Official Guide to

Self-Catering
holiday homes

MW00608292

England

There's something different
around every corner

The English Tourism Council

English Tourism Council is the national body for English Tourism. Its mission is to drive forward the quality, competitiveness and wise growth of England's tourism by providing intelligence, setting standards, creating partnerships and ensuring coherence. ETC sets out: to provide leadership and support for the industry – creating the right framework for tourism to flourish and providing a clear focus for tourism policy and promotion; to raise the quality of English tourism – ensuring consumers expectations are met and that tourism contributes to the quality of life; to improve the competitiveness of the industry; to ensure the wise growth of tourism – helping the tourism industry to take better account of the natural and built environment and the communities within which it operates.

Important:
The information contained in this guide has been published in good faith on the basis of information submitted to the English Tourism Council by the proprietors of the premises listed, who have paid for their entries to appear. The English Tourism Council cannot guarantee the accuracy of the information in this guide and accepts no responsibility for any error or misrepresentation. All liability for loss, disappointment, negligence or other damage caused by reliance on the information contained in this guide, or in the event of bankruptcy, or liquidation, or cessation of trade of any company, individual or firm mentioned, is hereby excluded. Please check carefully all prices and other details before confirming a reservation.

Cover Pictures:
  Front Cover: Bruern Stable Cottages, Burford, Oxfordshire
  Front Cover Inset: Darwin Lake, Matlock, Derbyshire
  Back Cover: (from top) Fornside Farm Cottages, Keswick, Cumbria
  The Olde House, Chapel Amble, Cornwall

Photo Credits:
  Cumbria - Cumbria Tourist Board
  Northumbria - Northumbria Tourist Board, Graeme Peacock, Mike Kipling, Colin Cuthbert and Michael Busselle
  North West - North West Tourist Board, Cheshire County Council, Lancashire County Council, Marketing Manchester
  Yorkshire - Yorkshire Tourist Board
  Heart of England - Heart of England Tourist Board
  East of England - East of England Tourist Board Collection
  South West - South West Tourism
  South of England - Southern Tourist Board,
  Peter Titmuss, Chris Cove-Smith and Iris Buckley
  South East England - South East England Tourist Board, Chris Parker and Iris Buckley

  Published by: The English Tourism Council, Thames Tower, Black's Road, Hammersmith, London W6 9EL.
  ISBN 0 86143 251 7

  Publishing Manager: Michael Dewing
  Production Manager: Iris Buckley
  Technical Manager: Marita Sen
  Compilation, Design & Production: www.jacksonlowe.com
  Typesetting: Tradespools Ltd, Somerset and Jackson Lowe Marketing, Lewes
  Maps: © Maps In Minutes™ (1999)
  Printing and Binding: Mozzon Giuntina S.p.A., Florence and Officine Grafiche De Agostini S.p.A., Novara.
  Advertisement Sales: Jackson Lowe Marketing, 173 High Street, Lewes, East Sussex BN7 1EH. (01273) 487487
  © English Tourism Council (except where stated)

Contents

Where to Stay in England 2002

WELCOME TO WHERE TO STAY
How to find your way around the guide including colour maps

How to use the guide	6
Finding your accommodation	6
Accommodation entries explained	7
Accommodation ratings and awards	8
Star Ratings	9
National Accessible Scheme	12-13
Regional Tourist Board areas	14
In which region is the county I wish to visit?	15
Accommodation location maps	18-30

PLACES TO STAY AND THINGS TO DO
Accommodation entries, places to visit, regional tourist board contact details and travel

London	31
Cumbria	45
Northumbria	85
North West	115
Yorkshire	129
Heart of England	167
East of England	235
South West	279
South of England	351
South East England	381
Complete listing of all English Tourism Council assessed Self Catering accommodation	411

FURTHER INFORMATION
Detailed information on accommodation ratings, guidance on how to book, events and more

The Quality Assurance Standards explained	670
General advice and information	671-672
About the guide entries	673
Travel information – by car and by train	674-675
Events for 2002	676-681
Town index	684

Key to Symbols
A key to symbols can be found on the inside back cover. Keep it open for easy reference.

For short breaks, family holidays, touring holidays or business stop-overs, Where to Stay is all you need. This guide contains details of thousands of places to stay in a wide choice of locations at prices to suit all budgets. Plus places to visit, tourist information centres, maps, events and a whole lot more.

There's no better way to feel refreshed and revitalised than by taking a short break or holiday in England. It offers a rich variety of interest, from dramatic coastal paths, rolling hills and hedgerows to vibrant cities and quality attractions.

Start by looking for a place to stay. The English Tourism Council has assessed all accommodation in this guide for quality, so you can book with confidence that it will meet your expectations.

a warm
welcome

Welcome to our 27th edition -
it's so easy to use, and packed with information.

Get away
and do yourself an English
world of good.

How to use the guide

The guide is divided into the 10 English Regional Tourist Board regions (these are shown on page 14). These regional sections give you all the information you need on the area: accommodation, places to visit, tourist information centres, travel and publications for further information.

Accommodation is listed alphabetically in order of place name. If you would like to know more about the city, town or village in which you wish to stay, you will find brief descriptions at the end of each regional section. Or you can contact the local Tourist Information Centre - the telephone number can be found next to the town name on the accommodation entry pages.

Finding your accommodation

Whether you know exactly where you want to stay or only have an idea of the area you wish to visit, it couldn't be easier to find accommodation:

BY PLACE if you know the town or village look in the town index at the back.

BY AREA if you know the area look at the full colour maps starting on page 18. All the places in black offer accommodation featured in this guide.

BY REGION if you know which part of England look in the relevant regional section. These are colour coded at the top of each page. A map showing the regions can be found on page 14.

BY COUNTY if you know which county look at the listing on page 15 to find the region it is in.

Types of accommodation

Self-catering accommodation is featured in this guide. This can be any of the following: Cottage, Houses, Bungalows, Flats, Studios, Apartments, Chalets, Villas. The type of accommodation is generally mentioned in the editorial description for each entry.

Making a Booking

Please remember that changes may occur after the guide is printed. When you have found a suitable place to stay we advise you to contact the establishment to check availability, and to confirm prices and any specific facilities which may be important to you. Further advice on booking can be found at the back of this guide, together with information about deposits and cancellations. It is always advisable to confirm your booking in writing.

Accommodation entries explained

Each accommodation entry contains detailed information to help you decide if it is right for you. This information has been provided by the proprietors themselves, and our aim has been to ensure that it is as objective and factual as possible. To the left of the establishment name you will find the Star rating.

At-a-glance symbols at the end of each entry give you additional information on services and facilities - a key can be found on the back cover flap. Keep this open to refer to as you read.

ROSS-ON-WYE Map ref 2A1 Tourist Information Centre Tel: (01423) 537300

★★★★

1 Unit
Sleeps 5

Ad p344

THE COACH HOUSE
5 Long Gate, Ross-on-Wye, Herefordshire HR0 0AB
Contact: Mrs C Dower, Pine Combe,
24 Waylands Avenue, Weybridge, Surrey KT13 1RY
T: (01989) 000121 F: (01989) 000123
E: info@coachhouse.co.uk
I: www.coachhouse.ross.co.uk

Converted from an old coach house, this beautiful character cottage has a delightful thatched roof. Spacious yet cosy and warm in winter with wood-burning stove. Two large bedrooms, recently fitted kitchen. Overlooking apple orchards with views of beautiful Herefordshire countryside. Town centre easily accessible, many fine amenities close by.

Open Apr-Oct
CC: Access, Visa
Switch/Delta

3 night stays available
Oct-Jan (except Xmas
and New Year)

Low season per wk
£150.00-£170.00
High season per wk
£170.00-£210.00

1. Listing under town or village with map reference
2. ETC Star rating
3. Number of units and how many they sleep
4. Accessible rating where applicable
5. Colour picture for enhanced entries
6. Description - standard entries 25 words; enhanced entries 50 words
7. At-a-glance facility symbols
8. Establishment name, contact address, telephone and fax numbers, e-mail and web site address
9. Prices per unit per week for low season and high season
10. Months open and credit cards accepted
11. Special promotions (enhanced entries only)

Exclusive accommodation listings

Where to Stay is the only guide to contain details of ALL self-catering accommodation in England which have been quality assessed by the English Tourism Council, giving you the widest choice of accommodation.

Accommodation Ratings & Awards

Ratings and awards are an indication of quality which will help you find the most suitable accommodation to meet your needs and expectations. You'll find several in this guide:

English Tourism Council

★ ★ ★
SELF CATERING

STAR RATINGS FOR QUALITY

The English Tourism Council's quality assurance standard for self-catering accommodation awards One to Five Stars. This gives you reliable information about the quality of the accommodation you can expect. (See page 9 for further information). You'll find something to suit all budgets and tastes.

SERVICED APARTMENTS

Within the self-catering standard we also include properties that have achieved a Star rating as Serviced Apartments. These provide self-catering accommodation with the following additional elements: concierge services, cleaning service.

NATIONAL ACCESSIBLE SCHEME FOR SPECIAL NEEDS

If you are a wheelchair user or have difficulty walking, please look on pages 12 and 13. You'll find a list of establishments which have a National Accessible rating, providing special access and facilities.

The *Safeway* Excellence in England AWARDS 2002

Safeway

EXCELLENCE IN ENGLAND
Awards for Tourism

ENGLISH TOURISM COUNCIL

GNER

The Safeway Excellence in England Awards are all about blowing English tourism's trumpet and telling the world what a fantastic place England is to visit, whether it's for a two week holiday, a weekend break or a day trip.

Formerly called England for Excellence, the Awards are now in their 13th year and are run by the English Tourism Council in association with England's ten regional tourist boards. There are 13 categories including B&B of the Year, Hotel of the Year and Visitor Attraction of the Year. New for 2002 are Short Break Destination of the Year and Most Improved Seaside Resort.

Winners of the 2002 awards will receive their trophies at a fun and festive event to be held on St George's Day (23 April) at the Royal Opera House in London. The day will not only celebrate excellence in tourism but also Englishness in all its diversity.

For a truly exceptional experience, look out for accommodation and attractions displaying a Safeway Excellence in England Award from April 2002 onwards.

Safeway, one of the UK's leading food retailers, is delighted to be sponsoring these awards as a part of a range of initiatives to help farming communities and the tourism industry.

For more information on Safeway Stores please visit: www.safeway.co.uk
For more information about the Excellence in England Awards visit: www.englishtourism.org.uk

How do we arrive at a Star rating?

The English Tourism Council has more than 50 trained assessors throughout England who visit properties annually, generally on a day visit arranged in advance with the owner.

They award ratings based on the overall level of quality and ensure that all requirements are met. There are strict guidelines to ensure every property is assessed to the same criteria. High standards of cleanliness are a major requirement; heating, lighting, comfort and convenience are also part of the assessment.

THE ASSESSOR'S ROLE

An assessor takes into account everything a guest will experience. This includes:

- how the initial enquiry is dealt with • the brochure or information supplied
- the arrival procedure
- help and contact for guests during their stay
- the quality of the accommodation and facilities.

In fact all aspects which contribute to the overall comfort and convenience for guests who may hire the property for a holiday or short break.

During their visit the assessor will take into consideration the quality and condition of all the fixtures and fittings. Most importantly excellent standards of cleanliness are noted. Personal touches which give a homely and welcoming feeling are encouraged. Spaciousness and convenience of use is also part of the assessment, taking into account the number of people who can be accommodated. The quality of information provided about places to visit, where to eat and how to operate equipment is all taken into account. To attract the highest Star rating everything must be of an exceptional standard, both inside and outside the property.

At the end of the visit the assessor will advise the owner of the Star rating they have awarded, discussing the reasons why, as well as suggesting areas for improvement. So you can see it's a very thorough process to ensure that when you book accommodation with a particular Star rating you can be confident it will meet your expectations. After all, meeting customer expectations is what makes happy guests.

Ratings you can trust

When you're looking for a place to stay, you need a rating system you can trust. The English Tourism Council's ratings give a clear guide to what to expect, in an easy-to-understand form. Properties are visited annually by trained, impartial assessors, so you can have the confidence that your accommodation has been thoroughly checked and rated for quality before you make your booking.

STAR RATINGS

The Star ratings reflect the quality that you're looking for when booking accommodation. All properties have to meet an extensive list of minimum requirements to take part in the scheme. From there, increased levels of quality apply. For instance, you'll find acceptable quality at One Star, good to very good quality at Three Star and exceptional quality at Five Star establishments.

Quite simply, the more Stars, the higher the overall level of quality you can expect. Establishments at higher rating levels also have to meet additional requirements for facilities.

Minimum requirements include the following:

- High standard of cleanliness throughout
- Pricing and conditions of booking made clear
- Local information to help you make the best of your stay
- Comfortable accommodation with a range of furniture to meet your needs
- Colour television (where signal available) at no extra charge
- Kitchen equipped to meet all essential requirements

The brief explanation of the Star ratings for self-catering accommodation outlined below shows what is included at each rating level (note that each rating also includes what is provided at a lower Star rating).

★ An acceptable overall level of quality with adequate furniture, furnishings and fittings.

★★ A good overall level of quality. All units are self-contained.

★★★ A good to very good overall level of quality with good standards of maintenance and decoration. Ample space and good quality furniture. All double beds have access from both sides. Microwave.

★★★★ An excellent overall level of quality with very good care and attention to detail throughout. Access to a washing machine and drier if it is not provided in the unit, or a 24 hour laundry service.

★★★★★ An exceptional overall level of quality with high levels of decor, fixtures and fittings, with personal touches. Excellent standards of management efficiency and guest services.

Many self-catering establishments have a range of accommodation units in the building or on the site, and in some cases the individual units may have different Star ratings. In such cases, the entry shows the range available.

Further information about the scheme can be found at the back of this guide.

BAY FORT MANSIONS
THE LUXURY HOLIDAY APARTMENTS

English Tourism Council

★★★★
SELF-CATERING

Elegant, Stylish, Comfortable, South facing Apartments complimenting probably the finest views of Torquay and the English Riviera.

Our 15 Apartments, 12 sea facing, many with patios and balconies, have been recently refurbished and equipped to a very high standard, and have been designed to provide you with a memorable holiday experience.

WARREN ROAD TORQUAY DEVON TQ2 5TN
TEL: 01803 213810 FAX: 01803 209057
www.bayfortapartments.co.uk

National
Accessible Scheme

The English Tourism Council and National and Regional Tourist Boards throughout Britain assess all types of places to stay, on holiday or business, that provide accessible accommodation for wheelchair users and others who may have difficulty walking.

Accommodation establishments taking part in the National Accessible Scheme, and which appear in the regional sections of this guide are listed opposite. Use the Town Index at the back to find the page numbers for their full entries.

The Tourist Boards recognise three categories of accessibility:

CATEGORY 1   Accessible to all wheelchair users including those travelling independently.

CATEGORY 2   Accessible to a wheelchair user with assistance.

CATEGORY 3   Accessible to a wheelchair user able to walk short distances and up at least three steps.

If you have additional needs or special requirements of any kind, we strongly recommend that you make sure these can be met by your chosen establishment before you confirm your booking.

The criteria the English Tourism Council and National and Regional Tourist Boards have adopted do not necessarily conform to British Standards or to Building Regulations. They reflect what the Boards understand to be acceptable to meet the practical needs of wheelchair users.

The National Accessible Scheme is currently in the process of being updated. Consultation has been conducted throughout 2001 with introduction during 2002.

The National Accessible Scheme forms part of the Tourism for All Campaign that is being promoted by the English Tourism Council and National and Regional Tourist Boards. Additional help and guidance on finding suitable holiday accommodation for those with special needs can be obtained from:

Holiday Care,
2nd Floor, Imperial Buildings,
Victoria Road,
Horley, Surrey RH6 7PZ

Tel: (01293) 774535
Fax: (01293) 784647
Email: holiday.care@virgin.net
Internet: www.holidaycare.org.uk
Minicom: (01293) 776943

CATEGORY 1

- **Kielder Water, Northumberland**
  - Calvert Trust Kielder
- **Colyton, Devon** - Smallicombe Farm
- **Cockfield, Durham** - Stonecroft and Swallows Nest
- **St Just-in-Penwith, Cornwall** - Swallows End

 CATEGORY 2

- **Atherstone, Warwickshire** - Hipsley Farm Cottages
- **Bakewell, Derbyshire** - Haddon Grove Farm Cottages
- **Barnard Castle, Durham**
  - East Briscoe Farm Cottages
  - Hauxwell Cottages (Bumpkin Byre and Puddles End)
- **Barnstaple, Devon** - Country Ways
- **Beaminster, Dorset** - Lewesdon Farm Holidays
  - Stable Cottage
- **Chale, Isle of Wight** - Atherfield Green Farm Holiday
- **Charlbury, Oxfordshire** - Banbury Hill Farm Cottages
- **Cotton, Suffolk** - Coda Cottages
- **Cranmer, Norfolk** - Home Farm
- **Dilham, Norfolk** - Dairy Farm Cottages
- **Dulverton, Somerset** - Northmoor House & Lodge
- **Harrogate, North Yorkshire** - Dinmore Cottages
- **Haworth, West Yorkshire** - Bronte Country Cottages
- **Holme next the Sea, Norfolk** - Whitegates
- **Horning, Norfolk** - Hall Farm Cottages
- **Kirkoswald, Cumbria** - Howscales
- **Llanyblodwel, Shropshire** - The Coach House
- **Moretonhampstead, Devon** - Budleigh Farm
- **Pickering, North Yorkshire** - Rawcliffe House Farm
- **Ravenstonedale, Cumbria** - Coldbeck Cottage
- **Salisbury, Wiltshire** - The Old Stables
- **Wisbech, Cambridgeshire** - Common Right Barns
- **York, North Yorkshire** - York Lakeside Lodges

 CATEGORY 3

- **Abberley, Worcestershire** - Old Yates Cottages
- **Alnwick, Northumberland**
  - Bog Mill Farm Holiday Cottages
  - Village Farm
- **Bamburgh, Northumberland**
  - Outchester & Ross Farm
  - Point Cottages
- **Bassenthwaite, Cumbria** - Irton House Farm
- **Bellingham, Northumberland**
  - Conheath Cottage
- **Bosley, Cheshire** - The Old Byre
- **Bridgnorth, Shropshire** - Bulls Head Cottages
- **Bude, Cornwall** - Kennacott Court
- **Buxton, Derbyshire** - The Bungalow at Litton Mill
- **Canterbury, Kent** - Ebury Hotel Cottages
- **Castle Acre, Norfolk** - Cherry Tree Cottage
- **Chapel Amble, Cornwall** - The Olde House
- **Chichester, West Sussex** - Cornerstones
- **Cratfield, Suffolk** - School Farm Cottages
- **Craven Arms, Shropshire** - Upper Onibury Cottages
- **Cressbrook, Derbyshire** - Cressbrook Hall Cottages
- **Dorking, Surrey** - Bulmer Farm
- **Foxley, Norfolk** - Moor Farm Stable Cottages
- **Grassington, North Yorkshire** - The Barn
- **Looe, Cornwall**
  - Bucklawren Farm
  - Well Meadow Cottage
- **Milton Abbas, Dorset** - Luccombe Farm
- **Moreton-in-Marsh, Gloucestershire** - The Cottage
- **Mosterton, Dorset** - Riverside
- **Nutley, East Sussex**
  - Whitehouse Farm Holiday Cottages
- **Ripon, North Yorkshire**
  - Byre Cottage & Swallow Cottage
- **Seahouses, Northumberland** - Dalfaber and Lynbank
- **Silverdale, Lancashire** - The Stables
- **Wickham Skeith, Suffolk** - The Netus
- **Wisbech, Cambridgeshire** - Common Right Barns

(The information contained on these pages was correct at the time of going to press.)

Regional Tourist Board Areas

This Where to Stay guide is divided into 10 regional sections as shown on the map below. To identify each regional section and its page number, please refer to the key below. The county index overleaf indicates in which regional section you will find a particular county.

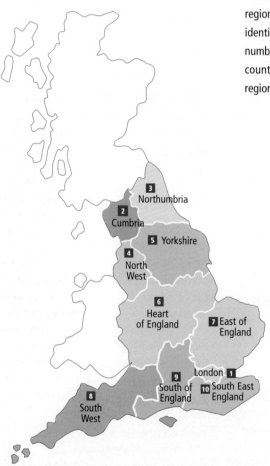

Key to Map	page
1 London	31
2 Cumbria	45
3 Northumbria	85
4 North West	115
5 Yorkshire	129
6 Heart of England	167
7 East of England	235
8 South West	279
9 South of England	351
10 South East England	381

Each of the ten English regions shown here has a Regional Tourist Board which can give you information about things to see or do locally. Contact details are given both at the beginning and end of each regional section.

LOCATION MAPS

Colour location maps showing all the cities, towns and villages with accommodation in the regional sections of this guide can be found on pages 18-30. Turn to the Town Index at the back of this guide for the page number on which you can find the relevant accommodation.

In which **region** is the **county** I wish to **visit**?

COUNTY/UNITARY AUTHORITY	REGION
Bath & North East Somerset	South West
Bedfordshire	East of England
Berkshire	South of England
Bristol	South West
Buckinghamshire	South of England
Cambridgeshire	East of England
Cheshire	North West
Cornwall	South West
Cumbria	Cumbria
Derbyshire	Heart of England
Devon	South West
Dorset (Eastern)	South of England
Dorset (Western)	South West
Durham	Northumbria
East Riding of Yorkshire	Yorkshire
East Sussex	South East England
Essex	East of England
Gloucestershire	Heart of England
Greater London	London
Greater Manchester	North West
Hampshire	South of England
Herefordshire	Heart of England
Hertfordshire	East of England
Isle of Wight	South of England
Isles of Scilly	South West
Kent	South East England
Lancashire	North West
Leicestershire	Heart of England
Lincolnshire	Heart of England
Merseyside	North West
Norfolk	East of England
North East Lincolnshire	Yorkshire
North Lincolnshire	Yorkshire
North Somerset	South West
North Yorkshire	Yorkshire
Northamptonshire	Heart of England
Northumberland	Northumbria
Nottinghamshire	Heart of England
Oxfordshire	South of England
Rutland	Heart of England
Shropshire	Heart of England
Somerset	South West
South Gloucestershire	South West
South Yorkshire	Yorkshire
Staffordshire	Heart of England
Suffolk	East of England
Surrey	South East England
Tees Valley	Northumbria
Tyne & Wear	Northumbria
Warwickshire	Heart of England
West Midlands	Heart of England
West Sussex	South East England
West Yorkshire	Yorkshire
Wiltshire	South West
Worcestershire	Heart of England
York	Yorkshire

UNITARY AUTHORITIES

Please note that many new unitary authorities have been formed - for example Brighton & Hove and Bristol - and are officially separate from the county in which they were previously located. To aid the reader we have only included the major unitary authorities in the list above and on the colour maps.

Our Countryside Matters!

Country Code

- Always follow the Country code
- Guard against all risk of fire
- Keep your dogs under close control
- Use gates and stiles to cross fences, hedges and walls
- Take your litter home
- Protect wildlife, plants and trees
- Make no unnecessary noise

- Enjoy the countryside and respect its life and work
- Fasten all gates
- Keep to public paths across farmland
- Leave livestock, crops and machinery alone
- Help to keep all water clean
- Take special care on country roads

We hope the countryside will fully open in 2002. However, given the serious nature of Foot and Mouth Disease please be ready to follow this additional advice and respect any further precautions given in local authority notices:

- Don't go onto farmland if you have handled farm animals in the last 7 days
- Avoid contact with farm animals and keep dogs on a lead where they are present
- If you step in dung, remove it before you leave the field • Don't go on paths with a local authority 'closed' notice.

For more information contact Tourist information Centres or
Countryside Agency web site www.countryside.gov.uk
which links to other local authority web sites providing details about rights
of way and access opportunities across England.

Welcome Host

Welcome Host is a nationally recognised customer care initiative, sponsored in England by the English Tourism Council. When visiting accommodation in this guide you may find this sign on display. It demonstrates commitment to courtesy and service and an aim to provide high standards of service and a warm welcome for all visitors.

Country Holidays

Britain's Favourite Cottage Holidays

English Tourism Council
★★★
SELF-CATERING

People who want the choice

Choose Country Holidays

Wouldn't you prefer a quiet stroll through the woods to the stressful morning rush hour? Or a revitalising jog on the beach instead of the dreaded school run? Then why not get away from the everyday with Country Holidays.

Relax on a cottage holiday...

- Over 3000 cottages to choose from throughout Britain
- Cottages for couples to parties of ten or more
- All cottages quality graded annually
- Pets welcome at many cottages
- Short Break offer - 4 midweek nights for the same price as 3 weekend nights
- Save £25 on a fortnight's holiday

Call **08700 725 725** QUOTING CMA80

for your FREE 2002 brochure or look and book at:

www.country-holidays.co.uk

English Tourism Council
★★★
SELF-CATERING

More choice and more freedom with Blakes

Whatever you're looking for, **BLAKES** have the perfect holiday for you...

The widest choice of self-catering accommodation throughout Britain, handpicked for quality and value. Our customers vary from couples looking for romantic oak beamed cottages to families seeking fun-packed holiday parks. With almost every inch of golden beach, rolling moor and fertile woodland covered in our brochure you're sure to find the perfect holiday.

It's Better with Blakes!

BLAKES

Call now for your free 2002 brochure - Quote BMA80

08700 70 80 99

or visit your local Travel Agent

www.blakes-cottages.co.uk

Great offers
ON HOLIDAY PARKS

MAP 1

Location
Maps

Every place name featured in the regional accommodation sections of this Where to Stay guide has a map reference to help you locate it on the maps which follow. For example, to find Colchester, Essex, which has 'Map ref 3B2', turn to Map 3 and refer to grid square B2.

All place names appearing in the regional sections are shown in black type on the maps. This enables you to find other places in your chosen area which may have suitable accommodation - the Town Index (at the back of this guide) gives page numbers.

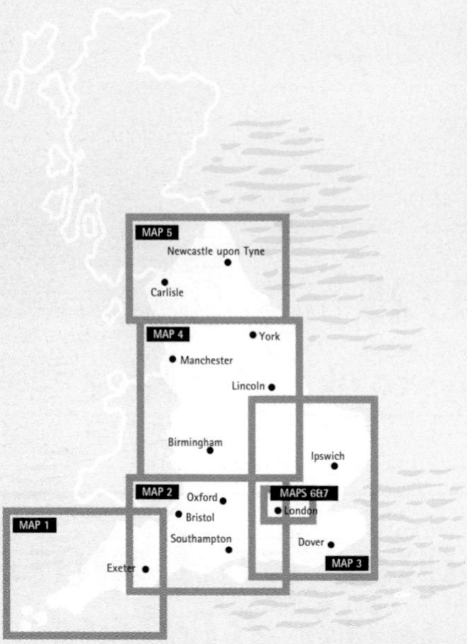

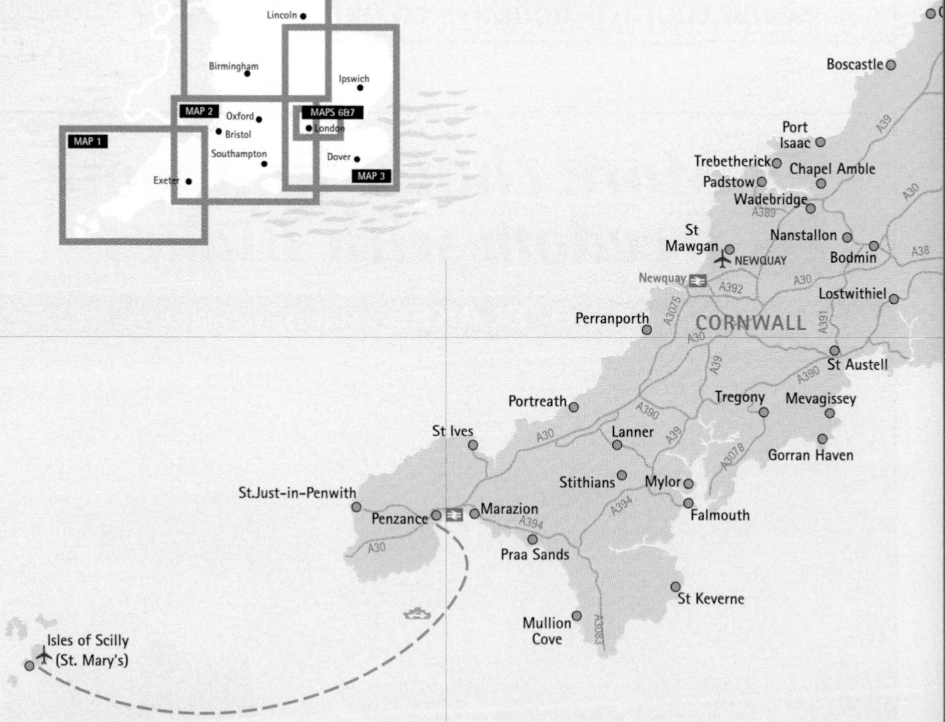

A **B**

1

2

3

MAP 5
Newcastle upon Tyne
Carlisle

MAP 4 • York
• Manchester
Lincoln •

Birmingham
Ipswich

MAP 2 Oxford •
• Bristol
MAPS 6&7
Southampton • London
MAP 1
Dover •
Exeter • MAP 3

Boscastle ○

Port
Isaac ○
Trebetherick ○ Chapel Amble
Padstow ○
Wadebridge
A389
St Nanstallon ○
Mawgan Bodmin
✈ NEWQUAY A38
Newquay A392 A30
Lostwithiel ○
Perranporth CORNWALL A391
A30
St Austell
A39 A380
Tregony Mevagissey
Portreath A390
St Ives A30 Lanner A39
Gorran Haven
Stithians Mylor ○
St.Just-in-Penwith A394 Falmouth
Penzance ○ Marazion
A30 A394
Praa Sands
St Keverne
A3083
Isles of Scilly Mullion
✈ (St. Mary's) Cove

Key to regions: South West

18

MAP 1

All place names in black offer accommodation in this guide.

MAP 2

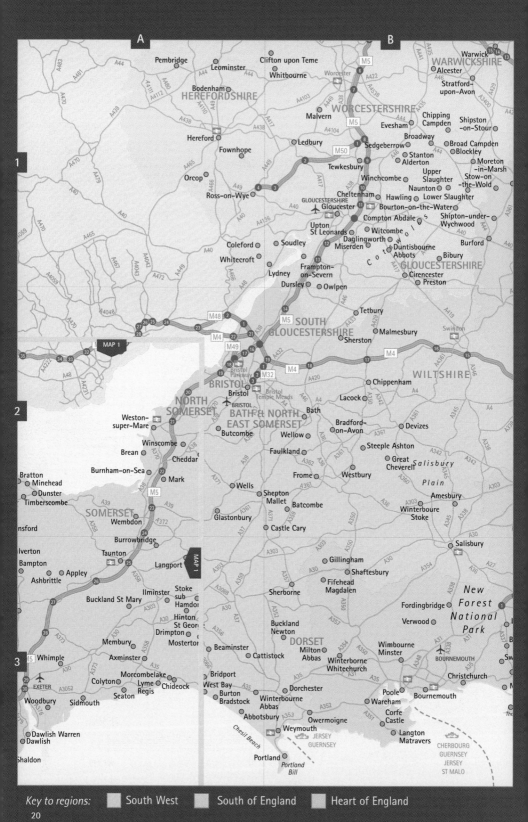

Key to regions: ■ South West ■ South of England ■ Heart of England

MAP 2

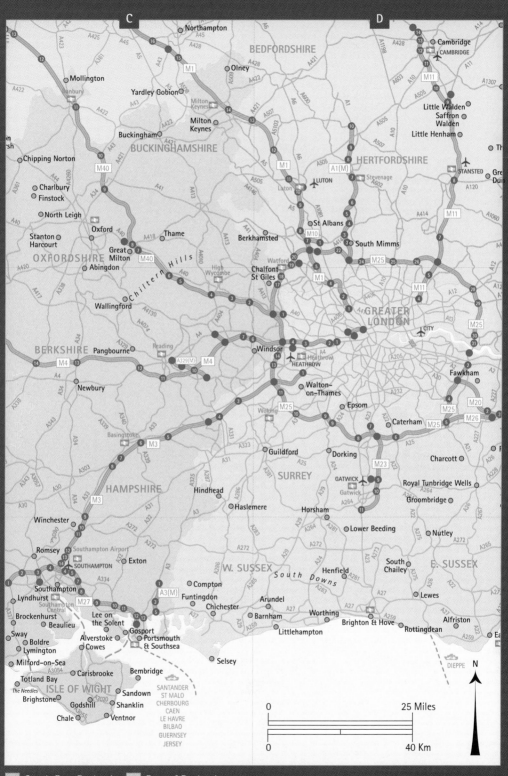

South East England   East of England   *All place names in black offer accommodation in this guide.*

MAP 3

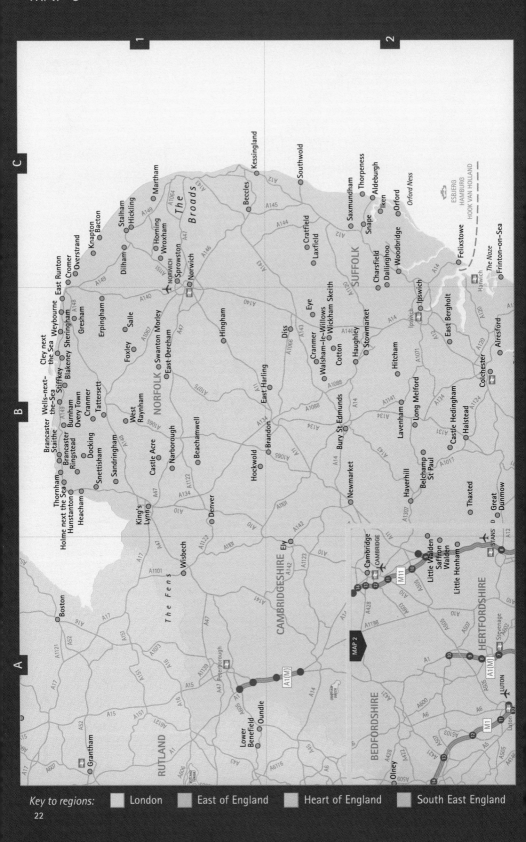

Key to regions: London | East of England | Heart of England | South East England

MAP 3

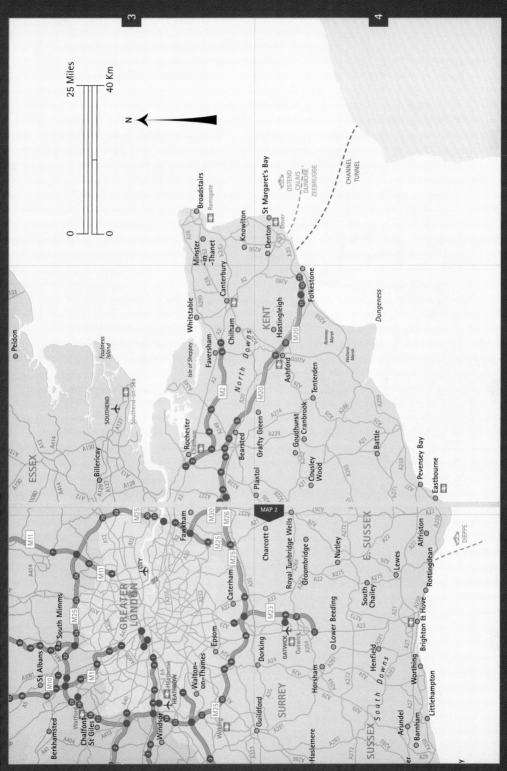

All place names in black offer accommodation in this guide.

MAP 4

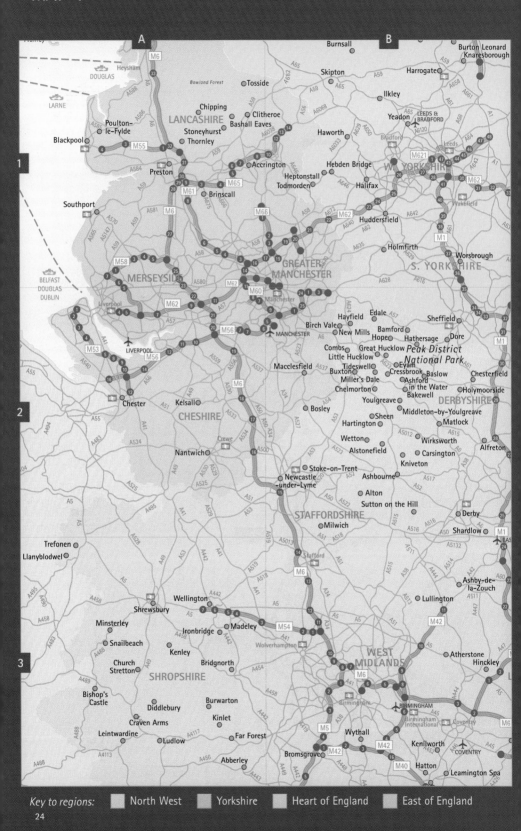

Key to regions: North West Yorkshire Heart of England East of England

All place names in black offer accommodation in this guide.

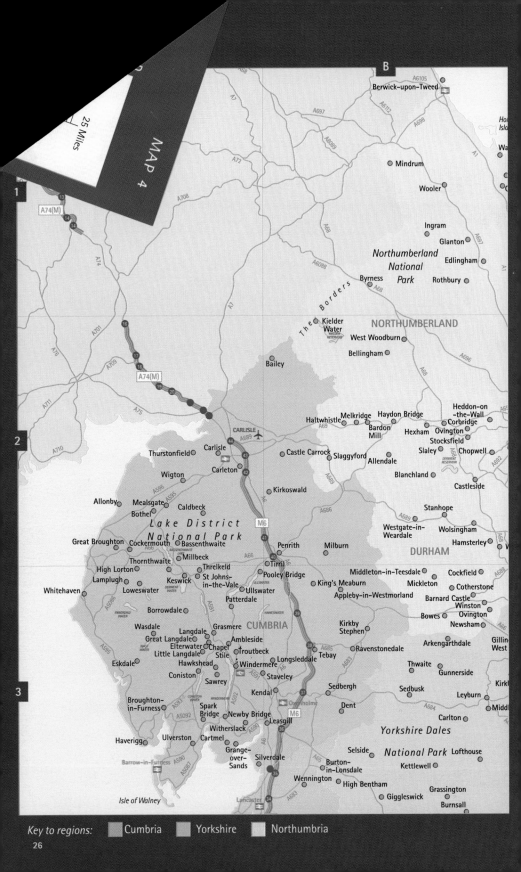

MAP 5

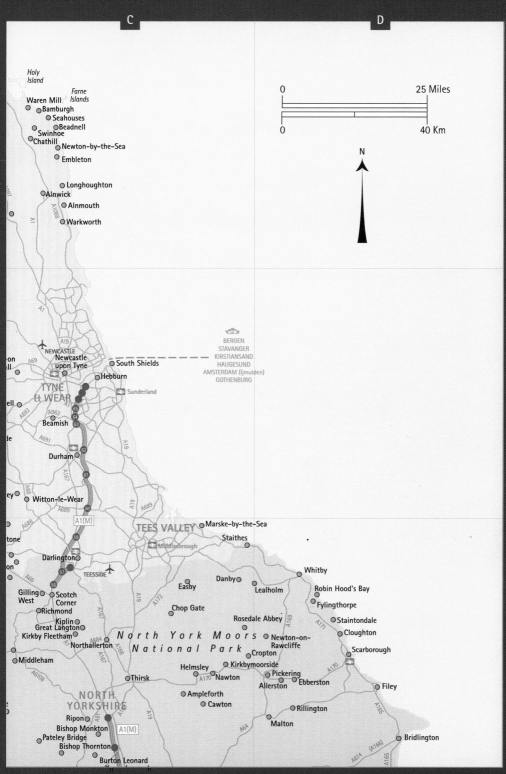

C

D

Holy
Island

Farne
Islands

Waren Mill
Bamburgh
Seahouses
Beadnell
Swinhoe
Chathill
Newton-by-the-Sea
Embleton

Longhoughton
Alnwick
Alnmouth
Warkworth

0   25 Miles
0   40 Km

N

NEWCASTLE
Newcastle
upon Tyne
South Shields
Hebburn

BERGEN
STAVANGER
KIRSTIANSAND
HAUGESUND
AMSTERDAM (Ijmuiden)
GOTHENBURG

TYNE
& WEAR
Sunderland

Beamish

Durham

Witton-le-Wear

A1(M)

TEES VALLEY
Middlesbrough
Marske-by-the-Sea
Staithes

Darlington

TEESIDE

Whitby

Gilling
West
Scotch
Corner
Richmond
Kiplin
Great Langton
Kirkby Fleetham
Northallerton
Middleham

Easby
Danby
Lealholm
Robin Hood's Bay
Fylingthorpe
Chop Gate

Rosedale Abbey
Staintondale
Cloughton

N o r t h   Y o r k   M o o r s
N a t i o n a l   P a r k
Newton-on-
Rawcliffe
Cropton
Scarborough

Helmsley
Kirkbymoorside
Thirsk
Nawton
Pickering
Ebberston
Filey
Allerston
Ampleforth
Cawton
Rillington

NORTH
YORKSHIRE
Malton

Ripon
Bishop Monkton
Pateley Bridge
Bishop Thornton
A1(M)
Burton Leonard
Bridlington

All place names in black offer accommodation in this guide.

MAP 6

MAP 6

© Arka Cartographics Ltd. 1999

MAP 7

Central London

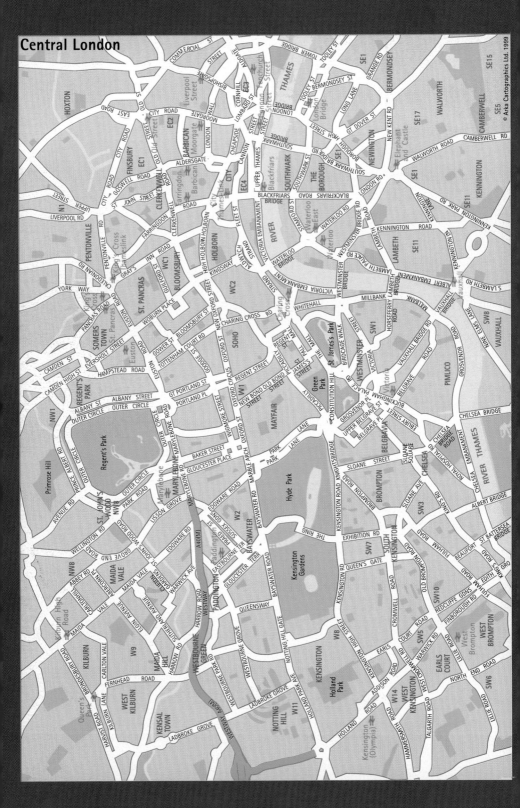

© Arka Cartographics Ltd. 1999

LONDON

A dynamic mix of history and heritage, cool and contemporary. Great museums, stunning art collections, royal palaces, hip nightlife and stylish shopping, from ritzy Bond Street to cutting-edge Hoxton.

classic sights

St Paul's Cathedral – Wren's famous church
Tower of London – 900 years of British history
London Eye – spectacular views from the world's highest 'big wheel'

arts for all

National Gallery – Botticelli, Rembrandt, Turner and more
Tate Modern – 20th century art in a former power station
Victoria & Albert Museum – decorative arts

city lights

Theatre: musicals – West End; drama – Royal Court and National Theatre;
Music: classical – Wigmore Hall and Royal Festival Hall;
jazz – Ronnie Scott's; ballet & opera – Royal Opera House

insider london

Dennis Severs's House, E1 – candlelit tours of this authentically 18th century house

Greater London, comprising the 32 London Boroughs

FOR MORE INFORMATION CONTACT:
London Tourist Board
6th Floor, Glen House, Stag Place,
London SW1E 5LT
Telephone enquiries - see London Line on page 36
Internet: www.LondonTouristBoard.com

The Pictures:
1 Tower Bridge
2 Hampton Court
3 Piccadilly Circus

Places to Visit - see pages 32-36
Where to Stay - see pages 37-43

PLACES to visit

You will find hundreds of interesting places to visit during your stay, just some of which are listed in these pages. Contact any Tourist Information Centre in and around London for more ideas on days out.

Bank of England Museum

Bartholomew Lane, London, EC2R 8AH
Tel: (020) 7601 5545 www.bankofengland.co.uk
The museum is housed within the Bank of England. It traces the history of the Bank from its foundation by Royal Charter in 1694 to its role today as the nation's central bank.

British Airways London Eye

Jubilee Gardens, South Bank, London, SE1
Tel: (0870) 5000 600 www.ba-londoneye.com
At 443 ft (135 m) high, this is the world's highest observation wheel. It provides a 30-minute slow-moving flight over London

British Library

96 Euston Road, London, NW1 2DB
Tel: (020) 7412 7332 www.bl.uk
Exhibition galleries, bookshop, piazza displaying Magna Carta, Gutenberg Bible, Shakespeare's First Folio and illuminated manuscripts, temporary exhibitions.

British Museum

Great Russell Street, London, WC1B 3DG
Tel: (020) 7323 8000 www.thebritishmuseum.ac.uk
One of the great museums of the world, showing the works of man from prehistoric to modern times with collections drawn from the whole world.

Cabinet War Rooms

Clive Steps, King Charles Street, London, SW1A 2AQ
Tel: (020) 7930 6961 www.iwm.org.uk
The underground headquarters used by Winston Churchill and the British Government during World War II. Includes Cabinet Room, Transatlantic Telephone Room and Map Room.

Chessington World of Adventures

Leatherhead Road, Chessington, KT9 2NE
Tel: (01372) 729560 www.chessington.com
Visitors will be in for a big adventure as they explore the theme park's amazing new attractions.

Design Museum

28 Shad Thames, London, SE1 2YD
Tel: (020) 7403 6933 www.designmuseum.org
The Design Museum is one of London's most inspiring attractions, concerned solely with the products, technologies and buildings of the 20thC and 21stC.

Hampton Court Palace

Hampton Court, East Molesey, KT8 9AU
Tel: (020) 8781 9500 www.hrp.org.uk
The oldest Tudor palace in England with many attractions including the Tudor kitchens, tennis courts, maze, State Apartments and King's Apartments.

HMS Belfast

Morgan's Lane, Tooley Street, London, SE1 2JH
Tel: (020) 7940 6300 www.iwm.org.uk
World War II cruiser weighing 11,500 tonnes, now a floating naval museum, with 9 decks to explore.

Imperial War Museum

Lambeth Road, London, SE1 6HZ
Tel: (020) 7416 5320 www.iwm.org.uk
Museum tells the story of 20thC war from Flanders to Bosnia. Special features include the Blitz Experience, the Trench Experience and the World of Espionage.

Kensington Palace State Apartments

Kensington Gardens, London, W8 4PX
Tel: (020) 7937 7079 www.hrp.org.uk
Furniture and ceiling paintings from Stuart-Hanoverian periods, rooms from Victorian era and works of art from the Royal Collection. Also Royal Ceremonial Dress Collection.

Kew Gardens (Royal Botanic Gardens)

Kew Richmond TW9 3AB
Tel: (020) 8940 1171 Rec.
300 acres (121 ha) containing living collections of over 40,000 varieties of plants. Seven spectacular glasshouses, 2 art galleries, Japanese and rock garden.

London Dungeon

28-34 Tooley Street, London, SE1 2SZ
Tel: (020) 7403 7221 www.thedungeons.com
The world's first medieval fully interactive horror attraction. Relive the 'Great Fire of London', unmask 'Jack the Ripper' and take the 'Judgement Day' ride.

London Planetarium

Marylebone Road, London, NW1 5LR
Tel: (0870) 400 3000 www.london-planetarium.com
Visitors can experience a virtual reality trip through space and wander through the interactive Space Zones before the show.

London Transport Museum

Covent Garden Piazza, London, WC2E 7BB
Tel: (020) 7379 6344 www.ltmuseum.co.uk
The history of transport for everyone, from spectacular vehicles, special exhibitions, actors and guided tours to film shows, gallery talks and children's craft workshops.

London Zoo

Regent's Park, London, NW1 4RY
Tel: (020) 7722 3333 www.londonzoo.co.uk
One of the world's most famous zoos and home to over 600 species. Including the new 'Web of Life' exhibition, as well as a full daily events programme.

Madame Tussaud's

Marylebone Road, London, NW1 5LR
Tel: (0870) 400 3000 www.madame-tussauds.com
World-famous collection of wax figures in themed settings which include The Garden Party, 200 Years, Superstars, The Grand Hall, The Chamber of Horrors and The Spirit of London.

National Army Museum

Royal Hospital Road, Chelsea, London, SW3 4HT
Tel: (020) 7730 0717
www.national-armymuseum.ac.uk
The story of the British soldier in peace and war, through five centuries. Exhibits range from paintings to uniforms and from the English Civil War to Kosovo.

National History Museum

Cromwell Road, London, SW7 5BD
Tel: (020) 7942 5000 www.nhm.ac.uk
Home of the wonders of the natural world, one of the most popular museums in the world and one of London's finest landmarks.

The Pictures:
1 London by night, Piccadilly Circus
2 Big Ben
3 Buckingham Palace
4 Albert Hall
5 Harrods
6 Horseguards Parade

National Portrait Gallery

St Martin's Place, London, WC2H 0HE
Tel: (020) 7306 0055 www.npg.org.uk
Permanent collection of portraits of famous men and women from the Middle Ages to the present day. Free, but charge for some exhibitions.

Royal Air Force Museum

Grahame Park Way, Hendon, London, NW9 5LL
Tel: (020) 8205 2266 www.rafmuseum.com
Britain's National Museum of Aviation features over 70 full-sized aircraft, Flight Simulator, 'Touch and Try' Jet Provost Trainer and Eurofighter 2000 Theatre.

Royal Mews

Buckingham Palace, London, SW1A 1AA
Tel: (020) 7839 1377 www.royal.gov.uk
Her Majesty The Queen's carriage horses, carriages and harness used on State occasions (Coronation Coach built 1761).

Royal Observatory Greenwich

Greenwich Park, London, SE10 9NF
Tel: (020) 8858 4422 www.nmm.ac.uk
Museum of time and space and site of the Greenwich Meridian. Working telescopes and planetarium, timeball, Wren's Octagon Room and intricate clocks and computer simulations.

Science Museum

Exhibition Road, London, SW7 2DD
Tel: (0870) 870 4868 www.sciencemuseum.org.uk
See, touch and experience the major scientific advances of the last 300 years. With over 40 galleries, and over 2,000 hands-on exhibits to captivate and inspire all.

Shakespeare's Globe Exhibition and Tour

New Globe Walk, Bankside, London, SE1 9DT
Tel: (020) 7902 1500 www.shakespeares-globe.org
Against the historical background of Elizabethan Bankside, the City of London's playground in Shakespeare's time, the exhibition focuses on actors, architecture and audiences.

St Paul's Cathedral

St Paul's Churchyard, London, EC4M 8AD
Tel: (020) 7236 4128 www.stpauls.co.uk
Wren's famous cathedral church of the diocese of London incorporating the Crypt, Ambulatory and Whispering Gallery.

Tate Britain

Millbank, London, SW1P 4RG
Tel: (020) 7887 8000 www.tate.org.uk
Tate Britain presents the world's greatest collection of British art in a dynamic series of new displays and exhibitions.

Theatre Museum

Russell Street, London, WC2E 7PA
Tel: (020) 7943 4700 www.theatremuseum.org
Five galleries illustrating the history of performance in the United Kingdom. The collection includes displays on theatre, ballet, dance, musical stage, rock and pop music.

Tower of London

Tower Hill, London, EC3N 4AB
Tel: (020) 7709 0765 www.hrp.org.uk
Home of the `Beefeaters' and ravens, the building spans 900 years of British history. On display are the nation's Crown Jewels, regalia and armoury robes.

Victoria and Albert Museum

Cromwell Road, London, SW7 2RL
Tel: (020) 7942 2000 www.vam.ac.uk
The V&A holds one of the world's largest and most diverse collections of the decorative arts, dating from 3000BC to the present day.

Vinopolis, City of Wine

1 Bank End, London, SE1 9BU
Tel: (0870) 241 4040 www.vinopolis.co.uk
Vinopolis offers all the pleasures of wine under one roof. The Wine Odyssey tour includes free tastings from over 200 wines; also 2 restaurants on site.

Westminster Abbey

Parliament Square, London, SW1P 3PA
Tel: (020) 7222 5152 www.westminster-abbey.org
One of Britain's finest Gothic buildings. Scene of the coronation, marriage and burial of British monarchs. Nave and cloisters, Royal Chapels and Undercroft Museum.

Find out more about London

Millennium Wheel

LONDON TOURIST BOARD

London Tourist Board and Convention Bureau
6th Floor, Glen House, Stag Place, London SW1E 5LT
www.LondonTouristBoard.com

TOURIST INFORMATION CENTRES

POINT OF ARRIVAL

- **Heathrow Terminals 1, 2, 3** Underground Station Concourse, Heathrow Airport, TW6 2JA.
  Open: Daily 0800-1800; 1 Jun-30 Sep, Mon-Sat 0800-1900, Sun 0800-1800.

- **Liverpool Street Underground Station,** EC2M 7PN.
  Open: Daily 0800-1800; 1 Jun-30 Sep, Mon-Sat 0800-1900, Sun 0800-1800.

- **Victoria Station Forecourt,** SW1V 1JU.
  Open: 1 Jun-30 Sep, Mon-Sat 0800-2100, Sun 0800-1800; 1 Oct-Easter, daily 0800-1800; Easter-31 May, Mon-Sat 0800-2000, Sun 0800-1800.

- **Waterloo International Terminal**
  Arrivals Hall, London SE1 7LT. Open: Daily 0830-2230.

INNER LONDON

- **Britain Visitor Centre,** 1 Regent Street, Piccadilly Circus, SW1Y 4XT.
  Open: Mon 0930-1830, Tue-Fri 0900-1830, Sat & Sun 1000-1600; Jun-Oct, Sat 0900-1700.

- **Greenwich TIC,** Pepys House, 2 Cutty Sark Gardens, Greenwich SE10 9LW.
  Tel: 0870 608 2000; Fax: 020 8853 4607.
  Open: Daily 1000-1700; 1 Jul-31 Aug, daily 1000-2000.

- **Lewisham TIC,** Lewisham Library, 199-201 Lewisham High Street, SE13 6LG.
  Tel: 020 8297 8317; Fax: 020 8297 9241.
  Open: Mon 1000-1700, Tue-Fri 0900-1700, Sat 1000-1600, Sun closed.

- **Liverpool Street Underground Station,** EC2M 7PN.
  Open: Mon-Fri 0800-1800, Sat 0800-1730, Sun 0900-1730.

- **Southwark Information Centre,**
  London Bridge, 6 Tooley Street, SE1 2SY.
  Tel: 020 7403 8299; Fax: 020 7357 6321.
  Open: Easter-31 Oct, Mon-Sat 1000-1800, Sun 1030-1730; 1 Nov-Easter, Mon-Sat 1000-1600, Sun 1100-1600.

- **Tower Hamlets TIC,** 18 Lamb Street, E1 6EA.
  Fax: 020 7375 2539.
  Open: Mon, Tue, Thu & Fri 0930-1330 & 1430-1630, Wed 0930-1300, Sat closed, Sun 1130-1430.

- **Victoria Station Forecourt,** SW1V 1JU.
  Open: Jan-Feb, Mon-Sat 0800-1900; Mar-May, Mon-Sat 0800-2000; Jun-Sep, Mon-Sat 0800-2100; Oct-Dec, Mon-Sat 0800-2000, Sun 0800-1815.

- **London Visitor Centre, Arrivals Hall,**
  Waterloo International Terminal, London SE1 7LT.
  Open: Daily 0830-2230.

OUTER LONDON

- **Bexley Hall Place TIC,** Bourne Road, Bexley, Kent, DA5 1PQ.
  Tel: 01322 558676; Fax 01322 522921.
  Open: Mon-Sat 1000-1630, Sun 1400-1730.

- **Croydon TIC, Katharine Street,** Croydon, CR9 1ET.
  Tel: 020 8253 1009; Fax: 020 8253 1008.
  Open: Mon, Tues, Wed & Fri 0900-1800, Thu 0930-1800, Sat 0900-1700, Sun 1400-1700.

- **Harrow TIC, Civic Centre,** Station Road, Harrow, HA1 2XF.
  Tel: 020 8424 1103; Fax: 020 8424 1134.
  Open: Mon-Fri 0900-1700, Sat & Sun closed.

- **Heathrow Terminals 1,2,3 Underground Station** Concourse, Heathrow Airport, TW6 2JA.
  Open: Daily 0800-1800.

- **Hillingdon TIC,** Central Library, 4-15 High Street, Uxbridge, UB8 1HD.
  Tel: 01895 250706; Fax: 01895 239794.
  Open: Mon, Tue & Thu 0930-2000, Wed 0930-1730, Fri 1000-1730, Sat 0930-1600, Sun closed.

- **Hounslow TIC,** The Treaty Centre, High Street, Hounslow, TW3 1ES.
  Tel: 020 8583 2929; Fax: 020 8583 4714.
  Open: Mon, Wed, Fri & Sat 0930-1730, Tue & Thu 0930-2000, Sun closed.

- **Kingston TIC,** Market House, Market Place,
  Kingston upon Thames, KT1 1JS.
  Tel: 020 8547 5592; Fax: 020 8547 5594.
  Open: Mon-Fri 1000-1700, Sat 0900-1600, Sun closed.

- **Richmond TIC,** Old Town Hall,
  Whittaker Avenue; Richmond, TW9 1TP.
  Tel: 020 8940 9125 Fax: 020 8940 6899.
  Open: Mon-Sat 1000-1700; Easter Sunday-end Sep,
  Sun 1030-1330.

- **Swanley TIC,** London Road, BR8 7AE.
  Tel: 01322 614660; Fax: 01322 666154.
  Open: Mon-Thur 0930-1730, Fri 0930-1800,
  Sat 0900-1600, Sun closed.

- **Twickenham TIC,** The Atrium, Civic Centre, York Street,
  Twickenham, Middlesex, TW1 3BZ.
  Tel: 020 8891 7272; Fax: 020 8891 7738.
  Open: Mon-Thu 0900-1715, Fri 0900-1700,
  Sat & Sun closed.

LONDON LINE

London Tourist Board's recorded telephone information
service provides information on museums, galleries,
attractions, river trips, sight seeing tours,
accommodation, theatre, what's on, changing of the
Guard, children's London, shopping, eating out and gay
and lesbian London.
Available 24 hours a day. Calls cost 60p per minute as at
July 2001. Call 09068 663344.

ARTSLINE

London's information and advice service for disabled
people on arts and entertainment. Call (020) 7388 2227.

WHICH PART OF LONDON?

The majority of tourist accommodation is situated in
the central parts of London and is therefore very
convenient for most of the city's attractions and
night life.

However, there are establishments in outer London which
provide other advantages, such as easier parking. In the
'Where to Stay' pages which follow, you will find
accommodation listed under INNER LONDON (covering
the E1 to W14 London Postal Area) and OUTER LONDON
(covering the remainder of Greater London). Colour maps
6 and 7 at the front of the guide show place names and
London Postal Area codes and will help you to locate
accommodation in your chosen area of London.

Getting to
London

BY ROAD: Major trunk roads into London include: A1, M1, A5, A10, A11, M11, A13,
A2, M2, A23, A3, M3, A4, M4, A40, M40, A41, M25 (London orbital).
London Transport is responsible for running London's bus services and the
underground rail network. (020) 7222 1234 (24 hour telephone service; calls
answered in rotation).

BY RAIL: Main rail termini:
Victoria/Waterloo/Charing Cross - serving the South/South East;
King's Cross - serving the North East; Euston - serving the North West/Midlands;
Liverpool Street - serving the East; Paddington - serving the Thames Valley/West.

The Pictures:
1 China Town
2 Houses of Parliament

Where to stay in London

Accommodation entries in this region are listed under Inner London (covering the postcode areas E1 to W14) and Outer London (covering the remainder of Greater London) - please refer to the colour location maps 6 and 7 at the front of this guide.

At-a-glance symbols at the end of each accommodation entry give useful information about services and facilities. A key to symbols can be found inside the back cover flap. Keep this open for easy reference.

A complete listing of all the English Tourism Council assessed accommodation covered by this guide appears at the back of the guide.

INNER LONDON
LONDON E3

★★★

1 Unit
Sleeping 4

THE FLAT
43 Tredegar Square, Bow, London E3 5AE
T: (020) 8981 2869
Contact: Mrs Alice Sielle

OPEN All year round
CC: Eurocard, Mastercard, Visa

Low season per wk
£375.00–£400.00
High season per wk
£375.00–£400.00

Lower ground floor flat with double bedroom, large kitchen/living room and access to patio. In a Georgian square, 2 minutes Mile End underground station. Easy access to City and Docklands.

QUALITY ASSURANCE SCHEME

For an explanation of the quality and facilities represented by the Stars please refer to the front of this guide. A more detailed explanation can be found in the information pages at the back.

★★★★

1 Unit
Sleeping 4

Two-bedroom house accommodating 4 in breathtaking waterscaped central area of London Docklands. Very peaceful, sunny garden. Master bedroom has balcony over water. Private parking. Docklands Light Railway 100 metres, Jubilee line 20 minutes to West End. Walk to Canary Wharf, London Arena. 30 restaurants, cafe, bars, shops and multi-screen. Flexible bookings, any number of nights. Nightly rates.

BRIDGE HOUSE–LONDON DOCKLANDS

31 Falcon Way, Clippers Quay, London E14 9UP
Contact: Mr J K Graham, 31 Falcon Way, London E14 9UP
T: (020) 7538 8980 & 07973 857187
F: (020) 7538 8980
E: johnkgraham31@hotmail.com
I: www.johnkgraham.com

OPEN All year round
CC: Barclaycard, Mastercard, Visa

High season per wk
£651.00

★★★★

1 Unit
Sleeping 6

First floor apartment. Lift. Secure parking. Double bedroom en suite and twin bedroom. Bathroom, lounge/dining room, fitted kitchen. All rooms and balcony overlooking River Thames and Dome. Canary Wharf 6 mins walk. Docklands Light Railway (South Quays), 3 mins' walk, trains to all of London (City and West End 20 mins).

RIVER THAMES APARTMENT

London Docklands, Galleons View, Stewart Street E14 3EX
Contact: Mrs Greta Paull, 35 Cheyne Avenue, South Woodford, London E18 2DP
T: (020) 8530 2336
F: (020) 8530 2336

OPEN All year round

Low season per wk
£400.00–£550.00
High season per wk
£550.00–£700.00

★★★★

1 Unit
Sleeping 6

RIVERSIDE
Capstan Square, London Docklands, London E14 3EU
Contact: Ms Christine James, Riverside,
35 Fairfield Drive, Codsall, Wolverhampton WV8 2AE
T: (01902) 843545 & 07967 375747 (Mobile)
F: (01902) 843545
E: christine@capstansq.fsnet.co.uk
I: www.capstansq.fsnet.co.uk

OPEN All year round

Low season per wk
£700.00–£900.00
High season per wk
£750.00–£950.00

This lovely spacious riverside townhouse has 4 bedrooms. Magnificent views. Dome, Greenwich, Canary Wharf and local Underground nearby, speedily reaches London's theatreland etc. for reasonable cost.

USE YOUR *i*s

There are more than 550 Tourist Information Centres throughout England offering friendly help with accommodation and holiday ideas as well as suggestions of places to visit and things to do. You'll find TIC addresses in the local Phone Book.

LONDON N1

★★–★★★

2 Units
Sleeping 5

RAY'S APARTMENTS
Northdown Street, King's Cross, London N1
Contact: Mr Raymond Dwek, Proprietor, 28 Abbottshall
Avenue, Southgate, London N14 7JX
T: 07944 313768 (mobile)
E: raydwek@shalom36.co.uk

OPEN All year round

Low season per wk
£600.00–£700.00
High season per wk
£650.00–£750.00

Two quiet maisonettes in the heart of London. The accommodation is smart, attractive and well equipped and is only 2 minutes from King's Cross station.

LONDON N7

★★–★★★

3 Units
Sleeping 2–5

CARENA HOLIDAY ACCOMMODATION
79 St George's Avenue, Tufnell Park, London N7 0AJ
Contact: Mr M Chouthi, 98 St George's Avenue,
Tufnell Park, London N7 0AH
T: (020) 7607 7453 (Answerphone) &
07860 329802 (Mobile)
F: (020) 7607 7453
E: colin.chouthi@talk21.com
I: carena.members.beeb.net

OPEN All year round

Low season per wk
£275.00–£475.00
High season per wk
£300.00–£500.00

In quiet road with free street parking. Comfortable apartments with a range of quality facilities and services. Perfectly positioned for easy access to London.

LONDON N16

★★

1 Unit
Sleeping 4

A self-catering penthouse apartment with roof terrace. It is split level with a glass bedroom upstairs that leads on to the roof terrace.

OLD STREET PENTHOUSE

London Holiday Accommodation, 34 Brunel Hse,
The Guinness Trust, London N16 5TE
Contact: Ms Karen Walker, London Holiday
Accommodation, 34 Brunel House, Guinness Trust,
Stamford Hill, London N16 5TF
T: (020) 8800 5908
E: sales@londonholiday.co.uk
I: www.londonholiday.co.uk

OPEN All year round
CC: Amex, Barclaycard,
Delta, Diners, Eurocard,
JCB, Maestro, Mastercard,
Solo, Switch, Visa, Visa
Electron

Low season per wk
£560.00
High season per wk
£560.00

LONDON N21

★★★★

1 Unit
Sleeping 6

Elegant, very spacious, luxurious yet homely units, fitted and maintained to the utmost standards of cleanliness and comfort, situated in a very fashionable and accessible part of North London. The property is set in a quiet and clean, tree-lined road, adorned with beautifully maintained gardens and immaculate playing fields.

FIRS APARTMENTS

28-30 Firs Lane, London N21 3ES
Contact: Mrs A M Turanli, 30 Firs Lane, London N21 3ES
T: (020) 8360 3890 & 7354 0802
F: (020) 8360 3890
E: information@firsapartments.com
I: www.firsapartments.com

OPEN All year round
CC: Barclaycard,
Mastercard, Visa

Low season per wk
£350.00–£400.00
High season per wk
£450.00–£500.00

RATING All accommodation in this guide has been rated, or is awaiting a rating, by a trained English Tourism Council assessor.

LONDON NW2

★

1 Unit
Sleeping 3–6

THE VILLAGE PROPERTY SERVICES
98 Dollis Hill Avenue, London NW2 6QX
T: (020) 8452 5327
F: (020) 8452 0903
Contact: Mr M A Abeyakoon

OPEN All year round
CC: Amex, Barclaycard,
Diners, Eurocard, JCB,
Mastercard, Visa

Low season per wk
£300.00–£600.00
High season per wk
£400.00–£1,200.00

*Self-contained apartment in safe residential location at realistic weekly rental.
Convenient for West End shops, theatre, cinema, etc.*

LONDON SE6

★★★–★★★★★

9 Units
Sleeping 2–6

*Two converted Victorian family
houses on adjoining plots offer
spacious accommodation. Use of
large garden, indoor heated pool,
steam room, sauna and games room.
Child friendly. Off-street parking.
Well-equipped apartments with
comfortable, homely, relaxing
atmosphere.*

GLENTHURSTON HOLIDAY APARTMENTS

27-29 Canadian Avenue, London SE6 3AU
T: (020) 8690 3992
F: (020) 8265 5872
E: suehalliday@cwcom.net
I: www.glenthurston.co.uk
Contact: Miss Sue Halliday & Mrs C E Halliday

OPEN All year round
CC: Delta, Eurocard,
Mastercard, Solo, Switch,
Visa, Visa Electron

Low season per wk
£485.00–£655.00
High season per wk
£510.00–£700.00

LONDON SE10

★★★★

1 Unit
Sleeping 4

HARBOUR MASTER'S HOUSE BASEMENT FLAT
20 Ballast Quay, London SE10 9PD
Contact: Dr Chris French, The Harbour Master's House,
20 Ballast Quay, London SE10 9PD
T: (020) 8293 9597
F: (020) 8853 2865
E: harbourmaster@lineone.net
I: www.website.lineone.net/~harbourmaster/

OPEN All year round

Low season per wk
£455.00–£595.00
High season per wk
£525.00–£665.00

*Superb self-contained flat, part of the historic Harbour Master's house (Grade II
Listed). Situated on attractive riverside enclave on the Thames in maritime Greenwich.*

LONDON SW3

★★★★★
SERVICED APARTMENTS

21 Units
Sleeping 2–8

*1-4 bedroom traditionally decorated,
luxury apartments in heart of
Knightsbridge. 24-hour guest
services and daily maid service
available. 250 yards from Harrods
and close to Hyde Park. West End
shopping, theatres and restaurants
and many attractions nearby.
Complimentary membership at
Champney's Health Club available
during your stay.*

BEAUFORT HOUSE

45-47 Beaufort Gardens, Knightsbridge, London SW3 1PN
Contact: Mr J Garcia, Beaufort House,
45-47 Beaufort Gardens, London SW3 1PN
T: (020) 7584 2600
F: (020) 7584 6532
E: info@beauforthouse.co.uk
I: www.beauforthouse.co.uk

OPEN All year round
CC: Amex, Barclaycard,
Delta, Diners, JCB,
Mastercard, Switch, Visa

Low season per wk
£245.00–£685.00
High season per wk
£270.00–£775.00

CONFIRM YOUR BOOKING
You are advised to confirm your booking in writing.

LONDON SW5

★★★

18 Units
Sleeping 4–5

Centrally located, high-standard apartments. Close to Knightsbridge, Earl's Court and Olympia. Daily rates available. Daily maid service. We welcome families. We have 3 children of our own and understand your needs for quality, cleanliness and good value for money. Robert and Polly Arnold look forward to welcoming you.

EMPERORS GATE SHORT STAY APARTMENTS

8 Knaresborough Place, Kensington, London SW5 0TG
T: (020) 7244 8409
F: (020) 7373 6455
E: info@apartment-hotels.com
I: www.apartment-hotels.com
Contact: Mr R G Arnold

OPEN All year round
CC: Amex, Barclaycard, Delta, Diners, Eurocard, JCB, Mastercard, Switch, Visa

Low season per wk
£595.00–£995.00
High season per wk
£700.00–£1,190.00

LONDON SW18

★★★–★★★★★

2 Units
Sleeping 3–6

BEAUMONT APARTMENTS
24 Combemartin Road, Southfields, London SW18 5PR
T: (020) 8789 2663
F: (020) 8265 5499
E: afriat@mistral.co.uk
I: www.beaumont-london-apartments.co.uk
Contact: Mr & Mrs A Afriat

OPEN All year round
CC: Amex, Barclaycard, Delta, Eurocard, JCB, Mastercard, Solo, Switch, Visa, Visa Electron

Low season per wk
£470.00–£650.00
High season per wk
£500.00–£780.00

Well-appointed flats in leafiest suburb within 25 minutes of West End. Close to zone 3 underground, Wimbledon tennis and convenient for A3, M4, M41, M25, Heathrow, Gatwick.

LONDON SW19

★★★

1 Unit
Sleeping 5

Just moments from Wimbledon Village's fashionable shops and restaurants, this delightful period cottage is tucked away in a quiet cul-de-sac. Charmingly and beautifully furnished sitting room, dining room. Compact, well-equipped kitchen and two small pretty bedrooms (one double, one twin). Sofa bed in the lounge. Bathroom with overhead shower.

HONEY COTTAGE

6 Oldfield Road, Wimbledon, London SW19 4SD
Contact: Mrs Jenny Humphries, 16 Dudley Road, Wimbledon, London SW19 8PN
T: (020) 8542 7798 & 8542 7798 (Home)
F: (020) 8395 7353
E: mikejenny@compuserve.com
I: www.honeycottage.com

OPEN All year round

Low season per wk
£350.00–£400.00
High season per wk
£400.00–£550.00

AT-A-GLANCE SYMBOLS

Symbols at the end of each accommodation entry give useful information about services and facilities. A key to symbols can be found inside the back cover flap. Keep this open for easy reference.

41

LONDON W4

★★★★

3 Units
Sleeping 4

Spacious, 2-bedroom 2-bathroom apartments, in a charming location very close to the River Thames, Hogarth House and miles of open space, but with excellent transport links into and out of London. Apartments have been professionally interior designed and equipped to accommodate both the business traveller and tourist.

MALTINGS LODGE

C & R Housing Services, Malden Way, New Malden KT3 5QX
Contact: Ms Anita Manger, C & R Housing Services, 167 Malden Way, New Malden KT3 5QX
T: (020) 8336 0119 (Mainline and Answerphone) & 07711 727181 (Mobile)
F: (020) 8336 0119
E: enquiries@crh.co.uk
I: www.crh.co.uk

OPEN All year round
CC: Amex, Barclaycard, Delta, Eurocard, JCB, Maestro, Mastercard, Solo, Switch, Visa

Low season per wk
£850.00
High season per wk
£850.00–£895.00

Special reduced rates for Christmas/New Year period.

LONDON W5

★★★–★★★★

2 Units
Sleeping 2–4

Situated in Ealing, a fashionable suburb with a vibrant university community. Three spacious apartments in a Victorian house, pretty garden with patio. Alternatively a ground floor apartment in a modern development. Locations in leafy residential areas, easy access to underground, motorways and buses. Excellent shops and restaurants. Free parking provided.

CLARENDON HOUSE APARTMENTS

Ranelagh Road, Ealing, London W5 5RJ
Contact: Mrs Anne Pedley, 21E Harewood Close, Bexhill TN39 3LX
T: (01424) 212954 & (020) 8567 0314 (Property)
F: (01424) 212954
E: clarendon.house@LineOne.net
I: www.clarendonhouseapartments.co.uk

OPEN All year round
CC: Delta, Mastercard, Solo, Switch, Visa

Low season per wk
£340.00–£520.00
High season per wk
£380.00–£570.00

LONDON W13

★★–★★★

6 Units
Sleeping 3–6

Attractive, fully-equipped apartments for business and holiday travellers. Located in quiet tree-lined residential street. Ealing Broadway Underground station, lively bars and restaurants, shopping malls and supermarkets within walking distance. Unrestricted parking. Fast tube connection to all London's tourist attractions and Heathrow Airport. Easy access to M40/M4 motorways.

APARTMENTS WEST LONDON

94 Gordon Road, and 10 Hastings Road, London W13 8PT
Contact: Mr W G Smith, Apartments West London, 94 Gordon Road, London W13 8PT
T: (020) 8566 8187 & (01895) 233365
F: (020) 8566 7670
E: info@apartmentswestlondon.com
I: www.apartmentswestlondon.com

OPEN All year round
CC: Barclaycard, Delta, Eurocard, JCB, Maestro, Mastercard, Solo, Switch, Visa, Visa Electron

Low season per wk
£320.00–£580.00
High season per wk
£320.00–£620.00

OUTER LONDON
BECKENHAM

★-★★★

8 Units
Sleeping 2–6

OAKFIELD ESTATES

107 South Eden Park Road, Beckenham BR3 3AX
T: (020) 8658 4441
F: (020) 8658 9198
E: hols@oakfield.co.uk
I: www.oakfield.co.uk
Contact: Mr J E Deane

Victorian mansion with a large garden in a semi-rural setting. 3 minutes' walk to Eden Park rail station. 25 minutes by rail or 14 kilometres by road to central London. Mr and Mrs Deane live on the premises and welcome children but not pets.

OPEN All year round
CC: Eurocard, Mastercard, Solo, Switch, Visa, Visa Electron

Low season per wk
£210.00–£600.00
High season per wk
£210.00–£600.00

CROYDON, Greater London *Tourist Information Centre Tel: (020) 8253 1009*

★★★

6 Units
Sleeping 4

S N D APARTMENTS
1 Mulgrave Road, Croydon CR0 1BL
T: (020) 8688 7870
F: (020) 8686 7835
E: mulgrave.road@ukgateway.net
Contact: Mrs Pamela Pereira

Apartments with own kitchen and bathroom, in quiet road near East Croydon station (London 15 minutes by train).

OPEN All year round
CC: Mastercard

Low season per wk
£350.00–£600.00

KINGSTON UPON THAMES, Greater London *Tourist Information Centre Tel: (020) 8547 5592*

★★★★

1 Unit
Sleeping 4

3 BECKETTS PLACE
Hampton Wick, Kingston upon Thames KT1 4EQ
Contact: Mr & Mrs A Bernhard, 2 Becketts Place, Hampton Wick, Kingston upon Thames KT1 4EQ
T: (020) 8943 3464 & 8943 3464
E: aebernhard@email.com

Self-contained riverside apartment with own balcony and garden, overlooking boats at their moorings. An establishment that offers a wonderful location and excellent facilities to its guests.

OPEN All year round

High season per wk
£600.00–£800.00

PINNER

★★★★

1 Unit
Sleeping 4–5

MOSS COTTAGE
2 Moss Lane, Pinner HA5 3AX
Contact: Ms Barbara Le Quesne, Proprietor, Moss Lane Cottages, 31 Paines Lane, Pinner HA5 3BU
T: (020) 8868 5507
F: (020) 8868 5507
E: bemail2@aol.com
I: www.moss-lane-cottages.com

Wing of 17thC Listed building overlooking woodland garden. 3 bedrooms, fully equipped kitchen, lounge/dining room, private patio. Convenient for rail, M25, M40 and Heathrow.

OPEN All year round
CC: Mastercard, Switch, Visa

Low season per wk
£650.00–£700.00
High season per wk
£700.00–£770.00

QUALITY ASSURANCE SCHEME

For an explanation of the quality and facilities represented by the Stars please refer to the front of this guide. A more detailed explanation can be found in the information pages at the back.

Where to Stay 2002

The official and best selling guides,
offering the reassurance of quality assured accommodation

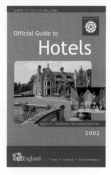

Hotels, Townhouses and
Travel Accommodation
in England 2002
£10.99

Guesthouses, Bed &
Breakfast, Farmhouses
and Inns in England 2002
£11.99

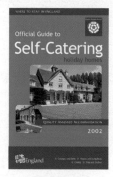

Self Catering
Holiday Homes
in England 2002
£9.99

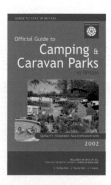

Camping & Caravan Parks
in Britain 2002
£5.99

Somewhere Special
in England 2002
£7.99

Look out also for:
SOMEWHERE SPECIAL
IN ENGLAND 2002

Accommodation
achieving the highest
standards in facilities
and quality of service -

the perfect guide for the
discerning traveller.

**NOW ALSO FEATURING
SELF CATERING
ACCOMMODATION**

The guides include

• **Accommodation entries packed with information** • **Full colour maps**
• **Places to visit** • **Tourist Information Centres**

INFORMATIVE • EASY TO USE • GREAT VALUE FOR MONEY

From all good bookshops or by mail order from the ETC Fulfilment Centre,
PO Box 22489, London W6 9FR
Tel: 0870 606 7204 Fax: 020 8563 3048
Email: fulfilment@englishtourism.org.uk Web: www.englishtourism.org.uk

CUMBRIA

Cumbria's dramatic and breathtaking landscapes, from the famous Lakes to the rugged mountains and fells, have inspired poets and artists for hundreds of years.

classic sights
Hadrian's Wall – a reminder of Roman occupation
Lake Windermere – largest lake in England

coast & country
Scafell Pike – England's highest mountain
Whitehaven – historic port

literary links
William Wordsworth – The poet's homes: Wordsworth House, Dove Cottage and Rydal Mount
Beatrix Potter – Her home, Hill Top; her watercolours at the Beatrix Potter Gallery and the tales at The World of Beatrix Potter

distinctively different
The Gondola – sail Coniston Water aboard the opulent 1859 steam yacht Gondola
Cars of the Stars Museum – cars from TV and film, including Chitty Chitty Bang Bang and the Batmobile

The county of Cumbria

FOR MORE INFORMATION CONTACT:
Cumbria Tourist Board
Ashleigh, Holly Road, Windermere,
Cumbria LA23 2AQ
Tel: (015394) 44444 Fax: (015394) 44041
Email: mail@cumbria-tourist-board.co.uk
Internet: www.golakes.co.uk

Places to Visit - see pages 46-49
Where to Stay - see pages 50-81

The Pictures:
1 Lake Windermere
2 Muncaster Castle
3 Walking at Wasdale

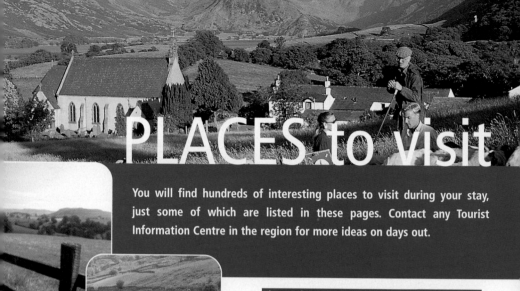

PLACES to visit

You will find hundreds of interesting places to visit during your stay, just some of which are listed in these pages. Contact any Tourist Information Centre in the region for more ideas on days out.

The Beacon

West Strand, Whitehaven, Cumbria CA28 7LY
Tel: (01946) 592302 www.copelandbc.gov.uk
Discover the industrial, maritime and social history of Whitehaven and surrounding area. Includes Meteorology Office weather gallery with satellite-linked equipment.

Birdoswald Roman Fort

Gilsland, Carlisle, Cumbria CA8 7DD
Tel: (016977) 47602
Remains of Roman fort on one of the best parts of Hadrian's Wall with excellent views of the Irthing Gorge. Exhibition, shop, tearooms and excavations.

Brantwood, Home of John Ruskin

Coniston, Cumbria LA21 8AD
Tel: (015394) 41396 www.brantwood.org.uk
Superb lake and mountain views. Works by Ruskin and contemporaries, memorabilia, Ruskin watercolours, craft and picture gallery, gardens.

Cars of the Stars Motor Museum

Standish Street, Keswick, Cumbria CA12 5LS
Tel: (017687) 73757 www.carsofthestars.com
Features TV and film vehicles including the Batmobile, Chitty Chitty Bang Bang, the James Bond collection, Herbie, FAB 1, plus many other famous cars and motorcycles.

The Dock Museum

North Road, Barrow-in-Furness, Cumbria LA14 2PW
Tel: (01229) 894444 www.barrowtourism.co.uk
The museum presents the story of steel shipbuilding, for which Barrow is famous, and straddles a Victorian graving dock. Interactive displays, nautical adventure playground.

Dove Cottage and Wandsworth Museum

Town End, Grasmere, Ambleside, Cumbria LA22 9SH
Tel: (015394) 35544 www.wordsworth.org.uk
Wordsworth's home 1799-1808. Poet's possessions. Museum with manuscripts, farmhouse reconstruction, paintings and drawings. Special events throughout the year.

Eden Ostrich World

Langwathby Hall Farm, Langwathby Hall, Langwathby, Penrith, Cumbria CA10 1LW
Tel: (01768) 881771 www.ostrich-world.com
Working farm with ostriches and other rare breed animals. Play areas, riverside walk, tearooms and gift shop. An enjoyable day out for the whole family.

Furness Abbey

Barrow-in-Furness, Cumbria LA13 0TJ
Tel: (01229) 823420
Ruins of 12thC Cistercian abbey, the 2nd wealthiest in England. Extensive remains include transepts, choir and west tower of church, canopied seats, arches, church.

Gleaston Water Mill

Gleaston, Ulverston, Cumbria LA12 0QH
Tel: (01229) 869244 www.watermill.co.uk
Water-driven corn mill in working order. Impressive
wooden machinery and water-wheel. Farm equipment
and tools display. Craft workshop, craft videos and
rare breeds.

Heron Glass

The Lakes Glass Centre, Oubas Hill, Ulverston,
Cumbria LA12 7LY
Tel: (01229) 581121
Heron Glass is a combined visitor centre and workshop
where you will find traditional glass-making
demonstrations daily with a chance of purchasing
glassware at the factory shop.

Hill Top

Near Sawrey, Ambleside, Cumbria LA22 0LF
Tel: (015394) 36269 www.nationaltrust.org.uk
Beatrix Potter wrote many of her popular Peter Rabbit
stories and other books in this charming little house
which still contains her own china and furniture.

Jennings Brothers, The Castle Brewery

Cockermouth, Cumbria CA13 9NE
Tel: (01900) 821011 www.jenningsbrewery.co.uk
Guided tours of Jennings traditional brewery. The brewery
uses the finest well water, malt, hops, sugar and yeast to
brew distinctive local beers.

K Village Outlet Centre

Lound Road, Netherfield, Kendal, Cumbria LA9 7DA
Tel: (01539) 732363 www.kvillage.co.uk
Famous named brands such as K-shoes, Van Heusen,
Denby, National Trust Shop, Tog24 and Ponden Mill,
all at discounts. Open 7 days per week with full
disabled access.

The Lake District Coast Aquarium

Maryport South Quay, Maryport, Cumbria CA15 8AB
Tel: (01900) 817760
www.lakedistrict-coastaquarium.co.uk
Purpose-built independent aquarium with over 35
displays. Largest collection of native marine species in
Cumbria. Cafe and gift shop.

The Lake District Visitor Centre

Brockhole, Windermere, Cumbria LA23 1LJ
Tel: (015394) 46601 www.lake-district.gov.uk
Interactive exhibitions, audio-visual show, shop, gardens,
grounds, adventure playground, dry-stone walling area,
trails, events and croquet. Cafe with home-cooked food.

Lakeland Motor Museum

Holker Hall, Cark in Cartmel, Grange-over-Sands,
Cumbria LA11 7PL
Tel: (015395) 58509 www.holker-hall.co.uk
Over 10,000 exhibits including rare motoring
automobilia. A 1930s garage re-creation and the
Campbell Legend Bluebird Exhibition.

Lakeland Sheep and Wool Centre

Egremont Road, Cockermouth, Cumbria CA13 0QX
Tel: (01900) 822673 www.shepherdshotel.co.uk
An all-weather attraction with live sheep shows including
working-dog demonstrations. Also large screen and other
tourism exhibitions on the area, a gift shop and cafe.

Lakeland Wildlife Oasis

Hale Milnthorpe, Cumbria LA7 7BW
Tel: (015395) 63027 www.wildlifeoasis.co.uk
A wildlife exhibition where both living animals and
inanimate hands-on displays are used to illustrate
evolution in the animal kingdom. Includes gift shop
and cafe.

The Pictures:
1 Kirkstile Inn
2 Watendlath Bridge
3 Loughrigg
4 Shoreline, Derwentwater

Lowther Parklands

Hackthorpe, Penrith, Cumbria CA10 2HG
Tel: (01931) 712523
Attractions include exotic birds and animals, rides, miniature railway, boating lake, play areas, adventure fort, Tarzan trail, international circus and a puppet theatre.

Muncaster Castle, Gardens, Owl Centre and Meadow Vole Maze

Ravenglass, Cumbria CA18 1RQ
Tel: (01229) 717614 www.muncastercastle.co.uk
Muncaster Castle has the most beautifully situated Owl Centre in the world. See the birds fly, picnic in the gardens, and visit the Pennington family home.

Ravenglass and Eskdale Railway

Ravenglass, Cumbria CA18 1SW
Tel: (01229) 717171 www.ravenglass-railway.co.uk
England's oldest narrow-gauge railway runs for 7 miles through glorious scenery to the foot of England's highest hills. Most trains are steam hauled.

Rheged - The Village in the Hill

Redhills, Penrith, Cumbria CA11 0DQ
Tel: (01768) 868000 www.rheged.com
Cumbria's new visitor attraction with Europe's largest grass-covered building. Discover speciality shops, restaurants, artist exhibitions, pottery demonstrations, children's play area and The National Mountaineering Exhibition.

The Rum Story

27 Lowther Street, Whitehaven, Cumbria CA28 7DN
Tel: (01946) 592933 www.rumstory.co.uk
'The Rum Story' - an authentic, heritage-based experience, depicting the unique story of the UK rum trade in the original Jefferson's wine merchant premises.

Sizergh Castle

Kendal, Cumbria LA8 8AE
Tel: (015395) 60070 www.nationaltrust.org.uk
Strickland family home for 750 years, now National Trust owned. With 14thC pele tower, 15thC great hall, 16thC wings. Stuart connections. Rock garden, rose garden, daffodils.

South Lakes Wild Animal Park Ltd

Crossgates, Dalton-in-Furness, Cumbria LA15 8JR
Tel: (01229) 466086 www.wildanimalpark.co.uk
Wild zoo park in over 17 acres (7 ha) of grounds. Large waterfowl ponds, cafe, toilets, car/coach park, miniature railway. Over 120 species of animals from all around the world.

South Tynedale Railway

Railway Station, Alston, Cumbria CA9 3JB
Tel: (01434) 381696 www.strps.org.uk
Narrow-gauge railway operating along 2.25 mile line from Alston to Kirkhaugh through the scenic South Tyne Valley. Steam- and diesel-hauled passenger trains.

Steam Yacht Gondola

Pier Cottage, Coniston, Cumbria LA21 8AJ
Tel: (015394) 41962
Victorian steam-powered vessel now National Trust owned and completely renovated with an opulently upholstered saloon. Superb way to appreciate the beauty of Coniston Water.

Theatre by the Lake

Lakeside, Keswick, Cumbria CA12 5DJ
Tel: (017687) 74411 www.theatrebythelake.com
Main auditorium of 400 seats, studio of 80. Exhibitions all year round. Cafe and bar.

Tullie House Museum and Art Gallery

Castle Street, Carlisle, Cumbria CA3 8TP
Tel: (01228) 534781 www.historic-carlisle.org.uk
Major tourist complex housing museum, art gallery, education facility, lecture theatre, shops, herb garden, restaurant and terrace bars.

Windermere Lake Cruises

Lakeside Pier, Newby Bridge, Ulverston, Cumbria LA12 8AS
Tel: (015395) 31188
www.windermere-lakecruises.co.uk
Steamers and launches sail between Ambleside, Bowness and Lakeside with connections for the Steam Railway, Brockhole, Ferry House, Fell Foot and the Aquarium of the Lakes.

Windermere Steamboat Museum

Rayrigg Road, Bowness-on-Windermere, Windermere, Cumbria LA23 1BN
Tel: (015394) 45565 www.steamboat.co.uk
A wealth of interest and information about life on bygone Windermere. Regular steam launch trips, vintage vessels and classic motorboats. Model boat pond, lakeside picnic area.

The World Famous Old Blacksmith's Shop Centre

Gretna Green, Gretna DG16 5EA
Tel: (01461) 338441 www.gretnagreen.com
The original Blacksmith's Shop museum and a shopping centre selling cashmere and woollen knitwear, crystal and china. Taste local produce in the Old Smithy Restaurant.

Find out more about
Cumbria

Further information about holidays and attractions in Cumbria is available from:

CUMBRIA TOURIST BOARD
Ashleigh, Holly Road, Windermere, Cumbria LA23 2AQ.
Tel: (015394) 44444 Fax: (015394) 44041
Email: mail@cumbria-tourist-board.co.uk
Internet: www.golakes.co.uk

The following publications are available from Cumbria Tourist Board:

Cumbria Tourist Board Holiday Guide (free) Tel: 08705 133059

Events Listings (free)

Cumbria The Lake District Touring Map
including tourist information and touring caravan and camping parks - £3.95

Laminated Poster - £4.50

Getting to
Cumbria

The Pictures:
1 Ullswater
2 Buttermere
3 Lake Windermere

BY ROAD: The M1/M6/M25/M40 provide a link with London and the South East and the M5/M6 provide access from the South West. The M62/M6 link Hull and Manchester with the region. Approximate journey time from London is 5 hours, from Manchester 2 hours.

BY RAIL: From London (Euston) to Oxenholme (Kendal) takes approximately 3 hours 30 minutes. From Oxenholme (connecting station for all main line trains) to Windermere takes approximately 20 minutes. From Carlisle to Barrow-in-Furness via the coastal route, with stops at many of the towns in between, takes approximately 2 hours. Trains from Edinburgh to Carlisle take 1 hour 45 minutes. The historic Settle-Carlisle line also runs through the county bringing passengers from Yorkshire via the Eden Valley.

www.travelcumbria.co.uk

Where to stay in Cumbria

Accommodation entries in this region are listed in alphabetical order of place name, and then in alphabetical order of establishment.

Map references refer to the colour location maps at the front of this guide. The first number indicates the map to use; the letter and number which follow refer to the grid reference on the map.

At-a-glance symbols at the end of each accommodation entry give useful information about services and facilities. A key to symbols can be found inside the back cover flap. Keep this open for easy reference.

A brief description of the towns and villages offering accommodation in the entries which follow, can be found at the end of this section.

A complete listing of all the English Tourism Council assessed accommodation covered by this guide appears at the back of the guide.

ALLONBY, Cumbria Map ref 5A2

★★★★

1 Unit
Sleeping 12

CROOKHURST
Crookhurst Farm, Allonby, Maryport CA15 6RB
Contact: Mrs B Wilson, Bowscale Farm, Allonby, Maryport CA15 6RB
T: (01900) 881228 & 0777 304 7591 (Mobile)
F: (01900) 881228
I: www.crookhurst.co.uk

Luxury 4-bedroomed spacious farmhouse set in open countryside 0.5 miles from village of Allonby and Solway Firth. Easy reach of Lake District and Southern Scotland. Homely environment, short breaks available. Bed linen, gas, electric, all included in price. Hire of towels on request.

OPEN All year round

Open Christmas, £950 for week. New Year also £950.

Low season per wk
£500.00–£600.00
High season per wk
£600.00–£660.00

AMBLESIDE, Cumbria Map ref 5A3 *Tourist Information Centre Tel: (015394) 32582*

✓

★★★

1 Unit
Sleeping 4

BIRCH COTTAGE
8 Edinboro, Ambleside LA22 9EN
Contact: Dr L Nash, 47 Goring Road, Bounds Green,
London N11 2BT
T: (020) 8888 1252 & (0115) 969 2190
F: (020) 8888 1252

OPEN All year round

Delightful 200-year-old traditional stone cottage in a quiet hamlet with mountain views. Five minutes' walk to village centre. Comfortably furnished, well-equipped. No smokers.

Low season per wk
Min £175.00
High season per wk
Max £335.00

AMBLESIDE continued

★★★★
1 Unit
Sleeping 4

Alpine-style log cabin set in 0.5 acres of tranquil woodland. Tastefully furnished and extravagantly equipped. Shared use of indoor heated pool, sauna and jacuzzi. Be close to nature, our neighbours and visitors often include red squirrels, deer, sheep and a badger. No smoking throughout. Family dog welcomed.

BLELHAM TARN AT NEAUM CRAG

✓
No

Foul Step Lane, Loughrigg, Ambleside LA22 9HG
Contact: Mrs Sue Witts, P O Box 73, Newport TF10 8WG
T: 07740 486947 (Mobile direct to owner)
& (01952) 810101
F: (01952) 810102
E: sales@pad-lok.com
I: www.pad-lok.com

OPEN Mar–Nov
CC: Barclaycard, Mastercard, Switch, Visa

3 night long weekends. 4 night mid-week breaks. 10% discount for 7 nights. Book on-line.

Low season per wk
£300.00–£450.00
High season per wk
£400.00–£600.00

★★★
3 Units
Sleeping 4–6

Two charming cottages and a bungalow converted from a former coach house and tack room, furnished to a high standard. Set in idyllic surroundings overlooking Lake Windermere with panoramic views of the Lakeland mountains. High Wray is a quiet hamlet between Ambleside and Hawkshead. Ideal base for walking/touring.

CHESTNUTS, BEECHES AND THE GRANARY

✓
No

High Wray Bank, High Wray, Ambleside LA22 0JD
Contact: Mr J R Benson, High Sett, Sun Hill Lane, Troutbeck Bridge, Windermere LA23 1HJ
T: (015394) 42731 & 07971 984232 (Mobile)
F: (015394) 42731
E: s.benson@talk21.com
I: www.accommodationlakedistrict.com

OPEN All year round

Low season per wk
£185.00–£500.00
High season per wk
£185.00–£450.00

★★★
1 Unit
Sleeping 5

DOWER HOUSE COTTAGE
Dower House, Wray Castle, Ambleside LA22 0JA
Contact: Mrs Margaret Rigg, The Dower House, Wray Castle, Ambleside LA22 0JA
T: (015394) 33211

OPEN All year round

Low season per wk
£233.00–£308.00
High season per wk
£352.00–£447.00

Self-catering cottage with 2 bedrooms, large kitchen, dining-room, large sitting-room, bathroom. French windows opening onto terrace and gardens.

★★★
1 Unit
Sleeping 6

HOLE HOUSE
High Wray, Ambleside LA22 0JF
Contact: Mrs Clare Irvine, Hole House, Tock How Farm, High Wray, Ambleside LA22 0JF
T: (015394) 36106 & 36294
F: (015394) 36294
I: www.tock-how-farm.com

OPEN All year round

Low season per wk
£190.00–£250.00
High season per wk
£450.00–£500.00

Charming 17thC cottage with wonderful panoramic views, once owned by Beatrix Potter. Restored to provide comfortable accommodation without losing its old world charm. Log fires.

WHERE TO STAY
Please mention this guide when making your booking.

AMBLESIDE continued

★★★★

3 Units
Sleeping 2–6

OLD COACH HOUSE, RIVERSIDE AND GARDEN COTTAGES
Clappersgate, Ambleside LA22 9ND   OPEN All year round
Contact: Mr V R Vyner-Brooks, Old Coach House,
Riverside and Garden Cottages, Middle Barrows Green,
Kendal LA8 0JG
T: (0151526) 5451/9321 & (015395) 60242
F: (0151) 526 1331
I: www.primecottages.co.uk

Low season per wk
£331.00–£419.00
High season per wk
£360.00–£935.00

*Cottages furnished and equipped to a very high standard. Old Coach House and
Riverside Cottage have 4-poster beds. Visit our website at www.primecottages.co.uk.*

★-★★

7 Units
Sleeping 4–6

RAMSTEADS
Outgate, Ambleside LA22 0NH   OPEN Mar–Nov
T: (015394) 36583
Contact: Mr G Evans

Low season per wk
£155.00–£300.00
High season per wk
£230.00–£380.00

*Timber lodges in 25 acres of natural woodland. Ideal centre for walkers, bird-watchers
and country lovers.*

★★★★

1 Unit
Sleeping 6

WAYSIDE COTTAGE
Clappersgate, Ambleside LA22 9LE   OPEN All year round
Contact: Dr Leech, 22 Styvechale Avenue, Coventry
CV5 6DX
T: (02476) 677549 (Home) & 07712 353201
E: waysidecottage@lineone.net
I: website.lineone.net/~waysidecottage

Low season per wk
£265.00–£365.00
High season per wk
£425.00–£520.00

*Charming old cottage, modernised to a high standard of comfort, retaining period
features. Oak beams, fireplace, antiques. Ambleside 1 mile. Many walks from the door.*

APPLEBY-IN-WESTMORLAND, Cumbria Map ref 5B3 *Tourist Information Centre Tel: (017683) 51177*

★★★★

1 Unit
Sleeping 9

DUNKIRK
Reagill, Penrith CA10 3ER   OPEN All year round
Contact: Mr Paul Crosbie, 30 Eagle Wharf Court,
Lafone Street, London SE1 2LZ
T: (020) 7403 7346 & 07970 940935 (Mobile)
E: paul.crosbie@the-sun.co.uk

Low season per wk
Min £340.00
High season per wk
Max £450.00

*Well-equipped cottage/barn conversion, oil central heating, wood-burning stove. In
quiet location, spacious grounds. Ideal for northern Lakes and Eden Valley.
Accommodates 8/9.*

BAILEY, Cumbria Map ref 5B2

★★★★

3 Units
Sleeping 4–8

SAUGHS FARM COTTAGES

Saughs Farm, Bailey, Newcastleton TD9 0TT
T: (016977) 48346 (Answerphone) & 48000
F: (016977) 48346
E: skylark@onholiday.co.uk
I: www.skylarkcottages.co.uk
Contact: Mrs Jane Gray

*Quality cottages converted from old byres on
conservation farm close to Scottish Border. Full
of character, cosy, stylish, each with a
woodburner stove. Panoramic views. Good
walking, cycling, riding. Forest bridleways, Reiver
Cycle Trail, stabling facilities. Historic area. Visit
Lake District, Scotland, Hadrian's Wall or Solway
Coast.*

OPEN All year round

Occasional short breaks from
£150. Discounts on multiple
bookings and longer stays.

Low season per wk
£200.00–£300.00
High season per wk
£285.00–£335.00

NB

IMPORTANT NOTE Information on accommodation listed
in this guide has been supplied by the proprietors. As changes may occur
you are advised to check details at the time of booking.

BASSENTHWAITE, Cumbria Map ref 5A2

★★★★
5 Units
Sleeping 2–6

Irton House Farm

Self Catering for you with a beautiful view

IRTON HOUSE FARM

Isel, Cockermouth CA13 9ST
T: (017687) 76380 (Answerphone)
F: (017687) 76090
E: almond@farmersweekly.net
I: www.almondirtonhousefarm.com
Contact: Mr and Mrs R W Almond

Immaculate, spacious properties for 2, 4 or 6 people. All furnished to a high specification for your enjoyment and convenience. Shopping centres at Keswick and Cockermouth. Superb views, walks and places of interest including the new Lakeside Theatre at Keswick. Also local inns and hotels serving good food. Prices are for 2 people.

OPEN All year round
CC: Barclaycard,
Mastercard, Visa

Short breaks (3 night minimum) in low season (excl Christmas and New Year).

Low season per wk
£250.00–£295.00
High season per wk
£295.00–£335.00

BORROWDALE, Cumbria Map ref 5A3

★★–★★★★★
2 Units
Sleeping 2

ROCKERY COTTAGE & MAIDEN MOOR COTTAGE
Greenbank Country House Hotel Ltd, Borrowdale,
Keswick CA12 5UY
Contact: Mrs Wood, Greenbank, Borrowdale, Keswick
CA12 5UY
T: (017687) 77215

OPEN All year round
CC: Barclaycard, Delta,
Maestro, Mastercard,
Switch, Visa

Low season per wk
£150.00–£250.00
High season per wk
£200.00–£450.00

Quiet and very well-equipped comfortable cottages. Central heating. Meals available in adjacent hotel. Magnificent views over Borrowdale Valley.

BOTHEL, Cumbria Map ref 5A2

★★★★
1 Unit
Sleeping 5

THE LODGE

Quarry House, Bothel, Wigton CA7 2HH
Contact: Mrs D E Shankland, Quarry House, Bothel,
Wigton CA7 2HH
T: (016973) 21674 & 07751 765087 (Mobile)
E: quarrylodgebothel@barclays.net

This timber lodge stands in an elevated position, with magnificent views across open countryside to the Solway Firth and the Scottish mountains beyond. Situated on the fringe of the national park, this is an ideal base for visiting the northern lakes and Solway coast.

OPEN All year round

Reductions for 2 persons and senior citizens. Short breaks available Nov-Dec.

Low season per wk
Min £165.00
High season per wk
Max £365.00

IDEAS For ideas on places to visit refer to the introduction at the beginning of this section.

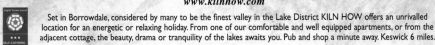

Borrowdale Self Catering Holidays

Resident Owners
Mr. & Mrs. P. Davis-Merry,
Kiln How, Rosthwaite, Keswick,
Cumbria CA12 5XB
Tel: 017687 77356 Fax: 017687 77727
Email: info@kilnhow.com
www.kilnhow.com

Kiln How

Set in Borrowdale, considered by many to be the finest valley in the Lake District KILN HOW offers an unrivalled location for an energetic or relaxing holiday. From one of our comfortable and well equipped apartments, or from the adjacent cottage, the beauty, drama or tranquility of the lakes awaits you. Pub and shop a minute away. Keswick 6 miles.

Per week £110–£495. Sleeps 2-6. Short winter breaks available.

BROUGHTON-IN-FURNESS, Cumbria Map ref 5A3

Rating
Applied For
4 Units
Sleeping 2–5

COOKSONS COTTAGES
Broadgate, Thwaites, Millom LA18 5JY
Contact: Mr David Lewthwaite, Broadgate, Thwaites,
Millom LA18 5JY
T: (01229) 716295
F: (01229) 716976
E: david@lewthwaite.fsbusiness.co.uk

OPEN All year round

Low season per wk
£85.00–£145.00
High season per wk
£145.00–£298.00

Whitewashed cottage in lovely countryside with good walks and beautiful views. Three bedrooms, sleeps up to 5 persons but available to couples. Open log fire.

★★★-★★★★
5 Units
Sleeping 2–6

RING HOUSE COTTAGES
Woodland, Broughton-in-Furness LA20 6DG
T: (01229) 716578
F: (01229) 716850
E: info@ringhouse.co.uk
I: www.ringhouse.co.uk
Contact: Mr and Mrs Stuart & Lynda Harrison

Cottages set in the beautiful and unspoilt 'Woodland Valley' provide an excellent base for outdoor activies or relaxing short breaks. All cottages are centrally heated and fully-equipped, including bedding and towels. Electricity, gas and fuel for log fires are also included in the price you pay.

OPEN All year round
CC: Barclaycard, Delta,
Mastercard, Switch, Visa

Low season per wk
£170.00–£275.00
High season per wk
£250.00–£490.00

[handwritten notes: 3 mile from Cumbian Lakes. Woodland Valley. 2 double + twin bed: pantry farmhouse! Latter Riggs natural play area]

[handwritten: Mon-Thurs only] *[handwritten: — 6/3 – 6/6 34 nights $255]*

CALDBECK, Cumbria Map ref 5A2

★★★★
1 Unit
Sleeping 3

MANOR COTTAGE
Fellside, Caldbeck, Wigton CA7 8HA
T: (016974) 78214
Contact: Mrs Ann Wade

OPEN All year round

Low season per wk
£120.00–£200.00
High season per wk
£200.00–£300.00

Converted barn with pine beams, nestling in the Caldbeck Fells in unspoilt Northern Lakeland. Comfortable, well-equipped. Panoramic views with garden and patio opening on to fells.

CARLETON, Cumbria Map ref 5A2

★★★★
2 Units
Sleeping 2–6

NEWBIGGIN HALL
Carleton, Carlisle CA4 0AJ
T: (01228) 527549
Contact: Mr and Mrs D Bates

Beautiful country mansion, built as a pele-tower in 1304, with late additions in the Queen Anne and Georgian periods. Set in 3 acres of delighful grounds, the house offers 2 charming apartments for 4/6, and a ground floor cotttage for 2/3. Only 4 miles south of Carlisle, yet with superb access to the Lakes, Borders, Solway Coast and Roman Wall.

OPEN All year round

Low season per wk
£185.00–£250.00
High season per wk
£270.00–£420.00

QUALITY ASSURANCE SCHEME
Star ratings were correct at the time of going to press but are subject to change. Please check at the time of booking.

★★★★
1 Unit
Sleeping 4

Situated 14 miles north Carlisle, midway Gretna Green and Hadrian's Wall, 3 superior 2-bedroom courtyard cottages enjoying extensive Borderland views. Touring base for Lake District and south Scotland. Swim in the pool, meander through the meadows, picnic by the stream, dine in the farm restaurant – simply unwind. Phone for colour brochure.

BESSIESTOWN FARM COUNTRY COTTAGES

Catlowdy, Longtown, Carlisle CA6 5QP
T: (01228) 577219 & 577019
F: (01228) 577219
E: bestbb2000@cs.com
I: www.bessiestown.co.uk
Contact: Mr John Sisson

OPEN All year round	Low season per wk
CC: Barclaycard, Mastercard, Visa	£195.00–£375.00
	High season per wk
3-night breaks. Specialist country craft courses. Phone for more details.	£200.00–£425.00

⚫⚫Ⓜ◎⚫⚫.☉⚫⚫Ⓣ🆅⚫⚫⚫P⚫U⚫⚫SP

★★★–★★★★★
4 Units
Sleeping 2–8

Set amidst beautiful countryside close to the Scottish Borders, our fully centrally heated cottages offer a high standard of accommodation with all modern-day facilites. A wide range of leisure and recreational activities are within a few minutes' drive from the farm. Our on-site dining room will make your stay more enjoyable.

MEADOW VIEW, BURN COTTAGE & ALD PALLYARDS

New Pallyards, Hethersgill, Carlisle CA6 6HZ
T: (01228) 577308 & 577315
F: (01228) 577308
E: info@newpallyards.freeserve.co.uk
I: www.newpallyards.freeserve.co.uk
Contact: Mrs G Elwen

OPEN All year round	Low season per wk
CC: Barclaycard, Delta, Mastercard, Visa	Min £120.00
	High season per wk
Book any promotional week and get a voucher for dinner for 2 in our dining room. Discount on 2-week stays.	Max £460.00

⚫⚫Ⓜ◎⚫⚫.☉⚫⚫⚫Ⓣ🆅⚫⚫⚫⚫//⚫PU⚫⚫🐴⚫SP

★★★–★★★★★
2 Units
Sleeping 2–5

Escape to relaxing Lakeland hamlet in the Cartmel Valley. Your chance to sit back, enjoy lovely gardens, peaceful surroundings and make a beautiful converted barn or dairy your home for a week or two. Easy walk to 800-year-old priory and traditional village pubs. Warm welcome assured.

BECKSIDE FARM

Cartmel, Grange-over-Sands LA11 7SP
T: (015395) 36141
F: (015395) 36141
E: beckside@dircon.co.uk
I: www.beckside.co.uk
Contact: Mr & Mrs Jeremy & Mary Ratcliff

OPEN All year round	Low season per wk
	£190.00–£340.00
	High season per wk
	£445.00–£495.00

⚫⚫⚫.☉⚫⚫Ⓣ🆅⚫⚫⚫P⚫SP⚫

CREDIT CARD BOOKINGS If you book by telephone and are asked for your credit card number it is advisable to check the proprietor's policy should you cancel your reservation.

CARTMEL continued

★★★★

2 Units
Sleeping 6

Grange End, originally a Georgian barn, has been converted into 2 holiday homes just oozing character and charm, complemented by solid tree-trunks supporting the ancient roof beams, exposed stone-work, wood-panelled window seats, and of course a log fire. Step back in time, yet luxuriate in the comforts of a modern, well-equipped home.

GRANGE END COTTAGES

4/5 Meadow View, Cark in Cartmel LA11 7NZ
Contact: Mr Brian Colling, 7 Rushside Road,
Cheadle Hulme, Cheadle SK8 6NW
T: (0161) 485 7015 (Answerphone) &
07774 141916 (Mobile)
F: (0161) 355 6346
E: ibex32@aol.com
I: www.holidaycottagescumbria.com

OPEN All year round

Short breaks available,
except in school holidays.

Low season per wk
£215.00–£380.00
High season per wk
£330.00–£495.00

CASTLE CARROCK, Cumbria Map ref 5B2

★★★★–★★★★★★

5 Units
Sleeping 3–8

320-acre livestock farm. Very well-equipped, finished to highest standards. Quality character cottages, oak beams, log burning stoves. All-inclusive prices. Offering a peaceful break. Outstanding panoramic views.

TOTTERGILL FARM

Castle Carrock, Brampton CA8 9DP
Contact: Mrs Alison Bridges, Owner, Tottergill Farm,
Castle Carrock, Brampton, Carlisle CA8 9DP
T: (01228) 670615 & 07785 996950
E: alison@tottergill.demon.co.uk
I: www.tottergill.demon.co.uk

OPEN All year round

Low season per wk
£185.00–£422.00
High season per wk
£422.00–£780.00

CHAPEL STILE, Cumbria Map ref 5A3

★★★

1 Unit
Sleeping 5

7 LINGMOOR VIEW
Chapel Stile, Ambleside LA22 9JP
Contact: Mrs Andrea Batho, High Hollin Bank, Coniston
LA21 8AG
T: (015394) 41680 (Answerphone)
E: a.batho@virgin.net

OPEN All year round

Low season per wk
£165.00–£246.00
High season per wk
£264.00–£345.00

Traditional lakeland cottage in prime fell-walking area. Two bedrooms, superb views. Open fire. Fitted kitchen. Shower. Comfortable and cosy. Linen provided. Off-road parking.

COCKERMOUTH, Cumbria Map ref 5A2 *Tourist Information Centre Tel: (01900) 822634*

★★–★★★★

1 Unit
Sleeping 8

BROADINGS HOLIDAY COTTAGES
Mockerkin, Cockermouth CA13 0ST
Contact: Mrs Christine Greening, Waverbank Farm,
Wigton CA7 8PN
T: (01697) 371315

OPEN All year round

Low season per wk
£255.00–£370.00
High season per wk
£380.00–£570.00

375-acre dairy farm. Well-equipped self-contained house, 5.5 miles from Cockermouth. Tennis court. Open fire for warm and cosy winter evenings.

CONISTON, Cumbria Map ref 5A3

★★★★

2 Units
Sleeping 6

1 AND 2 ASH GILL COTTAGES
Torver, Coniston LA21 8BE
Contact: Mrs Dorothy Cowburn, Lyndene, Pope Lane,
Whitestake, Preston PR4 4JR
T: (01772) 612832

OPEN All year round

Low season per wk
Min £260.00
High season per wk
Max £410.00

Two houses equipped to the highest standard. Ample parking, gardens and patios. Excellent base for walking, touring, watersports and pony trekking.

★★–★★★★

5 Units
Sleeping 2–14

BANK GROUND

talks
No

East of Lake, Coniston LA21 8AA
T: (015394) 41264
F: (015394) 41900
E: info@bankground.com
I: www.bankground.com
Contact: Mrs Lucy Batty

'Storybook' cottages, with Arthur Ransome's Swallows and Amazons being both written and filmed here. A mere 150 yards from the properties' own 0.5-mile stretch of Coniston shoreline, they command uninterrupted views over the lake to Coniston village and its magnificent backdrop of Lakeland fells. Ideal for all outdoor activities.

OPEN All year round
CC: Barclaycard, Delta, Eurocard, JCB, Mastercard, Solo, Switch, Visa, Visa Electron

Mini-breaks availble late Oct-mid Feb (excl Christmas and New Year).

Low season per wk
Min £280.00
High season per wk
Max £1,650.00

★★–★★★★

4 Units
Sleeping 2–30

Unique cottages and group accommodation of quality and character in stunning mountain scenery. Sleeps 2-30. Country, village and mountain cottages both large and small. Log fires, exposed beams, antique furniture. Great weeks, weekends, short breaks for couples, families or groups – pets welcome! Experience timeless romance and a real breath of fresh air.

THE COPPERMINES CONISTON COTTAGES

Yes

Heatment   Old Cottys : £620
Lancaster : 550 – 3 miles
The Estate Office, The Bridge, Coniston LA21 8HJ
South of
T: (015394) 41765 & 07721 584488   *Fri - Fri   Conist*
F: (015394) 41944
entrance
E: bookings@coppermines.co.uk
I: www.coppermines.co.uk
Contact: Mr Philip Johnston

OPEN All year round
CC: Amex, Barclaycard, Delta, JCB, Maestro, Mastercard, Solo, Switch, Visa, Visa Electron

Discounted late notice breaks, weekends or mid-weeks a speciality for couples or groups up to 30 people.

Low season per wk
£195.00–£5,000.00
High season per wk
£195.00–£5,000.00

Rating
Applied For
1 Unit
Sleeping 5

1 FAR END COTTAGES

Coniston LA21 8DD
Contact: Mrs Andrea Batho, High Hollin Bank, Coniston LA21 8AG
T: (015394) 41680
E: a.batho@virgin.net

This charming Grade II Listed cottage is in a lovely, peaceful location at the foot of the fell, close to the village and the lake. It is furnished and equipped to a high standard. There is an open fire in the snug sitting room and delighful views from the front rooms.

OPEN All year round

Low season per wk
£150.00–£234.00
High season per wk
£255.00–£360.00

---

www.travelengland.org.uk

Log on for information and inspiration. The latest information on places to visit, events and quality assessed accommodation.

★★★

1 Unit
Sleeping 8

10 GREEN COTTAGES

Torver, Coniston LA21 8BG
Contact: Mrs Cartledge, Lake Bank, Water Yeat, Ulverston
LA12 8DL
T: (01229) 885629 & 588828
E: moonshadowdh@aol.com

Spacious Victorian railway cottage in quiet terrace close to the lake with views of Coniston fells and the Old Man mountain. Newly refurbished to a high standard with quality fittings throughout and a lovely garden with patio. There are good pub/restaurants nearby and the cottage is ideally situated for walking, riding, sailing and cycling.

OPEN All year round
CC: Amex, Barclaycard,
Delta, Mastercard, Switch,
Visa

Low season per wk
£195.00–£395.00
High season per wk
£295.00–£495.00

★★★

1 Unit
Sleeping 8

5 HOLME GROUND COTTAGES

Coniston LA21 8DH
Contact: Mrs Kate Bradshaw, The Rookery, Oaklands,
Riding Mill NE44 6AR
T: (01434) 682526

Tranquilly located, traditionally built (1860s), former quarryman's cottage in (usually unoccupied) terrace of 8. Cosy, comfortable with double-glazing and open fire. Rates include coal and electricity throughout the year. Well equipped home-from-home surrounded by woodland and fell with attractive views. Enjoy great family fun and walking straight from the doorstep.

OPEN All year round

Free linen/towels supplied
(up to 4 people) low season
Oct-Feb.

Low season per wk
£210.00–£300.00
High season per wk
£330.00–£440.00

★★★

1 Unit
Sleeping 5

SHELT GILL
Haws Bank, Coniston LA21 8AW
Contact: Mrs R Dean, 9 The Fairway, Sheffield Sl0 4LX
T: (0114) 230 8077
F: (0114) 230 8077
E: holiday@sheltgill.co.uk
I: www.sheltgill.co.uk

OPEN All year round

Low season per wk
Min £170.00
High season per wk
Max £370.00

Medieval cottage with a view of Lake Coniston from the timbered living room, a stream in the garden and easy access to hill walks.

★★★★

1 Unit
Sleeping 12

SUNNY BANK FARM
Coniston Water LA21 8BL
Contact: Mr P Liddell, St James Vicarage,
Goschen Road, Carlisle CA2 5PF
T: (01228) 515639
F: (01228) 524569
E: sunnybankfarm@btinternet.com
I: www.bbbweb.com/sunnybank

OPEN All year round

Low season per wk
£640.00–£960.00
High season per wk
£1,080.00–£1,640.00

Superb traditional Lakeland farmhouse set in beautiful grounds, with extensive lake frontage. Games barn and chapel also available. Ideal for families/groups. Call for brochure.

ACCESSIBILITY

Look for the 🔣🔣🔣 symbols which indicate accessibility for wheelchair users. A list of establishments is at the front of this guide.

CONISTON continued

★★
7 Units
Sleeping 2–6

THURSTON HOUSE
Tiberthwaite Avenue, Coniston LA21 8EE
Contact: Mr and Mrs A Jefferson, 21 Chale Green,
Harwood, Bolton BL2 3NJ
T: (01204) 419261
E: alan@jefferson99.freeserve.co.uk
I: www.jefferson99.freeserve.co.uk

OPEN All year round

Low season per wk
£75.00–£175.00
High season per wk
£140.00–£250.00

Lakeland-stone house, converted into spacious, clean, comfortable flats. Quiet location, close to lake and village centre. Pets accepted.

ⓜ☥Ⓜ◎🖥☉🖵📺🗄🗄🗃🗟🖨P☂🐾SP

DENT, Cumbria Map ref 5B3

★★★★
1 Unit
Sleeping 4

BROOKS BARN
High Croft, Cowgill Road, Dent, Sedbergh LA10 5TF
Contact: Ms Ellen Kirton, High Croft, Cowgill Road,
Dent, Sedbergh LA10 5TF
T: (015396) 25003 & 07971 429822 (Mobile)
F: (015396) 25003
E: ellen.kirton@tesco.net
I: www.dentdale.com

OPEN All year round

Low season per wk
£170.00–£190.00
High season per wk
£210.00–£250.00

Flat in barn conversion. Sleeps 2-4. Extra room available. Own entrance, garden, washer/dryer, parking, linen included. Dogs welcome.

☥Ⓜ◎🖳☉🖵🖵🗄📺🗄🗄📨🔌🖨P☂🐾SP

★★★
2 Units
Sleeping 4

Two mid-17thC cottages in centre of small, quaint village. Both are modernised, comfortably furnished and decorated to high standards. Quiet unspoilt Dentdale offers a good base for walking, touring and exploring the Yorkshire Dales or the Lake District, with Kendal and Hawes nearby. Brochure available. Open all year.

MIDDLETON'S COTTAGE AND FOUNTAIN COTTAGE

Main Street, Dent, Sedbergh LA10 5QL
Contact: Mr and Mrs P M Ayers, The Old Rectory,
Litlington, Polegate BN26 5RB
T: (01323) 870032
F: (01323) 870032
E: candpayers@mistral.co.uk
I: www.dentcottages.co.uk

OPEN All year round

Short breaks welcome between Oct and Mar. Weekend or mid-week. Any combination subject to availability.

Low season per wk
£170.00–£220.00
High season per wk
£220.00–£295.00

ⓜ☥◎🖥📖☉🖵🖵🗄📺🗄🗄🖨P☂🐾SP

★★★
1 Unit
Sleeping 6

WILSEY HOUSE
Underwood, Gawthrop, Dent, Sedbergh LA10 5QF
Contact: Mrs Joan Saunders, 21 Church Street,
Somersham, Huntingdon PE28 3EG
T: (01487) 841556 (Answerphone)

OPEN Apr–Sep &
Christmas

Low season per wk
£260.00–£300.00
High season per wk
£310.00–£410.00

A 17thC Listed building retaining original features while including modern facilities. Quiet location, stunning views. Lakes 30 minutes' drive.

☥◎🖳☉🖵🖵📺🔌🗄🖋P🎣☂🐾SP🏠

ELTERWATER, Cumbria Map ref 5A3

★★★
3 Units
Sleeping 4–5

LANE ENDS COTTAGES
Elterwater, Ambleside LA22 9HN
Contact: Mrs M E Rice, Fellside,
3 and 4 Lane Ends Cottages, Elterwater, Ambleside
LA22 9HN
T: (015394) 37678

OPEN All year round

Low season per wk
Min £175.00
High season per wk
Min £330.00

Family-run stone-built cottages with open fireplaces. In a peaceful setting in Great Langdale on the edge of the common, with views of the surrounding fells.

☥Ⓜ◎🖳☉🖵📺🗄🗄🖨P

PRICES
Please check prices and other details at the time of booking.

ELTERWATER continued

★★★
2 Units
Sleeping 3–4

WISTARIA COTTAGE AND 3 MAIN STREET
Elterwater, Ambleside LA22 9HP
Contact: Mr & Mrs D Beardmore, 2 Beech Drive,
Kidsgrove, Stoke-on-Trent ST7 1BA
T: (01782) 783170
E: geoff.doreen.beardmore@ntlworld.com

OPEN All year round

Low season per wk
£289.00–£310.00
High season per wk
£325.00–£359.00

Traditional 18thC cottages near village centre. Tastefully renovated, well-equipped. Cleaned and maintained by owners. Warm and comfortable, off-peak heating, open fires. Fell and valley walking.

ESKDALE, Cumbria Map ref 5A3

★★★★
1 Unit
Sleeping 8

LONGRIGG GREEN
Eskdale Green, Holmrook CA19 1TW
Contact: Mrs C Carter, Booking Agent, Forest How,
Eskdale, Holmrook CA19 1TR
T: (019467) 23201
F: (019467) 23190
E: fcarter@easynet.co.uk

OPEN All year round

Low season per wk
£260.00–£430.00
High season per wk
£495.00–£575.00

Spacious detached house with garden and stream. 4 bedrooms, jacuzzi whirlpool bath, conservatory, log fire, drying room. Steam railway, pub and shop nearby. Brochure available.

★★★
1 Unit
Sleeping 6

OLD BRANTRAKE
Brant Rake, Eskdale, Holmrook CA19 1TT
Contact: Mr J B Tyson, Brant Rake, Eskdale, Holmrook
CA19 1TT
T: (019467) 23340
F: (019467) 23340
E: tyson@eskdale1.demon.co.uk

OPEN All year round

Low season per wk
£220.00–£345.00
High season per wk
£330.00–£445.00

Recently restored 17thC Listed farmhouse in rural setting, ideal for central fells or touring. 3 bedrooms, 2 WC, bath, shower, wood fire, modern kitchen.

GRANGE-OVER-SANDS, Cumbria Map ref 5A3 *Tourist Information Centre Tel: (015395) 34026*

★★★
1 Unit
Sleeping 4

CORNERWAYS BUNGALOW
Field Broughton, Grange-over-Sands LA11 6HR
Contact: Mrs Eunice Rigg, Prospect House,
Barber Green, Grange-over-Sands LA11 6HU
T: (015395) 36329 & 36587

OPEN Mar–Oct

Low season per wk
£250.00–£350.00
High season per wk
£300.00–£350.00

Pleasant bungalow in quiet situation, with double and twin bedroom. All-round views, private garden with parking. Ideal base for touring Lake District. Personal supervision.

GRASMERE, Cumbria Map ref 5A3

★★★–★★★★
3 Units
Sleeping 2–5

BROADRAYNE FARM COTTAGES

Grasmere, Ambleside LA22 9RU
Contact: Mrs Jo Dennison Drake, Broadrayne Farm,
Grasmere, Ambleside LA22 9RU
T: (015394) 35055 & 35055
F: (015394) 35733
E: jo@grasmere-accommodation.co.uk
I: www.grasmere-accommodation.co.uk

With dramatic mountains, gentle rolling fells, glorious lakes and peaceful valleys, Broadrayne Farm is at the very heart of the Lake District, superbly located for wonderful views. The atmospheric traditional farm properties have been lovingly renovated with today's creature comforts, including open coal fires, good heating and off-street parking.

OPEN All year round
CC: Eurocard, Mastercard,
Solo, Switch, Visa, Visa
Electron

Low season per wk
£182.00–£215.00
High season per wk
£304.00–£490.00

A week booked in the year
allows 10% off a 2nd week
booked in Mar.

★★

5 Units
Sleeping 2–4

Secluded, fellside converted coach house with exposed beams, on outskirts of Grasmere village. Free central heating in winter. Membership for 2 guests of exclusive health club. Guests will also receive 10% discount on meals at hotel. Bicycle hire.

GRASMERE LODGE

Forest Side, Grasmere, Ambleside LA22 9RN
Contact: Mr S Roberts & H McCarty, Manager,
Forest Side Country House Hotel, Forest Side, Grasmere,
Ambleside LA22 9KN
T: (015394) 35250
F: (015394) 35947
E: hotel@forestsidehotel.com
I: www.forestsidehotel.com

OPEN All year round

10% reduction in price if booked in 2001.

Low season per wk
£147.00–£266.00
High season per wk
£283.00–£350.00

★★★

3 Units
Sleeping 2–5

LAKE VIEW HOLIDAY APARTMENTS

Lake View Drive, Grasmere LA22 9TD
Contact: Mr & Mrs Stephen & Michelle King, Lake View
Holiday Apartments, Lake View Drive, Grasmere
LA22 9TD
T: (015394) 35384
E: info@lakeview-grasmere.com
I: www.lakeview-grasmere.com

OPEN All year round

Low season per wk
£151.00–£203.00
High season per wk
£247.00–£381.00

Three comfortable, well-equipped apartments in tranquil setting close to village centre. Large, attractive gardens, ample parking and private lakeshore access.

★★★

1 Unit
Sleeping 5

A personal welcome awaits you at this attractive Lakeland house. Furnished to high standard. Ideal situation on village outskirts, within minutes of local amenities. Three bedrooms. Large modern kitchen, dining room, comfortable lounge with magnificent views of fells. Spacious yet cosy and warm in winter (coal fire optional). Attractive garden.

SILVERGARTH

1 Low Riddings, Grasmere, Ambleside LA22 9QY
T: (015394) 35828
F: (015394) 35828
E: cowards.silvergarth@btinternet.com
I: www.cowards.silvergarth.btinternet.co.uk
Contact: Mrs Susan Coward

OPEN All year round

Low season per wk
£150.00–£275.00
High season per wk
£310.00–£425.00

★★★★

1 Unit
Sleeping 6

FERN COTTAGE

The Went, 60 Main Street, Great Broughton,
Cockermouth CA13 0YL
Contact: Mr M Winks, Manager, 179 Eccleshall Road,
Stafford ST16 1PD
T: (01785) 661365

OPEN All year round

Low season per wk
£125.00–£240.00
High season per wk
£250.00–£350.00

Four-bedroomed cottage with large games room, in the centre of quiet Broughton. Excellent touring base for North Lakes, Buttermere, Ennerdale and Cumbrian coast.

SPECIAL BREAKS

Many establishments offer special promotions and themed breaks. These are highlighted in red. (All such offers are subject to availability.)

GREAT LANGDALE, Cumbria Map ref 5A3

ELTERWATER HALL

★★★★★
6 Units
Sleeping 2–6

The Langdale Estate, Great Langdale,
Ambleside LA22 9JD
Contact: Mrs Paula Leyland, The Langdale Estate,
Great Langdale, Ambleside LA22 9JD
T: (015394) 37302, ext 512
F: (015394) 37394
E: itsgreat@langdale.co.uk
I: www.langdale.co.uk

OPEN All year round
CC: Amex, Barclaycard,
Delta, Diners, Eurocard,
JCB, Mastercard, Solo,
Switch, Visa, Visa Electron

Low season per wk
£585.00–£790.00
High season per wk
£1,080.00–£1,435.00

Elterwater Hall is situated in its own grounds and forms part of the award-winning Langdale Estate, with its hotel and country club a short walk away.

LANGDALE ESTATE CHAPEL STILE APARTMENTS

★★★★
10 Units
Sleeping 2–8

The Langdale Estate, Great Langdale,
Ambleside LA22 9JD
Contact: Mrs Paula Leyland, The Langdale Estate,
Great Langdale, Ambleside LA22 9JD
T: (015394) 37302, ext 512
F: (015394) 37394
E: itsgreat@langdale.co.uk
I: www.langdale.co.uk

OPEN All year round
CC: Amex, Barclaycard,
Delta, Mastercard, Solo,
Switch, Visa

Low season per wk
£465.00–£665.00
High season per wk
£870.00–£1,115.00

Chapel Stile is situated next to Wainwrights Inn and forms part of the award-winning Langdale Estate, with its hotel and country club a short walk away.

LANGDALE ESTATE LODGES

★★★★★
81 Units
Sleeping 2–8

Langdale Estate, Great Langdale, Ambleside LA22 9JD
Contact: Mrs Paula Leyland, The Langdale Estate,
Great Langdale, Ambleside LA22 9JD
T: (015394) 37302, ext 512
F: (015394) 37394
E: itsgreat@langdale.co.uk
I: www.langdale.co.uk

OPEN All year round
CC: Amex, Barclaycard,
Delta, Mastercard, Solo,
Switch, Visa

Low season per wk
£530.00–£825.00
High season per wk
£945.00–£1,500.00

Formerly an old gunpowder mill for the Elterwater Gunpowder Company and now a hotel and lodge complex, with a leisure centre and all facilities attached.

HAVERIGG, Cumbria Map ref 5A3

3 POOLSIDE

★★★
1 Unit
Sleeping 5

Haverigg, Millom LA18 4HW
Contact: Mr W Haston, 2 Pool Side, Haverigg, Millom
T: (01229) 772974
E: quietcottage@tinyworld.co.uk

OPEN All year round
CC: Amex, Barclaycard,
Delta, Diners, Mastercard,
Switch, Visa

Low season per wk
£150.00–£200.00
High season per wk
£200.00–£300.00

The cottage is 150-yards from the sandy beach. Walking, the Cumbrian Cycle Way and an RSPB bird sanctuary are all nearby.

HAWKSHEAD, Cumbria Map ref 5A3

BRIDGE VIEW

★★★
1 Unit
Sleeping 5

Hawkshead, Ambleside LA22 0PL
Contact: Mrs S Dewhurst, Bridge View, 2 Bridge View,
Hawkshead, Ambleside LA22 0PL
T: (015394) 36340

OPEN All year round

Low season per wk
Min £195.00
High season per wk
Max £390.00

Cottage quarter of a mile from the beautiful village of Hawkshead, famous for Beatrix Potter and Wordsworth. Central for all parts of the Lakes. Garden and parking.

CHECK THE MAPS

The colour maps at the front of this guide show all the cities, towns and villages for which you will find accommodation entries.
Refer to the town index to find the page on which they are listed.

★★★–★★★★

12 Units
Sleeping 2–6

BROOMRIGGS

Hawkshead, Ambleside LA22 0JX
Contact: Mrs F Taylforth, Secretary, Broomriggs,
Hawkshead, Ambleside LA22 0JX
T: (015394) 36280 & 36272
E: broomriggs@zoom.co.uk
I: www.broomriggs.co.uk/location.htm

Large country house converted into comfortable apartments, set in 100 acres of gardens, woodlands and lake frontage with rowing boats. All apartments have views of Esthwaite Water and surrounding fells. Located 1 mile from Hawkshead on the B5286 to Windermere ferry. Within easy access of all areas of the Lake District.

OPEN All year round

3-night stays available.

Low season per wk
£120.00–£350.00
High season per wk
£295.00–£450.00

★★★

8 Units
Sleeping 4–6

THE CROFT HOLIDAY FLATS

North Lonsdale Road, Hawkshead, Ambleside LA22 0NX
T: (015394) 36374
F: (015394) 36544
E: enquiries@hawkshead-croft.com
I: www.hawkshead-croft.com
Contact: Mrs R E Barr

OPEN All year round
CC: Barclaycard, Delta,
Eurocard, Mastercard,
Solo, Switch, Visa, Visa
Electron

Low season per wk
£155.00–£232.00
High season per wk
£235.00–£330.00

Large house with garden, converted into holiday flats. In village of Hawkshead on B5286 from Ambleside.

★★

1 Unit
Sleeping 4

MEADOW VIEW

Red Lion Yard, Hawkshead, Ambleside LA22 0NY
Contact: Agent, Blakes Cottages, Spring Mill, Earby,
Barnoldswick BB94 0AA
T: 08700 708090
F: 0870 5851150
I: www.blakes.cottages.co.uk

OPEN All year round
CC: Amex, Delta, Maestro,
Mastercard, Switch, Visa

Low season per wk
£195.00–£240.00
High season per wk
£250.00–£340.00

300-year-old cottage in the centre of Hawkshead. Entrance hall, bathroom, twin bedroom, double bedroom with wash basin and separate WC, kitchen and living accommodation. Central heating.

★★★★

2 Units
Sleeping 2–5

THE OLD BARN & BARN END COTTAGE

Field Head, Outgate, Ambleside LA22 0NH
Contact: Mrs Ann Gallagher, Hideaways,
The Minstrels Gallery, The Square, Hawkshead, Ambleside
LA22 0NZ
T: (015394) 42435
F: (015394) 36178
E: bookings@lakeland-hideaways.co.uk
I: www.lakeland-hideaways.co.uk

A superb barn conversion set amid stunning countryside. A quiet location within easy reach of Hawkshead village. Cosy, comfortable interior, furnished to a very high standard – all home comforts. Log fires. An excellent base for walking, cycling and sightseeing. Delightful private garden. Off-road parking. Lovely views.

OPEN All year round

Short breaks available
autumn, winter and early
spring.

Low season per wk
£200.00–£350.00
High season per wk
£260.00–£395.00

TOWN INDEX

This can be found at the back of this guide. If you know where you want to stay, the index will give you the page number listing accommodation in your chosen town, city or village.

★★★★
1 Unit
Sleeping 2

HOLEMIRE HOUSE BARN

Holemire House, High Lorton, Cockermouth CA13 9TX
T: (01900) 85225
Contact: Mrs A Fearfield

Traditional Lakeland barn with exposed beams, converted to quality accommodation for two. In beautiful Lorton Vale, overlooking local fells. Close to Keswick and northern Lakes. Warm in winter, light and sunny in summer. Situated in the midst of superb walking country. All prices include electricity, central heating and linen.

OPEN All year round

Low season per wk
£185.00–£200.00
High season per wk
£215.00–£300.00

★★★
2 Units
Sleeping 4

MIDTOWN COTTAGES

1 & 2 Midtown Cottages, High Lorton,
Cockermouth CA13 9UQ
Contact: Mr M Burrell, 20 Hillside, Abbotts Ann, Andover
SP11 7DF
T: (01264) 710165 (Answerphone)
F: (01264) 710165
E: info@midtowncottages.co.uk
I: www.midtowncottages.co.uk

Delightful cottages set by a paved courtyard with small lawned garden. Situated in a picturesque corner of the Lake District National Park close to Crummock Water and Buttermere, an ideal base for walking, cycling or just relaxing! The cottages are warm, comfortably furnished, with nearby pub and hotel serving excellent meals.

OPEN All year round

Short breaks available. See website for details.

Low season per wk
£180.00–£220.00
High season per wk
£360.00–£420.00

★★★–★★★★★
9 Units
Sleeping 4–9

FIELD END BARNS AND SHAW END MANSION

Patton, Kendal LA8 9DU
T: (01539) 824220 & 07778 596863
F: (01539) 824464
E: fshawend@globalnet.co.uk
I: www.diva-web.co.uk/fsendhols
Contact: Mr & Mrs E D Robinson

Field End Barns and Shaw End Mansion are set on a 200-acre estate in a beautiful location. The Barns provide 5 award-winning cottages of character with own private gardens, exposed oak beams and open fireplaces. Shaw End Mansion contains 4 apartments in a restored Georgian mansion.

OPEN All year round

Short breaks from 2 nights available most of the year, prices from £85.

Low season per wk
£160.00–£200.00
High season per wk
£190.00–£420.00

★★★
1 Unit
Sleeping 4

HIGH UNDERBROW COTTAGE
Burneside, Kendal LA8 9AY
Contact: Mrs Bateman, High Underbrow Farm,
Burneside, Kendal LA8 9AY
T: (01539) 721927

OPEN All year round

Low season per wk
Min £155.00
High season per wk
Max £205.00

100-acre mixed farm. Quiet location with lovely views. Ideal for touring Lakes and dales. 4 miles from Kendal, 8 miles from Windermere. Also 6-berth caravan.

KENDAL continued

★★★★
1 Unit
Sleeping 11

Classic period house set in 2-3 acres of mature gardens. The main house (which forms the major part of the property shown) has many original features, including oak panelled hall with snooker table and piano. Convenient for local shops and restaurants. Ideal base from which to explore the Lakes.

HYLANDS
Brigsteer Road, Kendal LA9 5DY
Contact: Mr S Lambeth, 5 Stable Close, Finmere,
Buckingham MK18 4AD
T: (01280) 848779 & 07973 716556
F: (01280) 847519
E: simonlambeth@aol.com
I: www.hylands-lakedistrict.co.uk

OPEN All year round

Low season per wk
£375.00–£610.00
High season per wk
£410.00–£975.00

---

1 Unit
Sleeping 4

MIDDLE SWINKLEBANK
Longsleddale, Kendal LA8 9BD
Contact: Mrs M Todd, Proprietor, Saddlers Croft,
Longsleddale, Kendal LA8 9BD
T: (01539) 823275

OPEN All year round

Low season per wk
Min £200.00
High season per wk
Min £200.00

Comfortable cottage, part of 17th C farmhouse, well-equipped, central heating, log fire. Idyllic setting in quiet, unspoilt valley. No additional charges. Warm welcome assured.

KESWICK, Cumbria Map ref 5A3 *Tourist Information Centre Tel: (017687) 72645*

★★★★-★★★★★
3 Units
Sleeping 2–6

ACORN APARTMENTS AND ACORN VIEW
Acorn House, Ambleside, Keswick CA12 4DL
Contact: Mr J Miller, Acorn Selfcatering, Acorn House,
Ambleside, Keswick CA12 4DL
T: (017687) 72553
F: (017687) 75332
E: info@acornselfcatering.co.uk
I: www.acornselfcatering.co.uk

OPEN All year round
CC: Barclaycard, Delta,
Mastercard, Solo, Switch,
Visa

Low season per wk
£125.00–£300.00
High season per wk
£225.00–£550.00

Fully contained spacious holiday house and flats situated 5 minutes' walk from town centre. Furnished to the highest standards. Cleanliness guaranteed, owner maintained.

★★★-★★★★★
3 Units
Sleeping 4

BELLE VUE
24 Lake Road, Keswick CA12 5BX
Contact: Mrs L G Ryder, Hillside, Portinscale, Keswick
CA12 5RS
T: (017687) 71065
E: lexieryder@hotmail.com

OPEN All year round

Low season per wk
£100.00–£160.00
High season per wk
£180.00–£350.00

Lovely detached Lakeland residence. Clean, comfortable and well-equipped. Close to lake. Lounge views of Catbells/Newlands Valley. Owner maintained.

★★★★
6 Units
Sleeping 2–4

Pleasantly secluded spacious apartments, with a garden area. Handsomely furnished, gas central heating. Half a mile from Keswick town centre. Ample parking. Owner maintained. Situated at the end of a private road.

BRIGHAM FARM
Low Brigham, Keswick CA12 4JN
Contact: Mr N Green, Fornside House,
St Johns-in-the-Vale, Keswick CA12 4TS
T: (017687) 79666
E: selfcatering@keswickholidays.co.uk
I: www.keswickholidays.co.uk

OPEN All year round

Low season per wk
£120.00–£200.00
High season per wk
£170.00–£325.00

KESWICK continued

3 CATHERINE COTTAGES

★★★

1 Unit
Sleeping 5

Keswick CA12 4HE
Contact: Mr and Mrs Peter & Margaret Hewitson,
17 Cedar Lane, Cockermouth CA13 9HN
T: (01900) 828039 & 07711 305075 (Mobile)
E: peter.hewitson1@btinternet.com

OPEN All year round

Low season per wk
£120.00–£180.00
High season per wk
£180.00–£250.00

Cottage in a quiet area near Fitz Park, 5 minutes' walk from the shops. Owner maintained. Car park. SAE for brochure.

★★★★

2 Units
Sleeping 3–5

CROFT HOUSE HOLIDAY HOMES CROFTSIDE AND CROFT CORNER

Croft House, Applethwaite, Keswick CA12 4PN
Contact: Mrs J L Boniface, Croft House, Applethwaite, Keswick CA12 4PN
T: (017687) 73693
E: holidays@crofthouselakes.co.uk
I: www.crofthouselakes.co.uk

Enjoy our stunning, panoramic views. Ground-floor apartment (sleeping 2-3 plus cot) and cottage (sleeping 5 plus cot) in Victorian country house. Peaceful setting near Applethwaite village, which nestles below Skiddaw, just 1.5 miles from Keswick. Own gardens, children's play area. Walk from the door or just mountain watch!

OPEN All year round

Vouchers available at discounted rate for nearby leisure centre.

Low season per wk
£200.00–£260.00
High season per wk
£350.00–£500.00

★★★

4 Units
Sleeping 2–6

DERWENT HOUSE AND BRANDELHOWE

Portinscale, Keswick CA12 5RS
Contact: Mr and Mrs Oliver Bull, Derwent House Holidays, Stone Heath, Hilderstone ST15 8SH
T: (01889) 505678 & (01782) 281321
F: (01889) 505679
E: thebulls@globalnet.co.uk

OPEN All year round

Low season per wk
£95.00–£180.00
High season per wk
£185.00–£320.00

Traditional stone and slate Lakeland building converted and renovated to form 4 comfortable holiday suites at Portinscale Village on Derwentwater. 1 mile from Keswick.

★★★★

19 Units
Sleeping 2–6

DERWENT MANOR

Portinscale, Keswick CA12 5RE
Contact: Mrs C Denwood, Proprietor, Derwent Manor, Portinscale, Keswick CA12 5RE
T: (017687) 72211
F: (017687) 71002
E: info@derwent-manor.co.uk
I: www.derwent-manor.co.uk

Enjoy village life at this former gentleman's residence. Refurbished to provide some of the most comfortable and well-equipped apartments available, or one bedroom cottage within grounds. Many extras, including Sunday lunch, entry to leisure club. Pets welcome. Lake on your doorstep, with 16 acres of conservation grounds to explore.

OPEN All year round
CC: Amex, Barclaycard, Delta, Eurocard, JCB, Maestro, Mastercard, Solo, Switch, Visa, Visa Electron

Low season per wk
£199.00–£550.00
High season per wk
£380.00–£650.00

SYMBOLS
The symbols in each entry give information about services and facilities. A key to these symbols appears at the back of this guide.

★★★★
4 Units
Sleeping 4–6

High quality cottages converted from traditional stone barns offering spacious and cosy accommodation. Stay on a working Lakeland sheep farm, feed the goats and ducks and enjoy the abundant wildlife. Walk the fells from the door. Farm trail available for visitors. Spectacular and peaceful location only 10 minutes from Keswick.

FORNSIDE FARM COTTAGES

Fornside Farm, St Johns-in-the-Vale, Keswick CA12 4TS
Contact: Mr & Mrs R M Hall, Fornside Farm,
St Johns-in-the-Vale, Keswick CA12 4TS
T: (017687) 79173
F: (017687) 79174
E: cottages@fornside.co.uk
I: www.fornside.co.uk

OPEN All year round

Low season per wk
£200.00–£250.00
High season per wk
£290.00–£575.00

★★★★
1 Unit
Sleeping 7

FOUNTAIN COTTAGE
High Hill, Keswick CA12 5NY
Contact: Dr and Mrs W E Preston, 5 Mill Bank, Lymm
WA13 9DG
T: (01925) 756479 (24 hrs)
E: preston@mail.talk-101.com

OPEN All year round

Low season per wk
Min £199.00
High season per wk
Max £399.00

Owner maintained, cosy, well-equipped cottage, on the edge of town with fell views. 3 bedrooms, central heating, private parking. Pets accepted.

★-★★★
3 Units
Sleeping 2–5

HILLSIDE
3 Borrowdale Road, Keswick CA12 5DD
Contact: Mr C F Howey, Cemetery Lodge,
Whitton Road, Rothbury NE65 7RX
T: (01669) 620451
E: lakesflat@aol.com
I: www.members.tripod.com/~lakesflats/

OPEN All year round

Low season per wk
£110.00–£255.00
High season per wk
£215.00–£350.00

Well-equipped apartments close to Lake Derwent Water and the centre of Keswick. Bed linen and services included. Pets welcome. Warm and comfortable. Short breaks available.

★★★★
16 Units
Sleeping 1–10

LOW BRIERY COTTAGES
Penrith Road, Keswick CA12 4RN
Contact: Mr Michael Atkinson, Low Briery Holiday
Village, Keswick CA12 4RN
F: (017687) 72044
I: www.keswick.uk.com

OPEN All year round
CC: Barclaycard, Delta,
Eurocard, JCB,
Mastercard, Solo, Switch,
Visa, Visa Electron

Low season per wk
£260.00–£330.00
High season per wk
£360.00–£530.00

Chalets beside the River Greta with magnificent views. Well-equipped properties offering comfortable accommodation in a choice setting.

★★
2 Units
Sleeping 4–6

19 SAINT JOHN'S STREET
Keswick CA12 5AE
T: (017687) 73571 (Answerphone)
Contact: Mr Peter Gee

OPEN All year round

Low season per wk
£150.00–£225.00
High season per wk
£225.00–£350.00

Ground floor and first floor flats in Listed building. Fully equipped, close to the town centre and lake.

MAP REFERENCES The map references refer to the colour maps at the front of this guide. The first figure is the map number; the letter and figure which follow indicate the grid reference on the map.

KING'S MEABURN, Cumbria Map ref 5B3

★★★-★★★★

4 Units
Sleeping 3–6

Attractive well-furnished cottages in quiet village, overlooking the beautiful Lyvennet Valley and the Lakeland hills. Some log fires in winter. Fishing, fuel and linen inclusive. Children and pets welcome. Ideal touring centre for Lakes, dales, Hadrian's Wall and Scottish Borders.

LYVENNET COTTAGES AND HILL TOP BARN
King's Meaburn, Penrith CA10 3BS
Contact: Mrs D M Addison, Keld, King's Meaburn, Penrith CA10 3BS
T: (01931) 714226 (Answerphone) & 714661
F: (01931) 714598
E: wendyaddison@yahoo.com
I: www.tumpline.co.uk/lyvennet

OPEN All year round

Low season per wk
£175.00–£260.00
High season per wk
£270.00–£425.00

KIRKBY STEPHEN, Cumbria Map ref 5B3 *Tourist Information Centre Tel: (017683) 71199*

★★★★

3 Units
Sleeping 4–6

Delightful farmhouse/barn conversions equipped to a very high standard for your every comfort. Can accommodate up to 16. Enjoy the splendid landscape surrounding you. Ideally situated for Lakes, Dales, Pennine Way. Abundance of footpaths and bridleways. Market town of Kirby Stephen 5 miles, Appleby 8 miles.

PENNISTONE GREEN
North Stainmore, Kirkby Stephen CA17 4DY
Contact: Mr T F Jackson, Ashmere, Rakes Road, Monyash, Bakewell DE45 1JL
T: (01629) 815683
E: sue@jackson-group.co.uk
I: www.jackson-group.co.uk

OPEN All year round

Low season per wk
Min £150.00
High season per wk
Max £360.00

KIRKOSWALD, Cumbria Map ref 5B2

★★★

5 Units
Sleeping 2–6

CROSSFIELD COTTAGES
Staffield, Kirkoswald, Penrith CA10 1EU
T: (01768) 898711
F: (01768) 898711
Contact: Mrs Susan Bottom

OPEN All year round

Low season per wk
£155.00–£230.00
High season per wk
£295.00–£380.00

Clean, secluded, quality cottages, central for the Lake District, North Pennines, Scotland's borderland and Hadrian's Wall. Private coarse fishing in adjacent lakes. Pets very welcome.

★★★★

5 Units
Sleeping 2–4

♿

HOWSCALES
Kirkoswald, Penrith CA10 1JG
T: (01768) 898666
F: (01768) 898710
E: liz@howscales.fsbusiness.co.uk
I: www.eden-in-cumbria.co.uk/howscales
Contact: Mrs S E Webster

OPEN Feb–Dec
CC: Mastercard, Visa

Low season per wk
£145.00–£220.00
High season per wk
£290.00–£420.00

Cosy, well-equipped converted 17thC farm cottages set in open, tranquil countryside with superb views. Touring base for Eden Valley, Lakes, Pennines. Brochure. Short breaks.

NB IMPORTANT NOTE Information on accommodation listed in this guide has been supplied by the proprietors. As changes may occur you are advised to check details at the time of booking.

LAMPLUGH, Cumbria Map ref 5A3

★★★★

1 Unit
Sleeping 4

This 19thC mid-terrace cottage enjoys panoramic views across farmland, ideally situated for walking from the door. Cosy lounge with Victorian fireplace. A traditional bread oven adds to the character of the kitchen/diner. Steep stairs lead to warm and cosy bedrooms – double and adult bunk. Shared rear garden.

2 FOLLY

Felldyke Cottages, Lamplugh, Workington CA14 4SH
Contact: Mrs Alison Wilson, Dockray Nook, Lamplugh, Workington CA14 4SH
T: (01946) 861151 (BT Callminder service) &
07740 697433
E: dockraynook@talk21.com
I: www.felldykecottageholidays.co.uk

OPEN All year round

Low season per wk
Max £200.00
High season per wk
Max £270.00

LANGDALE, Cumbria Map ref 5A3

★★★★

2 Units
Sleeping 6–8

OAKDENE
Chapel Stile, Ambleside LA22 9JE
Contact: Mrs Patricia Locke, 17 Shay Lane, Hale,
Altrincham WA15 8NZ
T: (0161) 904 9445

OPEN All year round

Low season per wk
£310.00–£470.00
High season per wk
£430.00–£920.00

Four-bedroomed and 3-bedroomed houses. Large garden with lovely views of fells. Shop, pub and river nearby. Membership of Langdale Leisure Club included until 31 March 2002.

£690

★★-★★★★★

48 Units
Sleeping 2–11

Welcome to Wheelwrights – an established family business featuring the very best in self-catering property in the heart of the English Lake District, with numerous quality properties for 2-11 people. You are guaranteed a holiday to remember. For more information visit our web site or telephone.

WHEELWRIGHTS HOLIDAY COTTAGES

Elterwater, Ambleside LA22 9HS
T: (015394) 37635 & 37571
F: (015394) 37618
E: enquiries@wheelwrights.com
I: www.wheelwrights.com
Contact: Mr I Price

OPEN All year round
CC: Barclaycard, Delta,
Mastercard, Switch, Visa

Low season per wk
£235.00–£850.00
High season per wk
£287.00–£1,500.00

LEASGILL, Cumbria Map ref 5A3

★★★

1 Unit
Sleeping 3

THE COTTAGE
1 Eversley Gardens, Leasgill, Milnthorpe LA7 7EY
Contact: Mrs Beverly Keatings, 1 Eversley Gardens,
Leasgill, Milnthorpe LA7 7EY
T: (015395) 63008
F: (015395) 62920

OPEN All year round

Low season per wk
£150.00–£205.00
High season per wk
£205.00–£230.00

Recently refurbished stone and slate cottage set in large, mature grounds with excellent views. Peaceful location with amenities close by. Suitable for year round use.

QUALITY ASSURANCE SCHEME

Star ratings were correct at the time of going to press but are subject to change. Please check at the time of booking.

LITTLE LANGDALE, Cumbria Map ref 5A3

★★★

1 Unit
Sleeping 5

HIGHFOLD COTTAGE
3 Greenbank Terrace, Little Langdale,
Ambleside LA22 9NX
Contact: Mrs C E Blair, 8 The Glebe, Chapel Stile,
Ambleside LA22 9JT
T: (015394) 37686

OPEN All year round

Low season per wk
£200.00–£260.00
High season per wk
£260.00–£330.00

Comfortable, well-equipped cottage, set in magnificent scenery. Ideally situated for walking and touring. Open fires, central heating. Pets and children welcome. Personally maintained.

LONGSLEDDALE, Cumbria Map ref 5B3

★★★

1 Unit
Sleeping 4

THE COACH HOUSE
Capplebarrow House, Longsleddale, Kendal LA8 9BB
T: (01539) 823686 & 07887 603282 (Mobile)
F: (01539) 823092
E: JENYFARMER@aol.com
Contact: Mrs Farmer

OPEN All year round

Low season per wk
£100.00–£150.00
High season per wk
£150.00–£210.00

Stone-built, converted coach house with ground floor shower room and bedroom and open staircase to first floor kitchen and lounge. Excellent views.

LOWESWATER, Cumbria Map ref 5A3

★★★★–★★★★★

7 Units
Sleeping 2–7

Nestling among magnificent fells and three beautiful lakes, luxury cottages, some serviced daily, available all year. Open fires, central heating and gardens. Children and pets welcome. Family-run. Crummock Water is only 10 minutes' walk through National Trust woods. Colour brochure.

LOWESWATER HOLIDAY COTTAGES

Scale Hill, Loweswater, Cockermouth CA13 9UX
T: (01900) 85232
F: (01900) 85232
E: mike@loweswaterholidaycottages.co.uk
I: www.loweswaterholidaycottages.co.uk
Contact: Mr M E Thompson

OPEN All year round

Low season per wk
£140.00–£360.00
High season per wk
£290.00–£730.00

MEALSGATE, Cumbria Map ref 5A2

★★★

1 Unit
Sleeping 8

WHITEHALL
Mealsgate, Carlisle CA5 1JS
Contact: Blakes HIB Ref: B4872, Spring Mill, Earby,
Barnoldswick BB94 0AA
T: (01282) 445096
F: (01282) 844288

OPEN May–Oct
CC: Amex, Barclaycard,
Delta, Maestro,
Mastercard, Switch, Visa

High season per wk
£478.00–£897.00

Grade I Listed pele tower in 1 acre of landscaped grounds. A central base for touring.

MILBURN, Cumbria Map ref 5B2

★★★★

1 Unit
Sleeping 4

BRAMLEY COTTAGE
Milburn, Penrith CA10 1TN
Contact: Mr & Mrs G Heelis, Orchard Cottage, Milburn,
Penrith CA10 1TN
T: (017683) 61074 (Answerphone)
F: (01768) 895528
E: guyheelis@aol.com
I: www.oas.co.uk/ukcottages/bramley

OPEN All year round
CC: Delta, Eurocard,
Mastercard, Solo, Switch,
Visa

Low season per wk
£190.00–£230.00
High season per wk
£280.00–£390.00

Charming 2-bedroomed cottage overlooking the large picturesque village green. Exposed beams, open fire, fully-equipped fitted kitchen, furnished and decorated to a high standard.

MILLBECK, Cumbria Map ref 5A2

★★★★

1 Unit
Sleeping 6

MILLBECK COTTAGES

3 Millbeck Cottages, Millbeck, Keswick CA12 4PT
Contact: Mr Richard Watson, 20 Hebing End, Benington,
Stevenage SG2 7DD
T: (01438) 359311 (Office) & 869286 (Home)
F: (01438) 740127
E: bcl@brignalls.co.uk

This spacious, 3-bedroom cottage is approached by private drive from Millbeck, a picturesque hamlet on the lower slopes of Skiddaw, 2 miles from Keswick. Set in woodland, it forms part of a recently converted 18thC mill. Warm and comfortable, it benefits from an open fire, private garden and parking.

OPEN All year round

Low season per wk
£400.00–£450.00
High season per wk
£480.00–£540.00

NEWBY BRIDGE, Cumbria Map ref 5A3

★★★★

1 Unit
Sleeping 4

WOODLAND COTTAGE

Newby Bridge Caravan Park, Canny Hill, Newby Bridge LA12 8NF
Contact: Mr Peter Newton, Hillside Lodge,
Newby Bridge Caravan Park, Canny Hill, Newby Bridge LA12 8NF
T: (015395) 31030
F: (015395) 30105
E: newbybridge@hopps.freeserve.co.uk

OPEN All year round
CC: Barclaycard, Delta,
Eurocard, Mastercard,
Switch, Visa

Low season per wk
£220.00–£340.00
High season per wk
£340.00–£460.00

Detached cottage with 2 en suite bedrooms, in own private gardens within the award-winning Newby Bridge Caravan Park. All on one level.

PATTERDALE, Cumbria Map ref 5A3

★★★–★★★★

3 Units
Sleeping 2–10

ELM HOW, CRUCK BARN AND EAGLE COTTAGE

Patterdale CA11 0PU
Contact: Miss M Scott/McGill,
Matson Ground Estate Company Ltd, 3 Lambrigg Terrace,
Kendal LA9 4BB
T: (01539) 726995 (Answerphone)
F: (01539) 741611
E: matsong@compuserve.com
I: www.matsonground.co.uk

Elm How and Cruck Barn, originally part of an 18thC farm, are in the Grisedale Valley, above Patterdale, surrounded by farmland. Ideal for walking, they are quiet, comfortable and well-equipped. Eagle cottage sits just above Glenridding. Both Eagle Cottage and Elm How have wood fires.

OPEN All year round
CC: Barclaycard, Delta,
Mastercard, Switch, Visa

Low season per wk
£180.00–£360.00
High season per wk
£290.00–£800.00

PENRITH, Cumbria Map ref 5B2 *Tourist Information Centre Tel: (01768) 867466*

★★★–★★★★★

3 Units
Sleeping 2–3

STONEFOLD COTTAGES

Stonefold, Newbiggin, Stainton, Penrith CA11 0HP
T: (01768) 866383
I: www.northlakes.co.uk/stonefold/
Contact: Mrs Gill Harrington

OPEN All year round

Low season per wk
£195.00–£235.00
High season per wk
£295.00–£325.00

Enjoy the sights and sounds of the countryside in idyllic rural setting. Relax in recently converted, well-equipped cottages with panoramic views. Send for brochure now.

REGIONAL TOURIST BOARD The **M** symbol in an establishment entry indicates that it is a Regional Tourist Board member.

★★★★
5 Units
Sleeping 3–8

WETHERAL COTTAGES
Great Salkeld, Penrith CA11 9NA
T: (01768) 898779
F: (01768) 898943
E: wetheralcottages@compuserve.com
Contact: Mr John Lowrey

Charming, well-equipped sandstone cottage, clustered amongst attractive gardens with grassed play area. Situated in Eden Valley on the edge of a quiet country village with pub. Easy access to the amenities of the Lakes, Northern England, Southern Scotland. Managed and served by resident proprietors. Prices all-inclusive. Colour brochure.

OPEN All year round
CC: Barclaycard, Delta, Mastercard, Switch, Visa

Short breaks Nov-Mar (excl Christmas and New Year). Log burning stove in Garth Cottage.

Low season per wk	£150.00–£350.00
High season per wk	£330.00–£550.00

POOLEY BRIDGE, Cumbria Map ref 5A3

★★★★
3 Units
Sleeping 2–8

HIGH WINDER COTTAGES
High Winder House, Celleron, Tirril, Penrith CA10 2LS
Contact: Mr R A Moss, High Winder House, Celleron,
Tirril, Penrith CA10 2LS
T: (017684) 86997 (Answerphone/fax)
& (017687) 72988 (Office (Mr Moss))
F: (017684) 86997
E: mossr@highwinder.freeserve.co.uk

Three cottages converted from a building in the grounds of the owner's secluded 17thC farmhouse high in the fells.

OPEN All year round

Low season per wk	£175.00–£320.00
High season per wk	£300.00–£590.00

RAVENSTONEDALE, Cumbria Map ref 5B3

★★★★
1 Unit
Sleeping 6

COLDBECK COTTAGE
Ravenstonedale, Kirkby Stephen CA17 4LW
Contact: Mrs Sally Cannon, Coldbeck House,
Ravenstonedale, Kirkby Stephen CA17 4LW
T: (015396) 23230
F: (015396) 23230
E: david.cannon@coldbeck.demon.co.uk

Comfortable, warm and spacious, with 3 en suite bedrooms, the cottage is surrounded by a 2-acre garden, in a tranquil and attractive Upper Eden village. Walks in the Howgills or Smardale Nature Reserve can be followed by good food and drink at nearby pubs, which are welcoming and wheelchair friendly.

OPEN All year round

Low season per wk	Min £350.00
High season per wk	Max £400.00

★★★
3 Units
Sleeping 4

MOSS COTTAGES
The Moss, Newbiggin-on-Lune,
Kirkby Stephen CA17 4NB
T: (015396) 23316
F: (015396) 23491
E: shallmoss@aol.com
Contact: Mrs H Shallcross

17thC farmhouse cottages, 2 of which are suitable for disabled visitors. Facing the Howgill Fells and ideal for fell walking and touring the Lakes and dales.

OPEN All year round

Low season per wk	£180.00–£200.00
High season per wk	£210.00–£270.00

CREDIT CARD BOOKINGS If you book by telephone and are asked for your credit card number it is advisable to check the proprietor's policy should you cancel your reservation.

ST JOHNS-IN-THE-VALE, Cumbria Map ref 5A3

★★★★
1 Unit
Sleeping 4

THE STUDIO
Fornside House, St Johns-in-the-Vale,
Keswick CA12 4TS
T: (017687) 79666
E: selfcatering@keswickholidays.co.uk
I: www.keswickholidays.co.uk
Contact: Mrs J Green

OPEN All year round

Low season per wk
£120.00–£185.00
High season per wk
£205.00–£275.00

Old barn adjoining house, converted into cosy, well-furnished apartment with splendid views towards Skiddaw. Own entrance and parking. One mile from Thirlmere, 6 from Keswick.

SAWREY, Cumbria Map ref 5A3

★★★
1 Unit
Sleeping 4

Family-run self-catering accommodation consisting of traditional farm buildings converted into attractive apartments and cottages in beautiful rural setting. Sunny terraces overlooking private paddock. Access to private lakeshore. Free coarse and trout fishing. Log fires, cosy and comfortable, excellent base for walking, cycling and sightseeing.

DERWENTWATER COTTAGE

Esthwaite Farm, Near Sawrey, Ambleside LA22 0LB
Contact: Mrs Ann Gallagher, Hideaways,
The Minstrels Gallery, The Square, Hawkshead, Ambleside
LA22 0NZ
T: (015394) 42435
F: (015394) 36178
E: bookings@lakeland-hideaways.co.uk
I: www.lakeland-hideaways.co.uk

OPEN All year round

Short breaks available autumn, winter and early spring.

Low season per wk
£220.00–£340.00
High season per wk
£290.00–£390.00

★★★
2 Units
Sleeping 3–5

LAKEFIELD
Near Sawrey, Ambleside LA22 0JZ
T: (015394) 36635 (24 hour answerphone)
F: (015394) 36635
Contact: Mr & Mrs John and Ann Taylor

OPEN All year round

Low season per wk
£180.00–£280.00
High season per wk
£280.00–£375.00

Two attractive, well-maintained modern apartments, equipped to a high standard. Beatrix Potter's former home 'Hilltop' nearby. Outstanding lake and mountain views. Resident owner.

Rating
Applied For
1 Unit
Sleeping 2

WEST VALE COTTAGE
West Vale, Far Sawrey, Ambleside LA22 0LQ
Contact: Mrs Dee Pennington, West Vale, Far Sawrey,
Ambleside LA22 0LQ
T: (015394) 42817
F: (015394) 45302

OPEN All year round
CC: Amex, Barclaycard,
Delta, JCB, Mastercard,
Solo, Switch, Visa, Visa
Electron

Low season per wk
£170.00–£180.00
High season per wk
£220.00–£295.00

Superbly situated in the heart of Beatrix Potter country. Warm, cosy, detached bungalow in own private garden. Heating and linen included. Decorated to high standard.

SEDBERGH, Cumbria Map ref 5B3

★★★–★★★★★
2 Units
Sleeping 4–8

FELL HOUSE
Howgill Lane, Sedbergh LA10 5DE
Contact: Mr Stephen Wickham, 8 Arnhem Wharf,
London E14 3RU
T: (020) 7538 4207 (Evening/Weekend) &
07778 901788 (Mobile)
F: (020) 7531 6552
E: steve@higround.co.uk
I: www.fellhouse.cwc.net

OPEN All year round

Low season per wk
£300.00–£400.00
High season per wk
£550.00–£750.00

Luxurious character warehouse conversion with linked, self-contained flat. Spacious living areas tastefully furnished. Quiet, but very close to pubs, shops, restaurant. Weekend bookings taken.

★★★
1 Unit
Sleeping 6

4 RAILWAY COTTAGES
Garsdale Head, Sedbergh LA10 5PP
Contact: Mrs W A Mills, 131 Glendale Gardens,
Leigh-on-Sea SS9 2BE
T: (01702) 478846
F: (01702) 482088
E: trewen@clara.co.uk
I: www.dalescottages.com

OPEN All year round
CC: Barclaycard, Delta,
Mastercard, Visa

Low season per wk
£225.00–£250.00
High season per wk
£325.00–£375.00

Attractive railwayman's cottage beside Garsdale Station, affording panoramic views. Warm and cosy in winter with open fire. Very comfortably furnished, fitted kitchen. Pets welcome.

★★★★
1 Unit
Sleeping 5

THWAITE COTTAGE
Thwaite Farm, Howgill, Sedbergh LA10 5JD
Contact: Mrs Dorothy Parker, Thwaite Farm, Howgill,
Sedbergh LA10 5JD
T: (015396) 20493

OPEN All year round

Low season per wk
Min £175.00
High season per wk
Min £300.00

Attractive farm cottage in peaceful location with excellent views of the Howgill fells and the River Lune. Good walking, fishing, touring lakes and dales. Short breaks.

★★
1 Unit
Sleeping 4

THURSTONVILLE HIGH LODGE
Lowick, Ulverston LA12 7SX
Contact: Mr R N Lord, Thurstonville, Lowick, Ulverston
LA12 7SX
T: (01229) 861 271

Thurstonville High Lodge is the gatehouse to a privately owned country house, 4 miles south of Coniston Water. Convenient for central Lakes and quieter Furness peninsula. Nearest shops 1.5 miles, Ulverston 4 miles. Rural outlook, private garden, 2 bedrooms (sleeping 4), bathroom (bath/shower), kitchen/diner, living room (open fire).

OPEN Jul–Oct, Bank
Holidays & Christmas

Low season per wk
Min £165.00
High season per wk
Max £245.00

Rating
Applied For
4 Units
Sleeping 2–5

BRUNT KNOTT FARM
Staveley, Kendal LA8 9QX
T: (01539) 821030 (Answerphone) & 822680
F: (01539) 821221
E: margaret@bruntknott.demon.co.uk
I: www.bruntknott.demon.co.uk
Contact: William & Margaret Beck

Cosy cottages on small 17thC farm. Peaceful, elevated, fellside location with superb views over Lakeland fells, 5 miles from Windermere. Lovely walks from your door. Central heating, three cottages also with woodburner/open fire. Laundry facilities. Ideal base Lakes and dales. Caring resident owners. Winter breaks available. Brochure.

OPEN All year round

Low season per wk
£152.00–£179.00
High season per wk
£215.00–£326.00

www.travelengland.org.uk
Log on for information and inspiration. The latest information on places to visit, events and quality assessed accommodation.

TEBAY, Cumbria Map ref 5B3

★★★
1 Unit
Sleeping 4

PRIMROSE FLAT

Primrose Cottage, Orton Road, Tebay, Penrith CA10 3TL OPEN All year round
Contact: Mrs Patricia Helen Jones, Primrose Cottage,
Orton Road, Tebay, Penrith CA10 3TL
T: (015396) 24791 & 07778 520930
E: primrosecottebay@aol.com

*Self-contained ground floor apartment. One double bedroom. Children/pets welcome.
One acre garden/woodland. New 2 bedroom bungalow, 2 bathrooms, suitable for
disabled.*

Low season per wk
£160.00–£220.00
High season per wk
£220.00–£320.00

THORNTHWAITE, Cumbria Map ref 5A3

★★★
1 Unit
Sleeping 4

SEAT HOWE

Thornthwaite, Keswick CA12 5SQ   OPEN All year round
T: (017687) 78371
Contact: Mrs Dorothy Bell

*Attractive, homely converted coach house (owner maintained). Extensive landscaped
gardens, wonderful views of lake and Skiddaw, ideal for bird-watching and red
squirrels.*

Low season per wk
£180.00–£200.00
High season per wk
£210.00–£300.00

THRELKELD, Cumbria Map ref 5A3

★★★
3 Units
Sleeping 2–6

BLENCATHRA CENTRE–LATRIGG VIEW, DERWENT VIEW, BORROWDALE VIEW

Threlkeld, Keswick CA12 4SG   OPEN All year round
Contact: Mr Simms, Blencathra Centre, Threlkeld,   CC: Barclaycard, Delta,
Keswick CA12 4SG   Mastercard, Switch, Visa
T: (017687) 79601
F: (017687) 79264
E: fsc.blencathra@ukonline.co.uk

*Three cottages high on the slopes of Blencathra, in grounds of award-winning Eco-
Centre. Walking from the door. Brochure available, dogs welcome.*

Low season per wk
£155.00–£260.00
High season per wk
£220.00–£340.00

THURSTONFIELD, Cumbria Map ref 5A2

★★★★
7 Units
Sleeping 4–6

THE TRANQUIL OTTER

The Lough, Thurstonfield, Carlisle CA5 6HB
Contact: Mr & Mrs Richard & Wendy Wise, Lough House,
Thurstonfield, Carlisle CA5 6HB
T: (01228) 576661 (Answerphone) & 576727
F: (01228) 576662
E: richard@the-tranquil-otter.co.uk
I: www.the-tranquil-otter.co.uk

*Idyllic and peaceful Cumbria beauty
spot. Seven cosy, well equipped
lodges at the water's edge. Each has
spectacular lake views and a rowing
boat. Woodland paths around lake
provide access to bird hide and
wetland board walk. Fabulous nature
including otters. Excellent flyfishing.
Wheelchair accessible lodges,
woodland paths and wheely boat.*

OPEN All year round
CC: Barclaycard, Delta,
Mastercard, Visa

Low season per wk
£250.00–£313.00
High season per wk
£425.00–£531.00

TIRRIL, Cumbria Map ref 5B2

★★★★
5 Units
Sleeping 2–10

TIRRIL FARM COTTAGES

Tirril View, Tirril, Penrith CA10 2JE   OPEN Apr–Dec
Contact: Mr David Owens, Tirril View, Tirril, Penrith
CA10 2JE
T: (01768) 864767
F: (01768) 864767

*Situated on a working farm, these tasteful barn conversions are set around a
courtyard with outstanding views over the fells.*

Low season per wk
£95.00–£390.00
High season per wk
£180.00–£790.00

TROUBECK, Cumbria Map ref 5A3

★★★★

1 Unit
Sleeping 5

HOLBECK GHYLL LODGE

Holbeck Lane, Windermere LA23 1LU
Contact: Mrs Maggie Kaye, Holmdene, Stoney Bank Road,
Thongsbridge, Holmfirth, Huddersfield HD9 7SL
T: (01484) 684605
F: (01484) 689051
E: maggiekaye@hotmail.com

Traditional single-storey Lakeland lodge with enclosed garden, available Easter to end-October. Two twin-bedded rooms, dining/living room with open fire and sofa bed. Modern kitchen. Bathroom with bath, shower and toilet. Antique pine throughout. Well situated for local walks, lake and pubs. Pets welcome. Ample parking.

OPEN Apr–Oct

Low season per wk
£350.00–£375.00
High season per wk
£395.00–£430.00

ULLSWATER, Cumbria Map ref 5A3

★★★★

1 Unit
Sleeping 6

CHERRY HOLM
Yanwath, Penrith
Contact: Mrs Susanne Sheard, 7 Bark Lane, Addingham,
Ilkley LS29 0RA
T: (01943) 830766

OPEN All year round

Low season per wk
Min £145.00
High season per wk
Max £385.00

New, well-equipped bungalow in peaceful country location 4 miles from Ullswater and 2 miles from Penrith. Three bedrooms, 2 bathrooms. Cosy and well organised.

★★★★

1 Unit
Sleeping 4

KNOTTSBANK

The Knotts, Watermillock, Penrith CA11 0JP
Contact: Mr & Mrs S Lamb, Woodbank, The Knotts,
Watermillock, Penrith CA11 0JP
T: (017684) 86355 (24 hours)

Detached cottage in beautiful, secluded grounds rich with wildlife. Panoramic views of Ullswater mountains and fells, Lake Ullswater within 10 minutes' walk. An ideal location for walking, touring or water-based activities. Knottsbank offers a very high standard of accommodation and cleanliness and is well-equipped. Resident owners. Brochure available.

OPEN All year round

Short breaks (minimum 3 nights) in low-mid season, high season according to availability.

Low season per wk
£270.00
High season per wk
£355.00–£385.00

★★★

4 Units
Sleeping 3–5

LAND ENDS

Watermillock, Ullswater CA11 0NB
T: (017684) 86438
F: (017684) 86959
E: infolandends@btinternet.com
I: www.landends.btinternet.co.uk
Contact: Ms Barbara Holmes

For those seeking total relaxation, Lands Ends is ideal. Only 1 mile from Ullswater, our 4 detached log cabins have a peaceful, fellside location in 25-acre grounds with 2 pretty lakes, red squirrels, ducks and wonderful birdlife. Inside, exposed logs and quality furnishings give a cosy, rustic appeal. Dogs welcome.

OPEN All year round

Low season per wk
£205.00–£408.00
High season per wk
£256.00–£411.00

MAP REFERENCES

Map references apply to the colour maps at the front of this guide.

ULLSWATER continued

★★★–★★★★

5 Units
Sleeping 6–14

160-acre hill livestock farm. All properties overlook Ullswater and have colour TV, freezer and central heating. Private access to lake with motor boats, sailing dinghies, canoes and mountain bikes for hire. Visitors can bring own boats. Horse-riding available for experienced adult riders – or bring own horse.

SWARTHBECK FARM HOLIDAY COTTAGES

Swarthbeck Farm, Howtown, Penrith CA10 2ND
Contact: Mr and Mrs W H Parkin, Swarthbeck Farm, Howtown, Penrith CA10 2ND
T: (017684) 86432 (Answerphone)
E: whparkin@ukonline.co.uk
I: www.cumbria.com/horsehols

OPEN All year round

Low season per wk
£200.00–£500.00
High season per wk
£310.00–£1,000.00

ULVERSTON, Cumbria Map ref 5A3 *Tourist Information Centre Tel: (01229) 587120*

★★–★★★★

6 Units
Sleeping 4–8

THE FALLS
Mansriggs, Ulverston LA12 7PX
T: (01229) 583781
F: (01229) 583781
I: www.thefalls.co.uk
Contact: Mrs Cheetham and Mrs Unger

OPEN All year round

Low season per wk
£135.00–£380.00
High season per wk
£200.00–£460.00

17thC farmstead in beautiful surroundings, converted into holiday homes in traditional Lakeland style. Resident proprietors. Children and dogs welcome.

★★★–★★★★★

3 Units
Sleeping 4–6

SWARTHMOOR HALL
Ulverston LA12 0JQ
Contact: Mr Steven Deeming, Swarthmoor Hall, Swarthmoor, Ulverston LA12 0JQ
T: (01229) 583204 (Answerphone/fax)
E: swarthmrhall@gn.apc.org
I: www.quaker.org.uk/swarth.html

OPEN All year round

Low season per wk
£180.00–£235.00
High season per wk
£260.00–£330.00

16thC Grade II* building, associated with the early Quaker movement. Two self-catering units within building, one unit (wheelchair friendly) in courtyard. Rural setting.

WASDALE, Cumbria Map ref 5A3

★★★

1 Unit
Sleeping 4

Cosy cottage-style 2-bedroomed ground floor apartment close to Wastwater Lake and within easy reach of Scafell, Great Gable, Yewbarrow and only 8 miles to the coast. Beautiful scenery and an excellent walking area. Other interests close by include Eskdale and Ravenglass miniature railway and Muncaster Castle.

GREENDALE HOLIDAY APARTMENTS

Greendale, Wasdale CA20 1EU
Contact: Mr and Mrs M D Burnett, Greendale Holiday Apartments, Greendale, Wasdale CA20 1EU
T: (019467) 26243

OPEN All year round

Low season per wk
£195.00–£245.00
High season per wk
£245.00–£300.00

ACCESSIBILITY

Look for the 🧑‍🦽 symbols which indicate accessibility for wheelchair users. A list of establishments is at the front of this guide.

★★★

1 Unit
Sleeping 7

HUNTING HOW FARMHOUSE

Moresby, Whitehaven CA28 6SF
Contact: J Messenger, Adamgill Farm, Moresby,
Whitehaven CA28 6SF
T: (01946) 693662 (Answerphone)
E: jmessenger.adamgill@farmersweekly.net

Lovely 17thC farmhouse, tastefully furnished and decorated. On 250-acre mixed farm. Elevated garden enjoying views over Solway to Scottish coast. 1.25 miles from Georgian port of Whitehaven, good centre for touring lakes and coast. Close to theatre, golf course, cycleways. Cooking by oil-fired Aga. Dishwasher. Open fire in lounge.

OPEN All year round

Low season per wk
Min £250.00
High season per wk
Max £375.00

★★★★

1 Unit
Sleeping 8

FOXGLOVES

Greenrigg Farm, Westward, Wigton CA7 8AH
Contact: Mr and Mrs E Kerr, Greenrigg Farm, Westward,
Wigton CA7 8AH
T: (016973) 42676 (Answerphone service)

Spacious, well-equipped, comfortable cottage on a working farm. Superlative setting and views, large kitchen/dining-room, Aga, lounge, open fire, storage heaters, TV/video, 3 bedrooms, bathroom, shower-room. Linen, towels, electricity, logs and coal inclusive. Children and pets very welcome. Extensive garden. Horse grazing and stabling available.

OPEN All year round

Low season per wk
£160.00–£400.00
High season per wk
£180.00–£428.00

★★★

2 Units
Sleeping 4–6

ABBEY COACH HOUSE
St Mary's Park, Windermere LA23 1AZ
T: (015394) 44027
F: (015394) 44027
E: abbeycoach@aol.com
Contact: Mrs P Bell

OPEN All year round

Low season per wk
£130.00–£295.00
High season per wk
£225.00–£395.00

Excellent location of ground floor apartment and bungalow in quiet, private area. Ample parking, extensive gardens. Ideal for families or retired.

★★★

1 Unit
Sleeping 6

BIRCH COTTAGE
C/O Birch Cottage, 35 Portland Road, Leeds LS12 4LT
Contact: Mr Roland Brown, 35 Portland Road, Leeds
LS12 4LT
T: (0113) 263 4260 & 07803 583267 (Mobile)
F: (0113) 263 4260
E: roland.brown@virgin.net
I: www.birchcottagewindermere.freeserve.co.uk

OPEN Jan–Oct, Dec
CC: Barclaycard, Delta,
JCB, Mastercard, Switch,
Visa

Low season per wk
£205.00–£255.00
High season per wk
£265.00–£385.00

Centrally-located in Windermere village, this recently renovated Victorian cottage is a short stroll from local shops, restaurants and pubs.

SPECIAL BREAKS

**Many establishments offer special promotions and themed breaks.
These are highlighted in red. (All such offers are subject to availability.)**

WINDERMERE continued

★★★ CANTERBURY FLATS

5 Units
Sleeping 2-8

Quarry Rigg, Bowness-on-Windermere,
Windermere LA23 3DT
Contact: Mr & Mrs M&I Zuniga, Bowness Holidays,
131 Radcliffe New Road, Whitefield, Manchester
M45 7RP
T: (0161) 796 3896
F: (0161) 796 1621

OPEN All year round

Low season per wk
£140.00–£250.00
High season per wk
£195.00–£485.00

Wonderful location. Apartments in the centre of the village, close to all amenities. Full membership of private leisure club, indoor swimming complex. Short breaks available.

★★★★ GAVEL COTTAGE

1 Unit
Sleeping 4

7 Meadowcroft Cottages, Storrs Park, Bowness-on-
Windermere LA23 3JE
Contact: Screetons, 25 Bridgegate, Howden, Goole
DN14 7AA
T: (01430) 431201
F: (01430) 432114
E: howden@screetons.co.uk
I: screetons.co.uk

OPEN All year round

Low season per wk
£195.00–£270.00
High season per wk
£360.00–£440.00

√† not how

Secluded period cottage close to marina. Tastefully furnished and well equipped. Two bedrooms, all modern facilities. Large garden with summer house. Member Burnside Leisure Complex.

CHECK THE MAPS

The colour maps at the front of this guide show all the cities, towns and villages for which you will find accommodation entries.
Refer to the town index to find the page on which they are listed.

Luxury Holiday Accommodation at Waters Edge Villa

"Actually on the shores of Lake Windermere"

This holiday accommodation at luxury level where attention has been given to the smallest detail to make this a memorable stay. This traditional Lakeland stone house has been converted into two three bedroomed suites and one studio apartment. Oil fired centrally heated and double glazed throughout, it is situated on the shores of Lake Windermere with unsurpassed views of the Lake, surrounding hills and mountains.

Plus FREE OF CHARGE unrestricted use of sailing or motor boat and entry into private leisure club. Phone today for free colour brochure **015394 43415**

Waters Edge Villa, Ferry Nab, Bowness-on-Windermere, Windermere, Cumbria LA23 3JH
Fax: 015394 88721 Website: www.windermere-lake-holidays-afloat.co.uk
Email: info@windermere-lake-holidays-afloat.co.uk

2001 WINNER SELF CATERING

OPEN ALL YEAR

★★★

8 Units
Sleeping 2–6

THE HEANING

Heaning Lane, Windermere LA23 1JW
T: (015394) 43453
E: info@theheaning.co.uk
I: www.theheaning.co.uk
Contact: Mrs Moulding

Clean and comfortable cottages. Beautifully situated Victorian mansion set in 7 acres of ground. The stables and barns have been converted into luxury cottages sleeping 2–6 people. A quiet, rural location yet only one mile from Windermere. An ideal base for walking and touring the area.

OPEN All year round
CC: Barclaycard, Delta, Mastercard, Switch, Visa, Visa Electron

Min 3-night break. From £100, 2 person to £200, 6 person during winter months.

Low season per wk
£200.00–£320.00
High season per wk
£290.00–£460.00

★★★

4 Units
Sleeping 2–6

LANGDALE VIEW HOLIDAY APARTMENTS
112 Craig Walk, Bowness-on-Windermere,
Windermere LA23 3AX
T: (015394) 46655
E: anything@langdale-view.co.uk
I: www.langdale-view.co.uk
Contact: Mrs Janice Fletcher

OPEN All year round
CC: Barclaycard, Delta, Eurocard, JCB, Mastercard, Solo, Switch, Visa

Low season per wk
£150.00–£250.00
High season per wk
£250.00–£420.00

Attractive, comfortable holiday apartments with car parking. Quiet, elevated position very close to village centre, lake, steamers, shops and restaurants.

★★★

8 Units
Sleeping 2–7

PINETHWAITE HOLIDAY COTTAGES
Lickbarrow Road, Windermere LA23 2NQ
T: (015394) 44558
F: (015394) 44556
E: legge@pinethwaite.freeserve.co.uk
I: www.pinecottages.co.uk
Contact: Mr P A Legge

OPEN All year round
CC: Mastercard, Visa

Low season per wk
£120.00–£380.00
High season per wk
£290.00–£520.00

Cottages and house nestling in delightful private woodland (roe deer, red squirrels). Log fires. Quiet, rural location, yet only 1 mile from Windermere and Bowness villages.

TOWN INDEX

This can be found at the back of this guide. If you know where you want to stay, the index will give you the page number listing accommodation in your chosen town, city or village.

BIRTHWAITE EDGE

Birthwaite Road, Windermere,
Cumbria LA23 1BS
Tel/Fax: 015394 42861
Email: etc@lakedge.com

Birthwaite Edge is the perfect base from which to explore the North of England. Public transport and bus tours nearby. Set in an exclusive area 10 minutes' stroll from Windermere village and lake. Central for restaurants, cafes and inns. Resident proprietors guarantee comfortable, clean apartments. No smoking or pets.

www.lakedge.com

★★★

4 Units
Sleeping 2–4

Old spinnery tastefully converted into 4 pleasant apartments, situated above Bowness village, close to Lake Windermere and fells. Ideal base from which to explore the Lake District. Quiet surroundings, private on-site car parking, leisure club facilities nearby, bargain breaks during the winter months.

SPINNERY COTTAGE HOLIDAY APARTMENTS

Brantfell Road, Bowness-on-Windermere,
Windermere LA23 3AE
T: (015394) 44884
F: (015394) 46565
E: Ray&barb@the-fairfield.co.uk
I: www.the-fairfield.co.uk
Contact: Mr Ray Hood

OPEN All year round	Low season per wk
CC: Barclaycard, Delta,	£190.00–£250.00
Mastercard, Switch, Visa	High season per wk
	£260.00–£310.00

Special breaks of minimum 2 nights available Nov–Mar.

★★★★

3 Units
Sleeping 5–8

WINDERMERE MARINA VILLAGE
Bowness-on-Windermere, Windermere LA23 3JQ
T: (015394) 46551 & 0800 917 4611 (Freephone)
F: (015394) 43233
E: info@wmv.co.uk
I: www.wmv.co.uk
Contact: Ms Pam Harvey

OPEN All year round	Low season per wk
CC: Amex, Barclaycard,	£350.00–£475.00
Delta, Diners, Eurocard,	High season per wk
Mastercard, Switch, Visa	£495.00–£1,050.00

Superbly appointed lakeside cottages with private leisure club and moorings. Short breaks and weekly bookings. Swimming pool, sauna, spas, bistro, playground.

★★★

2 Units
Sleeping 2

WINSTER HOUSE
Thornbarrow Road, Windermere LA23 2EN
Contact: Mrs S Jump, Winster House, Sunnybank Road,
Windermere LA23 2EN
T: (015394) 44723

OPEN Apr–Oct & Christmas	Low season per wk
	£150.00–£170.00
	High season per wk
	£170.00–£220.00

Two units each sleeping 2. Private parking and use of secluded garden. 5 minutes' walk to shops and restaurants, 10 minutes' walk to Lake Windermere. Brochure.

★★★

1 Unit
Sleeping 6

DYER DENE
Beck Head, Witherslack, Grange-over-Sands LA11 6SH
Contact: Mrs S Andrews, 121 Dorchester Road,
Garstang, Preston PR3 1FE
T: (01995) 602769
E: dyerdene@supanet.com

OPEN All year round	Low season per wk
	Min £160.00
	High season per wk
	Max £380.00

Comfortable cottage in tranquil valley. Beautiful views and excellent local walking. Garage-cum-games room and garden. Ideal for children. Coal/electric fire and radiators in all bedrooms.

USE YOUR *i*s

There are more than 550 Tourist Information Centres throughout England offering friendly help with accommodation and holiday ideas as well as suggestions of places to visit and things to do. You'll find TIC addresses in the local Phone Book.

A brief guide to the main Towns and Villages offering accommodation in Cumbria

A ALLONBY, CUMBRIA - Small village on Solway Firth with good sandy beaches, once famous for its herring fishing and as a fashionable resort of Victorian gentry. Good views across the Firth to Criffel and the Galloway mountains.

• **AMBLESIDE, CUMBRIA** - Market town situated at the head of Lake Windermere and surrounded by fells. The historic town centre is now a conservation area and the country around Ambleside is rich in historic and literary associations. Good centre for touring, walking and climbing.

• **APPLEBY-IN-WESTMORLAND, CUMBRIA** - Former county town of Westmorland, at the foot of the Pennines in the Eden Valley. The castle was rebuilt in the 17th C, except for its Norman keep, ditches and ramparts. It now houses a Rare Breeds Survival Trust Centre. Good centre for exploring the Eden Valley.

B BASSENTHWAITE LAKE, CUMBRIA - The northernmost and only true 'lake' in the Lake District. Visited annually by many species of migratory birds.

• **BORROWDALE, CUMBRIA** - Stretching south of Derwentwater to Seathwaite in the heart of the Lake District, the valley is walled by high fellsides. It can justly claim to be the most scenically impressive valley in the Lake District. Excellent centre for walking and climbing.

• **BOTHEL, CUMBRIA** - Small village situated on high ground to the north of Bassenthwaite Lake.

• **BROUGHTON-IN-FURNESS, CUMBRIA** - Old market village whose historic charter to hold fairs is still proclaimed every year on the first day of August in the market square. Good centre for touring the pretty Duddon Valley.

C CALDBECK, CUMBRIA - Quaint limestone village lying on the northern fringe of the Lake District National Park. John Peel, the famous huntsman who is immortalised in song, is buried in the churchyard. The fells surrounding Caldbeck were once heavily mined, being rich in lead, copper and barytes.

• **CARLISLE, CUMBRIA** - Cumbria's only city is rich in history. Attractions include the small red sandstone cathedral and 900-year-old castle with magnificent view from the keep. Award-winning Tullie House Museum and Art Gallery brings 2, 000 years of Border history dramatically to life. Excellent centre for shopping.

• **CARTMEL, CUMBRIA** - Picturesque conserved village based on a 12th C priory with a well-preserved church and gatehouse. Just half a mile outside the Lake District National Park, this is a peaceful base for walking and touring, with historic houses and beautiful scenery.

• **CASTLE CARROCK, CUMBRIA** - Small, tranquil village nestling at the north-western tip of the North Pennines, in an Area of Outstanding Natural Beauty.

• **COCKERMOUTH, CUMBRIA** - Ancient market town at confluence of Rivers Cocker and Derwent. Birthplace of William Wordsworth in 1770. The house where he was born is at the end of the town's broad, tree-lined main street and is now owned by the National Trust. Good touring base for the Lakes.

• **CONISTON, CUMBRIA** - The 803m fell Coniston Old Man dominates the skyline to the east of this village at the northern end of Coniston Water. Arthur Ransome set his 'Swallows and Amazons' stories here. Coniston's most famous resident was John Ruskin, whose home, Brantwood, is open to the public. Good centre for walking.

D DENT, CUMBRIA - Very picturesque village with narrow cobbled streets, lying within the boundaries of the Yorkshire Dales National Park.

E ELTERWATER, CUMBRIA - Attractive village at the foot of Great Langdale with a small village green as its focal point. Elterwater, one of the smallest lakes in the Lake District, was named by the Norsemen as 'Swan Lake' and swans still frequent the lake.

• **ESKDALE, CUMBRIA** - Several minor roads lead to the west end of this beautiful valley, or it can be approached via the east over the Hardknott Pass, the Lake District's steepest pass. Scafell Pike and Bow Fell lie to the north and a miniature railway links the Eskdale Valley with Ravenglass on the coast.

G GRANGE-OVER-SANDS, CUMBRIA - Set on the beautiful Cartmel Peninsula, this tranquil resort, known as Lakeland's Riviera, overlooks Morecambe Bay. Pleasant seafront walks and beautiful gardens. The bay attracts many species of wading birds.

• **GRASMERE, CUMBRIA** - Described by William Wordsworth as 'the loveliest spot that man hath ever found', this village, famous for its gingerbread, is in a beautiful setting overlooked by Helm Grag. Wordsworth lived at Dove Cottage. The cottage and museum are open to the public.

• **GREAT LANGDALE, CUMBRIA** - Picturesque valley at the foot of the Langdale Pikes, popular with walkers and climbers of every ability, with some of the Lake District's loveliest waterfalls.

H HAVERIGG, CUMBRIA - Village on the coast not far from the Duddon Valley.

• **HAWKSHEAD, CUMBRIA** - Lying near Esthwaite Water, this village has great charm and character. Its small squares are linked by flagged or cobbled alleys and the main square is dominated by the market house, or Shambles, where the butchers had their stalls in days gone by.

• **HIGH LORTON, CUMBRIA** - On the B5292 between Keswick and Cockermouth. Spectacular views from nearby Whinlatter Pass down this predominantly farming valley.

K KENDAL, CUMBRIA - The 'Auld Grey Town' lies in the valley of the River Kent with a backcloth of limestone fells. Situated just outside the Lake District National Park, it is a good centre for touring the Lakes and surrounding country. Ruined castle, reputed birthplace of Catherine Parr.

• **KESWICK, CUMBRIA** - Beautifully positioned town beside Derwentwater and below the mountains of Skiddaw and Blencathra. Excellent base for walking, climbing, watersports and touring. Motor-launches operate on Derwentwater and motor boats, rowing boats and canoes can be hired.

• **KINGS MEABURN, CUMBRIA** - Unspoilt Eden Valley village on the River Lyvennet.

- **KIRKBY STEPHEN, CUMBRIA** - Old market town close to the River Eden, with many fine Georgian buildings and an attractive market square. St Stephen's Church is known as the 'Cathedral of the Dales'. Good base for exploring the Eden Valley and the Dales.

- **KIRKOSWALD, CUMBRIA** - Village of red sandstone houses in the fertile Eden Valley, with the ruins of a 12th C castle. The village derives its name from the church of St Oswald.

- **L LAMPLUGH, CUMBRIA** - Scattered village famous for its 'Lamplugh Pudding'. Ideal touring base for the western Lake District.

- **LANGDALE, CUMBRIA** - The two Langdale valleys (Great Langdale and Little Langdale) lie in the heart of beautiful mountain scenery. The craggy Langdale Pikes are almost 2, 500 ft high. An ideal walking and climbing area and base for touring.

- **LITTLE LANGDALE, CUMBRIA** - See Langdale.

- **LONGSLEDDALE, CUMBRIA** - Quiet valley in the south-eastern fells, stretching 6 miles and lying 5 miles north of Kendal. Narrow roads, bordered by rolling hillsides, woodlands and craggy valley head.

- **LOWESWATER, CUMBRIA** - Scattered village lying between Loweswater, one of the smaller lakes, and Crummock Water. Mountains surround this quiet valley of three lakes, giving some marvellous views.

- **M MEALSGATE, CUMBRIA** - Scattered village between Cockermouth and Wigton, the birthplace of the 19th C philanthropist, George Moore.

- **N NEWBY BRIDGE, CUMBRIA** - At the southern end of Windermere on the River Leven, this village has an unusual stone bridge with arches of unequal size. The Lakeside and Haverthwaite Railway has a stop here, and steamer cruises on Lake Windermere leave from nearby Lakeside.

- **P PATTERDALE, CUMBRIA** - Amongst the fells at the southern end of the Ullswater Valley, this village is dominated by Helvellyn and St Sunday Crag. Ideal centre for touring and outdoor activities.

- **PENRITH, CUMBRIA** - Ancient and historic market town, the northern gateway to the Lake District. Penrith Castle was built as a defence against the Scots. Its ruins, open to the public, stand in the public park. High above the town is the Penrith Beacon, made famous by William Wordsworth.

- **POOLEY BRIDGE, CUMBRIA** - The bridge is on the northern tip of Lake Ullswater and spans the River Eamont where it emerges from the lake. Good centre for exploring, walking and sailing.

- **R RAVENSTONEDALE, CUMBRIA** - Surrounded by fells, the Howgills to the south-west and Wild Boar Fell to the south-east, this village has a fine church with an unusual interior where sections of the congregation sit facing one another.

- **S SAWREY, CUMBRIA** - Far Sawrey and Near Sawrey lie near Esthwaite Water. Both villages are small but Near Sawrey is famous for Hill Top Farm, home of Beatrix Potter, now owned by the National Trust and open to the public.

- **SEDBERGH, CUMBRIA** - This busy market town set below the Howgill Fells is an excellent centre for walkers and touring the Dales and Howgills. The noted boys' school was founded in 1525.

- **SPARK BRIDGE, CUMBRIA** - Small, attractive village beside the River Crake, south of Coniston Water. Cumbria's last bobbin mill recently closed here.

- **ST JOHNS-IN-THE-VALE, CUMBRIA** - Rugged valley linking Thirlmere and Threlkeld. At the north end it is dominated by Blencathra and at its south by Castle Rock.

- **STAVELEY, CUMBRIA** - Large village built in slate, set between Kendal and Windermere at the entrance to the lovely Kentmere Valley.

- **T TEBAY, CUMBRIA** - Village lying amongst high fells at the north end of the Lune Gorge.

- **THORNTHWAITE, CUMBRIA** - Small village, west of Keswick, at the southern tip of Bassenthwaite Lake. Forest trails in Thornthwaite Forest.

- **THRELKELD, CUMBRIA** - This village is a centre for climbing the Saddleback range of mountains, which tower high above it.

- **TROUTBECK, CUMBRIA** - Most of the houses in this picturesque village are 17th C, some retain their spinning galleries and oak-mullioned windows. At the south end of the village is Townend, owned by the National Trust and open to the public, an excellently preserved example of a yeoman farmer's or statesman's house.

- **U ULLSWATER, CUMBRIA** - This beautiful lake, which is over 7 miles long, runs from Glenridding to Pooley Bridge. Lofty peaks ranging around the lake make an impressive background. A steamer service operates along the lake between Pooley Bridge, Howtown and Glenridding in the summer.

- **ULVERSTON, CUMBRIA** - Market town lying between green fells and the sea. There is a replica of the Eddystone lighthouse on the Hoad which is a monument to Sir John Barrow, founder of the Royal Geographical Society. Birthplace of Stan Laurel, of Laurel and Hardy.

- **W WASDALE, CUMBRIA** - A very dramatic valley with England's deepest lake, Wastwater, highest mountain, Scafell Pike, and smallest church. The eastern shore of Wastwater is dominated by the 1,500 ft screes dropping steeply into the lake. A good centre for walking and climbing.

- **WHITEHAVEN, CUMBRIA** - Historic Georgian port on the west coast. The town was developed in the 17th C and many fine buildings have been preserved. The Beacon Heritage Centre includes a Meteorological Office Weather Gallery. Start or finishing point of Coast to Coast, Whitehaven to Sunderland, cycleway.

- **WIGTON, CUMBRIA** - Built on the site of a Roman fort, Wigton has a centuries-old market as well as cattle, sheep and horse auctions.

- **WINDERMERE, CUMBRIA** - Once a tiny hamlet before the introduction of the railway in 1847, now adjoins Bowness which is on the lakeside. Centre for sailing and boating. A good way to see the lake is a trip on a passenger steamer. Steamboat Museum has a fine collection of old boats.

- **WITHERSLACK, CUMBRIA** - Tranquil village on the east bank of the River Winster, at the south end of the Lyth Valley, famed for its damsons. Good base for touring.

CREDIT CARD BOOKINGS If you book by telephone and are asked for your credit card number it is advisable to check the proprietor's policy should you cancel your reservation.

Their
house is your home

Owners and agencies offering holiday homes in this guide want you to enjoy your holiday so please make yourself at home – but do also remember that it is someone else's property.

Here are a few tips to ensure a smooth-running, problem-free holiday:

Allow plenty of time for your journey but please do not arrive at the property before the stated time – and please leave by the stated time. This enables the owner to make sure everything is ready for you and for whoever follows you.

If you've booked for, say, six people please don't turn up with more.

Do respect the owner's rules on pets – if, for example, one small pet is allowed please don't take a Great Dane.

Do report any damages or breakages immediately (and offer the cost of repair), so that the owner can ensure everything is in order for the next letting.

Do leave the place clean and tidy – no dirty dishes in the sink, please – and all the furniture back where it was when you arrived.

Despite the best endeavours of the owners and agents, problems can occur from time to time. If you are dissatisfied in any way with your holiday home, please give the owner or agent a chance to put matters right by letting them know immediately.

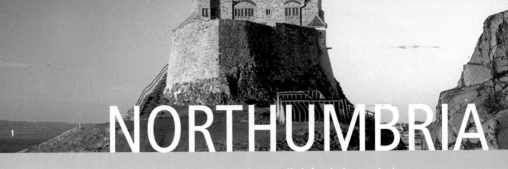

NORTHUMBRIA

Romans, sailors and industrial pioneers have all left their mark here. Northumbria's exciting cities, castle – studded countryside and white-sanded coastline make it an undiscovered gem.

classic sights

Lindisfarne Castle – on Holy Island
Housesteads Roman Fort – the most impressive Roman fort on Hadrian's Wall

coast & country

Kielder Water and Forest Park – perfect for walking, cycling and watersports
Saltburn – beach of broad sands
Seahouses – picturesque fishing village

maritime history

HMS Trincomalee – magnificent 1817 British warship
Captain Cook – birthplace museum and replica of his ship, Endeavour
Grace Darling – museum commemorating her rescue of shipwreck survivors in 1838

arts for all

Angel of the North – awe-inspiring sculpture by Antony Gormley

distinctively different

St Mary's lighthouse – great views from the top

The counties of County Durham, Northumberland, Tees Valley and Tyne & Wear

FOR MORE INFORMATION CONTACT:
Northumbria Tourist Board
Aykley Heads, Durham DH1 5UX
Tel: (0191) 375 3009 Fax: (0191) 386 0899
Internet: www.visitnorthumbria.com

The Pictures:
1 Lindisfarne Castle, Holy Island
2 Bamburgh, Northumberland
3 Washington Old Hall,
  Tyne & Wear

Places to Visit - see pages 86-89
Where to Stay - see pages 90-112

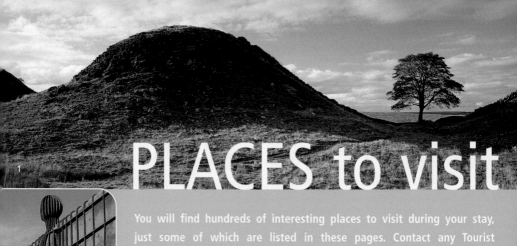

PLACES to visit

You will find hundreds of interesting places to visit during your stay, just some of which are listed in these pages. Contact any Tourist Information Centre in the region for more ideas on days out.

Alnwick Castle

The Estate Office, Alnwick, Northumberland NE66 1NQ
Tel: (01665) 510777 www.alnwickcastle.com
Largest inhabited castle in England, after Windsor Castle, and home of the Percys, Dukes of Northumberland since 1309.

ARC

Dovecot Street, Stockton-on-Tees, Stockton TS18 1LL
Tel: (01642) 666600 www.arconline.co.uk
Arts venue which aims to provide the region with an extensive and innovative programme. Two theatres, a dance studio, recording studio and rehearsal rooms.

Bamburgh Castle

Bamburgh, Northumberland NE69 7DF
Tel: (01668) 214515 www.bamburghcastle.com
Magnificent coastal castle completely restored in 1900. Collections of china, porcelain, furniture, paintings, arms and armour.

Bede's World

Church Bank, Jarrow, Tyne & Wear NE32 3DY
Tel: (0191) 489 2106 www.bedesworld.co.uk
Discover the exciting world of the Venerable Bede, early medieval Europe's greatest scholar. Church, monastic site, museum with exhibitions and recreated Anglo-Saxon farm.

Bowes Museum

Barnard Castle, Durham DL12 8NP
Tel: (01833) 690606 www.bowesmuseum.org.uk
French-style chateau housing art collections of national importance and archaeology of south west Durham.

Captain Cook Birthplace Museum

Stewart Park, Marton, Middlesbrough, Cleveland TS7 6AS
Tel: (01642) 311211
Early life and voyages of Captain Cook and the countries he visited. Temporary exhibitions. One person free with every group of 10 visiting.

Chesters Roman Fort (Cilurnum)

Chollerford, Hadrian's Wall, Humshaugh, Hexham, Northumberland NE46 4EP
Tel: (01434) 681379
Fort built for 500 cavalrymen. Remains include 5 gateways, barrack blocks, commandant's house and headquarters. Finest military bath house in Britain.

Cragside House, Gardens and Estate

Cragside, Rothbury, Morpeth, Northumberland NE65 7PX
Tel: (01669) 620333 www.nationaltrust.org.uk
House built 1864-84 for the first Lord Armstrong, a Tyneside industrialist. Cragside was the first house to be lit by electricity generated by water power.

Discovery Museum

Blandford House, Blandford Square, Newcastle upon Tyne, Tyne & Wear NE1 4JA
Tel: (0191) 232 6789
The Museum is currently undergoing a £10.7 million redevelopment. Visit the Science Maze, Fashion Works, Live Wires, Maritime Gallery, A Soldier's Life Gallery and The Newcastle Story (the new John George Jolcey Museum).

Durham Castle

Palace Green, Durham DH1 3RW
Tel: (0191) 374 3863 www.durhamcastle.com
Castle founded in 1072, Norman chapel dating from
1080, kitchens and great hall dated 1499 and 1284
respectively. Fine example of motte-and-bailey castle.

Durham Cathedral

The Chapter Office, The College, Durham DH1 3EH
Tel: (0191) 386 4266 www.durhamcathedral.co.uk
Durham Cathedral is thought by many to be the finest
example of Norman church architecture in England. Visit
the tombs of St Cuthbert and The Venerable Bede.

Gisborough Priory

Church Street, Guisborough, Redcar & Cleveland TS14 6HG
Tel: (01287) 633801
Remains of a priory founded by Robert de Brus in
AD1119. A priory for Augustinian canons in the grounds
of Guisborough Hall. Main arch and window of east wall
virtually intact.

Hall Hill Farm

Lanchester, Durham DH7 0TA
Tel: (01388) 730300 www.hallhillfarm.co.uk
Family fun set in attractive countryside with an
opportunity to see and touch the animals at close
quarters. Farm trailer ride, riverside walk, teashop and
play area.

Hartlepool Historic Quay

Maritime Avenue, Hartlepool, Cleveland TS24 0XZ
Tel: (01429) 860006 www.thisishartlepool.com
Hartlepool Historic Quay is an exciting reconstruction of
a seaport of the 1800s with buildings and lively quayside,
authentically reconstructed.

Housesteads Roman Fort (Vercovicum)

Hadrian's Wall, Haydon Bridge, Hexham,
Northumberland NE47 6NN
Tel: (01434) 344363
Best preserved and most impressive of the Roman forts.
Vercovicium was a 5-acre fort for an extensive 800 civil
settlement. Only example of a Roman hospital.

Killhope, The North of England Lead Mining Museum

Cowshill, Weardale, St John's Chapel, Bishop Auckland,
County Durham DL13 1AR
Tel: (01388) 537505 www.durham.gov.uk/killhope
Most complete lead mining site in Great Britain. Mine
tours available, 10m (34ft) diameter water-wheel,
reconstruction of Victorian machinery, miners lodging and
woodland walks.

Kirkleatham Old Hall Museum

Kirkleatham, Redcar, Redcar & Cleveland TS10 5NW
Tel: (01642) 479500
Displays depicting local life, industry, commerce, local
history, sea rescue, artists, social and natural history and
the story of Kirkleatham.

Laing Art Gallery

New Bridge Street, Newcastle upon Tyne,
Tyne & Wear NE1 8AJ
Tel: (0191) 232 7734
Paintings, including watercolours by Northumbrian-born
artist John Martin. Award-winning interactive displays
'Art on Tyneside' and 'Children's Gallery'. Cafe and shop.

Life Interactive World

Times Square, Scotswood Road, Newcastle upon Tyne,
Tyne & Wear NE1 4EP
Tel: (0191) 243 8210 www.lifeinteractiveworld.co.uk
Life Interactive World is an amazing action-packed
journey. Experience the longest motion ride in the world,
magical 3D, theatre shows, virtual games and
interactives.

The Pictures:
1 Hadrian's Wall
2 The Angel of the North, Gateshead
3 Tynemouth Priory and Castle, Tyne & Wear
4 Dunstanburgh, Northumberland
5 Boulby Cliff, Cleveland
6 Kielder Water, Northumberland

National Glass Centre

Liberty Way, Sunderland, Tyne & Wear SR6 0GL
Tel: (0191) 515 5555 www.nationalglasscentre.com
A large gallery presenting the best in contemporary and historical glass. Master craftspeople will demonstrate glass-making techniques. Classes and workshops available.

Nature's World at the Botanic Centre

Nature's World at the Botanic Centre
Ladgate Lane, Acklam, Middlesbrough,
Tees Valley TS5 7YN
Tel: (01642) 594895 www.naturesworld.org.uk
Demonstration gardens, wildlife pond, white garden, environmental exhibition hall, shop, tearooms and River Tees model now open. Hydroponicum and visitor exhibition centre.

Newcastle Cathedral Church of St Nicholas

St Nicholas Street, Newcastle upon Tyne,
Tyne & Wear NE1 1PF
Tel: (0191) 232 1939
www.newcastle-ang-cathedral-stnicholas.org.uk
13thC and 14thC church, added to in 18thC-20thC. Famous lantern tower, pre-reformation font and font cover, 15thC stained glass roundel in the side chapel.

The North of England Open Air Museum

Beamish, County Durham DH9 0RG
Tel: (0191) 370 4000 www.beamish.org.uk
Visit the town, colliery village, working farm, Pockerley Manor and 1825 railway, recreating life in the North East in the early 1800s and 1900s.

Ormesby Hall

Church Lane, Ormesby, Middlesbrough TS7 9AS
Tel: (01642) 324188 www.nationaltrust.org.uk
Georgian, 18thC mansion. Impressive contemporary plasterwork. Magnificent stable block attributed to Carr of York. Model railway exhibition and layout.

Raby Castle

PO Box 50, Staindrop, Darlington, County Durham DL2 3AH
Tel: (01833) 660202 www.rabycastle.com
The medieval castle, home of Lord Barnard's family since 1626, includes a 200-acre deer park, walled gardens, carriage collection, adventure playground, shop and tearooms.

Sea Life Aquarium

Grand Parade, Tynemouth, Tyne & Wear NE30 4JF
Tel: (0191) 257 6100
More than 30 hi-tech displays provide encounters with dozens of sea creatures. Journey beneath the North Sea and discover thousands of amazing creatures.

South Shields Museum and Art Gallery

Ocean Road, South Shields, Tyne & Wear NE33 2JA
Tel: (0191) 456 8740
Discover how the area's development has been influenced by its natural and industrial past through lively hands-on displays. Exciting programme of temporary exhibitions.

Thomas Bewick Birthplace Museum

Cherryburn, Station Bank, Mickley, Stocksfield,
Northumberland NE43 7DB
Tel: (01661) 843276
Birthplace cottage (1700) and farmyard. Printing house using original printing blocks. Introductory exhibition of the life, work and countryside.

Vindolanda (Chesterholm)

Chesterholm Museum, Hadrian's Wall, Bardon Mill,
Hexham, Northumberland NE47 7JN
Tel: (01434) 344277 www.vindolanda.com
Visitors may inspect the remains of the Roman fort and settlement, and see its extraordinary finds in the superb museum. Full-scale replicas of Roman buildings.

Washington Old Hall

The Avenue, District 4, Washington, Tyne & Wear NE38 7LE
Tel: (0191) 416 6879
From 1183 to 1399 the home of George Washington's direct ancestors, remaining in the family until 1613. The manor, from which the family took its name, was restored in 1936.

Wet 'N Wild

Rotary Way, Royal Quays, North Shields,
Tyne & Wear NE29 6DA
Tel: (0191) 296 1333 www.wetnwild.co.uk
Tropical indoor water park. A fun water playground providing the wildest and wettest indoor rapid experience. Whirlpools, slides and meandering lazy river.

Wildfowl and Wetlands Trust

Washington, District 15, Washington, Tyne & Wear NE38 8LE
Tel: (0191) 416 5454 www.wwt.org.uk
Collection of 1,000 wildfowl of 85 varieties. Viewing gallery, picnic areas, hides and winter wild bird-feeding station, flamingos and wild grey heron. Food available.

Find out more about Northumbria

Dunstanburgh Castle

Further information about holidays and attractions in Northumbria is available from:

NORTHUMBRIA TOURIST BOARD
Aykley Heads, Durham DH1 5UX.
Tel: (0191) 375 3009 Fax: (0191) 386 0899
Internet: www.visitnorthumbria.com

The following publications are available from Northumbria Tourist Board unless otherwise stated:

Northumbria 2002
information on the region, including hotels, bed and breakfast and self-catering accommodation, caravan and camping parks, attractions, shopping, eating and drinking

Going Places
information on where to go, what to see and what to do. Combined with the award-winning Powerpass promotion which offers 2-for-1 entry into many of the region's top attractions

Group Travel Directory
guide designed specifically for group organisers, detailing group accommodation providers, places to visit, suggested itineraries, coaching information and events

Educational Visits
information to help plan educational visits within the region. Uncover a wide variety of places

to visit with unique learning opportunities

Discover Northumbria on two wheels
information on cycling in the region including an order form allowing the reader to order maps/leaflets from a central ordering point

Freedom
caravan and camping guide to the North of England. Available from Freedom Holidays,

tel: 01202 252179

Getting to Northumbria

BY ROAD: The north/south routes on the A1 and A19 thread the region as does the A68. East/west routes like the A66 and A69 easily link with the western side of the country. Within Northumbria you will find fast, modern interconnecting roads between all the main centres, a vast network of scenic, traffic-free country roads to make motoring a pleasure and frequent local bus services operating to all towns and villages.

BY RAIL: London to Edinburgh InterCity service stops at Darlington, Durham, Newcastle and Berwick upon Tweed. 26 trains daily make the journey between London and Newcastle in just under 3 hours. The London to Middlesbrough journey takes 3 hours. Birmingham to Darlington 3 hours 15 minutes. Bristol to Durham 5 hours and Sheffield to Newcastle just over 2 hours. Direct services operate to Newcastle from Liverpool, Manchester, Glasgow, Stranraer and Carlisle. Regional services to areas of scenic beauty operate frequently, allowing the traveller easy access. The Tyne & Wear Metro makes it possible to travel to many destinations within the Tyneside area, such as Gateshead, South Shields, Whitley Bay and Newcastle International Airport, in minutes.

Where to stay in

Northumbria

Accommodation entries in this region are listed in alphabetical order of place name, and then in alphabetical order of establishment.

Map references refer to the colour location maps at front of this guide. The first number indicates the map to use; the letter and number which follow refer to the grid reference on the map.

At-a-glance symbols at the end of each accommodation entry give useful information about services and facilities. A key to symbols can be found inside the back cover flap. Keep this open for easy reference.

A brief description of the towns and villages offering accommodation in the entries which follow, can be found at the end of this section.

A complete listing of all the English Tourism Council assessed accommodation covered by this guide appears at the back of the guide.

ALLENDALE, Northumberland Map ref 5B2

★★

1 Unit
Sleeping 6

STATION HOUSE CARAVAN PARK
Catton, Hexham NE47 9QF
T: (01434) 683362
Contact: Mrs A G Dodsworth

OPEN All year round

Low season per wk
£120.00–£140.00
High season per wk
£150.00–£180.00

Ground-floor flat converted from booking office, station master's office and waiting room of Hexham-Allendale terminal railway station. Second bedroom entered via first.

ALNMOUTH, Northumberland Map ref 5C1

★★

3 Units
Sleeping 7

WOODEN FARM HOLIDAY COTTAGES
Wooden Farm, Lesbury, Alnwick NE66 2TW
T: (01665) 830342
Contact: Mr W G Farr

OPEN All year round

Low season per wk
Max £180.00
High season per wk
Max £210.00

Stone-built cottages in a quiet farm setting, overlooking the coast and the picturesque village of Alnmouth.

MAP REFERENCES The map references refer to the colour maps at the front of this guide. The first figure is the map number; the letter and figure which follow indicate the grid reference on the map.

ALNWICK, Northumberland Map ref 5C1 *Tourist Information Centre Tel: (01665) 510665*

★★★★

2 Units
Sleeping 2–4

Spacious cottages converted from 18thC farm buildings. Luxuriously equipped – 1 wheelchair friendly. Ideally situated 1 mile from the historic and picturesque town of Alnwick between Cheviot Hills and magnificent Heritage Coast. Perfect base for beaches, castles, walking, bird-watching, golfing, fishing, National Trust properties – or just relaxing.

BOG MILL FARM HOLIDAY COTTAGES

Bog Mill Farm, Alnwick NE66 3PA
Contact: Mrs A M Mason, Bog Mill Farm, Alnwick
NE66 3PA
T: (01665) 604529
F: (01665) 606972

OPEN All year round	Low season per wk Min £150.00
Short breaks 2, 3, 4 day available. Reductions for repeat or low season fortnights. Phone for details.	High season per wk Max £375.00

★★★

1 Unit
Sleeping 4

THE BUI
26 Lisburn Street, Alnwick NE66 1UR
Contact: Ms Diana Norris, Cosaig, Glenelg,
Kyle of Lochalsh IV40 8LB
T: (01599) 522365
F: (01599) 522365
E: diana_norris@hotmail.com

OPEN Mar–Oct

Low season per wk
£165.00–£210.00
High season per wk
£210.00–£300.00

Terraced sandstone house, antiques and open fire. Quiet location close to beautiful market town centre but with easy access to coast, castles and hills.

★★★★

2 Units
Sleeping 4–6

Enjoy panoramic views from cosy well-equipped cottages providing high quality accommodation on one level. Solid pine furniture, log fires, safe gardens, patio furniture. Central for coast and hills. Cot and highchair available. Secure private heated outbuildings. All fuel and linen inclusive. Washbasins in all bedrooms. No smokers or pets.

1 DENE VIEW COTTAGE AND 2 MOOR CROFT COTTAGE

Broome Hill Farm, Alnwick NE66 2BA
Contact: Mrs M E McGregor, Broome Hill Farm, Alnwick
NE66 2BA
T: (01665) 574460 (Answerphone)
F: (01665) 574460

OPEN All year round	Low season per wk £180.00–£256.00
Short breaks available Oct–Easter, prices on application. Sorry, no Stag or Hen parties.	High season per wk £400.00–£496.00

★★★

1 Unit
Sleeping 5

1 HOWICK STREET
Alnwick NE66 1UY
Contact: Mr Thomas Payton, Austrey House,
3 Grosvenor Terrace, Alnwick NE66 1LG
T: (01665) 510484
F: 0870 163 7533
E: tompayton@totalise.co.uk
I: www.howickhols.fsnet.co.uk

OPEN Feb–Sep &
Christmas

High season per wk
£200.00–£350.00

A traditional 3-bedroomed Georgian terraced house. Two minutes' walk from Alnwick town centre, conveniently situated for coast and hills.

QUALITY ASSURANCE SCHEME
Star ratings are explained at the back of this guide.

ALNWICK continued

★★★★
1 Unit
Sleeping 10–12

TIDAL WATCH

19 Lesbury Road, Hipsburn, Alnwick NE66 3NB
Contact: Mr K Bremner, Proprietor, Tidal Watch,
19 Lesbury Road, Lesbury, Alnwick NE66 3NB
T: 07947 624160 & 07714 276605
F: (01665) 510473
E: kevinbremner@aol.com

Looking southward over Alnmouth Estuary and coast, the house is well appointed including en suite facilities. There is a large, secure enclosed garden with luxurious summer house and garden furniture. Ample parking, central heating, pets allowed. Sleeps 10/12, one bedroom is on the ground floor. A warm and friendly home.

OPEN All year round

Low season per wk
£352.00–£407.00
High season per wk
£570.00–£842.00

★★★–★★★★★
11 Units
Sleeping 2–12

VILLAGE FARM

Shilbottle, Alnwick NE66 2XR
Contact: Mrs C M Stoker, Town Foot Farm, Shilbottle,
Alnwick NE66 2HG
T: (01665) 575591 & 0798 987 5749 (Mobile)
F: (01665) 575591
E: crissy@villagefarmcottages.co.uk
I: www.villagefarmcottages.co.uk

17thC farmhouse, cottages and beautifully appointed chalets, sleeping 2-12 persons. Complemented by excellent facilities – indoor heated swimming pool, fitness club, steam room, sauna, sunshower, beauty therapist, games room, tennis, riding, fishing and adventure playground. Situated between Alnwick and Heritage Coast. Warm personal welcome.

OPEN All year round

2-3 night stays available
Nov-Easter (excl Christmas
and New Year and half
terms).

Low season per wk
£128.00–£280.00
High season per wk
£225.00–£670.00

BAMBURGH, Northumberland Map ref 5C1

★★★★
1 Unit
Sleeping 6

BARN END
16 The Wynding, Bamburgh NE69 7DB
Contact: Mr George Bruce, The Steading, Westburn,
Crawcrook, Ryton NE40 4EU
T: (0191) 413 2353
E: george.e.bruce@talk21.com

OPEN Feb–Nov

Low season per wk
Min £250.00
High season per wk
Max £450.00

Cottage with 1 twin, 2 double rooms, bathroom/WC, en suite shower/WC. Fully carpeted and equipped. 200 yards to village and beach. Sorry, no pets.

★★★
1 Unit
Sleeping 4

THE COTTAGE
6 Armstrong Cottages, Bamburgh NE68 7BA
Contact: Mrs S Turnbull, 1 Friars Court, Bamburgh
NE69 7AE
T: (01668) 214494

OPEN All year round

Low season per wk
£200.00–£420.00

Charming, quality accommodation minutes from the beautiful sandy beach. With wonderful views of the magnificent Bamburgh Castle. Large private gardens and parking.

★★★
1 Unit
Sleeping 8

THE FAIRWAY
38 The Wynding, Bamburgh NE69 7DD
Contact: Mrs R S Middleton, High Close House, Wylam
NE41 8BL
T: (01661) 852125
E: rsmiddleton@talk21.com

OPEN Feb–Dec

Low season per wk
£420.00–£480.00
High season per wk
£480.00–£550.00

Beautifully situated cottage overlooking sea, 1 minute from beaches and golf course. Four bedrooms, open fire and central heating. Garden front and rear.

BAMBURGH continued

★★★★★

2 Units
Sleeping 4–8

GLEBE HOUSE AND GLEBE COTTAGE
The Glebe, Radcliffe Road, Bamburgh NE69 7AE
Contact: Mrs Maria Eliana Robinson, EMR Properties,
The Glebe, 16 Radcliffe Road, Bamburgh NE69 7AE
T: (01668) 214456
F: (01668) 214354
E: 101361.1343@compuserve.com
I: www.org.uk/holidays.uk

OPEN All year round

Low season per wk
£290.00–£495.00
High season per wk
£460.00–£875.00

In Bamburgh village, this lovely old vicarage has stunning views of the coast, church and castle. Cottages also available. Exclusive accommodation with private gardens.

★★★★

1 Unit
Sleeping 6

INGLENOOK COTTAGE
8 Front Street, Bamburgh NE69 7BW
Contact: Mrs A D Moore, Beckstones, Carperby,
Leyburn DL8 4DA
T: (01969) 663363

OPEN Jun–Sep &
Christmas

Low season per wk
£174.00–£342.00
High season per wk
£348.00–£525.00

Three-bedroomed Listed 17thC cottage beside the Grove (village green) and only 250 yards from Bamburgh Castle and beach.

★★★

1 Unit
Sleeping 5

NINETEEN
19 Lucker Road, Bamburgh NE69 7BS
Contact: Mr John McDougal, Glenander,
27 Lucker Road, Bamburgh NE69 7BS
T: (01668) 214336
F: (01668) 214100
E: clem500@btinternet.com

OPEN All year round

Low season per wk
Min £190.00
High season per wk
Max £490.00

Central village location. Comfortably furnished 3-bedroom house, sleeping up to five people, plus cot. Centrally heated, double glazed; modern electrical appliances; TV, Video, etc.

★★★–★★★★★

15 Units
Sleeping 2–6

Ross is in a superb location near the sea between Bamburgh and Holy Island – really 'away from it all'. A no-through-road farm hamlet with a choice of attractive farm and coastguard cottages modernised to a high standard to provide warm, comfortable accommodation. Please phone/fax for our colour brochure.

OUTCHESTER & ROSS FARM COTTAGES

Ross Farm, Belford NE70 7EN
Contact: Shirley McKie, Manager, 1 Cragview Road,
Belford NE70 7NT
T: (01668) 213336
F: (01668) 219385
E: enquiry@rosscottages.co.uk
I: www.rosscottages.co.uk

OPEN All year round

Low season per wk
£180.00–£316.00
High season per wk
£270.00–£550.00

★★★

5 Units
Sleeping 2–4

POINT COTTAGES
39 The Wynding, Bamburgh NE69 7DD
Contact: Mrs E Sanderson, 30 The Oval, Benton,
Newcastle upon Tyne NE12 9PP
T: (0191) 266 2800 & (01665) 720246
F: (0191) 215 1630
E: info@bamburgh-cottages.co.uk
I: www.bamburgh-cottages.co.uk

OPEN All year round

Low season per wk
£190.00–£230.00
High season per wk
£375.00–£425.00

Cluster of cottages, with fine sea views, located next to golf-course. Furnished to a high standard, log fires, large garden.

COLOUR MAPS Colour maps at the front of this guide pinpoint all places under which you will find accommodation listed.

BAMBURGH continued

★★★

1 Unit
Sleeping 11

STRUAN
30 Front Street, Bamburgh NE69 7BJ
Contact: Mr C E Wilkie-Smith, 27 Ridley Place,
Newcastle upon Tyne NE1 8LE
T: (0191) 232 8058 & (01434) 432333
F: (0191) 222 1391
E: kerry@daviesbellreed.co.uk

OPEN All year round

Low season per wk
Min £455.00
High season per wk
Max £969.00

*Situated in the heart of the village with superb views, this fully modernised
7-bedroomed house has a large south-facing garden.*

BARDON MILL, Northumberland Map ref 5B2

★★★

1 Unit
Sleeping 4

BIRKSHAW FARMHOUSE COTTAGE
Bardon Mill, Hexham NE47 7JL
Contact: Mr E C Story, Birkshaw Farmhouse,
Bardon Mill, Hexham NE47 7JL
T: (01434) 344394
E: cstory2723@aol.com
I: www.accomodata.co.uk/201299.htm

OPEN Mar–Oct

Low season per wk
£160.00
High season per wk
£170.00–£210.00

*Beautifully converted barn with Pennine views, half a mile south of Vindolanda in
open, Roman Wall country.*

BARNARD CASTLE, Durham Map ref 5B3 *Tourist Information Centre Tel: (01833) 690909*

★★★★

6 Units
Sleeping 2–6

EAST BRISCOE FARM COTTAGES
East Briscoe Farm, Baldersdale, Barnard Castle DL12 9UL
Contact: Mr & Mrs Peter & Ann Wilson, East Cottage,
East Briscoe Farm, Baldersdale, Barnard Castle DL12 9UL
T: (01833) 650087 (Answerphone)
F: (01833) 650027
E: peter@eastbriscoe.co.uk
I: www.eastbriscoe.co.uk

*Awarded Northumbria 'Self Catering
of the Year'. Charming country
cottages, delightfully situated in a
beautiful, peaceful, south facing
position on a 14-acre riverside
estate. By High Pennine moorland
and flower-strewn meadows; near
legendary waterfalls and busy
market towns. A paradise for
naturalists, tourists, cyclists or
walkers.*

OPEN Feb–Nov &
Christmas
CC: Barclaycard,
Mastercard, Visa

10% discount for 'last
minute' bookings, booked
within 7 days of arrival.

Low season per wk
£115.00–£165.00
High season per wk
£265.00–£380.00

★★★★

2 Units
Sleeping 2–6

HAUXWELL COTTAGES (BUMPKIN BYRE AND PUDDLES END)
Barnard Castle DL12 8QU
Contact: Mrs Penny Clark, Hauxwell Grange, Marwood,
Barnard Castle DL12 8QU
T: (01833) 695022 (Answerphone and fax)
F: (01833) 695022
E: jdclark@mail.sci-net.co.uk

OPEN All year round

Low season per wk
£185.00–£320.00
High season per wk
£160.00–£230.00

*Converted stable sleeps 4/6. Two bedrooms, bathroom, sitting room, dining/kitchen,
cloakroom. Converted cow byre sleeps 2/4 with bedroom, shower room, large sitting
room, dining/kitchen. Terraces.*

NB IMPORTANT NOTE Information on accommodation listed
in this guide has been supplied by the proprietors. As changes may occur
you are advised to check details at the time of booking.

BARNARD CASTLE continued

★★★

1 Unit
Sleeping 5

STAINDROP HOUSE MEWS

8a Office Square, Staindrop, Darlington DL2 3NG
Contact: Mrs D J Walton, Staindrop House,
14 Front street, Staindrop, Darlington DL2 3NH
T: (01833) 660951 (With answerphone)

Converted stable unit, comprising 3 bedrooms, 2 reception rooms, bathroom, shower room, fitted kitchen. The upstairs lounge has a small balcony and beamed ceiling. Sleeping up to 5 people plus baby. Pretty countryside village, A1(M) 12 miles. Use of large, landscaped garden. All linen provided. Pets accepted.

OPEN Feb–Dec

Coal fire (first bucket of coal free). Bottle of wine in fridge.

Low season per wk
£190.00–£240.00
High season per wk
£250.00–£391.00

BEADNELL, Northumberland Map ref 5C1

★★★

1 Unit
Sleeping 7

THE DELLS
44 Harbour Road, Beadnell, Chathill NE67 5BB
Contact: Mr & Mrs Iain and Andrea Slater,
25 Northumberland Gardens, Jesmond,
Newcastle upon Tyne NE2 1HA
T: (0191) 239 9934 (Evenings and weekends) &
0797 144 0085 (Mobile)
F: 07967 161515
E: andreaslater@beadnell.fsnet.co.uk

OPEN All year round

Low season per wk
£200.00–£350.00
High season per wk
£350.00–£500.00

Delightful 3-bedroomed detached bungalow with gardens, situated immediately on the seafront with spectacular sea views to the Farne Islands.

★★★

7 Units
Sleeping 2–5

TOWN FARM
Beadnell, Chathill NE67 5AU
Contact: Mr & Mrs P Thompson, South Lodge,
Swarland, Morpeth NE65 9JA
T: (01670) 787864 & 786188
F: (01670) 787336
E: pault@marishal.co.uk
I: www.northumberland-holidays.com

OPEN All year round
CC: Barclaycard, Delta,
Maestro, Mastercard,
Solo, Switch, Visa, Visa
Electron

Low season per wk
£100.00–£195.00
High season per wk
£175.00–£350.00

17thC stable block converted to cottages and apartments. Close to the sea and beaches, ideal for exploring lovely Northumbria. Easy walk to beach.

BEAMISH, Durham Map ref 5C2

★★★

4 Units
Sleeping 2

CHAPEL HOUSE STUDIO APARTMENTS

Causey Row, Marley Hill, Newcastle upon Tyne NE16 5EJ
Contact: Mr J MacLennan, Chapel House, Causey Row,
Marley Hill, Stanley NE16 5EJ
T: (01207) 290992

The 4 centrally heated studio apartments form part of a recently converted Methodist chapel, located on a quiet country lane overlooking farmland. Beamish Museum and Tanfield Railway are a short drive away and the MetroCentre can be reached in 20 minutes. Towels and linen provided.

OPEN All year round

3-day breaks from £85.

Low season per wk
£130.00
High season per wk
£145.00

QUALITY ASSURANCE SCHEME

Star ratings were correct at the time of going to press but are subject to change. Please check at the time of booking.

BELLINGHAM, Northumberland Map ref 5B2 *Tourist Information Centre Tel: (01434) 220616*

★★★★
1 Unit
Sleeping 5

CONHEATH COTTAGE
Bellingham, Hexham NE48 2EG
Contact: Mrs Zaina Riddle, Blakelaw Farm, Bellingham,
Hexham NE48 2EF
T: (01434) 220250
F: (01434) 220250
E: stay@conheath.co.uk
I: www.conheath.co.uk

OPEN All year round

Low season per wk
Min £170.00
High season per wk
Max £350.00

1146-acre hill farm. Quiet, semi-detached cottage. High standard of comfort, very well equipped. Open fire, large garden with furniture and barbecue.

★★★
4 Units
Sleeping 4

RIVERDALE APARTMENTS
Bellingham NE48 2JT
Contact: Mrs C Morris, Riverdale Hall Hotel,
Bellingham, Hexham NE48 2JT
T: (01434) 220254
F: (01434) 220457
E: iben@riverdalehall.demon.co.uk
I: www.riverdalehall.demon.co.uk

OPEN All year round
CC: Amex, Barclaycard,
Delta, Diners, Mastercard,
Switch, Visa

Low season per wk
£115.00–£175.00
High season per wk
£190.00–£240.00

Apartments with lounge (wardrobe beds), bedroom, bathroom and kitchen. Free use of indoor pool and facilities at nearby Riverdale Hall Hotel. Short breaks from £69.

BERWICK–UPON–TWEED, Northumberland Map ref 5B1 *Tourist Information Centre Tel: (01289) 330733*

★★★★
1 Unit
Sleeping 4

KINGSWAY COTTAGE
East Ord Farm, East Ord, Berwick-upon-
Tweed TD15 2NS
Contact: Mrs Judith King, East Ord Farmhouse,
East Ord, Berwick-upon-Tweed TD15 2NS
T: (01289) 306228 (Home) & 0798 980 0996 (Mobile)

OPEN All year round

Low season per wk
£200.00–£250.00
High season per wk
£250.00–£380.00

Delightful cottage situated in the quiet village of East Ord. It is central for coast and country. Edinburgh and Newcastle are 60 miles.

BLANCHLAND, Northumberland Map ref 5B2

★★★
1 Unit
Sleeping 4

Set in beautiful moorland, this is our family retreat. Two-bedroomed stone cottage with log stove, historic features and comfortable pine furnishings. Main bedroom recently refurbished. Central heating, telephone, VCR, garden with barbecue and stunning views. Sailing, fishing and golf nearby, 40 minutes to Beamish, Hadrian's Wall and Durham. Favourite honeymoon destination!

BOLTSLAW COTTAGE
Ramshaw, Blanchland, Consett DH8 9UU
Contact: Mrs N Smith, 6 Selborne Avenue, Gateshead
NE9 6ET
T: (0191) 487 9456
F: (01670) 510300
E: asmith6000@aol.com
I: www.oas.co.uk/ukcottages/boltslaw

OPEN All year round
CC: Mastercard

Mid-week breaks outside
school holidays £23 per night.

Low season per wk
£165.00–£185.00
High season per wk
£190.00–£245.00

BOWES, Durham Map ref 5B3

★★★
1 Unit
Sleeping 2

NUMBER 1 UNICORN COTTAGES
Bowes, Barnard Castle DL12 9HL
Contact: Mr & Mrs Mathew Hill, Church Lodge,
York Road, Shiptonthorpe, York YO43 3PH
T: (01430) 872560 (Evenings, Weekend) &
(01904) 432266 (Working hours)
E: anne.mat@ic24.net

OPEN All year round

Low season per wk
£150.00–£200.00
High season per wk
£200.00–£250.00

Once a stable block forming part of courtyard of 16thC coaching inn (the ancient Unicorn). Forms one side of stone archway, comfortable modern amenities within.

BYRNESS, Northumberland Map ref 5B1

Rating Applied For 1 Unit Sleeping 20	**CATCLEUGH FARM** Byrness, Newcastle upon Tyne NE19 1TX Contact: Mr Walter Nieuwkoop, P O Box 83, Morpeth NE61 4YY T: (01670) 772607 (Day/answerphone) & 07850 983128 (Mobile/answerphone) F: (01670) 772607 E: catcleugh@hotmail.com I: www.catcleugh.com	OPEN All year round	Low season per wk £165.00–£265.00 High season per wk £320.00–£550.00

Spacious 18thC shooting lodge which once belonged to the Dukes of Northumberland. Overlooking lake. Sleeps 2–20. Open all year.

★★★★
1 Unit
Sleeping 4

THE OLD SCHOOL HOUSE

Byrness, Rochester, Newcastle upon Tyne NE19 1TH
Contact: Dales Holiiday Cottages, Agents,
Carleton Business Park, Carleton New Road, Skipton
BD23 2DG
T: (01756) 799821
F: (01756) 797012

Northumbrian single-storey, stone cottage under slate. On Pennine Way with views over Kielder Forest Park. Exterior restored in vernacular style. Interior remodelled in pine with attic bedrooms and modern facilities. Spacious and cosy with oil-fired Rayburn for central heating and cooking and for touring Borders and Cheviot Hills.

OPEN Apr–Dec

Low season per wk
£195.00–£220.00
High season per wk
£332.00–£360.00

CASTLESIDE, Durham Map ref 5B2

★★ 1 Unit Sleeping 4	**MANOR PARK COTTAGE (MANOR PARK LTD)** Broadmeadows, Consett DH8 9HD Contact: Mr Brian Elstrop, Broadmeadows, Rippon Burn, Castleside, Consett DH8 9HD T: (01207) 501000 & 509308 F: (01207) 509271	OPEN Apr–Oct	Low season per wk £140.00–£150.00 High season per wk £180.00–£190.00

Completely self-contained country bungalow with 2 bedrooms. Family-run enterprise in an area of natural beauty. Secure parking for cars.

CHATHILL, Northumberland Map ref 5C1

★★ 2 Units Sleeping 5	**NEWSTEAD COTTAGE** Newstead Farm, Chathill NE67 5LH Contact: Mrs M Riddell, Newstead Farm, Chathill NE67 5LH T: (01665) 589263	OPEN Apr–Oct	Low season per wk £180.00–£220.00 High season per wk £220.00–£280.00

550-acre mixed farm. Cottages 4 miles from beautiful beaches, ideal for touring the Borders and Cheviot Hills. Fishing by arrangement.

AT-A-GLANCE SYMBOLS

Symbols at the end of each accommodation entry give useful information about services and facilities. A key to symbols can be found inside the back cover flap. Keep this open for easy reference.

★★★★

1 Unit
Sleeping 4

HIGH PASTURE COTTAGE

Bowser Hill Farm, Chopwell,
Newcastle upon Tyne NE17 7AY
Contact: Allan Low, Bowser Hill Farm, Chopwell,
Newcastle upon Tyne NE17 7AY
T: (01207) 560881
E: alow@btinternet.com

*Converted 17thC barn perched high above
Derwent Valley with superb long distance views.
Furnished to a very high standard with beams
and log-burning stove. Conveniently situated 15
minutes from MetroCentre, 12 miles from
Hexham market town and within easy reach of
Hadrian's Wall, Durham City and the coast.*

OPEN All year round

Low season per wk
£165.00–£270.00
High season per wk
£270.00–£350.00

★★★★

2 Units
Sleeping 4

STONECROFT AND SWALLOWS NEST

Low Lands Farm, Lowlands, Cockfield,
Bishop Auckland DL13 5AW
Contact: Mrs A Tallentire, Low Lands Farm, Cockfield,
Bishop Auckland DL13 5AW
T: (01388) 718251 (Answerphone)
F: (01388) 718251
E: info@farmholidaysuk.com
I: www.farmholidaysuk.com

*Two beautiful cottages on working
farm on borders of unspoilt Teesdale
and Weardale. Within 1 hour of
Durham city, Lake District,
Northumberland, Newcastle, east
coast. Very comfortable, superbly
equipped, log/coal fires, own
gardens, parking. All fuels, electric,
hot water, linen and towels included.
Children most welcome, pets by
arrangement.*

OPEN All year round

Mid-week and weekend
breaks available out of
season. Open Christmas and
New Year.

Low season per wk
£150.00–£200.00
High season per wk
£225.00–£295.00

★★★

1 Unit
Sleeping 6

OSWALD COTTAGE

10 Front Street, Corbridge NE45 5AP
Contact: Mrs H K Harriman, Swarden House,
Kyloe House Farm, Eachwick, Newcastle upon Tyne
NE18 0BB
T: (01661) 852909
F: (01661) 854106
E: pwh@littonproperties.co.uk

*Exceptional 18thC double-fronted
large stone cottage. Carved external
Latin inscription 'To the good all
things are good' reflects interior
ambience, beams and open fire. In
heart of historic village but quiet.
Stone's throw from river and superb
local shops. Lovely patio garden.
Perfect, winter or summer.*

OPEN All year round

Low season per wk
£350.00–£450.00
High season per wk
£500.00–£650.00

CREDIT CARD BOOKINGS If you book by telephone and are
asked for your credit card number it is advisable to check the proprietor's
policy should you cancel your reservation.

CORBRIDGE continued

WALLHOUSES SOUTH FARM COTTAGE

★★★★
1 Unit
Sleeping 4

Military Road, Corbridge NE45 5PU
Contact: Mrs E Lymburn, South Farm, Military Road,
Corbridge NE45 5PU
T: (01434) 672388
E: loraip@aol.com

OPEN All year round

Low season per wk
£250.00–£280.00
High season per wk
£250.00–£360.00

Traditional 2-bedroomed stone cottage in countryside location, but not isolated, on route of Roman Wall between Corbridge and Matfen. Pleasant garden.

WEST FELL COTTAGE

★★★
1 Unit
Sleeping 4

Ladycutter Lane, Corbridge NE45 5RZ
Contact: E J Smith, Proprietor, West Fell House,
Corbridge NE45 5RZ
T: (01434) 632044

OPEN All year round

Low season per wk
£100.00–£190.00
High season per wk
£190.00–£220.00

Two-bedroomed farm cottage near Dilston Castle and convenient for Corbridge and the Roman Wall.

COTHERSTONE, Durham Map ref 5B3

★★★
1 Unit
Sleeping 6

FARTHINGS

Cotherstone, Barnard Castle DL12 9QW
Contact: Mr C J Bainbridge, Glen Leigh, Cotherstone,
Barnard Castle DL12 9QW
T: (01833) 650331

Comfortable stone-built bungalow overlooking village green. Two bedrooms (double and twin), gas central heating, living room fire. Well equipped and decorated.

OPEN All year round

Low season per wk
£100.00–£170.00
High season per wk
£170.00–£250.00

DARLINGTON, Durham Map ref 5C3 *Tourist Information Centre Tel: (01325) 388666*

PEGASUS COTTAGE

★★★
1 Unit
Sleeping 4

4 Tees View, Hurworth Place, Darlington DL2 2DH
Contact: Mr & Mrs Stuart and Denise Chapman,
4 Tees View, Hurworth Place, Darlington DL2 2DH
T: (01325) 722542 (Weekend and evenings)
F: (01325) 722542
I: www.pegasuscottage.co.uk

OPEN All year round
CC: Barclaycard, Delta,
Eurocard, Maestro,
Mastercard, Solo, Switch,
Visa, Visa Electron

Low season per wk
£200.00–£290.00
High season per wk
£300.00–£320.00

Converted stable block of a Grade II Listed building, c1850. Local mayor's Design Award winner 1995. Set in small village 3 miles from Darlington.

DURHAM, Durham Map ref 5C2 *Tourist Information Centre Tel: (0191) 384 3720*

★★★★
1 Unit
Sleeping 4

THE OLD POWER HOUSE

Garden Cottage, Southill Hall, Plawsworth, Chester-le-Street DH3 4EQ
Contact: Mrs Anne Hall, Garden Cottage, Southill Hall, Plawsworth, Chester-le-Street DH3 4EQ
T: (0191) 387 3001 & 222 0626 (Work)
F: (0191) 389 3569
E: g.s.hall@talk21.com

Recently redeveloped former power house set in walled garden of old hall, providing compact 2-bedroom country cottage set in 3 acres of landscaped gardens. Idyllic location midway between Durham City (3 miles) and Chester-le-Street (3 miles). Newcastle, Sunderland and MetroCentre (Gateshead) within 25 minutes' drive.

OPEN All year round

Low season per wk
£200.00–£250.00
High season per wk
£250.00–£325.00

EDLINGHAM, Northumberland Map ref 5B1

★★★★

1 Unit
Sleeping 6

HAZELNUTHOUSE
3 Garden Terrace, Edlingham, Alnwick NE66 2BN
Contact: Ms Hazel Bennett, 61 Portsmouth Road,
Guildford GU2 4BS
T: (01483) 569346 (Answerphone, daytime no) &
07966 141895 (Mobile)
F: (01483) 569346
E: hazel.bennett@dial.pipex.com
I: www.bigfoot.com/~hazelnuthouse

OPEN Apr–Oct

High season per wk
£375.00–£450.00

Traditional Northumbrian stone-built cottage. Panoramic views of moorland valley from conservatory. Three bedrooms, lounge, kitchen/diner, luxury bathroom, log stove, double glazing and central heating.

EMBLETON, Northumberland Map ref 5C1

★★-★★★★★

10 Units
Sleeping 2–8

DOXFORD FARM COTTAGES

Doxford Farm, Chathill NE67 5DY
Contact: Mrs Sarah Shell, Doxford Farm, Chathill
NE67 5DY
T: (01665) 579348 (House) & 579477 (Shop)
F: (01665) 579331
E: doxfordfarm@hotmail.com
I: www.doxfordfarmcottages.com

Set in undulating wooded countryside 4 miles from sea, on a working mixed farm. Well equipped and furnished cottages with central heating and open fires. Wildlife trail and woodland walks. Doxford Country Store is nearby, with coffee shop, gift shop, country clothing and art gallery. Ideal base for Northumberland's castles and coastline.

OPEN All year round
CC: Amex, Barclaycard,
JCB, Mastercard, Switch,
Visa

Low season per wk
£150.00–£250.00
High season per wk
£295.00–£525.00

★★★

1 Unit
Sleeping 4

DUNSTANBURGH CASTLE COURTYARD COTTAGES
Embleton, Alnwick NE66 3UN
Contact: Mr Paul Thompson, Heritage Coast Holidays,
South Lodge, Swarland, Morpeth NE65 9JD
T: (01670) 787864 (0900-1700 only) & 786188 (After
1700)
F: (01670) 787336
E: pault@marishal.co.uk
I: www.northumberland-holidays.com

OPEN All year round

Low season per wk
£120.00–£199.00
High season per wk
£175.00–£350.00

The cottages have been converted from a 17thC coach house. Situated in a quiet courtyard, within easy walking distance of superb beaches and castle.

★★★★

4 Units
Sleeping 3–6

NORTHUMBRIAN HOLIDAY COTTAGES

Embleton, Alnwick
Contact: Mr & Mrs Chris Seal, 1 Westfield, Gosforth,
Newcastle upon Tyne NE3 4YE
T: (0191) 285 6930 & 07711 066584
E: seal@northumbrian-holiday-cottages.co.uk
I: www.northumbrian-holiday-cottages.co.uk

Four quality properties in Embleton village offering the ultimate in tranquillity, luxury and character. Secluded south-facing gardens and great emphasis on the provision of comfort and peace of mind. Ideal location for exploring Northumbrian coast, hills and castles. Enjoy a warm welcome and personal attention from our family-run business.

OPEN All year round

Low season per wk
£195.00–£250.00
High season per wk
£295.00–£480.00

GLANTON, Northumberland Map ref 5B1

★★★★
1 Unit
Sleeping 4

Lovely 18thC farmhouse retaining original features. Decorated, furnished and equipped to a very high standard. South-facing lawned garden. Secluded, peaceful location down private driveway, perfect for families, yet minutes from A697 and National Park. Stunning panoramic views. Great base for touring, walking or chilling out. Alnwick 7 miles, coast 11 miles.

THE FARMHOUSE

Northfield Farm, Glanton, Alnwick NE66 4AG
Contact: Mrs Jackie Stothard, Northfield Farm, Glanton, Alnwick NE66 4AG
T: (01665) 578203 (Answerphone available) &
0798 012 9386
F: (01665) 578203
E: jackie@lowalwinton.co.uk

OPEN All year round

Low season per wk
£160.00–£200.00
High season per wk
£220.00–£380.00

★★★
1 Unit
Sleeping 4

Detached, old stone property featuring wood-burning stoves and picturesque, secure private garden, situated in a peaceful country village. Ideally placed for walking, cycling, relaxing and exploring the unspoiled beaches and countryside of Northumbria. The cottage has recently been refurbished to a high standard and is extemely well-equipped. Children welcome, short breaks available.

HOLLY COTTAGE

Glanton, Alnwick NE66 4BJ
Contact: Mr Robert Johnston & Miss G Hibbert, Crag View Cottage, Glanton, Alnwick NE66 4AU
T: (01665) 578200 & 578336 (Answerphone)
F: (01665) 578336
E: g_hibbert@talk21.com

OPEN All year round

10% off any holiday consisting of 2 or more consecutive weeks for 2002.

Low season per wk
£195.00–£245.00
High season per wk
£295.00–£355.00

HALTWHISTLE, Northumberland Map ref 5B2 *Tourist Information Centre Tel: (01434) 322002*

★★★★
1 Unit
Sleeping 8

Traditional stone farmhouse in unique setting in national park. Ten minutes from Roman Army Museum/Hadrian's Wall and in close proximity to market town of Haltwhistle. Recently renovated to a high standard. Four bedrooms sleeping up to 8. Bathroom and separate shower, utility with laundry facilities, fully-fitted kitchen.

FARGLOW FARM

Greenhead, Gilsland, Carlisle CA6 7JB
Contact: Mrs C S Maclean, High Edge Cottage, Moss Kennels, Haydon Bridge, Hexham NE47 8JP
T: 07765 001005 (Mobile) & (01434) 344155
F: (01434) 344155

OPEN All year round

Low season per wk
£200.00–£350.00
High season per wk
£350.00–£500.00

---

www.travelengland.org.uk

Log on for information and inspiration. The latest information on places to visit, events and quality assessed accommodation.

HAMSTERLEY, Durham Map ref 5B2

★★★★
1 Unit
Sleeping 4

DIDDRIDGE FARM COTTAGE
Diddridge Dell, Diddridge Lane, Hamsterley,
Bishop Auckland DL13 3PG
Contact: Ms Sheila Petch, Diddridge Farm,
Diddridge Lane, Hamsterley, Bishop Auckland
DL13 3PG
T: (01388) 488520
E: diddridge@tinyworld.co.uk

OPEN All year round
CC: Delta, Eurocard, JCB,
Mastercard, Solo, Switch,
Visa, Visa Electron

Low season per wk
Min £375.00

Totally secluded dell on Linburn Beck. Sheltered by mature oak trees and period ginmill.

★★
2 Units
Sleeping 4

WEST HOPPYLAND CABINS
Hamsterley, Bishop Auckland DL13 3NP
T: (01388) 488196 & 07802 413923
Contact: Mrs C J Atkinson

Two cosy lodges set in peaceful birch wood with lovely views over Hamsterley Forest. Designated an Area of Outstanding Natural Beauty in the northern dales. An ideal base for touring the dales or for outdoor activities. Pony trekking and cycle hire on site. Owners at hand to help.

OPEN Mar–Oct

10% reduction on treks for
people staying in lodges.

Low season per wk
£140.00–£180.00
High season per wk
£200.00–£250.00

HAMSTERLEY FOREST

See under Barnard Castle, Stanhope, Wolsingham

HAYDON BRIDGE, Northumberland Map ref 5B2

★★–★★★
4 Units
Sleeping 4–6

Beautiful, peaceful rural location in open pasture bordered by pine forest with trout lakes (free fishing). Traditional stone-built hunting/ fishing lodge tastefully converted into attractive holiday cottages. Near Housesteads Roman Fort and Hadrian's Wall. Ideal for Northumberland National Park and historic border country. Bar/tearoom 2 minutes' walk. Ring for brochure.

HADRIAN'S WALL COUNTRY COTTAGES
Hindshield Moss, North Road, Above Haydon Bridge,
Hexham NE47 6NF
T: (01434) 688688
F: (01434) 684867
E: cottages@hadrianswall.co.uk
I: www.hadrianswall.co.uk
Contact: Mrs Lyn Murray

OPEN All year round

Free fishing on adjoining
private trout lake all year.

Low season per wk
£175.00–£195.00
High season per wk
£250.00–£295.00

HEBBURN, Tyne and Wear Map ref 5C2

Rating
Applied For
1 Unit
Sleeping 4

26 HAZELMOOR
Hebburn NE31 1DH
Contact: Mr P Goodall, 18 Coleridge Square, Hebburn
NE31 1QD
T: (0191) 428 6180 & 07941 611551 (Mobile)

OPEN All year round

Low season per wk
£180.00–£200.00
High season per wk
£200.00–£220.00

A self-contained modern 2 bedroom, fully-equipped flat. Situated at the end of a quiet cul-de-sac. Sleeps up to 4.

RATING All accommodation in this guide has been rated, or is awaiting
a rating, by a trained English Tourism Council assessor.

HEDDON-ON-THE-WALL, Northumberland Map ref 5B2

★★★
1 Unit
Sleeping 7

2 EAST TOWN HOUSE
Towne Gate, Heddon-on-the-Wall,
Newcastle upon Tyne NE15 0DR
Contact: Mr & Mrs C&B Amos, 1 East Town House,
Heddon-on-the-Wall, Newcastle upon Tyne NE15 0DR
T: (01661) 852277 & 852913
F: (01661) 853063

OPEN All year round

Low season per wk
£212.00–£269.00
High season per wk
£315.00–£365.00

Stone-built, well-equipped house furnished to a high standard, in historic village on Hadrian's Wall.

HEXHAM, Northumberland Map ref 5B2

★★★★
1 Unit
Sleeping 5

MOORGAIR COTTAGE
Slaley, Hexham NE47 0AN
T: (01434) 673473
E: g_ridley@lineone.net
I: www.moorgair.co.uk
Contact: Mrs V Ridley

OPEN All year round

Low season per wk
Min £180.00
High season per wk
Max £310.00

Superb cottage on small working farm. Private garden and parking. Excellent base for touring Northumberland, Durham, Borders. Lovely rural location – perfect for families.

★★★★★
1 Unit
Sleeping 4

SAMMY'S PLACE
26 St Wilfred's Road, Hexham NE46 2EA
Contact: Mr Roger McKechnie, Dilston House,
Corbridge NE45 5RH
T: (01434) 633653 & 07768 365343 (Mobile)
F: (01434) 6344640
E: roger@dilstonhouse.freeserve.co.uk
I: www.sammyshideaways.com

OPEN All year round

Low season per wk
£250.00
High season per wk
£425.00

Beautifully appointed 2-bedroomed apartment, with both rooms being en suite, sleeps 4. The property is situated in the heart of historic Hexham, Hadrian's Wall Country.

INGRAM, Northumberland Map ref 5B1

★★★★-★★★★★
3 Units
Sleeping 2–5

THE OLD RECTORY
Ingram, Alnwick NE66 4LT
Contact: Mrs T Stephenson, The Old Rectory, Ingram,
Alnwick NE66 4LT
T: (01665) 578236
E: trysha@cheviotholidaycottages.co.uk
I: www.cheviotholidaycottages.co.uk

Recapture the atmosphere and old world charm of a bygone era when staying at this 18thC rectory near River Breamish in National Park, an idyllic valley in the Cheviot Hills. Two beautifully appointed wings, superb coach house, stone detached Blacksmith's Forge and Honeysuckle Cottage, all delightfully presented and full of character.

OPEN All year round

Low season per wk
£200.00–£220.00
High season per wk
£330.00–£490.00

KIELDER FOREST

See under Bellingham, West Woodburn

ACCESSIBILITY
Look for the 🚾 symbols which indicate accessibility for wheelchair users. A list of establishments is at the front of this guide.

KIELDER WATER, Northumberland Map ref 5B2

★★★★

10 Units
Sleeping 6

CALVERT TRUST KIELDER

Kielder Water, Hexham NE48 1BS
T: (01434) 250232
F: (01434) 250015
E: enquiries@calvert-kielder.com
I: www.calvert-trust.org.uk
Contact: Miss Rachel Cowper

Ten fully accessible log chalets set in the heart of Kielder Forest providing an excellent base for exploring the magnificent Northumberland countryside. Each chalet can sleep 6 people in 3 large twin rooms; there is a spacious lounge and open plan kitchen and a veranda to relax on in the summer evenings.

OPEN All year round
CC: Mastercard, Visa

Low season per wk
£180.00–£320.00
High season per wk
£320.00–£580.00

LONGHOUGHTON, Northumberland Map ref 5C1

★★★

1 Unit
Sleeping 4

HARLAW HILL FARM COTTAGE
Harlow Hill, Longhoughton, Alnwick NE66 3AA
Contact: Mr & Mrs A&J Pringle, Harlow Hill,
Longhoughton, Alnwick NE66 3AA
T: (01665) 577215 (24 hours)

OPEN Jan, Mar–Dec

Low season per wk
£160.00–£240.00
High season per wk
£210.00–£330.00

400-acre arable farm. Traditional semi farm cottage in lovely surroundings. Easy access, good for all facilities, locally and north of the border.

MARSKE-BY-THE-SEA, Tees Valley Map ref 5C3

★★★

1 Unit
Sleeping 4

WHITE ROSE COTTAGE

7 Spain Hill, Marske-by-the-Sea TS11 7LE
Contact: Mr & Mrs Phillips, 21 Church Howle Crescent,
Marske-by-Sea, Redcar TS11 7EJ
T: (01642) 481064
F: (01642) 481064
E: phillipspcp@aol.com

A fully modernised cottage with all amenities. Converted in 1997 and furnished with pine throughout, 100 yards from the shops. Two minutes' walk from the beach. Cosy and warm in winter, hot and sunny in summer, with garden and conservatory.

OPEN All year round

Open all year. 3-night breaks available Oct-Apr.

Low season per wk
£150.00–£180.00
High season per wk
£200.00–£240.00

MELKRIDGE, Northumberland Map ref 5B2

★★★

5 Units
Sleeping 2–5

COMMON HOUSE FARM

Melkridge, Haltwhistle NE49 9PF
T: (01434) 321680 (Answerphone)
E: stay@commonhousefarm.com
I: www.commonhousefarm.com
Contact: Mr and Mrs R Goodchild

Near Hadrian's Wall, commanding spectacular valley views and surrounded by farmland, the comfortable south facing cottages provide a peaceful base for both walking holidays and touring Northern England. Centrally situated for Hexham, Kielder, the Lake District, Northumberland coast and North Pennines, Haltwhistle (2 miles). Provides all amenities. Acclaimed country inn nearby.

OPEN Mar–Dec
CC: Amex, Barclaycard,
Mastercard, Visa

Short breaks all year. Golf packages on request.

Low season per wk
£145.00–£180.00
High season per wk
£200.00–£350.00

CONFIRM YOUR BOOKING
You are advised to confirm your booking in writing.

MICKLETON, Durham Map ref 5B3

★★★
1 Unit
Sleeping 4

BLACKTHORN COTTAGE
Low Side, Mickleton, Barnard Castle DL12 0JU
Contact: Mrs D Garrett, 26 St Lawrence Road,
Upminster RM14 2UW
T: (01708) 225107 & 07710 530411 (Mobile)
E: coldigar@btinternet.com
I: www.teesdalecottages.co.uk

OPEN Apr–Sep &
Christmas

Low season per wk
£110.00–£150.00
High season per wk
£210.00–£250.00

Stone character cottage built in 1756. Two bedrooms, lounge and kitchen/diner. In quiet lane, close to village centre. Ideal walking in Teesdale. Pennine Way 2 miles.

MIDDLETON-IN-TEESDALE, Durham Map ref 5B3

★★★★
1 Unit
Sleeping 4

Stone built, converted from a farm worker's cottage. Situated close to Grassholme Reservoir in an idyllic position where peace and tranquillity are assured any time of the year. An ideal location for holiday-makers wishing to spend a carefree, relaxing holiday away from noise and stress.

BROCK SCAR COTTAGE
West Pasture, Middleton-in-Teesdale,
Barnard Castle DL12 0PW
Contact: Mrs Winfred Gargate, Brock Scar Farm,
Middleton-in-Teesdale, Barnard Castle DL12 0PW
T: (01833) 640495 & 0798 924 4786 (Mobile)
F: (01833) 640495
E: wyngargate@barclays.net
I: www.brockscar.co.uk

OPEN All year round

Low season per wk
£195.00
High season per wk
£350.00

★★
1 Unit
Sleeping 2–6

COUNTRY COTTAGE
Newbiggin-in-Teesdale, Middleton-in-Teesdale
DU12 0UQ
Contact: Mr R B Burman, Fairlawn, 1 Thorn Road,
Bramhall, Stockport SK7 1HG
T: (0161) 439 5435 (Evenings) & 860 7123 (Daytime)
E: familyburman@cwctv.net

OPEN All year round

Low season per wk
Min £150.00
High season per wk
Max £305.00

200-year-old cottage in quiet and peaceful location and with superb views, surrounded by farmland. Excellent walking countryside.

★★★
1 Unit
Sleeping 2

FIRETHORN COTTAGE
33 Town End, Middleton-in-Teesdale,
Barnard Castle DL12 0SY
Contact: Mrs J Thompson, Cutbush Farmhouse,
Hardingham Road, Hingham, Norwich NR9 4LY
T: (01953) 850 364

OPEN All year round

Low season per wk
£100.00–£120.00
High season per wk
£120.00–£160.00

Stone-built lead miner's cottage, 1 up/1 down, flagstone floors, traditional rag rugs, beamed ceilings. Superb walking, fishing, pubs and restaurants.

★★★
1 Unit
Sleeping 6

WESTFIELD COTTAGE
Laithkirk, Middleton-in-Teesdale,
Barnard Castle DL12 0PN
Contact: Mrs Doreen Scott, Westfield House, Laithkirk,
Middleton-in-Teesdale, Barnard Castle DL12 0PN
T: (01833) 640942

OPEN All year round

Low season per wk
£170.00–£200.00
High season per wk
£230.00–£380.00

Eighteenth-century farm cottage, tastefully renovated in the heart of beautiful Teesdale. Central for walking and with its own fishing on the River Lune.

SPECIAL BREAKS
**Many establishments offer special promotions and themed breaks.
These are highlighted in red. (All such offers are subject to availability.)**

MINDRUM, Northumberland Map ref 5B1

★★
1 Unit
Sleeping 4

BOWMONT COTTAGE
Bowmont Hill, Mindrum TD12 4QW
Contact: Mr & Mrs S Orpwood, Bowmont Hill, Mindrum
TD12 4QW
T: (01890) 852266 (Answerphone available)
F: (01890) 850245
E: s.orpwood@farmline.com
I: www.cottageguide.co.uk/bowmonthill

OPEN All year round

Low season per wk
£130.00–£175.00
High season per wk
£175.00–£275.00

Two-bedroomed cottage on arable and livestock farm with bathroom and separate shower. Log fire, kitchen/dining room with oil-fired Raeburn. Cot, high chair. Dogs by arrangement. Fishing.

NEWCASTLE UPON TYNE, Tyne and Wear Map ref 5C2 *Tourist Information Centre Tel: (0191) 277 8000*

★★★
1 Unit
Sleeping 6

135 AUDLEY ROAD
South Gosforth, Newcastle upon Tyne NE3 1QH
Contact: Miss Linda Wright, 137 Audley Road,
South Gosforth, Newcastle upon Tyne NE3 1QH
T: (0191) 285 6374 (Answerphone/day/pm)
E: lkw@audleyender.fsnet.co.uk

OPEN All year round

Low season per wk
£200.00–£250.00
High season per wk
£200.00–£250.00

Self-contained flat, close to shops and Metro and with easy access to city centre. All amenities. Sleeps up to 6.

NEWTON-BY-THE-SEA, Northumberland Map ref 5C1

★★★
2 Units
Sleeping 5

Situated in traditional Northumberland fishing village, cottages have views over Newton Bay to Dunstanburgh Castle. Cottages retain many of the original features and charm but with modern facilities. Close to safe, clean beaches, pub in village, large garden to front, National Trust coastline nearby, superb scenery.

3A & 3B COASTGUARD COTTAGES

Newton-by-the-Sea, Alnwick NE66 3EH
Contact: Mr & Mrs M Cottam, 13 St Georges Crescent,
Monkseaton, Whitley Bay NE25 8BJ
T: (0191) 251 2506 (Day) & 251 2506 (Evening)
F: (0191) 222 1017
E: mark&alisoncottam@hotmail.com
I: www.geocities.com/coastguardcottages

OPEN All year round

Short breaks available Oct–Mar. Minimum 3-nights (excl Christmas and New Year).

Low season per wk
£150.00–£275.00
High season per wk
£310.00–£450.00

★★★★
3 Units
Sleeping 5–6

NEWTON HALL COTTAGES
Newton Hall, Newton-by-the-Sea, Alnwick NE66 3DZ
Contact: Mrs S A Patterson, Newton Hall, Newton-by-
the-Sea, Alnwick NE66 3DZ
T: (01665) 576239
F: (01665) 576900
E: ian.patterson@newtonhall.prestel.co.uk
I: www.commercepark.co.uk/newtonhall

OPEN All year round
CC: Barclaycard, Delta,
Eurocard, JCB,
Mastercard, Switch, Visa,
Visa Electron

Low season per wk
£230.00–£250.00
High season per wk
£460.00–£475.00

Quality, spacious Georgian accommodation with 2 acres of gardens. Ideal base to enjoy magnificent coastline and panoramic countryside.

CHECK THE MAPS

The colour maps at the front of this guide show all the cities, towns and villages for which you will find accommodation entries.
Refer to the town index to find the page on which they are listed.

NEWTON-BY-THE-SEA continued

★★★
1 Unit
Sleeping 6

SEAWINDS
Boatmans Place, Newton-by-the-Sea,
Alnwick NE66 3EJ
Contact: Miss J Park, Low Buston Hall, Warkworth,
Morpeth NE65 0XY
T: (01665) 714805
F: (01665) 711345
E: jopark@farming.co.uk
I: www.seawinds.ntb.org.uk

OPEN All year round

Low season per wk
£275.00–£650.00
High season per wk
£450.00–£650.00

Former fisherman's cottage, 200 yards from sandy beach. Home-from-home with two ground floor bedrooms and bathroom. Excellent opportunity for families, bird watchers, walkers and golfers.

OVINGTON, Durham Map ref 5B3

★★★★
1 Unit
Sleeping 3

VILLAGE GREEN COTTAGE
Ovington, Richmond DL11 7BW
Contact: Mrs M J Green, The Cottage, Village Green,
Ovington, Richmond DL11 7BW
T: (01833) 627331

OPEN All year round

Low season per wk
£190.00
High season per wk
£250.00–£295.00

Cosy stone cottage with beams and pretty bedrooms, overlooking village green. Delightful garden leading to field, pond and summerhouse with fantastic views. Pub over green.

OVINGTON, Northumberland Map ref 5B2

★★★★
1 Unit
Sleeping 4

WESTGARTH COTTAGE
Old Brewery Square, Ovington NE42 6EB
Contact: Mrs C Graham, Stonecroft, Ovington
NE42 6EB
T: (01661) 832202

OPEN All year round

Low season per wk
£250.00–£280.00
High season per wk
£260.00–£300.00

Attractive stone-built cottage in a small, peaceful village surrounded by beautiful countryside, near the historic towns of Hexham and Corbridge.

ROTHBURY, Northumberland Map ref 5B1

★★★★
3 Units
Sleeping 4–8

Lovely cottages in valley beside River Coquet in Northumberland National Park. Beautiful, sheltered location. Wake up to the hills! Extensive lawned gardens. Private, secluded and safe for young families. Furnished and equipped to high standard, inclusive linen, power and heating. Open fires or wood burning stoves. Pets welcome. Rothbury 7 miles, Alnwick 14 miles.

LOW ALWINTON HOLIDAY COTTAGES

Low Alwinton, Harbottle, Morpeth NE65 5BE
Contact: Mrs Jackie Stothard, Northfield Farm, Glanton,
Alnwick NE66 4AG
T: (01665) 578203
E: jackie@lowalwinton.co.uk
I: www.lowalwinton.co.uk

OPEN All year round

If 4 people or less in Byre
Cottage (sleeps 8), £60 off.

Low season per wk
£110.00–£180.00
High season per wk
£200.00–£400.00

★★★★★
1 Unit
Sleeping 4

THE PELE TOWER
Whitton, Rothbury NE65 7RL
T: (01669) 620410
F: (01669) 621006
E: davidmalia@aol.com
I: www.thepeletower.com
Contact: Mr & Mrs J D Malia

OPEN All year round
CC: Barclaycard,
Mastercard, Visa

Low season per wk
£220.00–£340.00
High season per wk
£420.00–£560.00

19thC wing of Northumbrian pele tower, origins 1380. Includes whirlpool bath, dishwasher, satellite TV and video. Mountain bikes. Sorry, no smoking and no pets.

SEAHOUSES, Northumberland Map ref 5C1

★★★★
1 Unit
Sleeping 9

BROCKBURN
Monkshouses, Seahouses NE68 7SY
Contact: Mrs P Thompson, Highfield House,
Woodhill Farm, Ponteland, Newcastle upon Tyne
NE20 0JA
T: (01661) 860165

OPEN All year round

Low season per wk
£350.00–£600.00
High season per wk
£600.00–£850.00

Large 700-year-old house, retaining character and charm although thoroughly refurbished. Positioned on the beach, amongst sand dunes, with splendid views of Farne Islands.

★★★
2 Units
Sleeping 6–12

DALFABER AND LYNBANK
4 Mayfield, Seahouses NE68 7SG
Contact: Mrs Louise Donaldson, 4 Broad Road,
Seahouses NE68 7UP
T: (01665) 721066 (Home with answerphone) &
07889 855968 (Mobile)
F: (01665) 721066
I: www.dalfaber-lynbank.ntb.org.uk

OPEN All year round

Low season per wk
£180.00–£225.00
High season per wk
£225.00–£330.00

Clean comfortable houses sleeping 6 and 12. All facilities for children. Off-road parking, secure gardens with patio, barbecue. Pets welcome.

★★★
1 Unit
Sleeping 6

FISHERLASSES FLAT
2 South Street, Swallow Fish Ltd, Seahouses NE68 7RB
T: (01665) 721052
F: (01665) 721177
E: wilkin@swallowfish.co.uk
I: www.swallowfish.co.uk
Contact: Mrs Karen Wilkin

Well-equipped 2-bedroom flat with spacious living room, situated in the heart of Old Seahouses with impressive views of the North Sea. Few minutes' walk from the lively village, shops, friendly pubs, restaurants, superb beaches and golf course. A perfect base to explore the Secret Kingdom of Northumbria.

OPEN All year round
CC: Barclaycard,
Mastercard, Visa

Low season per wk
£220.00
High season per wk
£290.00

SLAGGYFORD, Northumberland Map ref 5B2

Rating
Applied For
1 Unit
Sleeping 6

BASTLE HOUSE
Greenhaugh Farm, Slaggyford, Brampton CA8 7NW
Contact: Mrs Deirdre Pepperdine, Greenhaugh Farm,
Slaggyford, Brampton CA8 7NW
T: (01434) 381123
F: (01434) 381124
E: kpepperdine@aol.com

Small country estate dedicated to conservation. Historic bastle house situated in Area of Outstanding Natural Beauty, with own trout lake. Beautiful scenic walks. We are located just off what has been acknowledged as one of the world's top ten drives – the Trans-Pennine A686 near Alston, England's highest market town.

OPEN All year round
CC: Visa

Welcome arrival hamper with
bottle of wine, 2 and 4 day
breaks available.

Low season per wk
£225.00–£250.00
High season per wk
£325.00–£450.00

SLALEY, Northumberland Map ref 5B2

★★★
1 Unit
Sleeping 5

COMBHILLS FARM
Slaley, Hexham NE47 0AQ
T: (01434) 673475
E: m.ogle@lineone.net
Contact: Mrs M A Ogle

OPEN All year round

Low season per wk
£180.00–£250.00
High season per wk
£180.00–£250.00

Comfortable, well-equipped, centrally-heated cottage on working family farm. Centrally located for Newcastle, Durham, MetroCentre and Hadrian's Wall. Beautiful countryside for walking. Ample parking.

Rating Applied For

11 Units
Sleeping 4–5

SANDHAVEN BEACH CHALETS
South Promenade, Sea Road, South Shields NE33 2LD
T: (0191) 455 8319 (Answerphone) &
07702 962884 (Mobile)
F: (0191) 455 8319
E: crowell@btconnect.com
I: www.sandhavenchalets.co.uk
Contact: Mrs Christine Rowell

OPEN All year round
CC: Mastercard, Visa

Low season per wk
£150.00–£200.00
High season per wk
£250.00–£300.00

Welcome to Catherine Cookson Country. Beautiful sea views from fully self-contained 2-bedroomed chalets, situated adjacent to South Shield's premier beach.

★★★

1 Unit
Sleeping 6

Large, stone-built, 3 bedroomed cottage in England's last great wilderness, yet with all modern conveniences and within walking distance of shops, tourist information centre, banks, etc. The cottage is in a high position with superb views of Weardale. Two separate central heating systems and double glazing throughout ensure comfort.

PRIMROSE COTTAGE

1 Wear View, Crawleyside, Stanhope,
Bishop Auckland DL13 2EG
Contact: Mrs D P Dickson, Agent, Northumbria Byways,
Crosby House, Crosby-on-Eden, Carlisle CA6 4QZ
T: (01228) 573337 & 573338
F: (01228) 573338
E: enquiries@northumbria-byways.com
I: www.northumbria-byways.com

OPEN All year round
CC: Barclaycard, Delta,
JCB, Mastercard, Solo,
Switch, Visa

Low season per wk
£185.00–£245.00
High season per wk
£225.00–£339.00

★★★

1 Unit
Sleeping 4

MOUNT FLAGGON
Hedley on the Hill, Stocksfield NE43 7SW
Contact: Mrs Bridget Smith, North View House,
Hedley on the Hill, Stocksfield NE43 7SW
T: (01661) 843867
F: (01661) 844097
E: gsmith9@compuserve.com

OPEN All year round

Low season per wk
£212.00–£250.00
High season per wk
£312.00–£365.00

Semi-detached cottage with garden and patio in small picturesque village with wonderful views and superb pub food a stroll away. Close to Durham, Newcastle, Hexham.

★★★

3 Units
Sleeping 4–6

3, 4 AND 5 SWINHOE COTTAGES
Belford NE70 7LJ
Contact: Mrs V Nixon, Swinhoe Farm House, Belford
NE70 7LJ
T: (01668) 213370
E: valerie@swinhoecottages.co.uk
I: www.swinhoecottages.co.uk

OPEN All year round

Low season per wk
£140.00–£320.00
High season per wk
£300.00–£370.00

Well-equipped cottages on working farm. Many walks including St Cuthbert's Cave. Approximately 10 minutes' drive from Bamburgh, with its sandy beaches, and Holy Island.

TOWN INDEX

This can be found at the back of this guide. If you know where you want to stay, the index will give you the page number listing accommodation in your chosen town, city or village.

WAREN MILL, Northumberland Map ref 5C1

★★★★

1 Unit
Sleeping 6

EIDER COTTAGE
Waren Mill, Belford NE70 7EE
Contact: Mrs S Turnbull, 1 Friars Court, Bamburgh
NE69 7AE
T: (01668) 214494
E: theturnbulls2k@btinternet.com

OPEN All year round

High season per wk
£200.00–£400.00

This charming stone-built, former miller's cottage is situated yards from Budle Bay, a renowned bird-watching area near Bamburgh. Ideal base for exploring Northumberland.

WARKWORTH, Northumberland Map ref 5C1

★★★★

4 Units
Sleeping 4–8

BUSTON FARM HOLIDAY COTTAGES
Low Buston, Morpeth NE65 0XY
Contact: Miss J Park, Low Buston Hall, Warkworth,
Morpeth NE65 0XY
T: (01665) 714805 (Answerphone)
F: (01665) 711345
E: jopark@farming.co.uk
I: www.bustonfarm.ntb.org.uk

OPEN All year round

Low season per wk
£200.00–£500.00
High season per wk
£250.00–£750.00

Listed 17thC farmhouse and stone farm cottages all with original character. Newly refurbished, home-from-home, excellent opportunity for families, bird watchers, walkers and golfers.

WEST WOODBURN, Northumberland Map ref 5B2

★★★

1 Unit
Sleeping 4

THE HOLLOW
West Woodburn
Contact: Mrs Marlene Robson, East Lodge, Nunnykirk,
Netherwitton, Morpeth NE61 4PB
T: (01670) 772580 & 772246

Comfortable 19thC 2-bedroomed cottage in peaceful unspoilt wooded valley on edge of National Park. 15 miles north Corbridge, quarter of a mile A68, 1 mile south-west West Woodburn village. Within easy reach of golf courses, Hadrian's Wall, Kielder Reservoir, castles, houses, gardens and many other attractions of this beautiful border county of Northumberland.

OPEN Mar–Dec

3 night stays available autumn and spring. All year-reduced price for only 2 people staying.

Low season per wk
£190.00–£280.00
High season per wk
£260.00–£315.00

WESTGATE-IN-WEARDALE, Durham Map ref 5B2

★★★★

1 Unit
Sleeping 5

THE OLD BARN
High Kitty Crag, Westgate-in-Weardale,
Bishop Auckland DL13 1LF
Contact: Mrs Angela Hackett, High Kitty Crag,
Westgate-in-Weardale, Bishop Auckland DL13 1LF
T: (01388) 517562 & 528555 (Work)
F: (01388) 526122
E: matthackett@talk21.com

OPEN May–Sep

Low season per wk
£140.00–£200.00
High season per wk
£200.00–£295.00

Characterful 18thC Dales barn conversion with woodburning stove and exposed beams. Adjacent to farmhouse in North Pennines AONB, commanding excellent views over Upper Weardale.

MAP REFERENCES
The map references refer to the colour maps at the front of this guide. The first figure is the map number; the letter and figure which follow indicate the grid reference on the map.

WINSTON, Durham Map ref 5B3

★★★★

2 Units
Sleeping 5–7

Two beautiful, fully-equipped Danish pine lodges in the heart of Teesdale. Set on the banks of the River Tees and surrounded by woodland. Private salmon and trout fishing included, excellent walking as the Teesdale Way passes through the site. An ideal base for touring the northern counties and Lake District.

HIGHCLIFFE WATERS
Highcliffe Farm, Winston, Darlington DL2 3PJ
Contact: Mr & Mrs Hodson, Highcliffe Farm, Winston, Darlington DL2 3PJ
T: (01325) 730427 (Answerphone)
F: (01325) 730740
E: mrshodson@aol.com
I: www.countryholidays.co.uk

OPEN All year round

Low season per wk
£155.00–£175.00
High season per wk
£290.00–£400.00

WITTON-LE-WEAR, Durham Map ref 5C2

★★★★

1 Unit
Sleeping 8

Very comfortable 4 bedroom, 2 bathroom, stone-built Victorian cottage in the charming and picturesque village of Witton-le-Wear. Suitable for groups of 2 to 8 people. On the village green with open panoramic views of the Wear Valley from the south-facing patio/garden. Convenient location for both Durham City and its lovely Dales.

CARRS TERRACE
The Green, Witton-le-Wear, Bishop Auckland DL14 0AU
Contact: Miss Merlyn Law, 93-99 Upper Richmond Road, London SW15 2TG
T: (020) 8780 1084
F: (020) 8789 9199
E: merlynlaw@aol.com

OPEN All year round

Low season per wk
£200.00–£300.00
High season per wk
£300.00–£550.00

WOLSINGHAM, Durham Map ref 5B2

★★★

1 Unit
Sleeping 4

ARDINE COTTAGE
7 Melbourne Place, Wolsingham,
Bishop Auckland DL13 3EQ
Contact: Mrs M Gardiner, 3 Melbourne Place,
Wolsingham, Bishop Auckland DL13 3EQ
T: (01388) 527538

OPEN All year round

Low season per wk
Min £120.00
High season per wk
Max £198.00

Cosy, 2-bedroomed terraced cottage, overlooking small village green in old part of Wolsingham. Excellent walking and touring centre.

★★★

1 Unit
Sleeping 7

WHITFIELD HOUSE COTTAGE
23 Front Street, Wolsingham,
Bishop Auckland DL13 3DF
Contact: Mrs M E Shepheard, 25 Front Street,
Wolsingham, Bishop Auckland DL13 3DF
T: (01388) 527466
E: enquiries@whitfieldhouse.clara.net
I: www.whitfieldhouse.clara.net

OPEN All year round

Low season per wk
£180.00–£250.00
High season per wk
£250.00–£390.00

Spacious accommodation in part of an attractive Queen Anne house. Near the centre of this small town, in a designated Area of Outstanding Natural Beauty.

NB

IMPORTANT NOTE Information on accommodation listed in this guide has been supplied by the proprietors. As changes may occur you are advised to check details at the time of booking.

WOOLER, Northumberland Map ref 5B1

★★★★

4 Units
Sleeping 4–6

Four delightful cottages with superb views of the Cheviot Hills. Centrally situated for lovely beaches, Scottish Borders, hills, and picturesque valleys. Ideal for walking, family holidays, cycling, bird-watching or just to get away and enjoy the peace in a beautiful place. Well-equipped with open fires. 'Home from home' comfort.

FENTON HILL FARM COTTAGES

Fenton Hill, Wooler NE71 6JJ
Contact: Mrs Margaret Logan, Fenton Hill, Wooler
NE71 6JJ
T: (01668) 216228
F: (01668) 216169
E: stay@fentonhillfarm.co.uk
I: www.fentonhillfarm.co.uk

OPEN All year round

Out of season breaks from £30 per night.

Low season per wk
£150.00–£200.00
High season per wk
£200.00–£385.00

★★

1 Unit
Sleeping 10

KIMMERSTON RIDING CENTRE
Kimmerston Farm, Wooler NE71 6JH
T: (01668) 216283
E: jane@kimmerston.com
I: www.kimmerston.com
Contact: Mr R Jeffreys

OPEN All year round

Low season per wk
£100.00–£300.00
High season per wk
£200.00–£350.00

Comfortable farm cottage with open fire. Situated in a riding centre. Spectacular views, walking, castles, bird-watching, golf, fishing, shooting, hunting. Garden barbecue. Dogs welcome.

TOWN INDEX

This can be found at the back of the guide. If you know where you want to stay, the index will give you the page number listing accommodation in your chosen town, city or village.

A brief guide to the main Towns and Villages offering accommodation in

Northumbria

A ALLENDALE, NORTHUMBERLAND
- Attractive small town set amongst moors, 10 miles south-west of Hexham and claimed to be the geographical centre of Britain. Surrounded by unspoilt walking country, with many well-signposted walks along the East and West Allen Rivers. Traditional Baal ceremony at New Year.

• **ALNMOUTH, NORTHUMBERLAND** - Quiet village with pleasant old buildings, at the mouth of the River Aln where extensive dunes and sands stretch along Alnmouth Bay. 18th C granaries, some converted to dwellings, still stand.

• **ALNWICK, NORTHUMBERLAND** - Ancient and historic market town, entered through the Hotspur Tower, an original gate in the town walls. The medieval castle, the second biggest in England and still the seat of the Dukes of Northumberland, was restored from ruin in the 18th C.

B BAMBURGH, NORTHUMBERLAND
- Village with a spectacular red sandstone castle standing 150 ft above the sea. On the village green the magnificent Norman church stands opposite a museum containing mementoes of the heroine Grace Darling.

• **BARDON MILL, NORTHUMBERLAND**
- Small hamlet midway between Haydon Bridge and Haltwhistle, within walking distance of Vindolanda, an excavated Roman settlement, and near the best stretches of Hadrian's Wall.

• **BARNARD CASTLE, DURHAM** - High over the Tees, a thriving market town with a busy market square. Bernard Baliol's 12th C castle (now ruins) stands nearby. The Bowes Museum, housed in a grand 19th C French chateau, holds fine paintings and furniture. Nearby are some magnificent buildings.

• **BEADNELL, NORTHUMBERLAND**
- Charming fishing village on Beadnell Bay. Seashore lime kilns (National Trust), dating from the 18th C, recall busier days as a coal and lime port and a pub is built on to a medieval pele tower which survives from days of the border wars.

• **BEAMISH, DURHAM** - Village made famous by the award-winning Beamish, North of England Open Air Museum, which covers every aspect of the life, buildings and artefacts of the North East of 1913. Also in the area are Causey Arch and Tanfield Railway.

• **BELLINGHAM, NORTHUMBERLAND** - Set in the beautiful valley of the North Tyne close to the Kielder Forest, Kielder Water and lonely moorland below the Cheviots. The church has an ancient stone wagon roof fortified in the 18th C with buttresses.

• **BERWICK-UPON-TWEED, NORTHUMBERLAND** - Guarding the mouth of the Tweed, England's northernmost town with the best 16th C city walls in Europe. The handsome Guildhall and barracks date from the 18th C. Three bridges cross to Tweedmouth, the oldest built in 1634.

• **BLANCHLAND, NORTHUMBERLAND** - Beautiful medieval village rebuilt in the 18th C with stone from its ruined abbey, for lead miners working on the surrounding wild moors. The village is approached over a stone bridge across the Derwent or, from the north, through the ancient gatehouse.

• **BOWES, DURHAM** - Old stone village high up on a Roman road crossing the Pennines. Settled since Roman times, the town has a sturdy Norman castle keep and an ancient church with a Norman font and Roman inscribed stone.

• **BYRNESS, NORTHUMBERLAND** - Forestry village in Redesdale Forest on the A68. Catcleugh Reservoir is nearby, the Pennine Way runs through the village and there is a forest toll road to Kielder Water.

C CASTLESIDE, DURHAM - Village on the edge of the North Pennines on the A68, one of the main routes from England to Scotland.

• **CHATHILL, NORTHUMBERLAND** - Rural hamlet with mainline station. Preston Tower, a border pele tower, is nearby.

• **CHOPWELL, TYNE AND WEAR** - Small village, 3 miles south east of Prudhoe. Ruined Prudhoe Castle stands on a wooded hillside overlooking the river Tyne.

• **CORBRIDGE, NORTHUMBERLAND** - Small town on the River Tyne. Close by are extensive remains of the Roman military town Corstopitum, with a museum housing important discoveries from excavations. The town itself is attractive with shady trees, a 17th C bridge and interesting old buildings, notably a 14th C vicarage.

• **COTHERSTONE, DURHAM** - Village with remains of Norman castle, 3 miles north-west of Barnard Castle. Home of Cotherstone cheese.

D DARLINGTON, DURHAM - Largest town in County Durham, standing on the River Skerne and home of the earliest passenger railway which first ran to Stockton in 1825. Now the home of a railway museum. Originally a prosperous market town occupying the site of an Anglo-Saxon settlement, it still holds an open market.

• **DURHAM, DURHAM** - Ancient city with its Norman castle and cathedral, now a World Heritage site, set on a bluff high over the Wear. A market and university town and regional centre, spreading beyond the market-place on both banks of the river.

E EDLINGHAM, NORTHUMBERLAND - Old village spread over the hillside climbing from a fertile river valley to the moors. On the hill's lower slopes the fortified church and ruined castle are reminders of medieval border wars.

• **EMBLETON, NORTHUMBERLAND**
- Coastal village beside a golf-course spread along the edge of Embleton Bay. The old church was extensively restored in the 19th C. The vicarage incorporates a medieval pele tower.

G GLANTON, NORTHUMBERLAND
- Attractive peaceful village in Northumberland National Park en route to Ingram Valley.

H HALTWHISTLE, NORTHUMBERLAND
- Small market town with interesting 12th C church, old inns and blacksmith's smithy. North of the town are several important sites and interpretation centres of Hadrian's Wall. Ideal centre for archaeology, outdoor activity or touring holidays.

RATING All accommodation in this guide has been rated, or is awaiting a rating, by a trained English Tourism Council assessor.

- **HAMSTERLEY, DURHAM** - Small village near Bedburn Beck, at the edge of the North Pennines. Just westward lies moorland country of Hamsterley Common and the beautiful Hamsterley Forest with picnic areas and nature trails.

- **HAYDON BRIDGE, NORTHUMBERLAND** - Small town on the banks of the South Tyne with an ancient church, built of stone from sites along the Roman Wall just north. Ideally situated for exploring Hadrian's Wall and the Border country.

- **HEDDON-ON-THE-WALL, NORTHUMBERLAND** - Village overlooking Hadrian's Wall near its eastern limit, at the edge of an industrial area spreading into Tyneside. The church, first rebuilt by the Normans, was originally constructed of stone from the Wall.

- **HEXHAM, NORTHUMBERLAND** - Old coaching and market town near Hadrian's Wall. Since pre-Norman times a weekly market has been held in the centre with its market-place and abbey park, and the richly-furnished 12th C abbey church has a superb Anglo-Saxon crypt.

- **INGRAM, NORTHUMBERLAND** - Hamlet in the Northumberland National Park at the foot of the Cheviot Hills, near the remains of many prehistoric forts. At the head of the valley is Linhope Spout, an interesting waterfall and deep pool.

- **KIELDER WATER, NORTHUMBERLAND** - A magnificent man-made lake, the largest in Northern Europe, with over 27 miles of shoreline. On the edge of the Northumberland National Park and near the Scottish border, Kielder can be explored by car, on foot or by ferry.

- **MARSKE-BY-THE-SEA, TEES VALLEY** - Residential town and resort 2 miles west of Saltburn.

- **MICKLETON, DURHAM** - Village 2 miles south-east of Middleton-in-Teesdale.

- **MIDDLETON-IN-TEESDALE, DURHAM** - Small stone town of hillside terraces overlooking the river, developed by the London Lead Company in the 18th C. Five miles up-river is the spectacular 70-ft waterfall, High Force.

- **MINDRUM, NORTHUMBERLAND** - Hamlet 4 miles south of Cornhill on Tweed by banks of Bowmont Water.

- **NEWCASTLE UPON TYNE, TYNE AND WEAR** - Commercial and cultural centre of the North East, with a large indoor shopping centre, Quayside market, museums and theatres which offer an annual 6 week season by the Royal Shakespeare Company. Norman castle keep, medieval alleys, old Guildhall.

- **NEWTON-BY-THE-SEA, NORTHUMBERLAND** - Attractive hamlet at the south end of Beadnell Bay with a sandy beach and splendid view of Dunstanburgh Castle. In a designated Area of Outstanding Natural Beauty, Low Newton, part of the village, is now owned by the National Trust.

- **OVINGTON, NORTHUMBERLAND** - Quiet village on the north bank of the River Tyne, linked to the village of Ovingham which has a 17th C packhorse bridge and was the birthplace of the famous artist and engraver Thomas Bewick.

- **ROTHBURY, NORTHUMBERLAND** - Old market town on the River Coquet near the Simonside Hills. It makes an ideal centre for walking and fishing or for exploring this beautiful area from the coast to the Cheviots. Cragside House and Gardens (National Trust) are open to the public.

- **SEAHOUSES, NORTHUMBERLAND** - Small modern resort developed around a 19th C herring port. Just offshore, and reached by boat from here, are the rocky Farne Islands (National Trust) where there is an important bird reserve. The bird observatory occupies a medieval pele tower.

- **SLAGGYFORD, NORTHUMBERLAND** - A most attractive hamlet on the Pennine Way in the South Tyne valley.

- **SLALEY, NORTHUMBERLAND** - Small hamlet, now a major golfing venue, south of Corbridge near the Derwent Reservoir.

- **SOUTH SHIELDS, TYNE AND WEAR** - At the mouth of the Tyne, shipbuilding and industrial centre developed around a 19th C coalport and occupying the site of an important Roman fort and granary port. The town's museum has mementoes of the earliest self-righting lifeboat, built here in 1789.

- **STANHOPE, DURHAM** - Old market town, 'Capital of Weardale', set amid moorland hills and former lead-mining country of the North Pennines. In the market square opposite the church is a mock medieval castle. Close to the town is a cave where important Bronze Age finds were made.

- **STOCKSFIELD, NORTHUMBERLAND** - Pretty rural village in Tyne Valley in area of good agricultural land. Bywell Hall, the home of Lord Allendale, is nearby as well as Cherryburn, the birthplace of Thomas Bewick, where a musuem dedicated to the life and works of this famous local engraver can be found.

- **WAREN MILL, NORTHUMBERLAND** - On Budle Bay just north of Bamburgh, in a designated Area of Outstanding Natural Beauty. This area is a favourite place for bird-watchers.

- **WARKWORTH, NORTHUMBERLAND** - A pretty village overlooked by its medieval castle. A 14th C fortified bridge across the wooded Coquet gives a superb view of 18th C terraces climbing to the castle. Upstream is a curious 14th C Hermitage and in the market square is the Norman church of St Lawrence.

- **WEST WOODBURN, NORTHUMBERLAND** - Small hamlet on the River Rede in rolling moorland country.

- **WESTGATE-IN-WEARDALE, DURHAM** - Small Weardale village with an old water-mill and a 19th C church. It is set at the entrance to the Bishops of Durham's former hunting ground, Old Park. Beautiful moorland, river and valley scenery to be explored.

- **WINSTON, DURHAM** - Attractive village overlooking the valley of the River Tees. Interesting Early English church and a manor house which once belonged to the powerful Neville family.

- **WITTON-LE-WEAR, DURHAM** - Hillside village rising from the river to its Norman church and triangular green. From here can be seen across the river the 15th C castle. Set in woodland by a stream it makes a romantic sight and its grounds provide secluded spots for campers and caravanners.

- **WOLSINGHAM, DURHAM** - Gateway to the moors of Upper Weardale, small town set at the confluence of the Wear and Waskerley Beck. The moors abound in old lead-workings and quarries; on Waskerley Beck, Tunstall Reservoir is the haunt of bird-watchers. Well placed for exploring the fells and dales.

- **WOOLER, NORTHUMBERLAND** - Old grey-stone town, market-place for foresters and hill farmers, set at the edge of the north-east Cheviots. This makes a good base for excursions to Northumberland's loveliest coastline, or for angling and walking in the Borderlands.market town occupying the site of an Anglo-Saxon settlement, it still holds an open market.

CREDIT CARD BOOKINGS If you book by telephone and are asked for your credit card number it is advisable to check the proprietor's policy should you cancel your reservation.

NORTH WEST

Home of pop stars, world famous football teams, Blackpool Tower and Coronation Street, the great North West has vibrant cities, idyllic countryside and world class art collections too.

classic sights

Blackpool Tower & Pleasure Beach – unashamed razzamatazz
Football – museums and tours at Manchester United and Liverpool football clubs
The Beatles – The Beatles Story, Magical Mystery Tour Bus and Macca's former home

coast & country

The Ribble Valley – unchanged rolling landscapes
Formby – a glorious beach of sand dunes and pine woods
Wildfowl & Wetlands Trust, near Ormskirk – 120 types of birds including flamingoes

arts for all

The Tate Liverpool – modern art
The Lowry – the world's largest collection of LS Lowry paintings

distinctively different

Granada Studios – tour the home of many TV classics

The counties of Cheshire, Greater Manchester, Lancashire, Merseyside and the High Peak District of Derbyshire

FOR MORE INFORMATION CONTACT:

**North West Tourist Board
Swan House, Swan Meadow Road,
Wigan Pier, Wigan WN3 5BB
Tel: (01942) 821222 Fax: (01942) 820002
Internet: www.visitnorthwest.com**

The Pictures:
1 Manchester United
   Football Club
2 Healey Dell, Rochdale
3 Blackpool Beach

Places to Visit - see pages 116-119
Where to Stay - see pages 120-127

PLACES to visit

You will find hundreds of interesting places to visit during your stay, just some of which are listed in these pages. Contact any Tourist Information Centre in the region for more ideas on days out.

The Albert Dock Company Limited

Suite 22, Edward Pavilion, Albert Dock, Liverpool, Merseyside L3 4AF
Tel: (0151) 708 7334 www.albertdock.com
Britain's largest Grade I Listed historic building. Restored four-sided dock including shops, bars, restaurants, entertainment, marina and the Maritime Museum.

The Beatles Story

Britannia Vaults, Albert Dock, Liverpool, Merseyside L3 4AA
Tel: (0151) 709 1963
Liverpool's award-winning visitor attraction with a replica of the original Cavern Club. Available for private parties.

Beeston Castle

Beeston, Tarporley, Cheshire CW6 9TX
Tel: (01829) 260464
A ruined 13thC castle situated on top of the Peckforton Hills, with views of the surrounding countryside. Exhibitions are also held featuring the castle's history.

Blackpool Pleasure Beach

525 Ocean Boulevard, South Shore, Blackpool, Lancashire FY4 1EZ
(0870) 444 5577
www.blackpoolpleasurebeach.co.uk
Europe's greatest show and amusement park. Blackpool Pleasure Beach offers over 145 rides and attractions, plus spectacular shows.

Blackpool Sea Life Centre

The Promenade, Blackpool, Lancashire FY1 5AA
Tel: (01253) 622445
Tropical sharks up to 8 ft (2.5 m) housed in a 100,000-gallon (454,609-litre) water display with an underwater walkway. The new 'Lost City of Atlantis' is back with the feature exhibition.

Blackpool Tower

The Promenade, Blackpool, Lancashire FY1 4BJ
Tel: (01253) 622242 www.blackpoollive.com
Inside Blackpool Tower you will find the Tower Ballroom, a circus, entertainment for the children, the Tower Top Ride and Undersea World.

Boat Museum

South Pier Road, Ellesmere Port, Cheshire CH5 4FW
Tel: (0151) 355 5017
Over 50 historic crafts, largest floating collection in the world with restored buildings, traditional cottages, workshops, steam engines, boat trips, shop and cafe.

Bridgemere Garden World

Bridgemere, Nantwich, Cheshire CW5 7QB
Tel: (01270) 520381
Bridgemere Garden World, 25 fascinating acres (10 ha) of plants, gardens, greenhouses and shop. Coffee shop, restaurant and over 20 different display gardens in the Garden Kingdom.

Camelot Theme Park

Park Hall Road, Charnock Richard, Chorley, Lancashire PR7 5LP
Tel: (01257) 453044 www.camelotthemepark.co.uk
The magical kingdom of Camelot is a world of thrilling rides, fantastic entertainment and family fun, with over 100 rides and attractions to enjoy.

CATALYST: The Museum of Chemical Industry

Gossage Building, Mersey Road, Widnes, Cheshire WA8 0DF
Tel: (0151) 420 1121
Catalyst is the award-winning family day out where science and technology come alive.

Chester Zoo

Upton-by-Chester, Chester, Cheshire CH2 1LH
Tel: (01244) 380280 www.demon.co.uk/chesterzoo
Chester Zoo is one of Europe's leading conservation zoos, with over 5,000 animals in spacious and natural enclosures. Now featuring the new 'Twilight Zone'.

Dunham Massey Hall Park and Garden

Altrincham, Cheshire WA14 4SJ
Tel: (0161) 941 1025 www.thenationaltrust.org.uk
An 18thC mansion in a 250-acre (100ha) wooded deer park with furniture, paintings and silver. A 25-acre (10ha) informal garden with mature trees and waterside plantings.

East Lancashire Railway

Bolton Street Station, Bury, Greater Manchester BL9 0EY
Tel: (0161) 764 7790 www.east-lancs-rly.co.uk
Eight miles of preserved railway, operated principally by steam. Traction Transport Museum close by.

Gawsworth Hall

Gawsworth, Macclesfield, Cheshire SK11 9RN
Tel: (01260) 223456 www.gawsworthhall.com
Gawsworth Hall is a Tudor half-timbered manor-house with tilting ground. Featuring pictures, sculpture and furniture and an open-air theatre.

Jodrell Bank Science Centre, Planetarium and Arboretum

Lower Withington, Macclesfield, Cheshire SK11 9DL
Tel: (01477) 571339 www.jb.man.ac.uk/scicen
Exhibition and interactive exhibits on astronomy, space, energy and the environment. Planetarium and the world-famous Lovell telescope, plus a 35-acre (14-ha) arboretum.

Knowsley Safari Park

Prescot, Merseyside L34 4AN
Tel: (0151) 430 9009 www.knowsley.com
A 5-mile safari through 500 acres (202 ha) of rolling countryside, and the world's wildest animals roaming free – that's the wonderful world of freedom you'll find at the park.

Lady Lever Art Gallery

Port Sunlight Village, Higher Bebington, Wirral, Merseyside CH62 5EQ
Tel: (0151) 478 4136 www.nmgm.org.uk
The 1st Lord Leverhulme's magnificent collection of British paintings dated 1750-1900, British furniture, Wedgwood pottery and oriental porcelain.

The Pictures:
1 The River Ribble and Pendle Hill, Lancashire
2 Japanese Garden, Tatton Park
3 Lytham, Lancashire
4 Pavilion Gardens, Buxton
5 Blackpool Pleasure Beach

Lancaster Castle

Shire Hall, Castle Parade, Lancaster, Lancashire LA1 1YJ
Tel: (01524) 64998
www.lancashire.gov.uk/resources/ps/castle/index.htm
Shire Hall has a collection of coats of arms, a crown
court, a grand jury room, a 'drop room' and dungeons.
Also external tour of castle.

Lyme Park

Disley, Stockport, Greater Manchester SK12 2NX
Tel: (01663) 762023 www.nationaltrust.org.uk
Lyme Park is a National Trust country estate set in 1,377
acres (541 ha) of moorland, woodland and park. This
magnificent house has 17 acres (7 ha) of historic gardens.

The Museum of Science & Industry, in Manchester

Liverpool Road, Castlefield, Manchester M3 4FP
Tel: (0161) 832 1830 www.msim.org.uk
The Museum of Science and Industry in Manchester is
based in the world's oldest passenger railway station
with galleries that amaze, amuse and entertain.

National Football Museum

Deepdale Stadium, Preston, Lancashire PR1 6RU
Tel: (01772) 908442
www.nationalfootballmuseum.com
The Football Museum exists to explain how and why
football has become the people's game.

Norton Priory Museum and Gardens

Tudor Road, Runcorn, Cheshire WA7 1SX
Tel: (01928) 569895 www.nortonpriory.org
Medieval priory remains, purpose-built museum,
St Christopher's statue, sculpture trail and award-winning
walled garden, all set in 39 acres (16 ha) of beautiful
gardens.

Quarry Bank Mill

Styal, Wilmslow, Cheshire SK9 4LA
Tel: (01625) 527468
www.rmplc.co.uk/orgs/quarrybankmill
A Georgian water-powered cotton-spinning mill, with
four floors of displays and demonstrations and 300 acres
(121 ha) of parkland surroundings.

Rufford Old Hall

Rufford, Ormskirk, Lancashire L40 1SG
Tel: (01704) 821254 www.nationaltrust.org.uk
One of the finest 16thC buildings in Lancashire with a
magnificent hall, particularly noted for its immense
moveable screen.

Sandcastle

South Promenade, Blackpool, Merseyside FY4 1BB
Tel: (01253) 343602
Wave pool, leisure pools, giant water flumes, white-
knuckle water slides, kiddies' safe harbour, play area,
catering, bar, shops and amusements.

Smithills Hall & Park Trust

Smithills Hall, Smithills Dean Road, Bolton,
Greater Manchester BL1 7NP
Tel: (01204) 332377
Smithills Hall is a fascinating example of the growth of a
great house which mirrors the changes in fashion and
living conditions from the late 14thC.

Southport Zoo and Conservation Trust

Princes Park, Southport, Merseyside PR8 1RX
Tel: (01704) 538102
Zoological gardens and conservation trust. Southport Zoo
has been run by the Petrie family since 1964. Talks on
natural history are held in the schoolroom.

Stapley Water Gardens & Palms Tropical Oasis

London Road, Stapeley, Nantwich, Cheshire CW5 7LH
Tel: (01270) 623868
www.stapeleywatergardens.com
Large water garden centre filled with display lakes, pools
and fountains. Trees and shrubs, pot plants, gifts, garden
sundries and pets. Thousand of items on display.

Tate Liverpool

Albert Dock, Liverpool, Merseyside L3 4BB
Tel: (0151) 702 7445 www.tate.org.uk
The Tate at Liverpool exhibits the National Collection of
Modern Art.

Tatton Park

Knutsford, Cheshire WA16 6QN
Tel: (01625) 534400 www.tattonpark.org.uk
Historic mansion with a 50-acre (20-ha) garden,
traditional working farm, Tudor manor-house, 2,000-acre
(809-ha) deer park and children's adventure playground.

Wigan Pier

Trencherfield Mill, Wigan, Lancashire WN3 4EF
Tel: (01942) 323666 www.wiganmbc.gov.uk
Wigan Pier combines interaction with displays and
reconstructions and the Wigan Pier Theatre Company.
Facilities include shops and a cafe.

Find out more about the
North West

Further information about holidays and attractions in the North West is available from:

NORTH WEST TOURIST BOARD
Swan House, Swan Meadow Road, Wigan Pier, Wigan WN3 5BB.
Tel: (01942) 821222 Fax: (01942) 820002
Internet: www.visitnorthwest.com

The following publications are available from North West Tourist Board:

Best of the North West
a guide to information on the region including hotels, self-catering establishments, caravan and camping parks. Also includes attractions, major events, shops and restaurants

Discovery Map
a non-accommodation guide, A1 folded to A4 map including list of visitor attractions, what to see and where to go

Bed and Breakfast Map
forming part of a family of maps for England, this guide provides information on bed and breakfast establishments in the North West region

Freedom
forming part of a family of publications about caravan and camping parks in the north of England

Stay on a Farm
a guide to farm accommodation in the north of England

Group Travel Planner
a guide to choosing the right accommodation, attraction or venue for group organisers

Venues
a 6-monthly newsletter about conference venues in the North West region

Schools Out
a 6-monthly newsletter aimed at schools providing information about where to go and what to see

Getting to the
North West

The Pictures:
1 Derbyshire
2 Barca Cafe Bar, Manchester

BY ROAD:
Motorways intersect within the region which has the best road network in the country. Travelling north or south use the M6 and east or west the M62.

BY RAIL:
Most North West coastal resorts are connected to InterCity routes with trains from many parts of the country and there are through trains to major cities and towns.

Where to stay in the North West

Accommodation entries in this region are listed in alphabetical order of place name, and then in alphabetical order of establishment.

Map references refer to the colour location maps at front of this guide. The first number indicates the map to use; the letter and number which follow refer to the grid reference on the map.

At-a-glance symbols at the end of each accommodation entry give useful information about services and facilities. A key to symbols can be found inside the back cover flap. Keep this open for easy reference.

A brief description of the towns and villages offering accommodation in the entries which follow, can be found at the end of this section.

A complete listing of all the English Tourism Council assessed accommodation covered by this guide appears at the back of the guide.

ACCRINGTON, Lancashire Map ref 4A1 *Tourist Information Centre Tel: (01254) 872595 (Public)*

★★★

1 Unit
Sleeping 6

LOW MOORSIDE FARM COTTAGE
Burnley Road, Clayton-le-Moors, Accrington BB5 5UG
Contact: Mr and Mrs C&E Hallworth, Elcliffe Cottage,
Burnley Road, Clayton-le-Moors, Accrington BB5 5UG
T: (01254) 237053

OPEN All year round

Low season per wk
£200.00–£250.00
High season per wk
£250.00–£300.00

Cottage set in open fields, formerly a working farm. Close to the Ribble Valley, easy access from M65. Children welcome. Sleeps 6, sorry no pets.

BASHALL EAVES, Lancashire Map ref 4A1

★★★★

1 Unit
Sleeping 4

THE COACH HOUSE
Clough Bottom, Bashall Eaves, Clitheroe BB7 3NA
T: (01254) 826285 (Reception 0900-1700)
F: (01254) 826015
E: focus.training@btinternet.com
Contact: Mrs Jane Backhouse

OPEN All year round
CC: Barclaycard, Delta,
JCB, Mastercard, Solo,
Switch, Visa, Visa Electron

Low season per wk
£180.00
High season per wk
£280.00

An organic farm set in idyllic surroundings. Historic buildings. Well maintained in superb grounds which are conservation focused.

QUALITY ASSURANCE SCHEME
Star ratings were correct at the time of going to press but are subject to change. Please check at the time of booking.

BLACKPOOL, Lancashire Map ref 4A1 *Tourist Information Centre Tel: (01253) 478 222*

★★★★

1 Unit
Sleeping 12

A large, luxuriously appointed thatched-roof coach house accommodating up to 12 guests in style and comfort. Situated in its own grounds, the Coach House is two minutes' walk from Ribby Hall Holiday Village with its superb sports, leisure and entertainment facilities. Country location yet only 10 miles from Blackpool.

THE COACH HOUSE AT RIBBY HALL HOLIDAY VILLAGE

Ribby Road, Wrea Green, Nr Blackpool PR4 2PR
Contact: Mr Mark Partington, Ribby Hall Holiday Village,
Ribby Road, Wrea Green, Preston PR4 2PR
T: (01772) 671111
F: (01772) 673113
E: enquiries@ribbyhall.co.uk
I: www.ribbyhall.co.uk

OPEN All year round	**Low season per wk**
CC: Amex, Barclaycard,	**£798.00–£1,200.00**
Delta, Eurocard, JCB,	**High season per wk**
Maestro, Mastercard,	**£1,200.00–£1,600.00**
Solo, Switch, Visa, Visa	
Electron	

Free use of swimming pool, sauna, spa and jacuzzi. Discounted rates on other facilities.

★★-★★★

4 Units
Sleeping 3–5

Select fully self-contained holiday flats, situated in a peaceful area 150 yards from Queens Promenade and 200 yards from all required shops. The friendly owners welcome couples and families and senior citizens to our apartments, where a high standard of cleanliness is assured. Tea, sugar, towels, provided.

DONANGE

29 Holmfield Road, Blackpool FY2 9TB
T: (01253) 355051
E: donange@bushinternet.com
I: www.de-zineuk.co.uk/donange
Contact: Ms Myra Hasson

OPEN All year round	**Low season per wk**
	£80.00–£150.00
Summer bookings before	**High season per wk**
May-10% discount.	**£130.00–£195.00**
Fortnightly bookings	
discount, senior citizens	
discount.	

★★★

167 Units
Sleeping 2–6

Award-winning holiday village occupying 100 acres of beautiful, peaceful landscaped woodland grounds, in a countryside setting yet only 10 miles from Blackpool and Lytham St Annes. Accommodation in a choice of 170 luxury, spacious stone cottages. Superb sports, leisure and entertainment facilities for all the family. Open all year.

RIBBY HALL HOLIDAY VILLAGE

Ribby Road, Wrea Green, Nr Blackpool PR4 2PR
Contact: Miss Helen Larkin, Reservations Supervisor, Ribby
Hall Holiday Village, Ribby Road, Wrea Green, Preston
PR4 2PR
T: (01772) 671111
F: (01772) 673113
E: enquiries@ribbyhall.co.uk
I: www.ribbyhall.co.uk

OPEN All year round	**Low season per wk**
CC: Amex, Barclaycard,	**£200.00–£595.00**
Delta, JCB, Maestro,	**High season per wk**
Mastercard, Solo, Switch,	**£375.00–£695.00**
Visa	

Special mid-week, weekend and full week offers available throughout the year subject to availability.

BLACKPOOL continued

★★
10 Units
Sleeping 2–8

SAN REMO HOLIDAY FLATS, APARTMENTS AND BUNGALOW
7 Empress Drive North, Blackpool FY2 9SE   OPEN All year round
T: (01253) 353487 & 884238
Contact: Mrs P Crowe

Superior, self-contained holiday flats, apartments and bungalow situated in select area 30 yards off Queens Promenade. All on ground or 1st floor. Car parking.

Low season per wk
£95.00–£200.00
High season per wk
£135.00–£330.00

★★-★★★
8 Units
Sleeping 2–8

STRATFORD APARTMENTS
36-38 Empress Drive, Blackpool FY2 9SD   OPEN All year round
Contact: Mr and Mrs W L Williams,
36-38 Empress Drive, Blackpool FY2 9SD
T: (01253) 500150 (Answerphone)
F: (01253) 357967

Situated close to Queens Promenade in Blackpool's select North Shore district with good local transport links to all attractions in central and South Shore areas.

Low season per wk
£100.00–£260.00
High season per wk
£145.00–£390.00

★★-★★★
12 Units
Sleeping 2–6

THORNCLIFFE HOLIDAY FLATS
1 Holmfield Road, Gynn Square, Blackpool FY2 9SL   OPEN All year round
T: (01253) 357561 & 357561
F: (01253) 405671
E: enquiries@thorncliffeholidayflats.co.uk
Contact: Mr & Mrs R J Jackson

Imposing property with uninterrupted views of Gynn Gardens and Promenade. Offering modernised comfortable accommodation with fire certificate. Private car park.

Low season per wk
£109.00–£242.00
High season per wk
£165.00–£361.00

BOSLEY, Cheshire Map ref 4B2

★★★
2 Units
Sleeping 4–6

THE OLD BYRE
Pye Ash Farm, Leek Road, Bosley,   OPEN All year round
Macclesfield SK11 0PN
Contact: Mrs D Gilman, Pedley House Farm,
Pedley Lane, Congleton CW12 3QD
T: (01260) 273650
F: (01260) 297115

110-acre mixed farm. Old beamed shippon in beautiful walking area, edge of Peak District and moorlands, 15 miles from Alton Towers. Heating and linen included.

Low season per wk
£150.00–£300.00
High season per wk
£200.00–£450.00

BRINSCALL, Lancashire Map ref 4A1

★★★
1 Unit
Sleeping 7

MOORS VIEW COTTAGE
117 School Lane, Brinscall, Chorley PR6 8PS   OPEN All year round
Contact: Mrs Sheila Smith, Four Seasons Guest House,
9 Cambridge Road, Cleveleys, Blackpool FY5 1EP
T: (01253) 853537 (Answerphone) &
07715 816281 (Mobile)
F: (01624) 662190

Two-bedroomed cottage with beautiful south-facing garden in semi-rural West Pennine village adjacent to canal, motorways and central for market towns and coast.

Low season per wk
£200.00–£250.00
High season per wk
£290.00–£315.00

CHECK THE MAPS

The colour maps at the front of this guide show all the cities, towns and villages for which you will find accommodation entries. Refer to the town index to find the page on which they are listed.

CHESTER, Cheshire Map ref 4A2 *Tourist Information Centre Tel: (01244) 402111*

★★★★
2 Units
Sleeping 2–4

The City Apartment is a double-bedroomed high standard property in the heart of the city. Quarry close has 2 bedrooms and is approximately 5 minutes' walk from the city centre and River Dee with views over landscaped gardens.

THE CITY APARTMENT & 14 QUARRY CLOSE

8 Back Queen Street, Chester CH1 3LW
Contact: Mrs Moira Martland, Upton Lodge, Wealstone Lane, Upton, Chester CH2 1HD
T: (01244) 372091
F: (01244) 374779
E: chesterhols@clara.co.uk
I: www.chesterholidays.co.uk

OPEN All year round

Guests arriving in Chester by train can be met and transported to the apartments if they wish.

Low season per wk
Min £250.00
High season per wk
Min £350.00

Rating
Applied For
1 Unit
Sleeping 4

IVY COTTAGE
11 Sandy Lane, Chester CH3 5UL
Contact: Mr & Mrs Joseph & Sonia Barry, Woodsorrel, 18 Dee Fords Avenue, Chester CH3 5UP
T: (01244) 403630 (Answerphone) & 07973 211582 (Mobile)
F: (01244) 403699
E: rmd.heritage@btconnect.com
I: rmd-heritage.co.uk

OPEN All year round

Low season per wk
£200.00–£600.00

A 3 storey detached cottage circa 1800. Situated within residential lane (B5130) with superb view across water meadows and city to the Welsh hills.

★★★★★
1 Unit
Sleeping 11

JASMINE MEWS STYLE COTTAGES
2 Meadowside Mews, Saughall Road, Chester CH1 4DB
Contact: Mrs Karen Buchan, Auchmacoy House, Llanfair Road, Abergele LL22 8DH
T: (01745) 825880 (Business line/answerphone) & 07831 580280 (Mobile)
F: (01745) 825880
E: k.buchan@btinternet.com
I: www.chesterholidaycottages.com

OPEN All year round

Low season per wk
£210.00–£225.00
High season per wk
£325.00–£410.00

Award-winning development of mews-style cottages. Built of reclaimed brick, sandstone windowsills. Modern interior, patio garden, parking. Approximately 10 minutes' walk to city centre.

★★★
1 Unit
Sleeping 4

KINGSWOOD COACH HOUSE
Kingswood, Parkgate Road, Saughall, Chester CH1 6JS
T: (01244) 851204 (Answerphone)
F: (01244) 851244
E: caroline.mcvey@psmconsulting.co.uk
Contact: Mrs Caroline Perry

OPEN All year round

Low season per wk
£160.00–£200.00
High season per wk
£200.00–£230.00

Ideal for couples. Large bedroom, fitted kitchen, living room, toilet and shower. Garden and patio, off-road parking. Close to bus route. Near Wales and Wirral.

★★
1 Unit
Sleeping 6

LITTLE MAYFIELD
Mayfield House, Warrington Road, Hoole Village, Chester CH2 4EX
T: (01244) 300231
F: (01244) 300231
Contact: Mr M J Cullen

OPEN Apr–Dec

Low season per wk
£165.00
High season per wk
£245.00

Self-contained wing of William IV house set in 3 acres of garden with hard tennis court. Spacious rooms. 7 minutes from Chester city centre.

CHESTER continued

3 THE MOUNT

★★★
1 Unit
Sleeping 6

4 Lancaster Drive, Chester CH3 5UD
Contact: Mrs Henderson, 4 Lancaster Drive, Chester
CH3 5JW
T: (01244) 326890 (Answerphone)

OPEN All year round

Low season per wk
£220.00–£320.00
High season per wk
£260.00–£380.00

Part Victorian, Grade II Listed property with a black and white exterior. Beautiful views onto the River Dee.

3 NORTHGATE AVENUE

★★★
1 Unit
Sleeping 2

Northgate Village, Chester CH2 2DX
Contact: Mrs Sue Byrne, Walnut Cottage, Rake Lane,
Chester CH2 4DB
T: (01244) 379824 (Answerphone) &
07801 045272 (Mobile)
E: k.byrne@chestercc.gov.uk

OPEN All year round

Low season per wk
£195.00–£225.00
High season per wk
£250.00–£365.00

Attractive house 10 minutes' walk city centre. Spacious lounge, patio doors to secluded garden. Well-equipped kitchen. Parking. Non-smoking. Sorry no pets. Brochure.

TATTERSALL GATE

★★★
1 Unit
Sleeping 6

1&3 Nuns Road, Chester CH1 2LZ
Contact: Mrs R A Randle, PO Box 247, Chester
CH1 2WA
T: (01244) 401591 & 07714 457940
F: (01244) 401591
E: rosrandle@cs.com
I: www.woodbank.co.uk/thatch

OPEN All year round
CC: Barclaycard,
Mastercard, Visa

Low season per wk
£200.00–£250.00
High season per wk
£350.00–£500.00

North West Tourism-Silver Award winner 2000. Charming Grade II Listed property, within 4 minutes' walk of Chester city centre, spectacular views. Garden, parking.

CHIPPING, Lancashire Map ref 4A1

RAKEFOOT BARN

★★★–★★★★★
4 Units
Sleeping 2–8

Rakefoot Farm, Chaigley, Clitheroe BB7 3LY
T: (01995) 61332 & 07889 279063
F: (01995) 61332
Contact: Mrs P M Gifford

OPEN All year round

Low season per wk
£80.00–£288.00
High season per wk
£147.00–£480.00

Traditional stone barn conversion. Family farm in Forest of Bowland between Chipping and Clitheroe. Three cottages interlinked. Most bedrooms en suite. Also B&B NWTB Silver Award winner 2000.

CLITHEROE, Lancashire Map ref 4A1 *Tourist Information Centre Tel: (01200) 425566*

GREENBANK COTTAGES

★★★★
5 Units
Sleeping 6

Greenbank Farm, Whalley Road, Sabden,
Clitheroe BB7 9DT
T: (01254) 823064
F: (01254) 822314
E: gordon.greenwood@ntlworld.com
Contact: Mr Gordon Greenwood

OPEN Mar–Oct

Low season per wk
£290.00–£345.00
High season per wk
£290.00–£400.00

Detached, 3-bedroomed cottages, set in farmland. Quiet location with easy road access.

KELSALL, Cheshire Map ref 4A2

NORTHWOOD HALL COURTYARD COTTAGES

★★★
3 Units
Sleeping 4–8

Northwood Hall, Dog Lane, Kelsall, Tarporley CW6 0RP
T: (01829) 752569
F: (01829) 751157
E: enquiries@northwood-hall.co.uk
I: www.northwoodhall-cottages.co.uk
Contact: Mrs C Nock

OPEN All year round

Low season per wk
£240.00–£285.00
High season per wk
£285.00–£305.00

Courtyard cottages sited adjacent to old Victorian farmhouse. Three detached cottages of varying sizes full of character with many original features.

MACCLESFIELD, Cheshire Map ref 4B2 *Tourist Information Centre Tel: (01625) 504114*

★★

1 Unit
Sleeping 6

MILL HOUSE FARM COTTAGE
Bosley, Macclesfield SK11 0NZ
Contact: Mrs L Whittaker, Mill House Farm, Bosley,
Macclesfield SK11 0NZ
T: (01260) 226265
E: lynne-whittaker@yahoo.co.uk

OPEN All year round

Low season per wk
£140.00–£170.00
High season per wk
£170.00–£220.00

Comfortable, spacious cottage on 130-acre dairy farm bordering the Peak District. Beautiful surrounding countryside and convenient for Alton Towers, Potteries, Chester, Manchester Airport.

MANCHESTER, Greater Manchester Map ref 4B1 *Tourist Information Centre Tel: (0161) 234 3157*

★★★

5 Units
Sleeping 3–4

LA SUISSE SELF-CATERING APARTMENTS
444 Bury Old Road, Prestwich, Manchester M25 1PQ
Contact: Mr and Mrs Phillips, 444 Bury Old Road,
Prestwich, Manchester M25 1PQ
T: (0161) 796 0545 & 07711 200551 (Mobile)
F: (0161) 796 0545
E: reservations@lasuisse.co.uk
I: www.lasuisse.co.uk

OPEN All year round
CC: Amex, Barclaycard,
Delta, Eurocard, JCB,
Mastercard, Solo, Switch,
Visa, Visa Electron

Low season per wk
£299.25–£365.75
High season per wk
£350.00–£455.00

Ideal for extended stay, relocations and vacations, with all the comforts of home. Daily rates available. Continental breakfast available on request. Maximum price excludes Commonwealth Games.

MANCHESTER AIRPORT

See under Manchester

NANTWICH, Cheshire Map ref 4A2 *Tourist Information Centre Tel: (01270) 610983*

★★★

2 Units
Sleeping 4–6

BANK FARM COTTAGES
Newcastle Road, Hough, Crewe CW2 5JG
T: (01270) 841809 & 841253
F: (01270) 841253
Contact: Mrs A Vaughan

OPEN All year round

Low season per wk
£200.00–£250.00
High season per wk
£250.00–£300.00

Charming holiday cottages created from Victorian farm buildings, furnished to a high standard. Full gas central heating, washing machines, microwaves. Ample parking. Excellent base for North Wales potteries.

POULTON-LE-FYLDE, Lancashire Map ref 4A1

★★★★

6 Units
Sleeping 4–6

SWANS REST
Garstang Road East, Singleton,
Poulton-le-Fylde FY6 8LX
T: (01253) 886617
F: (01253) 892563
E: swansrest@btconnect.com
I: www.swansrest.co.uk
Contact: Mrs Irene O'Connor

OPEN All year round

Low season per wk
£149.00–£299.00
High season per wk
£209.00–£410.00

Four luxury cottages set in 8 acres, including 2 new log cabins overlooking pond area with swans and ducks. Within 6 miles of Blackpool.

COUNTRY CODE Always follow the Country Code ✤ Enjoy the countryside and respect its life and work ✤ Guard against all risk of fire ✤ Fasten all gates ✤ Keep your dogs under close control ✤ Keep to public paths across farmland ✤ Use gates and stiles to cross fences, hedges and walls ✤ Leave livestock, crops and machinery alone ✤ Take your litter home ✤ Help to keep all water clean ✤ Protect wildlife, plants and trees ✤ Take special care on country roads ✤ Make no unnecessary noise

★★

16 Units
Sleeping 1

Near the town centre, with excellent road and rail links, the University's halls of residence offer comfortable, value-for-money accommodation. Grouped in small flats, all rooms are en suite with full self-catering facilities. Ideal base for visiting friends and family or a leisurely break to discover Lancashire and the surrounding countryside.

UNIVERSITY OF CENTRAL LANCASHIRE

Hospitality Services, Marsh Building, Preston PR1 2HE
Contact: Miss Maria Dominguez, University of Central Lancashire, Hospitality Services, Marsh Building, Preston PR1 2HE
T: (01772) 892650 (Direct line) & 892653
F: (01772) 892977
E: hospitalityservices@uclan.ac.uk
I: www.uclan.ac.uk

OPEN Jun–Sep
CC: Barclaycard, Delta, Eurocard, JCB, Maestro, Mastercard, Solo, Switch, Visa, Visa Electron

Low season per wk
£96.00–£112.00
High season per wk
£100.00–£117.00

RIBBLE VALLEY

See under Chipping, Clitheroe

SILVERDALE, Lancashire Map ref 5A3

★★★

1 Unit
Sleeping 3

The Stables are of 18thC construction and have been completely converted to a luxury standard, sleeps 2-3. Large bedroom, en suite shower room. Additional shower room. Facilities for disabled. Wheelchair access to all rooms. Situated in peaceful surroundings. AONB. Village and coast 0.25 miles. RSPB and golf course 1 mile.

THE STABLES

Lindeth House, Lindeth Road, Silverdale, Carnforth LA5 0TT
T: (01524) 702121
F: (01524) 702226
E: conquerors.maryk@virgin.net
Contact: Mrs C M Ranford

OPEN All year round

3 night stays available Oct–Feb (excl Christmas and New Year).

Low season per wk
£245.00–£265.00
High season per wk
£265.00–£315.00

★★★

2 Units
Sleeping 5–6

Beautiful, award-winning country cottages, nestling in the rich arable farmland of West Lancashire and just 4 miles from Southport and the seaside. Our cottages sleep from 4 to 6 people in a friendly, relaxed, family atmosphere. The ideal base for visiting all the North West's major attractions.

MARTIN LANE FARMHOUSE HOLIDAY COTTAGES

Martin Lane Farmhouse, Burscough, Ormskirk L40 8JH
T: (01704) 893527 & 07803 049128 (Mobile)
F: (01704) 893527
E: martinlanefarmhouse@btinternet.com
I: www.martinlanefarmhouse.btinternet.co.uk
Contact: Mrs Stubbs

OPEN All year round

Spring and autumn specials:
2 night stay plus extra night free.

Low season per wk
£135.00–£320.00
High season per wk
£200.00–£395.00

WHERE TO STAY

Please mention this guide when making your booking.

SOUTHPORT continued

★★★
5 Units
Sleeping 4–6

SANDY BROOK FARM
52 Wyke Cop Road, Scarisbrick, Southport PR8 5LR
Contact: Mr W Core, Sandy Brook Farm,
52 Wyke Cop Road, Scarisbrick, Southport PR8 5LR
T: (01704) 880337
F: (01704) 880337

OPEN All year round

Low season per wk
£100.00–£130.00
High season per wk
£240.00–£270.00

27-acre arable farm. Converted barn apartments furnished in traditional style. 3.5 miles from Southport in rural area of Scarisbrick. One apartment adapted for disabled.

STONYHURST, Lancashire Map ref 4A1

★★★★
1 Unit
Sleeping 2

ALDEN COTTAGE
Kemple End, Birdy Brow, Stonyhurst, Clitheroe BB7 9QY
Contact: Mr & Mrs P&B Carpenter, Alden Cottage,
Kemple End, Birdy Brow, Stonyhurst, Clitheroe BB7 9QY
T: (01254) 826468
E: carpenter@aldencottage.f9.co.uk

An idyllic and luxuriously appointed 17thC cottage situated in an Area of Outstanding Natural Beauty. Beamed sitting room with central heating and wood burner, well-equipped kitchen, bathroom with jacuzzi bath and shower. Perfect for a peaceful and relaxing stay. Double bedroom sleeps 2.

OPEN All year round

Short stays available, min 3 nights.

Low season per wk
£155.00–£185.00
High season per wk
£200.00–£235.00

THORNLEY, Lancashire Map ref 4A1

★★★
1 Unit
Sleeping 4

THORNLEY HALL
Thornley, Longridge, Preston PR3 2TN
Contact: Mrs G Airey, Proprietor, Thornley Hall,
Thornley, Longridge, Preston PR3 2TN
T: (01995) 61243

OPEN All year round

Low season per wk
£220.00–£250.00
High season per wk
£230.00–£260.00

Self-contained part of Thornley Hall in Forest of Bowland. Superb views. Spacious lounge/games room, dining-room and 2 bedrooms. Farmhouse with period features.

TOSSIDE, Lancashire Map ref 4A1

★★★★
1 Unit
Sleeping 10

LOWER GILL FARMHOUSE
Tosside, Skipton BD23 4SG
Contact: Agent, Holiday Cottages (Yorkshire) Ltd,
Water Street, Skipton BD23 4SJ
T: (01756) 700510
F: (01756) 701678
E: info@holidaycotts.demon.co.uk

OPEN All year round
CC: Barclaycard, Delta,
Eurocard, Mastercard,
Solo, Switch, Visa, Visa
Electron

Low season per wk
Max £295.00
High season per wk
Max £573.00

A 17thC farmhouse recently extensively renovated. Enjoying a quiet peaceful location. Character throughout, even wild deer graze on the lawn.

WENNINGTON, Lancashire Map ref 5B3

★★★★
1 Unit
Sleeping 4

EASTER COTTAGE
Wennington, Lancaster LA2 8NU
Contact: Mrs Jenny Herd, Mill Farm, Wennington,
Lancaster LA2 8NU
T: (015242) 21690

Award winning barn conversion, set in the Lune Valley, a conservation Area of Outstanding Natural Beauty. Equipped and furnished to a high standard, with oak beams, open stonework and woodburning stove. Retaining much charm and character. French windows to the lounge and master bedroom, overlook the beautiful 1-acre garden.

OPEN All year round

Short breaks available from end Oct–Easter (excl Christmas and New Year).

Low season per wk
Min £190.00
High season per wk
£290.00–£340.00

A brief guide to the main Towns and Villages offering accommodation in the

North West

A **ACCRINGTON, LANCASHIRE** - Situated halfway between Burnley and Blackburn. The mock-Jacobean Haworth Art Gallery, which has fine plaster ceilings, contains 130 pieces of Tiffany glass.

B **BLACKPOOL, LANCASHIRE** - Britain's largest fun resort, with Blackpool Pleasure Beach, 3 piers and the famous Tower. Host to the spectacular autumn illuminations.

C **CHESTER, CHESHIRE** - Roman and medieval walled city rich in treasures. Black and white buildings are a hallmark, including 'The Rows' - two-tier shopping galleries. 900-year-old cathedral and the famous Chester Zoo.

• **CHIPPING, LANCASHIRE** - Charming, well-preserved 17th C village, on the edge of the Forest of Bowland on the Pendle Witches' Trail. Ancient church, pub, craft shops, superb base for walking and touring the area. Best Kept Village award.

• **CLITHEROE, LANCASHIRE** - Ancient market town with a 800-year-old castle keep and a wide range of award-winning shops. Good base for touring Ribble Valley, Trough of Bowland and Pennine moorland. Country market on Tuesdays and Saturdays.

M **MACCLESFIELD, CHESHIRE** - Cobbled streets and quaint old buildings stand side by side with modern shops and three markets. Centuries of association with the silk industry; museums feature working exhibits and social history. Stunning views of the Peak District National Park.

• **MANCHESTER, GREATER MANCHESTER** - The Gateway to the North, offering one of Britain's largest selections of arts venues and theatre productions, a wide range of chain stores and specialist shops, a legendary, lively nightlife, spectacular architecture and a plethora of eating and drinking places.

N **NANTWICH, CHESHIRE** - Old market town on the River Weaver made prosperous in Roman times by salt springs. Fire destroyed the town in 1583 and many buildings were rebuilt in Elizabethan style. Churche's Mansion (open to the public) survived the fire.

P **POULTON-LE-FYLDE, LANCASHIRE** - Old market town, listed in the Domesday Book, whose most notable feature is the church of St Chad which has an early 17th C Perpendicular tower, Romanesque chancel, Georgian interior and wall monuments to the Fleetwoods and Heskeths.

• **PRESTON, LANCASHIRE** - Scene of decisive Royalist defeat by Cromwell in the Civil War and later of riots in the Industrial Revolution. Local history exhibited in Harris museum. Famous for its Guild and the celebration that takes place every 20 years.

S **SILVERDALE, LANCASHIRE** - On the shores of Morecambe Bay, this picturesque village is in the centre of a designated Area of Outstanding Natural Beauty.

• **SOUTHPORT, MERSEYSIDE** - Delightful Victorian resort noted for gardens, sandy beaches and 6 golf-courses, particularly Royal Birkdale. Attractions include the Atkinson Art Gallery, Southport Railway Centre, Pleasureland and the annual Southport Flower Show. Excellent shopping, particularly in Lord Street's elegant boulevard.

T **TOSSIDE, LANCASHIRE** - Small hillside hamlet with village school, church, public house and early 18th C Congregational Chapel. In beautiful countryside on the edge of the Forest of Bowland, close to the Stocks Reservoir.

Welcome Host

Welcome Host is a nationally recognised customer care initiative, sponsored in England by the English Tourism Council. When visiting accommodation in this guide you may find this sign on display. It demonstrates commitment to courtesy and service and an aim to provide high standards of service and a warm welcome for all visitors.

YORKSHIRE

Yorkshire combines wild and brooding moors with historic cities, elegant spa towns and a varied coastline of traditional resorts and working fishing ports.

classic sights

Fountains Abbey & Studley Royal – 12th century Cistercian abbey and Georgian water garden
Nostell Prior – 18th century house with outstanding art collection
York Minster – largest medieval Gothic cathedral north of the Alps

coast & country

The Pennines – dramatic moors and rocks
Whitby – unspoilt fishing port, famous for jet (black stone)

literary links

Brontë parsonage, Haworth – home of the Brontë sisters; inspiration for 'Wuthering Heights' and 'Jane Eyre'

arts for all

National Museum of Photography, Film and Television – hi-tech and hands-on

distinctively different

The Original Ghost Walk of York – spooky tours every night

The counties of North, South, East and West Yorkshire, and Northern Lincolnshire

FOR MORE INFORMATION CONTACT:
Yorkshire Tourist Board
312 Tadcaster Road, York YO24 1GS
Tel: (01904) 707070 (24-hr brochure line) Fax: (01904) 701414
Email: info@ytb.org.uk Internet: www.yorkshirevisitor.com

The Pictures:
1 Roseberry Topping
2 Skidby Windmill
3 The Beach at Bridlington

Places to Visit - see pages 130-133
Where to Stay - see pages 134-164

PLACES to visit

You will find hundreds of interesting places to visit during your stay, just some of which are listed in these pages. Contact any Tourist Information Centre in the region for more ideas on days out.

Eureka! The Museum for Children

Discovery Road, Halifax, West Yorkshire HX1 2NE
Tel: (01422) 330069 www.eureka.org.uk
Eureka! is the first museum of its kind designed especially for children up to the age of 12 with over 400 hands-on exhibits.

Beningbrough Hall & Gardens

Beningbrough, York, North Yorkshire YO30 1DD
Tel: (01904) 470666
Handsome Baroque house, built in 1716, with 100 pictures from the National Portrait Gallery, Victorian laundry, potting shed and restored walled garden.

Flamingo Land Theme Park, Zoo and Holiday Village

Kirby Misperton, Malton, North Yorkshire YO17 6UX
Tel: (01653) 668287 www.flamingoland.co.uk
One-price family funpark with over 100 attractions, 7 shows and Europe's largest privately owned zoo. Europe's only triple-looping coaster, Magnum Force.

Camp Modern History Theme Museum

Malton, North Yorkshire YO17 6RT
Tel: (01653) 697777 www.edencamp.co.uk
Modern history theme museum depicting civilian way of life during World War II. Millennium features.

Fountains Abbey and Studley Royal

Studley Park, Ripon, North Yorkshire HG4 3DY
Tel: (01765) 608888 www.fountainsabbey.org.uk
Largest monastic ruin in Britain, founded by Cistercian monks in 1132. Landscaped garden laid between 1720-40 with lake, formal water garden, temples and deer park.

Cusworth Hall Museum of South Yorkshire Life

Cusworth Hall, Cusworth Lane, Doncaster,
South Yorkshire DN5 7TU
Tel: (01302) 782342
www.museum@doncaster.gov.uk
Georgian mansion in landscaped park containing Museum of South Yorkshire Life. Special educational facilities.

Hornsea Freeport

Rolston Road, Hornsea,
East Riding of Yorkshire HU18 1UT
Tel: (01964) 534211
Set in 25 acres (10 ha) of landscaped gardens with over 40 quality high-street names all selling stock with discounts of up to 50%, licensed restaurant. Leisure attractions.

The Deep

79 Ferensway, Hull, Kingston upon Hull HU2 8LE
Tel: (01482) 615789 www.hull.ac.uk
The Deep consists of 4 elements: a visitor attraction, learning centre, research facility and a business centre.

Last of the Summer Wine Exhibition (Compo's House)

30 Huddersfield Road, Holmfirth, Huddersfield,
West Yorkshire HD6 1JS
Tel: (01484) 681408
Collection of photographs and memorabilia connected
with the television series 'Last of the Summer Wine'.

Leeds City Art Gallery

The Headrow, Leeds, West Yorkshire LS1 3AA
Tel: (0113) 247 8248
www.leeds.gov.uk/tourinfo/attract/museums/artgall.html
Art gallery containing British paintings, sculptures, prints
and drawings of the 19thC and 20thC. Henry Moore
gallery with permanent collection of 20thC sculpture.

Lightwater Valley Theme Park

North Stainley, Ripon, North Yorkshire HG4 3HT
Tel: (01765) 635321 www.lightwatervalley.net
Set in 175 acres (71 ha) of parkland, Lightwater Valley
features a number of white-knuckle rides and children's
rides along with shopping malls, a restaurant and picnic
areas.

Magna

Sheffield Road, Templeborough, Rotherham,
South Yorkshire S60 1DX
Tel: (01709) 720002 www.magnatrust.org.uk
Magna is the UK's first science adventure centre set in
the vast Templeborough steelworks in Rotherham. Fun is
unavoidable here with giant interactives.

Midland Railway Centre

Butterley Station, Ripley, North Yorkshire DE5 3QZ
Tel: (01773) 747674
Over 50 locomotives and over 100 items of historic
rolling stock of Midland and LMS origin with a steam-
hauled passenger service, a museum site, country and
farm park.

Mother Shipton's Cave & the Petrifying Well

Prophesy House, High Bridge, Knaresborough,
North Yorkshire HG5 8DD
Tel: (01423) 864600 www.mothershipton.co.uk
Mother Shipton's Cave and Petrifying Well are the oldest
tourist attractions in Britain, opened in 1630. Cave, well,
museum, playground and 12 acres (5 ha) of riverside
grounds.

National Museum of Photography, Film & Television

Bradford, West Yorkshire BD1 1NQ
Tel: (01274) 202030 www.nmpft.org.uk
This fascinating and innovative museum houses the three
types of media that have transformed the 20thC.
Millennium grant awarded.

National Railway Museum

Leeman Road, York, North Yorkshire YO26 4XJ
Tel: (01904) 621261 www.nrm.org.uk
For a fun-packed family day out come along to the
National Railway Museum and experience the incredible
story of the train.

North Yorkshire Moors Railway

Pickering Station, Park Street, Pickering,
North Yorkshire YO18 7AJ
Tel: (01751) 472508 www.nymr.demon.co.uk
Evening and Sunday lunchtime dining service trains offer
a unique and nostalgic experience with a wonderful
selection of menus to suit all tastes.

The Pictures:
1 Boats in harbour, Whitby, North Yorkshire
2 Hull Fair
3 Countryside near Grimsby
4 The Humber Bridge
5 Flamborough Head
6 Felixkirk, North York Moors

Piece Hall

Halifax, West Yorkshire HX1 1RE
Tel: (01422) 358087 www.calderdale.gov.uk
Built in 1779 and restored in 1976, this Grade I Listed
building forms a unique and striking monument to the
wealth and importance of the wool trade.

Pleasure Island Family Theme Park

Kings Road, Cleethorpes, North East Lincolnshire DN35 0PL
Tel: (01472) 211511 www.pleasure-island.co.uk
The East Coast's biggest fun day out, with over 50 rides
and attractions. Whatever the weather, fun is guaranteed
with lots of undercover attractions. Shows from around
the world.

Ripley Castle

Ripley, Harrogate, North Yorkshire HG3 3AY
Tel: (01423) 770152 www.ripleycastle.co.uk
Ripley Castle, home to the Ingilby family for over 26
generations, is set in the heart of a delightful estate with
Victorian walled gardens, deer park and pleasure
grounds.

Royal Armouries Museum

Armouries Drive, Leeds, West Yorkshire LS10 1LT
Tel: (0870) 510 6666 www.armouries.org.uk
Experience more than 3,000 years of history covered by
over 8,000 spectacular exhibits and stunning
surroundings. Arms and armour.

Sheffield Botanical Gardens

Clarkehouse Road, Sheffield, South Yorkshire S10 2LN
Tel: (0114) 250 0500 www.sbg.org.uk
Extensive gardens with over 5,500 species of plants,
Grade II Listed garden pavilion (now closed).

Skipton Castle

Skipton, North Yorkshire BD23 1AQ
Tel: (01756) 792442 www.skiptoncastle.co.uk
Fully-roofed Skipton Castle is in excellent condition. One
of the most complete and well-preserved medieval
castles in England.

Temple Newsam House

Leeds, West Yorkshire LS15 0AE
Tel: (0113) 264 7321 www.leeds.gov.uk
Tudor/Jacobean house, birthplace of Lord Darnley.
Paintings, furniture by Chippendale and others. Gold and
silver c1600 onwards. Ceramics, especially Leeds pottery.

Thirsk Museum

14-16 Kirkgate, Thirsk, North Yorkshire YO7 1PQ
Tel: (01845) 527707
Exhibits of local life and industry and cricket
memorabilia. The building was the home of Thomas Lord,
founder of Lords cricket ground in London.

The Viking City of Jorvick

Coppergate, York, North Yorkshire YO1 9WT
Tel: (01904) 643211 www.jorvik-viking-centre.co.uk
Technology of the 21stC transforms real archaeological
evidence into a dynamic vision of the City of York in
the10thC.

Wensleydale Cheese Visitor Centre

Wensleydale Creamery, Gayle Lane, Hawes,
North Yorkshire DL8 3RN
Tel: (01969) 667664
Museum, video and interpretation area, viewing gallery.
Handmade Wensleydale cheese, licensed restaurant,
specialist cheese shop, farm animals in natural
environment.

Wigfield Farm

Haverlands Lane, Worsbrough Bridge, Barnsley,
South Yorkshire S70 5NQ
Tel: (01226) 733702
Open working farm with rare and commercial breeds of
farm animals including pigs, cattle, sheep, goats, donkeys,
ponies, small animals, snakes and other reptiles.

York Castle Museum

The Eye of York, York, North Yorkshire YO1 9RY
Tel: (01904) 653611 www.york.gov.uk
England's most popular museum of everyday life
including reconstructed streets and period rooms.

York Dungeon

12 Clifford Street, York, North Yorkshire YO1 9RD
Tel: (01904) 632599 www.thedungeons.com
Set in dark, musty, atmospheric cellars and featuring life-
size tableaux of Dark Age deaths, medieval punishments
and persecution/torture of heretics.

York Minster

Deangate, York, North Yorkshire YO1 7HH
Tel: (01904) 557200 www.yorkminster.org
York Minster is the largest medieval Gothic cathedral
north of the Alps. Museum of Roman/Norman remains.
Chapter house.

Find out more about
Yorkshire

Further information about holidays and attractions in Yorkshire is available from:

YORKSHIRE TOURIST BOARD
312 Tadcaster Road, York YO24 1GS.
Tel: (01904) 707070 (24-hour brochure line)
Fax: (01904) 701414
Email: info@ytb.org.uk
Internet: www.yorkshirevisitor.com

The following publications are available from Yorkshire Tourist Board:

Yorkshire Visitor Guide 2002
information on the region, including hotels, self-catering, caravan and camping parks.
Also attractions, shops, restaurants and major events

Yorkshire - A Great Day Out
non-accommodation A5 guide listing where to go, what to see and where to eat,
the list goes on! Including map

Bed & Breakfast Touring Map
forming part of a 'family' of maps covering England, this guide provides information on
bed and breakfast establishments in Yorkshire

Group Operators' Guide 2002
a guide to choosing the right venue for travel trade and group organisers including hotels,
attractions and unusual venues

Conference and Venue Guide 2002
a full-colour, comprehensive guide to conference facilities in the region

The Pictures:
1 Walker in the Yorkshire Dales
2 York Minster

Getting to
Yorkshire

BY ROAD: Motorways: M1, M62, M606, M621, M18, M180, M181, A1(M). Trunk roads: A1, A19,
A57, A58, A59, A61, A62, A63, A64, A65, A66.

BY RAIL: InterCity services to Bradford, Doncaster, Harrogate, Kingston upon Hull, Leeds, Sheffield,
Wakefield and York. Frequent regional railway services city centre to city centre including
Manchester Airport service to Scarborough, York and Leeds.

Accommodation entries in this region are listed in alphabetical order of place name, and then in alphabetical order of establishment.

Map references refer to the colour location maps at front of this guide. The first number indicates the map to use; the letter and number which follow refer to the grid reference on the map.

At-a-glance symbols at the end of each accommodation entry give useful information about services and facilities. A key to symbols can be found inside the back cover flap. Keep this open for easy reference.

A brief description of the towns and villages offering accommodation in the entries which follow, can be found at the end of this section.

A complete listing of all the English Tourism Council assessed accommodation covered by this guide appears at the back of the guide.

ALLERSTON, North Yorkshire Map ref 5D3

★★★★

3 Units
Sleeping 6

THE OLD STATION
Main Street, Allerston, Pickering YO18 7PG
T: (01723) 859024
E: mcrbenson@aol.com
Contact: Mr & Mrs Mark & Carol Benson

Three superb railway carriage conversions, each self-contained and sleeping up to 6 people. Thoughtfully refurbished using new and original fittings, retaining a definite railway feel. Fully fitted modern kitchens and bathrooms. Personally attended by the proprietors living in the stationmaster's house. Plenty of space for children to play. Splendid views.

OPEN All year round

Low season per wk
£220.00–£286.00
High season per wk
£330.00–£412.00

AMPLEFORTH, North Yorkshire Map ref 5C3

★★★★

1 Unit
Sleeping 5

BROOK HOUSE
West End, Ampleforth, York YO6 4DY
Contact: Mrs Mary Sturges, Brook House Cottage,
West End, Ampleforth, York YO6 4DY
T: (01439) 788563
F: (01439) 788563
E: ykf31@dial.pipex.com

OPEN All year round

Low season per wk
£100.00–£180.00
High season per wk
£240.00–£300.00

Stone cottage situated by stream on edge of village. Within walking distance to shop and pub. Near to sporting facilities.

★★★★
1 Unit
Sleeping 4

Attractive stone cottage on the edge of national park, enjoying splendid views. Immaculate decorative order throughout. Price fully inclusive. Close to village amenities. Superb eating hostelries locally. Ideally situated for walking, moors, coast. 20 miles York, 10 miles Castle Howard. Non-smoking establishment. Personal attention by resident owners.

HILLSIDE COTTAGE

Hillside, West End, Ampleforth, York YO62 4DY
Contact: Mrs P Noble, Hillside, West End, Ampleforth, York YO62 4DY
T: (01439) 788303 (Answerphone) &
07941 687018 (Mobile)
F: (01439) 788303
E: hillsidecottage@westend-ampleforth.co.uk
I: www.cottageguide.co.uk/hillsidecottage

OPEN All year round

Low season per wk
£180.00–£235.00
High season per wk
£240.00–£285.00

ARKENGARTHDALE, North Yorkshire Map ref 5B3

★★★
1 Unit
Sleeping 2

LOW FAGGERGILL COTTAGE
Arkengarthdale, Richmond DL11 6RS
T: (01244) 345700 & (01748) 884550
F: (01244) 321442
Contact: Mrs G M Atkinson

OPEN Apr–Oct

Low season per wk
£170.00–£190.00
High season per wk
£190.00–£225.00

420-acre mixed farm. Small cottage adjacent to the owner's farmhouse. Evening meal available if required. No pets, please.

BEVERLEY, East Riding of Yorkshire Map ref 4C1 *Tourist Information Centre Tel: (01482) 867430*

★★★★
1 Unit
Sleeping 4

Superbly equipped 2-bedroom quality cottage, tastefully furnished and decorated to a high standard with all mod cons and safety requirements. In centre of picturesque village of Walkington in a quiet, private close. Ideal for historic York, Beverley, Lincoln and coastal resorts, walking, cycling and just relaxing. Private parking.

THE COTTAGE

3 Taylors Rise, Walkington, Beverley HU17 8SF
Contact: Mr Kenneth Hearne, 25 All Hallows Road, Walkington, Beverley HU17 8SH
T: (01482) 868310 (Answerphone)
E: knhearne@talk21.com
I: www.AKcottage.F25.com

OPEN All year round

Low season per wk
£180.00–£230.00
High season per wk
£250.00–£310.00

BISHOP MONKTON, North Yorkshire Map ref 5C3

★★★
1 Unit
Sleeping 2

The beamed single-storey barn conversion offers luxury twin accommodation with en suite bathroom and fitted kitchen area. Central heating and courtyard parking. Continental breakfast can be provided if required. This picturesque village is within easy reach of Ripon, York, Harrogate and the Yorkshire Dales. Two pubs in the village serve excellent food.

HALL FARM COTTAGE

Hall Farm, Boroughbridge Road, Bishop Monkton, Harrogate HG3 3QN
Contact: Mrs Jennifer Barker, Hall Farm, Boroughbridge Road, Bishop Monkton, Harrogate HG3 3QN
T: (01765) 677200 (Answerphone available)

OPEN All year round

Short breaks available 1, 2 and 3 nights with breakfast.

Low season per wk
Max £148.00
High season per wk
Max £198.00

★★★–★★★★

6 Units
Sleeping 2–6

Dukes Place is a well maintained, discreet conversion of a farm building which adjoins the Georgian farmhouse where the owners live. Working stables help to form an enclosed courtyard with a wealth of floral displays. In close proximity there is excellent parking, beechwood garden, barbecue, play area. Also 3 bed and breakfast rooms with en suite facilities.

THE COURTYARD AT 'DUKES PLACE'

Fountains Abbey Road, Bishop Thornton,
Harrogate HG3 3JY
T: (01765) 620229
F: (01765) 620454
E: jakimoorhouse@onetel.net.uk
Contact: Mrs Jaki Moorhouse

OPEN All year round	Low season per wk
CC: Mastercard, Visa	£175.00–£290.00
	High season per wk
Nov-Mar 3 night break £99	£250.00–£415.00
for 1-bedroom cottage (extra	
night free subject to	
availability).	

ᴀ ᵇ ◉ ⬛ ▥ ☉ ▭ ▤ �📺 🦆 🗲 🛏 ▥ ✖ ▯ P ∪ ❋ 🐾 ▥ ⊠

★★★

2 Units
Sleeping 2–5

WILD CHERRY COTTAGE & WEAVERS COTTAGE

Weaver's Cottage, 3 Finlay Cottages, Sewerby,
Bridlington YO15 1EG
Contact: Mrs Pauline Halstead, 33 Beverley Road,
Driffield YO25 6RZ
T: (01377) 253985 (Answerphone) &
0794 1141942 (Mobile)
F: (01377) 253985
E: pauline.halstead@virgin.net

Two early Victorian cottages in the centre of this Heritage Coast village. Weavers' Cottage has a studio available for guests who are experienced spinners/weavers.

OPEN Apr–Dec	Low season per wk
	£170.00–£240.00
	High season per wk
	£270.00–£330.00

ᴀ ◉ ▥ ▥ ▭ ▤ 📺 🦆 ▤ ▥ 🛏 P ❋ ⊠

★

3 Units
Sleeping 5–6

On the seafront, south facing, only 50 metres from sandy beach and promenade. All apartments have exceptional views along the beach to the harbour. Ideal position for main shopping centre, restaurants and Leisure World complex. Fully equipped, with high standard of furnishing, each with own private bathroom facilities.

HIGHCLIFFE HOLIDAY APARTMENTS

19 Albion Terrace, Bridlington YO15 2PJ
Contact: Mrs Pat Willcocks, Proprietor,
Highcliffe Holiday Apartments, 19 Albion Terrace,
Bridlington YO15 2PJ
T: (01262) 674127

OPEN All year round	Low season per wk
	£70.00–£150.00
	High season per wk
	£150.00–£300.00

ᴀ ᵇ Ⓜ ◉ ▥ ☉ ▭ 📺 🦆 ▤ ▥ 🛏 ▥ ⊠

QUALITY ASSURANCE SCHEME

For an explanation of the quality and facilities represented by the Stars please refer to the front of this guide. A more detailed explanation can be found in the information pages at the back.

★★★★
4 Units
Sleeping 4–6

PROSPECT FARM COTTAGES

Prospect Farm, Waltham Road, Brigsley,
Grimsby DN37 0RQ
Contact: Mrs Janet Speight, Prospect Farm,
Waltham Road, Brigsley, Grimsby DN37 0RQ
T: (01472) 826491 (Answerphone)
E: prospectfarm@btclick.com

Prospect Farm Cottages are situated down a long, leafy lane. They are in a courtyard, with views of horses and sheep grazing, and are tastefully appointed with fully-equipped kitchens to cater for your every need. All have 2 bedrooms. Number 2 is suitable for disabled clients.

OPEN All year round

Low season per wk
£250.00–£340.00
High season per wk
£320.00–£380.00

★★★
1 Unit
Sleeping 3

OATCROFT FARM BARN APARTMENT
Oatcroft Farm, Burnsall, Skipton BD23 6BN
T: (01756) 720268
Contact: Mrs J Stockdale

OPEN All year round

Low season per wk
£160.00–£185.00
High season per wk
£195.00–£220.00

A delightful first-floor barn conversion, with lounge, twin bedroom, dining/kitchen and bathroom. Beautiful views of Burnsall Fell. Sorry no pets. Private parking.

★★★★
2 Units
Sleeping 4–5

BRENTWOOD FARM COTTAGES

Barnoldswick Lane, Burton-in-Lonsdale LA6 3LZ
Contact: Mrs Anita Taylor, Brentwood Farm Cottages,
Banrnoldswick Lane, Burton-in-Lonsdale, Carnforth
LA6 3LZ
T: (015242) 62155
F: (015242) 62155
E: info@brentwoodfarmcottages.co.uk
I: www.brentwoodfarmcottages.co.uk

Relax in a spacious, yet cosy, new barn conversion located in a tranquil setting on a working dairy farm. Centrally situated for the Lake District, Yorkshire Dales, Lune Valley and Forest of Bowland. Ingleton waterfalls walk, three peaks and show caves nearby. Private walking and fishing available on site.

OPEN All year round
CC: Barclaycard, Delta,
Eurocard, JCB,
Mastercard, Solo, Switch,
Visa

Low season per wk
Min £210.00
High season per wk
Max £440.00

Winter short breaks available.
Seasonal hedge laying,
walling and computer tuition
available on request.

★★★★
4 Units
Sleeping 4–6

PARK HOUSE HOLIDAY COTTAGES
Park House, Station Lane, Burton Leonard,
Harrogate HG3 3RX
T: (01765) 677387 & 07976 935705
E: mail@parkhouseholidays.com
I: www.parkhouseholidays.com
Contact: Mr Russell Hammond

OPEN All year round
CC: Barclaycard,
Mastercard, Visa

Low season per wk
£125.00–£155.00
High season per wk
£325.00–£370.00

Spacious, comfortable and well-presented cottages converted from farm building. Large garden and playing field. Ideal base for exploring Yorkshire Dales and Moors. Near Harrogate.

IDEAS For ideas on places to visit refer to the introduction at the beginning of this section.

CARLTON, North Yorkshire Map ref 5B3

★★★
1 Unit
Sleeping 2

LITTLE HOLLIN
Carlton, Leyburn DL8 4AY
Contact: Mr & Mrs Anne & Peter Wright, 6 Garden Lane,
Southsea PO5 3DP
T: (023) 9273 6651 (Answerphone)
E: hollin@wright.globalnet.co.uk
I: www.users.globalnet.co.uk/~wright

Charming, traditional stone cottage in the Yorkshire Dales National Park. An ideal central base for visiting the Lake District, Cleveland Hills, both coasts, castles, stately homes and ancient abbeys. Offering guests well-appointed comfort after exploring picturesque dales or moorland walks. Local Forresters Arms serves outstanding food.

OPEN All year round

Low season per wk
£152.00–£195.00
High season per wk
£195.00–£246.00

CAWTON, North Yorkshire Map ref 5C3

★★★
1 Unit
Sleeping 7

MANOR FARM
Cawton, York YO62 4LW
Contact: Ms D Worsley, Manor Farm, Cawton Hall,
Cawton, York YO62 4LW
T: (01653) 628237 (Answerphone) & 628237

OPEN Mar–Oct &
Christmas

Low season per wk
£295.00–£310.00
High season per wk
£310.00–£370.00

17thC farmhouse on working farm, with open fires and secluded walled gardens. Convenient for the moors, coast and York. Children and pets welcome. Beautiful countryside.

CHOP GATE, North Yorkshire Map ref 5C3

★★★
1 Unit
Sleeping 7

BROADFIELDS COTTAGE
Broadfields, Chop Gate, Middlesbrough TS9 7JB
T: (01642) 778384 (Answerphone)
Contact: Mrs Judith Staples

OPEN All year round

Low season per wk
£325.00–£400.00
High season per wk
£425.00–£500.00

Stone-built semi-detached 4-bedroomed cottage of character. Outstanding views set in the national parks, in good walking country, between Stokesley and Helmsley.

★★
1 Unit
Sleeping 5

LAVROCK HALL FARMHOUSE COTTAGE
Chop Gate, Middlesbrough TS9 7LQ
Contact: Mrs Jane Brack, Lavrock Hall, Chop Gate,
Middlesbrough TS9 7LQ
T: (01439) 798275
F: (01439) 798337
E: info@lavrockhall.co.uk
I: www.lavrockhall.co.uk

OPEN All year round

Low season per wk
£120.00–£140.00
High season per wk
£140.00–£190.00

This pretty self-contained moorland cottage is part of the main 17thC traditional farmhouse. Quiet rural area with spectacular views. Easily accessible from main road.

USE YOUR *i*s
There are more than 550 Tourist Information Centres throughout England offering friendly help with accommodation and holiday ideas as well as suggestions of places to visit and things to do. You'll find TIC addresses in the local Phone Book.

CLOUGHTON, North Yorkshire Map ref 5D3

★★★★

4 Units
Sleeping 2–7

GOWLAND FARM COTTAGES

Gowland Farm, Gowland Lane, Cloughton,
Scarborough YO13 0DU
T: (01723) 870924
I: www.gowlandfarm.co.uk
Contact: Mr D P Martin

Four charming, converted stone barns overlooking Harwood Dale, 2 miles from coast, north of Scarborough. Fully carpeted, warm and cosy, with central heating and double glazing. Electric fires and colour TV in all lounges, well-equipped kitchens. Large pretty garden for guests' use (patio furniture provided). Beautiful views, quiet, peaceful.

OPEN All year round

Patchwork and quilting residential weekend courses in spring/autumn. Please ring for details.

Low season per wk
£115.00–£240.00
High season per wk
£170.00–£450.00

CROPTON, North Yorkshire Map ref 5C3

★★★★

7 Units
Sleeping 2–12

BECKHOUSE COTTAGES

Beckhouse Farm, Cropton, Pickering YO18 8ER
T: (01751) 417235
F: (01751) 417218
E: beckhousecarriages@hotmail.com
Contact: Mrs P Smith

OPEN All year round

Low season per wk
£150.00–£200.00
High season per wk
£250.00–£390.00

Working farm, keeping mostly horses for carriage driving and breeding. Private gardens. Beautiful walking countryside. Handy for forest, moors and sea. Winter breaks available.

DANBY, North Yorkshire Map ref 5C3

★★

1 Unit
Sleeping 6

CLITHERBECKS FARM

Danby, Whitby YO21 2NT
T: (01287) 660321
E: nharland@clitherbecks.freeserve.co.uk
I: www.clitherbecks.freeserve.co.uk
Contact: Mr Neil Harland

OPEN All year round

Low season per wk
£160.00–£260.00
High season per wk
£190.00–£300.00

Dwelling mentioned in Domesday Book. Present building built in 1780. Self-contained accommodation with separate entrance.

DORE, South Yorkshire Map ref 4B2

★★★

1 Unit
Sleeping 6

PAT'S COTTAGE

108 Townhead Road, Dore, Sheffield S17 3GB
Contact: Mr John Drakeford, 110 Townhead Road,
Dore, Sheffield S17 3GB
T: (0114) 236 6014 & 07850 200711 (Mobile)
F: (0114) 236 6014
E: johnmdrakeford@hotmail.com
I: www.patscottage.co.uk

OPEN All year round

Low season per wk
£200.00
High season per wk
£220.00–£310.00

An attractive 18thC stone cottage, sympathetically refurbished retaining original features including black beams. On the edge of the Peak District and the city of Sheffield.

EASBY, North Yorkshire Map ref 5C3

★★★★

2 Units
Sleeping 4–6

THE OLD STABLES

Easby Hall, Easby, Great Ayton TS9 6JQ
Contact: Mrs Catherine Hawman, Proprietor,
Park House, Easby Hall, Easby, Great Ayton TS9 6JQ
T: (01642) 722560
F: (01642) 722560
E: piglettoo@btinternet.com
I: www.stables.totalserve.co.uk

OPEN All year round

Low season per wk
£280.00–£360.00
High season per wk
£380.00–£500.00

Victorian former coach-house situated on a private country estate. Spacious, well-equipped cottages with antique furnishings. Comfortable base for exploring North Yorkshire Moors and coast.

EBBERSTON, North Yorkshire Map ref 5D3

★★★–★★★★★
8 Units
Sleeping 2–6

CLIFF HOUSE
Ebberston, Scarborough YO13 9PA
T: (01723) 859440
F: (01723) 850005
E: cliffhouseebberston@btinternet.com
Contact: Mr Simon Morris

OPEN All year round

Low season per wk
£205.00–£330.00
High season per wk
£335.00–£750.00

Comfortable cottages in the grounds of an historic former manor-house. Heated indoor pool, jacuzzi, hard tennis court, games room. Colour brochure available on request.

★★★★
1 Unit
Sleeping 4

NESFIELD COTTAGE
96 Main Street, Ebberston, Scarborough YO13 9NJ
Contact: Mrs J Wood, Nesfield Cottage, Ingleside,
Burton Road, Ashby-de-la-Zouch LE65 2TF
T: (01530) 416094
E: chris.wood4@virgin.net

OPEN All year round

Low season per wk
£180.00–£225.00
High season per wk
£225.00–£350.00

A 3-bedroomed stone, semi-detached cottage which has been extended and carefully modernised to retain character. In a pretty village between Pickering and Scarborough.

FILEY, North Yorkshire Map ref 5D3

★★–★★★
11 Units
Sleeping 2–7

BEACH HOLIDAY FLATS
9-10 The Beach, Filey YO14 9LA
T: (01723) 513178
E: anntindall@aol.com
I: www.thebeach-holidayflats.co.uk
Contact: Mr David Tindall

Probably the best position on the East Coast, 25 yards from the seafront, fabulous views over Filey Brigg, Bempton Rocks and Flamborough Head. We pride ourselves on the quality of our decor, fixtures, fittings, cleanliness and hospitality. The perfect location for your East Coast holiday. Filey – gem of the Yorkshire coast.

OPEN All year round

Low season per wk
£110.00–£170.00
High season per wk
£190.00–£475.00

★★★
5 Units
Sleeping 5

THE COTTAGES
Muston Grange, Muston Road, Filey YO14 0HU
T: (01723) 516620
F: (01723) 516620
Contact: Mr & Mrs David Teet

OPEN All year round
CC: Barclaycard, Delta,
JCB, Mastercard, Solo,
Switch, Visa

Low season per wk
£235.00–£290.00
High season per wk
£360.00–£440.00

Situated between Muston and Filey, the cottages are a range of converted traditional ex farm buildings providing quality accommodation in a private courtyard setting.

★★–★★★
4 Units
Sleeping 5–8

SAINT KITTS SELF CATERING HOLIDAY FLATS
2 The Beach, Filey YO14 9LA
T: (01723) 512141
E: dhmidgley@ukonline.co.uk
Contact: Mr & Mrs D H Midgley

OPEN All year round

Low season per wk
£110.00–£170.00
High season per wk
£310.00–£420.00

All flats have lounges facing the sea with views over the beach and bay. The ground floor flat has central heating.

FYLINGTHORPE, North Yorkshire Map ref 5D3

★★★
2 Units
Sleeping 4–6

SOUTH HOUSE FARM
Millbeck, Fylingthorpe, Whitby YO22 4UQ
T: (01947) 880243
F: (01947) 880243
Contact: Mrs N Pattinson

OPEN Apr–Oct &
Christmas

Low season per wk
£120.00–£270.00
High season per wk
£180.00–£375.00

Situated in valley between Robin Hood's Bay and Ravenscar. In national park close to sea. Many interesting walks on private land.

GIGGLESWICK, North Yorkshire Map ref 5B3

★★★★
2 Units
Sleeping 6

CLOSE HOUSE COTTAGE HOLIDAYS
Close House, Giggleswick, Settle BD24 0EA
Contact: Mr & Mrs Richard & Sue Hargreaves,
Close House, Giggleswick, Settle BD24 0EA
T: (01729) 822778 (Answerphone)
F: (01729) 822778

OPEN All year round

Low season per wk
Min £225.00
High season per wk
Max £392.00

Popular and beautiful cottages, newly renovated and offering high standard of accommodation, all in an idyllic setting with all amenities and ample parking.

GILLING WEST, North Yorkshire Map ref 5C3

★★★★
3 Units
Sleeping 4–11

GILLING OLD MILL
Gilling West, Richmond DL10 5JD
T: (01748) 822771
F: (01748) 822771
E: admin@yorkshiredales-cottages.com
I: www.yorkshiredales-cottages.com
Contact: Mr and Mrs H Bird

OPEN All year round

Low season per wk
£130.00–£280.00
High season per wk
£280.00–£600.00

Self-catering accommodation built in traditional courtyard buildings of great character. A warm welcome is assured.

GRASSINGTON, North Yorkshire Map ref 5B3 *Tourist Information Centre Tel: (01756) 752774*

★★★★
1 Unit
Sleeping 4

THE BARN
2A Broughton Fold, Grassington, Skipton BD23 5AL
Contact: Mrs P G Evans, 3 Delph Wood Close, Gilstead,
Bingley BD16 3LQ
T: (01274) 561546
E: grassington@ukonline.co.uk
I: www.qteq.co.uk/grassington

OPEN Feb–Dec

Low season per wk
£235.00–£260.00
High season per wk
£400.00–£425.00

Ground floor of a tastefully-converted Yorkshire Dales barn. In quiet, private fold off the main square. Secluded south-facing garden. Garage, parking for 2 cars.

★★★★
1 Unit
Sleeping 4

MANNA COTTAGE
63 Main Street, Grassington, Skipton BD23 5AA
Contact: Mrs Sheila Carr, Moor Green Farm, Tarns Lane,
Threshfield, Skipton BD23 5NR
T: (01756) 752435 & 07879 845771 (Mobile)
F: (01756) 752345
E: carr@totalise.co.uk
I: www.yorkshirenet.co.uk/stayat/mannacottage/

OPEN All year round

Low season per wk
£150.00–£250.00
High season per wk
£250.00–£350.00

An 18thC former lead miner's cottage, recently refurbished to a high standard. Warm, cosy and comfortable with many original features.

★★★★
1 Unit
Sleeping 2–5

Tastefully converted barn in delightful village setting 1.5 miles from Grassington. Spacious, yet cosy and warm in winter. Equipped to a high standard. Living flame stove in sitting-room, automatic Aga. Sleeps 2-5. Twin, double, sofabed in second sitting room. Ideal ground floor arrangement for the elderly or infirm.

SCALA GLEN BARN
Brook Street, Hebden, Skipton BD23 5DQ
Contact: Mr & Mrs C Roundhill, Beechcroft, Hardy Grange,
Grassington, Skipton BD23 5AJ
T: (01756) 752011 & 07759 926931
F: (01756) 752011
E: scalaglen@aol.com
I: www.oas.co.uk/ukcottages/scalaglen

OPEN All year round

Short breaks available.

Low season per wk
£230.00–£280.00
High season per wk
£325.00–£395.00

PRICES
Please check prices and other details at the time of booking.

GRASSINGTON continued

SUNNYSIDE COTTAGE

★★★
1 Unit
Sleeping 6

Moody Sty Lane, Grassington, Skipton BD23 6LJ
Contact: Mrs Carolyn Butt, Garris Lodge, Rylstone,
Skipton BD23 6LJ
T: (01756) 730391
F: (01756) 730391
E: c.butt@daelnet.co.uk
I: www.dalesaccommodation.com/sunnysidecottage

OPEN All year round

Low season per wk
£200.00–£250.00
High season per wk
£400.00–£450.00

Beautiful 300-year-old barn conversion. Ideally situated overlooking open fields, yet only 150 metres from the quaint old cobbled village square.

WELLHEAD COTTAGE

★★★★
1 Unit
Sleeping 4

42 Main Street, Grassington, Skipton BD23 5AG
Contact: Mr & Mrs Halliday, Proprietors,
2 Grange Drive, Horsforth, Leeds LS18 5EQ
T: (0113) 258 4212
F: (0113) 281 9455

OPEN All year round
CC: Amex, Barclaycard,
Delta, Diners, Mastercard,
Switch, Visa

Low season per wk
£220.00–£340.00
High season per wk
£340.00–£550.00

Finalist White Rose Awards 2001. Superb centrally located 17thC character cottage. Exposed beams, spacious lounge with open fireplace and leather sofas. Fully equipped. Private parking.

GREAT LANGTON, North Yorkshire Map ref 5C3

★★★★
1 Unit
Sleeping 6

STANHOW BUNGALOW

Stanhow Farm, Great Langton, Northallerton DL7 0TJ
Contact: Lady Mary Furness, Proprietor, Stanhow Farm,
Great Langton, Northallerton DL7 0TJ
T: (01609) 748614
F: (01609) 748614

Enjoy a peaceful location in beautiful countryside, yet close to market towns and historic cities. Detached with private enclosed garden, garage and parking. Open fire, 3 bedrooms. Clean, warm and comfortable, fully equipped and prepared for your arrival. Personally supervised. Good local hospitality and entertainment. Brochure available.

OPEN All year round

Short breaks. Business guests welcome.

Low season per wk
Min £225.00
High season per wk
Max £450.00

GUNNERSIDE, North Yorkshire Map ref 5B3

LEN HOUSE

★★
1 Unit
Sleeping 2

Gunnerside, Richmond DL11 6LE
Contact: Mrs R Marlein & Mrs G Anderson,
9 Littlethorpe Close, Strensall, York YO32 5WR
T: (01904) 490623
E: richard@marlein.freeserve.co.uk

OPEN All year round

Low season per wk
£165.00–£185.00
High season per wk
£175.00–£195.00

Well-equipped cottage set in the village of Gunnerside, in the heart of beautiful Swaledale. 'A walker's paradise'.

AT-A-GLANCE SYMBOLS

Symbols at the end of each accommodation entry give useful information about services and facilities. A key to symbols can be found inside the back cover flap. Keep this open for easy reference.

HALIFAX, West Yorkshire Map ref 4B1 *Tourist Information Centre Tel: (01422) 368725*

★★★★

2 Units
Sleeping 4

CHERRY TREE COTTAGES

Wall Nook, Barkisland, Ripponden, Halifax
T: (01422) 372662
F: (01422) 372662
E: cherry.tree@zen.co.uk
I: www.yorkshire-cottages.co.uk
Contact: Mr & Mrs Stan & Elaine Shaw

Two highly commended stone-built cottages set in 2 acres of natural woodland/heather garden with superb Pennine views and direct access to open countryside and footpaths. Close to a quiet Calderdale village with good pubs and restaurants nearby. Ideal location for exploring Bronte country and Pennine Yorkshire.

OPEN All year round
CC: Barclaycard, Delta,
Mastercard, Switch, Visa

Short breaks available outside high season. Minimum stay 3 nights.

Low season per wk
£220.00–£240.00
High season per wk
£295.00–£365.00

HARROGATE, North Yorkshire Map ref 4B1 *Tourist Information Centre Tel: (01423) 537300*

★★★★

23 Units
Sleeping 2–4

ASHNESS APARTMENTS

15 St Mary's Avenue, Harrogate HG2 0LP
Contact: Mrs B Batty and Mr J Spinlove,
15 St Mary's Avenue, Harrogate HG2 0LP
T: (01423) 526894
F: (01423) 700038

High quality apartments superbly situated in a nice, quiet road of fine Victorian townhouses very near the town centre of Harrogate. Excellent shops, restaurants and cafes are a short walk away through Montpellier Gardens with the 'Stray' and Valley Gardens just around the corner.

OPEN All year round
CC: Amex, Barclaycard,
Delta, JCB, Mastercard,
Solo, Switch, Visa

Short breaks available from £55 per night, minimum 2 nights.

Low season per wk
£245.00–£310.00
High season per wk
£285.00–£375.00

★★★-★★★★★

9 Units
Sleeping 2–8

BRIMHAM ROCKS COTTAGES

High North Farm, Fellbeck, Harrogate HG3 5EY
T: (01765) 620284
F: (01765) 620477
E: brimham@nascr.net
I: www.brimham.co.uk
Contact: Mrs J M Martin

Overlooking Brimham Rocks and with views of up to 60 miles, these individual cottages are ideally situated to explore both Dales and moors, York, Ripon, Harrogate, Leeds and the east coast. Converted from old farm buildings they are warm, cosy, comfortable and decorated with flair and imagination.

OPEN All year round

Short breaks at 66% of weekly rate.

Low season per wk
£165.00–£240.00
High season per wk
£340.00–£510.00

CREDIT CARD BOOKINGS If you book by telephone and are asked for your credit card number it is advisable to check the proprietor's policy should you cancel your reservation.

HARROGATE continued

★★★★

3 Units
Sleeping 3–5

Three award-winning dales cottages converted from 17thC farmstead. Peaceful situation, breathtaking views over Nidderdale, a protected Area of Outstanding Natural Beauty. Only 7 miles to spa town of Harrogate, close to York and Herriot country. Ideal for walkers and bird-watchers and for touring and sightseeing in the Yorkshire Dales.

DINMORE COTTAGES

Dinmore House, Burnt Yates, Harrogate HG3 3ET
Contact: Mrs Mabel Ward, Manager, Dovecote Cottage,
Dinmore House, Burnt Yates, Harrogate HG3 3ET
T: (01423) 770860 (Answerphone/fax) &
771711 (Answerphone)
F: (01423) 770860
E: aib@dinmore-cottages.freeserve.co.uk

OPEN All year round

Low season per wk
£225.00–£305.00
High season per wk
£380.00–£560.00

★★★★

3 Units
Sleeping 4–5

HARROGATE APARTMENTS
Crimple Head House, Beckwithshaw,
Harrogate HG3 1QU
Contact: Mr and Mrs K A Hartwell, Harrogate
Apartments, Crimple Head House, Beckwithshaw,
Harrogate HG3 1QU
T: (01423) 500655 & 07768 662734 (Mobile)
E: info@harrogateapartments.com
I: www.harrogateapartments.com

OPEN All year round

Low season per wk
£200.00–£230.00
High season per wk
£250.00–£360.00

Beautiful apartments both in the town centre of Harrogate and in the countryside. Ideal for conferences, holidays etc. Car parking, 4-poster beds. Apartments sleep up to 5 persons.

★★★

3 Units
Sleeping 4–5

HOLLY HOUSE FARM COTTAGES
Darley, Harrogate HG3 2QL
T: (01423) 780266 & 07710 125298
(Answerphone/mobile)
F: (01423) 780299
E: hollyhousecottages@supanet.com
Contact: Miss Mary Owen

OPEN All year round
CC: Delta, Mastercard,
Visa

Low season per wk
£215.00–£240.00
High season per wk
£340.00–£370.00

High standard character cottages with all amenities in converted milking parlour. Unrivalled Nidderdale views. Ideal walking, sightseeing, shopping and country pursuits. Children and pets welcome.

★★★

1 Unit
Sleeping 3

MOOR VIEW COTTAGE
Kings Road, Harrogate HG1 5HP
Contact: Mrs H L Sweeting, 45 Kingsley Drive,
Harrogate HG1 4TH
T: (014323) 885498
E: hlsweeting@easicom.com

OPEN Jan–Nov

Low season per wk
£130.00–£150.00
High season per wk
£150.00–£200.00

Moor View Cottage is a delightful, fully furnished 2 bedroomed cottage, 10 minutes' walk from the Harrogate Conference Centre and town shops. Shorter stays available.

TOWN INDEX

This can be found at the back of the guide. If you know where you want to stay, the index will give you the page number listing accommodation in your chosen town, city or village.

HARROGATE continued

★★★
1 Unit
Sleeping 4

REGENT COTTAGE
13a Regent Parade, Harrogate HG1 5AW
Contact: Mr Robert Blake, 1A Moorfield Road, Woodbridge
IP12 4JN
T: (01394) 382565
E: deben@btclick.com

Comfortable accommodation restored to a high standard and furnished with antiques. Two double bedrooms, bathroom, sitting room, kitchen/diner. Ideal base for many tourist attractions in Yorkshire Dales and Lake District. Walking distance of town centre. Full central heating and all linen provided. Car parking facilities. Additional annexe sleeps 2.

OPEN All year round

Low season per wk
Min £200.00
High season per wk
Min £320.00

★★★
9 Units
Sleeping 2–9

RUDDING HOLIDAY PARK
Rudding Park, Follifoot, Harrogate HG3 1JH
Contact: Mr Martin Hutchinson, Rudding Holiday Park,
Rudding Park, Follifoot, Harrogate HG3 1JH
T: (01423) 870439
F: (01423) 870859
E: holiday-park@ruddingpark.com
I: www.rudding-park.com

OPEN All year round
CC: Barclaycard, Delta,
Mastercard, Solo, Switch,
Visa

Low season per wk
£190.00–£360.00
High season per wk
£320.00–£710.00

Properties in and around the beautiful grounds of Rudding Park, 3 miles south of Harrogate. Shop, swimming pool, children's playground, games room, 18-hole golf course, driving range.

HAWORTH, West Yorkshire Map ref 4B1 *Tourist Information Centre Tel: (01535) 642329*

★★★-★★★★
7 Units
Sleeping 2–6

BRONTE COUNTRY COTTAGES
Westfield Farm, Tim Lane, Haworth, Keighley BD22 7SA
T: (01535) 644568 & 07771 597319
F: (01535) 646686
E: clare@brontecountrycottages.co.uk
I: www.brontecountrycottages.co.uk
Contact: Ms Clare Pickles

Splendid cottages, hand picked to offer the widest choice in the famous village. Stunning views, open fire, central village or countryside locations, modern amenities. Private children's indoor and outdoor play areas or cosy, quiet cottages for honeymoons or romantic holidays. Available all year. Full colour brochure on request.

OPEN All year round
CC: Barclaycard,
Mastercard, Visa

Low season per wk
£150.00–£230.00
High season per wk
£230.00–£420.00

CHECK THE MAPS
The colour maps at the front of this guide show all the cities, towns and villages for which you will find accommodation entries. Refer to the town index to find the page on which they are listed.

★★★★
2 Units
Sleeping 4

Ideally located in idyllic Bronte country, our cottages provide a perfect base for exploring northern England. Set in 10 acres of ancient woodland, they form part of an old water mill complex – recently renovated to provide luxury self-catering accommodation. Ideal for lovers of walking, wildlife and Wuthering Heights!

HEWENDEN MILL COTTAGES

Hewenden Mill, Cullingworth, Bradford BD13 5BP
Contact: Miss Janet & Susan Emanuel, Proprietors,
Hewenden Mill Cottages, Hewenden Mill, Cullingworth,
Bradford BD13 5BP
T: (01535) 271834
F: (01535) 273943
E: info@hewendenmillcottages.co.uk
I: www.hewendenmillcottages.co.uk

OPEN All year round
CC: Barclaycard,
Mastercard, Solo, Switch,
Visa

Short breaks our speciality:
3 night weekend and 4 night
mid-week (excl Bank Hols).

Low season per wk
£200.00–£300.00
High season per wk
£310.00–£400.00

★★★
1 Unit
Sleeping 4

3 BIRKS HALL COTTAGE
Cragg Vale, Hebden Bridge HX7 5SB
Contact: Mrs H Wilkinson, 1 Birks Hall, Cragg Vale,
Hebden Bridge HX7 5SB
T: (01422) 882064 & 884509

OPEN All year round

Low season per wk
£100.00–£120.00
High season per wk
£120.00–£180.00

Country cottage with 2 bedrooms, bathroom, kitchen and lounge with Georgian windows. In a small, picturesque village near the Pennine centre of Hebden Bridge.

★★★
2 Units
Sleeping 4–6

GREAT BURLEES FARM
Hebden Bridge HX7 8PS
T: (01422) 843382
Contact: Mr & Mrs B Wells

OPEN All year round

Low season per wk
£140.00–£170.00
High season per wk
£260.00–£310.00

The Mullions (East wing of 17thC farmhouse) and Mallard Cottage (an exquisite stable conversion) are located on secluded south-facing hillside with superb Pennine views.

★★★★
1 Unit
Sleeping 4

Originally part of an 18thC farmhouse, this is a very warm, comfortable 2-bedroomed stone cottage with oak beams. Situated off the main road in village 3 miles from charming market town of Helmsley. Ideal for walking or touring moors, coast and York. Central heating and log fire included in price.

TOWNEND COTTAGE

High Lane, Beadlam, Nawton, York YO62 7SY
Contact: Mrs M Begg, Townend Farmhouse, High Lane,
Beadlam, Nawton, York YO62 7SY
T: (01439) 770103
E: margaret.begg@ukgateway.net
I: www.visityorkshire.com

OPEN All year round

Low season per wk
Min £175.00
High season per wk
£270.00–£330.00

★★
1 Unit
Sleeping 5

5 DRAPER CORNER
Heptonstall, Hebden Bridge HX7 9DQ
Contact: Mrs S A Taylor, 4 Northfield Terrace,
Hebden Bridge HX7 7NG
T: (01422) 844323

OPEN All year round

Low season per wk
Min £160.00
High season per wk
Min £310.00

Delightful 18thC cottage overlooking spectacular moorland/national park views. Easy access to cities and dales. Author's home when in England, furnished with personal antiques, books, pictures.

HIGH BENTHAM, North Yorkshire Map ref 5B3

★★★★
1 Unit
Sleeping 4

HOLMES FARM COTTAGE
Holmes Farm, Low Bentham, Lancaster LA2 7DE
T: (015242) 61198
E: lucy@clucy.demon.co.uk
Contact: Mrs L J Story

OPEN All year round

Low season per wk
Min £175.00
High season per wk
Max £240.00

Tastefully converted stone cottage with large landscaped garden, surrounded by 127 acres of beautiful pastureland. Ideal base for visiting Lake District, dales and coast.

HOLMFIRTH, West Yorkshire Map ref 4B1 *Tourist Information Centre Tel: (01484) 222444*

★★★★
1 Unit
Sleeping 4

DAL-A-FR-SA
15 Hightown Lane, Holmfirth, Huddersfield HD9 3HY
Contact: Mr & Mrs David Babbings, 52 Meltham Road,
Honley, Huddersfield HD9 6HC
T: (01484) 323990 & 422150
E: davidbabbings@ntlworld.com

OPEN All year round
CC: Mastercard, Visa

Low season per wk
£95.00–£120.00
High season per wk
£180.00–£340.00

Beautiful beamed cottage, central location, quiet position. Enjoy a warm welcome at Dal-a-fr-sa, 'Where the Heart is' and Last of Summer Wine Country. Ideal base for sightseeing.

HUDDERSFIELD, West Yorkshire Map ref 4B1 *Tourist Information Centre Tel: (01484) 223200*

★★
1 Unit
Sleeping 4

BANK END
Netherton, Huddersfield
Contact: Mrs Rebecca Ng, 41 Mall Road, London
W6 9DG
T: (020) 8563 1186 (Home)
F: (020) 8748 1170
E: rebeccang80@hotmail.com
I: www.cottageguide.co.uk/netherton

OPEN All year round

Low season per wk
£150.00–£235.00
High season per wk
£195.00–£265.00

Stone cottage with Pennine views. Good walking from the door. Open fire in lounge. Well behaved pets only. Brochure on request.

ILKLEY, West Yorkshire Map ref 4B1

★★★★
1 Unit
Sleeping 13

Charming, spacious but cosy, well equipped, historic Listed cottages in grounds of Westwood Lodge, on the very edge of the famous Ilkley Moor. Peaceful yet close to the town centre. Ideal base for Dales and Bronte country. Free laundry, gym, sauna and spa. Extensive gardens, family friendly and a warm welcome!

WESTWOOD LODGE, ILKLEY MOOR

Wells Road, Ilkley LS29 9JF
Contact: Mr Tim Edwards and Mrs Paula Hunt,
Westwood Lodge, Wells Road, Ilkley LS29 9SF
T: (01943) 433430
F: (01943) 433431
E: welcome@westwoodlodge.co.uk
I: www.westwoodlodge.co.uk

OPEN All year round
CC: Barclaycard, Delta,
Eurocard, JCB, Maestro,
Mastercard, Solo, Switch,
Visa, Visa Electron

Low season per wk
£225.00–£330.00
High season per wk
£340.00–£500.00

Short breaks low season subject to availability for weekend (Fri-Mon) or mid-week (Mon-Fri).

www.travelengland.org.uk
Log on for information and inspiration. The latest information on places to visit, events and quality assessed accommodation.

KETTLEWELL, North Yorkshire Map ref 5B3

★★★★

4 Units
Sleeping 2–5

350-acre hill sheep farm. The stone-built cottages are beside the village stream and close to the farm. Beamed ceilings, open coal fires and fully-fitted kitchens. Linen is included. Private off road parking. Within easy walking distance are three public houses, three shops and the lovely church.

FOLD FARM COTTAGES

Fold Farm, Kettlewell, Skipton BD23 5RH
Contact: Mrs B Lambert, Fold Farm, Kettlewell, Skipton
BD23 5RH
T: (01756) 760886
F: (01756) 760464
E: fold.farm@lineone.net
I: www.foldfarm.co.uk

OPEN All year round

Low season per wk
£145.00–£280.00
High season per wk
£225.00–£425.00

KIPLIN, North Yorkshire Map ref 5C3

★★

2 Units
Sleeping 2

MARYLAND COTTAGE & BALTIMORE COTTAGE
Kiplin Hall, Scorton, Richmond DL10 6AT
Contact: Ms Elaine Bird, Calvert Cottage, Kiplin Hall,
Richmond DL10 6AT
T: (01748) 812863
F: (01748) 818178

The flats are part of the domestic quarters which served Kiplin Hall from approximately 1720.

OPEN All year round

Low season per wk
£180.00
High season per wk
£200.00

KIRKBY FLEETHAM, North Yorkshire Map ref 5C3

★★★

1 Unit
Sleeping 4

WREN COTTAGE
25 Forge Lane, Kirkby Fleetham, Northallerton DL7 0SA
Contact: Mrs J R Pybus, Old Street House Farm,
Little Holtby, Northallerton DL7 9LN
T: (01609) 748622
F: (01609) 748571
E: jp.st.house@farmersweekly.net

On a picturesque village green within easy reach of the dales, coast, many sites of historic interest and sporting attractions.

OPEN All year round

Low season per wk
Min £180.00
High season per wk
Max £305.00

KIRKBYMOORSIDE, North Yorkshire Map ref 5C3

★★★★

1 Unit
Sleeping 6

CHERRY VIEW COTTAGE
Hagg Lane, Kirkbymoorside, York YO62 7JF
Contact: Mrs SMP Drinkel, High Hagg Farm,
Kirkbymoorside, York YO62 7JF
T: (01751) 431714 & 433187 (After 1500)

Cottage set at edge of farm, breathtaking views across Vale of Pickering. Spacious and self-contained, 3-bedroom accommodation, furnished to a high standard. Lawned garden, ample parking.

OPEN All year round

Low season per wk
Min £275.00
High season per wk
Min £400.00

★★★

2 Units
Sleeping 4

KELDHOLME COTTAGES
Keldholme, Kirkbymoorside, York YO62 6NA
Contact: Mr B Hughes, Keldholme Cottages, Keldholme,
Kirkbymoorside, York YO62 6NA
T: (01751) 431933

Well-appointed stone cottages with beautiful gardens, in peaceful hamlet near small market town. Access to moors, coast, dales and York.

OPEN Apr–Oct

Low season per wk
£130.00
High season per wk
£190.00

ACCESSIBILITY

Look for the symbols which indicate accessibility for wheelchair users. A list of establishments is at the front of this guide.

KNARESBOROUGH, North Yorkshire Map ref 4B1

★★★
1 Unit
Sleeping 2

GARDEN APARTMENT
3 Aspin Way, Knaresborough HG5 8HL
T: (01423) 860463
E: gardenapartment@hotmail.com
Contact: Mrs A Rowinski

OPEN All year round
CC: Barclaycard, Eurocard,
Mastercard, Visa

Low season per wk
Max £150.00
High season per wk
Max £180.00

In beautiful market town. Ideal for touring dales, historic towns, coasts and lakes. Recommended by returning visitors. Clean and friendly apartment, all inclusive. Ideal for walking.

★★★
1 Unit
Sleeping 3

THE GRANARY
Gibbet Farm, Farnham Lane, Farnham,
Knaresborough HG5 9JP
T: (01423) 862065 & 862271
F: (01423) 862271
Contact: Mrs P M Thornton

OPEN Apr–Sep

High season per wk
£170.00–£210.00

90-acre arable farm. Well-appointed apartment, part of a 16thC farmhouse in 30 acres of parkland. Five miles from Harrogate, with the Yorkshire Dales and Herriot country close by.

★★★
1 Unit
Sleeping 4

33 KIRKGATE
Knaresborough HG5 8BZ
Contact: Ms Angela Durance, Agent, Harrogate Holiday
Cottages, The Old Post Office, Kettlesing, Harrogate
HG3 2LB
T: (01423) 772700
F: (01423) 772359
E: bookings@harrogateholidays.co.uk
I: www.harrogateholidays.co.uk

OPEN All year round
CC: Barclaycard,
Mastercard, Switch, Visa

Low season per wk
£220.00–£265.00
High season per wk
£295.00–£355.00

A 17thC Grade II Listed cottage with stunning views over the River Nidd Gorge and bridge. Situated near the market square and local amenities.

★★★-★★★★★
4 Units
Sleeping 2–8

Quality apartments for 2-8 persons in a spectacular setting. Tastefully appointed with many personal touches. Extensive grounds with woodland walks to River Nidd, Knaresborough and the Nidd Gorge, an Area of Outstanding Natural Beauty. Ideal holiday base with many nearby attractions. Convenient for Harrogate, York and Yorkshire Dales. Bed and breakfast also available.

WATERGATE LODGE HOLIDAY APARTMENTS

Watergate Haven, Ripley Road, Knaresborough HG5 9BU
T: (01423) 864627
F: (01423) 861087
E: watergate.haven@virgin.net
I: business.virgin.net/watergate.haven
Contact: Mr & Mrs Peter & Lesley Guest

OPEN All year round
CC: Barclaycard, Delta,
Mastercard, Visa

Short breaks and mid-week
bookings may be available.
Discounts for advance
payment.

Low season per wk
£195.00–£299.00
High season per wk
£265.00–£499.00

LEALHOLM, North Yorkshire Map ref 5C3

★★★
3 Units
Sleeping 3–6

GREENHOUSES FARM COTTAGES
Greenhouses Farm, Lealholm, Whitby YO21 2AD
T: (01947) 897486
F: (01947) 897486
E: n_eddleston@yahoo.com
I: www.greenhouses-farm-cottages.co.uk
Contact: Mr & Mrs Nick Eddleston

OPEN All year round

Low season per wk
£179.00–£220.00
High season per wk
£326.00–£497.00

Stone and pantile cottages converted from traditional farm buildings, providing well-equipped, comfortable, centrally heated accommodation. In beautiful, moorland hamlet within North York Moors National Park, 9 miles Whitby.

★★–★★★

5 Units
Sleeping 3–6

DALES VIEW HOLIDAY HOMES
Jenkins Garth, Leyburn DL8 5SP
T: (01969) 623707 (Answerphone available) &
622808 (Phone, answerphone)
F: (01969) 623707
E: daleshols@aol.com
I: www.daleshols.com
Contact: Messrs J&M Chilton

OPEN All year round

Low season per wk
£130.00–£175.00
High season per wk
£175.00–£260.00

Cottages and apartments in secluded courtyard off market place, some with views over Wensleydale. Private parking. Ideal touring/walking centre.

★★

1 Unit
Sleeping 7

LOW RISEBOROUGH
4 Ellerclose Road, Leyburn DL8 5EZ
Contact: Mr John Rowntree, 95 Chiswick Village,
London W4 3BZ
T: (020) 8994 9837 (Answerphone) & 8747 9080 (Office hours Mon–Fri)
F: (020) 8995 4674

OPEN Jun–Sep

High season per wk
£210.00–£250.00

Charmingly situated, well-appointed bungalow with garden on the edge of the town. Spectacular, panoramic views of Wensleydale and Coverdale.

★★★

1 Unit
Sleeping 2

THE OLD FIRE STATION
Shawl Terrace, Leyburn DL8 5DA
Contact: Miss C Wallace-Lowell, 4 Shawl Terrace, Leyburn
DL8 5DA
T: (01969) 623993

Comfortable, beamed stone cottage, thoughtfully converted in a quiet, terrace cul-de-sac off a town square. Cosy in winter, with central heating and a coal/gas fire. With good walking from the doorstep, Leyburn is an excellent centre for touring, with good shops, pubs and eating places. Non-smokers only.

OPEN Mar–Dec

Low season per wk
£193.00–£215.00
High season per wk
£230.00–£290.00

★★★★

2 Units
Sleeping 3–5

ACORN QUALITY COTTAGES
Lofthouse, Harrogate HG3 5SA
Contact: Mrs S Kerr, 82 Trafalgar Road, Birkdale,
Southport PR8 2NJ
T: (01704) 568941
E: acornqualitycottages@supanet.com
I: www.acornqualitycottages.co.uk

OPEN All year round
CC: Mastercard, Solo,
Switch, Visa, Visa Electron

Low season per wk
£200.00–£280.00
High season per wk
£320.00–£400.00

Traditional dales village cottages of exceptional quality and comfort, with log fires, dishwashers, 4-poster bed. Great walking and touring. Non-smoking.

★★★★

1 Unit
Sleeping 4

ROWGATE COTTAGE
Rowgate Farm, Thorpe Bassett, Malton YO17 8LU
Contact: Mrs Janet Clarkson, Rowgate Farm,
Thorpe Bassett, Malton YO17 8LU
T: (01944) 758277 (Answerphone available)

OPEN All year round

Low season per wk
£160.00–£250.00
High season per wk
£275.00–£310.00

Spacious, comfortable well-equipped cottage attached to owner's farmhouse. South-facing patio and own private garden. One mile from the village, all inclusive. Brochure available.

SYMBOLS The symbols in each entry give information about services and facilities. A key to these symbols appears at the back of this guide.

MALTON continued

★★★
1 Unit
Sleeping 3

SWANS NEST COTTAGE

Abbotts Farm House, Ryton, Malton YO17 6SA
Contact: Mrs Yvonne Dickinson, Abbots Farm House,
Ryton, Malton YO17 6SA
T: (01653) 694970
E: yvonnedickinson@excite.co.uk
I: www.oas.co.uk/ukcottages/swans-nest

A cosy two bedroom, fully equipped old farm cottage, caringly modernised to a very high standard, situated in the heart of rural Ryedale. Ideally located, being central to the North Yorkshire Moors, Yorkshire Wolds, east coast seaside, and the old City of York. Price includes logs for the open fire.

OPEN All year round
CC: Barclaycard, Delta,
Mastercard, Solo, Switch,
Visa

Mid-week and weekend
breaks generally available.

Low season per wk
£195.00–£265.00
High season per wk
£295.00–£345.00

MIDDLEHAM, North Yorkshire Map ref 5C3

★★★
1 Unit
Sleeping 6

THE COTTAGE
North Road, Middleham, Leyburn DL8 4PJ
Contact: Mrs Jacqueline Welch,
67 Saughton Road North, Edinburgh EH12 7JB
T: (0131) 334 3118 (Home) & 549 3691 (Work (daytime))

OPEN All year round

Low season per wk
£220.00–£250.00
High season per wk
£270.00–£320.00

Spacious cottage with 3 bedrooms (1 double, 1 twin and 1 single plus large sofa bed). Separate dining room and kitchen, fully-appointed bathroom plus WC.

NAWTON, North Yorkshire Map ref 5C3

★★
5 Units
Sleeping 2–6

VALLEY VIEW LODGES
Station Road, Nawton, York YO62 7RG
T: (01439) 770555
Contact: Mr and Mrs Harry and June Simpson

OPEN All year round

Low season per wk
£160.00–£210.00
High season per wk
£210.00–£320.00

Three-bedroomed timber lodges open all year. Quiet location, 25 miles north of York, 28 miles from the coast. Ideal base for walking and touring.

NEWSHAM, North Yorkshire Map ref 5B3

★★★★
1 Unit
Sleeping 6

DYSON HOUSE BARN

Newsham, Richmond DL11 7QP
Contact: Mr and Mrs R Clarkson, Dyson House, Newsham,
Richmond DL11 7QP
T: (01833) 627365 & 0771 444 5405 (Mobile)

Located on a working farm in open country between Richmond and Barnard Castle, this tastefully converted stone barn retains many features. Beautifully decorated and furnished throughout, it has 3 large bedrooms, 1 on ground floor with shower room. Patio with barbecue. Small pets welcome. Two public houses/restaurants within short walking distance.

OPEN All year round

Short stays available 6
Oct–31 Mar (excl school
holidays), minimum 2 nights.

Low season per wk
£205.00–£420.00
High season per wk
£295.00–£420.00

SPECIAL BREAKS
Many establishments offer special promotions and themed breaks. These are highlighted in red. (All such offers are subject to availability.)

★★★★

1 Unit
Sleeping 4

HIGH DALTON HALL COTTAGE

Newsham, Richmond DL11 7RG
Contact: Mrs Elizabeth Jopling, High Dalton Hall,
York Street, Newsham, Richmond DL11 7RG
T: (01833) 621450
F: (01833) 621450

Situated midway between Richmond/Barnard Castle and bordering Herriot Country, this superb detached stonebuilt cottage has been tastefully converted from an old farm building to offer spacious, light and airy accommodation with oak beams, log fire and panoramic views over open countryside. Ideally situated for walking, sightseeing or bird watching.

OPEN All year round
CC: Barclaycard, Delta,
Mastercard, Solo, Switch,
Visa, Visa Electron

Low season per wk
£200.00–£250.00
High season per wk
£300.00–£350.00

NEWTON-ON-RAWCLIFFE, North Yorkshire Map ref 5D3

★★★

3 Units
Sleeping 4–5

LET'S HOLIDAY
Mel House, Newton-on-Rawcliffe, Pickering YO18 8QA
T: (01751) 475396 (Answerphone/fax)
F: (01751) 475396
E: john.wicks@letsholiday.com
I: www.letsholiday.com
Contact: Mr John Wicks

OPEN Feb–Dec
CC: Visa

Low season per wk
£225.00–£238.00
High season per wk
£495.00–£513.00

Well-equipped and comfortable with shared indoor pool/jacuzzi/sauna in quiet village with pub next door. Ideal for steam railway, moors, coast and York.

NORTHALLERTON, North Yorkshire Map ref 5C3 *Tourist Information Centre Tel: (01609) 776864*

★★★

1 Unit
Sleeping 5

2 SUMMERFIELD COTTAGE
Welbury, Northallerton DL6 2SL
Contact: Mrs S H Holmes, Summerfield House Farm,
Welbury, Northallerton DL6 2SL
T: (01609) 882393
F: (01609) 882393
E: theholmeswelbury@talk21.com

OPEN All year round

Low season per wk
£120.00–£170.00
High season per wk
£170.00–£250.00

Enjoy the peaceful surroundings of this well-appointed 3-bedroomed farm cottage. Superb views over open countryside. Central for Yorkshire Dales, Moors, Herriot Country and York.

PATELEY BRIDGE, North Yorkshire Map ref 5C3

★★★★★

1 Unit
Sleeping 6

SCOTT HOUSE

Pateley Bridge, Harrogate
Contact: Mr & Mrs M F Halliday, 2 Grange Drive,
Horsforth, Leeds LS18 5EQ
T: (0113) 258 4212 (Day/Evening/Answerphone)
F: (0113) 281 9455

Finalist of the White Rose Awards 2001. Built in dedication to Captain Scott of the Antarctic. Superior 4-bedroomed quality interior designed house. Features large farmhouse kitchen with exposed beams, spacious lounge with open fireplace and luxurious corner leather suite. Hand carved 4-poster bed. Fully-equipped. Garden, barbecue, bicycles. Private parking.

OPEN All year round
CC: Delta, Eurocard,
Mastercard, Visa

Short breaks available from
£8pppn. 10% discount for
2-week bookings.

Low season per wk
£275.00–£400.00
High season per wk
£400.00–£660.00

PEAK DISTRICT

See under Dore

REGIONAL TOURIST BOARD The Ⓜ symbol in an
establishment entry indicates that it is a Regional Tourist Board member.

PICKERING, North Yorkshire Map ref 5D3 *Tourist Information Centre Tel: (01751) 473791*

★★★★-★★★★★★
8 Units
Sleeping 2–10

BEECH FARM COTTAGES

Wrelton, Pickering YO18 8PG
T: (01751) 476612
F: (01751) 475032
E: holiday@beechfarm.com
I: www.beechfarm.com
Contact: Mr Rooney Massara

Award-winning, luxury, stone cottages in courtyard setting in quiet village off the main road. Beautiful heated outdoor pool, whirlpool spa and sauna. Children's play area. On the edge of the North York Moors National Park. Also convenient for coast and York. Linen, towels, heating and electricity included in price.

OPEN All year round
CC: Delta, Eurocard, Mastercard, Visa

Open all year. Short breaks, 2-4 nights, available off season.

Low season per wk
£145.00–£700.00
High season per wk
£250.00–£1,500.00

★★★★
1 Unit
Sleeping 11

EAST KINGTHORPE HOUSE

East Kingthorpe, Whitby Road, Thornton Dale,
Pickering YO18 7NG
Contact: Mr and Mrs G Abbott, Buckthorn House,
Malton Road, Pickering YO18 8EA
T: (01751) 473848
E: geoffabbott@supanet.com
I: kingthorpe.freeservers.com/

Spacious Victorian farmhouse enjoying private gounds, sweeping views over North Yorkshire Moors National Parkland, Vale of Pickering and Wolds beyond. Two receptions plus enormous stone-flagged dining room, 5 bedrooms, 4 shower/ bathrooms. Wheelchair accessible. Quality furnishings. Cosy log fires in original period fireplace. Central for East coast, York, 'Herriot', 'Heartbeat', and 'Harry Potter' country.

OPEN All year round
CC: Delta, Eurocard, Mastercard, Visa

Free wine hamper with all 'Where to Stay' bookings. 3-night breaks Nov-Feb (excl public holidays).

Low season per wk
£465.00–£595.00
High season per wk
£690.00–£1,165.00

★★★-★★★★
5 Units
Sleeping 2–7

EASTGATE COTTAGES
117 Eastgate, Pickering YO18 7DW
T: (01751) 476653 & 471303
F: (01751) 471310
E: info@northyorkshirecottages.co.uk
I: www.northyorkshirecottages.co.uk
Contact: Mr and Mrs Kevin & Elaine Bedford

OPEN Jan, Mar–Dec

Low season per wk
£180.00–£400.00
High season per wk
£275.00–£700.00

Eastgate Cottages; 5 stone converted farm buildings dating back to the 1700s. The cottages are thoughtfully modernised and are located in a peaceful courtyard with gardens.

COUNTRY CODE Always follow the Country Code 🍀

Enjoy the countryside and respect its life and work 🍀 Guard against all risk of fire 🍀 Fasten all gates 🍀 Keep your dogs under close control 🍀 Keep to public paths across farmland 🍀 Use gates and stiles to cross fences, hedges and walls 🍀 Leave livestock, crops and machinery alone 🍀 Take your litter home 🍀 Help to keep all water clean 🍀 Protect wildlife, plants and trees 🍀 Take special care on country roads 🍀 Make no unnecessary noise

★★★★
7 Units
Sleeping 2–10

Beautifully equipped/furnished farmhouse, divided into 3 apartments (separate entrances) with adjoining cottage. Also 3 pine lodges nestled in woodland bordering landscaped gardens. All set in 2.5 acres including lawn tennis, putting, games room, hens, 3 little pigs and sheep. Friendly, personal supervision throughout. Central for North Yorkshire Moors, coast, forestry and York.

EASTHILL FARM HOUSE AND GARDENS

Wilton Road, Thornton Dale, Pickering YO18 7QP
T: (01751) 474561 (Answerphone available)
E: easthill@freeuk.com
I: www.easthill-farm-holidays.co.uk
Contact: Mrs Diane Stenton

OPEN All year round
CC: Delta, JCB, Maestro, Mastercard, Solo, Switch, Visa, Visa Electron

Short breaks available. OAP discounts out of season. Shortlisted for White Rose 'Self Catering Holiday of the Year' award.

Low season per wk
£165.00–£455.00
High season per wk
£325.00–£755.00

★★★
1 Unit
Sleeping 6

JOINERS COTTAGE
75 Outgang Road, Pickering YO18 7EL
Contact: Mr and Mrs P&C Fisher, Farndale House,
103 Eastgate, Pickering YO18 7DW
T: (01751) 475158 (With BT Callminder)

OPEN All year round

Low season per wk
£200.00–£350.00
High season per wk
£350.00–£500.00

Converted barn set in 0.75 acres of lawned garden. Situated 0.25 miles from the town centre. En suite bedroom, linen, towels, heating all included. Open all year.

★★★★
3 Units
Sleeping 2–7

Excellent cottages in fantastic location. Comfortable, spacious, luxurious stone barns in idyllic courtyard setting in North York Moors National Park. Close to York and coast. Traditional charm with today's comforts. Disabled facilities in cottage for 2. Children's play area. Meals available. Highly recommended. Resident owner.

RAWCLIFFE HOUSE FARM

Stape, Pickering YO18 8JA
T: (01751) 473292
F: (01751) 473766
E: sheilarh@yahoo.com
I: www.yorkshireaccommodation.com
Contact: Mrs Sheila Ducat

OPEN All year round
CC: Barclaycard, Mastercard, Visa

Short breaks available Nov-Mar. Special discounts for couples using larger cottages.

Low season per wk
Min £120.00
High season per wk
Max £595.00

RICHMOND, North Yorkshire Map ref 5C3 *Tourist Information Centre Tel: (01748) 850252*

★★★★
2 Units
Sleeping 4–6

BARN OWL COTTAGE AND KINGFISHER COTTAGE
Red House Farm, Easby, Richmond DL10 7EU
T: (01748) 822038 (Farmhouse)
Contact: Mr & Mrs G W Fothergill

OPEN All year round

Low season per wk
£200.00–£220.00
High season per wk
£300.00–£420.00

227-acre arable and mixed farm. Peacefully situated riverside barn conversions in beautiful Swaledale. Excellent for touring and walking. All welcome. Brochure available.

CHECK THE MAPS
The colour maps at the front of this guide show all the cities, towns and villages for which you will find accommodation entries. Refer to the town index to find the page on which they are listed.

RICHMOND continued

★★★★
1 Unit
Sleeping 5

ROSE COTTAGE
6 Pear Tree Close, Skeeby, Richmond DL10 5EJ
Contact: Mr David Hunt, 11 Richmond Road, Skeeby,
Richmond DL10 5DR
T: (01748) 823080
E: huntsholidays@hotmail.com
I: www.huntsholidays.co.uk

OPEN Apr–Dec
CC: Amex, Barclaycard,
Delta, JCB, Maestro,
Mastercard, Switch, Visa

Low season per wk
£180.00–£300.00
High season per wk
£300.00–£425.00

Newly built, beautifully furnished (en suite bedrooms) cottage in small picturesque village (pub/meals) close to historic Richmond, Dales, A1. Ideal for touring, walking or relaxing.

RILLINGTON, North Yorkshire Map ref 5D3

★★★
1 Unit
Sleeping 2

THORPE-RISE
10 High Street, Rillington, Malton YO17 8LA
T: (01944) 758446 (Answerphone available)
E: marilyn@mlegard.freeserve.co.uk
Contact: Mrs Marilyn Legard

OPEN All year round

Low season per wk
£120.00–£150.00
High season per wk
£150.00–£200.00

Comfortable, well-equipped bungalow adjoining the main house. Linen, towels provided. Patio, garage, own entrance. Ideal for a couple.

RIPON, North Yorkshire Map ref 5C3

★★★★
2 Units
Sleeping 2–4

BYRE COTTAGE & SWALLOW COTTAGE
Moor End Farm, Knaresborough Road, Littlethorpe,
Ripon HG4 3LU
Contact: Mr & Mrs R&P Spensley, Moor End Farm,
Knaresborough Road, Littlethorpe, Ripon HG4 3LU
T: (01765) 677419
E: pspensley@ukonline.co.uk
I: www.yorkshirebandb.co.uk

OPEN All year round

Low season per wk
£165.00–£220.00
High season per wk
£235.00–£320.00

Superb 1 and 2 bedroomed single-storey beamed cottages, converted from old farm buildings (for non-smokers). Enjoying a peaceful position, adjacent to owners' house.

ROBIN HOOD'S BAY, North Yorkshire Map ref 5D3

★★-★★★★★
5 Units
Sleeping 3–5

Adjacent to Robin Hood's Bay, beach, village and Boggle Hole, with fields/woodland paths. The stone and pantile cottages have attractive gardens, magnificent views. Horses and mountain bikes to ride, and Mistal Cottage guests enjoy private all-year-round swimming in the Chaletpool. Parking. Farm animals. Whitby 6 miles, Scarborough 16 miles.

FARSYDE HOUSE FARM COTTAGES

Robin Hood's Bay, Whitby YO22 4UG
T: (01947) 880249 (Answerphone available) & 880877
F: (01947) 880877
E: farsydestud@talk21.com
Contact: Mrs A Green

OPEN All year round

Short breaks in autumn, winter and spring. Minimum 2 nights. Special offers for early bookings and 2 occupants.

Low season per wk
£130.00–£300.00
High season per wk
£210.00–£530.00

★★★
1 Unit
Sleeping 4

LINGERS HILL
Thorpe Lane, Robin Hood's Bay, Whitby YO22 4TQ
Contact: Mrs F Harland, Lingers Hill Farm, Thorpe Lane,
Robin Hood's Bay, Whitby YO22 4TQ
T: (01947) 880608

OPEN All year round

Low season per wk
£160.00–£170.00
High season per wk
£195.00–£275.00

Cosy character cottage situated on the edge of the village at Robin Hood's Bay. Close to amenities, ideal walking and cycling area. Lovely views.

PRICES
Please check prices and other details at the time of booking.

ROSEDALE ABBEY, North Yorkshire Map ref 5C3

★★★

8 Units
Sleeping 3–8

CRAVEN GARTH HOLIDAY COTTAGES
Craven Garth Farm, Rosedale Abbey,
Pickering YO18 8RH
T: (01751) 417506 (Answerphone)
F: (01751) 417506
E: ena@cravengarth.com
I: www.cravengarth.com
Contact: Mrs Ena Dent

OPEN All year round

Low season per wk
£120.00–£325.00
High season per wk
£250.00–£600.00

Warm and cosy cottages in the centre of North York Moors National Park. Ideal for walking, sightseeing or just relaxing.

SCARBOROUGH, North Yorkshire Map ref 5D3 *Tourist Information Centre Tel: (01723) 373333*

★★★★

3 Units
Sleeping 2–5

FORGE VALLEY COTTAGES

East Ayton, Nr Scarborough
Contact: Mr David Beeley, Proprietor, Barn House,
8a Westgate, Old Malton, Malton YO17 7HE
T: (01653) 698251
F: (01653) 691962

Choice of 3 luxury stone-built cottages in East Ayton, a lovely village on the River Derwent. Your gateway to the North Yorkshire Moors and Scarborough only 4 miles. Highly equipped, well appointed, cosy and comfortable – an ideal holiday base! Private gardens and parking. Pets welcome. Non-smoking available.

OPEN All year round

Low season short breaks
from £75.

Low season per wk
£125.00
High season per wk
£125.00–£395.00

★★★★

9 Units
Sleeping 2–9

WREA HEAD COTTAGE HOLIDAYS

Wrea Head House, Barmoor Lane, Scalby,
Scarborough YO13 0PG
Contact: Wrea Head Cottage Holidays, Wrea Head House,
Barmoor Lane, Scalby, Scarborough YO13 0PG
T: (01723) 375844 & 07801 384994 (Mobile)
F: (01723) 500274
E: ytb@wreaheadcotghols.demon.co.uk
I: www.wreaheadcotghols.demon.co.uk

National winners of ETC 'England for Excellence' award for Best Self Catering Holiday of the Year. Superb indoor heated swimming pool, jacuzzi and sauna. Stunning panoramic sea views and beautiful countryside on edge of national park. Lovely award-winning gardens and croquet. Parking. Furnished Teddy Bear's cottage. York 1 hour, Whitby 30 minutes.

OPEN All year round
CC: Barclaycard,
Mastercard, Visa

Excellent value breaks, 4
nights for price of 3, 27 Oct
01-23 Mar 02 (excl Christmas
and New Year).

Low season per wk
£195.00–£525.00
High season per wk
£451.00–£1,150.00

SCOTCH CORNER, North Yorkshire Map ref 5C3

★★★

1 Unit
Sleeping 4

5 CEDAR GROVE
Barton, Richmond DL10 6JP
Contact: Mr and Mrs J P Lawson, The Close, Mill Lane,
Cloughton, Scarborough YO13 0AB
T: (01723) 870455 & 870017

OPEN All year round

Low season per wk
£120.00–£150.00
High season per wk
£150.00–£200.00

Semi-detached family home, near village green. Five miles south of Darlington, central for touring the Yorkshire Dales, Moors, Northumberland, Durham and Lake District.

QUALITY ASSURANCE SCHEME
Star ratings are explained at the back of this guide.

SEDBUSK, North Yorkshire Map ref 5B3

★★★★

1 Unit
Sleeping 8

JASMINE COTTAGE
Sedbusk, Hawes DL8 3PX
Contact: Mrs A D Moore, Beckstones, Carperby,
Leyburn DL8 4DA
T: (01969) 663363 (Answerphone available)

OPEN All year round

Low season per wk
£174.00–£342.00
High season per wk
£288.00–£396.00

Modernised, detached, south-facing cottage on the sunny side of the dale. Pleasant, secluded garden with a lane leading on to the moor behind. Flexible 3 or 4 bedrooms.

SELSIDE, North Yorkshire Map ref 5B3

★★★–★★★★★

2 Units
Sleeping 4–6

THE BYRES
Selside Farm, Selside, Settle BD24 0HZ
Contact: Mrs S E Lambert, Selside Farm, Selside, Settle
BD24 0HZ
T: (01729) 860367

OPEN All year round

Low season per wk
£200.00–£300.00
High season per wk
£250.00–£350.00

Three bedrooms, lounge, dining-room and kitchen. Coal fire, patio and garden to 3 sides. In centre of 3 peaks walking country. Weekend and short breaks.

SHEFFIELD, South Yorkshire Map ref 4B2 *Tourist Information Centre Tel: (0114) 221 1900*

★★★★

1 Unit
Sleeping 6

HANGRAM LANE FARMHOUSE
Hangram Lane Grange, Hangram Lane, Ringinglow,
Sheffield S11 7TQ
T: (0114) 230 3570
Contact: Mrs J Clark

OPEN All year round

Low season per wk
£258.50–£282.00
High season per wk
£293.75–£340.75

Comfortable, modernised farmhouse comprising large kitchen, dining room, lounge, 1 double bedroom, 2 twin-bedded rooms, bathroom and toilet. Two minutes' drive from the Peak District, shops and eating places.

SKIPTON, North Yorkshire Map ref 4B1 *Tourist Information Centre Tel: (01756) 792809*

★★★

1 Unit
Sleeping 5

HIGH MALSIS FARMHOUSE
High Malsis, Glusburn, Keighley BD20 8DU
T: (01535) 633309
Contact: Mrs S A Fort

Recently refurbished spacious farmhouse on small dairy farm. Sleeps 5, 1 double, 1 single, 1 twin and cot. Gas central heating, open fire, fuel provided. Edge of Bronte Country. Skipton 5 miles. Ideal base for exploring Yorkshire Dales and surrounding areas. A warm welcome awaits.

OPEN Apr–Oct

Low season per wk
Min £200.00
High season per wk
Min £320.00

★★★

1 Unit
Sleeping 6

7 PASTURE ROAD
Embsay, Skipton BD23 6RQ
Contact: Mr & Mrs C Lunnon, 17 Cherry Tree Way,
Helmshore, Rossendale BB4 4JZ
T: (01706) 230653 (Home)
E: j.lunnon@blackburn.ac.uk

OPEN All year round

Low season per wk
£160.00–£220.00
High season per wk
£270.00–£385.00

Stone-built house, on the edge of the Yorkshire Dales National Park. Three bedrooms, heating, linen and electricity included. Children and pets welcome. Non smokers only please.

TOWN INDEX
This can be found at the back of this guide. If you know where you want to stay, the index will give you the page number listing accommodation in your chosen town, city or village.

★★★

4 Units
Sleeping 2–6

Peace and tranquillity found on 170 acre sheep farm with stunning coastal and rural views. Ten minutes' walk from the Cleveland Way. Plenty of walks from the door amid cliffs, woodland and streams. Four, 'home from home', highly equipped, welcoming cottages. Ample parking. Pets made welcome.

WHITEHALL FARM HOLIDAY COTTAGES

Whitehall Farm, Staintondale, Scarborough YO13 0EY
T: (01723) 870234 (Answerphone) &
077698 684644 (Mobile)
E: celia@white66fs.business.co.uk
I: www.whitehallcottages.co.uk
Contact: Mr and Mrs James and Celia White

OPEN All year round

Low season per wk
£151.00–£169.00
High season per wk
£269.00–£422.00

★★

1 Unit
Sleeping 4

GLENCOE
Church Street, Staithes, Saltburn-by-the-Sea TS13 5DB
Contact: Rev David Purdy, The Vicarage, Church Street,
Kirkbymoorside, York YO62 6AZ
T: (01751) 431452

OPEN All year round

Low season per wk
£160.00–£195.00
High season per wk
£195.00–£250.00

Compact, cosy, mid-terrace former fisherman's cottage, in the heart of a fishing village steeped in history. Open fire. Two bedrooms. Close beach, shops, pubs.

★★★★

1 Unit
Sleeping 5

THE GRANARY
Thirlby, Thirsk YO7 2DJ
Contact: Mrs Mary Harrison, East Farm, Thirlby, Thirsk
YO7 2DJ
T: (01845) 597554 (Answerphone available)
E: mary@thegranary36.fsnet.co.uk

OPEN All year round

Low season per wk
£260.00
High season per wk
£310.00–£460.00

Converted granary with exposed beams, large open-plan lounge overlooking Whitestonecliffe. Set in extensive grounds including a small trout stream. Non-smoking property.

★★★

1 Unit
Sleeping 5

THE OLD SCHOOL HOUSE
Catton, Thirsk YO7 4SG
Contact: Mrs G Readman, School House, Catton, Thirsk
YO7 4SG
T: (01845) 567308

OPEN All year round

Low season per wk
£120.00–£150.00
High season per wk
£150.00–£200.00

Formerly the village school, attached to the owner's residence at the School House. Two bedrooms, 1 double with a single bed and 1 twin-bedded room, all ground floor.

★★★–★★★★★

2 Units
Sleeping 4

THWAITE FARM COTTAGES
Thwaite Farm, Thwaite, Richmond DL11 6DR
Contact: Mrs Gillian Whitehead, Thwaite Farm, Thwaite,
Richmond DL11 6DR
T: (01748) 886444
E: info@thwaitefarmcottages.co.uk
I: www.thwaitefarmcottages.co.uk

OPEN All year round

Low season per wk
£140.00–£200.00
High season per wk
£225.00–£275.00

Two barns converted to a high standard in small peaceful dales village in Upper Swaledale. Idyllic views, flower meadows, stone walls and barns. Ideal walking area.

MAP REFERENCES
The map references refer to the colour maps at the front of this guide. The first figure is the map number; the letter and figure which follow indicate the grid reference on the map.

★★★
1 Unit
Sleeping 4

THE COTTAGE
Causeway East Farmhouse, Lee Bottom Road,
Todmorden OL14 6HH
T: (01706) 815265
F: (01706) 815265
E: andrew@bentham5.freeserve.co.uk
Contact: Mr & Mrs A Bentham

OPEN All year round

Low season per wk
£130.00–£160.00
High season per wk
£160.00–£190.00

Part of a 17thC farmhouse beneath the Pennine Way. Ideal for walking and touring.

★-★★★★
3 Units
Sleeping 3–4

Three refurbished 2-bedroomed flats in Victorian terrace. Ideal location for beach, shops and restaurants. Personally supervised by the owners who are committed to very high quality standards. Linen and electricity included. Pets welcome. Unrestricted on-street parking outside the property on a first come basis. Phone for colour brochure.

ELIZABETH HOUSE HOLIDAY FLATS
12 John Street, Whitby YO21 3ET
Contact: Mrs Rosaline Cooper, Park View,
14 Chubb Hill Road, Whitby YO21 1JU
T: (01947) 604213 & 07867 618244 (Mobile)
F: (01947) 604213
E: cooperhouse@tinyworld.co.uk
I: www.elizabeth-house.fsnet.co.uk

OPEN All year round

Bargain breaks from £60 per flat. Nov–Mar excl Christmas and New Year.

Low season per wk
£130.00–£180.00
High season per wk
£200.00–£350.00

REGIONAL TOURIST BOARD The ΛΛ symbol in an establishment entry indicates that it is a Regional Tourist Board member.

Shoreline Cottages

Shoreline Cottages offer a selection of quality character cottages in the irresistible fishing town of Whitby on the Yorkshire coast. All of the properties have been beautifully furnished and decorated by a professional interior designer and are equipped to the highest of standards with washing machines, tumble dryers, microwaves, hi-fis and video players - combining convenience, character and comfort. Shoreline's commitment to quality and attention to detail make this the obvious choice for the discerning visitor. Shoreline Cottages - **More than you expect and all you desire.**

Cottages of distinction and character in Whitby, Yorkshire
Tel: 0113 289 3539
www.shoreline-cottages.com

★★★★
1 Unit
Sleeping 8

GLENCOE–GARDEN FLAT
c/o 18 Linden Close, Briggswath, Whitby YO21 1TA
Contact: Mrs Julie Charlton, Glencoe Holiday Flats,
18 Linden Close, Briggs Wath, Whitby YO21 1TA
T: (01947) 811531

OPEN All year round

Low season per wk
Min £350.00
High season per wk
Max £450.00

Luxury, holiday accommodation. Garden flat, West Cliff area, close to all amenities. Spacious and nicely furnished. Open all year. SAE for brochure.

★★
1 Unit
Sleeping 6

7 HENRIETTA STREET
Off Church Street, Whitby YO22 4DN
Contact: Mr William Usher, Proprietor,
2 Southlands Avenue, Whitby YO21 3DY
T: (01947) 605868

Cottage situated at the bottom of the 199 steps. Most rooms have a sea view of approximately 7 miles of coast and a view of the harbour. There is a small attractive harbour beach two minutes from the cottage suitable for a family.

OPEN All year round

Low season per wk
£200.00–£250.00
High season per wk
£300.00–£350.00

★★★
1 Unit
Sleeping 4

6 OLD COASTGUARD COTTAGES
East Cliff, Whitby YO22 4JS
Contact: Ms J M Noble, Howdale House, Browside,
Fylingdales, Whitby YO22
T: (01947) 881064

OPEN All year round

Low season per wk
Min £190.00
High season per wk
Max £390.00

A 2 bedroomed cottage situated on Whitby's east cliff. Close to the abbey, short walk from old town, with fantastic sea views.

★★
4 Units
Sleeping 3–5

SWALLOW HOLIDAY COTTAGES
The Farm, Stainsacre, Whitby YO22 4NT
Contact: Mr & Mrs McNeil, Swallow Holiday Cottages,
Long Lease Farm, Hawsker, Whitby YO22 4LA
T: (01947) 603790
F: (01947) 603790
I: www.swallowcottages.co.uk

OPEN All year round

Low season per wk
£115.00–£160.00
High season per wk
£225.00–£320.00

Mews of converted farm cottages in a private courtyard, in a small village close to the moors and the sea. Ideal for couples or family groups. Part weeks available low season.

RATING All accommodation in this guide has been rated, or is awaiting a rating, by a trained English Tourism Council assessor.

Fayvan Holiday Apartments

**Fayvan Holiday Apartments,
Crescent Avenue, West Cliff, Whitby YO21 3EQ
Tel/Fax: 01947 604813**

An elegant Victorian residence, containing superior apartments, on the West Cliff, with side views over the Royal Crescent Gardens to the sea.
The apartments are beautifully appointed with particular attention given to decor, furniture and fittings. You will find a welcoming atmosphere, with very high standards of service for all our guests.

English Tourism Council
★★★★
SELF-CATERING

WHITBY continued

★★★–★★★★

7 Units
Sleeping 2–6

Relax in superior village bungalows and cottages on the edge of the moors, 3.5 miles from Whitby and the sea. All tastefully decorated and well-equipped. Open fires, gardens. Pub, hotel and shops in village. Long or short winter breaks. Also, garden patio flat in Whitby.

WHITE ROSE HOLIDAY COTTAGES

5 Brooks Park, Sleights, Whitby YO21 1RT
Contact: Mrs J E Roberts, Greenacres, 5 Brook Park, Sleights, Whitby YO21 1RT
T: (01947) 810763
E: enquiries@whiterosecottages.com
I: www.whiterosecottages.com

OPEN All year round

Reduced rates for autumn/ winter breaks. Cosy, festively-decorated properties for Christmas/New Year.

Low season per wk
Min £205.00
High season per wk
Max £460.00

WORSBROUGH, South Yorkshire Map ref 4B1

★★★★

1 Unit
Sleeping 6

DELF COTTAGE
Houndhill Lane, Worsbrough, Barnsley S70 6TX
Contact: Mrs Julie Elmhirst, Delf House,
Houndhill Lane, Worsbrough, Barnsley S70 6TX
T: (01226) 282430 & 07768 766448 (Mobile)
F: (01226) 282430
E: t.elmhirst@btinternet.com
I: www.delfcottage.co.uk

Luxurious cottage in beautiful setting, overlooking trans-Pennine trail. Ideally placed for business or touring the north of England.

OPEN All year round

Low season per wk
£325.00–£350.00
High season per wk
£350.00

YEADON, West Yorkshire Map ref 4B1

★★★★

1 Unit
Sleeping 4

GILLCROFT COTTAGE
39 Gill Lane, Yeadon, Leeds LS19 7DE
Contact: Mrs I Croft, Gillcroft, 41 Gill Lane, Yeadon,
Leeds LS19 7DE
T: (0113) 250 4198
F: (0113) 250 4327

Cosy cottage, extensive garden with stream, used as 'Emmerdale' location. Off A65 within easy reach of dales, Bronte and 'Last of the Summer Wine' Country.

OPEN All year round

Low season per wk
Min £215.00
High season per wk
Max £285.00

YORK, North Yorkshire Map ref 4C1 *Tourist Information Centre Tel: (01904) 621756*

★★★★★

1 Unit
Sleeping 8

Luxurious Georgian-style townhouse with 5 bedrooms and 3 bathrooms in an outstanding position 5 minutes from city centre overlooking the medieval city walls on a prestigious riverside development. Furnished to an excellent standard, it has every facility including large lounge with 4 co-ordinated leather sofas and south facing balcony, jacuzzi, bath.

ABBEYGATE HOUSE

Bishopgate Street, York YO2 1JH
Contact: Mr & Mrs C Halliday, 3 Grange Drive, Horsforth, Leeds LS18 5EQ
T: (0113) 258 9833

OPEN All year round
CC: Barclaycard,
Mastercard, Visa

Short breaks available. Private parking for 2/3.

Low season per wk
Min £250.00

CONFIRM YOUR BOOKING
You are advised to confirm your booking in writing.

★★★

1 Unit
Sleeping 6

BAILE HILL COTTAGE
Bishophill, York
Contact: Mr & Mrs P&S Hodgson, Baile Hill Cottage,
Avalon, North Lane, Wheldrake, York YO19 6AY
T: (01904) 448670
F: (01904) 448908
E: holiday.cottage@btinternet.com
I: www.btinternet.com/~holiday.cottage

OPEN All year round

Low season per wk
£99.00–£186.00
High season per wk
£219.00–£379.00

Victorian town cottage with 2 bedrooms, dining room, lounge, modern fitted kitchen. Many original features, 4-poster bed. Peaceful, central location overlooking medieval city walls.

★★★★★

1 Unit
Sleeping 10

BAILLE HILL HOUSE
Bishopgate Street, York YO23 1JH
Contact: Mr & Mrs M F Halliday, 2 Grange Drive,
Horsforth, Leeds LS18 5EQ
T: (0113) 258 4212
F: (0113) 281 9455

Finalist of the White Rose Awards 2001. Superior Georgian-style 5-bedroomed quality end town house on 3 floors. Excellent location adjacent to prestigious riverside development and medieval City Walls. Fully-equipped to the highest standards. Interior designed lounge, immaculately furnished with luxurious corner leather suite and south-facing balcony. Private parking.

OPEN All year round
CC: Delta, Eurocard,
Mastercard, Visa

Short breaks available, from £9pppn. 10% discount for 2-week bookings.

Low season per wk
£500.00–£600.00
High season per wk
£600.00–£850.00

★★★

1 Unit
Sleeping 4

BARBICAN MEWS
18A Barbican Road, York YO10 5AA
Contact: Mrs Helen Jones, Homefinders Holidays,
11 Walmgate, York YO1 9TX
T: (01904) 632660 & 655200
F: (01904) 615388
E: c.thomas-letters.of.york@btinternet.com
I: www.letters.of.york.co.uk

OPEN All year round

Low season per wk
£225.00–£315.00
High season per wk
£335.00–£370.00

Two-bedroomed apartment, fully equipped to a high standard and with semi patio, ideally situated adjacent to city walls and leisure centre with pool.

★★★

1 Unit
Sleeping 4

19A BARBICAN MEWS
19A Barbican Road, York YO10 5BZ
Contact: Mrs Helen Jones, Homefinders Holidays,
11 Walmgate, York YO1 9TX
T: (01904) 632660 & 655200
F: (01904) 615388
E: c.thomas-letters.of.york.btinternet.com
I: www.letters.of.york.co.uk

OPEN All year round

Low season per wk
£225.00–£315.00
High season per wk
£335.00–£380.00

Modern 2-bedroomed first-floor apartment overlooking city walls. Near Barbican Centre and Clifford Tower. Ten minutes' walk to city centre.

★★

1 Unit
Sleeping 6

BISHOPHILL HOLIDAYS
5 Kyme Street, Bishophill, York YO1 6HG
Contact: Mrs Lesley Shimmin, 49 Moorgate, Acomb,
York YO24 4HP
T: (01904) 796118 (Answerphone available)
F: (01904) 796118
E: enquiries@bishophill.co.uk
I: www.bishophill.co.uk

OPEN All year round

Low season per wk
£120.00–£220.00
High season per wk
£240.00–£360.00

Comfortable Victorian artisan's terraced house in a quiet residential conservation area within the city walls. Family-run. Parking available. No extras.

YORK continued

★★★
1 Unit
Sleeping 5

1 BISHOPS COURT
Bishophill, York YO1 6EW
Contact: Mrs Helen Jones, Homefinders Holidays,
11 Walmgate, York YO1 9TX
T: (01904) 632660 & 655200
F: (01904) 651388
E: c.thomas-letters.of.york@btinternet.com
I: www.letters.of.york.co.uk

OPEN All year round

Low season per wk
£230.00–£320.00
High season per wk
£340.00–£375.00

Bright, spacious 3-bedroomed townhouse. Quality furnishings, private parking. Walking distance to city centre.

★★★
1 Unit
Sleeping 6

1 CLOISTERS WALK
St Maurice's Road, Monkgate, York YO31 7HZ
Contact: Mrs Helen Jones, Homefinders Holidays,
11 Walmgate, York YO1 9TX
T: (01904) 632660 & 655200
F: (01904) 651388
E: c.thomas-letters.of.york@btinternet.com
I: www.letters.of.york.co.uk

OPEN All year round

Low season per wk
£230.00–£320.00
High season per wk
£340.00–£380.00

Comfortable, modern house, beautifully placed 500 yards from York Minster. Excellent views, tranquil and spacious garden. Your 'corner shop' is Sainsbury's (200 yards).

★★★★
1 Unit
Sleeping 2

FLAT 24 MIDDLETON HOUSE
Lady Anne Court, Skeldergate, York YO1 6DT
Contact: Mrs Carole Bowes, Melrose House Farm,
Sutton Road, Thirsk YO7 2ES
T: (01845) 597334 (Answerphone available)

OPEN All year round

Low season per wk
£165.00–£265.00
High season per wk
£265.00–£310.00

One-bedroomed, first-floor flat within a 5-minute walk of York city centre. Parking for 1 car.

★★★★
1 Unit
Sleeping 4

FORGET ME NOTS
13 Victoria Court, Parkside, York YO26 4XE
Contact: Mrs Helen Jones, Homefinders Holidays,
11 Walmgate, York YO1 9TX
T: (01904) 632660 & 655200
F: (01904) 615388
E: c.thomas-letters.of.york@btinternet.com
I: www.letters.of.york.co.uk

OPEN All year round

Low season per wk
£230.00–£320.00
High season per wk
£340.00–£380.00

Beautiful 2-bedroomed house with lovely garden. Situated near the railway station and pleasant walk along riverside to town. Private garage.

★★
5 Units
Sleeping 2–4

KNOWLE HOUSE APARTMENTS
5 Bootham Terrace, York YO30 7DH
Contact: Mr Graham Harrand, Hedley House,
3 Bootham Terrace, York YO30 7DH
T: (01904) 637404
F: (01904) 639774
E: h.h@mcmail.com
I: www.hedleyhouse.com

OPEN All year round

Low season per wk
£100.00–£300.00
High season per wk
£200.00–£450.00

Studio, one bedroom and two bedroom apartments, within easy walking distance of city centre, next door to owner's hotel. Off-street parking. Three-day minimum stay.

★★★
6 Units
Sleeping 2–8

MERRICOTE COTTAGES
Malton Road, Stockton-on-the-Forest, York YO32 9TL
T: (01904) 400256 & 07939 522748
E: merricote@hotmail.com
Contact: Mr Andrew Williamson

OPEN All year round
CC: Amex, Barclaycard,
Delta, Mastercard, Switch,
Visa

Low season per wk
£136.50–£383.00
High season per wk
£226.00–£483.00

Beautiful spot from which to explore the historic city of York (3 miles), moors and coast. The cottages and bungalow are beautifully appointed, many amenities nearby.

WHERE TO STAY
Please mention this guide when making your booking.

★★★
1 Unit
Sleeping 4

PRIORY COTTAGE
12 Lower Darnborough Street, Bishopthorpe Road,
York YO23 1AR
Contact: Mrs Helen Jones, Homefinders Holidays,
11 Walmgate, York YO1 9TX
T: (01904) 632660 & 655200
F: (01904) 615388
E: c.thomas-letters.of.york.btinternet.com
I: www.letters.of.york.co.uk

OPEN All year round

Low season per wk
£230.00–£320.00
High season per wk
£340.00–£380.00

Edwardian cottage, refurbished to a high standard. Private walled garden. Parking available. Central heating, 2 double bedrooms, kitchen, separate dining room, living room and shower room.

★★★
1 Unit
Sleeping 6

29 RICHARDSON STREET
Clementhorpe, York YO23 1JU
Contact: Mrs Helen Jones, Homefinders Holidays,
11 Walmgate, York YO1 9TX
T: (01904) 632660 & 655200
F: (01904) 651388
E: c.thomas-letters.of.york@btinternet.com
I: www.letters.of.york.co.uk

OPEN All year round

Low season per wk
£230.00–£320.00
High season per wk
£340.00–£380.00

Comfortable and spacious house, short walk along riverside to the city centre. Three bedrooms, well furnished.

★★★★
1 Unit
Sleeping 3

RIVERSIDE HOLIDAY FLAT
61 Postern Close, York YO23 1JP
Contact: Mr P A Jackson, 17 Great Close, Cawood,
Selby YO8 3UG
T: (01757) 268207 & 07885 921691 (Mobile)
F: (01757) 268122
E: pajack@lineone.net
I: www.yorkriversideholidayflat.co.uk

OPEN All year round

Low season per wk
£200.00–£260.00
High season per wk
£275.00–£370.00

City-centre, double-bedroomed, first floor apartment with patio balcony. Overlooking the river and with fine views of the city. Own parking space.

★★★★
3 Units
Sleeping 1–3

SHAMBLES HOLIDAY APARTMENTS
The Art Shop, 27-27a Shambles, York YO1 7LX
T: (01904) 623898
F: (01904) 671283
E: shamblesholiday-york@tinyworld.co.uk
Contact: Mr and Mrs Fletcher

OPEN All year round
CC: Barclaycard, JCB,
Maestro, Mastercard,
Solo, Switch, Visa, Visa
Electron

Low season per wk
£175.00–£240.00
High season per wk
£245.00–£375.00

Grade II Listed Georgian building in York's most famous medieval street, The Shambles. Adjacent open-air market and all city centre facilities. No car parking.

★★★★–★★★★★★
16 Units
Sleeping 2–7

YORK LAKESIDE LODGES
Moor Lane, York YO24 2QU
T: (01904) 702346 & 07831 885824
F: (01904) 701631
E: neil@yorklakesidelodges.co.uk
I: www.yorklakesidelodges.co.uk
Contact: Mr N Manasir

OPEN All year round

Low season per wk
£195.00–£330.00
High season per wk
£400.00–£675.00

Well-equipped Scandinavian pine lodges in mature parkland surrounding private fishing lake. Coach to city centre every 10 minutes.

NB

IMPORTANT NOTE Information on accommodation listed in this guide has been supplied by the proprietors. As changes may occur you are advised to check details at the time of booking.

A brief guide to the main Towns and Villages offering accommodation in Yorkshire

A AMPLEFORTH, NORTH YORKSHIRE - Stone-built village in Hambleton Hills. Famous for its abbey and college, a Benedictine public school, founded in 1802, of which Cardinal Hume was once abbot. Romanesque-style church by Sir Giles Scott, completed in 1961 just after his death.

• **ARKENGARTHDALE, NORTH YORKSHIRE** - Picturesque Yorkshire dale, in the valley of Arkle Beck, once an important and prosperous lead-mining valley developed by Charles Bathurst in the 18th C.

B BEVERLEY, NORTH HUMBERSIDE - Beverley's most famous landmark is its beautiful medieval Minster dating from 1220, with Percy family tomb. Many attractive squares and streets, notably Wednesday and Saturday Market and North Bar Gateway. Famous racecourse. Market cross dates from 1714.

• **BISHOP THORNTON, NORTH YORKSHIRE** - Small village in Nidderdale, near Brimham Rocks.

• **BRIDLINGTON, EAST RIDING OF YORKSHIRE** - Lively seaside resort with long sandy beaches, Leisure World and busy harbour with fishing trips in cobles. Priory church of St Mary whose Bayle Gate is now a museum. Mementoes of flying pioneer, Amy Johnson, in Sewerby Hall. Harbour Museum and Aquarium.

• **BURNSALL, NORTH YORKSHIRE** - Attractive village of grey-stone buildings with massive 5-arched bridge over the River Wharfe, popular for fishing, boating and walking excursions. Annual feast day games, notably fell race held round maypole on the village green in August.

• **BURTON-IN-LONSDALE, NORTH YORKSHIRE** - On a hillside above the River Greta, this town was once the centre for 7 potteries, the last of which closed in 1930.

C CARLTON, NORTH YORKSHIRE - At the edge of the Yorkshire Dales, Carlton is a good base for exploring Coverdale and visiting the National Park Centre.

• **CLOUGHTON, NORTH YORKSHIRE** - Village north of Scarborough, close to the East Coast and North York Moors.

• **CROPTON, NORTH YORKSHIRE** - Moorland village at the top of a high ridge with stone houses, some of cruck construction, a Victorian church and the remains of a 12th C moated castle. Cropton Forest and Cropton Brewery nearby.

D DANBY, NORTH YORKSHIRE - Eskdale village 12 miles west of Whitby. Visit the Moors Centre at Danby Lodge, a former shooting lodge in 13 acres of grounds including woodland and riverside meadow. Remains of medieval Danby Castle.

E EBBERSTON, NORTH YORKSHIRE - Picturesque village with a Norman church and hall, overlooking the Vale of Pickering.

F FILEY, NORTH YORKSHIRE - Resort with elegant Regency buildings along the front and 6 miles of sandy beaches bounded by natural breakwater, Filey Brigg. Starting point of the Cleveland Way. St Oswald's church, overlooking a ravine, belonged to Augustinian canons until the Dissolution.

• **FYLINGTHORPE, NORTH YORKSHIRE** - Within a stone's throw of Robin Hood's Bay and the north east coast.

G GIGGLESWICK, NORTH YORKSHIRE - Picturesque Pennine village of period stone cottages with ancient market cross, stocks and tithe barn. Parish church is dedicated to St Alkeda, an Anglo-Saxon saint. During restoration work the tomb of a 15th C knight with his horse was discovered.

• **GRASSINGTON, NORTH YORKSHIRE** - Tourists visit this former lead-mining village to see its 'smiddy', antique and craft shops and Upper Wharfedale Museum of country trades. Popular with fishermen and walkers. Cobbled market square, numerous prehistoric sites. Grassington Feast in October. National Park Centre.

• **GREAT LANGTON, NORTH YORKSHIRE** - Village on the River Swale 5 miles north-west of Northallerton.

• **GUNNERSIDE, NORTH YORKSHIRE** - Taking its name from the Viking chieftain 'Gunner', the village has a humpbacked bridge known as 'Ivelet Bridge' spanning the river which is said to be haunted by a headless dog.

H HALIFAX, WEST YORKSHIRE - Founded on the cloth trade, and famous for its building society, textiles, carpets and toffee. Most notable landmark is Piece Hall where wool merchants traded, now restored to house shops, museums and art gallery. Home also to Eureka! The Museum for Children.

• **HARROGATE, NORTH YORKSHIRE** - Major conference, exhibition and shopping centre, renowned for its spa heritage and award-winning floral displays, spacious parks and gardens. Famous for antiques, toffee, fine shopping and excellent tea shops, also its Royal Pump Rooms and Baths. Annual Great Yorkshire Show in July.

• **HAWORTH, WEST YORKSHIRE** - Famous since 1820 as home of the Bronte family. The Parsonage is now a Bronte Museum where furniture and possessions of the family are displayed. Moors and Bronte waterfalls nearby and steam trains on the Keighley and Worth Valley Railway pass through.

• **HEBDEN BRIDGE, WEST YORKSHIRE** - Originally a small town on packhorse route, Hebden Bridge grew into a booming mill town in 18th C with rows of 'up-and-down' houses of several storeys built against hillsides. Ancient 'pace-egg play' custom held on Good Friday.

• **HELMSLEY, NORTH YORKSHIRE** - Delightful small market town with red roofs, warm stone buildings and cobbled market square, on the River Rye at the entrance to Ryedale and the North York Moors. Remains of 12th C castle, several inns and All Saints' Church.

• **HEPTONSTALL, WEST YORKSHIRE** - Quaint village above Hebden Bridge with an assortment of narrow streets, weavers' cottages, weather-worn houses and the ruins of a 12th C church. The 17th C grammar school is situated in a churchyard.

• **HIGH BENTHAM, NORTH YORKSHIRE** - Bentham is said to mean 'Home on the Common'. A weekly market has been held here since the 14th C. Good walking country.

• **HOLMFIRTH, WEST YORKSHIRE** - Village on the edge of the Peak District National Park, famous as the location for the filming of the TV series 'Last of the Summer Wine'.

• **HUDDERSFIELD, WEST YORKSHIRE** - Founded on wool and cloth, has a famous choral society. Town centre redeveloped, but several good Victorian buildings remain, including railway station, St Peter's Church, Tolson Memorial Museum, art gallery and nearby Colne Valley Museum.

I ILKLEY, WEST YORKSHIRE - Former spa with an elegant shopping centre and famous for its ballad. The 16th C manor house, now a museum, displays local prehistoric and Roman relics. Popular walk leads up Heber's Ghyll to Ilkley Moor, with the mysterious Swastika Stone and White Wells, 18th C plunge baths.

K KETTLEWELL, NORTH YORKSHIRE - Set in the spectacular scenery of the Yorkshire Dales National Park in Wharfedale, this former market town is a convenient stopping place for climbers and walkers. Dramatic rock formation of Kilnsey Crag is 3 miles south.

• **KIRKBY FLEETHAM, NORTH YORKSHIRE** - Village close to the A1 between dales and moors. Spacious village green has big lime trees and there is the interesting church of St Mary, some remains of moat and walling of a castle and the Hall.

• **KIRKBYMOORSIDE, NORTH YORKSHIRE** - Attractive market town with remains of Norman castle. Good centre for exploring moors. Nearby are wild daffodils of Farndale.

• **KNARESBOROUGH, NORTH YORKSHIRE** - Picturesque market town on the River Nidd. The 14th C keep is the best-preserved part of John of Gaunt's castle, and the manor house with its chequerboard walls was presented by James I to his son Charles as a fishing lodge. Prophetess Mother Shipton's cave. Boating on river.

L LEALHOLM, NORTH YORKSHIRE - Pretty moorland village on the River Esk below Leaholm Moor.

• **LEYBURN, NORTH YORKSHIRE** - Attractive dales market town where Mary Queen of Scots was reputedly captured after her escape from Bolton Castle. Fine views over Wensleydale from nearby.

• **LOFTHOUSE, NORTH YORKSHIRE** - Village on the river Nidd at the foot of bold limestone hills.

M MALTON, NORTH YORKSHIRE - Thriving farming town on the River Derwent with large livestock market. Famous for racehorse training. The local museum has Roman remains and the Eden Camp Modern History Theme Museum transports visitors back to wartime Britain. Castle Howard within easy reach.

• **MIDDLEHAM, NORTH YORKSHIRE** - Town famous for racehorse training, with cobbled squares and houses of local stone. Norman castle, once principal residence of Warwick the Kingmaker and later Richard III. Ancient stronghold of the Neville family was taken over by the Crown after the Battle of Barnet in 1471.

N NAWTON, NORTH YORKSHIRE - Village on the edge of the North York Moors National Park between Helmsley and Kirkbymoorside.

• **NEWTON-ON-RAWCLIFFE, NORTH YORKSHIRE** - Pretty village on the edge of the North York Moors National Park.

• **NORTHALLERTON, NORTH YORKSHIRE** - Formerly a staging post on coaching route to the North and later a railway town. Today a lively market town and administrative capital of North Yorkshire. Parish church of All Saints dates from 1200. Dickens stayed at The Fleece.

P PATELEY BRIDGE, NORTH YORKSHIRE - Market town at centre of Upper Nidderdale. Flax and linen industries once flourished in this remote and beautiful setting. Remains of Bronze Age settlements and disused lead mines.

• **PICKERING, NORTH YORKSHIRE** - Market town and tourist centre on edge of North York Moors. Parish church has complete set of 15th C wall paintings depicting lives of saints. Part of 12th C castle still stands. Beck Isle Museum. The North York Moors Railway begins here.

R RICHMOND, NORTH YORKSHIRE - Market town on edge of Swaledale with 11th C castle, Georgian and Victorian buildings surrounding cobbled market-place. Green Howards' Museum is in the former Holy Trinity Church. Attractions include the Georgian Theatre, restored Theatre Royal, Richmondshire Museum, Easby Abbey.

• **RILLINGTON, NORTH YORKSHIRE** - A stream runs through this large, attractive village which has a quaint old church and is on the main road to Scarborough.

• **RIPON, NORTH YORKSHIRE** - Ancient city with impressive cathedral containing Saxon crypt which houses church treasures from all over Yorkshire. Charter granted in 886 by Alfred the Great. 'Setting the Watch' tradition kept nightly by horn-blower in Market Square. Fountains Abbey nearby.

• **ROBIN HOOD'S BAY, NORTH YORKSHIRE** - Picturesque village of red-roofed cottages with main street running from cliff top down ravine to seashore, a magnet for artists. Scene of much smuggling and shipwrecks in 18th C. Robin Hood reputed to have escaped to continent by boat from here.

• **ROSEDALE ABBEY, NORTH YORKSHIRE** - Sturdy hamlet built around Cistercian nunnery in the reign of Henry II, in the middle of Rosedale, largest of the moorland valleys. Remains of 12th C priory. Disused lead mines on the surrounding moors.

S SCARBOROUGH, NORTH YORKSHIRE - Large, popular East Coast seaside resort, formerly a spa town. Beautiful gardens and two splendid sandy beaches. Castle ruins date from 1100; fine Georgian and Victorian houses. Scarborough Millennium depicts 1,000 years of town's history. Sea Life Centre.

• **SCOTCH CORNER, NORTH YORKSHIRE** - Famous milestone at the junction of the A1 and A66 near Richmond.

• **SEDBUSK, NORTH YORKSHIRE** - Wensleydale village on the River Ure, where hand knitting was once a local industry. Pony trekking centre.

• **SHEFFIELD, SOUTH YORKSHIRE** - Local iron ore and coal gave Sheffield its prosperous steel and cutlery industries. The modern city centre has many interesting buildings - cathedral, Cutlers' Hall, Crucible Theatre, Graves and Mappin Art Galleries. Meadowhall Shopping Centre nearby.

• **SKIPTON, NORTH YORKSHIRE** - Pleasant market town at gateway to dales, with farming community atmosphere, a Palladian Town Hall, parish church and fully roofed castle at the top of the High Street. The Clifford family motto, 'Desoramis' is sculpted in huge letters on the parapet over the castle gateway.

• **STAINTONDALE, NORTH YORKSHIRE** - Moors village north-west of Scarborough with shire horse farm and visitor centre.

• **STAITHES, NORTH YORKSHIRE** - Busy fishing village until growth of Whitby, Staithes is a maze of steep, cobbled streets packed with tall houses of red brick and bright paintwork. Smuggling was rife in 18th C. Cotton bonnets worn by fisherwomen can still be seen. Strong associations with Captain Cook.

T THIRSK, NORTH YORKSHIRE - Thriving market town with cobbled square surrounded by old shops and inns. St Mary's Church is probably the best example of Perpendicular work in Yorkshire. House of Thomas Lord - founder of Lord's Cricket Ground - is now a folk museum.

• **THWAITE, NORTH YORKSHIRE** - Quiet village, ideal for walking the fells of Great Shunner, Kisdon, High Seat, Rogan's Seat and Lovely Seat.

• **TODMORDEN, WEST YORKSHIRE** - In beautiful scenery on the edge of the Pennines at junction of 3 sweeping valleys. Until 1888 the county boundary between Yorkshire and Lancashire cut this old cotton town in half, running through the middle of the Town Hall.

W WHITBY, NORTH YORKSHIRE - Holiday town with narrow streets and steep alleys at the mouth of the River Esk. Captain James Cook, the famous navigator, lived in Grape Lane. 199 steps lead to St Mary's Church and St Hilda's Abbey overlooking harbour. Dracula connections. Gothic weekend every April.

Y YEADON, WEST YORKSHIRE - Once largely concerned with textiles. Close by is Novia House, a reminder of Hannah Green, the Ling Bob Witch. Leeds/Bradford Airport is here, and Yeadon Tarn, a small lake, is east of the town.

• **YORK, NORTH YORKSHIRE** - Ancient walled city nearly 2, 000 years old, containing many well-preserved medieval buildings. Its Minster has over 100 stained glass windows and is the largest Gothic cathedral in England. Attractions include Castle Museum, National Railway Museum, Jorvik Viking Centre and York Dungeon.

HEART of England

The home of Shakespeare, fine china and the grandest palaces in Britain, the region is full of surprises, from the thriving multicultural cities of Birmingham and Nottingham to countryside both dramatic and picturesque.

classic sights

Hardwick Hall – probably Britain's greatest Elizabethan house
Pottery & porcelain – factory tours of Royal Crown Derby, Wedgewood, Spode and more
Ironbridge Gorge – the world's first cast-iron bridge

country

The Cotswolds – picturebook England
The Peak District – moorland, limestone gorges and ancient woodlands

literary links

Stratford-upon-Avon – Royal Shakespeare Company; the homes of Shakespeare and his family
Nottingham – DH Lawrence Birthplace Museum

arts for all

Walsall – The New Art Gallery
Wightwick Manor – arts & crafts masterpiece
Arts Festivals – Bromsgrove, Malvern and Cheltenham

distinctively different

Cadbury World – Chocaholic heaven

The counties of Derbyshire, Gloucestershire, Herefordshire, Leicestershire, Lincolnshire, Northamptonshire, Nottinghamshire, Rutland, Shropshire, Staffordshire, Warwickshire, Worcestershire and West Midlands

FOR MORE INFORMATION CONTACT:

**Heart of England Tourist Board
Larkhill Road, Worcester WR5 2EZ
Tel: (01905) 761100 Fax: (01905) 763450
Internet: www.visitheartofengland.com**

The Pictures:
1 South Shropshire Hills
2 Brindley Place, Birmingham
3 Stratford-upon-Avon

Places to Visit - see pages 168-172
Where to Stay - see pages 173-229

PLACES to visit

You will find hundreds of interesting places to visit during your stay, just some of which are listed in these pages. Contact any Tourist Information Centre in the region for more ideas on days out.

Acton Scott Historic Working Farm

Wenlock Lodge, Acton Scott, Church Stretton, Shropshire SY6 6QN

Tel: (01694) 781306 www.actonscotmuseum.co.uk

Acton Scott Historic Working Farm demonstrates farming and rural life in south Shropshire at the close of the 19thC.

Alton Towers Theme Park

Alton, Stoke-on-Trent, Staffordshire ST10 4DB

Tel: (0870) 520 4060 www.alton-towers.co.uk

Theme Park with over 125 rides and attractions including Oblivion, Nemesis, Haunted House, Runaway Mine Train, Congo River Rapids, Log Flume and many children's rides.

The American Adventure

Ilkeston, Derbyshire DE7 5SX

Tel: (01773) 531521 www.americanadventure.co.uk

The American Adventure has action and entertainment for all ages including the Missile white-knuckle rollercoaster, Europe's tallest skycoaster and the world's wettest log flume.

Belton House, Park and Gardens

Belton, Grantham, Lincolnshire NG32 2LS

Tel: (01476) 566116

The crowning achievement of restoration country house architecture, built in 1685-88 for Sir John Brownlow with alterations by James Wyatt in 1777.

Belvoir Castle Estate Office

Belvoir, Grantham, Lincolnshire NG32 1PD

Tel: (01476) 870262 www.belvoircastle.com

The present castle is the fourth to be built on this site and dates from 1816. Art treasures include works by Poussin, Rubens, Holbein and Reynolds. Queen's Royal Lancers display.

Birmingham Botanical Gardens and Glasshouses

Westbourne Road, Edgbaston, Birmingham, West Midlands B15 3TR

Tel: (0121) 454 1860

www.bham-bot-gdns.demon.co.uk

15 acres (6 ha) of ornamental gardens and glasshouses. Widest range of plants in the Midlands from tropical rainforest to arid desert. Aviaries with exotic birds, children's play area.

Black Country Living Museum

Tipton Road, Dudley, West Midlands DY1 4SQ

Tel: (0121) 557 9643 www.bclm.co.uk

A warm welcome awaits you at Britain's friendliest open-air museum. Wander around original shops and houses, or ride on fair attractions and take a look down the mine.

Blenheim Palace

Woodstock, Oxford, Oxfordshire OX7 1PX
Tel: (01993) 811325
Home of the 11th Duke of Marlborough, birthplace of Sir Winston Churchill. Designed by Vanbrugh in the English Baroque style. Park landscaped by 'Capability' Brown.

Butlins Family Entertainment Resort

Roman Bank, Skegness, Lincolnshire PE25 1NJ
Tel: (01754) 762311
Butlins Family Entertainment Resort has a skyline pavilion, toyland, sub-tropical waterworld, tenpin bowling and entertainments' centre with live shows.

Cadbury World

Linden Road, Bournville, Birmingham, West Midlands B30 2LD
Tel: (0121) 451 4180 www.cadburyworld.co.uk
Story of Cabdury's chocolate includes chocolate-making demonstration and attractions for all ages.

Chatsworth House and Garden

Bakewell, Derbyshire DE45 1PP
Tel: (01246) 582204 www.chatsworth-house.co.uk
Built in 1687-1707 with a collection of fine pictures, books, drawings and furniture. Garden laid out by 'Capability' Brown with fountains, cascades, a farmyard and playground.

Cotswold Farm Park

Guiting Power, Cheltenham, Gloucestershire GL54 5UG
Tel: (01451) 850307
Collection of rare breeds of British farm animals. Pets' corner, adventure playground, Tractor School, picnic area, gift shop, cafe and seasonal farming displays.

Drayton Manor Family Theme Park

Tamworth, Staffordshire B78 3TW
Tel: (01827) 287979 www.draytonmanor.co.uk
A major theme park with over 100 rides and attractions, plus children's rides, Zoo, farm, museums and the new, live 'Popeye Show'.

The Elgar Birthplace Museum

Crown East Lane, Lower Broadheath, Worcester, Worcestershire WR2 6RH
Tel: (01905) 333224 www.elgar.org
Country cottage birthplace displaying Elgar's desk and family possessions, complemented by new Elgar Centre. Memorabilia, sounds and special events illustrate his life.

The Galleries of Justice

Shire Hall, High Pavement, Lace Market, Nottingham, Nottinghamshire NG1 1HN
Tel: (0115) 952 0555 www.galleriesofjustice.org.uk
A museum of law located in and around a 19thC courthouse and county gaol, brought to life by costumed interpreters.

The Heights of Abraham Cable Cars, Caverns and Country Park

Matlock Bath, Matlock, Derbyshire DE4 3PD
Tel: (01629) 582365 www.heights-of-abraham.co.uk
A spectacular cable car ride takes you to the summit where, within the grounds, there is a wide variety of attractions for young and old alike. Gift shop and coffee shop.

Ikon Gallery

1 Oozells Square, Brindleyplace, Birmingham, West Midlands B1 2HS
Tel: (0121) 248 0708 www.ikongallery.co.uk
Ikon Gallery is one of Europe's foremost galleries for presenting the work of living artists within an innovative educational framework.

The Pictures:
1 Cottage Gardens, River Arrow, Herefordshire
2 Darwin Statue, Shrewsbury
3 Packwood House, Warwickshire
4 Rutland Water
5 Rockingham Castle, Northamptonshire

Ironbridge Gorge Museum

Ironbridge, Telford, Shropshire TF8 7AW
Tel: (01952) 433522 www.ironbridge.org.uk
World's first cast-iron bridge, Museum of the Gorge
Visitor Centre, Tar Tunnel, Jackfield Tile Museum, Coalport
China Museum, Rosehill House, Blists Hill Museum and
Museum of Iron.

Lincoln Castle

Castle Hill, Lincoln, Lincolnshire LN1 3AA
Tel: (01522) 511068
A medieval castle, including towers and ramparts, with a
Magna Carta exhibition, a prison chapel experience,
reconstructed Westgate and popular events throughout
the summer.

Museum of British Road Transport

Hales Street, Coventry, West Midlands CV1 1PN
Tel: (024) 7683 2425 www.mbrt.co.uk
200 cars and commercial vehicles from 1896 to date, 200
cycles from 1818 to date, 90 motorcycles from 1920 to
date and the 'Thrust 2' land speed story.

National Sea Life Centre

The Water's Edge, Brindleyplace, Birmingham,
West Midlands B1 2HL
Tel: (0121) 633 4700 www.sealife.co.uk
Over 55 fascinating displays. The opportunity to come
face-to-face with literally hundreds of fascinating sea
creatures, from sharks to shrimps.

The National Tramway Museum

Crich, Matlock, Derbyshire DE4 5DP
Tel: (01773) 852565 www.tramway.co.uk
A collection of over 70 trams from Britain and overseas
from 1873-1969 with tram rides on a 1-mile route, a
period street scene, depots, a power station, workshops
and exhibitions.

Nottingham Industrial Museum

Courtyard Buildings, Wollaton Park, Nottingham,
Nottinghamshire NG8 2AE
Tel: (0115) 915 3910 www.nottinghamcity.gov.uk
An 18thC stables presenting the history of Nottingham's
industries: printing, pharmacy, hosiery and lace. There is
also a Victorian beam engine, a horse gin and transport.

Peak District Mining Museum

The Pavilion, Matlock Bath, Matlock, Derbyshire DE4 3NR
Tel: (01629) 583834 www.peakmines.co.uk
A large exhibition on 3,500 years of lead mining with
displays on geology, mines and miners, tools and
engines. The climbing shafts make it suitable for children
as well.

Rockingham Castle

Rockingham, Market Harborough, Leicestershire LE16 8TH
Tel: (01536) 770240 www.rockinghamcastle.com
An Elizabethan house within the walls of a Norman
castle with fine pictures, extensive views, gardens with
roses and an ancient yew hedge.

Rugby School Museum

10 Little Church Street, Rugby, Warwickshire CV21 3AW
Tel: (01788) 556109
Rugby School Museum tells the story of the school, scene
of 'Tom Brown's Schooldays', and contains the earlier
memorabilia of the game invented on the school close.

Severn Valley Railway

The Railway Station, Bewdley, Worcestershire DY12 1BG
Tel: (01299) 403816 www.svr.co.uk
Preserved standard gauge steam railway running 16
miles between Kidderminster, Bewdley and Bridgnorth.
Collection of locomotives and passenger coaches.

Shakespeare's Birthplace

Henley Street, Stratford-upon-Avon, Warwickshire CV37 6QW
Tel: (01789) 204016 www.shakespeare.org.uk
The world-famous house where William Shakespeare was
born in 1564 and where he grew up. See the highly
acclaimed Shakespeare Exhibition.

The Shrewsbury Quest

193 Abbey Foregate, Shrewsbury, Shropshire SY2 6AH
Tel: (01743) 243324 www.shrewsburyquest.com
12thC medieval visitor attraction. Solve mysteries, create
illuminated manuscripts, play medieval games and relax
in unique herb gardens. Gift shop and cafe.

Shugborough Estate

Shugborough, Milford, Stafford, Staffordshire ST17 0XB
Tel: (01889) 881388 www.staffordshire.gov.uk
18thC mansion house with fine collection of furniture.
Gardens and park contain beautiful neo-classical
monuments.

Skegness Natureland Seal Sanctuary

North Parade, The Promenade, Skegness,
Lincolnshire PE25 1DB
Tel: (01754) 764345 www.skegnessnatureland.co.uk
Collection of performing seals, baby seals, penguins,
aquarium, crocodiles, snakes, terrapins, scorpions, tropical
birds, butterflies (April-October) and pets.

Snibston Discovery Park

Ashby Road, Coalville, Leicester, Leicestershire LE67 3LN
Tel: (01530) 278444 www.leics.gov.uk/museums
An all-weather and award-winning science and
industrial heritage museum.

Spode Visitor Centre

Spode, Church Street, Stoke-on-Trent,
Staffordshire ST4 1BX
Tel: (01782) 744011 www.spode.co.uk
Visitors are shown the various processes in the making of
bone china. Samples can be bought at the Spode Shop.

The Tales of Robin Hood

30-38 Maid Marian Way, Nottingham,
Nottinghamshire NG1 6GF
Tel: (0115) 948 3284
Join the world's greatest medieval adventure. Ride
through the magical green wood and play the Silver
Arrow game, in the search for Robin Hood.

Twycross Zoo

Twycross, Atherstone, Warwickshire CV9 3PX
Tel: (01827) 880250 www.twycrosszoo.com
A zoo with gorillas, orang-utans, chimpanzees, a modern
gibbon complex, elephants, lions, giraffes, a reptile
house, pets' corner and rides.

Walsall Arboretum

Lichfield Street, Walsall, West Midlands WS1 1TJ
Tel: (01922) 653148 www.walsallarboretum.co.uk
Picturesque Victorian park with over 79 acres (32 ha) of
gardens, lakes and parkland.

Warwick Castle

Warwick, Warwickshire CV34 4QU
Tel: (01926) 406600 www.warwick-castle.co.uk
Set in 60 acres (24 ha) of grounds with state rooms,
armoury, dungeon, torture chamber, clock tower, A Royal
Weekend Party 1898, Kingmaker – a preparation for
battle attractions.

The Wedgwood Story Visitor Centre

Barlaston, Stoke-on-Trent, Staffordshire ST12 9ES
Tel: (01782) 204218 www.thewedgwoodstory.com
New £4.5 million visitor centre. It exhibits centuries of
craftsmanship on a plate. Audio guided tour includes
exhibition and demonstration areas. Shop and
restaurants.

The Wildfowl and Wetlands Trust

The Wildfowl and Wetlands Trust
Slimbridge, Gloucester, Gloucestershire GL2 7BT
Tel: (01453) 890333 www.wwt.org.uk
Tropical house, hides, heated observatory, exhibits, shop,
restaurant, children's playground, pond zone.

Worcester Cathedral

10A College Green, Worcester,
Worcestershire WR1 2LH
Tel: (01905) 611002
Norman crypt and chapter house, King John's Tomb,
Prince Arthur's Chantry, medieval cloisters and buildings.
Touch and hearing control visually impaired facilities
available.

The Pictures:
1 Alford Craft Market, Lincolnshire
2 Chatsworth House, Derbyshire

Find out more about
HEART of England

Further information about holidays and attractions in Heart of England is available from:

HEART OF ENGLAND TOURIST BOARD
Larkhill Road, Worcester WR5 2EZ.
Tel: (01905) 761100 Fax: (01905) 763450
Internet: www.visitheartofengland.com

The following publications are available free from the Heart of England Tourist Board:
Heart of England - The Official Guide 2002
Bed & Breakfast Touring Map including Caravan and Camping

Getting to the
HEART of England

BY ROAD: Britain's main motorways (M1/M6/M5) meet in the Heart of England; the M40 links with the M42 south of Birmingham while the M4 provides fast access from London to the south of the region. These road links ensure that the Heart of England is more accessible by road than any other region in the UK.

BY RAIL: The Heart of England lies at the centre of the country's rail network. There are direct trains from London and other major cities to many towns and cities within the region.

The Pictures:
1 River Avon, Evesham
2 Black Country Museum, Dudley

Accommodation entries in this region are listed in alphabetical order of place name, and then in alphabetical order of establishment. As West Oxfordshire and Cherwell are promoted in both Heart of England and South of England, places in these areas with accommodation are listed in this section. See South of England for full West Oxfordshire and Cherwell entries.

Map references refer to the colour location maps at front of this guide. The first number indicates the map to use; the letter and number which follow refer to the grid reference on the map.

At-a-glance symbols at the end of each accommodation entry give useful information about services and facilities. A key to symbols can be found inside the back cover flap. Keep this open for easy reference.

A brief description of the towns and villages offering accommodation in the entries which follow, can be found at the end of this section.

A complete listing of all the English Tourism Council assessed accommodation covered by this guide appears at the back of the guide.

ABBERLEY, Worcestershire Map ref 4A3

★★★

4 Units
Sleeping 2–4

OLD YATES COTTAGES
Old Yates Farm, Abberley, Worcester WR6 6AT
Contact: Mr & Mrs R M Goodman, Old Yates Farm,
Abberley, Worcester WR6 6AT
T: (01299) 896500
F: (01299) 896065
E: oldyates@aol.com
I: www.oldyatescottages.co.uk

OPEN All year round

Low season per wk
£140.00–£200.00
High season per wk
£260.00–£350.00

90-acre livestock farm. Cosy cottages in tranquil surroundings amidst beautiful countryside. A personal welcome awaits you. Convenient for exploring the Midlands and Welsh Borders.

QUALITY ASSURANCE SCHEME

For an explanation of the quality and facilities represented by the Stars please refer to the front of this guide. A more detailed explanation can be found in the information pages at the back.

ALCESTER, Warwickshire Map ref 2B1

★★★★

1 Unit
Sleeping 2

HERONVIEW

Cross Guns Cottage, Mill Lane, Oversley Green, Alcester, Stratford-upon-Avon B49 6LF
T: (01789) 766506 & 07966 201505 (Mobile)
F: (01789) 400851
E: heather@heronview.freeserve.co.uk
I: www.heronview.freeserve.co.uk
Contact: Mr & Mrs Heather and Mike Bosworth

A truly romantic setting 'just for two'. Tourist Board officials had no hesitation in awarding the first De-Luxe classification in Warwickshire. Beautiful gardens run down to the river and fishing lodge. Check out the website for full details or call for a brochure. Stratford-upon-Avon 6 miles.

OPEN All year round

Low season per wk
£280.00–£350.00
High season per wk
£350.00–£420.00

ALDERTON, Gloucestershire Map ref 2B1

★★★-★★★★★

7 Units
Sleeping 3–9

RECTORY FARM COTTAGES

Alderton, Tewkesbury GL20 8NW
T: (01242) 620455
F: (01242) 620455
E: prburton@talk21.com
I: www.rectoryfarmcottages.co.uk
Contact: Mr & Mrs M A Burton

Cotswold-stone house and 4 half-timbered cottages with shared gardens in a pretty courtyard setting in the centre of Alderton. Thatched and half-timbered cottage with own gardens nearby. All cottages have shared use of indoor heated swimming pool and snooker room (full size table). Full central heating. Linen supplied.

OPEN All year round

Low season per wk
£230.00–£500.00
High season per wk
£420.00–£1,100.00

ALFRETON, Derbyshire Map ref 4B2

★★★★

1 Unit
Sleeping 6

THE COACH HOUSE
136A Derby Road, Swanwick, Alfreton DE55 1AD
Contact: Mr & Mrs D M Whitaker, The Old Vicarage, 136 Derby Road, Swanwick, Alfreton DE55 1AD
T: (01773) 605116
F: (01773) 528703
E: pwhitaker@dial.pipex.com

OPEN All year round

Low season per wk
£321.00–£411.00
High season per wk
£329.00–£531.00

Spacious sitting room, dining room modern fitted kitchen with breakfast area. Three bedrooms, 1 double with en suite, shower/WC and 2 twin-bedded with bathroom/ WC. Games room.

USE YOUR *i*s

There are more than 550 Tourist Information Centres throughout England offering friendly help with accommodation and holiday ideas as well as suggestions of places to visit and things to do. You'll find TIC addresses in the local Phone Book.

ALSTONEFIELD, Staffordshire Map ref 4B2

★★★★
2 Units
Sleeping 5–6

Lovingly restored, the cottage originally formed part of Grade II Listed farmhouse. Has featured in 'Period Living' magazine. Warm, cosy, full of character and charm, with stone-flagged floors, low-beamed ceilings, antique furniture, richly coloured rugs, open fires in old range. Wonderful rambles from the cottage door. Organic farm. Exclusive barn also available.

CHURCH FARM COTTAGE
Church Farm, Stanshope, Ashbourne DE6 2AD
Contact: Mrs S Fowler, Church Farm, Stanshope,
Ashbourne DE6 2AD
T: (01335) 310243
F: (01335) 310243
E: sue@fowler89.fsnet.co.uk
I: www.dovedalecottages.co.uk

OPEN All year round

Low season per wk
£239.00–£286.00
High season per wk
£286.00–£430.00

👪♘◎🛏.☉🍴📠≡📺🧺🗑️🔌✂🗑️🐾🅿✿🐦🆂🏤

ALTON, Staffordshire Map ref 4B2

★★
3 Units
Sleeping 6

THE RADDLE INN
Quarry Bank, Hollington, Stoke-on-Trent ST10 4HQ
T: (01889) 507278 & 507568
F: (01889) 507355
E: peter@logcabin.co.uk
I: www.logcabin.co.uk
Contact: Mr P Wilkinson

OPEN All year round
CC: Amex, Barclaycard,
Delta, Eurocard, JCB,
Mastercard, Solo, Switch,
Visa, Visa Electron

Low season per wk
£150.00–£300.00
High season per wk
£200.00–£350.00

A public house/restaurant, set in the countryside, with a log cabin overlooking Croxden Abbey.

👪♘🥄🛏.☉📠📺🧺🗑️✂🗑️🅿✿🐦🆂

ASHBOURNE, Derbyshire Map ref 4B2 *Tourist Information Centre Tel: (01335) 343666*

★★★–★★★★★
4 Units
Sleeping 2–20

MOORE'S COTTAGE FARM
Slack Lane, Upper Mayfield, Ashbourne DE6 2JX
T: (01335) 346121 (Answerphone) &
07932 159895 (Mobile)
F: (01335) 300668
E: janetwatson@waitrose.com
Contact: Mr David Restrick and Janet Watson

OPEN All year round

Low season per wk
£165.00–£235.00
High season per wk
£245.00–£420.00

Family celebrations, friendship reunions. Four delightful cottages with Tara's Hall, games/dining room. Attractive gardens, country views, close to amenities. Safe for children. Pets welcome.

👪♘◎≡🛏.☉🍴📠📺🧺🗑️🗑️🅿✿🐦🆂🏤

★★★★
1 Unit
Sleeping 5

Enjoy the tranquility of an historic Grade II stone farmhouse in National Park and own valley, first founded by 12thC Cistercian monks. Spacious and comfortably modernised with two large double bedrooms. Mullion windows, stone flags, woodstove. Walking and cycling from door. Dogs by arrangement.

THE OLD FARMHOUSE
Roystone Grange, Pikehall, Matlock DE4 2PQ
Contact: Mrs H Quicke, Proprietor, Roystone Grange,
Pikehall, Matlock DE4 2PQ
T: (01335) 390288
F: (01335) 390382
E: roystone@msn.com

OPEN All year round

Low season per wk
£200.00–£240.00
High season per wk
£310.00–£390.00

👪♘◎🛏.☉🍴📠≡📺🧺🗑️🗑️✂🗑️🅿∪✿🐦🆂

IDEAS For ideas on places to visit refer to the introduction at the beginning of this section.

ASHBOURNE continued

★★★★★
1 Unit
Sleeping 2

THORPE CLOUD VIEW
Thorpe House, Thorpe, Ashbourne DE6 2AW
Contact: Mr Philip Ramsbottom, Thorpe House, Thorpe,
Ashbourne DE6 2AW
T: (01335) 350215 & 07801 839661 (Mobile)
E: phil@ramsbottomp.fsnet.co.uk

OPEN All year round

Low season per wk
£175.00–£190.00
High season per wk
£200.00–£225.00

Tastefully converted cottage with beautiful views, retaining its rural character yet providing the comfort of a modern dwelling. Indoor swimming pool. Near Dovedale.

ASHBY-DE-LA-ZOUCH, Leicestershire Map ref 4B3 *Tourist Information Centre Tel: (01530) 411767*

★★★★★
3 Units
Sleeping 2–8

UPPER RECTORY FARM COTTAGES
Snarestone Road, Appleby Magna, Tamworth DE12 7AJ
Contact: Mrs Jean Corbett, Cottage Farm,
Norton-Juxta-Twycross, Atherstone CV9 3QH
T: (01827) 880448
E: w.corbett@farmline.com

Set amidst the wheatfields of Leicestershire, these beautifully converted, single-storey barns are cosy and peaceful, luxuriously furnished and equipped and feature a wealth of oak beams. Lots to do locally; Bosworth Battlefield, Calke Abbey, National Forest etc. Stratford, Warwick, Peak District and Nottinghamshire are within an hour's drive.

OPEN All year round

Low season per wk
£250.00–£500.00
High season per wk
£285.00–£610.00

ASHFORD IN THE WATER, Derbyshire Map ref 4B2

★★★
1 Unit
Sleeping 2

GRITSTONE COTTAGE
c/o Gritstone House, Greaves Lane,
Ashford in the Water, Bakewell DE45 1QH
Contact: Mrs Ann Lindsay, Gritstone House,
Greaves Lane, Ashford in the Water, Bakewell
DE45 1QH
T: (01629) 813563
F: (01629) 813563

OPEN All year round

Low season per wk
£141.00–£183.00
High season per wk
£183.00–£225.00

18thC holiday cottage adjacent to owner's house. Price includes heat, light and bed-linen. Good base for stately homes and open country. No smoking, please.

★★★★★
1 Unit
Sleeping 4

LITTLE BATCH
Church Street, Ashford in the Water,
Bakewell DE44 1QB
Contact: Mrs J Stephens, 1 Hall End Lane,
Ashford in the Water, Bakewell DE45 1QJ
T: (01629) 813909
F: (01629) 813909

OPEN All year round

Low season per wk
£220.00–£240.00
High season per wk
£380.00–£400.00

Refurbished bungalow in grounds of Great Batch Hall. Two bedrooms, two bathrooms, double glazing. Freezer, washing machine, dryer, dishwasher, microwave. Garage. Fuel and linen included.

QUALITY ASSURANCE SCHEME
Star ratings were correct at the time of going to press but are subject to change. Please check at the time of booking.

ATHERSTONE, Warwickshire Map ref 4B3

★★★★

6 Units
Sleeping 2–4

Six superb cottages carefully converted from old farm barns. Each individually furnished to highest standards. Full central heating and all linen and towels included, fully equipped laundry. Enjoy the putting green, barbecue, lovely farm walks. Within easy reach of theatres, castles, cathedrals and museums of Stratford, Warwick, Lichfield and Birmingham.

HIPSLEY FARM COTTAGES

Hipsley Lane, Hurley, Atherstone CV9 2HS
Contact: Mrs A Prosser, Waste Farm, Hurley, Atherstone CV9 2LR
T: (01827) 872437
F: (01827) 872437
E: ann@hipsley.co.uk
I: www.hipsley.co.uk

OPEN All year round

Low season per wk
£245.00–£310.00
High season per wk
£285.00–£380.00

BAKEWELL, Derbyshire Map ref 4B2 *Tourist Information Centre Tel: (01629) 813227*

★★★★★

1 Unit
Sleeping 5

17thC luxuriously refurbished cottage with 2 en suite bedrooms. It has space, character, beams, exposed stonework, stripped pine doors, etc, and is situated within walking distance of ancient Bakewell town centre, famous for its Bakewell pudding. Also same standard en suite cottages availiable at Ashford, Baslow and Eyam. Phone for colour brochure.

ANNE COTTAGE

Yeld Road, Bakewell DE45 1FJ
Contact: Mrs Margaret Smith, Peak District Holidays, Bar End, Bar Road, Baslow, Bakewell DE45 1SF
T: (01246) 582140 (Answerphone) &
07711 457744 (Mobile)

OPEN All year round

Special welcome pack for all guests. Mid-week/weekend breaks available all year (excl Bank Hols).

Low season per wk
£230.00–£360.00
High season per wk
£360.00–£420.00

★★★★

3 Units
Sleeping 4

BALL CROSS FARM COTTAGES
Chatsworth Estate, Bakewell DE45 1PE
T: (01629) 815215
E: info@ballcrossfarm.com
I: www.ballcrossfarm.com
Contact: Mrs J Edwards

OPEN All year round

Low season per wk
£200.00–£250.00
High season per wk
£250.00–£325.00

Three luxury serviced self-contained cottages, sympathetically restored retaining many original architectural features, on the Chatsworth Estate. Breathtaking views, ample parking.

★★★★

1 Unit
Sleeping 6

THE BARN
Main Street, Great Longstone, Bakewell DE45 1TZ
Contact: Mr G J Raymont, 44 Newland Lane,
Ash Green, Coventry CV7 9BA
T: (024) 76644173 (answerphone) &
0774 8543829 (mobile)

OPEN All year round

Low season per wk
£200.00–£350.00
High season per wk
£350.00–£450.00

Detached barn conversion with oak beams and antique furniture. Three bedrooms, 2 bathrooms, living/dining room, kitchen, conservatory, garage and additional parking. Two miles Bakewell.

CREDIT CARD BOOKINGS
If you book by telephone and are asked for your credit card number it is advisable to check the proprietor's policy should you cancel your reservation.

BAKEWELL continued

DALE END FARM

★★★
3 Units
Sleeping 2–7

Gratton Dale, Youlgrave, Bakewell DE45 1LN
T: (01629) 650453
E: john.elizabeth.hague@talk21.com
Contact: Mrs E M Hague

OPEN All year round

Low season per wk
£175.00–£210.00
High season per wk
£225.00–£335.00

Delightful period cottage sleeping 2, and two 3-bedroomed bungalows each sleeping 6/7. Ideal for walking. Weekend breaks. Prices shown are for bungalow – cottage less. Spacious grounds including tennis court.

EDGE VIEW

★★★★
1 Unit
Sleeping 6

Monyash Road, Bakewell DE45 1FG
Contact: Mrs G P Rogers, Penylan, Monyash Road,
Bakewell DE45 1FG
T: (01629) 813336
F: (01629) 813336

OPEN All year round

Low season per wk
£240.00–£300.00
High season per wk
£300.00–£360.00

Three-bedroomed bungalow, with 2 bedrooms and bathroom/toilet on ground floor. Extensive views. Lawn, garden, ample off-road parking. Lock-up garage. Owner maintained.

HADDON GROVE FARM COTTAGES

★★★
10 Units
Sleeping 2–7

Haddon Grove Farm, Monyash Road, Bakewell
DE45 1JF
T: (01629) 813551
F: (01629) 815684
Contact: Mr J H Boxall

OPEN All year round

Low season per wk
£160.00–£310.00
High season per wk
£310.00–£780.00

Attractive collection of converted stone cottages overlooking Lathkill Dale and close to Bakewell. Facilities include recreation room and heated indoor swimming pool.

LIMESTONE COTTAGE

★★★
1 Unit
Sleeping 6

Monyash Road, Bakewell
Contact: Mrs V Hartley, 1 Church Street,
Ashford in the Water, Bakewell DE45 1QB
T: (01629) 813230
E: b&b@hartleycons.co.uk

Located in the heart of the Peak National Park, this popular market town is an ideal base from which to visit many of the attractions that the area has to offer, with the nearby houses of Chatsworth and Haddon, excellent walking in area.

OPEN All year round

Low season per wk
£236.00–£283.00
High season per wk
£338.00–£422.00

YULETIDE COTTAGE

★★★
1 Unit
Sleeping 4

Church Street, Youlgrave, Bakewell DE45 1UR
Contact: Mr & Mrs D Figg, c/o Hollands Butcher's Shop,
Church Street, Youlgrave, Bakewell DE45 1UR
T: (01629) 636234

OPEN All year round

Low season per wk
£170.00–£195.00
High season per wk
£260.00–£340.00

Cottage of character and charm (1740) with private sunny garden. Warm and cosy in winter. Close village pubs, scenic walks and numerous places of interest.

---

www.travelengland.org.uk

Log on for information and inspiration. The latest information on places to visit, events and quality assessed accommodation.

★★★★

3 Units
Sleeping 5–6

SHATTON HALL FARM

Bamford, Hope Valley S33 0BG
T: (01433) 620635 (answerphone/fax)
F: (01433) 620689
E: a.j.kellie@virgin.net
I: freespace.virgin.net/a.j.kellie/home.htm
Contact: Mrs A H Kellie

Three comfortable barn converted cottages, each with own garden or terrace, on this 'out of the way' beautifully situated farmstead, with good access. Waymarked woodland walks, trout lake, tennis court and gardens of interest, open NGS. Each cottage has double and twin bedded rooms, roomy living areas with open fires.

OPEN All year round

Newly converted barn suitable for art, craft and special interest groups.

Low season per wk
£200.00–£280.00
High season per wk
£325.00–£400.00

Rating
Applied For

1 Unit
Sleeping 5

HALL COTTAGE
Over Lane, Baslow, Bakewell DE45 1SA
Contact: Mr & Mrs R W Griffiths, Beechcroft,
School Lane, Baslow, Bakewell DE45 1RZ
T: (01246) 582900
F: (01246) 583675
E: hallcottage@btinternet.com

OPEN All year round

Low season per wk
£240.00–£260.00
High season per wk
£300.00–£350.00

Small stone barn, tastefully restored. Beamed ceilings, fireplace. Quiet location in oldest part of village. Walking distance to shops, pubs, restaurants, Chatsworth and open countryside.

★★★

1 Unit
Sleeping 6

GATHMAN'S COTTAGE

Baumber, Horncastle LN9 5ND
Contact: Mrs W Harrison, Manor Farm, Hemingby,
Horncastle LN9 5QF
T: (01507) 578352
F: (01507) 578352
E: gathmans@freenetname.co.uk
I: www.gathmanscottage.co.uk

This beautiful character cottage is a Grade II Listed building which has been carefully restored and modernised. Built in the early 18thC thatched and of 'mud and stud' construction. The interior is surprisingly roomy with the ceilings beamed throughout. The views are of the peaceful rolling countryside.

OPEN All year round

Short beaks available all year-minimum 3 nights (excl 2 Christmas weeks).

Low season per wk
£250.00
High season per wk
£350.00

★★★

4 Units
Sleeping 2–4

BIBURY HOLIDAY COTTAGES COLN COURT
Arlington, Bibury, Cirencester GL7 5NL
Contact: Mr A R Binns, Cotswold Heritage Ltd,
Coln Cottage, Arlington, Bibury, Cirencester GL7 5NL
T: (01285) 740314
F: (01285) 740314

OPEN All year round
CC: Amex, Barclaycard, Delta, Mastercard, Switch, Visa

Low season per wk
£180.00–£250.00
High season per wk
£250.00–£350.00

Delightful 17thC Cotswold cottages in lovely gardens, set in the beautiful riverside village of Bibury. Within walking distance of shops, pub and restaurants. Ample parking.

ACCESSIBILITY

Look for the symbols which indicate accessibility for wheelchair users. A list of establishments is at the front of this guide.

BIBURY continued

★★★★

2 Units
Sleeping 4

Situated in this picturesque village, these 2 delightful 2-bedroomed cottages offer tastefully furnished, spacious accommodation. Equipped to a high standard to include all the comforts of home. Heating/linen/ electricity included. Private parking. No smoking/pets. An ideal centre for touring Cotswolds and surrounding areas.

COTTESWOLD HOUSE COTTAGES

Arlington, Bibury, Cirencester GL7 5ND
Contact: Mrs Judith Underwood, Cotteswold House,
Arlington, Bibury, Cirencester GL7 5ND
T: (01285) 740609
F: (01285) 740609
E: cotteswold.house@btclick.com
I: home.btclick.com/cotteswold.house

OPEN All year round
CC: Mastercard, Visa

Low season per wk
Min £240.00
High season per wk
Max £350.00

BIRCH VALE, Derbyshire Map ref 4B2

★★★★

1 Unit
Sleeping 8

Relax and enjoy perfect seclusion and privacy in this tastefully converted detached barn of character. Situated on a small hill farm, the property has the advantage of its own private access road, and is surrounded by fields and wonderful dry-stone walls. Four bedrooms, 1 (en suite) with 4-poster bed.

HALLISHAW COTE

Birch Vale, New Mills, High Peak SK22 4QJ
Contact: Mrs Jennifer Hallam, Cold Harbour Farm,
New Mills, High Peak SK22 4QJ
T: (01663) 746155 & 749953
F: (01663) 743299
E: george.hallam@ic24.net
I: www.hallishawcote.co.uk

OPEN All year round

Winter short breaks available.

Low season per wk
£200.00–£400.00
High season per wk
£400.00–£600.00

BISHOP'S CASTLE, Shropshire Map ref 4A3

★★★★

1 Unit
Sleeping 6

The cottage, a wing of the house, is set in 10 acres of gardens and fields, surrounded by open countryside and hills. Lounge and kitchen upstairs for enjoyment of beautiful views. Private garden with patio and swing. Walking, fishing, riding close by. Explore mid-Wales and Shropshire.

APPLE TREE COTTAGE

White Gritt, Minsterley, Shrewsbury SY5 0JN
Contact: Mrs J Brickett, Apple Tree, White Gritt,
Minsterley, Shrewsbury SY5 0JN
T: (01588) 650331
E: JJ@331appletree.freeserve.co.uk
I: www.cottageguide.co.uk/appletree

OPEN All year round

Short breaks available from Nov-end Mar.

Low season per wk
Min £195.00
High season per wk
Max £340.00

SPECIAL BREAKS

Many establishments offer special promotions and themed breaks.
These are highlighted in red. (All such offers are subject to availability.)

BISHOP'S CASTLE continued

★★★

3 Units
Sleeping 2–6

CLAREMONT
Bishop's Castle SY9 5BW
T: (01588) 638170
F: (01588) 638170
E: price@claremontcottages.freeserve.co.uk
I: www.priceclaremont.co.uk
Contact: Mrs A Price

OPEN All year round
CC: Amex, Barclaycard,
Delta, Eurocard, JCB,
Mastercard, Solo, Switch,
Visa, Visa Electron

Low season per wk
£150.00–£250.00
High season per wk
£210.00–£400.00

Three self-contained cottages in grounds of owner's home close to centre of this historic market town. Ideally situated for exploring Shropshire, Herefordshire and Welsh Marches.

BLANKNEY, Lincolnshire Map ref 4C2

★★★

1 Unit
Sleeping 6

BLANKNEY GOLF CLUB
Blankney, Lincoln LN4 3AZ
T: (01526) 320263
F: (01526) 322521
Contact: Mr D Priest

OPEN All year round

Low season per wk
£190.00
High season per wk
£295.00

High quality detached bungalow in the heart of rural Lincolnshire, 1 hour's drive from the coast. Linen provided. Golf available 500 yards by prior booking.

BLOCKLEY, Gloucestershire Map ref 2B1

★★★

1 Unit
Sleeping 5

BROOKDALE
Brook Lane, Blockley, Moreton-in-Marsh GL56 9HR
Contact: Mrs A Taylor, The Stables, Mill Lane, Broom, Alcester B50 4HS
T: (01789) 778674

Brookdale is a mid-18thC 2-bedroomed cottage situated in a quiet lane, near stream, in the delightful village of Blockley. The cottage is very comfortable and has 2 open fires, logs provided. There is a lovely, large, secluded south-facing garden. Ideal for walking/touring. Good food nearby. Sorry no pets/young children.

OPEN All year round

Short breaks available Nov–Mar incl.

Low season per wk
£170.00–£230.00
High season per wk
£210.00–£290.00

★★★

1 Unit
Sleeping 4

HONEYSUCKLE COTTAGE
44 Park Road, Blockley, Moreton-in-Marsh GL56 9BZ
Contact: Miss P Street, Field House, Bibsworth Lane,
Broadway WR12 7LW
T: (01386) 858667
E: pamakin@talk21.com

OPEN All year round

Low season per wk
£205.00–£260.00
High season per wk
£225.00–£295.00

Cotswold-stone cottage with lovely views, completely renovated yet retaining original character. Tastefully furnished. Situated on edge of peaceful village. Ideal base for walking/touring.

★★★–★★★★★

9 Units
Sleeping 2–6

LOWER FARM COTTAGES
Blockley, Moreton-in-Marsh GL56 9DP
Contact: Mrs K Batchelor, Lower Farm Cottages,
Lower Farmhouse, Blockley, Moreton-in-Marsh GL56 9DP
T: (01386) 700237
F: (01386) 700237
I: www.lower-farm.co.uk

Converted barns and typical Cotswold cottages in an idyllic setting on the edge of this pretty Cotswold village, ideally situated to explore the numerous attractions of the Cotswolds, including Stratford, castles, gardens and wildlife parks. Cottages tastefully furnished with a blend of antique and new furnishings, together with modern facilities.

OPEN All year round

Winter breaks. Short breaks in season at short notice subject to availability.

Low season per wk
£160.00–£319.00
High season per wk
£289.00–£607.00

BODENHAM, Herefordshire Map ref 2A1

★★★-★★★★★

3 Units
Sleeping 4–6

THE FORGE

Bodenham, Hereford HR1 3JZ
T: (01568) 797144
E: andy-timmer@bodenham.freeserve.co.uk
I: www.bodenhamforge.co.uk
Contact: Mrs M E Timmer

Choose from an imaginatively converted smithy, granary or hayloft. Outstanding accommodation, picturesque orchard setting. Next to the river on the edge of a conservation village, with country walks. Hampton Court Gardens, Black and White Village trail, city of Hereford all within easy reach making this the perfect place to stay.

OPEN All year round
CC: Amex, Barclaycard, JCB, Mastercard, Switch, Visa

Low season per wk
£160.00–£220.00
High season per wk
£220.00–£420.00

BOSTON, Lincolnshire Map ref 3A1 *Tourist Information Centre Tel: (01205) 356656*

★★★

1 Unit
Sleeping 2

THE LODGE AT PINEWOOD

Pinewood, Ralphs Lane, Frampton West, Boston PE20 1QZ
Contact: Ms Sylvia Kilshaw, Pinewood, Ralphs Lane, Frampton West, Boston PE20 1QZ
T: (01205) 723739
F: (01205) 723739
E: skilshaw@pinewood99.demon.co.uk

The Lodge is an all-electric, centrally heated twin-bedded bungalow with conservatory, set in a large pleasant garden shared with the owner. Approximately 3 miles from the historic market town of Boston, it is close to the Wolds, sea, fishing and golf. Sorry, no pets. Brochure on request.

OPEN All year round

Low season per wk
Min £160.00
High season per wk
Max £210.00

BOURTON-ON-THE-WATER, Gloucestershire Map ref 2B1 *Tourist Information Centre Tel: (01451) 820211*

★★★★

1 Unit
Sleeping 4

ANNES COTTAGE
3 Colletts Court, Bourton-on-the-Water, Cheltenham GL54 2AR
Contact: Mrs A Oakes, White Rails Farm, Atch Lench, Evesham WR11 5SP
T: (01386) 870727 & 07712 112998
F: (01386) 870727
E: deborah.oakes@persona-mgt.co.uk

OPEN All year round

Low season per wk
Min £230.00
High season per wk
Max £380.00

An immaculate modern stone cottage. One double, one twin bedroom. Very comfortable and cosy. Two minutes' walk to village centre. Perfect for touring the Cotwolds.

★★★★

2 Units
Sleeping 6

OXLEIGH COTTAGES
Moore Road, Bourton-on-the-Water, Cheltenham GL54 2AZ
Contact: Mrs B Smith, Dairy House Farm, Croxton Lane, Middlewich CW10 9LA
T: (01606) 833245 & 07773 474108
F: (01606) 837139
E: bsmith_croxton@yahoo.co.uk

OPEN All year round

Low season per wk
£280.00–£320.00
High season per wk
£350.00–£720.00

Three-bedroomed cottages, semi-detached. Fully equipped. Four-poster beds, dishwashers, satellite TV, log fires, gas central heating, lawned garden, barbecue. Private off-road parking.

PRICES
Please check prices and other details at the time of booking.

BOURTON-ON-THE-WATER continued

★★★★
1 Unit
Sleeping 6–7

Pheasant Walk is a spacious well-furnished cottage attached to the owner's home. The attractive rear garden with pond overlooks open farmland. Village pub a short walk. Close to beauty spots of Bourton, the Slaughters and Stow. Cheltenham, Oxford and Stratford are withing easy driving distance. Sleeps 6/7.

PHEASANT WALK

Grove Farm, Cold Aston, Nr Boughton-on-the-Water, Cheltenham GL54 3BJ
Contact: Mrs P Avery, Proprietor, Grove Farm, Cold Aston, Cheltenham GL54 3BJ
T: (01451) 810942
F: (01451) 810942
E: grovefarm@coldaston.fsnet.co.uk

OPEN All year round

Short breaks available in low season.

Low season per wk	£345.00–£425.00
High season per wk	£485.00–£525.00

BRIDGNORTH, Shropshire Map ref 4A3 *Tourist Information Centre Tel: (01746) 763257*

★★★★★
1 Unit
Sleeping 4

The Barn has 2 double bedrooms, both offer the guests' opportunity to relax in a dream-like setting. Includes a spacious, beamed living room and dining room, fully equipped country kitchen. The Barn's very own walled garden is an oasis of flowering plants and fauna, and includes a built-in barbecue.

THE BARN

Turley Green, Alveley, Bridgnorth WV15 6LP
Contact: Mr K Hazelwood, Bay Horse Farm, Drakelow Lane, Wolverley, Kidderminster DY11 5RY
T: (01562) 850671 & 07850 287209

OPEN All year round

For special offers or late deals tel: 07850 287209.

Low season per wk	£200.00–£300.00
High season per wk	£350.00–£450.00

★★★
5 Units
Sleeping 3–9

Superbly furnished cottage with stone featured walls. Fully equipped, centrally heated. Quiet location near owner's 17thC inn. Sleeps 7. Ideally situated for visiting the many places of interest nearby. Choice of other cottages/apartments (3 on ground floor). Short breaks available.

BULLS HEAD COTTAGES

Chelmarsh, Bridgnorth WV16 6BA
Contact: Mr D Baxter, The Bulls Head, Chelmarsh, Bridgnorth WV16 6BA
T: (01746) 861469
F: (01746) 862646
E: dave@bullshead.fsnet.co.uk
I: www.stargate-uk.co.uk/bullshead

OPEN All year round
CC: Barclaycard, Delta, Mastercard, Solo, Switch, Visa, Visa Electron

Low season per wk	£200.00–£250.00
High season per wk	£250.00–£440.00

CHECK THE MAPS

The colour maps at the front of this guide show all the cities, towns and villages for which you will find accommodation entries.
Refer to the town index to find the page on which they are listed.

BRIDGNORTH continued

★★★
3 Units
Sleeping 4–5

Three cottages on a 330-acre dairy, arable and free-range poultry farm 3 miles south west of Bridgnorth. Situated in beautiful countryside, the Victorian cottages are very comfortably furnished and well-equipped with their own attractive gardens. Peaceful location, an ideal centre for exploring Shropshire and visiting Bridgnorth, Ironbridge, Ludlow and Shrewsbury.

EUDON BURNELL COTTAGES

Eudon Burnell Farm, Bridgnorth WV16 6UD
Contact: Mrs M A Crawford Clarke, Eudon Burnell, Bridgnorth WV16 6UD
T: (01746) 789235
F: (01746) 789550
E: eudonburnell@virtual-shropshire.co.uk
I: www.stargate-uk.co.uk/eudon-burnell-cottages

OPEN All year round	Low season per wk £180.00–£320.00
Winter/autumn short breaks, 2 nights minimum. Log fire in 2 cottages. £40–£65 per day.	High season per wk £200.00–£320.00

★★★
1 Unit
Sleeping 4

THE GRANARY
The Old Vicarage, Ditton Priors, Bridgnorth WV16 6SQ
T: (01746) 712272 & 712288
F: (01746) 712288
E: allens@oldvicditton.freeserve.co.uk
Contact: Mrs Sarah Allen

OPEN All year round

| Low season per wk £120.00 |
| High season per wk £170.00 |

Farm granary in unspoilt South Shropshire countryside. Bridgnorth within easy reach, Ludlow 16 miles. Studio sitting room, bedroom, kitchen, bathroom. Excellent walking.

★★★★
2 Units
Sleeping 4–6

Nestling beside the River Severn in a peaceful hamlet, our converted coach house provides exceptional accommodation. Two apartments, sleeping four and six. Large patios, landscaped gardens, separate barbecues, ample parking. Guests enjoy exclusive fishing rights on 0.5 mile of private water on River Severn.

NO.1 & 2 COACHMANS COTTAGE

Lower Forge, Eardington, Bridgnorth WV16 5LQ
Contact: Mrs Helen Turner, Severn House, Lower Forge, Eardington, Bridgnorth WV16 5LQ
T: (01746) 768197 (Answerphone) & 07778 807413 (Mobile)
F: (01746) 768847

OPEN All year round	Low season per wk £250.00–£275.00
Oct–Mar, long weekend, Fri, Sat, Sun night–just £100, all fishing included.	High season per wk £315.00–£350.00

★★
1 Unit
Sleeping 6

TUDOR COTTAGE
16 High Street, Claverley, Bridgnorth WV5 7DR
Contact: Mrs J B Henshaw, The White Cottage, 17 High Street, Claverley, Bridgnorth WV5 7DR
T: (01746) 710262

OPEN May–Oct

| Low season per wk Min £210.00 |
| High season per wk Max £250.00 |

Charming old cottage with beautiful garden in the old world village of Claverley. All amenities. Many places of interest within easy distance.

BROAD CAMPDEN, Gloucestershire Map ref 2B1

★★★
1 Unit
Sleeping 5

LION COTTAGE
Broad Campden, Chipping Campden GL55 6UR
T: (01386) 840077 (Answerphone)
Contact: Mrs B L Rawcliffe

OPEN All year round

| Low season per wk £215.00–£235.00 |
| High season per wk £260.00–£330.00 |

Cotswold stone-built cottage with beamed ceilings and open fireplace. Open plan living room with sitting, dining and kitchen areas; 1 double, 1 twin, 1 single bedroom.

BROADWAY, Worcestershire Map ref 2B1

★★★

1 Unit
Sleeping 2

HESTERS HOUSE
86 High Street, Broadway WR12 7AJ
Contact: Mrs L Dungate, Inglenook, Brokengate Lane,
Denham, Uxbridge UB9 4LA
T: (01895) 834357
F: (01895) 832904
E: pdungate@aol.com

OPEN All year round

Low season per wk
£175.00
High season per wk
£225.00

Charming, oak-beamed end of terrace cottage with small courtyard, fronting Broadway High Street. A delightful cosy home from which to tour Cotswolds. Prices include gas, electricity.

BROMSGROVE, Worcestershire Map ref 4B3 *Tourist Information Centre Tel: (01527) 831809*

★★★

1 Unit
Sleeping 4

EAST VIEW APARTMENT
Little Shortwood, Brockhill Lane, Tardebigge,
Bromsgrove B60 1LU
Contact: Mrs A Westwood, Little Shortwood,
Brockhill Lane, Tardebigge, Bromsgrove B60 1LU
T: (01527) 63180 (Answerphone)
F: (01527) 63180
E: westwoodja@hotmail.com

OPEN All year round

Low season per wk
Min £110.00
High season per wk
Max £180.00

Modernised flat in beamed 17thC cottage, on smallholding in open countryside near canal. Ten minutes M5/M42 junctions. Private 0.5 mile drive. Sleeps 2/4.

BURFORD, Oxfordshire

See South of England region

BURWARTON, Shropshire Map ref 4A3

★★★★

1 Unit
Sleeping 8

THE WICKET
Burwarton, Bridgnorth WV16 6QH
Contact: Mrs J M Millard,
Brown Clee Holidays Estate Office, Burwarton,
Bridgnorth WV16 6QQ
T: (01746) 787207 & 787422
E: millard@burwarton-estates.co.uk

OPEN Apr–Oct

Low season per wk
Min £385.00
High season per wk
Min £475.00

Peace and seclusion-fully equipped spacious 3-bedroomed cottage on a beautiful private estate. Dogs/horses allowed. Fishing. Suitable for 2 families.

BUXTON, Derbyshire Map ref 4B2 *Tourist Information Centre Tel: (01298) 25106*

★★★–★★★★★

1 Unit
Sleeping 14

Superbly equipped, elevated south-facing detached bungalow at end of riverside lane with unbroken views of Wye Valley (Monsal Trail). Peaceful paradise with 1 acre of private gardens. Immediate access to spectacular walks. Ideal for large groups, anniversaries, etc. Dining for 12 or more around same table. Weekenders welcome.

THE BUNGALOW AT LITTON MILL

Litton Mill, Miller's Dale, Buxton SK17 8SW
Contact: Mr Marcus Milton, 7 Mountlands,
Hardwick Square South, Buxton SK17 6QD
T: (01298) 27778 (Mobile diverts) & 27446 (Day)
F: (01298) 73045
E: hoe@litton-mill.clara.net
I: www.litton-mill.clara.net

OPEN All year round
CC: Eurocard

Weekend breaks special-3
nights, 14 adults, equivalent
to under £14pppn.

Low season per wk
£580.00–£990.00
High season per wk
£700.00–£1,200.00

TOWN INDEX

This can be found at the back of this guide. If you know where you want to stay, the index will give you the page number listing accommodation in your chosen town, city or village.

BUXTON continued

★★★
1 Unit
Sleeping 10

THE OLD STABLES
Back Torr Street, Buxton SK17 6HW
Contact: Mr & Mrs T B Cowlishaw, 136 Green Lane,
Buxton SK17 9DQ
T: (01298) 71086 (evenings/weekend) &
71086 (Evening)
F: (01298) 77678
E: jackie@cowlishawtravel.co.uk

OPEN All year round

Low season per wk
£256.00–£448.00
High season per wk
£448.00–£648.00

Converted town stables retaining character. Warm, comfortable, sleeps 10 in four bedrooms. 3 shower/bathrooms. Close to local facilities, opera house, pavilion gardens, shops and pubs.

★★★
1 Unit
Sleeping 2

SITTINGLOW FARM
Dove Holes, Buxton SK17 8DA
T: (01298) 812271
Contact: Mrs Ann S Buckley

OPEN All year round

Low season per wk
£100.00–£160.00
High season per wk
£160.00–£185.00

Superior ground level cottage adjoining farmhouse. Peaceful surroundings, magnificent views. Easy access from village. Buxton 4 miles. Storage radiators and linen included. Other electricity metered.

CARSINGTON, Derbyshire Map ref 4B2

★★★–★★★★★
17 Units
Sleeping 2–10

KNOCKERDOWN HOLIDAY COTTAGES
Knockerdown Farm, Knockerdown,
Ashbourne DE6 1NQ
Contact: Ms Cathy Lambert, Knockerdown Farm
Cottages, Knockerdown, Ashbourne DE6 1NQ
T: (01629) 540525
F: (01629) 540525
E: cathy@knockerdown-cottages.co.uk
I: www.derbyshireholidaycottages.co.uk

OPEN All year round
CC: Barclaycard, Delta,
Mastercard, Switch, Visa

Low season per wk
£230.00–£630.00
High season per wk
£416.00–£1,407.00

Adjacent to village inn. Indoor pool, sauna, gym, outdoor play area. Central for both Derbyshire and Staffordshire's many attractions. Five minutes to beautiful Carsington Reservoir.

CHARLBURY, Oxfordshire

See South of England region

CHELMORTON, Derbyshire Map ref 4B2

★★★
1 Unit
Sleeping 6

THE HALL
Town End Farm, Chelmorton, Buxton SK17 9SH
Contact: Mrs L F Marsden, Town End Farm, Chelmorton,
Buxton SK17 9SH
T: (01298) 85249
E: charles.marsden@nottingham.ac.uk

Three-bedroomed, self-contained part of a 17thC farmhouse set in open countryside within the historic landscape of the Peak District village of Chelmorton. Garden includes large lawn suitable for games. Eight kilometres from Buxton, 11 from Bakewell, close to Chatsworth and easy access to Alton Towers. Excellent walking and touring country.

OPEN Apr–Sep

Low season per wk
£230.00–£270.00
High season per wk
£270.00–£300.00

CHELTENHAM, Gloucestershire Map ref 2B1 *Tourist Information Centre Tel: (01242) 522878*

★★★
3 Units
Sleeping 2–4

BALCARRAS FARM HOLIDAY COTTAGES
Balcarras Farm, London Road, Charlton Kings,
Cheltenham GL52 6UT
Contact: Mr & Mrs D Ballinger, Balcarras Farm,
London Road, Charlton Kings, Cheltenham GL52 6UT
T: (01242) 584837 (Answerphone)
E: ballinger@bfhc.fsnet.co.uk

OPEN All year round

Low season per wk
£170.00–£185.00
High season per wk
£230.00–£300.00

Single-storey cottages built in 1992 around three sides of paved courtyard at rear of owner's former farmhouse. Footpaths to rear of property on to Cotswold Way.

CHELTENHAM continued

★★★★
1 Unit
Sleeping 4–6

THE GARDEN FLAT
20 Lansdown Parade, Cheltenham GL50 2LH
Contact: Ms Jenny Wardle, Change Forum Ltd,
20 Lansdown Parade, Cheltenham GL50 2LH
T: (01242) 577450
F: (01242) 527151
E: jennyw@changeforum.co.uk

OPEN All year round

Low season per wk
Min £350.00
High season per wk
Max £500.00

Set within a listed Regency terrace. Pretty private courtyard at rear. Within 10 minutes' walk of town centre and station. Ideal Cotswold touring base.

★★★★
3 Units
Sleeping 2–4

HOLMER COTTAGES
Haines Orchard, Woolstone, Cheltenham GL52 9RG
T: (01242) 672848 (Answerphone)
F: (01242) 672848
E: holmercottages@talk21.com
Contact: Mrs Jill Collins

Late 19thC semi-detached brick cottages, each with own separate sun terrace and private garden, overlooking old apple orchard. Situated in a small rural hamlet convenient for Cotswolds, Malverns, Severn Valley and racing at Cheltenham.

OPEN All year round

Low season per wk
£190.00–£250.00
High season per wk
£290.00–£360.00

★★★
1 Unit
Sleeping 4

PRIORY COTTAGE
Southam Lane, Southam, Cheltenham GL52 3NY
Contact: Mr I S Mant, Church Gate, Southam Lane,
Southam, Cheltenham GL52 3NY
T: (01242) 584693
F: (01242) 584693
E: iansmant@hotmail.com

Old Cotswold-stone cottage in own garden overlooking apple orchard. Cosy and warm in winter with wood-burning stove. Two bedrooms, one double, one twin; sitting room, dining room, modern fitted kitchen. Ideal touring base for Gloucestershire and surrounds. By Area of Outstanding Natural Beauty. Nearby footpaths include Cotswold Way.

OPEN All year round

Low season per wk
£250.00–£275.00
High season per wk
£275.00–£295.00

★★★
1 Unit
Sleeping 4

UPPER COBERLEY FARM
Upper Coberley, Cheltenham GL53 9RB
T: (01242) 870306
E: allen@uppercoberley.freeserve.co.uk
Contact: Mrs A Allen

OPEN All year round

Low season per wk
£205.00–£240.00
High season per wk
£240.00–£290.00

Spacious self-contained wing of 18thC Cotswold-stone farmhouse offering comfortable accommodation, set in Area of Outstanding Natural Beauty. Ideal touring and walking centre.

CHESTERFIELD, Derbyshire Map ref 4B2 *Tourist Information Centre Tel: (01246) 345777*

★★★★
1 Unit
Sleeping 5

PLOUGHMANS COTTAGE
Low Farm, Main Road, Marsh Lane, Sheffield S21 5RH
T: (01246) 435328
F: (01246) 435328
Contact: Mr and Mrs W G Fry

OPEN All year round

Low season per wk
£190.00–£220.00
High season per wk
£220.00–£240.00

Superb single-storey barn conversion with own garden and parking. Sleeps 4 plus cot. Open views. Many and varied places of interest to visit.

CHIPPING CAMPDEN, Gloucestershire Map ref 2B1

★★★★
1 Unit
Sleeping 4

CHAPTER COTTAGE
6 Park Road, Chipping Campden GL55 6EA
Contact: Mr P Revers, The Tyning, Blind Lane,
Chipping Campden GL55 6ED
T: (01386) 841450 & 07866 887495
E: prpco@dircon.co.uk
I: www.perpetuare.com

OPEN All year round

Low season per wk
Min £225.00
High season per wk
Min £325.00

Character cottage with 1st and 2nd floor apartment. Antique and co-ordinated furnishings. Double bedroom with bathroom, 1 twin bedroom with shower room.

★★★★
1 Unit
Sleeping 4

Exceptional cottage which has been lovingly renovated. Beautifully situated, tucked away at bottom of lane in picturesque Cotswold village, 1 mile from Chipping Campden. Exposed beams, wood floors, oriental rugs, log fire. Garden. Welcome tray with homemade cake and fresh flowers on arrival. Three other cottages and flat available, sleeping 2-8.

SHEPHERD'S COTTAGE

Broad Campden, Chipping Campden
Contact: Miss S Rolland, Campden Cottages, Folly Cottage,
Paxford, Chipping Campden GL55 6XG
T: (01386) 593315
F: (01386) 593057
E: campdencottages@btinternet.com
I: www.campdencottages.co.uk

OPEN All year round

Low season per wk
Min £275.00
High season per wk
Max £475.00

★★★★
1 Unit
Sleeping 5

WHISTLERS CORNER
6 West End Terrace, Chipping Campden GL55 6AX
Contact: Mr R Hutsby, Middle Hill Farm, Charlecote,
Warwick CV35 9EH
T: (01789) 841525 & 07778 153180 (mobile)
F: (01789) 841523
E: robert.hutsby@btinternet.com
I: www.broadway-cotswolds.co.uk/whistlers.html

OPEN All year round

Low season per wk
£240.00–£350.00
High season per wk
£335.00–£495.00

Victorian semi-detached cottage tastefully restored and furnished with many personal touches. Secluded patio. Quietly situated near centre with many eating establishments, restaurants and shops.

CHIPPING NORTON, Oxfordshire

See South of England region

CHURCH STRETTON, Shropshire Map ref 4A3

★★★★
1 Unit
Sleeping 3

BERRY'S COFFEE HOUSE
17 High Street, Church Stretton SY6 6BU
T: (01694) 724452
E: all@berryscoffeehouse.co.uk
I: www.berryscoffeehouse.co.uk
Contact: Mr J Gott

OPEN All year round
CC: Delta, Mastercard,
Visa

Low season per wk
£200.00–£250.00
High season per wk
£250.00–£300.00

Flat is on the 1st and 2nd floor of the early Victorian wing of a Queen Anne townhouse in the centre of Church Stretton.

MAP REFERENCES
The map references refer to the colour maps at the front of this guide. The first figure is the map number; the letter and figure which follow indicate the grid reference on the map.

CHURCH STRETTON continued

★★★

3 Units
Sleeping 2–6

BOTVYLE FARM

All Stretton, Church Stretton SY6 7JN
Contact: Mr & Mrs G Bebbington, Botvyle Farm,
All Stretton, Church Stretton SY6 7JN
T: (01694) 722869

In the heart of the Stretton Hills, sympathetically converted cottages retaining original character. Tastefully furnished and equipped to a high standard. Superb views. Ideal base for touring, walking, bird-watching. Easy access to Ludlow, Shrewsbury, Ironbridge. Pub, shop under 2 miles. Brochure available.

OPEN Jan, Mar–Dec

Short breaks (minimum 2 nights).

Low season per wk
£140.00–£220.00
High season per wk
£200.00–£350.00

★★★★

1 Unit
Sleeping 4

BROOK HOUSE FARM
Wall-under-Heywood, Church Stretton SY6 7DS
T: (01694) 771308
Contact: Mrs Joan Egerton

Delightfully converted farm cottage in Area of Outstanding Natural Beauty. Wheelchair friendly, non-smoking. Near Ludlow, Ironbridge and Shrewsbury. Also bed and breakfast.

OPEN All year round

Low season per wk
£250.00–£350.00
High season per wk
£250.00–£350.00

★★★★★

2 Units
Sleeping 8

BROOME FARM COTTAGES

Broome Farm, Chatwall, Church Stretton SY6 7LD
T: (01694) 771776 (answerphone) &
07968 057873 (mobile)
F: (01694) 771784
E: mark@broome-farm.co.uk
I: broome-farm.co.uk
Contact: Mr M Cavendish

A beautiful 160-acre farm with views over some of Shropshire's finest countryside. Two delightful 17thC former barns converted to luxury holiday cottages. Both properties include modern bathrooms, attractively decorated bedrooms with high ceilings and exposed beams, fully equipped kitchens, open fires, satellite television, telephone, etc. Smoking and pets permitted.

OPEN All year round

2, 3 and 4 night stays available.

Low season per wk
£359.00–£505.00
High season per wk
£362.00–£675.00

★★★★

1 Unit
Sleeping 4

GRANARY COTTAGE
Lower Day House, Church Preen, Church Stretton
SY6 7LH
Contact: Mr & Mrs J Kirkwood, Lower Day House,
Church Preen, Church Stretton SY6 7LH
T: (01694) 771521
E: jim@lowerdayhouse.freeserve.co.uk

Part of an 18thC farm courtyard. The cottage was originally a grain store and is sited next to a 17thC oak-framed threshing barn. Traditional Shropshire farm environment.

OPEN All year round

Low season per wk
Min £190.00
High season per wk
Max £300.00

★★★

8 Units
Sleeping 2–4

LONGMYND HOTEL
Cunnery Road, Church Stretton SY6 6AG
T: (01694) 722244
F: (01694) 722718
E: reservations@longmynd.co.uk
I: www.longmynd.co.uk
Contact: Mr M Chapman

The hotel offers restaurant meals, afternoon tea, bar snacks and use of swimming pool, sauna, solarium, trim gym, pitch 'n' putt and croquet lawn.

OPEN All year round
CC: Amex, Barclaycard,
Delta, Diners, Eurocard,
Mastercard, Switch, Visa

Low season per wk
£160.00–£300.00
High season per wk
£200.00–£375.00

CHURCH STRETTON continued

★★★
1 Unit
Sleeping 2

REDWOOD HEIGHTS
Watling Street South, Church Stretton SY6 7BJ
T: (01694) 724332 & 07703 413132
E: maureen@redwoodheights.freeserve.co.uk
Contact: Mrs M Bond

OPEN All year round

Low season per wk
£180.00
High season per wk
£180.00

Spacious wing of large modern house, built on a hill in Church Stretton. Private entrance off own sun-terraced lounge. Beautiful views.

CIRENCESTER, Gloucestershire Map ref 2B1 *Tourist Information Centre Tel: (01285) 654180*

★★★★
5 Units
Sleeping 2–6

GLEBE FARM HOLIDAY LETS
Glebe Farm, Barnsley Road, Cirencester GL7 5DY
T: (01285) 659226 (Answerphone)
F: (01285) 642622
Contact: Mrs P Handover

Five beamed cottages 3 miles from Cirencester, ideal for touring Cotswolds, Stratford, Bath and Oxford. Converted to a high standard, furnished with antiques and pine – all modern conveniences. Located in very peaceful surroundings. Patio, garden, barbecue, ample parking, laundry room, pay phone. Pets welcome. No hidden extras. Brochure.

OPEN All year round

Low season per wk
£150.00–£250.00
High season per wk
£250.00–£490.00

★★★★
1 Unit
Sleeping 2–5

THE MALTHOUSE GRANARY
Poulton, Cirencester GL7 5HN
Contact: Mrs B O'Leary, Proprietor, The Malthouse,
Poulton, Cirencester GL7 5HN
T: (01285) 850006 & 850433
F: (01285) 850437
E: bernie.oleary@btinternet.com

A delightful converted stable block adjoining Grade II Listed Cotswold Malthouse. Has a walled garden with summerhouse and patio, beamed kitchen with Aga and a handsome drawing room with a log burning fire. Within walking distance of horse riding facilities and a 5 minute drive to the Cotswold water parks.

OPEN All year round
CC: Barclaycard,
Mastercard, Visa

Low season per wk
£300.00–£400.00
High season per wk
£450.00–£550.00

★★
1 Unit
Sleeping 4

MAYFIELD COTTAGE
Cheltenham Road, Perrott's Brook, Cirencester GL7 7BH
Contact: Mrs J I Hutson, Mayfield House,
Cheltenham Road, Perrotts Brook, Cirencester GL7 7BH
T: (01285) 831301
F: (01285) 831301
E: jhutson@btclick.com

OPEN All year round
CC: Barclaycard, Delta,
Mastercard, Switch, Visa

Low season per wk
£180.00–£230.00
High season per wk
£255.00

Semi-detached, part Cotswold-stone cottage, overlooking open fields and Churn Valley. On A435, 2 miles north Cirencester. Ideal for touring Cotswolds. Area of Outstanding Natural Beauty. No pets please.

NB IMPORTANT NOTE
Information on accommodation listed in this guide has been supplied by the proprietors. As changes may occur you are advised to check details at the time of booking.

CIRENCESTER continued

★★★★

4 Units
Sleeping 2–7

110-acre mixed farm. Well-equipped, superior barn conversions, 4 miles from Cirencester. Quiet rural situation beside Thames. Adjacent Cotswold Water Park. Ideal touring centre for Oxford, Bath, Stratford, Stonehenge and Cotswolds. Good local walks including Thames path. Two single storey cottages. Central heating. Open all year. Ample parking. Linen provided.

OLD MILL COTTAGES

Old Mill Farm, Poole Keynes, Cirencester GL7 6ED
Contact: Mrs Catherine Hazell, Ermin House Farm, Syde,
Cheltenham GL53 9PN
T: (01285) 821255 & 07799 420020
F: (01285) 821531
E: catherine@oldmillcottages.fsnet.co.uk
I: www.oldmillcottages.co.uk

OPEN All year round

Low season per wk
£160.00–£300.00
High season per wk
£240.00–£650.00

★★★★★

1 Unit
Sleeping 10–12

Beautifully appointed farmhouse in 4 acres of stunning, secluded countryside. Sleeps up to 12 in 6 bedrooms all en suite. Large dining room, 2 kitchens, hall, spacious drawing room with wood-burning stove. Lawn, sheltered terrace and rough games field. Gourmet catering if required. Five miles from Cirencester. Good walking.

THE TALLET COTTAGE

Calmsden, Cirencester GL7 5ET
Contact: Mrs V J Arbuthnott, The Tallet, Calmsden,
Cirencester GL7 5ET
T: (01285) 831437
F: (01285) 831437
E: vanessa@thetallet.demon.co.uk
I: www.thetallet.co.uk

OPEN All year round

Low season per wk
£592.00–£890.00
High season per wk
£670.00–£995.00

CLIFTON UPON TEME, Worcestershire Map ref 2B1

★★★★★

1 Unit
Sleeping 4

Detached, timber-framed, single-storey cottage in centuries-old village set high above the river, within beautiful Teme Valley. Furnished to high standards, welcoming, warm, comfortable and spotlessly clean. Interesting visits, activities, walks and marvellous views abound. A place to unwind – come and discover it. Sorry, no smokers/pets. Brochure.

HOPEWAY COTTAGE

The Village, Clifton upon Teme, Worcester WR6 6EN
Contact: Mr & Mrs C&E White, Hope Wynd, The Village,
Clifton upon Teme, Worcester WR6 6EN
T: (01886) 812496
F: (01886) 812429
E: countryways@hopeway.co.uk
I: www.hopeway.co.uk

OPEN All year round

Low season per wk
£220.00–£260.00
High season per wk
£295.00–£395.00

SYMBOLS The symbols in each entry give information about services and facilities. A key to these symbols appears at the back of this guide.

COLEFORD, Gloucestershire Map ref 2A1 *Tourist Information Centre Tel: (01594) 812388*

★★★
1 Unit
Sleeping 4

FIRTREES HOLIDAY BUNGALOW
c/o Mr and Mrs P A Brain, Asgard House, 84 Park Road,   OPEN All year round
Christchurch, Coleford GL16 7AZ
Contact: Mr & Mrs P A Brain, Asgard House,
84 Park Road, Christchurch, Coleford GL16 7AZ
T: (01594) 832576 & 07885 615359 (Mobile)

Low season per wk
£135.00–£170.00
High season per wk
£220.00–£260.00

Modern, detached, easily accessible 2-bedroomed bungalow. Large lounge with sloping beamed ceiling. Small private garden, integral garage.

★★★
1 Unit
Sleeping 8

WOODSIDE COTTAGE
10 Cannop Villas, Cannop, Coleford GL16 7EH
Contact: Mrs Helen Evans, Peacked Rocks Cottage,
The Rocks, Joys Green, Lydbrook GL17 9RF
T: (01594) 823408 & 861119
F: (01594) 823408

Three bedroomed semi-detatched cottage set in the beautiful oak woodlands of the Cannop Valley Nature Reserve. Large garden adjacent to oak woodlands. Very well equipped. Family cycle trail 50 yards from the cottage. Cannop ponds and sculpture trail nearby.

OPEN All year round

Low season per wk
Min £120.00
High season per wk
Max £310.00

COMBS, Derbyshire Map ref 4B2

★★★★
1 Unit
Sleeping 4

PYEGREAVE COTTAGE
Pyegreave Farm, Combs, High Peak SK23 9UX
Contact: Mr N C Pollard, Pyegreave Farm, Combs,
High Peak SK23 9UX
T: (01298) 813444
F: (01298) 815381
E: n.pollard@allenpollard.co.uk
I: www.holidayapartments.org

Situated within the Peak District National Park and enjoying spectacular views, this cottage is finished and furnished to a very high standard whilst retaining original oak beams and many other interesting features. Ideal location for walking, golfing, the theatre (Buxton) or simply as an idyllic hideaway.

OPEN All year round

Low season per wk
£195.00–£240.00
High season per wk
£240.00–£325.00

COMPTON ABDALE, Gloucestershire Map ref 2B1

★★★
2 Units
Sleeping 2–4

SPRING HILL STABLE COTTAGES
Spring Hill, Compton Abdale, Cheltenham GL54 4DU
T: (01242) 890263 (Answerphone in day)
E: springhillcottages@yahoo.co.uk
Contact: Mrs M L Smail

Two charming cottages situated in countryside close to the village of Compton Abdale. These properties, with their magnificent views and rural surroundings, are ideal for those seeking complete relaxation and peace. Also within easy reach are Bath, Oxford and Stratford-upon-Avon. The Cotswold Way is readily accessible for walking.

OPEN All year round

3-night stays available Oct–Feb (excl Christmas and New Year).

Low season per wk
£110.00–£155.00
High season per wk
£210.00–£325.00

COSTOCK, Nottinghamshire Map ref 4C3

★★★★★

3 Units
Sleeping 3–5

COSTOCK MANOR LUXURY COTTAGES
The Manor, Church Lane, Costock,
Loughborough LE12 6UZ
T: (01509) 852250 & 853337
F: (01509) 853337
E: simblet@costock-manor.co.uk
I: www.costock-manor.co.uk
Contact: Mr and Mrs D Simblet

OPEN All year round

Low season per wk
£250.00–£320.00
High season per wk
£290.00–£530.00

A 13thC, oak-framed stone manor house set within 3 acres of walled grounds. Village location, close to Nottingham, with easy access to motorway and airport.

COTSWOLDS

See under Alderton, Bibury, Blockley, Bourton-on-the-Water, Broad Campden, Broadway, Cheltenham, Chipping Campden, Cirencester, Compton Abdale, Daglingworth, Dursley, Gloucester, Lower Slaughter, Miserden, Moreton-in-Marsh, Naunton, Owlpen, Stanton, Stow-on-the-Wold, Tetbury, Tewkesbury, Upton St Leonards, Winchcombe, Witcombe

See also Cotswolds in South of England region

CRAVEN ARMS, Shropshire Map ref 4A3

★★★★

4 Units
Sleeping 4–8

UPPER ONIBURY COTTAGES
Upper Onibury, Craven Arms SY7 9AW
Contact: Mrs V S Hickman, Upper Onibury Cottages,
Upper Onibury, Craven Arms SY7 9AW
T: (01584) 856206 & 856236
F: (01584) 856236
E: oniburycottages@yahoo.com

OPEN All year round

Low season per wk
£250.00–£400.00
High season per wk
£450.00–£800.00

250-acre mixed farm. Charming stone barns comprising 3 bungalows and 1 house, set around central courtyard. Beautifully furnished. Gardens and use of heated indoor swimming pool, tennis court.

CRESSBROOK, Derbyshire Map ref 4B2

★★★

3 Units
Sleeping 2–11

CRESSBROOK HALL COTTAGES
Cressbrook Hall, Cressbrook, Buxton SK17 8SY
Contact: Mrs B H Bailey, Cressbrook Hall Cottages Ltd,
Cressbrook Hall, Cressbrook, Buxton SK17 8SY
T: (01298) 871289
F: (01298) 871845
E: stay@cressbrookhall.co.uk
I: www.cressbrookhall.co.uk

OPEN All year round
CC: Barclaycard, Delta,
Eurocard, Maestro,
Mastercard, Solo, Switch,
Visa, Visa Electron

High season per wk
£275.00–£825.00

Accommodation with a difference! Self-catering or B&B in magnificent surroundings. Special catering services and leisure facilities ensure a carefree holiday. Colour brochure.

CRESWELL, Derbyshire Map ref 4C2

★★★★

1 Unit
Sleeping 6

DUKES COTTAGES
46 Sheffield Road, Creswell, Worksop S80 4HW
T: (01909) 722769
F: (01909) 722769
E: cottages@waywender.com
Contact: Mrs G Bateman

A warm welcome awaits you at this farmworker's cottage once of the Duke of Portland's estate. Superbly located for touring both Peak District and Robin Hood country. A real home from home. Private enclosed garden. Minutes from M1 and A1. Welcome tray with home-baked cake on arrival.

OPEN All year round

Short breaks available at special rates.

Low season per wk
£170.00–£313.00
High season per wk
£298.00–£327.00

REGIONAL TOURIST BOARD The ᴧ symbol in an establishment entry indicates that it is a Regional Tourist Board member.

DAGLINGWORTH, Gloucestershire Map ref 2B1

★★★★

1 Unit
Sleeping 2

CORNER COTTAGE
21 Farm Court, Church Lane, Daglingworth, Cirencester OPEN All year round
GL7 7AF
Contact: Mrs V M Bartlett, Brook Cottage,
23 Farm Court, Daglingworth, Cirencester GL7 7AF
T: (01285) 653478 (Answerphone)
F: (01285) 653478

Tastefully furnished, well-equipped, traditional Cotswold cottage in small village in tranquil valley. Cosy base for walking or touring. Non-smokers only, please.

Low season per wk
£200.00
High season per wk
£200.00

DERBY, Derbyshire Map ref 4B2 *Tourist Information Centre Tel: (01332) 255802*

★★★

1 Unit
Sleeping 4

BANK COTTAGE
3 The Hollow, Mickleover, Derby DE3 5DG   OPEN All year round
Contact: Mrs P K Pym, 2 The Hollow, Mickleover, Derby
DE3 5DG
T: (01332) 515607

Attractive 18thC oak-beamed cottage in a quiet conservation area of Derby, with easy access to the Derbyshire Dales and many other places of interest.

Low season per wk
£200.00
High season per wk
£200.00

DIDDLEBURY, Shropshire Map ref 4A3

★★★★

3 Units
Sleeping 4–6

GOOSEFOOT BARN COTTAGES
Pinstones, Diddlebury, Craven Arms SY7 9LB
T: (01584) 861326 (answerphone)
E: sally@goosefoot.freeserve.co.uk
I: www.goosefootbarn.co.uk
Contact: Mrs Sally Loft

Converted in 2000 from stone and timbered barns, the 3 cottages are individually decorated and equipped to the highest standards. Each cottage has en suite facilities and private garden or seating area. Situated in a secluded valley with walks from the doorstep through beautiful Corvedale. Ideally located for exploring South Shropshire.

OPEN All year round

Short breaks available
(minimum 2 nights).

Low season per wk
£190.00–£270.00
High season per wk
£290.00–£410.00

DORRINGTON, Lincolnshire Map ref 4C2

★★★

2 Units
Sleeping 5

DORRINGTON COTTAGES
12 Church Lane, Timberland, Lincoln LN4 3SB
Contact: Ms Crafer, Dorrington Cottages,
12 Church Lane, Timberland, Lincoln LN4 3SB
T: (01526) 378222

OPEN All year round
CC: Amex, Barclaycard,
Delta, Eurocard,
Mastercard, Visa

Low season per wk
£200.00–£250.00
High season per wk
£265.00–£300.00

Two Victorian cottages, very well equipped and decorated, comfortable throughout the year. 3 bedrooms. Private garden and parking. Price includes bed linen and central heating. Short breaks available.

AT-A-GLANCE SYMBOLS
Symbols at the end of each accommodation entry give useful information about services and facilities. A key to symbols can be found inside the back cover flap. Keep this open for easy reference.

DUNTISBOURNE ABBOTS, Gloucestershire Map ref 2B1

Rating
Applied For
1 Unit
Sleeping 4–6

Pretty 17thC cottage in a lovely, peaceful village. Delightful, private flagged terrace garden with seating area. Close to Cirencester and Cheltenham, and within an hour of many notable gardens and NT properties. Two bedrooms, both en suite. Additional accommodation for 2 guests in annexe. Regret no children, pets or smokers.

THE OLD COTTAGE
Duntisbourne Abbots, Cirencester GL7 7JN
Contact: Mrs G Simpson, Church Barn, Hawling,
Cheltenham GL54 5TA
T: (01451) 850118
F: (01451) 850118
E: paul.gill@btinternet.com
I: www.cottageguide.co.uk/cotswold-cottages

OPEN All year round	Low season per wk
CC: Barclaycard, Delta,	Min £200.00
JCB, Mastercard, Solo,	High season per wk
Switch, Visa, Visa Electron	Max £600.00

DURSLEY, Gloucestershire Map ref 2B1

★★★
1 Unit
Sleeping 4

TWO SPRINGBANK
37 Hopton Road, Upper Cam, Dursley GL11 5PD
Contact: Mrs F A Jones, 32 Everlands, Cam, Dursley
GL11 5NL
T: (01453) 543047
E: philippa.charters@care4free.net

OPEN All year round

Low season per wk
£132.00–£210.00
High season per wk
£177.00–£210.00

Renovated Victorian mid-terrace cottage, in pleasant rural location near 14thC church. Multi-fuel stove and night storage heaters. Close to Cotswold Way and an ideal touring centre.

EAST HADDON, Northamptonshire Map ref 4C3

★★★★★
1 Unit
Sleeping 6

MULBERRY COTTAGE
St Andrews Road, East Haddon, Northampton NN6 8DE
Contact: Mr & Mrs M Smerin, Lane Cottage,
St Andrews Road, East Haddon, Northampton NN6 8DE
T: (01604) 770244 (day/evening) &
(01327) 844822 (day/evening)
F: (01327) 844822
E: liz@smerin.freeserve.co.uk

OPEN All year round

Low season per wk
£200.00–£300.00
High season per wk
£350.00–£450.00

Attractive cottage, beamed sitting rooms, 2 bedrooms, en suite shower room and bathroom. Central heating and double glazing. Quiet location with garden and off-road parking.

EDALE, Derbyshire Map ref 4B2

★★★★
1 Unit
Sleeping 2

SKINNERS' HALL
Taylors' Croft, Edale, Hope Valley S33 7ZE
T: (01433) 670 281 (answerphone)
F: (01433) 670 481
E: sue@skinnershall.freeserve.co.uk
I: www.skinnershall.freeserve.co.uk
Contact: Mrs Susan Favell

OPEN All year round

Low season per wk
£200.00–£300.00
High season per wk
£300.00–£400.00

Luxury accommodation for 2, central heating, 20 ft living room, fitted kitchen, 4-poster, bathroom with separate shower and a 360 degree view.

QUALITY ASSURANCE SCHEME
Star ratings were correct at the time of going to press but are subject to change. Please check at the time of booking.

★★★★

1 Unit
Sleeping 4

Delightful 17thC converted granary with original oak beams, full of character and charm, set in beautiful countryside. Lovely garden with heated swimming pool (May to September) and barbecue facilities which guests are welcome to use. Lovely woodland walks. Host of stately homes close by as well as the National Sports Centre and golfing.

THE LOFT HOUSE

Criftin Farm, Epperstone, Nottingham NG14 6AT
Contact: Mrs J Esam, Criftin Farm, Epperstone,
Nottingham NG14 6AT
T: (0115) 965 2039
F: (0115) 965 5490
E: jennyesam@compuserve.com
I: www.nottsfarmtourism.co.uk

OPEN All year round

Low season per wk
£290.00
High season per wk
£330.00

★★★★

1 Unit
Sleeping 6

Delightful Grade II Listed thatched black and white cottage with many traditional and original period features. Spacious, tastefully furnished, all modern facilities. Large enclosed garden, patio area, garden furniture. Private and peacefully situated. Ample parking. Ideal touring base. Family supervised. No pets. Brochures available.

THATCHERS END

64 Pershore Road, Evesham WR11 6PQ
Contact: Mr & Mrs Wilson, 60 Pershore Road, Evesham
WR11 6PQ
T: (01386) 446269 & 07710 006949 (Mobile)
F: (01386) 446269
E: trad.accom@virgin.net
I: freespace.virgin.net/trad.accom

OPEN All year round
CC: Amex, Barclaycard,
Delta, Diners, Eurocard,
JCB, Maestro, Mastercard,
Solo, Switch, Visa, Visa
Electron

Low season per wk
£300.00–£400.00
High season per wk
£400.00–£495.00

★★★★

3 Units
Sleeping 2–6

DALEHEAD COURT COTTAGES
The Square, Eyam, Hope Valley S36 2RB
Contact: Mrs D M Neary, Laneside Farm, Hope,
Hope Valley S33 6RR
T: (01433) 620214
F: (01433) 620214
E: laneside@lineone.net
I: www.laneside.fsbusiness.co.uk

OPEN All year round

Low season per wk
£155.00–£285.00
High season per wk
£185.00–£400.00

Choice of imaginatively restored delightfully appointed cottages in the heart of Derbyshire's most historic village or cosy, beamed riverside farm cottages, bordering Hope village.

TOWN INDEX

This can be found at the back of the guide. If you
know where you want to stay, the index will give you
the page number listing accommodation in your
chosen town, city or village.

★★★★

1 Unit
Sleeping 4

WATCHMAKERS COTTAGE

Foolow, Eyam, Hope Valley S32 5QA
Contact: Mrs N J Carmichael, Proprietor,
Croft View Cottage, Foolow, Eyam, Hope Valley S32 5QA
T: (01433) 630711
E: carmichaelat@hotmail.com

This 17thC character cottage has been newly refurbished yet boasts several original features and is attractively furnished. Two pleasant bedrooms with good quality beds and bed linen, well-fitted kitchen, spacious sitting room with solid-fuel stove and stone-flagged dining room. Located in picturesque village with country walks from the door.

OPEN All year round

Low season per wk
£150.00–£250.00
High season per wk
£200.00–£350.00

FAR FOREST, Worcestershire Map ref 4A3

★★★

1 Unit
Sleeping 6

MANOR HOLDING
Far Forest, Bewdley
Contact: Mr & Mrs N Dobson-Smyth, 32 Church Street,
Hagley, Stourbridge DY9 0NA
T: 07970 260010 (Mobile) & (01562) 883609
E: nds@landscapeconsultancy.freeserve.co.uk

OPEN All year round

Low season per wk
£165.00–£195.00
High season per wk
£240.00–£320.00

Rustic 17thC half-timbered cottage hidden in the tranquil seclusion of the ancient Forest of Wyre. Half a kilometre from the nearest tarmac.

FINSTOCK, Oxfordshire

See South of England region

FOREST OF DEAN

See under Coleford, Lydney, Soudley, Whitecroft

FOWNHOPE, Herefordshire Map ref 2A1

★★★

1 Unit
Sleeping 4

BIRDS FARM COTTAGE
Lower Buckenhill, Fownhope, Hereford HR1 4PX
Contact: Mrs J Edwards, White House, How Caple,
Hereford HR1 4SR
T: (01989) 740644
F: (01989) 740388
E: birdscottage@yahoo.com

OPEN All year round

Low season per wk
£150.00–£170.00
High season per wk
£150.00–£300.00

120-acre organic farm. Small, well-equipped, recently refurbished country cottage in peaceful area close to Wye Valley walk. Plenty of parking, garden and grass field. Winter breaks available.

FRAMPTON–ON–SEVERN, Gloucestershire Map ref 2B1

★★★★–★★★★★★

2 Units
Sleeping 4

17thC Priest Cottage and adjacent Stable Cottage, both sleep four, set in a private courtyard. An abundance of exposed beams, sumptuously furnished with traditional oak furniture including a romantic 4-poster bed, grandfather clock, surround sound TV, DVD and CD. Good walking, ideal touring base for Cotswolds, Bath, Slimbridge, Westonbirt etc.

OLD PRIEST COTTAGE AND OLD STABLE COTTAGE

Church End, Frampton-on-Severn, Gloucester GL2 7EH
Contact: Mr and Mrs M R Williams, Tan House Farm,
Frampton-on-Severn, Gloucester GL2 7EH
T: (01452) 741072 (answerphone available)
F: (01452) 741072
E: tanhouse.farm@lineone.net

OPEN All year round

Autumn/winter short breaks-£60 per cottage per night.

Low season per wk
£280.00–£340.00
High season per wk
£340.00–£470.00

GLOUCESTER, Gloucestershire Map ref 2B1 *Tourist Information Centre Tel: (01452) 396572*

★★★
1 Unit
Sleeping 6

THE VINEARY
Vinetree Cottage, Solomons Tump, Huntley,   OPEN Mar–Sep
Gloucester GL19 3EB
Contact: Mrs A Snow, Vinetree Cottage,
Solomons Tump, Huntley, Gloucester GL19 3EB
T: (01452) 830006

Low season per wk
£155.00–£190.00
High season per wk
£200.00–£240.00

Annexe to owner's cottage in country lane. Open views. Local post office, golf course, country inns. Garden play area-great for children. Peaceful, central setting.

GRANTHAM, Lincolnshire Map ref 3A1 *Tourist Information Centre Tel: (01476) 406166*

★★★★
1 Unit
Sleeping 2

APPLETREE COTTAGE
Stone House, 4 Church Lane, Ropsley,   OPEN All year round
Grantham NG33 4DA
Contact: Elizabeth Puxty, Stone House, 4 Church Lane,
Ropsley, Grantham NG33 4DA
T: (01476) 585620

Low season per wk
£160.00–£190.00
High season per wk
£225.00

Early 18thC stone cottage, oak beams, with log fire and central heating. Spacious and comfortable. Village setting, quiet lanes, unspoilt countryside. All-inclusive price.

GREAT CARLTON, Lincolnshire Map ref 4D2

★★
1 Unit
Sleeping 5

WILLOW FARM
Great Carlton, Louth LN11 8JP   OPEN All year round
T: (01507) 338540 (answerphone)
Contact: Mr J Clark

Low season per wk
£120.00–£160.00
High season per wk
£180.00–£250.00

Comprising 2 double and 1 single bedrooms. Fly and coarse fishing available on site. Touring caravans welcome by arrangement.

GREAT HUCKLOW, Derbyshire Map ref 4B2

★★★★
1 Unit
Sleeping 4

SOUTH VIEW COTTAGE
Windmill, Great Hucklow, Buxton SK17 8RE   OPEN All year round
Contact: Mrs M Waterhouse, Holme Cottage, Windmill,
Great Hucklow, Buxton SK17 8RE
T: (01298) 871440 & 07785 791193
F: (01298) 871440

Low season per wk
£220.00–£250.00
High season per wk
£250.00–£295.00

Modernised country cottage in the hamlet of Windmill in the middle of the Peak District. Owner maintained. Furnished and decorated to a high standard. No smoking. Lock-up garage.

HARTINGTON, Derbyshire Map ref 4B2

★★★
1 Unit
Sleeping 7

BEECH COTTAGE
Church Steps, Hartington, Buxton SK17 0AR   OPEN All year round
Contact: Mrs L Birch, Dale House, Hartington, Buxton
SK17 0AS
T: (01298) 84532 (answerphone)
E: lesley@beechcottage99.freeserve.co.uk
I: www.beechcottage99.freeserve.co.uk

Low season per wk
£150.00–£185.00
High season per wk
£210.00–£370.00

Semi-detached stone-built cottage situated in Hartington. Close to the square, duck pond and tea shop. Super walks in scenic Wolfscote and Beresford Dales.

★★★
1 Unit
Sleeping 5

CHURCH VIEW
Hartington, Buxton SK17 0AW   OPEN All year round
Contact: Miss K Bassett, Digmer, Hartington, Buxton
SK17 0AQ
T: (01298) 84660

Low season per wk
£160.00–£185.00
High season per wk
£185.00–£240.00

Three-bedroomed cottage with part central heating. Open fire optional. Patio and lawned garden, lock-up garage.

MAP REFERENCES
Map references apply to the colour maps at the front of this guide.

HARTINGTON continued

★★★★
3 Units
Sleeping 4

CRUCK AND WOLFSCOTE COTTAGE

Wolfscote Grange Farm, Hartington, Buxton SK17 0AX
T: (01298) 84342
E: wolfscote@btinternet.com
I: www.cottageguide.co.uk/wolfscote
Contact: Mrs Jane Gibbs

Surrounded by walkable hills and dales. Cruck Cottage is cosy and peaceful with no neighbours. Nestling above the beautiful Dove Valley, Wolfscote Cottage is in a unique position on the edge of Wolfscote Dale with stunning scenery. Sparkles with interesting old world touches, pretty stencilling, en suite master bedroom and a main spa whirlpool bathroom.

OPEN All year round

Private farm trail weekend and short breaks available (especially Oct-Easter).

Low season per wk
Min £150.00
High season per wk
£400.00–£470.00

★★★-★★★★★
2 Units
Sleeping 5

1 STALEY COTTAGE AND VICTORIA HOUSE
Hartington, Buxton SK17 0AQ
Contact: Mr and Mrs J Oliver, Carr Head Farm,
Penistone, Sheffield S36 7GA
T: (01226) 762387

OPEN All year round

Low season per wk
£250.00–£280.00
High season per wk
£320.00–£450.00

Spacious cottage with 3 bedrooms, dining room, lounge, ground floor bathroom, upstairs shower room/WC and garden. In a pretty village near amenities, shops and restaurants. Also second property.

HATHERSAGE, Derbyshire Map ref 4B2

★★★
1 Unit
Sleeping 4

ST.MICHAEL'S COTTAGE
Main Road, Hathersage, Hope Valley S32 1BB
Contact: Miss H Turton, Saint Michael's Environmental Education Centre, Main Road, Hathersage, Hope Valley S32 1BB
T: (01433) 650309
F: (01433) 650089
E: stmichaels@education.nottscc.gov.uk

OPEN All year round

Low season per wk
£160.00–£180.00
High season per wk
£220.00–£290.00

Cosy character cottage with 1 double and 1 twin bedroom. Dramatic scenery, walks from the door, close to all amenities.

HATTON, Warwickshire Map ref 4B3

★★★
1 Unit
Sleeping 2

THE DAIRY
Green Gates Farm, Station Road, Hatton, Warwick CV35 7LJ
Contact: Mrs L Baker, Green Gates Farm, Station Road, Hatton, Warwick CV35 7LJ
T: (01926) 842438 (Answerphone)
E: greengatesfarm@hotmail.com

OPEN All year round

Low season per wk
£180.00–£250.00
High season per wk
£250.00–£330.00

Two-storey accommodation in old dairy with horseshoe beams. Overlooking stables, barn and fields beyond. Secluded but conveniently situated. Additional double sofa-bed in living room.

CREDIT CARD BOOKINGS If you book by telephone and are asked for your credit card number it is advisable to check the proprietor's policy should you cancel your reservation.

HATTON, Lincolnshire Map ref 4D2

★★★★

2 Units
Sleeping 2–4

THE GABLES
Hatton Hall Farm, Hatton, Market Rasen LN8 5QG
T: (01673) 858862 (answerphone) &
07702 271041 (mobile)
E: jmerivale@aol.com
I: www.thegables-nation.co.uk
Contact: Mrs J L Merivale

Beautiful, old red brick and pantile barn converted into two cottages. Filled with all mod cons to a high standard. Overlooking open countryside. Babysitting and meals available. Patio and barbecue for guests' use. Bicycles for hire. All towels and linen included.

OPEN All year round

Low season per wk
£160.00–£250.00
High season per wk
£200.00–£300.00

HAWLING, Gloucestershire Map ref 2B1

★★★★

2 Units
Sleeping 2–4

MIDDLE FARM COTTAGES
Middle Farm, Hawling, Cheltenham GL54 5SZ
T: (01451) 850744 (answerphone/fax)
E: nigel.woollacott@ukonline.co.uk
Contact: Mr & Mrs N J Woollacott

Newly converted 17thC barn cottages. Spacious, beautifully furnished. Log burners and beams. Cottage 1 sleeps 2, cottage 2 sleeps 4. All en suite, own gardens.

OPEN All year round

Low season per wk
£250.00–£345.00
High season per wk
£375.00–£595.00

HAYFIELD, Derbyshire Map ref 4B2

★★★★

1 Unit
Sleeping 2–4

BOWDEN BRIDGE COTTAGE
Kinder, Hayfield, High Peak SK22 2LH
T: (01663) 743975
F: (01663) 743812
E: j_easter@talk21.com
Contact: Mrs Margrith Easter

Cottage flat attached to main house, with double bedroom, lounge, kitchen, bathroom. Additional twin bedroom with washbasin available if required. Full central heating.

OPEN All year round

Low season per wk
£170.00–£200.00
High season per wk
£190.00–£220.00

HEREFORD, Herefordshire Map ref 2A1 *Tourist Information Centre Tel: (01432) 268430*

★★

2 Units
Sleeping 2–4

HOME FROM HOME HOLIDAYS
16 St Martins Avenue, Hereford HR2 7RQ
Contact: Mr & Mrs Bill & Maggie Matthews,
16 St Martins Avenue, Hereford HR2 7RQ
T: (01432) 272259
E: bandm@prospectpl.fsnet.co.uk

Quietly situated yet within 5 minutes' walk of the city, the apartments offer local leisure facilities and a base from which to visit local attractions.

OPEN All year round

Low season per wk
£145.00–£170.00
High season per wk
£165.00–£195.00

★★★

1 Unit
Sleeping 3

RUSHFORD
7 Belle Bank Avenue, Holmer, Hereford HR4 9RL
T: (01432) 273380
F: (01432) 273380
Contact: Mrs M W Roberts

Much praised wing of owner's detached house in pleasant surroundings and pretty garden with ancient cider mill. Situated on city fringe with rural views, close to church, pub, shop and bus service, it is half hour walk into the city centre. Comfortable and peaceful for non-smokers only.

OPEN All year round

Low season per wk
£120.00–£150.00
High season per wk
£160.00–£200.00

HINCKLEY, Leicestershire Map ref 4B3 *Tourist Information Centre Tel: (01455) 635106*

★★★★

1 Unit
Sleeping 1–5

CROSSWAYS COUNTRY HOLIDAYS
Crossways Farm, Lutterworth Road, Burbage, Hinckley   OPEN Apr–Sep
LE10 3AH
T: (01455) 239261 & 07946 421123 (Mobile)
F: (01445) 633889
E: user@burbage60.fsnet.co.uk
I: www.crossways-holidays.co.uk
Contact: Mr and Mrs John Mac and Carol Mac

Low season per wk
£350.00–£450.00
High season per wk
£450.00–£550.00

Superior comfortable cottage, gardens. Open country views. Easily accessible tourist attractions, airports. All mod cons, food hamper, linen, toiletries and a warm welcome.

HOLYMOORSIDE, Derbyshire Map ref 4B2

★★★

1 Unit
Sleeping 1–4

MILLCLOSE COTTAGE
Millclose Farm, Nether Loads, Holymoorside,
Chesterfield S42 7HW
T: (01246) 567624
F: (01246) 567624
E: allan.stockton@btinternet.com
Contact: Mr and Mrs A Stockton

A comfortable stone-built cottage on a small holding, farming traditional rare breeds. Surrounding buildings of historical interest, English Heritage scheduled area. Ideal for exploring the Peak District and visiting Derbyshire's stately homes. Easy access to walking, shopping, fishing.

OPEN All year round

Low season per wk
£140.00–£150.00
High season per wk
£200.00–£250.00

HOPE, Derbyshire Map ref 4B2

★★★★

2 Units
Sleeping 4–10

ASTON COTTAGES
The Dimings, Aston Lane, Hope Valley S33 6RA
T: (01433) 621619 (answerphone) &
07974 465758 (mobile)
E: rmorley@dimings.freeserve.co.uk
I: www.sallydog.co.uk/astoncottages/
Contact: Mrs R Morley

OPEN All year round

Low season per wk
£150.00–£250.00
High season per wk
£250.00–£400.00

Nestled under Winn Hill a true country hideaway, many walks from the cottage door. Recently converted sleeps 4, 6 or 10, beautifully furnished with every luxury.

HORSINGTON, Lincolnshire Map ref 4D2

★★★

1 Unit
Sleeping 4

WAYSIDE COTTAGE
Wayside Main Street, Horsington,
Woodhall Spa LN10 5EX
Contact: Mr & Mrs I G Williamson, 72 Mill Lane,
Woodhall Spa LN10 6QZ
T: (01526) 353101 & 07967 520289 (Mobile)
E: WILL@williamsoni.freeserve.co.uk
I: www.skegness.net/woodhallspa.htm

OPEN All year round

Low season per wk
£150.00–£180.00
High season per wk
£160.00–£200.00

Cottage bungalow in rural setting in sleepy Horsington, central to the county for exploring. Many walks.

IRONBRIDGE, Shropshire Map ref 4A3 *Tourist Information Centre Tel: (01952) 432166*

★★★

1 Unit
Sleeping 5

IVY COTTAGE
12 Church Hill, Ironbridge, Telford TF8 7PW
Contact: Mrs R Crofts, 36 Coneybury View, Broseley
TF12 5AX
T: (01952) 882203
E: ruthcrofts@aol.com

OPEN All year round

Low season per wk
£180.00–£200.00
High season per wk
£350.00–£400.00

Detached 3-bedroom Georgian house, part of Ironbridge townscape. Near to Ironbridge Gorge Museums, Wenlock Edge and lovely Shropshire medieval towns. Accessible leisure facilities nearby.

KENILWORTH, Warwickshire Map ref 4B3 *Tourist Information Centre Tel: (01926) 748900*

★★★★
1 Unit
Sleeping 4

JACKDAW COTTAGE
14 Castle Hill, Kenilworth CV8 1NB   OPEN All year round
Contact: Mrs L Grierson, Proprietor,
The White Bungalow, 6 Canterbury Close, Kenilworth
CV8 2PU
T: (01926) 855616 (Answerphone) &
07970 792131 (Mobile)
F: (01926) 513189
E: kgrierson@ukonline.co.uk

Cosy, well furnished and equipped, listed cottage. Conservation area on edge of historic town, picturesque setting by castle. Convenient for Stratford, Warwick, Cotswolds, NEC, NAC.

Low season per wk
£200.00–£300.00
High season per wk
£300.00–£370.00

KENLEY, Shropshire Map ref 4A3

★★★★
2 Units
Sleeping 2–4

NO 1 & 2 COURTYARD COTTAGES
Lower Springs Farm, Kenley, Shrewsbury SY5 6PA   OPEN All year round
T: (01952) 510841
E: a-gill@lineone.net
Contact: Mrs A Gill

Two immaculate, recenlty converted cottages with exposed oak beams. Large garden and stocked trout pools in lovely, peaceful valley with panoramic views of Wenlock Edge.

Low season per wk
£150.00–£250.00
High season per wk
£200.00–£350.00

KNIVETON, Derbyshire Map ref 4B2

★★★
1 Unit
Sleeping 4

WILLOW BANK
Kniveton, Ashbourne DE6 1JJ   OPEN All year round
T: (01335) 343308 & 07977 563093 (mobile)
E: maryvaughan@compuserve.com
I: www.vaughan77.fsnet.co.uk
Contact: Mrs ME Vaughan

Luxurious newly fitted ground floor flat, 1 double bedroom, 1 twin, an acre of garden with stream. Peak District village, Ashbourne 15 minutes.

Low season per wk
£250.00
High season per wk
£250.00–£300.00

LAMBLEY, Nottinghamshire Map ref 4C2

★★★
1 Unit
Sleeping 4

DICKMAN'S COTTAGE
4 Mill Lane, Lambley, Nottingham NG4 4PS   OPEN All year round
Contact: Mrs Rosamond J Marshall Smith, Springsyde,
Birdcage Walk, Otley LS21 3HB
T: (01943) 462719
F: (01943) 850925
E: marshallsmithuk@hotmail.com

Five miles north-east of Nottingham. Beamed cottage with garden. 2 bedrooms-1 double/1 twin. TV/video, dishwasher, washer/dryer. Private parking.

Low season per wk
£170.00–£190.00
High season per wk
£250.00–£270.00

LEAMINGTON SPA, Warwickshire Map ref 4B3 *Tourist Information Centre Tel: (01926) 742762*

★
2 Units
Sleeping 3–5

BLACKDOWN FARM COTTAGES
Blackdown Farm, Sandy Lane, Blackdown,   OPEN All year round
Leamington Spa CV32 6QS
Contact: Mr & Mrs R Solt, Blackdown Farm,
Sandy Lane, Leamington Spa CV32 6QS
T: (01926) 422522
F: (01926) 450996

Cottages converted from farm buildings, in the countryside between Leamington Spa and Kenilworth. Convenient for Shakespeare Country, Warwick, Coventry and the Cotswolds.

Low season per wk
£150.00–£250.00
High season per wk
£150.00–£350.00

★★★
3 Units
Sleeping 4–7

FURZEN HILL FARM
Cubbington Heath, Leamington Spa CV32 7UJ   OPEN All year round
T: (01926) 424791
F: (01926) 424791
Contact: Mrs C M Whitfield

Three cottages at Cubbington. Furzen Hill Cottage sleeps 7, The Barn 4 and Dairy Cottage 4. Ideally situated for Warwick, Stratford-upon-Avon and NEC.

Low season per wk
Min £160.00
High season per wk
Max £340.00

LEDBURY, Herefordshire Map ref 2B1 *Tourist Information Centre Tel: (01531) 636147*

★★★–★★★★★

5 Units
Sleeping 2–5

WHITE HOUSE COTTAGES
The White House, Aylton, Ledbury HR8 2RQ
Contact: Mrs Marianne Hills, The White House, Aylton,
Ledbury HR8 2RQ
T: (01531) 670349
F: (01531) 670057

OPEN All year round

Low season per wk
£171.00–£364.00
High season per wk
£306.00–£479.00

Listed 17thC farmhouse with 5 self-catering cottages from converted barns and oast house, with private garden/patios. Oak beams, fireplaces and many interesting features.

LEINTWARDINE, Herefordshire Map ref 4A3

★★★★

2 Units
Sleeping 4

BADGERS BLUFF HOLIDAY COTTAGES
The Todding Farmhouse, Leintwardine,
Craven Arms SY7 0LX
Contact: Mr R Norton, The Todding Farmhouse,
Leintwardine, Craven Arms SY7 0LX
T: (01547) 540648
F: (01547) 540648

OPEN All year round

Low season per wk
Min £181.00
High season per wk
Max £234.00

Set in a very quiet location with breathtaking views and abundant wildlife. Badgers Bluff is the perfect place to spend a peaceful country holiday.

★★★

1 Unit
Sleeping 4

OAK COTTAGE
22 Watling Street, Leintwardine, Craven Arms SY7 0LW
Contact: Mrs Vivienne Faulkner, Proprietor,
24 Watling Street, Leintwardine, Craven Arms SY7 0LW
T: (01547) 540629 (answerphone)
F: (01547) 540442
E: fmjones@axismundi.co.uk
I: www.oakenash.co.uk

OPEN All year round

Low season per wk
£180.00–£200.00
High season per wk
£200.00–£300.00

16thC, Grade II Listed timber-framed cottage, carefully restored and equipped in borderland village on River Teme. Glorious walking, fishing, good food. You can even coracle.

LEOMINSTER, Herefordshire Map ref 2A1 *Tourist Information Centre Tel: (01568) 616460*

★★★

1 Unit
Sleeping 4

MILL HOUSE FLAT
Woonton Court Farm, Leysters, Leominster HR6 0HL
Contact: Mrs E M Thomas, Woonton Court Farm,
Leysters, Leominster HR6 0HL
T: (01568) 750232 (Answerphone)
F: (01568) 750232
E: thomas.woontoncourt@famousweekly.net

OPEN All year round

Low season per wk
£140.00–£200.00
High season per wk
£180.00–£260.00

Comfortable converted cider house providing self-contained first floor flat. Sleeps 3/4. Excellent centre for Marches Gardens, N.T. properties, woodland walks, wildlife. Short breaks.

LINCOLN, Lincolnshire Map ref 4C2 *Tourist Information Centre Tel: (01522) 873213 & 873256*

★★

1 Unit
Sleeping 6

THE COBBLES
4 Well Lane, Lincoln LN2 1NA
Contact: Mr JM Scott, Sunnyside, Lincoln Road,
Brattleby, Lincoln LN1 2SQ
T: (01522) 730561 & 754904
F: (01522) 513995

OPEN All year round

Low season per wk
£200.00–£250.00
High season per wk
£260.00–£350.00

Edwardian cottage on a quiet cobbled lane in the heart of the city, close to cathedral and castle.

★★★

1 Unit
Sleeping 2

MARTINGALE COTTAGE
17 East Street, Nettleham, Lincoln LN2 2SL
Contact: Mrs P A Pate, 19 East Street, Nettleham,
Lincoln LN2 2SL
T: (01522) 751795
E: patsy.pate@ntlworld.com

OPEN All year round

Low season per wk
Min £120.00
High season per wk
Max £180.00

Comfortable, well-equipped 18thC stone cottage with private parking, near centre of village. Use of owner's attractive secluded garden. Good local shops and pubs.

★★★★

1 Unit
Sleeping 3

OLD VICARAGE COTTAGE

East Street, Nettleham, Lincoln LN2 2SL
Contact: Mrs S Downs, The Old Vicarage, East Street,
Nettleham, Lincoln LN2 2SL
T: (01522) 750819 (Answerphone)
F: (01522) 750819
E: susan@oldvic.net

*An 18thC stone-built property, one of the oldest
in the village. Spacious well-equipped
accommodation. Original exposed beams in the
living room. Own south-facing garden, off-road
parking. Quiet position, close to the centre of this
very attractive village with its shops, pubs,
village green and picturesque beckside.*

OPEN All year round

Low season per wk
Max £120.00
High season per wk
Max £160.00

★★★

1 Unit
Sleeping 4

PINGLES COTTAGE

Grange Farm, Broxholme, Lincoln LN1 2NG
T: (01522) 702441
Contact: Mrs P A Sutcliffe

*Well-equipped, secluded, cosy cottage with
private garden and ample parking, only 6 miles
from historic Lincoln and within easy reach of
trunk roads (A57, A1500). Free-range hens' eggs
and lamb are produced on the 100-acre organic
farm. A good variety of wildlife regularly visits
the garden. Coarse fishing in season at no extra
cost.*

OPEN All year round

Winter breaks; Nov-Easter, 3
nights £145.

Low season per wk
Min £215.00
High season per wk
Max £270.00

★★★

3 Units
Sleeping 2–3

ST CLEMENTS

Langworth Gate, Lincoln LN2 4AD
T: (01522) 538087 (Answerphone)
F: (01522) 560642
E: jroywood@aol.com
Contact: Mrs G Marshall

*Three well-equipped centrally heated
apartments in comfortable Victorian rectory: 1 is
twin-bedded, 2 are doubles. Situated down quiet
drive lined with mature trees. Cathedral views
and only 5 minutes' walk from historic up-hill
area. Plenty of car parking. A peaceful retreat in
the heart of the city. Short breaks when
available.*

OPEN All year round

Low season per wk
Min £110.00
High season per wk
Min £160.00

★★★★

2 Units
Sleeping 5

THE PARLOUR AND THE DAIRY
Forest Lane Farm, Little Hucklow, Buxton SK17 8JE
T: (01298) 871226 & 07974 181699 (mobile)
F: (01298) 871226
Contact: Mrs W Mycock

OPEN All year round

High season per wk
£180.00–£330.00

*Limestone barn restored to the highest standards, furnished in antique pine and
co-ordinated soft furnishings, all modern conveniences. Ideal for couples, families.
Pets welcome. Sorry no smoking.*

QUALITY ASSURANCE SCHEME

Star ratings are explained at the back of this guide.

LLANYBLODWEL, Shropshire Map ref 4A3

★★★★

1 Unit
Sleeping 10

THE COACH HOUSE

Huntsmans Lodge, Llanyblodwel, Oswestry SY10 8NF
Contact: Mr and Mrs S Perks, Proprietor,
Huntsmans Lodge, Llanyblodwel, Oswestry SY10 8NF
T: (01691) 828038

Superb comfortable 18thC coach house with cobbled stable yard and private garden, skilfully converted for comfort and style yet retaining character and history. Relax on our smallholding where the Tanat Valley crosses the Welsh border or choose from days out to castles, gardens, historic towns or activities locally. Brochure available.

OPEN All year round

Short breaks up to 4 nights available all year.

Low season per wk
£400.00–£500.00
High season per wk
£500.00–£700.00

LOUTH, Lincolnshire Map ref 4D2 *Tourist Information Centre Tel: (01507) 609289*

★★★–★★★★★

5 Units
Sleeping 4–6

ASHWATER HOUSE

Willow Drive, Louth LN11 0AH
Contact: Mrs H Mapletoft, Ashpot Cottage, Willow Drive, Louth LN11 0AH
T: (01507) 609295
F: (01507) 354624
E: robnholly@tesco.net
I: www.ashwaterhouse.co.uk

There are 5 relaxing cottages and cabins each with a view over the fishing lake and woodland, surrounded by open countryside, on the edge of Louth. Coarse fishing and an exclusive health and leisure club are complimentary. Pets welcome, retired discount, and our popular policy of no indoor smoking still continues.

OPEN All year round

3 night weekend and 4 night mid-week breaks available off-peak season from £125.

Low season per wk
£190.00–£250.00
High season per wk
£340.00–£410.00

★★★

1 Unit
Sleeping 4

MILL LODGE

Benniworth House Farm, Donington on Bain, Louth LN11 9RD
T: (01507) 343265 (preferably evenings)
Contact: Mrs P Cade

Ezra and Pamela Cade welcome you to a comfortable, warm, detached cottage, with conservatory, garden and garage, on lovely farm/nature reserve. Fitted kitchen, open log fire. Free first snack with home-produced honey. Good footpaths join the Viking Way, open access to countryside stewardship area. Children welcome.

OPEN All year round

Special rates for senior citizens.

Low season per wk
£200.00–£300.00
High season per wk
£250.00–£350.00

www.travelengland.org.uk

Log on for information and inspiration. The latest information on places to visit, events and quality assessed accommodation.

LOWER BENEFIELD, Northamptonshire Map ref 3A1

★★★

1 Unit
Sleeping 4

GRANARY COTTAGE

Brook Farm, Lower Benefield, Peterborough PE8 5AE
Contact: Mrs R C Singlehurst, Brook Farm,
Lower Benefield, Peterborough PE8 5AE
T: (01832) 205215

746-acre mixed farm. Comfortable, self-contained cottage converted from the old granary, with access to the garden. Off A427 between Oundle and Corby. Set in picturesque Northamptonshire countryside with the historic market towns of Oundle and Stamford within easy reach. Appealing walks and local attractions. Sorry, no pets please.

OPEN All year round

Low season per wk
Min £175.00
High season per wk
Min £225.00

LOWER SLAUGHTER, Gloucestershire Map ref 2B1

★★★★

1 Unit
Sleeping 5

MALT HOUSE COTTAGE
Mill Lane, Lower Slaughter, Cheltenham GL54 2HX
Contact: Mrs CE Hutsby, Little Hill Farm, Wellesbourne,
Warwick CV35 9EB
T: (01789) 840261 (mobile)
F: (01789) 842270
E: charhutsby@talk21.com
I: www.accomodata.co.uk/06099.htm

OPEN All year round

Low season per wk
£250.00–£300.00
High season per wk
£325.00–£475.00

Grade II Listed property, 4 stars. Private parking. This pretty beamed, stone-walled cottage is in a quiet position close to river Eye. All mod cons.

LUDLOW, Shropshire Map ref 4A3 *Tourist Information Centre Tel: (01584) 875053*

★★★★

1 Unit
Sleeping 6

THE AVENUE FLAT
The Avenue, Ashford Carbonell, Ludlow SY8 4DA
T: (01584) 831616
E: ronmeredithavenue@talk21.com
Contact: Mr R E Meredith

OPEN All year round

Low season per wk
£130.00–£170.00
High season per wk
£170.00–£290.00

Second floor of large, attractive, peaceful country residence set in 6 acres. Completely independent access with fine views and very comfortable, well equipped accommodation.

★★★

1 Unit
Sleeping 6

BRIBERY COTTAGE
23 Bell Lane, Ludlow SY8 1BN
Contact: Mr & Mrs R Caithness, 2 Dinham, Ludlow
SY8 1EJ
T: (01584) 872828 (Answerphone)
F: (01584) 872828
E: richard.caithness@virgin.net
I: www.virtual-shropshire.co.uk/bribery-cottage

OPEN All year round

Low season per wk
£125.00–£160.00
High season per wk
£230.00–£290.00

Three-storey terraced house, c1830 and a Grade II Listed building, set in historic surroundings near market square and castle. Rear conservatory leads into attractive walled garden.

CHECK THE MAPS

The colour maps at the front of this guide show all the cities, towns and villages for which you will find accommodation entries. Refer to the town index to find the page on which they are listed.

LUDLOW continued

★★
1 Unit
Sleeping 5

CHURCH BANK

Burrington, Ludlow SY8 2HT
Contact: Mrs K R Laurie, Church Bank, Burrington, Ludlow
SY8 2HT
T: (01568) 770426
E: laurie2502@lineone.net

This stone cottage lies in a beautiful peaceful valley near River Teme. There are excellent walks on the hills and forest trails. Wildlife abounds. Historic Ludlow is 5 winding miles away. Large comfortable sitting-room with woodburner and many books. Dinner can be provided by arrangement. Available all year.

OPEN Apr–Oct

Low season per wk
£150.00–£180.00
High season per wk
Max £200.00

★★★
1 Unit
Sleeping 3

THE GRANARY
Tana Leas Farm, Clee St Margaret,
Craven Arms SY7 9DZ
Contact: Mr & Mrs R Mercer, Tana Leas Farm,
Clee St Margaret, Craven Arms SY7 9DZ
T: (01584) 823272 (Answerphone)
F: (01584) 823272
E: r.mercer@tinyworld.co.uk

Recently refurbished converted granary in AONB. Ideal for quiet holiday. Ludlow 6 miles. Second property in Ludlow's historic Broad St. Sleeps 4.

OPEN Mar–Dec

Low season per wk
£175.00–£195.00
High season per wk
£195.00–£210.00

★★★
1 Unit
Sleeping 5

LILAC COTTAGE
11 Caynham Road, Knowbury, Ludlow SY8 3JQ
Contact: Mrs Elizabeth Grant, Wheelers Hope Cottage
Farm, Easthope, Much Wenlock TF13 6DN
T: (01746) 785564
I: www.cottagefarm@farmersweekly.net

Two-bedroomed detached beamed character cottage, situated in its own large garden and 4 acres, with spectacular views, lovely walks and only 4 miles from Ludlow.

OPEN All year round

Low season per wk
Min £130.00
High season per wk
Max £350.00

★★
1 Unit
Sleeping 4

POST HORN COTTAGE
Palmers Guild Court, Broad Street, Ludlow SY8 1NG
Contact: Ms H Davis, 32 Leamington Drive, Chilwell,
Beeston, Nottingham
T: (0115) 922 2383

Charming two-storey cottage in historic town centre building with exposed beams and small private patio. In quiet courtyard off Broad Street.

OPEN All year round

Low season per wk
£140.00–£180.00
High season per wk
£180.00–£210.00

★★★★
1 Unit
Sleeping 6

RAVENSCOURT MANOR

Woofferton, Ludlow SY8 4AL
Contact: Mrs Elizabeth Purnell, Ravenscourt Manor,
Woofferton, Ludlow SY8 4AL
T: (01584) 711905
F: (01584) 711905
I: www.virtual-shropshire.co.uk/ravencourt-manor

The cottage at Ravenscourt Manor is beautifully restored and furnished. Cottage sleeps 4-6 and has 2 bathrooms. Full CH, electric cooker, microwave oven, dishwasher, washing machine, fridge/freezer, TV and video, garden with furniture. Linen provided, welcome pack.

OPEN All year round

Low season per wk
£120.00–£180.00
High season per wk
£200.00–£300.00

REGIONAL TOURIST BOARD The 𝔐 symbol in an establishment entry indicates that it is a Regional Tourist Board member.

LUDLOW continued

★★★★

6 Units
Sleeping 2–6

SUTTON COURT FARM COTTAGES
Little Sutton, Stanton Lacy, Ludlow SY8 2AJ
Contact: Mr & Mrs S J Cronin, Sutton Court Farm,
Little Sutton, Stanton Lacy, Ludlow SY8 2AJ
T: (01584) 861305
F: (01584) 861441
E: suttoncourtfarm@go2.co.uk
I: www.go2.co.uk/suttoncourtfarm

OPEN All year round

Low season per wk
£200.00–£360.00
High season per wk
£320.00–£475.00

Comfortable cottages set around a peaceful courtyard in the beautiful Corvedale, just 5 miles from historic Ludlow. Evening meals, cream teas. Short breaks available all year.

LULLINGTON, Derbyshire Map ref 4B3

★★★★

1 Unit
Sleeping 5

AUBRIETIA COTTAGE
Lullington, Swadlincote DE12 8ED
Contact: Mrs R Cooper, The Grange, Lullington,
Swadlincote DE12 8ED
T: (01827) 373219 & 07774 885596 (mobile)
F: (01283) 515885

OPEN All year round

Low season per wk
£150.00–£200.00
High season per wk
£200.00–£250.00

Tastefully furnished cottage in Lullington, several times winner of the best kept village award. Pleasant outlook with many places of interest only a short drive away.

LYDNEY, Gloucestershire Map ref 2B1

★★★

3 Units
Sleeping 2–5

HIGHBURY COACH HOUSE
Bream Road, Lydney GL15 5JH
T: (01594) 842339 (Residential)
F: (01594) 844948
E: midgleya1@aol.com
Contact: Mr A R Midgley

OPEN All year round

Low season per wk
Min £130.00
High season per wk
Max £270.00

Three apartments in a Listed coach house close to Lydney, with panoramic views over the Forest of Dean and Severn Valley. Gardens, snooker and games rooms.

MADELEY, Shropshire Map ref 4A3

★★★★★

1 Unit
Sleeping 4–12

FLETCHER HOUSE
The Old Vicarage, Church Street, Madeley, Telford TF7 5BN
T: (01952) 525522 & 525524
E: houseoffletcher@aol.com
I: www.fletcherhouse.co.uk
Contact: Mrs Moira Shean

Elegant Grade II* Georgian vicarage once home of 'The Saint of Shropshire'. All rooms are tastefully refurbished and decorated. Set in lovely, peaceful gardens. Ideal base for Ironbridge museums and the beautiful Shropshire countryside. Also available – recently renovated coach house cottage in grounds for more intimate surroundings. Sleeps 4-6.

OPEN All year round
CC: Amex, Barclaycard,
Delta, Diners, Eurocard,
JCB, Maestro, Mastercard,
Solo, Switch, Visa, Visa
Electron

Murder Mystery and themed weekends for up to 12 people-special birthday/ anniversary packages arranged.

Low season per wk
£880.00–£935.00
High season per wk
£990.00–£1,650.00

MALVERN, Worcestershire Map ref 2B1 *Tourist Information Centre Tel: (01684) 892289*

★★★

1 Unit
Sleeping 4

THE COACH HOUSE
Como Road, Malvern WR14 2HS
Contact: Mrs J Jones, 58 North Malvern Road, Malvern
WR14 4LX
T: (01684) 569562

OPEN All year round

Low season per wk
£200.00–£250.00
High season per wk
£275.00–£360.00

Detached, turn of the century coach house conversion in the heart of Great Malvern. Set in a secluded garden.

MALVERN continued

★★★★

4 Units
Sleeping 2–6

Three traditional cottages and spacious garden flat in fine Regency house high on Elgar's Malvern Hills, with grandstand views over Herefordshire and the Black Mountains, offer exceptional cleanliness and detail to people who prefer to cater for themselves in private home comfort. Open all year but no pets please.

THE COTTAGES AT WESTWOOD HOUSE

Park Road, West Malvern, Malvern WR14 4DS
T: (01684) 892308 (Mrs Wright) & 578004 (Mrs Staddon)
F: (01684) 892882
E: DavidWrightTrans@cs.com
I: www.oas.co.uk/ukcottages/westwood
Contact: Mrs J Wright and Mrs J Staddon

OPEN All year round	Low season per wk £215.00–£405.00 High season per wk £360.00–£520.00

★★★

1 Unit
Sleeping 4

END COTTAGE
Malvern
Contact: Mr & Mrs Wight, The Rectory,
Fish House Lane, Stoke Prior, Bromsgrove B60 4JT
T: (01527) 832501
E: dennis.wight@tesco.net

OPEN All year round

Low season per wk
£180.00–£250.00
High season per wk
£200.00–£250.00

Comfortable, fully-equipped home, 1 mile from Great Malvern. Small garden, superb views, excellent walking on the hills nearby. Close to amenities.

★★★

1 Unit
Sleeping 2–4

GREENBANK HOUSE GARDEN FLAT
236 West Malvern Road, West Malvern, Malvern
WR14 4BG
T: (01684) 567328
Contact: Mrs S M Matthews

OPEN All year round

Low season per wk
Max £130.00
High season per wk
Max £200.00

On the Malvern Hills, close to shops and on a bus route. Excellent walking and touring centre. Fine outlook.

★★★

1 Unit
Sleeping 5

MYRTLE COTTAGE
6 Belvoir Bank, Malvern WR14 4LY
Contact: Country Holidays Ref: 15093, Agent, Country
Holidays, Springmill, Earby, Barnoldswick BB94 4OA
T: 08700 723723

OPEN All year round

Low season per wk
£189.00–£294.00
High season per wk
£315.00–£405.00

Victorian cottage on the slopes of the Malvern Hills. Sleeps 5 with oak beams, gas central heating, wood burning stove and a Victorian bath. Secluded garden.

MARKET RASEN, Lincolnshire Map ref 4D2

★★★–★★★★★

6 Units
Sleeping 2–6

30-acres livestock farm in a conservation Area of Outstanding Natural Beauty. Very old stone buildings lovingly restored and furnished and equipped to a very high standard. Near Viking Way. Hard tennis court.

PAPERMILL COTTAGES

Vale Farm, Caistor Lane, Tealby, Market Rasen LN8 3XN
Contact: Mr & Mrs Peter & Joyce Rhodes, Vale Farm,
Caistor Lane, Tealby, Market Rasen LN8 3XN
T: (01673) 838010
F: (01673) 838127
E: peter.rhodes1@btinternet.com
I: www.irac.org.uk/pmc

OPEN All year round CC: Barclaycard, Mastercard, Switch, Visa Short breaks-minimum 2 nights.	Low season per wk £100.00–£195.00 High season per wk £200.00–£385.00

MATLOCK, Derbyshire Map ref 4B2 *Tourist Information Centre Tel: (01629) 583388*

★★★★

10 Units
Sleeping 2–8

Set in 10 acres of private wooded grounds surrounding Darwin Lake, these superb luxury stone-built cottages provide a perfect setting for a tranquil, relaxing holiday, or are ideally located for those wishing to explore the Peaks and Dales. Central for bustling market towns, stately homes, quaint villages and many family attractions.

DARWIN LAKE

Jaggers Lane, Darley Moor, Matlock DE4 5LH
Contact: Ms Cath Lambert, Gainsborough Leisure Holiday Cottages, Knockerdown Farm, Knockerdown, Ashbourne DE6 1NQ
T: (01629) 540525 (Answerphone) & 735859
F: (01629) 540525
E: cathy@knockerdown-cottages.co.uk
I: www.derbyshireholidaycottages.co.uk

OPEN All year round CC: Barclaycard, Delta, Eurocard, JCB, Mastercard, Switch, Visa, Visa Electron	Low season per wk £316.00–£491.00 High season per wk £639.00–£930.00

3 and 4 night breaks available. Larger detatched cottages also available to sleep up to 8.

A⅍🐴M◎🗄.Ⅲ.☉🗂🖳☎TV🗄🛋🖉PU☼SP

★★★★

1 Unit
Sleeping 5

A quiet end cottage in the centre of a small Peak District village having two pubs and a shop. The village is surrounded by a network of public footpaths and stunning scenery in an Area of Outstanding Natural Beauty. Many attractions including stately Chatsworth House and Haddon Hall are nearby.

EAGLE COTTAGE

Birchover, Matlock DE4 2BN
Contact: Mrs M E Prince, Haresfield House, Birchover, Matlock DE4 2BL
T: (01629) 650634
E: maryprince@msn.com
I: www.cressbrook.co.uk/youlgve/eagle/

OPEN All year round	Low season per wk £180.00–£200.00 High season per wk £200.00–£220.00

A⅍◎🗄.Ⅲ.☉🗂🖳☎TV🗄🛋🖉P☼SP

★★★★-★★★★★

3 Units
Sleeping 5–8

These barns are set in a very rural location down a quiet country lane, having splendid panoramic views from the grounds of the whole surrounding area with Riber Castle sitting on the horizon overlooking Matlock. Choice of 3 cottages, sleeping 4, 6 and 8 persons. New indoor pool for 2002.

MOOREDGE BARNS

Tansley, Matlock
Contact: Mr C MacQueen, Agent, Peak Cottages, Strawberry Lee Lane, Totley Bents, Sheffield S17 3BA
T: (0114) 262 0777
F: (0114) 262 0666
E: enquiries@peakcottages.com
I: www.peakcottages.com

OPEN All year round CC: Barclaycard, Eurocard, Mastercard, Solo, Switch, Visa	Low season per wk £233.00–£361.00 High season per wk £416.00–£645.00

A⅍◎Ⅲ.☉🖳☎TV🗄🛋🖉✗🖉P☼🐕SP

ACCESSIBILITY

Look for the 🔳🔳🔳 symbols which indicate accessibility for wheelchair users. A list of establishments is at the front of this guide.

MIDDLETON-BY-YOULGREAVE, Derbyshire Map ref 4B2

★★★★
1 Unit
Sleeping 6

HOLLY HOMESTEAD COTTAGE
The Square, Middleton-by-Youlgreave,
Bakewell DE45 1LS
Contact: Mr & Mrs D W Edge, Ridgeway House,
Hillcliff Lane, Turnditch, Belper DE56 2EA
T: (01773) 550754
F: (01773) 550754
E: daveedge@turnditch82.freeserve.co.uk

OPEN All year round

Low season per wk
£230.00–£275.00
High season per wk
£330.00–£410.00

Comfortable Grade II Listed cottage, some 250 years old, provides character accommodation, retaining many original features, in the heart of this quiet and peaceful village.

MILLER'S DALE, Derbyshire Map ref 4B2

★★★-★★★★
5 Units
Sleeping 2–6

Cosy little cottage and quaint old-fashioned bungalow nestling beneath woods near river. Also three old world beamed, spacious cottages on the hillside above with views you dream of. All cottages maintained to very high standards and set within a Nature Conservation Area by peaceful rivered dales and towering limestone cliffs.

MILLER'S DALE COTTAGES & MONKS RETREAT

Miller's Dale, Buxton SK17 8SN
Contact: Mrs P Wilkson, Monks Dale Farm, Miller's Dale,
Buxton SK17 8SN
T: (01298) 871306
F: (01298) 871306
E: pamwilkson@hotmail.com
I: www.cressbrook.co.uk/tidza/monksdale

OPEN All year round

Low season short breaks.

Low season per wk
Min £120.00
High season per wk
Max £290.00

MILWICH, Staffordshire Map ref 4B2

★★★★
2 Units
Sleeping 4–6

SUMMERHILL FARM
Milwich, Stafford ST18 0EL
T: (01889) 505546
F: (01889) 505692
E: p.milward@btinternet.com
Contact: Mrs P A Milward

OPEN All year round

Low season per wk
£95.00–£130.00
High season per wk
£130.00–£241.00

Two and 3 bedroomed fully-equipped cottages, close to Alton Towers, Peak District, Shugborough Hall and Wedgwood. Riding and golf-course close at hand.

MINSTERLEY, Shropshire Map ref 4A3

★★★
1 Unit
Sleeping 4

OVENPIPE COTTAGE
Tankerville Lodge, Stiperstones, Minsterley,
Shrewsbury SY5 0NB
Contact: Mr A B & Mrs P Thornton, Tankerville Lodge,
Stiperstones, Minsterley, Shrewsbury SY5 0NB
T: (01743) 791401
F: (01743) 791401
E: tankervillelodge@supanet.com

OPEN All year round

Low season per wk
£100.00–£150.00
High season per wk
£150.00–£180.00

Attractively restored barn in peaceful countryside setting, close to Stiperstones nature reserve and Long Mynd in dramatic Shropshire Hills. Superb walking, touring, shop, inn, P.O. nearby.

SPECIAL BREAKS

Many establishments offer special promotions and themed breaks. These are highlighted in red. (All such offers are subject to availability.)

MISERDEN, Gloucestershire Map ref 2B1

★★★

3 Units
Sleeping 4–6

SUDGROVE COTTAGES

Miserden, Stroud GL6 7JD
T: (01285) 821322
F: (01285) 821322
E: enquiries@sudgrovecottages.co.uk
I: www.sudgrovecottages.co.uk
Contact: Martin and Carol Ractliffe

Three attractive Cotswold-stone cottages overlooking fields in a peaceful hamlet on a 'no through road'. Footpaths lead through valleys, woods and pasture to picturesque villages while Cirencester, Stroud, Cheltenham and Gloucester are easily reached by car. You will find Sudgrove a place to relax and unwind.

OPEN All year round

Low season per wk
£180.00–£270.00
High season per wk
£255.00–£395.00

MOLLINGTON, Oxfordshire

See South of England region

MORETON-IN-MARSH, Gloucestershire Map ref 2B1

★★★

1 Unit
Sleeping 5

THE COTTAGE

Broadmoor Farm, Little Wolford, Shipston-on-Stour CV36 5LZ
Contact: Mrs R M Warriner, Broadmoor Farm, Little Wolford, Shipston-on-Stour CV36 5LZ
T: (01608) 684223 (Answerphone)
F: (01608) 684261
E: rozwarriner@cs.com

OPEN All year round

Low season per wk
Min £200.00

Comfortable stone cottage with 3 spacious bedrooms, on our farm on the edge of a quiet hamlet in the Cotswold Area of Outstanding Natural Beauty.

★★★

1 Unit
Sleeping 4

THE LAURELS

9 St James Court, Moreton-in-Marsh GL56 0ER
Contact: Mrs S I Billinger, Blue Cedar House, Stow Road, Moreton-in-Marsh GL56 0DW
T: (01608) 650299
E: gandisb@dialstart.net

OPEN All year round

Low season per wk
Min £210.00
High season per wk
Min £364.00

Modern well-furnished bungalow with private garden in the North Cotswolds. Ideal touring centre, convenient for shops and services. Central heating and double glazing.

NAUNTON, Gloucestershire Map ref 2B1

★★★

1 Unit
Sleeping 7

BAKE HOUSE

Main Street, Naunton, Cheltenham GL54 3AT
Contact: Ms Joan Timmins, The Littons, Main Square, Naunton, Cheltenham GL54 3AT
T: (01451) 850443

OPEN All year round

Low season per wk
£400.00–£500.00
High season per wk
£500.00–£1,000.00

A peaceful 17thC cottage based in the centre of this idyllic unspoilt village. Three double bedrooms, 1 single, 2 bathrooms, 2 lounges, designer kitchen, library, secluded courtyard. Pretty stream running through village.

NEW MILLS, Derbyshire Map ref 4B2

★★★

1 Unit
Sleeping 6–8

SHAW FARM

Shaw Marsh, New Mills, High Peak SK22 4QE
T: (0161) 4271841
E: nicky.burgess@talk21.com
Contact: Mrs Nicky Burgess

OPEN All year round

Low season per wk
£240.00–£260.00
High season per wk
£300.00–£380.00

Semi-detached farmhouse on working dairy farm with views over open countryside. Garden with patio. Also for hire, 4 static caravans. Please apply for brochure.

RATING All accommodation in this guide has been rated, or is awaiting a rating, by a trained English Tourism Council assessor.

★★★

4 Units
Sleeping 4

SLATERS COUNTRY INN

Stone Road, Baldwins Gate, Newcastle-under-Lyme
ST5 5ED
T: (01782) 680052
F: (01782) 680136
I: www.slaterscountryinn.co.uk
Contact: Mrs Karen Slater

Tastefully converted 18thC farm surrounded by countryside. Five miles from J15 M6 and within easy reach of Alton Towers and the Potteries. The cottages are in the courtyard of this popular country inn with delightful gardens and excellent facilities. Opening in 2002 – Slaters Craft Village with tea rooms and garden centre.

OPEN All year round
CC: Barclaycard, Delta,
Eurocard, Mastercard,
Switch, Visa

Weekend and mid-week
breaks available.

Low season per wk
£200.00–£250.00
High season per wk
£280.00–£300.00

★★★

1 Unit
Sleeping 5–9

MILL BARN COTTAGE

The Mill House, Mill Lane, Earls Barton,
Northampton NN6 0NR
T: (01604) 810507
F: (01604) 810507
E: roger@themillbarn.free-online.co.uk
I: www.themillbarn.free-online.co.uk
Contact: Mr Roger Wolens

A centuries-old riverside barn converted into a fully-equipped cottage, retaining all the original stone and oak beam features. Unlimited access to gardens, river, barbecue, etc. Private and secluded but offering easy access to major tourist attractions. Well equipped including microwave, dishwasher, washer/dryer, TV, video, playhouse, babysitting, etc. Six miles Northampton.

OPEN All year round

Special short break and
weekend rates from £40 per
night.

Low season per wk
Min £150.00
High season per wk
Max £500.00

See South of England region

★★★★

3 Units
Sleeping 2–5

THE BURNETT FARMHOUSE

Orcop, Hereford HR2 8SF
T: (01981) 540 999 (answerphone/fax)
F: (01981) 540 999
E: burnett.farmhouse@talk21.com
Contact: Mr and Mrs M A Gooch

Set in magnificent rolling countryside, these beautifully renovated farm buildings adjoin The Burnett Farmhouse, with oak beams and old world charm. Far-reaching views across Orcop Valley to Garway Hill. Excellent base to discover the Wye Valley, Forest of Dean, Brecon Beacons, Malvern Hills, Welsh borders. Ideal walking/painting/wildlife.

OPEN All year round

Short breaks available all
year round.

Low season per wk
£195.00–£245.00
High season per wk
£295.00–£385.00

CONFIRM YOUR BOOKING
You are advised to confirm your booking in writing.

OUNDLE, Northamptonshire Map ref 3A1 *Tourist Information Centre Tel: (01832) 274333*

★★★★

1 Unit
Sleeping 3

THE BOLT HOLE
3 Ray Close, Off Cotterstock Road, Oundle,
Peterborough PE8 4QT
Contact: Mrs Anita Spurrell, Rose Cottage,
70 Glapthorne Road, Oundle, Peterborough PE8 4PT
T: (01832) 273521 (Work) & 272298 (Home)
F: (01832) 275409

OPEN All year round

Low season per wk
£240.00
High season per wk
£240.00

Comfortable modern bungalow. Lounge/diner, fitted kitchen. Garden room/single bedroom, double bedroom, large en suite shower. Separate cloak/utility room. Gas heating. Private garden and parking.

OWLPEN, Gloucestershire Map ref 2B1

★★★–★★★★★

9 Units
Sleeping 2–9

OWLPEN MANOR
Owlpen, Uley, Dursley GL11 5BZ
T: (01453) 860261
F: (01453) 860819
E: sales@owlpen.com
I: www.1travel.com/owlpen
Contact: Ms Julia Webb

OPEN All year round
CC: Amex, Barclaycard,
Delta, Eurocard, JCB,
Mastercard, Switch, Visa,
Visa Electron

Low season per wk
£250.00–£520.00
High season per wk
£355.00–£895.00

Period cottages in romantic Cotswold setting, on historic manorial estate in private wooded valley. Fully serviced, licensed restaurant, log fires, four-poster beds, antiques.

PEAK DISTRICT

See under Alstonefield, Ashbourne, Ashford in the Water, Bakewell, Bamford, Baslow, Buxton, Chelmorton, Cressbrook, Edale, Eyam, Calver, Great Hucklow, Hartington, Hathersage, Hayfield, Hope, Middleton-by-Youlgreave, Miller's Dale, New Mills, Tideswell, Youlgreave

PEMBRIDGE, Herefordshire Map ref 2A1

★★★

2 Units
Sleeping 4

THE GRANARY & THE DAIRY
Pembridge, Leominster HR6 9HP
T: (01544) 388268
F: (01544) 388154
E: nancy@grovedesign.co.uk
Contact: Mrs N Owens

Attractive barn conversions in 200-acre farm in secluded valley near black and white villages, Offa's Dyke and Mortimer Trail. Many historic and National Trust properties in the area. Friendly farm atmosphere. Children and pets welcome.

OPEN All year round

Low season per wk
£139.00–£222.00
High season per wk
£222.00–£300.00

★

1 Unit
Sleeping 5

ROWENA COTTAGE
2 East Street, Pembridge, Leominster HR6 9HA
Contact: Mrs D Malone, The Cottage, Holme, Newark
NG23 7RZ
T: (01636) 672914

OPEN All year round

Low season per wk
Min £180.00
High season per wk
Max £230.00

A comfortable black and white cottage with open fire and a wealth of beams. Located in the centre of picturesque village. An ideal touring centre.

COUNTRY CODE Always follow the Country Code ♧ Enjoy the countryside and respect its life and work ♧ Guard against all risk of fire ♧ Fasten all gates ♧ Keep your dogs under close control ♧ Keep to public paths across farmland ♧ Use gates and stiles to cross fences, hedges and walls ♧ Leave livestock, crops and machinery alone ♧ Take your litter home ♧ Help to keep all water clean ♧ Protect wildlife, plants and trees ♧ Take special care on country roads ♧ Make no unnecessary noise

PLUNGAR, Leicestershire Map ref 4C2

★★★★★

1 Unit
Sleeping 6

THE OLD WHARF

Grange Farm, Granby Lane, Plungar,
Nottingham NG13 0JJ
Contact: Mrs Elaine Pell, Grange Farm, Granby Lane,
Plungar, Nottingham NG13 0JJ
T: (01949) 860630 (answerphone)

Beautifully restored canalside cottage set in pretty countryside yet within easy reach of Nottingham, Melton Mowbray, Belvoir Castle, and National Watersports Centre. Spacious yet cosy and warm in winter, with inglenook fireplace and woodburning stove. Three double bedrooms, 2 bathrooms, well-equipped kitchen. An ideal base for walking, sightseeing holidays.

OPEN All year round

Short breaks available.

Low season per wk
£195.00–£295.00
High season per wk
£350.00–£400.00

PRESTON, Gloucestershire Map ref 2B1

★★★

1 Unit
Sleeping 2

THE TALLET
The Old Farmhouse, Preston, Cirencester GL7 5PR
T: (01285) 653405 (Anytime)
F: (01285) 653405
Contact: Mrs Susan Spivey

OPEN May–Oct

Low season per wk
Min £160.00
High season per wk
Max £230.00

An attractive Cotswold barn conversion approached by oustide stone steps. Beams in all rooms overlooking farmland with a small number of livestock. Parking.

ROSS-ON-WYE, Herefordshire Map ref 2A1 *Tourist Information Centre Tel: (01989) 562768*

★★★

4 Units
Sleeping 2–18

THE ASHE

Bridstow, Ross-on-Wye HR9 6QA
T: (01989) 563336
E: Holidaycottages.the.ashe@ukgateway.net
I: www.burnett24.freeserve.co.uk
Contact: Mrs M Ball

The Mill, Granary, Stable and Orchard Cottage, in the Wye Valley. Beamed 16thC converted stone barns, 2/3-bedroomed. Free use of on-site 18-hole par 3 golf course, tennis court, fishing lakes. Walks through beautiful Herefordshire countryside. Near Forest of Dean, Symonds Yat. Wales 10 miles.

OPEN All year round

Low season per wk
£120.00–£200.00
High season per wk
£250.00–£450.00

★★-★★★

4 Units
Sleeping 2–25

BARN HOUSE AND OAKLANDS

Llangarron, Ross-on-Wye HR9 6NZ
Contact: Mrs A Farr, Southwell Court, Broad Oak, Hereford HR2 8RA
T: (01600) 750333 (Answerphone)
E: farrcottages@yahoo.com
I: www.farrsouthwell.fsnet.co.uk

Oaklands is a superb country house in the village of Llangarron, just 3 miles off A40 at Ross-on-Wye. Set in 80 acres of private land ideal for country walking. It has 5 bedrooms and 2 sitting rooms and picture windows overlooking beautiful countryside. Central heating, log fires. Other smaller properties available.

OPEN All year round

3-night stays available off-season Oct–Mar.

Low season per wk
£250.00–£400.00
High season per wk
£500.00–£700.00

WHERE TO STAY
Please mention this guide when making your booking.

★★★★

1 Unit
Sleeping 2

OLD CIDER HOUSE
Glewstone, Ross-on-Wye HR9 6AN
Contact: Mrs H A Jackson, Lowcop, Glewstone, Ross-on-Wye HR9 6AN
T: (01989) 562827
F: (01989) 563877
E: man.of.ross.ltd@farming.co.uk

OPEN All year round

Low season per wk
£180.00–£200.00
High season per wk
£200.00–£250.00

Old cider house on fruit farm in Wye Valley, converted to character cottage with beams and antique furniture. Overlooking apple orchards. Warm in winter.

★★★

1 Unit
Sleeping 6

THE OLDE HOUSE
Upton Bishop, Ross-on-Wye HR9 7UE
Contact: P J & J Fray, Keepers Cottage, Upton Bishop, Ross-on-Wye HR9 7UE
T: (01989) 780383
F: (01989) 780383
E: peter@pjfray.co.uk
I: www.oldehouse.com

OPEN All year round

Low season per wk
£195.00–£230.00
High season per wk
£230.00–£350.00

Cosy beamed cottage with open fire and full central heating. Large garden and panoramic views.

★★★★

1 Unit
Sleeping 4

WATCHMAKER'S COTTAGE
Daffaluke House, Glewstone, Ross-on-Wye HR9 6BB
Contact: Mrs J Clark, Daffaluke House, Glewstone, Ross-on-Wye HR9 6BB
T: (01989) 770369 (Answerphone)
F: (01989) 770369
E: watchmakerscottage@madasafish.com

A peaceful detached coach house overlooking plum and apple orchards. Cosy and warm in winter with log fire. Four poster bedroom with bathroom and power-shower. Children's twin beds which convert to large double en suite. Own patio, shared garden. Wye Valley, Forest of Dean, walks, castles, bird watching, relaxing! Ross-on-Wye 4 miles.

OPEN All year round

Short breaks available.

Low season per wk
£210.00–£305.00
High season per wk
£320.00–£420.00

★★★

1 Unit
Sleeping 4

Y CRWYS
Goodrich, Ross-on-Wye HR9 6HU
Contact: Mr & Mrs Colin and Angie Fuller, Manager, 3 The Square, Goodrich, Ross-on-Wye HR9 6HX
T: (01600) 890799 (Answerphone)
E: rosiekeegan@yahoo.co.uk

Y Crwys is a unique 600-year-old detached stone cottage, with internal spiral staircase and external stairs, both stone. Two bedrooms, 2 toilets, kitchen/living area and lounge. There is a garden with unusual trees and patio.

OPEN All year round

Off-season short stays by arrangement.

Low season per wk
£140.00–£220.00
High season per wk
£220.00–£330.00

CHECK THE MAPS
The colour maps at the front of this guide show all the cities, towns and villages for which you will find accommodation entries.
Refer to the town index to find the page on which they are listed.

★★★★
3 Units
Sleeping 4–8

Attractive converted barns set within a farmyard. Fully equipped to ensure you are cosy and comfortable. Short breaks by arrangement. Fishing available. Located 3 miles from Rugby on Lawford Heath Lane. Midway between A428 and A45.

LAWFORD HILL FARM

Lawford Heath Lane, Rugby CV23 9HG
Contact: Mr & Mrs Susan Moses, Lawford Hill Farm,
Lawford Heath Lane, Rugby CV23 9HG
T: (01788) 542001
F: (01788) 537880
E: lawford.hill@talk21.com
I: www.lawfordhill.co.uk

OPEN All year round
CC: Delta, JCB,
Mastercard, Solo, Switch,
Visa, Visa Electron

Low season per wk
£300.00–£400.00
High season per wk
£400.00–£500.00

★★★★
1 Unit
Sleeping 5

THE CALF PEN
Barn Lane, Sedgeberrow, Evesham WR11 6UR
Contact: Mr and Mrs M Pilling, The Dower House,
Barn Lane, Sedgeberrow, Evesham WR11 6UR
T: (01386) 882095 & 07957 461391 (mobile)
E: calfpen_pilling@btinternet.com

OPEN Mar–Dec

Low season per wk
£350.00–£400.00
High season per wk
£430.00–£490.00

A delightful barn conversion on the fringe of the Cotswolds. Furnished and equipped to a high standard. The Calf Pen sleeps 5 plus a cot.

★★★★
1 Unit
Sleeping 4

THE OLD WORKSHOP
28 The Wharf, Shardlow, Derby DE72 2HG
Contact: Mrs D Hansen, 24 Mill Green, The Wharf,
Shardlow, Derby DE72 2WE
T: (01332) 799820 & (0115) 9742234

OPEN All year round

Low season per wk
£130.00–£150.00
High season per wk
£200.00–£250.00

Detached converted workshop. Open plan kitchen/diner/lounge with bed settee; shower room. Stairs to twin attic bedroom. Small patio garden.

★★★★★
1 Unit
Sleeping 8

FERNY KNOWLE
Sheen, Buxton SK17 0ER
Contact: Mr G Grindon, Ferny Knowle, Sheen, Buxton
SK17 0ER
T: (01298) 83264 (Answerphone)

OPEN All year round

Low season per wk
Min £213.00
High season per wk
Max £495.00

44-acre mixed farm. Renovated farmhouse on the Derbyshire/Staffordshire border. 3 bedrooms, plus bed/settee and bathroom downstairs. Full central heating, plus log fire.

See under Epperstone

★★★★
1 Unit
Sleeping 6

A recently renovated stone barn situated outside the hamlet of Ascott, a secluded valley surrounded by grass fields and oak trees. It will sleep 6 people in 2 double and 1 twin rooms. There are oak beams, stone floors and a Shaker-style kitchen.

LITTLE BARN

Ascott, Shipston-on-Stour CV36 5PP
Contact: Mrs K Lawrence, Acorns, Ascott, Shipston-on-
Stour CV36 5PP
T: (01608) 684240
E: johnandkaren.lawrence@ic24.net
I: www.littlebarn.members.easyspace.com/index.htm

OPEN All year round

Short breaks available to suit
your requirements. Please
contact us for details.

Low season per wk
£285.00–£325.00
High season per wk
£400.00–£475.00

SHIPTON-UNDER-WYCHWOOD, Oxfordshire

See South of England region

SHREWSBURY, Shropshire Map ref 4A3 *Tourist Information Centre Tel: (01743) 281200*

★★★

1 Unit
Sleeping 7

CROSS HILL
Shrewsbury SY1 1JH
Contact: Mrs E A Williams, 68 Church Hill, Penn,
Wolverhampton WV4 5JD
T: (01902) 341399
E: williams_letting@hotmail.com

OPEN All year round

Low season per wk
£180.00–£250.00
High season per wk
£250.00–£300.00

Four bedroomed Georgian house in heart of historic Shrewsbury. Easy walking distance of shops, restaurants, market, museums, churches, river and park. Courtyard garden. Private parking.

★★

1 Unit
Sleeping 4

INGLENOOK
Villa Lane, Bicton, Shrewsbury SY3 8EG
Contact: Mrs J M Mullineux, Fach-Hir, Brooks,
Welshpool SY21 8QP
T: (01686) 650361

OPEN All year round

Low season per wk
£80.00–£100.00
High season per wk
£150.00–£190.00

Bungalow in peaceful surroundings, 3 miles from the centre of historic Shrewsbury town. Ample parking alongside. Gardens and lawn.

SNAILBEACH, Shropshire Map ref 4A3

★★★

1 Unit
Sleeping 3

THE BLESSING
1 Farm Cottages, Snailbeach, Shrewsbury SY5 0LP
Contact: Mr & Mrs M J Dennis, 3 Farm Cottages,
Snailbeach, Shrewsbury SY5 0LP
T: (01743) 791489

OPEN All year round

Low season per wk
£175.00–£200.00
High season per wk
£225.00

In hills 12 miles from Shrewsbury, self-contained portion of centrally-heated, attractive cottage. Well carpeted and furnished, twin beds and sofa bed, garden and conservatory/porch.

SOUDLEY, Gloucestershire Map ref 2B1

★★★

1 Unit
Sleeping 6

THE COTTAGE
Soudley
Contact: Mrs Helen Evans, Peaked Rocks Cottage,
The Rocks, Joys Green, Lydbrook GL17 9RF
T: (01594) 861119 & 823408
F: (01594) 823408

Cottage situated in the quiet village of Soudley. Set in the beautiful Soudley Valley. Woodland walks and village pub 5 minutes' walk from the cottage. The tranquil Soudley Ponds set in woodlands and the Dean Heritage Museum 10 minutes' walk away. Very well-equipped.

OPEN All year round

Low season per wk
Min £120.00
High season per wk
Max £280.00

SPILSBY, Lincolnshire Map ref 4D2

★★★★

1 Unit
Sleeping 5

OWL BARN
Serena Lodge, Stonepit Lane, Skendleby, Spilsby
PE23 4QB
T: (01754) 890244 (BT call minder)
E: owlbreak@supanet.com
Contact: Mr D T Neal

OPEN All year round

High season per wk
£250.00–£450.00

A newly converted 19thC single storey barn in the grounds of Serena Lodge, the owner's home. Area of Outstanding Natural Beauty, 14 miles from the sea.

TOWN INDEX
This can be found at the back of this guide. If you know where you want to stay, the index will give you the page number listing accommodation in your chosen town, city or village.

STANTON, Gloucestershire Map ref 2B1

★★★
1 Unit
Sleeping 6

Charming Cotswold stone cottage in picturesque village. Three bedrooms, 2 bathrooms, spacious accommodation. The pretty garden offers al fresco dining. Village pub 5 minutes' walk from cottage, and Broadway (2 miles) has a selection of pubs and restaurants. Enjoy walking the Cotswold hills, or visit NT houses and gardens.

CHARITY COTTAGE
Stanton, Broadway WR12 7NE
Contact: Mrs V Ryland, Charity Farm, Stanton, Broadway WR12 7NE
T: (01386) 584339
F: (01386) 584270
E: kennethryland@ukonline.co.uk
I: www.myrtle-cottage.co.uk/ryland.htm

OPEN All year round

Short breaks available.

Low season per wk
£200.00–£350.00
High season per wk
£275.00–£450.00

STANTON HARCOURT, Oxfordshire

See South of England region

STANTON-ON-THE-WOLDS, Nottinghamshire Map ref 4C2

★★★★
1 Unit
Sleeping 6

Situated 7 miles south of Nottingham on the edge of the Vale of Belvoir, within easy reach of all attractions in the Midlands. The cottage stands well back from the A606, overlooking open countryside, with views of a lake and is set in a private well-maintained garden.

FOXCOTE COTTAGE
Hill Farm (Foxcote), Melton Road, Stanton-on-the-Wolds, Keyworth NG12 5PJ
T: (0115) 937 4337 (Answerphone and fax)
F: (0115) 937 4337
E: BJHinchley@aol.com
Contact: Mrs Joan Hinchley

OPEN All year round

Low season per wk
Min £350.00
High season per wk
Min £350.00

STOKE-ON-TRENT, Staffordshire Map ref 4B2 *Tourist Information Centre Tel: (01782) 236000*

★★★
1 Unit
Sleeping 5

Built in the 18thC, this delightful cottage was once the bake house to the Duke of Sutherland's estate at Trentham. Situated in a quiet lane, it contains oak beams, inglenook and private walled garden. Within easy reach of Alton Towers, 'Potteries' visitor centres and the Peak District National Park.

LOW ROOFS
7 Monument Lane, Tittensor, Stoke-on-Trent ST12 9JH
Contact: Mrs L Malkin, 62 Albert Terrace, Wolstanton, Newcastle-under-Lyme ST5 8AY
T: (01782) 627087
F: (01782) 627087

OPEN All year round

Low season per wk
£200.00–£250.00
High season per wk
£250.00–£350.00

MAP REFERENCES
The map references refer to the colour maps at the front of this guide. The first figure is the map number; the letter and figure which follow indicate the grid reference on the map.

STOW-ON-THE-WOLD, Gloucestershire Map ref 2B1 *Tourist Information Centre Tel: (01451) 831082*

★★★★-★★★★★
3 Units
Sleeping 4

Semi-detached Georgian cottage, quietly situated near centre. Great character, open fire, 2 bedrooms, bathroom, dining and sitting rooms, all beautifully equipped. Patio with barbecue. Regency-style cottage on one level also available. Double and twin bedrooms, bathroom, sitting/dining room and fully equipped kitchen. Pretty garden and barbecue.

BROAD OAK COTTAGES
Lower Park Street, Stow-on-the-Wold, Cheltenham GL54 1AQ
Contact: Mrs M Wilson, The Counting House, Stow-on-the-Wold, Cheltenham GL54 1AL
T: (01451) 830794 (Broad Oak Cottages) & 830794 (May Cottage)
F: (01451) 830794
E: rafw@aol.com

OPEN All year round

Short breaks available (except in high season).

Low season per wk
£220.00–£275.00
High season per wk
£285.00–£450.00

★★★
1 Unit
Sleeping 5

JOHNSTON COTTAGE
2 Oddfellows Row, Stow-on-the-Wold, Cheltenham GL54 1DB
Contact: Mrs Yvonne Johnston, Fosse Manor Hotel, Stow-on-the-Wold, Cheltenham GL54 1JX
T: (01451) 830354 (Day) & (01608) 650816 (Nights)
F: (01451) 832486

OPEN All year round

Low season per wk
£220.00–£330.00
High season per wk
£220.00–£330.00

Quiet location 5 minutes from town centre. Exposed beams and stonework, good quality throughout. Colourful flowers and hanging baskets in summer. Parking nearby.

★★★★
3 Units
Sleeping 2–16

LUCKLEY HOLIDAYS
Longborough, Moreton-in-Marsh GL56 0RD
T: (01451) 870885 & 07931 567525 (Mobile)
F: (01541) 831481
E: luckleyholidays@talk21.com
I: www.luckley-holidays.co.uk
Contact: Mr Robert Wharton

OPEN All year round

Low season per wk
£270.00–£417.00
High season per wk
£432.00–£828.00

Traditional Cotswold farm set in open countryside, with large swimming pool, tennis court and games room. Tranquillity in the heart of the north Cotswolds.

★★★
2 Units
Sleeping 3–6

MAUGERSBURY MANOR
Stow-on-the-Wold, Cheltenham GL54 1HP
T: (01451) 830581
F: (01451) 870902
E: karen@manorholidays.co.uk
I: www.manorholidays.co.uk
Contact: Mr C S Martin

OPEN All year round

Low season per wk
£120.00–£180.00
High season per wk
£250.00–£350.00

Quiet, comfortable apartment in old manor house. Sunny position with pleasant garden and grounds. Ample parking. Short breaks available. B&B available.

QUALITY ASSURANCE SCHEME

For an explanation of the quality and facilities represented by the Stars please refer to the front of this guide. A more detailed explanation can be found in the information pages at the back.

★★★★

1 Unit
Sleeping 7

OLD CORNER COTTAGE

Lower Oddington, Moreton-in-Marsh GL56 0XD
Contact: Mrs Cathy Terry, St. Helens Vicarage,
St. Helens Gardens, London W10 6LP
T: (0208) 960 5067
F: (0208) 965782
E: cathy.terry@cornercottage23.fsbusiness.co.uk

Delightful Grade II Listed Cotswold cottage built in the 1700s, has been tastefully refurbished whilst retaining original features like inglenook fireplace, flagstone floors. Three double bedrooms, bathroom, lounge, fully fitted kitchen, patio garden. In picturesque village with post office/shop, 11thC church and famous Fox Inn.

OPEN All year round

3 night breaks available
Oct-Apr.

Low season per wk
Min £185.00
High season per wk
Max £450.00

★★★★

4 Units
Sleeping 2–5

PARK FARM HOLIDAY COTTAGES

Park Farm, Maugersbury, Stow-on-the-Wold,
Cheltenham GL54 1HP
Contact: Mrs J C Ricketts, Park Farm, Maugersbury,
Cheltenham GL54 1HP
T: (01451) 830227
F: (01451) 870568
E: parkfarm.cottages@virgin.net

Situated on owners' mixed farm in small hamlet less than 10 minutes' walk from Stow-on-the-Wold, where there are excellent pubs and restaurants. Three south-facing, single-storey detached cottages with wonderful views accommodating 2/5 people. Romantic 4-poster beds in double rooms. Also, cosy 2-bedroomed wing to farmhouse. Log-burning stoves.

OPEN All year round

Low season per wk
£170.00–£250.00
High season per wk
£250.00–£510.00

★★★★

1 Unit
Sleeping 2

ROSE'S COTTAGE

The Green, Broadwell, Moreton-in-Marsh GL56 0UF
Contact: Mr & Mrs R Drinkwater, Rose's Cottage,
The Green, Broadwell, Moreton-in-Marsh GL56 0UF
T: (01451) 830007 & 870228

OPEN All year round

Low season per wk
£200.00–£230.00
High season per wk
£230.00–£300.00

Delightful cottage overlooking the green of charming Cotswold village, in an Area of Outstanding Natural Beauty, 1.5 miles from Stow-on-the-Wold. Ideal for touring.

★★★★★

1 Unit
Sleeping 4

VINTNERS COTTAGE

Broadwell, Moreton-in-Marsh GL56 0UF
Contact: Mrs P D Taylor, Booking Officer, 12 Dale Bank,
Oakdale, Harrogate HG1 2LP
T: (01423) 502355

Delightful 17thC cottage overlooking the green in Broadwell, a very pretty, unspoilt village outside Stow. Fully modernised and furnished to a high standard but retains all original features, fireplace, beams and exposed stone walls. A 2000 guest says 'one of the best cottages we have stayed in'. Can sleep a further 2.

OPEN All year round

Special mid-week rates
throughout the year.

Low season per wk
£350.00–£400.00
High season per wk
£475.00–£525.00

IDEAS For ideas on places to visit refer to the introduction at the beginning of this section.

STRATFORD-UPON-AVON, Warwickshire Map ref 2B1 *Tourist Information Centre Tel: (01789) 293127*

★★★★

2 Units
Sleeping 1–4

20-21 BANCROFT PLACE

Bridgefoot, Stratford-upon-Avon CV37 6YZ
Contact: Mrs Stella Carter, Park View, 57 Rother Street,
Stratford-upon-Avon CV37 6LT
T: (01789) 266839
F: (01789) 266839

First floor 2-bedroom apartments, centrally heated, in a quiet lane within 2 minutes' walk of town centre, river and theatre. Number 20 has a balcony with wonderful views of the river bridge on to Holy Trinity spire. Both apartments have off-road parking and are fully equipped.

OPEN All year round

Low season per wk
£255.00–£375.00
High season per wk
£375.00–£475.00

★★★★

1 Unit
Sleeping 5

BARD COTTAGE

Willicote Pastures, Willicote, Stratford-upon-Avon
CV37 8JT
Contact: Mrs M Hicks, 2 Beech Court, Stratford-upon-
Avon CV37 7UQ
T: (01789) 205039
F: (01789) 261386
E: Maureen.Hicks@btinternet.com
I: www.stratford-upon-avon.co.uk/bardcott.htm

Charming 19thC recently converted detached barn cottage retaining character and original beams. Tastefully furnished, equipped to high standard and all modern conveniences. Perfectly situated for exploring Stratford-upon-Avon, Warwick, Cotswolds, located 2 miles from Stratford town centre, in beautiful Shakespeare countryside. Well maintained gardens, patio. Convenient to M40, NEC.

OPEN All year round

Low season per wk
£300.00–£390.00
High season per wk
£400.00–£500.00

★★★★

2 Units
Sleeping 6

CHARLECOTE COTTAGE 2 WILLICOTE PASTURES
Warwickshire Avenue, Campden Road, Willicote,
Stratford-upon-Avon CV37 8LN
Contact: Mr J Lea, 6 Oak Wharf Mews, Birchdale Road,
Appleton, Warrington WA4 5AS
T: (01925) 604106 & (0151) 4952099 (Ask for Mr Lea)
F: (0151) 4246785
E: jplea@aol.com

OPEN All year round
CC: Barclaycard, Delta,
Mastercard, Switch, Visa,
Visa Electron

Low season per wk
£300.00–£600.00
High season per wk
£300.00–£600.00

Converted 120-year-old barn cottages. Exposed beams, splendid views, large gardens and private patio. Very well equipped with quality furnishings. Children welcome.

★★★

1 Unit
Sleeping 3

CHESTNUT COTTAGE
Gospel Oak House, Pathlow, Stratford-upon-
Avon CV37 0JA
Contact: Mrs J Rush, Gospel Oak House, Pathlow,
Stratford-upon-Avon CV37 0JA
T: (01789) 292764

OPEN All year round

Low season per wk
£160.00–£190.00
High season per wk
£190.00–£220.00

Set in splendid secluded grounds by woodland, with far reaching views. Well-appointed, attractively furnished, ample parking. 2.5 miles from Stratford-upon-Avon.

NB **IMPORTANT NOTE** Information on accommodation listed in this guide has been supplied by the proprietors. As changes may occur you are advised to check details at the time of booking.

STRATFORD-UPON-AVON continued

★★★

1 Unit
Sleeping 6

42 SHAKESPEARE STREET
Stratford-upon-Avon CV37 6RS
Contact: Mr K D Field, Avon House, Mulberry Street,
Stratford-upon-Avon CV37 6SD
T: (01789) 298141
F: (01789) 262272

OPEN All year round

Low season per wk
£200.00–£350.00
High season per wk
£300.00–£600.00

Grade II Listed cottage built 1840, in quiet back street in town centre, 300 metres from Shakespeare's birthplace. Very cosy. Private parking.

★★★★★

1 Unit
Sleeping 6

Spacious mews-style cottage set in woodland and garden surroundings. Tastefully furnished and fully equipped. Two double and 1 twin bedroom, 3 bath/shower rooms. Lounge, dining room, garden lounge, kitchen and breakfast room. In the village of Wilmcote, just outside Stratford-upon-Avon, ideal for Shakespeare Country and Cotswolds.

WOODCOTE
Park Close, Wilmcote, Stratford-upon-Avon CV37 9XE
Contact: Mr & Mrs W A Lucas, Tanglewood, Park Close,
Wilmcote, Stratford-upon-Avon CV37 9XE
T: (01789) 293932
F: (01789) 261855
E: lucasstratford@aol.com
I: www.lucasstratford.co.uk

OPEN All year round

Low season per wk
£295.00–£350.00
High season per wk
£395.00–£450.00

SUTTON ON THE HILL, Derbyshire Map ref 4B2

★★★★

1 Unit
Sleeping 6

THE CHOP HOUSE
Windle Hill Farm, Sutton on the Hill,
Ashbourne DE6 5JH
Contact: Mr and Mrs Lennard, Windle Hill Farm,
Sutton on the Hill, Ashbourne DE6 5JH
T: (01283) 732377 (Answerphone)
F: (01283) 732377
E: windlehill@btinternet.com
I: www.windlehill.btinternet.co.uk

OPEN All year round

Low season per wk
£140.00–£280.00
High season per wk
£280.00–£375.00

10-acre smallholding. Converted beamed barn on small working farm with traditional and rare breeds of livestock and poultry. Pleasant views. Ideal base for the Derbyshire Peak District.

TETBURY, Gloucestershire Map ref 2B2 *Tourist Information Centre Tel: (01666) 503552*

★★★

11 Units
Sleeping 2–8

Eleven superior 18thC cottages fitted with every convenience on a privately owned 200-acre estate set within the Royal Triangle in the magnificent Cotswolds. A peaceful, discreet location within a few minutes' walk of Tetbury. Ideal for touring, exploring, restaurants, pubs, historic venues, walking or just relaxing in comfort.

FOLLY FARM COTTAGES
Tetbury GL8 8XA
Contact: Mr J Benton, Folly Farm, Tetbury GL8 8XA
T: (01666) 502475
F: (01666) 502358
E: info@gtb.co.uk
I: www.gtb.co.uk

OPEN All year round
CC: Barclaycard,
Mastercard, Switch, Visa

Low season per wk
£250.00–£500.00
High season per wk
£300.00–£700.00

PRICES
Please check prices and other details at the time of booking.

★★★–★★★★★

3 Units
Sleeping 2–8

Georgian coach house and cottages, beautifully decorated and well-equipped. Antiques and 4-posters. Idyllic lakeside setting in 15-acre manor grounds in lovely village. Swimming, riding, clay shooting, tennis. On Bredon Hill near Cheltenham, perfect location for touring Cotswolds and Heart of England. Fine food and B&B available in manor.

COURTYARD COTTAGES

Upper Court, Kemerton, Tewkesbury GL20 7HY
Contact: Mr H W Herford, Upper Court, Kemerton, Tewkesbury GL20 7HY
T: (01386) 725351
F: (01386) 725472
E: sales@ttgihg.co.uk
I: www.country-holidays.co.uk

OPEN All year round
CC: Amex, Barclaycard, Mastercard, Switch, Visa

Low season per wk
£250.00–£950.00
High season per wk
£250.00–£1,400.00

★★★

1 Unit
Sleeping 8

Beautifully restored, this Grade II Listed house is located in the heart of the village, close to an excellent range of local amenities. Full central heating to all rooms plus wood-burning stove in the lounge. Ideal for groups or several families holidaying together. Huge loft room with second television.

GOLDSTRAWS

2 Curzon Terrace, Litton Mill, Buxton SK17 8SR
Contact: Mr & Mrs D J Sutherland, 2 Curzon Terrace, Litton Mill, Buxton SK17 8SR
T: (01298) 871100
F: (01298) 871641
E: enq@goldstrawshouse.co.uk
I: www.goldstrawshouse.co.uk

OPEN All year round
CC: Barclaycard, Delta, Eurocard, Mastercard, Switch, Visa

Low season per wk
£271.00–£327.00
High season per wk
£400.00–£525.00

3 night stays available at off-peak times.

★★★★

1 Unit
Sleeping 4

LITTLE BARN

Old Post Office Lane, Trefonen, Oswestry SY10 9DL
Contact: Mrs Sue Batley, Wulfruna Cottage, Old Post Office Lane, Trefonen, Oswestry SY10 9DL
T: (01691) 653387 (Answerphone)
E: info@little-barn.co.uk
I: www.little-barn.co.uk

OPEN All year round

Low season per wk
£100.00–£200.00
High season per wk
£200.00–£300.00

An old barn recently converted to high standard in a small village. Well-equipped modern kitchen, cosy lounge with wood burning stove. In Welsh Marches.

★★★★★

1 Unit
Sleeping 2

HOME FARM STABLE

Home Farmhouse, Upper Slaughter, Cheltenham GL54 2JF
Contact: Mrs M A Bayetto, Home Farmhouse, Upper Slaughter, Cheltenham GL54 2JF
T: (01451) 820487 (Answerphone) & 07901 684664
E: maureen.bayetto@virgin.net
I: www.home-farm-stable.co.uk

OPEN All year round

Low season per wk
Max £305.00
High season per wk
Max £395.00

Converted granary barn/stable with all original timbers and features, very sympathetically decorated and furnished to a good standard of comfort and style.

UPPINGHAM, Rutland Map ref 4C3

★★★
1 Unit
Sleeping 3

4 STOCKERSTON ROAD
Uppingham, Oakham LE15 9UD
T: (01572) 823478 & 823955
F: (01572) 823955
Contact: Mr or Mrs Lloyd

OPEN All year round

Low season per wk
£160.00
High season per wk
£160.00

Comfortably appointed flat with its own private walled garden. Designed for a couple, but can accommodate a third person. Enjoys a 3 Star rating with the ETC.

UPTON ST LEONARDS, Gloucestershire Map ref 2B1

★★
3 Units
Sleeping 3–4

HILL FARM COTTAGES
Hill Farm, Upton Hill, Upton St Leonards,
Gloucester GL4 8DA
T: (01452) 614081
Contact: Mrs M McLellan

OPEN All year round

Low season per wk
£170.00
High season per wk
£260.00–£270.00

Located 2 miles from Gloucester, with panoramic views of the Cotswolds. Close to dry-ski slopes and golfing facilities. Ideal for walking. Country pub nearby providing food.

WADDINGWORTH, Lincolnshire Map ref 4D2

★★★★
1 Unit
Sleeping 4

REDHOUSE COTTAGE
Redhouse Farm, Waddingworth,
Woodhall Spa LN10 5EE
Contact: Mr & Mrs A Pritchard, Redhouse Farm,
Waddingworth, Woodhall Spa LN10 5EE
T: (01507) 578285 & 07702 678241 (Mobile)
F: (01507) 578285

OPEN All year round

Low season per wk
Min £200.00
High season per wk
Max £350.00

This delightful well-equipped cottage is adjacent to the owner's farmhouse. Quiet picturesque setting overlooking St Margarets Church, a perfect base for walking, cycling, golf and bird watching.

WARWICK, Warwickshire Map ref 2B1 *Tourist Information Centre Tel: (01926) 492212*

★★★
1 Unit
Sleeping 3

COPES FLAT
Brook Street, Warwick CV34 4BL
Contact: Mrs E Draisey, Forth House, 44 High Street,
Warwick CV34 4AX
T: (01926) 401512
F: (01926) 490809
E: info@forthhouseuk.co.uk
I: www.forthhouseuk.co.uk

OPEN All year round
CC: Barclaycard, Delta,
Eurocard, JCB, Maestro,
Mastercard, Solo, Switch,
Visa, Visa Electron

Low season per wk
£180.00–£250.00
High season per wk
£280.00–£310.00

Secluded town centre self-contained coach house flat. Sitting room/dining room, bedroom, bathroom, kitchen, telephone. Close to shops and restaurants. Large roof garden. Non-smokers only, please.

WELLINGTON, Shropshire Map ref 4A3

★★★★
1 Unit
Sleeping 4

THE COACH HOUSE
Wrockwardine, Wellington, Telford TF6 5DG
Contact: Mrs M M Fellows, Old Vicarage,
Wrockwardine, Wellington, Telford TF6 5DG
T: (01952) 244859 & (0121) 212 2131
F: (0121) 212 1249

OPEN All year round

Low season per wk
£220.00–£250.00
High season per wk
£250.00–£350.00

Detached private house providing centrally heated 2-bedroomed accommodation. Pleasant location, surrounded by farms yet close to Ironbridge, Shrewsbury and the Welsh Marches.

WETTON, Staffordshire Map ref 4B2

★★★
1 Unit
Sleeping 5

STABLE BARN
Wetton, Ashbourne DE6 2AF
Contact: Mrs H Higton, The Old Post Office, Wetton,
Ashbourne DE6 2AP
T: (01335) 310312

OPEN All year round

Low season per wk
£180.00–£290.00
High season per wk
£180.00–£290.00

A barn conversion with 2 bedrooms, shower, wc, living room, dining and kitchen also storage heaters. Fully-equipped, bedding supplied, cot and high chair available. Car parking

★★★
1 Unit
Sleeping 8

ELCOCKS COTTAGE

Badley Wood, Whitbourne, Worcester WR6 5ST
Contact: Mr & Mrs M R Hogg, 61 Pereira Road, Harborne,
Birmingham B17 9JB
T: (0121) 427 1395 (Answerphone, evenings only)
E: mikehogguk@aol.com

A beautifully restored detached 17thC cottage set in 3 acres of fields. Features include exposed beams, wood-burning stove, period-style furnishings, cider mill and press. The garden and cottage face south towards the Malvern Hills. Situated 2 miles from Whitbourne. Very rural and secluded, with magnificent views.

OPEN All year round

Short breaks available including Fri and Sat nights. Minimum stay 2 nights.

Low season per wk
£300.00–£450.00
High season per wk
£490.00–£650.00

★★★
1 Unit
Sleeping 6

THE SIDINGS
10 Grove Park, Whitecroft, Lydney GL15 4SS
Contact: Mrs V Long, Fiddlers Green,
Mitchel Troy Common, Monmouth NP25 4JQ
T: (01600) 714464 (answerphone)
F: (01600) 714464
E: glong4464@aol.com

House on edge of village in the heart of the beautiful Forest of Dean, within 3 minutes of woodland.

OPEN All year round

Low season per wk
Min £200.00
High season per wk
Max £300.00

★★★★★
1 Unit
Sleeping 4–6

THE SADDLERY
Manor Farm Barns, Brooks Close, Willoughby,
Rugby CV23 8BY
Contact: Mrs E Heckford, Manor Farm, Brooks Close,
Willoughby, Rugby CV23 8BY
T: (01788) 890256 (answerphone)
E: thesaddlery@heckford.fsbusiness.co.uk

A recently converted barn on a working farm in quiet village. High standard, sleeps from 4 to 6, in a courtyard setting. Private patio and parking.

OPEN All year round

Low season per wk
£210.00–£360.00
High season per wk
£280.00–£420.00

★★★★
3 Units
Sleeping 6

COCKBURY COURT COTTAGES
1, 2 and 3 Cockbury Court, Cleeve Hill, Winchcombe,
Cheltenham GL54 5AD
Contact: Mr & Mrs J Charlton, Cotswold Cottages
Limited, Rowan Lodge, Neata Farm, Greet, Cheltenham
GL54 5BL
T: (01242) 604806
F: (01242) 604806
E: john@rowan-lodge.demon.co.uk
I: www.cotswoldcottagesltd.co.uk/bookings

Three detached cottages, set in private, secluded grounds, each sleeping 4/6. Gas central heating, fully refurbished. Inclusive of linen, utilities and welcome box. Gardens. Parking.

OPEN All year round
CC: Barclaycard,
Mastercard, Switch, Visa

Low season per wk
Min £200.00
High season per wk
Max £450.00

★★★
1 Unit
Sleeping 4

ORCHARD COTTAGE
Stanley Pontlarge, Winchcombe,
Cheltenham GL54 5HD
Contact: Mrs S M Rolt, Stanley Pontlarge,
Winchcombe, Cheltenham GL54 5HD
T: (01242) 602594

Ochard Cottage, Stanley Pontlarge – in grounds of 14thC hall house with private enclosure and access, amid secluded country of flocks and orchard. Magpie Cottage – secluded town cottage near Tewkesbury centre, with small garden.

OPEN All year round

Low season per wk
£200.00–£300.00
High season per wk
£260.00–£325.00

WINCHCOMBE continued

★★★

14 Units
Sleeping 2–5

Small, attractive complex of well-appointed Cotswold-stone cottages on the Sudeley Castle estate. Shared gardens and barbecue area. Short walk into the historic town of Winchcombe. Ideal location for walking holidays or touring the area.

SUDELEY CASTLE COUNTRY COTTAGES

Castle Street, Winchcombe, Cheltenham GL54 5JA
Contact: Mrs N Dyke, Central Support Administrator, Sudeley Castle, Winchcombe, Cheltenham GL54 5JD
T: (01242) 602308 (9am-5pm)
F: (01242) 602959
E: natalie.dyke@sudeley.org.uk

OPEN All year round
CC: Barclaycard, Delta, Mastercard, Switch, Visa

Complimentary entry to castle and gardens during normal opening hours for duration of stay. Short breaks available.

Low season per wk
Min £191.00
High season per wk
Max £648.00

A⅏◎▥.☉▭ℼ🖳🖭P✳SP🏠

★★★★-★★★★★★

5 Units
Sleeping 2–5

Traditional old barns of individual style and character finely restored to provide 4 spacious high quality properties. Original period features. Quality furnishings and all modern facilities. Gardens/patios, private parking and countryside views to each property. Also detached stone cottage (sleeps 4) nearby. All family supervised. Ideal touring base. No pets. Brochures available.

TRADITIONAL ACCOMMODATION

Greet Farm, Winchcombe, Cheltenham GL54 5LB
Contact: Mr & Mrs Wilson, 60 Pershore Road, Evesham WR11 6PQ
T: (01386) 446269 & 07710 006949 (Mobile)
F: (01386) 446269
E: trad.accom@virgin.net
I: freespace.virgin.net/trad.accom

OPEN All year round
CC: Amex, Barclaycard, Delta, Diners, Eurocard, JCB, Maestro, Mastercard, Solo, Switch, Visa, Visa Electron

Low season per wk
£210.00–£345.00
High season per wk
£345.00–£495.00

A⅏◎⌀▥.☉🍴▭🖳ℼ🍴🖭🖳P∪✳🐾SP🏠

WIRKSWORTH, Derbyshire Map ref 4B2

Rating Applied For

1 Unit
Sleeping 4

THE COTTAGE
Durhamhouse, 42 North End, Wirksworth, Derby DE4 4FG
T: (01629) 826159 (answerphone)
Contact: Mrs N Hagger

OPEN All year round

Low season per wk
£200.00–£250.00
High season per wk
£350.00–£400.00

A self-contained 2 bedroomed Grade II Listed cottage. Situated in a market town, access to Peak Park and Derbyshire Dales.

⅏⌀▥.☉🍴ℼ🖳🖭P🐾🏠SP

USE YOUR *i*s

There are more than 550 Tourist Information Centres throughout England offering friendly help with accommodation and holiday ideas as well as suggestions of places to visit and things to do. You'll find TIC addresses in the local Phone Book.

WITCOMBE, Gloucestershire Map ref 2B1

★★★

3 Units
Sleeping 2–5

Located on a 400-year-old private family estate of 1.5 acres, in an Area of Outstanding Natural Beauty. The cottages are set adjacent to parkland, converted from a granary barn. Here you can trout fish on well stocked reservoirs. The Cotswold Way runs through the estate.

WITCOMBE PARK HOLIDAY COTTAGES

Witcombe Farm, Great Witcombe, Gloucester GL3 4TR
Contact: Mrs Hicks-Beach, Witcombe Farm,
Great Witcombe, Gloucester GL3 4TR
T: (01452) 863591
F: (01452) 863591

OPEN All year round

Low season per wk
£130.00–£190.00
High season per wk
£210.00–£330.00

WOODHALL SPA, Lincolnshire Map ref 4D2

★★

1 Unit
Sleeping 4

MILL LANE COTTAGE
70 Mill Lane, Woodhall Spa LN10 6QZ
Contact: Mr & Mrs I G Williamson, 72 Mill Lane,
Woodhall Spa LN10 6QZ
T: (01526) 353101 & 07967 520289 (Mobile)
E: WILL@williamsoni.freeserve.co.uk
I: www.skegness.net/woodhallspa.htm

Renovated cottage down quiet residential lane. Walks to river and pub. Cottage has all amenities, sports can be catered for.

OPEN All year round

Low season per wk
£150.00–£175.00
High season per wk
£155.00–£185.00

WYE VALLEY

See under Fownhope, Hereford, Ross-on-Wye

WYTHALL, Worcestershire Map ref 4B3

★★★–★★★★

6 Units
Sleeping 4–6

INKFORD COURT COTTAGES
Alcester Road, Wythall, Birmingham B47 6DL
T: (01564) 822304 & 07831 462451 (Mobile)
F: (01564) 829618
Contact: Mr J S Bedford

Cottages, part of a restoration and conversion of 18thC period farm buildings, set in 6.5 acres. Ideally located for Heart of England.

OPEN All year round

Low season per wk
£195.00–£325.00
High season per wk
£200.00–£365.00

YARDLEY GOBION, Northamptonshire Map ref 2C1

★★

1 Unit
Sleeping 4

Self-contained stable cottage in rural canal-side location, built about 1850 by former French prisoners of war, with ground floor stables, shower room, toilet and twin bedroom. The 1st floor has open-plan living accommodation, kitchen and double bedroom.

THE STABLE

Old Wharf Farm, The Wharf, Yardley Gobion,
Towcester NN12 7UE
T: (01908) 542293 & 07850 772370 (Mobile)
F: (01908) 542293
Contact: Mr Alan Paine

OPEN All year round
CC: Delta, Switch

Low season per wk
Max £225.00
High season per wk
Max £300.00

QUALITY ASSURANCE SCHEME

Star ratings were correct at the time of going to press but are subject to change. Please check at the time of booking.

YOULGREAVE, Derbyshire Map ref 4B2

★★★★

1 Unit

Sleeping 3

THYME COTTAGE
1 Bankside, Bank Top, Youlgreave, Bakewell DE45 1WD   OPEN All year round
Contact: Mrs S A MacDonald, Hardanger, Main Street,
Youlgrave, Bakewell DE45 1UW
T: (01629) 636472
F: (01629) 636472
E: lm@maccolour.co.uk

Low season per wk
£175.00–£225.00
High season per wk
£235.00–£295.00

200-year-old lovingly restored stone cottage; beams, antique oak, wood-burning
stove, sofa bed, super king/twin. Pubs, shops nearby. Superb walks from doorstep.

COUNTRY CODE
Always follow the Country Code
Enjoy the countryside and respect
its life and work   Guard against
all risk of fire   Fasten all gates
Keep your dogs under close control
Keep to public paths across
farmland   Use gates and stiles to
cross fences, hedges and walls
Leave livestock, crops and machinery
alone   Take your litter home
Help to keep all water clean
Protect wildlife, plants and trees
Take special care on country roads
Make no unnecessary noise

A brief guide to the main Towns and Villages offering accommodation in the

Heart of England

A ABBERLEY, WORCESTERSHIRE - Village with some interesting buildings including a pre-Reformation rectory and a Gothic clock tower with 20 bells. At Great Witley nearby is a magnificent 18th C church with rich plasterwork, paintings and carving and the gardens and ruins of Witley Court.

• **ALCESTER, WARWICKSHIRE** - Town has Roman origins and many old buildings around the High Street. It is close to Ragley Hall, the 18th C Palladian mansion with its magnificent baroque Great Hall.

• **ALDERTON, GLOUCESTERSHIRE** - Hillside village with wide views of Evesham Vale. The restored church has a 15th C tower, a broken Saxon font and some medieval glass. Some stone from the previous Norman church has been incorporated into its structure.

• **ALSTONEFIELD, STAFFORDSHIRE** - Peaceful village well situated for exploring the pleasant countryside of Dovedale, much of which is owned by the National Trust.

• **ALTON, STAFFORDSHIRE** - Alton Castle, an impressive 19th C building, dominates the village which is set in spectacular scenery. Nearby is Alton Towers, a romantic 19th C ruin with innumerable tourist attractions within one of England's largest theme parks in its 800 acres of magnificent gardens.

• **ASHBOURNE, DERBYSHIRE** - Market town on the edge of the Peak District National Park and an excellent centre for walking. Its impressive church with 212-ft spire stands in an unspoilt old street. Ashbourne is well-known for gingerbread and its Shrovetide football match.

• **ASHBY-DE-LA-ZOUCH, LEICESTERSHIRE** - Lovely market town with late 15th C church, impressive ruined 15th C castle, an interesting small museum and a wide, sloping main street with Georgian buildings. Twycross Zoo is nearby.

• **ASHFORD IN THE WATER, DERBYSHIRE** - Limestone village in attractive surroundings of the Peak District approached by 3 bridges over the River Wye. There is an annual well-dressing ceremony and the village was well-known in the 18th C for its black marble quarries.

• **ATHERSTONE, WARWICKSHIRE** - Pleasant market town with some 18th C houses and interesting old inns. Every Shrove Tuesday a game of football is played in the streets, a tradition which dates from the 13th C. Twycross Zoo is nearby with an extensive collection of reptiles and butterflies.

B BAKEWELL, DERBYSHIRE - Pleasant market town, famous for its pudding. It is set in beautiful countryside on the River Wye and is an excellent centre for exploring the Derbyshire Dales, the Peak District National Park, Chatsworth and Haddon Hall.

• **BAMFORD, DERBYSHIRE** - Village in the Peak District near the Upper Derwent Reservoirs of Ladybower, Derwent and Howden. An excellent centre for walking.

• **BASLOW, DERBYSHIRE** - Small village on the River Derwent with a stone-built toll-house and a packhorse bridge. Chatsworth, home of the Duke of Devonshire, is nearby.

• **BIBURY, GLOUCESTERSHIRE** - Village on the River Coln with stone houses and the famous 17th C Arlington Row, former weavers' cottages. Arlington Mill is now a folk museum. Trout farm and Barnsley House Gardens nearby are open to the public.

• **BISHOP'S CASTLE, SHROPSHIRE** - A 12th C Planned Town with a castle site at the top of the hill and a church at the bottom of the main street. Many interesting buildings with original timber frames hidden behind present day houses. On the Welsh border close to the Clun Forest in quiet, unspoilt countryside.

• **BLOCKLEY, GLOUCESTERSHIRE** - This village's prosperity was founded in silk mills and other factories but now it is a quiet, unspoilt place. An excellent centre for exploring pretty Cotswold villages, especially Chipping Campden and Broadway.

• **BODENHAM, HEREFORDSHIRE** - Attractive village with old timbered cottages and stone houses and an interesting church. Here the River Lugg makes a loop and flows under an ancient bridge at the end of the village.

• **BOSTON, LINCOLNSHIRE** - Historic town famous for its church tower, the Boston Stump, 272 ft high. Still a busy port, the town is full of interest and has links with Boston, Massachusetts, through the Pilgrim Fathers. The cells where they were imprisoned can be seen in the medieval Guildhall.

• **BOURTON-ON-THE-WATER, GLOUCESTERSHIRE** - The River Windrush flows through this famous Cotswold village which has a green, and cottages and houses of Cotswold stone. Its many attractions include a model village, Birdland, a Motor Museum and the Cotswold Perfumery.

• **BRIDGNORTH, SHROPSHIRE** - Red sandstone riverside town in 2 parts - High and Low - linked by a cliff railway. Much of interest including a ruined Norman keep, half-timbered 16th C houses, Midland Motor Museum and Severn Valley Railway.

• **BROAD CAMPDEN, GLOUCESTERSHIRE** - Attractive village with interesting church by Prichard of Llandaff a mile outside the picturesque Cotswold town of Chipping Campden.

• **BROADWAY, WORCESTERSHIRE** - Beautiful Cotswold village called the 'Show village of England', with 16th C stone houses and cottages. Near the village is Broadway Tower with magnificent views over 12 counties and a country park with nature trails and adventure playground.

• **BROMSGROVE, WORCESTERSHIRE** - This market town near the Lickey Hills has an interesting museum and craft centre and 14th C church with fine tombs and a Carillon tower. The Avoncroft Museum of Buildings is nearby where many old buildings have been re-assembled, having been saved from destruction.

• **BURWARTON, SHROPSHIRE** - Stately village between Ludlow and Bridgnorth, with the magnificent park of Burwarton Hall, an attractive Georgian inn and the ruin of an old Norman church.

• **BUXTON, DERBYSHIRE** - The highest market town in England and one of the oldest spas, with an elegant Crescent, Poole's Cavern, Opera House and attractive Pavilion Gardens. An excellent centre for exploring the Peak District.

C CARSINGTON, DERBYSHIRE - The visitor centre at Britain's newest reservoir, Carsington Water, allows visitors to learn about the surrounding countryside and wildlife. Around the reservoir many activities are available including cycling, sailing and horse riding.

- **CHELTENHAM, GLOUCESTERSHIRE** - Cheltenham was developed as a spa town in the 18th C and has some beautiful Regency architecture, in particular the Pittville Pump Room. It holds international music and literature festivals and is also famous for its race meetings and cricket.

- **CHESTERFIELD, DERBYSHIRE** - Famous for the twisted spire of its parish church, Chesterfield has some fine modern buildings and excellent shopping facilities, including a large, traditional open-air market. Hardwick Hall and Bolsover Castle are nearby.

- **CHIPPING CAMPDEN, GLOUCESTERSHIRE** - Outstanding Cotswold wool town with many old stone gabled houses, a splendid church and 17th C almshouses. Nearby are Kiftsgate Court Gardens and Hidcote Manor Gardens (National Trust).

- **CHURCH STRETTON, SHROPSHIRE** - Church Stretton lies under the eastern slope of the Longmynd surrounded by hills. It is ideal for walkers, with marvellous views, golf and gliding. Wenlock Edge is not far away.

- **CIRENCESTER, GLOUCESTERSHIRE** - 'Capital of the Cotswolds', Cirencester was Britain's second most important Roman town with many finds housed in the Corinium Museum. It has a very fine Perpendicular church and old houses around the market place.

- **CLIFTON UPON TEME, WORCESTERSHIRE** - Small, picturesque village high above the River Teme, with magnificent views over the Worcestershire and Herefordshire countryside. With its ancient church and pub, village green and flower-adorned half-timbered cottages, it is the epitome of a traditional English village.

- **COLEFORD, GLOUCESTERSHIRE** - Small town in the Forest of Dean with the ancient iron mines at Clearwell Caves nearby, where mining equipment and geological samples are displayed. There are several forest trails in the area.

- **COMPTON ABDALE, GLOUCESTERSHIRE** - High on the hills this Cotswold village is quietly located 4 miles outside Northleach, off the main A40 towards Cheltenham and is ideally located to tour the area and visit the main attractions.

- **CRAVEN ARMS, SHROPSHIRE** - Busy village on A49 renowned for its sheep markets. Close to Wenlock Edge and the Longmynd and an ideal centre for walking with many fine views. Nearby Stokesay Castle, a 13th C fortified manor house, the ruins of Hopton Castle and Ludlow.

- **CRESSBROOK, DERBYSHIRE** - Delightful dale with stone hall and pleasant houses, steep wooded slopes and superb views.

- **CRESWELL, DERBYSHIRE** - Village close to limestone gorge and caves noted for Stone Age finds, with displays in Visitor Centre.

- **D DAGLINGWORTH, GLOUCESTERSHIRE** - Delightful village in the valley of the River Dunt near Cirencester, with a church which has remnants of Saxon work as well as 3 well-preserved sculptures. There is a medieval dovecote at the manor house.

- **DERBY, DERBYSHIRE** - Modern industrial city but with ancient origins. There is a wide range of attractions including several museums (notably Royal Crown Derby), a theatre, a concert hall, and the cathedral with fine ironwork and Bess of Hardwick's tomb.

- **DIDDLEBURY, SHROPSHIRE** - Village close to the beautiful countryside of Wenlock Edge and the Longmynd.

- **DORRINGTON, LINCOLNSHIRE** - Small village with several pretty cottages and an interesting church.

- **DURSLEY, GLOUCESTERSHIRE** - Market town with some Georgian houses and an 18th C arched market hall with a statue of Queen Anne. Nearby is the weaving village of Uley with 17th C houses.

- **E EAST HADDON, NORTHAMPTONSHIRE** - Pretty village with a stone-towered church, thatched cottages and a thatched village pump.

- **EDALE, DERBYSHIRE** - Deep, 1, 250 ft valley, a mecca for walkers. The Pennine Way starts here, also the easiest way on to Kinder via Jacobs Ladder. Most of the buildings and walls are traditionally made of stone in this picturesque village.

- **EPPERSTONE, NOTTINGHAMSHIRE** - The settlement here was mentioned in the Domesday Book. Its medieval church stands high above the village and there is a manor house and an old dovecote.

- **EVESHAM, WORCESTERSHIRE** - Market town in the centre of a fruit-growing area. There are pleasant walks along the River Avon and many old houses and inns. A fine 16th C bell tower stands between 2 churches near the medieval Almonry Museum.

- **EYAM, DERBYSHIRE** - Attractive village famous for the courage its people showed during the plague of 1665. The church has several memorials to this time and there is a well-dressing ceremony in August. The fine 17th C manor house of Eyam Hall is open in summer, and Chatsworth is nearby.

- **F FOWNHOPE, HEREFORDSHIRE** - Attractive village close to the River Wye with black and white cottages and other interesting houses. It has a large church with a Norman tower and a 14th C spire.

- **FRAMPTON-ON-SEVERN, GLOUCESTERSHIRE** - Near the River Severn in the Berkeley Vale, the village has a remarkably large green with an interesting range of buildings, the most notable being Frampton Court built around 1733. Beside the Sharpness Canal, close by is Berkeley Castle and Slimbridge Wildfowl Trust.

- **G GLOUCESTER, GLOUCESTERSHIRE** - A Roman city and inland port, its cathedral is one of the most beautiful in Britain. Gloucester's many attractions include museums and the restored warehouses in the Victorian docks containing the National Waterways Museum, Robert Opie Packaging Collection and other attractions.

- **GRANTHAM, LINCOLNSHIRE** - On the old Great North Road (A1), Grantham's splendid parish church has a fine spire and chained library. Sir Isaac Newton was educated here and his statue stands in front of the museum which includes displays on Newton and other famous local people.

- **GREAT HUCKLOW, DERBYSHIRE** - Small village in the Peak District. Headquarters of the Derbyshire and Lancashire Gliding Club.

- **H HARTINGTON, DERBYSHIRE** - Village with a large market-place set in fine surroundings near the River Dove, well-known for its fishing and Izaak Walton, author of 'The Compleat Angler'.

- **HATHERSAGE, DERBYSHIRE** - Hillside village in the Peak District, dominated by the church with many good brasses and monuments to the Eyre family which provide a link with Charlotte Bronte. Little John, friend of Robin Hood, is said to be buried here.

- **HATTON, WARWICKSHIRE** - Surrounded by woodlands 2 miles north-west of Warwick, close to a flight of 21 locks on the canal and Hatton Country World.

- **HAWLING, GLOUCESTERSHIRE** - Hamlet high in the Cotswold farmlands with a small Georgian church.

- **HAYFIELD, DERBYSHIRE** - Village set in spectacular scenery at the highest point of the Peak District with the best approach to the Kinder Scout plateau via the Kinder Downfall. An excellent centre for walking. Three reservoirs close by.

- **HEREFORD, HEREFORDSHIRE** - Agricultural county town, its cathedral containing much Norman work, a large chained library and the world-famous Mappa Mundi exhibition. Among the city's varied attractions are several museums including the Cider Museum and the Old House.

- **HINCKLEY, LEICESTERSHIRE** - The town has an excellent leisure centre, Bosworth Battlefield, with its Visitor Centre and Battle Trail, is 5 miles away.

- **HOPE, DERBYSHIRE** - Village in the Hope Valley which is an excellent base for walking in the Peak District and for fishing and shooting. There is a well-dressing ceremony each June and its August sheep dog trials are well-known. Castleton Caves are nearby.

- **IRONBRIDGE, SHROPSHIRE** - Small town on the Severn where the Industrial Revolution began. It has the world's first iron bridge built in 1779. The Ironbridge Gorge Museum, of exceptional interest, comprises a rebuilt turn-of-the-century town and sites spread over 6 square miles.

- **KENILWORTH, WARWICKSHIRE** - The main feature of the town is the ruined 12th C castle. It has many royal associations but was damaged by Cromwell. A good base for visiting Coventry, Leamington Spa and Warwick.

- **LAMBLEY, NOTTINGHAMSHIRE** - Pretty village 5 miles NE of Nottingham. Playworld outdoor children's adventure park in Floralands Garden Centre is in the village and nearby is Sherwood Forest and Robin Hood Country.

- **LEAMINGTON SPA, WARWICKSHIRE** - 18th C spa town with many fine Georgian and Regency houses. The refurbished 19th C Pump Rooms with Heritage Centre. The attractive Jephson Gardens are laid out alongside the river.

- **LEDBURY, HEREFORDSHIRE** - Town with cobbled streets and many black and white timbered houses, including the 17th C market house and old inns. In attractive countryside nearby is Eastnor Castle, a venue for many events, with an interesting collection of tapestries and armour.

- **LEINTWARDINE, HEREFORDSHIRE** - Attractive border village where the Rivers Teme and Clun meet. It has some black and white cottages, old inns and an impressive church. It is near Hopton Castle and the beautiful scenery around Clun.

- **LEOMINSTER, HEREFORDSHIRE** - The town owed its prosperity to wool and has many interesting buildings, notably the timber-framed Grange Court, a former town hall. The impressive Norman priory church has 3 naves and a ducking stool. Berrington Hall (National Trust) is nearby.

- **LINCOLN, LINCOLNSHIRE** - Ancient city dominated by the magnificent 11th C cathedral with its triple towers. A Roman gateway is still used and there are medieval houses lining narrow, cobbled streets. Other attractions include the Norman castle, several museums and the Usher Gallery.

- **LOUTH, LINCOLNSHIRE** - Attractive old market town set on the eastern edge of the Lincolnshire Wolds. St James's Church has an impressive tower and spire and there are the remains of a Cistercian abbey. The museum contains an interesting collection of local material.

- **LOWER BENEFIELD, NORTHAMPTONSHIRE** - 3 miles W of the attractive town of Oundle, Lower and Upper Benefield are small villages near to Rockingham Forest and Castle, and within easy reach of Southwick Hall and the Nene Valley.

- **LOWER SLAUGHTER, GLOUCESTERSHIRE** - Pretty Cotswold village of stone cottages with a river running through the main street.

- **LUDLOW, SHROPSHIRE** - Outstandingly interesting border town with a magnificent castle high above the River Teme, 2 half-timbered old inns and an impressive 15th C church. The Reader's House, with its 3-storey Jacobean porch, should also be seen.

- **LULLINGTON, DERBYSHIRE** - In the extreme south of Derbyshire, near the Staffordshire border. Beautiful flowers and plants fill the village green, churchyard and gardens of the Great House.

- **LYDNEY, GLOUCESTERSHIRE** - Small town in the Forest of Dean close to the River Severn, where Roman remains have been found. It has a steam centre with engines, coaches and wagons.

- **MALVERN, WORCESTERSHIRE** - Spa town in Victorian times, its water is still bottled and sold worldwide. 6 resorts, set on the slopes of the Hills, form part of Malvern. Great Malvern Priory has splendid 15th C windows. It is an excellent walking centre.

- **MARKET RASEN, LINCOLNSHIRE** - Market town on the edge of the Lincolnshire Wolds. The racecourse and the picnic site and forest walks at Willingham Woods are to the east of the town.

- **MATLOCK, DERBYSHIRE** - The town lies beside the narrow valley of the River Derwent surrounded by steep wooded hills. Good centre for exploring Derbyshire's best scenery.

- **MIDDLETON-BY-YOULGREAVE, DERBYSHIRE** - Small hamlet nestling on the River Bradford, a mile from Youlgreave.

- **MILLER'S DALE, DERBYSHIRE** - Village located in fine countryside near Buxton and Chatsworth.

- **MILWICH, STAFFORDSHIRE** - Village midway between Stone and Uttoxeter. The oldest dated bell in Staffordshire, purported to have rung for Agincourt, is here.

- **MINSTERLEY, SHROPSHIRE** - Village with a curious little church of 1692 and a fine old black and white hall. The lofty ridge known as the Stiperstones is 4 miles to the south.

- **MISERDEN, GLOUCESTERSHIRE** - Village in wooded valley country with a church of late Saxon origin. The Camp is a hamlet with an interesting group of old houses and Miserden Park Gardens can be visited between April and September.

- **MORETON-IN-MARSH, GLOUCESTERSHIRE** - Attractive town of Cotswold stone with 17th C houses, an ideal base for touring the Cotswolds. Some of the local attractions include Batsford Park Arboretum, the Jacobean Chastleton House and Sezincote Garden.

- **NAUNTON, GLOUCESTERSHIRE** - A high place on the Windrush, renowned for its wild flowers and with an attractive dovecote.

- **NEWCASTLE-UNDER-LYME, STAFFORDSHIRE** - Industrial town whose museum and art gallery give evidence of its past. The Guildhall was built in the 18th C and there is the modern University of Keele.

- **NORTHAMPTON, NORTHAMPTONSHIRE** - A bustling town and a shoe manufacturing centre, with excellent shopping facilities, several museums and parks, a theatre and a concert hall. Several old churches include 1 of only 4 round churches in Britain.

- **OUNDLE, NORTHAMPTONSHIRE** - Historic town situated on the River Nene with narrow alleys and courtyards and many stone buildings, including a fine church and historic inns.

- **OWLPEN, GLOUCESTERSHIRE** - Near the Severn Estuary, the 15th C Owlpen Manor, (open to visitors April-September) together with its outbuildings and church form a delightful group of Cotswold stone buildings. The weaving village of Uley with its 17th C houses is close by.

- **PEMBRIDGE, HEREFORDSHIRE** - Delightful village close to the Welsh border with many black and white half-timbered cottages, some dating from the 14th C. There is a market hall supported by 8 wooden pillars in the market place, also old inns and a 14th C church with interesting separate bell tower.

R ROSS-ON-WYE, HEREFORDSHIRE
- Attractive market town with a 17th C market hall, set above the River Wye. There are lovely views over the surrounding countryside from the Prospect and the town is close to Goodrich Castle and the Welsh border.

• **RUGBY, WARWICKSHIRE** - Town famous for its public school which gave its name to Rugby Union football and which featured in Tom Brown's Schooldays.

S SEDGEBERROW, WORCESTERSHIRE
- Village on the edge of the Vale of Evesham, with Bredon Hill to the east and westward views of the Cotswold hills.

• **SHEEN, STAFFORDSHIRE** - Overlooking the River Dore. Sheen Hill to the north provides a lovely view of the valley and uplands.

• **SHIPSTON-ON-STOUR, WARWICKSHIRE**
- Old market town with many Georgian houses and inns. Honington Hall, a small Carolean house, is nearby and Stratford, the Cotswolds, Chipping Campden and Hidcote Manor Gardens can be easily reached.

• **SHREWSBURY, SHROPSHIRE** - Beautiful historic town on the River Severn retaining many fine old timber-framed houses. Its attractions include Rowley's Museum with Roman finds, remains of a castle, Clive House Museum, St Chad's 18th C round church, rowing on the river and the Shrewsbury Flower Show in August.

• **SNAILBEACH, SHROPSHIRE** - Tiny village (no beach - the word is a corruption of batch meaning open ground near a river), in the hills leading to the Stiperstones, this attractive area is about 10 miles SW of Shrewsbury and delightful touring country.

• **SPILSBY, LINCOLNSHIRE** - Market town in attractive countryside on the edge of the Lincolnshire Wolds and the Fens. Birthplace of explorer Sir John Franklin and has associations with the poet Tennyson, born in nearby Somersby. It has a medieval market cross.

• **STANTON, GLOUCESTERSHIRE** - Unspoilt Cotswold village with picturesque stone houses built around 1600. The church dates from Norman times but has 20th C furnishings and glass. Nearby is Stanway House, a Jacobean manor, open to summer visitors, and ruins of Hailes Abbey (English Heritage).

• **STANTON-ON-THE-WOLDS, NOTTINGHAMSHIRE** - Quiet village with golf course, just off the main route between Nottingham and Melton Mowbray, giving easy access to nearby attractions.

• **STOKE-ON-TRENT, STAFFORDSHIRE**
- Famous for its pottery. Factories of several famous makers, including Josiah Wedgwood, can be visited. The City Museum has one of the finest pottery and porcelain collections in the world.

• **STOW-ON-THE-WOLD, GLOUCESTERSHIRE** - Attractive Cotswold wool town with a large market-place and some fine houses, especially the old grammar school. There is an interesting church dating from Norman times. Stow-on-the-Wold is surrounded by lovely countryside and Cotswold villages.

• **STRATFORD-UPON-AVON, WARWICKSHIRE** - Famous as Shakespeare's home town, Stratford's many attractions include his birthplace, New Place where he died, the Royal Shakespeare Theatre and Gallery and Hall's Croft (his daughter's house).

• **SUTTON ON THE HILL, DERBYSHIRE**
- Rural community, although only 8 miles west of Derby. The church is slightly elevated and provides excellent views of the Peak District.

T TETBURY, GLOUCESTERSHIRE - Small market town with 18th C houses and an attractive 17th C Town Hall. It is a good touring centre with many places of interest nearby including Badminton House and Westonbirt Arboretum.

• **TEWKESBURY, GLOUCESTERSHIRE**
- Tewkesbury's outstanding possession is its magnificent church, built as an abbey, with a great Norman tower and beautiful 14th C interior. The town stands at the confluence of the Severn and Avon and has many medieval houses, inns and several museums.

• **TIDESWELL, DERBYSHIRE** - Small town with a large 14th C church known as the 'Cathedral of the Peak'. There is a well-dressing ceremony each June with Morris dancing, and many choral events throughout the year.

U UPPER SLAUGHTER, GLOUCESTERSHIRE
- Pretty Cotswold village with a tributary of the River Windrush flowing through it. It has an attractive Elizabethan manor house which incorporates the remains of a 15th C priory.

• **UPPINGHAM, RUTLAND** - Quiet market town dominated by its famous public school which was founded in 1584. It has many stone houses and is surrounded by attractive countryside.

• **UPTON ST LEONARDS, GLOUCESTERSHIRE** - Village in a lovely setting below hills, with many old houses and a part-Norman church.

W WARWICK, WARWICKSHIRE - Castle rising above the River Avon, 15th C Beauchamp Chapel attached to St Mary's Church, medieval Lord Leycester's Hospital almshouses and several museums. Nearby is Ashorne Hall Nickelodeon and the National Heritage museum at Gaydon.

• **WELLINGTON, SHROPSHIRE** - On the west side of Telford district, under the Wrekin and with easy access to Shrewsbury and Ironbridge.

• **WETTON, STAFFORDSHIRE** - High-lying village with many old limestone buildings and some of Staffordshire's most glorious countryside around it. Near here one of the country's most spectacular sights, Thor's Cave, gapes from a limestone precipice in the Manifold Valley.

• **WHITBOURNE, HEREFORDSHIRE** - Large parish on both sides of the Worcester to Bromyard road, the location of a medieval moated building, once the palace of the Bishops of Hereford. In the delightfully peaceful village are some houses of cruck construction and some unusual 16th C brick chimneys.

• **WINCHCOMBE, GLOUCESTERSHIRE**
- Ancient town with a folk museum and railway museum. To the south lies Sudeley Castle with its fine collection of paintings and toys and an Elizabethan garden.

• **WIRKSWORTH, DERBYSHIRE** - Small town which was once the centre of the lead-mining industry in Derbyshire. It has many old buildings of interest, including the church of St Mary, narrow streets and alleys, a Heritage Centre and the National Stone Centre. There is a well-dressing ceremony in May.

• **WITCOMBE, GLOUCESTERSHIRE**
- Combination of villages scattered south-west of Gloucester on the lower slopes of the Cotswold escarpment up to Birdlip Hill. Remains of a Roman villa.

• **WOODHALL SPA, LINCOLNSHIRE** - Attractive town which was formerly a spa. It has excellent sporting facilities with a championship golf-course and is surrounded by pine woods.

• **WYTHALL, WORCESTERSHIRE** - On the southern outskirts of Birmingham heading towards Evesham.

Y YARDLEY GOBION, NORTHAMPTONSHIRE - Picturesque village in the southern tip of the county near the Grand Union Canal. Some expansion since the 1950s.

• **YOULGREAVE, DERBYSHIRE** - Small town in the Peak District with an impressive church, much of which dates from Norman times. There are some interesting monuments in the church and stained glass by William Morris. The stone circle of Arbor Low is nearby.

Finding
accommodation
is as easy as 1 2 3

Where to Stay makes it quick and easy to find a place to stay.
There are several ways to use this guide.

1

Town Index
The town index, starting on page 684, lists all the places with
accommodation featured in the regional sections. The index gives a page
number where you can find full accommodation and contact details.

2

Colour Maps
All the place names in black on the colour maps at the front have an
entry in the regional sections. Refer to the town index for the page
number where you will find one or more establishments offering
accommodation in your chosen town or village.

3

Accommodation listing
Contact details for **all** English Tourism Council assessed accommodation
throughout England, together with their national Star rating are given in
the listing section of this guide. Establishments with a full entry in the
regional sections are shown in blue. Look in the town index for the page
number on which their full entry appears.

EAST of England

A region of remote and wild beauty, with vast expanses of open country, unspoilt coastline, sweeping views and big skies. It's renowned for its charming half-timbered towns and villages, ancient sites, historic country houses and nature reserves.

classic sights
Blickling Hall – one of England's great Jacobean houses
Sutton Hoo – important Anglo-Saxon burial site

coast & country
Blakeney Point – good for seal and bird watching
Hatfield Forest – medieval royal hunting forest
Norfolk Broads – miles of waterways through glorious countryside

arts for all
Aldeburgh Festival – classical music in a picturesque setting
Dedham Vale – the landscapes of John Constable; his home and early studio are at East Bergholt. Also the home of Sir Alfred Munnings, famous for his paintings of horses
Sudbury – Gainsborough's house, with fine collection of paintings

delightfully different
Whipsnade Tree Cathedral – unique, 26 acres (10.5ha) cathedral made of trees

The counties of Bedfordshire, Cambridgeshire, Essex, Hertfordshire, Norfolk and Suffolk

FOR MORE INFORMATION CONTACT:
East of England Tourist Board
Toppesfield Hall, Hadleigh, Suffolk IP7 5DN
Tel: (01473) 822922 Fax: (01473) 823063
Email: eastofenglandtouristboard@compuserve.com
Internet: www.eastofenglandtouristboard.com

The Pictures:
1 Horsey Mere, Norfolk
2 King's College, Cambridge
3 Norwich

Places to Visit - see pages 236-240
Where to Stay - see pages 241-275

235

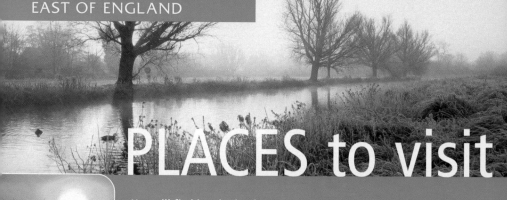

PLACES to visit

You will find hundreds of interesting places to visit during your stay, just some of which are listed in these pages. Contact any Tourist Information Centre in the region for more ideas on days out.

Blickling Hall

Blickling, Norwich, Norfolk NR11 6NF
Tel: (01263) 738030 www.nationaltrust.org.uk
A Jacobean redbrick mansion with garden, orangery, parkland and lake. There is also a display of fine tapestries and furniture.

Audley End House and Park

Audley End, Saffron Walden, Essex CB11 4JF
Tel: (01799) 522399
A palatial Jacobean house remodelled in the 18thC-19thC with a magnificent Great Hall with 17thC plaster ceilings. Rooms and furniture by Robert Adam and park by 'Capability' Brown.

Bressingham Steam Experience and Gardens

Bressingham, Diss, Norfolk IP22 2AB
Tel: (01379) 687386 www.bressingham.co.uk
Steam rides through five miles of woodland. Six acres (2 ha) of the Island Beds plant centre. Mainline locomotives, the Victorian Gallopers and over 50 steam engines.

Banham Zoo

The Grove, Banham, Norwich, Norfolk NR16 2HE
Tel: (01953) 887771 www.banhamzoo.co.uk
Wildlife spectacular which will take you on a journey to experience tigers, leopards and zebra and some of the world's most exotic, rare and endangered animals.

Bure Valley Railway

Aylsham Station, Norwich Road, Aylsham, Norwich, Norfolk NR11 6BW
Tel: (01263) 733858 www.bvrw.co.uk
A 15-inch narrow-gauge steam railway covering nine miles of track from Wroxham, in the heart of the Norfolk Broads, to Aylsham, a bustling market town.

Barleylands Farm

Barleylands Road, Billericay, Essex CM11 2UD
Tel: (01268) 290229
Visitor centre with a rural museum, animal centre, craft studios, blacksmith's shop, glass-blowing studio with a viewing gallery, miniature steam railway and a restaurant.

Colchester Castle

Colchester, Essex CO1 1TJ
Tel: (01206) 282931
www.colchestermuseums.org.uk
A Norman keep on the foundations of a Roman temple. The archaeological material includes much on Roman Colchester (Camulodunum).

Colchester Zoo

Maldon Road, Stanway, Colchester, Essex CO3 5SL
Tel: (01206) 331292 www.colchester-zoo.co.uk
Zoo with 200 species and some of the best cat and
primate collections in the UK, 60 acres (27 ha) of gardens
and lakes, award-winning animal enclosures and picnic
areas.

Ely Cathedral

Chapter House, The College, Ely, Cambridgeshire CB7 4DL
Tel: (01353) 667735
One of England's finest cathedrals with guided tours and
tours of the Octagon and West Tower, monastic precincts
and also a brass-rubbing centre and Stained Glass
Museum.

Fritton Lake Country World

Fritton, Great Yarmouth, Norfolk NR31 9HA
Tel: (01493) 488208
A 250-acre (101-ha) centre with a children's assault
course, putting, an adventure playground, golf, fishing,
boating, wildfowl, heavy horses, cart rides, falconry and
flying displays.

The Gardens of the Rose

The Royal National Rose Society, Chiswell Green,
St Albans, Hertfordshire AL2 3NR
Tel: (01727) 850461 www.roses.co.uk
The Royal National Rose Society's Garden with 27 acres
(11 ha) of garden and trial grounds for new varieties of
rose. Roses of all types displayed with 1,700 different
varieties.

Hatfield House, Park and Gardens

Hatfield, Hertfordshire AL9 5NQ
Tel: (01707) 287010 www.hatfield-house.co.uk
Magnificent Jacobean house, home of the Marquess of
Salisbury. Exquisite gardens, model soldiers and park
trails. Childhood home of Queen Elizabeth I.

Hedingham Castle

Castle Hedingham, Halstead, Essex CO9 3DJ
Tel: (01787) 460261
www.hedinghamcastle@aspects.net
The finest Norman keep in England, built in 1140 by the
deVeres, Earls of Oxford. Visited by Kings Henry VII and
VIII and Queen Elizabeth I and besieged by King John.

Holkham Hall

Wells-next-the-Sea, Norfolk NR23 1AB
Tel: (01328) 710227 www.holkham.co.uk
A classic 18thC Palladian-style mansion. Part of a great
agricultural estate and a living treasure house of artistic
and architectural history along with a bygones collection.

Ickworth House, Park and Gardens

The Rotunda, Horringer, Bury St Edmunds, Suffolk IP29 5QE
Tel: (01284) 735270 www.nationaltrust.org.uk
An extraordinary oval house with flanking wings, begun
in 1795. Fine paintings, a beautiful collection of Georgian
silver, an Italian garden and stunning parkland.

Imperial War Museum

Duxford, Cambridge, Cambridgeshire CB2 4QR
Tel: (01223) 835000 www.iwm.org.uk
Over 180 aircraft on display with tanks, vehicles and
guns, an adventure playground, shops and a restaurant.

The Pictures:
1 River Wensum, Norfolk
2 Punting on the River Cam, Cambridge
3 Globe Inn, Linslade, Bedfordshire
4 Thorpeness, Suffolk
5 Tulip fields

Kentwell Hall

Long Melford, Sudbury, Suffolk CO10 9BA
Tel: (01787) 310207 www.kentwell.co.uk
A mellow redbrick Tudor manor surrounded by a moat, this family home has been interestingly restored with Tudor costume displays, a 16thC house and mosaic Tudor rose maze.

Knebworth House, Gardens and Park

Knebworth, Stevenage, Hertfordshire SG3 6PY
Tel: (01438) 812661 www.knebworthhouse.com
Tudor manor house, re-fashioned in the 19thC, housing a collection of manuscripts, portraits and Jacobean banquet hall. Formal gardens and adventure playground.

Leighton Buzzard Railway

Page's Park Station, Billington Road, Leighton Buzzard, Bedfordshire LU7 4TN
Tel: (01525) 373888 www.buzzrail.co.uk
An authentic narrow-gauge light railway, built in 1919, offering a 65-minute return journey into the Bedfordshire countryside.

Marsh Farm Country Park

Marsh Farm Road, South Woodham Ferrers, Chelmsford, Essex CM3 5WP
Tel: (01245) 321552
www.marshfarmcountrypark.co.uk
A farm centre with sheep, a pig unit, free-range chickens, milking demonstrations, indoor and outdoor adventure play areas, nature reserve, walks, picnic area and pets' corner.

Melford Hall

Long Melford, Sudbury, Suffolk CO10 9AA
Tel: (01787) 880286
www.nationaltrust.org.uk/eastanglia
Turreted brick Tudor mansion with 18thC and Regency interiors. Collection of Chinese porcelain, gardens and a walk in the grounds. Dogs on leads, where permitted.

Minsmere Nature Reserve

Westleton, Saxmundham, Suffolk IP17 3BY
Tel: (01728) 648281 www.rspb.org.uk
RSPB reserve on the Suffolk coast with bird-watching hides and trails, year-round events, guided walk and visitor centre with large shop and welcoming tearooms.

National Horseracing Museum and Tours

99 High Street, Newmarket, Suffolk CB8 8JL
Tel: (01638) 667333 www.nhrm.co.uk
Award-winning display of the people and horses involved in racing's amazing history. Minibus tours to gallops, stables and equine pool. Hands-on gallery with horse simulator.

National Stud

Newmarket, Suffolk CB8 0XE
Tel: (01638) 663464 www.nationalstud.co.uk
A visit to the National Stud consists of a conducted tour which will include top thoroughbred stallions, mares and foals.

Norfolk Lavender Limited

Caley Mill, Heacham, King's Lynn, Norfolk PE31 7JE
Tel: (01485) 570384 www.norfolk-lavender.co.uk
Lavender is distilled from the flowers and the oil made into a wide range of gifts. There is a slide show when the distillery is not working.

Norwich Cathedral

The Close, Norwich, Norfolk NR1 4EH
Tel: (01603) 218321 www.cathedral.org.uk
A Norman cathedral from 1096 with 14thC roof bosses depicting bible scenes from Adam and Eve to the Day of Judgement. Cloisters, cathedral close, shop and restaurant.

Oliver Cromwell's House

29 St Marys Street, Ely, Cambridgeshire CB7 4HF
Tel: (01353) 662062 www.elyeastcambs.co.uk
The family home of Oliver Cromwell with a 17thC kitchen, parlour, a haunted bedroom, a Tourist Information Centre, souvenirs and craft shop.

Peter Beales Roses

London Road, Attleborough, Norfolk NR17 1AY
Tel: (01953) 454707 www.classicroses.co.uk
Two and a half acres (1 ha) of display rose garden set in rural surroundings.

Pleasure Beach

South Beach Parade, Great Yarmouth, Norfolk NR30 3EH
Tel: (01493) 844585
Rollercoaster, Terminator, log flume, Twister, monorail, galloping horses, caterpillar, ghost train and fun house. Height restrictions are in force on some rides.

Pleasurewood Hills Theme Park

Leisure Way, Corton, Lowestoft, Suffolk NR32 5DZ
Tel: (01502) 586000 pleasurewoodhills.co.uk
Crazy coaster, tidal wave watercoaster, log flume,
chairlift, two railways, pirate ship, Aladdin's cave, parrot
and sea-lion shows, the cannonball express and
rattlesnake rides.

Sainsbury Centre for Visual Arts

University of East Anglia, Norwich, Norfolk NR4 7TJ
Tel: (01603) 456060 www.uea.ac.uk/scva
Housing the Sainsbury collection of works by Picasso,
Bacon and Henry Moore alongside many objects of
pottery and art. Also a cafe and an art bookshop with
activities monthly.

Sandringham

Sandringham, King's Lynn, Norfolk PE35 6EN
Tel: (01553) 772675 www.sandringhamestate.co.uk
The country retreat of HM The Queen. A delightful house
and 60 acres (24 ha) of grounds and lakes. There is also a
museum of royal vehicles and royal memorabilia.

Shuttleworth Collection

Old Warden Aerodrome, Biggleswade, Bedfordshire SG18 9EP
Tel: (01767) 627288 www.shuttleworth.org
A unique historical collection of aircraft, from a 1909
Bleriot to a 1942 Spitfire (in flying condition), and cars,
dating from an 1898 Panhard (in running order).

Somerleyton Hall and Gardens

Somerleyton, Lowestoft, Suffolk NR32 5QQ
Tel: (01502) 730224 www.somerleyton.co.uk
Anglo Italian-style mansion with state rooms, a maze,
12-acre (5-ha) gardens with azaleas and rhododendrons,
miniature railway, shop and tearooms.

Stondon Museum

Station Road, Lower Stondon, Henlow Camp, Henlow,
Bedfordshire SG16 6JN
Tel: (01462) 850339 www.transportmuseum.co.uk
A museum with transport exhibits from the early 1900s
to the 1980s. The largest private collection in England of
bygone vehicles from the beginning of the century.

Thursford Collection

Thursford Green, Thursford, Fakenham, Norfolk NR21 0AS
Tel: (01328) 878477
Musical evenings some Tuesdays from mid-July to the
end of September. A live musical show with nine
mechanical organs and a Wurlitzer show starring Robert
Wolfe (daily 29 March-mid October).

Whipsnade Wild Animal Park

Dunstable, Bedfordshire LU6 2LF
Tel: (01582) 872171 www.whipsnade.co.uk
Whipsnade Wild Animal Park has over 2,500 animals and
is set in 600 acres (243 ha) of beautiful parkland. The
Great Whipsnade Railway and free animal
demonstrations.

Wimpole Hall and Home Farm

Arrington, Royston, Hertfordshire SG8 0BW
Tel: (01223) 207257 www.wimpole.org
An 18thC house in a landscaped park with a folly,
Chinese bridge. Plunge bath and yellow drawing room in
the house, the work of John Soane. Home Farm has a
rare breeds centre.

Woburn Abbey

Woburn, Milton Keynes, Bedfordshire MK17 9WA
Tel: (01525) 290666 www.woburnabbey.co.uk
An 18thC Palladian mansion, altered by Henry Holland,
the Prince Regent's architect, containing a collection of
English silver, French and English furniture and art.

Woburn Safari Park

Woburn, Milton Keynes, Bedfordshire MK17 9QN
Tel: (01525) 290407 www.woburnsafari.co.uk
Drive through the safari park with 30 species of animals
in natural groups just a windscreen's width away, plus
the action-packed Wild World Leisure Area with shows
for all.

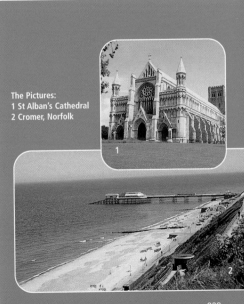

The Pictures:
1 St Alban's Cathedral
2 Cromer, Norfolk

Find out more about the East of England

Further information about holidays and attractions in the East of England is available from:

EAST OF ENGLAND TOURIST BOARD
Toppesfield Hall, Hadleigh, Suffolk IP7 5DN
Tel: (01473) 822922 Fax: (01473) 823063
Email: eastofenglandtouristboard@compuserve.com
Internet: www.eastofenglandtouristboard.com

The following publications are available from The East of England Tourist Board:

East of England - The Official Guide 2002
an information packed A5 guide featuring all you need to know about places to visit and things to see and do in the East of England. From historic houses to garden centres, from animal collections to craft centres - the Guide has it all, including film and TV locations, city, town and village information, events, shopping, car tours plus lots more! Price £3.99 (excl. p&p)

England's Cycling Country
the East of England offers perfect cycling country - from quiet country lanes to ancient trackways. This free publication promotes the many Cycling Discovery Maps that are available to buy (£1.50 excl. p&p), as well as providing useful information for anyone planning a cycling tour of the region

Getting to the East of England

BY ROAD: The region is easily accessible. From London and the south via the A1, M11, M25, A10, M1, A46 and A12. From the north via the A17, A1, A15, A5, M1 and A6. From the west via the A14, A47, A421, A428, A418, A41 and A427.

BY RAIL: Regular fast trains run to all major cities and towns in the region. London stations which serve the region are Liverpool Street, Kings Cross, Fenchurch Street, Moorgate, St Pancras, London Marylebone and London Euston. Bedford, Luton and St Albans are on the Thameslink line which runs to Kings Cross and onto London Gatwick Airport. There is also a direct link between London Stansted Airport and Liverpool Street. Through the Channel Tunnel, there are trains direct from Paris and Brussels to Waterloo Station, London. A short journey on the Underground will bring passengers to those stations operating services into the East of England. Further information on rail journeys in the East of England can be obtained on (0845) 748 4950.

Where to stay in the East of England

Accommodation entries in this region are listed in alphabetical order of place name, and then in alphabetical order of establishment.

Map references refer to the colour location maps at front of this guide. The first number indicates the map to use; the letter and number which follow refer to the grid reference on the map.

At-a-glance symbols at the end of each accommodation entry give useful information about services and facilities. A key to symbols can be found inside the back cover flap. Keep this open for easy reference.

A brief description of the towns and villages offering accommodation in the entries which follow, can be found at the end of this section.

A complete listing of all the English Tourism Council assessed accommodation covered by this guide appears at the back of the guide.

ALDEBURGH, Suffolk Map ref 3C2 *Tourist Information Centre Tel: (01728) 453637*

★★★

1 Unit
Sleeping 2

COSY CORNER
41 Mariners Way, Aldeburgh IP15 5QH
T: (01728) 453121
Contact: Mrs B A Fryer

Ten minutes' walk to beach, town and bird reserve. Very comfortable ground floor annexe, having one internal step. Hand rails fitted in fully tiled shower room. Double bedroom, lounge/ diner, well-fitted kitchen. Quiet location at end of cul-de-sac with private off-road parking. Linen provided.

OPEN Jun–Sep &
Christmas

Short breaks available for minimum of 2 nights in low season at £40 per night.

Low season per wk
£210.00–£250.00
High season per wk
£250.00–£275.00

⊚ ▥ ⊙ ⌸ ▭ ▤ 📺 ⌇ ◷ ⅏ ⛿ ♠ P SP

TOWN INDEX
This can be found at the back of the guide. If you know where you want to stay, the index will give you the page number listing accommodation in your chosen town, city or village.

241

★★★★

1 Unit
Sleeping 3

CRAGSIDE

9 Hertford Place, Aldeburgh, Ipswich IP15 5DB
Contact: Mrs L Valentine, Rookery Farm, Cratfield,
Halesworth IP19 0QE
T: (01986) 798609
F: (01986) 798609
E: j.r.valentine@btinternet.com

*Deceptively spacious ground floor flat with twin
and single bedroom in large house on Crag Path.
Recently completely refurbished. Twenty yards
sea. Well equipped for a really comfortable
holiday with 2 TVs, microwave, dishwasher,
washer/dryer, telephone/answerphone.
Inglenook fireplaces. Cosy for winter with central
heating, down duvets, electric blankets. No pets
and no children, please.*

OPEN All year round

Low season per wk
£150.00–£260.00
High season per wk
£260.00–£350.00

★★★

1 Unit
Sleeping 4

THE DUTCH HOUSE FLAT

217 High Street, Aldeburgh IP15 5DN
Contact: Mr Christopher Bacon, Dodnash Priory Farm,
Bentley, Ipswich IP9 2DF
T: (01473) 310682 (Home) & 07836 731821 (Mobile)
F: (01473) 311131
E: cbacon@freeuk.com

*Recently created centrally heated ground floor
flat in high street position near sea and shops.
Comfortably sleeps 4 in 2 bedrooms, one double
and one twin. Galley kitchen fully fitted with
microwave, dishwasher and washing machine.
Tastefully furnished accommodation. Lounge/
dining room with stereo TV/video.*

OPEN All year round

Weekend breaks available in
low season.

Low season per wk
Max £290.00
High season per wk
Max £330.00

★★★

1 Unit
Sleeping 15

ORLANDO

25 King Street, Aldeburgh IP15 5BY
Contact: Mr Peter Hatcher, Martlesham Hall, Church Lane,
Martlesham, Woodbridge IP12 4PQ
T: (01394) 382126 (answerphone) & 274321 (work-day)
F: (01394) 382126
E: peter@hatcher.co.uk

*Orlando is a spacious, 6 bedroomed house
adjacent to the beach with magnificent,
panoramic views of the sea. The house is well-
equipped with all modern facilities. There is an
open plan kitchen with Aga and dining area for
sociable meals. Two living rooms on two floors –
ideal for grown-ups and kids alike.*

OPEN All year round

Low season per wk
£800.00–£900.00

★★★

2 Units
Sleeping 2–4

TELEGRAPH COTTAGE AND BARN
Warren Hill Lane, Aldeburgh IP15 5QD
Contact: Mr Richard John Balls, Gorse Hill,
Leiston Road, Aldeburgh IP15 5QD
T: (01728) 452162 & 07855 390185
F: (01728) 452162
E: gorse40@hotmail.com
I: www.selfcateringsuffolk.co.uk

OPEN All year round

Low season per wk
£160.00–£325.00
High season per wk
£335.00–£410.00

*Traditional timber framed barn and Suffolk cottage with panoramic views over North
Warren bird reserve, Thorpeness, sea and Aldeburgh golf course. Very cosy and well
equipped.*

ALRESFORD, Essex Map ref 3B2

★★★

1 Unit

Sleeping 2

CREEK LODGE
Ford Lane, Alresford, Colchester CO7 8BE
T: (01206) 825411
Contact: Mrs Patricia Mountney

OPEN All year round

Low season per wk
Max £130.00
High season per wk
Max £200.00

Tranquil riverside cottage set in extensive landscaped gardens, perfectly situated for sailing, walking and bird-watching. Only 5 miles from historic Colchester.

BACTON, Norfolk Map ref 3C1

★★★★

1 Unit

Sleeping 6

SWISS COTTAGE
8 Anne Stannard Way, Bacton, Norwich NR12 0HX
Contact: Linda Weinberg
T: 00 411 8442222
F: 00 411 8400222
E: swissonthebeach@cs.com

Few properties enjoy sea and sand views at such close proximity. With just a few steps to a quiet sandy beach, this recently built brick and flint cottage is within easy reach of the Norfolk Broads. The spacious conservatory and open-plan continental-style living accommodation enhance this idyllic picture.

OPEN All year round

Short breaks available on request.

Low season per wk
£320.00–£440.00
High season per wk
£500.00–£660.00

BEACHAMWELL, Norfolk Map ref 3B1

★★★

1 Unit

Sleeping 2

CAROLE WILSONS RECTORY HOLIDAYS
The Old Rectory, Beachamwell, Swaffham PE37 8BE
T: (01366) 328628 (answerphone)
E: rectoryholidays@talkgas.net
Contact: Mrs C Wilson

OPEN Mar–Nov

Low season per wk
Max £150.00
High season per wk
Max £175.00

Studio flat attached to Victorian Rectory which stands in 2 acres of lovely gardens and lawns, in a conservation village. The church is saxon.

BECCLES, Suffolk Map ref 3C1

★★★

1 Unit

Sleeping 6

9 THE MALTINGS
Fen Lane, Beccles NR34 9BB
Contact: Mrs Brenda Lanchester & Mr Birch, Brick Kiln
Barn, Kings Lane, Weston, Beccles NR34 8TG
T: (01502) 717362 & 711888
F: (01502) 711888
E: bircharch@aol.com

OPEN All year round

Low season per wk
£175.00–£280.00
High season per wk
£300.00–£420.00

Riverside converted maltings, large galleried living room, 2 twin-bedded rooms (plus double sofa bed in living room). Mooring for 16ft boat, kitchen and bathroom.

BELCHAMP ST PAUL, Essex Map ref 3B2

★★★★

1 Unit

Sleeping 5

COLEFAIR COTTAGE
Gages Road, Belchamp St Paul, Sudbury CO10 7BT
Contact: Mr Kirk Forrest, Suffolk & Norfolk Country
Cottages, Hillside Orchard, Rectory Farm Lane, Orwell,
Royston SG8 5RB
T: (01223) 207946
F: (01223) 208893
E: admin@suffolkandnorfolkcottages.co.uk
I: www.suffolkandnorfolkcottages.co.uk

OPEN All year round
CC: Barclaycard, Delta,
Eurocard, JCB,
Mastercard, Solo, Switch,
Visa

Low season per wk
£200.00–£240.00
High season per wk
£240.00–£352.00

Semi-detached character cottage in small village. Sitting room with open fire, dining room, kitchen, shower room, double bedroom, twin bedroom, bathroom, futon. Delightful garden.

SYMBOLS The symbols in each entry give information about services and facilities. A key to these symbols appears at the back of this guide.

BERKHAMSTED, Hertfordshire Map ref 2D1

★★★
2 Units
Sleeping 5

HOLLY TREE & JACK'S COTTAGE
22 & 23 Ringshall, Little Gaddesden, Berkhamsted
HP4 1ND
Contact: Mrs D Barrington, 20 & 21 Ringshall,
Little Gaddesden, Berkhamsted HP4 1ND
T: (01442) 843464
F: (01442) 842051
E: RBBarrington@aol.com

OPEN All year round

Low season per wk
£250.00–£275.00
High season per wk
£275.00–£350.00

Restored, period cottages with all modern amenities provided, in a village set in National Trust woodland. London 28 miles. Excellent food and rail connections.

🌣3 ⊚ ⊞ ⊙ 🗗 ▭ 🖨 📺 📞 🗄 📇 📱 ♿ P 📌 🐾 🐎 🏛

BILLERICAY, Essex Map ref 3B3

★★★★★
1 Unit
Sleeping 2–6

THE PUMP HOUSE APARTMENT
132 Church Street, Great Burstead, Billericay CM11 2TR
Contact: Mrs E R Bayliss, Pump House, Church Street,
Great Burstead, Billericay CM11 2TR
T: (01277) 656579
F: (01277) 631160
E: john.bayliss@willmottdixon.co.uk

The apartment is on 2 floors and luxuriously furnished, with air conditioning. The accommodation comprises 2 living rooms, fully fitted kitchen/diner and the option of 1, 2 or 3 bedrooms with 1, 2 or 3 bath/shower rooms, sleeping up to 6 persons. Guests have use of heated (May-Sept) outdoor pool, hot tub, gazebo and gardens. Personal supervision.

OPEN All year round
CC: Amex, Barclaycard,
Mastercard, Visa

5% discount for stays of 4 weeks. 10% discount for stays of 8 weeks.

Low season per wk
£400.00–£800.00
High season per wk
£525.00–£900.00

🅰🌣⊚⊞⊙🗗▭🖨📺📞🗄📇📱✂🔌♿P🐾📌❄🆂

BLAKENEY, Norfolk Map ref 3B1

★★★
1 Unit
Sleeping 5

CURRIE'S COTTAGE
Blakeney NR25 7NX
Contact: Dr & Mrs Fogarty, 202 Unthank Road,
Norwich NR2 2AH
T: (01603) 502007 (answerphone)
E: curriescottage@cs.com

OPEN All year round

Low season per wk
£215.00–£300.00
High season per wk
£340.00–£420.00

A traditional, newly refurbished flint cottage, looking on to a communal lawn and set back behind the high street. Shops, pubs and quayside nearby.

🌣⊚🛏⊙🗗▭🖨📺🗄📇✂🆂

★★★
4 Units
Sleeping 3–8

MARINERS HILL COTTAGES
Mariners Hill, Blakeney, Holt NR25 7NB
Contact: Mrs B Pope, The Lodge, Back Lane, Blakeney,
Holt NR25 7NR
T: (01263) 740477
F: (01263) 741356

OPEN All year round

Low season per wk
£100.00–£300.00
High season per wk
£400.00–£675.00

Flint bungalows and converted barns in quiet cul-de-sac facing the harbour. Tastefully furnished. Personally supervised by owners. Ideal for golf, bird-watching, sailing, riding, walking. Private parking.

🌣🅼⊚🛏⊙▭🖨📺📞🗄📇📱♿PU❄🐎🆂

CHECK THE MAPS
The colour maps at the front of this guide show all the cities, towns and villages for which you will find accommodation entries. Refer to the town index to find the page on which they are listed.

★★★
3 Units
Sleeping 4–8

A beautiful conversion of 18thC stables and farmhouse in an idyllic location in the grounds of the owner's manor house, 2 miles from the unspoilt North Norfolk coast. All properties are spacious, attractively decorated and well-equipped. Ideal for family holidays. Superb base for beaches, historic sites, walking and wildlife.

THE STABLE COURT AND APARTMENTS

Langham Hall, Langham, Holt NR25 7BX
Contact: Mr & Mrs Peter Darling, Langham Hall, Langham, Holt NR25 7BX
T: (01328) 830375 (Answerphone)
F: (01328) 830775
E: peter.darling1@btinternet.com
I: www.ukcoastalholidays.com/go/langhamhall

OPEN All year round	Low season per wk £300.00–£600.00
Short breaks available. Prices excl Easter, Christmas, New Year, Bank Hols.	High season per wk £400.00–£850.00

★★★
11 Units
Sleeping 4–10

Beautifully restored, fully fitted, traditional flint farm cottages. Stunning location, remote yet accessible, big skies, unspoilt rolling farmland, woodlands, long empty beaches, cosy pubs, RSPB nature reserves, log fires, barbecues, gardens, tennis court, high chairs, cots, stairgates, wooden playhouse, linen supplied, laundry, microwave ovens, TV, videos, radios, some with dishwashers.

THOMPSON BRANCASTER FARMS

Field House, Brancaster, King's Lynn PE31 8AG
Contact: Mrs Sue Lane, 4 Stiffkey Road, Warham, Wells-next-the-Sea NR23 1NP
T: 07885 269538 (Mobile)
F: (01328) 710144
E: sue@rsdlane.freeserve.co.uk
I: www.tbfholidayhomes.co.uk

OPEN All year round CC: Barclaycard, Delta, Eurocard, Mastercard, Solo, Switch, Visa	Low season per wk £200.00–£380.00 High season per wk £440.00–£890.00
Open all year-short breaks available (excl peak times).	

★★★★
1 Unit
Sleeping 6

21 DALE END
Brancaster Staithe, King's Lynn PE31 8DA
Contact: Mrs Debbie Clark, Stone House,
19 Main Street, Seaton, Oakham LE15 9HU
T: (01572) 747389
F: (01572) 747693
E: debbie@courtneycampbell.com
I: www.hemingwayclark.com/norfolk

OPEN All year round	Low season per wk £240.00–£350.00 High season per wk £350.00–£550.00

Light, airy, modern house, sleeping 6 and cot, in 3 bedrooms. Spacious accommodation and all appliances. Sunny south facing garden. Two minutes' walk to coastal path.

CREDIT CARD BOOKINGS
If you book by telephone and are asked for your credit card number it is advisable to check the proprietor's policy should you cancel your reservation.

★★★
2 Units
Sleeping 2–6

VISTA & CARPENTERS COTTAGES

Main Road, Brancaster Staithe, King's Lynn PE31 8BY
Contact: Mrs G J Smith, Dale View, Brancaster Staithe,
King's Lynn PE31 8BY
T: (01485) 210497
F: (01485) 210497

These two lovely cottages enjoy one of the best views along the Norfolk coast (see picture). Walking down the cottage gardens you meet the saltmarsh and the Norfolk coastal path. Both cottages have exposed beams and open fires as well as central heating throughout. Close to amenities, pets welcome.

OPEN All year round

Short breaks (weekend and mid-week) available during low season; minimum 3 nights.

Low season per wk	£180.00–£280.00
High season per wk	£230.00–£600.00

★★
1 Unit
Sleeping 4

DEACONS COTTAGE
South Street, Hockwold, Thetford IP26 4JG
T: (01842) 828023 & 878739
Contact: Mrs B D Deacon

OPEN All year round

Low season per wk	£100.00–£150.00
High season per wk	£150.00–£200.00

Terrace of cottages built 1742. In the Breckland Forest area, within 40 miles of historic cities of Ely, Cambridge, Norwich.

★★★★
2 Units
Sleeping 3–6

POPLAR HALL
Frostenden Corner, Frostenden, Wangford NR34 7JA
T: (01502) 578549
I: www.southwold.co.uk/poplar-hall/
Contact: Mrs Anna Garwood

OPEN All year round

Low season per wk	£180.00–£270.00
High season per wk	£300.00–£390.00

Poplar Hall Cottage and Lofthouse are well-equipped, beautifully appointed and have their own gardens and patios, private parking and cycle store. 3.5 miles from Southwold.

★★★
1 Unit
Sleeping 4

MILL HOUSE ANNEXE

Mill Farm, Burnham Overy Town, King's Lynn PE31 8DX
Contact: Mrs Anthea Moore Ede, 16 Victoria Grove,
London W8 5RW
T: (0207) 5848826 (work & home) &
(01328) 730384 (weekends)
F: (0207) 5818694
E: antheamooreede@zoom.co.uk

Comfortable newly refurbished cottage. Linen and electricity included. Sleeps 4/5, cot available. Close to picturesque village of Burnham Market with excellent shops, wide sandy beaches at Holkham and Brancaster. Golf, bird-watching, sailing.

OPEN Feb–Dec

3 day stays available Oct-Feb (excl Christmas and New Year).

Low season per wk	Max £250.00
High season per wk	Max £400.00

---

www.travelengland.org.uk
Log on for information and inspiration. The latest information on places to visit, events and quality assessed accommodation.

★★-★★★★
3 Units
Sleeping 2-7

Get away from it all in the heart of the Suffolk countryside. The Court and Granary suites are tastefully converted old farmhouse and buildings from 1 to 3 bedrooms. The Court (illustrated) has 3 bedrooms (1 en suite), family bathroom, lounge and kitchen/diner. Linen provided. Gardens and farm trail to explore. Send SAE for brochure.

THE COURT & THE GRANARY SUITES

Melford Road, Lawshall, Bury St Edmunds IP29 4PX
T: (01284) 830385 & 07711 829546 (Mobile)
F: (01284) 830385
E: brighthousefarm@supanet.com
I: www.brighthousefarm.fsnet.co.uk
Contact: Mrs Roberta Truin

OPEN All year round	Low season per wk £250.00-£450.00 High season per wk £400.00-£600.00

★★★★★
1 Unit
Sleeping 6

Originally an early 17thC cottage, the Manse now has an early Victorian facade. For a hundred years it was the residence of the pastor of the neighbouring congregational church. Features inglenook fireplace, beams, fine furnishings and private garden. Sleeps 6. Situated on a very picturesque village green.

THE MANSE

The Green, Hartest, Bury St Edmunds IP29 4DH
Contact: Pat, Secretary, Sturgeons Hall, The Green, Hartest, Bury St Edmunds IP29 4DH
T: (01284) 830690
F: (01284) 830228
E: gig_manning@lineone.net
I: www.themanse.uk.com

OPEN All year round CC: Amex, Delta, Maestro, Mastercard, Solo, Switch, Visa, Visa Electron	Low season per wk £450.00 High season per wk £600.00

★★★★
2 Units
Sleeping 4

BROOKLANDS COURT
Brooklands Avenue, Cambridge
Contact: Mr & Mrs Oliver Digney, 9a Cambridge Road, Great Shelford, Cambridge CB2 5JE
T: (01223) 841294
F: (01223) 841294
E: sdigney@clarencehouse.fsnet.co.uk
I: www.clarencehouse.org.uk

Brooklands Court is a prestigious group of apartments very close to the botanic gardens and the railway station.

OPEN All year round CC: Barclaycard, Delta, Eurocard, JCB, Mastercard, Switch, Visa	Low season per wk Max £485.00 High season per wk Max £485.00

★★★★
4 Units
Sleeping 2-4

CLARENCE HOUSE
13 Clarendon Street, Cambridge CB1 1JU
Contact: Mr & Mrs Oliver Digney, 9a Cambridge Road, Great Shelford, Cambridge CB2 5JE
T: (01223) 841294
F: (01223) 841294
E: sdigney@clarence.house.fsnet.co.uk
I: www.clarencehouse.org.uk

A 4-storey Victorian house in the centre of this historic city. All apartments furnished and equipped to a very high standard.

OPEN All year round CC: Barclaycard, Delta, JCB, Mastercard, Switch, Visa	Low season per wk £345.00-£395.00 High season per wk £395.00-£445.00

REGIONAL TOURIST BOARD The ⋀ symbol in an establishment entry indicates that it is a Regional Tourist Board member.

CAMBRIDGE continued

★★★
2 Units
Sleeping 2–4

HOME FROM HOME APARTMENTS
74 Milton Road, Cambridge CB4 1LA
Contact: Mrs E Fasano, Bungalow rear of,
78 Milton Road, Cambridge CB4 1LA
T: (01223) 323555 & 07740 594306
F: (01223) 563509
E: homefromhome@tesco.net
I: www.smoothhound.co.uk/hotels/homefrom.html

OPEN All year round
CC: Barclaycard, Delta,
JCB, Mastercard, Solo,
Switch, Visa, Visa Electron

Low season per wk
£280.00–£395.00
High season per wk
£350.00–£490.00

Victorian house centrally located to river and colleges. Both apartments are fully-equipped and furnished to a high standard. Smoking is not permitted.

★★★★
1 Unit
Sleeping 4

VICTORIA APARTMENT
4 Poynters Lodge, 148 Chesterton Road, Cambridge
CB4 1JB
Contact: Mrs Maria Fasano, Victoria, 57 Arbury Road,
Cambridge CB4 2JB
T: (01223) 350086 & 07803 906619
F: (01223) 350086
E: vicmaria@globalnet.co.uk
I: www.victoriaguesthouse.co.uk

OPEN All year round
CC: Barclaycard, Delta,
Eurocard, Mastercard,
Solo, Switch, Visa, Visa
Electron

Low season per wk
£275.00–£350.00
High season per wk
£335.00–£495.00

A comfortable ground floor apartment, situated in Cambridge City Centre which can accommodate 2 to 4 people. Furnished and equipped to high standard. Bed and breakfast also available.

CASTLE ACRE, Norfolk Map ref 3B1

★★★★
1 Unit
Sleeping 6

CHERRY TREE COTTAGE
Back Lane, Castle Acre, King's Lynn PE32 2AR
Contact: Mr & Mrs C J Boswell, Wellington House,
Back Lane, Castle Acre, King's Lynn PE32 2AR
T: (01760) 755000
F: (01760) 755000
E: boswell@paston.co.uk

Exceptionally comfortable and charming 4-bedroomed cottage in historic conservation village. Furnished and equipped to very high standards. Features include a magnificent king-sized 4-poster, a large conservatory and cottage gardens. Easy access to Sandringham and all regional attractions. Shops, pubs, restaurants and English Heritage sites within 300 yards. Inclusive rates.

OPEN All year round

10% discount on bookings of
2 weeks or more.

Low season per wk
£195.00–£265.00
High season per wk
£265.00–£425.00

★★★
1 Unit
Sleeping 6

PEDDARS COTTAGE
5 Bailey Gate, Castle Acre, King's Lynn PE32 2AF
Contact: Mrs Angela Swindell, St Saviour's Rectory,
St Saviour, Jersey JE2 7NP
T: (01534) 727480 & 736679
F: (01534) 727480
E: jsyedu71@localdial.com

OPEN Mar–Sep

Low season per wk
Max £200.00
High season per wk
Max £275.00

Well-equipped cottage-style house situated in centre of historic village. Close to castle, priory and shops. On the Peddars Way footpath.

CASTLE HEDINGHAM, Essex Map ref 3B2

★★★–★★★★★
2 Units
Sleeping 2

ROSEMARY FARM
Rosemary Lane, Castle Hedingham, Halstead CO9 3AJ
T: (01787) 461653 & 370399
Contact: Mr Garry Ian Henderson

OPEN All year round

Low season per wk
£191.00–£298.00

Two cottages in barn conversion offering lounge, kitchen, 1 and 2 bedrooms, shower/toilet, patio area, parking within premises, open countryside. Village, pubs and restaurant nearby.

CHARSFIELD, Suffolk Map ref 3C2

★★★★

1 Unit
Sleeping 7

ROSEHILL COTTAGE

Charsfield, Woodbridge
Contact: Ms Di Janus, 33 Freegrove Road, London N7 9RG
T: (0207) 6096610 (evenings) & 6072133 (days)
F: (0207) 6871070
E: di@dijanus.freeserve.co.uk
I: www.suffolk-cottage.co.uk

*Lovely timber-framed cottage (1750).
Approximately 1 acre garden with good views.
Beautifully renovated, fully equipped, 3
bedrooms, 2 bathrooms, magnificent lounge.
Tranquil, picturesque village with good pub/
restaurant and shop. Walking, cycling, tennis,
horse riding. Near Woodbridge and coast. No
smoking. No pets. Short breaks pro rata to price
shown.*

OPEN All year round

Low season per wk
Min £195.00
High season per wk
Max £550.00

CLEY NEXT THE SEA, Norfolk Map ref 3B1

★★★

1 Unit
Sleeping 7

ARCHWAY COTTAGE

Coast Road, Cley next the Sea, Holt NR25 7RN
Contact: Mrs V Jackson, 3A Brickendon Lane, Brickendon,
Hertford SG13 8NU
T: (01992) 511303 & 503196
F: (01992) 511303

*Pretty 18thC flint cottage, well furnished and
comfortable, with 4 bedrooms, 2 bathrooms and
garage. Near village centre, bird sanctuaries and
the sea. Also, another similar cottage in Wells-
next-the-Sea. Illustrated brochures available for
both cottages. Both sleep 7.*

OPEN All year round

Low season per wk
£150.00–£200.00
High season per wk
£250.00–£420.00

★★★

1 Unit
Sleeping 4

THURN COTTAGE

The Fairstead, Cley next the Sea, Holt NR25 7RL
Contact: Mr & Mrs Chris & Carol Smith, 15 South
Hanningfield Way, Runwell, Wickford SS11 7DR
T: (01268) 769801 & (01708) 722179
E: cjcksmith@btinternet.com

*Exceptionally attractive, brick-flint detached
cottage peacefully set in the heart of Cley. Light
and bright decoration complements high quality
furnishings offering above average comfort. A
must for year round holidays for families,
twitchers and walkers wishing to explore the
beautiful North Norfolk coast or simply relax.
Walled garden/parking.*

OPEN All year round

Low season per wk
£200.00–£360.00
High season per wk
£340.00–£420.00

COUNTRY CODE Always follow the Country Code 🌾
Enjoy the countryside and respect its life and work 🌾 Guard
against all risk of fire 🌾 Fasten all gates 🌾 Keep your dogs
under close control 🌾 Keep to public paths across farmland
🌾 Use gates and stiles to cross fences, hedges and walls 🌾
Leave livestock, crops and machinery alone 🌾 Take your litter
home 🌾 Help to keep all water clean 🌾 Protect wildlife,
plants and trees 🌾 Take special care on country roads 🌾
Make no unnecessary noise

COLCHESTER, Essex Map ref 3B2 *Tourist Information Centre Tel: (01206) 282920*

★★★★-★★★★★★
3 Units
Sleeping 4–5

CASTLE ROAD COTTAGES

6,17 & 64 Castle Road, Colchester CO1 1UN
Contact: Mrs Patsie Ford, 19 High Street, Nayland,
Colchester CO6 4JG
T: (01206) 262210
F: (01206) 262210

Superbly situated in quiet cul-de-sac in conservation area, by castle park in central Colchester. Two cosy Victorian cottages refurbished to provide every comfort, whilst retaining original character. Each has its own private courtyard and garden. Guests may arrive on any day for any number of days. Brochure on request.

OPEN All year round

Discounts available for those staying over 28 nights. Nightly rates available.

Low season per wk
£315.00
High season per wk
£385.00

🛏10 🎠 🍴 🏠 ☺ 🖥 📻 📺 🍳 🔥 🗑 ✖ 🔌 🚗 P ✿ 🐴

★★★
1 Unit
Sleeping 4

MUNDY
The Crescent, West Bergholt, Colchester CO6 3DA
Contact: Mrs Jan Blackwell, Grebe House, The Crescent,
West Bergholt, Colchester CO6 3DA
T: (01206) 240910

OPEN Jan–Nov

Low season per wk
£150.00–£180.00
High season per wk
£210.00–£250.00

Restored timbered cottage. 1 double, 1 twin, lounge, kitchen, garden room. Between Colne and Stour Valleys, close to Constable Country. Comfortable, quiet, excellent touring base.

🛏 🎠 🏠 🖥 📻 📺 🍳 🔥 ✖ 🔌 🚗 P ✿ 🐴 🏕

★★★
1 Unit
Sleeping 6

50 ROSEBERY AVENUE
Colchester CO1 2UP
Contact: Mrs K Webb, 51 Rosebery Avenue, Colchester
CO1 2UP
T: (01206) 866888
E: katowebb@ntlworld.com

OPEN All year round

Low season per wk
£170.00–£190.00
High season per wk
£210.00–£240.00

Modernised house in quiet town centre location. Castle, park, shops, museums and sports centre within walking distance. Ideal for East Coast. Bus/trains close by.

🛏 Ⓜ 🎠 🏠 🖥 ☺ 🖥 📻 📺 🍳 🔥 ✖ 🔌 🚗 P ✿ SP

★★★★
1 Unit
Sleeping 4

THE TEA HOUSE

Layer Marney Tower, Colchester CO5 9US
Contact: Mr Nicholas Charrington, Layer Marney Tower,
Layer Marney, Colchester CO5 9US
T: (01206) 330784
F: (01206) 330784
E: nicholas@layermarney.demon.co.uk
I: layermarneytower.com

Beautiful, Edwardian folly in the grounds of a Tudor palace. Tastefully restored and fully equipped to the highest standards. Peaceful, rural setting with spectacular views of Layer Marney Tower and the surrounding deer park. Ideally located for bird-watching at Aberton Reservoir, or visiting historic Colchester and Constable Country at Dedham.

OPEN All year round
CC: Barclaycard,
Mastercard, Visa

Late availability discounts offered. Also short breaks available from 8 weeks before arrival.

Low season per wk
£250.00–£340.00
High season per wk
£340.00–£485.00

🅰 🛏 🎠 🏠 ☺ 🖥 📻 📺 🍳 🔥 🗑 🚗 P ✿ SP 🏕

ACCESSIBILITY
Look for the 🅳🅳🅳 symbols which indicate accessibility for wheelchair users. A list of establishments is at the front of this guide.

COTTON, Suffolk Map ref 3B2

★★★★

3 Units
Sleeping 2–3

CODA COTTAGES
Poplar Farm, Dandy Corner, Cotton,
Stowmarket IP14 4QX
Contact: Mrs Kate Sida-Nicholls, Manager, Coda
Cottages, Poplar Farm, Dandy Corner, Cotton,
Stowmarket IP14 4QX
T: (01449) 780076
F: (01449) 780280
E: codacottages@dandycorner.co.uk

OPEN Jan, Mar–Dec

Low season per wk
£140.00–£210.00
High season per wk
£210.00–£320.00

Listed 17thC timber barn comprising of 2, 2-storey units and 1 single-story unit restored for wheelchair bound clients. Situated in Mid Suffolk.

CRANMER, Norfolk Map ref 3B1

★★★★

4 Units
Sleeping 4–5

HOME FARM
Cranmer Holiday Cottages, Cranmer, Fakenham NR21 9HY
T: (01328) 823135
E: bookings@homefarmcranmer.co.uk
I: www.homefarmcranmer.co.uk
Contact: Mrs Lynne & John Johnson

4 luxuriously converted Victorian barns in grounds of owner's home. Cottages are all on one level, spacious and modern, sleeping 4-20 (when combined). Each has private terrace overlooking gardens and farmland. Well situated for exploring beaches at Holkham, Burnhams and Brancaster, for sailing and local bird reserves.

OPEN All year round

Low season per wk
£220.00–£250.00
High season per wk
£350.00–£550.00

CRATFIELD, Suffolk Map ref 3C2

★★★

1 Unit
Sleeping 6

CHERRY TREES
Cratfield Hall, Cratfield, Halesworth IP19 0DR
T: (01379) 586709
F: (01349) 586709
E: j.l.knox@farming.co.uk
Contact: Mrs Chris Knox

OPEN All year round

Low season per wk
£200.00–£295.00
High season per wk
£380.00–£420.00

A chalet/bungalow situated in Suffolk with an enclosed garden set well back from the road and in the grounds of a working farm.

★★★★

4 Units
Sleeping 2–6

SCHOOL FARM COTTAGES
Church Road, Cratfield, Halesworth IP19 0BU
Contact: Mrs Claire Sillett, School Farm, Cratfield,
Halesworth IP19 0BU
T: (01986) 798844
F: (01986) 798394
E: schoolfarmcotts@aol.com

OPEN All year round

Low season per wk
£150.00–£240.00
High season per wk
£250.00–£425.00

Four high quality, well-equipped cottages converted from traditional farm buildings. Attractive setting on working farm in beautiful Suffolk countryside. Near Heritage Coast.

CROMER, Norfolk Map ref 3C1 *Tourist Information Centre Tel: (01263) 512497*

★★

1 Unit
Sleeping 6

CLIFF HOLLOW
41 Cliff Drive, Overstrand Road, Cromer NR27 0AL
Contact: Miss L M Willins, Cliff Haven,
35 Overstrand Road, Cromer NR27 0AL
T: (01263) 512447 (Answerphone)
F: (01263) 512447

OPEN Apr–Oct &
Christmas

Low season per wk
£160.00
High season per wk
£235.00

Family home, secluded area, own garden, 4 bedrooms, combined bathroom and WC, lounge, dining room and kitchen. Sleeps 6 plus baby. Cot and highchair.

MAP REFERENCES
Map references apply to the colour maps at the front of this guide.

CROMER continued

★★
1 Unit
Sleeping 24

SHELLY HOUSE

Cromer
Contact: Mr Steven Ballantyne, Property Manager,
5 Whites Row, Bishopsgate, London E1 7NF
T: (020) 73750184 (Office)
F: (020) 73750553
E: draxballantyne@aol.com

*Newly refurbished substantial Victorian house
with excellent sea views, close to town centre
and beach. Adaptable accommodation to suit
groups of all sizes: 9-10 bedrooms, observation
room with balcony, dining room to seat 22, large
living room, 2 kitchens and 3 bathrooms.
Furnished with antiques, comfortable chairs and
stripped floors.*

OPEN All year round

Discounts offered for low
season weekend breaks. (Excl
Christmas and New Year).

Low season per wk
£421.00–£861.00
High season per wk
£917.00–£1,293.00

DALLINGHOO, Suffolk Map ref 3C2

★★★★
1 Unit
Sleeping 6

ROBINS NEST

Dallinghoo, Woodbridge IP13 0LD
Contact: Mr Robert Blake, 1a Moorfield Road, Woodbridge
IP12 4JN
T: (01394) 382565 & (01473) 736220
E: deben@btclick.com

*16thC cottage with exposed beams, in quiet rural
position overlooking countryside. Ideal base for
many local tourist attractions. Refurbished to
high standard. Three first floor double bedrooms,
bathroom, toilet. Downstairs toilet, shower room,
kitchen, dining room with inglenook fire, sitting
room, study, sun room. Full central heating, linen
provided.*

OPEN All year round

Low season per wk
Min £250.00
High season per wk
Min £420.00

DENVER, Norfolk Map ref 3B1

★★★
3 Units
Sleeping 4

DENVER WINDMILL
Sluice Road, Denver, Downham Market PE38 0EG
T: (01366) 384009 (answerphone & fax)
F: (01366) 384009

OPEN All year round
CC: Barclaycard, Delta,
Mastercard, Switch, Visa,
Visa Electron

Low season per wk
£150.00–£250.00
High season per wk
£200.00–£350.00

*A wonderful working windmill offers unique stay in original miller's house. Three
cottages each sleeping 4 people, available all year. Fully-equipped, recently restored.
Rural location.*

DILHAM, Norfolk Map ref 3C1

★★★★
7 Units
Sleeping 4–11

DAIRY FARM COTTAGES
Dilham, North Walsham NR28 9QA
Contact: Mr & Mrs James & Annabel Paterson,
Rumford Limited, Manor Farm, Dilham, North Walsham
NR28 9PZ
T: (01692) 535178 & 536883
F: (01692) 536723
E: japdilman@farmline.com

OPEN All year round
CC: Barclaycard, Visa

Low season per wk
£140.00–£200.00
High season per wk
£200.00–£290.00

*500-acre mixed farm. Traditional farm buildings converted into cottages. Beautiful,
country setting in heart of Broadland. Secure play area, games room, farm animals.
Coast 15 minutes. Brochure available.*

SPECIAL BREAKS

**Many establishments offer special promotions and themed breaks.
These are highlighted in red. (All such offers are subject to availability.)**

★★★★
1 Unit
Sleeping 5

Set in peaceful, idyllic countryside, central for exploring Norfolk and Suffolk's many attractions. The well-equipped cottage, spacious safe garden and indoor swimming pool make for a relaxing holiday. Family room, 1 bunk, 1 single. Bed linen, towels, electricity, central heating all included. Cot, highchair available. Sorry no pets. Colour brochure.

WALCOT GREEN FARM COTTAGE
Diss IP22 5SU
Contact: Mrs Nannette Catchpole, Walcot Green Farm,
Diss IP22 5SU
T: (01379) 652806
F: (01379) 652806
E: n.catchpole.wgf@virgin.net
I: website.lineone.net/~walcotgreenfarm

OPEN Mar–Oct

Low season per wk
£240.00–£310.00
High season per wk
£310.00–£400.00

★★★★★
2 Units
Sleeping 6

Irresistible cottage overlooking courtyard garden. Wonderful acccommodation – en suites and every comfort. Luxurious Victorian townhouse. Outstanding features: lounge – leather sofas, stone fireplace; bedrooms – wash basins, heated towel rails, TV/video, radio/CDs. Fabulous 4-poster. Three baths, 1 shower. Both properties: luxury kitchen, log fires, welcome supplies. Quality assurance. Shared laundry. Music room with keyboard.

COURTYARD COTTAGE & NORFOLK HOUSE
High Street, Docking PE31 8NH
Contact: Mr Alan Witley, Cherry Tree Cottage,
17 Peddars Way South, Ringstead, Hunstanton PE36 5LF
T: (01485) 525341 & 532543
F: (01485) 532715
E: holidays@witleypress.co.uk

OPEN All year round

'Last minute' holidays at reduced rate. Winter breaks 27 Oct-29 Mar from £150. Phone for tariff.

Low season per wk
Min £240.00
High season per wk
Max £650.00

★★★
1 Unit
Sleeping 6

ROSE COTTAGE
70 Little Lane, Docking, King's Lynn PE31
Contact: Mrs Rick and Sue Tunnard, Keepers Cottage,
Little Lane, Docking, King's Lynn PE31 8NT
T: (01485) 518000

OPEN All year round

Low season per wk
£135.00–£170.00
High season per wk
£190.00–£300.00

A country cottage restored to its original character. Situated in a quiet location on the edge of Docking village. Good car parking and garden.

★★★
1 Unit
Sleeping 5

WOODSTOCK WING
Woodstock, Gaston Street, East Bergholt,
Colchester CO7 6SD
T: (01206) 298724
Contact: Mr & Mrs Keith & Janet Alcoe

OPEN All year round

Low season per wk
£250.00
High season per wk
£260.00

Close to centre of picturesque village, John Constable's birthplace. Ideal location to explore Suffolk and beyond. Comfortably furnished, all facilities – parking. Brochure available on request.

QUALITY ASSURANCE SCHEME
Star ratings are explained at the back of this guide.

★★★★

2 Units
Sleeping 2–10

Handsomely appointed 18thC country house (sleeps 8-10) and detached bungalow (sleeps 2-4). Both self-contained and very private, patios/garden, tennis/croquet. Quiet rural retreat in pretty countryside, excellent centre for exploring East Anglia. Tastefully furnished accommodation. House has beautiful conservatory, washbasins all 4 bedrooms, lounge with beams, inglenook and woodburner.

CLINTON COTTAGE AND CLINTON HOUSE

Well Hill, Clint Green, Yaxham NR19 1RX
Contact: Mrs M R Searle, Clinton Willows, Cutthroat Lane, Yaxham, East Dereham NR19 1RZ
T: (01362) 692079
F: (01362) 692079
E: clintonholidays@tesco.net
I: www.norfolkcountrycottage.co.uk

OPEN All year round

Low season per wk
Min £130.00
High season per wk
Max £870.00

★★★★

2 Units
Sleeping 5

900-acre arable farm. Escape to the Norfolk countryside. Our cosy cottages, with beams and woodburners, are ideal for a relaxing break or a busy sightseeing holiday. Why not book both cottages and bring family and friends? Set in large garden by Thetford Forest, the cottages are fully equipped and carefully prepared for you.

DOLPHIN LODGE

Roudham Farm, East Harling, Norwich NR16 2RJ
T: (01953) 717126
F: (01953) 718593
E: jolly@roudhamfarm.co.uk
I: www.farmstayanglia.co.uk
Contact: Mrs E Jolly

OPEN All year round

Short breaks available autumn/spring. Return transport for walkers.

Low season per wk
£180.00–£265.00
High season per wk
£265.00–£415.00

★★–★★★★

8 Units
Sleeping 2–6

POPLARS CARAVAN AND CHALET PARK
Brick Lane, East Runton, Cromer NR27 9PL
Contact: Mr & Mrs K Parfitt, Managers, Poplars Caravan and Chalet Park, Brick Lane, East Runton, Cromer NR27 9PL
T: (01263) 512892

Coastal village brick bungalows set on edge of woodlands in peaceful, spacious grounds. Fully equipped and comfortably furnished. Family-run.

OPEN Mar–Oct

Low season per wk
£140.00–£190.00
High season per wk
£210.00–£380.00

QUALITY ASSURANCE SCHEME

For an explanation of the quality and facilities represented by the Stars please refer to the front of this guide. A more detailed explanation can be found in the information pages at the back.

★★★★
1 Unit
Sleeping 6

HILL HOUSE FARM COTTAGE
9 Main Street, Coveney, Ely CB6 2DJ
T: (01353) 778369
E: hill_house@madasafish.com
Contact: Mrs H E Nix

Tasteful barn conversion in farm yard, furnished to a high quality. Comfortable lounge/dining room with colour TV and video. Garden. Set in quiet village location with open views of Ely Cathedral and surrounding countryside, 3 miles west of Ely. Easy access to Cambridge, Huntingdon and Newmarket. Warm and friendly atmosphere.

OPEN All year round
CC: Barclaycard, Delta, Eurocard, Mastercard, Solo, Switch, Visa

Low season per wk
£250.00–£350.00
High season per wk
£300.00–£500.00

★★★
5 Units
Sleeping 4–7

GRANGE FARM
The Grange, Erpingham, Norwich NR11 7QX
Contact: Mrs Jane Bell, The Grange, Erpingham, Norwich NR11 7QX
T: (01263) 761241 (Answerphone)
F: (01263) 761241
E: jane@bellkitchen.freeserve.co.uk
I: www.grangefarmholidays.fsnet.co.uk

A 17thC farmhouse and 4 converted period farm buildings around a courtyard. The conversions sleep 4 each, the farmhouse sleeps 7. All in large garden in the middle of a 250-acre farm beside a river. Heated indoor swimming pool. Open Christmas and New Year.

OPEN All year round

Weekends (up to 4 nights) from £125 in low season.

Low season per wk
£195.00–£300.00
High season per wk
£300.00–£600.00

★★★–★★★★★
4 Units
Sleeping 2–6

MANOR HOUSE COTTAGES
Yaxley Manor House, Mellis Road, Yaxley, Eye IP23 8DG
T: (01379) 788181 & 07860 797874
F: (01379) 788422
E: david@dmenterprises.demon.co.uk
I: www.manorhousecottages.co.uk
Contact: Mr David Mason

OPEN All year round
CC: Barclaycard, Mastercard, Visa

Low season per wk
£153.00–£250.00
High season per wk
£250.00–£377.00

Yaxley Manor House was built in 1520. To the rear of the manor are the barns and stables converted to holiday cottages.

★★★
1 Unit
Sleeping 4

FLAT 2
7 Brownlow Road, Felixstowe IP11 7EX
Contact: Mrs Gwen Lynch, Cedar House, 20 The Close, Tattingstone, Ipswich IP9 2PD
T: (01473) 328729 (Answerphone)

OPEN Apr–Oct

Low season per wk
£130.00–£160.00
High season per wk
£160.00–£200.00

Two-bedroomed 1st-floor flat with balcony overlooking the sea. In quiet area and within walking distance of the town centre, with own parking space.

★★
3 Units
Sleeping 3–6

KIMBERLEY HOLIDAY FLATS
105-107 Undercliff Road, Felixstowe IP11 2AF
Contact: Mrs Valerie Reed, Kimberley Holiday Flats, 105-107 Undercliff Road, Felixstowe IP11 2AF
T: (01394) 672157

OPEN All year round

Low season per wk
£175.00–£285.00
High season per wk
£195.00–£400.00

All flats are self-contained with balconies, and overlook the sea. The town centre is nearby. Car spaces off road at rear. Telephone for brochure.

FOXLEY, Norfolk Map ref 3B1

★★-★★★
10 Units
Sleeping 3–7

MOOR FARM STABLE COTTAGES
Moor Farm, Foxley, Dereham NR20 4QN
Contact: Mr P Davis, Moor Farm, Foxley, Dereham
NR20 4QN
T: (01362) 688523 (Answerphone)
F: (01362) 688523
E: moorfarm@aol.com

Located on working farm, a courtyard of 2 and 3
bed self-catering chalets, all fully equipped and
centrally heated, 2 specially adapted for
disabled. Ideally situated for coast, Broads,
Norwich, Sandringham. 365 acres of mature
woodland adjoining owners' farm to walk.
Fishing available close by. Pets welcome.

OPEN All year round

Low season per wk
£170.00–£220.00
High season per wk
£250.00–£400.00

FRINTON-ON-SEA, Essex Map ref 3C2

★★★
1 Unit
Sleeping 6

QUARTETTE
Frinton-on-Sea
Contact: Mr Robert Bucke, Agent, Boydens,
73 Connaught Ave, Frinton-on-Sea CO13 9PP
T: 07010 716013
F: 0870 765 3746
E: ipsw@btinternet.com
I: www.ipsw.btinternet.co.uk/quartette.htm

Comfortable bungalow, large secluded garden, 10 minutes' walk from wonderful
beach, near shops, Constable Country, Harwich and the continent.

OPEN May–Sep

Low season per wk
£299.00–£385.00
High season per wk
£395.00–£475.00

GREAT DUNMOW, Essex Map ref 3B2

★★★★
2 Units
Sleeping 4–6

THE GRANARY
Moor End Farm, Broxted, Dunmow CM6 2EL
T: (01371) 870821
I: www.moorendfarm.com
Contact: Mr & Mrs J P Burton

A beautifully converted Victorian granary in a rural location close to Stansted Airport.
Breakfast pack provided. Ample off-road parking available.

OPEN All year round
CC: Amex, Barclaycard,
Delta, Diners, Mastercard,
Switch, Visa

Low season per wk
£250.00–£650.00
High season per wk
£275.00–£675.00

GRESHAM, Norfolk Map ref 3B1

★★
2 Units
Sleeping 3–4

ASTALOT AND AVALON COTTAGES
Gooseberry Alley, Sustead Road, Lower Gresham
NR11 8RE
Contact: Mrs J J Murray, Mariners Hard High Street,
Cley, Holt NR25 7RX
T: (01263) 740404 (Answerphone) &
740801 (Answerphone)
F: (01263) 740404

Adjoining flint/brick cottages built over 160 years ago. Completely renovated. Warm
and very comfortable, with small enclosed gardens. Dogs welcome. Sea 2 miles.
Electricity included.

OPEN All year round

Low season per wk
£120.00–£195.00
High season per wk
£210.00–£275.00

USE YOUR *i*s
There are more than 550 Tourist Information
Centres throughout England offering friendly help
with accommodation and holiday ideas as well as
suggestions of places to visit and things to do.
You'll find TIC addresses in the local Phone Book.

HALSTEAD, Essex Map ref 3B2

★★★★
1 Unit
Sleeping 4

GAINSFORD HALL
Gainsford End, Toppesfield, Halstead CO9 4EJ
Contact: Mr Chris Barnard & Ms Archer, Houghtons Farm,
Gainsford End, Toppesfield, Halstead CO9 4EH
T: (01787) 237334

Gainsford Hall is a working dairy farm. A timber-framed Tudor farmhouse showing exposed beams and mullion window. Spacious lounge/dining room with wood-burning stove. Kitchen, shower room, 2 twin bedrooms, en suite bathroom, hall and landing. Fuel, bedding and towels included. Large garden with own parking.

OPEN All year round

3 night stays available all year round.

Low season per wk
Max £400.00
High season per wk
Max £500.00

HAUGHLEY, Suffolk Map ref 3B2

★★★
1 Unit
Sleeping 2–4

THE COTTAGE
Red House Farm, Station Road, Haughley,
Stowmarket IP14 3QP
Contact: Mrs Mary Noy, Red House Farm, Station Road,
Haughley, Stowmarket IP14 3QP
T: (01449) 673323
F: (01449) 675413

OPEN All year round

Low season per wk
£190.00
High season per wk
£220.00

Delightful well-equipped cottage adjoining farmhouse on small grassland farm. Ideal for exploring the many attractions in Suffolk, Norfolk and Essex.

HAVERHILL, Suffolk Map ref 3B2

★★★
1 Unit
Sleeping 4

WINDSWEPT
Withersfield, Haverhill CB9 7RY
Contact: Mrs J R Notley, The Chestnuts, Withersfield,
Haverhill CB9 7RY
T: (01440) 704582
F: (01440) 704582
E: jane@ikidunot.freeserve.co.uk
I: www.geocities.com/thetropics/core/2353

OPEN All year round

Low season per wk
£200.00–£250.00
High season per wk
£250.00–£300.00

Overlooking village green. Thirty minutes drive from Cambridge, Newmarket, Bury St Edmunds and Saffron Walden. Uninterrupted view across rolling countryside. Two-bedroomed bungalow in own grounds.

HEACHAM, Norfolk Map ref 3B1

★★-★★★
5 Units
Sleeping 4–6

CEDAR SPRINGS
Bankside, Jubilee Road, Heacham, King's Lynn PE31 7LJ
Contact: Mrs A Howe, Owl Lodge, Jubilee Road,
Heacham, King's Lynn PE31 7AR
T: (01485) 570609

OPEN Apr–Sep

Low season per wk
£95.00–£160.00
High season per wk
£195.00–£295.00

Fully equipped 2-3 bed chalets on quiet garden site, 300 yards from beach, 3 miles from Hunstanton. Adjacent car parking. Sorry no pets.

★
8 Units
Sleeping 4

CEDAR SPRINGS CHALETS
Bankside, Heacham, King's Lynn PE31 7AU
Contact: Mr & Mrs Michael Chestney,
35 West Raynham, Fakenham NR21 7EY
T: (01328) 838341

OPEN Mar–Sep

Low season per wk
£85.00–£105.00
High season per wk
£105.00–£175.00

2-bedroomed chalets on quiet garden site 300 yards from beach. No dogs, please. Conservation Area of Outstanding Natural Beauty. Sandringham within 6 miles.

CHECK THE MAPS
The colour maps at the front of this guide show all the cities, towns and villages for which you will find accommodation entries.
Refer to the town index to find the page on which they are listed.

HEACHAM continued

★★★★
1 Unit
Sleeping 6

11 THE DRIFT
Heacham, King's Lynn PE31 7DT
Contact: Mrs Rachel Holliday, 15 Wilson Drive,
East Winch, King's Lynn PE32 1NX
T: (01553) 842134 (answerphone)

OPEN All year round

Low season per wk
£180.00–£300.00
High season per wk
£300.00–£450.00

Newly renovated Victorian stone cottage retaining many original features. Wooden floors and open fireplaces etc. Pretty patio garden. Central village location.

★★
1 Unit
Sleeping 6

2 RETREAT COTTAGE
Off Caley Street, Heacham, King's Lynn PE31 7DR
Contact: Mrs I J Rooth, 32 Church Green,
Hunstanton Road, Heacham, King's Lynn PE31 7HH
T: (01485) 572072 & 571438
E: clare@clarerooth.demon.co.uk

OPEN All year round

Low season per wk
£140.00–£270.00
High season per wk
£275.00–£390.00

Retreat cottage is a 4-bedroomed detached cottage with a sunny enclosed garden in the heart of Heacham village, approximately 20 minutes walk from the beach.

HICKLING, Norfolk Map ref 3C1

★★★
1 Unit
Sleeping 4

OLD CHAPEL COTTAGE
Stubb Road, Hickling, Norwich NR12 0YS
Contact: Mrs C Brown, Hollingbery, Guilt Cross,
Kenninghall, Norwich NR16 2LJ
T: (01953) 681314
F: (01953) 681681

OPEN All year round

Low season per wk
£210.00
High season per wk
£220.00

Traditional Norfolk flint and brick cottage. Sitting room with dining area, kitchen and hall. One double and one twin bedroom. Bathroom with WC. Night storage heaters.

HINGHAM, Norfolk Map ref 3B1

★★★★
1 Unit
Sleeping 6

THE GRANARY
College Farm, Hingham, Norwich NR9 4PP
Contact: Mrs C Dunnett, College Farm, Hingham, Norwich NR9 4PP
T: (01953) 850596
F: (01953) 851364
E: christine.dunnett@lineone.net

Tastefully converted and furnished 18thC granary. Peaceful location on small thoroughbred stud farm with pets galore. Very attractive, well-equipped accommodation with original oak beams throughout. Warm and cosy in winter with woodburning stove. Children's play area with outdoor above-ground pool. Perfect location to explore Norfolk.

OPEN All year round

3-night low season breaks available for only £100.

Low season per wk
£170.00
High season per wk
£265.00–£310.00

AT-A-GLANCE SYMBOLS
Symbols at the end of each accommodation entry give useful information about services and facilities. A key to symbols can be found inside the back cover flap. Keep this open for easy reference.

★★-★★★

3 Units
Sleeping 3–6

Peacefully situated, ground floor cottages in 4 acres of beautiful gardens. Two cottages (photographed) have conservatories overlooking natural ponds with wildlife. The Bakery, a listed building, converted into a cosy retreat, retaining original features with own delightful secluded garden. Central for touring. Good walks, cycling, golf, fishing, etc, locally.

THE BAKERY, LILY COTTAGE AND FRANZ COTTAGE

c/o Mill House, Water Run, Hitcham, Ipswich IP7 7LN
T: (01449) 740315 (Answerphone & fax) &
07767 304762 (Mobile)
F: (01449) 740315
E: hitcham@aol.com
Contact: Ms Melanie Rieger

OPEN All year round

Low season per wk
£140.00–£225.00
High season per wk
£225.00–£245.00

★★★★

3 Units
Sleeping 2–6

Three converted barn cottages in rural Norfolk, bordering Breckland, with heathland, ancient forests, nature reserves and the romantic Fens. Little Barn sleeps 2, Chalk Barn 4, Red Barn 6–8. Ideal for all seasons. Cambridge, Ely and seaside all within 1 hour. Excellently equipped kitchens and woodburning stoves. Pets very welcome.

LILAC BARNS

The Lilacs, South Street, Hockwold, Thetford IP26 4JG
Contact: Agent, Hoseasons Country Cottages,
Sunway House, Lowestoft NR32 2LW
T: (01502) 501515
I: www.hoseasons.co.uk

OPEN All year round
CC: Barclaycard,
Mastercard, Solo, Switch,
Visa

Short breaks available for winter, off-season and last minute bookings.

Low season per wk
£170.00–£443.00
High season per wk
£285.00–£608.00

★★★★

1 Unit
Sleeping 8

WHITEGATES
Peddars Way, Holme next the Sea,
Hunstanton PE36 6LE
Contact: Mr & Mrs K Felgate, Caretaker, 51 Kirkgate
Street, Holme next the Sea, Hunstanton PE36 6LH
T: (01485) 525556
E: kevin.felgate@talk21.com

OPEN Jun–Sep

High season per wk
£550.00

Cottage-style modern home, set in a 1-acre garden in quiet picturesque village on unspoilt North Norfolk Coast. Wheelchair accessible.

TOWN INDEX

This can be found at the back of the guide. If you know where you want to stay, the index will give you the page number listing accommodation in your chosen town, city or village.

★★★★
1 Unit
Sleeping 6

A 3-bedroomed, 1930s, spacious, thatched house in lawned garden with trees, standing back from the road, near the river and towards the edge of the village. Plenty of space in the garden that includes a swimming pool and a Wendy house for small children.

BURE HOUSE

131 Lower Street, Horning, Norwich NR12 8PF
Contact: 50, Norfolk Country Cottages, Carlton House, Market Place, Reepham, Norwich NR10 4JJ
T: (01603) 871872
F: (01603) 870304
E: cottages@paston.co.uk
I: www.norfolkcottages.co.uk

OPEN All year round
CC: Mastercard, Switch, Visa

High season per wk
£350.00–£650.00

Short breaks available in low season and occasionally at other times.

★★★★
8 Units
Sleeping 2–6

HALL FARM COTTAGES
Hall Farm, Horning, Norwich NR12 8NJ
T: (01692) 630385 & 07050 101746
F: (01692) 630385
E: cottages@hallfarm.com
I: www.hallfarm.com
Contact: Mrs & Mr Linda & Ivor Hudson

OPEN All year round
CC: Amex, Barclaycard, Eurocard, Mastercard, Solo, Switch, Visa

Low season per wk
£150.00–£205.00
High season per wk
£265.00–£570.00

Traditional barns converted to luxury, spacious 2 and 3 bedroom, two-bathroom cottages around cloistered courtyard. Central heating, laundry, games room. Rural setting. Heating and electricity included.

★★★
6 Units
Sleeping 4–9

HORNING LODGES 1,2,3, KATES & LADY LODGE & EAGLE COTTAGE
King Line Cottages/Ellis Frost Marine, Ferry View Estate, Horning, Norwich NR12 8PT
Contact: Mr Robert King, King Line Cottages, Ferry View Estate, Horning, Norwich NR12 8PT
T: (01692) 630297 (Office) & 630030 (Home)
F: (01692) 630498
E: kingline@norfolk-broads.co.uk
I: www.norfolk-broads.co.uk

OPEN All year round
CC: Barclaycard, Mastercard, Visa

Low season per wk
£130.00–£285.00
High season per wk
£285.00–£775.00

Main riverside lodges on the River Bure at Horning Ferry. Suitable for disability category 2 and 3 ratings.

★★★
1 Unit
Sleeping 5

This fully modernised coachman's cottage provides comfortable and private accommodation for 5 adults and 1 baby. Situated by the town green it has delightful and unobstructed views of the 'Wash' and is conveniently placed for the local shops, directly opposite the sea and about 200 yards from the beach.

MINNA COTTAGE

23 The Green, Hunstanton PE36 5AH
Contact: Mr T Cassie, 21 The Green, Hunstanton PE36 5AH
T: (01485) 532448
E: cassie@globalnet.co.uk

OPEN All year round
CC: Barclaycard, Delta, Mastercard, Switch, Visa

Low season per wk
£275.00–£325.00
High season per wk
£325.00–£385.00

COLOUR MAPS Colour maps at the front of this guide pinpoint all places under which you will find accommodation listed.

HUNSTANTON continued

★★★
1 Unit
Sleeping 3

WEST LODGE
Cole Green, Sedgeford, Hunstanton PE36 5LS
Contact: Mrs G Tibbs, Cole Green Cottage, Cole Green,
Sedgeford, Hunstanton PE36 5LS
T: (01485) 571770 & 07711 569388 (mobile)
F: (01485) 571770

OPEN All year round

Low season per wk
£130.00–£200.00
High season per wk
£200.00–£290.00

Charming Edwardian cottage situated in a quiet conservation area near the unspoilt, beautiful Norfolk coast. Furnished to a high standard, overlooking own garden. Parking.

〓8 ◎ ⅏ ▥ ⊙ ▯ ▣ ▤ TV ⬚ ⬚ ▱ ✂ ⬚ ◆ P ▶ ✿ ⬚ SP ▥

IKEN, Suffolk Map ref 3C2

★★★★
1 Unit
Sleeping 6

THE OLD STABLE
The Anchorage, Church Lane, Iken, Woodbridge IP12 2ES
Contact: Mrs Gunilla Hailes, The Anchorage, Church Lane,
Iken, Woodbridge IP12 2ES
T: (01728) 688263 (9am-9pm also answerphone)
F: (01728) 688262

Luxury converted stable/coach house, sleeps 4-6, overlooking the historic Iken church. Unrivalled views over tidal views over tidal River Alde. Ideally situated for Snape Maltings, Aldeburgh, Orford and Woodbridge. Excellent walking cycling and bird-watching. Slipway available for dinghy launch.

Weekend breaks available
from £70 per night.

Low season per wk
£330.00–£380.00
High season per wk
£450.00–£500.00

〓 ◎ ⬚ ⅏ ▥ ⊙ ▯ ▣ ▤ TV ⬚ ▱ ⬚ ◆ P ♪ ✿ SP

IPSWICH, Suffolk Map ref 3B2 *Tourist Information Centre Tel: (01473) 258070*

Rating
Applied For
1 Unit
Sleeping 5

MOCKBEGGARS FLAT
Mockbeggars, Claydon, Ipswich IP6 0AH
Contact: Mrs Priscilla Clayton-Mead, Mockbeggars
Hall, Claydon, Ipswich IP6 0AH
T: (01473) 830239
F: (01473) 832989
E: pru@mockbeggars.co.uk
I: www.mockbeggars.co.uk

OPEN Jun–Dec
CC: Barclaycard, Delta,
JCB, Mastercard, Solo,
Switch, Visa

Low season per wk
£199.00–£250.00
High season per wk
£260.00–£420.00

Recently converted coaching stables creating a comfortable first floor flat. Ideal location for visiting Suffolk. Set in rural surroundings, in grounds of B&B. Brochure available.

Ⓜ〓 ◎ ▥ ⊙ ▯ ▣ ▤ TV ⬚ ▱ ⬚ ⬚ ∥ ◆ ✿ SP

KESSINGLAND, Suffolk Map ref 3C1

★★★
1 Unit
Sleeping 5

KEW COTTAGE
44 Church Road, Kessingland, Lowestoft NR33 7QT
Contact: Mrs J Gill, 46 St Georges Avenue, Northampton
NN2 6JA
T: (01604) 717301 (after 6.00 p.m) & 791424
(answer phone/fax)
F: (01604) 791424
E: b.s.g.@btinternet.com

Modernised 2-bedroomed semi-detached cottage in the middle of village, 10 minutes' walk from the sea. Large back garden with patio area. Sleeps 4-5. Norfolk Broads 3 miles, Lowestoft 3 miles, Southwold 5 miles.

OPEN Feb–Nov

Low season per wk
£160.00–£180.00
High season per wk
Max £235.00

〓 ◎ ⅏ ⊙ ▯ ▣ ▤ TV ⬚ ▱ ⬚ ◆ ✿

TOWN INDEX
This can be found at the back of this guide. If you know where you want to stay, the index will give you the page number listing accommodation in your chosen town, city or village.

KING'S LYNN, Norfolk Map ref 3B1 *Tourist Information Centre Tel: (01553) 763044*

★★★

1 Unit
Sleeping 5

GRANERY
Manor House, Churchgate Way, Terrington St Clement,   OPEN All year round
King's Lynn PE34 4LZ
Contact: Mrs Ann Jones, Manor House,
Churchgate Way, Terrington St Clement, King's Lynn
PE34 4LZ
T: (01553) 828700 (answer machine)

Low season per wk
£175.00–£250.00
High season per wk
£300.00–£350.00

*A 19thC conversion next to manor house (seen on TV's House Detectives) and
Cathedral of the Fens. Eat vegetables and fruit from walled garden. Dogs and horses
welcome.*

KNAPTON, Norfolk Map ref 3C1

★★★★

1 Unit
Sleeping 4

CORNERSTONE COTTAGE
The Street, Knapton, North Walsham NR28 0AD
Contact: Mr & Mrs Eves, Cornerstone House, The Street,
Knapton, North Walsham NR28 0AD
T: (01263) 722884 & 07780 612254
I: www.broadland.com/cornerstone

*Attractive, beamed cottage set in rural village.
1.5 miles from sandy beaches. Eight miles from
Broads and National Trust properties. Ideal for
walking, cycling and bird-watching.
Accommodation for 4 in 1 double and 1 twin
room. Ample storage for cycles. Short breaks
available and last minute bookings.*

OPEN Apr–Sep &
Christmas

Low season per wk
£120.00–£180.00
High season per wk
£180.00–£300.00

LAVENHAM, Suffolk Map ref 3B2

★★★★

5 Units
Sleeping 2–6

THE GROVE
Priory Green, Edwardstone, Lavenham, Sudbury CO10 5PP
T: (01787) 211115
F: (01787) 211220
E: stefanie@edwardstone.demon.co.uk
I: www.grove-cottages.co.uk
Contact: Mr & Mrs Mark Scott & Stefanie Wege

*Our 300-year-old, romantic farm cottages set in
beautiful countryside, combine authentic rural
character with the convenience of modern
amenities. Ancient beams, an old baking oven
and copper kettle, open fires, period farmhouse
furniture, original brick and wood floors
transport you back in time. Bikes are free, canoes
available.*

OPEN All year round
CC: Mastercard

Low season per wk
£150.00–£240.00
High season per wk
£299.00–£600.00

CHECK THE MAPS
The colour maps at the front of this guide show
all the cities, towns and villages for which you will
find accommodation entries. Refer to the town
index to find the page on which they are listed.

★★★★★

1 Unit
Sleeping 4

Superbly converted coach house in the centre of the medieval village of Lavenham. Two bedrooms with bathrooms, first floor living area with stunning views down Lady Street of the Market Place and Guildhall. Dishwasher, washer/dryer, TV, hi-fi, video and CD library. Private garden with barbecue. Linen included.

THE HAYLOFT

Lady Street, Lavenham, Sudbury CO10 9RA
Contact: Mrs Annabel Jackson, Market House,
Market Place, Lavenham, Sudbury CO10 9QZ
T: (01787) 249129 (Hayloft Lettings) & 249122 (Private)
F: (01787) 249122
E: annabeljjackson@hotmail.com
I: www.thehayloft.net

OPEN All year round

Much more information on our website.

Low season per wk
£275.00
High season per wk
£280.00–£530.00

★★★

1 Unit
Sleeping 6

OLD WETHERDEN HALL
Hitcham, Ipswich IP7 7PZ
T: (01449) 740574 & 07798 728406 (Mobile)
F: (01449) 740574
E: farm@weatherdenhall.force9.co.uk
Contact: Mrs J Elsden

OPEN All year round

Low season per wk
Min £185.00
High season per wk
Max £350.00

360-acre arable farm. Recently restored 15thC oak-beamed moated hall, fully modernised. Beautiful secluded setting, large garden, abundance of wildlife.

★★★

4 Units
Sleeping 4–6

QUAKERS YARD
Water Street, Lavenham, Sudbury CO10 9RW
Contact: Mr David Aldous, Two A's Hoggards Green,
Stanningfield, Bury St Edmunds IP29 4RG
T: (01284) 827271

OPEN All year round
CC: Barclaycard, Delta,
Mastercard, Switch, Visa

Low season per wk
£180.00–£220.00
High season per wk
£250.00–£375.00

Two bungalows and 2 cottage-style units in Lavenham, set in landscaped gardens and with off-road parking. Open all year. Short breaks available.

★★★

2 Units
Sleeping 2–4

THE LOOSEBOX & THE OLD STABLES
The Villa, High Street, Laxfield, Woodbridge IP13 8DU
Contact: Mr & Mrs John & Jane Reeve, Laxfield Leisure
Ltd, High Street, Laxfield, Woodbridge IP13 8DU
T: (01986) 798019 (answerphone)
F: (01986) 798019
E: laxfieldleisure@talk21.com

OPEN All year round

Low season per wk
£160.00–£250.00
High season per wk
£245.00–£365.00

The Old Stables (sleeps 4), and The Loose Box (sleeps 2), are listed properties in the village centre. Superb modern conversions retaining all their character.

★★★★

1 Unit
Sleeping 3

STABLE COTTAGE
Little Henham Hall, Little Henham,
Saffron Walden CB11 3XR
Contact: Mrs Kate Muskett, Little Henham Hall,
Little Henham, Saffron Walden CB11 3XR
T: (01279) 850228
F: (01279) 850397

OPEN All year round

Low season per wk
£200.00–£250.00
High season per wk
£200.00–£250.00

Renovated and modernised cottage, once a Victorian stable, situated within farm complex overlooking open farmland. Beautiful local walks and delightful villages nearby.

RATING All accommodation in this guide has been rated, or is awaiting a rating, by a trained English Tourism Council assessor.

LITTLE WALDEN, Essex Map ref 2D1

★★★
4 Units
Sleeping 2–4

ORCHARD VIEW NUMBERS 1-4
Little Bowsers Farm, Bowsers Lane, Little Walden,
Saffron Walden CB10 1XQ
Contact: Mrs Maureen Chapman-Barker, Little Bowsers
Farm, Bowsers Lane, Little Walden, Saffron Walden
CB10 1XQ
T: (01799) 527315
F: (01799) 527315
E: sales@farmerkit.co.uk
I: www.farmerkit.co.uk

OPEN All year round

High season per wk
£200.00–£250.00

Little Bowsers Farm is a 30 acre organic holding. The farm produces free range organic eggs. There are apple, plum, pear and cherry orchards planted over the past 3 years.

LONG MELFORD, Suffolk Map ref 3B2

★★★★
1 Unit
Sleeping 4

Delightful Grade II Listed flint cottage in the heart of this historic and picturesque village. Recently renovated, retaining many traditional features. Attractively furnished to high levels of comfort. Secluded garden backing onto meadowlands. All amenities in the village are close by, including restaurants and shops.

HOPE COTTAGE
Little St Marys, Long Melford CO10 9LG
Contact: Ms S Jamil, 219 Parkwood Drive, Sudbury
CO10 1LX
T: (01787) 310199 & 07970 808701 (Mobile)
F: (01787) 310199
E: sns.jam@tesco.net
I: www.hope-cottage-suffolk.co.uk

OPEN All year round

Short breaks available all
year (subject to availability
in high season).

Low season per wk
£205.00
High season per wk
£220.00–£325.00

MARTHAM, Norfolk Map ref 3C1

★★★
1 Unit
Sleeping 5

GREENSIDE COTTAGE
32 The Green, Martham, Great Yarmouth NR29 4PA
Contact: Mrs B I Dyball, Greenside, 30 The Green,
Martham, Great Yarmouth NR29 4PA
T: (01493) 740375

OPEN All year round

Low season per wk
£140.00–£200.00
High season per wk
£200.00–£330.00

Part-thatched cottage overlooking village green. Fitted kitchen, shower with hand basin and toilet, double bedroom (3 beds) single bedroom, lounge and lounge/diner. No pets.

NARBOROUGH, Norfolk Map ref 3B1

★★★★
2 Units
Sleeping 2–4

CHURCH FARM HOLIDAY HOMES
Church Farm, Narborough, King's Lynn PE32 1TE
T: (01760) 337696 & 07801 641570 (mobile)
F: (01760) 337858
E: nickystlawrence@ouvip.com
I: www.churchfarmholidayhomes.com
Contact: Mrs Nicky St Lawrence

OPEN All year round

Low season per wk
Min £220.00
High season per wk
Max £350.00

Two self-catering farm cottages, sleeping 2 and 4, alongside River Nar. Wood-burners, beams and 4-poster beds. Private swimming and beach hut facility. Horses/dogs welcome.

MAP REFERENCES
The map references refer to the colour maps at the front of this guide. The first figure is the map number; the letter and figure which follow indicate the grid reference on the map.

NEWMARKET, Suffolk Map ref 3B2 *Tourist Information Centre Tel: (01638) 667200*

★★★★
1 Unit
Sleeping 6

LA HOGUE COTTAGE
Chippenham, Ely CB7 5PZ
Contact: Mr & Mrs J M Tilbrook, La Hogue Hall,
Chippenham, Ely CB7 5PZ
T: (01638) 750433 & 712253
F: (01638) 712833
E: r.tilbrook@farming.co.uk

*Very spacious renovated farm cottage with log
fire and comfortable accommodation
overlooking fields. Close to many places of
historic and sporting interest. Ideally situated 2
miles from Newmarket in a quiet, rural setting.
Perfect for holidays, race weeks and sales.*

OPEN All year round

Low season per wk
£380.00–£450.00
High season per wk
£450.00–£500.00

★★★★
1 Unit
Sleeping 2

SWALLOWS REST
6 Ditton Green, Woodditton, Newmarket CB8 9SQ
T: (01638) 730823
F: (01638) 731767
Contact: Mrs Gill Woodward

OPEN Mar–Nov

Low season per wk
£150.00–£180.00
High season per wk
£180.00–£220.00

*Comfortable annexe off owners' secluded property in quiet rural village 3 miles
Newmarket. Own entrance and garden. Pub with food 400 yards. Country walks.
Cambridge 20 minutes.*

NORFOLK BROADS

See under Beccles, Hickling, Horning, Norwich, Salle, Sprowston, Stalham, Wroxham

NORWICH, Norfolk Map ref 3C1 *Tourist Information Centre Tel: (01603) 666071*

★★★
1 Unit
Sleeping 5

30 KINGSLEY ROAD
Norwich NR1 3RB
Contact: Miss Sally Clarke, 3 Kingsley Road, Norwich
NR1 3RB
T: (01603) 615819
F: (01603) 615819
E: kingsley@paston.co.uk

OPEN All year round

Low season per wk
£285.00–£300.00
High season per wk
£365.00

*Spacious and quiet city centre Edwardian 3-bedroomed house near bus station.
Central heating and bed linen included. First floor bath/WC, ground floor shower/WC.
Small garden.*

ORFORD, Suffolk Map ref 3C2

★★★
1 Unit
Sleeping 6

41 DAPHNE ROAD
Orford, Woodbridge IP12 2NH
Contact: Mrs Phyllida Flint, Green Lane House,
Castle Green, Orford, Woodbridge IP12 2NF
T: (01394) 450159
F: (01394) 450827

OPEN All year round

Low season per wk
£255.00–£330.00
High season per wk
£380.00–£470.00

*Comfortable, well appointed end-of-terrace cottage, close all village amenities. Open
fire, oil central heating. Lovely secluded enclosed garden.*

★★★
1 Unit
Sleeping 5

47 DAPHNE ROAD
Orford, Woodbridge IP12 2NH
Contact: Mrs Sheila Hitchcock, Church Farm Cottage,
Sudbourne, Woodbridge IP12 2BP
T: (01394) 450714
F: (01394) 450714
E: barryhitchcock@compuserve.com

OPEN All year round

Low season per wk
£175.00–£250.00
High season per wk
£300.00–£375.00

*Delightful 3-bedroomed Edwardian cottage in centre of village. Quiet road near River
Alde. Electric heating and open fire. Unrestricted parking.*

CONFIRM YOUR BOOKING
You are advised to confirm your booking in writing.

OVERSTRAND, Norfolk Map ref 3C1

★★★–★★★★

5 Units
Sleeping 4–7

Poppyland offers 7 individual award-winning properties, 5 in the fishing village of Overstrand, close to its safe sandy beaches and amenities and 2 in Wickmere, 7 miles from Sheringham in the heart of unspoilt rural North Norfolk surrounded by open countryside. Ideal walking, cycling and birdwatching.

POPPYLAND HOLIDAY COTTAGES

High Street, Overstrand, Cromer NR27 0AB
Contact: Mrs T Riches, Poppyland Holiday Cottages,
21 Regent Street, Wickmere, Norwich NR11 7ND
T: (01263) 577473
F: (01265) 570087
E: poppyland@totalise.co.uk
I: www.broadland.com/poppyland

OPEN All year round
CC: Barclaycard, Delta, Mastercard, Solo, Switch, Visa

Low season per wk
£165.00–£245.00
High season per wk
£275.00–£499.00

PELDON, Essex Map ref 3B3

★★★★

1 Unit
Sleeping 6

Self-catering annexe to a converted barn-type property, in 4 acres. Five Lakes Country Club golf 10 minutes, Colchester 10 minutes, beach 5 minutes. Brochure available. Rose Barn Cottage is 50 yards from the famous Peldon Rose Inn, a 600-year-old inn with a renowned kitchen.

ROSE BARN COTTAGE

Rose Barn, Mersea Road, Peldon, Colchester CO5 7QJ
Contact: Mrs A Everett, Rose Barn, Mersea Road, Peldon,
Colchester CO5 7QJ
T: (01206) 735317
F: (01206) 735311
E: everettaj@aol.com

OPEN All year round

Low season per wk
£200.00–£250.00
High season per wk
£200.00–£375.00

RINGSTEAD, Norfolk Map ref 3B1

★★★★

1 Unit
Sleeping 4

BREW HOUSE BARN
Gin Trap Inn, Ringstead, Hunstanton PE36 5JU
T: (01485) 525264
E: margaret@gintrap.co.uk
I: www.gintrap.co.uk
Contact: Mrs M Harmes

17thC Brew House Barn is set apart from the pub and has its own parking and separate entrance with an enclosed patio area.

OPEN All year round

Low season per wk
£250.00–£295.00
High season per wk
£300.00–£425.00

SAFFRON WALDEN, Essex Map ref 2D1 *Tourist Information Centre Tel: (01799) 510444*

★★

1 Unit
Sleeping 4

THE BARN
Burntwood End, Little Walden, Saffron Walden
CB10 1XE
Contact: Mr John Goose, Burntwood End,
Little Walden, Saffron Walden CB10 1XE
T: (01799) 523202 & (01638) 730518 (Katie-daughter)
E: john.goose@aventis.com

Very quietly situated barn conversion in the countryside, approximately 1 mile from Little Walden (excellent pub), 4 miles from Saffron Walden and only 20 minutes from Cambridge. About 1 hour from London by road or rail.

OPEN All year round

Low season per wk
Min £140.00
High season per wk
Max £260.00

IMPORTANT NOTE Information on accommodation listed in this guide has been supplied by the proprietors. As changes may occur you are advised to check details at the time of booking.

★★★★
1 Unit
Sleeping 6

NEWHOUSE FARM
Walden Road, Radwinter, Saffron Walden CB10 2SP
T: (01799) 599211
F: (01799) 599967
E: emmaredcliffe@hotmail.com
Contact: Mrs Emma Redcliffe

OPEN All year round

Low season per wk
£250.00–£350.00
High season per wk
£350.00–£450.00

60-acre farm. Elizabethan/Georgian farmhouse with extensive grounds and traditional yard where 2 converted brick buildings provide cosy and attractive accommodation.

ST ALBANS, Hertfordshire Map ref 2D1 *Tourist Information Centre Tel: (01727) 864511*

★★★★
1 Unit
Sleeping 2

THE HOLLIES

11 Spencer Place, Sandridge, St Albans AL4 9DW
T: (01727) 859845
E: martin.newbury@ntlworld.co.uk
Contact: Mrs Anne Newbury

Delightful self-contained ground floor annexe attached to owner's home. Pretty double bedroom, shower room/WC and sunny kitchen/ diner. The lounge has French doors on to patio, leading to large, peaceful garden which guests are welcome to enjoy. Close to countryside yet only 2.5 miles from historic St Albans.

OPEN All year round

Low season per wk
Max £260.00
High season per wk
Max £260.00

SALLE, Norfolk Map ref 3B1

★★★
1 Unit
Sleeping 4

COACHMAN'S COTTAGE

Salle Place, Salle, Norwich NR10 4SF
Contact: Mrs Glynis Pratt, Walk Gates Cottages, Salle, Norwich NR10 4SF
T: (01603) 870417 & (020) 7584 5047

Small, typical Norfolk coachman's cottage, in lovely grounds with orchard, wood, lawns, stream and half moat. Wood-burning stove. Heating by night storage heaters. Ideal holiday accommodation.

OPEN All year round

Low season per wk
£110.00–£180.00
High season per wk
£190.00–£250.00

SANDRINGHAM, Norfolk Map ref 3B1

★★★★
1 Unit
Sleeping 9

FOLK ON THE HILL

Mill Cottage, Mill Road, Dersingham,
King's Lynn PE31 6HY
Contact: Mrs L Skerritt, Mill Cottage, Mill Road,
Dersingham, King's Lynn PE31 6HY
T: (01485) 544411 (Answerphone) &
07798 946334 (Mobile)
E: lili@skerritt-euwe.freeserve.co.uk

An 18thC coach house in carrstone, recently restored in original pine. Overlooks quiet, undulating countryside against a backcloth of sea and sky. A private courtyard faces south and west. Gardens and paddock offer further retreat and relaxation. Children are a focus. A beach hut is available at Old Hunstanton.

OPEN All year round

Special 3 day breaks-prices negotiable.

Low season per wk
£390.00–£440.00
High season per wk
£500.00–£750.00

★★–★★★
3 Units
Sleeping 2–6

Snape Maltings is a unique collection of Victorian granaries and malthouses set on the River Alde – now housing a variety of shops, galleries and restaurants, and famous as home to the Aldeburgh Festival. Three cottages and one flat have been tastefully converted to make an ideal base for touring the Suffolk coast.

SNAPE MALTINGS
Snape, Saxmundham IP17 1SR
Contact: Ms Dawn Hannan, Administrator, Snape Maltings, Snape, Saxmundham IP17 1SR
T: (01728) 688303
F: (01728) 688930
E: dawn@snapemaltings.co.uk
I: www.snapemaltings.co.uk

OPEN All year round
CC: Amex, Barclaycard, Delta, Mastercard, Switch, Visa

Low season per wk
£215.00–£340.00
High season per wk
£350.00–£540.00

★★★
1 Unit
Sleeping 6

THE HAVEN
31 Nelson Road, Sheringham NR26 8BX
Contact: Mrs P Pilkington, 2 Moorgreen, Newthorpe, Nottingham NG16 2FB
T: (01773) 763010

OPEN All year round

Low season per wk
£180.00–£275.00
High season per wk
£270.00–£345.00

Detached holiday dorma bungalow in own grounds with parking. Comfortably furnished, within easy reach of all local amenities.

★★★★
2 Units
Sleeping 4

VICTORIA COURT
Cliff Road, Sheringham NR26 8BJ
Contact: Mr Graham Simmons, Camberley, 62 Cliff Road, Sheringham NR26 8BJ
T: (01263) 823101
F: (01263) 821433

OPEN All year round

Low season per wk
£170.00–£285.00
High season per wk
£315.00–£430.00

Two immaculate fully-equipped apartments, each sleeping 4, enjoying excellent coastal and sea views. Direct access to beach. Safe parking in own grounds.

★★★★
1 Unit
Sleeping 6

THE GRANARY
Croft Farm, Snape, Saxmundham IP17 1QU
Contact: Mrs Sally Gillett, Croft Farm, Snape, Saxmundham IP17 1QU
T: (01728) 688254
E: e.r.gillett@btinternet.com

OPEN Aug–Dec

Low season per wk
£450.00–£550.00
High season per wk
£580.00–£620.00

Converted to a spacious cottage of exceptional standards, the Granary has its own patio and fenced garden area. Peaceful location with access to farm walks.

★★★★
3 Units
Sleeping 2–4

VALLEY FARM BARNS
Aldeburgh Road, Snape, Saxmundham IP17 1QH
T: (01728) 689071
E: chrisvalleyfarm@aol.com
Contact: C Nicholson

OPEN All year round

Low season per wk
£200.00–£260.00
High season per wk
£295.00–£395.00

Cottages formed from conversion of thatched, timber framed 16thC barn and associated buildings.

QUALITY ASSURANCE SCHEME
Star ratings were correct at the time of going to press but are subject to change. Please check at the time of booking.

SNETTISHAM, Norfolk Map ref 3B1

★★★
1 Unit
Sleeping 5

CARPENTERS LODGE
6 Norton Hill, Snettisham, King's Lynn PE31 7LZ
Contact: Mr N Madgett, Carpenters Bungalow,
6 Norton Hill, Snettisham, King's Lynn PE31 7LZ
T: (01485) 541580
E: nmmadgett@hotmail.com
I: www.carpenterslodge.co.uk

OPEN Mar–Oct

Low season per wk
£210.00–£240.00
High season per wk
£270.00–£340.00

Unique self-contained property in picturesque, peaceful location. Outdoor heated pool, galleried main bedroom, large lounge with open fire. Close Sandringham, bird reserves and beaches.

★★★
1 Unit
Sleeping 4

CURSONS COTTAGE
Lynn Road, Snettisham, King's Lynn PE31 7LW
Contact: Mrs A Campbell, Craven House, Lynn Road,
Snettisham, King's Lynn PE31 7LW
T: (01485) 541179 & 535678
F: (01485) 543259
E: ian.averilcampbell@btinternet.com

OPEN All year round

Low season per wk
£170.00–£250.00
High season per wk
£275.00–£350.00

Attractive and comfortable stone cottages in centre of by-passed village. Near Sandringham and north-west Norfolk heritage coastline. Sensitively modernised to retain character.

SOUTH MIMMS, Hertfordshire Map ref 2D1

★★–★★★
3 Units
Sleeping 2–6

THE BLACK SWAN
62-64 Blanche Lane, South Mimms,
Potters Bar EN6 3PD
T: (01707) 644180
F: (01707) 642344
Contact: Mr W A Marsterson

OPEN All year round

Low season per wk
£145.00–£205.00
High season per wk
£185.00–£290.00

Cottage and self-contained flats, 16thC listed building. Rail connections at Potters Bar and London Underground at Barnet allow travel to London within 45 minutes.

SOUTHWOLD, Suffolk Map ref 3C2

★★★
1 Unit
Sleeping 8

HARBOUR COTTAGE
40 Ferry Road, Southwold IP18
Contact: Mrs S E Harris, 2 Ullswater, Carlton Colville,
Lowestoft NR33 8WG
T: (01502) 513658 & 07860 426559 (Mobile)

OPEN All year round

Low season per wk
£325.00–£350.00
High season per wk
£475.00–£525.00

A 4-bedroom cottage, sleeping 8, with garden gate opening to dunes and beach. Close to picturesque harbour, golf course and town centre. Full gas-fired central heating.

★★
1 Unit
Sleeping 6

HORSESHOE COTTAGE
7 Lorne Road, Southwold IP18 6EP
Contact: Debbie & Jennifer Frost & Tallon, Accountants,
Acanthus Property Letting Services, 9 Trinity Street,
Southwold IP18 6JH
T: (01502) 724033 & 722806
F: (01502) 725168
E: sales@southwold-holidays.co.uk
I: www.southwold-holidays.co.uk

OPEN All year round
CC: Amex, Barclaycard,
Mastercard, Visa

Low season per wk
£260.00–£350.00
High season per wk
£350.00–£450.00

A comfortable family house with views over South Green. Near to sea, shops and common. Small yard at rear. Open fire and new kitchen 2001.

★★
1 Unit
Sleeping 4

THE LITTLE BLUE HOUSE
26 East Street, Southwold IP18
Contact: Mrs Diana Wright, The Kiln, The Folley,
Layer-de-la-Haye, Colchester CO2 0HZ
T: (01206) 738003

OPEN All year round

Low season per wk
£220.00–£250.00
High season per wk
£260.00–£355.00

Small, cosy cottage close to shops and seafront with an attractive enclosed paved garden at the rear. Sleeps 2 adults and 2 children.

SOUTHWOLD continued

★★★★
1 Unit
Sleeping 12

SHELL HOUSE
25 North Parade, Southwold IP18 6LT
Contact: Mrs Elisabeth Fairs, Home Farm,
Heveningham, Halesworth IP19 0EL
T: (01986) 798250 (business and home) & 798240
F: (01986) 798754

OPEN All year round

Low season per wk
Min £600.00
High season per wk
Max £950.00

Lovely, spacious seafront house, sleeps 12 and 2 cots. No pets. Private parking, gas central heating, linen, electricity all included. Aga. Stairlift. 3 bathrooms. Enclosed patio. No smoking. Weekends available.

🎠 ⊙ 𝄞 ▥ ⌁ ⊙ 🗔 ▭ 🖥 TV 🔌 🗄 🛎 🖩 ⌫ 🖵 🖳 P ✿ SP

SPROWSTON, Norfolk Map ref 3C1

★★
1 Unit
Sleeping 4

HOLME
3 Recreation Ground Road, Sprowston,
Norwich NR7 8EN
Contact: Mrs P Guyton, 2 Recreation Ground Road,
Sprowston, Norwich NR7 8EN
T: (01603) 465703

OPEN All year round

Low season per wk
£120.00–£145.00
High season per wk
£155.00–£200.00

Traditional, detached bungalow 2 miles north of Norwich. Non-smoking accommodation consists of 2 twin bedrooms, lounge, kitchen/diner, bathroom. Enclosed garden with patio furniture.

🎠8 Ⓜ ▦ ▥ ⊙ ▭ 🖥 TV 🛎 ⌫ 🖵 🖳 🚗 P ✿ SP

STALHAM, Norfolk Map ref 3C1

★★
1 Unit
Sleeping 4

144 BROADSIDE CHALET PARK
Stalham, Norwich NR12 9PN
Contact: Mr J J Crawford, 5 Collingwood Avenue,
Surbiton KT5 9PT
T: (020) 8241 0658 & 8337 4487
F: (020) 8241 0658
E: crawfcall@compuserve.com
I: www.norfolkholiday.co.uk

OPEN Mar–Oct

Low season per wk
£75.00–£125.00
High season per wk
£125.00–£199.00

South-facing, detached chalet on landscaped park, with pleasant lawns for quiet relaxation or where children may play safely. Swimming pool, licensed club, shop. 4 miles to Blue Flag beach.

🎠 Ⓜ ◎ ▦ ⊙ ▭ 🖥 TV 🔌 🛎 🖩 ☒ ⚲ ∪ 🏊 ♪ ✿ 🐎 SP

STIFFKEY, Norfolk Map ref 3B1

★★
1 Unit
Sleeping 5

HAWTHORNS
Holly Road, Stiffkey, Wells-next-the-Sea NR23 1QE
Contact: Mrs M C Hickey-Smith, 18 Poplar Road,
Histon, Cambridge CB4 9LN
T: (01223) 572316
E: hawthorns_norfolk@hotmail.com

OPEN Apr–Oct

Low season per wk
Min £140.00
High season per wk
Max £300.00

Chalet in peaceful, rural location, 1 minute's walk from the coast. Comfortable accommodation with 3 bedrooms, kitchen, bathroom with shower, sitting/dining room and garden.

🎠 Ⓜ ◎ ▦ ⊙ ▭ TV 🛎 ⌫ ☒ 🚗 P ✿ 🐎 SP

STOWMARKET, Suffolk Map ref 3B2 *Tourist Information Centre Tel: (01449) 676800*

★★★★
5 Units
Sleeping 2–3

Immaculate, spacious cottages for two people amidst 4 acres of peaceful and tranquil surroundings in the heart of the Suffolk countryside. Cottages fully equipped and owner maintained. Ideally situated for exploring Constable country, Lavenham, Southwold and the Heritage Coast.

BARN COTTAGES

Goldings, East End Lane, Stonham Aspal,
Stowmarket IP14 6AS
Contact: Mrs M Tydeman, Goldings, East End Lane,
Stonham Aspal, Stowmarket IP14 6AS
T: (01449) 711229 (Business Number)
E: maria@barncottages.co.uk
I: www.barncottages.co.uk

OPEN All year round

Low season per wk
£140.00–£260.00
High season per wk
£260.00–£298.00

Ⓜ 🎠 ◎ ▦ ▥ ⊙ ▭ TV 🗄 🛎 🖩 🚗 P ∪ ✿ 🐎 ⚲ SP

SWANTON MORLEY, Norfolk Map ref 3B1

★★★

2 Units
Sleeping 4

TEAL AND HERON COTTAGE
Waterfall Farm Cottages, Worthing Road,
Swanton Morley, East Dereham NR20 4QD
Contact: Mrs Sally Marsham, Waterfall Farm,
Worthing Road, Swanton Morley, East Dereham
NR20 4QD
T: (01362) 637300 & 0797 4395571 (Mobile)
F: (01362) 637300

OPEN All year round

Low season per wk
Min £165.00
High season per wk
£195.00–£240.00

The cottages were converted from farm buildings. Fully equipped. Both sleep 4, 1 double, 1 twin. No smoking. A small holding with goats, hens, small pets-hands on.

TATTERSETT, Norfolk Map ref 31B

★★★-★★★★★

5 Units
Sleeping 4–6

TAT VALLEY HOLIDAY COTTAGES
Lower Farm, Tattersett, King's Lynn PE31 8RT
T: (01485) 528506
E: enquiries@norfolkholidayhomes.co.uk
I: www.norfolkholidayhomes.co.uk
Contact: Mr T W Hurn

These 5 luxury barn conversions offer accommodation to the highest standards, whilst retaining many original features. A large games barn with facilities for all ages is an added bonus for this tranquil setting. Tatt Valley Cottages are situated on a working farm in beautiful North Norfolk near to Burnham Market and the Norfolk coast.

OPEN All year round

3-night stays available
Oct–Mar (excl holiday
periods).

Low season per wk
£183.00–£247.00
High season per wk
£351.00–£460.00

THAXTED, Essex Map ref 3B2

★★★★

2 Units
Sleeping 4

THAXTED HOLIDAY COTTAGES
Totmans Farm, Dunmow Road, Thaxted,
Dunmow CM6 2LU
T: (01371) 830233
E: enquiries@thaxtedholidaycottages.co.uk
I: www.thaxtedholidaycottages.co.uk
Contact: Mrs Yolanda De Bono

Converted from an old farm building, Mill View and Orchard Cottage are well placed in an elevated rural position on the edge of town. Excellent views can be enjoyed of Thaxted's cathedral-like church and windmill. Private patio and use of 2.5 acre meadow. Shops, pubs and public transport a few minutes' walk.

OPEN All year round

Short stays available. Special
prices for long stay.

Low season per wk
Min £200.00
High season per wk
Max £400.00

THORNHAM, Norfolk Map ref 3B1

★★★-★★★★★

7 Units
Sleeping 4–8

MANOR FARM COTTAGES
Ringstead Road, Thornham, Hunstanton PE36 6NN
Contact: Mr/Mrs M Goddard, Manor Farm House,
Thornham, Hunstanton PE36 6NB
T: (01485) 512272 & 07836 685266
F: (01485) 512241

OPEN All year round

Low season per wk
£185.00–£260.00
High season per wk
£240.00–£495.00

Carefully furnished cottages converted from barns, standing in 6 acres, with wonderful views, in this unspoilt village. Close to beaches, pubs and shop.

CREDIT CARD BOOKINGS If you book by telephone and are asked for your credit card number it is advisable to check the proprietor's policy should you cancel your reservation.

THORNHAM continued

★★★

1 Unit
Sleeping 5

OYSTER COTTAGE
Main Road, Thornham, Hunstanton PE36 6LY
Contact: Mrs G Tibbs, Cole Green Cottage, Sedgeford,
Hunstanton PE36 5LS
T: (01485) 571770 & 07711 569388 (Mobile)
F: (01485) 571770

OPEN All year round

Low season per wk
£130.00–£200.00
High season per wk
£210.00–£295.00

Traditional period flint and brick cottage, in conservation area. Close to RSPB and coastal paths. Well equipped comfortable accommodation. Small walled garden. Pretty village.

THORPENESS, Suffolk Map ref 3C2

★★★★

9 Units
Sleeping 7

Family 2 and 3 bedroomed apartments with sea views. Fully fitted kitchens with dishwasher and washing machine. TV in lounge. Linen, towels, electricity included. Pets, smoking, allowed in some apartments. Discounted tennis and golf facilities. Beach, cycling and wonderful walks make up this perfect holiday. Larger houses in village also available.

THE COUNTRY CLUB APARTMENTS

The Benthills, Thorpeness, Leiston IP16 4NU
Contact: Reception, Thorpeness Golf Club and Hotel
Limited, The Golf Club, Thorpeness, Leiston IP16 4NH
T: (01728) 452176
F: (01728) 453868
E: info@thorpeness.co.uk
I: www.thorpeness.co.uk

OPEN All year round
CC: Barclaycard, Delta,
Mastercard, Solo, Switch,
Visa, Visa Electron

Low season per wk
£200.00–£375.00
High season per wk
£340.00–£680.00

★★★

1 Unit
Sleeping 12

A true family holiday in this wonderfully eccentric 'fantasy unmatched in England'. The House in the Clouds has 5 bedrooms, 3 bathrooms, unrivalled views from the 'Room at the Top'. Play billards, snooker, table tennis, tennis, and boules. Overlooking sea, golf course, Meare and bird-watching on RSPB reserves.

THE HOUSE IN THE CLOUDS

Thorpeness, Leiston IP16 4PD
Contact: Mrs S Le Comber, The House in The Clouds,
4 Hinde House, 14 Hinde Street, London W1U 3BG
T: (0207) 2243615 & 0771 845 5988
F: (020) 7224 3615

OPEN All year round

Low season per wk
£1,160.00–£1,290.00
High season per wk
£1,690.00–£1,880.00

WALSHAM-LE-WILLOWS, Suffolk Map ref 3B2

★★

1 Unit
Sleeping 1–5

Fully modernised 17thC cottage set in pretty Suffolk village with good shops and pubs, 11 miles north east of Bury St Edmunds. Well-behaved pets welcome. Owner managed. Oil central heating, electricity and bed linen included in rent. Tennis court and swimming pool available in summer by arrangement.

BRIDGE COTTAGE

Grove Road, Walsham-le-Willows,
Bury St Edmunds IP31 3AD
Contact: Mrs H M Russell, The Beeches,
Walsham-le-Willows, Bury St Edmunds IP31 3AD
T: (01359) 259227
F: (01359) 258206

OPEN All year round

Low season per wk
Min £200.00
High season per wk
Max £320.00

WELLS-NEXT-THE-SEA, Norfolk Map ref 3B1

★★★

1 Unit
Sleeping 4

HONEYPOT COTTAGE
3 Claxtons Yard, Wells-next-the-Sea NR23 1DB
Contact: Mrs Joan Price, Shingles, Southgate Close,
Wells-next-the-Sea NR23 1HG
T: (01328) 711982 (Answerphone)
F: (01328) 711982
E: walker.al@talk21.com
I: members.tripod.com/honeypothouse

OPEN All year round

Low season per wk
Max £200.00
High season per wk
£300.00–£400.00

Offering comfortable accommodation on the picturesque North Norfolk coast with quaint shopping streets and harbour within easy walking distance. Ideally situated for bird-watching, walking, sightseeing, etc.

WEST RAYNHAM, Norfolk Map ref 3B1

★★

1 Unit
Sleeping 4

24 THE STREET
West Raynham, Fakenham NR21 7AD
Contact: Mrs A M Hook, 19 Northolme Road, Highbury,
London N5 2UZ
T: (020) 7226 9640
F: (020) 7226 9640
E: ammlon@aol.com

OPEN All year round

Low season per wk
£160.00–£200.00
High season per wk
£260.00

Pretty flint cottage in quiet village with 1 double and 2 single rooms. Large orchard and garden at the back. Within reach of sea, birding country.

WEYBOURNE, Norfolk Map ref 3B1

★★★

1 Unit
Sleeping 6

The Coach House, within the grounds of the guesthouse is sympathetically restored and well-equipped. Garden, swimming pool and parking are shared with guesthouse. Evening meals are available by arrangement. Excellent walks are easily accessible on Kelling Heath and coastal footpaths. Patio furniture, dishwasher and microwave are available for your enhanced enjoyment.

THE COACH HOUSE
Rosedale Farm Guesthouse, Holt Road, Weybourne,
Holt NR25 7ST
Contact: Mr & Mrs Charles Lacoste, Rosedale Farm
Guesthouse, Holt Road, Weybourne, Holt NR25 7ST
T: (01263) 588778 & 07760 493538
E: rosedale.lacostes@tinyworld.co.uk
I: www.sheringham-network.co.uk/rosedale

OPEN All year round

3 night mid-week breaks in
winter from £40 per night for
2 incl breakfast. Weekends 2
nights from £50 per night
incl breakfast.

Low season per wk
£140.00–£240.00
High season per wk
£260.00–£420.00

WICKHAM SKEITH, Suffolk Map ref 3B2

★★★

1 Unit
Sleeping 4

THE NETUS
Street Farm, Wickham Skeith, Eye IP23 8LP
Contact: Mrs Joy Homan, Street Farm, Wickham Skeith,
Eye IP23 8LP
T: (01449) 766275 (Answerphone)

OPEN All year round

Low season per wk
£125.00–£175.00
High season per wk
£200.00–£250.00

Single-storey, wheelchair accessible, well-equipped kitchen-cum-living room, bathroom with shower, 2 twin bedrooms sleeping 4. Parking and patio garden. Rural views.

www.travelengland.org.uk
Log on for information and inspiration. The latest information on places to visit, events and quality assessed accommodation.

WISBECH, Cambridgeshire Map ref 3A1 *Tourist Information Centre Tel: (01945) 583263*

★★★★

2 Units
Sleeping 2–4

COMMON RIGHT BARNS
Common Right Farm, Plash Drove, Wisbech St Mary,   OPEN All year round
Wisbech PE13 4SP
T: (01945) 410424 (Answerphone)
F: (01945) 410424
E: teresa@commonrightbarns.co.uk
I: www.commonrightbarns.co.uk
Contact: Mrs T M Fowler

Low season per wk
£160.00–£180.00
High season per wk
£220.00–£360.00

Rurally situated in beamed barn buildings, 2 wheelchair friendly, self-contained cottages with enclosed gardens for 4 and 2 persons. Linen, electricity and heating inclusive.

᠕ ᠔3 ◎ ▥ ⊙ ▤ ▭ ▤ TV ◎ ▰ ▨ ♣ P ✿ ☂ ⚲ SP

WOODBRIDGE, Suffolk Map ref 3C2 *Tourist Information Centre Tel: (01394) 382240*

★★★★

2 Units
Sleeping 6–10

EASTON FARM PARK
Easton, Woodbridge IP13 0EQ   OPEN All year round
Contact: Mr Mark Clixby, Easton Farm Park, Easton,   CC: Barclaycard, Delta,
Woodbridge IP13 0EQ   Mastercard, Switch, Visa,
T: (01728) 746475   Visa Electron
F: (01728) 747861
E: easton@eastonfarmpark.co.uk
I: www.eastonfarmpark.co.uk

Low season per wk
£392.00–£481.00
High season per wk
£511.00–£675.00

Easton Farm Park is a well established visitor attraction set in 35 acres of attractive rural countryside beside the Deben River.

᠕ ᠔ ◎ ▥ ⊙ ▭ ▤ TV ◎ ▰ ✕ ▨ P ⚲ SP ⛪

★★★

1 Unit
Sleeping 2

QUAYSIDE COTTAGE
The Quay, Waldringfield, Woodbridge IP12 4QZ   OPEN All year round
Contact: Mr Richard Leigh, Quayside, The Quay,
Waldringfield, Woodbridge IP12 4QZ
T: (01473) 736724 (home)
E: quayside@waldringfield.org.uk

Low season per wk
£200.00–£250.00
High season per wk
£250.00–£300.00

Single-storey accommodation for two adults in quiet village. Cottage is very comfortably furnished, with double bed. Sunroom with stunning views of river activities.

◎ ▤ ▥ ⊙ ▭ ▤ TV ⚲ ▰ ⛴ ✕ ▨ ♣ P ✿ ⚲ SP

WROXHAM, Norfolk Map ref 3C1

★★★★

4 Units
Sleeping 8–16

DAISY BROAD LODGES
Riverside Road, Wroxham, Norwich NR12 8UD   OPEN All year round
Contact: Mr Daniel Thwaites, Barns Brinkcraft,   CC: Barclaycard, Delta,
Riverside Road, Wroxham, Norwich NR12 8UD   Eurocard, JCB,
T: (01603) 782625 & 782333   Mastercard, Solo, Switch,
F: (01603) 784072   Visa, Visa Electron
E: daniel@barnesbrinkcraft.co.uk
I: www.barnesbrinkcraft.co.uk

Low season per wk
£495.00–£559.00
High season per wk
£645.00–£1,161.00

New in 1998/2000, river frontage, 1st-floor living area, balcony and bedrooms downstairs. Two minutes' walk from village Daylaunch (not Jul/Aug) and sailing dinghy free of charge.

᠔ ∅ ▥ ⊙ ▤ ▭ ▤ TV ⚲ ◎ ▰ ▨ ♣ P ✿ ☂ ⚲ SP

★★★★

1 Unit
Sleeping 6

Built in 1999, the lodge has spacious accommodation with full gas central heating. Three large bedrooms (2 doubles, 1 twin). Two toilets, one with shower and one with bath. Large communal room with kitchen/diner. Lawn to river frontage with own dinghy. Quietly situated but within walking distance of village.

KINGFISHER LODGE

Fineway Cruises, Riverside Road, Wroxham,
Norwich NR12 8UD
Contact: Mrs D Campling, Fineway Cruises,
Riverside Road, Wroxham, Norwich NR12 8UD
T: (01603) 782309
F: (01603) 784838
E: steve@fineway.freeserve.co.uk
I: www.finewayleisure.co.uk

OPEN All year round
CC: Barclaycard, Delta,
Maestro, Mastercard,
Switch, Visa

Low season per wk
Min £310.00
High season per wk
Max £715.00

᠔ ◎ ▥ ⊙ ▤ ▭ ▤ TV ◎ ▰ ▨ ♣ P ✿ ☂ ⚲ SP

★★★

1 Unit
Sleeping 2

WHITEGATES APARTMENT

181 Norwich Road, Wroxham, Norwich NR12 8RZ
T: (01603) 781037
Contact: Mrs CM Youd

Whitegates Apartment is a fully equipped self-catering ground floor apartment with en suite facilities, secure parking, swimming pool, sauna, games room and barbecue. Ten minutes' walk from Wroxham with boat hire and restaurants, 8 miles from Norwich and within easy reach of Great Yarmouth and the North Norfolk coast.

OPEN All year round

3 night stays available.
Oct-Mar incl Christmas and
New Year.

Low season per wk
£200.00–£225.00
High season per wk
£250.00–£285.00

USE YOUR *i*s

There are more than 550 Tourist Information Centres throughout England offering friendly help with accommodation and holiday ideas as well as suggestions of places to visit and things to do. There may well be a centre in your home town which can help you before you set out. You'll find addresses in the local Phone Book.

A brief guide to the main Towns and Villages offering accommodation in the East of England

ALDEBURGH, SUFFOLK - A prosperous port in the 16th C, now famous for the Aldeburgh Music Festival held annually in June. The 16th C Moot Hall, now a museum, is a timber-framed building once used as an open market.

• **ALRESFORD, ESSEX** - Village easily accessible from the Essex Sunshine Coast and Colchester.

BECCLES, SUFFOLK - Fire destroyed the town in the 16th C and it was rebuilt in Georgian red brick. The River Waveney, on which the town stands, is popular with boating enthusiasts and has an annual regatta. Home of Beccles and District Museum.

• **BERKHAMSTED, HERTFORDSHIRE** - Hilltop town on Grand Union Canal surrounded by pleasant countryside and a 1200-acre common. It has remains of an important castle with earthworks and moat. Birthplace of William Cowper, the poet.

• **BILLERICAY, ESSEX** - Site of both Roman and Saxon settlements and a popular overnight stop for Canterbury pilgrims. Historic links with famous Mayflower voyage. Now a flourishing town with a wide variety of sports, leisure and cultural activities and some fine examples of Georgian architecture.

• **BLAKENEY, NORFOLK** - Picturesque village on the north coast of Norfolk and a former port and fishing village. 15th C Guildhall. Marshy creeks extend towards Blakeney Point (National Trust) and are a paradise for naturalists, with trips to the reserve and to see the seals from Blakeney Quay.

• **BRANCASTER, NORFOLK** - On the North Norfolk Coast. One mile from the pebble beach. Close to Holkham Hall and Sandringham. Many nature reserves nearby.

• **BRANCASTER STAITHE, NORFOLK** - Small harbour with a boat service to Scolt Head Island, a bird sanctuary and nature study area.

• **BRANDON, SUFFOLK** - Set on the edge of Thetford Forest in an area known as Breckland. Old stone 5-arched bridge links Suffolk with Norfolk. 3 miles north-east is Grime's Graves, the largest prehistoric flint mine in Europe.

• **BURY ST EDMUNDS, SUFFOLK** - Ancient market and cathedral town which takes its name from the martyred Saxon King, St Edmund. Bury St Edmunds has many fine buildings including the Athenaeum and Moyses Hall, reputed to be the oldest Norman house in the county.

CAMBRIDGE, CAMBRIDGESHIRE - A most important and beautiful city on the River Cam with 31 colleges forming one of the oldest universities in the world. Numerous museums, good shopping centre, restaurants, theatres, cinema and fine bookshops.

• **CASTLE ACRE, NORFOLK** - Remains of castle and priory. Possibly the grandest castle earthworks in England.

• **CASTLE HEDINGHAM, ESSEX** - Here is a splendid Norman keep, built in by the famous deVeres, Earls of Oxford with the finest Norman arch in England. All beside a medieval village with a fine Norman church.

• **CHARSFIELD, SUFFOLK** - This village was the principal model for Akenfield in Ronald Blythe's book of that name. The church is worth visiting to see its glowing red bricks.

• **CLEY NEXT THE SEA, NORFOLK** - Due to land reclamation the village has not been next the sea since the 17th C. Behind the old quay the main street winds between flint-built houses. The marshes between Cley and Salthouse are bird reserves. Cley Windmill is a 160-year-old tower mill converted into a guesthouse.

• **COLCHESTER, ESSEX** - Britain's oldest recorded town standing on the River Colne and famous for its oysters. Numerous historic buildings, ancient remains and museums. Plenty of parks and gardens, extensive shopping centre, theatre and zoo.

• **CROMER, NORFOLK** - Once a small fishing village and now famous for its fishing boats that still work off the beach and offer freshly caught crabs. Excellent bathing on sandy beaches fringed by cliffs. The town boasts a fine pier, theatre, museum and a lifeboat station.

DALLINGHOO, SUFFOLK - Small quiet rural village with an interesting church, 8 miles from Woodbridge.

• **DILHAM, NORFOLK** - Set in beautiful, quiet country in heart of Broadland. Acres to roam over, including Dilham Islands (Victorian Folly).

• **DISS, NORFOLK** - Old market town built around 3 sides of the Mere, a 6-acre stretch of water. Although modernised, some interesting Tudor, Georgian and Victorian buildings around the market-place remain. St Mary's church has a fine knapped flint chancel.

• **DOCKING, NORFOLK** - Conservation village still retaining village stocks, lock-up, blacksmith's forge and ponds. Well situated for the North Norfolk coast 5 miles away.

EAST BERGHOLT, SUFFOLK - John Constable, the famous East Anglian artist, was born here in 1776 and at the church of St Mary are reminders of his family's associations with the area. 1 mile south of the village are Flatford Mill and Willy Lott's cottage, both made famous by Constable in his paintings.

• **EAST HARLING, NORFOLK** - In the heart of Norfolk countryside, near Thetford forest.

• **ELY, CAMBRIDGESHIRE** - Until the 17th C, when the Fens were drained, Ely was an island. The cathedral, completed in 1189, dominates the surrounding area. One particular feature is the central octagonal tower with a fan-vaulted timber roof and wooden lantern.

• **ERPINGHAM, NORFOLK** - Quiet rural setting, yet well placed for Cromer and North Norfolk Coast.

• **EYE, SUFFOLK** - 'Eye' means island and this town was once surrounded by marsh. The fine church of SS Peter and Paul has a tower over 100ft

FELIXSTOWE, SUFFOLK - Seaside resort that developed at the end of the 19th C. Lying in a gently curving bay with a 2-mile-long beach and backed by a wide promenade of lawns and floral gardens.

RATING All accommodation in this guide has been rated, or is awaiting a rating, by a trained English Tourism Council assessor.

- **FOXLEY, NORFOLK** - Small quiet rural village, close to Fakenham and East Dereham.

- **FRINTON-ON-SEA, ESSEX** - Sedate town that developed as a resort at the end of the 19th C and still retains an air of Victorian gentility. Fine sandy beaches, good fishing and golf.

G GREAT DUNMOW, ESSEX - On the main Roman road from Bishop's Stortford to Braintree. Doctor's Pond near the square was where the first lifeboat was tested in 1785. Home of the Dunmow Flitch trials held every 4 years on Whit Monday.

- **GRESHAM, NORFOLK** - A rural village with a round-towered church which has a fine Seven Sacraments font.

H HALSTEAD, ESSEX - Situated close to the Roman city of Colchester and Braintree, Halstead is notable for the Blue Bridge House. A Queen Anne facade was built over the existing Tudor house between 1700 and 1712 and it contains collections of 17th C European furniture.

- **HAUGHLEY, SUFFOLK** - In the heart of Suffolk, very well placed for touring.

- **HEACHAM, NORFOLK** - The portrait of a Red Indian princess who married John Rolfe of Heacham Hall in 1614 appears on the village sign. Caley Mill is the centre of lavender growing.

- **HICKLING, NORFOLK** - Hickling Broad is one of the largest and most popular of all the Broads and is noted for its birds. Nearby is Sutton Windmill, the tallest in the country.

- **HINGHAM, NORFOLK** - Small market town with a 14th C church, 15 miles from Norwich.

- **HITCHAM, SUFFOLK** - Six miles from Lavenham.

- **HOLME NEXT THE SEA, NORFOLK** - At the north end of the Peddar's Way on the West Norfolk Coast.

- **HORNING, NORFOLK** - Riverside village and well-known Broadland centre. Occasional glimpses of the river can be caught between picturesque thatched cottages.

- **HUNSTANTON, NORFOLK** - Seaside resort which faces the Wash. The shingle and sand beach is backed by striped cliffs and many unusual fossils can be found here. The town is predominantly Victorian. The Oasis family leisure centre has indoor and outdoor pools.

I IPSWICH, SUFFOLK - Interesting county town and major port on the River Orwell. Birthplace of Cardinal Wolsey. Christchurch Mansion, set in a fine park, contains a good collection of furniture and pictures, with works by Gainsborough, Constable and Munnings.

K KESSINGLAND, SUFFOLK - Seaside village whose church tower has served as a landmark to sailors for generations. Nearby is the Suffolk Wildlife and Country Park.

- **KING'S LYNN, NORFOLK** - A busy town with many outstanding buildings. The Guildhall and Town Hall are both built of flint in a striking chequer design. Behind the Guildhall in the Old Gaol House the sounds and smells of prison life 2 centuries ago are recreated.

- **KNAPTON, NORFOLK** - The church is visited for the beauty of its roof and font. The former, dated 1504, is 30 ft wide and adorned with a host of angels. The latter is 13th C, built of Purbeck marble and has an interesting Decorative cover.

L LAVENHAM, SUFFOLK - A former prosperous wool town of timber-framed buildings with the cathedral-like church and its tall tower. The market-place is 13th C and the Guildhall now houses a museum.

- **LONG MELFORD, SUFFOLK** - One of Suffolk's loveliest villages, remarkable for the length of its main street. Holy Trinity Church is considered to be the finest village church in England. The National Trust own the Eizabethan Melford Hall and nearby Kentwell Hall is also open to the public.

N NEWMARKET, SUFFOLK - Centre of the English horse-racing world and the headquarters of the Jockey Club and National Stud. Racecourse and horse sales. The National Horse Racing Museum traces the history and development of the Sport of Kings.

- **NORWICH, NORFOLK** - Beautiful cathedral city and county town on the River Wensum with many fine museums and medieval churches. Norman castle, Guildhall and interesting medieval streets. Good shopping centre and market.

O ORFORD, SUFFOLK - Once a thriving port, now a quiet village of brick and timber buildings, famous for its castle. Orford comes to life during the summer when boats tie up at the quay.

- **OVERSTRAND, NORFOLK** - Village with extensive sandy beach. Church of St Martin, built in 14th C but much rebuilt since, has a round tower and ancient oven for baking the sacrament.

S SAFFRON WALDEN, ESSEX - Takes its name from the saffron crocus once grown around the town. The church of St Mary has superb carvings, magnificent roofs and brasses. A town maze can be seen on the common. Two miles south-west is Audley End, a magnificent Jacobean mansion owned by English Heritage.

- **SALLE, NORFOLK** - Pronounced Saul and famous for the magnificent 15th C church of SS Peter and Paul which is considered to be the finest in the county.

- **SANDRINGHAM, NORFOLK** - Famous as the country retreat of Her Majesty the Queen. The house and grounds are open to the public at certain times.

- **SAXMUNDHAM, SUFFOLK** - The church of St John the Baptist has a hammer-beam roof and contains a number of good monuments.

- **SHERINGHAM, NORFOLK** - Holiday resort with Victorian and Edwardian hotels and a sand and shingle beach where the fishing boats are hauled up. The North Norfolk Railway operates from Sheringham station during the summer. Other attractions include museums, theatre and Splash Fun Pool.

- **SNAPE, SUFFOLK** - The Maltings are 19th C buildings built to receive barges of barley, but in 1965 they were converted to an opera house and concert hall. Its situation on the edge of the salt marshes is very beautiful.

- **SNETTISHAM, NORFOLK** - Village with a superb Decorated church. The 17th C Old Hall is a distinguished-looking house with Dutch gables over the 2 bays. Snettisham Pits is a reserve of the Royal Society for the Protection of Birds. Red deer herd and other animals, farm trails and nature walks at Park Farm.

- **SOUTH MIMMS, HERTFORDSHIRE** - Best known today for its location at the junction of the M25 and the A1M.

- **SOUTHWOLD, SUFFOLK** - Pleasant and attractive seaside town with a triangular market square and spacious greens around which stand flint, brick and colour-washed cottages. The parish church of St Edmund is one of the greatest churches in Suffolk.

- **SPROWSTON, NORFOLK** - Two miles north of Norwich, six miles from the Broads.

- **ST ALBANS, HERTFORDSHIRE** - As Verulamium this was one of the largest towns in Roman Britain and its remains can be seen in the museum. The Norman cathedral was built from Roman materials to commemorate Alban, the first British Christian martyr.

- **STALHAM, NORFOLK** - Lies on the edge of the Broads.

- **STIFFKEY, NORFOLK** - A brick and flint village on the edge of the marshes, famous for cockles.

- **STOWMARKET, SUFFOLK** - Small market town where routes converge. There is an open-air museum of rural life at the Museum of East Anglian Life.

- **SWANTON MORLEY, NORFOLK** - All Saints Church, built around 1400, has an eye-catching west tower with large bell-openings at the top. The remains of a cottage belonging to the ancestors of Abraham Lincoln can also be seen.

T THAXTED, ESSEX - Small town rich in outstanding buildings and dominated by its hilltop medieval church. The magnificent Guildhall was built by the Cutlers' Guild in the late 14th C. A windmill built in 1804 has been restored and houses a rural museum.

• **THORPENESS, SUFFOLK** - A planned mock-Tudor seaside resort, built in the early 20th C, with a 65-acre artificial lake. The House in the Clouds was built to disguise a water-tower. The windmill contains an exhibition on Suffolk's heritage coast.

W WALSHAM-LE-WILLOWS, SUFFOLK - Pretty Suffolk village with good shops and pubs. Eleven miles north east of Bury St Edmunds.

• **WELLS-NEXT-THE-SEA, NORFOLK** - Seaside resort and small port on the north coast. The Buttlands is a large tree-lined green surrounded by Georgian houses and from here narrow streets lead to the quay.

• **WEYBOURNE, NORFOLK** - Used as an embarkation point for troops off to France in World War I, Weybourne was a deep-water port of strategic importance. Home of the Muckleburgh collection, the largest collection of World War II military vehicles.

• **WISBECH, CAMBRIDGESHIRE** - The town is the centre of the agricultural and flower-growing industries of Fenland. Peckover House (National Trust) is an important example of domestic architecture.

• **WOODBRIDGE, SUFFOLK** - Once a busy seaport, the town is now a sailing centre on the River Deben. There are many buildings of architectural merit including the Bell and Angel Inns. The 18th C Tide Mill is now restored and open to the public.

• **WROXHAM, NORFOLK** - Yachting centre on the River Bure which houses the headquarters of the Norfolk Broads Yacht Club. The church of St Mary has a famous doorway and the manor house nearby dates back to 1623.

The *Safeway*
Excellence in England
AWARDS 2002

Safeway

EXCELLENCE
IN ENGLAND
Awards for Tourism

ENGLISH TOURISM COUNCIL

GNER

The Safeway Excellence in England Awards are all about blowing English tourism's trumpet and telling the world what a fantastic place England is to visit, whether it's for a two week holiday, a weekend break or a day trip.

Formerly called England for Excellence, the Awards are now in their 13th year and are run by the English Tourism Council in association with England's ten regional tourist boards. There are 13 categories including B&B of the Year, Hotel of the Year and Visitor Attraction of the Year. New for 2002 are Short Break Destination of the Year and Most Improved Seaside Resort.

Winners of the 2002 awards will receive their trophies at a fun and festive event to be held on St George's Day (23 April) at the Royal Opera House in London. The day will not only celebrate excellence in tourism but also Englishness in all its diversity.

For a truly exceptional experience, look out for accommodation and attractions displaying a Safeway Excellence in England Award from April 2002 onwards.

Safeway, one of the UK's leading food retailers, is delighted to be sponsoring these awards as a part of a range of initiatives to help farming communities and the tourism industry.

For more information on Safeway Stores please visit: www.safeway.co.uk
For more information about the Excellence in England Awards visit: www.englishtourism.org.uk

SOUTH WEST

A land of myths and legends – and beautiful beaches. The region has cathedral cities, Georgian Bath and maritime Bristol, mysterious castles, evocative country houses and sub-tropical gardens to discover too.

classic sights
Newquay – surfers' paradise
English Riviera – family-friendly beaches
Dartmoor – wild open moorland and rocky tors

coast & country
Runnymede – riverside meadows and woodland
Pegwell Bay & Goodwin Sands – a haven for birds and seals

glorious gardens
Stourhead – 18th century landscape garden
Lost Gardens of Heligan – 19th century gardens

art for all
Tate Gallery St Ives – modern art and the St Ives School
Arnolfini Gallery, Bristol – contemporary arts

distinctively different
Daphne du Maurier – Cornwall inspired many of her novels
Agatha Christie – follow the trail in Torquay

The counties of Bath, Bristol, Cornwall, Devon, Dorset (Western),Isles of Scilly, Somerset, South Gloucestershire and Wiltshire

FOR MORE INFORMATION CONTACT:
South West Tourism
Admail 3186, Exeter EX2 7WH
Tel: (0870) 442 0880 Fax: (0870) 442 0881
Email: info@westcountryholidays.com
Internet: www.westcountryholidays.com

The Pictures:
1 Weston-super-Mare
2 Bath

Places to Visit - see pages 280-284
Where to Stay - see pages 285-345

279

PLACES to visit

You will find hundreds of interesting places to visit during your stay, just some of which are listed in these pages. Contact any Tourist Information Centre in the region for more ideas on days out.

At Bristol Harbourside

Bristol, Avon BS1 5DB
Tel: (0117) 915 5000 www.at-bristol.org.uk
A £97 million Millennium Landmark project on Bristol's revitalised harbourside. It consists of 3 world-class visitor attractions.

Atwell-Wilson Motor Museum Trust

Downside, Stockley Lane, Calne, Wiltshire SN11 0NF
Tel: (01249) 813119 www.atwell-wilson.org
Motor museum with vintage, post-vintage and classic cars, including American models. Classic motorbikes. A 17thC water meadow walk. Car clubs welcome for rallies. Play area.

Avebury Manor and Garden

Avebury, Marlborough, Wiltshire SN8 1RF
Tel: (01672) 539250
Manor house, regularly altered and of monastic origins. Present buildings date from the early 16thC with Queen Anne alterations and Edwardian renovations. Gardens.

Babbacombe Model Village

Hampton Avenue, Babbacombe, Torquay, Devon TQ1 3LA
Tel: (01803) 315315
www.babbacombemodelvillage.co.uk
Over 400 models, many with sound and animation, with four acres (1.6 ha) of award-winning gardens. See modern towns, villages and rural areas. Stunning illuminations.

Bristol City Museum & Art Gallery

Queen's Road, Bristol, Avon BS8 1RL
Tel: (0117) 922 3571
www.bristol-city.gov.uk/museums
Collection representing applied, oriental and fine art, archaeology, geology, natural history, ethnography and Egyptology.

Bristol Zoo Gardens

Clifton, Bristol, Avon BS8 3HA
Tel: (0117) 973 8951 www.bristolzoo.org.uk
Enjoy an exciting, real life experience and see over 300 species of wildlife in beautiful gardens.

Buckland Abbey

Yelverton, Devon PL20 6EY
Tel: (01822) 853607
Originally a Cistercian monastery, then home of Sir Francis Drake. Ancient buildings, exhibitions, herb garden, craft workshops and estate walks.

Cheddar Caves and Gorge

Cheddar, Somerset BS27 3QF
Tel: (01934) 742343 www.cheddarcaves.co.uk
Beautiful caves located in Cheddar Gorge. Gough's Cave with its cathedral-like caverns, and Cox's Cave with stalagmites and stalactites. Also 'The Crystal Quest' fantasy adventure.

The Combe Martin Motor Cycle Collection

Cross Street, Combe Martin, Ilfracombe, Devon EX34 0DH
Tel: (01271) 882346
www.motorcycle-collection.co.uk
Collection of motorcycles, scooters and invalid carriages, displayed against a background of old petrol pumps, signs and garage equipment. Motoring nostalgia.

Combe Martin Wildlife and Dinosaur Park

Jurassic Hotel, Combe Martin, Ilfracombe,
Devon EX34 0NG
Tel: (01271) 882486
Wildlife park and life-size models of dinosaurs.

Crealy Park

Sidmouth Road, Clyst St Mary, Exeter, Devon EX5 1DR
Tel: (01395) 233200 www.crealy.co.uk
One of Devon's largest animal farms. Milk a cow, feed a lamb and pick up a piglet. Adventure playgrounds. Dragonfly Lake and farm trails.

Dairyland Farm World

Newquay, Cornwall TR8 5AA
Tel: (01872) 510246 www.dairylandfarmworld.com
One hundred and seventy cows milked in rotary parlour. Heritage centre. Farm nature trail. Farm park with animals, pets and wildfowl. Daily events. Also conservation area.

Eden Project

Watering Lane Nursery, Pentewan, St Austell,
Cornwall PL26 6EN
Tel: (01726) 222900
A 37-acre (15-ha) china clay pit has been dramatically transformed to accommodate the planthouses, visitor centre and temperate parkland.

Exmoor Falconry & Animal Farm

West Lynch Farm, Allerford, Minehead, Somerset TA24 8HJ
Tel: (01643) 862816 www.exmoorfalconry.co.uk
Farm animals, rare breeds, pets' corner, birds of prey and owls. Flying displays daily. Historic farm buildings.

Flambards Village

Culdrose Manor, Helston, Cornwall TR13 0QA
Tel: (01326) 573404 www.flambards.co.uk
Life-size Victorian village with fully stocked shops, plus carriages and fashions. 'Britain in the Blitz' life-size wartime street, historic aircraft, exploratorium.

Heale Garden & Plant Centre

Middle Woodford, Salisbury, Wiltshire SP4 6NT
Tel: (01722) 782504
Mature, traditional-type garden with shrubs, musk and other roses, and kitchen garden. Authentic Japanese teahouse in water garden. Magnolias. Snowdrops and aconites in winter.

International Animal Rescue Animal Tracks

Ash Mill, South Molton, Devon EX36 4QW
Tel: (01769) 550277 www.iar.org.uk
A 60-acre (24-ha) animal sanctuary with a wide range of rescued animals, from monkeys to chinchillas and shire horses to other horses and ponies. Also rare plant nursery.

The Pictures:
1 Lands End, Cornwall
2 Clifton Suspension Bridge, Bristol
3 Stonehenge
4 Interior of Salisbury Cathedral
5 Shaftesbury Hill, Dorset

Jamaica Inn Museums (Potters Museum of Curiosity)

Jamaica Inn Courtyard, Bolventor, Launceston, Cornwall PL15 7TS
Tel: (01566) 86838
Museums contain lifetime work of Walter Potter, a Victorian taxidermist. Exhibits include Kittens' Wedding, Death of Cock Robin and The Story of Smuggling.

Longleat

The Estate Office, Warminster, Wiltshire BA12 7NW
Tel: (01985) 844400 www.longleat.co.uk
Elizabethan stately home, safari park, plus a wonderland of family attractions. 'World's Longest Hedge Maze', Safari Boats, Pets' Corner, Longleat railway.

The Lost Gardens of Heligan

Heligan, Pentewan, St Austell, Cornwall PL26 6EN
Tel: (01726) 845100 www.heligan.com
Heligan Gardens is the scene of the largest garden restoration project undertaken since the war. Public access to parts of 'Home Farm'.

Lyme Regis Philpot Museum

Bridge Street, Lyme Regis, Dorset DT7 3QA
Tel: (01297) 443370 www.lymeregismuseum.co.uk
Fossils, geology, local history and lace exhibitions. Museum shop.

National Marine Aquarium

Rope Walk, Coxside, Plymouth, Devon PL4 0LF
Tel: (01752) 600301 www.national-aquarium.co.uk
The United Kingdom's only world-class aquarium, located in the heart of Plymouth. Visitor experiences will include a mountain stream and Caribbean reef complete with sharks.

Newquay Zoo

Trenance Park, Newquay, Cornwall TR7 2LZ
Tel: (01637) 873342 www.newquayzoo.co.uk
A modern, award-winning zoo where you can have fun and learn at the same time. A varied collection of animals, from Acouchi to Zebra.

Paignton Zoo Environmental Park

Totnes Road, Paignton, Devon TQ4 7EU
Tel: (01803) 557479 www.paigntonzoo.org.uk
One of England's largest zoos with over 1,200 animals in the beautiful setting of 75 acres (30 ha) of botanical gardens. The zoo is one of Devon's most popular family days out.

Plant World

St Marychurch Road, Newton Abbot, Devon TQ12 4SE
Tel: (01803) 872939
Four acres (1.6 ha) of gardens including the unique 'map of the world' gardens. Cottage garden. Panoramic views. Comprehensive nursery of rare and more unusual plants.

Powderham Castle

The Estate Office, Kenton, Exeter, Devon EX6 8JQ
Tel: (01626) 890243 www.powderham.co.uk
Built c1390, restored in the 18thC. Georgian interiors, china, furnishings and paintings. Family home of the Courtenays for over 600 years. Fine views across deer park and River Exe.

Plymouth Dome

The Hoe, Plymouth, Devon PL1 2NZ
Tel: (01752) 603300
Purpose-built visitor interpretation centre showing the history of Plymouth and its people from Stone Age beginnings to satellite technology. Situated on Plymouth Hoe.

Railway Village Museum

34 Faringdon Road, Swindon, Wiltshire SN1 5BJ
Tel: (01793) 466553 www.swindon.gov.uk
Foreman's house in original Great Western Railway village. Furnished to re-create a Victorian working-class home.

Roman Baths

Pump Room, Abbey Church Yard, Bath BA1 1LZ
Tel: (01225) 477785 www.romanbaths.co.uk
Roman baths and temple precinct, hot springs and Roman temple. Jewellery, coins, curses and votive offerings from the sacred spring.

St Michael's Mount

Marazion, Cornwall TR17 0HT
Tel: (01736) 710507
Originally the site of a Benedictine chapel, the castle on its rock dates from the14thC. Fine views towards Land's End and the Lizard. Reached by foot, or ferry at high tide in summer.

Steam – Museum of the Great Western Railway

Kemble Drive, Churchward, Swindon, Wiltshire SN2 2TA
Tel: (01793) 466646 www.steam-museum.org.uk
Historic Great Western Railway locomotives, wide range of nameplates, models, illustrations, posters and tickets.

Stonehenge

Amesbury, Salisbury, Wiltshire SP4 7DE
Tel: (01980) 623108
www.stonehengemasterplan.org
World-famous prehistoric monument built as a ceremonial centre. Started 5,000 years ago and remodelled several times in next 1,500 years.

Stourhead House and Garden

The Estate Office, Stourton, Warminster, Wiltshire BA12 6QD
Tel: (01747) 841152 www.nationaltrust.org.uk
Landscaped garden, laid out c1741-80, with lakes, temples, rare trees and plants. House, begun in c1721 by Colen Campbell, contains fine paintings and Chippendale furniture.

Tate Gallery St Ives

Porthmeor Beach, St Ives, Cornwall TR26 1TG
Tel: (01736) 796226 www.tate.org.uk
Opened in 1993 and offering a unique introduction to modern art. Changing displays focus on the modern movement St Ives is famous for. Also an extensive education programme.

Teignmouth Museum

29 French Street, Teignmouth, Devon TQ14 8ST
Tel: (01626) 777041
Exhibits include a16thC cannon and artefacts from the Armada wreck, local history, c1920s pier machines and c1877 cannon.

Tintagel Castle

Tintagel, Cornwall PL34 0HE
Tel: (01840) 770328 www.english-heritage.org.uk
Medieval ruined castle on wild, wind-swept coast. Famous for associations with Arthurian legend. Built largely in the 13thC by Richard, Earl of Cornwall. Used as a prison in the 14thC.

Tithe Barn Children's Farm

New Barn Road, Abbotsbury, Weymouth, Dorset DT3 4JF
Tel: (01305) 871817
Extensive children's farm for children under 11 years. Activities include hand-feeding (with bottles) milk to lambs and kids. Replicas of Terracotta Warriors on display in barn.

Totnes Costume Museum – Devonshire Collection of Period Costume

Bogan House, 43 High Street, Totnes, Devon TQ9 5NP
Tel: (01803) 863821
New exhibition of costumes and accessories each season, displayed in one of the historic merchant's houses of Totnes. Bogan House recently restored by Mitchell Trust.

Woodlands Leisure Park

Blackawton, Totnes, Devon TQ9 7DQ
Tel: (01803) 712598
www.woodlands-leisure-park.co.uk
All-weather fun guaranteed with unique combination of indoor and outdoor attractions: 3 watercoasters, toboggan run, massive indoor adventure centre with rides. Falconry and animals.

Wookey Hole Caves and Papermill

Wookey Hole, Wells, Somerset BA5 1BB
Tel: (01749) 672243 www.wookey.co.uk
Spectacular caves and legendary home of the Witch of Wookey. Working Victorian papermill including Old Penny Arcade, Magical Mirror Maze and Cave Diving Museum.

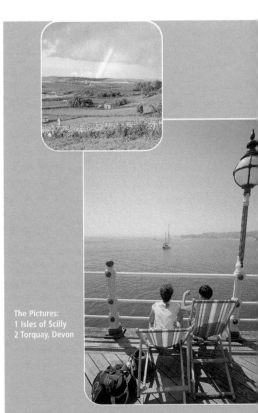

The Pictures:
1 Isles of Scilly
2 Torquay, Devon

Find out more about the
SOUTH WEST

Further information about holidays and attractions in the South West is available from:

SOUTH WEST TOURISM
Admail 3186, Exeter EX2 7WH.
Tel: (0870) 442 0880
Fax: (0870) 442 0881
Email: info@westcountryholidays.com
Internet: www.westcountryholidays.com

The following publications are available free from South West Tourism:
Bed & Breakfast Touring Map
West Country Holiday Homes & Apartments
West Country Hotels and Guesthouses
Glorious Gardens of the West Country
Camping and Caravan Touring Map
Tourist Attractions Touring Map
Trencherman's West Country, Restaurant Guide

Getting to the
SOUTH WEST

BY ROAD: Somerset, Devon and Cornwall are well served from the North and Midlands by the M6/M5 which extends just beyond Exeter, where it links in with the dual carriageways of the A38 to Plymouth, A380 to Torbay and the A30 into Cornwall. The North Devon Link Road A361 joins Junction 37 with the coast of north Devon and A39, which then becomes the Atlantic Highway into Cornwall.

BY RAIL: The main towns in the South West are served throughout the year by fast, direct and frequent rail services from all over the country. InterCity 125 trains operate from London (Paddington) to Chippenham, Swindon, Bath, Bristol, Weston-super-Mare, Taunton, Exeter, Plymouth and Penzance, and also from Scotland, the North East and the Midlands to the South West. A service runs from London (Waterloo) to Exeter, via Salisbury, Yeovil and Crewkerne. Sleeper services operate between Devon and Cornwall and London as well as between Bristol and Glasgow and Edinburgh. Motorail services operate from strategic points to key South West locations.

Where to stay in the South West

Accommodation entries in this region are listed in alphabetical order of place name, and then in alphabetical order of establishment.

Map references refer to the colour location maps at front of this guide. The first number indicates the map to use; the letter and number which follow refer to the grid reference on the map.

At-a-glance symbols at the end of each accommodation entry give useful information about services and facilities. A key to symbols can be found inside the back cover flap. Keep this open for easy reference.

A brief description of the towns and villages offering accommodation in the entries which follow, can be found at the end of this section.

A complete listing of all the English Tourism Council assessed accommodation covered by this guide appears at the back of the guide.

ABBOTSBURY, Dorset Map ref 2A3

★★★
1 Unit
Sleeping 4

THE COTTAGE
Grove Lane, Abbotsbury, Weymouth DT3 4JH
T: (01305) 871462
E: val@thecottage-abbotsbury.co.uk
I: www.thecottage-abbotsbury.co.uk
Contact: Mrs Val Dredge

OPEN All year round

Low season per wk
Min £135.00
High season per wk
Max £325.00

17thC character cottage with secluded garden. Renovated and equipped with thought and care. Owner supervised. Idyllic setting near sea, swannery and village. Good walking country.

★★★★
4 Units
Sleeping 4–8

THE OLD COASTGUARDS
Abbotsbury, Weymouth DT3 4LB
T: (01305) 871335 (Ansaphone)
F: (01305) 871766
E: reception@oldcoastguards.com
I: www.oldcoastguards.com
Contact: Mrs Cheryl Varley

Owner-maintained, well-equipped character cottages 'away from it all' in a simply stunning position. Large gardens overlooking the magnificent Chesil Beach and Lyme Bay with farmland and hills rising behind to nearly 700 feet. Finest scenery, walking, bird watching, fishing and flora. Historic village with lots to do. Excellent eating out.

OPEN All year round

Low season per wk
£410.00–£578.00
High season per wk
£794.00–£931.00

★★★★
7 Units
Sleeping 2–8

LYNCH COUNTRY HOUSE HOLIDAY APARTMENTS

Allerford, Minehead TA24 8HJ
T: (01643) 862800
F: (01643) 862800
E: admin@lynchcountryhouse.co.uk
I: www.lynchcountryhouse.co.uk
Contact: Mr and Mrs B Tacchi

Delightful country house in woodland setting, overlooking moors and sea, tastefully converted to comfortable apartments. Seven acres informal gardens. Lynch is an ideal base for those on a walking holiday. There are many well-made paths leading to combes, moors and wooded hillsides.

OPEN All year round

Low season per wk
£225.00–£350.00
High season per wk
£280.00–£560.00

★★★★
1 Unit
Sleeping 5

THE STABLES
Ivy Cottage, Netheravon, Salisbury SP4 9QW
Contact: Mrs A Thatcher, Ivy Cottage, Netheravon,
Salisbury SP4 9QW
T: (01980) 670557
F: (01980) 670557
E: athatcher@bigfoot.com
I: www.oas.co.uk/ukcottages/thestables

OPEN All year round
CC: Mastercard, Visa

High season per wk
£220.00–£390.00

Charming cottage, in village 5 miles north of Stonehenge, in Avon valley. Self-catering or half-board. Short breaks available.

★★★
3 Units
Sleeping 4–2

STONE BARN COTTAGE

Appley Court Farm, Appley, Nr Wellington TA21 0HJ
Contact: Mrs A Champion, Proprietor, Appley Court Farm,
Appley, Nr Wellington TA21 0HJ
T: (01823) 673263
F: (01823) 673287
E: goappleycourt@aol.com

On 135-acre farm in village surrounded by beautiful countryside, ideal for walkers and nature lovers. Three adjoining cottages in old stone barn, furnished to a high standard, with oak beams and French windows opening to individual patios. Free trout fishing on River Tone. Pub serving excellent food in village.

OPEN All year round

Discount if more than one cottage booked.

Low season per wk
£145.00–£175.00
High season per wk
£189.00–£308.00

★★★★
1 Unit
Sleeping 4

THE OLD DAIRY
Chackeridge Farm, Ashbrittle, Wellington TA21 0LT
Contact: Mr & Mrs CR Buswell, Owners,
Chackeridge Farm, Ashbrittle, Wellington TA21 0LT
T: (01823) 672757

Low season per wk
£150.00–£220.00
High season per wk
£250.00–£350.00

Tastefully converted dairy, furnished to high standard and incorporating many antiques. Beautiful view over Blackdown Hills with Wellington Monument.

ACCESSIBILITY

Look for the 🔲 🔲 🔲 symbols which indicate accessibility for wheelchair users. A list of establishments is at the front of this guide.

ASHBURTON, Devon Map ref 1C2

★★
1 Unit
Sleeping 5

STARES NEST COTTAGE

Holne, Ashburton TQ13 7SL
Contact: Mrs Anne Mortimore, Hazelwood, Holne,
Ashburton TQ13 7SJ
T: (01364) 631235

Well-equipped period cottage in village of Holne near Ashburton. Close to shop, pub and church. In Dartmoor National Park. Central for moor, River Dart and beaches. Large, peaceful garden.

OPEN Apr–Sep

High season per wk
£200.00–£450.00

🛋 Ⓜ ◎ 🛏 ☉ 🖥 📺 🗑 🔌 ⌨ 🏄 P ☀ 🛍 🎁

★★-★★★
6 Units
Sleeping 2–12

WOODER MANOR HOLIDAY HOMES

Widecombe-in-the-Moor, Newton Abbot TQ13 7TR
T: (01364) 621391
F: (01364) 621391
E: angelabell@woodermanor.co.uk
I: www.woodermanor.co.uk
Contact: Mrs Angela Bell

Cottages in picturesque valley in Dartmoor National Park. Peaceful location with beautiful views of woodland, moors and granite tors. Central for touring Devon, exploring Dartmoor, coast, National Trust properties and attractions. Clean and very well-equipped. Gardens. Easy off-road parking, good food at local inn (0.5 miles). Colour brochure. Wheelchair access in 2 units.

OPEN All year round

Nightly rates available.
Riding stables 1 mile. Tennis
court 0.5 miles. Walking
from doorstep.

Low season per wk
£140.00–£500.00
High season per wk
£200.00–£880.00

🅰 🛋 Ⓜ ◎ 🛏 📶 ☉ 🖥 📺 🗑 🔌 ⌨ 🏄 P ⌖ ☀ 🛍 🔅 SP 🎁

ASHWATER, Devon Map ref 1C2

★★★
6 Units
Sleeping 8–14

BRADDON COTTAGES

Ashwater, Beaworthy EX21 5EP
T: (01409) 211350
F: (01409) 211350
I: www.braddoncottages.co.uk
Contact: Mr & Mrs George & Anne Ridge

For country lovers. Six separate cottages with gardens and lawns, on 150-acre estate of meadows and forest, 2 miles from Ashwater. All look south over ornamental fishing lake to Dartmoor. Games field, nature trails, adults' snooker, children's games rooms, wood fires, shop. Owner managed. Colour brochure.

OPEN All year round
CC: Barclaycard, Delta,
Eurocard, Mastercard,
Switch, Visa

Low season per wk
£90.00–£150.00
High season per wk
£150.00–£1,000.00

🅰 🛋 Ⓜ ◎ 🍴 🛏 📶 ☉ 🖥 📺 🗑 🔌 ⌨ 🏄 P ⌖ U ♪ ☀ 🛍 🔅 SP 🎁

QUALITY ASSURANCE SCHEME

For an explanation of the quality and facilities represented by the Stars please refer to the front of this guide. A more detailed explanation can be found in the information pages at the back.

AXMINSTER, Devon Map ref 1D2

★★★

1 Unit
Sleeping 6

HILLTOP

All Saints, Axminster EX13 7LY
Contact: Mrs A Morris, Townshayne Farm, Northleigh,
Colyton EX24 6BU
T: (01404) 831714

*Idyllic 3-bedroomed country cottage close to
Devon/Dorset/Somerset border. Quietly situated
within its own pretty garden with glorious views
over open farmland to the Axe Valley. Easy
access to the coast at Lyme Regis. Exposed
timbers and open fireplaces create a cosy
atmosphere. Very comfortable and well-
equipped.*

OPEN Mar–Oct

Low season per wk
Min £270.00
High season per wk
Max £430.00

BAMPTON, Devon Map ref 1D1

★★★★

5 Units
Sleeping 2–6

THREE GATES FARM

Huntsham, Tiverton EX16 7QH
T: (01398) 331280 (Ansaphone)
Contact: Mrs Alison Spencer

*Peaceful setting for 5 excellent self-catering
cottages. Superb indoor heated pool with sauna
and small fitness room attached. Two acres with
safely fenced pond, play area and games room.
Perfect place for relaxing or base for exploring
beaches, moors and the many attractions of
Devon and Somerset.*

OPEN All year round
CC: Mastercard, Visa

Short breaks available Oct–
Mar (excl Christmas and New
Year), also short break B&B.

Low season per wk
£110.00–£300.00
High season per wk
£130.00–£740.00

★★★

1 Unit
Sleeping 4–6

WONHAM BARTON

Bampton, Tiverton EX16 9JZ
T: (01398) 331312 (Ansaphone)
F: (01398) 331312
E: anne@devonfarms.co.uk
I: www.devonfarms.co.uk
Contact: Mrs A McLean Williams

*From friendly accommodation
overlooking Exe Valley, conveniently
explore secretive, historic Devon,
rolling moorlands and dramatic
coastlines; enjoy country pursuits
and leisurely cream teas. Savour 300
tranquil acres, glimpsing Exmoor red
deer, soaring buzzards and
traditional shepherding; share
romantic scenes from TV drama and
'Landgirls' filmed here. Tell us when
you're coming!*

OPEN All year round
CC: Barclaycard, Delta,
Mastercard, Solo, Switch,
Visa

Low season per wk
£130.00–£265.00
High season per wk
£265.00–£325.00

SPECIAL BREAKS

**Many establishments offer special promotions and themed breaks.
These are highlighted in red. (All such offers are subject to availability.)**

BARNSTAPLE, Devon Map ref 1C1 *Tourist Information Centre Tel: 0845 458 2003*

★★★★
5 Units
Sleeping 2–9

COUNTRY WAYS
Little Knowle Farm, High Bickington, Umberleigh,
Barnstaple EX37 9BJ
T: (01769) 560503
F: (01769) 560503
E: kate.price@virgin.net
I: www.devon-holiday.co.uk
Contact: Mrs Kate Price

OPEN All year round

Low season per wk
£175.00–£550.00
High season per wk
£264.00–£625.00

42-acre mixed farm. Beautifully converted barns, hidden away on a small farm with lovely gardens and magnificent views. Within easy reach Exmoor and coast. Barnstaple 8 miles.

★★★
8 Units
Sleeping 2–6

NORTH HILL COTTAGES
North Hill, Shirwell, Barnstaple EX31 4LG
Contact: Ms Nicky Hann, Best Leisure, North Hill,
Shirwell, Barnstaple EX31 4LG
T: (01271) 850611
F: (01271) 850693
I: www.bestleisure.co.uk

OPEN All year round

Low season per wk
£210.00–£301.00
High season per wk
£287.00–£793.00

Converted 17thC farm buildings with exposed beams, wood stove and central heating. Set in 9 acres of pastures and gardens, close to Barnstaple town.

BATCOMBE, Somerset Map ref 2B2

★★★★
1 Unit
Sleeping 2–6

Recently converted coach house in grounds of 16thC thatched farmhouse equipped to high standard for comfort: rural setting on edge of beautiful village. Twin and double bedrooms, each with own bathroom. Woodburning stove, central heating. Local walks, good touring location Stourhead, Longleat, Bath, Wells. Short walk to excellent pub.

THE COACH HOUSE AT BOORDS FARM
Batcombe, Shepton Mallet BA4 6HD
T: (01749) 850372
F: (01749) 850372
E: boordsfarm@michaelp.demon.co.uk
Contact: Mr & Mrs Michael & Anne Page

OPEN All year round

Short breaks available.
Flexible changeover days on all lengths of bookings.

Low season per wk
Min £350.00
High season per wk
£400.00–£420.00

BATH, Bath and North East Somerset Map ref 2B2 *Tourist Information Centre Tel: (01225) 477101*

★★★★
5 Units
Sleeping 2–4

Delightful single-storey cottages, formerly old cow byres. Tastefully converted. Exposed beams. Countryside location in an Area of Outstanding Natural Beauty. Village shop and pub 500 metres. Kennet and Avon Canal nearby for boating, cycling and walking. Bath 5 miles. Regular buses. Welcome pack. Short breaks when available. Colour brochure.

CHURCH FARM COTTAGES
Winsley, Bradford-on-Avon BA15 2JH
Contact: Mrs Trish Bowles, Church Farm, Winsley,
Bradford-on-Avon BA15 2JH
T: (01225) 722246 & 07768 543027 (Mobile)
F: (01225) 722246
E: stay@churchfarmcottages.com
I: www.churchfarmcottages.com

OPEN All year round
CC: Barclaycard, Delta,
Eurocard, JCB, Maestro,
Mastercard, Solo, Switch,
Visa, Visa Electron

Low season per wk
£185.00–£225.00
High season per wk
£250.00–£375.00

Welcome bottle of wine for stays of 1 week or more.

BEAMINSTER, Dorset Map ref 2A3

★★★

3 Units
Sleeping 4

GREENS CROSS FARM
Stoke Road, Beaminster DT8 3JL
T: (01308) 862661
F: (01308) 863800
Contact: Mr DG Baker

OPEN All year round

Low season per wk
£180.00–£220.00
High season per wk
£250.00–£300.00

Three well-equipped holiday units. Within walking distance of Beaminster in heart of Dorset and close to coast. Short winter breaks. Field for horse.

★★★★

2 Units
Sleeping 4–6

LEWESDON FARM HOLIDAYS
Lewesdon Farm, Stoke Abbott, Beaminster DT8 3JZ
T: (01308) 868270
Contact: Mr & Mrs Smith

Two peacefully situated cottages both with en suite bedrooms. Amidst open countryside in an Area of Outstanding Natural Beauty, with wonderful views in all directions. Thoughtfully converted using mellow local stone. Designed to be wheelchair accessible. Excellent walks from the door, an abundance of wildlife, close to coast, unspoilt beaches. Non-smokers, please.

OPEN Jan, Mar–Dec

Special rates for out-of-season short breaks. Please call establishment direct for more details.

Low season per wk
£260.00–£280.00
High season per wk
£400.00–£445.00

★★★

1 Unit
Sleeping 6

ORCHARD END
Hooke, Beaminster DT8 3PD
Contact: Mrs P M Wallbridge, Watermeadow House,
Bridge Farm, Hooke, Beaminster DT8 3PD
T: (01308) 862619
F: (01308) 862619
E: enquiries@watermeadowhouse.co.uk
I: www.watermeadowhouse.co.uk

OPEN All year round
CC: Barclaycard, Delta,
Mastercard, Solo, Switch,
Visa

Low season per wk
£210.00–£300.00
High season per wk
£300.00–£420.00

280-acre dairy & livestock farm. Working dairy farm in a quiet village 9 miles from the coast. Good walking country and near Hooke Working Woodland Trust land and trout fishing.

★★★★

1 Unit
Sleeping 3

STABLE COTTAGE
Meerhay Manor, Beaminster DT8 3SB
Contact: Mrs Diana Clarke, Meerhay Manor,
Beaminster DT8 3SB
T: (01308) 862305
F: (01308) 863977
E: meerhay@aol.com
I: www.meerhay.co.uk

OPEN All year round

Low season per wk
Min £150.00
High season per wk
Max £375.00

New ground floor conversion of old barn in grounds of old manor. Wheelchair accessible. Fifty acres farmland, plantsman's garden, tennis court, stabling. Seven miles coast, idyllic setting.

BELSTONE, Devon Map ref 1C2

★★★

1 Unit
Sleeping 4

1 CHURCH COTTAGES
Belstone, Okehampton EX20 1QZ
Contact: Mr and Mrs R S Kingwell, St Annes House,
7 Vicar Street, Wymondham NR18 0PL
T: (01953) 601271
E: mandrkingwell@btinternet.com

OPEN All year round

Low season per wk
£170.00–£210.00
High season per wk
£310.00–£365.00

Comfortable stone cottage in Dartmoor National Park. Situated beside church in centre of Belstone village near Okehampton. Scenic area, ideal for walking.

WHERE TO STAY
Please mention this guide when making your booking.

BERRYNARBOR, Devon Map ref 1C1

★★★-★★★★
9 Units
Sleeping 2–8

SMYTHEN FARM COASTAL HOLIDAY COTTAGES

Smythen, Sterridge Valley, Berrynarbor,
Ilfracombe EX34 9TB
T: (01271) 882875
Contact: Mr & Ms Thompson & Elstone

Near golden sands with sea and coastal views. Heated covered swimming pool in a suntrap enclosure, gardens and games room with pool table, table tennis, football machine. Tree house on two levels. Free pony rides, ball pond and bouncy castle, 14-acre recreation field and dog walk. For colour brochure phone Jayne.

OPEN Mar–Oct

Low season per wk
£105.00–£174.00
High season per wk
£267.00–£670.00

BIDEFORD, Devon Map ref 1C1 *Tourist Information Centre Tel: (01237) 477676*

★★★
1 Unit
Sleeping 2

COACHMANS COTTAGE
Staddon House, Monkleigh, Bideford EX39 5JR
Contact: Mr and Mrs T M Downie, Staddon House,
Monkleigh, Bideford EX39 5JR
T: (01805) 623670

Charming character cottage in courtyard setting, within easy reach of national parks and beaches. Price includes cream tea on arrival, linen and fuel for woodburner.

OPEN All year round

Low season per wk
£115.00–£145.00
High season per wk
£145.00–£190.00

BIGBURY-ON-SEA, Devon Map ref 1C3

★★
9 Units
Sleeping 4–6

BEACHDOWN
Challaborough Bay, Challaborough,
Kingsbridge TQ7 4JB
Contact: Mr W S Menzies,
Beachdown Holiday Bungalows, Challaborough Bay,
Challaborough, Kingsbridge TQ7 4JB
T: (01548) 810089
F: (01548) 810089
E: beachdown@yahoo.com

Comfortable bungalows in peaceful surroundings, 200 yards from sandy beach. Superb cliff walks, many local attractions, including golf, watersports. Dartmoor 30 minutes. Dogs welcome.

OPEN All year round

Low season per wk
Min £110.00
High season per wk
Max £395.00

★★★★
1 Unit
Sleeping 6

FERRYCOMBE
Avon Court, Folly Hill, Bigbury-on-Sea,
Kingsbridge TQ7 4AR
Contact: Mrs Juliet Fooks, Little Grassington,
The Spinneys, Heathfield TN21 8YN
T: (01435) 863045 & 0705 0030231

Unique, old Devon stone barn in a small courtyard with private garden. Spectacular sea views overlook the sweep of Bigbury Bay with its glorious sandy beaches and famous Burgh Island. Ideal for the family with children.

OPEN All year round

Low season per wk
£248.00–£380.00
High season per wk
£342.00–£650.00

USE YOUR *i*s

There are more than 550 Tourist Information Centres throughout England offering friendly help with accommodation and holiday ideas as well as suggestions of places to visit and things to do. You'll find TIC addresses in the local Phone Book.

★★★★

1 Unit
Sleeping 4

18thC mill in idyllic setting beside River Torridge – free trout fishing. Forty acres gardens, water meadows. Hard tennis court. Good centre for beaches, sightseeing. Two twin bedrooms, bath with shower over, WC and separate WC. Patio, barbecue. Please view website for a wider selection of our English Tourism Council assessed properties.

KINGSLEY MILL

Black Torrington, Beaworthy EX21 5HS
Contact: Mr Peter Morris, Farm & Cottage Holidays, Victoria House, 12 Fore Street, Northam, Bideford EX39 1AW
T: (01237) 479146
F: (01237) 421512
E: farmcott@cix.co.uk
I: www.farmcott.co.uk

OPEN All year round

Low season per wk
£194.00–£324.00
High season per wk
£342.00–£476.00

★★★

3 Units
Sleeping 2–6

MENNABROOM FARM

Warleggan, Mount, Bodmin PL30 4HE
T: (01208) 821272
F: (01208) 821555
E: lucas@nmadial.co.uk
Contact: Mrs J G Lucas

OPEN All year round

Low season per wk
£150.00–£225.00
High season per wk
£290.00–£510.00

Medieval farmhouse with 3 listed cottages on south-facing edge of Bodmin Moor. Woods, rivers, lakes, peace, seclusion. Easy access to both coasts.

★★★★

1 Unit
Sleeping 2

THE BOATHOUSE

The Harbour, Boscastle PL35 0AG
Contact: Mrs T E Webster, Seagulls, The Harbour, Boscastle PL35 0AG
T: (01840) 250413 & 250374
I: www.businessthisiscornwall.co.uk/boathouse/

OPEN All year round

Low season per wk
£150.00–£250.00
High season per wk
£265.00–£350.00

Recently converted boathouse in harbour area. Open beamed ceilings, wood floors, galley kitchen, nautical decor. Spacious, comfortable and warm.

★★★★

5 Units
Sleeping 4–6

Traditional 3-bedroomed cottage, sleeps 6. Plus 4 cottages converted from Victorian barn sleeping 2–4, with full central heating. All with well appointed kitchens. Private road with ample parking, Boscastle 2 miles. Tranquil farm setting with views of Valency Valley. Gardens with barbecue. Games room with pool, table tennis and payphone.

CARGURRA COTTAGE

St Juliot, Boscastle PL35 0BU
Contact: Mrs Elson, Hennett, St Juliot, Boscastle PL35 0BT
T: (01840) 261206
F: (01840) 261206
E: gillian@cargurra.co.uk
I: www.cargurra.co.uk

OPEN All year round
CC: Barclaycard, Delta, Eurocard, JCB, Mastercard, Visa

Low season per wk
£95.00–£195.00
High season per wk
£200.00–£410.00

CHECK THE MAPS

The colour maps at the front of this guide show all the cities, towns and villages for which you will find accommodation entries.
Refer to the town index to find the page on which they are listed.

BOSCASTLE continued

★★★
1 Unit
Sleeping 5

PARADISE FARM COTTAGE
Boscastle PL35 0BL
Contact: Mrs D M Hancock, Owner, Paradise Farm,
Boscastle PL35 0BL
T: (01840) 250528

OPEN All year round

Low season per wk
£120.00–£170.00
High season per wk
£190.00–£395.00

Peaceful bygone surroundings, magical harbour village. Pets, ponies, ducks. Suntrap garden, fields, views. Log fire. Super pub meals, shop, cliff and country walks from the doorstep.

★★★
6 Units
Sleeping 2–5

WESTERINGS
Forrabury, Boscastle PL35 0DJ
T: (01840) 250314
E: shirley@westeringsholidays.co.uk
I: www.westeringsholidays.co.uk
Contact: Mrs S A Wakelin

OPEN All year round

Low season per wk
£110.00–£160.00
High season per wk
£160.00–£420.00

Self-catering apartments in Georgian rectory with bungalows in grounds. Quietly situated near National Trust coastline and harbour of Boscastle.

BOWDEN, Devon Map ref 1D3

★★★★
13 Units
Sleeping 2–8

HIGHER BOWDEN
Bowden, Dartmouth TQ6 0LH
T: (01803) 770745
F: (01803) 770262
E: cottages@higherbowden.com
I: www.higherbowden.com
Contact: Mrs & Mr Monica & Paul Khosla

A collection of 13 cottages developed from 2 adjoining 17thC farms, set in beautiful countryside, 1 mile inland from Blackpool Sands and 4 miles from Dartmouth. Indoor swimming pool, sauna, jacuzzi, gym, snooker and games room plus special facilities for young children including playgrounds, trampoline and under 5s' playroom.

OPEN All year round

Low season per wk
£257.00–£643.00
High season per wk
£495.00–£1,449.00

BRADFORD-ON-AVON, Wiltshire Map ref 2B2 *Tourist Information Centre Tel: (01225) 865797*

★★★
1 Unit
Sleeping 4

GREYSTONE COTTAGE
19 Bridge Street, Bradford-on-Avon BA15 1BY
Contact: Mrs Gillian Mary Patel, 19 Church Street,
Bradford-on-Avon BA15 1LN
T: (01225) 868179 & 0771 4494006 (mobile)
F: (01225) 867084
E: vivandgill@yahoo.co.uk

OPEN All year round

Low season per wk
£200.00–£260.00
High season per wk
£260.00–£310.00

Comfortable 18thC Grade II Listed terraced cottage, overlooking medieval town bridge. Ample public parking nearby. Close to all amenities. Garden with patio and views. Welcome tray.

BRATTON, Somerset Map ref 1D1

★★★★
6 Units
Sleeping 2–5

WOODCOMBE LODGES
Bratton, Minehead TA24 8SQ
T: (01643) 702789 & 07974 844914 (Mobile)
F: (01643) 702789
E: nicola@woodcombelodge.co.uk
I: www.woodcombelodge.co.uk
Contact: Mrs N Hanson

Timber lodges and stone cottages in a tranquil rural setting on the edge of Exmoor National Park. Standing in a beautiful 2.5 acre garden with wonderful views towards the wooded slopes of Exmoor. Minehead's seafront, harbour, shops, etc, 1.5 miles. Close to Dunster, Selworthy, Porlock and many local beauty spots.

OPEN All year round
CC: Barclaycard, Delta,
Eurocard, Mastercard,
Visa

Low season per wk
£105.00–£240.00
High season per wk
£190.00–£435.00

BRAYFORD, Devon Map ref 1C1

★★
1 Unit
Sleeping 6

MUXWORTHY COTTAGE
Muxworthy Farm, Brayford, Barnstaple EX32 7QP
Contact: Mrs G M Bament, Muxworthy Farm, Brayford,
Barnstaple EX32 7QP
T: (01598) 710342

OPEN All year round

Low season per wk
Min £125.00
High season per wk
Max £255.00

Secluded old world cottage 3 miles from the village of Brayford, 11 miles from Barnstaple and surrounded by beautiful countryside, in heart of Exmoor.

BREAN, Somerset Map ref 1D1

★★
1 Unit
Sleeping 8

GADARA BUNGALOW
Diamond Farm, Weston Road, Brean, Burnham-on-
Sea TA8 2RL
T: (01278) 751263
E: feelfreetoemailme@diamondfarm42.freeserve.co.uk
I: www.diamondfarm.co.uk
Contact: Mr T M Hicks

OPEN All year round

Low season per wk
£140.00–£220.00
High season per wk
£280.00–£370.00

Gadara bungalow is a spacious 3-bedroomed bungalow in its own grounds with direct access to beach. Accommodation includes lounge, kitchen. Central heating is provided for main rooms.

BRIDPORT, Dorset Map ref 2A3 *Tourist Information Centre Tel: (01308) 424901*

★★★
4 Units
Sleeping 2–6

CONISTON HOLIDAY APARTMENTS

Coniston House, Victoria Grove, Bridport DT6 3AE
T: (01308) 424049
F: (01308) 424049
Contact: Mrs Jackie Murphy

Spacious, self-contained, fully-equipped apartments with summer swimming pool. Play area, gardens and garage parking. Ideally situated overlooking the Dorset hills, yet only 2 minutes' walk to market town. Harbour and beaches 1 mile. A warm welcome awaits from resident proprietors. Brochure available.

OPEN All year round

Short and long breaks available in low season.

Low season per wk
Min £95.00
High season per wk
Max £405.00

★★★
1 Unit
Sleeping 4

SUNNYSIDE FARM
Loscombe, Bridport DT6 3TL
T: (01308) 488481
F: (01308) 488136
Contact: Major and Mrs M A Everitt

OPEN All year round

Low season per wk
£225.00–£250.00
High season per wk
£250.00–£325.00

Very comfortable detached timber bungalow (sleeps 4) in garden of main house in rural conservation Area of Outstanding Natural Beauty. Dorset coast 5 miles.

BRISTOL Map ref 2A2 *Tourist Information Centre Tel: (0117) 926 0767*

★★★
1 Unit
Sleeping 4

AVONSIDE
19 St Edyth's Road, Sea Mills, Bristol BS9 2EP
T: (0117) 968 1967
Contact: Mrs D M Ridout

OPEN All year round

Low season per wk
Min £225.00
High season per wk
Max £250.00

Comfortable first-floor flat, well-furnished, equipped and maintained to a high standard. Convenient, pleasant residential area 3 miles from city centre. Motorway nearby.

★★★
1 Unit
Sleeping 2

REDLAND FLAT
Redland, Bristol
Contact: Mr H I Jones, Flat 1, Elm Lodge, Elm Grove,
London NW2 3AE
T: (020) 8450 6761
E: redlandflat.btc@ondigital.com

OPEN All year round

Low season per wk
£225.00–£250.00
High season per wk
£325.00–£350.00

Spacious flat with panoramic views over city from south-facing balconies off the lounge and kitchen. City centre 1.5 miles, Durdham Downs 2 minutes.

★★
6 Units
Sleeping 5–6

DEVONCOURT HOLIDAY FLATS

Berry Head Road, Brixham TQ5 9AB
T: (01803) 853748 & 07050 338889
F: (01803) 855775
E: devoncourt@devoncoast.com
I: www.devoncourt.net
Contact: Mr Robin Hooker

Panoramic sea views from your balcony and lounge over Torbay, Brixham harbour and marina. The beach is opposite, only 50 metres. Each flat is fully self contained, with colour TV, full cooker, fully carpeted. Private gardens. Car park. Children, pets and credit cards welcome. For colour brochure telephone 01803 853748 or 07050 338889.

OPEN All year round
CC: Barclaycard, Delta,
Eurocard, Mastercard,
Switch, Visa, Visa Electron

10% discount for pensioners.

Low season per wk
£130.00–£190.00
High season per wk
£260.00–£340.00

★★★★
3 Units
Sleeping 4

DOMINEYS COTTAGES

Domineys Yard, Buckland Newton, Dorchester DT2 7BS
T: (01300) 345295
F: (01300) 345596
Contact: Mrs J D Gueterbock

Delightful Victorian 2-bedroom cottages, comfortably furnished and equipped and maintained to highest standards. Surrounded by beautiful gardens with patios. Heated summer swimming pool. Peaceful location on village edge in heart of Hardy's Dorset. Well situated for touring Wessex, walking and country pursuits. Regrets no pets. Children 5+ and babies welcome.

OPEN All year round

Low season per wk
£200.00–£360.00
High season per wk
£360.00–£440.00

★★★★
1 Unit
Sleeping 2

THE APARTMENT
Hillside, Buckland St Mary, Chard TA20 3TQ
Contact: Mr Roy Harkness, Hillside, Buckland St Mary,
Chard TA20 3TQ
T: (01460) 234599 & 07703 633770 (Mobile)
F: (01460) 234599
E: royandmarge@hillsidebsm.freeserve.co.uk

OPEN All year round

Low season per wk
£120.00–£170.00
High season per wk
£180.00–£220.00

Tastefully extended Victorian cottage on the edge of Blackdown Hills (off A303), bordering South Somerset and North Devon. Comfortable and quiet. Ideal for Lyme, Exmoor, Dartmoor, Quantocks.

AT-A-GLANCE SYMBOLS

Symbols at the end of each accommodation entry give useful information about services and facilities. A key to symbols can be found inside the back cover flap. Keep this open for easy reference.

★★★★
7 Units
Sleeping 4–6

GLEBE HOUSE COTTAGES LIMITED

Bridgerule, Holsworthy EX22 7EW
T: (01288) 381272
E: holidays@glebehousecottages.freeserve.co.uk
I: www.glebehousecottages.co.uk
Contact: Mr and Mrs James Varley

Beautiful period cottages with exposed beams, some 4-poster beds, en suite facilities and double spa baths. Set in 5 acres of tranquil countryside on Grade II Listed Georgian estate but only 10 minutes' drive from Bude and sandy beaches. Cellar bar and restaurant serving superb home-cooked food. Baby listening monitors.

OPEN All year round
CC: Barclaycard,
Mastercard, Visa

Short breaks available most of the year (excl during school summer holidays).

Low season per wk
£220.00–£490.00
High season per wk
£370.00–£765.00

★★★
8 Units
Sleeping 4–9

HOUNDAPITT FARM COTTAGES
Sandymouth Bay, Stibb, Bude EX23 9HW
T: (01288) 355455
E: anthony@houndapitt.co.uk
I: www.houndapitt.co.uk
Contact: Mr A Heard

OPEN Feb–Oct, Dec

Low season per wk
£140.00–£230.00
High season per wk
£530.00–£795.00

Cottages in 100-acre estate 1 mile from beach. Quality accommodation at competitive prices. Countryside setting, spectacular views. Free coarse fishing, adventure playground, pony rides and more.

★★-★★★★
6 Units
Sleeping 2–7

IVYLEAF BARTON COTTAGES
Ivyleaf Hill, Bude EX23 9LD
Contact: Mr & Mrs P McIntyre, Ivyleaf Barton,
Ivyleaf Hill, Bude EX23 9LD
T: (01288) 321237
F: (01288) 321937
E: ivyleafbarton@hotmail.com

OPEN All year round

Low season per wk
£160.00–£310.00
High season per wk
£280.00–£670.00

Converted stone barns. Well equipped, cosy in winter with focal point fires. Adjacent to 9-hole golf course. Three miles from Bude. Short breaks available.

★★★★★
18 Units
Sleeping 2–10

KENNACOTT COURT

Widemouth Bay, Bude EX23 0ND
T: (01288) 361766 & 361683
F: (01288) 361434
E: maureen@kennacottcourt.co.uk
I: www.kennacottcourt.co.uk
Contact: Mr & Mrs R H Davis

An outstanding collection of cottages which are beautifully furnished, very comfortable and comprehensively equipped. Kennacott Court has a wide range of activities: indoor swimming pool, games room, snooker, sauna and solarium together with tennis courts and our own golf course. All set in 75 acres overlooking the sea at Widemouth Bay.

OPEN All year round
CC: Barclaycard,
Mastercard, Switch, Visa

Open all year with attractive out-of-season short breaks.

Low season per wk
£225.00–£720.00
High season per wk
£450.00–£1,870.00

TOWN INDEX

This can be found at the back of this guide. If you know where you want to stay, the index will give you the page number listing accommodation in your chosen town, city or village.

★★★

7 Units
Sleeping 2–6

LANGFIELD MANOR

Broadclose, Bude EX23 8DP
T: (01288) 352415
F: (01288) 353416
E: freestone.langfield@virgin.net
I: www.bude.co.uk/langfield
Contact: Mr & Mrs Keith & Christa Freestone

Seven quality apartments within fine Edwardian house. Games room with full-sized snooker table, pool and table-tennis tables. Three minutes' walk to the shops and 10 to beautiful sandy beaches, yet peacefully situated in delightful sheltered south-facing gardens with solar-heated outdoor swimming pool. Golf course adjacent.

OPEN All year round

Low season per wk
Min £130.00
High season per wk
£285.00–£685.00

★★★

3 Units
Sleeping 4–9

PENHALT FARM

Widemouth Bay, Bude EX23 0DG
Contact: Mr & Mrs D J Marks, Penhalt Farm,
Widemouth Bay, Bude EX23 0DG
T: (01288) 361210
F: (01288) 361210
I: www.holidaybank.co.uk/penhaltfarm

Spectacular sea and country views. Farmhouse sleeps up to 9 in 4 bedrooms. Comfortable, well-equipped accommodation with enclosed garden, ample parking and close to the coastal footpath. Ideal for walking, surfing and touring the dramatic North Cornwall coastline and countryside. Outside children's play area. Reduced rates for smaller parties from September-Easter.

OPEN All year round

Low season per wk
£130.00–£330.00
High season per wk
£380.00–£599.00

★★★

2 Units
Sleeping 6

AALSMEER

Marine Drive, Widemouth Bay, Bude EX23 0AQ
Contact: Mr & Mrs D Marks, Penhalt Farm,
Widemouth Bay, Poundstock, Bude EX23 0DG
T: (01288) 361210
F: (01288) 361210
I: www.holidaybank.co.uk/penhaltfarm

Just 200 yards from the beach at Widemouth Bay. Panoramic sea views from this detached, double glazed 3 bedroomed bungalow. Set back from coast road on a service road with deep front garden. Very well-equipped, comfortable accommodation with Aga, open fire, all convenience kitchen, bathroom, shower room and garage. Suitable for partially disabled.

OPEN All year round

Low season per wk
£175.00–£230.00
High season per wk
£280.00–£520.00

CHECK THE MAPS

The colour maps at the front of this guide show all the cities, towns and villages for which you will find accommodation entries. Refer to the town index to find the page on which they are listed.

★

1 Unit
Sleeping 6

8 ALLANDALE ROAD
Burnham-on-Sea
Contact: Ms M J Mayo, Maeswalter, Heol Senni, Brecon
LD3 8SU
T: (01874) 636629
E: maeswalter@talk21.com

Large self-contained ground floor flat in quiet cul-de-sac leading down to sandy beach. Sleeps 6. Central heating, washing machine, microwave, slow cooker, gas cooker. Linen and towels provided. Close to shops and amenities.

OPEN All year round

Short breaks out of season available. Reductions for OAPs and disabled visitors.

Low season per wk
Min £190.00
High season per wk
Max £310.00

★★★

4 Units
Sleeping 4–9

PROSPECT FARM
Prospect Farm Guest House &t, Holiday Cottages,
East Brent, Highbridge TA9 4JH
T: (01278) 760507
Contact: Mrs Gillian Wall

17thC tastefully restored country cottages set amidst flower gardens and surrounded by the natural West Country beauty of the Somerset Levels, near the legendary Brent Knoll, with remains of Iron Age and Roman settlements. Two miles junction 22 M5, 3 miles Burnham-on-Sea. Variety of small farm animals and pets. Children welcome.

OPEN All year round

Special tariffs quoted for mid-week and weekend breaks in low season.

Low season per wk
£100.00–£120.00
High season per wk
£190.00–£460.00

★★★

1 Unit
Sleeping 2

HILLVIEW
Stanmoor Road, Burrowbridge, Bridgwater TA7 0RX
T: (01823) 698308
F: (01823) 698308
Contact: Mrs Rosalind Griffiths

OPEN All year round

Low season per wk
Max £130.00
High season per wk
Max £165.00

Compact bungalow, fully equipped and centrally heated, in its own grounds. Conservatory.

★★★

1 Unit
Sleeping 2

PEBBLE BEACH LODGE
Coast Road, Burton Bradstock, Bridport DT6 4RJ
T: (01308) 897428
F: (01308) 897428
Contact: Mr and Mrs Bruce and Jan Hemingway

OPEN All year round

Low season per wk
Min £150.00
High season per wk
Max £350.00

One double bedroomed apartment with two single bed settees for children, within charming guesthouse, affording wonderful views of heritage coastline and direct access to beach.

MAP REFERENCES The map references refer to the colour maps at the front of this guide. The first figure is the map number; the letter and figure which follow indicate the grid reference on the map.

★★★

8 Units
Sleeping 2–6

BUTCOMBE FARM

Aldwick Lane, Butcombe BS40 7UW
T: (01761) 462380
F: (01761) 462300
E: info@butcombe-farm.demon.co.uk
I: www.butcombe-farm.demon.co.uk
Contact: Mr Barry Harvey

Originally a 14thC medieval hall house, Butcombe Farm is now a beautiful manor-house with en suite bed and breakfast and individual self-catering accommodation. Set in several acres amid peaceful countryside. Close to Bath, Bristol, Cheddar, Wells, Mendips and Exmoor. For more information, please contact Barry and Josephine Harvey.

OPEN All year round
CC: Barclaycard, Eurocard, Maestro, Mastercard, Solo, Switch, Visa, Visa Electron

Breaks available with clay pigeon shoots, horse riding, archery, aromatherapy massage, wine tasting and more.

Low season per wk
£230.00–£475.00
High season per wk
£265.00–£540.00

★★★★

1 Unit
Sleeping 5

COCKHILL OLD BARN

Lower Cockhill Farm, Castle Cary BA7 7NZ
Contact: Mrs A Peppin, Lower Cockhill Farm, Castle Cary BA7 7NZ
T: (01963) 351288 (Ansaphone)
F: (01963) 351840
E: bookings@cockhill.co.uk

This expertly converted 2-bedroomed Listed medieval barn combines modern comfort with the original character of fine ancient beams and flagstone floors. Set in lovely countryside yet near town, it is ideally placed for touring this fascinating part of the world. Good views over fields and fabulous sunsets. South-facing patio.

OPEN All year round

Low season per wk
£220.00–£300.00
High season per wk
£325.00–£450.00

★★★

1 Unit
Sleeping 6

LITTLE GREYSTONES
Cattistock, Dorchester DT2 0JB
Contact: Mr & Mrs A&J Fletcher, Greystones,
Cattistock, Dorchester DT2 0JB
T: (01300) 320477
E: j_f.fletcher@virgin-net.uk

OPEN All year round

Low season per wk
£185.00–£260.00
High season per wk
£240.00–£410.00

Modern, detached bungalow. Two bedrooms, 2 bathrooms, very well equipped. In small village in beautiful countryside, with easy access to coast.

TOWN INDEX

This can be found at the back of the guide. If you know where you want to stay, the index will give you the page number listing accommodation in your chosen town, city or village.

★★★

4 Units
Sleeping 2–6

HOME PLACE FARM COTTAGES

Challacombe, Barnstaple EX31 4TS
T: (01598) 763283
F: (01598) 763283
E: markandsarah@holidayexmoor.co.uk
I: www.holidayexmoor.co.uk
Contact: Mr Mark Ravenscroft

Four comfortable cottages set amidst atmospheric moorland in the tranquil River Bray valley in Exmoor National Park, close to the spectacular coast. Excellent walks from the door with village pub an easy stroll. Wood-burning stoves, mini spa with sauna hot tub, private coarse fishing, pet pig.

OPEN Mar–Dec
CC: Barclaycard,
Mastercard, Visa

Mid-week Mon-Fri, cottage for sleeping 4: £145 (excl school holidays).

Low season per wk
£105.00–£250.00
High season per wk
£150.00–£550.00

★★★★

4 Units
Sleeping 2–6

CARCLAZE FARM

Chapel Amble, Wadebridge PL27 6EP
T: (01208) 813886
E: enquires@carclaze.dabsol.co.uk
I: www.carclaze.co.uk
Contact: Mrs J Nicholls

Peaceful setting in the heart of the countryside, with superb views yet only 10 minutes from the spectacular coast. An ideal location to explore North Cornwall, with its sailing, surfing, sandy beaches, golf and cliff walks. Quality cottages furnished to high standards, suitable for those who seek something special.

OPEN All year round

Low season per wk
£230.00–£315.00
High season per wk
£440.00–£890.00

★★★

37 Units
Sleeping 2–8

THE OLDE HOUSE

Chapel Amble, Wadebridge PL27 6EN
T: (01208) 813219 & 815230
F: (01208) 815689
E: info@theoldhouse.co.uk
I: www.theoldehouse.co.uk
Contact: Mr and Mrs A Hawkey

Self-catering cottages on working farm with indoor heated swimming pool, toddlers' pool, sauna, solarium, jacuzzi, games room with full-size snooker table, darts, colour TV. Outside are tennis courts, adventure playground, pets' corner, farm trail, playbarn with ball pool, Wendy house, ropes, slides. Laundry facilities included, baby-sitting service available.

OPEN All year round
CC: Mastercard, Visa

Short breaks available all year round. Long weekends, mid-week breaks. Pay by credit card.

Low season per wk
£300.00–£325.00
High season per wk
Min £490.00

★★★

1 Unit
Sleeping 6

CHEDDAR LODGE
Old Cheddar Cottage, Draycott Road, Cheddar
BS27 3RP
T: (01934) 743859 & 07974 579070 (Mobile)
F: (01934) 741550
E: jon@1rawlings.freeserve.co.uk
Contact: Mr Jon Rawlings

OPEN All year round

High season per wk
£200.00–£300.00

Detached single-storey attractive stone cottage with its own garden, offering comfortable family-sized accommodation. Close to owner's home but with private off-street parking.

CHIDEOCK, Dorset Map ref 1D2

★★★★
1 Unit
Sleeping 5

ACORN COTTAGE

Willowhayne Farm, Chideock, Bridport DT6 6HY
Contact: Mr Grant Roberts, 20 Eastland Road,
Thornbury, Bristol BS35 1DS
T: (01454) 415140 (Ansaphone) & 413056 (Evening)
F: (01454) 415140
E: grant@robe87.freeserve.co.uk

OPEN Apr–Dec

Low season per wk
£265.00–£395.00
High season per wk
£395.00–£560.00

Charming mews cottage converted from stone barn. Beautiful views of countryside and within 0.5 mile from the sea.

CHIPPENHAM, Wiltshire Map ref 2B2 *Tourist Information Centre Tel: (01249) 706333*

★★★★
2 Units
Sleeping 2–4

ROWARD FARM

Roward Farm, Draycot Cerne, Chippenham SN15 4SG
T: (01249) 758147
F: (01249) 758149
E: d.humphrey@roward.demon.co.uk
Contact: Mr David Humphrey

Three character cottages converted from traditional farm barns with many original features. Set on a small farm in peaceful Wiltshire countryside with easy access to Bath, Cotswolds and many local attractions. Each cottage has its own garden or patio, is fully equipped and very comfortable.

OPEN All year round

Low season per wk
£190.00–£260.00
High season per wk
£275.00–£335.00

★★★★
1 Unit
Sleeping 6

SWALLOW COTTAGE

Olivemead Farm, Dauntsey, Chippenham SN15 4JQ
Contact: Mrs Suzanne Candy, Olivemead Farm,
Olivemead Lane, Dauntsey, Chippenham SN15 4JQ
T: (01666) 510205
F: (01666) 510205
E: olivemead@farming.co.uk

Imagine a delightful, comfortable well-equipped cottage on a working dairy farm, converted to offer the luxuries of modern living but retaining its traditional features. Bed settee available for extra guests. Perfectly positioned for days out in Wiltshire, Bath and the Cotswolds. Convenient M4. Brochure available.

OPEN All year round

Low season per wk
£200.00
High season per wk
£300.00–£400.00

CHUDLEIGH, Devon Map ref 1D2

★★★
3 Units
Sleeping 6–8

COOMBESHEAD FARM

Coombeshead Cross, Chudleigh,
Newton Abbot TQ13 0NQ
T: (01626) 853334 (Answerphone)
E: anne-coombeshead@supanet.com
Contact: Mr & Mrs R Smith

OPEN Mar–Dec

Low season per wk
£180.00–£280.00
High season per wk
£250.00–£400.00

Comfortable holiday cottages converted from stone farm buildings. Quiet but not isolated, between Dartmoor and sea. Owners in residence.

IMPORTANT NOTE Information on accommodation listed in this guide has been supplied by the proprietors. As changes may occur you are advised to check details at the time of booking.

★★★
1 Unit
Sleeping 4

FARMBOROUGH HOUSE

Old Exeter Road, Chudleigh, Newton Abbot TQ13 0DR
T: (01626) 853258
F: (01626) 853258
E: holidays@farmborough-house.com
I: www.farmborough-house.com
Contact: Mrs Deirdre Aldridge

Hidden away from the road and nestling in a superb rural location, this comfortable 1st floor apartment for non-smoking, country-loving couples overlooks gardens and wildlife. Glimpse the occasional deer in 10 acres of former vineyard. Convenient for Dartmoor, coast, M5. A cream tea awaits you. No pets. Brochure.

OPEN All year round

Low season per wk
£205.00–£240.00
High season per wk
£280.00

★★★
1 Unit
Sleeping 4

SILVER COTTAGE

Chudleigh, Newton Abbot TQ13 0JX
Contact: Mr E J Gardner, 75 Old Exeter Street, Chudleigh, Newton Abbot TQ13 0JX
T: (01626) 854571 (Ansaphone)
F: (01626) 854571

Delightful character cottage well situated for country walks yet within few minutes of shopping centre in this friendly, historic town. Ideal base for touring being central for Dartmoor National Park, Exeter, Plymouth, and the coast for Dawlish and Torbay. Children welcomed. Brochure sent on request.

OPEN All year round

Low season short breaks. Discounts available for senior citizens. Special rates on application. Book early.

Low season per wk
£100.00–£150.00
High season per wk
£185.00–£265.00

★★★★
1 Unit
Sleeping 2

DEER COTT

Middle Garland, Chulmleigh EX18 7DU
T: (01769) 580461 (Ansaphone)
F: (01769) 580461
E: deercott@sosi.net
I: www.sosi.net/users/deercott
Contact: Mr & Mrs George & Mary Simpson

Discover the peace and beauty of the Devonshire countryside and relax in comfortable accommodation offering every convenience for couples at any time of the year. In a park-like setting of 20 acres within the Devon heartland, handy for the moors and shores. Amenities at South Molton/Barnstaple a short drive away.

OPEN All year round

Low season per wk
£180.00–£210.00
High season per wk
£225.00–£375.00

COUNTRY CODE Always follow the Country Code ⚘ Enjoy the countryside and respect its life and work ⚘ Guard against all risk of fire ⚘ Fasten all gates ⚘ Keep your dogs under close control ⚘ Keep to public paths across farmland ⚘ Use gates and stiles to cross fences, hedges and walls ⚘ Leave livestock, crops and machinery alone ⚘ Take your litter home ⚘ Help to keep all water clean ⚘ Protect wildlife, plants and trees ⚘ Take special care on country roads ⚘ Make no unnecessary noise

COLYTON, Devon Map ref 1D2

★★★★

5 Units
Sleeping 2–8

SMALLICOMBE FARM

Northleigh, Colyton EX24 6BU
T: (01404) 831310
F: (01404) 831431
E: maggie_todd@yahoo.com
I: www.smallicombe.com
Contact: Mrs M A Todd

*Relax in award-winning converted barns
surrounded by abundance of wildlife in an Area
of Outstanding Natural Beauty. Hear the sounds
of the countryside yet be near our World
Heritage Coastline. Meet friendly farm animals
including prize-winning rare breed pigs. Enjoy a
farmhouse breakfast or evening meals in our
licensed restaurant.*

OPEN All year round

'Piggy Weekend': 2 nights
self-catering plus 1 day with
the pigs from £85 per
couple–£125 family of 4.

Low season per wk
£95.00–£295.00
High season per wk
£295.00–£695.00

COMBE MARTIN, Devon Map ref 1C1

★★★★

1 Unit
Sleeping 6

PRETORIA
Cross Street, Seaside, Combe Martin,
Ilfracombe EX34 0DH
Contact: Mrs Heather Trueman, 6 Cross Mead, Lynton
EX35 6DG
T: (01598) 753517 (Ansaphone)
E: russ@crown-inn.freeserve.co.uk

OPEN All year round

Low season per wk
£175.00–£285.00
High season per wk
£300.00–£495.00

*Four-bedroomed, seaside cottage. Sleeps 6. Garden. Free parking for 2 cars. Tastefully
furnished. Fully equipped kitchen. Close to beach. Open all year.*

★★-★★★

9 Units
Sleeping 2–6

WIDMOUTH FARM COTTAGES

Watermouth, Ilfracombe EX24 9RX
T: (01271) 863743
F: (01271) 866479
E: holidays@widmouthfarmcottages.co.uk
I: www.widmouthfarmcottages.co.uk
Contact: Mrs Elizabeth Sansom

*Delightful cottages, some early 1800s (including
a unique round barn conversion) set in 35 acres
of National Heritage coastland with private
beach. The coastal footpath borders our land
and the views are stunning. Easily accessible and
near places of interest. Activities for all ages.
Grocery and meal delivery services.*

OPEN All year round
CC: Amex, Barclaycard,
Delta, JCB, Maestro,
Mastercard, Solo, Switch,
Visa, Visa Electron

2, 3 and 4 night stays may be
booked in advance Oct–May.

Low season per wk
£150.00–£340.00
High season per wk
£275.00–£550.00

CRACKINGTON HAVEN, Cornwall Map ref 1C2

★★★★-★★★★★★

6 Units
Sleeping 3–6

ROSECARE FARM COTTAGES

Rosecare, St Gennys, Bude EX23 0BE
T: (01840) 230375
E: gilljohn@rosecare.freeserve.co.uk
I: www.cottageguide.co.uk/rosecare
Contact: Mr and Mrs John Stone

*Five stone cottages and 1 farmhouse sleeping
2-6 in a peaceful hamlet 1.5 miles from the
spectacular north Cornwall coastline. An ideal
location to explore Cornwall's many attractions
including lovely beaches, walks and sub-tropical
gardens, plus the Eden Project. Dogs welcome.
Log-burning stoves. Resident proprietors.*

OPEN Mar–Dec

Low season per wk
£125.00–£290.00
High season per wk
£295.00–£635.00

CROYDE, Devon Map ref 1C1

★★★
1 Unit
Sleeping 4–6

OCEANSIDE
Leadengate Close, Croyde, Braunton EX33 1PT
Contact: Mr & Mrs D Scarlett, 7 Glebe Lane,
Long Street, Hanslope MK19 7DD
T: (01908) 516444
F: (01908) 516174
E: mail@oceansidecroyde.co.uk
I: www.oceansidecroyde.co.uk

OPEN Apr–Oct

Low season per wk
£150.00–£250.00
High season per wk
£250.00–£525.00

Spacious, fully equipped 2 bedroomed bungalow. Quiet location, 5 minutes walk to beach and village centre. All mod cons. Enclosed garden. No smoking or pets.

DARTMOOR

See under Ashburton, Belstone, Dunsford, Moretonhampstead, Okehampton, Tavistock

DARTMOUTH, Devon Map ref 1D3 *Tourist Information Centre Tel: (01803) 834224*

★★★★
1 Unit
Sleeping 9

33 CLARENCE HILL
Dartmouth TQ6 9NY
Contact: Mrs Sally Pool, Lansdown, Magpie Lane, Coleshill,
Amersham HP7 0LS
T: (01494) 727687

Grade II Listed Regency house. Very comfortable, well-equipped, sleeps 7 to 9 people. Close to town centre. Small garden, garage, spectacular harbour and sea views. Available all year. Linen provided.

OPEN All year round

Low season per wk
£300.00–£400.00
High season per wk
£500.00–£700.00

★★★★★
1 Unit
Sleeping 4

LITTLE COOMBE COTTAGE
Dittisham, Dartmouth TQ6 0JB
Contact: Mr & Mrs Unitt, Little Coombe Farm, Dittisham,
Dartmouth TQ6 0JB
T: (01803) 722599
F: (01803) 722599

Top Tourist Board rating. Idyllic cottage tucked away on small 20-acre estate, overlooking stream-fed pools and woodland. Rare breeds of geese, poultry, highland cattle. Lovely walks. Two en suite bedrooms, 4-poster and twin. Well-fitted kitchen, separate lounge/dining room, central heating, woodburner. Cosy winter breaks. No steps throughout. Non-smoking.

OPEN All year round

Low season per wk
£230.00–£330.00
High season per wk
£345.00–£495.00

★★-★★★
4 Units
Sleeping 2–6

THE OLD BAKEHOUSE
7 Broadstone, Dartmouth TQ6 9NR
T: (01803) 834585 & 07909 680884
F: (01803) 834585
Contact: Mrs S R Ridalls

OPEN All year round

Low season per wk
£150.00–£295.00
High season per wk
£240.00–£555.00

Character cottages with beams, old stone fireplaces, one with 4-poster bed, in a conservation area, 2 minutes from historic town centre and river. Free parking.

QUALITY ASSURANCE SCHEME
Star ratings were correct at the time of going to press but are subject to change. Please check at the time of booking.

DAWLISH, Devon Map ref 1D2

★★★★
5 Units
Sleeping 4–6

On the edge of privately-owned Cofton Country Holiday Park, converted 100-year-old farm buildings overlooked by ancient Cofton church. Coarse fishing lakes. Woodland walks. Within a short drive to the Exe estuary and Dawlish Warren. All amenities of the park available during season, including swimming pool and pub.

COFTON COUNTRY COTTAGE HOLIDAYS

Starcross, Nr Dawlish, Exeter EX6 8RP
T: (01626) 890111
F: (01626) 891572
E: enquiries@cofton-holidays-devon.co.uk
I: www.cofton-holidays-devon.co.uk
Contact: Mr & Mrs W G Jeffery

OPEN All year round		Low season per wk
CC: Barclaycard, Delta,		£235.00–£369.00
Eurocard, Maestro,		High season per wk
Mastercard, Solo, Switch,		£355.00–£599.00
Visa, Visa Electron		

Short breaks early and late season, 3 or 4 night breaks at most times.

DAWLISH WARREN, Devon Map ref 1D2

★★★★
9 Units
Sleeping 4–6

Magnificent 18thC house converted into 6 luxury apartments. Woodside Cottages – 3 estate workers' cottage conversions. New properties for 2002. Exe estuary views, surrounded by fields and 50 acres of unspoilt woodlands. Quiet and restful holidays in a perfect setting. Amenities at Cofton during season.

EASTDON ESTATE

Eastdon House &, Woodside Cottages, Starcross, Nr Dawlish, Exeter EX6
Contact: Mrs V Jeffery, Cofton Country Holidays, Starcross, Exeter EX6 8RP
T: (01626) 890111
F: (01626) 891572
E: enquiries@cofton-holidays-devon.co.uk
I: www.cofton-holidays-devon.co.uk

OPEN All year round	Low season per wk
	£235.00–£399.00
Short breaks early and late	High season per wk
season. 3 or 4 night breaks at	£355.00–£629.00
most times.	

DEVIZES, Wiltshire Map ref 2B2 *Tourist Information Centre Tel: (01380) 729408*

★★★★
1 Unit
Sleeping 5

OWLS COTTAGE
48 White Street, Easterton, Devizes SN10 4PA
T: (01380) 818804
F: (01380) 818804
E: gill_whittome@yahoo.co.uk
Contact: Mrs G C Whittome

OPEN All year round	Low season per wk
	£265.00
	High season per wk
	£395.00

Superior quality cottage in peaceful rural location, outstanding downland views. Excellent walking, White Horse way, Wiltshire cycle way, birdwatching. Ideal for Stonehenge and Bath. Brochure.

★★★
2 Units
Sleeping 8

RENDELLS FARM HOLIDAY COTTAGES
All Cannings, Devizes SN10 3PA
Contact: Mr & Mrs Keith & Sue Roper & Baron,
The Barn, Rendells Farm, All Cannings, Devizes
SN10 3PA
T: (01380) 860243 & 07778 355873 (Mobile)
F: (01895) 270708
E: sroper@waitrose.com
I: www.rendellsfarmcottages.com

OPEN All year round	Low season per wk
	£188.00–£298.00
	High season per wk
	£330.00–£415.00

Set in 10 acres with a small lake and beautiful views of the Pewsey Downs, our holiday cottages are fully equipped, warm and welcoming.

DORCHESTER, Dorset Map ref 2B3 *Tourist Information Centre Tel: (01305) 267992*

★★★★–★★★★★

18 Units
Sleeping 2–7

Converted brick and stone barns, tastefully furnished in cottage style and fully heated. Three beautifully appointed houses with dishwasher, washing machine/dryer, en suite facilities. Some cottages for couples, others sleeping up to 7. Superb indoor heated pool, games and fitness facilities, 2 en tout cas hard tennis courts. Restaurant now fully open.

GREENWOOD GRANGE FARM COTTAGES

Higher Bockhampton, Dorchester DT2 8QH
Contact: Mrs Jayne O'Brien, Owner, Greenwood Grange Farm Cottages, Higher Bockhampton, Dorchester DT2 8QH
T: (01305) 268874 & 260212 (Resident's payphone)
F: (01305) 268874
E: enquiries@greenwoodgrange.co.uk
I: www.greenwoodgrange.co.uk

OPEN All year round
CC: Delta, Mastercard, Solo, Switch, Visa

Low season per wk
£291.00–£702.00
High season per wk
£480.00–£1,625.00

DRIMPTON, Dorset Map ref 1D2

★★★

1 Unit
Sleeping 5

LITTLE BROOKFIELD
Chard Road, Drimpton, Beaminster DT8 3RF
Contact: Mrs J Angold, Brookfield, Chard Road, Drimpton, Beaminster DT8 3RF
T: (01308) 867058
F: (01308) 867080

OPEN May–Oct

Low season per wk
Min £160.00
High season per wk
Max £310.00

Rural retreat. Comfortable attached bungalow in quiet village. Beautiful countryside. Coast 10 miles.

DULVERTON, Somerset Map ref 1D1

★★★★

2 Units
Sleeping 5–22

Victorian country house set in 4 acres lovely garden and surrounded by woodland of the Barle River Valley. Perfect for family and other gatherings in the peace and beauty of Exmoor. House sleeps 22 and 3 cots. Lodge sleeps 5 and 1 cot.

NORTHMOOR HOUSE & LODGE

Northmoor, Dulverton TA22 9QG
Contact: Mr Tim Tarling, Manager, Northmoor, Dulverton TA22 9QF
T: (01398) 323720
E: timtarling@northmoor.fsnet.co.uk
I: www.northmoorhouse.co.uk

OPEN All year round

3 night breaks out of high season.

Low season per wk
Min £200.00
High season per wk
Max £2,500.00

★★★

1 Unit
Sleeping 4

PADDONS
Northmoor Road, Dulverton TA22 9PW
T: (01398) 323514
F: (01398) 324283
E: marymm@bscd.org.uk
Contact: Mrs Mary McMichael

OPEN All year round

Low season per wk
£215.00–£250.00
High season per wk
£340.00–£415.00

Wing of owner's 300-year-old home. Quarter mile private fishing River Baile, 12 acres private woodland. Large sunny garden. 10 minutes from Dulverton shops.

CREDIT CARD BOOKINGS If you book by telephone and are asked for your credit card number it is advisable to check the proprietor's policy should you cancel your reservation.

DUNSFORD, Devon Map ref 1D2

★★★
1 Unit
Sleeping 2

POPPY COTTAGE
3 Bridge Street, Dunsford, Exeter EX6 7AA
Contact: Miss Hazel Cant, 23 Fox Brook,
Wootton Bassett, Swindon SN4 8QD
T: (01793) 850555 (Ansaphone)
E: hazel@hcant.freeserve.co.uk

OPEN All year round

Low season per wk
£125.00–£165.00
High season per wk
£165.00–£195.00

17thC terraced cottage, fully modernised. One spacious bedroom, bathroom with shower attachment, fully fitted kitchen and lounge. Village setting with pub, shop, golf and river nearby.

DUNSTER, Somerset Map ref 1D1

★★★-★★★★
12 Units
Sleeping 2–12

DUDDINGS COUNTRY HOLIDAYS
Duddings, Timberscombe, Minehead TA24 7TB
T: (01643) 841123
F: (01643) 841165
E: richard@duddings.co.uk
I: www.duddings.co.uk
Contact: Mr Richard Tilke

Thatched longhouse and attractive cottages, beautifully converted from old stone barns on small country estate 2 miles from picturesque village of Dunster in Exmoor National Park. Facilities include heated indoor pool, hard tennis court, putting green, pool and table tennis. Walking, riding, fishing, beaches nearby. Off-peak short breaks available. Families welcome.

OPEN All year round

Low season per wk
£175.00–£660.00
High season per wk
£325.00–£1,650.00

★★★★-★★★★★
6 Units
Sleeping 2–6

LITTLE QUARME COTTAGES
Wheddon Cross, Exmoor National Park TA24 7EA
T: (01643) 841249
F: (01643) 841249
E: 106425.743@compuserve.com
I: www.littlequarme-cottages.co.uk
Contact: Mrs Tammy Cody-Boutcher

Stone cottages offering discerning guests a rare combination of quality cottages and outstanding location with panoramic views in central Exmoor. The cottages are on a village-like complex, all have small private gardens and stand amid superb larger gardens and 18 acres. Quality, comfort and cleanliness, ample parking, non-smoking, resident owner.

OPEN All year round

Short breaks available on request.

Low season per wk
£120.00–£285.00
High season per wk
£285.00–£520.00

EAST ALLINGTON, Devon Map ref 1C3

★★★
1 Unit
Sleeping 4

HOMELEIGH
3 Vineyard Terrace, East Allington, Totnes TQ9 7QZ
Contact: Miss Jennifer Tibbs, Agent, 24 Fairlop Close,
Calcot, Reading RG31 7EF
T: (0118) 9412889 (Answerphone)
F: (0118) 9412889
E: j.tibbs@mail.excite.com

OPEN All year round

Low season per wk
£160.00–£190.00
High season per wk
£220.00–£290.00

Pretty stone cottage in quiet village. Comfortable and well-equipped with full central heating and private garden. Dartmoor and sandy beaches are within easy reach.

www.travelengland.org.uk
Log on for information and inspiration. The latest information on places to visit, events and quality assessed accommodation.

EAST ALLINGTON continued

★★★–★★★★★

7 Units
Sleeping 2–12

PITT FARM
East Allington, Totnes TQ9 7QD
Contact: Mr & Mrs C&D Bates, Pitt Farm, Green Lane,
East Allington, Totnes TQ9 7QD
T: (01548) 521234 (Ansaphone)
F: (01548) 521518
E: christopher.bates@ukonline.co.uk
I: www.ukonline.co.uk/christopher.bates/

OPEN All year round
CC: Barclaycard, Delta,
Mastercard, Switch, Visa

Low season per wk
£230.00–£740.00
High season per wk
£437.00–£1,625.00

Located in the heart of South Devon, 7 cottages created by the imaginative conversion of farm buildings to provide spacious and private accommodation. Sleep 2-12 people.

EXBOURNE, Devon Map ref 1C2

★★★

2 Units
Sleeping 4–5

EASTERBROOK FARM COTTAGES
Easterbrook Farm, Exbourne, Okehampton EX20 3QY
Contact: Mr M A Pryce, Easterbrook Farm, Exbourne,
Okehampton EX20 3QY
T: (01837) 851674 & 07831 588183
E: pryce.easterbrook@btinternet.com

Three sympathetically converted barns, 2 sleep 4, 1 sleeps 5, full central heating, linen, gas and electricity included. Peaceful 70-acre farm away from crowded tourist areas. Ideal touring base. Horses and a variety of small animals.

OPEN All year round

Low season per wk
£150.00–£220.00
High season per wk
£350.00–£500.00

EXMOOR

See under Allerford, Bratton, Brayford, Challacombe, Combe Martin, Dulverton, Dunster, Lynton, Minehead, North Molton, Parracombe, Porlock, Timberscombe, Winsford, Withypool, Parracombe

FALMOUTH, Cornwall Map ref 1B3 *Tourist Information Centre Tel: (01326) 312300*

★★★★★

1 Unit
Sleeping 5

TALL SHIPS
12 Campbeltown Way, Port Pendenis, Falmouth TR11 3YE
Contact: Mr M Couldry, 8 Campbeltown Way,
Port Pendennis, Falmouth TR11 3YE
T: (01326) 311440 & 219390 (evenings)
F: (01326) 316781
E: mike.couldry@virgin.net
I: www.cornwall-online.co.uk/tallships

Beautifully equipped 3 bedroom holiday house on Port Pendennis Marina, south facing with patio and balcony. Situated in a private and secure road in Falmouth town close to restaurants etc. Parking and garage, en suite, Sky TV, tennis court. Marina berths can be arranged. Adjacent to the National Maritime Museum.

OPEN All year round

Low season per wk
Min £480.00
High season per wk
Max £880.00

QUALITY ASSURANCE SCHEME
For an explanation of the quality and facilities represented by the Stars please refer to the front of this guide. A more detailed explanation can be found in the information pages at the back.

FAULKLAND, Somerset Map ref 2B2

★★★★★

2 Units
Sleeping 8

LIME KILN FARM

Faulkland, Bath BA3 5XE
Contact: Mrs M J Kendall, Lime Kiln Farm, Faulkland, Bath
BA3 5XE
T: (01373) 834305
E: limekiln@btinternet.com

*Non-working small holding with ponies,
labradors, chickens and 2 flats. Set in the peace
and tranquility of the countryside, 15 minutes
south of Bath. Easy access all major tourist
attractions. Ample parking. Ideal short or long
breaks including winter breaks.*

OPEN All year round

Low season per wk
£285.00–£360.00
High season per wk
£365.00–£495.00

FROME, Somerset Map ref 2B2 *Tourist Information Centre Tel: (01373) 467271*

★★★★–★★★★★★

10 Units
Sleeping 6–12

EXECUTIVE HOLIDAYS

Whitemill Farm, Iron Mills Lane, Oldford, Frome BA11 2NR
T: (01373) 452907 & 07860 147525 (Mobile)
F: (01373) 453253
E: info@executiveholidays.co.uk
I: www.executiveholidays.co.uk
Contact: Mr R A Gregory

*16thC mill and cottage set in their own
individual grounds sleeping up to 12 and 10
respectively. Eight holiday cottages set alongside
our private trout stream, appointed to the
highest standards, sleeping up to 6. Country
setting, 12 miles from Bath, ideal centre for
touring, walking or sporting breaks. Free colour
brochure.*

OPEN All year round
CC: Barclaycard,
Mastercard, Visa

Minimum 2-day breaks
available throughout most of
the year.

Low season per wk
£350.00–£770.00
High season per wk
£790.00–£1,575.00

GLASTONBURY, Somerset Map ref 2A2 *Tourist Information Centre Tel: (01458) 832954*

★★

1 Unit
Sleeping 6

MAGDALENE HOUSE TRUST
38 Magdalene Street, Glastonbury BA6 9EJ
T: (01458) 835235 (During business hours)
Contact: Ms Anne Stallybrass

*Comfortable, first floor flat in Glastonbury between the Abbey and the Tor. Suitable
for holidays, pilgrimage and retreat.*

OPEN All year round

Low season per wk
Min £125.00
High season per wk
Max £300.00

GOODRINGTON, Devon Map ref 1D2

★★–★★★

5 Units
Sleeping 2–6

ASHDENE HOLIDAY APARTMENTS
Cliff Park Road, Goodrington, Paignton TQ4 6NB
T: (01803) 558397 (Ansaphone & fax)
F: (01803) 558397
E: ashdene.apts@goodrington.fsbusiness.co.uk
I: www.paigntondevon.co.uk/ashdene.htm
Contact: Mrs & Mr Jill & David Beckett

*Detached property comprising of 5 self-contained apartments. Private parking.
Goodrington Sands 150 yards, close to zoo and water park.*

OPEN All year round

Low season per wk
£105.00–£385.00
High season per wk
£375.00–£420.00

GORRAN HAVEN, Cornwall Map ref 1B3

★★★

2 Units
Sleeping 6

TREGILLAN
Trewollock Lane, Gorran Haven, St Austell PL26 6NT
T: (01726) 842452
E: tregillan-hol-apts@talk21.com
Contact: Mr and Mrs K Pike

*Comfortable self-contained holiday apartments. Beautiful rural area, 600 yards from
sandy beach and coastal walks. Private parking, garden. Open all year. Winter short
breaks.*

OPEN All year round

Low season per wk
Min £110.00
High season per wk
Max £420.00

GREAT CHEVERELL, Wiltshire Map ref 2B2

★

1 Unit
Sleeping 4

DOWNSWOOD
Great Cheverell, Devizes SN10 5TW
T: (01380) 813304
Contact: Mrs Ros Shepherd

7-acre stud farm. Annexe to small country house. Gardens, lovely surroundings. Adjacent to Salisbury Plain and ideal for touring, walking or riding (horses welcome).

OPEN Feb–Dec

Low season per wk
Max £175.00
High season per wk
Max £180.00

HARTLAND, Devon Map ref 1C1

★★★

3 Units
Sleeping 2–4

YAPHAM COTTAGES

Hartland, Bideford EX39 6AN
Contact: Mrs J Young, Yapham Farm, Hartland, Bideford
EX39 6AN
T: (01237) 441916
E: jane.yapham@virgin.net

Stunning location, wonderful views set down a private half mile drive in 5 acres of beautiful countryside. Yapham offers complete tranquillity yet is perfect for visiting nearby tourist attractions. All 3 cottages are skilful barn conversions, tastefully decorated. A Devon cream tea, fresh fruit and flowers await you on arrival.

OPEN All year round

2-day 'Foodie' break–2 delicious evening meals at local hostelries included in your stay.

Low season per wk
£170.00–£190.00
High season per wk
£270.00–£390.00

HINTON ST GEORGE, Somerset Map ref 1D2

★★★

1 Unit
Sleeping 6

OLD FARM

Hinton St George TA17 8SA
T: (01460) 72553
E: khandavis@btinternet.com
Contact: Mr & Ms Khan-Davis

Thoughtfully converted barn, part of a thatched Grade II Listed property, in the heart of the picturesque Somerset village of Hinton St George. Main bedroom, kitchen/dining area, living room and bathroom on ground floor, additional bedroom in attic. Special features for elderly and disabled. Village shop/post office and office within walking distance.

OPEN All year round

Low season per wk
£175.00–£225.00
High season per wk
£175.00–£250.00

HOLSWORTHY, Devon Map ref 1C2

★★★

1 Unit
Sleeping 6

LEWORTHY COTTAGE

Leworthy Farmhouse, Lower Leworthy, Pyworthy,
Holsworthy EX22 6SJ
T: (01409) 259469
Contact: Mrs Patricia Jennings

Immaculate wing of charming Georgian farmhouse, set in idyllic backwater. Relax in tranquil gardens, orchard. Fish lake. Patio, barbecue, play area. Delightfully appointed lounge. Spacious kitchen, comfortable bedrooms, all with peaceful rural views. Forests, country lanes, meadows, deer, buzzard, pheasant. Profusion of wild flowers, 20 minutes spectacular, beautiful and rugged coast.

OPEN All year round

Discounts for couples.

Low season per wk
£150.00–£210.00
High season per wk
£260.00–£495.00

★★
10 Units
Sleeping 4–7

THORNE MANOR FARM

Holsworthy EX22 7JD
T: (01409) 253685 & 0797 038059 (Mobile phone)
Contact: Mr & Mrs SW Graham

Nine self-catering cottages converted from the old farm buildings. Games room and outdoor pool, squash and tennis courts. Nine miles Bude and beaches. Golf, fishing, cycling and walking within easy reach.

OPEN All year round

Low season per wk
£140.00–£180.00
High season per wk
£200.00–£350.00

HOPE COVE, Devon Map ref 1C3

★★★
10 Units
Sleeping 2–7

THORNLEA MEWS HOLIDAY COTTAGES

Hope Cove, Salcombe TQ7 3HB
T: (01548) 561319
F: (01548) 561319
E: thornleamews@rdplus.net
Contact: Mr & Mrs John & Ann Wilton

Large flat, mews cottages and split level bungalow in pretty south-facing garden, 400 yards from the beach. Superb cliff walks, swimming and sailing. Kingsbridge and Salcombe 10 minutes' drive. Windsurfing and riding nearby. Wide range of good restaurants and pubs in the locality.

OPEN Mar–Oct

Short breaks available in the low season.

Low season per wk
£70.00–£445.00
High season per wk
£140.00–£500.00

HUXHAM, Devon Map ref 1D2

★★★★
7 Units
Sleeping 6–8

BUSSELLS FARM
Huxham, Exeter EX5 4EN
T: (01392) 841238
F: (01392) 841345
E: rob.downey@bussellsfarm.co.uk
I: www.bussellsfarm.co.uk
Contact: Mr & Mrs RS Downey

OPEN All year round
CC: Barclaycard,
Mastercard, Visa

Low season per wk
£300.00–£350.00
High season per wk
£475.00–£650.00

Very high quality barn conversions, beautiful setting in the Exe Valley close to Exeter, with swimming pool, secure fishing lakes, stables and playground.

ILFRACOMBE, Devon Map ref 1C1 *Tourist Information Centre Tel: 0845 458 3630*

★★★★
5 Units
Sleeping 4–6

THE ADMIRALS HOUSE

Ilfracombe
Contact: Miss D Marshall, The Ilfracombe Carlton Hotel, Runnacleave Road, Ilfracombe EX34 8AR
T: (01271) 862446 & 863711
F: (01271) 865379

Stunning apartments in a converted Georgian manor house situated on the quayside in glorious Ilfracombe. All amenities for your convenience and comfort and fabulous harbour views just waiting for you to enjoy.

OPEN All year round
CC: Amex, Barclaycard,
Delta, Mastercard, Switch,
Visa

Short breaks off-season.
Special discounts for couples.

Low season per wk
£180.00–£270.00
High season per wk
£325.00–£550.00

ILMINSTER, Somerset Map ref 1D2

★★★★

1 Unit
Sleeping 8

MYRTLE HOUSE
Church Lane, Horton, Ilminster TA19 9RN
Contact: Mr & Mrs G Denman, 16 Challis Green,
Barrington, Cambridge CB2 5RJ
T: (01223) 871294
E: gordon.denman@earthling.net
I: www.appleorchard.freeserve.co.uk

OPEN All year round
CC: Barclaycard, Delta,
Eurocard, JCB, Maestro,
Mastercard, Solo, Switch,
Visa, Visa Electron

Low season per wk
Min £250.00
High season per wk
Max £550.00

Comfortable and spacious renovated 19thC farmhouse with some features dating back to 17thC. Log fire available. Adjoins fields in quiet village, convenient for countryside and coast.

ISLES OF SCILLY Map ref 1A3 *Tourist Information Centre Tel: (01720) 422536*

★★★

1 Unit
Sleeping 4

PEDNBROSE
McFarlands Down, St Mary's TR21 0NS
Contact: Miss E H Astbury, 23 Wonford Road, Exeter
EX2 4LH
T: (01392) 250050

OPEN Apr–Sep

Low season per wk
£250.00–£400.00
High season per wk
£400.00–£500.00

Cosy, well-equipped bungalow. Quiet, sandy beach, superb sea and island views, golf-course nearby. Bed linen provided. Non-smokers only, please. Dogs by arrangement.

KING'S NYMPTON, Devon Map ref 1C1

★★★

5 Units
Sleeping 2–7

VENN FARM HOLIDAYS
Venn Farm, King's Nympton, Umberleigh EX37 9TR
T: (01769) 572448
E: isla@bmvenn.demon.co.uk
I: www.bmvenn.demon.co.uk
Contact: Mrs I Martin

OPEN Mar–Dec

Low season per wk
£125.00–£300.00
High season per wk
£400.00–£525.00

50-acre livestock farm. Cottages converted from old stone barn situated on small working farm, with views over beautiful countryside to Exmoor and Dartmoor.

KINGSBRIDGE, Devon Map ref 1C3 *Tourist Information Centre Tel: (01548) 853195*

★★★–★★★★★

3 Units
Sleeping 4–7

Set in 4 acres of mature gardens, a 2-bedroomed flat tastefully furnished and with kitchen/diner. Also 2 houses sleeping 6–7, recently converted to a high standard. Ideal for the beach, walkers, bird-watchers. Tennis court. Seven miles from Kingsbridge, between Start Point and Prawle Point. Ten miles Dartmouth.

THE LAURELS, COACH HOUSE & COACHMANS LODGE

Kingsbridge
Contact: Mrs B J Baker, South Allington House,
Chivelstone, Kingsbridge TQ7 2NB
T: (01548) 511272
F: (01548) 511421
E: barbara@sthallingtonbnb.demon.co.uk
I: www.sthallingtonbnb.demon.co.uk

OPEN All year round

Low season per wk
£157.00–£263.00
High season per wk
£276.00–£594.00

★★★

2 Units
Sleeping 4–6

READS FARM
Loddiswell, Kingsbridge TQ7 4RT
T: (01548) 550317
F: (01548) 550317
Contact: Mrs A Pethybridge

OPEN Apr–Oct

Low season per wk
£90.00–£180.00
High season per wk
£190.00–£350.00

Flats are part of farmhouse in an Area of Outstanding Natural Beauty. Farmland adjoins River Avon. Fishing. Heated swimming pool.

IDEAS For ideas on places to visit refer to the introduction at the beginning of this section.

LACOCK, Wiltshire Map ref 2B2

★★★★

2 Units
Sleeping 4–5

Tastefully converted beamed farm building with many original features, 1.5 miles from NT village. Cheese House sleeps 5 plus cot and has an extra seating area on 2nd floor – 'The Gallery' with portable TV. Cyder House sleeps 4. Stepped fireplace with woodburning stove. Private garden with furniture and barbecue.

CYDER HOUSE AND CHEESE HOUSE

Wick Farm, Wick Lane, Lacock, Chippenham SN15 2LU
T: (01249) 730244 & 07957 417915
F: (01249) 730072
E: kingsilverlands2@btinternet.com
Contact: Mr and Mrs Philip & Susan King

OPEN All year round

3 night stays Oct–Apr (excl holiday times).

Low season per wk
£200.00–£265.00
High season per wk
£295.00–£420.00

LANGPORT, Somerset Map ref 1D1

★★★–★★★★★

2 Units
Sleeping 5

MUCHELNEY HAM FARM
Muchelney, Langport TA10 0DJ
T: (01458) 250737
F: (01458) 250737
I: www.muchelneyhamfarm.co.uk
Contact: Mrs Ann Woodborne

OPEN All year round

Low season per wk
Min £150.00
High season per wk
Max £395.00

Cider house, extension built in c1979 to main farmhouse. Two bedrooms, 1 double, 1 double and single, 2 bathrooms-1 shower en suite. Large sitting, dining, kitchen. Ample parking.

LANNER, Cornwall Map ref 1B3

★★★

1 Unit

Ground floor flat, part of detached house in 0.75 acre garden with countryside views. Comprises spacious lounge/dining, patio doors, modern pine kitchen, bathroom, double bedroom leading to single bedroom. Ideally situated to explore north and south coasts, with walking, cycling, riding, sailing, local country pubs and village shops nearby.

LITTLE SHALOM

Pennance Road, Lanner, Redruth TR16 5TQ
Contact: Powell's Cottage Holidays, High Street, Saundersfoot SA69 9EJ
T: (01834) 812791
F: (01834) 811731
E: info@powells.co.uk
I: www.powells.co.uk

OPEN All year round

Low season per wk
£200.00–£300.00
High season per wk
£350.00–£450.00

USE YOUR *i*s

There are more than 550 Tourist Information Centres throughout England offering friendly help with accommodation and holiday ideas as well as suggestions of places to visit and things to do. You'll find TIC addresses in the local Phone Book.

★★★

5 Units
Sleeping 3–7

THE OLD RECTORY

Lanreath-by-Looe, Looe PL13 2NU
T: (01503) 220247
F: (01503) 220108
E: ask@oldrectory-lanreath.co.uk
I: www.oldrectory-lanreath.co.uk
Contact: Mr and Mrs C Duncan

Gracious Georgian mansion with spacious, fully-equipped apartments. Enjoy large, beautiful, secluded gardens with heated swimming pool. Edge of picturesque, tranquil village offering all amenities – set in breathtaking countryside only minutes from pretty fishing villages and beaches. Many superb stately homes and beautiful gardens to visit. Parking for 8 cars.

OPEN All year round
CC: Barclaycard, Delta,
Eurocard, Mastercard,
Switch, Visa

Low season per wk
£110.00–£240.00
High season per wk
£285.00–£640.00

★★★–★★★★

8 Units
Sleeping 4–8

BAMHAM FARM COTTAGES

Higher Bamham Farm, Launceston PL15 9LD
T: (01566) 772141
F: (01566) 775266
E: jackie@bamhamfarm.co.uk
I: www.cottages-cornwall.co.uk
Contact: Mrs J A Chapman

Eight individually designed cottages, ideally situated in beautiful countryside 1 mile from Launceston, the ancient capital of Cornwall, dominated by its Norman castle. The north and south coasts are easily accessible as are both Dartmoor and Bodmin Moor. Facilities include a heated indoor swimming pool, sauna, solarium, video recorders and trout fishing.

OPEN All year round
CC: Barclaycard, Delta,
Eurocard, Mastercard,
Solo, Switch, Visa

For special offers see our website www.cottages-cornwall.co.uk

Low season per wk
£190.00–£360.00
High season per wk
£250.00–£850.00

★★–★★★★

3 Units
Sleeping 2–5

LANGDON FARM COTTAGE
Langdon Farm, Boyton, Launceston PL15 8NW
Contact: Mrs F Rawlinson, Langdon Farm, Boyton,
Launceston PL15 8NW
T: (01566) 785389
E: g.f.rawlinson@btinternet.com

South-facing 1 bedroomed Victorian cottage, attached to the end of a 17thC farmhouse. Private garden and south-facing terrace. Local pub, telephone about half a mile away.

OPEN Mar–Dec

Low season per wk
£140.00–£210.00
High season per wk
£230.00–£250.00

★★★

1 Unit
Sleeping 2–6

SWALLOWS

Lower Dutson Farm, Launceston PL15 9SP
Contact: Mrs Kathryn Broad, Lower Dutson Farm,
Launceston PL15 9SP
T: (01566) 776456
F: (01566) 776456
E: francis.broad@btclick.com

The charm of a 17thC farmhouse furnished with up-to-date comforts makes an ideal touring base. First farm in Cornwall by the A388 halfway between north/south coasts. NT properties and moors. Two miles from Launceston's Norman castle, winding streets and unique carved church. River and lake fishing.

OPEN All year round

Salmon and trout in the River Tamar and coarse lake fishing available free for guests.

Low season per wk
£120.00–£250.00
High season per wk
£280.00–£400.00

★★★

7 Units
Sleeping 2–8

LOWER CAMPSCOTT FARM

Lee, Ilfracombe EX34 8LS
T: (01271) 863479
F: (01271) 867639
E: setaside@msn.com
Contact: Mrs M Cowell

Converted from our farm buildings, we have 4 charming character cottages. Tastefully furnished and everything supplied to make your stay special as is also in our 2 holiday homes and new lodge home. Peaceful farm setting with views across the Bristol Channel. Lee and Woolacombe beaches are easily accessible.

OPEN All year round

Short breaks available out of school holidays.

Low season per wk
£140.00–£300.00
High season per wk
£280.00–£560.00

★★★★

1 Unit
Sleeping 4

BEECHLEIGH COTTAGE
Tregondale Farm, Menheniot, Liskeard PL14 3RG
T: (01579) 342407
F: (01579) 342407
E: tregondale@connectfree.co.uk
I: www.tregondalefarm.co.uk
Contact: Mrs S Rowe

OPEN All year round

Low season per wk
£120.00–£250.00
High season per wk
£300.00–£500.00

'Something Special'. Charming, cosy, peaceful, en suite character cottage. Woodburner, barbecue, tennis court. Woodland farm trail, beautiful wild flowers, fishing, walking, cycling. Just come and explore.

★★★

2 Units
Sleeping 4–5

LODGE BARTON
Lamellion, Liskeard PL14 4JX
T: (01579) 344432
F: (01579) 344432
E: lodgebart@aol.com
I: www.selectideas.co.uk/lodgebarton
Contact: Mrs R Hodin

OPEN All year round

Low season per wk
£120.00–£150.00
High season per wk
£350.00–£450.00

Idyllic farm setting with goats, ducks, woods. Sunny character cottages, well-equipped and within easy reach of beaches and moors.

★★★

2 Units
Sleeping 5

LOOKWEEP FARM COTTAGES
Lookweep Farm, Liverton, Newton Abbot TQ12 6HT
T: (01626) 833277
F: (01626) 834412
E: holidays@lookweep.co.uk
I: www.lookweep.co.uk
Contact: Mrs Helen Griffiths

OPEN All year round
CC: Barclaycard, Delta,
Eurocard, Mastercard,
Switch, Visa

Low season per wk
£210.00–£240.00
High season per wk
£300.00–£500.00

Two attractive well-equipped stone cottages with swimming pool in tranquil Dartmoor setting surrounded by open farmland and woods. Two miles from Bovey Tracey and Haytor.

AT-A-GLANCE SYMBOLS

Symbols at the end of each accommodation entry give useful information about services and facilities. A key to symbols can be found inside the back cover flap. Keep this open for easy reference.

★★★★–★★★★★★

5 Units
Sleeping 2–8

BUCKLAWREN FARM

St Martins, Looe PL13 1NZ
T: (01503) 240738
F: (01503) 240481
E: bucklawren@compuserve.com
I: www.cornwallexplore.co.uk/bucklawren
Contact: Mrs J Henly

Set deep in unspoilt countryside, with a large garden and exceptional sea views, these delightful stone cottages on an award-winning farm are just 1 mile from the beach and 3 miles from the fishing port of Looe. The Granary Restaurant close by.

OPEN All year round
CC: Barclaycard,
Mastercard, Visa

Low season per wk
£130.00–£250.00
High season per wk
£270.00–£750.00

★★★★

23 Units
Sleeping 2–10

CRYLLA VALLEY COTTAGES

Notter Bridge, Saltash PL12 4RN
T: (01752) 851133
F: (01752) 851666
E: sales@cryllacottages.co.uk
I: www.cryllacottages.co.uk
Contact: Mrs M Walsh

Award-winning cottages and bungalows in beautiful riverside setting between Looe and Plymouth. 18 acres of grounds and attractive flower gardens. Play area. Ideal for fishing, golf, walking, riding, sailing, town and coast, visiting historic houses and gardens and touring Cornwall and Devon. Country inn close by for good food.

OPEN All year round
CC: Barclaycard, Delta,
Mastercard, Switch, Visa

Free leisure membership to nearby Golf and Country Club: 3 pools, gym, sauna, jacuzzi, racquets.

Low season per wk
£137.00–£364.00
High season per wk
£235.00–£651.00

★★★★

11 Units
Sleeping 4–8

ROCK TOWERS APARTMENTS
Marine Drive, Hannafore, West Looe, Looe PL13 2DQ
Contact: Mr Clive Dixon, Cornish Collection,
73 Bodrigan Road, Barbican, East Looe, Looe PL13 1EH
T: (01503) 262736 & 07768 752936
F: (01503) 262736
E: cornishcol@aol.com
I: www.cornishcollection.co.uk

The apartments are situated on the front at West Looe with excellent views of the beach, estuary and sea.

OPEN All year round
CC: Barclaycard, Delta,
Mastercard, Switch, Visa,
Visa Electron

Low season per wk
£185.00–£395.00
High season per wk
£485.00–£850.00

★★★★

1 Unit
Sleeping 4

WELL MEADOW COTTAGE
Coldrinnick Farm, Duloe, Liskeard PL14 4QF
Contact: Mrs Kaye Chapman, Coldrinnick Farm, Duloe,
Liskeard PL14 4QF
T: (01503) 220251 & 07977 378916
E: kaye@coldrinnick.fsnet.co.uk

An attractively converted barn with large garden, in secluded countryside. On working dairy farm, outstanding views and walks. Dogs and children welcome.

OPEN All year round

Low season per wk
£150.00–£260.00
High season per wk
£260.00–£395.00

ACCESSIBILITY

Look for the symbols which indicate accessibility for wheelchair users. A list of establishments is at the front of this guide.

LOSTWITHIEL, Cornwall Map ref 1B2

★★★-★★★★

7 Units
Sleeping 2–6

Charming selection of Georgian estate cottages nestling in the Fowey Valley with two delightful waterside properties. Cottages with leaded light windows, real fires, 4-poster bed and well lit. Working water wheel, parkland, river frontage and boat. Woodland and riverside walks from your cottage door. So much more than just a cottage!

LANWITHAN MANOR, FARM & WATERSIDE COTTAGES

Lanwithan Cottages, Lostwithiel PL22 0LA
Contact: Mr H F Edward-Collins, Lanwithan Cottages, Lostwithiel PL22 0LA
T: (01208) 872444
F: (01208) 872444
E: HEC@ukgateway.net

OPEN All year round
CC: Barclaycard, Mastercard, Visa

Short breaks out of season. Pets accepted in some cottages.

Low season per wk
£125.00–£195.00
High season per wk
£320.00–£750.00

★★★★

9 Units
Sleeping 2–6

Winners of 6 awards in 5 years, including 'Best Self-Catering Holiday of the Year' for the whole of England. With all the ingredients for a perfect holiday you are bound to want to come back. Equally suitable for couples or families. Visit our website or phone for a brochure.

TREDETHICK FARM COTTAGES

Little Bakes, Tredethick, Lostwithiel PL22 0LE
T: (01208) 873618
F: (01208) 873618
E: holidays@tredethick.co.uk
I: www.tredethick.co.uk
Contact: Mr & Mrs Tim & Nicky Reed

OPEN All year round
CC: Amex, Barclaycard, Delta, Diners, Eurocard, JCB, Maestro, Mastercard, Solo, Switch, Visa, Visa Electron

Short breaks from Nov-Apr (excl Christmas and New Year).

Low season per wk
£170.00–£250.00
High season per wk
£250.00–£880.00

LYME REGIS, Dorset Map ref 1D2 *Tourist Information Centre Tel: (01297) 442138*

★★★

1 Unit
Sleeping 6

COOMBE HAYES FARM COTTAGE
Wadley Hill, Uplyme, Lyme Regis DT7 3SU
T: (01297) 445744
E: rozduffin@excite.co.uk
I: www.lymeregis.com
Contact: Mrs R Duffin

Attractive stone cottage on small farm near sea and Lyme Regis. Spacious, comfortably furnished rooms. Large private garden. Ample parking. Lovely rural views. Quiet location.

OPEN All year round

Low season per wk
£200.00–£325.00
High season per wk
£350.00–£495.00

★★★

4 Units
Sleeping 4–6

ST ANDREWS HOLIDAY FLATS
Uplyme Road, Lyme Regis DT7 3LP
T: (01297) 445495 (Ansaphone)
F: (01297) 445495
Contact: Mrs Cynthia Wendy McHardy

Luxury accommodation 10 minutes to beach and town, parking, swimming pool, play area, patio, lawns and views.

OPEN All year round

Low season per wk
£120.00–£150.00
High season per wk
£150.00–£320.00

PRICES

Please check prices and other details at the time of booking.

★★★★

4 Units
Sleeping 3–4

SEA TREE HOUSE

18 Broad Street, Lyme Regis DT7 3QE
T: (01297) 442244
F: (01297) 442244
E: seatree.house@ukonline.co.uk
I: www.lymeregis.com/seatreehouse
Contact: Mr David Parker

Romantic, elegant apartments overlooking the sea, 3 minutes from the beach. Spacious living room with dining area overlooking the sea. Central position giving easy access to restaurants, pubs and walks in Area of Outstanding Natural Beauty. Warm, friendly welcome from owners.

OPEN All year round

Additional art studio available to small groups and individuals.

Low season per wk
£210.00–£320.00
High season per wk
£350.00–£525.00

LYNTON, Devon Map ref 1C1 *Tourist Information Centre Tel: 0845 458 3775*

★★★★

1 Unit
Sleeping 2

ROYAL CASTLE LODGE

Castle Hill, Lynton EX35
Contact: Mr M Wolverson, Prime Spot Holiday Cottages, Stag Cottage, Holdstone Down, Combe Martin, Ilfracombe EX34 0PF
T: (01271) 882449 & 0777 9861643 (Mobile)

Something special! High quality 16thC, detached, thatched, stone cottage with rustic balcony, stable door, real fire, garden. Idyllic coastal setting in England's 'Little Switzerland', Exmoor National Park, wooded outlook with harbour, pubs, restaurants, shops within walking distance. Spectacular walks, spotless, warm and cosy, off-season short breaks, perfect honeymoon/anniversaries.

OPEN All year round

De-stressing breaks Nov–Mar. All welcome who appreciate quality, privacy and no petty restrictions.

Low season per wk
£205.00–£300.00
High season per wk
£300.00–£495.00

MALMESBURY, Wiltshire Map ref 2B2 *Tourist Information Centre Tel: (01666) 823748*

★★★

2 Units
Sleeping 3

COW BYRE AND BULL PEN

Stonehill Farm, Charlton, Malmesbury SN16 9DY
T: (01666) 823310
F: (01666) 823310
E: johnedna@stonehillfarm.fsnet.co.uk
Contact: Mrs Edna Edwards

Superbly located on edge of Cotswolds in rolling countryside. Two converted barns offering cosy comfort in bedroom, sitting room, kitchen/diner and bathroom. Pets and children welcome. Perfect for visiting the Cotswold hills and villages, Bath, Oxford and Stonehenge.

OPEN All year round

Low season per wk
Min £180.00
High season per wk
Max £230.00

MARAZION, Cornwall Map ref 1B3

★★

1 Unit
Sleeping 3

TREGEW VEAN
Rose Hill, Marazion TR17 0HB
Contact: Mrs J H Pool, Tregew, Rose Hill, Marazion TR17 0HB
T: (01736) 710247

OPEN All year round

Low season per wk
£150.00–£200.00
High season per wk
£240.00–£330.00

Quiet, self-contained flat with magnificent views over Mount's Bay. Few minutes' walk to beach and village. Parking. Personally supervised. Regret no pets.

SYMBOLS The symbols in each entry give information about services and facilities. A key to these symbols appears at the back of this guide.

MARK, Somerset Map ref 1D1

★★★

1 Unit
Sleeping 4

YARDWALL HOUSE
Yardwall Road, Mark, Highbridge TA9 4QE
T: (01278) 641453 (Ansaphone)
F: (01278) 641673
E: yardwall@tesco.net
Contact: Mrs Lynne Smith

OPEN Mar–Nov

Low season per wk
£200.00–£230.00
High season per wk
£230.00–£295.00

Peaceful detached cottage, 2 bedrooms, sitting room, bathroom, modern kitchen, conservatory opens on to garden. Overlooks open Somerset countryside. Easy access M5.

MEMBURY, Devon Map ref 1D2

★★★★

5 Units
Sleeping 2–5

GOODMANS HOUSE

Furley, Membury, Nr Axminster EX13 7TU
T: (01404) 881690
Contact: Mrs Patricia Spencer

Cleverly converted stone cottages/suites in 9-acre grounds of Georgian country house. All units enjoy peace, tranquility, privacy and wonderful views. Country soft furnishings, antique pine. Central heating. Colour TV, microwave, etc. Pretty bathrooms. Restored 16thC house, inglenooks, offers candlelit dining with superb food, imaginative menus, only fresh produce, lots organic.

OPEN Feb–Nov &
Christmas

Inclusive break packages
Christmas, New Year,
Valentines, Easter.
Complimentary bottle of
wine. Year 2000 prices held.

Low season per wk
£190.00–£305.00
High season per wk
£305.00–£400.00

MENHENIOT, Cornwall Map ref 1C2

★★★-★★★★★

2 Units
Sleeping 2–5

TREWINT FARM

Menheniot, Liskeard PL14 3RE
T: (01579) 347155
F: (01579) 347155
I: www.geocities.com/trewint_2000
Contact: Mrs Elizabeth Rowe

Come and enjoy a relaxing holiday at Trewint Farm. Two cottages sleeping 2-5 with all the extras to provide 'home from home' comforts. Wander around our working family farm, children can enjoy Rusty the pony, Pets Corner, trampoline, new games and fitness room. Ideal for touring garden visits, National Trust, Eden Project, Looe and Polperro.

OPEN All year round

Low season per wk
£150.00–£300.00
High season per wk
£300.00–£500.00

TOWN INDEX

This can be found at the back of the guide. If you know where you want to stay, the index will give you the page number listing accommodation in your chosen town, city or village.

MEVAGISSEY, Cornwall Map ref 1B3

★★★★

3 Units
Sleeping 4–6

TRELEAVEN FARM COTTAGES

Treleaven Farm, Mevagissey, St Austell PL26 6RZ
T: (01726) 843558 & 842413
F: (01726) 843558
E: linda.hennah@btinternet.com
I: www.treleavenfarm.co.uk
Contact: Mr L Hennah

Delightful, well-cared for cottages overlooking the village and within easy walking distance. Close to Heligan, Eden, many other gardens, walks and attractions. Kitchens with full-size cooker, dishwasher, fridge/freezer, microwave. TV, video, hi-fi. Laundry room, games barn, putting green. Equipped to a very high standard. Sorry, no pets.

OPEN All year round

Short stay breaks, 3 nights from £100 for 2. Oct–Easter (excl Christmas).

Low season per wk
£100.00–£250.00
High season per wk
£350.00–£650.00

★★★

13 Units
Sleeping 2–6

TRELOEN HOLIDAY APARTMENTS
Dept E, Polkirt Hill, Mevagissey, St Austell PL26 6UX
T: (01726) 842406
F: (01726) 842406
E: holidays@treloen.co.uk
I: www.treloen.co.uk
Contact: Mr and Mrs C J Seamark

Quality apartments in secluded clifftop setting, all with spectacular sea views and private balconies/patios. 450 metres picturesque harbour, shops, beach. Ten miles Eden project.

OPEN All year round
CC: Barclaycard, Delta, Diners, Eurocard, JCB, Switch, Visa, Visa Electron

Low season per wk
£129.00–£182.00
High season per wk
£284.00–£510.00

MINEHEAD, Somerset Map ref 1D1 *Tourist Information Centre Tel: (01643) 702624*

★★★★

1 Unit
Sleeping 4

ANCHOR COTTAGE
21 Quay Street, Minehead TA24 5UL
Contact: Dr J C Malin, 3 The Courtyard, Bancks Street,
Minehead TA24 5DJ
T: (01643) 707529
F: (01643) 708712

Delightful 17thC fisherman's cottage facing Bristol Channel, with rear patio giving superb views. Two double bedrooms, attic bedroom, bathroom/WC, fully-equipped kitchen, lounge and downstairs WC.

OPEN Apr–Dec

Low season per wk
£255.00–£300.00
High season per wk
£305.00–£410.00

★★★

2 Units
Sleeping 4–5

FISHERMANS COTTAGES
59/41 Quay Street, Minehead TA24 5UL
Contact: Mrs PDR Martin, 57 Quay Street, Minehead
TA24 5UL
T: (01643) 704263

Both cottages are situated overlooking Minehead Harbour and Minehead Bay. Close to the town centre and seafront.

OPEN All year round

Low season per wk
£130.00–£160.00
High season per wk
£260.00

MINIONS, Cornwall Map ref 1C2

★★★★

3 Units
Sleeping 3–4

TREWALLA FARM

Minions, Liskeard PL14 6ED
Contact: Fiona Cotter, Trewalla Farm, Minions, Liskeard
PL14 6ED
T: (01579) 342385
F: (01579) 342385

Three cottages equipped and furnished to a high standard on a small farm in an Area of Outstanding Natural Beauty. overlooking Siblyback Lake, the location offers perfect peace and an ideal base for walking as well as touring both coastlines or visiting the Eden project – if you can tear yourself away!

OPEN Mar–Dec

Weekend breaks available on low season.

Low season per wk
£205.00–£260.00
High season per wk
£340.00–£415.00

MODBURY, Devon Map ref 1C3

★★★★

4 Units
Sleeping 2–6

OLDAPORT FARM COTTAGES
Modbury, Ivybridge PL21 0TG
T: (01548) 830842
F: (01548) 830998
E: cathy.evans@dial.pipex.com
I: www.oldaport.dial.pipex.com
Contact: Miss C M Evans

OPEN All year round

Low season per wk
£149.00–£238.00
High season per wk
£288.00–£448.00

Comfortable cottages sited on historic small sheep farm in the beautiful Erme Valley, 8 miles from Dartmoor. Sandy beach nearby.

MORCOMBELAKE, Dorset Map ref 1D2

★★★

1 Unit
Sleeping 6

NORCHARD FARMHOUSE
Norchard Barn, Morcombelake, Bridport DT6 6EP
T: (01297) 489263
F: (01297) 489661
Contact: Mrs M Ollard

OPEN Mar–Dec

Low season per wk
Min £250.00
High season per wk
Min £550.00

Spacious converted barn in spectacular coastal setting, surrounded by Natonal Trust land. No traffic, no bright lights.

MORETONHAMPSTEAD, Devon Map ref 1C2

★★–★★★★

7 Units
Sleeping 2–6

BUDLEIGH FARM
Moretonhampstead, Newton Abbot TQ13 8SB
T: (01647) 440835 & 440436
E: swharvey@budleighfarm.co.uk
I: www.budleighfarm.co.uk
Contact: Mrs J Harvey

Seven properties created with flair from granite barns, on a farm at the end of a stunning valley – rural but not remote. Easy to find. Superb gardens, pubs of character, beaches and castles are all accessible. Superb walking country. In Dartmoor National Park.

OPEN All year round
CC: Barclaycard, Eurocard, Mastercard, Visa

Low season per wk
£115.00–£269.00
High season per wk
£215.00–£399.00

MOSTERTON, Dorset Map ref 1D2

★★

1 Unit
Sleeping 6

RIVERSIDE
Bakers Mill Farm, Mosterton, Beaminster DT8 3HQ
Contact: Mrs Young, 61 Clifton Road, Southampton
SO15 4GY
T: (023) 8077 1729

OPEN All year round

Low season per wk
£100.00–£200.00
High season per wk
£200.00–£410.00

Bungalow on working farm between Crewkerne and Beaminster. Access and facilities for wheelchairs and disabled. Large sun lounge overlooking fields, large secure kennel and secure gardens.

CHECK THE MAPS
The colour maps at the front of this guide show all the cities, towns and villages for which you will find accommodation entries. Refer to the town index to find the page on which they are listed.

MOTHECOMBE, Devon Map ref 1C3

★★★-★★★★★
7 Units
Sleeping 5–12

The Flete Estate is undoubtedly the Jewel in the Crown of the beautiful South Hams. This private 5,000-acre estate is designated an Area of Outstanding Natural Beauty, encompassing large broadleaf woodlands, rolling pastures, cliff paths and sandy beaches, secluded cottages, little hamlets and a tantalising lacework of private drives and pathways.

THE FLETE ESTATE HOLIDAY COTTAGES

Mothecombe, Holbeton, Plymouth PL8 1LA
T: (01752) 830253
F: (01752) 830500
E: cottages@flete.co.uk
I: www.flete.co.uk
Contact: Miss J Webb

OPEN All year round		Low season per wk £330.00–£750.00
Winter breaks minimum 3 nights Nov–Mar (excl Christmas and New Year) from £85 per night.		High season per wk £710.00–£1,230.00

ⓂⓈ M ◎ ▤ ⊙ 🖥 📺 🎱 🔥 ☕️ 📞 P ∪ ♪ ✿ 🐴 🐾 SP

MULLION COVE, Cornwall Map ref 1B3

★★★-★★★★
5 Units
Sleeping 2–5

Our properties at Mullion Cove are situated in 2.5 acres of grounds, a quarter of a mile off road with superb sea views and close to the National Trust harbour and the coastal footpath. Central heating all year, bed linen included, pets accepted. Friday and Saturday changeover.

POLPEOR HOLIDAY APARTMENTS AND COTTAGES

Mullion Cove, Helston TR12 7EU
Contact: Mr M Raftery, Mullion Cottages, Churchtown, Mullion, Helston TR12 7HN
T: (01326) 240315
F: (01326) 241090
E: bookings@mullioncottages.com
I: www.mullioncottages.com

OPEN Feb–Dec		Low season per wk £175.00–£260.00
CC: Barclaycard, Delta, Eurocard, JCB, Maestro, Mastercard, Solo, Switch, Visa, Visa Electron		High season per wk £375.00–£625.00

ⓂⓈ M ◎ ▤ ▥ ⊙ 🖥 📺 🔥 ☕️ 📞 P ✿ 🐴 SP

MYLOR, Cornwall Map ref 1B3

★
2 Units
Sleeping 2–6

ALBION HOUSE COTTAGES
Mylor, Falmouth TR11 5SQ
Contact: Mrs P Polglase, Albion House, Mylor,
Falmouth TR11 5SQ
T: (01326) 373607
F: (01326) 377607

OPEN Mar–Nov

Low season per wk £195.00–£365.00	High season per wk £395.00–£525.00

Situated in an AONB close to waterside pub. Convenient for surf beaches, yacht harbour, gardens and National Maritime Museum. Converted stable and coach house. Patio courtyard, barbecue.

ⓂⓈ M ◎ ▤ ▥ ⊙ 🖥 📺 🔥 ☕️ 📞 P ⚲ ♪ ✿ 🐴 SP

NANSTALLON, Cornwall Map ref 1B2

★★★★★
2 Units
Sleeping 5–6

TREGARTHEN COTTAGES
Nanstallon, Bodmin PL30 5LB
T: (01208) 831570 (Ansaphone) &
(01841) 533147 (Mornings, not Wed)
F: (01208) 831570
E: enquiries@tregarthencottages.co.uk
I: www.tregarthencottages.co.uk
Contact: Mrs Margaret Bealing

OPEN All year round

Low season per wk £150.00–£250.00	High season per wk £250.00–£500.00

Three-bedroomed property with 1 room en suite. Two-bedroomed property with 1 room en suite. Fully-equipped, detached properties with own garden areas, 50 yards from Camel Trail.

ⓂⓈ ◎ ▥ ⊙ 🖥 📺 🔥 ☕️ 📞 P ∪ ✿ 🐴 🐾 SP

NEWTON FERRERS, Devon Map ref 1C3

★★★

1 Unit
Sleeping 5

UPWOOD
Court Road, Newton Ferrers, Plymouth PL8 1DA
T: (01752) 872286
E: aline@upwood54.freeserve.co.uk
Contact: Mrs A M Stackhouse

OPEN All year round

Low season per wk
Min £170.00
High season per wk
Max £270.00

Ground floor flat, equipped to high standard. Easy reach of sea, moors, National Trust coastline. Sailing, riding, walking. Cot available. Garden, delightful views.

NORTH MOLTON, Devon Map ref 1C1

★★★★

1 Unit
Sleeping 5

THE BYRE
Limeslake, North Molton, South Molton EX36 3LY
T: (01598) 740494
E: fade@limeslake.freeserve.co.uk
Contact: Mr C R Fade

Close to quiet, southern edge of Exmoor. Spacious accommodation in tranquil setting at end of private drive with outstanding views. Ideal for walking, cycling or riding. The sandy beaches of the north Devon coastline, the North Devon Coastal Path, Saunton Sands and Royal North Devon golf clubs are within a short car ride.

OPEN All year round

Low season per wk
£250.00–£395.00
High season per wk
£350.00–£395.00

★★-★★★★

3 Units
Sleeping 2–8

WEST MILLBROOK FARM
West Millbrook, Twitchen, South Molton EX36 3LP
T: (01598) 740382
I: www.north.molton.co.uk
Contact: Mrs R J Courtney

Farm bordering Exmoor surrounded by pleasant gardens and beautiful, peaceful countryside. Situated a mile from North Molton village with easy access from North Devon link road. Ideal for touring Exmoor and North Devon/Somerset coast and beaches. Games room, play area. Out-of-season short breaks. Colour brochure available.

OPEN All year round

Low season per wk
Min £65.00
High season per wk
Max £350.00

OAKFORD, Devon Map ref 1D1

★★★★

1 Unit
Sleeping 5

APPLE TREE COTTAGE
Oakford, Tiverton EX16 9EW
Contact: Ms C Booth, 47 Bradley Gardens, Ealing,
London W13 8HE
T: (020) 8997 8028 (Ansaphone) & 7330 4955
F: (020) 8997 3633
E: claire@appletreeoakford.fsnet.co.uk
I: www.appletree-oakford.co.uk

OPEN All year round
CC: Barclaycard, Delta,
Mastercard, Solo, Switch,
Visa

Low season per wk
£265.00–£350.00
High season per wk
£350.00–£525.00

Pretty stone cottage in peaceful conservation village above beautiful Exe Valley, close to Exmoor. Very comfortable accommodation, log fire, 3 bedrooms, 2 WCs. Sunny garden.

SPECIAL BREAKS
Many establishments offer special promotions and themed breaks. These are highlighted in red. (All such offers are subject to availability.)

★★★★
1 Unit
Sleeping 4

Set deep in the heart of Devon's beautiful countryside, this charming well-maintained annexe is ideally situated for exploring Exmoor. Or if you prefer you can relax and enjoy the peaceful surroundings in our picturesque garden with its pond and summerhouse. An adjoining paddock is available for your pets to play in.

COOMBE COTTAGE

Oakford, Tiverton EX16 9HF
Contact: Mrs Mary Reed, Coombe House, Oakford,
Tiverton EX16 9HF
T: (01398) 351281
F: (01398) 351211
E: coombehse@aol.com
I: www.exmoor-holiday-cottage.co.uk

OPEN All year round

Low season per wk
£125.00–£200.00
High season per wk
£200.00–£330.00

OKEHAMPTON, Devon Map ref 1C2

★★★★
2 Units
Sleeping 4–6

BEER FARM
Okehampton EX20 1SG
T: (01837) 840265
F: (01837) 840245
E: beerfarm.oke@which.net
I: www.beerfarm.co.uk
Contact: Mr & Mrs R&S Annear

OPEN All year round

Low season per wk
£160.00–£290.00
High season per wk
£350.00–£490.00

Former barn, now 2 comfortable cottages, on small farm, edge of Dartmoor. Video, microwave, dishwasher. Children welcome. Dogs/horse by arrangement. Excellent walking/touring base.

★★★★
4 Units
Sleeping 2–12

LITTLE BIDLAKE BARNS

Bridestowe, Okehampton EX20 4NS
T: (01837) 861233
F: (01837) 861233
E: bidlakefrm@aol.com
I: www.littlebidlakefarm.co.uk
Contact: Mrs J Down

Luxury fully-equipped barn conversions on fringe of Dartmoor. Four units sleeping 2, 4, 6 and 12. Original beams, arched windows and underfloor heating. Most rooms en suite with TVs. Perfect for touring Devon and Cornwall. Cycling, fishing, golf, riding, walking or water pursuits all local. Bring your own horse on holiday and try our Dartmoor Horse Trails.

OPEN All year round
CC: Barclaycard, Eurocard,
Mastercard, Switch, Visa

Special offer short breaks
available Nov–Mar (excl
Christmas and New Year).

Low season per wk
£230.00–£600.00
High season per wk
£370.00–£875.00

COUNTRY CODE Always follow the Country Code ✿ Enjoy the countryside and respect its life and work ✿ Guard against all risk of fire ✿ Fasten all gates ✿ Keep your dogs under close control ✿ Keep to public paths across farmland ✿ Use gates and stiles to cross fences, hedges and walls ✿ Leave livestock, crops and machinery alone ✿ Take your litter home ✿ Help to keep all water clean ✿ Protect wildlife, plants and trees ✿ Take special care on country roads ✿ Make no unnecessary noise

★★★★
4 Units
Sleeping 4–8

Delightful barn conversions on working sheep farm, furnished to high standards. Lounge, well equipped fitted kitchens/dining areas, outdoor heated swimming pool, gardens and patio, barbecue areas. Dartmoor just a walk away. Pony trekking, walking, cycling, fishing or just simply relax. Home from home, cream tea. 3 new coarse fishing lakes.

WEEK FARM COUNTRY HOLIDAYS

Week Farm, Bridestowe, Okehampton EX20 4HZ
T: (01837) 861221
F: (01837) 861221
E: accomm@weekfarmonline.com
I: www.weekfarmonline.com
Contact: Mrs Margaret Hockridge

OPEN All year round

Fishing weekends based on 3 well-stocked coarse fishing lakes.

Low season per wk
£200.00–£530.00
High season per wk
£480.00–£740.00

OWERMOIGNE, Dorset Map ref 2B3

★★
1 Unit
Sleeping 7

JASMINE COTTAGE
11 Moreton Road, Owermoigne, Dorchester DT2 8HT
Contact: Mrs J Lawton, 9 Moreton Road, Owermoigne,
Dorchester DT2 8HT
T: (01305) 854457

OPEN All year round

Low season per wk
£200.00–£275.00
High season per wk
£275.00–£385.00

Enjoy the pleasure of village life at this country cottage, 3 miles from the sea.

PADSTOW, Cornwall Map ref 1B2 *Tourist Information Centre Tel: (01841) 533449*

★★★
1 Unit
Sleeping 4

FUCHSIA COTTAGE
16 Sarah's View, Sarah's Lane, Padstow PL28 8DU
Contact: Mrs N Lumley, Magnolia Cottage,
1 College Mews, Stokesley, Middlesbrough TS9 5DJ
T: (01642) 710732
E: lumley@magnolia1.fsnet.co.uk
I: www.fuchsiacottage.co.uk

OPEN All year round

Low season per wk
£110.00–£140.00
High season per wk
£240.00–£370.00

A modern cottage-style property with front and rear gardens. Garage and parking. Short walk from lovely harbour and Camel Trail.

★★★–★★★★★
4 Units
Sleeping 3–8

THE LAURELS HOLIDAY PARK
Padstow Road, Whitecross, Wadebridge PL27 7JQ
Contact: Mr A D Nicholson, The Laurels, Padstow Road,
Whitecross, Wadebridge PL27 7JQ
T: (01208) 813341 (Ansaphone)
F: (01208) 813341
E: anicholson@thelaurels-park.freeserve.co.uk
I: www.thelaurels-park.freeserve.co.uk

OPEN All year round

Low season per wk
£70.00–£420.00
High season per wk
£255.00–£575.00

Four very attractive Cornish stone cottages near Padstow, sleeping from 2 to 12, overlooking Camel estuary. All modern facilities, play area for children. Ideal touring centre.

★★★★
3 Units
Sleeping 2–8

THE OLD BAKERY
6 Cross Street, Padstow PL28 8AT
Contact: Mr Anthony Tippett, T W Properties,
6 Cross Street, Padstow PL28 8AT
T: (01841) 532885
F: (01841) 873517
E: tony.twproperties@virgin.net

OPEN All year round

Low season per wk
£210.00–£465.00
High season per wk
£345.00–£690.00

Three adjoining cottages set in the heart of Padstow. 3 minutes' walk from harbour, shops, restaurants and inns. Comfortable accommodation at any time of year.

REGIONAL TOURIST BOARD The ▲ symbol in an establishment entry indicates that it is a Regional Tourist Board member.

★★★

3 Units
Sleeping 4–6

PADSTOW HOLIDAY COTTAGES
1 Sarahs Gate, Little Petherick, Wadebridge PL27 7QT
Contact: Mrs Pat Walker, 1 Sarah's Gate,
Little Petherick, Wadebridge PL27 7QT
T: (01841) 541180
E: info@padstow-selfcatering.co.uk
I: www.padstow-selfcatering.co.uk

OPEN All year round
CC: Mastercard, Visa

Low season per wk
£140.00–£220.00
High season per wk
£350.00–£530.00

Padstow properties in quiet locations a short walk from the harbour. Providing comfortable, quality accommodation. Private parking. Patio gardens. Gas/electricity and linen included. Owner-supervised.

★★★★★

2 Units
Sleeping 2–5

Beautifully restored, tastefully furnished cottages in old part of Padstow. Ideal location for those who appreciate comfort and quality. Lovers of good food are catered for by fine restaurants including 3 Rick Stein establishments. Three minutes' walk to the delightful harbour, beautiful unspoilt coastline and beaches all around.

SUNDAY & SUNRISE COTTAGE
Ruthys Lane, Padstow PL28
Contact: Mrs D E Hoe, 14 The Green, Snitterfield,
Stratford-upon-Avon CV37 0JG
T: (01789) 730223 (Evenings, BT ansaphone)
F: (01789) 730199
E: mail@sundaycottage.co.uk
I: www.sundaycottage.co.uk

OPEN All year round

Low season per wk
£180.00–£360.00
High season per wk
£400.00–£525.00

★★★★

2 Units
Sleeping 6

Nestling in 50 acres in a secluded Exmoor valley at the convergence of 3 footpaths, our 2 spacious, comfortable cottages have been sympathetically converted from a fine Victorian barn overlooking a pretty, cobbled courtyard. Woodburners, fully-equipped kitchen, high-beamed ceilings, canopied bedrooms, laundry room. Panoramic views, splendid walking and riding.

VOLEY FARM
Parracombe, Barnstaple EX31 4PG
T: (01598) 763315 (Ansaphone)
F: (01598) 763660
E: voleyfarm@tesco.net
I: www.voleyfarm.com
Contact: Ms Judith Killen

OPEN Mar–Dec

Low season per wk
£195.00–£295.00
High season per wk
£310.00–£485.00

★★★★

1 Unit
Sleeping 6

THE OLD FARMHOUSE
Chegwidden Farm, St Levan, Penzance TR19 6LP
T: (01736) 810516 & 07831 834013 (Mobile)
F: (01736) 810516
E: halls@chegwidden.fsnet.co.uk
I: www.chegwidden.fsnet.co.uk
Contact: Mrs Vivienne Hall

OPEN All year round

Low season per wk
£300.00–£350.00
High season per wk
£550.00–£675.00

A 17thC farmhouse on Land's End peninsular. Listed in Book of Legends. Near beaches and coastal paths and Minack Theatre.

MAP REFERENCES
Map references apply to the colour maps at the front of this guide.

★★★
2 Units
Sleeping 3–8

ROSPANNEL FARM
Crows-an-Wra, Penzance TR19 6HS   OPEN Jul–Dec
T: (01736) 810262
E: gbernard@thefreeinternet.co.uk
Contact: Mr GB Hocking

Low season per wk
£220.00–£350.00
High season per wk
£270.00–£390.00

Old fashioned, very quiet and peaceful farm. Own pool and hide for birdwatchers. Moth light for insect enthusiasts. Badgers, foxes and lots of wildlife.

★★★
5 Units
Sleeping 2–5

SAINT PIRANS COTTAGES
Perranuthnoe, Penzance TR20 9NJ   OPEN All year round
Contact: Mrs Caroline Gresswell, The White House,
Micheldever, Winchester SO21 3AJ
T: (01962) 774379

Low season per wk
£120.00–£250.00
High season per wk
£410.00–£440.00

Comfortable cottages 400 metres from sandy cove in pretty village, 5 miles east Penzance. Ideal for family holidays, excellent centre for touring West Cornwall. Regret no pets.

★★★
1 Unit
Sleeping 6

4 EUREKA VALE
Perranporth TR6 0BS   OPEN All year round
Contact: Mr and Mrs J A Cuthill, 27 St George's Hill,
Perranporth TR6 0JS
T: (01872) 573624 (Answerphone)

Low season per wk
£180.00–£325.00
High season per wk
£330.00–£475.00

Early Victorian cottage in a quiet, private location with a sheltered garden, 150 metres from a sandy surfing beach. Close to all amenities.

★★★★–★★★★★★
4 Units
Sleeping 2–16

CLASSY COTTAGES

Blanches Windsor, Polperro, Looe PL13 2PT
Contact: Mrs & Mr Fiona & Martin Nicolle,
Blanches Windsor, Polperro, Looe PL13 2PT
T: 07000 423000
E: nicolle@classycottages.co.uk
I: www.classycottages.co.uk

Two romantic fishermen's cottages sitting on Polperro's harbour wall. Two isolated houses situated in 3 acres of gardens with sea views, short walk down valley to deserted cove and rock pools. Log fires. Use of private indoor swimming pool, sauna, spa, solarium at our farm cottages. Cornish cream tea to complete our welcome.

OPEN All year round
CC: Barclaycard, Delta,
JCB, Mastercard, Solo,
Switch, Visa, Visa Electron

Weekend breaks-out of
season, mid-week breaks.

Low season per wk
£240.00–£550.00
High season per wk
£1,120.00–£1,795.00

★★★–★★★★
8 Units
Sleeping 2–7

CRUMPLEHORN COTTAGES
The Anchorage, Portuan Road, Polperro,   OPEN All year round
Looe PL13 2DN
Contact: Mr M Collings, Crumplehorn Cottages,
The Anchorage, Portuan Road, Hannafore, Looe
PL13 2DN
T: (01503) 262523
F: (01503) 262523
E: gloria@crumplehorncottages.co.uk
I: www.crumplehorncottage.co.uk

Low season per wk
£135.00–£310.00
High season per wk
£290.00–£555.00

Traditional Cornish cottages, close to harbour, safe sandy beaches. Resident local owner. Not part of a holiday complex-individually sited within the village. Cottage at Looe also available.

★ **QUALITY ASSURANCE SCHEME**
Star ratings are explained at the back of this guide.

★★★★
1 Unit
Sleeping 4

GREEN CHANTRY
Porlock, Minehead TA24 8LB
Contact: M Payton, Home Farm, Burrowbridge, Bridgwater
TA7 0RF
T: (01823) 698330
F: (01823) 698169
E: maggie_payton@hotmail.com

*Pretty Victorian cottage in a tranquil setting,
close to the high street of this charming village
with its range of shops and restaurants. Pretty
fabrics, wooden floors downstairs, brightly
coloured rugs, co-ordinating bedlinen make this
a perfect place to unwind. Sun-trap garden.
Garage nearby.*

OPEN All year round

Short breaks Nov-Feb
minimum 2 nights. Special
offers for Christmas and New
Year.

Low season per wk
Min £185.00
High season per wk
Max £400.00

★★★-★★★★
10 Units
Sleeping 2–12

TREVATHAN FARM
St Endellion, Port Isaac PL29 3TT
T: (01208) 880248
F: (01208) 880248
E: symons@trevathanfarm.com
I: www.trevethanfarm.com
Contact: Mrs J Symons

OPEN All year round

Low season per wk
£120.00–£700.00
High season per wk
£360.00–£1,200.00

*Beautiful cottages with countryside views, games room and tennis court, set on
working farm. Beaches, golf, riding within 3 miles. Also large period house sleeping 12.*

★★★
1 Unit
Sleeping 4

LILAC COTTAGE
171 Wakeham, Portland DT5 1HR
Contact: Mrs Gill Morris, 1 Mermaid Cottages,
Wakeham, Portland DT5 1HS
T: (01305) 823359
E: portmorris@aol.com

OPEN All year round

Low season per wk
Min £125.00
High season per wk
Max £350.00

*A delightful Victorian terraced cottage with modern amenities but which retains
many of its original features. Located in a highly scenic area 5 minutes from Church
Ope Cove.*

★★★
7 Units
Sleeping 2–7

TRENGOVE FARM COTTAGES
Trengove Farm, Cot Road, Illogan, Redruth TR16 4PU
Contact: Mrs Lindsey Richards, Trengove Farm, Cot Road,
Illogan, Redruth TR16 4PU
T: (01209) 843008
F: (01209) 843682
E: richards@farming.co.uk

*Traditional, well-equipped cottages and
farmhouse on a 140-acre arable farm. Close to
beautiful beaches, cliffs and countryside park,
yet within easy reach of the main towns.
Centrally heated, some with woodburners – ideal
for inexpensive winter breaks. A superb location
for walking, swimming, touring or just switching
off.*

OPEN All year round

Short breaks available from
£80 during low season.

Low season per wk
£135.00–£350.00
High season per wk
£200.00–£500.00

CHECK THE MAPS
The colour maps at the front of this guide show all the cities, towns
and villages for which you will find accommodation entries.
Refer to the town index to find the page on which they are listed.

★★★

5 Units
Sleeping 5–8

SEA MEADS HOLIDAY HOMES
Sea Meads Lodge Sea Meads Estate, Praa Sands,
Penzance TR20 9TA
Contact: Miss Nicky Hann, Best Leisure, North Hill,
Shirwell, Barnstaple EX31 4LG
T: (01271) 850611
F: (01271) 850693

OPEN All year round

Low season per wk
£195.00
High season per wk
£200.00–£895.00

Spacious detached holiday homes just yards from the sea and beach. Fitted to very high standards. Own sun patios, gardens, garages. Sleeps up to 8.

Ⱥ ⱦ Ⓜ ◎ 🅼 ☉ 🗖 💻 TV 🗑 🔥 (🖉 💬 P ∪ ⸙ ❋ 🐎 🐕 SP

★★–★★★★★

18 Units
Sleeping 2–11

BOSINVER FARM COTTAGES
Bosinver Farm, Trelowth, St Austell PL26 7DT
T: (01726) 72128
F: (01726) 72128
E: bosinver@holidays2000.freeserve.co.uk
I: www.bosinver.co.uk
Contact: Mrs Pat Smith

Nestling in a hidden valley near the sea, Heligan Gardens and the Eden Project, our small farm has friendly animals and ponies. 16thC thatched farmhouse or cottages, privately set in their own mature gardens surrounded by wildflower meadows. Fishing, tennis, swimming pool and a short walk to the village pub.

OPEN All year round
CC: Barclaycard, Delta,
Eurocard, Mastercard,
Switch, Visa

Short breaks Sep–May, £35
per night for 2 persons
(minimum 3 nights).

Low season per wk
£130.00–£700.00
High season per wk
£235.00–£1,350.00

Ⱥ ⱦ Ⓜ ◎ 🖉 🅼 ☉ 💻 🗖 TV 🗑 🔥 (🖉 💬 ✈ P ⸙ ⚲ ∪ ♪ ⸙ ❋ 🐎 🐕 SP 🏠

★★★★

3 Units
Sleeping 2–6

NANJEATH FARM
Lanjeth, St Austell PL26 7TN
T: (01726) 70666 (Ansaphone) & 07810 005636 (Mobile)
I: www.nanjeath.co.uk
Contact: Mrs J Sandercock

Situated in the heart of Cornwall, Nanjeath Farm is a 17thC Listed farmhouse with 3 delightful cottages offering the utmost comfort, peace and tranquility. Set among mature trees and beautifully unspoilt meadows, Nanjeath is ideally suited to couples or those with older children seeking a quiet and relaxing holiday.

OPEN May–Dec

Short breaks available–min 3
nights (excl Christmas and
New Year).

Low season per wk
£180.00–£250.00

Ⱥ ⱦ 12 ◎ 🅼 🎛 ☉ 🗖 💻 🗖 TV 🗑 🔥 ❋ 💬 ✈ P ⚲ ❋ SP 🏠

★★★★

1 Unit
Sleeping 4

CARRACK WIDDEN
The Terrace, St Ives TR26 2BP
Contact: Mrs C Perry, Tros-an-Mor,
Treloyhan Manor Drive, St Ives TR26 2AS
T: (01736) 793370

OPEN Feb–Oct
CC: Solo

Low season per wk
£141.00–£157.00
High season per wk
£405.00

Well established, well furnished and equipped apartment, close to beach, town, bus and rail station. Magnificent views overlooking Porthminster Beach.

ⱦ Ⓜ ◎ 🅼 🎛 ☉ 💻 🗖 TV 🗑 🔥 (🖉 💬 P SP

★★★★

4 Units
Sleeping 2–4

CASA BELLA
Hain Walk, St Ives TR26 2AF
Contact: Mrs C Perry, Tros-an-Mor,
Treloyhan Manor Drive, St Ives TR26 2AS
T: (01736) 793370

OPEN Mar–Oct

Low season per wk
£140.00–£175.00
High season per wk
£336.00–£474.00

Apartments with magnificent sea and coastal views, set in beautiful gardens in peaceful setting.

Ⱥ ⱦ ◎ 🅼 🎛 ☉ 🗖 💻 TV 🗑 🔥 (🖉 💬 ✈ P ❋ SP

ST IVES continued

★★★
7 Units
Sleeping 4–7

CHY MOR AND PREMIER APARTMENTS
Beach House, The Wharf, St Ives TR26 1QA
Contact: Mr M Gill, Beach House, The Wharf, St Ives
TR26 1QA
T: (01736) 798798 (Ansaphone) & 07887 653165
F: (01736) 796831
E: mgill@stivesharbour.com
I: www.stivesharbour.com

OPEN All year round

Low season per wk
£160.00–£170.00
High season per wk
£330.00–£540.00

*Situated on St Ives harbour front with uninterrupted views of the harbour and bay.
Visit our website, www.stivesharbour.com.*

★★★★
7 Units
Sleeping 2–6

TREVALGAN HOLIDAY FARM
Trevalgan Farm, St Ives TR26 3BJ
T: (01736) 796433
F: (01736) 796433
I: www.trevalgan.co.uk
Contact: Mrs J S Osborne

OPEN All year round
CC: Mastercard, Visa

Low season per wk
£190.00–£330.00
High season per wk
£355.00–£455.00

*Traditional granite barns converted to a high standard, on coastal stock rearing farm
in magnificent scenery. Cliff walks. Short breaks (excl. Jul, Aug) available.*

ST JUST-IN-PENWITH, Cornwall Map ref 1A3

★★★
1 Unit
Sleeping 4

NANQUIDNO VEAN
Nanquidno, St Just-in-Penwith TR19 7NU
Contact: Mrs P M Gildea, 4 Tyer Street,
Stratford-upon-Avon CV37 6TY
T: (01789) 299338

OPEN All year round

Low season per wk
£260.00–£280.00
High season per wk
Min £425.00

*A period granite cottage in beautiful valley running down to the sea-a very peaceful
location perfect for bird watching, walking or seaside holidays.*

★★★★
1 Unit
Sleeping 4

SWALLOWS END
Kelynack Moor Farmhouse, Bosworlas, St Just-in-Penwith,
Penzance TR19 7RQ
T: (01736) 787011 (Answerphone)
Contact: Mr & Mrs Richens

*Annexe to traditional farmhouse in Area of
Outstanding Natural Beauty with ancient
moorland and Heritage Coast nearby. Stylish,
well-equipped accommodation, specially
designed to meet the needs of wheelchair users
and others with mobility difficulties. Set in
tranquil gardens with natural pond and views
across valley. Town facilities available.*

OPEN Apr–Oct &
Christmas

Specialist mobility
equipment hired on request.
Short breaks available Oct–
Mar.

Low season per wk
£190.00–£260.00
High season per wk
£280.00–£450.00

ST KEVERNE, Cornwall Map ref 1B3

★★★★
3 Units
Sleeping 2–4

FATTY OWLS
Trenoweth, St Keverne, Helston TR12 6QQ
Contact: Ms Y Cole, Trenoweth, St Keverne, Helston
TR12 6QQ
T: (01326) 280199 (Answerphone)
E: trenoweth@compuserve.com

*Three attractive single-storey cottages sleeping 2
to 4, set in 4-acre garden in peaceful
conservation valley. Streamside footpaths to
village/sea. Coastal/country walks. Non-smoking.
Pets welcome. Personally supervised by resident
owner.*

OPEN Mar–Oct

Low season per wk
£145.00–£160.00
High season per wk
£160.00–£340.00

ST MAWES

See display advertisement below

ST MAWGAN, Cornwall Map ref 1B2

★★★

1 Unit
Sleeping 5

POLGREEN MANOR

St Mawgan, Newquay TR8 4AG
T: (01637) 860700
F: (01637) 875165
Contact: Mrs J A Wake, NDD

Rural cottage adjoining traditional Cornish farmhouse, the residence of landscape artist Judith Wake, NDD, and her ornithologist husband Robin Wake. Mawgan Porth beach 1 mile. St Mawgan village, 0.75 miles. Popular with families (badminton lawn) and ideal for garden-loving couples from late March – end June. BA Link flights Gatwick-Newquay.

OPEN Apr–Oct

Low season per wk
£220.00–£306.00
High season per wk
£394.00–£420.00

SALCOMBE, Devon Map ref 1C3 *Tourist Information Centre Tel: 0906 302 0180*

★★★

1 Unit
Sleeping 6

COXSWAIN'S WATCH

59 Fore Street, Salcombe TQ8 8ET
Contact: Mr Andrew Oulsnam, Robert Oulsnam & Co,
79 Hewell Road, Barnt Green, Birmingham B45 8NL
T: (0121) 445 3311
F: (0121) 445 6026
E: barntgreen@oulsnam-online.com

Delightfully appointed period residence, with magnificent views over harbour and estuary and lying close to shops, pubs, restaurants and ferry to beaches, in this superb sailing resort. Hall, cloaks/shower room, lounge, kitchen/breakfast room, laundry, 3 bedrooms (sleeping 6) bathroom, patio, central heating. Free use of motor-boat and indoor swimming pool.

OPEN All year round

Low season per wk
Min £475.00
High season per wk
Min £1,150.00

TOWN INDEX

This can be found at the back of this guide. If you know where you want to stay, the index will give you the page number listing accommodation in your chosen town, city or village.

ETC 2-4 STARS ALL PROPERTIES INSPECTED

specialplaces

www.specialplacescornwall.co.uk

Self-catering at its best. A small selection of very Special Places at beautiful waterside and countryside locations, including St. Mawes, Falmouth, Flushing, Feock, Perranwell, Truro and Constantine. Well placed for Eden, Heligan and Western Cornwall. Comfortable, well equipped and carefully maintained. Sleeping from 2 to 8 people. A warm welcome awaits you at any time of year. Also member of Cornwall Tourist Board.

SPECIAL PLACES IN CORNWALL POACHERS FEACH, FEOCK TRURO, CORNWALL TR3 6SQ TEL/FAX 01872 864400

SALISBURY, Wiltshire Map ref 2B3 *Tourist Information Centre Tel: (01722) 334956*

★★★★

3 Units
Sleeping 5–6

THE OLD STABLES
Bridge Farm, Lower Road, Britford, Salisbury SP5 4DY
T: (01722) 349002
F: (01722) 349003
E: mail@old-stables.co.uk
I: www.old-stables.co.uk
Contact: Mr G Gould

Newly converted 19thC stable block. Three units, traditionally decorated, spiral staircase. Downstairs: 1 en suite twin bedroom, kitchen/ dining room. Upstairs: 1 double, 1 single, shower room. Ideal touring base. Non-smoking. Pets by arrangement.

OPEN All year round
CC: Barclaycard, Delta, Mastercard, Solo, Switch, Visa, Visa Electron

Low season per wk
£195.00–£325.00
High season per wk
£345.00–£495.00

SALISBURY PLAIN

See under Amesbury, Hindon, Great Cheverell, Salisbury, Winterbourne Stoke

SEATON, Devon Map ref 1D2 *Tourist Information Centre Tel: (01297) 21660*

★★★

1 Unit
Sleeping 5

WEST RIDGE BUNGALOW
Harepath Hill, Seaton EX12 2TA
T: (01297) 22398
F: (01297) 22398
E: foxfamily@westridge.fsbusiness.co.uk
I: www.cottageguide.co.uk/westridge
Contact: Mrs H Fox

Comfortably-furnished bungalow on elevated ground in 1.5 acres of lawns and gardens. Beautiful panoramic views of Axe Estuary and sea. Close by are Beer and Branscombe. Lyme Regis 7 miles, Sidmouth 10 miles. An excellent centre for touring, walking, sailing, fishing, golf. Full gas central heating, double glazing throughout.

OPEN Mar–Oct

Low season per wk
£175.00–£295.00
High season per wk
£295.00–£385.00

SHALDON, Devon Map ref 1D2

★★

3 Units
Sleeping 6

BADGERS BROOK HOLIDAY COTTAGES
Stoke-in-Teignhead, Newton Abbot TQ12 4QW
Contact: Mr & Mrs KT Price, Badgers Brook, Higher Gabwell, Stoke-in-Teignhead, Newton Abbot TQ12 4QW
T: (01803) 327398
F: (01803) 327398
E: badgers@aisthorpe.freeserve.co.uk

OPEN All year round
CC: Switch

Low season per wk
£185.00–£215.00
High season per wk
£290.00–£410.00

Barn conversions in peaceful rural location between Teignmouth and Torbay. Ideal touring base or tranquil location for relaxing in large gardens. Beaches half a mile.

★★★

1 Unit
Sleeping 5

BARTON COTTAGE
Court Barton, Stokeinteignhead, Newton Abbot TQ12 4QL
Contact: Miss Susan Elizabeth Witt, Barton Cottage Holiday Lettings, Court Barton, Stokeinteignhead, Newton Abbot TQ12 4QL
T: (01626) 872441 (Ansaphone) & 07703 240218 (Mobile)
E: bartoncottage@stokeinteignhead.freeserve.co.uk

OPEN Apr–Sep

Low season per wk
£249.00–£399.00
High season per wk
£449.00

Pretty red sandstone cottage in peaceful picturesque Rocombe Valley. Attractive courtyard setting with walled patio garden containing climbing jasmine and roses.

COLOUR MAPS Colour maps at the front of this guide pinpoint all places under which you will find accommodation listed.

SHALDON continued

★★★

3 Units
Sleeping 4–6

Relax in our cosy cottage, spacious bungalow or delightful garden apartment in this peaceful coastal hamlet. Ideal for walkers, nature lovers and those who enjoy a quieter holiday. All properties are well maintained, within walking distance of beach/coastal paths, with gardens and glorious sea views. Sorry no pets.

COOMBE CLOSE HOLIDAYS

Coombe Close, Maidencombe, Torquay TQ1 4TR
Contact: Mr & Mrs M&P Huff, Coombe Close Holidays,
Coombe Close, Brim Hill, Maidencombe, Torquay TQ1 4TR
T: (01803) 327215
F: (01803) 327215
E: peterhuff@onetel.net.uk
I: www.shines.net/maidencombe

OPEN All year round

Short breaks available Oct–
Apr (excl Christmas, New
Year and Easter).

Low season per wk
£120.00–£210.00
High season per wk
£275.00–£500.00

ⒶᎧ7 Ⓜ ∅ ⊞ ⊙ ᘐ ▭ TV ⊋ ᗧ ᗧ ⤬ ⊠ ⟟ P ✿ SP

SHEPTON MALLET, Somerset Map ref 2A2 *Tourist Information Centre Tel: (01749) 345258*

★★★

4 Units
Sleeping 2–6

KNOWLE FARM COTTAGES
West Compton, Shepton Mallet BA4 4PD
T: (01749) 890482
F: (01749) 890405
Contact: Mrs J A Boyce

OPEN All year round

Low season per wk
£170.00–£270.00
High season per wk
£270.00–£425.00

Cottages converted from old farm buildings, set in a pleasant garden in quiet, unspoilt countryside. Ideal for touring. Separate play area for children.

ⒶᎧ Ⓜ ∅ ⊞ ⊙ ᘐ ▭ TV ⊋ ᗧ ᗧ ᗧ P ✿ SP ⤉

SHERBORNE, Dorset Map ref 2B3 *Tourist Information Centre Tel: (01935) 815341*

★★★

1 Unit
Sleeping 4

BLACKBERRY COTTAGE
3 Bristol Road, Sherborne DT9 4HS
Contact: Mr John Michael Farr, 17 Marsh Lane, Yeovil
BA21 3BX
T: (01935) 423148 & 433538 (Office)

OPEN All year round

Low season per wk
£150.00–£180.00
High season per wk
£220.00–£310.00

An ideal base for discovering the delights of Dorset. This 19thC stone cottage is close to the centre of the historic town of Sherborne.

ⒶᎧ ◉ 🛋 ⊙ ▭ ⊟ TV ᗧ ᗧ ⤬ ᗧ ✿ SP

SHERSTON, Wiltshire Map ref 2B2

★★★★

1 Unit
Sleeping 3

Cotswold-stone cottage rebuilt in 1991 from original stable and hayloft. Situated in quiet valley in AONB on edge of village designated a conservation area. Secluded gardens with river running through. Parking adjacent cottage. No pets and no smoking please.

MAY COTTAGE

c/o Mill Cottage, Thompsons Hill, Sherston,
Malmesbury SN16 0NE
Contact: Mrs S M Bristow, Mill Cottage, Thompsons Hill,
Sherston, Malmesbury SN16 0NE
T: (01666) 840655

OPEN All year round

Low season per wk
Min £220.00
High season per wk
Max £260.00

ⒶᎧ ◉ ⊞ ⊙ ▭ ⊟ TV ᗧ ⤬ ᗧ ᗧ P ✿ SP

ACCESSIBILITY

Look for the 🔸🔸🔸 symbols which indicate accessibility for
wheelchair users. A list of establishments is at the front of this guide.

★★★★

7 Units
Sleeping 4–6

Two miles from Heritage Coastline and beaches, cradled in 45 acres of idyllic, peaceful valley. Listed 17thC farmhouse with period cottages lovingly converted from original farm buildings each with own delightful enclosed garden. Studio facilities in restored Victorian kennels. Tennis court, trout pond. 14thC inn and amenities within walking distance.

BOSWELL FARM COTTAGES

Boswell Farm, Sidford, Sidmouth EX10 0PP
Contact: Mr & Mrs B P Dillon, Boswell Farm Holiday
Cottages, Boswell Farm, Sidford, Sidmouth EX10 0PP
T: (01395) 514162
F: (01395) 514162
E: dillon@boswell-farm.co.uk
I: www.boswell-farm.co.uk

OPEN All year round
CC: Barclaycard, Delta,
Eurocard, Mastercard,
Switch, Visa

25% reduction-2 people (and baby) Nov-Mar (for full week only, excl Bank Hols).

Low season per wk
£180.00–£285.00
High season per wk
£340.00–£770.00

★★★★

5 Units
Sleeping 2–4

We are 150 yards from a National Trust valley which leads to the Coastal Path and Weston beach. Excellent walking and touring area. Our bungalows face south onto a lawn and each has a patio table and chairs for your use. Perfect location for an interesting and relaxing holiday.

LEIGH FARM

Weston, Sidmouth EX10 0PH
T: (01395) 516065
F: (01395) 579582
E: leigh.farm@virgin.net
I: www.streets-ahead.com/leighfarm
Contact: Mr & Mrs Geoff & Gill Davis

OPEN All year round
CC: Barclaycard, Delta,
JCB, Mastercard, Solo,
Switch, Visa, Visa Electron

Weekend and mid-week breaks available Oct-Mar (excl Christmas and New Year).

Low season per wk
£140.00–£160.00
High season per wk
£196.00–£428.00

★★★

1 Unit
Sleeping 6

The cottage is situated near the centre of Steeple Ashton, one of Wiltshire's most picturesque villages. This delightful, sympathetically modernised cottage dates from the 18thC. There are lots of exposed beams and stonework and a free supply of wood for blazing fires. Within easy reach are Bath, Castle Combe, Stourhead Gardens, Stonehenge and much, much more.

JASMINE COTTAGE

1 High Street, Steeple Ashton, Trowbridge BA14 6EL
Contact: Mr NA Sharples, 4 St Margarets, Little Aston,
Sutton Coldfield B74 4HU
T: (0121) 353 5258
E: jasminecottage@netscapeonline.co.uk
I: www.jasminecottage.co.uk

OPEN All year round

Low season per wk
Min £189.00
High season per wk
Max £449.00

IMPORTANT NOTE Information on accommodation listed in this guide has been supplied by the proprietors. As changes may occur you are advised to check details at the time of booking.

STITHIANS, Cornwall Map ref 1B3

★★★

10 Units
Sleeping 2–9

HIGHER TREWITHEN

Stithians, Truro TR3 7DR
T: (01209) 860863 & 07785 752373
F: (01209) 860785
E: trewithen@talk21.com
I: www.trewithenholidaycottages.co.uk
Contact: Mrs Avril Stokes

Comfortable cottages converted from an old farmstead. Surrounded by open farmland and within easy walking distance of Stithians village facilities. The cottages sleep from 2 to 9 persons in 1 to 4 bedrooms. Six miles to both Riviera and Atlantic Coasts. Ample parking. A central location for all holiday activities.

OPEN All year round

Low season per wk
£125.00–£200.00
High season per wk
£290.00–£650.00

STOKE SUB HAMDON, Somerset Map ref 1D2

★★★★

1 Unit
Sleeping 4

ONE FAIR PLACE
Chiselborough, Stoke sub Hamdon TA14 6TL
Contact: Mrs A A Wright, Holly Lodge, 39 The Avenue,
Crowthorne RG45 6PB
T: (01344) 772461
F: (01344) 772461
E: petewright@compuserve.com

OPEN All year round

Low season per wk
£170.00–£190.00
High season per wk
£205.00–£300.00

Golden hamstone cottage in picturesque Chiselborough village. Open log fire and pretty cottage garden. Lovely countryside walks, views, touring and NT properties nearby. Brochure available.

TAUNTON, Somerset Map ref 1D1 *Tourist Information Centre Tel: (01823) 336344*

★★★

3 Units
Sleeping 4–8

Comfortable holiday cottages with character in idyllic countryside. The cottages (with 1-4 bedrooms) are converted stone barns and adjoin the historic 17thC Listed farmhouse. Spacious and equipped to a high standard, surrounded by the beautiful countryside of our working dairy farm. Bring your horse on holiday – purpose built stabling. Taunton, M5, J25 4 miles.

MEARE COURT HOLIDAY COTTAGES

Meare Court, Wrantage, Taunton TA3 6DA
T: (01823) 480570 & 07980 601670
F: (01823) 481123
E: mearecourt@farming.co.uk
I: www.mearecourt.co.uk
Contact: Mrs E J Bray

OPEN All year round
CC: Amex, Barclaycard,
Delta, Diners, Eurocard,
JCB, Maestro, Mastercard,
Solo, Switch, Visa

Short breaks/weekends
available. Min 2 nights except
Jul-Aug. All linen, towels, etc
included.

Low season per wk
£180.00–£500.00
High season per wk
£350.00–£1,200.00

TAVISTOCK, Devon Map ref 1C2 *Tourist Information Centre Tel: (01822) 612938*

★★★

1 Unit
Sleeping 5

ACORN COTTAGE – CEDAR LODGE
Heathfield, Tavistock PL19 0LQ
Contact: Mrs Vivien Powell-Thomas, Acorn Cottage,
Heathfield, Tavistock PL19 0LQ
T: (01822) 810038
E: viv@acorncot.fsnet.co.uk
I: www.fsmail.net

OPEN All year round

Low season per wk
£75.00–£100.00
High season per wk
£140.00–£300.00

Cedar lodge at Acorn Cottage, spacious cabin-style bungalow, set in quiet rural location central to beaches and many recreational activities. Close Dartmoor National Park. Map Ref O/S sheet 201:463787. Send for brochure.

TAVISTOCK continued

★★★
1 Unit
Sleeping 4

HIGHER CHADDLEHANGER FARM
Tavistock PL19 0LG
T: (01822) 810268
F: (01822) 810268
Contact: Mrs R Cole

OPEN All year round

Low season per wk
£130.00
High season per wk
£130.00

Holiday flatlet in farmhouse on beef and sheep farm, close to moors. Own entrance, private garden.

THURLESTONE, Devon Map ref 1C3

★★★★
1 Unit
Sleeping 6

APRIL COTTAGE
Thurlestone, Kingsbridge TQ7 3NE
Contact: Mrs Joy Jordan, F P Holidays, 76 Main Road,
Long Bennington, Newark NG23 5DJ
T: (01400) 281937
F: (01400) 282051
E: joy.jordan@focalpointuk.com
I: www.fpholidays.com

OPEN All year round

Low season per wk
£260.00–£290.00
High season per wk
£655.00–£670.00

Welcoming, comfortable 19thC cottage in quiet conservation village. Secret garden. Walking distance to sea, pub, shop, golf. Glorious walks and views. Once experienced, never forgotten.

TIMBERSCOMBE, Somerset Map ref 1D1

★★★★
1 Unit
Sleeping 4

MILL LEAT
Great House Street, Timberscombe,
Minehead TA24 7TQ
Contact: Mrs Judith Ford, Rowan Cottage,
Great House Street, Timberscombe, Minehead
TA24 7TQ
T: (01643) 841336 (Ansaphone)

OPEN All year round

Low season per wk
£180.00
High season per wk
£250.00–£300.00

In Exmoor National Park, convenient for coast and moorland. Comfortable modern detached bungalow equipped to high standard in delightful situation overlooking pond. Own garden. Brochure available.

TIVERTON, Devon Map ref 1D2 *Tourist Information Centre Tel: (01884) 255827*

★★★★
4 Units
Sleeping 2–4

TIVERTON CASTLE
Tiverton EX16 6RP
T: (01884) 253200 & 255200 (Ansaphone)
F: (01884) 254200
E: tiverton.castle@ukf.net
I: www.tivertoncastle.com
Contact: Mrs A Gordon

OPEN All year round

Low season per wk
£216.00–£407.00
High season per wk
£266.00–£534.00

Extremely comfortable, well equipped apartments inside historic castle in centre of Tiverton. Wonderful touring centre for the best that Devon offers. Beautiful gardens.

TORQUAY, Devon Map ref 1D2 *Tourist Information Centre Tel: 0906 680 1268 (Premium rate number)*

★★★
14 Units
Sleeping 2–6

BURLEY COURT APARTMENTS
Wheatridge Lane, Livermead, Torquay TQ2 6RA
T: (01803) 607879 & 606101
F: (01803) 605516
Contact: Mrs B Palmer

Architecturally-designed apartments superbly appointed and furnished and to a high standard, many having sea views and some with their own private sun terrace. Situated in secluded south-facing gardens, 200 metres from Livermead beach. Leisure facilities include heated indoor and outdoor swimming pools, spa bath, sauna, solarium, games room.

OPEN All year round
CC: Barclaycard,
Mastercard, Visa

Low season per wk
£100.00–£260.00
High season per wk
£205.00–£535.00

★★★
4 Units
Sleeping 2–7

An elegant Victorian residence in the leafy neighbourhood of Wellswood, a stroll up the road from Torquay harbour and Meadfoot beach. Set in its own grounds, the property has been converted into a number of well-appointed, light and spacious apartments plus a lovely cottage. TVs, playstations. Laundry facilities. Secure parking.

HOLLINGTON HOUSE APARTMENTS

Acadia Road, Wellswood, Torquay TQ1 2PY
Contact: Mr & Mrs R & S Vaughton, Proprietors,
21 Bishops Close, Torquay TQ1 2PL
T: (01803) 293555
E: aldworth@caribbeancourt.co.uk
I: www.caribbeancourt.co.uk

OPEN All year round	Low season per wk
CC: Delta, JCB, Maestro,	£140.00–£310.00
Mastercard, Solo, Switch,	High season per wk
Visa, Visa Electron	£320.00–£500.00

★★
9 Units
Sleeping 2–6

LORNA DOONE HOLIDAY APARTMENTS
Torwood Gardens Road, Torquay TQ1 1EQ
Contact: Mr Lee & Max Chapman, Teddesley Leisure
Limited, Longmynd Hotel, Cunnery Road,
Church Stretton SY6 6AG
T: (01694) 722244
F: (01694) 722718
E: reservations@longmynd.co.uk
I: www.longmynd.co.uk

OPEN All year round
CC: Amex, Barclaycard,
Delta, Diners, Mastercard,
Switch, Visa

Low season per wk
£135.00–£300.00
High season per wk
£180.00–£425.00

Newly converted Georgian mansion in central Torquay. Each apartment has been tastefully decorated and has a comprehensive inventory.

BAY FORT MANSIONS
THE LUXURY HOLIDAY APARTMENTS

English Tourism Council

★★★★
SELF-CATERING

Elegant, Stylish, Comfortable, South facing Apartments complimenting probably the finest views of Torquay and the English Riviera.

Our 15 Apartments, 12 sea facing, many with patios and balconies, have been recently refurbished and equipped to a very high standard, and have been designed to provide you with a memorable holiday experience.

WARREN ROAD TORQUAY DEVON TQ2 5TN
TEL: 01803 213810 FAX: 01803 209057
www.bayfortapartments.co.uk

★★★

24 Units
Sleeping 3–6

Well-appointed self-contained apartments providing superior accommodation. Close to shops and seafront and an ideal base for touring. Superb leisure facilities including indoor/outdoor pools, spa, sauna and gymnasium. Beauty salon, solarium, games room, licensed bar and restaurant also available.

MAXTON LODGE HOLIDAY APARTMENTS

Rousdown Road, Chelston, Torquay TQ2 6PB
T: (01803) 607811
F: (01803) 605357
E: stay@redhouse-hotel.co.uk
I: www.redhouse-hotel.co.uk
Contact: Mr Richard Hassell

OPEN All year round
CC: Barclaycard, Delta, Mastercard, Solo, Switch, Visa

Low season per wk
£158.00–£250.00
High season per wk
£240.00–£620.00

Fully serviced apartments available with a choice of meals built into an inclusive tariff.

★★★

6 Units
Sleeping 3–6

Beautifully appointed, spacious Victorian self-contained apartments in level woodland setting in exclusive peaceful conservation area. Walks through woods to beaches, close to excellent shops. One mile from harbour. Regular bus service. Gardens, off-road parking. All accommodation is well equipped, tastefully decorated and immaculately maintained. Pets and children welcome.

MOORCOT SELF CONTAINED HOLIDAY APARTMENTS

Kents Road, Wellswood, Torquay TQ1 2NN
T: (01803) 293710
E: margaret-neilson@moorcot.fsnet.co.uk
I: www.moorcot.fsnet.co.uk
Contact: Mrs M C Neilson

OPEN All year round

Short breaks Oct-Apr, 4 nights for the price of 3.

Low season per wk
£100.00–£160.00
High season per wk
£170.00–£330.00

★★★

9 Units
Sleeping 1–5

A Victorian villa with a modern block of 9 flats, set in beautiful grounds with heated pool and safe parking.

MOORHAVEN HOLIDAY FLATS

43 Barton Road, Torquay TQ1 4DT
T: (01803) 328567
E: info@moorhaven.co.uk
I: www.moorhaven.co.uk
Contact: Mr & Mrs T&J Chandler

OPEN All year round
CC: Barclaycard, Delta, Mastercard, Switch, Visa

Low season per wk
£130.00–£200.00
High season per wk
£210.00–£380.00

Out of season 3-day break rates on application.

QUALITY ASSURANCE SCHEME

Star ratings were correct at the time of going to press but are subject to change. Please check at the time of booking.

TORQUAY continued

★★★★ 8 Units Sleeping 2–6	**MUNTHAM HOLIDAY APARTMENTS** Barrington Road, Wellswood, Torquay TQ1 1SG T: (01803) 292958 F: (01803) 291715 E: muntham@btinternet.com I: www.torbay.gov.uk Contact: Mr & Mrs Peter & Trudie Cross	OPEN All year round CC: Barclaycard, Delta, JCB, Mastercard, Solo, Switch, Visa, Visa Electron	Low season per wk £130.00–£195.00 High season per wk £247.00–£390.00

Gracious Victorian villa with large gardens and car park. Quiet residential area close to local shops, beaches and Torbay. Resident proprietors.

★★★ 18 Units Sleeping 1–5	**SOUTH SANDS APARTMENTS** Torbay Road, Torquay TQ2 6RG T: (01803) 293521 F: (01803) 293502 E: southsands.torquay@virgin.net I: www.southsands.co.uk Contact: Mr P W Moorhouse	OPEN All year round CC: Amex, Barclaycard, Delta, Mastercard, Visa	Low season per wk £100.00–£180.00 High season per wk £220.00–£375.00

Superb apartments conveniently situated on seafront. Nearest beach 100 yards. Ground/first floor only. Short breaks and mid-week bookings except summer season.

★★★
8 Units
Sleeping 1–7

WOODFIELD HOLIDAY APARTMENTS

Lower Woodfield Road, Torquay TQ1 2JY
T: (01803) 295974
Contact: Mr and Mrs T W Gaylard

Grade II Listed neo-Gothic villa built in 1841, of architectural and historic interest. Clean, homely apartments, most with views over Torquay harbour. Convenient for all amenities. 600 yards to harbour and town. Free car parking, central heating for early/late season visitors. Family-run business, resident proprietors. Telephone or write for free colour brochure.

OPEN All year round

Low season per wk
£90.00–£185.00
High season per wk
£245.00–£440.00

TORRINGTON, Devon Map ref 1C1 *Tourist Information Centre Tel: (01805) 626140*

★★★ 6 Units Sleeping 4–6	**STOWFORD LODGE & SOUTH HILL COTTAGES** Torrington EX38 8NU Contact: Mrs S Milsom, Stowford Lodge, Langtree, Torrington EX38 8NU T: (01805) 601540 F: (01805) 601487 E: stowford@dial.pipex.com I: www.stowford.dial.pipex.com	OPEN All year round	Low season per wk £190.00–£310.00 High season per wk £310.00–£490.00

Four delightful cottages converted from Victorian stone farm buildings. Heated indoor pool. Also, pair of period cottages on edge of farm. Pets welcome.

TOWN INDEX

This can be found at the back of the guide. If you know where you want to stay, the index will give you the page number listing accommodation in your chosen town, city or village.

TREBETHERICK, Cornwall Map ref 1B2

★★★★

18 Units

Collection of luxury holiday homes situated between Rock and Polzeath and the famous Camel Estuary. Easy walking distance from surfing beaches and quiet coves. Deluxe cottages offer full central heating and log fires, telephone/fax machines and every possible convenience. Ideal for out of season walking holidays.

HIGHCLIFFE

Trebetherick, Wadebridge PL27 6TS
Contact: Mr Robert Mably, Highcliffe Agency Ltd,
Bosneives, Withiel, Bodmin PL30 5NQ
T: (01208) 831167 (Office) & 07768 586807 (Mobile)
F: (01208) 831198
E: sales@highcliffeagency.com
I: www.highcliffeholidays.co.uk

OPEN All year round

Out of season long weekend breaks. Special rates for Christmas.

Low season per wk
£370.00–£500.00
High season per wk
£500.00–£950.00

TREGONY, Cornwall Map ref 1B3

★★★★

1 Unit
Sleeping 2

THE BOLT HOLE
Tregony, Truro
Contact: Ms B F Hunt, The Pines,
Lower Golf Links Road, Broadstone BH18 8BG
T: (01202) 693817 (Ansaphone) &
07885 951942 (Mobile)
E: barbara@aaacott.freeserve.co.uk

OPEN All year round

Low season per wk
£165.00–£250.00
High season per wk
£250.00–£360.00

18thC cottage, fully refurbished and equipped. Tastefully furnished. Vaulted ceiling and beams, delightful garden. Amenities 3 minutes' walk. Quiet. Coastal path nearby, glorious scenery.

TREMAINE, Cornwall Map ref 1C2

★★★★

2 Units
Sleeping 2–4

TREMAINE BARN
West Tremaine, Tremaine, Launceston PL15 8SA
Contact: Mr & Mrs Alan & Jillie Lamb, Owners,
West Tremaine, Tremaine, Launceston PL15 8SA
T: (01566) 781636
F: (01566) 781309
E: welcome@stay-in-cornwall.co.uk
I: www.stay-in-cornwall.co.uk

OPEN All year round

Low season per wk
£195.00–£295.00
High season per wk
£275.00–£495.00

A luxury stone barn and round house conversion in beautiful countryside between historic Launceston, Bodmin Moor and the north Cornwall coast.

WADEBRIDGE, Cornwall Map ref 1B2 Tourist Information Centre Tel: (01208) 813725

★★★★

3 Units
Sleeping 4–8

Luxury barn conversions set in a picturesque valley overlooking fields of cows and sheep. Four-poster beds; meal delivery service; games room; log fires; pets' corner; farm trail linking with Saints Way footpath. Ideal for walkers. Padstow, Eden and Heligan within 25 minutes' drive.

TREGOLLS FARM COTTAGES

Tregolls Farm, St Wenn, Bodmin PL30 5PG
Contact: Mrs Marilyn Hawkey, Tregolls Farm, St Wenn,
Bodmin PL30 5PG
T: (01208) 812154
F: (01208) 812154
E: tregollsfarm@btclick.com
I: www.tregollsfarm.co.uk

OPEN All year round
CC: Barclaycard,
Mastercard, Visa

3 and 4-night breaks from
Oct-Apr.

Low season per wk
£148.00–£320.00
High season per wk
£290.00–£560.00

RATING All accommodation in this guide has been rated, or is awaiting a rating, by a trained English Tourism Council assessor.

WELLOW, Bath and North East Somerset Map ref 2B2

★★★★
1 Unit
Sleeping 4–6

HOLLY COTTAGE

The Hollies, Mill Hill, Wellow, Bath BA2 8QJ
Contact: Mr & Mrs Alick & Mari Bartholowmew,
Proprietors, The Hollies, Mill Hill, Wellow, Bath BA2 8QJ
T: (01225) 840889
E: enquiries@bath-holidays.co.uk
I: www.bath-holidays.co.uk

Sample the gracious culture of Bath while enjoying the comforts of a cosy cottage on the edge of a conservation village only 6 miles distant. Exceptional location overlooking stream. Newly renovated, modern kitchen, woodburning stove, sunny conservatory, private garden. Riding, lovely country walks. Two double bedrooms, sofa bed and cot.

OPEN All year round
CC: Barclaycard, Delta,
Mastercard, Solo, Switch,
Visa

Weekend and mid-week breaks are available outside school holidays usually at only 7 days' notice.

Low season per wk
£265.00–£320.00
High season per wk
£340.00–£395.00

WELLS, Somerset Map ref 2A2 *Tourist Information Centre Tel: (01749) 672552*

★★★★
1 Unit
Sleeping 2–6

5 HIGH STREET

Wells BA5 2AA
Contact: Mr & Mrs Alan & Margaret Southwood,
40a South Street, Wells BA5 1SL
T: (01749) 675510

Centrally situated character apartment in Listed building overlooking Market Place, furnished to a high standard, large walled garden at rear. Three minutes' walk to cathedral and Bishops' Palace. Good location for visits to Cheddar, Wookey Hole, Glastonbury, Bath, the Quantocks and Exmoor National Park.

OPEN Apr–Oct

Low season per wk
£220.00–£250.00
High season per wk
£250.00–£280.00

★★–★★★
2 Units
Sleeping 2–3

MODEL FARM COTTAGES
Model Farm, Milton, Wells BA5 3AE
T: (01749) 673363
F: (01749) 671566
E: creedmodelfarm@faxvia.net
Contact: Mrs Gill Creed

These well-equipped cottages are situated in peaceful countryside away from traffic. Both have private patios leading on to open fields.

OPEN All year round

Low season per wk
£195.00–£220.00
High season per wk
£220.00–£250.00

WEMBDON, Somerset Map ref 1D1

★★★★
1 Unit
Sleeping 4

GRANGE FARM COTTAGE
Grange Farm, Wembdon, Bridgwater TA5 2BB
Contact: Agent, English Country Cottages,
Stoney Bank, Earby, Barnoldswick BB94 0AA
T: 0870 585 1155
F: 0870 585 1150
I: www.english-country-cottages.co.uk

Beautifully converted single-storey barn with 2 en suite bedrooms, within ground of Grade II Listed Georgian home. Own secluded garden with natural duck pond.

OPEN Apr–Oct

High season per wk
£325.00–£515.00

CREDIT CARD BOOKINGS If you book by telephone and are asked for your credit card number it is advisable to check the proprietor's policy should you cancel your reservation.

WEST BAY, Dorset Map ref 2A3

★★★–★★★★
8 Units
Sleeping 2–6

WESTPOINT APARTMENTS
The Esplanade, West Bay, Bridport DT6 4HG
T: (01308) 423636
F: (01308) 458871
E: bea@westpoint-apartments.co.uk
I: www.westpoint-apartments.co.uk
Contact: Mr & Mrs D&B Slade

OPEN All year round
CC: Barclaycard,
Mastercard, Switch, Visa

Low season per wk
£140.00–£260.00
High season per wk
£290.00–£480.00

On seafront overlooking sea and harbour. Golf, fishing, cliff walks. 3 and 4 day breaks available. Home of TV series 'Harbour Lights'. Thomas Hardy Country.

WESTBURY, Wiltshire Map ref 2B2 *Tourist Information Centre Tel: (01373) 827158*

★★★★
1 Unit
Sleeping 2–5

IRON BOX COTTAGE
Whitecroft, Dilton Marsh, Westbury BA13 4DJ
Contact: Mrs SA Hansford, 1 Carpenters Lane, Bratton,
Westbury BA13 4SS
T: (01380) 830169 & 830670
E: sue.hansford@tesco.net

A charming 18thC cottage in a quiet country lane close to footpaths and open countryside. This spacious yet cosy cottage has 3 bedrooms, exposed beams, open fireplace and enclosed private courtyard. Many activities and places of historical interest are nearby with Bath, Salisbury, Stonehenge and Longleat within easy reach.

OPEN All year round

Short breaks available Oct–Mar inclusive (excl Christmas and New Year).

Low season per wk
Min £200.00
High season per wk
Max £450.00

WESTON-SUPER-MARE, North Somerset Map ref 1D1 *Tourist Information Centre Tel: (01934) 888800*

★★★★
1 Unit
Sleeping 6

CLARENCE VIEW
36a Clarence Road South, Weston-super-Mare BS22
Contact: Ms A Cantle, Champagne Holiday Lets,
Broomrigg House, Broomrigg Road, Fleet, Aldershot
GU13 8LR
T: (01252) 622789 & 07831 845643
F: (01252) 812948
E: alison@broomrigg.madasafish.com
I: www.holiday-rentals.com

Luxury 3-bedroomed apartment overlooking the park. Spacious rooms, elegantly furnished. Three minutes beach, golf. Quiet end of town. Sleeps 6. Weekends, 3-day breaks and nightly rates available. Open all year.

OPEN All year round

£50 off your spring or summer break if you book in Jan.

Low season per wk
£290.00–£396.00
High season per wk
£396.00–£475.00

USE YOUR *i*s

There are more than 550 Tourist Information Centres throughout England offering friendly help with accommodation and holiday ideas as well as suggestions of places to visit and things to do. You'll find TIC addresses in the local Phone Book.

★★★★

1 Unit
Sleeping 4

Luxury conversion of a Victorian sanatorium on the seafront. Security access, private parking, patio. Sleeps 4. One double, one twin, en suite plus family bathroom. Ground floor. Explore Wells, Bath, Cheddar and Bristol. Visit Wookey Hole, the designer shopping outlets at Street or simply relax on the beach. Family holidays to remember.

ROYAL SANDS

6 Royal Court, Royal Sands, Weston-super-Mare BS23
Contact: Ms A Cantle, Champagne Holiday Lets, Broomrigg House, Broomrigg Road, Fleet, Aldershot GU13 8LR
T: (01252) 622789 & 07831 845643
F: (01252) 812948
E: alison@broomrigg.madasafish.com
I: www.holiday-rentals.com

OPEN All year round

£50 off if you book ahead (in Jan).

Low season per wk	£250.00–£356.00
High season per wk	£356.00–£450.00

WEYMOUTH, Dorset Map ref 2B3 *Tourist Information Centre Tel: (01305) 785747*

★★★

5 Units
Sleeping 4–6

Centre of Weymouth's Georgian Esplanade, 20 yards from beach, close to town centre. Georgian house converted into 2 bedroomed self-contained holiday flats, most with panoramic sea views. Close to train and bus station.

BELVIDERE HOUSE HOLIDAY FLATS

119 The Esplanade, Weymouth DT4 7EH
Contact: Mrs V J Brown, 16 Nottington Lane, Weymouth DT3 5DF
T: (01305) 814152
F: (01305) 5760301
E: enquiries@belviderehouse.co.uk
I: www.belviderehouse.co.uk

OPEN All year round

Low season per wk	£250.00–£300.00
High season per wk	£375.00–£500.00

★★★

3 Units
Sleeping 4–7

Spectacular sea and castle views across peaceful, landscaped gardens with heated pool, woodland pond, summerhouse, play areas, pirate lookout and viewing deck leading to secluded, sandy beach and footpath. Ideal for sailing, diving, windsurfing in Portland Harbour; walking, bird-watching in Hardy country; visiting stately homes, gardens, picturesque harbours, traditional seaside resorts.

GLENTHORNE

Castle Cove, 15 Old Castle Road, Weymouth DT4 8QB
T: (01305) 777281 & 07831 751526
Contact: Mrs Olivia Nurrish

OPEN All year round

Short stays Oct-Apr (excl Christmas and New Year).

Low season per wk	£200.00–£375.00
High season per wk	£375.00–£500.00

www.travelengland.org.uk

Log on for information and inspiration. The latest information on places to visit, events and quality assessed accommodation.

WHIMPLE, Devon Map ref 1D2

★★

3 Units
Sleeping 6

LSF HOLIDAY COTTAGES
Lower Southbrook Farm, Southbrook Lane, Whimple,
Exeter EX5 2PG
T: (01404) 822989
F: (01404) 822989
E: angela.lang@btinternet.com
Contact: Mrs S Lang

OPEN All year round

Low season per wk
£135.00–£192.00
High season per wk
£239.00–£343.00

Three comfortable cottages in 4 acres, surrounded by beautiful countryside. Ideally located for visiting Exeter and many of the popular tourist attractions.

WINSCOMBE, North Somerset Map ref 1D1

★★★★

1 Unit
Sleeping 8

Luxury accommodation in south wing of Gothic Victorian manor house. Newly refurbished, period features and modern comforts. Log fires in winter, relax and barbecue in summer under Mulberry Tree. Beach 15 minutes, good local pub and restaurant; visit Cheddar Gorge, Bath, Bristol and Wells. Children's secret garden and tennis court.

MULBERRY SOUTH WING OF WINSCOMBE COURT

Winscombe Court, Winscombe Hill, Winscombe BS25 1DE
Contact: Mrs J Symons, Winscombe Court,
Winscombe Hill, Winscombe BS25 1DE
T: (01934) 842171 (Ansaphone) & 844665
F: (01934) 842171
E: jsymons@winscombecourt.fsnet.co.uk
I: www.winscombecourt.co.uk

OPEN All year round
CC: Barclaycard, Delta,
JCB, Mastercard, Solo,
Switch, Visa, Visa Electron

Low season per wk
Min £490.00
High season per wk
Max £850.00

Special weekend breaks
off-season.

WINSFORD, Somerset Map ref 1D1

★★

1 Unit
Sleeping 7

HILL HOUSE
Halse Lane, Winsford, Minehead TA24 7JE
Contact: Mrs S Maxse, Homestead Farm, Selborne,
Alton GU34 3LN
T: (01420) 511216
F: (01420) 511024

OPEN Apr–Oct

Low season per wk
Min £195.00
High season per wk
Max £375.00

Spacious, comfortable, detached house for 7 people, with lovely views.

WINTERBOURNE ABBAS, Dorset Map ref 2A3

★★★

1 Unit
Sleeping 2

GARDEN STUDIO
5a Butt Farm Close, Winterbourne Abbas,
Dorchester DT2 9SU
Contact: Mrs Anne Slattery, 14 Diggory Crescent,
Dorchester DT1 2SP
T: (01305) 259127
E: anne@slattery.fsnet.co.uk

OPEN May–Sep

Low season per wk
£220.00
High season per wk
£220.00

Purpose-built self-contained apartment with own entrance and garden area. Only 14 years old, but attractively refurbished. In the heart of Hardy Country.

WINTERBOURNE STOKE, Wiltshire Map ref 2B2

★★

1 Unit
Sleeping 2

SCOTLAND LODGE
Winterbourne Stoke, Salisbury SP3 4TF
T: (01980) 620943 & 07957 856302 (Mobile)
F: (01980) 621403
E: scotland.lodge@virgin.net.co.uk
I: www.scotland-lodge.co.uk
Contact: Mrs Jane Singleton

OPEN All year round

Low season per wk
Min £150.00
High season per wk
£175.00–£220.00

Well-appointed and comfortable self-catering unit within a country house. Ideal touring base near Stonehenge and Salisbury. Bed and breakfast also available. No smoking.

★★★★★

3 Units
Sleeping 2–8

Thatched 16thC cottage in a village location, close to the sea at Budleigh Salterton. Lovely furnishings and antiques, and high standards throughout. Ideal base for West Country touring, beach holidays or walking. Well-behaved dogs welcome. Pub and shop within walking distance.

THE THATCHED COTTAGE COMPANY

Broadmead, Woodbury, Exeter EX5
Contact: Mrs G M Barlow, The Thatched Cottage Company, 56 Fore Street, Otterton, Budleigh Salterton EX9 7HB
T: (01395) 567676
F: (01395) 567440
I: www.thethatchedcottagecompany.com

OPEN All year round

Winter 3 day breaks from £175.

Low season per wk
£300.00–£550.00
High season per wk
£450.00–£1,192.00

COUNTRY CODE

Always follow the Country Code 🌳
Enjoy the countryside and respect its life and work 🌳 Guard against all risk of fire 🌳 Fasten all gates 🌳 Keep your dogs under close control 🌳 Keep to public paths across farmland 🌳 Use gates and stiles to cross fences, hedges and walls 🌳 Leave livestock, crops and machinery alone 🌳 Take your litter home 🌳 Help to keep all water clean 🌳 Protect wildlife, plants and trees 🌳 Take special care on country roads 🌳 Make no unnecessary noise 🌳

A brief guide to the main Towns and Villages offering accommodation in the

South West of England

A **ABBOTSBURY, DORSET** - Beautiful village near Chesil Beach, with a long main street of mellow stone and thatched cottages and the ruins of a Benedictine monastery. High above the village on a hill is a prominent 15th C chapel. Abbotsbury's famous swannery and sub-tropical gardens lie just outside the village.

- **ALLERFORD, SOMERSET** - Village with picturesque stone and thatch cottages and a packhorse bridge, set in the beautiful Vale of Porlock.

- **AMESBURY, WILTSHIRE** - Standing on the banks of the River Avon, this is the nearest town to Stonehenge on Salisbury Plain. The area is rich in prehistoric sites.

- **ASHBRITTLE, SOMERSET** - Village on the Somerset/Devon border, close to the River Tone.

- **ASHBURTON, DEVON** - Formerly a thriving wool centre and important as one of Dartmoor's four stannary towns. Today's busy market town has many period buildings. Ancient tradition is maintained in the annual ale-tasting and bread-weighing ceremony. Good centre for exploring Dartmoor or the south Devon coast.

- **ASHWATER, DEVON** - Village 6 miles south-east of Holsworthy, with a pleasant village green dominated by its church.

- **AXMINSTER, DEVON** - This tree-shaded market town on the banks of the River Axe was one of Devon's earliest West Saxon settlements, but is better known for its carpet making. Based on Turkish methods, the industry began in 1755, declined in the 1830s and was revived in 1937.

B **BAMPTON, DEVON** - Riverside market town, famous for its fair each October.

- **BARNSTAPLE, DEVON** - At the head of the Taw Estuary, once a ship-building and textile town, now an agricultural centre with attractive period buildings, a modern civic centre and leisure centre. Attractions include Queen Anne's Walk, a charming colonnaded arcade and Pannier Market.

- **BATCOMBE, SOMERSET** - Village tucked into a fold of the hills, close to the uppermost reaches of the River Alham, giving superb views of the countryside. The church has a splendid 15th C tower.

- **BATH, BATH AND NORTH EAST SOMERSET** - Georgian spa city beside the River Avon. Important Roman site with impressive reconstructed baths, uncovered in 19th C. Bath Abbey built on site of monastery where first king of England was crowned (AD 973). Fine architecture in mellow local stone. Pump Room and museums.

- **BEAMINSTER, DORSET** - Old country town of mellow local stone set amid hills and rural vales. Mainly Georgian buildings; attractive almshouses date from 1603. The 17th C church with its ornate, pinnacled tower was restored inside by the Victorians. Parnham, a Tudor manor house, lies 1 mile south.

- **BELSTONE, DEVON** - Village in picturesque Dartmoor setting, retaining its stocks and whipping post. Several prehistoric stone circles to be seen in the area.

- **BERRYNARBOR, DEVON** - Picturesque, old-world village, winner of best-kept village awards, adjoining the lovely, wooded Sterridge Valley. On scenic route between Ilfracombe and Combe Martin.

- **BIDEFORD, DEVON** - The home port of Sir Richard Grenville, the town with its 17th C merchants' houses flourished as a shipbuilding and cloth town. The bridge of 24 arches was built about 1460. Charles Kingsley stayed here while writing Westward Ho!

- **BIGBURY-ON-SEA, DEVON** - Small resort on Bigbury Bay at the mouth of the River Avon. Wide sands, rugged cliffs. Burgh Island can be reached on foot at low tide.

- **BODMIN, CORNWALL** - County town south-west of Bodmin Moor with a ruined priory and church dedicated to St Petroc. Nearby are Lanhydrock House and Pencarrow House.

- **BOSCASTLE, CORNWALL** - Small, unspoilt village in Valency Valley. Active as a port until onset of railway era, its natural harbour affords rare shelter on this wild coast. Attractions include spectacular blow-hole, Celtic field strips, part-Norman church. Nearby St Juliot Church was restored by Thomas Hardy.

- **BRADFORD-ON-AVON, WILTSHIRE** - Huddled beside the river, the buildings of this former cloth-weaving town reflect continuing prosperity from the Middle Ages. There is a tiny Anglo-Saxon church, part of a monastery. The part-14th C bridge carries a medieval chapel, later used as a gaol.

- **BRATTON, SOMERSET** - Hamlet on the edge of the Exmoor National Park, close to the resort of Minehead.

- **BRAYFORD, DEVON** - Village lies 6 miles north-west of South Molton and marks the crossing of the River Bray by one of the main roads from Exmoor to the sea.

- **BREAN, SOMERSET** - Caravans and holiday bungalows by sand dunes on the flat shoreline south of Brean Down. This rocky promontory has exhilarating cliff walks, bird-watching and an Iron Age fort.

- **BRIDPORT, DORSET** - Market town and chief producer of nets and ropes just inland of dramatic Dorset coast. Old, broad streets built for drying and twisting and long gardens for rope-walks. Grand arcaded Town Hall and Georgian buildings. Local history museum has Roman relics.

- **BRISTOL** - Famous for maritime links, historic harbour, Georgian terraces and Brunel's Clifton suspension bridge. Many attractions including SS Great Britain, Bristol Zoo, museums and art galleries and top name entertainments. Events include Balloon Fiesta and Regatta.

- **BRIXHAM, DEVON** - Famous for its trawling fleet in the 19th C, a steeply-built fishing port overlooking the harbour and fish market. A statue of William of Orange recalls his landing here before deposing James II. There is an aquarium and museum. Good cliff views and walks.

- **BUCKLAND NEWTON, DORSET** - Village in an Area of Outstanding Natural Beauty, on the edge of the Dorset Downs midway between Dorchester and Sherborne.

- **BUDE, CORNWALL** - Resort on dramatic Atlantic coast. High cliffs give spectacular sea and inland views. Golf-course, cricket pitch, folly, surfing, coarse-fishing and boating. Mother-town Stratton was base of Royalist Sir Bevil Grenville.

- **BURNHAM-ON-SEA, SOMERSET** - Small Victorian resort famous for sunsets and sandy beaches, a few minutes from junction 22 of the M5. Ideal base for touring Somerset, Cheddar and Bath. Good sporting facilities, championship golf-course.

- **BURTON BRADSTOCK, DORSET** - Lying amid fields beside the River Bride, a village of old stone houses, a 14th C church and a village green. The beautiful coast road from Abbotsbury to Bridport passes by and Iron Age forts top the surrounding hills. The sheltered river valley makes a staging post for migrating birds.

C CASTLE CARY, SOMERSET - One of south Somerset's most attractive market towns, with a picturesque winding high street of golden stone and thatch, market-house and famous round 18th C lock-up.

- **CATTISTOCK, DORSET** - 9 miles north-west of Dorchester, amidst fine downland scenery near the River Frome.
- **CHALLACOMBE, DEVON** - Small, attractive village surrounded by the stunning countryside of the Exmoor National Park. Close to the North Devon coast, a number of National Trust properties and family attractions.
- **CHAPEL AMBLE, CORNWALL** - Village 2 miles north of Wadebridge and within easy reach of the Camel Estuary and the North Cornwall coast.
- **CHEDDAR, SOMERSET** - Large village at foot of Mendips just south of the spectacular Cheddar Gorge. Close by are Roman and Saxon sites and famous show caves. Traditional Cheddar cheese is still made here.
- **CHIDEOCK, DORSET** - Village of sandstone thatched cottages in a valley near the dramatic Dorset coast. The church holds an interesting processional cross in mother-of-pearl and the manor house close by is associated with the Victorian Roman Catholic church. Seatown has a pebble beach and limestone cliffs.
- **CHIPPENHAM, WILTSHIRE** - Ancient market town with modern industry. Notable early buildings include the medieval Town Hall and the gabled 15th C Yelde Hall, now a local history museum. On the outskirts Hardenhuish has a charming hilltop church by the Georgian architect John Wood of Bath.
- **CHUDLEIGH, DEVON** - Small market town close to main Exeter to Plymouth road. To the south is Chudleigh Rock, a dramatic limestone outcrop containing prehistoric caves.
- **CHULMLEIGH, DEVON** - Small, hilly town above the Little Dart River, long since by-passed by the main road. The large 15th C church is noted for its splendid rood screen and 38 carved wooden angels on the roof.
- **COLYTON, DEVON** - Surrounded by fertile farmland, this small riverside town was an early Saxon settlement. Medieval prosperity from the wool trade built the grand church tower with its octagonal lantern and the church's fine west window.

- **COMBE MARTIN, DEVON** - On the edge of the Exmoor National Park, this seaside village is set in a long narrow valley with its natural harbour lying between towering cliffs. The main beach is a mixture of sand, rocks and pebbles and the lack of strong currents ensures safe bathing.
- **CRACKINGTON HAVEN, CORNWALL** - Tiny village on the North Cornwall coast, with a small sandy beach and surf bathing. The highest cliffs in Cornwall lie to the south.
- **CROYDE, DEVON** - Pretty village with thatched cottages near Croyde Bay. To the south stretch Saunton Sands and their dunelands Braunton Burrows with interesting flowers and plants, nature reserve and golf-course. Cliff walks and bird-watching at Baggy Point, west of the village.

D DARTMOUTH, DEVON - Ancient port at mouth of Dart. Has fine period buildings, notably town houses near Quay and Butterwalk of 1635. Harbour castle ruin. In 12th C Crusader fleets assembled here. Royal Naval College dominates from Hill. Carnival, June; Regatta, August.

- **DAWLISH, DEVON** - Small resort, developed in Regency and Victorian periods beside Dawlish Water. Town centre has ornamental riverside gardens with black swans. One of England's most scenic stretches of railway was built by Brunel alongside jagged red cliffs between the sands and the town.
- **DAWLISH WARREN, DEVON** - Popular with campers and caravanners, a sandy spit of land at the mouth of the River Exe. The sand dunes with their golf links are rich in plant and bird life. Brunel's atmospheric railway once ran along the dramatic line between jagged red cliffs and sandy shore.
- **DEVIZES, WILTSHIRE** - Old market town standing on the Kennet and Avon Canal. Rebuilt Norman castle, good 18th C buildings. St John's church has 12th C work and Norman tower. Museum of Wiltshire's archaeology and natural history reflects wealth of prehistoric sites in the county.
- **DORCHESTER, DORSET** - Busy medieval county town destroyed by fires in 17th and 18th C. Cromwellian stronghold and scene of Judge Jeffreys' Bloody Assize after Monmouth Rebellion of 1685. Tolpuddle Martyrs were tried in Shire Hall. Museum has Roman and earlier exhibits and Hardy relics.
- **DULVERTON, SOMERSET** - Set among woods and hills of south-west Exmoor, a busy riverside town with a 13th C church. The Rivers Barle and Exe are rich in salmon and trout. The information centre at the Exmoor National Park Headquarters at Dulverton is open throughout the year.

- **DUNSFORD, DEVON** - Picturesque village of thatched white walled cottages 4 miles north-east of Moretonhampstead and on the edge of the Dartmoor National Park.
- **DUNSTER, SOMERSET** - Ancient town with views of Exmoor. The hilltop castle has been continuously occupied since 1070. Medieval prosperity from cloth built 16th C octagonal Yarn Market and the church. A riverside mill, packhorse bridge and 18th C hilltop folly occupy other interesting corners in the town.

E EAST ALLINGTON, DEVON - Village 3 miles north-east of Kingsbridge and within easy reach of the South Devon coast.

F FALMOUTH, CORNWALL - Busy port and fishing harbour, popular resort on the balmy Cornish Riviera. Henry VIII's Pendennis Castle faces St Mawes Castle across the broad natural harbour and yacht basin Carrick Roads, which receives 7 rivers.

- **FROME, SOMERSET** - Old market town with modern light industry, its medieval centre watered by the River Frome. Above Cheap Street with its flagstones and watercourse is the church showing work of varying periods. Interesting buildings include 18th C wool merchants' houses.

G GLASTONBURY, SOMERSET - Market town associated with Joseph of Arimathea and the birth of English Christianity. Built around its 7th C abbey said to be the site of King Arthur's burial. Glastonbury Tor with its ancient tower gives panoramic views over flat country and the Mendip Hills.

- **GORRAN HAVEN, CORNWALL** - Once important in the pilchard fisheries, now a seaside village gathered at the mouth of its valley. A medieval chapel and Methodist church stand among the cottages overlooking the quay and beautiful unspoilt cliffs spread south-west of Dodman Point.

H HARTLAND, DEVON - Hamlet on high, wild country near Hartland Point. Just west, the parish church tower makes a magnificent landmark; the light, unrestored interior holds one of Devon's finest rood screens. There are spectacular cliffs around Hartland Point and the lighthouse.

- **HOLSWORTHY, DEVON** - Busy rural town and centre of a large farming community. Market day attracts many visitors.
- **HOPE COVE, DEVON** - Sheltered by the 400-ft headland of Bolt Tail, Hope Cove lies close to a small resort with thatched cottages, Inner Hope. Between Bolt Tail and Bolt Head lie 6 miles of beautiful National Trust cliffs.

I ILFRACOMBE, DEVON - Resort of Victorian grandeur set on hillside between cliffs with sandy coves. At the mouth of the harbour stands an 18th C lighthouse, built over a medieval chapel. There are fine formal gardens and a museum. Chambercombe Manor, an interesting old house, is nearby.

• **ILMINSTER, SOMERSET** - Former wool town with modern industry, set in undulating, pastoral country. Fine market square of mellow Ham stone and Elizabethan school house. The 15th C church has a handsome tower and lofty, light interior with notable brass memorials. Nearby is an art centre with theatre and gardens.

• **ISLES OF SCILLY** - Picturesque group of islands and granitic rocks south-west of Lands End. Peaceful and unspoilt, they are noted for natural beauty, romantic maritime history, silver sands, early flowers and sub-tropical gardens on Tresco. Main island is St. Mary's.

K KING'S NYMPTON, DEVON - Village 3 miles north of Chulmleigh. The church is famous for its fine roofs and rood screen and below the village is Junction Pool which features in 'Tarka the Otter' by Henry Williamson.

• **KINGSBRIDGE, DEVON** - Formerly important as a port, now a market town overlooking head of beautiful, wooded estuary winding deep into rural countryside. Summer art exhibitions; Cookworthy Museum.

L LACOCK, WILTSHIRE - Village of great charm. Medieval buildings of stone, brick or timber-frame have jutting storeys, gables, oriel windows. Magnificent church has perpendicular fan-vaulted chapel with grand tomb to benefactor who, after Dissolution, bought Augustinian nunnery, Lacock Abbey.

• **LANGPORT, SOMERSET** - Small market town with Anglo-Saxon origins, sloping to River Parrett. Well-known for glove making and, formerly, for eels. Interesting old buildings include some fine local churches.

• **LANREATH-BY-LOOE, CORNWALL** - Village 5 miles north-west of Looe. Folk and farm museum in the village tithe barn and Shillamill Lakes nearby.

• **LAUNCESTON, CORNWALL** - Medieval 'Gateway to Cornwall', county town until 1838, founded by the Normans under their hilltop castle near the original monastic settlement. This market town, overlooked by its castle ruin, has a square with Georgian houses and an elaborately-carved granite church.

• **LEE, DEVON** - Village 2 miles west of Ilfracombe, nestling in a coombe leading down to Lee Bay and sometimes called Fuchsia Valley.

• **LISKEARD, CORNWALL** - Former stannary town with a livestock market and light industry, at the head of a valley running to the coast. Handsome Georgian and Victorian residences and a Victorian Guildhall reflect the prosperity of the mining boom. The large church has an early 20th C tower and a Norman font.

• **LIVERTON, DEVON** - Hamlet 4 miles north-west of Newton Abbot and within the Dartmoor National Park.

• **LOOE, CORNWALL** - Small resort developed around former fishing and smuggling ports occupying the deep estuary of the East and West Looe Rivers. Narrow winding streets, with old inns; museum and art gallery are housed in interesting old buildings. Shark fishing centre, boat trips; busy harbour.

• **LOSTWITHIEL, CORNWALL** - Cornwall's ancient capital which gained its Royal Charter in 1189. Tin from the mines around the town was smelted and coined in the Duchy Palace. Norman Restormel Castle, with its circular keep and deep moat, overlooks the town.

• **LYME REGIS, DORSET** - Pretty, historic fishing town and resort set against the fossil-rich cliffs of Lyme Bay. In medieval times it was an important port and cloth centre. The Cobb, a massive stone breakwater, shelters the ancient harbour which is still lively with boats.

• **LYNTON, DEVON** - Hilltop resort on Exmoor coast linked to its seaside twin, Lynmouth, by a water-operated cliff railway which descends from the town hall. Spectacular surroundings of moorland cliffs with steep chasms of conifer and rocks through which rivers cascade.

M MALMESBURY, WILTSHIRE - Overlooking the River Avon, an old town dominated by its great church, once a Benedictine abbey. The surviving Norman nave and porch are noted for fine sculptures, 12th C arches and musicians' gallery.

• **MARAZION, CORNWALL** - Old town sloping to Mount's Bay with views of St Michael's Mount and a causeway to the island revealed at low tide. In medieval times it catered for pilgrims. The Mount is crowned by a 15th C castle built around the former Benedictine monastery of 1044.

• **MEVAGISSEY, CORNWALL** - Small fishing town, a favourite with holidaymakers. Earlier prosperity came from pilchard fisheries, boat-building and smuggling. By the harbour are fish cellars, some converted, and a local history museum is housed in an old boat-building shed. Handsome Methodist chapel; shark fishing, sailing.

• **MINEHEAD, SOMERSET** - Victorian resort with spreading sands developed around old fishing port on the coast below Exmoor. Former fishermen's cottages stand beside the 17th C harbour; cobbled streets climb the hill in steps to the church. Boat trips, steam railway. Hobby Horse festival 1 May.

• **MINIONS, CORNWALL** - Village on the southern edge of Bodmin Moor with many pre-historic sites nearby. Paths lead to the Cheesewring, a stone formation where thick oval slabs balance precariously.

• **MODBURY, DEVON** - Attractive South Hams town set in rolling countryside, whose Perpendicular church has a rare Devon spire.

• **MORETONHAMPSTEAD, DEVON** - Small market town with a row of 17th C almshouses standing on the Exeter road. Surrounding moorland is scattered with ancient farmhouses, prehistoric sites.

• **MOTHECOMBE, DEVON** - Situated on the western side of the Erme Estuary and close to the coast of Bigbury Bay. Within easy reach of Plymouth and Kingsbridge.

N NEWTON FERRERS, DEVON - Hillside village overlooking wooded estuary of the River Yealm, with attractive waterside cottages and yacht anchorage.

• **NORTH MOLTON, DEVON** - Village on the southern slopes of Exmoor, a centre for local copper mines in the 19th C. A 17th C monument in the church shows the effigies of a mining landlord and his family.

O OAKFORD, DEVON - Village in the Exe Valley, close to the market town of Bampton and the Exmoor National Park.

• **OKEHAMPTON, DEVON** - Busy market town near the high tors of northern Dartmoor. The Victorian church, with William Morris windows and a 15th C tower, stands on the site of a Saxon church. A Norman castle ruin overlooks the river to the west of the town. Museum of Dartmoor Life in a restored mill.

• **OWERMOIGNE, DORSET** - Village 6 miles east of Dorchester, within easy reach of the Dorset coast and the family resort of Weymouth.

P PADSTOW, CORNWALL - Old town encircling its harbour on the Camel Estuary. The 15th C church has notable bench-ends. There are fine houses on North Quay and Raleigh's Court House on South Quay. Tall cliffs and golden sands along the coast and ferry to Rock. Famous 'Obby 'Oss Festival on 1 May.

• **PARRACOMBE, DEVON** - Pretty village spreading over the slopes of a river valley on the western edge of Exmoor.

- **PENZANCE, CORNWALL** - Resort and fishing port on Mount's Bay with mainly Victorian promenade and some fine Regency terraces. Former prosperity came from tin trade and pilchard fishing. Grand Georgian style church by harbour. Georgian Egyptian building at head of Chapel Street and Morrab Gardens.

- **PERRANPORTH, CORNWALL** - Small seaside resort developed around a former mining village. Today's attractions include exciting surf, rocks, caves and extensive sand dunes.

- **POLPERRO, CORNWALL** - Picturesque fishing village clinging to steep valley slopes about its harbour. A river splashes past cottages and narrow lanes twist between. The harbour mouth, guarded by jagged rocks, is closed by heavy timbers during storms.

- **PORLOCK, SOMERSET** - Village set between steep Exmoor hills and the sea at the head of beautiful Porlock Vale. The narrow street shows a medley of building styles. South-westward is Porlock Weir with its old houses and tiny harbour and further along the shore at Culbone is England's smallest church.

- **PORT ISAAC, CORNWALL** - Old fishing port of whitewashed cottages, twisting stairways and narrow alleys. A stream splashes down through the centre to the harbour. Nearby stands a 19th C folly, Doyden Castle, with a magnificent view of the coast.

- **PORTLAND, DORSET** - Joined by a narrow isthmus to the coast, a stony promontory sloping from the lofty landward side to a lighthouse on Portland Bill at its southern tip. Villages are built of the white limestone for which the 'isle' is famous.

- **PORTREATH, CORNWALL** - Formerly developed as a mining port, small resort with some handsome 19th C buildings. Cliffs, sands and good surf.

- **PRAA SANDS, CORNWALL** - Small village named after long, sandy bathing beach to the south. Picturesque Prussia Cove, a former haunt of smugglers, lies to the west and is sheltered by Crudden Point. A tower of the 16th C Pengersick Castle remains.

- **S** SALCOMBE, DEVON - Sheltered yachting resort of whitewashed houses and narrow streets in a balmy setting on the Salcombe Estuary. Palm, myrtle and other Mediterranean plants flourish. There are sandy bays and creeks for boating.

- **SALISBURY, WILTSHIRE** - Beautiful city and ancient regional capital set amid water meadows. Buildings of all periods are dominated by the cathedral whose spire is the tallest in England. Built between 1220 and 1258, it is one of the purest examples of Early English architecture.

- **SEATON, DEVON** - Small resort lying near the mouth of the River Axe. A mile-long beach extends to the dramatic cliffs of Beer Head. Annual art exhibition in July.

- **SHALDON, DEVON** - Pretty resort facing Teignmouth from the south bank of the Teign Estuary. Regency houses harmonise with others of later periods; there are old cottages and narrow lanes. On the Ness, a sandstone promontory nearby, a tunnel built in the 19th C leads to a beach revealed at low tide.

- **SHEPTON MALLET, SOMERSET** - Historic town in the Mendip foothills, important in Roman times and site of many significant archaeological finds. Cloth industry reached its peak in the 17th C, and many fine examples of cloth merchants' houses remain. Beautiful parish church, market cross, local history museum, Collett Park.

- **SHERBORNE, DORSET** - Dorset's 'Cathedral City' of medieval streets, golden hamstone buildings and great abbey church, resting place of Saxon kings. Formidable 12th C castle ruins and Sir Walter Raleigh's splendid Tudor mansion and deer park. Street markets, leisure centre, many cultural activities.

- **SHERSTON, WILTSHIRE** - Village situated 5 miles south west of Malmesbury, with 16th C to 18th C houses in the High Street. Site of a battle against the Danes in 1016.

- **SHIPHAM, SOMERSET** - Peaceful village on the slopes of the Mendip Hills.

- **SIDMOUTH, DEVON** - Charming resort set amid lofty red cliffs where the River Sid meets the sea. The wealth of ornate Regency and Victorian villas recalls the time when this was one of the south coast's most exclusive resorts. Museum; August International Festival of Folk Arts.

- **ST AUSTELL, CORNWALL** - Leading market town, the meeting point of old and new Cornwall. One mile from St Austell Bay with its sandy beaches, old fishing villages and attractive countryside. Ancient narrow streets, pedestrian shopping precincts. Fine church of Pentewan stone and Italianate Town Hall.

- **ST IVES, CORNWALL** - Old fishing port, artists' colony and holiday town with good surfing beach. Fishermen's cottages, granite fish cellars, a sandy harbour and magnificent headlands typify a charm that has survived since the 19th C pilchard boom. Tate Gallery opened in 1993.

- **ST JUST-IN-PENWITH, CORNWALL** - Coastal parish of craggy moorland scattered with engine houses and chimney stacks of disused mines. The old mining town of St Just has handsome 19th C granite buildings. North of the town are the dramatic ruined tin mines at Botallack.

- **ST KEVERNE, CORNWALL** - Standing on the windswept Lizard Peninsula, a village of cob and stone houses gathered round a spacious square. The church has an interesting octagonal spire, rebuilt in 1770 and was a landmark for ships negotiating the dreaded Manacle Rocks, 1 mile offshore.

- **ST MAWGAN, CORNWALL** - Pretty village of great historic interest, on wooded slopes in the Vale of Lanherne. At its centre, an old stone bridge over the River Menahyl is overlooked by the church with its lofty buttressed tower. Among ancient stone crosses in the churchyard is a 15th C lantern cross with carved figures.

- **STEEPLE ASHTON, WILTSHIRE** - Old village dominated by its magnificent Perpendicular church, built at a time of prosperity from the medieval wool trade.

- **T** TAUNTON, SOMERSET - County town, well-known for its public schools, sheltered by gentle hill-ranges on the River Tone. Medieval prosperity from wool has continued in marketing and manufacturing and the town retains many fine period buildings. Museum.

- **TAVISTOCK, DEVON** - Old market town beside the River Tavy on the western edge of Dartmoor. Developed around its 10th C abbey, of which some fragments remain, it became a stannary town in 1305 when tin-streaming thrived on the moors. Tavistock Goose Fair, October.

- **THURLESTONE, DEVON** - Small resort of thatched cottages standing above coastal cliffs near the winding estuary of Devon's River Avon. The village has a fine golf-course and a good beach.

- **TIVERTON, DEVON** - Busy market and textile town, settled since the 9th C, at the meeting of 2 rivers. Town houses, Tudor almshouses and parts of the fine church were built by wealthy cloth merchants; a medieval castle is incorporated into a private house; Blundells School.

- **TORQUAY, DEVON** - Devon's grandest resort, developed from a fishing village. Smart apartments and terraces rise from the seafront and Marine Drive along the headland gives views of beaches and colourful cliffs.

- **TORRINGTON, DEVON** - Perched high above the River Torridge, with a charming market square, Georgian Town Hall and a museum. The famous Dartington Crystal Factory, Rosemoor Gardens and Plough Arts Centre are all located in the town.

- **TREGONY, CORNWALL** - Old village, once a significant port and market town, rising from the River Fal. An inscribed stone of the 6th C forms a cornerstone of the church, which stands above the village and was almost entirely rebuilt in 1899.

- **WADEBRIDGE, CORNWALL** - Old market town with Cornwall's finest medieval bridge, spanning the Camel at its highest navigable point. Twice widened, the bridge is said to have been built on woolpacks sunk in the unstable sands of the river bed.

- **WELLS, SOMERSET** - Small city set beneath the southern slopes of the Mendips. Built between 1180 and 1424, the magnificent cathedral is preserved in much of its original glory and with its ancient precincts forms one of our loveliest and most unified groups of medieval buildings.

- **WEST BAY, DORSET** - Picturesque resort with a busy harbour, the perfect base for exploring this spectacular stretch of coastline.

- **WESTBURY, WILTSHIRE** - Wiltshire's best-known white horse looks down on the town with its Georgian houses around the Market Place. Handsome Perpendicular church with fine carved chancel screen and stone reredos. Above the white horse are the prehistoric earthworks of Bratton Castle.

- **WESTON-SUPER-MARE, NORTH SOMERSET** - Large, friendly resort developed in the 19th C. Traditional seaside attractions include theatres and a dance hall. The museum has a Victorian seaside gallery and Iron Age finds from a hill fort on Worlebury Hill in Weston Woods.

- **WEYMOUTH, DORSET** - Ancient port and one of the south's earliest resorts. Curving beside a long, sandy beach, the elegant Georgian esplanade is graced with a statue of George III and a cheerful Victorian Jubilee clock tower. Museum, Sea-Life Centre.

- **WINSCOMBE, NORTH SOMERSET** - Winscombe Hill and the prominent Crook's Peak dominate this Mendip Valley village. The church displays 15th C glass and a splendid tower.

- **WINSFORD, SOMERSET** - Small village in Exmoor National Park, on the River Exe in splendid walking country under Winsford Hill. On the other side of the hill is a Celtic standing stone, the Caratacus Stone, and nearby across the River Barle stretches an ancient packhorse bridge, Tarr Steps.

- **WINTERBOURNE ABBAS, DORSET** - Main road village with numerous prehistoric remains nearby. Maiden Castle 3 miles south-east.

- **WITHYPOOL, SOMERSET** - Pretty village high on Exmoor near the beautiful River Barle. On Winsford Hill (National Trust) are Bronze Age barrows known as the Wambarrows.

- **WOODBURY, DEVON** - Attractive village, with Woodbury Common to the east, affording a panoramic coastal view from Berry Head to Portland Bill. Woodbury Castle Iron Age fort lies at a height of some 600 ft.

Our Countryside Matters!

Country Code

- Always follow the Country code
- Guard against all risk of fire
- Keep your dogs under close control
- Use gates and stiles to cross fences, hedges and walls
- Take your litter home
- Protect wildlife, plants and trees
- Make no unnecessary noise

- Enjoy the countryside and respect its life and work
- Fasten all gates
- Keep to public paths across farmland
- Leave livestock, crops and machinery alone
- Help to keep all water clean
- Take special care on country roads

We hope the countryside will fully open in 2002. However, given the serious nature of Foot and Mouth Disease please be ready to follow this additional advice and respect any further precautions given in local authority notices:

- Don't go onto farmland if you have handled farm animals in the last 7 days
- Avoid contact with farm animals and keep dogs on a lead where they are present
- If you step in dung, remove it before you leave the field • Don't go on paths with a local authority 'closed' notice.

For more information contact Tourist information Centres or Countryside Agency web site www.countryside.gov.uk which links to other local authority web sites providing details about rights of way and access opportunities across England.

SOUTH of England

A seafaring region with 800 years of nautical heritage to enjoy in its busy harbours and family resorts. For landlubbers there's gentle countryside, Georgian towns, modern cities and outstanding historic houses too.

classic sights

Blenheim Palace – a gilded Italian palace in an English park
Oxford – University town with ancient colleges
Claydon House – unusual interiors in the Rococo, Gothick and Chinoiserie styles

coast & country

Chiltern Hills – tranquil country walks
New Forest – historic wood and heathland
Studland Bay – glorious sweeping beach

glorious gardens

Cliveden – a series of distinctive and delightful gardens
Mottisfont Abbey – the perfect English rose garden

maritime history

Portsmouth Historic Dockyard – Henry VIII's Mary Rose, HMS Victory and HMS Warrior

distinctively different

Sandham Memorial Chapel – houses Stanley Spencer's WW1 murals

The counties of Berkshire, Buckinghamshire, Dorset (Eastern), Hampshire, Isle of Wight and Oxfordshire

FOR MORE INFORMATION CONTACT:
Southern Tourist Board
40 Chamberlayne Road, Eastleigh,
Hampshire S050 5JH
Tel: (023) 8062 5505 Fax: (023) 8062 0010
Email: info@southerntb.co.uk
Internet: www.visitbritain.com

The Pictures:
1 Freshwater Bay, Isle of Wight
2 Radcliffe Camera, Oxford
3 Lulworth Cove, Dorset

Places to Visit - see pages 352-355
Where to Stay - see pages 356-377

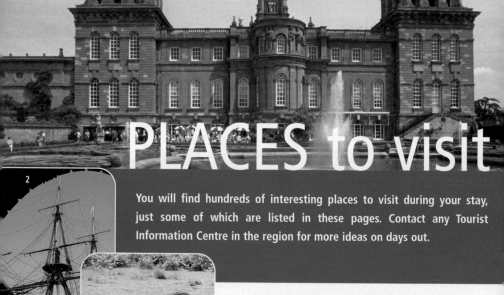

PLACES to visit

You will find hundreds of interesting places to visit during your stay, just some of which are listed in these pages. Contact any Tourist Information Centre in the region for more ideas on days out.

Beaulieu National Motor Museum

Beaulieu, Brockenhurst, Hampshire SO42 7ZN
Tel: (01590) 612345 www.beaulieu.co.uk
Motor museum with over 250 exhibits showing the history of motoring from 1896. Also Palace House, Wheels Experience, Beaulieu Abbey ruins and a display of monastic life.

Bekonscot Model Village

Warwick Road, Beaconsfield, Buckinghamshire HP9 2PL
Tel: (01494) 672919 www.bekonscot.org.uk
The oldest model village in the world, Bekonscot depicts rural England in the 1930s, where time has stood still for 70 years.

Blenheim Palace

Woodstock, Oxfordshire OX20 1PX
Tel: (01993) 811325 www.blenheimpalace.com
Home of the 11th Duke of Marlborough. Birthplace of Sir Winston Churchill. Designed by Vanbrugh in the English baroque style. Landscaped by `Capability' Brown.

Breamore House

Breamore, Fordingbridge, Hampshire SP6 2DF
Tel: (01725) 512233
Elizabethan manor house of 1583, with fine collection of works of art. Furniture, tapestries, needlework, paintings mainly 17thC and 18thC Dutch School.

Broughton Castle

Banbury, Oxfordshire OX15 5EB
Tel: (01295) 276070
Medieval moated house built in 1300 and enlarged between 1550 and 1600. The home of Lord and Lady Saye and Sele and family home for 600 years. Has Civil War connections.

Buckinghamshire County Museum

Church Street, Aylesbury, Buckinghamshire HP20 2QP
Tel: (01296) 331441
www.buckscc.gov.uk/tourism/museum
Lively hands-on, innovative museum complex consisting of county heritage displays, regional art gallery and Roald Dahl Children's Gallery in lovely garden setting.

Carisbrooke Castle

Newport, Isle of Wight PO30 1XY
Tel: (01983) 522107 www.english-heritage.org.uk
A splendid Norman castle where Charles I was imprisoned. The governor's lodge houses the county museum. Wheelhouse with wheel operated by donkeys.

Compton Acres

Canford Cliffs Road, Canford Cliffs,
Poole, Dorset BH13 7ES
Tel: (01202) 700778 www.comptonacres.co.uk
Ten separate and distinct gardens of the world. The gardens include Italian, Japanese, Indian glen and Spanish water garden. Country crafts and 'Off the Beaten Track Trail'.

Cotswold Wildlife Park

Bradwell Grove, Burford, Oxford, Oxfordshire OX18 4JW
Tel: (01993) 823006
Wildlife park in 200 acres (81 ha) of gardens and woodland with a variety of animals from all over the world.

The D Day Museum and Overlord Embroidery

Clarence Esplanade, Portsmouth, Hampshire PO5 3NT
Tel: (023) 9282 7261
www.portsmouthmuseums.co.uk
The magnificent 272 ft- (83 m-) long 'Overlord Embroidery' depicts the allied invasion of Normandy on 6 June 1944. Sound guides available in 4 languages.

Dicot Railway Centre

Great Western Society, Didcot, Oxfordshire OX11 7NJ
Tel: (01235) 817200
www.didcotrailwaycentre.org.uk
Living museum recreating the golden age of the Great Western Railway. Steam locomotives and trains, engine shed and small relics museum.

Exbury Gardens

Exbury Estate Office, Exbury, Southampton, Hampshire SO45 1AZ
Tel: (023) 8089 1203 www.exbury.co.uk.
Over 200 acres (81 ha) of woodland garden, including the Rothschild collection of rhododendrons, azaleas, camellias and magnolias.

Flagship Portsmouth

Porter's Lodge, 1/7 College Road, HM Naval Base, Portsmouth, Hampshire PO1 3LJ
Tel: (023) 9286 1533 www.flagship.org.uk
The world's greatest historic ships: Mary Rose, HMS Victory, HMS Warrior 1860. Royal Naval Museum, 'Warships by Water' tours, Dockyard Apprentice exhibition.

Gilbert White's House and Garden and The Oats Museum

The Wakes, High Street, Selborne, Alton, Hampshire GU34 3JH
Tel: (01420) 511275
Historic house and garden, home of Gilbert White, author of 'The Natural History of Selborne'. Exhibition on Frank Oates, explorer, and Captain Lawrence Oates of Antarctica fame.

The Hawk Conservancy and Country Park

Andover, Hampshire SP11 8DY
Tel: (01264) 772252 www.hawk-conservancy.org
Unique to Great Britain – 'Valley of the Eagles' held here daily at 1400.

Jane Austen's House

Chawton, Alton, Hampshire GU34 1SD
Tel: (01420) 83262
A 17thC house where Jane Austen lived from 1809-1817 and wrote or revised her six great novels. Letters, pictures, memorabilia, garden with old-fashioned flowers.

Kingston Lacy

Wimborne Minster, Dorset BH21 4EA
Tel: (01202) 883402 www.nationaltrust.org.uk
A 17thC house designed for Sir Ralph Bankes by Sir Roger Pratt, altered by Sir Charles Barry in the19thC. Collection of paintings, 250-acre (101-ha) wooded park, herd of Devon cattle.

Legoland Windsor

Winkfield Road, Windsor, Berkshire SL4 4AY
Tel: (0870) 504 0404 www.legoland.co.uk
A family park with hands-on activities, rides, themed playscapes and more Lego bricks than you ever dreamed possible!

The Pictures:
1 Blenheim Palace, Oxfordshire
2 HMS Victory, Portsmouth
3 Deer at Bolderwood, New Forest
4 Poole, Dorset
5 Oxford
6 Swan Green, New Forest

The Living Rainforest

Hampstead Norreys, Newbury, Berkshire RG18 0TN
Tel: (01635) 202444 www.livingrainforest.org
Two tropical rainforests, all under cover, approximately
20,000 sq ft (1,858 sq m). Collection of rare and exotic
tropical plants together with small representation of
wildlife in rainforest.

Manor Farm (Farm and Museum)

Manor Farm Country Park, Pylands Lane, Bursledon,
Southampton, Hampshire SO30 2ER
Tel: (01489) 787055
www.hants.gov.uk/countryside/manorfarm
Traditional Hampshire farmstead with range of buildings,
farm animals, machinery and equipment, pre-1950s
farmhouse and 13thC church set for 1900.
Living history site.

Marwell Zoological Park

Colden Common, Winchester, Hampshire SO21 1JH
Tel: (01962) 777407
Set in 100 acres (40.5 ha) of parkland surrounding
Marwell Hall. Venue suitable for all age groups including
disabled.

Oceanarium

Pier Approach, West Beach, Bournemouth, Dorset BH2 5AA
Tel: (01202) 311993 www.oceanarium.co.uk
Situated in the heart of Bournemouth next to the pier,
the Oceanarium will take you on a fascinating voyage of
the undersea world with creatures such as elegant
seahorses and sinister sharks.

Osborne House

Yorke Avenue, East Cowes, Isle of Wight PO32 6JY
Tel: (01983) 200022 www.english-heritage.com
Queen Victoria and Prince Albert's seaside holiday home.
Swiss Cottage where royal children learnt cooking and
gardening. Victorian carriage service to Swiss Cottage.

The Oxford Story

6 Broad Street, Oxford, Oxfordshire OX1 3AJ
Tel: (01865) 728822 www.heritageattractions.co.uk
An excellent introduction to Oxford – experience 900
years of University history in one hour. From scientists to
poets, astronomers to comedians.

Paultons Park

Ower, Romsey, Hampshire SO51 6AL
Tel: (023) 8081 4442
A full day out for all the family with over 40 attractions.
Rides, play areas, entertainments, museums, birds and
animals, beautiful gardens and lots more.

River and Rowing Museum

Mill Meadows, Henley-on-Thames, Oxfordshire RG9 1BF
Tel: (01491) 415600 www.rrm.co.uk
A unique, award-winning museum with galleries
dedicated to rowing, the River Thames and the town of
Henley. Special exhibitions run throughout the year.

Royal Navy Submarine Museum and HMS Alliance

Haslar Jetty Road, Gosport, Hampshire PO12 2AS
Tel: (023) 9252 9217 www.rnsubmus.co.uk
HM Submarine Alliance, HM Submarine No 1 (Holland 1),
midget submarines and models of every type of
submarine from earliest days to present nuclear age.

Swanage Railway

Station House, Swanage, Dorset BH19 1HB
Tel: (01929) 425800 www.swanrail.demon.co.uk
Enjoy a nostalgic steam train ride on the Purbeck line.
Steam trains run every weekend throughout the year
with daily running from April to October.

The Vyne

Sherborne St John, Basingstoke, Hampshire RG24 9HL
Tel: (01256) 881337 www.nationaltrust.org.uk
Original house dating back to Henry VIII's time.
Extensively altered in the mid 17thC. Tudor chapel,
beautiful gardens and lake.

Waterperry Gardens

Waterperry, Oxford, Oxfordshire OX33 1JZ
Tel: (01844) 339254 www.waterperrygardens.co.uk
Ornamental gardens covering six acres (2 ha) of the
83-acre (33.5-ha) 18thC Waterperry House estate.
Saxon village church, garden shop, teashop and art and
craft gallery.

Whitchurch Silk Mill

28 Winchester Street, Whitchurch, Hampshire RG28 7AL
Tel: (01256) 892065
Unique Georgian silk-weaving watermill, now a working
museum producing fine silk fabrics on Victorian
machinery. Riverside garden, tearooms for light meals,
silk gift shop.

Windsor Castle

Windsor, Berkshire SL4 1NJ
Tel: (01753) 869898 www.royal.gov.uk
Official residence of HM The Queen and royal residence
for 9 centuries. State apartments, Queen Mary's Doll's
House.

Find out more about the
SOUTH of England

Further information about holidays and attractions in the South of England is available from:

SOUTHERN TOURIST BOARD
40 Chamberlayne Road, Eastleigh, Hampshire SO50 5JH.
Tel: (023) 8062 5505 Fax: (023) 8062 0010
Email: info@southerntb.co.uk
Internet: www.visitbritain.com

Getting to the
SOUTH of England

BY ROAD: A good road network links London and the rest of the UK with major Southern destinations. The M27 provides a near continuous motorway route along the south coast and the M25/M3/A33 provides a direct route from London to Winchester and Southampton. The scenic A31 stretches from London, through Hampshire and to mid Dorset, whilst the M40/A34 have considerably cut travelling times from the West Midlands to the South. The M25 has speeded up access to Berkshire on the M4, Buckinghamshire and Oxfordshire on the M40.

BY RAIL: From London's Waterloo, trains travel to Portsmouth, Southampton and Bournemouth approximately three times an hour. From these stations, frequent trains go to Poole, Salisbury and Winchester. Further information on rail journeys in the South of England can be obtained from 08457 484950.

The Pictures:
River Isis, Oxford
2 Alum Bay, Isle of Wight

Where to stay in the South of England

Accommodation entries in this region are listed in alphabetical order of place name, and then in alphabetical order of establishment.

Map references refer to the colour location maps at front of this guide. The first number indicates the map to use; the letter and number which follow refer to the grid reference on the map.

At-a-glance symbols at the end of each accommodation entry give useful information about services and facilities. A key to symbols can be found inside the back cover flap. Keep this open for easy reference.

A brief description of the towns and villages offering accommodation in the entries which follow, can be found at the end of this section.

A complete listing of all the English Tourism Council assessed accommodation covered by this guide appears at the back of the guide.

ABINGDON, Oxfordshire Map ref 2C1 *Tourist Information Centre Tel: (01235) 522711*

★★★
3 Units
Sleeping 2–6

Three recently converted and very pretty, well-appointed cottages. Offering guests a comfortable countryside stay while being only 5 minutes' walk from the town centre of Abingdon and the River Thames. An ideal base for visiting Oxford, Cotswolds, Woodstock and Henley. Only 1 hour from central London.

KINGFISHER BARN HOLIDAY COTTAGES

Kingfisher Barn Ltd, Rye Farm, Abingdon OX14 3NN
T: (01235) 537538
F: (01235) 537538
E: info@kingfisherbarn.com
I: www.kingfisherbarn.com
Contact: Ms Liz Beaumont

OPEN All year round
CC: Amex, Delta, Diners, JCB, Mastercard, Switch, Visa

Free use of heated indoor swimming pool.

Low season per wk	£275.00–£495.00
High season per wk	£275.00–£495.00

🅰 ⚲ 🄰 🚻 🎨 ⊙ 🗕 🖵 🖳 📺 🍴 🗄 🍳 🌙 P ⛾ ❄ 🐎 🆂🅿

★★★
1 Unit
Sleeping 4–5

THE OLD SCHOOL
16 High Street, Drayton, Abingdon OX14 4JL
T: (01235) 531557 (Answerphone (24 hrs))
E: gordon@theoldeschool.freeserve.co.uk
Contact: Mrs C A Radburn

OPEN All year round

Low season per wk	£210.00–£255.00
High season per wk	£255.00–£295.00

Part of 19thC village school, converted to provide a spacious, well-equipped, tastefully furnished maisonette. Ideal for Oxford, Thames Valley, Cotswolds. Fast train service to London from nearby Didcot.

⚲7 🅼 🄰 🚻 🎨 ⊙ 🗕 🖵 🖳 📺 🍴 🗄 🍳 ✂ 🌙 ♠ P ∪ ⛾ ❄ 🆂🅿 🏠

ALVERSTOKE, Hampshire Map ref 2C3

★★
1 Unit
Sleeping 6

28 THE AVENUE
Alverstoke, Gosport PO12 2JR
Contact: Mr Martin Lawson, 18 Upper Paddock Road,
Watford WD1 4DZ
T: (01923) 244042
F: (01923) 244042

OPEN All year round

Low season per wk
£280.00–£320.00
High season per wk
£320.00–£350.00

Three-bedroomed house with pleasant garden, 10 minutes from uncrowded beach. Opportunities for fishing, sailing and windsurfing. Close to Portsmouth, Southampton and New Forest.

BEAULIEU, Hampshire Map ref 2C3

★★★★
1 Unit
Sleeping 4

HILL TOP HOUSE COTTAGE
Palace Lane, Beaulieu SO42 7YG
Contact: Mr & Mrs Brett Johnson, Hill Top House,
Palace Lane, Beaulieu SO42 7YG
T: (01590) 612731 & 07836 247896 (Mobile)
F: (01590) 612743
E: bretros@cs.com

OPEN All year round
CC: Barclaycard, Delta,
Eurocard, Mastercard,
Visa

Low season per wk
£295.00–£320.00
High season per wk
£420.00–£505.00

Set in the grounds of a period manor house, this comfortable single storey cottage enjoys superb views. Renovated to the highest standards.

★★★
1 Unit
Sleeping 7

IVY COTTAGE
Main Road, East Boldre, Brockenhurst SO42 7WD
Contact: Mr & Mrs B R Gibb, 28 Church Street,
Littlehampton BN17 5PX
T: (01903) 715595 (Answerphone when no reply) &
07778 933172
E: gibb28@breathemail.net

OPEN All year round

Low season per wk
£340.00–£440.00
High season per wk
£440.00–£540.00

Comfortable well-equipped 4-bedroom holiday cottage between Beaulieu and Lymington, with direct access to open forest. Village shop and pub nearby.

★★★★
1 Unit
Sleeping 2

MARES TAILS COTTAGE
Mares Tails, Furzey Lane, Beaulieu,
Brockenhurst SO42 7WB
Contact: Mrs Alice Barber, Mares Tails, Furzey Lane,
Beaulieu, Brockenhurst SO42 7WB
T: (01590) 612160
E: marestails612160@cs.com

OPEN May–Oct

Low season per wk
£250.00–£310.00
High season per wk
£320.00–£345.00

Well-appointed cottage in own secluded garden in grounds of architect's house. One mile from lovely village of Beaulieu, with direct access to open forest. 30 ft conservatory.

BEMBRIDGE, Isle of Wight Map ref 2C3

★★
1 Unit
Sleeping 10

NINE
Lane End Road, Bembridge PO35 5SU
Contact: Mrs B C Cripps, High Point, Brook Green,
Cuckfield, Haywards Heath RH17 5JJ
T: (01444) 454474

OPEN All year round

Low season per wk
£150.00–£250.00
High season per wk
£350.00–£550.00

Ideal holiday home 400 yards from sea. Five double bedrooms, sun parlour, good garden. TV, video, washing machine/dryer, dishwasher, fridge/freezer. Parking. Dogs welcome.

★★★★
1 Unit
Sleeping 6

SHIP-N-SHORE
1 Kings House, Kings Road, Bembridge PO35 5NT
Contact: Mrs C M Morris, Ash Hill Farm, Atherfield,
Chale, Ventnor PO38 2LH
T: (01983) 551350 (Answerphone)

OPEN All year round

Low season per wk
Min £200.00
High season per wk
Max £450.00

A tastefully decorated apartment with some harbour views, 2 minutes' walk to harbour/beach. Two bedrooms, master bedroom en suite. Furnished patio. Beautiful countryside walks nearby.

★★

1 Unit
Sleeping 2

CLOSE COTTAGE

Brockenhurst Road, Battramsley, Boldre,
Lymington SO41 8PT
T: (01590) 675343
Contact: Mr or Mrs C J White

*Cosy annexe of period cottage with beamed
ceilings and antique decor. French doors to
garden with rural views. Totally self-contained,
with double bed. Ample parking. Nearest
neighbour is country pub serving meals. Ideal for
forest walks, 2 miles to Lymington and coast, 2
miles to Brockenhurst shops/eating.*

OPEN All year round

Low season per wk
£120.00–£180.00
High season per wk
£220.00

★★★

1 Unit
Sleeping 4

ORCHARD HOUSE
Battramsley, Boldre, Lymington SO41 8ND
Contact: Mrs Valerie Barnes, Orchard House,
Battramsley, Boldre, Lymington SO41 8ND
T: (01590) 676686

OPEN All year round

Low season per wk
£200.00–£220.00
High season per wk
£220.00–£250.00

*Self-contained, ground floor annexe to country house. Set in 3 acres, south facing,
with patio doors to garden. Midway between Brockenhurst and Lymington.*

★★★

8 Units
Sleeping 2–6

SHALBOURNE HOUSE HOLIDAY FLATS

17 Grand Avenue, Southbourne, Bournemouth BH6 3SY
Contact: Mrs Margaret Stubbs, Manager,
83 Southbourne East Road, Bournemouth BH6 4DX
T: (01202) 432735 & 0797 9492252 (Mobile)

*Our recently modernised fully self-contained
holiday flats offer excellent standards of
cleanliness and comfort, at competitive prices. A
short walk from a 'Blue Flag' beach, shopping
centre, pubs and restaurants, we are
conveniently located for visiting Bournemouth
and Christchurch town centres, and for touring
Dorset, Hampshire and the New Forest.*

OPEN Apr–Oct

2001 tariff for 2002 season
providing £50 per week
deposit received before
31 Jan 2002.

Low season per wk
£110.00–£190.00
High season per wk
£190.00–£400.00

★★★★★

1 Unit
Sleeping 4

ROSE COTTAGE

Thorncross Farm, Brighstone, Newport PO30 4PN
Contact: Mr John Russell, Thorncross Farm, Brighstone,
Newport PO30 4PN
T: (01983) 740291
F: (01983) 741408

*Delightful 17thC semi-detached cottage in open
countryside. Tastefully refurbished to high
standard. One bedroom sleeping 4, beamed
living room with inglenook fireplace, well-
equipped kitchen leading to bathroom on
ground floor. Large garden with patio area. One
mile from village with shops and pubs serving
food.*

OPEN All year round

Low season per wk
£300.00–£325.00
High season per wk
£325.00–£475.00

CONFIRM YOUR BOOKING
You are advised to confirm your booking in writing.

★★★★★
1 Unit
Sleeping 4

Cottage/bungalow on open forest road, set in its own secluded garden. Many luxury fittings, beautifully furnished, cosy rooms, dining hall with log fire, luxury whirlpool bathroom, modern fitted kitchen and new large conservatory. Easy access to village, many amenities close by in ideal holiday area. Pets welcome.

GORSE COTTAGE
Balmer Lawn Road, Brockenhurst SO42 7TT
Contact: Mr & Mrs J Bareford, Whins, Hook Heath Avenue, Woking GU22 0HN
T: (01483) 760803 (Answerphone)
F: (01483) 764227
E: jon@bareford.com
I: www.bareford.com

OPEN All year round

Low season per wk
£380.00–£500.00
High season per wk
£650.00–£680.00

★★★★
1 Unit
Sleeping 6

2 WATERS GREEN COURT
Brockenhurst SO42 7QR
Contact: Mrs Sharon Hough, 5 Barton Drive, Knowle, Solihull B93 0PE
T: (01564) 771582
F: (01564) 774733
E: sharon.hough@talk21.com

House sleeping up to 6 in Brockenhurst. Ideal base for touring the New Forest and surrounding attractions.

OPEN All year round

Low season per wk
£380.00–£500.00
High season per wk
£450.00–£650.00

★★★★
1 Unit
Sleeping 6

Unusual accommodation in our beautiful 17thC manor house. The Nursery Flat has recently been refurbished and decorated to reflect its youthful connections. A small wood, orchard and tennis court, as well as a natural therapy clinic with a full range of complementary therapies available.

THE COURTYARD CENTRE AT BARTON MANOR
Barton Hartshorn, Buckingham MK18 4JU
T: (01280) 848943
F: (01280) 847517
E: enquiries@bartonmanor.co.uk
I: www.bartonmanor.co.uk
Contact: Mrs Susannah Petszaft

OPEN All year round

Individual and group retreats-options of yoga, t'ai chi, aromatherapy, reflexology, herbal medicine, osteopathy, massage etc.

High season per wk
£450.00

Rating Applied For
3 Units
Sleeping 4

HUNTSMILL HOLIDAYS
Huntsmill Farm, Shalstone, Buckingham MK18 5ND
Contact: Mrs Fiona Hilsdon, Huntsmill Holidays, Huntsmill Farm, Shalstone, Buckingham MK18 5ND
T: (01280) 704852
F: (01280) 704852

Cottages in a courtyard, tastefully converted from stone and slate barns. Peaceful countryside location, yet only 10 minutes from M40. Fully equipped, friendly service.

OPEN All year round

Low season per wk
Min £180.00
High season per wk
Max £450.00

ACCESSIBILITY
Look for the 🔲 🔲 🔲 symbols which indicate accessibility for wheelchair users. A list of establishments is at the front of this guide.

★★★★★

10 Units
Sleeping 2–8

England for Excellence Winner 1998. Cotswold-stone Victorian stableyard with grassed courtyard in front and beautiful walled garden with wisteria and apple tunnel and 120 foot long border behind. Open fires, 4-poster beds, antiques, designer fabrics and specialist paint effects. Two storey playhouse, toys, dressing-up box and climbing frame for children.

BRUERN STABLE COTTAGES

Bruern, Chipping Norton OX7 6PY
Contact: Ms Frances Curtin, Red Brick House, Bruern,
Chipping Norton OX7 6PY
T: (01993) 830415 (Home & Office)
F: (01993) 831750
E: judy.astor@easynet.co.uk
I: www.bruern.co.uk

OPEN All year round
CC: Amex, Barclaycard,
Delta, Mastercard, Switch,
Visa

Short breaks available in the
low season.

Low season per wk
£438.00–£943.00
High season per wk
£744.00–£2,012.00

★★-★★★

5 Units
Sleeping 2–5

Secluded riverside and woodland setting with waterfall and waterwheel, but only 5 minutes' walk from historic Burford, pubs, restaurants and shops. Free use of bikes and rowing boat. Warm 18thC cottage and 4 apartments with country antiques. Excellent base for Cotswolds, Oxford, Stratford.

THE MILL AT BURFORD

83 Witney Street, Burford OX18 4RX
T: (01993) 822379 & 878151
F: (01993) 822759
E: cottages@themillatburford.co.uk
I: www.themillatburford.co.uk
Contact: Mr & Mrs Tony Waddell

OPEN All year round
CC: Eurocard, Mastercard,
Solo, Switch, Visa, Visa
Electron

Short breaks available Nov-
Mar

Low season per wk
£190.00–£300.00
High season per wk
£245.00–£492.00

★★★★

1 Unit
Sleeping 6

DAIRY COTTAGE
Bowcombe Road, Carisbrooke, Newport PO30 3HT
Contact: Mrs E R Yapp, Luckington Farm,
Bowcombe Road, Carisbrooke, Newport PO30 3HT
T: (01983) 822951

OPEN All year round

Low season per wk
Min £350.00
High season per wk
Max £500.00

Detached stone cottage in rural position. Castle close by, excellent walking and beaches nearby. Separate garden, barbecue.

★★★★

4 Units
Sleeping 2–10

ATHERFIELD GREEN FARM HOLIDAY COTTAGES
Chale, Ventnor PO38 2LG
Contact: A Jupe, The Laurels, High Street, Newchurch,
Sandown PO36 0NJ
T: (01983) 867613
F: (01983) 868214
E: alistair.jupe@btinternet.com

OPEN All year round

Low season per wk
£120.00–£260.00
High season per wk
£300.00–£750.00

Four holiday units constructed from 18thC farm courtyard in very quiet rural location. Suitable for wheelchair users. ETC 4 star grading and disability grade 2.

SPECIAL BREAKS

Many establishments offer special promotions and themed breaks. These are highlighted in red. (All such offers are subject to availability.)

CHALFONT ST GILES, Buckinghamshire Map ref 2D2

★★★

1 Unit
Sleeping 2

STUDIO FLAT AT APPLEWOOD
Mill Lane, Chalfont St Giles HP8 4NX
Contact: Mr & Mrs J E Newcombe, Applewood, Mill Lane,
Chalfont St Giles HP8 4NX
T: (01494) 873343 (answerphone)
E: JnA@stgiles98.fsnet.co.uk

In pretty, historic Buckinghamshire village – a very comfortable apartment overlooking owner's attractive garden. Quiet, self-contained, fully equipped – all linen. Centrally heated 'home from home' – colour TV and private telephone. Inclusive terms (reductions for longer stays). Visit London (only 20 miles), Oxford, Windsor, Henley, the Cotswolds, famous country houses and gardens.

OPEN All year round

Low season per wk
£180.00–£200.00
High season per wk
£200.00–£220.00

CHARLBURY, Oxfordshire Map ref 2C1

★★★

7 Units
Sleeping 2–6

BANBURY HILL FARM COTTAGES
Banbury Hill Farm, Charlbury, Oxford OX7 3JH
Contact: Mrs Angela Widdows, Banbury Hill Farm,
Charlbury, Oxford OX7 3JH
T: (01608) 810314
F: (01608) 811891
E: angelawiddows@gfwiddowsf9.co.uk
I: www.charlburyoxfordaccom.co.uk

54-acre mixed farm. Farm cottages well situated for touring Cotswolds, Oxford and Stratford. Many bridleways and footpaths, delightful scenery overlooking Evenlode Valley and famous Wychwood Forest.

OPEN All year round
CC: Barclaycard, Delta,
Eurocard, Mastercard,
Switch, Visa

High season per wk
£185.00–£375.00

CHIPPING NORTON, Oxfordshire Map ref 2C1 *Tourist Information Centre Tel: (01608) 644379*

★★★

1 Unit
Sleeping 2

COMPTON HOUSE
71 Burford Road, Chipping Norton OX7 5EE
T: (01608) 642964 & 644575 (Business hours only)
F: (01608) 642964
E: mark@questfs.co.uk
Contact: Mrs J Roach

Situated 5 minutes' walk from the centre of town, our holiday apartment offers excellent accommodation in an ideal location for exploring the beautiful Cotswold countryside.

OPEN All year round

Low season per wk
£150.00–£180.00
High season per wk
£180.00–£210.00

CHRISTCHURCH, Dorset Map ref 2B3 *Tourist Information Centre Tel: (01202) 471780*

★–★★

3 Units
Sleeping 2

THE CAUSEWAY
32-34 Stanpit, Mudeford, Christchurch BH23 3LZ
T: (01202) 470149 & 07979 607993 (Mobile)
F: (01202) 477558
E: thecauseway@nascr.net
Contact: Mrs L Tomkinson

Attractive, clean, well-equipped studio flats. Ideally situated midway between town and harbour of Christchurch and Mudeford quay and beaches.

OPEN All year round

Low season per wk
£90.00–£120.00
High season per wk
£120.00–£175.00

TOWN INDEX
This can be found at the back of the guide. If you know where you want to stay, the index will give you the page number listing accommodation in your chosen town, city or village.

CORFE CASTLE, Dorset Map ref 2B3

★★★
5 Units
Sleeping 2–6

KINGSTON COUNTRY COURTYARD
Greystone Court, Kingston, Corfe Castle,
Wareham BH20 5LR
Contact: Mrs Ann Fry, Kingston Country Courtyard,
Greystone Court, Kingston, Corfe Castle, Wareham
BH20 5LR
T: (01929) 481066
F: (01929) 481256
E: annfry@kingstoncountrycourtyard.co.uk
I: www.kingstoncountrycourtyard.co.uk

*Kingston Country Courtyard offers a variety of apartments and suites in converted
outbuildings, retaining their original character and charm.*

OPEN Feb–Dec

Low season per wk
£200.00–£300.00
High season per wk
£300.00–£400.00

★★★★
3 Units
Sleeping 4–10

SCOLES MANOR
Kingston, Corfe Castle BH20 5LG
T: (01929) 480312
F: (01929) 481237
E: peter@scoles.co.uk
I: www.scoles.co.uk
Contact: Mr & Mrs Peter Bell

*Scoles Manor Barns are next to historic Scoles
Manor (Listed Grade II*) and have been
converted into three beautifully appointed units
sleeping 2 to 10 people. They are in a superb
rural setting with 30 acres of meadows and
woodlands and spectacular views over Corfe
Castle and the Purbeck countryside.*

OPEN All year round

Winter breaks–perfect for
groups up to 20.

Low season per wk
£210.00–£350.00
High season per wk
£495.00–£925.00

COTSWOLDS

See under Alvescot, Burford, Charlbury, Chipping Norton, North Leigh, Shipton-under-
Wychwood, Stanton Harcourt

See also Cotswolds in Heart of England region

COWES, Isle of Wight Map ref 2C3 *Tourist Information Centre Tel: (01983) 291914*

★★★
1 Unit
Sleeping 4

FARTHINGS
27 St Andrews Street, Cowes PO31 7DF
Contact: Mr Michael Rabjohns, Firestone Cottage,
Kite Hill, Wootton Bridge, Ryde PO33 4LE
T: (01983) 884122

*Well-equipped fisherman's cottage with enclosed patio garden. Quiet location, close
to amenities and ferries. Ideal for families and yachtsmen. Parking.*

OPEN All year round

Low season per wk
£150.00–£190.00
High season per wk
£180.00–£300.00

★★
1 Unit
Sleeping 4

110 GURNARD PINES
Cockleton Lane, Gurnard, Cowes PO31 8QE
Contact: Mr Graham Reed, 21 Roull Road,
Corstorphine, Edinburgh EH12 7JW
T: (0131) 334 9184 & 07966 726389
E: reedg@callnetuk.com
I: www.callnetuk.com/home/reedg

*A 2-bedroom chalet in holiday village with excellent facilities for all the family. Ideal
location for a wonderfully relaxed holiday. Sleeps 4 and cot.*

OPEN Mar–Dec

Low season per wk
£80.00–£250.00
High season per wk
£250.00–£450.00

★★
1 Unit
Sleeping 4–6

127 GURNARD PINES
Cockleton Lane, Gurnard, Cowes PO31 8RJ
Contact: Mrs Karin Wales, Hazelmount Lodge,
Church Road, Binstead, Ryde PO33 3TB
T: (01983) 567484 & 07884 364717 (Mobile)
E: karin-wales@hotmail.com

*Furnished and equipped for 4-6 persons. Full, on-site facilities and entertainment. Set
in woodland surroundings.*

OPEN All year round

Low season per wk
£160.00–£200.00
High season per wk
£275.00–£420.00

COWES continued

★★★

2 Units
Sleeping 2–10

1 MIDDLETON TERRACE
20 Cross Street, Cowes PO31 7TD
Contact: Mrs Sarah Cotton, 49 Linden Road, Newport
PO30 1RJ
T: (01983) 523648

OPEN Apr–Sep, Dec

Low season per wk
Min £210.00
High season per wk
Max £420.00

Large townhouse in central Cowes, close to all amenities including marina and yacht clubs. Fully equipped including Sky TV. Sleeps from 1-2 or a maximum of 10.

EXTON, Hampshire Map ref 2C3

★★★★

4 Units
Sleeping 5

BEACON HILL FARM COTTAGES
The Farm Office, Beacon Hill Farm, Warnford Road,
Exton, Southampton SO32 3NW
Contact: Mrs J Smith, The Farm Office Manor Farm,
Beacon Hill Lane, Warnford Road, Exton, Southampton
SO32 3NW
T: (01730) 829724
F: (01730) 829833
E: chris.martin@farmline.com
I: www.beaconhillcottages.co.uk

OPEN All year round

Low season per wk
Min £300.00
High season per wk
Min £450.00

Four cottages in a converted barn, formerly part of a working farm. Idyllic setting, stunning views of Meon Valley farmland.

FIFEHEAD MAGDALEN, Dorset Map ref 2B3

★★★–★★★★★

3 Units
Sleeping 6–8

Charming detached cottages situated in courtyard of working farm. Picturesque walks along the river, riding, cycling, golf, fishing are available. Coast within an hour. Many National Trust properties to visit. Children and small pets welcome. All cottages suitable for wheelchair user.

STABLE COTTAGE, SHIRE COTTAGE & GRANARY COTTAGE
Middle Farm, Fifehead Magdalen, Gillingham SP8 5RR
Contact: Mrs R Trevor, Middle Farm, Fifehead Magdalen,
Gillingham SP8 5RR
T: (01258) 820220 & 821074
F: (01258) 820220

OPEN All year round

High season per wk
£300.00–£500.00

FINSTOCK, Oxfordshire Map ref 2C1

★★

1 Unit
Sleeping 4–5

17thC cottage situated on the edge of the Cotswolds in peaceful Oxfordshire village. Many attractions include scenic countryside, walking and easy access to Oxford and Stratford. Sleeps 4 + cot.

WYCHWOOD
School Road, Finstock, Chipping Norton OX7 3DJ
Contact: Mrs Bodil Grain, 40 School Road, Finstock,
Oxford OX7 3DJ
T: (01993) 868249 (Answerphone)
E: bgrain@wychwoodcottage.co.uk
I: www.wychwoodcottage.co.uk

OPEN All year round

Weekend breaks available.
Prices on application.

Low season per wk
£175.00–£225.00
High season per wk
£250.00–£325.00

CHECK THE MAPS
The colour maps at the front of this guide show all the cities, towns and villages for which you will find accommodation entries. Refer to the town index to find the page on which they are listed.

★★★★
6 Units
Sleeping 4–8

BURGATE MANOR FARM HOLIDAYS
Burgate Manor Farm, Fordingbridge SP6 1LX
T: (01425) 653908
F: (01425) 653908
E: holidays@newforestcottages.com
I: www.newforestcottages.com
Contact: Mrs Bridget Stallard

OPEN All year round

Low season per wk
£210.00–£420.00
High season per wk
£474.00–£660.00

*New Forest/Avon Valley. Farm cottages. Avon fishing. Pub/restaurant short walk.
Private farmland for walks/picnics/bird watching. Walk picturesque water meadows
into New Forest. Beach 15 miles.*

★★★
1 Unit
Sleeping 4–6

GARDEN COTTAGE
The Terrace, Rockbourne, Fordingbridge SP6 3NE
Contact: Mr & Mrs A Holmes, The Dial House,
Rockbourne, Fordingbridge SP6 3NA
T: (01725) 518083
F: (01725) 518083
E: rockbourneprop@freeuk.com
I: www.rockbourne.4dw.com

OPEN All year round

Low season per wk
£220.00–£300.00
High season per wk
£300.00–£400.00

*Comfortable country cottage with 2 bedrooms in picturesque downland village close
to New Forest and Salisbury. Fully equipped. Large secluded gardens. Winterbourne
stream. Lovely views.*

★★★
1 Unit
Sleeping 4

GLENCAIRN
High Street, Damerham, Fordingbridge SP6 3EU
Contact: Mrs C Tiller, 2 Fernlea, Sandleheath,
Fordingbridge SP6 1PN
T: (01425) 652506

OPEN Mar–Oct &
Christmas

Low season per wk
£190.00–£295.00
High season per wk
£295.00–£355.00

*Detached cottage in pleasant, friendly village close to New Forest. Comfortably
furnished and newly decorated throughout. Three bedrooms, well equipped kitchen,
large quiet garden. Brochure available.*

Rating
Applied For
1 Unit
Sleeping 6

5 RIVERSIDE PLACE
Fordingbridge SP6 1RR
Contact: Ms Lindsay Burgess, 71 Christchurch Road,
Ringwood BH24 1DH
T: (01425) 476106
F: (01425) 479097

OPEN Apr–Sep

Low season per wk
£210.00–£300.00
High season per wk
£305.00–£440.00

*A new townhouse situated on the banks of the River Avon in the centre of
Fordingbridge. Delightful river views.*

★★★★
1 Unit
Sleeping 6

MEADS FARM
Stour Provost, Gillingham SP8 5RX
T: (01747) 838265
F: (01258) 821123
Contact: Mrs June Wallis

*Superb detached bungalow with spacious, very
well equipped accommodation. Two double, one
twin bedroom. Half an acre of lawns. Coarse
fishing 150 yards, also lake fishing half a mile.
Outstanding views over the Blackmore Vale.
Many places of interest just a short car ride
away.*

OPEN All year round

Low season per wk
Min £210.00
High season per wk
Max £420.00

WHERE TO STAY
Please mention this guide when making your booking.

GILLINGHAM continued

★★★★
1 Unit
Sleeping 2

WOOLFIELDS BARN
Woolfields Farm, Milton on Stour, Gillingham SP8 5PX
T: (01747) 824729 & 07836 772264
F: (01747) 824986
E: OThomas453@aol.com
Contact: Mr & Mrs B Thomas

OPEN All year round

Low season per wk
£140.00–£180.00
High season per wk
£180.00–£245.00

Barn conversion equipped to a high standard. Games room, centrally heated, linen provided.

Ⓜ ◎ ▦ Ⅲ ⊙ ▭ ▤ TV ⌇ 🖸 🛆 🖳 🖋 P ∪ ✻ 🐾 SP

GODSHILL, Isle of Wight Map ref 2C3

★★★
2 Units
Sleeping 3–6

SEYMOUR COTTAGES
Lower Yard Farm, Godshill, Ventnor PO38 3LY
T: (01983) 840536
Contact: Mr & Mrs P Lazenby

OPEN Mar–Oct &
Christmas

Low season per wk
£160.00–£350.00
High season per wk
£350.00–£505.00

Beautifully converted stone cottages on non-working farm, retaining character of hay loft and milking parlour.

🐖 Ⓜ ◎ ▦ ⊙ ▭ TV 🖸 🛆 ✕ 🖳 🖋 P ✻ 🐾 SP

GOSPORT, Hampshire Map ref 2C3 *Tourist Information Centre Tel: (023) 9252 2944*

★★★
1 Unit
Sleeping 6–10

CAPTAINS FOLLY
The Hardway, 69 Priory Road, Gosport PO12 4LF
Contact: Mr J M White, 8 Cambridge Road,
Lee on the Solent PO13 9DH
T: (023) 9255 0883

OPEN All year round

Low season per wk
£325.00–£350.00
High season per wk
£475.00–£500.00

Character house with 4 bedrooms and 3 bathrooms. Large garden leading to shore. Adjacent Priddy's Hard waterbus to Portsmouth. Ideal for New Forest, Winchester and Salisbury. Parking.

🐖 ◎ Ⅲ ⊙ 🖸 ▭ ▤ TV ⌇ 🖸 🛆 🗍 🖳 🖋 P ✻ ⤳ SP 🏛

★★
1 Unit
Sleeping 6

KEEFONS
6a Village Road, Alverstoke, Gosport PO12 2LF
Contact: Mr & Mrs Keith & Yvonne Hoskins,
6 Village Road, Alverstoke, Gosport PO12 2LF
T: (023) 9252 0982

OPEN All year round

Low season per wk
Min £180.00
High season per wk
Max £250.00

Spacious Georgian flat sleeping 6 in 3 bedrooms. Local to maritime England and Isle of Wight. Five minutes' walk from beach. Off-road parking.

Ⓜ ◎ Ⅲ ▭ TV 🛆 🖳 🖋 P 🐾 SP

GREAT MILTON, Oxfordshire Map ref 2C1

★★★★
6 Units
Sleeping 3–5

VIEWS FARM BARNS
Views Farm, Great Milton, Oxford OX44 7NW
T: (01844) 279352 & 07836 273541
F: (01844) 279362
E: viewsfarm@callnetuk.com
Contact: Mr & Mrs C O Peers

OPEN All year round
CC: Mastercard, Visa

Low season per wk
£200.00–£250.00
High season per wk
£300.00–£360.00

400-acre arable and mixed farm. Converted stable block forming well-appointed holiday flats. Close to Oxford and the M40. Superb views of Thame Valley.

Ⓜ 🐖 ◎ Ⅲ ⊙ 🖸 ▭ TV ⌇ 🖸 🛆 🗍 🖳 🖋 P ⌇ ✂ ✻ 🐾 ⤳ 🏛

ISLE OF WIGHT

See under Bembridge, Brighstone, Carisbrooke, Chale, Cowes, Godshill, Sandown, Shanklin, Totland Bay, Ventnor

LANGTON MATRAVERS, Dorset Map ref 2B3

★★★
1 Unit
Sleeping 4

FLAT 5 GARFIELD HOUSE
Langton Matravers, Swanage BH19 3HJ
Contact: Miss Susan Inge, Flat A, 147 Holland Road,
London W14 8AS
T: (020) 7602 4945
E: sueinge@hotmail.com

OPEN All year round

Low season per wk
£210.00–£245.00
High season per wk
£245.00–£315.00

Spacious and homely well equipped flat in large Purbeck stone house in friendly village. Lovely views over sea and hills. 10 minutes' walk to cliff top.

🐖5 ◎ Ⅲ ⊙ 🖸 ▭ ▤ TV 🖸 🛆 🗍 🖳 🖋 P ✻ ⤳ SP

IDEAS For ideas on places to visit refer to the introduction at the beginning of this section.

LEE ON THE SOLENT, Hampshire Map ref 2C3

★★★

1 Unit
Sleeping 6

THE CHART HOUSE
4 Cambridge Road, Lee on the Solent PO13 9DH
Contact: Ms Marion Kinnear-White, 6 Cambridge Road,
Lee on the Solent PO13 9DH
T: (023) 9255 4145 (Call minder available) & 9255 0883
E: marion_kinnear-white@talk21.com

OPEN All year round

Low season per wk
£260.00–£300.00
High season per wk
£290.00–£320.00

Detached, 3-bedroomed house, close to seafront. Fully carpeted. Enclosed garden/patio. Off-road parking. Heated indoor pool available for private hire next door.

 (symbols)

LYMINGTON, Hampshire Map ref 2C3

★★★

1 Unit
Sleeping 5

FIR TREE COTTAGE
Lower Buckland Road, Lymington SO41 9DU
Contact: Mrs B Saword, 1 Merlewood Court,
Lyon Avenue, New Milton BH25 6AP
T: (01425) 617219

OPEN All year round

Low season per wk
£175.00–£255.00
High season per wk
£260.00–£370.00

Period cottage 1.5 miles from open forest. Enclosed garden, good for pets and children. Traditional furnishings, books, fitted carpets, double glazing, toys.

LYNDHURST, Hampshire Map ref 2C3

★★★–★★★★★

3 Units
Sleeping 4–6

We pride ourselves on quality interiors giving guests the benefit of comfortable living areas within the heart of the New Forest. All properties completely refurnished. Linen provided, washing machines, TVs, stereo/CD players and parking. Ideally situated in Lyndhurst village (Southampton 9 miles/18 minutes, Bournemouth 25 miles/35 minutes).

ALICE COTTAGE, DORMOUSE CORNER & DUCHESS PLACE

Queens Parade, Lyndhurst SO43 7AH
Contact: Mr Mike Saqui, The Penny Farthing Hotel,
Romsey Road, Lyndhurst SO43 7AA
T: (023) 8028 4422
F: (023) 8028 4488
E: cottages@pennyfarthinghotel.co.uk
I: www.pennyfarthinghotel.co.uk

OPEN All year round
CC: Amex, Barclaycard,
Delta, Diners, Eurocard,
JCB, Mastercard, Solo,
Switch, Visa, Visa Electron

High season per wk
£475.00–£675.00

★★★★

1 Unit
Sleeping 4

HOLLY COTTAGE
Southampton Road, Lyndhurst SO43 7BU
Contact: Mr & Mrs F S Turner, Greensward,
The Crescent, Woodlands Road, Ashurst, Southampton
SO40 7AQ
T: (023) 8029 2374
F: (023) 8029 2374

OPEN All year round

Low season per wk
£230.00–£350.00
High season per wk
£350.00–£425.00

Cosy, comfortably furnished 19thC cottage 50 yards from forest. Personally renovated and maintained by local owner. Children welcome. No short breaks. Sleeps 4 + cot.

★★★★

1 Unit
Sleeping 4

YORKE COTTAGE
9 Pemberton Road, Lyndhurst SO43 7AN
Contact: Mr John Drew, Burwood Lodge,
27 Romsey Road, Lyndhurst SO43 7AA
T: (023) 8028 2445
F: (023) 8028 4104
E: burwoodl@ukonline.co.uk

OPEN All year round

Low season per wk
£165.00–£350.00
High season per wk
£350.00–£450.00

Pretty Victorian cottage in peaceful location, minutes from open forest and village high street. Superbly and tastefully appointed, linen, gas, electricity included. Private parking.

PRICES
Please check prices and other details at the time of booking.

MILFORD-ON-SEA, Hampshire Map ref 2C3

★★
2 Units
Sleeping 2–6

FOREST FARM
Barnes Lane, Milford-on-Sea, Lymington SO41 0RR
T: (01590) 644365
F: (01590) 644365
E: driving@ffarm.fsnet.co.uk
I: www.forestfarmdriving.com
Contact: Ms Debbie Butler

OPEN All year round

Low season per wk
Min £160.00
High season per wk
Min £210.00

Studio apartment on 30-acre carriage driving centre close to forest and sea. Ample parking and excellent local amenities. Luxury stabling and grazing available.

◎ ⌀ ▥ ▥ ☉ ▤ TV ⬚ ⬚ ⬚ 🐾 ✳ ⌁ SP

★★★★
1 Unit
Sleeping 5

HARMONY
53A Knowland Drive, Milford-on-Sea,
Lymington SO41 0RH
Contact: Mrs C R Ling, 9 The White House,
Westover Road, Milford-on-Sea, Lymington SO41 0PW
T: (01590) 641779 & 07808 215567 (Mobile)

OPEN All year round

Low season per wk
£210.00–£365.00
High season per wk
£385.00–£535.00

Modern, spacious, detached bungalow and garage in secluded surroundings. Patio and conservatory. Easy walk to village and sea. New Forest 5 miles.

🛏12 ◎ ⌀ ▥ ☉ ▤ ▥ ▥ TV ⬚ ⬚ ⬚ ✕ P ✳ ⌁ P SP

★★★
1 Unit
Sleeping 5

WINDMILL COTTAGE
22 Windmill Close, Milford-on-Sea,
Lymington SO41 0SX
Contact: Mrs S M Perham, Danescourt,
14 Kivernell Road, Milford-on-Sea, Lymington SO41 0PQ
T: (01590) 643516
F: (01590) 641255

OPEN All year round

Low season per wk
£210.00–£235.00
High season per wk
£265.00–£495.00

3-bedroomed, Georgian-style house in select residential area close to village, sea and the New Forest.

🛏 ◎ ▥ ▥ ☉ ▤ ▥ ▥ TV ⬚ ⬚ ⬚ P ∪ ✳ ⌁ SP

MILTON ABBAS, Dorset Map ref 2B3

★★★★★
1 Unit
Sleeping 4

LITTLE HEWISH BARN
Milton Abbas, Blandford Forum DT11 0DP
Contact: Mr Terry Dunn, 2 Little Hewish Cottages,
Milton Abbas, Blandford Forum DT11 0DP
T: (01258) 881235 (Answerphone) & 07778 966843
F: (01258) 881393
E: terry@littlehewish.co.uk
I: www.littlehewish.co.uk

Converted 150-year-old brick and flint barn in lovely rural setting. Spacious open-plan living/dining area, wood-burning stove. Children welcome, well-behaved pets by arrangement, small private garden. Pre-arrival shopping/baby-sitting available at cost. Flexible, family-run business. Fully inclusive prices, no hidden extras!

OPEN All year round

'Per person per night' pricing, outside peak periods.

Low season per wk
Min £336.00
High season per wk
Max £550.00

🅰 🛏 ◎ ▥ ☉ ▤ ▥ ▥ TV ⬚ ⬚ ⬚ P ∪ ✳ ⌁ SP ▦

CHECK THE MAPS
The colour maps at the front of this guide show all the cities, towns and villages for which you will find accommodation entries. Refer to the town index to find the page on which they are listed.

MILTON ABBAS continued

★★★★

4 Units
Sleeping 2–5

LUCCOMBE FARM

Milton Abbas, Blandford Forum DT11 0BE
T: (01258) 880558
F: (01258) 881384
Contact: Mr & Mrs Murray & Amanda Kayll

Sympathetically converted Georgian barns with landscaped gardens and ponds in idyllic countryside, away from roads, ideal as a touring base. We provide many services and leisure activities including a riding school with indoor arena, tennis court and games room. Other country activities can be arranged on farm or nearby.

OPEN All year round

We try to be flexibly with booking dates. Out of season weekends always available.

Low season per wk	Min £175.00
High season per wk	Max £600.00

★★-★★★★★

3 Units
Sleeping 5–10

Architect-designed conversion of Grade II Listed thatched barn. Underfloor heating, inglenook fireplace with woodburner. Enjoy stunning views to Poole harbour and the Purbeck Hills. A very peaceful site where the woodland walking and riding are superb.

PARK FARM

Milton Abbas, Blandford Forum DT11 0AX
Contact: Mrs Audrey Burch, Park Farm, Milton Abbas, Blandford Forum DT11 0AX
T: (01258) 880828
F: (01258) 881788
E: burch@parkfarmcottages.co.uk
I: www.parkfarmcottages.co.uk

OPEN All year round

2 or 3 night stay available in off-peak periods.

Low season per wk	£195.00–£500.00
High season per wk	£375.00–£750.00

★★★

1 Unit
Sleeping 6

Grade II Listed, 18thC thatched cob cottage set in The Street, in the unique village of Milton Abbas created by Lord Milton and landscaped by 'Capability' Brown. This cosy and comfortable cottage has everything you would expect, from low doors to inglenook fireplace. In the centre of Hardy Country, an ideal base for walkers and romantics.

PRIMROSE COTTAGE

29 The Street, Milton Abbas, Blandford Forum DT11 0BL
Contact: Mrs G D Garvey, Brook Cottage, 1 Long Street, Cerne Abbas, Dorchester DT2 7JF
T: (01300) 341352
F: (01300) 341352
E: tgarvey@ragtime99.freeserve.co.uk

OPEN All year round

Low season per wk	£195.00–£225.00
High season per wk	£345.00–£445.00

COUNTRY CODE Always follow the Country Code 🌱 Enjoy the countryside and respect its life and work 🌱 Guard against all risk of fire 🌱 Fasten all gates 🌱 Keep your dogs under close control 🌱 Keep to public paths across farmland 🌱 Use gates and stiles to cross fences, hedges and walls 🌱 Leave livestock, crops and machinery alone 🌱 Take your litter home 🌱 Help to keep all water clean 🌱 Protect wildlife, plants and trees 🌱 Take special care on country roads 🌱 Make no unnecessary noise

MILTON KEYNES, Buckinghamshire Map ref 2C1

★★★

1 Unit
Sleeping 3

35 BROOKSIDE CLOSE

Old Stratford, Milton Keynes MK19 6BE
Contact: Mrs A Hepher, The Old Bakery Hotel, Main Street,
Cosgrove, Milton Keynes MK19 7JL
T: (01908) 262255
F: (01908) 263620
E: avh@hepher.demon.co.uk

One of several high quality self-catering apartments. Available by the day or week; let on a fully serviced basis – charge covers gas, electricity, cleaning linen, welcome basket and taxes. Only telephone is extra. Located on a quiet residential estate, decorated and furnished to a high standard. Personal service.

OPEN All year round
CC: Amex, Barclaycard,
Delta, Diners, Eurocard,
JCB, Maestro, Mastercard,
Solo, Switch, Visa, Visa
Electron

Low season per wk
Min £250.00
High season per wk
Min £250.00

MOLLINGTON, Oxfordshire Map ref 2C1

★★-★★★★

2 Units
Sleeping 2–4

THE YEWS

Anita Holiday Cottages, The Shipton & The Byre,
Mollington, Banbury OX17 1AZ
Contact: Mr & Mrs Darrel & Gail Jeffries, Anitas Holiday
Cottages, The Yews, Church Farm, Mollington, Banbury
OX17 1AZ
T: (01295) 750731

Converted from an old cow byre these cottages are superbly finished to a high standard. Only walking distance to our village pub and situated in the lovely village of Mollington. Central to Oxford, Stratford on Avon, Blenheim, Warwick and Cotswolds. Lovely walks and cycling, even fishing close by.

OPEN All year round

Short breaks available on request.

Low season per wk
£130.00–£160.00
High season per wk
£160.00–£220.00

NEW FOREST

See under Beaulieu, Boldre, Brockenhurst, Fordingbridge, Lymington, Lyndhurst, Milford-on-Sea, Sway

NEWBURY, Berkshire Map ref 2C2 *Tourist Information Centre Tel: (01635) 30267*

★★★★

1 Unit
Sleeping 4

BARN HOUSE
Enborne Street Farm, Enborne, Newbury RG20 0JP
Contact: Mrs M Edwards, Enborne Street Farm,
Enborne, Newbury RG20 0JP
T: (01635) 253443
F: (01635) 253443

OPEN All year round

Low season per wk
£270.00
High season per wk
£270.00

Beautifully converted barn in quiet country position. Every modern convenience. Double bedroom and separate minstrels' gallery with sofa-bed. Tennis court and walks on farm.

★★★★★

1 Unit
Sleeping 5

PEREGRINE COTTAGE

Enborne Street, Enborne, Newbury RG14 6RP
Contact: Mrs Elizabeth Knight, Peregrine House,
Enborne Street, Enborne, Newbury RG14 6RP
T: (01635) 42585
F: (01635) 528775
E: lizziek1eak@hotmail.com

South of historic Newbury in open countryside. Five minutes from M4 Jct 13. Town centre 10 minutes, London 1 hour, Heathrow 45 minutes. Beautifully furnished and cared for with private terrace by old orchard. Use of swimming pool, tennis court and barbecue. Extra cleaning if required. Given highest rating.

OPEN All year round
CC: Barclaycard, Delta,
Mastercard, Switch, Visa

Low season per wk
Min £385.00
High season per wk
Min £500.00

NEWBURY continued

★★★-★★★★★

2 Units

Sleeping 4–6

YAFFLES
Red Shute Hill, Hermitage, Thatcham RG18 9QH
Contact: Mr & Mrs Tony & Jean Bradford, Yaffles,
Red Shute Hill, Hermitage, Thatcham RG18 9QH
T: (01635) 201100 & 0777 5681821 (Mobile)
F: (01635) 201100
E: yaffles@ukonline.co.uk
I: www.cottagesdirect.com/yaffles

OPEN All year round

Low season per wk
Min £240.00
High season per wk
Max £305.00

Comfortable secluded self-contained garden flat and studio set in spacious peaceful grounds just north of Newbury yet near jct 13 of M4 motorway. Prices are for 2 people.

NORTH LEIGH, Oxfordshire Map ref 2C1

★★★

1 Unit

Sleeping 4

WYLCOT COTTAGE
New Yatt Road, North Leigh, Witney OX8 6TT
Contact: Mrs Joy Crew, Hollywell Cottage, New Yatt,
Witney OX29 6TF
T: (01993) 868614

OPEN Mar–Nov

Low season per wk
£195.00
High season per wk
£260.00

Charming, detached stone cottage in pretty walled garden, located on the edge of the Cotswolds. Convenient for Oxford, Burford and Woodstock. Close shops and pubs.

OLNEY, Buckinghamshire Map ref 2C1

★★★★

2 Units

Sleeping 4

HYDE FARM COTTAGES
Hyde Farm, Warrington Road, Olney MK46 4DU
T: (01234) 711223 & 07778 412975
Contact: Mrs Penny Reynolds

Beautifully situated at the end of a long drive with lovely views over open farmland, these cottages are comfortable and homely with their own garden, patio and parking. Ideal central location for many tourist attractions, with easy access to Milton Keynes, Northampton and Bedford. Olney market town just 1.5 miles.

OPEN All year round

Low season per wk
Max £325.00
High season per wk
Max £375.00

OXFORD, Oxfordshire Map ref 2C1 *Tourist Information Centre Tel: (01865) 726871*

★★★★

4 Units

Sleeping 2–7

OTMOOR HOLIDAYS
Lower Farm, Noke, Oxford OX3 9TX
T: (01865) 373766
F: (01865) 371911
E: info@oxfordholidays.co.uk
I: www.oxfordholidays.co.uk
Contact: Mrs Emma Righton

Four delightful cottages nestled around a beautifully landscaped courtyard garden in a peaceful location, adjacent to RSPB reserve, yet only 15 minutes from Oxford city centre. All with stable doors and plenty of old beams, the cottages have been finished to a high standard to provide comfort, warmth and space.

OPEN All year round
CC: Barclaycard, Delta,
Eurocard, JCB,
Mastercard, Solo, Switch,
Visa, Visa Electron

Low season per wk
£275.00–£595.00
High season per wk
£305.00–£720.00

TOWN INDEX
This can be found at the back of this guide. If you know where you want to stay, the index will give you the page number listing accommodation in your chosen town, city or village.

★★★

1 Unit
Sleeping 5

Picturebook, brick and flint, thatched cottage, on 300-acre beef and arable farm. Ideal base for visiting London, Oxford, Stonehenge and Stratford, and for sightseeing in the Thames Valley, Chilterns, Cotswolds and beyond. A warm and friendly 'home from home' for a holiday to remember.

BRAMBLY THATCH
Goring Heath, Pangbourne, Reading RG8 7TA
Contact: Mr & Mrs J N Hatt, Merricroft Farming,
Goring Heath, Reading RG8 7TA
T: (0118) 984 3121
F: (0118) 984 4662
E: hatts@merricroft.demon.co.uk

OPEN All year round

Pay by credit card free of charge, if you mention this advert.

Low season per wk
£335.00–£395.00
High season per wk
£335.00–£395.00

★★★★

1 Unit
Sleeping 8

Pennycroft is set among woodland and fields in the Chiltern Hills above the River Thames between Streatley and Pangbourne, made famous in 'The Wind in the Willows'. London is only 1 hour away and Oxford, Windsor and Heathrow 45 minutes. The 100-year-old house is fully modernised and centrally heated.

PENNYCROFT
Pennycroft Cottage, Pangbourne, Reading
Contact: Mr C J Collingwood, 34 Ambleside Avenue,
London SW16 1QP
T: (020) 8769 2742
F: (020) 8677 3023
E: pennycroft@cwcom.net
I: www.pennycroft.cwc.net

OPEN All year round
CC: Barclaycard, Delta,
JCB, Mastercard, Solo,
Switch, Visa, Visa Electron

Discounts for stays of more than 2 weeks. See our website.

Low season per wk
£350.00–£420.00
High season per wk
£420.00–£630.00

★★★

3 Units
Sleeping 2–4

DOLPHIN COTTAGE, SEAHORSE & STARFISH APARTMENTS
18 Pinewood Road, Branksome Park, Poole BH13 6JS
Contact: Mrs Middler, The Grovefield Manor Hotel,
18 Pinewood Road, Branksome Park, Poole BH13 6JS
T: (01202) 766798

OPEN All year round

Low season per wk
£350.00–£425.00
High season per wk
£525.00–£575.00

Attached to an Edwardian mansion house, the ground floor apartment is modern, spacious and has its own garden. The cottage is purpose built with 2 en suite bedrooms and own garden. Only 400yds from beach.

★★★

1 Unit
Sleeping 4

17 GREEN GARDENS
Baiter Park, Poole BH15 1XX
Contact: Ms Christina Harris, Victoria, Beech Close,
Spetisbury, Blandford Forum DT11 9HG
T: (01258) 456609
E: christina.harris@breathemail.net

OPEN May–Oct

Low season per wk
£200.00–£275.00
High season per wk
£300.00–£375.00

End of terrace 2-bedroom house on Baiter Park with partial views of sea. Easy walking distance of Poole Quay.

★★

3 Units
Sleeping 6–10

WYCHCOTT, SPINNAKER REACH & QUAY COTTAGE
1 Harbour Shallows, 15 Whitecliff Road, Poole
BH14 8DU
T: (01202) 741637
Contact: Mrs B Saunders

OPEN All year round

Low season per wk
£125.00–£250.00
High season per wk
£300.00–£550.00

Wychcott is a bungalow with garden. Spinnaker is a first floor apartment with views of Harbour and Purbecks. Quay overlooks Fishermen's Dock and Brownsea Island. Pets welcome.

★★★
6 Units
Sleeping 2–7

ATLANTIC APARTMENTS
61A Festing Road, Southsea PO4 0NQ
Contact: Mr F Hamdani, 61A Festing Road, Southsea
PO4 0NQ
T: (023) 92735574 & 92734233
F: (023) 92820955
E: feris@oceanhotel.freeserve.co.uk
I: www.oceanhotel.freeserve.co.uk

OPEN All year round

Low season per wk
£180.00–£250.00
High season per wk
£200.00–£300.00

Situated in one of the most attractive areas of Southsea, only a few yards from the canoe lake and seafront. All apartments are fully self-contained. Large car park.

★★★
10 Units
Sleeping 1–2

LAKESIDE HOLIDAY & BUSINESS APARTMENTS
5 Helena Road, Southsea, Portsmouth PO4 9RH
T: (023) 9282 0690
F: (023) 9282 0690
Contact: Mrs V Hamza

Ten double self-catering apartments in a lovely detached house, 2 minutes' walk to the sea, rose gardens, bowling greens and lake. A home from home. Newly refurbished and top 3 Star award. Open all year, parking available for 6 cars.

OPEN All year round
CC: Amex, Barclaycard,
Diners, Maestro,
Mastercard, Switch, Visa

Low season per wk
£140.00–£180.00
High season per wk
£180.00–£240.00

★★★
6 Units
Sleeping 2–8

OCEAN APARTMENTS
8-10 St Helens Parade, Southsea,
Portsmouth PO4 0RW
Contact: Mrs Dawn Sait, Assistant Manager,
Ocean Apartments, 8-10 St Helens Parade, Southsea,
Portsmouth PO4 0RW
T: (023) 92734233 & 92734342
F: (023) 92297046
E: feris@oceanhotel.freeserve.co.uk
I: www.oceanhotel.freeserve.co.uk

OPEN All year round
CC: Barclaycard,
Mastercard, Visa

Low season per wk
£200.00–£500.00
High season per wk
£250.00–£700.00

Imposing seafront building with magnificent views. Recently refurbished. From 1 to 4 bedroomed self-contained apartments, very spacious, lift, private car parking. Executive suites available.

★★★
6 Units
Sleeping 2–8

SOUTH PARADE APARTMENTS
29b South Parade, Southsea PO4 0SH
Contact: Mr & Mrs Sait, South Parade Apartments
c/o, 61A Festing Road, Southsea PO4 0NQ
T: (023) 92817007 & 92734342
F: (023) 92297046
E: feris@oceanhotel.freeserve.co.uk
I: www.oceanhotel.freeserve.co.uk

OPEN All year round

Low season per wk
£200.00–£350.00
High season per wk
£250.00–£450.00

Magnificent, Listed seafront building in its own grounds. Self-contained, spacious apartments from 1 to 5 bedrooms. Lift, car park. Close to all amenities, superb sea views.

★★★
1 Unit
Sleeping 4

THE OLD SMITHY
Awbridge Hill, Romsey SO51 0HF
T: (01794) 511778 & 07831 452018
F: (01794) 521446
E: paul@paulreevesphotography.co.uk
Contact: Mr Paul Reeves

OPEN All year round

Low season per wk
£180.00–£200.00
High season per wk
£250.00–£350.00

Grade II Listed building, formerly a blacksmith's shop, now fully renovated. Wonderful country views and walks.

SYMBOLS
The symbols in each entry give information about services and facilities. A key to these symbols appears at the back of this guide.

★★
11 Units
Sleeping 2–6

PARKLANDS APARTMENTS
9 Winchester Park Road, Sandown PO36 8HJ
T: (01983) 409602
Contact: Mr Hugh McGee

Spotlessly clean, very well-equipped flats in well-kept house. Personal supervision by caring resident proprietors. Friendly atmosphere, inspection invited. In a quiet road just a few minutes' walk from the town, station and 6 miles of the safe sandy beach of Sandown Bay.

OPEN All year round

Low season per wk
£100.00–£210.00
High season per wk
£220.00–£520.00

★★
1 Unit
Sleeping 4

DAIRY COTTAGE
Broadlea Farm, Sutton Waldron,
Blandford Forum DT11 8NS
Contact: Mrs Mary Pryce, Broadlea Farm,
Sutton Waldron, Blandford Forum DT11 8NS
T: (01747) 811330 (And Answerphone)
F: (01747) 811330
E: mary2@tinyworld.co.uk

OPEN All year round

Low season per wk
Max £210.00
High season per wk
Max £240.00

Fully equipped cottage amidst lovely countryside, south of Shaftesbury. 2 bedrooms, spacious lounge/dining room, separate kitchen and bathroom. Good base for visiting tourist attractions.

★★★
2 Units
Sleeping 6

ELMVALE & SOUTH VIEW
Woodville Farm, Green Lane, Stour Row,
Shaftesbury SP7 0QD
Contact: Mr J K Westcott, Stonebank, 14 West Street,
Chickerell, Weymouth DT3 4DY
T: (01305) 760120
F: (01305) 760871
E: keithstonebank@aol.com
I: www.stonebank-chickerell.com

OPEN All year round

Low season per wk
£270.00–£330.00
High season per wk
£360.00–£435.00

Spacious bungalow on working farm in quiet village. Beautiful views across Blackmore Vale. Central for walking and touring Dorset and surrounding counties.

★★★
4 Units
Sleeping 2–3

FERNHURST HOLIDAY APARTMENTS
42 Western Road, Shanklin PO37 7NF
T: (01983) 862126 (Answerphone) &
0778 8757167 (Mobile)
E: dpetcher@talk21.com
I: www.isleofwight.uk.com/fernhurst
Contact: Mrs Sandra Petcher

OPEN All year round

Low season per wk
£125.00–£215.00
High season per wk
£260.00–£460.00

Individually designed apartments, well-equipped and meticulously clean. Centrally positioned but extremely quiet. Sorry no pets. Children welcome. Electric, gas, linen inclusive.

QUALITY ASSURANCE SCHEME
For an explanation of the quality and facilities represented by the Stars please refer to the front of this guide. A more detailed explanation can be found in the information pages at the back.

SHIPTON-UNDER-WYCHWOOD, Oxfordshire Map ref 2B1

★★★

1 Unit
Sleeping 2

6 WESTGATE

Shipton Court, Shipton-under-Wychwood OX7 6DG
Contact: Mrs Helen Harrison, Northgate, Shipton Court,
Shipton-under-Wychwood OX7 6DG
T: (01993) 830202 (Answerphone)
F: (01993) 830202

*Delightful cottage in charming setting in
grounds of 17thC manor house, suitable 2
adults. Double bedroom with en suite bath and
shower. Beautiful, spacious beamed sitting room
with lovely view over gardens. Large well-
equipped kitchen. Immaculate condition. No
children or pets. Many historic towns and tourist
attractions nearby.*

OPEN Apr–Oct

Low season per wk
£190.00–£225.00
High season per wk
£250.00–£265.00

SOUTHAMPTON, Hampshire Map ref 2C3

★★★

2 Units
Sleeping 2

PINEWOOD LODGE APARTMENTS
Pinewood Lodge, Kanes Hill, Southampton SO19 6AJ
T: (023) 8040 2925
Contact: Dr or Mrs S W Bradberry

OPEN All year round

Low season per wk
Min £140.00
High season per wk
Max £170.00

*Double or twin-bedded, fully-equipped, self-contained apartments, in pleasant
wooded area, each with separate kitchen, bathroom and lounge. Private verandah or
patio.*

SOUTHSEA

See under Portsmouth & Southsea

STANTON HARCOURT, Oxfordshire Map ref 2C1

★★★★★

1 Unit
Sleeping 9

AKERS

Duck End Lane, Sutton, Stanton Harcourt OX29 5RH
Contact: Ms Barbara Harding, Lower Farm, Duck End Lane,
Sutton, Stanton Harcourt OX29 5RH
T: (01865) 881553
E: barbaraharding@yahoo.co.uk
I: www.oxfordshirecottages.com

*Thatched, 17thC Listed cottage on the edge of an
historic village near Oxford. Privately situated at
the end of a no-through lane. Recently
renovated to a high standard. Five bedrooms, 3
bathrooms, 2 sitting rooms, spacious kitchen/
diner, utility. Two inglenooks. Spectacular 3-acre
garden. Large duck pond.*

OPEN All year round

Three night stays available.

Low season per wk
£750.00–£850.00
High season per wk
£1,100.00–£1,550.00

SWAY, Hampshire Map ref 2C3

★★★

1 Unit
Sleeping 6

HACKNEY PARK
Mount Pleasant Lane, Sway, Lymington SO41 8LS
T: (01590) 682049
Contact: Mrs Helen Beale

OPEN All year round

Low season per wk
£160.00–£280.00
High season per wk
£280.00–£340.00

*Modern, spacious and comfortable, self-contained apartment (more bedrooms
available if required), in tranquil setting with delightful forest views. Excellent touring/
walking and horse riding area.*

MAP REFERENCES The map references refer to the colour maps at the front of this guide. The first figure is the map number; the letter and figure which follow indicate the grid reference on the map.

SWAY continued

★★
1 Unit
Sleeping 4

HIGHBANK
Silver Street, Sway, Lymington SO41 6DG
Contact: Mr Stuart Bailey, Homefield, Silver Street,
Sway, Lymington SO41 6DG
T: (01590) 682025 & 683410
F: (01590) 683782
E: baileyhome@aol.com
I: www.stuartbailey.net

OPEN All year round

Low season per wk
£100.00–£200.00
High season per wk
£200.00–£300.00

Two bedroom cottage with 1 double and 1 adult bunk bed, all with duvets. Small enclosed garden with gas barbecue. Garage and off-road parking.

THAME, Oxfordshire Map ref 2C1 *Tourist Information Centre Tel: (01844) 212834*

★★★
1 Unit
Sleeping 3

HONEYSUCKLE COTTAGE
Frogmore Lane, Long Crendon, Aylesbury HP18 9DZ
T: (01844) 208697
Contact: Mr & Mrs A Lester

OPEN All year round

Low season per wk
£170.00–£190.00
High season per wk
Max £210.00

Very comfortable, well-equipped, self-contained annexe to cottage, with private garden and off-lane parking.

TOTLAND BAY, Isle of Wight Map ref 2C3

★★★
1 Unit
Sleeping 6

STONEWIND FARM
Summers Lane, Totland Bay PO39 0HJ
Contact: Mrs Pat Hayles, Barn Cottage, Middleton,
Freshwater PO40 9RW
T: (01983) 752912 (answerphone/fax)
F: (01983) 752912

OPEN All year round

Low season per wk
£150.00–£180.00
High season per wk
£180.00–£450.00

Recently renovated 2-bedroom farmhouse. Sleeps 6. Central heating, fully-equipped kitchen. Electricity, linen and towels provided. Secluded garden with barbecue.

VENTNOR, Isle of Wight Map ref 2C3

★★
1 Unit
Sleeping 6

SUNRISE
29 St Catherine Street, Ventnor PO38 1HG
Contact: Mrs Cherry Owens, Appletrees,
Post Office Road, Inkpen, Hungerford RG17 9PU
T: (01488) 668216

OPEN All year round

Low season per wk
Min £180.00
High season per wk
Max £330.00

Two-bedroom cottage with sea views. Near shops and beach. Sleeps 4 adults, 2 children and baby. Available all year. Ideal beach, walking, cycling holidays.

★★★
5 Units
Sleeping 4

WESTFIELD LODGES
Shore Road, Bonchurch, Ventnor PO38 1RH
T: (01983) 852268
F: (01983) 853992
E: info@westfieldlodges.fsnet.co.uk
I: www.westfieldlodges.co.uk
Contact: Mrs J MacLean

Five timber-clad detached lodges with 2 bedroom accommodation within an attractive woodland setting on a quiet site 5 minutes from beach. Situated on the south coast within the historic village of Bonchurch, the island offers a range of attractions and activities, perfect for walks, beaches, exploring or just relaxing.

OPEN Jan–Nov & Christmas

3-4 night short breaks available Oct–Mar. Open Christmas and New Year. Pets welcome.

Low season per wk
£125.00–£225.00
High season per wk
£245.00–£460.00

IMPORTANT NOTE Information on accommodation listed in this guide has been supplied by the proprietors. As changes may occur you are advised to check details at the time of booking.

VERWOOD, Dorset Map ref 2B3

★★★

1 Unit
Sleeping 4

FOREST EDGE
59 Coopers Lane, Verwood,
Wimborne Minster BH31 7PG
T: (01202) 822093
E: psingle@waitrose.com
Contact: Mr Patrick Singleton

OPEN All year round

Low season per wk
£150.00–£250.00
High season per wk
£250.00–£325.00

Holiday home pleasantly situated on the very edge of Ringwood Forest, with own courtyard garden. Ideal for touring New Forest with Bournemouth, Sailsbury and Poole easily reached. Comprehensive brochure available.

WALLINGFORD, Oxfordshire Map ref 2C2 *Tourist Information Centre Tel: (01491) 826972*

★★★

1 Unit
Sleeping 2–3

THE ANNEXE
Alders Croft, South Moreton, Didcot OX11 9AD
T: (01235) 813104
F: (01235) 813104
Contact: Mrs R A Ryder

OPEN All year round

Low season per wk
£155.00–£165.00
High season per wk
£165.00–£175.00

Single-storey annexe to main house overlooking garden. Convenient for River Thames, Oxford, Cotswolds, Windsor. Good walking on Ridgeway. Third person charged extra. Friday to Friday.

WAREHAM, Dorset Map ref 2B3 *Tourist Information Centre Tel: (01929) 552740*

★★★

1 Unit
Sleeping 6

EAST CREECH FARM HOUSE
East Creech, Wareham BH20 5AP
T: (01929) 480519 & 481312
F: (01929) 481312
E: debbie.best@euphony.net
I: www.pages.euphony.net/debbie.best/holiday
Contact: Mrs V Best

The farm is a dairy and beef farm. (It is possible to watch the milking). Ideal location for walking the Purbeck Hills and coastal paths.

OPEN Feb–Nov

Low season per wk
£160.00–£195.00
High season per wk
£345.00–£495.00

WIMBORNE MINSTER, Dorset Map ref 2B3

★

1 Unit
Sleeping 6

HILLBERRY
Blandford Road, Corfe Mullen,
Wimborne Minster BH21 3HF
T: (01202) 658906
Contact: Mr & Mrs P L Cheyne

OPEN All year round

Low season per wk
£105.00–£700.00
High season per wk
£105.00–£700.00

Upper ground floor of split-level house on south-facing hillside. Spacious, comfortable, level accommodation with large secluded verandah, overlooking natural gardens and peaceful countryside.

WINCHESTER, Hampshire Map ref 2C3 *Tourist Information Centre Tel: (01962) 840500*

★★

1 Unit
Sleeping 4

FLAT 7 KINGSWAY COURT
Kingsway Gardens, Chandlers Ford, Eastleigh SO53 1FG
Contact: Mr Peter Bulmer, Flat 14 Kingsway Court,
Kingsway Gardens, Chandlers Ford, Eastleigh SO53 1FG
T: (023) 8025 3159

OPEN All year round

Low season per wk
£200.00–£230.00
High season per wk
£230.00–£275.00

First floor flat with 2 bedrooms and balcony overlooking gardens. One hour from London, between Winchester and Southampton, close to New Forest.

QUALITY ASSURANCE SCHEME
Star ratings were correct at the time of going to press but are subject to change. Please check at the time of booking.

WINCHESTER continued

★★★★
1 Unit
Sleeping 6

GYLEEN
11 Mount View Road, Olivers Battery, Winchester
SO22 4JJ
Contact: Mr & Mrs Paul Tipple, 9 Mount View Road,
Olivers Battery, Winchester SO22 4JJ
T: (01962) 861918
F: 0870 0542801
E: pauliz@tipple.demon.co.uk
I: www.cottageguide.co.uk/gyleen

OPEN All year round

Low season per wk
£220.00–£275.00
High season per wk
£304.00–£344.00

Detached, centrally heated 2-bedroomed bungalow with large mature garden in quiet cul-de-sac overlooking golf-course, 2 miles west of Winchester city centre.

WINDSOR, Berkshire Map ref 2D2 *Tourist Information Centre Tel: (01753) 743900*

★★★
1 Unit
Sleeping 4

9 THE COURTYARD
4 High Street, Windsor SL4 1LD
Contact: Mrs N J Hitchcock, 1 Agar's Place, Datchet,
Slough SL3 9AH
T: (01753) 545005
F: (01753) 545005
E: jhhitchcock@btinternet.com

OPEN All year round

Low season per wk
£425.00–£465.00
High season per wk
£465.00–£525.00

Attractively furnished modern apartment served by lift. Courtyard setting just off High Street. Well located for Ascot, Henley and London.

★★★
1 Unit
Sleeping 4

MANOR VIEW APARTMENT
19 Dedworth Manor, Thames Mead, Windsor SL4 5NF
Contact: Mrs M C Smith, 32 Matthews Chase, Binfield,
Bracknell RG42 4UR
T: (01344) 485658
E: manorview@care4free.net
I: www.manorview.care4free.net

OPEN Jan–Aug

Low season per wk
£415.00
High season per wk
£415.00

Cosy and comfortable apartment tucked away in the grounds of an old manor house yet only 1.5 miles from the heart of Royal Windsor.

WINTERBORNE WHITECHURCH, Dorset Map ref 2B3

★★★
1 Unit
Sleeping 4

A pretty 17thC thatched cottage, overlooking the unspoilt Dorset countryside. Perfectly situated for exploring the beautiful Thomas Hardy country and the dramatic coastline from Lulworth Cove to Chesil beach. Dorchester 12 miles, Blandford Forum 5 miles. Weymouth, Poole and Bournemouth all within easy reach.

3 ROSE COTTAGES
Rook Lane, Winterborne Whitechurch,
Blandford Forum DT11 0AH
Contact: Mrs Anne Macfarlane, Barn Court, West Street,
Winterborne Kingston, Blandford Forum DT11 9AX
T: (01929) 471612
F: (01929) 472293
E: rosecottages5137@aol.com
I: www.cottageguide.co.uk/rose.cottage

OPEN All year round

Short breaks available.

Low season per wk
£166.00–£186.00
High season per wk
£197.00–£363.00

CREDIT CARD BOOKINGS If you book by telephone and are asked for your credit card number it is advisable to check the proprietor's policy should you cancel your reservation.

A brief guide to the main Towns and Villages offering accommodation in the South of England

A ABINGDON, OXFORDSHIRE - Attractive former county town on River Thames with many interesting buildings, including 17th C County Hall, now a museum, in the market-place and the remains of an abbey.

• **ALVERSTOKE, HAMPSHIRE** - Village located at the head the Haslar Creek. Within easy reach of Gosport.

B BEAULIEU, HAMPSHIRE - Beautifully situated among woods and hills on the Beaulieu river, the village is both charming and unspoilt. The 13th C ruined Cistercian abbey and 14th C Palace House stand close to the National Motor Museum. There is a maritime museum at Bucklers Hard.

• **BEMBRIDGE, ISLE OF WIGHT** - Village with harbour and bay below Bembridge Down - the most easterly village on the island. Bembridge Sailing Club is one of the most important in southern England.

• **BOLDRE, HAMPSHIRE** - An attractive village with pretty views of the village from the bridge. The white plastered church sits on top of a hill.

• **BOURNEMOUTH, DORSET** - Seaside town set among the pines with a mild climate, sandy beaches and fine coastal views. The town has wide streets with excellent shops, a pier, a pavilion, museums and conference centre.

• **BRIGHSTONE, ISLE OF WIGHT** - Excellent centre for visitors who want somewhere quiet. Calbourne nearby is ideal for picnics and the sea at Chilton Chie has safe bathing at high tide.

• **BROCKENHURST, HAMPSHIRE** - Attractive village with thatched cottages and a ford in its main street. Well placed for visiting the New Forest.

• **BUCKINGHAM, BUCKINGHAMSHIRE** - Interesting old market town surrounded by rich farmland. It has many Georgian buildings, including the Town Hall and Old Jail and many old almshouses and inns. Stowe School nearby has magnificent 18th C landscaped gardens.

• **BURFORD, OXFORDSHIRE** - One of the most beautiful Cotswold wool towns with Georgian and Tudor houses, many antique shops and a picturesque High Street sloping to the River Windrush.

C CARISBROOKE, ISLE OF WIGHT - Situated at the heart of the Isle of Wight and an ideal base for touring. Boasts a Norman church, formerly a monastic church, and a castle built on the site of a Roman fortress.

• **CHALE, ISLE OF WIGHT** - Village overlooking Chale Bay and near Blackgang Chine which has a children's maze, a water garden and a museum displaying many objects from shipwrecks.

• **CHALFONT ST GILES, BUCKINGHAMSHIRE** - Pretty, old village in wooded Chiltern Hills yet only 20 miles from London and a good base for visiting the city. Excellent base for Windsor, Henley, the Thames Valley, Oxford and the Cotswolds.

• **CHARLBURY, OXFORDSHIRE** - Large Cotswold village with beautiful views of the Evenlode Valley just outside the village and close to the ancient Forest of Wychwood.

• **CHIPPING NORTON, OXFORDSHIRE** - Old market town set high in the Cotswolds and an ideal touring centre. The wide market-place contains many 16th C and 17th C stone houses and the Town Hall and Tudor Guildhall.

• **CHRISTCHURCH, DORSET** - Tranquil town lying between the Avon and Stour just before they converge and flow into Christchurch Harbour. A fine 11th C church and the remains of a Norman castle and house can be seen.

• **CORFE CASTLE, DORSET** - One of the most spectacular ruined castles in Britain. Norman in origin, the castle was a Royalist stronghold during the Civil War and held out until 1645. The village had a considerable marble-carving industry in the Middle Ages.

• **CORFE MULLEN, DORSET** - Village 3 miles south-west of Wimborne. Church and mill are of interest.

• **COWES, ISLE OF WIGHT** - There are regular ferry and hydrofoil services across the Solent to Cowes. The town is the headquarters of the Royal Yacht Squadron and Cowes Week is held every August.

F FINSTOCK, OXFORDSHIRE - This charming village on the edge of the Wychwood Forest was the home of John Wesley.

• **FORDINGBRIDGE, HAMPSHIRE** - On the north-west edge of the New Forest. A medieval bridge crosses the Avon at this point and gave the town its name. A good centre for walking, exploring and fishing.

G GILLINGHAM, DORSET - A good shopping centre for tourists in the dairy vale of Dorset on the River Stour. Acclaimed as a beauty spot by the painter John Constable.

• **GODSHILL, ISLE OF WIGHT** - On the Shanklin road. Hill-top church and museum.

• **GOSPORT, HAMPSHIRE** - From a tiny fishing hamlet, Gosport has grown into an important centre with many naval establishments, including HMS Dolphin, the submarine base, with the Naval Submarine Museum which preserves HMS Alliance and Holland I.

• **GREAT MILTON, OXFORDSHIRE** - One of Oxfordshire's most famous villages situated in the Chiltern foothills. Thought to once be the home of John Milton who it is suggested wrote Paradise Lost while living here.

L LANGTON MATRAVERS, DORSET - 18th C Purbeck stone village surrounded by National Trust downland, about a mile from the sea and 350 ft above sea level. Excellent walking.

• **LEE ON THE SOLENT, HAMPSHIRE** - Resort and residential area with fine views across the Solent to Cowes and Calshot.

• **LYMINGTON, HAMPSHIRE** - Small, pleasant town with bright cottages and attractive Georgian houses, lying on the edge of the New Forest with a ferry service to the Isle of Wight. A sheltered harbour makes it a busy yachting centre.

• **LYNDHURST, HAMPSHIRE** - The 'capital' of the New Forest, surrounded by attractive woodland scenery and delightful villages. The town is dominated by the Victorian Gothic-style church where the original Alice in Wonderland is buried.

M MILFORD-ON-SEA, HAMPSHIRE - Victorian seaside resort with shingle beach and good bathing, set in pleasant countryside and looking out over the Isle of Wight. Nearby is Hurst Castle, built by Henry VIII. The school chapel, former abbey church, can be visited.

• **MILTON ABBAS, DORSET** - Sloping village street of thatched houses. A boys' school lies in Capability Brown's landscaped gardens amid hills and woods where the town once stood. The school chapel, former abbey church, can be visited.

• **MILTON KEYNES, BUCKINGHAMSHIRE** - Designated a New Town in 1967, Milton Keynes offers a wide range of housing and is abundantly planted with trees. It has excellent shopping facilities and 3 centres for leisure and sporting activities. The Open University is based here.

NEWBURY, BERKSHIRE - Ancient town surrounded by the Downs and on the Kennet and Avon Canal. It has many buildings of interest, including the 17th C Cloth Hall, which is now a museum. The famous racecourse is nearby.

• **NORTH LEIGH, OXFORDSHIRE** - Small village with an ancient church whose tower was built in Anglo-Saxon times. There is a disused windmill on a hilltop and remains of a Roman villa nearby with a hypocaust and a tessellated pavement.

OXFORD, OXFORDSHIRE - Beautiful university town with many ancient colleges, some dating from the 13th C, and numerous buildings of historic and architectural interest. The Ashmolean Museum has outstanding collections. Lovely gardens and meadows with punting on the Cherwell.

PANGBOURNE, BERKSHIRE - A pretty stretch of river where the Pang joins the Thames with views of the lock, weir and toll bridge. Once the home of Kenneth Grahame, author of 'Wind in the Willows'.

• **POOLE, DORSET** - Tremendous natural harbour makes Poole a superb boating centre. The harbour area is crowded with historic buildings including the 15th C Town Cellars housing a maritime museum.

• **PORTSMOUTH & SOUTHSEA, HAMPSHIRE** - There have been connections with the Navy since early times and the first dock was built in 1194. HMS Victory, Nelson's flagship, is here and Charles Dickens' former home is open to the public. Neighbouring Southsea has a promenade with magnificent views of Spithead.

ROMSEY, HAMPSHIRE - Town grew up around the important abbey and lies on the banks of the River Test, famous for trout and salmon. Broadlands House, home of the late Lord Mountbatten, is open to the public.

SANDOWN, ISLE OF WIGHT - The 6-mile sweep of Sandown Bay is one of the island's finest stretches, with excellent sands. The pier has a pavilion and sun terrace; the esplanade has amusements, bars, eating-places and gardens.

• **SHAFTESBURY, DORSET** - Hilltop town with a long history. The ancient and cobbled Gold Hill is one of the most attractive in Dorset. There is an excellent small museum containing a collection of buttons for which the town is famous.

• **SHANKLIN, ISLE OF WIGHT** - Set on a cliff with gentle slopes leading down to the beach, esplanade and marine gardens. The picturesque, old thatched village nestles at the end of the wooded chine.

• **SHIPTON-UNDER-WYCHWOOD, OXFORDSHIRE** - Situated in the ancient Forest of Wychwood with many fine old houses and an interesting parish church. Nearby is Shipton Court, a gabled Elizabethan house set in beautiful grounds that include an ornamental lake and a tree-lined avenue approach.

• **SOUTHAMPTON, HAMPSHIRE** - One of Britain's leading seaports with a long history, now a major container port. In the 18th C it became a fashionable resort with the assembly rooms and theatre. The old Guildhall and the Wool House are now museums. Sections of the medieval wall can still be seen.

• **SWAY, HAMPSHIRE** - Small village on the south-western edge of the New Forest. It is noted for its 220-ft tower, Peterson's Folly, built in the 1870s by a retired Indian judge to demonstrate the value of concrete as a building material.

THAME, OXFORDSHIRE - Historic market town on the River Thames. The wide, unspoilt High Street has many styles of architecture with medieval timber-framed cottages, Georgian houses and some famous inns.

• **TOTLAND BAY, ISLE OF WIGHT** - On the Freshwater Peninsula. It is possible to walk from here around to Alum Bay.

VENTNOR, ISLE OF WIGHT - Town lies at the bottom of an 800-ft hill and has a reputation as a winter holiday and health resort due to its mild climate. The mile-long esplanade reaches the shore of the delightful village of Bonchurch, and in the other direction are the 22-acre Botanical Gardens.

WALLINGFORD, OXFORDSHIRE - Site of an ancient ford over the River Thames, now crossed by a 900-ft-long bridge. The town has many timber-framed and Georgian buildings, Gainsborough portraits in the 17th C Town Hall and a few remains of a Norman Castle.

• **WAREHAM, DORSET** - This site has been occupied since pre-Roman times and has a turbulent history. In 1762 fire destroyed much of the town, so the buildings now are mostly Georgian.

• **WINCHESTER, HAMPSHIRE** - King Alfred the Great made Winchester the capital of Saxon England. A magnificent Norman cathedral, with one of the longest naves in Europe, dominates the city. Home of Winchester College founded in 1382.

• **WINDSOR, BERKSHIRE** - Town dominated by the spectacular castle, home of the Royal Family for over 900 years. Parts are open to the public. There are many attractions including the Great Park, Eton and trips on the river.

• **WINTERBORNE WHITECHURCH, DORSET** - Village astride the A354.

QUALITY ASSURANCE SCHEME

For an explanation of the quality and facilities represented by the Stars please refer to the front of this guide. A more detailed explanation can be found in the information pages at the back.

Where to Stay
2002

The official and best selling guides,
offering the reassurance of quality assured accommodation

Hotels, Townhouses and
Travel Accommodation
in England 2002
£10.99

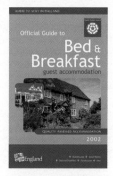

Guesthouses, Bed &
Breakfast, Farmhouses
and Inns in England 2002
£11.99

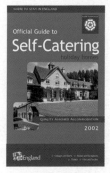

Self Catering
Holiday Homes
in England 2002
£9.99

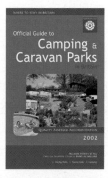

Camping & Caravan Parks
in Britain 2002
£5.99

Somewhere Special
in England 2002
£7.99

Look out also for:
SOMEWHERE SPECIAL
IN ENGLAND 2002

Accommodation
achieving the highest
standards in facilities
and quality of service -

the perfect guide for the
discerning traveller.

**NOW ALSO FEATURING
SELF CATERING
ACCOMMODATION**

The guides include

• Accommodation entries packed with information • Full colour maps
• Places to visit • Tourist Information Centres

INFORMATIVE • EASY TO USE • GREAT VALUE FOR MONEY

From all good bookshops or by mail order from the ETC Fulfilment Centre,
PO Box 22489, London W6 9FR
Tel: 0870 606 7204 Fax: 020 8563 3048
Email: fulfilment@englishtourism.org.uk Web: www.englishtourism.org.uk

SOUTH EAST England

The White cliffs of Dover, beach huts and piers, yachts at Chichester – this distinctive coast combines with famous gardens and the apples and hops of Kent to make a quintessentially English region.

classic sights
Battle of Hastings – audio tour brings the battle to life
Hever Castle – romantic moated castle, home of Anne Boleyn

coast & country
Runnymede – riverside meadows and woodland
Pegwell Bay & Goodwin Sands – a haven for birds and seals

gorgeous gardens
Sissinghurst – celebrated garden of Vita Sackville-West
Leonardslee – rhododendrons and azaleas ablaze with colour in May

literary links
Charles Dickens – Rochester; his home Gad's Hill Place
Rudyard Kipling – Bateman's, his momento filled home
Chaucer – The Canterbury Tales

arts for all
Brighton Festival – international performers, artists and writers every May

distinctively different
Royal Pavilion – exotic palace of King George IV

The counties of East Sussex, Kent, Surrey and West Sussex

FOR MORE INFORMATION CONTACT:
South East England Tourist Board
The Old Brew House, Warwick Park,
Tunbridge Wells, Kent TN2 5TU
Tel: (01892) 540766 Fax: (01892) 511008
Email: enquiries@seetb.org.uk
Internet: www.SouthEastEngland.uk.com

The Pictures:
1 Bodiam Castle, East Sussex
2 Southover Grange Gardens,
   Lewes, East Sussex

Places to Visit - see pages 382-385
Where to Stay - see pages 386-403

381

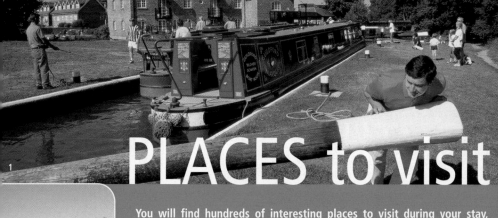

PLACES to visit

You will find hundreds of interesting places to visit during your stay, just some of which are listed in these pages. Contact any Tourist Information Centre in the region for more ideas on days out.

Alfriston Clergy House

The Tye, Alfriston, Polegate, East Sussex BN26 5TL
Tel: (01323) 870001 www.nationaltrust.org.uk
A thatched, half-timbered 14thC building with exhibition on Wealden house-building. It was the first building acquired by The National Trust in 1896. Cottage garden.

Amberley Museum

Houghton Bridge, Amberley, Arundel, West Sussex BN18 9LT
Tel: (01798) 831370 www.amberleymuseum.co.uk
Open-air industrial history centre in chalk quarry. Working craftsmen, narrow-gauge railway, early buses, working machines and other exhibits. Nature trail/visitor centre.

Anne of Cleves House Museum

52 Southover High Street, Lewes, East Sussex BN7 1JA
Tel: (01273) 474610 www.sussexpast.co.uk
A 16thC timber-framed Wealden hall-house which contains collections of Sussex interest. Displays feature Lewes from the 16thC to the present day.

Arundel Castle

Arundel, West Sussex BN18 9AB
Tel: (01903) 883136 www.arundelcastle.org
An impressive Norman stronghold in extensive grounds, much restored in the 18thC and 19thC. 11thC keep, 13thC barbican, barons' hall, armoury, chapel. Van Dyck and Gainsborough paintings.

Basingstoke Canal Visitor Centre

Mytchett Place Road, Mytchett, Camberley, Hampshire GU16 6DD
Tel: (01252) 370073 www.basingstoke-canal.co.uk
A canal interpretation centre with an exhibition displaying the history of canals over the past 200 years. Boat trips and boat hire available. Adventure playground.

Battle Abbey and Battlefield

High Street, Battle, East Sussex TN33 0AD
Tel: (01424) 773792 www.english-heritage.org.uk
An abbey founded by William the Conqueror on the site of the Battle of Hastings. The church altar is on the spot where King Harold was killed. Battlefield views and exhibition.

Beaver Zoological Gardens

Waylands Farm, Approach Road, Tatsfield, Westerham, Kent TN16 2JT
Tel: (01959) 577747 www.beaverwaterworld.com
Visitors to Beaver Zoological Gardens can see reptiles, tropical and cold water fish, Canadian beavers, aviary birds, rabbits and chipmunks. Play area, sandpit and cafe.

Borde Hill Garden

Balcombe Road, Haywards Heath, West Sussex RH16 1XP
Tel: (01444) 450326 www.bordehill.co.uk
Winner of two prestigious awards. A garden of contrasts where botanical interest and garden design play equally important roles. Extended colour throughout the year.

Brooklands Museum

Brooklands Road, Weybridge, Surrey KT13 0QN
Tel: (01932) 857381 www.motor-software.co.uk
Original 1907 motor racing circuit. Features the most historic and steepest section of the old banked track and 1-in-4 test hill. Motoring village and Grand Prix exhibition.

The Canterbury Tales Visitor Attraction

St Margaret's Street, Canterbury, Kent CT1 2TG
Tel: (01227) 479227 www.canterburytales.org.uk
An audiovisual recreation of life in medieval England. Visitors join Chaucer's pilgrims on their journey from London's Tabard Inn to Thomas Becket's shrine at Canterbury.

Charleston

Firle, Lewes, East Sussex BN8 6LL
Tel: (01323) 811265 www.charleston.org.uk
A 17thC-18thC farmhouse, home of Vanessa Bell and Duncan Grant of the Bloomsbury Set. House and contents decorated by the artists. Traditional walled garden.

Chartwell

Westerham, Kent TN16 1PS
Tel: (01732) 866368 www.nationaltrust.org.uk
The home of Sir Winston Churchill with study, studio, museum rooms with gifts, uniforms and photos. Garden, Golden Rose Walk, lakes. 'Years at Chartwell' exhibition.

Chatley Heath Semaphore Tower

Pointers Road, Cobham, Surrey KT11 1PQ
Tel: (01483) 517595
A restored historic semaphore tower, set in woodland, displaying the history of overland naval communications in the early 19thC. Working semaphore mast and models.

Drusillas Park

Alfriston, East Sussex BN26 5QS
Tel: (01323) 874100 www.drusillas.co.uk
South East England Tourist Board Visitor Attraction of the Year. Jungle Adventure Golf, adventure playground, toddlers' play village, zoolympics and small-gauge railway.

Eagle Heights

Hulberry Farm, Lullingstone Lane, Eynsford, Dartford, Kent DA4 0JB
Tel: (01322) 866466 www.eagleheights.co.uk
Bird of prey centre housed undercover where visitors can see eagles, hawks, falcons, owls and vultures from all over the world. Reptile centre, play area and sandpit.

English Wine Centre

Alfriston Roundabout, Alfriston, East Sussex BN26 5QS
Tel: (01323) 870164 www.weddingwine.co.uk
The English Wine Centre was established in 1972 and stocks a large range of English wines, fruit wines and ciders within the attractive wine shop. Tours and tastings available.

Goodwood House

Goodwood, Chichester, West Sussex PO18 OPX
Tel: (01243) 755040 www.goodwood.co.uk
A magnificent Regency house, home to the Earl of March, extensively refurbished in 1997 and set in a large area of open parkland. Fine furnishings, tapestries and porcelain.

Kent & East Sussex Railway

Tenterden Town Station, Tenterden, Kent TN30 6HE
Tel: (01580) 765155 www.kesr.org.uk
Full-size steam railway with restored Edwardian stations at Tenterden and Northiam. 14 steam engines, Victorian coaches and Pullman carriages. Museum and children's play area.

Leeds Castle and Gardens

Maidstone, Kent ME17 1PL
Tel: (01622) 765400 www.leeds-castle.co.uk
A castle built on two islands in a lake, dating from the 9thC. Furniture, tapestries, art treasures, dog collar museum, gardens, duckery, aviaries, maze, grotto, vineyard and greenhouses.

The Pictures:
1 River Wey, Nr. Guildford
2 Chiddingfold Village, Surrey
3 Leeds Castle, Kent
4 Bateman's, East Sussex
5 Chichester Cathedral Gardens, West Sussex
6 Brighton Pier

Port Lympne Wild Animal Park, Mansion and Gardens

Port Lympne, Hythe, Kent CT21 4PD
Tel: (01303) 264647 www.howletts.net
A 300-acre (121-ha) wild animal park specialising in rare breeds including gorillas, deer, rhino, tigers, elephants etc. Mansion with art gallery exhibitions, murals and gardens. Trailer rides.

Rural Life Centre

Old Kiln Museum, Reeds Road, Tilford,
Farnham, Surrey GU10 2DL
Tel: (01252) 792300
www.surreyweb.org.uk/rural-life
A museum with a comprehensive collection of farm machines, implements, wagons, displays on past village life, small arboretum and a woodland walk.

The Savill Garden

Windsor Great Park, Wick Lane, Englefield Green,
Egham, Surrey TW20 0UU
Tel: (01753) 847518 www.savillgarden.co.uk
Woodland garden with formal gardens and herbaceous borders offering much of great interest and beauty in all seasons. Landscaped Queen Elizabeth Temperate House.

Scotney Castle Garden

Lamberhurst, Royal Tunbridge Wells, Kent TN3 8JN
Tel: (01892) 891081 www.nationaltrust.org.uk
Romantic gardens created around the ruins of a 14thC moated castle containing exhibitions. Gardens created by the Hussey family with shrubs, winding paths and good views.

Sculpture at Goodwood

Hat Hill Copse, Goodwood, Chichester, West Sussex PO18 0QP
Tel: (01243) 538449 www.sculpture.org.uk
A changing collection of contemporary British sculpture set in 20 acres (8 ha) of beautiful grounds on the South Downs overlooking Chichester.

St Mary's House and Gardens

Bramber, Steyning, West Sussex BN44 3WE
Tel: (01903) 816205
A medieval, timber-framed Grade I Listed house with rare 16thC wall-leather, fine panelled rooms and a unique painted room. Topiary gardens.

South of England Rare Breeds Centre

Highlands Farm, Woodchurch, Ashford, Kent TN26 3RJ
Tel: (01233) 861493 www.rarebreeds.org.uk
Large collection of rare farm breeds on a working farm with children's play activities. Georgian farmstead under reconstruction. Home to the 'Tamworth Two'. Woodland walks.

Titsey Place and Gardens

Oxted, Surrey RH8 0SD
Tel: (01273) 407056 www.titsey.com
A guided tour of Titsey Place includes the library, old servants' hall, dining room and drawing room. The gardens comprise 10 acres (4 ha) of formal gardens and a walled garden.

Weald and Downland Open Air Museum

Singleton, Chichester, West Sussex PO18 0EU
Tel: (01243) 811348 www.wealddown.co.uk
Over 40 rescued historic buildings from South East England, reconstructed on a downland country park site. Homes and workplaces of the past include a medieval farmstead.

West Dean Gardens

West Dean Estate, West Dean, Chichester,
West Sussex PO18 0QZ
Tel: (01243) 818210 www.westdean.org.uk
Extensive downland garden with specimen trees, 300 ft (91 m) pergola, rustic summerhouses and restored walled kitchen garden. Walk in parkland and 45-acre (18-ha) arboretum.

Wilderness Wood

Hadlow Down, Uckfield, East Sussex TN22 4HJ
Tel: (01825) 830509 www.wildernesswood.co.uk
A family-run working woodland of 60 acres (24 ha), beautiful in all seasons. There are trails, a bluebell walk, a play area, workshop and a timber barn with exhibitions.

The Wildfowl and Wetlands Trust

Mill Road, Arundel, West Sussex BN18 9PB
Tel: (01903) 883355 www.wwt.org.uk
A wildlife paradise and a haven of peace and tranquility for swans, ducks and geese from around the world. Visitor centre and viewing gallery.

Winkworth Arboretum

Hascombe Road, Hascombe, Godalming, Surrey GU8 4AD
Tel: (01483) 208477 www.cornuswwweb.co.uk
One hundred acres (40 ha) of hillside planted with rare trees and shrubs. Good views, lakes, newly restored boathouse, azaleas, bluebells, wild spring flowers and autumn colours.

Find out more about
SOUTH EAST England

Further information about holidays and attractions in South East England is available from:

SOUTH EAST ENGLAND TOURIST BOARD
The Old Brew House, Warwick Park, Tunbridge Wells, Kent TN2 5TU.
Tel: (01892) 540766 Fax: (01892) 511008
Email: enquiries@seetb.org.uk
Internet: www.SouthEastEngland.uk.com

The following publications are available from the South East England Tourist Board:

South East Holiday and Short Breaks Guide
a detailed guide to the region including places to visit and inspected accommodation

Bed and Breakfast Touring map 2002 - including Camping and Caravan Parks in the South East
a useful touring map detailing inspected guest accommodation in the South East and London regions. Also contains camping and caravan parks

Eating and Drinking at Traditional Inns
in partnership with Whitbread Pubs, a guide to some of the fine inns to be found in the South and South East of England

Churches and Cathedrals of the South of England
a guide detailing some of the region's finest churches and cathedrals, their fascinating history and architecture

Spoilt for Choice - 100s of Places to Visit in South East England
the definitive guide to over 300 places to visit in South East England. Also contains a Web site directory, map and information on the network of Tourist Information Centres

Leisure Map and Gazetteer - South East England
produced in conjunction with Estate Publications Ltd, a colourful tourist map of the South East showing roads, railways, hundreds of places to visit and the topography of the region

e pictures:
Guildford Castle

Getting to
SOUTH EAST England

BY ROAD: From the north of England - M1/M25; the west and Wales - M4/M25; the east of England - M25; the south of England M3/M25; London - M20 or M2.

BY RAIL: Regular services from London's Charing Cross, Victoria and Waterloo East stations to all parts of South East England.

Where to stay in South East England

Accommodation entries in this region are listed in alphabetical order of place name, and then in alphabetical order of establishment.

Map references refer to the colour location maps at front of this guide. The first number indicates the map to use; the letter and number which follow refer to the grid reference on the map.

At-a-glance symbols at the end of each accommodation entry give useful information about services and facilities. A key to symbols can be found inside the back cover flap. Keep this open for easy reference.

A brief description of the towns and villages offering accommodation in the entries which follow, can be found at the end of this section.

A complete listing of all the English Tourism Council assessed accommodation covered by this guide appears at the back of the guide.

ALFRISTON, East Sussex Map ref 2D3

★★★★

1 Unit
Sleeping 4

Delightful Listed 16thC cottage with many charming period features. Convenient village location with many speciality shops, inns and restaurants within 5 minutes' walk. Peaceful courtyard garden and private parking. Double and twin bedrooms, bathroom and shower room. Fully equipped. Ideal walking, cycling, fishing etc. Adjacent to Southdown Way.

FLINT COTTAGE
12 North Street, Alfriston, Polegate BN26 5UG
Contact: Mrs Linda Garwood, Downland Cottages,
Allington Lodge, Allington Lane, Offham, Lewes BN7 3QJ
T: (01273) 477044
F: (01273) 479855
E: cgarwood@dircon.co.uk
I: www.flintcottagesussex.co.uk

OPEN All year round

Low season per wk
Min £195.00
High season per wk
Max £475.00

---

www.travelengland.org.uk
Log on for information and inspiration. The latest information on places to visit, events and quality assessed accommodation.

ARUNDEL, West Sussex Map ref 2D3 *Tourist Information Centre Tel: (01903) 882268*

★★

2 Units
Sleeping 4

THE COACHMAN'S FLAT AND THE COTTAGE
Mill Lane House, Slindon, Arundel BN18 0RP
Contact: Mrs Sarah Fuente, Mill Lane House, Slindon,
Arundel BN18 0RP
T: (01243) 814440
F: (01243) 814436

OPEN All year round

Low season per wk
£140.00–£250.00
High season per wk
£315.00–£350.00

Flat and cottage in 16thC property. Spectacular views to coast. In National Trust village on South Downs. Use of large gardens. Animals by arrangement.

ASHDOWN FOREST

See under Nutley

ASHFORD, Kent Map ref 3B4 *Tourist Information Centre Tel: (01233) 629165*

★★★

6 Units
Sleeping 4

EVERSLEIGH WOODLAND LODGES
Eversleigh House, Hornash Lane, Shadoxhurst,
Ashford TN26 1HX
T: (01233) 733248 & 07703 349744 (Mobile)
F: (01233) 733248
E: cjdrury@freeuk.com
Contact: Mrs C J Drury

OPEN Feb–Dec
CC: Barclaycard,
Mastercard, Visa

Low season per wk
£215.00–£375.00
High season per wk
£425.00–£525.00

Spacious detached lodges in woodland setting. Heated indoor swimming pool, games room, gymnasium, solarium, gardens. Easy access South Coast, London, Canterbury, Channel ports and tunnel.

ACCESSIBILITY

Look for the 🄰🄰🄰 symbols which indicate accessibility for wheelchair users. A list of establishments is at the front of this guide.

FOR SELF CATERING HOLIDAYS IN THE SOUTH EAST OF ENGLAND, SEASCA MEMBERS OFFER THE WIDEST CHOICE PLUS FRIENDLY HELP AND EXPERT LOCAL KNOWLEDGE

Best of Brighton & Sussex Cottages

Tel: 01273 308779
Fax: 01273 390211
Email: brightoncottages@pavilion.co.uk
www.bestofbrighton.co.uk

Fairhaven Holiday Cottages

Tel: 01634 300089
Fax: 01634 570157
Email: fairhaven@pavilion.co.uk
www.fairhaven-holidays.co.uk

Freedom Holiday Homes

Tel: 01580 720770
Fax: 01580 720771
Email: mail@freedomholidayhomes.co.uk
www.freedomholidayhomes.co.uk

Garden of England Cottages

Tel: 01732 369168
Fax: 01732 358817
Email: holidays@gardenofenglandcottages.co.uk
www.gardenofenglandcottages.co.uk

All SEASCA (South East Association of Self Catering Agencies) agencies are members of the SEETB and participate in the ETC Star Grading Scheme

BARNHAM, West Sussex Map ref 2C3

★★★★

1 Unit
Sleeping 2

A converted barn, spacious, beamed and well furnished. Sleeps 2. Peaceful rural location. Ideal for exploring coast and country. Historic Arundel and Chichester close by. Pet animals kept on the small farm. Exclusive garden. Dogs welcomed open April-October. Brochure available.

WELLDIGGERS

Church Farm Barns, Hill Lane, Barnham,
Bognor Regis PO22 0BN
Contact: Mrs Penelope Crawford, Church Farm Barns,
Hill Lane, Barnham, Bognor Regis PO22 0BN
T: (01243) 555119
F: (01243) 552779
E: welldiggers@hotmail.com
I: www.welldiggers.co.uk

OPEN Apr-Oct

High season per wk
£325.00-£425.00

BATTLE, East Sussex Map ref 3B4 *Tourist Information Centre Tel: (01424) 773721*

★★★

2 Units
Sleeping 2-4

NETHERFIELD HALL COTTAGES
Netherfield Hall, Netherfield, Battle TN33 9PQ
T: (01424) 774450 (Answerphone)
F: (01424) 774450
Contact: Mrs Jean Hawes

OPEN Jan, Mar-Dec

Low season per wk
£220.00-£295.00
High season per wk
£270.00-£395.00

Single-storey country cottages set in woodland in grounds of Netherfield Hall. One bedroom, lounge with sofa-bed, kitchen/diner. 2 miles from Battle.

★★★

1 Unit
Sleeping 5

PRIOR'S WELL
6 Upper Lake, Battle TN33 0AN
Contact: Mrs Yvonne Apps, Manager,
50 Wellington Gardens, Battle TN33 0HD
T: (01424) 772914 & 0796 7902183

OPEN All year round

Low season per wk
£350.00
High season per wk
£400.00

Grade II Listed building, 300-year-old beamed cottage, originally ostler's cottage for Chequers Inn, on Battle of Hastings field. Flexible bookings.

BEARSTED, Kent Map ref 3B3

★★★

1 Unit
Sleeping 6

LAUREL COTTAGE
83 Ware Street, Bearsted, Maidstone ME14 4PG
Contact: Mrs Chris Street, 43 The Landway, Bearsted,
Maidstone ME14 4BG
T: (01622) 739713
F: (01622) 631249

OPEN All year round

Low season per wk
£200.00
High season per wk
£400.00

Semi detached Victorian cottage, 3 twin bedrooms and cot, bathroom/shower, dining room, lounge, kitchen, 2nd toilet downstairs, garden with patio. Sorry no smokers or pets.

BRIGHTON & HOVE, East Sussex Map ref 2D3

★-★★

17 Units
Sleeping 1-2

THE ABBEY SELF-CATERING FLATLETS
14-19 Norfolk Terrace, Brighton BN1 3AD
Contact: Reservations, The Abbey Self-Catering Flatlets,
14-19 Norfolk Terrace, Brighton BN1 3AD
T: (01273) 778771
F: (01273) 729147
E: theabbey@brighton.co.uk
I: www.brighton.co.uk/hotels/theabbey

OPEN All year round
CC: Barclaycard, Delta,
Eurocard, JCB, Maestro,
Mastercard, Solo, Switch,
Visa, Visa Electron

Low season per wk
£125.00-£195.00
High season per wk
£145.00-£250.00

Specialising in self-catering. Lift, licensed bar. Everything provided. Prices to suit everyone. Easy parking. Children welcome. Open all year. All major credit cards.

REGIONAL TOURIST BOARD The ⋀ symbol in an establishment entry indicates that it is a Regional Tourist Board member.

BRIGHTON HOLIDAY FLATS

★★★
20 Units
Sleeping 2–5

50 Kings Road, Brighton BN1 1NA
Contact: Mrs L Bowler, Little Shepham, Shepham Lane,
Polegate BN26 6NB
T: (01323) 483119
F: (01323) 488322
E: bookings@brightonflats.co.uk
I: www.brightonflats.co.uk

OPEN All year round
CC: Mastercard, Switch,
Visa

Low season per wk
Min £220.00
High season per wk
Max £480.00

Newly refurbished apartments in prime seafront location in the heart of Brighton, near The Lanes, numerous restaurants, shops and entertainments.

BRIGHTON MARINA HOLIDAY APARTMENTS

★★★★
2 Units
Sleeping 2–4

5 Mariners Quay, Brighton Marina Village, Brighton
BN2 5UZ
T: (01273) 693569
F: (01273) 693569
Contact: Mrs S B Wills

OPEN All year round

Low season per wk
£250.00–£450.00
High season per wk
£350.00–£600.00

Luxury apartments in waterside village. Beautifully furnished; modern kitchens/ bathrooms; satellite TV. Extensive shopping, dining, leisure facilites at the Marina. One mile Pier and town.

METROPOLE COURT APARTMENTS

★★★–★★★★
4 Units
Sleeping 4–5

Well-appointed, privately owned apartments located above the Hilton Brighton Metropole, with panoramic sea and/or town views. Direct access to hotel facilities including the health club with indoor swimming pool. Close to all local entertainments and world-famous Brighton Lanes. Trains to London 50 minutes; Gatwick Airport 40 minutes.

The Hilton Brighton Metropole Hotel, Kings Road,
Brighton BN1 2FA
Contact: Mr & Mrs Harold & Valerie Williams, Cliff Edge,
28 Marine Drive, Rottingdean, Brighton BN2 7HQ
T: (01273) 302431
F: (01273) 307744
E: harval@brighton-apartments.com
I: www.brighton-apartments.com

OPEN All year round
CC: Barclaycard, Delta,
Eurocard, JCB,
Mastercard, Visa

Low season per wk
£300.00–£400.00
High season per wk
£360.00–£580.00

SEAPOINT

★★★★
1 Unit
Sleeping 6–7

2 Roedean Terrace, Brighton BN2 5RN
Contact: Mrs R T Salmon, Best of Brighton & Sussex
Cottages Ltd, Windmill Lodge, Vicarage Lane,
Rottingdean, Brighton BN2 7HD
T: (01273) 308779 & 07956 662457
F: (01273) 300266
E: brightoncottages@pavilion.co.uk
I: www.bestofbrighton.co.uk

OPEN All year round
CC: Barclaycard, Delta,
Eurocard, Mastercard,
Switch, Visa

Low season per wk
£375.00–£430.00
High season per wk
£515.00–£675.00

Former coastguard's cottage offering unrivalled panoramic views of Brighton Marina and English Channel. Lovely south-facing garden and patio. One mile Brighton centre. Three bedrooms, 2 bathrooms. Sleeps 6/7 people.

BEACON LIGHT COTTAGE

★★★
1 Unit
Sleeping 6–7

14 Alexandra Road, Broadstairs CT10 1EP
Contact: Mr Patrick Vandervorst, Duinhelmlaan 11,
B-8420 Wenduine, Belgium
T: 0032 504 23207 (business) & 504 12566 (home)
F: 0032 504 23207
E: beaconlight.cottage@worldonline.be
I: www.beaconlightcottage.com

OPEN All year round

Low season per wk
£190.00–£250.00
High season per wk
£220.00–£380.00

Clean and cosy old English cottage. Sleeps 6 with cot. Open log fire, close to beach in conservation area. Video, satellite TV.

CANTERBURY, Kent Map ref 3B3 *Tourist Information Centre Tel: (01227) 766567*

★★★★
3 Units
Sleeping 3–6

THE CANTERBURY HOTEL & APARTMENTS
71 New Dover Road, Canterbury CT1 3DZ
Contact: Mr D Standen, Reception Manager,
The Canterbury Hotel and Apartments,
71 New Dover Road, Canterbury CT1 3DZ
T: (01227) 450551
F: (01227) 780145
E: canterbury.hotel@btinternet.com
I: www.canterbury-hotel-apartments.co.uk

OPEN All year round
CC: Amex, Barclaycard,
Delta, Diners, Eurocard,
Mastercard, Switch, Visa

Low season per wk
£290.00–£400.00
High season per wk
£320.00–£440.00

Superior apartments in hotel grounds, close to city centre. Colour TV, direct-dial telephone, fully equipped. Out of season long stay discounts.

★★★★
6 Units
Sleeping 2–4

EBURY HOTEL COTTAGES
65–67 New Dover Road, Canterbury CT1 3DX
Contact: Mr Henry Mason, Ebury Hotel,
New Dover Road, Canterbury CT1 3DX
T: (01227) 768433 & 811550
F: (01227) 459187
E: info@ebury-hotel.co.uk
I: www.ebury-hotel.co.uk

OPEN All year round
CC: Amex, Barclaycard,
Delta, Diners, JCB,
Maestro, Mastercard,
Solo, Switch, Visa, Visa
Electron

Low season per wk
£240.00–£330.00
High season per wk
£340.00–£480.00

Quiet, comfortable hotel flats, bungalows and cottages standing in grounds, half a mile from the city centre. Heated indoor pool and spa.

★★★
1 Unit
Sleeping 3

HENRY'S OF ASH
51 The Street, Ash, Canterbury CT3 2EN
Contact: Mr P H Robinson, Henry's of Ash, Darrington,
Durlock Road, Ash, Canterbury CT3 2HU
T: (01304) 812563

OPEN All year round

Low season per wk
£110.00–£146.00
High season per wk
£146.00–£170.00

Comfortable self-contained maisonette, over central village antiques shop. Double glazing. Handy for touring East Kent and for Channel trips.

★★★
2 Units
Sleeping 2–4

WAGONERS & SHEPHERDS COTTAGE
Denstroude Farm, Blean, Canterbury CT2 9JZ
T: (01227) 471513
Contact: Mrs M K Heathcote

OPEN All year round

Low season per wk
£160.00–£180.00
High season per wk
£180.00–£220.00

Two small, comfortable cottages on working farm. Close to Canterbury and within easy reach of Dover and many places of interest. Ideal for walking and bird watching.

★★★
3 Units
Sleeping 6

YEW TREE PARK
Stone Street, Petham, Canterbury CT4 5PL
T: (01227) 700306
F: (01227) 700306
E: enquiries@yewtreepark.com
I: www.yewtreepark.com
Contact: Mr Derek Zanders

OPEN Mar–Oct
CC: Barclaycard, Delta,
Eurocard, JCB, Maestro,
Mastercard, Solo, Switch,
Visa

Low season per wk
£165.00–£205.00
High season per wk
£205.00–£325.00

Picturesque country park close to Canterbury and M20 on B2068. Ideally situated for exploring, local heritage, Kent and beaches. Large outdoor pool.

CATERHAM, Surrey Map ref 2D2

★★★
1 Unit
Sleeping 4–6

THE WHITE COTTAGE
Birchwood House, Woldingham Road, Woldingham,
Caterham CR3 7LR
Contact: Mrs Josephine Crux, Birchwood House,
Woldingham Road, Woldingham, Caterham CR3 7LR
T: (01883) 343287
F: (01883) 348066
E: jocrux@birchwoodhouse.freeserve.co.uk
I: www.oas.co.uk/ukcottages

OPEN All year round

Low season per wk
Min £220.00
High season per wk
Max £240.00

230-acre mixed farm. Detached bungalow in country setting near rail and buses. Easy access to London. Fully-fitted kitchen, 2 bedrooms, dining room/lounge with bed settee, bathroom.

★★★★
2 Units
Sleeping 2–4

THE OLD DAIRY & STABLE COTTAGE

The Old Barn, Charcott Farm, Charcott,
Tonbridge TN11 8LG
Contact: Mrs Sandra Bell, The Old Barn, Charcott Farm,
Charcott, Tonbridge TN11 8LG
T: (01892) 870138 & 07850 018811
F: (01892) 870138

OPEN All year round

Low season per wk
£265.00–£325.00
High season per wk
£395.00–£500.00

One and two bedroomed cottages in rural location, heart of Kent. Wealth of beams, full central heating. Linen, hamper, toiletries provided. Well equipped. Enclosed gardens.

★★★★
1 Unit
Sleeping 6

5 CALEDONIAN ROAD

Caledonian Road, Chichester PO19 2LH
Contact: Miss Victoria Chubb, 33 Hillier Road, London SW11 6AX
T: (020) 7924 5446
E: victoriachubb@hotmail.com
I: www.sussexlive.com

Recently restored and furnished old townhouse with high quality contemporary interior. Modern kitchen, real fire, books and games. Sunny patio garden. City centre 3 minutes' walk. House in quiet road. Ideal for beach or exploring the South Downs, Goodwood and evenings at theatre, cinema, restaurants. Wonderful location summer or winter.

OPEN All year round

Low season per wk
£250.00–£300.00
High season per wk
£300.00–£425.00

★★★★
1 Unit
Sleeping 6

CORNERSTONES

Brookside Close, Runcton, Chichester PO20 6PY
Contact: Mrs V J Higgins, Greenacre, Goodwood Gardens, Runcton, Chichester PO20 6SP
T: (01243) 839096
F: (01243) 779658
E: vjrmhiggins@hotmail.com
I: www.visitbritain.com

Built in local style. 2 bedrooms upstairs, 1 downstairs. Quiet village south of Chichester. Easy walking distance to pub/restaurant, church and post office/shop. Recently renovated, central heating. Equipped/furnished to a high standard. Garaging for 2 cars. Enclosed gardens with patio, tables and chairs. No smoking. Brochure available.

OPEN All year round
CC: Mastercard, Visa

Low season per wk
£325.00–£485.00
High season per wk
£485.00–£565.00

USE YOUR *i*s

There are more than 550 Tourist Information Centres throughout England offering friendly help with accommodation and holiday ideas as well as suggestions of places to visit and things to do. You'll find TIC addresses in the local Phone Book.

CHICHESTER continued

★★★★

1 Unit
Sleeping 2

Distinctive, modernised 1-bedroom cottage. Quiet village south of Chichester. Within easy walking distance of pub/restaurant, church, village post office/shop. Equipped and furnished to a high standard. Off-road parking. Sun trap patio with table and chairs. No smoking. Brochure available.

CYGNET COTTAGE
Mill Lane, Runcton, Chichester PO20 6PP
Contact: Mrs V J Higgins, Greenacre, Goodwood Gardens, Runcton, Chichester PO20 6SP
T: (01243) 839096
F: (01243) 779658
E: vjrmhiggins@hotmail.com
I: www.visitbritain.com

OPEN All year round
CC: Mastercard, Visa

Low season per wk
£185.00–£250.00
High season per wk
£250.00–£295.00

★★★★

1 Unit
Sleeping 2

Luxury studio-style cottage in quiet village. Furnished and equipped to a very high standard. Own enclosed garden with patio furniture. Five minutes' drive from Chichester. Village shop and pub within easy walking distance. All linen and towels included. Small, well-behaved dogs welcome. No smoking. Fri-Fri. Brochure available.

FOOTPATH NURSERY
Post Office Lane, North Mundham, Chichester PO20 6JY
T: (01243) 779823
F: (01243) 779823
E: noeljenny@onetel.net.uk
Contact: Mr & Mrs Noel Bettridge

OPEN All year round

Short breaks available in low season. Min 2 nights.

Low season per wk
£175.00–£235.00
High season per wk
£235.00–£285.00

★★★★

4 Units
Sleeping 2–5

18thC windmill and adjoining buildings converted into comfortable holiday homes, set in nearly an acre of attractive gardens with croquet, putting and barbecue. Situated in the country between the historic city of Chichester and the sea, with views over farmland, golf course and to the Downs.

HUNSTON MILL
Selsey Road, Hunston, Chichester PO20 6AU
T: (01243) 783375
F: (01243) 785179
E: hunston.mill@virgin.net
I: www.hunstonmill.co.uk
Contact: Mr & Mrs R Beeny

OPEN All year round
CC: Barclaycard,
Mastercard, Visa

Low season per wk
£195.00–£240.00
High season per wk
£235.00–£400.00

CHILHAM, Kent Map ref 3B3

★★★

2 Units
Sleeping 2–3

MONCKTON COTTAGES
Heron Manor, Mountain Street, Chilham,
Canterbury CT4 8DG
T: (01227) 730256 (Answerphone)
F: (01227) 730256
E: monckton@rw-kirwan.demon.co.uk
Contact: Dr R W Kirwan

OPEN All year round

Low season per wk
£130.00–£240.00
High season per wk
£240.00–£360.00

Charming self-contained cottages, part of 15thC manor, in 3 acres. Picturesque setting on North Downs Way. Immaculately maintained, each with private garden and fully equipped.

★★★★
1 Unit
Sleeping 2

3 THE OLD SCHOOL HOUSE

School Lane, Compton, Chichester PO18 9EZ
Contact: Mr & Mrs Brian & Val Parkinson,
47-48 Castle Garden, Petersfield GU32 3AG
T: (01730) 233747
E: val@comptoncottage.co.uk
I: www.comptoncottage.co.uk

Grade II Listed. East wing of mid-Victorian former village school in conservation area. Comfortable, light, spacious yet cosy. Pine spiral staircase to large bedroom. Open stone hearth for log fires. Sun-trap courtyard and garden with barbecue. Next to bridleway. Superb walking and cycling. Shop, pub, restaurant 2 minutes' stroll.

OPEN All year round

3-night stays available (except Christmas and New Year).

Low season per wk
£285.00–£325.00
High season per wk
£325.00–£450.00

★★★
1 Unit
Sleeping 2

THE COWSHED AT THE CARRIAGE HOUSE
Monks Lane, Cousley Wood, Wadhurst TN5 6EN
Contact: Mrs Maureen Parker, The Carriage House,
Monks Lane, Cousley Wood, Wadhurst TN5 6EN
T: (01892) 783188 (Home) & 723800 (Work)
F: (01892) 784380

OPEN All year round

Low season per wk
Max £200.00
High season per wk
Max £250.00

Fully equipped converted cowshed in rural setting. Sleeps 2. Parking. Main line to London. Ideal touring centre for South Coast and National Trust properties.

★★★-★★★★★
2 Units
Sleeping 5–6

TURNDEN WING

Turnden, Hartley Road, Cranbrook TN17 3QX
Contact: Mr Peter Hopper, Turnden, Hartley Road,
Cranbrook TN17 3QX
T: (01580) 713183 (Answerphone)
F: (01580) 713183
E: turnden@globalnet.co.uk

Adjoining 16thC farmhouse surrounded by 70 acres of grassland, Turnden Wing accommodates 11-12 persons as one large house or 2 self-contained flats for 5-6. Ground floor: comfortably furnished, 1 double, 1 3-bedded, 2 WCs, showers and bath, large kitchen, patio doors to garden. First floor: 1 double, 2 twins, lounge/diner and access to large garden.

OPEN All year round

Low season per wk
£250.00–£400.00
High season per wk
£400.00–£450.00

★★★★
1 Unit
Sleeping 5

LOW BORRANS
The Street, Denton, Canterbury CT4 6QZ
T: (01303) 844289
F: (01303) 844289
E: paul@downland-cycles.freeserve.co.uk
Contact: Mr & Mrs P Lucock

OPEN All year round

Low season per wk
£180.00–£270.00
High season per wk
£270.00–£320.00

17thC country cottage with exposed beams, inglenook fireplace and antique furniture. Centre of small village 8 miles from Canterbury, Folkestone, Dover. Comfortable, warm, relaxed atmosphere for winter breaks.

MAP REFERENCES
Map references apply to the colour maps at the front of this guide.

DORKING, Surrey Map ref 2D2

★★★
2 Units
Sleeping 2–4

BULMER FARM
Holmbury St Mary, Dorking RH5 6LG
Contact: Mrs Gill Hill, Bulmer Farm, Holmbury St Mary,
Dorking RH5 6LG
T: (01306) 730210

OPEN All year round

Low season per wk
£190.00–£280.00
High season per wk
£250.00–£340.00

30-acre beef farm. Two single-storey units converted from 17thC farm building. Two-person unit suitable for disabled and four-person unit form courtyard to farmhouse.

EASTBOURNE, East Sussex Map ref 3B4 *Tourist Information Centre Tel: (01323) 411400*

★★★★
4 Units
Sleeping 6

BLACK ROBIN FARM
Beachy Head, Eastbourne BN20 7XX
T: (01323) 643357 & 0797 0905809 (Mobile)
F: (01323) 643357
Contact: Mrs Jane Higgs

OPEN All year round
CC: Barclaycard,
Mastercard, Switch, Visa

Low season per wk
Min £160.00
High season per wk
Max £380.00

1000-acre livestock farm. Peaceful farm bungalows set in middle of South Downs. Excellent views. Close to town, beach and South Downs Way. Dogs and children welcome.

★★★★
5 Units
Sleeping 2–5

COURTNEY HOUSE HOLIDAY FLATS
53 Royal Parade, Eastbourne BN22 7AQ
T: (01323) 410202 & 732697
E: holidays@courtneyhouse.org.uk
I: www.eastbourne-web.co.uk/sites/courteneyhouse/index.html
Contact: Mr A Beney

OPEN All year round

Low season per wk
£90.00–£130.00
High season per wk
£230.00–£295.00

Self-contained holiday flats, ideally situated on seafront, with sea views. Close to all amenities. Unrestricted street parking. Golf and boating nearby. Non-smoking.

EPSOM, Surrey Map ref 2D2

★★★
1 Unit
Sleeping 5

7 GREAT TATTENHAMS
Epsom KT18 5RF
T: (01737) 354112
Contact: Mrs Mary Willis

OPEN All year round

Low season per wk
£130.00–£155.00
High season per wk
£180.00–£205.00

Modern, spacious, comfortably furnished first floor flat. A good touring centre for London and the south east.

FAVERSHAM, Kent Map ref 3B3 *Tourist Information Centre Tel: (01795) 534542*

★★★
1 Unit
Sleeping 4

MONKS COTTAGE
Leaveland, Faversham ME13 0NP
T: (01233) 740419
F: (01233) 740419
Contact: Mr & Mrs Graham Darby

Modern cottage of brick construction in grounds of our period thatched family home. Set in 4 acres in quiet, picturesque valley. Ideal for country walks. Situated within 4 miles M2/M20. Easy access to coastal resorts, Channel ports.

OPEN May–Aug &
Christmas

High season per wk
£300.00–£400.00

★★★
1 Unit
Sleeping 6

UPLEES FARM
Uplees Road, Luddenham, Faversham ME13 0QR
T: (01795) 532133
Contact: Mr & Mrs Chris & Heather Flood

OPEN All year round

Low season per wk
£147.00–£212.00
High season per wk
£265.00–£353.00

Farmhouse in a rural location in the Kent countryside. Many original features including beams and an inglenook fireplace. Canterbury, Dover and Whitstable nearby.

FAWKHAM, Kent Map ref 2D2

★★★

5 Units
Sleeping 2–5

THREE GATES STABLES HOLIDAY COTTAGES

Speedgate Hill, Fawkham, Longfield DA3 8NJ
T: (01474) 872739
F: (01474) 879455
Contact: Mr Thomas Cramer

Set in beautiful Kent countryside around a converted stable courtyard. Near motorways, airports and convenient for Channel ports (around 1 hour drive). London is only 40 minutes by train or car.

OPEN All year round

Low season per wk
£260.00–£340.00
High season per wk
£300.00–£280.00

FOLKESTONE, Kent Map ref 3B4 *Tourist Information Centre Tel: (01303) 258594*

★★★

3 Units
Sleeping 3–6

PARKVIEW APARTMENTS

1 Grimston Gardens, Folkestone CT20 2PT
T: (01303) 251482
E: paulamcglynn6@hotmail.com
Contact: Miss Paula McGlynn

Modernised, traditional self-contained flats close to Leas, 7 minutes' walk from town centre. Available low season for company relocations etc.

OPEN All year round

OAP and registered disability discounts available.

Low season per wk
Min £130.00
High season per wk
Min £245.00

FUNTINGTON, West Sussex Map ref 2C3

★★★★

1 Unit
Sleeping 4

THE COURTYARD

Adsdean Farm, Funtington, Chichester PO18 9DN
Contact: Ms Claire Hoare, 3 The Cottages,
Adsdean Farm, Funtington, Chichester PO18 9DN
T: (01243) 575464
F: (01243) 575586
E: tim.hoare@farming.co.uk

OPEN All year round
CC: Delta, Mastercard,
Switch, Visa

Low season per wk
£200.00–£300.00
High season per wk
£300.00–£400.00

A delightful farm conversion with its own secluded courtyard. The South Downs on the doorstep, and easy access to the town and local amenties.

GATWICK AIRPORT

See under Horsham

GOUDHURST, Kent Map ref 3B4

★★★★

4 Units
Sleeping 2–8

THREE CHIMNEYS FARM

Bedgebury Road, Goudhurst, Cranbrook TN17 2RA
T: (01580) 212175 & 07785 734639
F: (01580) 212175
E: marionfuller@threechimneysfarm.co.uk
I: www.threechimneysfarm.co.uk
Contact: Mrs Marion Fuller

OPEN All year round
CC: Barclaycard, Delta,
Eurocard, Mastercard,
Switch, Visa

Low season per wk
£200.00–£300.00
High season per wk
£300.00–£600.00

80-acre mixed farm. Spacious cottages in a beautiful location, very quiet but not isolated.

SPECIAL BREAKS

Many establishments offer special promotions and themed breaks. These are highlighted in red. (All such offers are subject to availability.)

GRAFTY GREEN, Kent Map ref 3B4

★★★

1 Unit
Sleeping 3

2 FERMOR COTTAGES
Headcorn Road, Grafty Green, Maidstone ME17 2AN
Contact: Mrs Rosemary Smith, Fermor Cottage,
Headcorn Road, Grafty Green, Maidstone ME17 2AN
T: (01622) 850526
F: (01622) 850526

OPEN All year round

Low season per wk
£210.00–£235.00
High season per wk
£260.00–£270.00

*A 15thC Listed cottage, white weatherboarded, with beams and inglenook fireplace.
Lounge, kitchen/diner, bathroom, 1 double and 1 single bedroom.*

GROOMBRIDGE, East Sussex Map ref 2D2

★★★

3 Units
Sleeping 8

HOLLAMBYS
Eridge Road, Groombridge, Royal Tunbridge Wells TN3 9NJ
T: (01892) 864203
E: ajoad@hollambys.force9.co.uk
Contact: Mr Andrew Joad & I Smith

*Three pretty and comfortable cottages with
wonderful views set in delightful quiet position
on 20-acre working farm. Many National Trust
houses and gardens nearby. Royal Tunbridge
Wells 4.5 miles, Groombridge village 0.75 miles.
Plenty of parking. Linen included.*

OPEN All year round

Nov–Feb one evening meal
included at local pub.

Low season per wk
£150.00–£300.00
High season per wk
£275.00–£375.00

GUILDFORD, Surrey Map ref 2D2 *Tourist Information Centre Tel: (01483) 444333*

★★

36 Units
Sleeping 4–6

UNIVERSITY OF SURREY
Guildford GU2 7XH
Contact: Conference Office, University of Surrey,
Stag Hill, Guildford GU2 5XH
T: (01483) 259093 & 259157
F: (01483) 579266
E: k.stacey@surrey.ac.uk
I: www.surrey.ac.uk/conferences

OPEN Jun–Aug
CC: Visa

High season per wk
£300.00–£360.00

*Modern, self-contained flats or houses for self-catering holidays. One mile from
Guildford with excellent transport links. Guests welcome to use campus facilities.*

HASLEMERE, Surrey Map ref 2C2

★★

1 Unit
Sleeping 4–5

SHEPS HOLLOW
Henley Common, Haslemere GU27 3HB
Contact: Mrs Elizabeth Cattell, Sheps Hollow,
Henley Common, Haslemere GU27 3HB
T: (01428) 653120

OPEN All year round

Low season per wk
£150.00–£200.00
High season per wk
£150.00–£200.00

*Attractive hamlet between Haslemere and Midhurst. Newly converted, beautifully
furnished very small 16thC open-plan barn with minstrels' gallery bedroom. Meals
provided if required.*

AT-A-GLANCE SYMBOLS
Symbols at the end of each accommodation entry give
useful information about services and facilities. A key
to symbols can be found inside the back cover flap.
Keep this open for easy reference.

★★★★
1 Unit
Sleeping 2

STAPLE FARM
Hastingleigh, Ashford TN25 5HF
T: (01233) 750248
F: (01233) 750249
Contact: Mr & Mrs C H Martindale

Stable conversion displaying beams and original features, yet offering all modern amenities. Situated in Area of Outstanding Natural Beauty with excellent walks from front door, including the North Downs Way. Within easy reach of Canterbury, Eurostar terminals, Channel ports of Dover and Folkestone plus many places of historic interest.

OPEN Jun–Sep

Low season per wk
£220.00
High season per wk
£220.00–£300.00

★★
1 Unit
Sleeping 3

DEARS FARM
West End Lane, Henfield BN5 9RD
T: (01273) 492334
Contact: Mrs M G Paul

OPEN Feb–Dec

Low season per wk
Min £175.00
High season per wk
Min £210.00

Cosy self-catering studio apartment in a converted farm building in the grounds of a 15thC timber-framed listed building. Easy parking.

★★★
2 Units
Sleeping 4–5

NEW HALL COTTAGE & NEW HALL HOLIDAY FLAT
New Hall, Small Dole, Henfield BN5 9YJ
Contact: Mrs M W Carreck, New Hall, Small Dole, Henfield BN5 9YJ
T: (01273) 492546 (Answerphone)

Self-contained flat and 17thC cottage attached to manor house. Set in 3.5 acres of mature gardens and surrounded by farmland. Within easy reach of famous Sussex gardens, Nymans, High Beeches, Wakehurst Place, Leonardslee and less than an hour from Wisley.

OPEN All year round

Short breaks available out-of-season: £90 for 2 nights, each extra night £35.

Low season per wk
£150.00–£250.00
High season per wk
£270.00–£315.00

★★★★
1 Unit
Sleeping 4

TYNDALLS COTTAGE
26 Tyndalls, Hindhead GU26 6AP
T: (01428) 609028
F: (01428) 609028
E: tyndallscottage@tinyworld.co.uk
Contact: Mrs Christine Foster

Comfortable cottage adjoining the beautiful Hindhead Commons and Devil's Punchbowl (National Trust), comprising twin bedroom, living room (with double bed settee) opening to dining conservatory, kitchen and bathroom. Wonderful walking country and ideal base for touring Surrey, Sussex and Hampshire. Midway London and south coast. Village facilities 1 mile.

OPEN All year round

Low season per wk
£250.00
High season per wk
£300.00

QUALITY ASSURANCE SCHEME
Star ratings are explained at the back of this guide.

★★★★-★★★★★

2 Units
Sleeping 3–8

Former farm buildings arranged around a courtyard, in the grounds of the owners' 16thC farmhouse, in lush Sussex countryside. Most rooms have exposed beams. Guests enjoy the use of the owners' heated outdoor pool and extensive gardens. Games area, with table tennis and pool table. Fresh flowers and welcome groceries.

WALNUT BARN & WALNUT COTTAGE

Kerves Lane, Horsham RH13 6RJ
Contact: Mrs Sally Cole, Hard's Farm Cottage, Kerves Lane, Horsham RH13 6RJ
T: (01403) 249159
E: jpcole@lineone.net
I: www.sussexholidaycottages.com

OPEN All year round	Low season per wk £315.00–£1,260.00
10% discount for visitors who return within 12 months.	High season per wk £525.00–£2,100.00

🏃 🚗 ◎ Ⅲ ⊙ ⟐ 📻 TV 🗗 ⌂ 🐾 🖐 🗑 🚗 ⌖ ✿ 🐕 SP

HOVE

See under Brighton & Hove

KNOWLTON, Kent Map ref 3C3

★★★-★★★★★

6 Units
Sleeping 2–19

KNOWLTON COURT
The Estate Office, Knowlton Court, Knowlton,
Canterbury CT3 1PT
T: (01304) 842402
F: (01304) 842403
E: knowlton.cottages@farmline.com
Contact: Mrs Mary Smith

OPEN All year round	Low season per wk £140.00–£1,175.00
CC: Delta, Mastercard, Solo, Switch, Visa, Visa Electron	High season per wk £315.00–£1,650.00

Elizabethan house and former farm cottages. Golf courses at Sandwich, Channel Tunnel at Folkestone, port of Dover and cathedral city of Canterbury all easily accessible.

🏔 🏃 Ⅿ ◎ 🚪 ⊙ ⟐ TV 🗗 ⌂ 🖂 ᜘ ✿ 🐕 🏛

LEWES, East Sussex Map ref 2D3 *Tourist Information Centre Tel: (01273) 483448*

★★★

1 Unit
Sleeping 4

5 BUCKHURST CLOSE
Lewes BN7 2ES
Contact: Mrs S Foulds, 66 Houndean Rise, Lewes BN7 1EJ
T: (01273) 474755
F: (01273) 474755

OPEN All year round	Low season per wk Min £120.00
	High season per wk Max £210.00

Modern terraced house, fully equipped. Sleeps 4 in 2 bedrooms. Small garden, parking space. Easy walking distance to town. Five minutes' drive to station or Glyndebourne.

◎ 🚪 ⟐ 📻 TV ⌂ 🖂 🚗 ✿ 🐕

LITTLEHAMPTON, West Sussex Map ref 2D3

★★★

1 Unit
Sleeping 4

RACING GREENS
Littlehampton BN17 5LQ
Contact: 70 South Terrace, Littlehampton BN17 5LQ
T: (01903) 732972 & 07887 572098
F: (01903) 732932
E: urban.surfer@easynet.co.uk
Contact: Ms Edith Ballantine

OPEN All year round	Low season per wk £225.00–£275.00
CC: Barclaycard, Delta, Mastercard, Switch, Visa	High season per wk £225.00–£275.00

A charming, private self-catering apartment entered through a herb garden for your exclusive use, right on beachfront.

🏃 ◎ 🚪 ⊙ ⟐ TV 🗗 ⌂ 🖾 ✿ 🐾 SP

CHECK THE MAPS

The colour maps at the front of this guide show all the cities, towns and villages for which you will find accommodation entries.
Refer to the town index to find the page on which they are listed.

LOWER BEEDING, West Sussex Map ref 2D3

★★-★★★★

3 Units
Sleeping 4-6

BLACK COTTAGE, THE LITTLE BARN & THE OLD DAIRY
Newells Farmhouse, Newells Lane, Lower Beeding,   OPEN All year round
Horsham RH13 6LN
Contact: Mrs V Storey, Newells Farm,
Newells Farmhouse, Newells Lane, Lower Beeding,
Horsham RH13 6LN
T: (01403) 891326
F: (01403) 891530

Low season per wk
£200.00-£300.00
High season per wk
£230.00-£450.00

Secluded 19thC cottage, sleeping 4, lovely views. Two newly-converted cottages in farmyard, each sleeping 6. All with gardens. 650-acre arable and woodland farm.

🅰🕭◎🖪🎢.☉🖪🖵🖳📺🗔🛆🗝🦮🅿♙🖎❄🐾🐎 SP

MINSTER-IN-THANET, Kent Map ref 3C3

★★★

1 Unit
Sleeping 2

DURLOCK LODGE
Durlock, Minster-in-Thanet, Ramsgate CT12 4HD
Contact: Mr David Sworder, Durlock Lodge, Durlock,
Minster-in-Thanet, Ramsgate CT12 4HD
T: (01843) 821219
E: david@durlocklodge.co.uk
I: www.durlocklodge.co.uk

OPEN All year round
CC: Amex, Barclaycard,
Delta, Mastercard, Solo,
Switch, Visa, Visa Electron

Low season per wk
£175.00-£250.00
High season per wk
£250.00-£270.00

Quality accommodation in charming historical village, shops and restaurants within walking distance. Beaches and golf courses within 5 mile drive.

🐎◎🖉🎢.☉🖪🖵🖳📺🗨🛆🗝🦮🅿♙❄🐾🐎 SP

NUTLEY, East Sussex Map ref 2D3

★★-★★★

10 Units
Sleeping 4-5

Former smallholding overlooking open countryside and Ashdown Forest. Shower room, kitchen/diner/ lounge. Fully equipped wheelchair. Pet and smoker-friendly cottages available. Spare campbeds. Ideally situated for London, castles, gardens and coast. Both Friday and Saturday turnaround.

WHITEHOUSE FARM HOLIDAY COTTAGES

Whitehouse Farm, Horney Common, Nutley,
Uckfield TN22 3EE
T: (01825) 712377
F: (01825) 712377
E: keith.g.r.wilson@btinternet.com
I: www.streets-ahead.com/whitehousefarm
Contact: Mr Keith Wilson

OPEN All year round
CC: Barclaycard, Delta,
Mastercard, Visa

Low season per wk
£220.00-£306.00
High season per wk
£306.00-£409.00

🅰🐎◎🖪🎢.☉🖪🖵📺🗔🛆🗨🗝🅿♙🐎🕭 SP🏨

PEVENSEY BAY, East Sussex Map ref 3B4

★★★★

1 Unit
Sleeping 2-4

This delightful 2 bed chalet-style bungalow is situated right on the beach at Pevensey Bay. Located in the heart of 1066 Country with its rich history and beautiful countryside, Sunpatch offers you the opportunity to tour this fascinating area, or simply relax in comfort by the sea.

SUNPATCH

254 Coast Road, Pevensey Bay, Pevensey BN24 6NT
Contact: Mr Lindsay Davis, Willow Cottage,
8 Kingswood Way, Selsdon, South Croydon CR2 8QP
T: (020) 8651 2444 & 07711 616550
E: lindsay.davis@btinternet.com
I: www.beachbungalow.freeservers.com

OPEN Mar-Oct

Low season per wk
£295.00-£350.00
High season per wk
£350.00-£450.00

🐎◎🖪🎢.☉🖪🖵🖳📺🗔🛆🗨✂🗝🅿♙

TOWN INDEX

This can be found at the back of this guide. If you know where you want to stay, the index will give you the page number listing accommodation in your chosen town, city or village.

PLAXTOL, Kent Map ref 3B4

★★★
1 Unit
Sleeping 5

GOLDING HOP FARM COTTAGE

Bewley Lane, Plaxtol, Sevenoaks TN15 0PS
Contact: Mrs J Vincent, Golding Hop Farm,
Bewley Lane, Plaxtol, Sevenoaks TN15 0PS
T: (01732) 885432
F: (01732) 885432
E: adrian@mvvincent.freeserve.co.uk
I: www.mvvincent.freeserve.co.uk

OPEN All year round

Low season per wk
Min £200.00
High season per wk
Max £420.00

12-acre cobnut farm. South-facing cottage with garden and all modern conveniences. Quiet position but not isolated.

ROCHESTER, Kent Map ref 3B3 *Tourist Information Centre Tel: (01634) 843666*

★★★★
1 Unit
Sleeping 3

NEWLANDS FARM HOUSE

Fenn Corner, St Mary Hoo, Rochester ME3 8RE
T: (01634) 253083 (Weekday daytime) & 272388 (All Other times)
F: (01634) 255053
E: knweld@aol.com
Contact: Mrs Patricia Kelly

Small converted grain store overlooking pond and stableyard. RSPB site nearby, suit bird-watchers, walkers, cyclists. Five minutes to unbroken views over Thames estuary, 6 miles to Rochester. Chatham Dockyard World Heritage Centre, 25 miles London.

3 night stays available Oct-Jan (excl Christmas and New Year).

Low season per wk
£250.00–£295.00
High season per wk
£325.00–£395.00

Rating
Applied For
4 Units
Sleeping 6

STABLE COTTAGES

Fenn Croft, Newlands Farm Road, St Mary's Hoo,
Rochester ME3 8QS
T: (01634) 272439
F: (01634) 272205
Contact: Mr & Mrs Jason Symonds

Low season per wk
£150.00–£240.00
High season per wk
£180.00–£400.00

Family-run. Twenty acres of secluded grounds. Overlooking Thames. Access to motorways, ports, London 45 minutes. Ideal base for walking, bird-watching, sightseeing. Warm welcome.

ROTTINGDEAN, East Sussex Map ref 2D3

★★★
1 Unit
Sleeping 4–5
Ad p???

HORSESHOE COTTAGE

Whipping Post Lane, Rottingdean, Brighton BN2 7HZ
Contact: Best of Brighton & Sussex Cottages Ltd,
Windmill Lodge, Vicarage Lane, Rottingdean, Brighton
BN2 7HD
T: (01273) 308779 & 07956 662457
F: (01273) 300266
E: brightoncottages@pavilion.co.uk
I: www.bestofbrighton.co.uk

Low season per wk
£355.00–£400.00
High season per wk
£400.00–£535.00

Charming 2-bedroomed, 2 bathroom flint cottage in the centre of this village and close to the seafront and shops, pond and church. Sleeps 4/5 people.

ROYAL TUNBRIDGE WELLS, Kent Map ref 2D2 *Tourist Information Centre Tel: (01892) 515675*

★★★
1 Unit
Sleeping 8

BROAD OAK HOUSE

9 Linden Park Road, Royal Tunbridge Wells TN2 5QL
T: (01892) 619065 & 619064
F: (01892) 619066
E: tina@tlctraing.co.uk
Contact: Ms Tina Seymour

Low season per wk
£385.00–£575.00
High season per wk
£445.00–£675.00

Newly refurbished self contained top floor flat in Victorian house. Quiet location within minutes of the Pantiles. Three double bedrooms. Sleeps 8. Off street parking.

COLOUR MAPS Colour maps at the front of this guide pinpoint all places under which you will find accommodation listed.

★★★

2 Units
Sleeping 2–4

FORD COTTAGE

Linden Park Road, Royal Tunbridge Wells TN2 5QL
Contact: Mrs Wendy Cusdin, Ford Cottage,
Linden Park Road, Royal Tunbridge Wells TN2 5QL
T: (01892) 531419 (Answerphone)
E: fordcottage@tinyworld.co.uk

Ford Cottage is a picturesque Victorian cottage, 3 minutes' walk from Pantiles. Offer 2 self-contained studio flats – own front doors and sleeping 2 and 4 people. Fully fitted kitchens with en suites and showers. Linen and towels provided. Off-street parking. Ideal for visiting many local gardens, castles and historic houses.

OPEN All year round

Short breaks available–terms on request.

Low season per wk
£220.00–£280.00
High season per wk
£250.00–£320.00

★★★★

6 Units
Sleeping 2–4

ITARIS PROPERTIES LIMITED

Itaris Properties, 60 Mount Ephraim,
Royal Tunbridge Wells TN4 8BB
Contact: Mr Edward Chattell, Itaris Properties Ltd,
12 Mount Ephraim, Royal Tunbridge Wells TN4 8AS
T: (01892) 511065
F: (01892) 540171
E: aechattell@msn.com
I: www.itaris.co.uk

Royal Tunbridge Wells is surrounded by beautiful and unspoilt countryside and is the ideal location for a short break or relaxing holiday. Our 6 self-contained and fully equipped, self-catering holiday apartments, sleeping 2-4 persons, are situated in the very heart of Tunbridge Wells within walking distance of its many amenities.

OPEN All year round

Low season per wk
£210.00–£231.00
High season per wk
£310.00–£330.00

ST MARGARET'S BAY, Kent Map ref 3C4

★★★★

5 Units
Sleeping 4–6

REACH COURT FARM COTTAGES

Reach Court Farm, St Margaret's Bay, Dover CT15 6AQ
T: (01304) 852159
F: (01304) 853902
Contact: Mrs J Mitchell

OPEN All year round

Low season per wk
£185.00–£290.00
High season per wk
£240.00–£420.00

Four Star barn conversion in centre of farm. Perfect rural setting, short walk to bay and 'White Cliffs'. Village nearby. Full brochure on request.

SELSEY, West Sussex Map ref 2C3

★★

1 Unit
Sleeping 2

STABLE ANNEXE

Post Cottage, Rectory Lane, Selsey,
Chichester PO20 9DU
Contact: Mr & Mrs Kenneth Child, Post Cottage,
Rectory Lane, Selsey, Chichester PO20 9DU
T: (01243) 604264

OPEN All year round

Low season per wk
Min £135.00
High season per wk
Max £205.00

The converted thatch stables is built of flint and brick and dates from 1745.

SOUTH CHAILEY, East Sussex Map ref 2D3

★★★

2 Units
Sleeping 3–6

FANTASY COTTAGES

Fantasy, Kilnwood Lane, South Chailey, Lewes BN8 4AU
T: (01273) 400445 (Answerphone) & 401619
F: (01273) 400445
E: comesailing@btinternet.com
Contact: Mrs Alison Bullar

OPEN May–Sep

Low season per wk
£200.00–£325.00
High season per wk
£310.00–£475.00

Converted from Chailey Potteries in attractive cottage garden. Mix antique/pine furniture. Well equipped kitchens. Good location for walking, cycling, riding on Sussex Downs/Ashdown Forest.

TENTERDEN, Kent Map ref 3B4

★★★★

1 Unit
Sleeping 5

Listed beamed cottage on residential side of tree-lined High Street. Comfortable 'home from home', 1 single, 2 double bedrooms, cot available. Rear secluded courtyard. Close to all amenities, including steam railway and leisure centre. Children welcome. Sorry no pets, no smoking. Good centre for exploring Kent and East Sussex. Brochure available.

QUINCE COTTAGE
143 High Street, Tenterden TN30 6JS
Contact: Mrs H E Crease, Laurelhurst, 38 Ashford Road, Tenterden TN30 6LL
T: (01580) 765636
F: (01580) 765922
E: quincott@zetnet.co.uk
I: quincecottage.co.uk

OPEN All year round

On bookings for 2 or more consecutive weeks we are happy to give 5% discount.

Low season per wk
£220.00–£320.00
High season per wk
£360.00–£410.00

TUNBRIDGE WELLS

See under Royal Tunbridge Wells

WALTON-ON-THAMES, Surrey Map ref 2D2

★★★★

1 Unit
Sleeping 4

GUEST WING
30 Mayfield Gardens, Walton-on-Thames KT12 5PP
Contact: Mr A R Dominy, 30 Mayfield Gardens,
Walton-on-Thames KT12 5PP
T: (01932) 241223

OPEN All year round

Low season per wk
£235.00–£280.00
High season per wk
£280.00–£310.00

Attractive 2-bedroom, self-contained wing of neo-Georgian house in residential cul-de-sac, adjacent to Walton station. Ideal for London, Hampton Court, Windsor and motorway network.

WHITSTABLE, Kent Map ref 3B3 *Tourist Information Centre Tel: (01227) 275482*

★★★

1 Unit
Sleeping 6

19 ACTON ROAD
Whitstable CT5
Contact: Ms Stephanie Brunton, Georgia,
17 Pierpoint Road, Whitstable CT5 4NW
T: (01227) 272206
E: stormbrunton@clara.co.uk
I: www.whitstableaccommodation.co.uk

OPEN All year round

Low season per wk
£180.00–£245.00
High season per wk
£255.00–£400.00

Three bedroom holiday cottage in quiet residential road. Close to town centre and seafront.

★★★

1 Unit
Sleeping 6

TRAPPERS END
Whitstable
Contact: Mrs J M Reed, 11 Woodlands Avenue,
New Malden KT3 3UL
T: (020) 8942 0342 & 07710 591735 (Mobile)
F: (020) 8942 0342
E: janette.reed@cwcom.net

OPEN Apr, Jun–Sep, Dec
CC: Barclaycard, Delta,
Mastercard, Visa

Low season per wk
Min £500.00
High season per wk
Max £600.00

Detached house overlooking Whitstable. Fresh linen and towels provided, central heating, dishwasher, video/TV.

MAP REFERENCES The map references refer to the colour maps at the front of this guide. The first figure is the map number; the letter and figure which follow indicate the grid reference on the map.

★★

3 Units
Sleeping 2–5

TORRINGTON HOLIDAY FLATS

60 Manor Road, Worthing BN11 4SL
T: (01903) 238582 & 07860 699268 (Mobile)
F: (01903) 230266
Contact: Mrs Elsden & Mary Fitzgerald

Handsome Edwardian house. Quiet conservation area. Five minutes' level walk to sea and shops. Spacious well furnished flats in excellent condition.

OPEN All year round

Low season per wk
£140.00–£230.00
High season per wk
£140.00–£300.00

USE YOUR *i*s

There are more than 550 Tourist Information Centres throughout England offering friendly help with accommodation and holiday ideas as well as suggestions of places to visit and things to do. There may well be a centre in your home town which can help you before you set out. You'll find addresses in the local Phone Book.

A brief guide to the main Towns and Villages offering accommodation in the

South East

A ALFRISTON, EAST SUSSEX - Old village in the Cuckmere Valley and a former smugglers' haunt. The 14th C Clergy House was the first building to be bought by the National Trust. Spacious 14th C St Andrew's church is known as the 'Cathedral of the South Downs' and the 13th C Star Inn is one of the oldest in England.

• **ARUNDEL, WEST SUSSEX** - Picturesque, historic town on the River Arun, dominated by Arundel Castle, home of the Dukes of Norfolk. There are many 18th C houses, the Wildfowl and Wetlands Centre and Museum and Heritage Centre.

• **ASHFORD, KENT** - Once a market centre for the farmers of the Weald of Kent and Romney Marsh. The town centre has a number of Tudor and Georgian houses and a museum. Eurostar trains stop at Ashford International station.

B BATTLE, EAST SUSSEX - The Abbey at Battle was built on the site of the Battle of Hastings, when William defeated Harold II and so became the Conqueror in 1066. The museum has a fine collection relating to the Sussex iron industry and there is a social history museum - Buckleys Yesterday's World.

• **BEARSTED, KENT** - Many old houses and oasts surround the village green, which is still used for cricket and football. Nearby is Leeds Castle.

• **BRIGHTON & HOVE, EAST SUSSEX** - Brighton's attractions include the Royal Pavilion, Volks Electric Railway, Sea Life Centre and Marina Village, Conference Centre, 'The Lanes' and several theatres.

• **BROADSTAIRS, KENT** - Popular seaside resort with numerous sandy bays. Charles Dickens spent his summers at Bleak House where he wrote parts of 'David Copperfield'. The Dickens Festival is held in June, when many people wear Dickensian costume.

C CANTERBURY, KENT - Place of pilgrimage since the martyrdom of Becket in 1170 and the site of Canterbury Cathedral. Visit St Augustine's Abbey, St Martin's (the oldest church in England), Royal Museum and Art Gallery and the Canterbury Tales. Nearby is Howletts Wild Animal Park. Good shopping centre.

• **CATERHAM, SURREY** - Town on the North Downs 6 miles south of Croydon.

• **CHARCOTT, KENT** - A pretty, rural hamlet set in the heart of the Kent countryside. Convenient for Hever Castle, Chartwell, Penshurst Place and Chiddingstone Castle.

• **CHICHESTER, WEST SUSSEX** - The county town of West Sussex with a beautiful Norman cathedral. Noted for its Georgian architecture but also has modern buildings like the Festival Theatre. Surrounded by places of interest, including Fishbourne Roman Palace, Weald and Downland Open-Air Museum and West Dean Gardens.

• **CHILHAM, KENT** - Extremely pretty village of mostly Tudor and Jacobean houses. The village rises to the spacious square with the castle and the 15th C church.

• **COMPTON, WEST SUSSEX** - Brick and flint village on the West Sussex/Hampshire border, with mainly Victorian church.

• **CRANBROOK, KENT** - Old town, a centre for the weaving industry in the 15th C. The 72-ft high Union Mill is a 3-storey windmill, still in working order. Sissinghurst Gardens (National Trust) nearby.

D DENTON, KENT - Hamlet of tile-hung houses and a little Early English church reached via a grassy track.

• **DORKING, SURREY** - Ancient market town and a good centre for walking, delightfully set between Box Hill and the Downs. Denbies Wine Estate - England's largest vineyard - is situated here.

E EASTBOURNE, EAST SUSSEX - One of the finest, most elegant resorts on the south-east coast situated beside Beachy Head. Long promenade, well known Carpet Gardens on the seafront, Devonshire Park tennis and indoor leisure complex, theatres, Towner Art Gallery, 'How We Lived Then' Museum of Shops and Social History.

• **EPSOM, SURREY** - Horse races have been held on the slopes of Epsom Downs for centuries. The racecourse is the home of the world-famous Derby. Many famous old homes are here, among them the 17th C Waterloo House.

F FAVERSHAM, KENT - Historic town, once a port, dating back to prehistoric times. Abbey Street has more than 50 listed buildings. Roman and Anglo-Saxon finds and other exhibits can be seen in a museum in the Maison Dieu at Ospringe. Fleur de Lys Heritage Centre.

• **FAWKHAM, KENT** - Village with small, pretty church set amongst trees. Nearby is the famous motor-racing circuit of Brands Hatch.

• **FOLKESTONE, KENT** - Popular resort. The town has a fine promenade, the Leas, from where orchestral Horse-racing at Westenhanger Racecourse nearby.

G GOUDHURST, KENT - Village on a hill surmounted by a square-towered church with fine views of orchards and hopfields. Achieved prosperity through weaving in the Middle Ages. Finchcocks houses a living museum of historic early keyboard instruments.

• **GROOMBRIDGE, EAST SUSSEX** - The Kent/East Sussex boundary divides the old village from the new. A triangular village green is flanked on one side by a church beyond which lies the 17th C Groombridge Place, set within its large medieval moat, with gardens open to the public.

• **GUILDFORD, SURREY** - Bustling town with Lewis Carroll connections and many historic monuments, one of which is the Guildhall clock jutting out over the old High Street. The modern cathedral occupies a commanding position on Stag Hill.

H HASLEMERE, SURREY - Town set in hilly, wooded countryside, much of it in the care of the National Trust. Its attractions include the educational museum and the annual music festival.

• **HENFIELD, WEST SUSSEX** - Ancient village with many old houses and good shopping facilities, on a ridge of high ground overlooking the Adur Valley. Views to the South Downs.

• **HINDHEAD, SURREY** - One of Surrey's best known beauty spots and good for views over Sussex and the Weald. Much of the woodland and heath belongs to the National Trust.

- **HORSHAM, WEST SUSSEX** - Busy town with much modern development but still retaining its old character. The museum in Causeway House is devoted chiefly to local history and the agricultural life of the county.

K KNOWLTON, KENT - Kentish hamlet within easy reach of Sandwich, Deal and Canterbury, with Knowlton Court, an Elizabethan house (not open) and the flint church of St Clement, restored in 1855.

L LEWES, EAST SUSSEX - Historic county town with Norman castle. The steep High Street has mainly Georgian buildings. There is a folk museum at Anne of Cleves House and the archaeological museum is in Barbican House.

- **LITTLEHAMPTON, WEST SUSSEX** - Ancient port at the mouth of the River Arun, now a popular holiday resort, offering flat, sandy beaches, sailing, fishing and boat trips. The Sussex Downs are a short walk inland.

- **LOWER BEEDING, WEST SUSSEX** - Close to St Leonard's Forest, once a royal hunting ground. The area is also well-known for its hammer ponds, used when the iron was smelted here. Leonardslee Gardens are especially beautiful in spring and autumn.

M MINSTER-IN-THANET, KENT - Small town in rural setting has a noteworthy parish church with 15th C choir stalls.

N NUTLEY, EAST SUSSEX - Richard II had a hunting lodge at Nutley, which he used when hunting in the Ashdown Forest. To the north of the village is Nutley Mill, built in 1690.

P PEVENSEY BAY, EAST SUSSEX - Small but popular resort, with spacious beach, near the village of Pevensey.

- **PLAXTOL, KENT** - Village standing high above the Kent Weald, with a 17th C church in the centre and a rare medieval domestic house.

R ROCHESTER, KENT- Ancient cathedral city on the River Medway. Has many places of interest connected with Charles Dickens (who lived nearby) including the fascinating Dickens Centre. Also massive castle overlooking the river and Guildhall Museum.

- **ROTTINGDEAN, EAST SUSSEX** - The quiet High Street contains a number of fine old buildings and the village pond and green are close by.

- **ROYAL TUNBRIDGE WELLS, KENT** - This 'Royal' town became famous as a spa in the 17th C and much of its charm is retained, as in the Pantiles, a shaded walk lined with elegant shops. Heritage attraction 'A Day at the Wells'. Excellent shopping centre.

S SELSEY, WEST SUSSEX - Almost surrounded by water, with the English Channel on two sides and an inland lake, once Pagham Harbour, and the Brook on the other two. Ideal for yachting, swimming, fishing and wildlife.

- **SOUTH CHAILEY, EAST SUSSEX** - Although not far from the busy market towns of Lewes and Haywards Heath, South Chailey is close to the North Common Nature Reserve, the attractive Sheffield Park Gardens (National Trust) and the Bluebell Railway.

- **ST MARGARET'S BAY, KENT** - Traditional starting and arrival point for the grease-covered cross-Channel swimmers. North and east of the bay, towards Kingsdown, the National Trust has safeguarded almost 300 acres of farmland, including a magnificent clifftop walk.

T TENTERDEN, KENT - Most attractive market town with a broad main street full of 16th C houses and shops. The tower of the 15th C parish church is the finest in Kent. Fine antiques centre.

W WALTON-ON-THAMES, SURREY - Busy town beside the Thames, retaining a distinctive atmosphere despite being only 12 miles from central London. Close to Hampton Court Palace, Sandown Park racecourse and Claremont Landscape Garden (National Trust), Esher.

- **WHITSTABLE, KENT** - Seaside resort and yachting centre on Kent's north shore. The beach is shingle and there are the usual seaside amenities and entertainments and a museum.

- **WORTHING, WEST SUSSEX** - Town in the West Sussex countryside and by the South Coast, with excellent shopping and many pavement cafes and restaurants. Attractions include the award-winning Museum and Art Gallery, beautiful gardens, pier, elegant town houses, Cissbury Ring hill fort and the South Downs.

www.travelengland.org.uk

Log on to travelengland.org.uk and discover something different around every corner. Meander through pages for ideas of places to visit and things to do. Spend time in each region and discover the diversity – from busy vibrant cities to rural village greens; rugged peaks to gentle rolling hills; dramatic coastline to idyllic sandy beaches. England might be a small country but it is brimming with choice and opportunity. Visit www.travelengland.org.uk and see for yourself.

England

Self-Catering
Agencies

This section of the guide lists agencies which have a selection of holiday homes to let in various parts of the country. Some agencies specialise in a particular area or region while others have properties in all parts of England.

The agencies listed here are grouped first into those who have had all properties assessed by the English Tourism Council and secondly into those who have had at least 50% of their properties assessed by the English Tourism Council. This second section is then divided into two sub-sections; agencies with 75% or more properties assessed followed by those with between 50% and 75% of properties assessed.

To obtain further information on individual properties please contact the agency or agencies direct, indicating the time of year when the accommodation is required, the number of people to be accommodated and any preferred locations.

The prices shown in each agency entry are weekly terms per unit.

The symbol [T] in an agency entry means that accommodation may be booked with that agency through a bona fide travel agent.

TOTALLY QUALITY ASSESSED

The agencies in this first section have had **all their properties assessed** by the English Tourism Council.

Cumbrian Cottages

7 The Crescent
Carlisle, Cumbria CA1 1OW
T: (01228) 599960
F: (01228) 599970
E: enquiries@cumbrian-cottages.co.uk
I: www.cumbrian-cottages.co.uk

Short breaks also available.

Low season
From £150-£890

High season
From £260-£1,950

Three hundred luxury cottages, houses and apartments throughout the Lake District, Eden Valley and Cumbria. We can offer secluded cottages sleeping two, to properties in the heart of towns sleeping 16. Some have lake views and most of our properties have leisure club facilities available. Many properties accept pets. All electric, gas, fuel and bed linen included. Fully ETC assessed from 3-5 Stars.

Diana Bullivant – North Cornwall

South Winds, Trebell Green, Bodmin,Cornwall PL30 5HR
T: (01208) 831336
F: (01208) 831336
E: diana@dbullivant.fsnet.co.uk
I: www.cornwall–online.co.uk/diana–bullivant
Short breaks also available.

Low season
(November-April)
£185-£550

High season
(July-August)
£340-£1,350

Excellent choice of high quality holiday homes from beach houses to country cottages, all under personal management. I can organise meals, babysitting and help you have the best holiday ever.

'Heart of the Lakes' and 'Cottage Life'

Fisherbeck Mill,
Old Lake Road, Ambleside,
Cumbria LA22 0DH
T: (015394) 32321
F: (015394) 33251
E: info@heartofthelakes.co.uk
I: www.heartofthelakes.co.uk

Short breaks also available

Low season
(November-March,
excluding Christmas
and New Year)
£150-£600

High season
(April-October,
plus Christmas
and New Year)
£200-£1,600

Wide selection of well presented holiday homes throughout central Lakeland, some with lake views, many with gardens. Rural locations or village centre properties available. Ideal for holidays at any time of the year. Cottages, apartments and houses all shown in our fully illustrated colour brochure, or visit our website.

ACCESSIBILITY
Look for the 🅑 🅑 🅑 symbols which indicate accessibility for wheelchair users. A list of establishments is at the front of this guide.

Island Cottage Holidays - Isle of Wight

T: (01929) 480080
F: (01929) 481070
E: enq@islandcottageholidays.com
I: www.islandcottageholidays.com
Short breaks also available. T

Low season
(October-May)
£129-£495

High season
(June-September)
£179-£1,200

Charming cottages in delightful rural surroundings and close to the sea. Beautiful views - attractive gardens. Carefully selected individual cottages situated throughout the Isle of Wight. Properties sleeping 1-14. All properties assessed for quality by the English Tourism Council – 3-5 Stars.

The Lakeland Cottage Company

Waterside House,
Newby Bridge,
Cumbria LA12 8AN
T: (015395) 30024
F: (015395) 31932
E: John@lakelandcottageco.com
I: www.lakelandcottageco.com
Out of season short breaks also available.

Low season
From £220-£2,700

High season
From £300-£2,700

Fine cottages in delightful locations south and central Lakeland. Snug romantic retreats and grand houses sleeping 2/21, prepared with pride and care. Free or discounted leisure club. To help in your choice we produce a beautiful colour brochure and CD ROM with virtual tours of each property and a film of the lake district.

Lakelovers Holiday Homes

Belmont House, Lake Road,
Bowness-on-Windermere,
Cumbria LA23 3BJ
T: (015394) 88855
F: (015394) 88857
E: bookings@lakelovers.co.uk
I: www.lakelovers.co.uk
Short breaks also available

Low season
(November-March)
excluding Christmas
and New Year
£130-£500

High season
(April-October)
including Christmas
and New Year
£190-£1,500

For the ultimate in Lakeland holidays, Lakelovers have it all, from traditional farmhouses sleeping up to 14 steeped in character, to luxury modern apartments sleeping 2, complete with private tennis facilities. Over 140 retreats to choose from. We pride ourselves on hand picking individual properties equipped to the highest standard to suit every taste and pocket. We include FREE leisure club membership with every holiday.

WHERE TO STAY
Please mention this guide when making your booking.

Marsdens Cottage Holidays

2 The Square,
Braunton,
North Devon EX33 2JB
T: (01271) 813777
F: (01271) 813664
E: holidays@marsdens.co.uk
I: www.marsdens.co.uk
Short breaks also available.

Low season
(October-March)
£129-£1,632

High season
(April-September)
£302-£2,226

For the finest holiday homes on North Devon's spectacular National Trust coastline, Exmoor and rural Devon, look no further than the West Country's largest agency of assessed holiday cottages. It's no wonder so many of our customers return year after year. Free brochure or visit our website with all our properties, online availability and booking at www.marsdens.co.uk

Suffolk Secrets

7 Frenze Road, Diss, IP22 4PA
T: (01379) 651297
F: (01379) 641555
I: www.suffolk-secrets.co.uk
Short breaks also available.

Low season
(November-April)
excluding Christmas
& New Year
£165-£450

High season
(May-October)
£330-£850

Discover the unspoilt Heritage Coast from Woodbridge to Southwold, including Aldeburgh, Snape and the world renowned Minsmere nature reserve. Select and book on-line or phone for a brochure.

COMMITTED TO ETC QUALITY ASSURANCE

The agencies in this section are divided into two sections. Firstly those which have had 75% or more properties assessed and secondly those which have had at least 50% of properties assessed. It is advisable to enquire whether or not the property you choose has been assessed by the ETC at the time of booking.

MORE THAN 75% OF PROPERTIES ASSESSED

Mackay's Agency

30 Frederick Street, Edinburgh EH2 2JR
T: (0131) 225 3539 24-hour brochure line: (0131) 226 4364
F: (0131) 226 5284
E: etc@mackays-scotland.co.uk
I: www.mackays-scotland.co.uk
Short breaks also available. [T]

Low season
(November-April)
£135-£375

High season
(May-October)
£250-£595

A selection of cottages, houses and farmhouses throughout the North of England and the Borders. Personally inspected properties, ideal for families, walking or fishing holidays.

IMPORTANT NOTE Information on accommodation listed in this guide has been supplied by the proprietors. As changes may occur you are advised to check details at the time of booking.

Norfolk Holiday Homes

62 Westgate, Hunstanton,
Norfolk, PE36 5EL
T: (01485) 534267
F: (01485) 535230
E: shchol@birdsnorfolkholidayhomes.co.uk
I: www.norfolkholidayhomes-birds.co.uk

Low season
(January-May)
(September-December)
£200-£350

High season
(June-September)
£350-£1,500

A wide and varied selection of properties in this lovely area ideally situated for exploring. Superb for families and couples. Disabled guests and pets welcome. Discounts available. Short Breaks. All close to holiday amenities either by foot, car or bus. Sleeping 2-10.

Rumsey Holiday Homes

2, Banks Road, Sandbanks, Poole BH13 7QD
T: (01202) 707357
F: (01202) 701955
E: info@rhh.org
I: www.rhh.org

Low season
(Varies)
£140-£600

High season
(9 weeks July-August)
£225-£1,700

Around 100 of the best houses, cottages, bungalows and flats in and around Poole. A unique selection directly in front of the award winning Sandbanks Beaches. Over 80% of units ETC inspected.

BETWEEN 50% AND 75% OF PROPERTIES ASSESSED

Cornish Cottage Holidays

The Old Turnpike Dairy, Godolphin Road, Helston, Cornwall TR13 8QL
T: (01326) 573808
F: (01326) 564992
E: inquiry@cornishcottageholidays.co.uk
I: www.cornishcottageholidays.co.uk

Short breaks also available.

Low season
(October-Easter)
£100-£300

High season
(Easter-October)
£250-£1,000

One of Cornwall's leading agencies, we have an extensive portfolio of self-catering properties to let. Our cottages offer comfortable accommodation in a variety of situations. All personally or Tourism Council Assessed.

Cottage in the Country

Forest Gate, Frog Lane,
Milton-under-Wychwood,
Oxfordshire OX7 6JZ
T: (01993) 831495/831743
F: (01993) 831095
E: cottage@cottageinthecountry.co.uk
I: www.cottageinthecountry.co.uk

Short breaks also available. [T]

Low season
(November-March)
£165-£1,200

High season
(April-October)
£200-£1,200

Gentle Cotswold villages – Stow, Blockley, The Slaughters; bustling markets towns – Banbury, Abingdon; historic cities – Oxford, Windsor, Worcester, Stratford or tranquil countryside...wherever, you'll never be far from our rich English Heritage. Personally known properties to help you with your choice. For town properties also see www.stayintown.co.uk

English Tourism Council

English Tourism Council
assessed
Accommodation

On the following pages you will find an exclusive listing of every self-catering establishment in England that has been assessed for quality by the English Tourism Council.

The information includes brief contact details for each place to stay, together with its Star rating. The listing also shows if an establishment has a National Accessible rating (see the front of the guide for further information).

More detailed information on all the places shown in blue can be found in the regional sections (where establishments have paid to have their details included). To find these entries please refer to the appropriate regional section, or look in the town index at the back of this guide.

The list which follows was compiled slightly later than the regional sections. For this reason you may find that, in a few instances, a Star rating may differ between the two sections. This list contains the most up-to-date information and was correct at the time of going to press.

LONDON

INNER LONDON
E1

Hamlet UK Ltd ★★–★★★
Contact: Miss R Naufal, Hamlet UK Ltd, 74 Onslow Gardens, Muswell Hill, London N10 3JX
T: (020) 8883 0024
E: hamlet_uk@globalnet.co.uk
I: www.users.globalnet.co.uk/~hamlet_uk

E3

The Flat ★★★
Contact: Mrs Alice Sielle, The Flat, 43 Tredegar Square, Bow, London E3 5AE
T: (020) 8981 2869

E11

Greenstone Mews ★★★
Contact: Mrs Teresa Farnham, 46 Preston Drive, Wanstead, London E11 2JB
T: (020) 8530 6729 & 8989 5923
E: stayfarnham@aol.com

E14

Bridge House–London Docklands ★★★★
Contact: Mr J K Graham, 31 Falcon Way, London E14 9UP
T: (020) 7538 8980 & 07973 857187
F: (020) 7538 8980
E: johnkgraham31@hotmail.com
I: www.johnkgraham.com

River Thames Apartment ★★★★
Contact: Mrs Greta Paull, 35 Cheyne Avenue, South Woodford, London E18 2DP
T: (020) 8530 2336
F: (020) 8530 2336

Riverside ★★★★
Contact: Ms Christine James, Riverside, 5 Fairfield Drive, Codsall, Wolverhampton WV8 2AE
T: (01902) 843545 & 07967 375747
F: (01902) 843545
E: christine@capstansq.fsnet.co.uk
I: www.capstansq.fsnet.co.uk

EC1

Citadines Barbican ★★★
Contact: Miss Anabala Almaila, 18-21 Northumberland Avenue, London WC2N 5BJ
T: (020) 7766 3800
F: (020) 7766 3766
E: reslondon@citadines.com
I: www.citadines.com

N1

Danbury Court Estates Rating Applied For
Contact: Mr Peter Edgar, 26 Danbury Street, Islington, London N1 8JU
T: 070 7870 0600
F: 070 7870 0604
E: peter@danburycourt.co.uk

Old Street Penthouse ★★
Contact: Ms Karen Walker, London Holiday Accommodation, 34 Brunel House, Guinness Trust, Stamford Hill, London N16 5TF
T: (020) 8800 5908
E: sales@londonholiday.co.uk
I: www.londonholiday.co.uk

Ray's Apartments ★★–★★★
Contact: Mr Raymond Dwek, 28 Abbottshall Avenue, Southgate, London N14 7JX
T: 07944 313768
E: raydwek@shalom36.co.uk

N7

Carena Holiday Accommodation ★★–★★★
Contact: Mr M Chouthi, 98 St George's Avenue, Tufnell Park, London N7 0AH
T: (020) 7607 7453 & 07860 329802
F: (020) 7607 7453
E: colin.chouthi@talk21.com
I: carena.members.beeb.net

N21

Firs Apartments ★★★★
Contact: Mrs A M Turanli, 30 Firs Lane, London N21 3ES
T: (020) 8360 3890 & 7354 0802
F: (020) 8360 3890
E: information@firsapartments.com
I: www.firsapartments.com

NW2

305 Jubilee Heights ★★★★
Contact: Ms Jacqueline Bass, 32 Hunts Cross Avenue, Woolton, Liverpool L25 5NX
T: (0151) 428 2859 & 07970 997970

The Village Property Services ★
Contact: Mr M A Abeyakoon, The Village Property Services, 98 Dollis Hill Avenue, London NW2 6QX
T: (020) 8452 5327
F: (020) 8452 0903

SE1

London Riverside Apartments ★★★★
Contact: Mr John Dillon, London Riverside Apartments, 566 Manhattan Building, Bow Quarter, London E3 2UL
T: (020) 8983 1260
I: www.londonriverside.co.uk

SE3

Sunfields ★★
Contact: Mrs J Poole, Sunfields, 135 Shooters Hill Road, Basement Flat, London SE3 8UQ
T: (020) 8858 1420
E: jpoole@currantbun.com

SE6

Glenthurston Holiday Apartments ★★★–★★★★
Contact: Miss Sue Halliday & Mrs C E Halliday, Glenthurston Holiday Apartments, 27-29 Canadian Avenue, London SE6 3AU
T: (020) 8690 3992
F: (020) 8265 5872
E: suehalliday@cwcom.net
I: www.glenthurston.co.uk

SE10

Harbour Master's House Basement Flat★★★★
Contact: Dr Chris French, The Harbour Master's House, 20 Ballast Quay, London SE10 9PD
T: (020) 8293 9597
F: (020) 8853 2865
E: harbourmaster@lineone.net
I: www.website.lineone.net/~harbourmaster/

51 Hyde Vale ★★★
Contact: Mrs Jane Baker, 51 Hyde Vale, Greenwich, London SE10 8QQ
T: (020) 8692 9677
F: (020) 8355 1208
E: jane@pgingold.demon.co.uk

SE13

Studio Cottage Rating Applied For
Contact: Ms Pamela Burke, Welcome Homes & Hotels, 21 Kellerton Road, London SE13 5RB
T: (020) 8265 1212
F: (020) 8852 3243
E: info@welcomehomes.co.uk
I: www.welcomehomes.co.uk

SE16

Flat A, 4 Dunnage Crescent ★★★
Contact: Mr & Mrs Beesley, 147 Ormside Street, Peckham, London SE15 1TF
T: (020) 7358 1272 & (013224) 31728
F: (020) 7732 0408
E: info@mayflowerletting.co.uk
I: www.mayflowerletting.co.uk

SE18

River Hope Mansions ★★★★
Contact: Mr & Mrs J J Aune, 18 Beaconsfield Road, London SE3 7LZ
T: (020) 8305 0996
F: (020) 8305 0996
E: jjama@btinternet.com

SW1

Club Suites ★★★–★★★★
Contact: Ms Anne-Marie Webster, 52 Lower Sloane Street, London SW1W 8BS
T: (020) 7730 9131
F: (020) 7730 6146
E: reservations@sloaneclub.co.uk
I: www.sloaneclub.co.uk

SW3

Beaufort House ★★★★★
Serviced Apartments
Contact: Mr J Garcia, Beaufort House, 45-47 Beaufort Gardens, London SW3 1PN
T: (020) 7584 2600
F: (020) 7584 6532
E: info@beauforthouse.co.uk
I: www.beauforthouse.co.uk

SW5

Emperors Gate Short Stay Apartments ★★★
Contact: Mr R G Arnold, Emperors Gate Short Stay Apartments, 8 Knaresborough Place, Kensington, London SW5 0TG
T: (020) 7244 8409
F: (020) 7373 6455
E: info@apartment-hotels.com
I: www.apartment-hotels.com

SW7

Ashburn Garden Apartments ★★★
Serviced Apartments
Contact: Mr A Aresti, Ashburn Garden Apartments, 3 Ashburn Gardens, London SW7 4DG
T: (020) 7370 2663
F: (020) 7370 6743
E: info@ashburngardens.co.uk
I: www.ashburngardens.co.uk

Snow White Properties Ltd ★★–★★★
Contact: Miss M White, Snow White Properties Ltd, 55 Ennismore Gardens, Knightsbridge, London SW7 1AJ
T: (020) 7584 3307
F: (020) 7581 4686
E: snow.white@virgin.net
I: www.snowwhitelondon.com

SW14

East Sheen Studio Flat Flat 1 ★★★
Contact: Mrs Angela Butt, 179 Mortlake Road, Kew, Kew, Richmond, Surrey TW9 4AW
T: (020) 8876 0584 & 8876 5375
F: (020) 8876 0584

SW18

Beaumont Apartments ★★★–★★★★
Contact: Mr & Mrs A Afriat, Beaumont Apartments, 24 Combemartin Road, Southfields, London SW18 5PR
T: (020) 8789 2663
F: (020) 8265 5499
E: afriat@mistral.co.uk
I: www.beaumont-london-apartments.co.uk

SW19

Honey Cottage ★★★
Contact: Mrs Jenny Humphries, 16 Dudley Road, Wimbledon, London SW19 8PN
T: (020) 8542 7798 & 8542 7798
F: (020) 8395 7353
E: mikejenny@compuserve.com
I: www.honeycottage.com

Establishments printed in blue have a detailed entry in this guide

Montague House ★★★
Contact: Mrs Jenny Humphries,
16 Dudley Road, Wimbledon,
London SW19 8PN
T: (020) 85427798
E: mikejenny@compuserve.co.uk
I: www.montaguehouse.co.uk

SW20

Thalia & Hebe Holiday Homes
★★★
Contact: Mr & Mrs Briscoe-
Smith, 150 Westway, Raynes
Park, West Wimbledon, London
SW20 9LS
T: (020) 8542 0505
F: (020) 8287 0637
E: peter@briscoe-smith.org.uk
I: briscoe-smith.org.uk/thalia/

W1

The Ascott Mayfair
Rating Applied For
Contact: Mr Martin King, The
Ascott Mayfair, 49 Hill Street,
Mayfair, London W1J 5NB
T: (020) 7499 6868
F: (020) 7499 0705
E: martin.king@the-ascott.com
I: www.the-ascott.com

23 Greengarden House
★★★★
Serviced Apartments
Contact: Miss Nikki Pybus, 23
Greengarden House, St
Christopher's Place, London
W1U 1NL
T: (020) 7935 9191 & 7935 8858
F: (020) 7935 8858
E: info@greengardenhouse.com
I: www.greengardenhouse.com

Tustin Holiday Flats
★★–★★★
Contact: Reservations Office,
Tustin Holiday Flats, 94 York
Street, London W1H 1QX
T: (020) 7723 9611
F: (020) 7724 0224
E: pctustinuk@btconnect.com
I: www.pctustin.com

W2

Royal Court Apartments
★–★★★
Contact: Ms Natalin Brown,
Royal Court Apartments, 51-53
Gloucester Terrace, London
W2 3DQ
T: (020) 7402 5077
F: (020) 7724 0286
E: info@rcahotels.co.uk
I: www.rcahotels.co.uk

W4

Maltings Lodge ★★★★
Contact: Ms Anita Manger, C &
R Housing Services, 167 Malden
Way, New Malden, Surrey
KT3 5QX
T: (020) 8336 0119 &
07711 727181
F: (020) 8336 0119
E: enquiries@crh.co.uk
I: www.crh.co.uk

W5

Clarendon House Apartments
★★★–★★★★
Contact: Mrs Anne Pedley, 21E
Harewood Close, Bexhill, East
Sussex TN39 3LX
T: (01424) 212954 & (020) 8567
0314
F: (01424) 212954
E: clarendon.house@LineOne.
net
I: www.
clarendonhouseapartments.
co.uk

W8

51 Kensington Court ★★★★
Contact: Mr Mohamed Elhafedi,
51 Kensington Court, London
W8 5DB
T: (020) 7937 2030
F: (020) 7938 5312
E: bookings@kensingtoncourt.
co.uk

W13

Apartments West London
★★–★★★
Contact: Mr W G Smith,
Apartments West London, 94
Gordon Road, London W13 8PT
T: (020) 8566 8187 &
(01895) 233365
F: (020) 8566 7670
E: info@apartmentswestlondon.
com
I: www.apartmentswestlondon.
com

OUTER LONDON
Beckenham

Oakfield Estates ★–★★★
Contact: Mr J E Deane, Oakfield
Estates, 107 South Eden Park
Road, Beckenham, Kent BR3 3AX
T: (020) 8658 4441
F: (020) 8658 9198
E: hols@oakfield.co.uk
I: www.oakfield.co.uk

CHESSINGTON

1 Ashby Avenue ★★
Contact: Mrs V Hastings, 57
Gorings Mead, Horsham, West
Sussex RH13 5BS
T: (01403) 256420

CROYDON

Ballards Farm Cottage ★★★
Contact: Mr & Mrs M
McDermott, Ballards Farm
Cottage, 2 Ballards Farm Road,
Croydon, CR0 5RL
T: (020) 8657 1080
I: www.website.lineone.
net/~michaelmed

London Country Apartments
Ltd ★★★★–★★★★★
Contact: Ms Rochelle Anselm,
London Country Apartments Ltd,
121 Cherry Orchard Road, East
Croydon, Croydon, CR0 6BE
T: (020) 8686 8068
F: (020) 8686 0678
E: 101327.1320@compuserve.
com
I: www.lcaliving.com

S N D Apartments ★★★
Contact: Mrs Pamela Pereira, S
N D Apartments, 1 Mulgrave
Road, Croydon, Surrey CR0 1BL
T: (020) 8688 7870
F: (020) 8686 7835
E: mulgrave.road@ukgateway.
net

HAMPTON

Courtlands
Rating Applied For
Contact: Mr C Deuster, 36 High
Street, Hampton, Middlesex
TW12 2SJ
T: (0208) 9798822
E: cdeuster@aol.com

KINGSTON UPON THAMES

3 Becketts Place ★★★★
Contact: Mr & Mrs A Bernhard, 2
Becketts Place, Hampton Wick,
Kingston upon Thames, Surrey
KT1 4EQ
T: (020) 8943 3464 & 8943 3464
E: aebernhard@email.com

PINNER

Moss Cottage ★★★★
Contact: Ms Barbara Le Quesne,
Moss Lane Cottages, 31 Paines
Lane, Pinner, Middlesex
HA5 3BU
T: (020) 8868 5507
F: (020) 8868 5507
E: bemail2@aol.com
I: www.moss-lane-cottages.com

TEDDINGTON

Stoney Deep ★★★
Contact: Ms Chingfu Pang, Flat
18 Stoney Deep, 48 Twickenham
Road, Teddington, Middlesex
TW11 8BL
T: (020) 8943 1757 & 8941 8660
F: (020) 8941 8681
E: chingfupang@yahoo.com

TWICKENHAM

Flat 4 Friston House ★★★
Contact: Mr Arthur Shipp, 5
Cambridge Road, Twickenham,
Middlesex TW1 2HN
T: (020) 8892 6778
F: (020) 8892 6778
E: shipplets@ukgateway.net

CUMBRIA

AINSTABLE
Cumbria

The Old Dairy Cottage ★★★
Contact: Dales Hol Cot Ref:3172,
Dales Holiday Cottages, Carleton
Business Park, Carleton New
Road, Skipton, North Yorkshire
BD23 2AA
T: (01756) 799821 & 790919
F: (01756) 797012
E: info@dalesholcot.com
I: www.dalesholcot.com

ALLITHWAITE
Cumbria

The Flat ★★★
Contact: Country Holidays
ref:6726, Spring Mill, Earby,
Barnoldswick, Lancashire
BB94 0AA
T: 08700 723723
F: (01282) 844288
E: sales@ttgihg.co.uk
I: www.country-holidays.co.uk

Trevelyan Cottage ★★
Contact: Sykes Cottages Ref:
669, Sykes Cottages, York House,
York Street, Chester, CH1 3LR
T: (01244) 345700
F: (01244) 321442
E: info@sykescottages.co.uk
I: www.sykescottages.co.uk

ALLONBY
Cumbria

Crookhurst ★★★★
Contact: Mrs B Wilson, Bowscale
Farm, Allonby, Maryport,
Cumbria CA15 6RB
T: (01900) 881228 & 0777 304
7591
F: (01900) 881228
I: www.crookhurst.co.uk

Spring Lea ★★★★
Contact: Mr J Williamson, Spring
Lea, Allonby, Maryport, Cumbria
CA15 6QF
T: (01900) 881331
F: (01900) 881209
E: mail@springlea.co.uk

ALSTON
Cumbria

Connelly ★★★
Contact: Mr D A Timms, 51
Silver Street, Ely, Cambridgeshire
CB7 4JB
T: (01353) 662171

Ghyll Burn Cottage ★★★
Contact: Mrs S Huntley, Ghyll
Burn Cottage, Hartside Nursery
Garden, Alston, Cumbria
CA9 3BL
T: (01434) 381372 & 381428
F: (01434) 381372
E: ghyllburn@appleonline.net
I: www.cumbria1st.com/towns

Stone Barn Cottage ★★★★★
Contact: Mrs Dee Ellis, Stone
Barn Cottage, Low Galligill Farm,
Nentsberry, Alston, Cumbria
CA9 3LW
T: (01434) 381672
E: lowgalligillfarm@btinternet.
com
I: www.btinternet.
com/~stonebarncottage

AMBLESIDE
Cumbria

1,2,3,4 & 5 Riverside Cottages
Rating Applied For
Contact: Mr Paul Liddell,
Lakelovers, The New Toffee Loft,
Kendal Road, Bowness-on-
Windermere, Windermere,
Cumbria LA23 3RA
T: (015394) 88855
F: (015394) 88857
E: bookings@lakelovers.co.uk
I: www.lakelovers.co.uk

Above Stock Rating Applied For
Contact: Mr Paul Liddell, Lakelovers, The New Toffee Loft, Kendal Road, Bowness-on-Windermere, Windermere, Cumbria LA23 3RA
T: (015394) 88855
F: (015394) 88857
E: bookings@lakelovers.co.uk
I: www.lakelovers.co.uk

Acorns ★★★★
Contact: Mrs Susan Jackson, Heart of the Lakes, Fisherbeck Hill, Old Lake Road, Ambleside, Cumbria LA22 0DH
T: (015394) 32321
F: (015394) 33251
E: info@heartofthelakes.co.uk
I: www.heartofthelakes.co.uk

Altar End ★★★★
Contact: Mrs Susan Jackson, Heart of the Lakes, Fisherbeck Hill, Old Lake Road, Ambleside, Cumbria LA22 0DH
T: (015394) 32321
F: (015394) 33251
E: info@heartofthelakes.co.uk
I: www.heartofthelakes.co.uk

20 and 21 The Falls ★★★
Contact: Mr Paul Liddell, Lakelovers, The New Toffee Loft, Kendal Road, Windermere, Cumbria LA23 3RA
T: (015394) 88855
F: (015394) 88857
E: bookings@lakelovers.co.uk
I: www.lakelovers.co.uk

Ashburne Cottage ★★★
Contact: Mrs S Jackson, Heart of the Lakes, Fisherbeck Mill, Old Lake Road, Ambleside, Cumbria LA22 0DH
T: (015394) 32321
F: (015394) 33251
E: info@heartofthelakes.co.uk
I: www.heartofthelakes.co.uk

Babbling Brook ★★★★
Contact: Mrs Susan Jackson, Heart of the Lakes, Fisherbeck Hill, Old Lake Road, Ambleside, Cumbria LA22 0DH
T: (015394) 32321
F: (015394) 33251
E: info@heartofthelakes.co.uk
I: www.heartofthelakes.co.uk

Baddeley Cottage ★★★
Contact: Mrs S Jackson, Heart of the Lakes, Fisherbeck Mill, Old Lake Road, Ambleside, Cumbria LA22 0DH
T: (015394) 32321
F: (015394) 33251
E: info@heartofthelakes.co.uk
I: www.heartofthelakes.co.uk

7 Badgers Rake (The Garden Flat) ★★★
Contact: Mr D Hogarth, Cumbrian Cottages, 7 The Crescent, Carlisle, CA1 1QW
T: (01228) 599960
F: (01228) 599970
E: enquiries@cumbrian-cottages.co.uk
I: www.cumbrian-cottages.co.uk

10 Badgers Rake ★★★★
Contact: Mr D Hogarth, Cumbrian Cottages, 7 The Crescent, Carlisle, CA1 1QW
T: (01228) 599960 & 599950
F: (01228) 599970
E: enquiries@cumbrian-cottages.co.uk
I: www.cumbrian-cottages.co.uk

9 Badgers Rake ★★★
Contact: Mr D Hogarth, Cumbrian Cottages, 7 The Crescent, Carlisle, CA1 1QW
T: (01228) 599960 & 599950
F: (01228) 599970
E: enquiries@cumbrian-cottages.co.uk
I: www.cumbrian-cottages.co.uk

Bakestones Cottage ★★★★
Contact: Mrs Susan Jackson, Heart of the Lakes, Fisherbeck Hill, Old Lake Road, Ambleside, Cumbria LA22 0DH
T: (015394) 32321
F: (015394) 33251
E: info@heartofthelakes.co.uk
I: www.heartofthelakes.co.uk

Barn Waterhead ★★★★
Contact: Mrs Susan Jackson, Heart of the Lakes, Fisherbeck Hill, Old Lake Road, Ambleside, Cumbria LA22 0DH
T: (015394) 32321
F: (015394) 33251
E: info@heartofthelakes.co.uk
I: www.heartofthelakes.co.uk

Beck, Hillside and Couter Cottages ★★★
Contact: Mrs N K Morris, 11 Maple Grove, Worsley, Manchester M28 7ED
T: (0161) 790 8023 & 07747 794790
I: www.amblesideselfcatering.co.uk

Birch Cottage ★★★
Contact: Dr L Nash, 47 Goring Road, Bounds Green, London N11 2BT
T: (020) 8888 1252 & (0115) 969 2190
F: (020) 8888 1252

Birchcroft ★★★★
Contact: Mr Susan Jackson, Heart of the Lakes, Fisherbeck Mill, Old Lake Road, Ambleside, Cumbria LA22 0DH
T: (015394) 32321
F: (015394) 33251
E: info@heartofthelakes.co.uk
I: www.heartofthelakes.co.uk

Blelham Tarn at Neaum Crag ★★★★
Contact: Mrs Sue Witts, P O Box 73, Newport, Shropshire TF10 8WG
T: 07740 486947 & (01952) 810101
F: (01952) 810102
E: sales@pad-lok.com
I: www.pad-lok.com

Bobbin Cottage ★★★★
Contact: Mr Paul Liddell, Lakelovers, The New Toffee Loft, Kendal Road, Windermere, Cumbria LA23 3RA
T: (015394) 88855
F: (015394) 88857
E: bookings@lakelovers.co.uk
I: www.lakelovers.co.uk

Bobbin Mill ★★★★
Contact: Mrs Susan Jackson, Heart of the Lakes, Fisherbeck Mill, Old Lake Road, Ambleside, Cumbria LA22 0DH
T: (015394) 32321
F: (015394) 33251
E: info@heartofthelakes.co.uk
I: www.heartofthelakes.co.uk

Bowfell ★★★
Contact: Mrs Susan Jackson, Heart of the Lakes, Fisherbeck Hill, Old Lake Road, Ambleside, Cumbria LA22 0DH
T: (015394) 32321
F: (015394) 33251
E: info@heartofthelakes.co.uk
I: www.heartofthelakes.co.uk

Brackenrigg ★★★
Contact: Mr Paul Liddell, Lakelovers, The New Toffee Loft, Kendal Road, Windermere, Cumbria LA23 3RA
T: (015394) 88855
F: (015394) 88857
E: bookings@lakelovers.co.uk
I: www.lakelovers.co.uk

Brae Cottage ★★★
Contact: Mr Paul Liddell, Lakelovers, The New Toffee Loft, Kendal Road, Windermere, Cumbria LA23 3RA
T: (015394) 88855
F: (015394) 88857
E: bookings@lakelovers.co.uk
I: www.lakelovers.co.uk

Braebeck ★★★★
Contact: Mr Paul Liddell, Lakelovers, The New Toffee Loft, Kendal Road, Windermere, Cumbria LA23 3RA
T: (015394) 88855
F: (015394) 88857
E: bookings@lakelovers.co.uk
I: www.lakelovers.co.uk

15 Brathay ★★★★
Contact: Mrs Susan Jackson, Heart of the Lakes, Fisherbeck Mill, Old Lake Road, Ambleside, Cumbria LA22 0DH
T: (015394) 32321
F: (015394) 33251
E: info@heartofthelakes.co.uk
I: www.heartofthelakes.co.uk

Briar Nook ★★★★
Contact: Mr D Hogarth, Cumbrian Cottages, 7 The Crescent, Carlisle, CA1 1QW
T: (01228) 599960 & 599950
F: (01228) 599970
E: enquiries@cumbrian-cottages.co.uk
I: www.cumbrian-cottages.co.uk

Briardale Cottage ★★★
Contact: Mrs Susan Jackson, Heart of the Lakes, Fisherbeck Hill, Old Lake Road, Ambleside, Cumbria LA22 0DH
T: (015394) 32321
F: (015394) 33251
E: info@heartofthelakes.co.uk
I: www.heartofthelakes.co.uk

Broad Oak ★★★
Contact: Mrs S Jackson, Heart of the Lakes, Fisherbeck Mill, Old Lake Road, Ambleside, Cumbria LA22 0DH
T: (015394) 32321
F: (015394) 33251
E: info@heartofthelakes.co.uk
I: www.heartofthelakes.co.uk

Byways ★★
Contact: Mrs Susan Jackson, Heart of the Lakes, Fisherbeck Mill, Old Lake Road, Ambleside, Cumbria LA22 0DH
T: (015394) 32321
F: (015394) 33251
E: info@heartofthelakes.co.uk
I: www.heartofthelakes.co.uk

Cedar House ★★★★
Contact: Mrs Susan Jackson, Heart of the Lakes, Fisherbeck Hill, Old Lake Road, Ambleside, Cumbria LA22 0DH
T: (015394) 32321
F: (015394) 33251
E: info@heartofthelakes.co.uk
I: www.heartofthelakes.co.uk

Chestnuts, Beeches and The Granary ★★★
Contact: Mr J R Benson, High Sett, Sun Hill Lane, Troutbeck Bridge, Windermere, Cumbria LA23 1HJ
T: (015394) 42731 & 07971 984232
F: (015394) 42731
E: s.benson@talk21.com
I: www.accommodationlakedistrict.com

Church View ★★★
Contact: Mr D Hogarth, Cumbrian Cottages, 7 The Crescent, Carlisle, CA1 1QW
T: (01228) 599960 & 599950
F: (01228) 599970
E: enquiries@cumbrian-cottages.co.uk
I: www.cumbrian-cottages.co.uk

Clover Cottage ★★★
Contact: Proprietor, Heart of the Lakes, Fisherbeck Mill, Old Lake Road, Ambleside, Cumbria LA22 0DH
T: (015394) 32321
F: (015394) 33251
E: info@heartofthelakes.co.uk
I: www.heartofthelakes.co.uk

Cobblestone House ★★★★
Contact: Mr D Hogarth, Cumbrian Cottages, 7 The Crescent, Carlisle, CA1 1QW
T: (01228) 599960 & 599950
F: (01228) 599970
E: enquiries@cumbrian-cottages.co.uk
I: www.cumbrian-cottages.co.uk

Cobblestones ★★★
Contact: Mr D Hogarth, Cumbrian Cottages, 7 The Crescent, Carlisle, CA1 1QW
T: (01228) 599960 & 599950
F: (01228) 599970
E: enquiries@cumbrian-cottages.co.uk
I: www.cumbrian-cottages.co.uk

Establishments printed in blue have a detailed entry in this guide

Crag View ★★★
Contact: Mrs P Davies, 21
Dowhills Road, Blundellsands,
Liverpool, L23 8SH
T: (0151) 924 6995
F: (0151) 285 9107
E: pdavies@bsg.uu-net.com

Cranford Cottage ★★
Contact: Sykes Cottages
Ref:301, Sykes Cottages, York
House, York Street, Chester,
CH1 3LR
T: (01244) 345700
F: (01244) 321442
E: info@sykescottages.co.uk
I: www.sykescottages.co.uk

Cringol Cottage ★★★
Contact: Mrs Susan Jackson,
Heart of the Lakes, Fisherbeck
Hill, Old Lake Road, Ambleside,
Cumbria LA22 0DH
T: (015394) 32321
F: (015394) 33251
E: info@heartofthelakes.co.uk
I: www.heartofthelakes.co.uk

Crinkle Crags ★★★
Contact: Mrs Susan Jackson,
Heart of the Lakes, Fisherbeck
Hill, Old Lake Road, Ambleside,
Cumbria LA22 0DH
T: (015394) 32321
F: (015394) 33251
E: info@heartofthelakes.co.uk
I: www.heartofthelakes.co.uk

8 Croft Courtyard ★★★
Contact: Mr P L Mors, Silkwater,
East Hill, Evershot, Dorchester,
Dorset DT2 0LB
T: (01935) 83673
F: (01935) 83673
E: croft.courtyard@virgin.net

Derby Cottage ★★★
Contact: Mr D Hogarth,
Cumbrian Cottages, 7 The
Crescent, Carlisle, CA1 1QW
T: (01228) 599960 & 599950
F: (01228) 599970
E: enquiries@
cumbrian-cottages.co.uk
I: www.cumbrian-cottages.co.uk

Dower House Cottage ★★★
Contact: Mrs Margaret Rigg, The
Dower House, Wray Castle,
Ambleside, Cumbria LA22 0JA
T: (015394) 33211

Ecclerigg Cottage ★★★
Contact: Mrs Susan Jackson,
Heart of the Lakes, Fisherbeck
Hill, Old Lake Road, Ambleside,
Cumbria LA22 0DH
T: (015394) 32321
F: (015394) 33251
E: info@heartofthelakes.co.uk
I: www.heartofthelakes.co.uk

Edelweiss ★★★★
Contact: Mrs Susan Jackson,
Heart of the Lakes, Fisherbeck
Hill, Old Lake Road, Ambleside,
Cumbria LA22 0DH
T: (015394) 32321
F: (015394) 33251
E: info@heartofthelakes.co.uk
I: www.heartofthelakes.co.uk

Ellerview ★★★
Contact: Mr Paul Liddell,
Lakelovers, The New Toffee Loft,
Kendal Road, Windermere,
Cumbria LA23 3RA
T: (015394) 88855
F: (015394) 88857
E: bookings@lakelovers.co.uk
I: www.lakelovers.co.uk

Eskdale ★★★★
Contact: Mr D Hogarth,
Cumbrian Cottages, 7 The
Crescent, Carlisle, CA1 1QW
T: (01228) 599960 & 599950
F: (01228) 599970
E: enquiries@
cumbrian-cottages.co.uk
I: www.cumbrian-cottages.co.uk

Falls View Cottage ★★★
Contact: Mrs Susan Jackson,
Heart of the Lakes, Fisherbeck
Hill, Old Lake Road, Ambleside,
Cumbria LA22 0DH
T: (015394) 32321
F: (015394) 33251
E: info@heartofthelakes.co.uk
I: www.heartofthelakes.co.uk

Fellside ★★★★
Contact: Mr Paul Liddell,
Lakelovers, The New Toffee Loft,
Kendal Road, Windermere,
Cumbria LA23 3RA
T: (015394) 88855
F: (015394) 88857
E: bookings@lakelovers.co.uk
I: www.lakelovers.co.uk

Fern Ghyll ★★★★
Contact: Mrs Susan Jackson,
Heart of the Lakes, Fisherbeck
Hill, Old Lake Road, Ambleside,
Cumbria LA22 0DH
T: (015394) 32321
F: (015394) 33251
E: info@heartofthelakes.co.uk
I: www.heartofthelakes.co.uk

The Flat ★★★
Contact: Mrs Susan Jackson,
Heart of the Lakes, Fisherbeck
Mill, Old Lake Road, Ambleside,
Cumbria LA22 0DH
T: (015394) 32321
F: (015394) 33251
E: info@heartofthelakes.co.uk
I: www.heartofthelakes.co.uk

Forge Side ★★★
Contact: Mrs Susan Jackson,
Heart of the Lakes, Fisherbeck
Mill, Old Lake Road, Ambleside,
Cumbria LA22 0DH
T: (015394) 32321
F: (015394) 33251
E: info@heartofthelakes.co.uk
I: www.heartofthelakes.co.uk

Four Seasons Cottage ★★★
Contact: Mrs Susan Jackson,
Heart of the Lakes, Fisherbeck
Mill, Old Lake Road, Ambleside,
Cumbria LA22 0DH
T: (015394) 32321
F: (015394) 33251
E: info@heartofthelakes.co.uk
I: www.heartofthelakes.co.uk

Gale House Cottage ★★★★
Contact: Mrs Susan Jackson,
Heart of the Lakes, Fisherbeck
Mill, Old Lake Road, Ambleside,
Cumbria LA22 0DH
T: (015394) 32321
F: (015394) 33251
E: info@heartofthelakes.co.uk
I: www.heartofthelakes.co.uk

Gale Howe Barn ★★★★
Contact: Mrs Susan Jackson,
Heart of the Lakes, Fisherbeck
Mill, Old Lake Road, Ambleside,
Cumbria LA22 0DH
T: (015394) 32321
F: (015394) 33251
E: info@heartofthelakes.co.uk
I: www.heartofthelakes.co.uk

**Gale Lodge (Coachmans,
Lingmel & Scafell) ★★★★**
Contact: Mrs Susan Jackson,
Heart of the Lakes, Fisherbeck
Hill, Old Lake Road, Ambleside,
Cumbria LA22 0DH
T: (015394) 32321
F: (015394) 33251
E: info@heartofthelakes.co.uk
I: www.heartofthelakes.co.uk

Gale Mews ★★★★
Contact: Mrs Susan Jackson,
Heart of the Lakes, Fisherbeck
Hill, Old Lake Road, Ambleside,
Cumbria LA22 0DH
T: (015394) 32321
F: (015394) 33251
E: info@heartofthelakes.co.uk
I: www.heartofthelakes.co.uk

The Garden Flat ★★★
Contact: Mr and Mrs Alan
Wardle, North Lodge, Longtail
Hill, Bowness-on-Windermere,
Windermere, Cumbria LA23 3JD
T: (01539) 447905
I: www.lakeland-holidays.net

Ghyll Bank ★★★★
Contact: Mrs Susan Jackson,
Heart of the Lakes, Fisherbeck
Mill, Old Lake Road, Ambleside,
Cumbria LA22 0DH
T: (015394) 32321
F: (015394) 33251
E: info@heartofthelakes.co.uk
I: www.heartofthelakes.co.uk

Ghyll Heights ★★★★
Contact: Mr D Hogarth,
Cumbrian Cottages, 7 The
Crescent, Carlisle, CA1 1QW
T: (01228) 599960
F: (01228) 599970
E: enquiries@
cumbrian-cottages.co.uk
I: www.cumbrian-cottages.co.uk

Ghyll View ★★★
Contact: Mrs Susan Jackson,
Heart of the Lakes, Fisherbeck
Hill, Old Lake Road, Ambleside,
Cumbria LA22 0DH
T: (015394) 32321
F: (015394) 33251
E: info@heartofthelakes.co.uk
I: www.heartofthelakes.co.uk

3 Ghyllside ★★★
Contact: Mr Paul Liddell,
Lakelovers, The New Toffee Loft,
Kendal Road, Windermere,
Cumbria LA23 3RA
T: (015394) 88855
F: (015394) 88857
E: bookings@lakelovers.co.uk
I: www.lakelovers.co.uk

Gilbert Scar House ★★★★
Contact: Mrs Susan Jackson,
Heart of the Lakes, Fisherbeck
Hill, Old Lake Road, Ambleside,
Cumbria LA22 0DH
T: (015394) 32321
F: (015394) 33251
E: info@heartofthelakes.co.uk
I: www.heartofthelakes.co.uk

Gillybeck, The Falls ★★★★
Contact: Mrs Susan Jackson,
Heart of the Lakes, Fisherbeck
Hill, Old Lake Road, Ambleside,
Cumbria LA22 0DH
T: (015394) 32321
F: (015394) 33251
E: info@heartofthelakes.co.uk
I: www.heartofthelakes.co.uk

The Granny Flat ★★★
Contact: Mrs Susan Jackson,
Heart of the Lakes, Fisherbeck
Hill, Old Lake Road, Ambleside,
Cumbria LA22 0DH
T: (015394) 32321
F: (015394) 33251
E: info@heartofthelakes.co.uk
I: www.heartofthelakes.co.uk

**The Grove Farm
★★★★-★★★★★**
Contact: Mrs Zorika Thompson,
The Grove Farm, Stockghyll Lane,
Ambleside, Cumbria LA22 9LG
T: (015394) 33074
F: (015394) 31881

Hayrake ★★
Contact: Mrs Susan Jackson,
Heart of the Lakes, Fisherbeck
Mill, Old Lake Road, Ambleside,
Cumbria LA22 0DH
T: (015394) 32321
F: (015394) 33251
E: info@heartofthelakes.co.uk
I: www.heartofthelakes.co.uk

Hazelhurst ★★★★
Contact: Mr D Hogarth,
Cumbrian Cottages, 7 The
Crescent, Carlisle, CA1 1QW
T: (01228) 599960 & 599950
F: (01228) 599970
E: enquiries@
cumbrian-cottages.co.uk
I: www.cumbrian-cottages.co.uk

Heather Cottage ★★★
Contact: Mr Paul Liddell,
Lakelovers, The New Toffee Loft,
Kendal Road, Windermere,
Cumbria LA23 3RA
T: (015394) 88855
F: (015394) 88857
E: bookings@lakelovers.co.uk
I: www.lakelovers.co.uk

Herald Cottage ★★★★
Contact: Mr D Hogarth,
Cumbrian Cottages, 7 The
Crescent, Carlisle, CA1 1QW
T: (01228) 599960
F: (01228) 599970
E: enquiries@
cumbrian-cottages.co.uk
I: www.cumbrian-cottages.co.uk

High Bank ★★★
Contact: Mrs Susan Jackson,
Heart of the Lakes, Fisherbeck
Hill, Old Lake Road, Ambleside,
Cumbria LA22 0DH
T: (015394) 32321
F: (015394) 33251
E: info@heartofthelakes.co.uk
I: www.heartofthelakes.co.uk

High Nook ★★★
Contact: Mrs Susan Jackson,
Heart of the Lakes, Fisherbeck
Mill, Old Lake Road, Ambleside,
Cumbria LA22 0DH
T: (015394) 32321
F: (015394) 33251
E: info@heartofthelakes.co.uk
I: www.heartofthelakes.co.uk

High Pike Cottage ★★★
Contact: Mrs Susan Jackson,
Heart of the Lakes, Fisherbeck
Hill, Old Lake Road, Ambleside,
Cumbria LA22 0DH
T: (015394) 32321
F: (015394) 33251
E: info@heartofthelakes.co.uk
I: www.heartofthelakes.co.uk

Hillandale
Rating Applied For
Contact: Mr Paul Liddell,
Lakelovers, The New Toffee Loft,
Kendal Road, Windermere,
Cumbria LA23 3RA
T: (015394) 88855
F: (015394) 88857
E: bookings@lakelovers.co.uk
I: www.lakelovers.co.uk

Hillside Cottage ★★★
Contact: Mrs Susan Jackson,
Heart of the Lakes, Fisherbeck
Mill, Old Lake Road, Ambleside,
Cumbria LA22 0DH
T: (015394) 32321
F: (015394) 33251
E: info@heartofthelakes.co.uk
I: www.heartofthelakes.co.uk

Hilltop (Ambleside Suite)
★★★★★
Contact: Mrs Susan Jackson,
Heart of the Lakes, Fisherbeck
Hill, Old Lake Road, Ambleside,
Cumbria LA22 0DH
T: (015394) 32321
F: (015394) 33251
E: info@heartofthelakes.co.uk
I: www.heartofthelakes.co.uk

Holbeck ★★★★★
Contact: Mrs Susan Jackson,
Heart of the Lakes, Fisherbeck
Hill, Old Lake Road, Ambleside,
Cumbria LA22 0DH
T: (015394) 32321
F: (015394) 33251
E: info@heartofthelakes.co.uk
I: www.heartofthelakes.co.uk

Hole House ★★★
Contact: Mrs Clare Irvine, Hole
House, Tock How Farm, High
Wray, Ambleside, Cumbria
LA22 0JF
T: (015394) 36106 & 36294
F: (015394) 36294
I: www.tock-how-farm.com

The Hollies ★★★
Contact: Mr D Hogarth,
Cumbrian Cottages, 7 The
Crescent, Carlisle, CA1 1QW
T: (01228) 599960 & 599950
F: (01228) 599970
E: enquiries@
cumbrian-cottages.co.uk
I: www.cumbrian-cottages.co.uk

Honeypot Cottage ★★★★
Contact: Mrs Susan Jackson,
Heart of the Lakes, Fisherbeck
Mill, Old Lake Road, Ambleside,
Cumbria LA22 0DH
T: (015394) 32321
F: (015394) 33251
E: info@heartofthelakes.co.uk
I: www.heartofthelakes.co.uk

Horseshoe Cottage ★★★
Contact: Mrs Susan Jackson,
Heart of the Lakes, Fisherbeck
Hill, Old Lake Road, Ambleside,
Cumbria LA22 0DH
T: (015394) 32321
F: (015394) 33251
E: info@heartofthelakes.co.uk
I: www.heartofthelakes.co.uk

2 How Head ★★★
Contact: Mrs Susan Jackson,
Heart of the Lakes, Fisherbeck
Hill, Old Lake Road, Ambleside,
Cumbria LA22 0DH
T: (015394) 32321
F: (015394) 33251
E: info@heartofthelakes.co.uk
I: www.heartofthelakes.co.uk

4 How Head ★★★
Contact: Mr R D Holland, How
Head Cottage, East of Lake,
Coniston, Cumbria LA21 8AA
T: (015394) 41594
E: howhead@lineone.net
I: www.howheadcottages.co.uk

Iona ★★★
Contact: Mrs Susan Jackson,
Heart of the Lakes, Fisherbeck
Hill, Old Lake Road, Ambleside,
Cumbria LA22 0DH
T: (015394) 32321
F: (015394) 33251
E: info@heartofthelakes.co.uk
I: www.heartofthelakes.co.uk

Juniper Cottage ★★★
Contact: Mr Paul Liddell,
Lakelovers, The New Toffee Loft,
Kendal Road, Windermere,
Cumbria LA23 3RA
T: (015394) 88855
F: (015394) 88857
E: bookings@lakelovers.co.uk
I: www.lakelovers.co.uk

3 Kiln Cottages ★★★
Contact: Mr Paul Liddell,
Lakelovers, The New Toffee Loft,
Kendal Road, Windermere,
Cumbria LA23 3RA
T: (015394) 88855
F: (015394) 88857
E: bookings@lakelovers.co.uk
I: www.lakelovers.co.uk

Kingfisher Cottage ★★★★
Contact: Mr Paul Liddell,
Lakelovers, The New Toffee Loft,
Kendal Road, Windermere,
Cumbria LA23 3RA
T: (015394) 88855
F: (015394) 88857
E: bookings@lakelovers.co.uk
I: www.lakelovers.co.uk

Kirkstone Cottage ★★★
Contact: Mr D Hogarth,
Cumbrian Cottages, 7 The
Crescent, Carlisle, CA1 1QW
T: (01228) 599960
F: (01228) 599970
E: enquiries@
cumbrian-cottages.co.uk
I: www.cumbrian-cottages.co.uk

**Kirkstone Foot Cottages and
Apartments ★★★★**
Contact: Mr Norfolk, Kirkstone
Foot Cottages and Apartments,
Kirkstone Pass Road, Ambleside,
Cumbria LA22 9EH
T: (01524) 410777
F: (01524) 417573
E: kirkstone@breathemail.net
I: www.kirkstonefoot.co.uk

Lakeland Cottage ★★★★
Contact: Mr Paul Liddell,
Lakelovers, The New Toffee Loft,
Kendal Road, Windermere,
Cumbria LA23 3RA
T: (015394) 88855
F: (015394) 88857
E: bookings@lakelovers.co.uk
I: www.lakelovers.co.uk

The Lakelands
★★★★-★★★★★
Contact: Mrs Catrina Fletcher,
The Lakelands, Lower Gale,
Ambleside, Cumbria LA22 0BD
T: (015394) 33777
F: (015394) 31301
E: lakeland@globalnet.co.uk
I: www.thelakelands.com

19 The Lakelands ★★★★
Contact: Mr Paul Liddell,
Lakelovers, The New Toffee Loft,
Kendal Road, Windermere,
Cumbria LA23 3RA
T: (015394) 88855
F: (015394) 88857
E: bookings@lakelovers.co.uk
I: www.lakelovers.co.uk

The Larches ★★★★
Contact: Mrs Susan Jackson,
Heart of the Lakes, Fisherbeck
Hill, Old Lake Road, Ambleside,
Cumbria LA22 0DH
T: (015394) 32321
F: (015394) 33251
E: info@heartofthelakes.co.uk
I: www.heartofthelakes.co.uk
🏠

Leafy Nook ★★★★
Contact: Mrs Susan Jackson,
Heart of the Lakes, Fisherbeck
Hill, Old Lake Road, Ambleside,
Cumbria LA22 0DH
T: (015394) 32321
F: (015394) 33251
E: info@heartofthelakes.co.uk
I: www.heartofthelakes.co.uk

Lingmell Gale Lodge
Rating Applied For
Contact: Mrs Susan Jackson,
Heart of the Lakes, Fisherbeck
Mill, Old Lake Road, Ambleside,
Cumbria LA22 0DH
T: (015394) 32321
F: (015394) 33251
E: info@heartofthelakes.co.uk
I: www.heartofthelakes.co.uk

Long Mynd ★★★★
Contact: Mr D Hogarth,
Cumbrian Cottages, 7 The
Crescent, Carlisle, CA1 1QW
T: (01228) 599960
F: (01228) 599970
E: enquiries@
cumbrian-cottages.co.uk
I: www.cumbrian-cottages.co.uk

Longmeadow ★★★★
Contact: Mr D Hogarth,
Cumbrian Cottages, 7 The
Crescent, Carlisle, CA1 1QW
T: (01228) 599960
F: (01228) 599970
E: enquiries@
cumbrian-cottages.co.uk
I: www.cumbrian-cottages.co.uk

The Lookout ★★★★★
Contact: Mrs Susan Jackson,
Heart of the Lakes, Fisherbeck
Hill, Old Lake Road, Ambleside,
Cumbria LA22 0DH
T: (015394) 32321
F: (015394) 33251
E: info@heartofthelakes.co.uk
I: www.heartofthelakes.co.uk

Loughrigg ★★★★
Contact: Mr D Hogarth,
Cumbrian Cottages, 7 The
Crescent, Carlisle, CA1 1QW
T: (01228) 599960
F: (01228) 599970
I: www.cumbrian-cottages.co.uk

Loughrigg
Rating Applied For
Contact: Mrs Susan Jackson,
Heart of the Lakes, Fisherbeck
Mill, Old Lake Road, Ambleside,
Cumbria LA22 0DH
T: (015394) 32321
F: (015394) 33251
E: info@heartofthelakes.co.uk
I: www.heartofthelakes.co.uk

5 Loughrigg Park ★★★
Contact: Mr Paul Liddell,
Lakelovers, The New Toffee Loft,
Kendal Road, Windermere,
Cumbria LA23 3RA
T: (015394) 88855
F: (015394) 88857
E: bookings@lakelovers.co.uk
I: www.lakelovers.co.uk

Loughrigg Suite ★★★★★
Contact: Mrs Susan Jackson,
Heart of the Lakes, Fisherbeck
Hill, Old Lake Road, Ambleside,
Cumbria LA22 0DH
T: (015394) 32321
F: (015394) 33251
E: info@heartofthelakes.co.uk
I: www.heartofthelakes.co.uk

Loughrigg View
Rating Applied For
Contact: Mrs Susan Jackson,
Heart of the Lakes, Fisherbeck
Mill, Old Lake Road, Ambleside,
Cumbria LA22 0DH
T: (015394) 32321
F: (015394) 33251
E: info@heartofthelakes.co.uk
I: www.heartofthelakes.co.uk

Establishments printed in blue have a detailed entry in this guide

Loughrigg View Cottage ★★★
Contact: Mr and Mrs James and
Patricia Redman, Crow How
Hotel, Rydal Road, Ambleside,
Cumbria LA22 9PN
T: (015394) 32193
F: (015394) 31770
E: patredman200@
netscapeonline.com

Low Brow Barn
Rating Applied For
Contact: Mrs Susan Jackson,
Heart of the Lakes, Fisherbeck
Mill, Old Lake Road, Ambleside,
Cumbria LA22 0DH
T: (015394) 32321
F: (015394) 33251
E: info@heartofthelakes.co.uk
I: www.heartofthelakes.co.uk

Low Grove Cottage ★★★★
Contact: Mrs Susan Jackson,
Heart of the Lakes, Fisherbeck
Hill, Old Lake Road, Ambleside,
Cumbria LA22 0DH
T: (015394) 32321
F: (015394) 33251
E: info@heartofthelakes.co.uk
I: www.heartofthelakes.co.uk

Low White Stones ★★★★
Contact: Mrs Susan Jackson,
Heart of the Lakes, Fisherbeck
Hill, Old Lake Road, Ambleside,
Cumbria LA22 0DH
T: (015394) 32321
F: (015394) 33251
E: info@heartofthelakes.co.uk
I: www.heartofthelakes.co.uk

Martins Nest ★★★★
Contact: Mrs Susan Jackson,
Heart of the Lakes, Fisherbeck
Hill, Old Lake Road, Ambleside,
Cumbria LA22 0DH
T: (015394) 32321
F: (015394) 33251
E: info@heartofthelakes.co.uk
I: www.heartofthelakes.co.uk

May Cottage ★★★★
Contact: Mr C Evans, 3 Freshwell
Street, Saffron Walden, Essex
CB10 1BY

Melverley ★★★
Contact: Mrs Susan Jackson,
Heart of the Lakes, Fisherbeck
Mill, Old Lake Road, Ambleside,
Cumbria LA22 0DH
T: (015394) 32321
F: (015394) 33251
E: info@heartofthelakes.co.uk
I: www.heartofthelakes.co.uk

Mickle Moss ★★
Contact: Mr Paul Liddell,
Lakelovers, The New Toffee Loft,
Kendal Road, Windermere,
Cumbria LA23 3RA
T: (015394) 88855
F: (015394) 88857
E: bookings@lakelovers.co.uk
I: www.lakelovers.co.uk

Milestones ★★★★
Contact: Mr Paul Liddell,
Lakelovers, The New Toffee Loft,
Kendal Road, Windermere,
Cumbria LA23 3RA
T: (015394) 88855
F: (015394) 88857
E: bookings@lakelovers.co.uk
I: www.lakelovers.co.uk

Mill Brow Farm Cottage
★★★★
Contact: Mrs Pat Long, Mill
Brow Farm, Skelwith Bridge,
Ambleside, Cumbria LA22 9NH
T: (015394) 33253

Miller Bridge
Rating Applied For
Contact: Mr Paul Liddell,
Lakelovers, The New Toffee Loft,
Kendal Road, Bowness-on-
Windermere, Windermere,
Cumbria LA23 3RA
T: (015394) 88855
F: (015394) 88857
E: bookings@lakelovers.co.uk
I: www.lakelovers.co.uk

Mountain View ★★★
Contact: Mr D Hogarth,
Cumbrian Cottages, 7 The
Crescent, Carlisle, CA1 1QW
T: (01228) 599960 & 599950
F: (01228) 599970
E: enquiries@
cumbrian-cottages.co.uk
I: www.cumbrian-cottages.co.uk

Nook End Annexe ★★★
Contact: Mr John Serginson, The
Lakeland Cottage Company,
Waterside House, Newby Bridge,
Ulverston, Cumbria LA12 8AN
T: (015395) 30024
F: (015395) 31932
E: john@
lakeland-cottage-company.
co.uk
I: www.
lakeland-cottage-company.
co.uk

Nook End Farm ★★★★
Contact: Mr John Serginson, The
Lakeland Cottage Company,
Waterside House, Newby Bridge,
Ulverston, Cumbria LA12 8AN
T: (015395) 30024
F: (015395) 31932
E: john@
lakeland-cottage-company.
co.uk
I: www.
lakeland-cottage-company.
co.uk

North Cottage ★★★
Contact: Mrs Susan Jackson,
Heart of the Lakes, Fisherbeck
Hill, Old Lake Road, Ambleside,
Cumbria LA22 0DH
T: (015394) 32321
F: (015394) 33251
E: info@heartofthelakes.co.uk
I: www.heartofthelakes.co.uk

Oak Cottage ★★★
Contact: Mrs Susan Jackson,
Heart of the Lakes, Fisherbeck
Mill, Old Lake Road, Ambleside,
Cumbria LA22 0DH
T: (015394) 32321
F: (015394) 33251
E: info@heartofthelakes.co.uk
I: www.heartofthelakes.co.uk

Oaklands's ★★★
Contact: Mr D Hogarth,
Cumbrian Cottages, 7 The
Crescent, Carlisle, CA1 1QW
T: (01228) 599960
F: (01228) 599970
E: enquiries@
cumbrian-cottages.co.uk
I: www.cumbrian-cottages.co.uk

Old Coach House, Riverside
and Garden Cottages★★★★
Contact: Mr V R Vyner-Brooks,
Old Coach House, Riverside and
Garden Cottages, Middle
Barrows Green, Kendal, Cumbria
LA8 0JG
T: (0151526) 5451/9321 &
(015395) 60242
F: (0151) 526 1331
I: www.primecottages.co.uk

Old Gale Farmhouse ★★★
Contact: Mr D Hogarth,
Cumbrian Cottages, 7 The
Crescent, Carlisle, CA1 1QW
T: (01228) 599960
F: (01228) 599970
E: enquiries@
cumbrian-cottages.co.uk
I: www.cumbrian-cottages.co.uk

Old Mill Cottage ★★★
Contact: Mrs Susan Jackson,
Heart of the Lakes, Fisherbeck
Hill, Old Lake Road, Ambleside,
Cumbria LA22 0DH
T: (015394) 32321
F: (015394) 33251
E: info@heartofthelakes.co.uk
I: www.heartofthelakes.co.uk

Otters Holt ★★★★
Contact: Mrs Susan Jackson,
Heart of the Lakes, Fisherbeck
Mill, Old Lake Road, Ambleside,
Cumbria LA22 0DH
T: (015394) 32321
F: (015394) 33251
E: info@heartofthelakes.co.uk
I: www.heartofthelakes.co.uk

Overbeck Cottage ★★★★
Contact: Mr and Mrs A T Rhone,
Riverside Lodge, Rothay Bridge,
Ambleside, Cumbria LA22 0EH
T: (015394) 34208
E: alanrhone@riversidelodge.
co.uk
I: www.riversidelodge.co.uk

Overghyll ★★★
Contact: Mrs Susan Jackson,
Heart of the Lakes, Fisherbeck
Hill, Old Lake Road, Ambleside,
Cumbria LA22 0DH
T: (015394) 32321
F: (015394) 33251
E: info@heartofthelakes.co.uk
I: www.heartofthelakes.co.uk

Printers Cottage ★★★
Contact: Mrs Susan Jackson,
Heart of the Lakes, Fisherbeck
Hill, Old Lake Road, Ambleside,
Cumbria LA22 0DH
T: (015394) 32321
F: (015394) 33251
E: info@heartofthelakes.co.uk
I: www.heartofthelakes.co.uk

Ramsteads ★-★★
Contact: Mr G Evans,
Ramsteads, Outgate, Ambleside,
Cumbria LA22 0NH
T: (015394) 36583

The Retreat ★★★
Contact: Mrs Susan Jackson,
Heart of the Lakes, Fisherbeck
Hill, Old Lake Road, Ambleside,
Cumbria LA22 0DH
T: (015394) 32321
F: (015394) 33251
E: info@heartofthelakes.co.uk
I: www.heartofthelakes.co.uk

River Falls View ★★★★
Contact: Mr Paul Liddell,
Lakelovers, The New Toffee Loft,
Kendal Road, Windermere,
Cumbria LA23 3RA
T: (015394) 88855
F: (015394) 88857
E: bookings@lakelovers.co.uk
I: www.lakelovers.co.uk

Robin Cottage ★★
Contact: Mrs Susan Jackson,
Heart of the Lakes, Fisherbeck
Hill, Old Lake Road, Ambleside,
Cumbria LA22 0DH
T: (015394) 32321
F: (015394) 33251
E: info@heartofthelakes.co.uk
I: www.heartofthelakes.co.uk

Rose Cottage ★★★
Contact: Mrs Susan Jackson,
Heart of the Lakes, Fisherbeck
Hill, Old Lake Road, Ambleside,
Cumbria LA22 0DH
T: (015394) 32321
F: (015394) 33251
E: info@heartofthelakes.co.uk
I: www.heartofthelakes.co.uk

Rushbrook Cottage ★★★★
Contact: Mrs Susan Jackson,
Heart of the Lakes, Fisherbeck
Hill, Old Lake Road, Ambleside,
Cumbria LA22 0DH
T: (015394) 32321
F: (015394) 33251
E: info@heartofthelakes.co.uk
I: www.heartofthelakes.co.uk

Sarum ★★★
Contact: Ms J Hughes, 95 Lark
Hill Lane, Formby, Liverpool,
L37 1LU
T: (01704) 831558

Scandale Bridge Cottage ★★★
Contact: Mr and Mrs Derek
Sweeney, Lakeland Traditional
Inns and Cottages, Kings Head
Hotel, Thirlspot, Keswick,
Cumbria CA12 4TN
T: 0870 2142 & (017687) 72393
F: (017687) 72309
E: scandale@lakelandsheart.
demon.co.uk
I: www.lakelandsheart.com

Spring Cottage ★★★
Contact: Mrs Susan Jackson,
Heart of the Lakes, Fisherbeck
Hill, Old Lake Road, Ambleside,
Cumbria LA22 0DH
T: (015394) 32321
F: (015394) 33251
E: info@heartofthelakes.co.uk
I: www.heartofthelakes.co.uk

Spring Cottage
Rating Applied For
Contact: Mr Paul Liddell,
Lakelovers, The New Toffee Loft,
Kendal Road, Bowness-on-
Windermere, Windermere,
Cumbria LA23 3RA
T: (015394) 88855
F: (015394) 88857
E: bookings@lakelovers.co.uk
I: www.lakelovers.co.uk

Establishments printed in blue have a detailed entry in this guide

Squirrel Bank ★★★
Contact: Mr D Hogarth,
Cumbrian Cottages, 7 The
Crescent, Carlisle, CA1 1QW
T: (01228) 599960 & 599950
F: (01228) 599970
E: enquiries@
cumbrian-cottages.co.uk
I: www.cumbrian-cottages.co.uk

Squirrel's Nest ★★★★
Contact: Mrs Susan Jackson,
Heart of the Lakes, Fisherbeck
Mill, Old Lake Road, Ambleside,
Cumbria LA22 0DH
T: (015394) 32321
F: (015394) 33251
E: info@heartofthelakes.co.uk
I: www.heartofthelakes.co.uk

The Stables ★★★★★
Contact: Mrs Susan Jackson,
Heart of the Lakes, Fisherbeck
Hill, Old Lake Road, Ambleside,
Cumbria LA22 0DH
T: (015394) 32321
F: (015394) 33251
E: info@heartofthelakes.co.uk
I: www.heartofthelakes.co.uk

Steeple View ★★★
Contact: Mrs Susan Jackson,
Heart of the Lakes, Fisherbeck
Hill, Old Lake Road, Ambleside,
Cumbria LA22 0DH
T: (015394) 32321
F: (015394) 33251
E: info@heartofthelakes.co.uk
I: www.heartofthelakes.co.uk

Striding Home ★★★★
Contact: Mrs Susan Jackson,
Heart of the Lakes, Fisherbeck
Mill, Old Lake Road, Ambleside,
Cumbria LA22 0DH
T: (015394) 32321
F: (015394) 33251
E: info@heartofthelakes.co.uk
I: www.heartofthelakes.co.uk

2 Sunny Bank Cottages ★★
Contact: Mrs Susan Jackson,
Heart of the Lakes, Fisherbeck
Mill, Old Lake Road, Ambleside,
Cumbria LA22 0DH
T: (015394) 32321
F: (015394) 33251
E: info@heartofthelakes.co.uk
I: www.heartofthelakes.co.uk

Swallowdale ★★★★
Contact: Mrs Susan Jackson,
Heart of the Lakes, Fisherbeck
Hill, Old Lake Road, Ambleside,
Cumbria LA22 0DH
T: (015394) 32321
F: (015394) 33251
E: info@heartofthelakes.co.uk
I: www.heartofthelakes.co.uk

Sweden Bank ★★★★
Contact: Mrs Susan Jackson,
Heart of the Lakes, Fisherbeck
Hill, Old Lake Road, Ambleside,
Cumbria LA22 0DH
T: (015394) 32321
F: (015394) 33251
E: info@heartofthelakes.co.uk
I: www.heartofthelakes.co.uk

Thomas Fold Cottage ★★★★
Contact: Mrs Susan Jackson,
Heart of the Lakes, Fisherbeck
Hill, Old Lake Road, Ambleside,
Cumbria LA22 0DH
T: (015394) 32321
F: (015394) 33251
E: info@heartofthelakes.co.uk
I: www.heartofthelakes.co.uk

1 Tom Fold ★★★
Contact: Mr Paul Liddell,
Lakelovers, The New Toffee Loft,
Kendal Road, Windermere,
Cumbria LA23 3RA
T: (015394) 88855
F: (015394) 88857
E: bookings@lakelovers.co.uk
I: www.lakelovers.co.uk

Top O' The Stairs ★★★★
Contact: Mrs Susan Jackson,
Heart of the Lakes, Fisherbeck
Mill, Old Lake Road, Ambleside,
Cumbria LA22 0DH
T: (015394) 32321
F: (015394) 33251
E: info@heartofthelakes.co.uk
I: www.heartofthelakes.co.uk

Tottle Bank ★★★
Contact: Mr D Hogarth,
Cumbrian Cottages, 7 The
Crescent, Carlisle, CA1 1QW
T: (01228) 599960
F: (01228) 599970
E: enquiries@
cumbrian-cottages.co.uk
I: www.cumbrian-cottages.co.uk

Tree Tops ★★★★
Contact: Mr D Hogarth,
Cumbrian Cottages, 7 The
Crescent, Carlisle, CA1 1QW
T: (01228) 599960
F: (01228) 599970
E: enquiries@
cumbrian-cottages.co.uk
I: www.cumbrian-cottages.co.uk

Upper Tweenways ★★★★
Contact: Mrs Susan Jackson,
Heart of the Lakes, Fisherbeck
Hill, Old Lake Road, Ambleside,
Cumbria LA22 0DH
T: (015394) 32321
F: (015394) 33251
E: info@heartofthelakes.co.uk
I: www.heartofthelakes.co.uk

Wansfell ★★★★
Contact: Mrs Susan Jackson,
Heart of the Lakes, Fisherbeck
Hill, Old Lake Road, Ambleside,
Cumbria LA22 0DH
T: (015394) 32321
F: (015394) 33251
E: info@heartofthelakes.co.uk
I: www.heartofthelakes.co.uk

Waterfalls ★★★★
Contact: Mrs Susan Jackson,
Heart of the Lakes, Fisherbeck
Mill, Old Lake Road, Ambleside,
Cumbria LA22 0DH
T: (015394) 32321
F: (015394) 33251
E: info@heartofthelakes.co.uk
I: www.heartofthelakes.co.uk

Wayside Cottage ★★★★
Contact: Dr Leech, 22 Styvechale
Avenue, Coventry, Warwickshire
CV5 6DX
T: (02476) 677549 &
07712 353201
E: waysidecottage@lineone.net
I: website.lineone.
net/~waysidecottage

Wetherlam ★★★
Contact: Mrs Susan Jackson,
Heart of the Lakes, Fisherbeck
Hill, Old Lake Road, Ambleside,
Cumbria LA22 0DH
T: (015394) 32321
F: (015394) 33251
E: info@heartofthelakes.co.uk
I: www.heartofthelakes.co.uk

Wilmar Cottage ★★
Contact: Mrs Susan Jackson,
Heart of the Lakes, Fisherbeck
Mill, Old Lake Road, Ambleside,
Cumbria LA22 0DH
T: (015394) 32321
F: (015394) 33251
E: info@heartofthelakes.co.uk
I: www.heartofthelakes.co.uk

Windermere Suite ★★★★★
Contact: Mrs Susan Jackson,
Heart of the Lakes, Fisherbeck
Hill, Old Lake Road, Ambleside,
Cumbria LA22 0DH
T: (015394) 32321
F: (015394) 33251
E: info@heartofthelakes.co.uk
I: www.heartofthelakes.co.uk

Woolly End
Rating Applied For
Contact: Mr Paul Liddell,
Lakelovers, The New Toffee Loft,
Kendal Road, Windermere,
Cumbria LA23 3RA
T: (015394) 88855
F: (015394) 88857
E: bookings@lakelovers.co.uk
I: www.lakelovers.co.uk

Wren Cottage ★★★
Contact: Mrs Susan Jackson,
Heart of the Lakes, Fisherbeck
Mill, Old Lake Road, Ambleside,
Cumbria LA22 0DH
T: (015394) 32321
F: (015394) 33251
E: info@heartofthelakes.co.uk
I: www.heartofthelakes.co.uk

Wykefield Cottages ★★★★
Contact: Mr D Hogarth,
Cumbrian Cottages, 7 The
Crescent, Carlisle, CA1 1QW
T: (01228) 599960 & 599950
F: (01228) 599970
E: enquiries@
cumbrian-cottages.co.uk
I: www.cumbrian-cottages.co.uk

APPLEBY-IN-WESTMORLAND
Cumbria

Black Bull ★★★★
Contact: Mr D Hogarth,
Cumbrian Cottages, 7 The
Crescent, Carlisle, CA1 1QW
T: (01228) 599960 & 599950
F: (01228) 599970
E: enquiries@
cumbrian-cottages.co.uk
I: www.cumbrian-cottages.co.uk

Dunkirk ★★★★
Contact: Mr Paul Crosbie, 30
Eagle Wharf Court, Lafone
Street, London SE1 2LZ
T: (020) 7403 7346 &
07970 940935
E: paul.crosbie@the-sun.co.uk

Holly Lodge ★★★
Contact: Mr Nigel Hodgkinson,
Holly Lodge, Roman Road,
Appleby-in-Westmorland,
Cumbria CA16 6JH
T: (017683) 51850

Ivy Cottage ★★★
Contact: Mrs H Grisdale,
Penerin, Long Marton, Appleby-
in-Westmorland, Cumbria
CA16 6BN
T: (017683) 61233

**Milburn Grange Holiday
Cottages★★★**
Contact: Mrs Margaret Burke,
Milburn Grange Holiday
Cottages, Milburn Grange,
Knock, Appleby-in-
Westmorland, Cumbria
CA16 6DR
T: (017683) 61867 & 0780 104
4399
F: (017683) 61867
E: mburke2606@aol.com
I: www.oas.
co.uk/ukcottages/
milburngrange/

Owl Cottage ★★
Contact: Dales Hol Cot Ref:2923,
Dales Holiday Cottages, Carleton
Business Park, Carleton New
Road, Skipton, North Yorkshire
BD23 2AA
T: (01756) 799821 & 790919
F: (01756) 797012
E: info@dalesholcot.com
I: www.dalesholcot.com

APPLETHWAITE
Cumbria

The Manesty ★★★★
Contact: Mr D Hogarth,
Cumbrian Cottages, 7 The
Crescent, Carlisle, CA1 1QW
T: (01228) 599960 & 599950
F: (01228) 599970
E: enquiries@
cumbrian-cottages.co.uk
I: www.cumbrian-cottages.co.uk

No1 – No5 Gale Cottages
Rating Applied For
Contact: Mr Thomas Ryan, Gale
Cottage, Applethwaite, Keswick,
Cumbria CA12 4PL
T: (017687) 72413
F: (017687) 75706
E: ryan@applethwaite.com
I: www.galecottages.com

ARMATHWAITE
Cumbria

Coombs Cottage ★★★★
Contact: Mr D Hogarth,
Cumbrian Cottages, 7 The
Crescent, Carlisle, CA1 1QW
T: (01228) 599960 & 599950
F: (01228) 599970
E: enquiries@
cumbrian-cottages.co.uk
I: www.cumbrian-cottages.co.uk

Establishments printed in blue have a detailed entry in this guide

Longdales Cottage ★★★
Contact: Mr D Hogarth,
Cumbrian Cottages, 7 The
Crescent, Carlisle, CA1 1QW
T: (01228) 599960
F: (01228) 599970
E: enquiries@
cumbrian-cottages.co.uk
I: www.cumbrian-cottages.co.uk

ASPATRIA
Cumbria

Halls Bank Farm ★★★★★
Contact: Messrs G H Wilkinson,
Arkleby House, Arkleby, Aspatria,
Carlisle, Cumbria CA5 2BP
T: (016973) 20374

AYSIDE
Cumbria

Brookfield Cotttage ★★★★
Contact: Dales Hold Cot
Ref:2649, Dales Holiday
Cottages, Carleton Business
Park, Carleton New Road,
Skipton, North Yorkshire
BD23 2AA
T: (01756) 799821 & 790919
F: (01756) 797012
E: inf@dalesholcot.com
I: www.dalesholcot.com

BACKBARROW
Cumbria

Megan's Retreat ★★★★
Contact: Mr and Mrs Steven and
Lorraine Brierley, 68 Forge
Fields, Sandbach, Cheshire
CW11 3RN
T: (01270) 765068 & 766213
F: (01270) 765068
E: megansretreat@yahoo.co.uk
I: www.geocities.
com/megansretreat

BAILEY
Cumbria

Bailey Mill ★★-★★★
Contact: Mrs P Copeland, Bailey
Mill, Bailey, Newcastleton,
Roxburghshire TD9 0TR
T: (016977) 48617 & 48057
F: (016977) 48617
I: www.holidaycottagescumbria.
co.uk

Saughs Farm Cottages ★★★★
Contact: Mrs Jane Gray, Saughs
Farm Cottages, Saughs Farm,
Bailey, Newcastleton,
Roxburghshire TD9 0TT
T: (016977) 48346 & 48000
F: (016977) 48346
E: skylark@onholiday.co.uk
I: www.skylarkcottages.co.uk

BAMPTON
Cumbria

Tethera ★★★★
Contact: Mr Martin Wardle,
Lakes and Valleys, North Lodge,
Longtail Hill, Bowness-on-
Windermere, Windermere,
Cumbria LA23 3JD
T: (015394) 88612
F: (015394) 48988
E: lakesandvalleys@aol.com
I: www.lakesandvalleys.co.uk

Well Cottage ★★★
Contact: Mr Martin Wardle,
Lakes and Valleys, North Lodge,
Longtail Hill, Bowness-on-
Windermere, Windermere,
Cumbria LA23 3JD
T: (015394) 88612
F: (015394) 48988
E: lakesandvalleys@aol.com
I: www.lakesandvalleys.co.uk

BAMPTON GRANGE
Cumbria

Town End Cottage ★★★★
Contact: Mr Martin Wardle,
Lakes and Valleys, North Lodge,
Longtail Hill, Bowness-on-
Windermere, Windermere,
Cumbria LA23 3JD
T: (015394) 47477
F: (015394) 48988
E: lakesandvalleys@aol.com
I: www.lakesandvalleys.co.uk

BARRAS
Cumbria

Manor House ★★★★
Contact: Country Holidays
ref:1573, Spring Mill, Earby,
Barnoldswick, Lancashire
BB94 0AA
T: (01282) 445096
F: (01282) 844288
E: sales@ttgihg.co.uk
I: www.country-holidays.co.uk

BASSENTHWAITE
Cumbria

Apple Tree Cottage ★★★★
Contact: Mrs Jill Pointon, The
Lodge, Low Lorton,
Cockermouth, Cumbria
CA13 9UP
T: (01900) 85011 & 85637

Brook Cottage ★★★★
Contact: Mr D Hogarth,
Cumbrian Cottages, 7 The
Crescent, Carlisle, CA1 1QW
T: (01228) 599960
F: (01228) 599970
E: enquiries@
cumbrian-cottages.co.uk
I: www.cumbrian-cottages.co.uk

Castle Hill Cottage ★★★★
Contact: Mr D Hogarth,
Cumbrian Cottages, 7 The
Crescent, Carlisle, CA1 1QW
T: (01228) 599960 & 599950
F: (01228) 599970
E: enquiries@
cumbrian-cottages.co.uk
I: www.cumbrian-cottages.co.uk

Garries Cottage ★★★
Contact: Mr D Hogarth,
Cumbrian Cottages, 7 The
Crescent, Carlisle, CA1 1QW
T: (01228) 599960
F: (01228) 599970
E: enquiries@
cumbrian-cottages.co.uk
I: www.cumbrian-cottages.co.uk

High Spy ★★★
Contact: Mr D Hogarth,
Cumbrian Cottages, 7 The
Crescent, Carlisle, CA1 1QW
T: (01228) 599960 & 599950
F: (01228) 599970
E: enquiries@
cumbrian-cottages.co.uk
I: www.cumbrian-cottages.co.uk

Irton House Farm ★★★★
Contact: Mr and Mrs R W
Almond, Irton House Farm, Isel,
Cockermouth, Cumbria
CA13 9ST
T: (017687) 76380
F: (017687) 76090
E: almond@farmersweekly.net
I: www.almondirtonhousefarm.
com

6 Low Kiln Court ★★★★
Contact: Mr D Hogarth,
Cumbrian Cottages, 7 The
Crescent, Carlisle, CA1 1QW
T: (01228) 599960
F: (01228) 599970
E: enquiries@
cumbrian-cottages.co.uk
I: www.cumbrian-cottages.co.uk

Low Kiln Hill ★★★
Contact: Mr D Hogarth,
Cumbrian Cottages, 7 The
Crescent, Carlisle, CA1 1QW
T: (01228) 599960
F: (01228) 599970
E: enquiries@
cumbrian-cottages.co.uk
I: www.cumbrian-cottages.co.uk

**Melbecks Holidays Homes
★★★-★★★★**
Contact: Mr and Mrs Burton,
Melbecks Holidays Homes,
Bassenthwaite, Keswick,
Cumbria CA12 4QX
T: (017687) 76451
F: (017687) 76451

Mireside Farmhouse ★★★★
Contact: Ms Sally Phillips,
Parkergate, Bassenthwaite,
Keswick, Cumbria CA12 4QG
T: (017687) 76962
F: (017687) 76911
E: sally@keswick.org.uk

Random Stones ★★★★
Contact: Mrs Susan Jackson,
Heart of the Lakes, Fisherbeck
Mill, Old Lake Road, Ambleside,
Cumbria LA22 0DH
T: (015394) 32321
F: (015394) 33251
E: info@heartofthelakes.co.uk
I: www.heartofthelakes.co.uk

**Riggs Cottage
Rating Applied For**
Contact: Mr D Hogarth,
Cumbrian Cottages, 7 The
Crescent, Carlisle, CA1 1QW
T: (01228) 599960 & 599950
F: (01228) 599970
E: enquiries@
cumbrian-cottages.co.uk
I: www.cumbrian-cottages.co.uk

The Ruddings ★★★
Contact: Mr D Hogarth,
Cumbrian Cottages, 7 The
Crescent, Carlisle, CA1 1QW
T: (01228) 599960
F: (01228) 599970
E: enquiries@
cumbrian-cottages.co.uk
I: www.cumbrian-cottages.co.uk

BECKFOOT
Cumbria

Seaview Farmhouse ★★★★★
Contact: Mr & Mrs P&B Doherty,
Seaview Cottage, Beckfoot,
Silloth, Carlisle CA5 4LA
T: 07720 572203
E: patbren@compuserve.com

BEETHAM
Cumbria

Ashton Lodge ★★★
Contact: Country Holidays
ref:9647, Spring Mill, Earby,
Barnoldswick, Lancashire
BB94 0AA
T: (01282) 445096
F: (01282) 844288
E: sales@ttgihg.co.uk
I: www.country-holidays.co.uk

BERRIER
Cumbria

Bells Farm ★★★
Contact: Mr D Hogarth,
Cumbrian Cottages, 7 The
Crescent, Carlisle, CA1 1QW
T: (01228) 599960 & 599950
F: (01228) 599970
E: enquiries@
cumbrian-cottages.co.uk
I: www.cumbrian-cottages.co.uk

BEWCASTLE
Cumbria

Arch View ★★★-★★★★
Contact: Mrs J James, Arch View,
Midtodhills Farm, Bew Castle,
Roadhead, Carlisle CA6 6PF
T: (016977) 48213
F: (016977) 48213
E: bewcastlecott@aol.com
I: www.holidaycottagescarlisle.
co.uk

**Bank End Farm Cottages (Old
Farm Cottage and Barn
Cottage)★★★**
Contact: Mrs J Liddle, Bank End
Farm Cottages (Old Farm
Cottage and Barn Cottage), Bank
End Farm, Bewcastle, Roadhead,
Carlisle CA6 6NU
T: (016977) 48644
F: (016977) 48644

BLAWITH
Cumbria

Birchbank Cottage ★★★★
Contact: Mrs L M Nicholson,
Birchbank, Blawith, Ulverston,
Cumbria LA12 8EW
T: (01229) 885277
E: birchbank@btinternet.com

Blea Brows ★★★
Contact: Mr Philip Johnston, The
Coppermines Coniston,
Coppermines Valley, Coniston,
Cumbria LA21 8HX
T: (015394) 41765 &
07721 584488
E: bookings@coppermines.co.uk
I: www.coppermines.co.uk

BOLTON
Cumbria

**The Stable Annexe and Glebe
Stables★★★**
Contact: Dales Hol Cot
Ref:3129/2889, Dales Holiday
Cottages, Carleton Business
Park, Carleton New Road,
Skipton, North Yorkshire
BD23 2AA
T: (01756) 799821 & 790919
F: (01756) 797012
E: info@dalesholcot.com
I: www.dalesholcot.com

BORROWDALE
Cumbria

Barrow Gate ★★
Contact: Mr David Burton,
Lakeland Cottage Holidays, 3 The
Heads, Keswick, Cumbria
CA12 5ES
T: (017687) 71071
F: (017687) 75036

Derwent Farmhouse ★★
Contact: Mr David Burton,
Lakeland Cottage Holidays, 3 The
Heads, Keswick, Cumbria
CA12 5ES
T: (017687) 71071
F: (017687) 75036
E: info@lakelandcottages.co.uk
I: www.lakelandcottages.co.uk/

Hazel Bank Cottage ★★★★
Contact: Mr and Mrs Glen and
Brenda Davies, Hazel Bank
Country House, Rosthwaite,
Keswick, Cumbria CA12 5XB
T: (017687) 77248
F: (017687) 77373
E: enquiries@hazelbankhotel.
co.uk
I: www.hazelbankhotel.co.uk

**Rockery Cottage & Maiden
Moor Cottage**★★-★★★★
Contact: Mrs Wood, Greenbank,
Borrowdale, Keswick, Cumbria
CA12 5UY
T: (017687) 77215

Scale Force Cottage ★★★
Contact: Mr David Burton,
Lakeland Cottage Holidays, 3 The
Heads, Keswick, Cumbria
CA12 5ES
T: (017687) 71071
F: (017687) 75036
E: info@lakelandcottages.co.uk
I: www.lakelandcottages.co.uk/

Tan Cottage ★★★
Contact: Mr David Burton,
Lakeland Cottage Holidays, 3 The
Heads, Keswick, Cumbria
CA12 5ES
T: (017687) 71071
F: (017687) 75036
E: info@lakelandcottages.co.uk
I: www.lakelandcottages.co.uk/

BOTHEL
Cumbria

The Lodge ★★★★
Contact: Mrs D E Shankland,
Quarry House, Bothel, Wigton,
Cumbria CA7 2HH
T: (016973) 21674 &
07751 765087
E: quarrylodgebothel@barclays.
net

BOUTH
Cumbria

Crag House Cottage ★★★★
Contact: Mr John Serginson, The
Lakeland Cottage Company,
Waterside House, Newby Bridge,
Ulverston, Cumbria LA12 8AN
T: (015395) 30024
F: (015395) 31932
E: john@
lakeland-cottage-company.
co.uk
I: www.
lakeland-cottage-company.
co.uk

Rose Cottage ★★★★
Contact: Mr John Serginson, The
Lakeland Cottage Company,
Waterside House, Newby Bridge,
Ulverston, Cumbria LA12 8AN
T: (015395) 30024
F: (015395) 31932
E: john@
lakeland-cottage-company.
co.uk
I: www.
lakeland-cottage-company.
co.uk

BOWMANSTEAD
Cumbria

Number One Lake View
★★★★
Contact: Mr Philip Johnson,
Coppermines & Coniston
Cottages, The Powder Magazine,
Coppermines Valley, Coniston,
Cumbria LA21 8HX
T: (01539) 41765
I: www.coppermines.co.uk

BOWNESS-ON-WINDERMERE
Cumbria

April Cottage
Rating Applied For
Contact: Mr Sam Lindley, G E
Lindley & Son, Pontey Farm,
Meltham Road, Honley,
Huddersfield, Yorkshire HD7
T: (01484) 661723
F: (01484) 663839
E: lindleys@ponteyfarm.fsnet.
co.uk
I: www.lakeholidays.com

Beau Penny ★★★
Contact: Ms Lynne Lewthwaite,
Lakelovers, The New Toffee Loft,
Kendal Road, Bowness-on-
Windermere, Windermere,
Cumbria LA23 3RA
T: (015394) 88855
F: (015394) 88857
E: bookings@lakelovers.co.uk
I: www.lakelovers.co.uk

Beech How Cottage ★★★
Contact: Mr Paul Liddell,
Lakelovers, The New Toffee Loft,
Kendal Road, Windermere,
Cumbria LA23 3RA
T: (015394) 88855
F: (015394) 88857
E: bookings@lakelovers.co.uk
I: www.lakelovers.co.uk

3 Beechwood Close ★★★
Contact: Mr Paul Liddell,
Lakelovers, The New Toffee Loft,
Kendal Road, Windermere,
Cumbria LA23 3RA
T: (015394) 88855
F: (015394) 88857
E: bookings@lakelovers.co.uk
I: www.lakelovers.co.uk

The Birds Nest ★★★
Contact: Mrs Susan Jackson,
Heart of the Lakes, Fisherbeck
Hill, Old Lake Road, Ambleside,
Cumbria LA22 0DH
T: (015394) 32321
F: (015394) 33251
E: info@heartofthelakes.co.uk
I: www.heartofthelakes.co.uk

Biskey Rise ★★★★
Contact: Mrs Susan Jackson,
Heart of the Lakes, Fisherbeck
Hill, Old Lake Road, Ambleside,
Cumbria LA22 0DH
T: (015394) 32321
F: (015394) 33251
E: info@heartofthelakes.co.uk
I: www.heartofthelakes.co.uk

Black Beck Cottage ★★★★★
Contact: Mr D Hogarth,
Cumbrian Cottages, 7 The
Crescent, Carlisle, CA1 1QW
T: (01228) 599960 & 599950
F: (01228) 599970
E: enquiries@
cumbrian-cottages.co.uk
I: www.cumbrian-cottages.co.uk

**Bluebells Ground & 1st Floor
Flat** ★★★★
Contact: Mr D Hogarth,
Cumbrian Cottages, 7 The
Crescent, Carlisle, CA1 1QW
T: (01228) 599960 & 599950
F: (01228) 599970
E: enquiries@
cumbrian-cottages.co.uk
I: www.cumbrian-cottages.co.uk

The Bothy ★★★
Contact: Mr D Hogarth,
Cumbrian Cottages, 7 The
Crescent, Carlisle, CA1 1QW
T: (01228) 599960 & 599950
F: (01228) 599970
E: enquiries@
cumbrian-cottages.co.uk
I: www.cumbrian-cottages.co.uk

Bowmere ★★★★
Contact: Mr D Hogarth,
Cumbrian Cottages, 7 The
Crescent, Carlisle, CA1 1QW
T: (01228) 599960 & 599950
F: (01228) 599970
E: enquiries@
cumbrian-cottages.co.uk
I: www.cumbrian-cottages.co.uk

Brackenrigg Lodge ★★★★★
Contact: Mrs Susan Jackson,
Heart of the Lakes, Fisherbeck
Hill, Old Lake Road, Ambleside,
Cumbria LA22 0DH
T: (015394) 32321
F: (015394) 33251
E: info@heartofthelakes.co.uk
I: www.heartofthelakes.co.uk

Brantfield Cottage ★★★
Contact: Mr D Hogarth,
Cumbrian Cottages, 7 The
Crescent, Carlisle, CA1 1QW
T: (01228) 599960 & 599950
F: (01228) 599970
E: enquiries@
cumbrian-cottages.co.uk
I: www.cumbrian-cottages.co.uk

Brantmere ★★★
Contact: Mr and Mrs Norman
and Christine McVeigh, 24 Oak
Street, Windermere, Cumbria
LA23 1EN
T: (015394) 43404 & 44444
E: brantmere@email.com

Briarwood ★★★
Contact: Mr David Hogarth,
Cumbrian Cottages, 7 The
Crescent, Carlisle, CA1 1QW
T: (01228) 599960 & 599950
F: (01228) 599970
E: enquiries@
cumbrian-cottages.co.uk
I: www.cumbrian-cottages.co.uk

Canons Craig ★★★★
Contact: Bowness Lakeland
Holidays, 131 Radcliff New
Road, Whitfield, Manchester,
Manchester M45 7RP
T: (0161) 796 3896
E: paul.denby@btinternet.com
I: www.freeyellow.
com/pdfedrkd/

Cherry Vale ★★★★
Contact: Mr D Hogarth,
Cumbrian Cottages, 7 The
Crescent, Carlisle, CA1 1QW
T: (01228) 599960 & 599950
F: (01228) 599970
E: enquiries@
cumbrian-cottages.co.uk
I: www.cumbrian-cottages.co.uk

Chestnut House ★★★★
Contact: Mr D Hogarth,
Cumbrian Cottages, 7 The
Crescent, Carlisle, CA1 1QW
T: (01228) 599960 & 599950
F: (01228) 599970
E: enquiries@
cumbrian-cottages.co.uk
I: www.cumbrian-cottages.co.uk

Cockshott Wood ★★★★
Contact: Mrs Susan Jackson,
Heart of the Lakes, Fisherbeck
Mill, Old Lake Road, Ambleside,
Cumbria LA22 0DH
T: (015394) 32321
F: (015394) 33251
E: info@heartofthelakes.co.uk
I: www.heartofthelakes.co.uk

Craglands ★★★
Contact: Mr D Hogarth,
Cumbrian Cottages, 7 The
Crescent, Carlisle, CA1 1QW
T: (01228) 599960 & 599950
F: (01228) 599970
E: enquiries@
cumbrian-cottages.co.uk
I: www.cumbrian-cottages.co.uk

Daisy Bank Cottage ★★★
Contact: Mr D Hogarth,
Cumbrian Cottages, 7 The
Crescent, Carlisle, CA1 1QW
T: (01228) 599960 & 599950
F: (01228) 599970
E: enquiries@
cumbrian-cottages.co.uk
I: www.cumbrian-cottages.co.uk

Deloraine ★★★
Contact: Mr G H and Mrs
Pauline Fanstone, Deloraine,
Helm Road, Bowness-on-
Windermere, Windermere,
Cumbria LA23 2HS
T: (015394) 45557
F: (015394) 43221
E: gordon@deloraine.demon.
co.uk
I: www.deloraine.demon.co.uk
🖨

Elim Cottage ★★★
Contact: Mr D Hogarth,
Cumbrian Cottages, 7 The
Crescent, Carlisle, CA1 1QW
T: (01228) 599960 & 599950
F: (01228) 599970
E: enquiries@
cumbrian-cottages.co.uk
I: www.cumbrian-cottages.co.uk

Establishments printed in blue have a detailed entry in this guide

Fair View ★★★★
Contact: Mrs Susan Jackson,
Heart of the Lakes, Fisherbeck
Hill, Old Lake Road, Ambleside,
Cumbria LA22 0DH
T: (015394) 32321
F: (015394) 33251
E: info@heartofthelakes.co.uk
I: www.heartofthelakes.co.uk

11 Fairfield ★★★
Contact: Mr and Mrs Michael
and Susan Smyth, Windy Ridge,
Beamish Lane, Albrighton,
Wolverhampton WV7 3JJ
T: (01902) 372806 & 372382
F: (01902) 372382
E: michael@smythassociates.
freeserve.co.uk

6 Fairfield ★★★★
Contact: Mrs B Killip, 6 Fairfield,
Off Brantfell Road, Bowness-on-
Windermere, Cumbria LA23 3AL
T: (015394) 45305

9 Fairfield ★★★
Contact: Mr D Hogarth,
Cumbrian Cottages, 7 The
Crescent, Carlisle, CA1 1QW
T: (01228) 599960 & 599950
F: (01228) 599970
E: enquiries@
cumbrian-cottages.co.uk
I: www.cumbrian-cottages.co.uk

Fairhaven ★★★★
Contact: Mr D Hogarth,
Cumbrian Cottages, 7 The
Crescent, Carlisle, CA1 1QW
T: (01228) 599960 & 599950
F: (01228) 599970
E: enquiries@
cumbrian-cottages.co.uk
I: www.cumbrian-cottages.co.uk

Fell Beck ★★★★
Contact: Mr John Serginson, The
Lakeland Cottage Company,
Waterside House, Newby Bridge,
Ulverston, Cumbria LA12 8AN
T: (015395) 30024
F: (015395) 31932
E: john@
lakeland-cottage-company.
co.uk
I: www.
lakeland-cottage-company.
co.uk

5 Fir Tree Crescent ★★★
Contact: Mr Paul Liddell,
Lakelovers, The New Toffee Loft,
Kendal Road, Windermere,
Cumbria LA23 3RA
T: (015394) 88855
F: (015394) 88857
E: bookings@lakelovers.co.uk
I: www.lakelovers.co.uk

Glebe Holme ★★★★
Contact: Mr D Hogarth,
Cumbrian Cottages, 7 The
Crescent, Carlisle, CA1 1QW
T: (01228) 599960
F: (01228) 599970
E: enquiries@
cumbrian-cottages.co.uk
I: www.cumbrian-cottages.co.uk

Heatherbank ★★★
Contact: Mr D Hogarth,
Cumbrian Cottages, 7 The
Crescent, Carlisle, CA1 1QW
T: (01228) 599960 & 599950
F: (01228) 599970
E: enquiries@
cumbrian-cottages.co.uk
I: www.cumbrian-cottages.co.uk

High Croft ★★★★
Contact: Mrs Susan Jackson,
Heart of the Lakes, Fisherbeck
Hill, Old Lake Road, Ambleside,
Cumbria LA22 0DH
T: (015394) 32321
F: (015394) 33251
E: info@heartofthelakes.co.uk
I: www.heartofthelakes.co.uk

Hill Crest Cottage ★★★
Contact: Mr D Hogarth,
Cumbrian Cottages, 7 The
Crescent, Carlisle, CA1 1QW
T: (01228) 599960
F: (01228) 599970
E: enquiries@
cumbrian-cottages.co.uk
I: www.cumbrian-cottages.co.uk

Hollinfield ★★★★
Contact: Mrs Susan Jackson,
Heart of the Lakes, Fisherbeck
Hill, Old Lake Road, Ambleside,
Cumbria LA22 0DH
T: (015394) 32321
F: (015394) 33251
E: info@heartofthelakes.co.uk
I: www.heartofthelakes.co.uk

Honeysuckle Cottage ★★★
Contact: Mr D Hogarth,
Cumbrian Cottages, 7 The
Crescent, Carlisle, CA1 1QW
T: (01228) 599960
F: (01228) 599970
E: enquiries@
cumbrian-cottages.co.uk
I: www.cumbrian-cottages.co.uk

Kent Cottage ★★★
Contact: Mr D Hogarth,
Cumbrian Cottages, 7 The
Crescent, Carlisle, CA1 1QW
T: (01228) 599960 & 599950
F: (01228) 599970
E: enquiries@
cumbrian-cottages.co.uk
I: www.cumbrian-cottages.co.uk

Lake View ★★★★
Contact: Mr Paul Liddell,
Lakelovers, The New Toffee Loft,
Kendal Road, Windermere,
Cumbria LA23 3RA
T: (015394) 88855
F: (015394) 88857
E: bookings@lakelovers.co.uk
I: www.lakelovers.co.uk

Ling Howe ★★★★★
Contact: Mr D Hogarth,
Cumbrian Cottages, 7 The
Crescent, Carlisle, CA1 1QW
T: (01228) 599960 & 599950
F: (01228) 599970
E: enquiries@
cumbrian-cottages.co.uk
I: www.cumbrian-cottages.co.uk

Little Gill Cottage ★★
Contact: Mr Paul Liddell,
Lakelovers, The New Toffee Loft,
Kendal Road, Windermere,
Cumbria LA23 3RA
T: (015394) 88855
F: (015394) 88857
E: bookings@lakelovers.co.uk
I: www.lakelovers.co.uk

1 Meadowcroft ★★★★
Contact: Mr D Hogarth,
Cumbrian Cottages, 7 The
Crescent, Carlisle, CA1 1QW
T: (01228) 599960 & 599950
F: (01228) 599970
E: enquiries@
cumbrian-cottages.co.uk
I: www.cumbrian-cottages.co.uk

12 Meadowcroft ★★★
Contact: Mr Paul Liddell,
Lakelovers, The New Toffee Loft,
Kendal Road, Bowness-on-
Windermere, Windermere,
Cumbria LA23 3RA
T: (015394) 88855
F: (015394) 88857
E: bookings@lakelovers.co.uk
I: www.lakelovers.co.uk

14 Meadowcroft ★★★★
Contact: Mr D Hogarth,
Cumbrian Cottages, 7 The
Crescent, Carlisle, CA1 1QW
T: (01228) 599960 & 599950
F: (01228) 599970
E: enquiries@
cumbrian-cottages.co.uk
I: www.cumbrian-cottages.co.uk

3 Meadowcroft ★★★★
Contact: Mr D Hogarth,
Cumbrian Cottages, 7 The
Crescent, Carlisle, CA1 1QW
T: (01228) 599960 & 599950
F: (01228) 599970
E: enquiries@
cumbrian-cottages.co.uk
I: www.cumbrian-cottages.co.uk

7 Meadowcroft ★★★★
Contact: Mr D Hogarth,
Cumbrian Cottages, 7 The
Crescent, Carlisle, CA1 1QW
T: (01228) 599960
F: (01228) 599970
E: enquiries@
cumbrian-cottages.co.uk
I: www.cumbrian-cottages.co.uk

Mere View ★★★★
Contact: Mr Paul Liddell,
Lakelovers, The New Toffee Loft,
Kendal Road, Windermere,
Cumbria LA23 3RA
T: (015394) 88855
F: (015394) 88857
E: bookings@lakelovers.co.uk
I: www.lakelovers.co.uk

The Oaks ★★★★
Contact: Mr D Hogarth,
Cumbrian Cottages, 7 The
Crescent, Carlisle, CA1 1QW
T: (01228) 599960 & 599950
F: (01228) 599970
E: enquiries@
cumbrian-cottages.co.uk
I: www.cumbrian-cottages.co.uk

Oakwood Cottages ★★★
Contact: Mrs J Moore, Pavey Ark,
Brantfell Road, Bowness-on-
Windermere, Windermere,
Cumbria LA23 3AE
T: (015394) 88685 &
07808 458346
F: (015394) 88685
E: mooredsr@freeserve.co.uk

Orchard House
Rating Applied For
Contact: Ms Lynne Lewthwaite,
Lakelovers, The New Toffee Loft,
Kendal Road, Bowness-on-
Windermere, Windermere,
Cumbria LA23 3RA
T: (015394) 88855
F: (015394) 88857
E: bookings@lakelovers.co.uk
I: www.lakelovers.co.uk

Penny's Nest ★★★★
Contact: Mr Paul Liddell,
Lakelovers, The New Toffee Loft,
Kendal Road, Windermere,
Cumbria LA23 3RA
T: (015394) 88855
F: (015394) 88857
E: bookings@lakelovers.co.uk
I: www.lakelovers.co.uk

Pine View ★★★
Contact: Mr D Hogarth,
Cumbrian Cottages, 7 The
Crescent, Carlisle, CA1 1QW
T: (01228) 599960 & 599950
F: (01228) 599970
E: enquiries@
cumbrian-cottages.co.uk
I: www.cumbrian-cottages.co.uk

Primrose Cottage ★★★
Contact: Mr D Hogarth,
Cumbrian Cottages, 7 The
Crescent, Carlisle, CA1 1QW
T: (01228) 599960
F: (01228) 599970
E: enquiries@
cumbrian-cottages.co.uk
I: www.cumbrian-cottages.co.uk

2B Quarry Brow ★★★
Contact: Mr Paul Liddell,
Lakelovers, The New Toffee Loft,
Kendal Road, Windermere,
Cumbria LA23 3RA
T: (015394) 88855
F: (015394) 88857
E: bookings@lakelovers.co.uk
I: www.lakelovers.co.uk

35A Quarry Rigg ★★
Contact: Mr D Hogarth,
Cumbrian Cottages, 7 The
Crescent, Carlisle, CA1 1QW
T: (01228) 599960
F: (01228) 599970
E: enquiries@
cumbrian-cottages.co.uk
I: www.cumbrian-cottages.co.uk

48A Quarry Rigg ★★★
Contact: Mr Paul Liddell,
Lakelovers, The New Toffee Loft,
Kendal Road, Bowness-on-
Windermere, Windermere,
Cumbria LA23 3RA
T: (015394) 88855
F: (015394) 88857
E: bookings@lakelovers.co.uk
I: www.lakelovers.co.uk

Rattle Beck ★★★★
Contact: Mr D Hogarth,
Cumbrian Cottages, 7 The
Crescent, Carlisle, CA1 1QW
T: (01228) 599960
F: (01228) 599970
E: enquiries@
cumbrian-cottages.co.uk
I: www.cumbrian-cottages.co.uk

Rose Cottage ★★★
Contact: Mr and Mrs Alan
Wardle, North Lodge, Longtail
Hill, Bowness-on-Windermere,
Windermere, Cumbria LA23 3JD
T: (01539) 447905
I: www.lakeland-holidays.net

Saw Mill Cottage ★★★
Contact: Mrs Susan Jackson,
Heart of the Lakes, Fisherbeck
Hill, Old Lake Road, Ambleside,
Cumbria LA22 0DH
T: (015394) 32321
F: (015394) 33251
E: info@heartofthelakes.co.uk
I: www.heartofthelakes.co.uk

Skylark ★★★★
Contact: Mr D Hogarth,
Cumbrian Cottages, 7 The
Crescent, Carlisle, CA1 1QW
T: (01228) 599960 & 599950
F: (01228) 599970
E: enquiries@
cumbrian-cottages.co.uk
I: www.cumbrian-cottages.co.uk

Solstice Cottage
Rating Applied For
Contact: Mr Paul Liddell,
Lakelovers, The New Toffee Loft,
Kendal Road, Windermere,
Cumbria LA23 3RA
T: (015394) 88855
F: (015394) 88857
E: bookings@lakelovers.co.uk
I: www.lakelovers.co.uk

Southside Cottage ★★★
Contact: Ms Lynne Lewthwaite,
Lakelovers, The New Toffee Loft,
Kendal Road, Bowness-on-
Windermere, Windermere,
Cumbria LA23 3RA
T: (015394) 88855
F: (015394) 88857
E: bookings@lakelovers.co.uk
I: www.lakelovers.co.uk

Squirrel's Nest ★★★
Contact: Mr D Hogarth,
Cumbrian Cottages, 7 The
Crescent, Carlisle, CA1 1QW
T: (01228) 599960 & 599950
F: (01228) 599970
E: enquiries@
cumbrian-cottages.co.uk
I: www.cumbrian-cottages.co.uk

Swallow's Rest ★★★
Contact: Mr Paul Liddell,
Lakelovers, The New Toffee Loft,
Kendal Road, Bowness-on-
Windermere, Windermere,
Cumbria LA23 3RA
T: (015394) 88855
F: (015394) 88857
E: bookings@lakelovers.co.uk
I: www.lakelovers.co.uk

Swan's Nest
Rating Applied For
Contact: Mr Paul Liddell,
Lakelovers, The New Toffee Loft,
Kendal Road, Bowness-on-
Windermere, Windermere,
Cumbria LA23 3RA
T: (015394) 88855
F: (015394) 88857
E: bookings@lakelovers.co.uk
I: www.lakelovers.co.uk

Tanglewood ★★★★
Contact: Mr D Hogarth,
Cumbrian Cottages, 7 The
Crescent, Carlisle, CA1 1QW
T: (01228) 599960
F: (01228) 599970
E: enquiries@
cumbrian-cottages.co.uk
I: www.cumbrian-cottages.co.uk

Waters Edge Villa ★★★★
Contact: Mr & Ms Bernard &
Michelle Twitchett & Weir,
WLHA, Waters Edge Villa, Ferry
Nab, Bowness-on-Windermere,
Windermere, Cumbria LA23 3JH
T: (015394) 43415
F: (015394) 88721
E: info@wlha.freeserve.co.uk
I: www.
windermere-lake-holidays-
afloat.co.uk

Welkom Cottage
Rating Applied For
Contact: Ms Lynne Lewthwaite,
Lakelovers, The New Toffee Loft,
Kendal Road, Bowness-on-
Windermere, Windermere,
Cumbria LA23 3RA
T: (015394) 88855
F: (015394) 88857
E: bookings@lakelovers.co.uk
I: www.lakelovers.co.uk

BOWSTON
Cumbria

Winstanley Cottage ★★★
Contact: Mr D Hogarth,
Cumbrian Cottages, 7 The
Crescent, Carlisle, CA1 1QW
T: (01228) 599960 & 599950
F: (01228) 599970
E: enquiries@
cumbrian-cottages.co.uk
I: www.cumbrian-cottages.co.uk

BRAITHWAITE
Cumbria

**Barrow View Cottage and
Cedar Cottage★★★★**
Contact: Mr C C Horton, 5 St
John's Street, Keswick, Cumbria
CA12 5AP
T: (017687) 74627
E: c.c.horton@talk21.com

Beech End ★★
Contact: Mr David Burton,
Lakeland Cottage Holidays, 3 The
Heads, Keswick, Cumbria
CA12 5ES
T: (017687) 71071
F: (017687) 75036
E: info@lakelandcottages.co.uk
I: www.lakelandcottages.co.uk

Coledale House ★★★★
Contact: Mr D Hogarth,
Cumbrian Cottages, 7 The
Crescent, Carlisle, CA1 1QW
T: (01228) 599960 & 599950
F: (01228) 599970
E: enquiries@
cumbrian-cottages.co.uk
I: www.cumbrian-cottages.co.uk

Cosy Cottage ★★★
Contact: Mr David Burton,
Lakeland Cottage Holidays, 3 The
Heads, Keswick, Cumbria
CA12 5ES
T: (017687) 71071
F: (017687) 75036
E: info@lakelandcottages.co.uk
I: www.lakelandcottages.co.uk/

Glen Cottage ★★★★
Contact: Mrs J Pilling, The Shiel,
Applethwaite, Keswick, Cumbria
CA12 4PL
T: (017687) 72171
F: (017687) 72171
E: lel@btinternet.com
I: www.cottagel.freeserve.co.uk

Green Hill ★★★★
Contact: Mrs Helen Peters, 23
Eden Park, Kirkoswald, Penrith,
Cumbria CA10 1EA
T: (01768) 898944
F: (01768) 898944
E: peters@kirkoswald.fslife.
co.uk

Highbridge Cottage ★★★★
Contact: Mr D Hogarth,
Cumbrian Cottages, 7 The
Crescent, Carlisle, CA1 1QW
T: (01228) 599960 & 599950
F: (01228) 599970
E: enquiries@
cumbrian-cottages.co.uk
I: www.cumbrian-cottages.co.uk

Kinn ★★★
Contact: Mr David Burton,
Lakeland Cottage Holidays, 3 The
Heads, Keswick, Cumbria
CA12 5ES
T: (017687) 71071
F: (017687) 75036
E: info@lakelandcottages.co.uk
I: www.lakelandcottages.co.uk

Millside Cottage ★★★★
Contact: Mr David Burton,
Lakeland Cottage Holidays, 3 The
Heads, Keswick, Cumbria
CA12 5ES
T: (017687) 71071
F: (017687) 75036
E: info@lakelandcottages.co.uk
I: www.lakelandcottages.co.uk/

Olives Cottage
Rating Applied For
Contact: Mr D Hogarth,
Cumbrian Cottages, 7 The
Crescent, Carlisle, CA1 1QW
T: (01228) 599960 & 599950
F: (01228) 599970
E: enquiries@
cumbrian-cottages.co.uk
I: www.cumbrian-cottages.co.uk

Western Cottage ★★★
Contact: Mr and Mrs D K Dutta,
38 High Street, Bugbrooke,
Northampton, Northants
NN7 3PG
T: (01604) 831279

Windrush ★★★★
Contact: Mr David Burton,
Lakeland Cottage Holidays, 3 The
Heads, Keswick, Cumbria
CA12 5ES
T: (017687) 71071
F: (017687) 75036
E: info@lakelandcottages.co.uk
I: www.lakelandcottages.co.uk/

BRAMPTON
Cumbria

Chapel House ★★★
Contact: Mrs D Potts, Chapel
House, Talkin, Brampton,
Cumbria CA8 1LP
T: (01228) 670535

Hadrian's View ★★★★
Contact: Country Holidays
ref:9870, Spring Mill, Earby,
Barnoldswick, Lancashire
BB94 0AA
T: (01282) 445096
F: (01282) 844288
E: sales@ttgihg.co.uk
I: www.country-holidays.co.uk

**Long Byres at Talkin Head
★★-★★★**
Contact: Mrs Harriet Sykes,
Talkin Head, Brampton, Cumbria
CA8 1LT
T: (016977) 3435
F: (016977) 2228
E: harriet@talkinhead.demon.
co.uk
I: www.talkinhead.demon.co.uk

**Warren Bank Cottage
★★★★★**
Contact: Mrs Margaret Douglas,
6 St Cuthberts Terrace, Hexham,
Northumberland NE46 2EL
T: (01434) 607544 &
07970 927439
E: margie@warrenbankcottage.
com
I: www.
stay@warrenbankcottage.com

BRANTHWAITE
Cumbria

The Corn Mill ★★★
Contact: Country Holidays
ref:4334, Spring Mill, Earby,
Barnoldswick, Lancashire
BB94 0AA
T: (01282) 445096
F: (01282) 844288
E: sales@ttgihg.co.uk
I: www.country-holidays.co.uk

BRIGSTEER
Cumbria

Garden Cottage ★★★★
Contact: Mr D Hogarth,
Cumbrian Cottages, 7 The
Crescent, Carlisle, CA1 1QW
T: (01228) 599960
F: (01228) 599970
E: enquiries@
cumbrian-cottages.co.uk
I: www.cumbrian-cottages.co.uk

Moss Rigg ★★★
Contact: Mr D Hogarth,
Cumbrian Cottages, 7 The
Crescent, Carlisle, CA1 1QW
T: (01228) 599960 & 599950
F: (01228) 599970
E: enquiries@
cumbrian-cottages.co.uk
I: www.cumbrian-cottages.co.uk

BROUGHTON–IN–FURNESS
Cumbria

Cooksons Cottages
Rating Applied For
Contact: Mr David Lewthwaite,
Broadgate, Thwaites, Millom,
Cumbria LA18 5JY
T: (01229) 716295
F: (01229) 716976
E: david@lewthwaite.
fsbusiness.co.uk

Holebeck Farm Cottages
★★★-★★★★
Contact: Mr Philip Johnston, The
Coppermines Coniston,
Coppermines Valley, Coniston,
Cumbria LA21 8HX
T: (015394) 41765 &
07721 584488
F: (015394) 41944
E: estateoffice@coppermines.
co.uk
I: www.coppermines.co.uk

Ring House Cottages
★★★-★★★★
Contact: Mr and Mrs Stuart &
Lynda Harrison, Ring House
Cottages, Woodland,
Broughton-in-Furness, Cumbria
LA20 6DG
T: (01229) 716578
F: (01229) 716850
E: info@ringhouse.co.uk
I: www.ringhouse.co.uk

Rose Cottage ★★★
Contact: Mrs M Harrison, Lane
End Farm, Broughton Mills,
Broughton-in-Furness, Cumbria
LA20 6AX
T: (01229) 716332
I: www.lakesbreaks.co.uk

Seathwaite Lodge ★★★
Contact: Country Holidays
ref:10194, Spring Mill, Earby,
Barnoldswick, Lancashire
BB94 0AA
T: 08700 723723
F: (01282) 844288
I: www.country-holidays.co.uk

Thornthwaite Farm ★★★
Contact: Mrs J Jackson,
Thornthwaite Farm, Woodland
Hall, Woodland, Broughton-in-
Furness, Cumbria LA20 6DF
T: (01229) 716340
F: (01229) 716340
I: www.lakedistrictcottages.
co.uk

BURNESIDE
Cumbria

Houseman Tenement Farm
★★★★
Contact: Mrs R Bland,
Houseman Tenement Farm,
Burneside, Kendal, Cumbria
LA8 9AG
T: (01539) 723362

BURTON-IN-KENDAL
Cumbria

Cornmillers Cottage ★★★★
Contact: Mrs K Duckett,
Cornmillers Cottage, Coat Green
Farm, Burton, Carnforth,
Lancashire LA6 1JG
T: (01524) 781535
F: (01524) 781535
E: cornmiller@supanet.com

BUTTERMERE
Cumbria

Bridge Hotel Self Catering
Apartments★★★★
Contact: Bridge Hotel,
Buttermere, Cockermouth,
Cumbria CA13 9UZ
T: (017687) 70252
F: (017687) 70215
E: enquiries@bridge-hotel.com
I: www.bridge-hotel.com

Lanthwaite Green Farm
Cottage ★★★★
Contact: Ms Catherine McGuire,
Bridge Hotel, Buttermere,
Cockermouth, Cumbria
CA13 9UZ
T: (017687) 70252
F: (017687) 70215
E: enquiries@bridge-hotel.com
I: www.bridge-hotel.com

Rannerdale Close And
Rannderdale Croft★★★
Contact: Mrs P E Beard,
Rannerdale Close And
Rannderdale Croft, Rannerdale
Farm, Buttermere, Cockermouth,
Cumbria CA13 9UY
T: (017687) 70232

CALDBECK
Cumbria

Brae Fell, High Pike ★★★
Contact: Mr Dales Hol Cot
Ref:1979/1980, Dales Holiday
Cottages, Carleton Business
Park, Carleton New Road,
Skipton, North Yorkshire
BD23 2AA
T: (01756) 799821 & 790919
F: (01756) 797012
E: info@dalesholcot.com
I: www.dalesholcot.com

High Pike and Brae Fell ★★★
Contact: Dales Hol Cot
Ref:1979/1980, Dales Holiday
Cottages, Carleton Business
Park, Carleton New Road,
Skipton, North Yorkshire
BD23 2AA
T: (01756) 799821 & 790919
F: (01756) 797012
E: info@dalesholcot.com
I: www.dalesholcot.com

Manor Cottage ★★★★
Contact: Mrs Ann Wade, Manor
Cottage, Fellside, Caldbeck,
Wigton, Cumbria CA7 8HA
T: (016974) 78214

Monkhouse Hill
★★★★-★★★★★
Contact: Mrs Jennifer Collard,
Monkhouse Hill, Sebergham,
Carlisle CA5 7HW
T: (016974) 76254
F: (016974) 76254
E: cottages@monkhousehill.
co.uk
I: www.monkhousehill.co.uk

1 Riverside Cottage ★★★★
Contact: Mr D Hogarth,
Cumbrian Cottages, 7 The
Crescent, Carlisle, CA1 1QW
T: (01228) 599960
F: (01228) 599970
E: enquiries@
cumbrian-cottages.co.uk
I: www.cumbrian-cottages.co.uk

CALDEWGATE
Cumbria

University of Northumbria
(Carlisle Campus)★★★
Contact: Mrs Dee Carruthers,
University of Northumbria
(Carlisle Campus), Old Brewery
Residences, Bridge Lane,
Caldewgate, Carlisle CA2 5SR
T: (01228) 597352 & (0191) 227
4808
F: (01228) 597352
E: d.carruthers@unn.ac.uk

CARK IN CARTMEL
Cumbria

The Mill Holiday Apartment
★★★
Contact: Mrs Teresa Watson, 12
Millstream Court, Cark in
Cartmel, Grange-over-Sands,
Cumbria LA11 7NW
T: (015395) 58519 &
079298 74479
I: www.millholidayapartment.
co.uk

Salesbrook ★★★★
Contact: Mr John Serginson, The
Lakeland Cottage Company,
Waterside House, Newby Bridge,
Ulverston, Cumbria LA12 8AN
T: (015395) 30024
F: (015395) 31932
E: john@
lakeland-cottage-company.
co.uk
I: www.
lakeland-cottage-company.
co.uk

CARLETON
Cumbria

Newbiggin Hall ★★★★
Contact: Mr and Mrs D Bates,
Newbiggin Hall, Carleton,
Carlisle CA4 0AJ
T: (01228) 527549

CARLISLE
Cumbria

Bessiestown Farm Country
Cottages ★★★★
Contact: Mr John Sisson,
Bessiestown Farm Country
Cottages, Catlowdy, Longtown,
Carlisle CA6 5QP
T: (01228) 577219 & 577019
F: (01228) 577219
E: bestbb2000@cs.com
I: www.bessiestown.co.uk

Bull Pen, Homestead and
Cottage ★★★★
Contact: Mrs J G Simpson, 4
Thiefside, Calthwaite, Penrith,
Cumbria CA11 9RG
T: (017688) 85288
F: (017688) 85288

Green View Lodges and Well
Cottage
Rating Applied For
Contact: Mrs A E Ivinson, Green
View Lodges and Well Cottage,
Welton, Carlisle, Cumbria
CA5 7ES
T: (016974) 76230
F: (016974) 76523
E: grnvlodges@aol.com
I: www.green-view-lodges.com

Kokied Cottage ★★★★
Contact: Mr & Mrs Fisher, 105
Manchester Road, Knutsford,
Cheshire WA16 0NX
T: (01565) 650507

Meadow View, Burn Cottage &
Ald Pallyards★★★-★★★★
Contact: Mrs G Elwen, Meadow
View, Burn Cottage & Ald
Pallyards, New Pallyards,
Hethersgill, Carlisle CA6 6HZ
T: (01228) 577308 & 577315
F: (01228) 577308
E: info@newpallyards.freeserve.
co.uk
I: www.newpallyards.freeserve.
co.uk

Stonewalls ★★★
Contact: Country Holidays
ref:9809, Spring Mill, Earby,
Barnoldswick, Lancashire
BB94 0AA
T: 08700 723723
F: (01282) 844288
E: sales@ttgihg.co.uk
I: www.country-holidays.co.uk

CARTMEL
Cumbria

Aynsome Manor Park 10 & 15
★★★
Contact: Mr Paul Liddell,
Lakelovers, The New Toffee Loft,
Kendal Road, Windermere,
Cumbria LA23 3RA
T: (015394) 88855
F: (015394) 88857
E: bookings@lakelovers.co.uk
I: www.lakelovers.co.uk

Beckside Farm ★★★-★★★★
Contact: Mr & Mrs Jeremy &
Mary Ratcliff, Beckside Farm,
Cartmel, Grange-over-Sands,
Cumbria LA11 7SP
T: (015395) 36141
F: (015395) 36141
E: beckside@dircon.co.uk
I: www.beckside.co.uk

Byways ★★★★
Contact: Mr D Hogarth,
Cumbrian Cottages, 7 The
Crescent, Carlisle, CA1 1QW
T: (01228) 599960
F: (01228) 599970
E: enquiries@
cumbrian-cottages.co.uk
I: www.cumbrian-cottages.co.uk

Causeway Cottage
Rating Applied For
Contact: Mr D Hogarth,
Cumbrian Cottages, 7 The
Crescent, Carlisle, CA1 1QW
T: (01228) 599960 & 59950
F: (01228) 599970
E: enquiries@
cumbrian-cottages.co.uk
I: www.cumbrian-cottages.co.uk

Grange End Cottages ★★★★
Contact: Mr Brian Colling, 7
Rushside Road, Cheadle Hulme,
Cheadle, Cheshire SK8 6NW
T: (0161) 485 7015 &
07774 141916
F: (0161) 355 6346
E: ibex32@aol.com
I: www.holidaycottagescumbria.
com

Hampsfell View
Rating Applied For
Contact: Mrs Angela Bennett, 8
Fell Cottages, Grange Fell Road,
Grange-over-Sands, Cumbria
LA11
T: (015395) 33553 & 36097

Longlands at Cartmel ★★★★
Contact: Mr Martin Ainscough,
Longlands at Cartmel, Cartmel,
Grange-over-Sands, Cumbria
LA11 6HG
T: (015395) 36475
F: (015395) 36172
E: longlands@cartmel.com
I: www.cartmel.com

Longlands Farm Cottage ★★
Contact: Mrs J A Dixon,
Longlands Farm Cottage,
Longlands Farm, Cartmel,
Grange-over-Sands, Cumbria
LA11 6HJ
T: (015395) 36406

The Old Vicarage ★★★★
Contact: Mrs S V Sharphouse,
The Old Vicarage, Field
Broughton, Cartmel, Grange-
over-Sands, Cumbria LA11 6HW
T: (015395) 36540
E: theflat@sharphouse.co.uk
I: www.sharphouse.co.uk/theflat

Wharton Barn ★★★★
Contact: Mr John Serginson, The
Lakeland Cottage Company,
Waterside House, Newby Bridge,
Ulverston, Cumbria LA12 8AN
T: (015395) 30024
F: (015395) 31932
E: john@
lakeland-cottage-company.
co.uk
I: www.
lakeland-cottage-company.
co.uk

Wharton Cottage ★★★★
Contact: Mr John Serginson, The
Lakeland Cottage Company,
Waterside House, Newby Bridge,
Ulverston, Cumbria LA12 8AN
T: (015395) 30024
F: (015395) 31932
E: john@
lakeland-cottage-company.
co.uk
I: www.
lakeland-cottage-company.
co.uk

CASTLE CARROCK
Cumbria

Tottergill Farm
★★★★-★★★★★
Contact: Mrs Alison Bridges,
Tottergill Farm, Castle Carrock,
Carlisle CA8 9DP
T: (01228) 670615 &
07785 996950
E: alison@tottergill.demon.
co.uk
I: www.tottergill.demon.co.uk

CHAPEL STILE
Cumbria

Bank View ★★★
Contact: Mr D Hogarth,
Cumbrian Cottages, 7 The
Crescent, Carlisle, CA1 1QW
T: (01228) 599960 & 599950
F: (01228) 599970
E: enquiries@
cumbrian-cottages.co.uk
I: www.cumbrian-cottages.co.uk

Dulcanter ★★★
Contact: Mr D Hogarth,
Cumbrian Cottages, 7 The
Crescent, Carlisle, CA1 1QW
T: (01228) 599960 & 599950
F: (01228) 599970
E: enquiries@
cumbrian-cottages.co.uk
I: www.cumbrian-cottages.co.uk

Fir Garth ★★★
Contact: Mr D Hogarth,
Cumbrian Cottages, 7 The
Crescent, Carlisle, CA1 1QW
T: (01228) 599960
F: (01228) 599970
E: enquiries@
cumbrian-cottages.co.uk
I: www.cumbrian-cottages.co.uk

1 Lingmoor View ★★★
Contact: Mrs P R Robinson, 3
Whinfield Road, Ulverston,
Cumbria LA12 7HG
T: (01229) 583889
E: pauline@lakelandcottage.
com
I: www.lakelandcottage.com

2 Lingmoor View ★★★
Contact: Mr J Batho, High Hollin
Bank, Coniston, Cumbria
LA21 8AG
T: (015394) 41680
E: charlie.batho@maginus.com

7 Lingmoor View ★★★
Contact: Mrs Andrea Batho,
High Hollin Bank, Coniston,
Cumbria LA21 8AG
T: (015394) 41680
E: a.batho@virgin.net

8 Lingmoor View ★★
Contact: Mr Paul Liddell,
Lakelovers, The New Toffee Loft,
Kendal Road, Windermere,
Cumbria LA23 3RA
T: (015394) 88855
F: (015394) 88857
E: bookings@lakelovers.co.uk
I: www.lakelovers.co.uk

27 Thrang Brow ★★★★
Contact: Country Holidays
ref:14588, Holiday Cottages
Group Owner Services Dept,
Spring Mill, Earby, Barnoldswick,
Lancashire BB18 0AA
T: (01282) 445096
F: (01282) 844288
E: sales@ttgihg.co.uk
I: www.country-holidays.co.uk

CLAPPERSGATE
Cumbria

Blackcombe, Whitecrags
★★★★
Contact: Mrs Susan Jackson,
Heart of the Lakes, Fisherbeck
Hill, Old Lake Road, Ambleside,
Cumbria LA22 0DH
T: (015394) 32321
F: (015394) 33251
E: info@heartofthelakes.co.uk
I: www.heartofthelakes.co.uk

Brathay Cottage ★★★
Contact: Mr D Hogarth,
Cumbrian Cottages, 7 The
Crescent, Carlisle, CA1 1QW
T: (01228) 599960 & 599950
F: (01228) 599970
E: enquiries@
cumbrian-cottages.co.uk
I: www.cumbrian-cottages.co.uk

Fell View ★★★
Contact: Mrs Susan Jackson,
Heart of the Lakes, Fisherbeck
Hill, Old Lake Road, Ambleside,
Cumbria LA22 0DH
T: (015394) 32321
F: (015394) 33251
E: info@heartofthelakes.co.uk
I: www.heartofthelakes.co.uk

The Hayloft ★★★
Contact: Mrs Susan Jackson,
Heart of the Lakes, Fisherbeck
Mill, Old Lake Road, Ambleside,
Cumbria LA22 0DH
T: (015394) 32321
F: (015394) 33251
E: info@heartofthelakes.co.uk
I: www.heartofthelakes.co.uk

Rock Cottage ★★★
Contact: Mrs Susan Jackson,
Heart of the Lakes, Fisherbeck
Hill, Old Lake Road, Ambleside,
Cumbria LA22 0DH
T: (015394) 32321
F: (015394) 33251
E: info@heartofthelakes.co.uk
I: www.heartofthelakes.co.uk

Scafell Pike, White Crags
★★★★
Contact: Mrs Susan Jackson,
Heart of the Lakes, Fisherbeck
Hill, Old Lake Road, Ambleside,
Cumbria LA22 0DH
T: (015394) 32321
F: (015394) 33251
E: info@heartofthelakes.co.uk
I: www.heartofthelakes.co.uk

Skiddaw, Whitecrags ★★★★
Contact: Mrs Susan Jackson,
Heart of the Lakes, Fisherbeck
Hill, Old Lake Road, Ambleside,
Cumbria LA22 0DH
T: (015394) 32321
F: (015394) 33251
E: info@heartofthelakes.co.uk
I: www.heartofthelakes.co.uk

The Treetops ★★
Contact: Mrs Susan Jackson,
Heart of the Lakes, Fisherbeck
Hill, Old Lake Road, Ambleside,
Cumbria LA22 0DH
T: (015394) 32321
F: (015394) 33251
E: info@heartofthelakes.co.uk
I: www.heartofthelakes.co.uk

CLEATOR
Cumbria

The Coach House ★
Contact: Mr and Mrs H Porter,
The Coach House, Hazelholme,
Cleator, Cumbria CA23 9YP
T: (01946) 810436

CLEATOR MOOR
Cumbria

Scalelands Cottage ★★★
Contact: Mrs Lawson, Scalelands
Cottage, Scalelands Farm,
Parkside, Cleator Moor, Cumbria
CA25 5HQ
T: (01946) 810323

COCKERMOUTH
Cumbria

Broadings Holiday Cottages
★★-★★★
Contact: Mrs Christine Greening,
Waverbank Farm, Wigton,
Cumbria CA7 8PN
T: (01697) 371315

Corner Cottage ★★★
Contact: Mrs Sue Hannah,
Limelighting, Grand Theatre,
Station Road, Cockermouth,
Cumbria CA13 9PZ
T: (01900) 822480 & 826021
F: (01900) 822480
E: suehannah@limelighting.
demon.co.uk
I: www.cottageguide.
co.uk/greatbroughton

The Garden Cottage ★★
Contact: Country Holidays
ref:7456, Spring Mill, Earby,
Barnoldswick, Lancashire
BD94 0AA
T: 08700 723723
F: (01282) 844288
E: sales@ttgihg.co.uk
I: www.country-holidays.co.uk

Ghyll Yeat ★★★★
Contact: Mrs A Haworth, 1 Park
Villas, Keswick, Cumbria
CA12 5LQ
T: (017687) 80321
E: peter_anneghyllyeat@
lineone.net

Jenkin Cottage ★★★★
Contact: Mrs M E Teasdale,
Jenkin Cottage, Jenkin Farm,
Embleton, Cockermouth,
Cumbria CA13 9TN
T: (017687) 76387

37 Kirkgate
Rating Applied For
Contact: Mr & Mrs Nelson
Chicken, 39 Kirkgate,
Cockermouth, Cumbria
CA13 9PJ
T: (01900) 823236
F: (01900) 825983

46 Kirkgate ★★★★
Contact: Mrs P M Livesey,
Fawcett House, High Brigham,
Cockermouth, Cumbria
CA13 0TG
T: (01900) 825442
E: tricia.livesey@euphony.net

14 Lawson Garth ★★★
Contact: Country Holidays
ref:7572, Spring Mill, Earby,
Barnoldswick, Lancashire
BB94 0AA
T: 08700 723723
F: (01282) 844288
I: www.country-holidays.co.uk

Moorside ★★★
Contact: Mr D Hogarth,
Cumbrian Cottages, 7 The
Crescent, Carlisle, CA1 1QW
T: (01228) 599960
F: (01228) 599970
E: enquiries@
cumbrian-cottages.co.uk
I: www.cumbrian-cottages.co.uk

The Retreat ★★★★
Contact: Mr David Burton,
Lakeland Cottage Holidays, 3 The
Heads, Keswick, Cumbria
CA12 5ES
T: (017687) 71071
F: (017687) 75036
E: info@lakelandcottages.co.uk
I: www.lakelandcottages.co.uk/

Establishments printed in blue have a detailed entry in this guide

Southwaite Mill Holiday Cottages ★★★-★★★★
Contact: Mr David Warner, Southwaite Holidays Limited, Greysouthen House, The Went, Greysouthen, Cockermouth, Cumbria CA13 0UQ
T: (01900) 827270
F: (01900) 821168

Turner How Cottage
Rating Applied For
Contact: Mr D Hogarth, Cumbrian Cottages, 7 The Crescent, Carlisle, CA1 1QW
T: (01228) 599960 & 599950
F: (01228) 599970
E: enquiries@
cumbrian-cottages.co.uk
I: www.cumbrian-cottages.co.uk

Wood Hall ★★★
Contact: Mrs D Jackson, Wood Hall, Cockermouth, Cumbria CA13 0NX
T: (01900) 823585 & 07860 873965
E: d.jackson@ukonline.co.uk
I: www.wood-hall.co.uk

COLTHOUSE
Cumbria

Croft Foot Barn ★★★
Contact: Mrs Susan Jackson, Heart of the Lakes, Fisherbeck Hill, Old Lake Road, Ambleside, Cumbria LA22 0DH
T: (015394) 32321
F: (015394) 33251
E: info@heartofthelakes.co.uk
I: www.heartofthelakes.co.uk

Croft Head Cottage ★★★★
Contact: Mr D Hogarth, Cumbrian Cottages, 7 The Crescent, Carlisle, CA1 1QW
T: (01228) 599960 & 599950
F: (01228) 599970
E: enquiries@
cumbrian-cottages.co.uk
I: www.cumbrian-cottages.co.uk

CONISTON
Cumbria

1 and 2 Ash Gill Cottages ★★★★
Contact: Mrs Dorothy Cowburn, Lyndene, Pope Lane, Whitestake, Preston, Lancashire PR4 4JR
T: (01772) 612832

Atkinson Ground Cottages ★★★
Contact: Mr John Serginson, The Lakeland Cottage Company, Waterside House, Newby Bridge, Ulverston, Cumbria LA12 8AN
T: (015395) 30024
F: (015395) 31932
E: john@
lakeland-cottage-company.
co.uk
I: www.
lakeland-cottage-company.
co.uk

Bank Ground ★★-★★★★
Contact: Mrs Lucy Batty, Bank Ground, East of Lake, Coniston, Cumbria LA21 8AA
T: (015394) 41264
F: (015394) 41900
E: info@bankground.com
I: www.bankground.com

Beech Grove ★★★★
Contact: Mrs Jean Johnson, Beech Grove, Esk Villa, Tilberthwaite Avenue, Coniston, Cumbria LA21 8ED
T: (015394) 41319
E: jean@eskvilla.freeserve.co.uk
I: www.conistonholidays.co.uk

Bramble Cottage ★★★★
Contact: Mr & Mrs R Newport, Brigg House, Torver, Coniston, Cumbria LA21 8AY
T: (015394) 41592
F: (015394) 41092
E: info@lakesabout.co.uk
I: www.lakesabout.co.uk

The Bridge Cottages ★★★★
Contact: Mr Philip Johnston, The Coppermines Coniston, Coppermines Valley, Coniston, Cumbria LA21 8HX
T: (015394) 41765 & 07721 584488
F: (015394) 41944
E: bookings@coppermines.co.uk
I: www.coppermines.co.uk

The Coach House ★★★★
Contact: Mr and Mrs Ray Newport, The Coach House, Brigg House, Torver, Coniston, Cumbria LA21 8AY
E: info@lakesabout.co.uk
I: www.lakesabout.co.uk

Coniston Country Cottages ★★★-★★★★
Contact: Mr and Mrs Roger and Joan Lupton, Coniston Country Cottages, Little Arrow, Coniston, Cumbria LA21 8AU
T: (015394) 41114
F: (015394) 41114
E: rlupton@conistoncottages.co.uk
I: www.conistoncottages.co.uk

Coniston View Cottage ★★★
Contact: Mrs Susan Jackson, Heart of the Lakes, Fisherbeck Mill, Old Lake Road, Ambleside, Cumbria LA22 0DH
T: (015394) 32321
F: (015394) 33251
E: info@heartofthelakes.co.uk
I: www.heartofthelakes.co.uk

The Coppermines Coniston Cottages ★★-★★★★
Contact: Mr Philip Johnston, The Coppermines Coniston Cottages, Coniston, Cumbria LA21 8HJ
T: (015394) 41765 & 07721 584488
F: (015394) 41944
E: bookings@coppermines.co.uk
I: www.coppermines.co.uk

4 Coppermines Cottages ★★★
Contact: Mr Philip Johnston, The Coppermines Coniston, Coppermines Valley, Coniston, Cumbria LA21 8HX
T: (015394) 41765 & 07721 584488
E: bookings@coppermines.co.uk
I: www.coppermines.co.uk

The Craggs and Maple Craggs ★★★
Contact: Mrs Susan Jackson, Heart of the Lakes, Fisherbeck Hill, Old Lake Road, Ambleside, Cumbria LA22 0DH
T: (015394) 32321
F: (015394) 33251
E: info@heartofthelakes.co.uk
I: www.heartofthelakes.co.uk

Curdle Dub ★★★
Contact: Mr Paul Liddell, Lakelovers, The New Toffee Loft, Kendal Road, Windermere, Cumbria LA23 3RA
T: (015394) 88855
F: (015394) 88857
E: bookings@lakelovers.co.uk
I: www.lakelovers.co.uk

Damson Cottage ★★★★
Contact: Mr D Hogarth, Cumbrian Cottages, 7 The Crescent, Carlisle, CA1 1QW
T: (01228) 599960 & 599950
F: (01228) 599970
E: enquiries@
cumbrian-cottages.co.uk
I: www.cumbrian-cottages.co.uk

25 Days Bank ★★★
Contact: Mrs P M Thornton, 129 Burneside Road, Kendal, Cumbria LA9 6EB
T: (01539) 720684

1 Far End Cottages
Rating Applied For
Contact: Mrs Andrea Batho, High Hollin Bank, Coniston, Cumbria LA21 8AG
T: (015394) 41680
E: a.batho@virgin.net

Fisherbeck Nest, Fisherbeck Fold ★★★★
Contact: Mr D Hogarth, Cumbrian Cottages, 7 The Crescent, Carlisle, CA1 1QW
T: (01228) 599960 & 599950
F: (01228) 599970
E: enquiries@
cumbrian-cottages.co.uk
I: www.cumbrian-cottages.co.uk

Gable End ★★★
Contact: Mr John Serginson, The Lakeland Cottage Company, Waterside House, Newby Bridge, Ulverston, Cumbria LA12 8AN
T: (015395) 30024
F: (015395) 31932
E: john@
lakeland-cottage-company.
co.uk
I: www.lakelandcottageco.com

10 Green Cottages ★★★
Contact: Mrs Cartledge, Lake Bank, Water Yeat, Ulverston, Cumbria LA12 8DL
T: (01229) 885629 & 588828
E: moonshadowdh@aol.com

Greenbeck Cottage ★★★
Contact: Mr & Mrs Gerald & Rosslyn Rager, Hall Farm, Brickley Lane, Ingoldisthorpe, King's Lynn, Norfolk PE31 6PF
T: (01485) 543340 & 0773 415267
F: (01485) 543340
E: rosslyn@rager99.freeserve.co.uk

High Arnside ★★-★★★
Contact: Mrs J Meredith, High Arnside, High Arnside Farm, Coniston, Cumbria LA21 8DW
T: (01539) 432261
E: JanMeredith@bigwig.net
I: www.bigwig.net/high-arnside

High Dixon Barn ★★★
Contact: Mrs Susan Jackson, Heart of the Lakes, Fisherbeck Hill, Old Lake Road, Ambleside, Cumbria LA22 0DH
T: (015394) 32321
F: (015394) 33251
E: info@heartofthelakes.co.uk
I: www.heartofthelakes.co.uk

High Dixon Ground ★★★
Contact: Mrs Susan Jackson, Heart of the Lakes, Fisherbeck Hill, Old Lake Road, Ambleside, Cumbria LA22 0DH
T: (015394) 32321
F: (015394) 33251
E: info@heartofthelakes.co.uk
I: www.heartofthelakes.co.uk

Hollin & Richmond House Apartments ★★★
Contact: Mrs J Johnson, Esk Villa, Tilberthwaite Avenue, Coniston, Cumbria LA21 8ED
T: (015394) 41319
E: jean@eskvilla.freeserve.co.uk
I: www.conistonholidays.co.uk

Hollygarth ★★★★
Contact: Mrs Susan Jackson, Heart of the Lakes, Fisherbeck Hill, Old Lake Road, Ambleside, Cumbria LA22 0DH
T: (015394) 32321
F: (015394) 33251
E: info@heartofthelakes.co.uk
I: www.heartofthelakes.co.uk

5 Holme Ground Cottages ★★★
Contact: Mrs Kate Bradshaw, The Rookery, Oaklands, Riding Mill, Northumberland NE44 6AR
T: (01434) 682526

How Head Cottages ★★★
Contact: Mr R D Holland, How Head Cottages, East of Lake, Coniston, Cumbria LA21 8AA
T: (015394) 41594
E: howhead@lineone.net
I: www.howheadcottages.co.uk

Howhead ★★★★
Contact: Mr John Serginson, The Lakeland Cottage Company, Waterside House, Newby Bridge, Ulverston, Cumbria LA12 8AN
T: (015395) 30024
F: (015395) 31932
E: john@
lakeland-cottage-company.
co.uk
I: www.
lakeland-cottage-company.
co.uk

Lake View Cottage ★★★
Contact: Mrs Susan Jackson, Heart of the Lakes, Fisherbeck Hill, Old Lake Road, Ambleside, Cumbria LA22 0DH
T: (015394) 32321
F: (015394) 33251
E: info@heartofthelakes.co.uk
I: www.heartofthelakes.co.uk

Line Cottage ★★★
Contact: Mr John Serginson, The Lakeland Cottage Company, Waterside House, Newby Bridge, Ulverston, Cumbria LA12 8AN
T: (015395) 30024
F: (015395) 31932
E: john@lakeland-cottage-company.co.uk
I: www.lakeland-cottage-company.co.uk

Maple Crags
Rating Applied For
Contact: Mrs Susan Jackson, Heart of the Lakes, Fisherbeck Mill, Old Lake Road, Ambleside, Cumbria LA22 0DH
T: (015394) 32321
F: (015394) 33251
E: info@heartofthelakes.co.uk
I: www.heartofthelakes.co.uk

Rockleigh
Rating Applied For
Contact: Mr Paul Liddell, Lakelovers, The New Toffee Loft, Kendal Road, Windermere, Cumbria LA23 3RA
T: (015394) 88855
F: (015394) 88857
E: bookings@lakelovers.co.uk
I: www.lakelovers.co.uk

Shelt Gill ★★★
Contact: Mrs R Dean, 9 The Fairway, Sheffield, South Yorkshire S10 4LX
T: (0114) 230 8077
F: (0114) 230 8077
E: holiday@sheltgill.co.uk
I: www.sheltgill.co.uk

The Shieling
Rating Applied For
Contact: Mr Paul Liddell, Lakelovers, The New Toffee Loft, Kendal Road, Bowness-on-Windermere, Windermere, Cumbria LA23 3RA
T: (015394) 88855
F: (015394) 88857
E: bookings@lakelovers.co.uk
I: www.lakelovers.co.uk

Station House & Station Cottage
Rating Applied For
Contact: Mr Paul Liddell, Lakelovers, The New Toffee Loft, Kendal Road, Bowness-on-Windermere, Windermere, Cumbria LA23 3RA
T: (015394) 88855
F: (015394) 88857
E: bookings@lakelovers.co.uk
I: www.lakelovers.co.uk

Sunbeam Cottage ★★★
Contact: Mr Paul Liddell, Lakelovers, The New Toffee Loft, Kendal Road, Windermere, Cumbria LA23 3RA
T: (015394) 88855
F: (015394) 88857
E: bookings@lakelovers.co.uk
I: www.lakelovers.co.uk

Sunny Bank Farm ★★★★
Contact: Mr P Liddell, St James Vicarage, Goschen Road, Carlisle, CA2 5PF
T: (01228) 515639
F: (01228) 524569
E: sunnybankfarm@btinternet.com
I: www.bbbweb.com/sunnybank

Sunny Bank Mill ★★★
Contact: Lakelovers, The New Toffee Loft, Kendal Road, Windermere, Cumbria LA23 3RA
T: (015394) 88857
E: bookings@lakelovers.co.uk
I: www.lakelovers.co.uk

Three Springs ★★★
Contact: Mr John Serginson, The Lakeland Cottage Company, Waterside House, Newby Bridge, Ulverston, Cumbria LA12 8AN
T: (015395) 30024
F: (015395) 31932
E: john@lakeland-cottage-company.co.uk
I: www.lakeland-cottage-company.co.uk

Thurston House ★★
Contact: Mr and Mrs A Jefferson, 21 Chale Green, Harwood, Bolton, BL2 3NJ
T: (01204) 419261
E: alan@jefferson99.freeserve.co.uk
I: www.jefferson99.freeserve.co.uk

Tilberthwaite Farm Cottage ★★★
Contact: Mrs D Wilkinson, Tilberthwaite Farm Cottage, Tilberthwaite Farm, Coniston, Cumbria LA21 8DG
T: (015394) 37281
I: tilberthwaitefarmcottage.com

Tinklerbeck Farm ★★★★★
Contact: Mr John Serginson, The Lakeland Cottage Company, Waterside House, Newby Bridge, Ulverston, Cumbria LA12 8AN
T: (015395) 30024
F: (015395) 31932
E: john@lakeland-cottage-company.co.uk
I: www.lakeland-cottage-company.co.uk

Townson Ground ★★★
Contact: Mrs B E Nelson, East of Lake Road, Coniston, Cumbria LA21 8AA
T: (015394) 41272
F: (015394) 41110
E: info@townsonground.co.uk
I: www.townsonground.co.uk

Yewdale Holiday Apartments 'Yewdale View'★★★
Contact: Mrs M Elwell, Skelcies Cottage, Nook Lane, Crosthwaite, Windermere, Cumbria LA8 8HX
T: (015395) 68745
F: (015395) 68272
E: yewdaleholidayapartments@hotmail.com

COUPLAND BECK
Cumbria

Westmorland Cottages ★★★
Contact: Mrs Clare Patterson, Westmorland Cottages, Coupland Beck Farm, Coupland Beck, Appleby-in-Westmorland, Cumbria CA16 6LN
T: (017683) 51449 & 0771 858 4323
E: westmorlandcott.@btconnect.com

COWAN HEAD
Cumbria

River View ★★★
Contact: Mr D Hogarth, Cumbrian Cottages, 7 The Crescent, Carlisle, CA1 1QW
T: (01228) 599960 & 599950
F: (01228) 599970
E: enquiries@cumbrian-cottages.co.uk
I: www.cumbrian-cottages.co.uk

COWGILL
Cumbria

Allen Haw Farmhouse
Rating Applied For
Contact: Dales Hol Cot Ref:2280, Dales Holiday Cottages, Carleton Business Park, Carleton New Road, Skipton, North Yorkshire BD23 2AA
T: (01756) 799821 & 790919
F: (01756) 797012
E: info@dalesholcot.com
I: www.dalesholcot.com

Dee Cottage ★★★
Contact: Mr J Bolton & Miss D Clark, Huds House, Cowgill, Sedbergh, Cumbria LA10 5TQ
T: (015396) 25234
E: deecott@callnetuk.com

Hill Farmhouse ★★★
Contact: Mr and Mrs Ron and Yvonne Metcalfe, Hill Farmhouse, Cowgill, Sedbergh, Cumbria LA10 5RF
T: (015396) 25144

CROOK
Cumbria

Mitchelland Cottage ★★★
Contact: Mrs Marie Turner, Mitchelland House, Crook, Kendal, Cumbria LA8 8LL
T: (015394) 48589
E: marie.mitchelland@talk21.com

Tarn Close ★★★★
Contact: Mr John Serginson, The Lakeland Cottage Company, Waterside House, Newby Bridge, Ulverston, Cumbria LA12 8AN
T: (015395) 30024
F: (015395) 31932
E: john@lakeland-cottage-company.co.uk
I: www.lakeland-cottage-company.co.uk

Waingap ★★★★
Contact: Mr Paul Liddell, Lakelovers, The New Toffee Loft, Kendal Road, Windermere, Cumbria LA23 3RA
T: (015394) 88855
F: (015394) 88857
E: bookings@lakelovers.co.uk
I: www.lakelovers.co.uk

CROOKLANDS
Cumbria

Old Farmhouse ★★★
Contact: Mrs J Norman, Old Farmhouse, Crooklands, Milnthorpe, Cumbria LA7 7NW
T: (015395) 67716
E: theoldfarmhouse@supalife.com

CROSBY GARRETT
Cumbria

The Cottage ★★★
Contact: Country Holidays ref:5687, Spring Mill, Earby, Barnoldswick, Lancashire BB94 0AA
T: 08700 723723
F: (01282) 844288
E: sales@ttgihg.co.uk
I: www.country-holidays.co.uk

The Old Wash House Cottage ★★★
Contact: Mrs J Lane, Absolute Escapes, Orchard Farm House, Lynn Road, Gayton, King's Lynn, Norfolk PE32 1PA
T: 07553 636989
F: 07553 636989
E: janelane@absolute-escapes.co.uk
I: www.absolute-escapes.co.uk

CROSBY-ON-EDEN
Cumbria

Crosby House Cottages ★★★★
Contact: Mrs D Dickson, Crosby House Cottages, Crosby House, Crosby-on-Eden, Carlisle CA6 4QZ
T: (01228) 573239
F: (01228) 573338
E: info@norbyways.demon.co.uk
I: www.northumbria-byways.com/crosby

CROSBY RAVENSWORTH
Cumbria

The Stable ★★★★
Contact: Mrs Christine Jackson, The Stable, Wickerslack Farm, Crosby Ravensworth, Penrith, Cumbria CA10 3LN
T: (01931) 715236

CROSTHWAITE
Cumbria

Cloverdale ★★★★
Contact: Mr John Serginson, The Lakeland Cottage Company, Waterside House, Newby Bridge, Ulverston, Cumbria LA12 8AN
T: (015395) 30024
F: (015395) 31932

Corner Cottage ★★★★
Contact: Mr Paul Liddell, Lakelovers, The New Toffee Loft, Kendal Road, Windermere, Cumbria LA23 3RA
T: (015394) 88855
F: (015394) 88857
E: bookings@lakelovers.co.uk
I: www.lakelovers.co.uk

Crosthwaite Cottages ★★★
Contact: Mr John Serginson, The Lakeland Cottage Company, Waterside House, Newby Bridge, Ulverston, Cumbria LA12 8AN
T: (015395) 30024
F: (015395) 31932

Damson Barn ★★★
Contact: Mr D Hogarth,
Cumbrian Cottages, 7 The
Crescent, Carlisle, CA1 1QW
T: (01228) 599960
F: (01228) 599970
I: www.cumbrian-cottages.co.uk

Gilpin View ★★★
Contact: Mr Paul Liddell,
Lakelovers, The New Toffee Loft,
Kendal Road, Windermere,
Cumbria LA23 3RA
T: (015394) 88855
F: (015394) 88857
E: bookings@lakelovers.co.uk
I: www.lakelovers.co.uk

Greenbank ★★★★
Contact: Jackie Gaskell,
Greenbank, Crosthwaite, Kendal,
Cumbria LA8 8JD
T: (015395) 68598
🚶

High Beck Cottage
Rating Applied For
Contact: Mr Paul Liddell,
Lakelovers, The New Toffee Loft,
Kendal Road, Windermere,
Cumbria LA23 3RA
T: (015394) 88855
F: (015394) 88857
E: bookings@lakelovers.co.uk
I: www.lakelovers.co.uk

CUMWHINTON
Cumbria
West Cottage ★★★★
Contact: Mrs Allison Stamper,
Cringles Farm, Cumwhinton,
Carlisle CA4 8DL
T: (01228) 561600

DEAN
Cumbria
Barn House ★★★
Contact: Country Holidays
ref:4333, Spring Mill, Earby,
Barnoldswick, Lancashire
BB94 0AA
T: (01282) 445096
F: (01282) 844288
E: sales@ttgihg.co.uk
I: www.country-holidays.co.uk

DENT
Cumbria
Bamford Cottage ★★
Contact: Sykes Cottages Ref:
402, Sykes Cottages, York House,
York Street, Chester, CH1 3LR
T: (01244) 345700
F: (01244) 321442
E: info@sykescottages.co.uk
I: www.sykescottages.co.uk

Brooks House ★★★★
Contact: Ms Ellen Kirton, High
Croft, Cowgill Road, Dent,
Sedbergh, Cumbria LA10 5TF
T: (015396) 25003 &
07971 429822
F: (015396) 25003
E: ellen.kirton@tesco.net
I: www.dentdale.com

Buzzard's Cottage ★★★★
Contact: Dales Hol Cot Ref:2865,
Dales Holiday Cottages, Carleton
Business Park, Carleton New
Road, Skipton, North Yorkshire
BD23 2AA
T: (01756) 799821 & 790919
F: (01756) 797012
E: info@dalesholcot.com
I: www.dalesholcot.com

Fern Lea ★★
Contact: Mrs B Harlow, 32 Main
Street, Woodborough,
Nottingham NE14 6EA
T: (0115) 965 2795
F: (0115) 965 2795

High Chapel Cottage ★★★
Contact: Dales Hol Cot Ref:2074,
Dales Holiday Cottages, Carleton
Business Park, Carleton New
Road, Skipton, North Yorkshire
BD23 2AA
T: (01756) 799821 & 790919
F: (01756) 797012
E: info@dalesholcot.com
I: www.dalesholcot.com

Lea Yeat Cottage ★★★
Contact: Mrs Jo Chapman, Wray
Rigg, Dent, Sedbergh, Cumbria
LA10 5RF
T: (015396) 25091
E: billyjo@tesco.net
I: www.cottageguide.
co.uk/leayeat

Middleton's Cottage and
Fountain Cottage★★★
Contact: Mr and Mrs P M Ayers,
The Old Rectory, Litlington,
Polegate, East Sussex BN26 5RB
T: (01323) 870032 & 870920
F: (01323) 870032
E: candpayers@mistral.co.uk
I: www.dentcottages.co.uk

Mire Garth ★★★
Contact: Mrs Jean Middleton,
Deepdale Head, Dent, Sedbergh,
Cumbria LA10 5RA
T: (015396) 25235

Old Parsonage
Rating Applied For
Contact: Dales Hol Cot Ref:2595,
Dales Holiday Cottages, Carleton
Business Park, Carleton New
Road, Skipton, North Yorkshire
BD23 2AA
T: (01756) 799821 & 790919
F: (01756) 797012
E: info@dalesholcot.com
I: www.dalesholcot.com

Stonecroft ★★★
Contact: Country Holidays
ref:5555, Spring Mill, Earby,
Barnoldswick, Lancashire
BB94 0AA
T: 0870 723723
F: (01282) 844288
I: www.country-holidays.co.uk

West Garth ★★
Contact: Mr Wales, Holiday
Cottages (Yorkshire) Ltd, Water
Street, Skipton, North Yorkshire
BD23 1PB
T: (01756) 700510

Wilsey House ★★★
Contact: Mrs Joan Saunders, 21
Church Street, Somersham,
Huntingdon, Cambridgeshire
PE28 3EG
T: (01487) 841556

DOCKRAY
Cumbria
East View ★★★
Contact: Mr D Hogarth,
Cumbrian Cottages, 7 The
Crescent, Carlisle, CA1 1QW
T: (01228) 599960 & 599950
F: (01228) 599970
E: enquiries@
cumbrian-cottages.co.uk
I: www.cumbrian-cottages.co.uk

Lookin How ★★★★★
Contact: Mr D Hogarth,
Cumbrian Cottages, 7 The
Crescent, Carlisle, CA1 1QW
T: (01228) 599960
F: (01228) 599970
E: enquiries@
cumbrian-cottages.co.uk
I: www.cumbrian-cottages.co.uk

DOVENBY
Cumbria
Beck House ★★★
Contact: Dales Hol Cot Ref:2571,
Dales Holiday Cottages, Carleton
Business Park, Carleton New
Road, Skipton, North Yorkshire
BD23 2AA
T: (01756) 799821 & 790919
F: (01756) 797012
E: info@dalesholcot.com
I: www.dalesholcot.com

DRUMBURGH
Cumbria
Grange Cottage ★★★
Contact: Mrs S Hodgson, The
Grange, Drumburgh, Carlisle
CA7 5DW
T: (01228) 576551

EAGLESFIELD
Cumbria
John Dalton Cottage ★★★
Contact: Country Holidays
ref:732, Spring Mill, Earby,
Barnoldswick, Lancashire
BB94 0AA
T: 08700 723723
F: (01282) 844288
E: sales@ttgihg.co.uk
I: www.country-holidays.co.uk

EDDERSIDE
Cumbria
Centre Farm ★★★
Contact: Mr D Hogarth,
Cumbrian Cottages, 7 The
Crescent, Carlisle, CA1 1QW
T: (01228) 599960 & 599950
F: (01228) 599970
E: enquiries@
cumbrian-cottages.co.uk
I: www.cumbrian-cottages.co.uk

ELTERWATER
Cumbria
Bridge End Cottage
Rating Applied For
Contact: Mr Paul Liddell,
Lakelovers, The New Toffee Loft,
Kendal Road, Windermere,
Cumbria LA23 3RA
T: (015394) 88855
F: (015394) 88857
E: bookings@lakelovers.co.uk
I: www.lakelovers.co.uk

2 Bridge Syke ★★
Contact: Mr Paul Liddell,
Lakelovers, The New Toffee Loft,
Kendal Road, Windermere,
Cumbria LA23 3RA
T: (015394) 88855
F: (015394) 88857
E: bookings@lakelovers.co.uk
I: www.lakelovers.co.uk

Eltermere Old Barn ★★★★
Contact: Mrs Susan Jackson,
Heart of the Lakes, Fisherbeck
Mill, Old Lake Road, Ambleside,
Cumbria LA22 0DH
T: (015394) 32321
F: (015394) 33251
E: info@heartofthelakes.co.uk
I: www.heartofthelakes.co.uk

Gunpowder Cottage
Rating Applied For
Contact: Mr Paul Liddell,
Lakelovers, The New Toffee Loft,
Kendal Road, Bowness-on-
Windermere, Windermere,
Cumbria LA23 3RA
T: (015394) 88855
F: (015394) 88857
E: bookings@lakelovers.co.uk
I: www.lakelovers.co.uk

Lane Ends Cottages ★★★
Contact: Mrs M E Rice, Fellside,
3 and 4 Lane Ends Cottages,
Elterwater, Ambleside, Cumbria
LA22 9HN
T: (015394) 37678

Oakbank ★★★★
Contact: Mrs Susan Jackson,
Heart of the Lakes, Fisherbeck
Mill, Old Lake Road, Ambleside,
Cumbria LA22 0DH
T: (015394) 32321
F: (015394) 33251
E: info@heartofthelakes.co.uk
I: www.heartofthelakes.co.uk

St Giles ★★★
Contact: Mrs Susan Jackson,
Heart of the Lakes, Fisherbeck
Mill, Old Lake Road, Ambleside,
Cumbria LA22 0DH
T: (015394) 32321
F: (015394) 33251
E: info@heartofthelakes.co.uk
I: www.heartofthelakes.co.uk

Wistaria Cottage and 3 Main
Street ★★★
Contact: Mr & Mrs D Beardmore,
2 Beech Drive, Kidsgrove, Stoke-
on-Trent ST7 1BA
T: (01782) 783170
E: geoff.doreen.beardmore@
ntlworld.com

EMBLETON
Cumbria
Sunny Bank Cottage, Rakefoot
★★★
Contact: Mrs M Bell, 2 Rakefoot
Cottages, Embleton,
Cockermouth, Cumbria
CA13 9XU
T: (017687) 76273

ENDMOOR
Cumbria
West View Flat ★★★
Contact: Mrs M Bainbridge,
West View Flat, West View Farm,
Endmoor, Kendal, Cumbria
LA8 0HY
T: (015395) 67278

ENNERDALE
Cumbria
Beck Cottage ★★★-★★★★
Contact: Mr & Mrs H&S
Branney, Croasdale Farm,
Ennerdale, Cleator, Cumbria
T: (01946) 861813

ESKDALE
Cumbria
Bridge End Farm Cottages
★★★★-★★★★★
Contact: Mr G M Poole, Select
Cottages Office No 1, Unit 11,
Lansdown Industrial Estate,
Gloucester Road, Cheltenham,
Gloucestershire GL51 8PL
T: (01242) 679900
F: (01242) 679911
E: greg@selectcottages.com
I: www.selectcottages.com

Fisherground Farm ★★★
Contact: Mrs J E Hall,
Fisherground Farm, Eskdale,
Holmrook, Cumbria CA19 1TF
T: (019467) 23319
E: holidays@fisherground.co.uk
I: www.fisherground.co.uk

Longrigg Green ★★★★
Contact: Mrs C Carter, Forest
How, Eskdale, Holmrook,
Cumbria CA19 1TR
T: (019467) 23201
F: (019467) 23190
E: fcarter@easynet.co.uk

Old Brantrake ★★★
Contact: Mr J B Tyson, Brant
Rake, Eskdale, Holmrook,
Cumbria CA19 1TT
T: (019467) 23340
F: (019467) 23340
E: tyson@eskdale1.demon.co.uk

Whin Rigg ★★★★
Contact: Mrs Jennifer
Prestwood, The Ferns, Eskdale
Green, Holmrook, Cumbria
CA19 1UA
T: (019467) 23217
F: (019467) 23217
E: j.prestwood@talk21.com

FAR SAWREY
Cumbria

1 & 2 Church Cottage ★★★★
Contact: Mr P Liddell, Heart of
Lakes, Fisherbeck Hill, Old Lake
Road, Ambleside, Cumbria
LA22 0DH
T: (015394) 32321
F: (015394) 32321
E: info@heartofthelakes.co.uk
I: www.heartofthelakes.co.uk

Claife Cottage ★★★
Contact: Mr D Hogarth,
Cumbrian Cottages, 7 The
Crescent, Carlisle, CA1 1QW
T: (01228) 599960 & 599950
F: (01228) 599970
E: enquiries@
cumbrian-cottages.co.uk
I: www.cumbrian-cottages.co.uk

FINSTHWAITE
Cumbria

The Barn ★★★★
Contact: Mr D Hogarth,
Cumbrian Cottages, 7 The
Crescent, Carlisle, CA1 1QW
T: (01228) 599960
F: (01228) 599970
E: enquiries@
cumbrian-cottages.co.uk
I: www.cumbrian-cottages.co.uk

FIRBANK
Cumbria

Bowers House
Rating Applied For
Contact: Country Holidays
ref:10961, Spring Mill, Earby,
Barnoldswick, Lancashire
BB94 0AA
T: 0870 723723
F: (01282) 844288
I: www.country-holidays.co.uk

GARNETT BRIDGE
Cumbria

Cocks Close ★★★
Contact: Mrs Denny, Lindens,
Ashley Park Road, Walton-on-
Thames, Surrey KT12 1JU
T: (01932) 246432
F: (01932) 253174
E: mikericky@aol.com

The Mill Cottage ★★★★
Contact: Country Holidays
ref:10152, Spring Mill, Earby,
Barnoldswick, Lancashire
BB94 0AA
T: (01282) 445096
F: (01282) 844288
E: sales@ttgihg.co.uk
I: www.country-holidays.co.uk

GARRIGILL
Cumbria

Brook Cottage ★★★★
Contact: Mr and Mrs Gifford,
Moordale, Garrigill, Alston,
Cumbria CA9 3EB
T: (01434) 381688
F: (01434) 381688
E: mggarrigill@aol.com
I: members.aol.com/brookcot
🖫

GARSDALE
Cumbria

Cloughside Cottage
Rating Applied For
Contact: Dales Hol Cot Ref:2599,
Dales Holiday Cottages, Carleton
Business Park, Carleton New
Road, Skipton, North Yorkshire
BD23 2AA
T: (01756) 799821 & 790919
F: (01756) 797012
E: info@dalesholcot.com
I: www.dalesholcot.com

GARSDALE HEAD
Cumbria

Dandry Cottage
Rating Applied For
Contact: Dales Hol Cot Ref:1637,
Dales Holiday Cottages, Carleton
Business Park, Carleton New
Road, Skipton, North Yorkshire
BD23 2AA
T: (01756) 799821 & 790919
F: (01756) 797012
E: info@dalesholcot.com
I: www.dalesholcot.com

GILCRUX
Cumbria

Ellen Hall
Rating Applied For
Contact: Mrs Alison Dunlop,
Ellen Hall, Gilcrux, Cockermouth,
Cumbria CA7 2QB
T: (016973) 21439
F: (016973) 22675
E: data.dunlop@virgin.net
I: www.cottagesmadefortwo.
co.uk

GLENRIDDING
Cumbria

Birkside Cottage ★★★
Contact: Mr D Hogarth,
Cumbrian Cottages, 7 The
Crescent, Carlisle, CA1 1QW
T: (01228) 599960 & 599950
F: (01228) 599970
E: enquiries@
cumbrian-cottages.co.uk
I: www.cumbrian-cottages.co.uk

Brown Howe ★★★
Contact: Dales Hol Cot Ref:1933,
Dales Holiday Cottages, Carleton
Business Park, Carleton New
Road, Skipton, North Yorkshire
BD23 2AA
T: (01756) 799821 & 790919
F: (01756) 797012
E: info@dalesholcot.com
I: www.dalesholcot.com

Chapel Cottage ★★★★
Contact: Mrs Susan Jackson,
Heart of the Lakes, Fisherbeck
Hill, Old Lake Road, Ambleside,
Cumbria LA22 0DH
T: (015394) 32321
F: (015394) 33251
E: info@heartofthelakes.co.uk
I: www.heartofthelakes.co.uk

Chapel House ★★★★★
Contact: Mrs Susan Jackson,
Heart of the Lakes, Fisherbeck
Hill, Old Lake Road, Ambleside,
Cumbria LA22 0DH
T: (015394) 32321
F: (015394) 33251
E: info@heartofthelakes.co.uk
I: www.heartofthelakes.co.uk

Fell View Holidays ★★★
Contact: Mr and Mrs J Burnett,
Fell View Holidays, Fell View,
Grisedale Bridge, Glenridding,
Penrith, Cumbria CA11 0PJ
T: (017684) 82342 &
(01768) 867420
F: (017684) 82342

Grassthwaite How ★★★★
Contact: Mrs Susan Jackson,
Heart of the Lakes, Fisherbeck
Mill, Old Lake Road, Ambleside,
Cumbria LA22 0DH
T: (015394) 32321
F: (015394) 33251
E: info@heartofthelakes.co.uk
I: www.heartofthelakes.co.uk

Mistal Cottage ★★★★
Contact: Mrs Susan Jackson,
Heart of the Lakes, Fisherbeck
Hill, Old Lake Road, Ambleside,
Cumbria LA22 0DH
T: (015394) 32321
F: (015394) 33251
E: info@heartofthelakes.co.uk
I: www.heartofthelakes.co.uk

Rathmore ★★★
Contact: Mrs Susan Jackson,
Heart of the Lakes, Fisherbeck
Mill, Old Lake Road, Ambleside,
Cumbria LA22 0DH
T: (015394) 32321
F: (015394) 33251
E: info@heartofthelakes.co.uk
I: www.heartofthelakes.co.uk

GOSFORTH
Cumbria

Potters Barn
Rating Applied For
Contact: Mrs Barbara Wright,
Potters Barn, Gosforth Pottery,
Gosforth, Seascale, Cumbria
CA20 1AH
T: (019467) 25296
E: pottersbarn@potterycourses.
co.uk
I: www.potters-barn.co.uk

GRANGE-OVER-SANDS
Cumbria

The Chalet Studio ★★★
Contact: Mrs Margaret Wilson,
The Chalet, Highfield Road,
Grange-over-Sands, Cumbria
LA11 7JA
T: (015395) 34695

Cornerways Bungalow ★★★
Contact: Mrs Eunice Rigg,
Prospect House, Barber Green,
Grange-over-Sands, Cumbria
LA11 6HU
T: (015395) 36329 & 36587

**Hazelwood Court Country
House Self-Catering
★★★-★★★★**
Contact: Mr M Stilling,
Hazelwood Court Country
House Self-Catering, Lindale
Road, Grange-over-Sands,
Cumbria LA11 6SP
T: (015395) 34196
E: martstilling@hazelcourt
I: hazelwoodcourt.co.uk

Helens ★★★
Contact: Mrs B Atkins,
Woodside, Charney Road,
Grange-over-Sands, Cumbria
T: (015395) 34647

The Nook ★★★
Contact: Mr John Serginson, The
Lakeland Cottage Company,
Waterside House, Newby Bridge,
Ulverston, Cumbria LA12 8AN
T: (015395) 30024
F: (015395) 31932
E: john@
lakeland-cottage-company.
co.uk
I: www.
lakeland-cottage-company.
co.uk

Spring Bank Cottage ★★★★
Contact: Mrs J Brocklebank,
Spring Bank Farm, Grange-over-
Sands, Cumbria LA11 6HA
T: (015395) 32606

Swimmers Farm ★★★★★
Contact: Mr D Hogarth,
Cumbrian Cottages, 7 The
Crescent, Carlisle, CA1 1QW
T: (01228) 599960 & 599950
F: (01228) 599970
E: enquiries@
cumbrian-cottages.co.uk
I: www.cumbrian-cottages.co.uk

Wycombe Holiday Flats ★★★
Contact: Mrs W G Benson,
Wycombe Holiday Flats,
Wycombe, The Esplanade,
Grange-over-Sands, Cumbria
LA11 7HH
T: (015395) 32297
F: (015395) 32295
E: whf@btinternet.com
I: www.wycombeholidayflats.
co.uk

GRASMERE
Cumbria

Above Beck ★★★
Contact: Mrs Susan Jackson,
Heart of the Lakes, Fisherbeck
Hill, Old Lake Road, Ambleside,
Cumbria LA22 0DH
T: (015394) 32321
F: (015394) 33251
E: info@heartofthelakes.co.uk
I: www.heartofthelakes.co.uk

Acorn Cottage ★★★
Contact: Mr & Mrs F Bowers,
Kirk Allans, Church Bridge,
Grasmere, Cumbria LA22 9SN
T: (015394) 35219
F: (015394) 35219
E: fran@folklore.co.uk

Establishments printed in blue have a detailed entry in this guide

Acorn Cottage
Rating Applied For
Contact: Mr Paul Liddell,
Lakelovers, The New Toffee Loft,
Kendal Road, Windermere,
Cumbria LA23 3RA
T: (015394) 88855
F: (015394) 88857
E: bookings@lakelovers.co.uk
I: www.lakelovers.co.uk

The Barn (How Head) ★★★
Contact: Mrs Susan Jackson,
Heart of the Lakes, Fisherbeck
Mill, Old Lake Road, Ambleside,
Cumbria LA22 0DH
T: (015394) 32321
F: (015394) 33251
E: info@heartofthelakes.co.uk
I: www.heartofthelakes.co.uk

Beck Allans ★★★-★★★★
Contact: Mr P Taylor, Beck
Allans, College Street, Grasmere,
Cumbria LA22 9SZ
T: (015394) 35563
F: (015394) 35563
E: mail@beckallans.com
I: www.beckallans.com

Bellfoot ★★★★
Contact: Mrs Susan Jackson,
Heart of the Lakes, Fisherbeck
Mill, Old Lake Road, Ambleside,
Cumbria LA22 0DH
T: (015394) 32321
F: (015394) 33251
E: info@heartofthelakes.co.uk
I: www.heartofthelakes.co.uk

**Broadrayne Farm Cottages
★★★-★★★★**
Contact: Mrs Jo Dennison Drake,
Broadrayne Farm, Grasmere,
Ambleside, Cumbria LA22 9RU
T: (015394) 35055 & 35055
F: (015394) 35733
E: jo@
grasmere-accommodation.co.uk
I: www.
grasmere-accommodation.co.uk

Buttercrags ★★★
Contact: Mr Martin Wood,
Grasmere Cottages, Moss Grove
Hotel, Grasmere, Ambleside,
Cumbria LA22 9SW
T: (015394) 35395
F: (015394) 35691
E: martinw@globalnet.co.uk
I: www.mossgrove.co.uk

**Bydews Cottage and Studio
Flat ★★**
Contact: Mr Paul Nelson,
Undercrag, Easedale Road,
Grasmere, Ambleside, Cumbria
LA22 9QD
T: (015394) 35349 & 35301
E: paul@grasmerevillage.
demon.co.uk
I: www.grasmerevillage.demon.
co.uk

Chapel Cottage ★★★★
Contact: Mr Martin Wood,
Grasmere Cottages, Moss Grove
Hotel, Grasmere, Ambleside,
Cumbria LA22 9SW
T: (015394) 35395
F: (015394) 35691
E: martinw@globalnet.co.uk
I: www.grasmerecottages.co.uk

Coachmans Cottage ★★★★
Contact: Mrs Susan Jackson,
Heart of the Lakes, Fisherbeck
Hill, Old Lake Road, Ambleside,
Cumbria LA22 0DH
T: (015394) 32321
F: (015394) 33251
E: info@heartofthelakes.co.uk
I: www.heartofthelakes.co.uk

Crag Cottage ★★★
Contact: Mrs Susan Jackson,
Heart of the Lakes, Fisherbeck
Hill, Old Lake Road, Ambleside,
Cumbria LA22 0DH
T: (015394) 32321
F: (015394) 33251
E: info@heartofthelakes.co.uk
I: www.heartofthelakes.co.uk

3 Dale End ★★
Contact: Mrs Anne Truelove, 98
Antrobus Road, Sutton Coldfield,
West Midlands B73 5EL
T: (0121) 3547915 &
(015394) 35200
E: p.f.truelove@aston.ac.uk
I: www.civ.aston.ac.
uk/civ/notes/truelove

Dippers Bank ★★★★
Contact: Mrs Susan Jackson,
Heart of the Lakes, Fisherbeck
Hill, Old Lake Road, Ambleside,
Cumbria LA22 0DH
T: (015394) 32321
F: (015394) 33251
E: info@heartofthelakes.co.uk
I: www.heartofthelakes.co.uk

Dove Holme ★★★★
Contact: Mr D Hogarth,
Cumbrian Cottages, 7 The
Crescent, Carlisle, CA1 1QW
T: (01228) 599960 & 599950
F: (01228) 599970
E: enquiries@
cumbrian-cottages.co.uk
I: www.cumbrian-cottages.co.uk

Dunnabeck ★★★★
Contact: Mrs Susan Jackson,
Heart of the Lakes, Fisherbeck
Hill, Old Lake Road, Ambleside,
Cumbria LA22 0DH
T: (015394) 32321
F: (015394) 33251
E: info@heartofthelakes.co.uk
I: www.heartofthelakes.co.uk

Easedale ★★★
Contact: Mrs Susan Jackson,
Heart of the Lakes, Fisherbeck
Hill, Old Lake Road, Ambleside,
Cumbria LA22 0DH
T: (015394) 32321
F: (015394) 33251
E: info@heartofthelakes.co.uk
I: www.heartofthelakes.co.uk

Fairfield, Wood Close ★★★★
Contact: Mrs Susan Jackson,
Heart of the Lakes, Fisherbeck
Hill, Old Lake Road, Ambleside,
Cumbria LA22 0DH
T: (015394) 32321
F: (015394) 33251
E: info@heartofthelakes.co.uk
I: www.heartofthelakes.co.uk

Fairfield Cottage ★★★★
Contact: Mrs Susan Jackson,
Heart of the Lakes, Fisherbeck
Hill, Old Lake Road, Ambleside,
Cumbria LA22 0DH
T: (015394) 32321
F: (015394) 33251
E: info@heartofthelakes.co.uk
I: www.heartofthelakes.co.uk

1 Field Foot ★★★
Contact: Mrs Jean Morrison, 11
Park Crescent, Wigan,
Lancashire WN1 1RZ
T: (01942) 236350
F: (015394) 35475

Glendene ★★★★
Contact: Mrs Susan Jackson,
Heart of the Lakes, Fisherbeck
Hill, Old Lake Road, Ambleside,
Cumbria LA22 0DH
T: (015394) 32321
F: (015394) 33251
E: info@heartofthelakes.co.uk
I: www.heartofthelakes.co.uk

Goody Bridge Barn ★★★★
Contact: Mrs Susan Jackson,
Heart of the Lakes, Fisherbeck
Mill, Old Lake Road, Ambleside,
Cumbria LA22 0DH
T: (015394) 32321
F: (015394) 33251
E: info@heartofthelakes.co.uk
I: www.heartofthelakes.co.uk

Goody Bridge Cottage ★★★★
Contact: Mrs Susan Jackson,
Heart of the Lakes, Fisherbeck
Mill, Old Lake Road, Ambleside,
Cumbria LA22 0DH
T: (015394) 32321
F: (015394) 33251
E: info@heartofthelakes.co.uk
I: www.heartofthelakes.co.uk

Grasmere Lodge ★★
Contact: Mr S Roberts & H
McCarty, Forest Side Country
House Hotel, Forest Side,
Grasmere, Ambleside, Cumbria
LA22 9KN
T: (015394) 35250
F: (015394) 35947
E: hotel@forestsidehotel.com
I: www.forestsidehotel.com

Grasmere View ★★★
Contact: Mr D Hogarth,
Cumbrian Cottages, 7 The
Crescent, Carlisle, CA1 1QW
T: (01228) 599960 & 599950
F: (01228) 599970
E: enquiries@
cumbrian-cottages.co.uk
I: www.cumbrian-cottages.co.uk

Grey Crag Barn ★★★
Contact: Mrs Susan Jackson,
Heart of the Lakes, Fisherbeck
Mill, Old Lake Road, Ambleside,
Cumbria LA22 0DH
T: (015394) 32321
F: (015394) 33251
E: info@heartofthelakes.co.uk
I: www.heartofthelakes.co.uk

Helm Cottage ★★★★
Contact: Mr D Hogarth,
Cumbrian Cottages, 7 The
Crescent, Carlisle, CA1 1QW
T: (01228) 599960 & 599950
F: (01228) 599970
E: enquiries@
cumbrian-cottages.co.uk
I: www.cumbrian-cottages.co.uk

Helm Crag ★★★
Contact: Mr and Mrs Alan
Wardle, North Lodge, Longtail
Hill, Bowness-on-Windermere,
Windermere, Cumbria LA23 3JD
T: (015394) 47905
I: www.lakeland-holidays.net

Heron View Cottage ★★★★
Contact: Mr D Hogarth,
Cumbrian Cottages, 7 The
Crescent, Carlisle, CA1 1QW
T: (01228) 599960
F: (01228) 599970
E: enquiries@
cumbrian-cottages.co.uk
I: www.cumbrian-cottages.co.uk

Heronsyde ★★★★
Contact: Mrs Susan Jackson,
Heart of the Lakes, Fisherbeck
Hill, Old Lake Road, Ambleside,
Cumbria LA22 0DH
T: (015394) 32321
F: (015394) 33251
E: info@heartofthelakes.co.uk
I: www.heartofthelakes.co.uk

Hollen Farm Cottage ★★★★
Contact: Mrs Susan Jackson,
Heart of the Lakes, Fisherbeck
Hill, Old Lake Road, Ambleside,
Cumbria LA22 0DH
T: (015394) 32321
F: (015394) 33251
E: info@heartofthelakes.co.uk
I: www.heartofthelakes.co.uk

Hollens Farm ★★★★
Contact: Mrs Susan Jackson,
Heart of the Lakes, Fisherbeck
Hill, Old Lake Road, Ambleside,
Cumbria LA22 0DH
T: (015394) 32321
F: (015394) 33251
E: info@heartofthelakes.co.uk
I: www.heartofthelakes.co.uk

Holly Cottage ★★★★
Contact: Mr D Hogarth,
Cumbrian Cottages, 7 The
Crescent, Carlisle, CA1 1QW
T: (01228) 599960
F: (01228) 599970
E: enquiries@
cumbrian-cottages.co.uk
I: www.cumbrian-cottages.co.uk

Huntingstile South ★★★★
Contact: Mrs Susan Jackson,
Heart of the Lakes, Fisherbeck
Hill, Old Lake Road, Ambleside,
Cumbria LA22 0DH
T: (015394) 32321
F: (015394) 33251
E: info@heartofthelakes.co.uk
I: www.heartofthelakes.co.uk

Kelbarrow West ★★★
Contact: Mrs Susan Jackson,
Heart of the Lakes, Fisherbeck
Mill, Old Lake Road, Ambleside,
Cumbria LA22 0DH
T: (015394) 32321
F: (015394) 33251
E: info@heartofthelakes.co.uk
I: www.heartofthelakes.co.uk

**Lake View Holiday Apartments
★★★**
Contact: Mr & Mrs Stephen &
Michelle King, Lake View Holiday
Apartments, Lake View Drive,
Grasmere, Cumbria LA22 9TD
T: (015394) 35384
E: info@lakeview-grasmere.com
I: www.lakeview-grasmere.com

Le Tholonet ★★★★
Contact: Mrs Susan Jackson,
Heart of the Lakes, Fisherbeck
Hill, Old Lake Road, Ambleside,
Cumbria LA22 0DH
T: (015394) 32321
F: (015394) 33251
E: info@heartofthelakes.co.uk
I: www.heartofthelakes.co.uk

Little Beeches ★★★
Contact: Mrs Susan Jackson,
Heart of the Lakes, Fisherbeck
Mill, Old Lake Road, Ambleside,
Cumbria LA22 0DH
T: (015394) 32321
F: (015394) 33251
E: info@heartofthelakes.co.uk
I: www.heartofthelakes.co.uk

Low Croft and Croft End ★★★
Contact: Mrs Ann Dixon, Tongue
Ghyll, Grasmere, Ambleside,
Cumbria LA22 9RU
T: (015394) 35571
E: ann@grasmere-holidays.
co.uk
I: www.grasmere-holidays.co.uk

Meadow Brow ★★★
Contact: Mr J A and Mrs W
Wade, Meadow Brow, Grasmere,
Ambleside, Cumbria LA22 9RR
T: (015394) 35275
I: www.meadowbrow.com

Mews Cottage
Rating Applied For
Contact: Mrs Susan Jackson,
Heart of the Lakes, Fisherbeck
Mill, Old Lake Road, Ambleside,
Cumbria LA22 0DH
T: (015394) 32321
F: (015394) 33251
E: info@heartofthelakes.co.uk
I: www.heartofthelakes.co.uk

2 Michael's Fold ★★★★
Contact: Mr Paul Nelson,
Undercrag, Easedale Road,
Grasmere, Ambleside, Cumbria
LA22 9QD
T: (015394) 35349 & 35301
E: paul@grassmerevillage.
demon.co.uk
I: www.grassmerevillage.demon.
co.uk

North Lodge ★★★
Contact: Mrs Susan Jackson,
Heart of the Lakes, Fisherbeck
Hill, Old Lake Road, Ambleside,
Cumbria LA22 0DH
T: (015394) 32321
F: (015394) 33251
E: info@heartofthelakes.co.uk
I: www.heartofthelakes.co.uk

Oak Bank Apartment ★★★
Contact: Mr D Hogarth,
Cumbrian Cottages, 7 The
Crescent, Carlisle, CA1 1QW
T: (01228) 599960 & 599950
F: (01228) 599970
E: enquiries@
cumbrian-cottages.co.uk
I: www.cumbrian-cottages.co.uk

**Old Bakers Cottage and Bakers
Rest ★★★★**
Contact: Mr D Hogarth,
Cumbrian Cottages, 7 The
Crescent, Carlisle, CA1 1QW
T: (01228) 599960
F: (01228) 599970
E: enquiries@
cumbrian-cottages.co.uk
I: www.cumbrian-cottages.co.uk

Old Bakery Cottage ★★★
Contact: Mr Martin Wood,
Grasmere Cottages, Moss Grove
Hotel, Grasmere, Ambleside,
Cumbria LA22 9SW
T: (015394) 35395
F: (015394) 35691
E: martinw@globalnet.co.uk
I: www.grasmerecottages.co.uk

Overmere ★★★★
Contact: Mrs Susan Jackson,
Heart of the Lakes, Fisherbeck
Hill, Old Lake Road, Ambleside,
Cumbria LA22 0DH
T: (015394) 32321
F: (015394) 33251
E: info@heartofthelakes.co.uk
I: www.heartofthelakes.co.uk

Poets View Cottage ★★★★★
Contact: Mr D Hogarth,
Cumbrian Cottages, 7 The
Crescent, Carlisle, CA1 1QW
T: (01228) 599960 & 599950
F: (01228) 599970
E: enquiries@
cumbrian-cottages.co.uk
I: www.cumbrian-cottages.co.uk

Ramblers Roost ★★★
Contact: Mr D Hogarth,
Cumbrian Cottages, 7 The
Crescent, Carlisle, CA1 1QW
T: (01228) 599960 & 599950
F: (01228) 599970
E: enquiries@
cumbrian-cottages.co.uk
I: www.cumbrian-cottages.co.uk

Riverville ★★★★
Contact: Mr D Hogarth,
Cumbrian Cottages, 7 The
Crescent, Carlisle, CA1 1QW
T: (01228) 599960 & 599950
F: (01228) 599970
E: enquiries@
cumbrian-cottages.co.uk
I: www.cumbrian-cottages.co.uk

**Rothay Lodge Garden
Apartment ★★★★**
Contact: Mrs Jean Allan, Rothay
Lodge Garden Apartment, White
Bridge, Grasmere, Ambleside,
Cumbria LA22 9RH
T: (015394) 35341
F: (015394) 39545
E: enquiries@rothay-lodge.
co.uk
I: www.rothay-lodge.co.uk

Rowan Cottage ★★★★
Contact: Mr D Hogarth,
Cumbrian Cottages, 7 The
Crescent, Carlisle, CA1 1QW
T: (01228) 599960 & 599950
F: (01228) 599970
E: enquiries@
cumbrian-cottages.co.uk
I: www.cumbrian-cottages.co.uk

Silver Fell ★★★★★
Contact: Mrs Beryl Mansbridge,
Field End, Brigsteer, Kendal,
Cumbria LA8 8AN
T: (015395) 68570
F: (015395) 68570
E: beryl.mansbridge@which.net
I: homepages.which.net/beryl.
mansbridge/home.html

Silvergarth ★★★
Contact: Mrs Susan Coward,
Silvergarth, 1 Low Riddings,
Grasmere, Ambleside, Cumbria
LA22 9QY
T: (015394) 35828
F: (015394) 35828
E: cowards.silvergarth@
btinternet.com
I: www.cowards.silvergarth.
btinternet.co.uk

Spinners ★★★★
Contact: Mrs Susan Jackson,
Heart of the Lakes, Fisherbeck
Mill, Old Lake Road, Ambleside,
Cumbria LA22 0DH
T: (015394) 32321
F: (015394) 33251
E: info@heartofthelakes.co.uk
I: www.heartofthelakes.co.uk

Stonebeck ★★★★
Contact: Mrs Susan Jackson,
Heart of the Lakes, Fisherbeck
Mill, Old Lake Road, Ambleside,
Cumbria LA22 0DH
T: (015394) 32321
F: (015394) 33251
E: info@heartofthelakes.co.uk

Swallows Cottage ★★★★
Contact: Mr Paul Liddell,
Lakelovers, The New Toffee Loft,
Kendal Road, Windermere,
Cumbria LA23 3RA
T: (015394) 88855
F: (015394) 88857
E: bookings@lakelovers.co.uk
I: www.lakelovers.co.uk

3 Tarn Cottages ★★★
Contact: Mrs Isobel Yates,
Brookside, Underbarrow, Kendal,
Cumbria LA8 8HH
T: (015395) 68843
I: www.lakes-online.
co.uk/info/accommodation/
self_catering/03.htm

Thirlmere Cottage ★★★
Contact: Mrs Susan Jackson,
Heart of the Lakes, Fisherbeck
Mill, Old Lake Road, Ambleside,
Cumbria LA22 0DH
T: (015394) 32321
F: (015394) 33251
E: info@heartofthelakes.co.uk
I: www.heartofthelakes.co.uk

Tilly's Cottage
Rating Applied For
Contact: Mr Paul Liddell,
Lakelovers, The New Toffee Loft,
Kendal Road, Bowness-on-
Windermere, Windermere,
Cumbria LA23 3RA
T: (015394) 88855
F: (015394) 88857
E: bookings@lakelovers.co.uk
I: www.lakelovers.co.uk

2 Townhead Cottages
Rating Applied For
Contact: Mr P Liddell, Lakelovers,
The New Toffee Loft, Kendal
Road, Windermere, Cumbria
LA23 3RA
T: (015394) 88855
F: (015394) 88857
E: bookings@lakelovers.co.uk
I: www.lakelovers.co.uk

Underheron ★★★★
Contact: Mrs Susan Jackson,
Heart of the Lakes, Fisherbeck
Mill, Old Lake Road, Ambleside,
Cumbria LA22 0DH
T: (015394) 32321
F: (015394) 33251
E: info@heartofthelakes.co.uk
I: www.heartofthelakes.co.uk

Weavers ★★★★
Contact: Mrs Susan Jackson,
Heart of the Lakes, Fisherbeck
Hill, Old Lake Road, Ambleside,
Cumbria LA22 0DH
T: (015394) 32321
F: (015394) 33251
E: info@heartofthelakes.co.uk
I: www.heartofthelakes.co.uk

Willowbank ★★★
Contact: Mrs Susan Jackson,
Heart of the Lakes, Fisherbeck
Hill, Old Lake Road, Ambleside,
Cumbria LA22 0DH
T: (015394) 32321
F: (015394) 33251
E: info@heartofthelakes.co.uk
I: www.heartofthelakes.co.uk

**Woodland Crag Cottage
★★★★**
Contact: Mrs Susan Jackson,
Heart of the Lakes, Fisherbeck
Hill, Old Lake Road, Ambleside,
Cumbria LA22 0DH
T: (015394) 32321
F: (015394) 33251
E: info@heartofthelakes.co.uk
I: www.heartofthelakes.co.uk

GRAYRIGG
Cumbria

Punchbowl House ★★★
Contact: Mrs D Johnson,
Punchbowl House, Grayrigg,
Kendal, Cumbria LA8 9BU
T: (01539) 824345
F: (01539) 824345
E: enquiries@punchbowlhouse.
co.uk
I: www.punchbowlhouse.co.uk

GREAT ASBY
Cumbria

Wray Cottage ★★★
Contact: Pamela Cowey, The
Hunting House, Great Asby,
Appleby-in-Westmorland,
Cumbria CA16 6HD
T: (017683) 52485

GREAT BROUGHTON
Cumbria

Fern Cottage ★★★★
Contact: Mr M Winks, 179
Eccleshall Road, Stafford,
Staffordshire ST16 1PD
T: (01785) 661365

GREAT LANGDALE
Cumbria

Elterwater Hall ★★★★★
Contact: Mrs Paula Leyland, The
Langdale Estate, Great Langdale,
Ambleside, Cumbria LA22 9JD
T: (015394) 37302
F: (015394) 37394
E: itsgreat@langdale.co.uk
I: www.langdale.co.uk

Establishments printed in blue have a detailed entry in this guide

Harry Place Farm Cottage ★★★★
Contact: Mrs Susan Jackson, Heart of the Lakes, Fisherbeck Hill, Old Lake Road, Ambleside, Cumbria LA22 0DH
T: (015394) 32321
F: (015394) 33251
E: info@heartofthelakes.co.uk
I: www.heartofthelakes.co.uk

Langdale Estate Chapel Stile Apartments★★★★
Contact: Mrs Paula Leyland, The Langdale Estate, Great Langdale, Ambleside, Cumbria LA22 9JD
T: (015394) 37302
F: (015394) 37394
E: itsgreat@langdale.co.uk
I: www.langdale.co.uk

Langdale Estate Lodges ★★★★★
Contact: Mrs Paula Leyland, The Langdale Estate, Great Langdale, Ambleside, Cumbria LA22 9JD
T: (015394) 37302
F: (015394) 37394
E: itsgreat@langdale.co.uk
I: www.langdale.co.uk

Middlefell Farm Cottage ★★★
Contact: Mrs Susan Jackson, Heart of the Lakes, Fisherbeck Mill, Old Lake Road, Ambleside, Cumbria LA22 0DH
T: (015394) 32321
F: (015394) 33251
E: info@heartofthelakes.co.uk
I: www.heartofthelakes.co.uk

Rawfell ★★★★
Contact: Mrs Susan Jackson, Heart of the Lakes, Fisherbeck Hill, Old Lake Road, Ambleside, Cumbria LA22 0DH
T: (015394) 32321
F: (015394) 33251
E: info@heartofthelakes.co.uk
I: www.heartofthelakes.co.uk

GREAT MUSGRAVE
Cumbria

Blandswath Cottage ★★★
Contact: Dales Hol Cot Ref:1914, Dales Holiday Cottages, Carleton Business Park, Carleton New Road, Skipton, North Yorkshire BD23 2AA
T: (01756) 799821 & 790919
F: (01756) 797012
E: info@dalesholcot.com
I: www.dalesholcot.com

GREAT STRICKLAND
Cumbria

Sherif Park ★★★★
Contact: Sykes Cottages Ref:, Sykes Cottages, York House, York Street, Chester, CH1 3LR
T: (01244) 345700
F: (01244) 321442
E: info@sykescottages.co.uk
I: www.sykescottages.co.uk

GREYSOUTHEN
Cumbria

Swallow Barn Cottage ★★★★
Contact: Mr & Mrs R G James, 6 Evening Hill View, Brigham Road, Cockermouth, Cumbria CA13 0BB
T: (01900) 823016
F: (01900) 821446
E: swallowbarn@millenium-uk.net
I: www.swallowbarn.co.uk

GREYSTOKE
Cumbria

Brathen Cottage ★★★★
Contact: Mrs Christine Mole, Brathen the Thorpe, Greystoke, Penrith, Cumbria CA11 0TJ
T: (017684) 83595

Duck Down Cottage ★★★★
Contact: Mr Kevin Duckenfield, 10 Leconfield Garth, Follifoot, Harrogate, North Yorkshire HG3 1NF
T: (01423) 870490
F: (01423) 874175
E: sales@duckdowncottage.co.uk
I: www.duckdowncottage.co.uk

The Tack Room ★★★
Contact: Dales Hol Cot Ref:2104, Dales Holiday Cottages, Carleton Business Park, Carleton New Road, Skipton, North Yorkshire BD23 2AA
T: (01756) 799821 & 790919
F: (01756) 797012
E: info@dalesholcot.com
I: www.dalesholcot.com

Whakatane ★★★★
Contact: Dales Hol Cot Ref:2955, Dales Holiday Cottages, Carleton Business Park, Carleton New Road, Skipton, North Yorkshire BD23 2AA
T: (01756) 799821 & 790919
F: (01756) 797012
E: info@dalesholcot.com
I: www.dalesholcot.com

GRIZEBECK
Cumbria

The Cart House ★★★★
Contact: Mr John Serginson, The Lakeland Cottage Company, Waterside House, Newby Bridge, Ulverston, Cumbria LA12 8AN
T: (015395) 30024
F: (015395) 31932
E: john@lakeland-cottage-company.co.uk
I: www.lakeland-cottage-company.co.uk

GRIZEDALE
Cumbria

High Dale Park Barn ★★★
Contact: Mr P Brown, High Dale Park Farm, High Dale Park, Satterthwaite, Ulverston, Cumbria LA12 8LJ
T: (01229) 860226
E: peterbrown@highdalepark.demon.co.uk

HALE
Cumbria

Yew Tree Cottage ★★★★
Contact: Mr and Mrs T Wood, Littlebank, 6 Ancliffe Lane, Bolton-le-Sands, Carnforth, Lancashire LA5 8DS
T: (01524) 823179

HARTLEY
Cumbria

The Barn ★★★
Contact: Dales Hol Cot Ref:2852, Dales Holiday Cottages, Carleton Business Park, Carleton New Road, Skipton, North Yorkshire BD23 2AA
T: (01756) 799821 & 790919
F: (01756) 797012
E: info@dalesholcot.com
I: www.dalesholcot.com

Hartley Castle Barn ★★★★
Contact: Mrs Sally Dixon, Hartley Castle Barn, Hartley Castle, Hartley, Kirkby Stephen, Cumbria CA17 4JJ
T: (017683) 71331

HARTSOP
Cumbria

Brothersfield Cottage ★★★★
Contact: Country Holidays ref:12828, Spring Mill, Earby, Barnoldswick, Lancashire BB94 0AA
T: (01282) 445096
F: (01282) 844288
E: sales@ttgihg.co.uk
I: www.country-holidays.co.uk

Caudale Beck ★★
Contact: Mrs Susan Jackson, Heart of the Lakes, Fisherbeck Hill, Old Lake Road, Ambleside, Cumbria LA22 0DH
T: (015394) 32321
F: (015394) 33251
E: info@heartofthelakes.co.uk
I: www.heartofthelakes.co.uk

Dovedale ★★
Contact: Mrs Susan Jackson, Heart of the Lakes, Fisherbeck Hill, Old Lake Road, Ambleside, Cumbria LA22 0DH
T: (015394) 32321
F: (015394) 33251
E: info@heartofthelakes.co.uk
I: www.heartofthelakes.co.uk

Greenbank ★★★★
Contact: Mrs Susan Jackson, Heart of the Lakes, Fisherbeck Hill, Old Lake Road, Ambleside, Cumbria LA22 0DH
T: (015394) 32321
F: (015394) 33251
E: info@heartofthelakes.co.uk
I: www.heartofthelakes.co.uk

High Beckside ★★★
Contact: Mrs S Jackson, Heart of the Lakes, Fisherbeck Mill, Old Lake Road, Ambleside, Cumbria LA22 0DH
T: (015394) 32321
F: (015394) 33251
E: info@heartofthelakes.co.uk
I: www.heartofthelakes.co.uk

HAVERIGG
Cumbria

Harbour Cottage ★★★★
Contact: Country Holidays ref:8982, Spring Mill, Earby, Barnoldswick, Lancashire BB94 0AA
T: (01282) 445096
F: (01282) 844288
E: sales@ttgihhg.co.uk
I: www.country-holidays.co.uk

Haverings ★★★
Contact: Country Holidays ref:4902, Spring Mill, Earby, Barnoldswick, Lancashire BB94 0AA
T: 08700 723723
F: (01282) 844288
I: www.country-holidays.co.uk

Lazey Cottage ★★★★
Contact: Mrs Gloria Parsons and Mrs P Jenkinson, Orchard House, The Hill, Millom, Cumbria LA18 5HE
T: (01229) 772515

3 Poolside ★★★
Contact: Mr W Haston, 2 Pool Side, Haverigg, Millom, Cumbria
T: (01229) 772974
E: quietcottage@tinyworld.co.uk

HAVERTHWAITE
Cumbria

Close Cottage ★★★★
Contact: Mr John Serginson, The Lakeland Cottage Company, Waterside House, Newby Bridge, Ulverston, Cumbria LA12 8AN
T: (015395) 30024
F: (015395) 31932
E: john@lakeland-cottage-company.co.uk
I: www.lakeland-cottage-company.co.uk

Outwood
Rating Applied For
Contact: Mr P Liddell, Lakelovers, The New Toffee Loft, Kendal Road, Windermere, Cumbria LA23 3RA
T: (015394) 88855
F: (015394) 88857
E: bookings@lakelovers.co.uk
I: www.lakelovers.co.uk

Woodcroft House ★★★★
Contact: Mr John Serginson, The Lakeland Cottage Company, Waterside House, Newby Bridge, Ulverston, Cumbria LA12 8AN
T: (015395) 30024
F: (015395) 31932
E: john@lakeland-cottage-company.co.uk
I: www.lakeland-cottage-company.co.uk

HAWKSHEAD
Cumbria

Barn Syke
Rating Applied For
Contact: Mr Paul Liddell, Lakelovers, The New Toffee Loft, Kendal Road, Bowness-on-Windermere, Windermere, Cumbria LA23 3RA
T: (015394) 88855
F: (015394) 88857
E: bookings@lakelovers.co.uk
I: www.lakelovers.co.uk

Ben Fold ★★★★
Contact: Mrs Susan Jackson, Heart of the Lakes, Fisherbeck Hill, Old Lake Road, Ambleside, Cumbria LA22 0DH
T: (015394) 32321
F: (015394) 33251
E: info@heartofthelakes.co.uk
I: www.heartofthelakes.co.uk

431

Betty Fold Country House
★★★
Contact: Mr A J Marsden, Betty
Fold Country House, Hawkshead
Hill, Ambleside, Cumbria
LA22 0PS
T: (015394) 36611
E: holidays@bettyfold.freeserve.
co.uk
I: www.bettyfold.co.uk

Birkwray Farmhouse ★★★
Contact: Mr Paul Liddell,
Lakelovers, The New Toffee Loft,
Kendal Road, Windermere,
Cumbria LA23 3RA
T: (015394) 88855
F: (015394) 88857
E: bookings@lakelovers.co.uk
I: www.lakelovers.co.uk

Bridge View ★★★
Contact: Mrs S Dewhurst, Bridge
View, 2 Bridge View, Hawkshead,
Ambleside, Cumbria LA22 0PL
T: (015394) 36340

Broomriggs ★★★-★★★★
Contact: Mrs F Taylforth,
Broomriggs, Hawkshead,
Ambleside, Cumbria LA22 0JX
T: (015394) 36280 & 36272
E: broomriggs@zoom.co.uk
I: www.broomriggs.
co.uk/location.htm

Coachman's Loft ★★★★
Contact: Mrs Susan Jackson,
Heart of the Lakes, Fisherbeck
Hill, Old Lake Road, Ambleside,
Cumbria LA22 0DH
T: (015394) 32321
F: (015394) 33251
E: info@heartofthelakes.co.uk
I: www.heartofthelakes.co.uk

Columbine Cottage
Rating Applied For
Contact: Mr Paul Liddell,
Lakelovers, The New Toffee Loft,
Kendal Road, Bowness-on-
Windermere, Windermere,
Cumbria LA23 3RA
T: (015394) 88855
F: (015394) 88857
E: bookings@lakelovers.co.uk
I: www.lakelovers.co.uk

The Croft Holiday Flats ★★★
Contact: Mrs R E Barr, The Croft
Holiday Flats, North Lonsdale
Road, Hawkshead, Ambleside,
Cumbria LA22 0NX
T: (015394) 36374
F: (015394) 36544
E: enquiries@hawkshead-croft.
com
I: www.hawkshead-croft.com

Fair Cop ★★★★
Contact: Mrs Susan Jackson,
Heart of the Lakes, Fisherbeck
Hill, Old Lake Road, Ambleside,
Cumbria LA22 0DH
T: (015394) 32321
F: (015394) 33251
E: info@heartofthelakes.co.uk
I: www.heartofthelakes.co.uk

Gilpin Cottage ★★★
Contact: Mrs Susan Jackson,
Heart of the Lakes, Fisherbeck
Hill, Old Lake Road, Ambleside,
Cumbria LA22 0DH
T: (015394) 32321
F: (015394) 33251
E: info@heartofthelakes.co.uk
I: www.heartofthelakes.co.uk

Goosifoot ★★★
Contact: Mrs Susan Jackson,
Heart of the Lakes, Fisherbeck
Hill, Old Lake Road, Ambleside,
Cumbria LA22 0DH
T: (015394) 32321
F: (015394) 33251
E: info@heartofthelakes.co.uk
I: www.heartofthelakes.co.uk

Greenbank House
Rating Applied For
Contact: Mrs Susan Jackson,
Heart of the Lakes, Fisherbeck
Mill, Old Lake Road, Ambleside,
Cumbria LA22 0DH
T: (015394) 32321
F: (015394) 33251
E: info@heartofthelakes.co.uk
I: www.heartofthelakes.co.uk

Hatters Cottage ★★★
Contact: Mr and Mrs J Gunner,
Hawkshead Hill Farm,
Hawkshead Hill, Ambleside,
Cumbria LA22 0PW
T: (015394) 36203
E: mail@hatters-cottage.
freeserve.co.uk
I: www.hatters-cottage.
freeserve.co.uk

Heron Cottage
Rating Applied For
Contact: Mr Paul Liddell,
Lakelovers, The New Toffee Loft,
Kendal Road, Bowness-on-
Windermere, Windermere,
Cumbria LA23 3RA
T: (015394) 88855
F: (015394) 88857
E: bookings@lakelovers.co.uk
I: www.lakelovers.co.uk

High Orchard ★★★★
Contact: Mrs Susan Jackson,
Heart of the Lakes, Fisherbeck
Hill, Old Lake Road, Ambleside,
Cumbria LA22 0DH
T: (015394) 32321
F: (015394) 33251
E: info@heartofthelakes.co.uk
I: www.heartofthelakes.co.uk

Keen Ground Cottage ★★★
Contact: Mr John Serginson, The
Lakeland Cottage Company,
Waterside House, Newby Bridge,
Ulverston, Cumbria LA12 8AN
T: (015395) 30024
F: (015395) 31932
E: john@
lakeland-cottage-company.
co.uk
I: www.
lakeland-cottage-company.
co.uk

Kings Yard Cottage ★★★
Contact: Mr D Hogarth,
Cumbrian Cottages, 7 The
Crescent, Carlisle, CA1 1QW
T: (01228) 599960
F: (01228) 599970
E: enquiries@
cumbrian-cottages.co.uk
I: www.cumbrian-cottages.co.uk

Lantern Cottage ★★★
Contact: Mr D Hogarth,
Cumbrian Cottages, 7 The
Crescent, Carlisle, CA1 1QW
T: (01228) 599960
F: (01228) 599970
E: enquiries@
cumbrian-cottages.co.uk
I: www.cumbrian-cottages.co.uk

Larch Cottage ★★★
Contact: Mrs Susan Jackson,
Heart of the Lakes, Fisherbeck
Mill, Old Lake Road, Ambleside,
Cumbria LA22 0DH
T: (015394) 32321
F: (015394) 33251
E: info@heartofthelakes.co.uk
I: www.heartofthelakes.co.uk

Meadow View ★★
Contact: Blakes Cottages, Spring
Mill, Earby, Barnoldswick,
Lancashire BB94 0AA
T: 08700 708090
F: 0870 5851150
I: www.blakes.cottages.co.uk

Oak Apple Cottage ★★★★
Contact: Mrs N Penrice, Oak
Apple Cottage, Violet Bank,
Hawkshead, Ambleside, Cumbria
LA22 0PL
T: (015394) 36222
E: chp@violetbank.freeserve.
co.uk

**The Old Barn & Barn End
Cottage** ★★★★
Contact: Mrs Ann Gallagher,
Hideaways, The Minstrels
Gallery, The Square, Hawkshead,
Ambleside, Cumbria LA22 0NZ
T: (015394) 42435
F: (015394) 36178
E: bookings@
lakeland-hideaways.co.uk
I: www.lakeland-hideaways.
co.uk

Old Farm ★★★★
Contact: Mr John Serginson, The
Lakeland Cottage Company,
Waterside House, Newby Bridge,
Ulverston, Cumbria LA12 8AN
T: (015395) 30024
F: (015395) 31932
E: john@
lakeland-cottage-company.
co.uk
I: www.
lakeland-cottage-company.
co.uk

Rigges Wood Cottage ★★★★
Contact: Mr Paul Liddell,
Lakelovers, The New Toffee Loft,
Kendal Road, Windermere,
Cumbria LA23 3RA
T: (015394) 88855
F: (015394) 88857
E: bookings@lakelovers.co.uk
I: www.lakelovers.co.uk

Rose Cottage ★★★★★
Contact: Mrs A Gallagher,
Hideaways, Minstel Gallery, The
Square, Hawkshead, Ambleside,
Cumbria LA22 0NZ
T: (015394) 42435
F: (015394) 36178
E: email@sawrey-house.co.uk
I: www.hawkshead-cottages.
com

Rose Howe ★★★★
Contact: Mrs Susan Jackson,
Heart of the Lakes, Fisherbeck
Mill, Old Lake Road, Ambleside,
Cumbria LA22 0DH
T: (015394) 32321
F: (015394) 33251
E: info@heartofthelakes.co.uk
I: www.heartofthelakes.co.uk

Sand Ground Barn ★★★
Contact: Mrs Susan Jackson,
Heart of the Lakes, Fisherbeck
Mill, Old Lake Road, Ambleside,
Cumbria LA22 0DH
T: (015394) 32321
F: (015394) 33251
E: info@heartofthelakes.co.uk

Sandy Wyke ★★★★
Contact: Mrs Susan Jackson,
Heart of the Lakes, Fisherbeck
Hill, Old Lake Road, Ambleside,
Cumbria LA22 0DH
T: (015394) 32321
F: (015394) 33251
E: info@heartofthelakes.co.uk
I: www.heartofthelakes.co.uk

Sergeant Man ★★★★
Contact: Mrs Susan Jackson,
Heart of the Lakes, Fisherbeck
Hill, Old Lake Road, Ambleside,
Cumbria LA22 0DH
T: (015394) 32321
F: (015394) 33251
E: info@heartofthelakes.co.uk
I: www.heartofthelakes.co.uk

Shepherd's Cottage ★★★★
Contact: Hideaways, The
Minstrels Gallery, The Square,
Hawkshead, Ambleside, Cumbria
LA22 0NZ
T: (015394) 42435
F: (015394) 36178
E: bookings@lakeland-holidays.
co.uk
I: www.lakeland-hideaways.
co.uk

Swallow's Nest ★★★★
Contact: Mrs Susan Jackson,
Heart of the Lakes, Fisherbeck
Hill, Old Lake Road, Ambleside,
Cumbria LA22 0DH
T: (015394) 32321
F: (015394) 33251
E: info@heartofthelakes.co.uk
I: www.heartofthelakes.co.uk

Tarn Hows ★★★★
Contact: Mrs Susan Jackson,
Heart of the Lakes, Fisherbeck
Hill, Old Lake Road, Ambleside,
Cumbria LA22 0DH
T: (015394) 32321
F: (015394) 33251
E: info@heartofthelakes.co.uk
I: www.heartofthelakes.co.uk

Thompson Ground Farm
★★★★
Contact: Mr Paul Liddell,
Lakelovers, The New Toffee Loft,
Kendal Road, Windermere,
Cumbria LA23 3RA
T: (015394) 88855
F: (015394) 88857
E: bookings@lakelovers.co.uk
I: www.lakelovers.co.uk

Walker Ground Barn ★★★★
Contact: Mrs Susan Jackson,
Heart of the Lakes, Fisherbeck
Mill, Old Lake Road, Ambleside,
Cumbria LA22 0DH
T: (015394) 32321
F: (015394) 33251
E: info@heartofthelakes.co.uk
I: www.heartofthelakes.co.uk

Establishments printed in blue have a detailed entry in this guide

Woodlands, Roger Ground ★★★★
Contact: Mrs Susan Jackson,
Heart of the Lakes, Fisherbeck
Hill, Old Lake Road, Ambleside,
Cumbria LA22 0DH
T: (015394) 32321
F: (015394) 33251
E: info@heartofthelakes.co.uk
I: www.heartofthelakes.co.uk

Yew Trees ★★★★
Contact: Mrs Susan Jackson,
Heart of the Lakes, Fisherbeck
Hill, Old Lake Road, Ambleside,
Cumbria LA22 0DH
T: (015394) 32321
F: (015394) 33251
E: info@heartofthelakes.co.uk
I: www.heartofthelakes.co.uk

HEAVES
Cumbria

Wain Gap Cottage
Rating Applied For
Contact: Mrs C Whitelock,
Heaves Hotel, Heaves, Kendal,
Cumbria LA8 8EF
T: (015395) 60396
F: (015395) 60269
E: cottages@heaves.freeserve.
co.uk

HELTON
Cumbria

Talbot Studio ★★★★
Contact: Mr Martin Wardle,
Lakes and Valleys, North Lodge,
Longtail Hill, Bowness-on-
Windermere, Windermere,
Cumbria LA23 3JD
T: (015394) 88612
F: (015394) 48988
E: lakesandvalleys@aol.com
I: www.lakesandvalleys.co.uk

HESKET NEWMARKET
Cumbria

Bannest Hill Cottage ★★★
Contact: Mr and Mrs J D Clay,
Bannest Hill Cottage, Bannest
Hill, Haltcliffe, Hesket
Newmarket, Wigton, Cumbria
CA7 8JT
T: (017684) 84394

Syke House ★★★
Contact: Sykes Cottages Ref:
692, Sykes Cottages, York House,
York Street, Chester, CH1 3LR
T: (01244) 345700
F: (01244) 321442
E: info@sykescottages.co.uk
I: www.sykescottages.co.uk

HIGH LORTON
Cumbria

Boon Beck Farmhouse ★★★★
Contact: Mr D Hogarth,
Cumbrian Cottages, 7 The
Crescent, Carlisle, CA1 1QW
T: (01228) 599960 & 599950
F: (01228) 599970
E: enquiries@
cumbrian-cottages.co.uk
I: www.cumbrian-cottages.co.uk

Brewery House ★★★★★
Contact: Mr D Hogarth,
Cumbrian Cottages, 7 The
Crescent, Carlisle, CA1 1QW
T: (01228) 599960 & 599950
F: (01228) 599970
E: enquiries@
cumbrian-cottages.co.uk
I: www.cumbrian-cottages.co.uk

High Groom Cottage ★★★
Contact: Mr D Hogarth,
Cumbrian Cottages, 7 The
Crescent, Carlisle, CA1 1QW
T: (01228) 599960 & 599950
F: (01228) 599970
E: enquiries@
cumbrian-cottages.co.uk
I: www.cumbrian-cottages.co.uk

Holemire House Barn ★★★★
Contact: Mrs A Fearfield,
Holemire House Barn, Holemire
House, High Lorton,
Cockermouth, Cumbria
CA13 9TX
T: (01900) 85225

Midtown Cottages ★★★
Contact: Mr M Burrell, 20
Hillside, Abbotts Ann, Andover,
Hampshire SP11 7DF
T: (01264) 710165
F: (01264) 710165
E: info@midtowncottages.co.uk
I: www.midtowncottages.co.uk

Wayside Cottage ★★★
Contact: Dales Hol Cot Ref:2376,
Dales Holiday Cottages, Carleton
Business Park, Carleton New
Road, Skipton, North Yorkshire
BD23 2AA
T: (01756) 799821 & 790919
F: (01756) 797012
E: info@dalesholcot.com
I: www.dalesholcot.com

HILTON
Cumbria

Joiners Cottage
Rating Applied For
Contact: Dales Hol Cot Ref:2762,
Dales Holiday Cottages, Carleton
Business Park, Carleton New
Road, Skipton, North Yorkshire
BD23 2AA
T: (01756) 799821 & 790919
F: (01756) 797012
E: info@dalesholcot.com
I: www.dalesholcot.com

HOLMROOK
Cumbria

**Hollin Head Cottage and Esk
View ★★★-★★★★**
Contact: Mrs D M Postlethwaite,
Hollin Head Cottage and Esk
View, Spout House Farm, Boot,
Holmrook, Cumbria CA19 1TF
T: (019467) 23235
F: (019467) 23235

Yattus ★★★★★
Contact: Mr D Hogarth,
Cumbrian Cottages, 7 The
Crescent, Carlisle, CA1 1QW
T: (01228) 599960 & 599950
F: (01228) 599970
E: enquiries@
cumbrian-cottages.co.uk
I: www.cumbrian-cottages.co.uk

HUTTON ROOF
Cumbria

Barn Cottage ★★★
Contact: Mr J Newton,
Hegglehead, Hutton Roof,
Penrith, Cumbria CA11 0XS
T: (017684) 84566
F: (017684) 84460
E: hegglehead@aol.com
I: www.hegglehead.co.uk

INGS
Cumbria

Ghyll Cottage ★★★
Contact: Mr D Hogarth,
Cumbrian Cottages, 7 The
Crescent, Carlisle, CA1 1QW
T: (01228) 599960 & 599950
F: (01228) 599970
E: enquiries@
cumbrian-cottages.co.uk
I: www.cumbrian-cottages.co.uk

Topiary Cottage
Rating Applied For
Contact: Mr Paul Liddell,
Lakelovers, The New Toffee Loft,
Kendal Road, Windermere,
Cumbria LA23 3RA
T: (015394) 88855
F: (015394) 88857
E: bookings@lakelovers.co.uk
I: www.lakelovers.co.uk

IREBY
Cumbria

Fell Cottage ★★★★★
Contact: Mr D Hogarth,
Cumbrian Cottages, 7 The
Crescent, Carlisle, CA1 1QW
T: (01228) 599960 & 599950
F: (01228) 599970
E: enquiries@
cumbrian-cottages.co.uk
I: www.cumbrian-cottages.co.uk

Millers Cottage ★★★★
Contact: Mrs Anne Marrs,
Millers Cottage, Uldale Mill,
Ireby, Carlisle, Cumbria CA7 1DS
T: (016973) 71582
F: (016973) 71582

Rowan Cottage ★★★
Contact: Dales Hol Cot Ref:2349,
Dales Holiday Cottages, Carleton
Business Park, Carleton New
Road, Skipton, North Yorkshire
BD23 2AA
T: (01756) 799821 & 790919
F: (01756) 797012
E: info@dalesholcot.com
I: www.dalesholcot.com

KENDAL
Cumbria

Dora's Cottage ★★★
Contact: Mrs Val Sunter, Higher
House Farm, Oxenholme Lane,
Natland, Kendal, Cumbria
LA9 7QH
T: (015395) 61177
F: (015395) 61520

**Field End Barns and Shaw End
Mansion ★★★-★★★★**
Contact: Mr & Mrs E D
Robinson, Field End Barns and
Shaw End Mansion, Patton,
Kendal, Cumbria LA8 9DU
T: (01539) 824220 &
07778 596863
F: (01539) 824464
E: fshawend@globalnet.co.uk
I: www.diva-web.
co.uk/fsendhols

The Garden Flat
Rating Applied For
Contact: Sykes Cottages Ref:
784, Sykes Cottages, York House,
York Street, Chester, CH1 3LR
T: (01244) 345700
F: (01244) 321442
E: info@sykescottages.co.uk
I: www.sykescottages.co.uk

Gilcruce
Rating Applied For
Contact: Mr Paul Liddell,
Lakelovers, The New Toffee Loft,
Kendal Road, Windermere,
Cumbria LA23 3RA
T: (015394) 88855
F: (015394) 88857
E: bookings@lakelovers.co.uk
I: www.lakelovers.co.uk

High Swinklebank Farm ★★★
Contact: Mrs O B Simpson, High
Swinklebank Farm, Longsleddale,
Kendal, Cumbria LA8 9BD
T: (01539) 823682

**High Underbrow Cottage
★★★**
Contact: Mrs Bateman, High
Underbrow Farm, Burneside,
Kendal, Cumbria LA8 9AY
T: (01539) 721927

Hylands ★★★★
Contact: Mr S Lambeth, 5 Stable
Close, Finmere, Buckingham,
Buckinghamshire MK18 4AD
T: (01280) 848779 &
07973 716556
F: (01280) 847519
E: simonlambeth@aol.com
I: www.hylands-lakedistrict.
co.uk

**Moresdale Bank Cottage
★★★★**
Contact: Mrs Helen Parkins,
Moresdale Cottage, Lambrigg,
Kendal, Cumbria LA8 0DH
T: (01539) 824227
E: rgpkendal@btinternet.com
I: www.diva-web.
co.uk/moresdale

8 Old Lound Cottages ★★★
Contact: Country Holidays
ref:10962, Spring Mill, Earby,
Barnoldswick, Lancashire
BB94 0AA
T: 08700 723723
F: (01282) 844288
E: sales@ttgihg.co.uk
I: www.country-holidays.co.uk

**Plumgarths Self-catering
Holidays ★★★★**
Contact: Mr and Mrs Wharram,
Plumgarths Self-catering
Holidays, Crook Road, Kendal,
Cumbria LA8 8LX
T: (01539) 720010
F: (01539) 735367
E: kath@plumgarths.f9.co.uk
I: fp.plumgarths.f9.co.uk

Todd Meadow ★★★★
Contact: Mr D Hogarth,
Cumbrian Cottages, 7 The
Crescent, Carlisle, CA1 1QW
T: (01228) 599960
F: (01228) 599970
E: enquiries@
cumbrian-cottages.co.uk
I: www.cumbrian-cottages.co.uk

KENTMERE
Cumbria

Fell View ★★★
Contact: Dales Hol Cot Ref:2035,
Dales Holiday Cottages, Carleton
Business Park, Carleton New
Road, Skipton, North Yorkshire
BD23 2AA
T: (01756) 799821 & 790919
F: (01756) 797012
E: info@dalesholcot.com
I: www.dalesholcot.com

High Fold ★★★★★
Contact: Mr D Hogarth,
Cumbrian Cottages, 7 The
Crescent, Carlisle, CA1 1QW
T: (01228) 599960
F: (01228) 599970
E: enquiries@
cumbrian-cottages.co.uk
I: www.cumbrian-cottages.co.uk

The Nook Cottage – Kentmere Valley ★★★
Contact: Mr John Serginson, The
Lakeland Cottage Company,
Waterside House, Newby Bridge,
Ulverston, Cumbria LA12 8AN
T: (015395) 30024
F: (015395) 31932
E: john@
lakeland-cottage-company.
co.uk
I: www.
lakeland-cottage-company.
co.uk

KESWICK
Cumbria

Acorn Apartments and Acorn View ★★★★–★★★★★
Contact: Mr J Miller, Acorn
Selfcatering, Acorn House,
Ambleside, Keswick, Cumbria
CA12 4DL
T: (017687) 72553
F: (017687) 75332
E: info@acornselfcatering.co.uk
I: www.acornselfcatering.co.uk

Alison's Cottage and Alison's View ★★★–★★★★
Contact: Mrs Alison Milner, 9
Fearon Close, Gunthorpe,
Nottingham, NG14 7FA
T: (0115) 966 4049 &
07798 770616

Amba ★★★★
Contact: Mr D Hogarth,
Cumbrian Cottages, 7 The
Crescent, Carlisle, CA1 1QW
T: (01228) 599960 & 599950
F: (01228) 599970
E: enquiries@
cumbrian-cottages.co.uk
I: www.cumbrian-cottages.co.uk

Applemere ★★★★
Contact: Mr D Hogarth,
Cumbrian Cottages, 7 The
Crescent, Carlisle, CA1 1QW
T: (01228) 599960 & 599950
F: (01228) 599970
E: enquiries@
cumbrian-cottages.co.uk
I: www.cumbrian-cottages.co.uk

Appletree ★★★★
Contact: Mr D Hogarth,
Cumbrian Cottages, 7 The
Crescent, Carlisle, CA1 1QW
T: (01228) 599960 & 599950
F: (01228) 599970
E: enquiries@
cumbrian-cottages.co.uk
I: www.cumbrian-cottages.co.uk

Armathwaite Hall ★★★★–★★★★★
Contact: Ms Carolyn Graves,
Armathwaite Hall, Keswick,
Cumbria CA12 4RE
T: (017687) 76551
F: (017687) 76220
E: reservations@
armathwaite-hall.com
I: www.armathwaite-hall.com

Ashbrooke ★★★
Contact: Mr D Hogarth,
Cumbrian Cottages, 7 The
Crescent, Carlisle, CA1 1QW
T: (01228) 599960
F: (01228) 599970
E: enquiries@
cumbrian-cottages.co.uk
I: www.cumbrian-cottages.co.uk

3 Beech ★★★
Contact: Mrs S Johnstone,
Timbers, York Lane, Langho,
Blackburn, Lancashire BB6 8DW
T: (01254) 247776

Belle Vue ★★★–★★★★
Contact: Mrs L G Ryder, Hillside,
Portinscale, Keswick, Cumbria
CA12 5RS
T: (017687) 71065
E: lexieryder@hotmail.com

Bleech Green Cottages ★★★
Contact: Mr D Hogarth,
Cumbrian Cottages, 7 The
Crescent, Carlisle, CA1 1QW
T: (01228) 599960 & 599950
F: (01228) 599970
E: enquiries@
cumbrian-cottages.co.uk
I: www.cumbrian-cottages.co.uk

Blencathra House ★★★★
Contact: Mr D Hogarth,
Cumbrian Cottages, 7 The
Crescent, Carlisle, CA1 1QW
T: (01228) 599960 & 599950
F: (01228) 599970
E: enquiries@
cumbrian-cottages.co.uk
I: www.cumbrian-cottages.co.uk

Bracken Lodge ★★★★
Contact: Mr D Hogarth,
Cumbrian Cottages, 7 The
Crescent, Carlisle, CA1 1QW
T: (01228) 599960 & 599950
F: (01228) 599970
E: enquiries@
cumbrian-cottages.co.uk
I: www.cumbrian-cottages.co.uk

Brandelhow ★★★★
Contact: Mrs Wendy Ferry,
Smithy House, Armathwaite,
Carlisle, Cumbria CA4 9ST
T: (016974) 72269

Brewery Lane Holiday Cottages ★★★
Contact: Mr J Stephenson,
Beechtrees, Lonsties, Keswick,
Cumbria CA12 5ER
T: (017687) 73525
F: (017687) 75435
E: helen8@supanet.com
I: www.selfcateringkeswick.com

Brigham Farm ★★★★
Contact: Mr N Green, Fornside
House, St Johns-in-the-Vale,
Keswick, Cumbria CA12 4TS
T: (017687) 79666
E: selfcatering@
keswickholidays.co.uk
I: www.keswickholidays.co.uk

Bunbury Cottage ★★★
Contact: Mr D Hogarth,
Cumbrian Cottages, 7 The
Crescent, Carlisle, CA1 1QW
T: (01228) 599960
F: (01228) 599970
E: enquiries@
cumbrian-cottages.co.uk
I: www.cumbrian-cottages.co.uk

11 Burnside Park ★★★★
Contact: Mr D Hogarth,
Cumbrian Cottages, 7 The
Crescent, Carlisle, CA1 1QW
T: (01228) 599960 & 599950
F: (01228) 599970
E: enquiries@
cumbrian-cottages.co.uk
I: www.cumbrian-cottages.co.uk

Cairnway ★★★★
Contact: Mr D Hogarth,
Cumbrian Cottages, 7 The
Crescent, Carlisle, CA1 1QW
T: (01228) 599960 & 599950
F: (01228) 599970
E: enquiries@
cumbrian-cottages.co.uk
I: www.cumbrian-cottages.co.uk

Carolyn's Cottage ★★★
Contact: Mr D Hogarth,
Cumbrian Cottages, 7 The
Crescent, Carlisle, CA1 1QW
T: (01228) 599960
F: (01228) 599970
E: enquiries@
cumbrian-cottages.co.uk
I: www.cumbrian-cottages.co.uk

Castlerigg Manor Lodge ★★★★
Contact: Mr D Hogarth,
Cumbrian Cottages, 7 The
Crescent, Carlisle, CA1 1QW
T: (01228) 599960 & 599950
F: (01228) 599970
E: enquiries@
cumbrian-cottages.co.uk
I: www.cumbrian-cottages.co.uk

Catbells ★★★
Contact: Mr David Burton,
Lakeland Cottage Holidays, 3 The
Heads, Keswick, Cumbria
CA12 5ES
T: (017687) 71071
F: (017687) 75036
E: info@lakelandcottages.co.uk
I: www.lakelandcottages.co.uk

3 Catherine Cottages ★★★
Contact: Mr and Mrs Peter &
Margaret Hewitson, 17 Cedar
Lane, Cockermouth, Cumbria
CA13 9HN
T: (01900) 828039 &
07711 305075
E: peter.hewitson1@btinternet.
com

Cosy Nook ★★★
Contact: Mr D Hogarth,
Cumbrian Cottages, 7 The
Crescent, Carlisle, CA1 1QW
T: (01228) 599960 & 599950
F: (01228) 599970
E: enquiries@
cumbrian-cottages.co.uk
I: www.cumbrian-cottages.co.uk

The Cottage ★★★
Contact: Mrs M Beaty, The
Cottage, Birkrigg, Newlands,
Keswick, Cumbria CA12 5TS
T: (017687) 78278

The Cottage ★★★★
Contact: Mrs Susan Jackson,
Heart of the Lakes, Fisherbeck
Hill, Old Lake Road, Ambleside,
Cumbria LA22 0DH
T: (015394) 32321
F: (015394) 33251
E: info@heartofthelakes.co.uk
I: www.heartofthelakes.co.uk

The Cottage ★★★
Contact: Mr and Mrs D Brown, 4
Ashtree Avenue, Keswick,
Cumbria CA12 5PF
T: (017687) 74324
E: cottages@keswickcumbria.
freeserve.co.uk
I: www.keswickcumbria.
freeserve.co.uk

Crag Lea ★★★
Contact: Mr D Hogarth,
Cumbrian Cottages, 7 The
Crescent, Carlisle, CA1 1QW
T: (01228) 599960 & 599950
F: (01228) 599970
E: enquiries@
cumbrian-cottages.co.uk
I: www.cumbrian-cottages.co.uk

Croft House Holiday Homes Croftside and Croft Corner ★★★★
Contact: Mrs J L Boniface, Croft
House, Applethwaite, Keswick,
Cumbria CA12 4PN
T: (017687) 73693
E: holidays@crofthouselakes.
co.uk
I: www.crofthouselakes.co.uk

Dale Head Hall Lakeside Hotel ★★★★–★★★★★
Contact: Mr H Bonkenburg, Dale
Head Hall Lakeside Hotel,
Thirlmere, Keswick, Cumbria
CA12 4TN
T: (017687) 72478
F: (017687) 71070
E: onthelakeside@
dale-head-hall.co.uk
I: www.dale-head-hall.co.uk

Dalrymple ★★
Contact: Mr David Burton,
Lakeland Cottage Holidays, 3 The
Heads, Keswick, Cumbria
CA12 5ES
T: (017687) 71071
F: (017687) 75036
E: info@lakelandcottages.co.uk
I: www.lakelandcottages.co.uk/

Denholm ★★★
Contact: Mr D Hogarth,
Cumbrian Cottages, 7 The
Crescent, Carlisle, CA1 1QW
T: (01228) 599960 & 599950
F: (01228) 599970
E: enquiries@
cumbrian-cottages.co.uk
I: www.cumbrian-cottages.co.uk

Derwent House and Brandelhowe ★★★
Contact: Mr and Mrs Oliver Bull,
Derwent House Holidays, Stone
Heath, Hilderstone, Staffordshire
ST15 8SH
T: (01889) 505678 &
(01782) 281321
F: (01889) 505679
E: thebulls@globalnet.co.uk

Derwent Manor ★★★★
Contact: Mrs C Denwood,
Derwent Manor, Portinscale,
Keswick, Cumbria CA12 5RE
T: (017687) 72211
F: (017687) 71002
E: info@derwent-manor.co.uk
I: www.derwent-manor.co.uk

Establishments printed in blue have a detailed entry in this guide

Dove House ★★★★
Contact: Mrs Susan Jackson,
Heart of the Lakes, Fisherbeck
Hill, Old Lake Road, Ambleside,
Cumbria LA22 0DH
T: (015394) 32321
F: (015394) 33251
E: info@heartofthelakes.co.uk
I: www.heartofthelakes.co.uk

Dowthwaite ★★★★
Contact: Mrs Susan Jackson,
Heart of the Lakes, Fisherbeck
Hill, Old Lake Road, Ambleside,
Cumbria LA22 0DH
T: (015394) 32321
F: (015394) 33251
E: info@heartofthelakes.co.uk
I: www.heartofthelakes.co.uk

Drystones ★★★★
Contact: Mr D Hogarth,
Cumbrian Cottages, 7 The
Crescent, Carlisle, CA1 1QW
T: (01228) 599960 & 599950
F: (01228) 599970
E: enquiries@
cumbrian-cottages.co.uk
I: www.cumbrian-cottages.co.uk

Dunmallet ★★★
Contact: Mr D Hogarth,
Cumbrian Cottages, 7 The
Crescent, Carlisle, CA1 1QW
T: (01228) 599960 & 599950
F: (01228) 599970
E: enquiries@
cumbrian-cottages.co.uk
I: www.cumbrian-cottages.co.uk

14 Elm Court ★★★
Contact: Mr D Hogarth,
Cumbrian Cottages, 7 The
Crescent, Carlisle, CA1 1QW
T: (01228) 599960 & 599950
F: (01228) 599970
E: enquiries@
cumbrian-cottages.co.uk
I: www.cumbrian-cottages.co.uk

15 Elm Court ★★★★
Contact: Mr D Hogarth,
Cumbrian Cottages, 7 The
Crescent, Carlisle, CA1 1QW
T: (01228) 599960 & 599950
F: (01228) 599970
E: enquiries@
cumbrian-cottages.co.uk
I: www.cumbrian-cottages.co.uk

5 Elm Court ★★★
Contact: Mr and Mrs Frank and
Pauline Bergin, 46 Lakeland
Park, Keswick, Cumbria
CA12 4AT
T: (017687) 75405

Elmcot ★★★★
Contact: Mr D Hogarth,
Cumbrian Cottages, 7 The
Crescent, Carlisle, CA1 1QW
T: (01228) 599960 & 599950
F: (01228) 599970
E: enquiries@
cumbrian-cottages.co.uk
I: www.cumbrian-cottages.co.uk

Fell View ★★★
Contact: Mr D Hogarth,
Cumbrian Cottages, 7 The
Crescent, Carlisle, CA1 1QW
T: (01228) 599960 & 599950
F: (01228) 599970
E: enquiries@
cumbrian-cottages.co.uk
I: www.cumbrian-cottages.co.uk

The Fells ★★★★
Contact: Mr D Hogarth,
Cumbrian Cottages, 7 The
Crescent, Carlisle, CA1 1QW
T: (01228) 599960 & 599950
F: (01228) 599970
E: enquiries@
cumbrian-cottages.co.uk
I: www.cumbrian-cottages.co.uk

Fernbank House ★★★★★
Contact: Mr Stephen Mason,
Stonegarth Guest House, 2 Eskin
Street, Keswick, Cumbria
CA12 4DH
T: (017687) 74457 & 72436
E: info@fernbankhouse.com
I: www.fernbankhouse.com

Ferndale ★★
Contact: Mr David Burton,
Lakeland Cottage Holidays, 3 The
Heads, Keswick, Cumbria
CA12 5ES
T: (017687) 71071
F: (017687) 75036
E: info@lakelandcottages.co.uk
I: www.lakelandcottages.co.uk/

**Fieldside Grange
★★★-★★★★**
Contact: Mr David Mitchell,
Fieldside Grange, Keswick,
Cumbria
T: (017687) 74444
F: (017687) 75088
E: fieldgrangekeswick@
tinyonline.co.uk
I: www.cottageguide.
co.uk/fielgrange

Fieldside Lodge ★★★★
Contact: Mr D Hogarth,
Cumbrian Cottages, 7 The
Crescent, Carlisle, CA1 1QW
T: (01228) 599960 & 599950
F: (01228) 599970
E: enquiries@
cumbrian-cottages.co.uk
I: www.cumbrian-cottages.co.uk

**Fornside Farm Cottages
★★★★**
Contact: Mr & Mrs R M Hall,
Fornside Farm, St Johns-in-the-
Vale, Keswick, Cumbria CA12 4TS
T: (017687) 79173
F: (017687) 79174
E: cottages@fornside.co.uk
I: www.fornside.co.uk

Fountain Cottage ★★★★
Contact: Dr and Mrs W E
Preston, 5 Mill Bank, Lymm,
Cheshire WA13 9DG
T: (01925) 756479
E: preston@mail.talk-101.com

Gable Cottage ★★★
Contact: Mr D Hogarth,
Cumbrian Cottages, 7 The
Crescent, Carlisle, CA1 1QW
T: (01228) 599960
F: (01228) 599970
E: enquiries@
cumbrian-cottages.co.uk
I: wwww.cumbrian-cottages.
co.uk

Gallery Mews Cottages ★★★
Contact: Mr P Graham,
Randlehow, Mockerkin,
Cockermouth, Cumbria
CA13 0ST
T: (01946) 861018
E: enquiries@thornthwaite.net
I: www.thornthwaite.net

Glendera ★★★
Contact: Mr David Burton,
Lakeland Cottage Holidays, 3 The
Heads, Keswick, Cumbria
CA12 5ES
T: (017687) 71071
F: (017687) 75036
E: info@lakelandcottages.co.uk
I: www.lakelandcottages.co.uk/

Glenmore ★★★
Contact: Mr D Hogarth,
Cumbrian Cottages, 7 The
Crescent, Carlisle, CA1 1QW
T: (01228) 599960
F: (01228) 599970
E: enquiries@
cumbrian-cottages.co.uk
I: www.cumbrian-cottages.co.uk

Grange Cottage ★★★
Contact: Mr David Burton,
Lakeland Cottage Holidays, 3 The
Heads, Keswick, Cumbria
CA12 5ES
T: (017687) 71071
F: (017687) 75036
E: info@lakelandcottages.co.uk
I: www.lakelandcottages.co.uk

1 Greta Side Court ★★★
Contact: Mr D Hogarth,
Cumbrian Cottages, 7 The
Crescent, Carlisle, CA1 1QW
T: (01228) 599960 & 599950
F: (01228) 599970
E: enquiries@
cumbrian-cottages.co.uk
I: www.cumbrian-cottages.co.uk

2 Greta Side Court ★★★
Contact: Mr D Hogarth,
Cumbrian Cottages, 7 The
Crescent, Carlisle, CA1 1QW
T: (01228) 599960 & 599950
F: (01228) 599970
E: enquiries@
cumbrian-cottages.co.uk
I: www.cumbrian-cottages.co.uk

4 Greta Side Court ★★★
Contact: Mr D Hogarth,
Cumbrian Cottages, 7 The
Crescent, Carlisle, CA1 1QW
T: (01228) 599960 & 599950
F: (01228) 599970
E: enquiries@
cumbrian-cottages.co.uk
I: www.cumbrian-cottages.co.uk

Greta View ★★★
Contact: Mr David Burton,
Lakeland Cottage Holidays, 3 The
Heads, Keswick, Cumbria
CA12 5ES
T: (017687) 71071
F: (017687) 75036
E: info@lakelandcottages.co.uk
I: www.lakelandcottages.co.uk/

5 The Hawthorns ★★★★
Contact: Mr & Mrs Ralph and
Hazel Hetherington, Whitbarrow
Cottage, Berrier, Penrith,
Cumbria CA11 0XB
T: (017684) 83689
F: (017684) 83689

Herries ★★★
Contact: Mr David Burton,
Lakeland Cottage Holidays, 3 The
Heads, Keswick, Cumbria
CA12 5ES
T: (017687) 71071
F: (017687) 75036
E: info@lakelandcottages.co.uk
I: www.lakelandcottages.co.uk/

High Rigg ★★★★
Contact: Mr T C Sayer, High
Rigg, Fasnakyle, Oldhill Wood,
Studham, Dunstable,
Bedfordshire LU6 2NF
T: (01582) 872574

Hillside ★-★★★
Contact: Mr C F Howey,
Cemetery Lodge, Whitton Road,
Rothbury, Northumberland
NE65 7RX
T: (01669) 620451
E: lakesflat@aol.com
I: www.members.tripod.
com/~lakesflats/

11 Howrah's Court ★★★★
Contact: Mr D Hogarth,
Cumbrian Cottages, 7 The
Crescent, Carlisle, CA1 1QW
T: (01228) 599960
F: (01228) 599970
E: enquiries@
cumbrian-cottages.co.uk
I: www.cumbrian-cottages.co.uk

Inglewood ★★★
Contact: Country Holidays Ref:
15288, Holiday Cottages Group
Owner Services Dept, Spring
Mill, Earby, Barnoldswick,
Lancashire BB18 6RN
T: (01282) 445444
F: (01282) 841539
E: sales@tthigh.co.uk
I: www.country-holidays.co.uk

**Keswick Timeshare Limited
★★★★**
Contact: Mr David Etherden,
Keswick Timeshare Limited,
Keswick Bridge, Brundholme
Road, Keswick, Cumbria
CA12 4NL
T: (017687) 73591
F: (017687) 75811
E: enquiries@keswickb.com
I: www.keswickb.com

**Kingsfell and Kingstarn
★★★★**
Contact: Mr Nicholas Gillham, 3
Salisbury House, Abbey Mills,
Abbey Mill Lane, St Albans,
Hertfordshire AL3 4HG
T: (01727) 853531 &
(017687) 74444
E: nick.gillham@tinyworld.co.uk

Kylesku ★★★
Contact: Mr D Hogarth,
Cumbrian Cottages, 7 The
Crescent, Carlisle, CA1 1QW
T: (01228) 599960 & 599950
F: (01228) 599970
E: enquiries@
cumbrian-cottages.co.uk
I: www.cumbrian-cottages.co.uk

Latrigg View ★★★★
Contact: Mr D Hogarth,
Cumbrian Cottages, 7 The
Crescent, Carlisle, CA1 1QW
T: (01228) 599960
F: (01228) 599970
E: enquiries@
cumbrian-cottages.co.uk
I: www.cumbrian-cottages.co.uk

Little Haven ★★★★
Contact: Mr D Hogarth,
Cumbrian Cottages, 7 The
Crescent, Carlisle, CA1 1QW
T: (01228) 599960
F: (01228) 599970
E: enquiries@
cumbrian-cottages.co.uk
I: www.cumbrian-cottages.co.uk

1 Lonsdale House ★★★★
Contact: Mr D Hogarth,
Cumbrian Cottages, 7 The
Crescent, Carlisle, CA1 1QW
T: (01228) 599960
F: (01228) 599970
E: enquiries@
cumbrian-cottages.co.uk
I: www.cumbrian-cottages.co.uk

5 Lonsdale House ★★★★
Contact: Mr D Hogarth,
Cumbrian Cottages, 7 The
Crescent, Carlisle, CA1 1QW
T: (01228) 599960
F: (01228) 599970
E: enquiries@
cumbrian-cottages.co.uk
I: www.cumbrian-cottages.co.uk

Low Briery Cottages ★★★★
Contact: Mr Michael Atkinson,
Low Briery Holiday Village,
Keswick, Cumbria CA12 4RN
F: (017687) 72044
I: www.keswick.uk.com

Luxurious Lakeland ★★
Contact: Mr John Mitchell,
Luxurious Lakeland, 35 Main
Street, Keswick, Cumbria
CA12 5BL
T: (017687) 72790 &
(016973) 20220
F: (017687) 75750

8 Lydia's Cottages ★★★★
Contact: Mrs J Hutchinson, 6
Mountain View, Borrowdale,
Keswick, Cumbria CA12 5XH
T: (017687) 77631
E: jean@jhutch.demon.co.uk
I: www.jhutch.demon.
co.uk/jean/lydias.htm

Meadow Cottage ★★★
Contact: Mr David Burton,
Lakeland Cottage Holidays, 3 The
Heads, Keswick, Cumbria
CA12 5ES
T: (017687) 71071
F: (017687) 75036
E: info@lakelandcottages.co.uk
I: www.lakelandcottages.co.uk/

Mill House ★★★★
Contact: Mr D Hogarth,
Cumbrian Cottages, 7 The
Crescent, Carlisle, CA1 1QW
T: (01228) 599960 & 599950
F: (01228) 599970
E: enquiries@
cumbrian-cottages.co.uk
I: www.cumbrian-cottages.co.uk

Millbeck Cottages ★★★★
Contact: Mr D Hogarth,
Cumbrian Cottages, 7 The
Crescent, Carlisle, CA1 1QW
T: (01228) 599960
F: (01228) 599970
E: enquiries@
cumbrian-cottages.co.uk
I: www.cumbrian-cottages.co.uk

Mountain View ★★★★
Contact: Country Hoidays
ref:1905, Spring Mill, Earby,
Barnoldswick, Lancashire
BB94 0AA
T: (01282) 445096
F: (01282) 844288
E: sales@ttgihg.co.uk
I: www.coutnry-holidays.co.uk

Northside ★★★
Contact: Mr David Burton,
Lakeland Cottage Holidays, 3 The
Heads, Keswick, Cumbria
CA12 5ES
T: (017687) 71071
F: (017687) 75036
E: info@lakelandcottages.co.uk
I: www.lakelandcottages.co.uk/

Olivet ★★★
Contact: Mr D Hogarth,
Cumbrian Cottages, 7 The
Crescent, Carlisle, CA1 1QW
T: (01228) 599960 & 599950
F: (01228) 599970
E: enquiries@
cumbrian-cottages.co.uk
I: www.cumbrian-cottages.co.uk

Orchard Barn ★★★
Contact: Mr & Mrs I C Hall,
Fisherground Farm, Eskdale,
Cumbria CA19 1TF
T: (01946) 723319
E: holidays@fisherground.co.uk
I: www.orchardhouseholidays.
co.uk

Poet's Corner ★★★★
Contact: Mr D Hogarth,
Cumbrian Cottages, 7 The
Crescent, Carlisle, CA1 1QW
T: (01228) 599960 & 599950
F: (01228) 599970
E: enquiries@
cumbrian-cottages.co.uk
I: www.cumbrian-cottages.co.uk

Poplar Cottage ★★★
Contact: Mr D Hogarth,
Cumbrian Cottages, 7 The
Crescent, Carlisle, CA1 1QW
T: (01228) 599960
F: (01228) 599970
E: enquiries@
cumbrian-cottages.co.uk
I: www.cumbrian-cottages.co.uk

Primrose Cottage ★★★★
Contact: Mr & Mrs Geoff
Holloway, Bramble Cottage,
Helmingham Road, Otley,
Suffolk IP9 5NS
T: (01473) 890035
F: (01473) 890463
E: primrose.cott@btinternet.
com
I: www.primrose.cott.btinternet.
co.uk

Ptarmigan House ★★★★
Contact: Mr D Hogarth,
Cumbrian Cottages, 7 The
Crescent, Carlisle, CA1 1QW
T: (01228) 599960 & 599950
F: (01228) 599970
E: enquiries@
cumbrian-cottages.co.uk
I: www.cumbrian-cottages.co.uk

Quintok ★★★★
Contact: Mr David Burton,
Lakeland Cottage Holidays, 3 The
Heads, Keswick, Cumbria
CA12 5ES
T: (017687) 71071
F: (017687) 75036
E: info@lakelandcottages.co.uk
I: www.lakelandcottages.co.uk/

24 Ratcliffe Place ★★★
Contact: Mrs W Plant, The
Rectory, Church Lane, Garforth,
Leeds LS25 1NR
T: (0113) 2863737
E: wendy@planet.go-legend.net

Rivendell ★★★
Contact: Mr David Burton,
Lakeland Cottage Holidays, 3 The
Heads, Keswick, Cumbria
CA12 5ES
T: (017687) 71071
F: (017687) 75036
E: info@lakelandcottages.co.uk
I: www.lakelandcottages.co.uk/

Riverside Holiday Flats ★★
Contact: Mr J Stephenson,
Riverside Holiday Flats, Burleigh
Mead, The Heads, Keswick,
Cumbria CA12 5ER
T: (017687) 72750
F: (017687) 75435
E: helen8@supanet.com
I: www.selfcateringkeswick.com

Saddleback Cottage ★★★
Contact: Mr D Hogarth,
Cumbrian Cottages, 7 The
Crescent, Carlisle, CA1 1QW
T: (01228) 599960
F: (01228) 599970
E: enquiries@
cumbrian-cottages.co.uk
I: www.cumbrian-cottages.co.uk

19 Saint John's Street ★★
Contact: Mr Peter Gee, 19 Saint
John's Street, Keswick, Cumbria
CA12 5AE
T: (017687) 73571

Sandburne Cottage ★★★★
Contact: Mrs Susan Jackson,
Heart of the Lakes, Fisherbeck
Mill, Old Lake Road, Ambleside,
Cumbria LA22 0DH
T: (015394) 32321
F: (015394) 33251
E: info@heartofthelakes.co.uk
I: www.heartofthelakes.co.uk

Sandholme ★★
Contact: Mr David Burton,
Lakeland Cottage Holidays, 3 The
Heads, Keswick, Cumbria
CA12 5ES
T: (017687) 71071
F: (017687) 75036
E: info@lakelandcottages.co.uk
I: www.lakelandcottages.co.uk/

Shelter Stone ★★
Contact: Mr David Burton,
Lakeland Cottage Holidays, 3 The
Heads, Keswick, Cumbria
CA12 5ES
T: (017687) 71071
F: (017687) 75036
E: info@lakelandcottages.co.uk
I: www.lakelandcottages.co.uk/

Skiddaw View ★★★
Contact: Mrs Winifred Cartmell,
Skiddaw View, 1 Heads Road,
Keswick, Cumbria CA12 5HA
T: (017687) 73574

Skiddaw View ★★★
Contact: Mr D Hogarth,
Cumbrian Cottages, 7 The
Crescent, Carlisle, CA1 1QW
T: (01228) 599960
F: (01228) 599970
E: enquiries@
cumbrian-cottages.co.uk
I: www.cumbrian-cottages.co.uk

Slate Cottage ★★★★
Contact: Mr D Hogarth,
Cumbrian Cottages, 7 The
Crescent, Carlisle, CA1 1QW
T: (01228) 599960
F: (01228) 599970
E: enquiries@
cumbrian-cottages.co.uk
I: www.cumbrian-cottages.co.uk

The Steps ★★★
Contact: Mr D Hogarth,
Cumbrian Cottages, 7 The
Crescent, Carlisle, CA1 1QW
T: (01228) 599960 & 599950
F: (01228) 599970
E: enquiries@
cumbrian-cottages.co.uk
I: www.cumbrian-cottages.co.uk

Stone Ledges ★★★
Contact: Mr D Hogarth,
Cumbrian Cottages, 7 The
Crescent, Carlisle, CA1 1QW
T: (01228) 599960 & 599950
F: (01228) 599970
E: enquiries@
cumbrian-cottages.co.uk
I: www.cumbrian-cottages.co.uk

Stone Steps ★★★
Contact: Mr D Hogarth,
Cumbrian Cottages, 7 The
Crescent, Carlisle, CA1 1QW
T: (01228) 599960 & 599950
F: (01228) 599970
E: enquiries@
cumbrian-cottages.co.uk
I: www.cumbrian-cottages.co.uk

Swinside Cottage
Rating Applied For
Contact: Dales Hol Cot Ref:2568,
Dales Holiday Cottages, Carleton
Business Park, Carleton New
Road, Skipton, North Yorkshire
BD23 2AA
T: (01756) 799821 & 790919
F: (01756) 797012
E: info@dalesholcot.com
I: www.dalesholcot.com

Threeways ★★★★
Contact: Mr D Hogarth,
Cumbrian Cottages, 7 The
Crescent, Carlisle, CA1 1QW
T: (01228) 599960
F: (01228) 599970
E: enquiries@
cumbrian-cottages.co.uk
I: www.cumbrian-cottages.co.uk

Topsey Turvey ★★★
Contact: Mr D Hogarth,
Cumbrian Cottages, 7 The
Crescent, Carlisle, CA1 1QW
T: (01228) 599960
F: (01228) 599970
E: enquiries@
cumbrian-cottages.co.uk
I: www.cumbrian-cottages.co.uk

Twentymans Court ★★★
Contact: Mr D Hogarth,
Cumbrian Cottages, 7 The
Crescent, Carlisle, CA1 1QW
T: (01228) 599960 & 599950
F: (01228) 599970
E: enquiries@
cumbrian-cottages.co.uk
I: www.cumbrian-cottages.co.uk

Underne ★★★
Contact: Mr David Burton,
Lakeland Cottage Holidays, 3 The
Heads, Keswick, Cumbria
CA12 5ES
T: (017687) 71071
F: (017687) 75036
E: info@lakelandcottages.co.uk
I: www.lakelandcottages.co.uk/

Underscar ★★★★★
Contact: Mrs Susan Jackson,
Heart of the Lakes, Fisherbeck
Hill, Old Lake Road, Ambleside,
Cumbria LA22 0DH
T: (015394) 32321
F: (015394) 33251
E: info@heartofthelakes.co.uk
I: www.heartofthelakes.co.uk

Upton Glen ★★★★
Contact: Mr D Hogarth,
Cumbrian Cottages, 7 The
Crescent, Carlisle, CA1 1QW
T: (01228) 599960 & 599950
F: (01228) 599970
E: enquiries@
cumbrian-cottages.co.uk
I: www.cumbrian-cottages.co.uk

Victoria Cottage
Rating Applied For
Contact: Mr D Hogarth,
Cumbrian Cottages, 7 The
Crescent, Carlisle, CA1 1QW
T: (01228) 599960
F: (01228) 599970
E: enquiries@
cumbrian-cottages.co.uk
I: www.cumbrian-cottages.co.uk

Walkers Retreat ★★★
Contact: Mr and Mrs M
Walkingshaw, 10a Tithebarn
Street, Keswick, Cumbria
CA12 5ED
T: (017687) 75505

White Wicket ★★★
Contact: Mr D Hogarth,
Cumbrian Cottages, 7 The
Crescent, Carlisle, CA1 1QW
T: (01228) 599960 & 599950
F: (01228) 599970
E: enquiries@
cumbrian-cottages.co.uk
I: www.cumbrian-cottages.co.uk

Woodleigh ★★★★
Contact: Mr D Hogarth,
Cumbrian Cottages, 7 The
Crescent, Carlisle, CA1 1QW
T: (01228) 599960 & 599950
F: (01228) 599970
E: enquiries@
cumbrian-cottages.co.uk
I: www.cumbrian-cottages.co.uk

The Wool Store ★★★
Contact: Mr D Hogarth,
Cumbrian Cottages, 7 The
Crescent, Carlisle, CA1 1QW
T: (01228) 599960 & 599950
F: (01228) 599970
E: enquiries@
cumbrian-cottages.co.uk
I: www.cumbrian-cottages.co.uk

KILLINGTON
Cumbria

Ghyll Stile Mill Cottage ★★★
Contact: Mrs Janet Chetwood,
Ghyll Stile Mill Cottage,
Killington, Sedbergh, Cumbria
LA10 5EH
T: (015396) 21715
E: janetghyll@aol.com

The Granary
Rating Applied For
Contact: Dales Hol Cot Ref:2457,
Dales Holiday Cottages, Carleton
Business Park, Carleton New
Road, Skipton, North Yorkshire
BD23 2AA
T: (01756) 799821 & 790919
F: (01756) 797012
E: info@dalesholcot.com
I: www.dalesholcot.com

KING'S MEABURN
Cumbria

**Lyvennet Cottages and Hill Top
Barn** ★★★-★★★★
Contact: Mrs D M Addison, Keld,
King's Meaburn, Penrith,
Cumbria CA10 3BS
T: (01931) 714226 & 714661
F: (01931) 714598
E: wendyaddison@yahoo.com
I: www.tumpline.co.uk/lyvennet

KIRKBY-IN-FURNESS
Cumbria

One Headgate ★★★
Contact: Mrs M Carmichael, 4
Village Paddock, Stockton-on-
Tees, Cleveland TS18 5DT
T: (01642) 645960
F: (01642) 645960
E: gm.c@ntlworld.com

KIRKBY LONSDALE
Cumbria

Barkinbeck Cottage ★★★
Contact: Mrs A Hamilton,
Barkinbeck House, Gatebeck,
Kendal, Cumbria LA8 0HX
T: (015395) 67122
&

The Stables
Rating Applied For
Contact: Mr D Hogarth,
Cumbrian Cottages, 7 The
Crescent, Carlisle, CA1 1QW
T: (01228) 599960 & 599950
F: (01228) 599970
E: enquiries@
cumbrian-cottages.co.uk
I: www.cumbrian-cottages.co.uk

KIRKBY STEPHEN
Cumbria

The Lodge ★★★
Contact: Mr Wales, Holiday
Cottages (Yorkshire) Ltd, Water
Street, Skipton, North Yorkshire
BD23 1PB
T: (01756) 700510

Pennistone Green ★★★★
Contact: Mr T F Jackson,
Ashmere, Rakes Road, Monyash,
Bakewell, Derbyshire DE45 1JL
T: (01629) 815683
E: sue@jackson-group.co.uk
I: www.jackson-group.co.uk

Swallows Barn ★★★★
Contact: Mrs J Atkinson,
Swallows Barn, Augill House,
Brough, Kirkby Stephen,
Cumbria CA17 4DX
T: (017683) 41272

KIRKLAND
Cumbria

Kirkland Hall Cottages
Rating Applied For
Contact: Mr and Mrs Ian Howes,
Kirkland Hall Cottages, Kirkland
Hall, Kirkland, Penrith, Cumbria
CA10 1RN
T: (01768) 88295
F: (01768) 88295
E: kirklandhallcottages@
hotmail.com
I: www.kirkland-hall-cottages.
co.uk

KIRKLINTON
Cumbria

Dovecote ★★★★
Contact: Mrs S L Chandley,
Dovecote, Cleughside Farm,
Kirklinton, Carlisle CA6 6BE
T: (01228) 675650

Keepers Cottage ★★★★
Contact: Mrs P Armstrong,
Slealands, Longtown, Carlisle,
Cumbria CA6 5RQ
T: (01228) 791378

KIRKOSWALD
Cumbria

Crossfield Cottages ★★★
Contact: Mrs Susan Bottom,
Crossfield Cottages, Staffield,
Kirkoswald, Penrith, Cumbria
CA10 1EU
T: (01768) 898711
F: (01768) 898711

Howscales ★★★★
Contact: Mrs S E Webster,
Howscales, Kirkoswald, Penrith,
Cumbria CA10 1JG
T: (01768) 898666
F: (01768) 898710
E: liz@howscales.fsbusiness.
co.uk
I: www.eden-in-cumbria.
co.uk/howscales
&

KIRKSANTON
Cumbria

12 The Green ★★★
Contact: Country Holidays
ref:4762, Spring Mill, Earby,
Barnoldswick, Lancashire
BB94 0AA
T: 0870 723724
F: (01282) 844288
E: sales@tthigh.co.uk
I: www.country-holidays.co.uk

LAKESIDE
Cumbria

The Loft ★★★★
Contact: Cumbrian Cottages Ltd,
7 the Crescent, Carlisle,
CA1 1QW
T: (01228) 599960
F: (01228) 599970
E: enquiries@
cumbrian-cottages.co.uk
I: www.cumbrian-cottages.co.uk

Nutwood ★★★★
Contact: Mr Paul Liddell,
Lakelovers, The New Toffee Loft,
Kendal Road, Windermere,
Cumbria LA23 3RA
T: (015394) 88855
F: (015394) 88857
E: bookings@lakelovers.co.uk
I: www.lakelovers.co.uk

LAMPLUGH
Cumbria

2 Folly ★★★★
Contact: Mrs Alison Wilson,
Dockray Nook, Lamplugh,
Workington, Cumbria CA14 4SH
T: (01946) 861151 &
07740 697433
E: dockraynook@talk21.com
I: www.felldykecottageholidays.
co.uk

The Old Farmhouse Streetgate
★★★★
Contact: Country Holidays
ref:11325, Spring Mill, Earby,
Barnoldswick, Lancashire
BB94 0AA
T: 08700 723723
F: (01282) 844288
E: sales@ttgihg.co.uk
I: www.country-holidays.co.uk

LANGDALE
Cumbria

The Britannia Holiday Cottages
★★★-★★★★
Contact: Mrs Judith Fry, The
Britannia Inn, Elterwater,
Ambleside, Cumbria LA22 9HP
T: (015394) 37210
F: (015394) 37311
E: info@britinn.co.uk
I: www.britinn.co.uk

Long House Cottages ★★★
Contact: Mr Ian Grayston, Long
House Cottages, Great Langdale,
Ambleside, Cumbria LA22 9JS
T: (015394) 37222
E: enquiries@
longhousecottages.co.uk
I: www.longhousecottages.co.uk

Oakdene ★★★★
Contact: Mrs Patricia Locke, 17
Shay Lane, Hale, Altrincham,
Cheshire WA15 8NZ
T: (0161) 904 9445

**Wheelwrights Holiday
Cottages** ★★-★★★★
Contact: Mr I Price,
Wheelwrights Holiday Cottages,
Elterwater, Ambleside, Cumbria
LA22 9HS
T: (015394) 37635 & 37571
F: (015394) 37618
E: enquiries@wheelwrights.com
I: www.wheelwrights.com

Establishments printed in blue have a detailed entry in this guide

White Lion Cottage ★★★
Contact: Mrs Susan Jackson, Heart of the Lakes, Fisherbeck Hill, Old Lake Road, Ambleside, Cumbria LA22 0DH
T: (015394) 32321
F: (015394) 33251
E: info@heartofthelakes.co.uk
I: www.heartofthelakes.co.uk

LANGWATHBY
Cumbria

Byre Cottage ★★★★
Contact: Mrs J Lane, Absolute Escapes, Orchard Farmhouse, Lynn Road, Gayton, King's Lynn, Norfolk PE32 1PA
T: (01553) 636989
F: (01553) 636989
E: janelane@absolute-escapes.co.uk
I: www.absolute-escapes.co.uk

LEASGILL
Cumbria

The Cottage ★★★★
Contact: Mrs Beverly Keatings, 1 Eversley Gardens, Leasgill, Milnthorpe, Cumbria LA7 7EY
T: (015395) 63008
F: (015395) 62920

LEVENS
Cumbria

Underhill ★★★★
Contact: Mrs C Phillips, Underhill, Levens, Kendal, Cumbria LA8 8PH
T: (015395) 60298
E: c-phillips@msn.com

LINDALE
Cumbria

7 New Cottages ★★★
Contact: Country Holidays ref:3625, Spring Mill, Earby, Barnoldswick, Lancashire BB94 0AA
T: (01282) 445096
F: (01282) 844288
E: sales@ttgihg.co.uk
I: www.country-holidays.co.uk

Redriggs Country Cottages ★★★
Contact: Mr and Mrs W D Bleakley, Redriggs Country Cottages, Redriggs, High Hampsfield, Lindale, Grange-over-Sands, Cumbria LA11 6LY
T: (015395) 33608

LITTLE LANGDALE
Cumbria

The Bield ★★★★
Contact: Mrs Susan Jackson, Heart of the Lakes, Fisherbeck Hill, Old Lake Road, Ambleside, Cumbria LA22 0DH
T: (015394) 32321
F: (015394) 33251
E: info@heartofthelakes.co.uk
I: www.heartofthelakes.co.uk

Birch House
Rating Applied For
Contact: Mr Paul Liddell, Lakelovers, The New Toffee Loft, Kendal Road, Bowness-on-Windermere, Windermere, Cumbria LA23 3RA
T: (015394) 88855
F: (015394) 88857
E: bookings@lakelovers.co.uk
I: www.lakelovers.co.uk

Farragrain ★★★★
Contact: Mrs Susan Jackson, Heart of the Lakes, Fisherbeck Hill, Old Lake Road, Ambleside, Cumbria LA22 0DH
T: (015394) 32321
F: (015394) 33251
I: www.heartofthelakes.co.uk

Highfold Cottage ★★★
Contact: Mrs C E Blair, 8 The Glebe, Chapel Stile, Ambleside, Cumbria LA22 9JT
T: (015394) 37686

Lang Parrock ★★★
Contact: Mrs Susan Jackson, Heart of the Lakes, Fisherbeck Mill, Old Lake Road, Ambleside, Cumbria LA22 0DH
T: (015394) 32321
F: (015394) 33251
E: info@heartofthelakes.co.uk
I: www.heartofthelakes.co.uk

The Peat House ★★★★
Contact: Mrs Susan Jackson, Heart of the Lakes, Fisherbeck Hill, Old Lake Road, Ambleside, Cumbria LA22 0DH
T: (015394) 32321
F: (015394) 33251
E: info@heartofthelakes.co.uk
I: www.heartofthelakes.co.uk

LITTLE STRICKLAND
Cumbria

Old School ★★★★
Contact: Mr Geoff Hancock, Choice Homes, 11 Highlands Road, Bamford, Rochdale OL11 5PD
T: (01706) 368486 &
07899 846818
F: (01706) 368486

Spring Bank ★★★★
Contact: Mrs J Ostle, Meadowfield, Little Strickland, Penrith, Cumbria CA10 3EG
T: (01931) 716246
E: springbank17@hotmail.com

LONGSLEDDALE
Cumbria

The Coach House ★★★
Contact: Mrs Farmer, The Coach House, Capplebarrow House, Longsleddale, Kendal, Cumbria LA8 9BB
T: (01539) 823686 &
07887 603282
F: (01539) 823092
E: JENYFARMER@aol.com

LORTON
Cumbria

Green Trees ★★★★
Contact: Mr D Hogarth, Cumbrian Cottages, 7 The Crescent, Carlisle, CA1 1QW
T: (01228) 599960
F: (01228) 599970
E: enquiries@cumbrian-cottages.co.uk
I: www.cumbrian-cottages.co.uk

High Swinside Farm Holiday Cottages★★–★★★
Contact: Mr & Mrs A Cresswell, High Swinside Farm Holiday Cottages, High Swinside Farm, Lorton, Cockermouth, Cumbria CA13 9UA
T: (01900) 85206 & 85033
F: (01900) 85076
E: tony.cresswell@btinternet.com
I: www.btinternet.com/~tony.cresswell

LOUGHRIGG
Cumbria

1 Brunt Howe ★★★★
Contact: Mr Paul Liddell, Lakelovers, The New Toffee Loft, Kendal Road, Windermere, Cumbria LA23 3RA
T: (015394) 88855
F: (015394) 88857
E: bookings@lakelovers.co.uk
I: www.lakelovers.co.uk

LOWESWATER
Cumbria

Askhill Farm
Rating Applied For
Contact: Mrs M Vickers, Askhill Farm, Loweswater, Cockermouth, Cumbria CA13 0SU
T: (01946) 861640

The Coach House ★★★★★
Contact: Country Holidays ref:8368, Spring Mill, Earby, Barnoldswick, Lancashire BB94 0AA
T: (01282) 445096
F: (01282) 844288
E: sales@ttgihg.co.uk
I: www.country-holidays.co.uk

Crummock Water Holiday Cottages and Foulsyke House ★★★–★★★★★
Contact: Mrs Carol Thompson, Foulsyke, Loweswater, Cockermouth, Cumbria CA13 0RS
T: (01900) 85637
E: crummockcottages@netscapeonline.co.uk
I: www.crummockcottages.co.uk

Low Park Cottage ★★★
Contact: Mr R Watkins, Low Park Cottage, Loweswater, Cockermouth, Cumbria CA13 0RU
T: (01900) 85242

Loweswater Holiday Cottages ★★★–★★★★★
Contact: Mr M E Thompson, Loweswater Holiday Cottages, Scale Hill, Loweswater, Cockermouth, Cumbria CA13 9UX
T: (01900) 85232
F: (01900) 85232
E: mike@loweswaterholidaycottages.co.uk
I: www.loweswaterholidaycottages.co.uk

Melbreak Cottage ★★★★★
Contact: Mr and Mrs D J Edwards, Osborne Cottage, Garden Lane, Allonby, Maryport, Cumbria CA15 6PX
T: (01900) 881404
E: danianddavid@compuserve.com

LOWICK
Cumbria

Alltmaen ★★★
Contact: Mr John Serginson, The Lakeland Cottage Company, Waterside House, Newby Bridge, Ulverston, Cumbria LA12 8AN
T: (015395) 30024
F: (015395) 31932
E: john@lakeland-cottage-company.co.uk
I: www.lakeland-cottage-company.co.uk

Bark Cottage ★★★
Contact: Miss Jenny Tancock & Mr Joe Fairclough, Tannery Barn, The Meadows, Lowick Green, Ulverston, Cumbria LA12 8DX
T: (01229) 885416
E: barkcottage@tannerybarn.freeserve.co.uk
I: www.tannerybarn.freeserve.co.uk

Tsukudu ★★★★
Contact: Mr Martin Wardle, Lakes and Valleys, North Lodge, Longtail Hill, Bowness-on-Windermere, Windermere, Cumbria LA23 3JD
T: (015394) 88612
F: (015394) 48988
E: lakesandvalleys@aol.com
I: www.lakesandvalleys.co.uk

MALLERSTANG
Cumbria

Old Faw Cottage ★★★
Contact: Mr Wales, Holiday Cottages (Yorkshire) Ltd, Water Street, Skipton, North Yorkshire BD23 1PB
T: (01756) 700510

MANESTY
Cumbria

The Coppice ★★
Contact: Mr David Burton, Lakeland Cottage Holidays, 3 The Heads, Keswick, Cumbria CA12 5ES
T: (017687) 71071
F: (017687) 75036
E: info@lakelandcottages.co.uk
I: www.lakelandcottages.co.uk

High Ground ★★★
Contact: Mr D Hogarth, Cumbrian Cottages, 7 The Crescent, Carlisle, CA1 1QW
T: (01228) 599960 & 599950
F: (01228) 599970
E: enquiries@cumbrian-cottages.co.uk
I: www.cumbrian-cottages.co.uk

Establishments printed in blue have a detailed entry in this guide

Manesty Holiday Cottages
★★★
Contact: Mr and Mrs A T
Leyland, Manesty Holiday
Cottages, Youdale Knot,
Manesty, Keswick, Cumbria
CA12 5UG
T: (017687) 77216
F: (017687) 77384
I: www.borrowdale.
com/manesty

MATTERDALE END
Cumbria

Bank House Farm ★★★
Contact: Mr & Mrs T J
Hargreaves, Bank House Farm,
Matterdale End, Penrith,
Cumbria CA11 0LF
T: (01768) 482040

MEALSGATE
Cumbria

West Court and East Court
★★★
Contact: Dales Hol Cot
Ref:2315/2075, Dales Holiday
Cottages, Carleton Business
Park, Carleton New Road,
Skipton, North Yorkshire
BD23 2AA
T: (01756) 799821 & 790919
F: (01756) 797012
E: info@dalesholcot.com
I: www.dalesholcot.com

Whitehall ★★★
Contact: Blakes HIB Ref: B4872,
Spring Mill, Earby, Barnoldswick,
Lancashire BB94 0AA
T: (01282) 445096
F: (01282) 844288

MILBURN
Cumbria

Bramley Cottage ★★★★
Contact: Mr & Mrs G Heelis,
Orchard Cottage, Milburn,
Penrith, Cumbria CA10 1TN
T: (01683) 61074
F: (01768) 895528
E: guyheelis@aol.com
I: www.oas.
co.uk/ukcottages/bramley

Gullom Cottage ★★★
Contact: Mr D Hogarth,
Cumbrian Cottages, 7 The
Crescent, Carlisle, CA1 1QW
T: (01228) 599960 & 599950
F: (01228) 599970
E: enquiries@
cumbrian-cottages.co.uk
I: www.cumbrian-cottages.co.uk

High Slakes ★★★★
Contact: Mr Wales, Holiday
Cottages (Yorkshire) Ltd, Water
Street, Skipton, North Yorkshire
BD23 1PB
T: (01756) 700510

MILLBECK
Cumbria

Millbeck Cottages ★★★★
Contact: Mr Richard Watson, 20
Hebing End, Benington,
Stevenage, Hertfordshire
SG2 7DD
T: (01438) 359311 & 869286
F: (01438) 740127
E: bcl@brignalls.co.uk

MILLOM
Cumbria

The Haws ★★★★
Contact: Country Holidays
ref:13991, Spring Mill, Earby,
Barnoldswick, Lancashire
BB94 0AA
T: 08700 723723
F: (01282) 844288
I: www.country-holidays.co.uk

MILNTHORPE
Cumbria

2 Crooklands Court ★★★
Contact: Miss Julie Sumner, 3
The Avenue, Rainford, St Helens,
Merseyside WA11 8DR
T: (01744) 883229 & 0700 560
9000
F: 0870 744 3311

MORLAND
Cumbria

Lowergate House ★★★★
Contact: Dales Hol Cot Ref:3148,
Dales Holiday Cottages, Carleton
Business Park, Carleton New
Road, Skipton, North Yorkshire
BD23 2AA
T: (01756) 799821 & 790919
F: (01756) 797012
E: info@dalesholcot.com
I: www.dalesholcot.com

MOTHERBY
Cumbria

Nettle How Cottage ★★★
Contact: Mr and Mrs Andy
Hamnett, Nettle How Cottage,
Motherby, Penrith, Cumbria
CA11 0RJ
T: (017684) 83544
F: (017684) 83544

MUNGRISDALE
Cumbria

Grisedale View, Howe Top
★★★★
Contact: Mrs C A Weightman,
Grisedale View, Howe Top, Near
Howe, Mungrisdale, Penrith,
Cumbria CA11 0SH
T: (017687) 79678
F: (017687) 79678

NADDLE
Cumbria

The Bungalow ★★★
Contact: Mrs J Nicholson,
Causeway Foot Farm, Naddle,
Keswick, Cumbria CA12 4TF
T: (017687) 72290
E: jacknic@bluecarrots.com
I: www.lakesholidaycottage.
co.uk

NATLAND
Cumbria

Stonegable ★★★
Contact: Mr D Hogarth,
Cumbrian Cottages, 7 The
Crescent, Carlisle, CA1 1QW
T: (01228) 599960 & 599950
F: (01228) 599970
E: enquiries@
cumbrian-cottages.co.uk
I: www.cumbrian-cottages.co.uk

NEAR SAWREY
Cumbria

Smithy Cottage
Rating Applied For
Contact: Mr Paul Liddell,
Lakelovers, The New Toffee Loft,
Kendal Road, Bowness-on-
Windermere, Windermere,
Cumbria LA23 3RA
T: (015394) 88855
F: (015394) 88857
E: bookings@lakelovers.co.uk
I: www.lakelovers.co.uk

NENTHEAD
Cumbria

Rock House Farm Cottages
★★★
Contact: Mrs J Palmer, Durham
Pine, Colima Avenue,
Sunderland Enterprise Park,
Sunderland, Tyne & Wear
SR5 3XF
T: (0191) 516 2600
F: (0191) 516 9528

NEW HUTTON
Cumbria

High Butterbent Cottage
★★★★
Contact: Country Holidays
ref:2524, Spring Mill, Earby,
Barnoldswick, Lancashire
BB94 0AA
T: 0870 723723
F: (01282) 844288
E: sales@ttgihg.co.uk
I: www.country-holidays.co.uk

NEWBIGGIN
Cumbria

The Old Post Office
Rating Applied For
Contact: Dales Hol Cot Ref:2799,
Dales Holiday Cottages, Carleton
Business Park, Carleton New
Road, Skipton, North Yorkshire
BD23 2AA
T: (01756) 799821 & 790919
F: (01756) 797012
E: info@dalesholcot.com
I: www.dalesholcot.com

NEWBIGGIN–ON–LUNE
Cumbria

Ashley Cottage ★★★
Contact: Mr and Mrs Hickman,
Ashley Cottage, Ashley Bank,
Newbiggin-on-Lune, Kirkby
Stephen, Cumbria CA17 4LZ
T: (015396) 23214
F: (015396) 23214
E: ashleybnk@aol.com
I: www.eden-in-cumbria.
co.uk/ashleybank

NEWBY
Cumbria

**Midtown Cottage & Dairy
Cottage** ★★★★
Contact: The Wardle Family,
Goosemire Cottages, North
Lodge, Longtail Hill, Bowness-
on-Windermere, Windermere,
Cumbria LA23 3JD
T: (015394) 47477
F: (015394) 48988
E: martin@goosemire.freeserve.
co.uk

NEWBY BRIDGE
Cumbria

Cherry Tree House ★★★★
Contact: Heart of the Lakes,
Heart of the Lakes, Fisherbeck
Hill, Old Lake Road, Ambleside,
Cumbria LA22 0DH
T: (015394) 32321
F: (015394) 33251
E: info@heartofthelakes.co.uk
I: www.heartofthelakes.co.uk

Flat 2 Stock Park Mansion
Rating Applied For
Contact: Mrs Diane Watson, 17
Argarmeols Road, Formby,
Liverpool L37 7BX
T: (01704) 871144 &
0710 819598
E: rogerwatson@ic24.net

Woodland Cottage ★★★★
Contact: Mr Peter Newton,
Hillside Lodge, Newby Bridge
Caravan Park, Canny Hill, Newby
Bridge, Cumbria LA12 8NF
T: (015395) 31030
F: (015395) 30105
E: newbybridge@hopps.
freeserve.co.uk

NEWLAND
Cumbria

Curlew Rise and Heron Beck
★★★★
Contact: Mr John Serginson, The
Lakeland Cottage Company,
Waterside House, Newby Bridge,
Ulverston, Cumbria LA12 8AN
T: (015395) 30024
F: (015395) 31932
E: john@
lakeland-cottage-company.
co.uk
I: www.
lakeland-cottage-company.
co.uk

NEWLANDS
Cumbria

Fell Cottage ★★★
Contact: Mr David Burton,
Lakeland Cottage Holidays, 3 The
Heads, Keswick, Cumbria
CA12 5ES
T: (017687) 71071
F: (017687) 75036
E: info@lakelandcottages.co.uk
I: www.lakelandcottages.co.uk/

ORTON
Cumbria

Barugh ★★
Contact: Mrs J Lane, Absolute
Escapes, Orchard Farm House,
Lynn Road, Gayton, King's Lynn,
Norfolk PE32 1PA
T: 07553 636989
F: 07553 636989
E: janelane@absolute-escapes.
co.uk
I: www.absolute-escapes.co.uk

OUSBY
Cumbria

Hole Bank ★★★★
Contact: Mrs Lesley McVey, 10
Helvellyn Court, Penrith,
Cumbria CA11 8PZ
T: (01768) 892247
F: (01768) 892247

OUTGATE
Cumbria

Borwick Fold Cottages ★★★★
Contact: Mr and Mrs J Johnson,
Borwick Fold, Hawkshead,
Ambleside, Cumbria LA22 0PU
T: (015394) 36742
F: (015394) 36094
E: borwickfold@cwcom.net

OUTHGILL
Cumbria

**Ing Hill Barn Apartments
★★★★**
Contact: Country Holidays
ref:14815, Spring Mill, Earby,
Barnoldswick, Lancashire
BB94 0AA
T: (01282) 445096
F: (01282) 844288

PAPCASTLE
Cumbria

Sunny Brae ★★★★
Contact: Mr D Hogarth,
Cumbrian Cottages, 7 The
Crescent, Carlisle, CA1 1QW
T: (01228) 599960 & 599950
F: (01228) 599970
E: enquiries@
cumbrian-cottages.co.uk
I: www.cumbrian-cottages.co.uk

PARDSHAW
Cumbria

Stoneygate Cottage ★★★★
Contact: Country Holidays
ref:12243, Spring Mill, Earby,
Barnoldswick, Lancashire
BB94 0AA
T: 08700 723723
F: (01282) 844288
E: sales@ttgihg.co.uk
I: www.country-holidays.co.uk

Sunny Corner ★★★★
Contact: Mr S Hill, Sunny
Corner, The Croft, Pardshaw,
Cockermouth, Cumbria
CA13 0SP
T: (01900) 826380

PATTERDALE
Cumbria

Bleaze End ★★★★
Contact: Mrs Susan Jackson,
Heart of the Lakes, Fisherbeck
Hill, Old Lake Road, Ambleside,
Cumbria LA22 0DH
T: (015394) 32321
F: (015394) 33251
E: info@heartofthelakes.co.uk
I: www.heartofthelakes.co.uk

Broad How ★★★★
Contact: Country Holidays
ref:8478, Spring Mill, Earby,
Barnoldswick, Lancashire
BB94 0AA
T: 0870 723723
F: (01282) 844288
I: www.country-holidays.co.uk

Deepdale Hall Cottage ★★★
Contact: Mr C A Brown,
Deepdale Hall, Patterdale,
Penrith, Cumbria CA11 0NR
T: (017684) 82369 & 82608
E: brown@deepdalehall.
freeserve.co.uk
I: www.deepdalehall.co.uk

**Elm How, Cruck Barn and
Eagle Cottage ★★★-★★★★**
Contact: Miss M Scott/McGill,
Matson Ground Estate Company
Ltd, 3 Lambrigg Terrace, Kendal,
Cumbria LA9 4BB
T: (01539) 726995
F: (01539) 741611
E: matsong@compuserve.com
I: www.matsonground.co.uk

Fellside ★★★
Contact: Mrs Anne-Marie
Knight, Fellside, Hartsop,
Penrith, Cumbria CA11 0NZ
T: (017684) 82532

Grove Cottage ★★★
Contact: Mr J B Sinclair, Grove
Cottage, Hartsop, Penrith,
Cumbria CA11 0NZ
T: (017684) 82438

Hartsop Fold ★★★
Contact: Mrs Lesley Hennedy,
Merlin Crag, Marthwaite,
Sedbergh, Cumbria LA10 5HU
T: (015396) 22069
F: (015396) 20899
E: bookings@hartsop-fold.co.uk
I: www.hartsop-fold.co.uk

Lower Grisedale Lodge ★★★
Contact: Mrs Susan Jackson,
Heart of the Lakes, Fisherbeck
Hill, Old Lake Road, Ambleside,
Cumbria LA22 0DH
T: (015394) 32321
F: (015394) 33251
E: info@heartofthelakes.co.uk
I: www.heartofthelakes.co.uk

PENRITH
Cumbria

**Barn Croft and Barn End
★★★★**
Contact: Mr R M Walton,
Carthanet, Soulby, Dacre,
Penrith, Cumbria CA11 0JF

**Croft House
Rating Applied For**
Contact: Dales Hol Cot Ref:3007,
Dales Holiday Cottages, Carleton
Business Park, Carleton New
Road, Skipton, North Yorkshire
BD23 2AA
T: (01756) 799821 & 790919
F: (01756) 797012
E: info@dalesholcot.com
I: www.dalesholcot.com

The Dower Tower ★★★★
Contact: Mrs B Blyth, Carleton
Derrick, Carleton Derrick Drive,
Penrith, Cumbria CA11 8LS
T: (01768) 867450
E: bevanneblyth@hotmail.com
I: members.tripod.com/blyth58

Meaburn Lodge ★★★
Contact: Holiday Cottages
(Yorkshire), Water Street,
Skipton, North Yorkshire
BD23 1PB
T: (01756) 700510
E: info@holidaycotts.co.uk

**Skirwith Hall Cottage and
Smithy Cottage ★★★**
Contact: Mrs L I Wilson, Skirwith
Hall Cottage and Smithy
Cottage, Skirwith Hall, Skirwith,
Penrith, Cumbria CA10 1RH
T: (01768) 88241 &
07710 969156
F: (01768) 88241
E: idawilson@aol.com
I: www.eden-in-cumbria.
co.uk/skirwith

**Stonefold Cottages
★★★-★★★★**
Contact: Mrs Gill Harrington,
Stonefold Cottages, Stonefold,
Newbiggin, Stainton, Penrith,
Cumbria CA11 0HP
T: (01768) 866383
I: www.northlakes.
co.uk/stonefold/

West View Cottages ★★★★
Contact: Mr and Mrs A J Grave,
West View Farm, Winskill,
Penrith, Cumbria CA10 1PD
T: (01768) 881356
F: (01768) 881356
E: westviewfarm@talk21.com
I: www.eden-in-cumbria.
co.uk/westview

Wetheral Cottages ★★★★
Contact: Mr John Lowrey,
Wetheral Cottages, Great
Salkeld, Penrith, Cumbria
CA11 9NA
T: (01768) 898779
F: (01768) 898943
E: wetheralcottages@
compuserve.com

PENRUDDOCK
Cumbria

Beckses Cottage ★★★★
Contact: Mr D Hogarth,
Cumbrian Cottages, 7 The
Crescent, Carlisle, CA1 1QW
T: (01228) 599960 & 599950
F: (01228) 599970
E: enquiries@
cumbrian-cottages.co.uk
I: www.cumbrian-cottages.co.uk

Beckside Cottage ★★★
Contact: Dales Hol Cot Ref:2591,
Dales Holiday Cottages, Carleton
Business Park, Carleton New
Road, Skipton, North Yorkshire
BD23 2AA
T: (01756) 799821 & 790919
F: (01756) 797012
E: info@dalesholcot.com
I: www.dalesholcot.com

POOLEY BRIDGE
Cumbria

**Barton Hall Farm Holiday
Cottages ★★★★**
Contact: Mrs Amanda Strong,
Barton Hall Farm Holiday
Cottages, Pooley Bridge, Penrith,
Cumbria CA10 2NG
T: (017684) 86034
E: amanda@pooleybridge.
demon.co.uk

Beauthorn Coach House ★★★
Contact: Mr & Mrs Alan &
Margaret Wardle, North Lodge,
Longtail Hill, Bowness-on-
Windermere, Windermere,
Cumbria LA23 3JD
T: (015394) 447905

Blacksmith's Cottages ★★★★
Contact: Mr D Hogarth,
Cumbrian Cottages, 7 The
Crescent, Carlisle, CA1 1QW
T: (01228) 599960 & 599950
F: (01228) 599970
E: enquiries@
cumbrian-cottages.co.uk
I: www.cumbrian-cottages.co.uk

High Winder Cottages ★★★★
Contact: Mr R A Moss, High
Winder House, Celleron, Tirril,
Penrith, Cumbria CA10 2LS
T: (017684) 86997 &
(017687) 72988
F: (017684) 86997
E: mossr@highwinder.freeserve.
co.uk

Winn's Cottage ★★★
Contact: The Hon. Mrs C
Fortescue, Bowerbank House,
Pooley Bridge, Penrith, Cumbria
CA10 2NG
T: (017684) 86304 & 86642
F: (017684) 86977

PORTINSCALE
Cumbria

Cosey Cottage ★★★
Contact: Mr David Brown, 4
Ashtree Avenue, Keswick,
Cumbria CA12 5PF
T: (017687) 74324
E: cottages@keswickcumbria.
freeserve.co.uk
I: www.keswickcumbria.
freeserve.co.uk

Jasmine Cottage ★★★
Contact: Mr D Hogarth,
Cumbrian Cottages, 7 The
Crescent, Carlisle, CA1 1QW
T: (01228) 599960
F: (01228) 599970
E: enquiries@
cumbrian-cottages.co.uk
I: www.cumbrian-cottages.co.uk

Smithy Cottage ★★★
Contact: Mr D Hogarth,
Cumbrian Cottages, 7 The
Crescent, Carlisle, CA1 1QW
T: (01228) 599960 & 599950
F: (01228) 599970
E: enquiries@
cumbrian-cottages.co.uk
I: www.cumbrian-cottages.co.uk

Stable Cottage ★★★
Contact: Mrs Pope, 1 Portinscale
House, Portinscale, Keswick,
Cumbria CA12 5RF
T: (017687) 75161

RAVENSTONEDALE
Cumbria

Coldbeck Cottage ★★★★
Contact: Mrs Sally Cannon,
Coldbeck House,
Ravenstonedale, Kirkby Stephen,
Cumbria CA17 4LW
T: (015396) 23230
F: (015396) 23230
E: david.cannon@coldbeck.
demon.co.uk
♿

**Low Springthyll
Rating Applied For**
Contact: Mr & Mrs N Burton,
Low Haygarth Farm, Cautley,
Sedbergh, Cumbria LA10 5NE
T: (015396) 20349
F: (015396) 20349

Establishments printed in blue have a detailed entry in this guide

Moss Cottages ★★★
Contact: Mrs H Shallcross, Moss
Cottages, The Moss, Newbiggin-
on-Lune, Kirkby Stephen,
Cumbria CA17 4NB
T: (015396) 23316
F: (015396) 23491
E: shallmoss@aol.com

REDMAIN
Cumbria

**Huddlestone Cottage and The
Hayloft ★★★★**
Contact: Mrs Christine Neale,
Huddlestone Cottage and The
Hayloft, Pooley House, Redmain,
Cockermouth, Cumbria
CA13 0PZ
T: (01900) 825695
F: (01900) 825695
E: hudcot@lakesnw.co.uk
I: www.lakesnw.co.uk

ROSTHWAITE
Cumbria

**Borrowdale Self-Catering
Holidays ★★★**
Contact: Mr & Mrs Peter Davis-
Merry, Borrowdale Self-Catering
Holidays, Kiln How, Rosthwaite,
Keswick, Cumbria CA12 5XB
T: (017687) 77356
F: (017687) 77727
E: kiln.how@classicfm.net
I: www.kilnhow.com

Castle How ★★★
Contact: Mr D Hogarth,
Cumbrian Cottages, 7 The
Crescent, Carlisle, CA1 1QW
T: (01228) 599960 & 599950
F: (01228) 599970
E: enquiries@
cumbrian-cottages.co.uk
I: www.cumbrian-cottages.co.uk

Clare's Cottage ★★
Contact: Ms Janice Diamond, 20
James Street, Horwich, Bolton
BL6 7QS
T: (01204) 668681
E: janctb@clarescottage.com
I: www.clarescottage.com

High Knott ★★★★
Contact: Mr D Hogarth,
Cumbrian Cottages, 7 The
Crescent, Carlisle, CA1 1QW
T: (01228) 599960
F: (01228) 599970
E: enquiries@
cumbrian-cottages.co.uk
I: www.cumbrian-cottages.co.uk

Larch Cottage ★★
Contact: Mr David Burton,
Lakeland Cottage Holidays, 3 The
Heads, Keswick, Cumbria
CA12 5ES
T: (017687) 71071
F: (017687) 75036
E: info@lakelandcottages.co.uk
I: www.lakelandcottages.co.uk/

Thwaite How ★★★
Contact: Mr and Mrs C H
Brewerton, 3 Sycamore Way,
Market Bosworth, Nuneaton,
Warwickshire CV13 0LU
T: (01455) 290168

ROWELTOWN
Cumbria

**Low Luckens Organic Resource
Centre
Rating Applied For**
Contact: Mr & Mrs Mike
Downham, Low Luckens,
Roweltown, Carlisle CA6 6LJ
T: (016977) 48331 & 47637
E: lowluckensorc@hotmail.com
I: www.whiteholmefarm.com

RUCKCROFT
Cumbria

Ruckcroft Cottage ★★★
Contact: Mr D Hogarth,
Cumbrian Cottages, 7 The
Crescent, Carlisle, CA1 1QW
T: (01228) 599960 & 599950
F: (01228) 599970
E: enquiries@
cumbrian-cottages.co.uk
I: www.cumbrian-cottages.co.uk

RUSLAND
Cumbria

**Crosslands House Cottage
★★★**
Contact: Mr John Serginson, The
Lakeland Cottage Company,
Waterside House, Newby Bridge,
Ulverston, Cumbria LA12 8AN
T: (015395) 30024
F: (015395) 31932
E: john@
lakeland-cottage-company.
co.uk
I: www.
lakeland-cottage-company.
co.uk

Ford Cottage ★★★★★
Contact: Mr Paul Liddell,
Lakelovers, The New Toffee Loft,
Kendal Road, Windermere,
Cumbria LA23 3RA
T: (015394) 88855
F: (015394) 88857
E: bookings@lakelovers.co.uk
I: www.lakelovers.co.uk

RYDAL
Cumbria

Fox Cottage ★★★★
Contact: Mrs Susan Jackson,
Heart of the Lakes, Fisherbeck
Hill, Old Lake Road, Ambleside,
Cumbria LA22 0DH
T: (015394) 32321
F: (015394) 33251
E: info@heartofthelakes.co.uk
I: www.heartofthelakes.co.uk

Hall Bank Cottage ★★
Contact: Mr Lumpton, Rydal
Estate Carter Jonas, 52 Kirkland,
Kendal, Cumbria LA9 5AP
T: (01539) 722592
F: (01539) 729587
E: valerie.dickinson@
carterjonas.co.uk

Rydal Mount Cottage ★★★★
Contact: Mrs Susan Jackson,
Heart of the Lakes, Fisherbeck
Mill, Old Lake Road, Ambleside,
Cumbria LA22 0DH
T: (015394) 32321
F: (015394) 33251
E: info@heartofthelakes.co.uk
I: www.heartofthelakes.co.uk

Stepping Stones ★★★★
Contact: Mrs Susan Jackson,
Heart of the Lakes, Fisherbeck
Hill, Old Lake Road, Ambleside,
Cumbria LA22 0DH
T: (015394) 32321
F: (015394) 33251
E: info@heartofthelakes.co.uk
I: www.heartofthelakes.co.uk

Steps End Cottage ★★★
Contact: Mr John Serginson, The
Lakeland Cottage Company,
Waterside House, Newby Bridge,
Ulverston, Cumbria LA12 8AN
T: (015395) 30024
F: (015395) 31932
E: john@
lakeland-cottage-company.
co.uk
I: www.
lakeland-cottage-company.
co.uk

ST JOHNS-IN-THE-VALE
Cumbria

Fornside Cottage ★★★★
Contact: Mr D Hogarth,
Cumbrian Cottages, 7 The
Crescent, Carlisle, CA1 1QW
T: (01228) 599960
F: (01228) 599970
E: enquiries@
cumbrian-cottages.co.uk
I: www.cumbrian-cottages.co.uk

Lowthwaite Cottage ★★★
Contact: Mr D Hogarth,
Cumbrian Cottages, 7 The
Crescent, Carlisle, CA1 1QW
T: (01228) 599960
F: (01228) 599970
E: enquiries@
cumbrian-cottages.co.uk
I: www.cumbrian-cottages.co.uk

The Studio ★★★★
Contact: Mrs J Green, The
Studio, Fornside House, St
Johns-in-the-Vale, Keswick,
Cumbria CA12 4TS
T: (017687) 79666
E: selfcatering@
keswickholidays.co.uk
I: www.keswickholidays.co.uk

SATTERTHWAITE
Cumbria

Tanwood Barn ★★★★
Contact: Mrs Susan Jackson,
Heart of the Lakes, Fisherbeck
Hill, Old Lake Road, Ambleside,
Cumbria LA22 0DH
T: (015394) 32321
F: (015394) 33251
E: info@heartofthelakes.co.uk
I: www.heartofthelakes.co.uk

SAWREY
Cumbria

Anvil Cottage ★★★★
Contact: Mr D Hogarth,
Cumbrian Cottages, 7 The
Crescent, Carlisle, CA1 1QW
T: (01228) 599960 & 599950
F: (01228) 599970
E: enquiries@
cumbrian-cottages.co.uk
I: www.cumbrian-cottages.co.uk

2 Cunsey House ★★★
Contact: Country Holidays
ref:11039, Spring Mill, Earby,
Barnoldswick, Lancashire
BB94 0AA
T: 08700 723723
F: (01282) 844288
E: sales@ttgihg.co.uk
I: www.country-holidays.co.uk

Derwentwater Cottage ★★★
Contact: Mrs Ann Gallagher,
Hideaways, The Minstrels
Gallery, The Square, Hawkshead,
Ambleside, Cumbria LA22 0NZ
T: (015394) 42435
F: (015394) 36178
E: bookings@
lakeland-hideaways.co.uk
I: www.lakeland-hideaways.
co.uk

**The Forge
Rating Applied For**
Contact: Mr P Liddell, Lakelovers,
The New Toffee Loft, Kendal
Road, Windermere, Cumbria
LA23 3RA
T: (015394) 88855
F: (015394) 88857
E: bookings@lakelovers.co.uk
I: www.lakelovers.co.uk

Lakefield ★★★
Contact: Mr & Mrs John and
Ann Taylor, Lakefield, Near
Sawrey, Ambleside, Cumbria
LA22 0JZ
T: (015394) 36635
F: (015394) 36635

**Sawrey Knotts
★★★-★★★★★**
Contact: Mrs Stephanie Barnes,
Sawrey Knotts, Far Sawrey,
Ambleside, Cumbria LA22 0LG
T: (015394) 88625
F: (015394) 88625
E: sawrey-knotts@lake-district.
net
I: www.lake-district.
net/sawrey-knotts

Sunnyside Cottage ★★★★
Contact: Mr John Serginson, The
Lakeland Cottage Company,
Waterside House, Newby Bridge,
Ulverston, Cumbria LA12 8AN
T: (015395) 30024
F: (015395) 31932
E: john@
lakeland-cottage-company.
co.uk
I: www.
lakeland-cottge-company.co.uk

**West Vale Cottage
Rating Applied For**
Contact: Mrs Dee Pennington,
West Vale, Far Sawrey,
Ambleside, Cumbria LA22 0LQ
T: (015394) 42817
F: (015394) 45302

SEATHWAITE
Cumbria

2 High Moss House ★★
Contact: Mrs Helen Barnard, 13
Herries Road, Glasgow, G41 4DE
T: (0141) 423 1060
F: (0141) 424 1441
E: helen@cognit.co.uk

CUMBRIA

SEATOLLER
Cumbria

The Barn ★★★★
Contact: Mr D Hogarth,
Cumbrian Cottages, 7 The
Crescent, Carlisle, CA1 1QW
T: (01228) 599960
F: (01228) 599970
E: enquiries@
cumbrian-cottages.co.uk
I: www.cumbrain-cottages.co.uk

Bell Crags ★★★
Contact: Mr David Burton,
Lakeland Cottage Holidays, 3 The
Heads, Keswick, Cumbria
CA12 5ES
T: (017687) 71071
F: (017687) 75036
E: info@lakelandcottages.co.uk
I: www.lakelandcottages.co.uk

Brasscam ★★★★
Contact: Mr D Hogarth,
Cumbrian Cottages, 7 The
Crescent, Carlisle, CA1 1QW
T: (01228) 599960 & 599950
F: (01228) 599970
E: enquiries@
cumbrian-cottages.co.uk
I: www.cumbrian-cottages.co.uk

Ghyllside ★★★★
Contact: Mr D Hogarth,
Cumbrian Cottages, 7 The
Crescent, Carlisle, CA1 1QW
T: (01228) 599960
F: (01228) 599970
E: enquiries@
cumbrian-cottages.co.uk
I: www.cumbrian-cottages.co.uk

High Stile ★★
Contact: Mr David Burton,
Lakeland Cottage Holidays, 3 The
Heads, Keswick, Cumbria
CA12 5ES
T: (017687) 71071
F: (017687) 75036
E: info@lakelandcottages.co.uk
I: www.lakelandcottages.co.uk/

Honister ★★★
Contact: Mr D Hogarth,
Cumbrian Cottages, 7 The
Crescent, Carlisle, CA1 1QW
T: (01228) 599960 & 599950
F: (01228) 599970
E: enquiries@
cumbrian-cottages.co.uk
I: www.cumbrian-cottages.co.uk

SEDBERGH
Cumbria

**Bainbridge Court and Moss
Bank ★★–★★★★**
Contact: Mrs P A Holme, Cobble
Country Holidays, 59 Main
Street, Sedbergh, Cumbria
LA10 5AB
T: (015396) 21000
F: (015396) 21710
E: admin@cobblecountry.co.uk
I: www.cobblecountry.co.uk

Beckside Hall ★★★
Contact: Dales Hol Cot Ref:3141,
Dales Holiday Cottages, Carleton
Business Park, Carleton New
Road, Skipton, North Yorkshire
BD23 2AA
T: (01756) 799821 & 790919
F: (01756) 797012
E: info@dalesholcot.com
I: www.dalesholcot.com

Carriers Cottage ★★★
Contact: Mr & Mrs T&K Ellis, Sun
Ridge, Joss Lane, Sedbergh,
Cumbria LA10 5AS
T: (015396) 20566

Craigan ★★★★
Contact: Country Hoidays
ref:5661, Spring Mill, Earby,
Barnoldswick, Lancashire
BB94 0AA
T: 08700 723723
F: (01282) 844288
E: sales@ttgihg.co.uk
I: www.country-holidays.co.uk

Fell House ★★★–★★★★
Contact: Mr Stephen Wickham,
8 Arnhem Wharf, London
E14 3RU
T: (020) 7538 4207 &
07778 901788
E: (020) 7531 6552
E: steve@higround.co.uk
I: www.fellhouse.cwc.net

High Brigflatts ★★★
Contact: Mr and Mrs Jones, High
Brigflatts, Brigflatts Lane,
Sedbergh, Cumbria LA10 5HN
T: (015396) 20570
E: hjhilaryjones@cs.com

Ingmire Hall ★★★★
Contact: Mr & Mrs S Gardner,
Ingmire Hall, Sedbergh, Cumbria
LA10 5HR
T: (015396) 21012 & 21116
F: (015396) 21116

**Oakdene Country House
Rating Applied For**
Contact: Mr David & Hilary
Collier & Dixon, Oakdene
Country House, Garsdale Road,
Sedbergh, Cumbria LA10 5JN
T: (015396) 20280
F: (0589) 621501
E: oakdene@compuserve.com
I: www.meetforworkorleisure.
co.uk

4 Railway Cottages ★★★
Contact: Mrs W A Mills, 131
Glendale Gardens, Leigh-on-Sea,
Essex SS9 2BE
T: (01702) 478846
F: (01702) 482088
E: trewen@clara.co.uk
I: www.dalescottages.com

Randall Hill Cottage ★★★
Contact: Dales Hol Cot Ref:2177,
Dales Holiday Cottages, Carleton
Business Park, Carleton New
Road, Skipton, North Yorkshire
BD23 2AA
T: (01756) 799821 & 790919
F: (01756) 797012
E: info@dalesholcot.com
I: www.dalesholcot.com

Thwaite Cottage ★★★★
Contact: Mrs Dorothy Parker,
Thwaite Farm, Howgill,
Sedbergh, Cumbria LA10 5JD
T: (015396) 20493

SEDGWICK
Cumbria

**Wilson Cottage
Rating Applied For**
Contact: Mr Paul Liddell,
Lakelovers, The New Toffee Loft,
Kendal Road, Windermere,
Cumbria LA23 3RA
T: (015394) 88855
F: (015394) 88857
E: bookings@lakelovers.co.uk
I: www.lakelovers.co.uk

Woodside ★★★★
Contact: Mr D Hogarth,
Cumbrian Cottages, 7 The
Crescent, Carlisle, CA1 1QW
T: (01228) 599960 & 599950
F: (01228) 599970
E: enquiries@
cumbrian-cottages.co.uk
I: www.cumbrian-cottages.co.uk

SELSIDE
Cumbria

Shapellon ★★★
Contact: Mrs L Knowles,
Hollowgate Farm, Selside,
Kendal, Cumbria LA8 9LG
T: (01539) 823258
E: hollowgate@talk21.com

SILECROFT
Cumbria

Lowsha Cottage ★★★
Contact: Dales Hol Cot Ref:3126,
Dales Holiday Cottages, Carleton
Business Park, Carleton New
Road, Skipton, North Yorkshire
BD23 2AA
T: (01756) 799821 & 790919
F: (01756) 797012
E: info@dalesholcot.com
I: www.daleshicot.com

SKELSMERGH
Cumbria

Cornerways ★★★
Contact: Mr Paul Liddell,
Lakelovers, The New Toffee Loft,
Kendal Road, Windermere,
Cumbria LA23 3RA
T: (015394) 88855
F: (015394) 88857
E: bookings@lakelovers.co.uk
I: www.lakelovers.co.uk

SKELTON
Cumbria

**Saddleback Cottage
Rating Applied For**
Contact: Dales Hol Cot Ref:2204,
Dales Holiday Cottages, Carleton
Business Park, Carleton New
Road, Skipton, North Yorkshire
BD23 2AA
T: (01756) 799821 & 790919
F: (01756) 797012
E: info@dalesholcot.com
I: www.dalesholcot.com

SKELWITH BRIDGE
Cumbria

Brathay View ★★★★
Contact: Mrs Susan Jackson,
Heart of the Lakes, Fisherbeck
Mill, Old Lake Road, Ambleside,
Cumbria LA22 0DH
T: (015394) 32321
F: (015394) 33251
E: info@heartofthelakes.co.uk
I: www.heartofthelakes.co.uk

**Byron
Rating Applied For**
Contact: Mr Paul Liddell,
Lakelovers, The New Toffee Loft,
Kendal Road, Bowness-on-
Windermere, Windermere,
Cumbria LA23 3RA
T: (015394) 88855
F: (015394) 88857
E: bookings@lakelovers.co.uk
I: www.lakelovers.co.uk

**The Coach House
Rating Applied For**
Contact: Mr Paul Liddell,
Lakelovers, The New Toffee Loft,
Kendal Road, Windermere,
Cumbria LA23 3RA
T: (015394) 88855
F: (015394) 88857
E: bookings@lakelovers.co.uk
I: www.lakelovers.co.uk

Ghyll Pool Lodge ★★★
Contact: Mr D Hogarth,
Cumbrian Cottages, 7 The
Crescent, Carlisle, CA1 1QW
T: (01228) 599960
F: (01228) 599970
E: enquiries@
cumbrian-cottages.co.uk
I: www.cumbrian-cottages.co.uk

**Ivy Cottage
Rating Applied For**
Contact: Mr D Hogarth,
Cumbrian Cottages, 7 The
Crescent, Carlisle, CA1 1QW
T: (01228) 599960 & 599950
F: (01228) 599970
E: enquiries@
cumbrian-cottages.co.uk
I: www.cumbrian-cottages.co.uk

Kalamunda ★★★★
Contact: Mr Paul Liddell,
Lakelovers, The New Toffee Loft,
Kendal Road, Windermere,
Cumbria LA23 3RA
T: (015394) 88855
F: (015394) 88857
E: bookings@lakelovers.co.uk
I: www.lakelovers.co.uk

Little Greenbank ★★★★
Contact: Mrs Lilian Green,
Greenbank, Skelwith Bridge,
Ambleside, Cumbria LA22 9NW
T: (015394) 33236
E: greenbank@bigwig.net
I: www.visitgreenbank.co.uk

Maison Hector ★★★★
Contact: Mr D Hogarth,
Cumbrian Cottages, 7 The
Crescent, Carlisle, CA1 1QW
T: (01228) 599960 & 599950
F: (01228) 599970
E: enquiries@
cumbrian-cottages.co.uk
I: www.cumbrian-cottages.co.uk

Merlin's ★★★★
Contact: Mrs Susan Jackson,
Heart of the Lakes, Fisherbeck
Hill, Old Lake Road, Ambleside,
Cumbria LA22 0DH
T: (015394) 32321
F: (015394) 33251
E: info@heartofthelakes.co.uk
I: www.heartofthelakes.co.uk

Establishments printed in blue have a detailed entry in this guide

2 Neaum Crag Court ★★★
Contact: Mr D Hogarth,
Cumbrian Cottages, 7 The
Crescent, Carlisle, CA1 1QW
T: (01228) 599960
F: (01228) 599970
E: enquiries@
cumbrian-cottages.co.uk
I: www.cumbrian-cottages.co.uk

4 Neaum Crag Court ★★★
Contact: Mr D Hogarth,
Cumbrian Cottages, 7 The
Crescent, Carlisle, CA1 1QW
T: (01228) 599960
F: (01228) 599970
E: enquiries@
cumbrian-cottages.co.uk
I: www.cumbrian-cottages.co.uk

Oakdene ★★★★
Contact: Mrs Susan Jackson,
Heart of the Lakes, Fisherbeck
Hill, Old Lake Road, Ambleside,
Cumbria LA22 0DH
T: (015394) 32321
F: (015394) 33251
E: info@heartofthelakes.co.uk
I: www.heartofthelakes.co.uk

Ramblers Rest ★★★★
Contact: Mr Paul Liddell,
Lakelovers, The New Toffee Loft,
Kendal Road, Windermere,
Cumbria LA23 3RA
T: (015394) 88855
F: (015394) 88857
E: bookings@lakelovers.co.uk
I: www.lakelovers.co.uk

River Bank Cottage ★★★★
Contact: Mr D Hogarth,
Cumbrian Cottages, 7 The
Crescent, Carlisle, CA1 1QW
T: (01228) 599960 & 599950
F: (01228) 599970
E: enquiries@
cumbrian-cottages.co.uk
I: www.cumbrian-cottages.co.uk

Riverbank Cottage ★★★
Contact: Mrs Jackson, Heart of
the Lakes, Fisherbeck Mill, Old
Lake Road, Ambleside, Cumbria
LA22 0DH
T: (015394) 32321
F: (015394) 33251
E: info@heartofthelakes.co.uk
I: www.heartofthelakes.co.uk

Tarn Howes
Rating Applied For
Contact: Mr Paul Liddell,
Lakelovers, The New Toffee Loft,
Kendal Road, Bowness-on-
Windermere, Windermere,
Cumbria LA23 3RA
T: (015394) 88855
F: (015394) 88857
E: bookings@lakelovers.co.uk
I: www.lakelovers.co.uk

Wordsworth, Neaum Crag
★★★
Contact: Mrs Susan Jackson,
Heart of the Lakes, Fisherbeck
Hill, Old Lake Road, Ambleside,
Cumbria LA22 0DH
T: (015394) 32321
F: (015394) 33251
E: info@heartofthelakes.co.uk
I: www.heartofthelakes.co.uk

SKELWITH FOLD
Cumbria

Crophowe ★★★
Contact: Mr Paul Liddell,
Lakelovers, The New Toffee Loft,
Kendal Road, Windermere,
Cumbria LA23 3RA
T: (015394) 88855
F: (015394) 88857
E: bookings@lakelovers.co.uk
I: www.lakelovers.co.uk

Hillcrest ★★★★
Contact: Mr Paul Liddell,
Lakelovers, The New Toffee Loft,
Kendal Road, Windermere,
Cumbria LA23 3RA
T: (015394) 88855
F: (015394) 88857
E: bookings@lakelovers.co.uk
I: www.lakelovers.co.uk

Rivendell Cottage ★★★
Contact: Mrs Susan Jackson,
Heart of the Lakes, Fisherbeck
Hill, Old Lake Road, Ambleside,
Cumbria LA22 0DH
T: (015394) 32321
F: (015394) 33251
E: info@heartofthelakes.co.uk
I: www.heartofthelakes.co.uk

SKINBURNESS
Cumbria

Lucknow ★★★★
Contact: Mrs Joy Ross, 10
Brittons Close, Sharnbrook,
Bedford, Bedfordshire
MK44 1PN
T: 07774 888480 &
(01234) 781991
F: 07860 275142
E: lucknowcottage@btinternet.
com
I: www.btinternet.
com/~lucknowcottage

SMARDALE
Cumbria

Leases ★★★
Contact: Mrs C M Galloway,
Leases, Smardale, Kirkby
Stephen, Cumbria CA17 4HQ
T: (01683) 71198
E: leasesgall@aol.com

SOCKBRIDGE
Cumbria

Eastwards Cottage ★★★★
Contact: Mr Martin Wardle,
Lakes and Valleys, North Lodge,
Longtail Hill, Bowness-on-
Windermere, Windermere,
Cumbria LA23 3JD
T: (015394) 88612 & 47477
F: (015394) 48988
E: lakesandvalleys@aol.com
I: www.lakesandvalleys.co.uk

Primrose Bank, Hall Croft
★★★
Contact: Mrs J Lane, Absolute
Escapes, Orchard Farm House,
Lynn Road, Gayton, King's Lynn,
Norfolk PE32 1PA
T: 07553 636989
F: 07553 636989
E: janelane@absolute-escapes.
co.uk
I: www.absolute-escapes.co.uk

SOUTHWAITE
Cumbria

Serendipity Cottage ★★★
Contact: Dales Holiday Cottages,
Carleton Business Park, Carleton
New Road, Skipton, North
Yorkshire BD23 2AA
T: (01756) 799821 & 790919
F: (01756) 797012
I: www.dales-holiday-cottages.
com

SPARK BRIDGE
Cumbria

Dicky Cragg ★★★
Contact: Mrs D Lever, 27 East
Beach, Lytham, Lytham St
Annes, Lancashire FY8 5EX
T: (01253) 736438 & 795905
F: (01253) 731555
E: lettings@jgl.com
I: www.jgl.co.uk/dickycragg

Riversdale ★★★
Contact: Mr John Serginson, The
Lakeland Cottage Company,
Waterside House, Newby Bridge,
Ulverston, Cumbria LA12 8AN
T: (015395) 30024
F: (015395) 31932
E: john@
lakeland-cottage-company.
co.uk
I: www.
lakeland-cottage-company.
co.uk

Summer Hill Holidays
★★★-★★★★★
Contact: Mrs R Campbell,
Summer Hill Holidays, Summer
Hill, Spark Bridge, Ulverston,
Cumbria LA12 7SS
T: (01229) 861510
F: (01229) 861090
E: rosemary@summerhill.co.uk
I: www.summerhill.co.uk

Thurstonville High Lodge ★★
Contact: Mr R N Lord,
Thurstonville, Lowick, Ulverston,
Cumbria LA12 7SX
T: (01229) 861 271

STAINTON
Cumbria

Andrew Cottage ★★★
Contact: Dales Hol Cot Ref:2098,
Dales Holiday Cottages, Carleton
Business Park, Carleton New
Road, Skipton, North Yorkshire
BD23 2AA
T: (01756) 799821 & 790919
F: (01756) 797012
E: info@dalesholcot.com
I: www.dalesholcot.com

Mill Race View ★★★
Contact: Dales Hol Cot Ref:2264,
Dales Holiday Cottages, Carleton
Business Park, Carleton New
Road, Skipton, North Yorkshire
BD23 2AA
T: (01756) 799821 & 790919
F: (01756) 797012
E: info@dalesholcot.com
I: www.dalesholcot.com

STAIR
Cumbria

Grizedale Cottage ★★★
Contact: Mr David Burton,
Lakeland Cottage Holidays, 3 The
Heads, Keswick, Cumbria
CA12 5ES
T: (017687) 71071
F: (017687) 75036
E: info@lakelandcottages.co.uk
I: www.lakelandcottages.co.uk

The Parrock ★★★
Contact: Mrs J Williams, Stair
Mill, Stair, Keswick, Cumbria
CA12 5UF
T: (017687) 78333

STAVELEY
Cumbria

Ashleigh ★★★★
Contact: Mr John Serginson, The
Lakeland Cottage Company,
Waterside House, Newby Bridge,
Ulverston, Cumbria LA12 8AN
T: (015395) 30024
F: (015395) 31932
E: john@
lakeland-cottage-company.
co.uk
I: www.
lakeland-cottage-company.
co.uk

Avondale ★★★
Contact: Miss Helen Whalley, 2
Lynstead, Thornbarrow Road,
Windermere, Cumbria LA23 2DG
T: (015394) 45713
E: helen.whalley@avondale.uk.
net
⬆

Bobbin Cottage ★★★
Contact: Dales Hol Cot Ref:2284,
Dales Holiday Cottages, Carleton
Business Park, Carleton New
Road, Skipton, North Yorkshire
BD23 2AA
T: (01756) 799821 & 790919
F: (01756) 797012
E: info@dalesholcot.com
I: www.dalesholcot.com

Brunt Knott Farm Holiday
Cottages
Rating Applied For
Contact: William and Margaret
Beck, Brunt Knott Farm Holiday
Cottages, Brunt Knott Farm,
Staveley, Kendal, Cumbria
LA8 9QX
T: (01539) 821030 & 822680
F: (01539) 821221
E: margaret@bruntknott.
demon.co.uk
I: www.bruntknott.demon.co.uk

Capple Howe ★★★★
Contact: Ms Grange, Capple
Howe, Browfoot Farm, Staveley,
Kendal, Cumbria LA8 9JQ
T: (01539) 821210

Ghyllbank ★★
Contact: Mrs Sylvia Beaty,
Garnett House Farm, Burneside,
Kendal, Cumbria LA8 5SF
T: (01539) 724542
F: (01539) 724542

Marsden ★★
Contact: Mr Paul Liddell,
Lakelovers, The New Toffee Loft,
Kendal Road, Windermere,
Cumbria LA23 3RA
T: (015394) 88855
F: (015394) 88857
E: bookings@lakelovers.co.uk
I: www.lakelovers.co.uk

Mill House ★★
Contact: Mr Paul Liddell,
Lakelovers, The New Toffee Loft,
Kendal Road, Windermere,
Cumbria LA23 3RA
T: (015394) 88855
F: (015394) 88857
E: bookings@lakelovers.co.uk
I: www.lakelovers.co.uk

Mill Race Cottage ★★★
Contact: Mr Paul Liddell,
Lakelovers, The New Toffee Loft,
Kendal Road, Windermere,
Cumbria LA23 3RA
T: (015394) 88855
F: (015394) 88857
E: bookings@lakelovers.co.uk
I: www.lakelovers.co.uk

Nook House ★★★
Contact: Mr John Serginson, The
Lakeland Cottage Company,
Waterside House, Newby Bridge,
Ulverston, Cumbria LA12 8AN
T: (015395) 30024
F: (015395) 31932
E: john@
lakeland-cottage-company.
co.uk
I: www.lakeland.
cottage-company.co.uk

Whinfield ★★★
Contact: Mrs P M Taylor,
Whinfield, 18 Rawes Garth,
Staveley, Kendal, Cumbria
LA8 9QH
T: (01539) 821002

STAVELEY-IN-CARTMEL
Cumbria

April Cottage
Rating Applied For
Contact: Mr Paul Liddell,
Lakelovers, The New Toffee Loft,
Kendal Road, Windermere,
Cumbria LA23 3RA
T: (015394) 88855
F: (015394) 88857
E: bookings@lakelovers.co.uk
I: www.lakelovers.co.uk

Croft Cottage ★★★
Contact: Mr D Hogarth,
Cumbrian Cottages, 7 The
Crescent, Carlisle, CA1 1QW
T: (01228) 599960 & 599950
F: (01228) 599970
E: enquiries@
cumbrian-cottages.co.uk
I: www.cumbrian-cottages.co.uk

Staveley House Cottage
★★★★
Contact: Mr John Serginson, The
Lakeland Cottage Company,
Waterside House, Newby Bridge,
Ulverston, Cumbria LA12 8AN
T: (015395) 30024
F: (015395) 31932
E: john@
lakeland-cottage-company.
co.uk
I: www.
lakeland-cottage-company.
co.uk

TEBAY
Cumbria

Primrose Flat ★★★
Contact: Mrs Patricia Helen
Jones, Primrose Cottage, Orton
Road, Tebay, Penrith, Cumbria
CA10 3TL
T: (015396) 24791 &
07778 520930
E: primrosecottebay@aol.com

THORNTHWAITE
Cumbria

Beck View ★★★
Contact: Mr D Hogarth,
Cumbrian Cottages, 7 The
Crescent, Carlisle, CA1 1QW
T: (01228) 599960 & 599950
F: (01228) 599970
E: enquiries@
cumbrian-cottages.co.uk
I: www.cumbrian-cottages.co.uk

Beck Wythop Cottage ★★★★
Contact: Mr D Hogarth,
Cumbrian Cottages, 7 The
Crescent, Carlisle, CA1 1QW
T: (01228) 599960 & 599950
F: (01228) 599970
E: enquiries@
cumbrian-cottages.co.uk
I: www.cumbrian-cottages.co.uk

Harriets Hideaway ★★★★
Contact: Mrs Jane Miller, 24 Elm
Court, Whickham, Newcastle
upon Tyne NE16 4PS
T: (0191) 488 0549
F: (0191) 422 3303
E: mtekk@ic24.net

Kirkstones ★★★
Contact: Mr Malcolm Prentice,
Parkside Farm, Stony Gate,
Houghton-le-Spring, Tyne and
Wear DH4 4NN
T: (0191) 528 0233
I: www.kirkstones.co.uk

The Larches ★★★
Contact: Mr David Burton,
Lakeland Cottage Holidays, 3 The
Heads, Keswick, Cumbria
CA12 5ES
T: (017687) 71071
F: (017687) 75036
E: info@lakelandcottages.co.uk
I: www.lakelandcottages.co.uk/

Seat Howe ★★★
Contact: Mrs Dorothy Bell, Seat
Howe, Thornthwaite, Keswick,
Cumbria CA12 5SQ
T: (017687) 78371

Talcomb ★★★
Contact: Mr Howard King, 14
Brooklands, Darras Hall,
Ponteland, Newcastle upon
Tyne, Northumberland NE20
T: 07973 420179

Thwaite Hill Cottage ★★★★
Contact: Mr David Burton,
Lakeland Cottage Holidays, 3 The
Heads, Keswick, Cumbria
CA12 5ES
T: (017687) 71071
F: (017687) 75036
E: info@lakelandcottages.co.uk
I: www.lakelandcottages.co.uk/

THRELKELD
Cumbria

1 The Barns ★★★
Contact: Mrs J Browne, One The
Barns, Langdale Merritts Hill,
Illogan, Redruth, Cornwall
TR16 4DF
T: (01209) 215553
E: tom.joan@lineone.net

Blencathra Centre - Latrigg
View, Derwent View,
Borrowdale View ★★★
Contact: Mr A Simms,
Blencathra Centre, Threlkeld,
Keswick, Cumbria CA12 4SG
T: (017687) 79601
F: (017687) 79264
E: fsc.blencathra@ukonline.
co.uk

Blencathra View ★★★
Contact: Mr D Hogarth,
Cumbrian Cottages, 7 The
Crescent, Carlisle, CA1 1QW
T: (01228) 599960 & 599950
F: (01228) 599970
E: enquiries@
cumbrian-cottages.co.uk
I: www.cumbrian-cottages.co.uk

Heather View ★★★★
Contact: Mr D Hogarth,
Cumbrian Cottages, 7 The
Crescent, Carlisle, CA1 1QW
T: (01228) 599960 & 599950
F: (01228) 599970
E: enquiries@
cumbrian-cottages.co.uk
I: www.cumbrian-cottages.co.uk

Katellen Cottage ★★★★
Contact: Mr D Hogarth,
Cumbrian Cottages, 7 The
Crescent, Carlisle, CA1 1QW
T: (01228) 599960 & 599950
F: (01228) 599970
E: enquiries@
cumbrian-cottages.co.uk
I: www.cumbrian-cottages.co.uk

Latcrag ★★★★
Contact: Mrs D Benson, High
Row Farm, Threlkeld, Keswick,
Cumbria CA12 4SF
T: (017687) 79256

Lingclose Cottage ★★★★
Contact: Dales Hol Cot Ref:2469,
Dales Holiday Cottages, Carleton
Business Park, Carleton New
Road, Skipton, North Yorkshire
BD23 2AA
T: (01756) 799821 & 790919
F: (01756) 797012
E: info@dalesholcot.com
I: www.dalesholcot.com

Nightingale Cottage ★★
Contact: Mr D Hogarth,
Cumbrian Cottages, 7 The
Crescent, Carlisle, CA1 1QW
T: (01228) 599960 & 599950
F: (01228) 599970
E: enquiries@
cumbrian-cottages.co.uk
I: www.cumbrian-cottages.co.uk

Old Manse Barn ★★★
Contact: Mrs L Deadman, Old
Manse Barn, Threlkeld, Keswick,
Cumbria CA12 4SQ
T: (017687) 79270
E: jon@deadman.freeserve.
co.uk
I: www.deadman.freeserve.co.uk

Townhead Byre ★★★
Contact: Mr David Burton,
Lakeland Cottage Holidays, 3 The
Heads, Keswick, Cumbria
CA12 5ES
T: (017687) 71071
F: (017687) 75036
E: info@lakelandcottages.co.uk
I: www.lakelandcottages.co.uk/

White Pike ★★★
Contact: Mr D Hogarth,
Cumbrian Cottages, 7 The
Crescent, Carlisle, CA1 1QW
T: (01228) 599960 & 599950
F: (01228) 599970
E: enquiries@
cumbrian-cottages.co.uk
I: www.cumbrian-cottages.co.uk

THURSBY
Cumbria

Meadow Cottage ★★★★
Contact: Dr Malcolm Quigley, 22
Newby Cross, Wigton Road,
Carlisle, Cumbria CA5 6JP
T: (01228) 710180

THURSTONFIELD
Cumbria

The Tranquil Otter ★★★★
Contact: Mr & Mrs Richard &
Wendy Wise, Lough House,
Thurstonfield, Carlisle, Cumbria
CA5 6HB
T: (01228) 576661 & 576727
F: (01228) 576662
E: richard@the-tranquil-otter.
co.uk
I: www.the-tranquil-otter.co.uk

TIRRIL
Cumbria

Tirril Farm Cottages ★★★★
Contact: Mr David Owens, Tirril
View, Tirril, Penrith, Cumbria
CA10 2JE
T: (01768) 864767
F: (01768) 864767

TORVER
Cumbria

Dipper Cottage, Robin Cottage
& Wren Cottage
Rating Applied For
Contact: Mr Paul Liddell,
Lakelovers, The New Toffee Loft,
Kendal Road, Windermere,
Cumbria LA23 3RA
T: (015394) 88855
F: (015394) 88857
E: bookings@lakelovers.co.uk
I: www.lakelovers.co.uk

Ellice Howe
Rating Applied For
Contact: Mr Paul Liddell,
Lakelovers, The New Toffee Loft,
Kendal Road, Bowness-on-
Windermere, Windermere,
Cumbria LA23 3RA
T: (015394) 88855
F: (015394) 88857
E: bookings@lakelovers.co.uk
I: www.lakelovers.co.uk

The Old Pottery ★★★
Contact: Mr Philip Johnston, The
Coppermines Coniston,
Coppermines Valley, Coniston,
Cumbria LA21 8HX
T: (015394) 41765 &
07721 584488
F: (015394) 41944
E: estateoffice@coppermines.
co.uk
I: www.coppermines.co.uk

Old Stable Cottage ★★★
Contact: Mr Philip Johnston, The
Coppermines Coniston,
Coppermines Valley, Coniston,
Cumbria LA21 8HX
T: (015394) 41765 &
07721 584488
F: (015394) 41944
E: bookings@coppermines.co.uk
I: www.coppermines.co.uk

Scarr Head Cottage ★★★★
Contact: Mr D Hogarth,
Cumbrian Cottages, 7 The
Crescent, Carlisle, CA1 1QW
T: (01228) 599960
F: (01228) 599970
E: enquiries@
cumbrian-cottages.co.uk
I: www.cumbrian-cottages.co.uk

TROUBECK
Cumbria

**1 and 2 Butt Hill Cottage
★★★**
Contact: Mr Paul Liddell,
Lakelovers, The New Toffee Loft,
Kendal Road, Windermere,
Cumbria LA23 3RA
T: (015394) 88855
F: (015394) 88857
E: bookings@lakelovers.co.uk
I: www.lakelovers.co.uk

Barn Cottage ★★★
Contact: Mrs J Cochrane, High
Green House, Troutbeck,
Windermere, Cumbria LA23 1PN
T: (015394) 34421
E: james.cochrane@ukonline.
co.uk

Betty's Cottage ★★★★
Contact: Mrs Susan Jackson,
Heart of the Lakes, Fisherbeck
Mill, Old Lake Road, Ambleside,
Cumbria LA22 0DH
T: (015394) 32321
F: (015394) 33251
E: info@heartofthelakes.co.uk
I: www.heartofthelakes.co.uk

**Gill Head Apartment and Bald
Howe ★★★**
Contact: Dales Hol Cot
Ref:2069/2097, Dales Holiday
Cottages, Carleton Business
Park, Carleton New Road,
Skipton, North Yorkshire
BD23 2AA
T: (01756) 799821 & 790919
F: (01756) 797012
E: info@dalesholcot.com
I: www.dalesholcot.com

Glenside ★★★
Contact: Mrs Susan Jackson,
Heart of the Lakes, Fisherbeck
Hill, Old Lake Road, Ambleside,
Cumbria LA22 0DH
T: (015394) 32321
F: (015394) 33251
E: info@heartofthelakes.co.uk
I: www.heartofthelakes.co.uk

Holbeck Ghyll Lodge ★★★★
Contact: Mrs Maggie Kaye,
Holmdene, Stoney Bank Road,
Thongsbridge, Holmfirth,
Huddersfield HD9 7SL
T: (01484) 684605
F: (01484) 689051
E: maggiekaye@hotmail.com

Knotts Farm ★★★★
Contact: Proprietor, Heart of the
Lakes, Fisherbeck Mill, Old Lake
Road, Ambleside, Cumbria
LA22 0DH
T: (015394) 32321
F: (015394) 33251
E: info@heartofthelakes.co.uk
I: www.heartofthelakes.co.uk

Knotts Farm Cottage ★★★
Contact: Mrs Susan Jackson,
Heart of the Lakes, Fisherbeck
Hill, Old Lake Road, Ambleside,
Cumbria LA22 0DH
T: (015394) 32321
F: (015394) 33251
E: info@heartofthelakes.co.uk
I: www.heartofthelakes.co.uk

Long Mire Yeat ★★★
Contact: Mrs Susan Jackson,
Heart of the Lakes, Fisherbeck
Hill, Old Lake Road, Ambleside,
Cumbria LA22 0DH
T: (015394) 32321
F: (015394) 33251
E: info@heartofthelakes.co.uk
I: www.heartofthelakes.co.uk

Low House ★★★★
Contact: Mrs E Dale, Moorend,
Troutbeck, Penrith, Cumbria
CA11 0SX
T: (017687) 79388 & 79731

Orchard Cottage ★★★★
Contact: Mr Paul Liddell,
Lakelovers, The New Toffee Loft,
Kendal Road, Windermere,
Cumbria LA23 3RA
T: (015394) 88855
F: (015394) 88857
E: bookings@lakelovers.co.uk
I: www.lakelovers.co.uk

Robin Cottage ★★★★
Contact: Mr D Hogarth,
Cumbrian Cottages, 7 The
Crescent, Carlisle, CA1 1QW
T: (01228) 599960 & 599950
F: (01228) 599970
E: enquiries@
cumbrian-cottages.co.uk
I: www.cumbrian-cottages.co.uk

South View ★★★
Contact: Mr D Hogarth,
Cumbrian Cottages, 7 The
Crescent, Carlisle, CA1 1QW
T: (01228) 599960 & 599950
F: (01228) 599970
E: enquiries@
cumbrian-cottages.co.uk
I: www.cumbrian-cottages.co.uk

Stamp Howe ★★★★
Contact: Mrs Susan Jackson,
Heart of the Lakes, Fisherbeck
Hill, Old Lake Road, Ambleside,
Cumbria LA22 0DH
T: (015394) 32321
F: (015394) 33251
E: info@heartofthelakes.co.uk
I: www.heartofthelakes.co.uk

Troutbeck Mews ★★★★
Contact: Mr and Mrs T J Bowers,
Troutbeck Mews, Troutbeck Inn,
Troutbeck, Penrith, Cumbria
CA11 0SJ
T: (017684) 83635
F: (017684) 83928
E: enquiries@troutbeck-inn.
com
I: www.troutbeck-inn.com

Wetherlam ★★★
Contact: Mr P Liddell, Heart of
the Lakes, Fisherbeck Hill, Old
Lake Road, Ambleside, Cumbria
LA22 0DH
T: (015394) 32321
F: (015394) 33251
E: info@heartofthelakes.co.uk
I: www.heartofthelakes.co.uk

TROUTBECK BRIDGE
Cumbria

Briery Lodge ★★★
Contact: Mrs S Jackson, Heart of
the Lakes, Fisherbeck Mill, Old
Lake Road, Ambleside, Cumbria
LA22 0DH
T: (015394) 32321
F: (015394) 33251
E: info@heartofthelakes.co.uk
I: www.heartofthelakes.co.uk

**Cornerways
Rating Applied For**
Contact: Sykes Cottages
Ref:777, Sykes Cottages, York
House, York Street, Chester,
CH1 3LR
T: (01244) 345700
F: (01244) 321442
E: info@sykescottages.co.uk
I: www.sykescottages.co.uk

Grooms Cottage ★★★
Contact: Mr D Hogarth,
Cumbrian Cottages, 7 The
Crescent, Carlisle, CA1 1QW
T: (01228) 599960 & 599950
F: (01228) 599970
E: enquiries@
cumbrian-cottages.co.uk
I: www.cumbrian-cottages.co.uk

Howarth Cottage ★★★
Contact: Mr D Hogarth,
Cumbrian Cottages, 7 The
Crescent, Carlisle, CA1 1QW
T: (01228) 599960
F: (01228) 599970
E: enquiries@
cumbrian-cottages.co.uk
I: www.cumbrian-cottages.co.uk

**Quarry Garth Lodge
Rating Applied For**
Contact: Mr Richard Bee,
Lakeland Estates, Quarry Garth,
Windermere, Cumbria LA23 1LF
T: (015394) 45111 & 45222
F: (015394) 45333

School Cottage ★★★
Contact: Mrs Susan Jackson,
Heart of the Lakes, Fisherbeck
Hill, Old Lake Road, Ambleside,
Cumbria LA22 0DH
T: (015394) 32321
F: (015394) 33251
E: info@heartofthelakes.co.uk
I: www.heartofthelakes.co.uk

The School House ★★★★
Contact: Mrs Susan Jackson,
Heart of the Lakes, Fisherbeck
Mill, Old Lake Road, Ambleside,
Cumbria LA22 0DH
T: (015394) 32321
F: (015394) 33251
E: info@heartofthelakes.co.uk
I: www.heartofthelakes.co.uk

ULDALE
Cumbria

**Coach House and Groom
Cottage ★★★**
Contact: Mr D Hogarth,
Cumbrian Cottages, 7 The
Crescent, Carlisle, CA1 1QW
T: (01228) 599960 & 599950
F: (01228) 599970
E: enquiries@
cumbrian-cottages.co.uk
I: www.cumbrian-cottages.co.uk

Knaifan Cottage ★★★★
Contact: Mr D Hogarth,
Cumbrian Cottages, 7 The
Crescent, Carlisle, CA1 1QW
T: (01228) 599960
F: (01228) 599970
E: enquiries@
cumbrian-cottages.co.uk
I: www.cumbrian-cottages.co.uk

The Old Vicarage ★★★
Contact: Mr David Lowden, The
Granary, The Old Vicarage,
Uldale, Carlisle CA7 1HA
T: (016973) 71907 &
07855 532246
E: catford@dircon.co.uk

Trusmadoor ★★★★
Contact: Mr D Hogarth,
Cumbrian Cottages, 7 The
Crescent, Carlisle, CA1 1QW
T: (01228) 599960 & 599950
F: (01228) 599970
E: enquiries@
cumbrian-cottages.co.uk
I: www.cumbrian-cottages.co.uk

ULLOCK
Cumbria

Tree Tops ★★★
Contact: Dales Hol Cot Ref:2884,
Dales Holiday Cottages, Carleton
Business Park, Carleton New
Road, Skipton, North Yorkshire
BD23 2AA
T: (01756) 799821 & 790919
F: (01756) 797012
E: info@dalesholcot.com
I: www.dalesholcot.com

ULLSWATER
Cumbria

**Arcos Holiday Cottages
(Hutton) ★★★**
Contact: Mr R Cowperthwaite,
Arcos Holiday Cottages (Hutton),
Ullswater, Penrith, Cumbria
CA11 0LZ
T: (017684) 83300
F: (017684) 83300
E: ray-c@arcos-holidays.
freeserve.co.uk
I: arcos-holidays.freeserve.co.uk

Cherry Holm ★★★★
Contact: Mrs Susanne Sheard, 7
Bark Lane, Addingham, Ilkley,
West Yorkshire LS29 0RA
T: (01943) 830766

**Estate Office Patterdale Hall
Estate★★-★★★**
Contact: Mr Stephen Foxall,
Estate Office Patterdale Hall
Estate, Glenridding, Penrith,
Cumbria CA11 0PJ
T: (017684) 82308
F: (017684) 82308
E: welcome@phel.co.uk
I: www.phel.co.uk

Ghyll Cottage ★★★★
Contact: Mrs Elizabeth
Darbyshire, Crossgates Farm,
Hartsop, Penrith, Cumbria
CA11 0NZ
T: (017684) 82566
F: (017684) 82566
E: erdarbyshire@aol.com
I: www.lakesinfo.
com/ghyllcottage

Knottsbank ★★★★
Contact: Mr & Mrs S Lamb,
Woodbank, The Knotts,
Watermillock, Penrith, Cumbria
CA11 0JP
T: (017684) 86355

Lakefield ★★★★
Contact: Mrs Susan Jackson,
Heart of the Lakes, Fisherbeck
Mill, Old Lake Road, Ambleside,
Cumbria LA22 0DH
T: (015394) 32321
F: (015394) 33251
E: info@heartofthelakes.co.uk
I: www.heartofthelakes.co.uk

Land Ends ★★★
Contact: Ms Barbara Holmes,
Land Ends, Watermillock,
Ullswater, Cumbria CA11 0NB
T: (017684) 86438
F: (017684) 86959
E: infolandends@btinternet.
com
I: www.landends.btinternet.
co.uk

**Swarthbeck Farm Holiday
Cottages ★★★-★★★★★**
Contact: Mr and Mrs W H
Parkin, Swarthbeck Farm,
Howtown, Penrith, Cumbria
CA10 2ND
T: (017684) 86432
E: whparkin@ukonline.co.uk
I: www.cumbria.com/horsehols

ULVERSTON
Cumbria

**Ashlack Cottages
Rating Applied For**
Contact: Mrs Amanda Keegan,
Ashlack Hall, Grizebeck, Kirkby-
in-Furness, Cumbria LA17 7XN
T: (01229) 889108
F: (01229) 889111
E: allkeegan@breathemail.net
I: ashlackcottages.co.uk

Cosy Cottage ★★
Contact: Mrs Joyce Atkinson,
Bridge Close, Pennington Lane,
Lindal, Ulverston, Cumbria
LA12 0LA
T: (01229) 582012

The Falls ★★-★★★
Contact: Mrs Cheetham and Mrs
Unger, The Falls, Mansriggs,
Ulverston, Cumbria LA12 7PX
T: (01229) 583781
F: (01229) 583781
I: www.thefalls.co.uk

**Lile Cottage at Gleaston Water
Mill★★★★**
Contact: Mrs V Brereton, Lile
Cottage at Gleaston Water Mill,
Gleaston Water Mill, Gleaston,
Ulverston, Cumbria LA12 0QH
T: (01229) 869244
F: (01229) 869764
E: pigsty@watermill.co.uk
I: www.watermill.co.uk

Orchard Cottage ★★★
Contact: Mrs Martin, Mascalles
Bungalow, Mascalles, Ulverston,
Cumbria LA12 0TQ
T: (01229) 463591

3 Rosside Cottages ★★★
Contact: Sykes Cottages
Ref:608, Sykes Cottages, York
House, York Street, Chester,
CH1 3LR
T: (01244) 345700
F: (01244) 321442
E: info@sykescottages.co.uk
I: www.sykescottages.co.uk

Rusland Hall ★★★
Contact: Mr John Serginson, The
Lakeland Cottage Company,
Waterside House, Newby Bridge,
Ulverston, Cumbria LA12 8AN
T: (015395) 30024
F: (015395) 31932
E: john@
lakeland-cottage-company.
co.uk
I: www.
lakeland-cottage-company.
co.uk

**Swarthmoor Hall
★★★-★★★★**
Contact: Mr Steven Deeming,
Swarthmoor Hall, Swarthmoor,
Ulverston, Cumbria LA12 0JQ
T: (01229) 583204
E: swarthmrhall@gn.apc.org
I: www.quaker.org.uk/swarth.
html

Waters Yeat Mill ★★★★
Contact: Mr D Hogarth,
Cumbrian Cottages, 7 The
Crescent, Carlisle, CA1 1QW
T: (01228) 599960 & 599950
F: (01228) 599970
E: enquiries@
cumbrian-cottages.co.uk
I: www.cumbrian-cottages.co.uk

**Woodview and Stablend
★★★★**
Contact: Mr John Serginson, The
Lakeland Cottage Company,
Waterside House, Newby Bridge,
Ulverston, Cumbria LA12 8AN
T: (015395) 30024
F: (015395) 31932
E: john@
lakeland-cottage-company.
co.uk
I: www.
lakeland-cottage-company.
co.uk

UNDERBARROW
Cumbria

Crispin Cottage ★★★
Contact: Country Holidays
ref:11252, Spring Mill, Earby,
Barnoldswick, Lancashire
BB94 0AA
T: 08700 732732
F: (01282) 844288
I: www.country-holidays.co.uk

Garth Row ★★★★
Contact: Sykes Cottages Ref:
702, Sykes Cottages, York House,
York Street, Chester, CH1 3LR
T: (01244) 345700
F: (01244) 321442
E: info@sykescottages.co.uk
I: www.sykescottages.co.uk

Honey Pot ★★★★★
Contact: Mr D Hogarth,
Cumbrian Cottages, 7 The
Crescent, Carlisle, CA1 1QW
T: (01228) 599960 & 599950
F: (01228) 599970
E: enquiries@
cumbrian-cottages.co.uk
I: www.cumbrian-cottages.co.uk

Nanny Goat ★★★★★
Contact: Mr D Hogarth,
Cumbrian Cottages, 7 The
Crescent, Carlisle, CA1 1QW
T: (01228) 599960 & 599950
F: (01228) 599970
E: enquiries@
cumbrian-cottages.co.uk
I: www.cumbrian-cottages.co.uk

UNDERSKIDDAW
Cumbria

**Apartment 1, Oakfield House
★★★★**
Contact: Mr D Hogarth,
Cumbrian Cottages Limited, 7
The Crescent, Carlisle, CA1 1QW
T: (01228) 599960
F: (01228) 599970
E: enquiries@
cumbrian-cottages.co.uk
I: www.cumbrian-cottages.co.uk

Garth Cottage ★★★★
Contact: Mr D Hogarth,
Cumbrian Cottages, 7 The
Crescent, Carlisle, CA1 1QW
T: (01228) 599960
F: (01228) 599970
E: enquiries@
cumbrian-cottages.co.uk
I: www.cumbrian-cottages.co.uk

**White Stones Cottage
Rating Applied For**
Contact: Mr & Mrs John
Houldershaw, White Stones,
Underskiddaw, Keswick, Cumbria
CA12 4QD
T: (017687) 72762

UNTHANK
Cumbria

**Cottage 1,2,3
Rating Applied For**
Contact: Dales Hol Cot
Ref:3212/3/4, Dales Holiday
Cottages, Carleton Business
Park, Carleton New Road,
Skipton, North Yorkshire
BD23 2AA
T: (01756) 799821 & 790919
F: (01756) 797012
E: info@dalesholcot.com
I: www.dalesholcot.com

WASDALE
Cumbria

**Greendale Holiday Apartments
★★★**
Contact: Mr and Mrs M D
Burnett, Greendale Holiday
Apartments, Greendale,
Wasdale, Cumbria CA20 1EU
T: (019467) 26243

Little Ground ★★★
Contact: Mr D Hogarth,
Cumbrian Cottages, 7 The
Crescent, Carlisle, CA1 1QW
T: (01228) 599960 & 599950
F: (01228) 599970
E: enquiries@
cumbrian-cottages.co.uk
I: www.cumbrian-cottages.co.uk

Little Ground Cottage ★★★
Contact: Mr D Hogarth,
Cumbrian Cottages, 7 The
Crescent, Carlisle, CA1 1QW
T: (01228) 599960 & 599950
F: (01228) 599970
E: enquiries@
cumbrian-cottages.co.uk
I: www.cumbrian-cottages.co.uk

**Stoneleigh
Rating Applied For**
Contact: Mr D Hogarth,
Cumbrian Cottages, 7 The
Crescent, Carlisle, CA1 1QW
T: (01228) 599960 & 599950
F: (01228) 599970
E: enquiries@
cumbrian-cottages.co.uk
I: www.cumbrian-cottages.co.uk

Sundial Cottage ★★★
Contact: Mr & Mrs M McKinley,
Sundial Cottage, Galesyke,
Wasdale, Seascale, Cumbria
CA20 1ET
T: (01946) 726225

Woodhow Farm ★★
Contact: Mr D J Kaminski, The
Squirrels, 55 Broadway, Cheadle,
Cheshire SK8 1LB
T: (0161) 428 9116
F: (0161) 428 9116
E: woodhow_farm@kaminsk.
fsnet.co.uk

Yewtree Farm ★★★-★★★★
Contact: Mrs Pauline Corley,
Yewtree Farm, Wasdale,
Seascale, Cumbria CA20 1EU
T: (019467) 26285
E: pauline@corleyp.freeserve.
co.uk

WATERHEAD
Cumbria

Betamere ★★★★
Contact: Mrs Susan Jackson,
Heart of the Lakes, Fisherbeck
Mill, Old Lake Road, Ambleside,
Cumbria LA22 0DH
T: (015394) 32321
F: (015394) 33251
E: info@heartofthelakes.co.uk
I: www.heartofthelakes.co.uk

Brathay Wyke ★★★
Contact: Mrs Susan Jackson,
Heart of the Lakes, Fisherbeck
Mill, Old Lake Road, Ambleside,
Cumbria LA22 0DH
T: (015394) 32321
F: (015394) 33251
E: info@heartofthelakes.co.uk
I: www.heartofthelakes.co.uk

Claife Heights ★★★
Contact: Mrs Susan Jackson,
Heart of the Lakes, Fisherbeck
Hill, Old Lake Road, Ambleside,
Cumbria LA22 0DH
T: (015394) 32321
F: (015394) 33251
E: info@heartofthelakes.co.uk
I: www.heartofthelakes.co.uk

High Borrans ★★★★
Contact: Mrs S Jackson, Heart of
the Lakes, Fisherbeck Mill, Old
Lake Road, Ambleside, Cumbria
LA22 0DH
T: (015394) 32321
F: (015394) 33251
E: info@heartofthelakes.co.uk
I: www.heartofthelakes.co.uk

Establishments printed in blue have a detailed entry in this guide

Jenkins Crag ★★★★★
Contact: Mrs Susan Jackson,
Heart of the Lakes, Fisherbeck
Hill, Old Lake Road, Ambleside,
Cumbria LA22 0DH
T: (015394) 32321
F: (015394) 33251
E: info@heartofthelakes.co.uk
I: www.heartofthelakes.co.uk

Latterbarrow ★★★★★
Contact: Mrs Susan Jackson,
Heart of the Lakes, Fisherbeck
Hill, Old Lake Road, Ambleside,
Cumbria LA22 0DH
T: (015394) 32321
F: (015394) 33251
E: info@heartofthelakes.co.uk
I: www.heartofthelakes.co.uk

Romney Grange ★★★★★
Contact: Mrs Susan Jackson,
Heart of the Lakes, Fisherbeck
Hill, Old Lake Road, Ambleside,
Cumbria LA22 0DH
T: (015394) 32321
F: (015394) 33251
E: info@heartofthelakes.co.uk
I: www.heartofthelakes.co.uk

Skelghyll ★★★★
Contact: Mrs Susan Jackson,
Heart of the Lakes, Fisherbeck
Mill, Old Lake Road, Ambleside,
Cumbria LA22 0DH
T: (015394) 32321
F: (015394) 33251
E: info@heartofthelakes.co.uk
I: www.heartofthelakes.co.uk

WATERMILLOCK
Cumbria

Beauthorn Cottage ★★★
Contact: Mr Martin Wardle,
Lakes and Valleys, North Lodge,
Longtail Hill, Bowness-on-
Windermere, Windermere,
Cumbria LA23 3JD
T: (015394) 88612
F: (015394) 48988
E: lakesandvalleys@aol.com
I: www.lakesandvalleys.co.uk

Fair Place Cottage ★★★
Contact: CH Ref:11224, 13649,
Spring Mill, Earby, Barnoldswick,
Lancashire BB94 0AA
T: 08700 723723
F: (01282) 844288
I: www.country-holidays.co.uk

Middlegate ★★★
Contact: Mrs Susan Jackson,
Heart of the Lakes, Fisherbeck
Hill, Old Lake Road, Ambleside,
Cumbria LA22 0DH
T: (015394) 32321
F: (015394) 33251
E: info@heartofthelakes.co.uk
I: www.heartofthelakes.co.uk

WESTNEWTON
Cumbria

Home Farm Cottage ★★★★
Contact: Mr Martin King, Home
Farmhouse, Westnewton,
Wigton CA7 3NX
T: (016973) 22480
E: martin@homefarmhouse.
freeserve.co.uk
I: www.homefarmhouse.
freeserve.co.uk

WESTWARD
Cumbria

High Hall Cottage ★★★★
Contact: Mrs J Thompson, High
Hall, Westward, Wigton,
Cumbria CA7 8NQ
T: (016973) 42584

WETHERAL
Cumbria

Geltsdale ★★★★★
Contact: Mr D Hogarth,
Cumbrian Cottages, 7 The
Crescent, Carlisle, CA1 1QW
T: (01228) 599960
F: (01228) 599970
E: enquiries@
cumbrian-cottages.co.uk
I: www.cumbrian-cottages.co.uk

Sarah's Cottage ★★★★★
Contact: Mr D Hogarth,
Cumbrian Cottages, 7 The
Crescent, Carlisle, CA1 1QW
T: (01228) 599960 & 599950
F: (01228) 599970
E: enquiries@
cumbrian-cottages.co.uk
I: www.cumbrian-cottages.co.uk

WHARTON
Cumbria

Moor End Farm ★★★
Contact: Mrs J Lane, Absolute
Escapes, Orchard Farm House,
Lynn Road, Gayton, King's Lynn,
Norfolk PE32 1PA
T: 07553 636989
F: 07553 636989
E: janelane@absolute-escapes.
co.uk
I: www.absolute-escapes.co.uk

WHITE MOSS
Cumbria

Ladywood Lodge ★★
Contact: Mrs Susan Jackson,
Heart of the Lakes, Fisherbeck
Mill, Old Lake Road, Ambleside,
Cumbria LA22 0DH
T: (015394) 32321
F: (015394) 33251
E: info@heartofthelakes.co.uk
I: www.heartofthelakes.co.uk

WHITEHAVEN
Cumbria

**Hunting How Farmhouse
★★★**
Contact: J Messenger, Adamgill
Farm, Moresby, Whitehaven,
Cumbria CA28 6SF
T: (01946) 693662
E: jmessenger.adamgill@
farmersweekly.net

**Swallows Return and Owls
Retreat ★★★**
Contact: Mr and Mrs James
Moore, Swallows Return and
Owls Retreat, Moresby Hall
Cottage, Moresby, Whitehaven,
Cumbria CA28 6PJ
T: (01946) 64078
I: www.cottageguide.
co.uk/moresby

WIGTON
Cumbria

The Barn ★★★★
Contact: Mr & Mrs R Hill,
Highside, Parton, Wigton,
Cumbria CA7 0HE
T: (016973) 42938
F: (016973) 42938

Foxgloves ★★★★
Contact: Mr and Mrs E Kerr,
Greenrigg Farm, Westward,
Wigton, Cumbria CA7 8AH
T: (016973) 42676

WINDERMERE
Cumbria

Abbey Coach House ★★★
Contact: Mrs P Bell, Abbey
Coach House, St Mary's Park,
Windermere, Cumbria LA23 1AZ
T: (015394) 44027
F: (015394) 44027
E: abbeycoach@aol.com

Above Cot ★★★★
Contact: Mr D Hogarth,
Cumbrian Cottages, 7 The
Crescent, Carlisle, CA1 1QW
T: (01228) 599960 & 599950
F: (01228) 599970
E: enquiries@
cumbrian-cottages.co.uk
I: www.cumbrian-cottages.co.uk

Annisgarth ★★★
Contact: Mr D Hogarth,
Cumbrian Cottages, 7 The
Crescent, Carlisle, CA1 1QW
T: (01228) 599960 & 599950
F: (01228) 599970
E: enquiries@
cumbrian-cottages.co.uk
I: www.cumbrian-cottages.co.uk

Bank Cottage ★★★★
Contact: Captain and Mrs
Beighton, The Gables, 180
Singlewell Road, Gravesend,
Kent DA11 7RB
T: (01474) 533028

Beaumont ★★★★
Contact: Mr & Mrs Robert
Theobald, Beaumont,
Thornbarrow Road, Windermere,
Cumbria LA23 2DG
T: (015394) 45521
F: (015394) 46267
E: etc@beaumont-holidays.
co.uk
I: beaumont-holidays.co.uk

Belmont ★★★
Contact: Mrs Susan Jackson,
Heart of the Lakes, Fisherbeck
Hill, Old Lake Road, Ambleside,
Cumbria LA22 0DH
T: (015394) 32321
F: (015394) 33251
E: info@heartofthelakes.co.uk
I: www.heartofthelakes.co.uk

Birch Cottage ★★★
Contact: Mr Roland Brown, 35
Portland Road, Leeds, West
Yorkshire LS12 4LT
T: (0113) 263 4260 &
07803 583267
F: (0113) 263 4260
E: roland.brown@virgin.net
I: www.birchcottagewindermere.
freeserve.co.uk

Birthwaite Edge ★★★
Contact: Mr Bruce Dodsworth,
Birthwaite Edge, Birthwaite
Edge, Birthwaite Road,
Windermere, Cumbria LA23 1BS
T: (015394) 42861
E: etc@lakedge.com
I: www.lakedge.com

**6 Biskey Howe Park
Rating Applied For**
Contact: Mr P Liddell, Lakelovers,
The New Toffee Loft, Kendal
Road, Windermere, Cumbria
LA23 3RA
T: (015394) 88855
F: (015394) 88857
E: bookings@lakelovers.co.uk
I: www.lakelovers.co.uk

4 Brantfell Cottages ★★★
Contact: Mr D Hogarth,
Cumbrian Cottages, 7 The
Crescent, Carlisle, CA1 1QW
T: (01228) 599960 & 599950
F: (01228) 599970
E: enquiries@
cumbrian-cottages.co.uk
I: www.cumbrian-cottages.co.uk

Brent Cottage ★★★★
Contact: Mr Paul Liddell,
Lakelovers, The New Toffee Loft,
Kendal Road, Windermere,
Cumbria LA23 3RA
T: (015394) 88855
F: (015394) 88857
E: bookings@lakelovers.co.uk
I: www.lakelovers.co.uk

Briscoe Lodge ★★★
Contact: Mrs M A Cook, Briscoe
Lodge, Ellerthwaite Road,
Windermere, Cumbria LA23 2AH
T: (015394) 42928

Burnside Park ★★★★
Contact: Mrs Candy Philip,
Burnside Park, The Lodge,
Bowness-on-Windermere,
Windermere, Cumbria LA23 3EW
T: (015394) 46624 & 44530
F: (015394) 47754
E: cottages@burnsidehotel.com
I: www.burnsidehotel.com

Calgarth ★★★
Contact: Mr D Hogarth,
Cumbrian Cottages, 7 The
Crescent, Carlisle, CA1 1QW
T: (01228) 599960 & 599950
F: (01228) 599970
E: enquiries@
cumbrian-cottages.co.uk
I: www.cumbrian-cottages.co.uk

Canterbury Flats ★★★
Contact: Mr & Mrs M&I Zuniga,
Bowness Holidays, 131 Radcliffe
New Road, Whitefield,
Manchester M45 7RP
T: (0161) 796 3896
F: (0161) 796 1621

Caxton Nook ★★★
Contact: Mr D Hogarth,
Cumbrian Cottages, 7 The
Crescent, Carlisle, CA1 1QW
T: (01228) 599960 & 599950
F: (01228) 599970
E: enquiries@
cumbrian-cottages.co.uk
I: www.cumbrian-cottages.co.uk

Claife Heights Flat ★★★
Contact: Mr and Mrs Ray &
Barbara Hood, The Fairfield,
Brantfell Road, Bowness-on-
Windermere, Windermere,
Cumbria LA23 3AE
T: (015394) 46565
F: (015394) 46565
E: Ray&barb@the-fairfield.co.uk
I: www.the-fairfield.co.uk

Claife View ★★★
Contact: Mr D Hogarth,
Cumbrian Cottages, 7 The
Crescent, Carlisle, CA1 1QW
T: (01228) 599960 & 599950
F: (01228) 599970
E: enquiries@
cumbrian-cottages.co.uk
I: www.cumbrian-cottages.co.uk

Clara's Cottage ★★★
Contact: Mr D Hogarth,
Cumbrian Cottages, 7 The
Crescent, Carlisle, CA1 1QW
T: (01228) 599960 & 599950
F: (01228) 599970
E: enquiries@
cumbrian-cottages.co.uk
I: www.cumbrian-cottages.co.uk

Claremont ★★★
Contact: Mrs Susan Jackson,
Heart of the Lakes, Fisherbeck
Hill, Old Lake Road, Ambleside,
Cumbria LA22 0DH
T: (015394) 32321
F: (015394) 33251
E: info@heartofthelakes.co.uk
I: www.heartofthelakes.co.uk

3 College Court ★★★
Contact: Mr Paul Liddell,
Lakelovers, The New Toffee Loft,
Kendal Road, Windermere,
Cumbria LA23 3RA
T: (015394) 88855
F: (015394) 88857
E: bookings@lakelovers.co.uk
I: www.lakelovers.co.uk

4 College Court ★★★
Contact: Mr Paul Liddell,
Lakelovers, The New Toffee Loft,
Kendal Road, Windermere,
Cumbria LA23 3RA
T: (015394) 88855
F: (015394) 88857
E: bookings@lakelovers.co.uk
I: www.lakelovers.co.uk

5 College Gate ★★★
Contact: Mr Paul Liddell,
Lakelovers, The New Toffee Loft,
Kendal Road, Windermere,
Cumbria LA23 3RA
T: (015394) 88855
F: (015394) 88857
E: bookings@lakelovers.co.uk
I: www.lakelovers.co.uk

Coppice View ★★★★
Contact: Mr D Hogarth,
Cumbrian Cottages, 7 The
Crescent, Carlisle, CA1 1QW
T: (01228) 599960 & 599950
F: (01228) 599970
E: enquiries@
cumbrian-cottages.co.uk
I: www.cumbrian-cottages.co.uk

1 The Court ★★★★
Contact: Mrs Rosalind
Hutchison, 11 Mount Charles
Crescent, Alloway, Ayr, Ayrshire
KA7 4NY
T: (01292) 443979
F: (01292) 443979
E: rosiehutchison@aol.com

Craigside ★★★★
Contact: Mr Paul Liddell,
Lakelovers, The New Toffee Loft,
Kendal Road, Windermere,
Cumbria LA23 3RA
T: (015394) 88855
F: (015394) 88857
E: bookings@lakelovers.co.uk
I: www.lakelovers.co.uk

Cross Cottage ★★★
Contact: Mr D Hogarth,
Cumbrian Cottages, 7 The
Crescent, Carlisle, CA1 1QW
T: (01228) 599960 & 599950
F: (01228) 599970
E: enquiries@
cumbrian-cottages.co.uk
I: www.cumbrian-cottages.co.uk

8 Denewood ★★★
Contact: Mr Paul Liddell,
Lakelovers, The New Toffee Loft,
Kendal Road, Windermere,
Cumbria LA23 3RA
T: (015394) 88855
F: (015394) 88857
E: bookings@lakelovers.co.uk
I: www.lakelovers.co.uk

Four Winds ★★★★
Contact: Mrs B N Monks, Four
Winds, Victoria Road,
Windermere, Cumbria LA23 2DP
T: (015394) 43612
E: brigid@fourwind.demon.
co.uk

Gavel Cottage ★★★★
Contact: Screetons,
25 Bridgegate, Howden, Goole,
East Yorskhire DN14 7AA
T: (01430) 431201
F: (01430) 432114
E: howden@screetons.co.uk
I: screetons.co.uk

Gildabrook Cottage ★★★★
Contact: Mr Paul Liddell,
Lakelovers, The New Toffee Loft,
Kendal Road, Windermere,
Cumbria LA23 3RA
T: (015394) 88855
F: (015394) 88857
E: bookings@lakelovers.co.uk
I: www.lakelovers.co.uk

Greystones ★★★
Contact: Mr D Hogarth,
Cumbrian Cottages, 7 The
Crescent, Carlisle, CA1 1QW
T: (01228) 599960 & 599950
F: (01228) 599970
E: enquiries@
cumbrian-cottages.co.uk
I: www.cumbrian-cottages.cu.uk

The Heaning ★★★
Contact: Mrs Moulding, The
Heaning, Heaning Lane,
Windermere, Cumbria LA23 1JW
T: (015394) 43453
F: (015394) 43453
E: info@theheaning.co.uk
I: www.theheaning.co.uk

Helm Farm ★★★
Contact: Mrs M McGill, Matson
Ground Estate Co Ltd, 3
Lambrigg Terrace, Kendal,
Cumbria LA9 4BB
T: (01539) 726995 & 794191
F: (01539) 741611
E: matsong@compuserve.com
I: www.matsonground.co.uk

5 Helm Rigg ★★★
Contact: Mr Paul Liddell,
Lakelovers, The New Toffee Loft,
Kendal Road, Windermere,
Cumbria LA23 3RA
T: (015394) 88855
F: (015394) 88857
E: bookings@lakelovers.co.uk
I: www.lakelovers.co.uk

Hilltop ★★★★
Contact: Mr D Hogarth,
Cumbrian Cottages, 7 The
Crescent, Carlisle, CA1 1QW
T: (01228) 599960 & 599950
F: (01228) 599970
E: enquiries@
cumbrian-cottages.co.uk
I: www.cumbrian-cottages.co.uk

Hodge Howe ★★★★★
Contact: Mrs Susan Jackson,
Heart of the Lakes, Fisherbeck
Mill, Old Lake Road, Ambleside,
Cumbria LA22 0DH
T: (015394) 32321
F: (015394) 33251
E: info@heartofthelakes.co.uk
I: www.heartofthelakes.co.uk

Hunters Moon ★★★★
Contact: Mr Paul Liddell,
Lakelovers, The New Toffee Loft,
Kendal Road, Windermere,
Cumbria LA23 3RA
T: (015394) 88855
F: (015394) 88857
E: bookings@lakelovers.co.uk
I: www.lakelovers.co.uk

Ivy Cottage ★★
Contact: Mr Paul Liddell,
Lakelovers, The New Toffee Loft,
Kendal Road, Windermere,
Cumbria LA23 3RA
T: (015394) 88855
F: (015394) 88857
E: bookings@lakelovers.co.uk
I: www.lakelovers.co.uk

Lakeside Lodge ★★★★
Contact: Ms Jennifer Denison,
Lakeside Lodge, Newby Bridge,
Ulverston, Cumbria LA12 8AT
T: (015395) 30001
F: (015395) 31699
E: sales@lakesidehotel.co.uk
I: www.lakesidehotel.co.uk

Lakeview ★★★
Contact: Mr D Hogarth,
Cumbrian Cottages, 7 The
Crescent, Carlisle, CA1 1QW
T: (01228) 599960
F: (01228) 599970
E: enquiries@
cumbrian-cottages.co.uk
I: www.cumbrian-cottages.co.uk

Langdale View Holiday
Apartments ★★★
Contact: Mrs Janice Fletcher,
Langdale View Holiday
Apartments, 112 Craig Walk,
Bowness-on-Windermere,
Windermere, Cumbria LA23 3AX
T: (015394) 46655
E: anything@langdale-view.
co.uk
I: www.langdale-view.co.uk

7 Langrigge Park ★★
Contact: Mr Paul Liddell,
Lakelovers, The New Toffee Loft,
Kendal Road, Windermere,
Cumbria LA23 3RA
T: (015394) 88855
F: (015394) 88857
E: bookings@lakelovers.co.uk
I: www.lakelovers.co.uk

Low Fell Cottage ★★★
Contact: Mr D Hogarth,
Cumbrian Cottages, 7 The
Crescent, Carlisle, CA1 1QW
T: (01228) 599960 & 599950
F: (01228) 599970
E: enquiries@
cumbrian-cottages.co.uk
I: www.cumbrian-cottages.co.uk

Lowther Cottage ★★★★
Contact: Mr and Mrs Derek
Sweeney, Lakeland Traditional
Inns and Cottages, Kings Head
Hotel, Thirlspot, Keswick,
Cumbria CA12 4TN
T: 0500 600725 &
(017687) 72393
F: (017687) 72309
E: lowther@lakelandsheart.
demon.co.uk
I: www.lakelandsheart.demon.
co.uk

Meadows End ★★★
Contact: Mr D Hogarth,
Cumbrian Cottages, 7 The
Crescent, Carlisle, CA1 1QW
T: (01228) 599960
F: (01228) 599970
E: enquiries@
cumbrian-cottages.co.uk
I: www.cumbrian-cottages.co.uk

Oak Terrace Cottage ★★
Contact: Mr D Hogarth,
Cumbrian Cottages, 7 The
Crescent, Carlisle, CA1 1QW
T: (01228) 599960
F: (01228) 599970
E: enquiries@
cumbrian-cottages.co.uk
I: www.cumbrian-cottages.co.uk

Oakdene ★★★
Contact: Country Holidays
ref:12088, Spring Mill, Earby,
Barnoldswick, Lancashire
BB94 0AA
T: 08700 723723
F: (01282) 844288
E: sales@ttgihg.co.uk
I: www.country-holidays.co.uk

Oakdene ★★★★
Contact: Mr D Hogarth,
Cumbrian Cottages, 7 The
Crescent, Carlisle, CA1 1QW
T: (01228) 599960 & 599950
F: (01228) 599970
E: enquiries@
cumbrian-cottages.co.uk
I: www.cumbrian-cottages.co.uk

Old Oak Cottage
Rating Applied For
Contact: Mr Paul Liddell,
Lakelovers, The New Toffee Loft,
Kendal Road, Windermere,
Cumbria LA23 3RA
T: (015394) 88855
F: (015394) 88857
E: bookings@lakelovers.co.uk
I: www.lakelovers.co.uk

Establishments printed in blue have a detailed entry in this guide

Olde Coach House and Stables ★★★
Contact: Mr & Mrs Alan & Margaret Wardle, North Lodge, Longtail Hill, Bowness-on-Windermere, Windermere, Cumbria LA23 3JD
T: (015394) 47905 & 88612
F: (015394) 48988
I: www.lakeland-holidays.net

Orchard Fold ★★★
Contact: Mr D Hogarth, Cumbrian Cottages, 7 The Crescent, Carlisle, CA1 1QW
T: (01228) 599960 & 599950
F: (01228) 599970
E: enquiries@cumbrian-cottages.co.uk
I: www.cumbrian-cottages.co.uk

Penny Place ★★★
Contact: Mr Paul Liddell, Lakelovers, The New Toffee Loft, Kendal Road, Windermere, Cumbria LA23 3RA
T: (015394) 88855
F: (015394) 88857
E: bookings@lakelovers.co.uk
I: www.lakelovers.co.uk

Pine Lodge
Rating Applied For
Contact: Mr Paul Liddell, Lakelovers, The New Toffee Loft, Kendal Road, Windermere, Cumbria LA23 3RA
T: (015394) 88855
F: (015394) 88857
E: bookings@lakelovers.co.uk
I: www.lakelovers.co.uk

Pinethwaite Holiday Cottages ★★★
Contact: Mr P A Legge, Pinethwaite Holiday Cottages, Lickbarrow Road, Windermere, Cumbria LA23 2NQ
T: (015394) 44558
F: (015394) 44556
E: legge@pinethwaite.freeserve.co.uk
I: www.pinecottages.co.uk

Pipers Howe ★★★★
Contact: Mr Paul Liddell, Lakelovers, The New Toffee Loft, Kendal Road, Windermere, Cumbria LA23 3RA
T: (015394) 88855
F: (015394) 88857
E: bookings@lakelovers.co.uk
I: www.lakelovers.co.uk

Post Masters House ★★★★
Contact: Mr D Hogarth, Cumbrian Cottages, 7 The Crescent, Carlisle, CA1 1QW
T: (01228) 599960 & 599950
F: (01228) 599970
E: enquiries@cumbrian-cottages.co.uk
I: www.cumbrian-cottages.co.uk

Priory Coach House ★★★★
Contact: Mr Paul Liddell, Lakelovers, The New Toffee Loft, Kendal Road, Windermere, Cumbria LA23 3RA
T: (015394) 88855
F: (015394) 88857
E: bookings@lakelovers.co.uk
I: www.lakelovers.co.uk

Priory Lodge ★★★★
Contact: Mr D Hogarth, Cumbrian Cottages, 7 The Crescent, Carlisle, CA1 1QW
T: (01228) 599960
F: (01228) 599970
E: enquiries@cumbrian-cottages.co.uk
I: www.cumbrian-cottages.co.uk

Rayriggs ★★★★
Contact: Mr Paul Liddell, Lakelovers, The New Toffee Loft, Kendal Road, Bowness-on-Windermere, Windermere, Cumbria LA23 3RA
T: (015394) 88855
F: (015394) 88857
E: bookings@lakelovers.co.uk
I: www.lakelovers.co.uk

Rose Cottage ★★★★
Contact: Mr D Hogarth, Cumbrian Cottages, 7 The Crescent, Carlisle, CA1 1QW
T: (01228) 599960
F: (01228) 599970
E: enquiries@cumbrian-cottages.co.uk
I: www.cumbrian-cottages.co.uk

Rose Cottage ★★★★
Contact: Mr Paul Liddell, Lakelovers, The New Toffee Loft, Kendal Road, Bowness-on-Windermere, Windermere, Cumbria LA23 3RA
T: (015394) 88855
F: (015394) 88857
E: bookings@lakelovers.co.uk
I: www.lakelovers.co.uk

Spinnery Cottage Holiday Apartments ★★★
Contact: Mr Ray Hood, Spinnery Cottage Holiday Apartments, Brantfell Road, Bowness-on-Windermere, Windermere, Cumbria LA23 3AE
T: (015394) 44884
F: (015394) 46565
E: Ray&barb@the-fairfield.co.uk
I: www.the-fairfield.co.uk

Springfield Cottage ★★★
Contact: Mr D Hogarth, Cumbrian Cottages, 7 The Crescent, Carlisle, CA1 1QW
T: (01228) 599960 & 599950
F: (01228) 599970
E: enquiries@cumbrian-cottages.co.uk
I: www.cumbrian-cottages.co.uk

Storrs Hall ★★★
Contact: Mr D Hogarth, Cumbrian Cottages, 7 The Crescent, Carlisle, CA1 1QW
T: (01228) 599960 & 599950
F: (01228) 599970
E: enquiries@cumbrian-cottages.co.uk
I: www.cumbrian-cottages.co.uk

Sunny Bec ★★★★
Contact: Mr D Hogarth, Cumbrian Cottages, 7 The Crescent, Carlisle, CA1 1QW
T: (01228) 599960 & 599950
F: (01228) 599970
E: enquiries@cumbrian-cottages.co.uk
I: www.cumbrian-cottages.co.uk

Sunnybank House ★★★
Contact: Sunnybank House, Sunnybank Road, Windermere, Cumbria LA23 2BP

Treetops ★★★★
Contact: Mr & Mrs J S Alcock, 6 Ghyllside, Ambleside, Cumbria LA22 0QU
T: (015394) 32819
E: pat.john@lakedistrictcumbria.co.uk
I: www.lakedistrictcumbria.co.uk

24 Victoria Terrace ★★
Contact: Mrs E Lishman, 22 Victoria Terrace, Windermere, Cumbria LA23 1AB
T: (015394) 42982

The Wendy House ★★★
Contact: Mr Paul Liddell, Lakelovers, The New Toffee Loft, Kendal Road, Windermere, Cumbria LA23 3RA
T: (015394) 88855
F: (015394) 88857
E: bookings@lakelovers.co.uk
I: www.lakelovers.co.uk

White Moss ★★★★
Contact: Mrs Susan Jackson, Heart of the Lakes, Fisherbeck Hill, Old Lake Road, Ambleside, Cumbria LA22 0DH
T: (015394) 32321
F: (015394) 33251
E: info@heartofthelakes.co.uk
I: www.heartofthelakes.co.uk

Windermere Marina Village ★★★★
Contact: Ms Pam Harvey, Windermere Marina Village, Bowness-on-Windermere, Windermere, Cumbria LA23 3JQ
T: (015394) 46551 & 0800 917 4611
F: (015394) 43233
E: info@wmv.co.uk
I: www.wmv.co.uk

Winster House ★★★
Contact: Mrs S Jump, Winster House, Sunnybank Road, Windermere, Cumbria LA23 2EN
T: (015394) 44723

Yewdale Holiday Apartments 'The Old Picture House' ★★★
Contact: Mrs M Elwell, Skelcies Cottage, Nook Lane, Crosthwaite, Windermere, Cumbria LA8 8HX
T: (015395) 68745
F: (015395) 68272
E: yewdaleholidayapartments@hotmail.com

WINTON
Cumbria

Manor House ★★★★
Contact: Mr D Hogarth, Cumbrian Cottages, 7 The Crescent, Carlisle, CA1 1QW
T: (01228) 599960 & 599950
F: (01228) 599970
E: enquiries@cumbrian-cottages.co.uk
I: www.cumbrian-cottages.co.uk

WITHERSLACK
Cumbria

Dyer Dene ★★★
Contact: Mrs S Andrews, 121 Dorchester Road, Garstang, Preston, Lancashire PR3 1FE
T: (01995) 602769
E: dyerdene@supanet.com

Fern Lea Rose Mount Mole End Ingle Nook Primrose Cottage Delph Cottage ★★
Contact: CH ref:11182-11184,4970,4971, Spring Mill, Earby, Barnoldswick, Lancashire BB94 0AA
T: (01282) 445096
F: (01282) 844288
E: sales@ttgihg.co.uk
I: www.country-holidays.co.uk

The Old Coachhouse ★★★★
Contact: Mr John Serginson, The Lakeland Cottage Company, Waterside House, Newby Bridge, Ulverston, Cumbria LA12 8AN
T: (015395) 30024
F: (015395) 31932
E: john@lakeland-cottage-company.co.uk
I: www.lakeland-cottage-company.co.uk

Spa Inn House ★★★★
Contact: Mr D Hogarth, Cumbrian Cottages, 7 The Crescent, Carlisle, CA1 1QW
T: (01228) 599960 & 599950
F: (01228) 599970
E: enquiries@cumbrian-cottages.co.uk
I: www.cumbrian-cottages.co.uk

Thornbarrow Hill Cottage ★★★
Contact: Mr John Serginson, The Lakeland Cottage Company, Waterside House, Newby Bridge, Ulverston, Cumbria LA12 8AN
T: (015395) 30024
F: (015395) 31932
E: john@lakeland-cottage-company.co.uk
I: www.lakeland-cottage-company.co.uk

YANWATH
Cumbria

Copper Beech Cottage ★★★★
Contact: S M Beattie, 2 Barnside, Glendowlin Park, Yanwath, Penrith, Cumbria CA10 2LA
T: (01768) 892855

ACKLINGTON
Northumberland

Morwick Farm Cottage ★★
Contact: Sykes Cottages
Ref:642, Sykes Cottages, York
House, York Street, Chester,
Cheshire CH1 3LR
T: (01244) 345700
F: (01244) 321442
E: info@sykescottages.co.uk
I: www.sykescottages.co.uk

ALLENDALE
Northumberland

2 Allen Mill Cottages ★★★★
Contact: Ms Jan Simmonds, 2
Wooley Burnfoot, Allendale,
Hexham, Northumberland
NE47 9NE
T: (01434) 683019
F: (0191) 281 5655
E: jsimmonds@tinyworld.co.uk
I: digilander.iol.it/rdowen

Low Huntwell Cottage ★★
Contact: Mr R P Ridley, Low
Huntwell Farm, Sparty Lea,
Hexham, Northumberland
NE47 9UL
T: (01434) 685 223
E: robertridley@hotmail.com

**Station House Caravan Park
★★**
Contact: Mrs A G Dodsworth,
Station House Caravan Park,
Catton, Hexham,
Northumberland NE47 9QF
T: (01434) 683362

ALLENHEADS
Northumberland

Englewood ★★★
Contact: Sykes Cottages
Ref:291, Sykes Cottages, York
House, York Street, Chester,
Cheshire CH1 3LR
T: (01244) 345700
F: (01244) 321442
E: info@sykescottages.co.uk
I: www.sykescottages.co.uk

ALNMOUTH
Northumberland

Bilton Barns ★★★★
Contact: Mrs D Jackson, Bilton
Barns, Alnmouth, Alnwick,
Northumberland NE66 2TB
T: (01665) 830427

Cuthbert's Landing ★★★
Contact: Mr Joan Davidson,
Blue Dolpins, 11 Riverside Road,
Alnmouth, Alnwick,
Northumberland NE66 2SD
T: (01665) 830893
E: jackandjoan@hotmail.com

**Grange Cottages
★★★-★★★★**
Contact: Mr & Mrs Jennifer &
Peter Cossins, The Grange, 20
Northumberland Street,
Alnmouth, Alnwick,
Northumberland NE66 2RJ
T: (01665) 830401
F: (01665) 830401
E: thegrange.alnmouth@virgin.
net

**The Old Stables, High Buston
Hall ★★★★**
Contact: Mr Edwards, The
Stables, High Buston Hall, High
Buston, Alnmouth, Alnwick,
Northumberland NE66 3QH
T: (01665) 830341
I: www.
holiday-cottages-
northumberland.com

Prospect House ★★★
Contact: Mrs A Yeadon, 2
Prospect Place, Alnmouth,
Alnwick, Northumberland
NE66 2RL
T: (01665) 830649
E: prospect.holidays@talk21.
com
I: www.cottageguide.
co.uk/alnmouth

Quality Self Catering ★★★★
Contact: Mrs Vicki Taylor, Letton
Lodge, Alnmouth, Alnwick,
Northumberland NE66 2RJ
T: (01665) 830633
F: (01665) 830122
E: LettonLodge@aol.com
I: www.almouth.co.uk

Riverdale ★★★
Contact: Mrs D Spark, 6 Peep O'
Sea, Howick, Alnwick,
Northumberland NE66 3LD
T: (01665) 577261 & 577285
F: (01665) 577285
E: spark@holidays.
northumberland.fsbusiness.
co.uk

Sunnyside Cottage ★★★★
Contact: Mrs Mary Hollins,
Longridge, Longridge Road,
Blaydon-on-Tyne, Tyne and
Wear NE21 6JW
T: (0191) 413 1331
F: (0191) 413 1331
E: sunnysidecott@lineone.net

**Wooden Farm Holiday
Cottages ★★**
Contact: Mr W G Farr, Wooden
Farm Holiday Cottages, Wooden
Farm, Lesbury, Alnwick,
Northumberland NE66 2TW
T: (01665) 830342

ALNWICK
Northumberland

**Bog Mill Farm Holiday
Cottages ★★★★**
Contact: Mrs A M Mason, Bog
Mill Farm, Alnwick,
Northumberland NE66 3PA
T: (01665) 604529
F: (01665) 606972

The Bui ★★★
Contact: Ms Diana Norris,
Cosaig, Glenelg, Kyle of
Lochalsh, Ross-shire IV40 8LB
T: (01599) 522365
F: (01599) 522365
E: diana_norris@hotmail.com

**Cheviot View and Dipper
Cottage ★★★-★★★★**
Contact: CH ref:13062, N625,
Spring Mill, Earby, Barnoldswick,
Lancashire BB94 0AA
T: 08700 723723
F: (01282) 844288
E: sales@ttgihg.co.uk
I: www.country-holidays.co.uk

**1 Dene View Cottage and 2
Moor Croft Cottage ★★★★**
Contact: Mrs M E McGregor,
Broome Hill Farm, Alnwick,
Northumberland NE66 2BA
T: (01665) 574460
F: (01665) 574460

Farm Cottage ★★★
Contact: Mrs J A Renner,
Farmhouse, Shipley Hill, Alnwick,
Northumberland NE66 2LX
T: (01665) 579266

Garden Cottages ★★★★
Contact: Mrs A J Hardisty,
Garden Cottages, Lemmington
Hall, Alnwick, Northumberland
NE66 2BH
T: (01665) 574129
F: (01665) 574129

Green Batt Cottages ★★★
Contact: Dr Emma Wady, Green
Batt House, The Pinfold, Alnwick,
Northumberland NE66 1TY
T: (01665) 602429
F: (01665) 602429
E: wadyone@cs.com
I: www.cottageguide.
co.uk/greenbatt

Green Batt Studio ★★★
Contact: Mr David Surtees,
David Surtees & Associates, 146
Whitley Road, Whitley Bay, Tyne
and Wear NE25 2NA
T: (0191) 253 3714 & 258 5286
F: (0191) 251 0614
E: davidsurtees@msn.com
I: www.
northumberlandcottageholidays.
co.uk

**Henhill and Birchwood Hall
Cottages★★★-★★★★**
Contact: Mrs Jane Mallen,
Northumberland Estates,
Alnwick Castle, Alnwick,
Northumberland NE66 1NQ
T: (01665) 602094 &
07774 606123
F: (01665) 608126
E: nehc@farmline.com
I: www.alnwickcastle.
com/holidaycottages/

1 Howick Street ★★★
Contact: Mr Thomas Payton,
Austrey House, 3 Grosvenor
Terrace, Alnwick,
Northumberland NE66 1LG
T: (01665) 510484
F: 0870 163 7533
E: tompayton@totalise.co.uk
I: www.howickhols.fsnet.co.uk

Limpet Cottage ★★★
Contact: Mrs Jane Mallen,
Northumberland Estates,
Alnwick Castle, Alnwick,
Northumberland NE66 1NQ
T: (01665) 602094 &
07774 606123
F: (01665) 608126
E: nehc@farmline.com
I: www.alnwickcastle.
com/holidaycottages/

Market Townhouse ★★★
Contact: Mrs P Straughan, 8
Walkergate, Alnwick,
Northumberland NE66 1NB
T: (01665) 605017
E: pamstraughan@tinyworld.
co.uk

The Rocket House ★★
Contact: Mrs J Walwyn-James,
Oakland House, Moorfield, High
West Jesmond, Newcastle upon
Tyne, NE2 3NL
T: (0191) 213 1507
F: (0191) 213 1507

Sawmill Cottage ★★★
Contact: Ms Alison Wrangham,
Harehope Hall, Eglingham,
Alnwick, Northumberland
NE66 2DP
T: (01668) 217329 & 217129
F: (01668) 217346
E: ali.wrangham@farming.co.uk

**Stamford & Embleton Mill
Farm Cottages★★★★**
Contact: Mrs H G Grahamslaw,
The Farmhouse, Gallowmoor,
Rock, Alnwick, Northumberland
NE66 3SB
T: (01665) 579425
F: (01665) 579425

Thorn Rigg ★★★★
Contact: Country Holidays
ref:12730, Spring Mill, Earby,
Barnoldswick, Lancashire
BB18 6RN
T: 08700 723723
F: (01282) 844288
I: www.country-holidays.co.uk

Tidal Watch ★★★★
Contact: Mr K Bremner, Tidal
Watch, 19 Lesbury Road,
Lesbury, Alnwick,
Northumberland NE66 3NB
T: 07947 624160 &
07714 276605
F: (01665) 510473
E: kevinbremner@aol.com

Village Farm ★★★-★★★★
Contact: Mrs C M Stoker, Town
Foot Farm, Shilbottle, Alnwick,
Northumberland NE66 2HG
T: (01665) 575591 & 0798 987
5749
F: (01665) 575591
E: crissy@villagefarmcottages.
co.uk
I: www.villagefarmcottages.
co.uk

Wakefield Cottage ★★★
Contact: Mrs Juliet Wakefield,
Wakefield Cottage, 1 Bailiffgate,
Alnwick, Northumberland
NE66 1LZ
T: (01665) 602078

Establishments printed in blue have a detailed entry in this guide

2 White House Folly Cottages
★★★
Contact: Mrs J M Gilroy, White
House Folly Farm, Alnwick,
Northumberland NE66 2LW
T: (01665) 579265

ALWINTON
Northumberland

Stonecrop Cottage ★★★
Contact: Mrs Mason, 73 Barling
Road, Southend-on-Sea, Essex
SS3 0QG
T: (01702) 582693
F: (01669) 650361

AMBLE-BY-THE-SEA
Northumberland

Brent Cottage ★★★
Contact: Mr M A Clarke, 18 The
Green, Thrussington, Leicester
LE7 4UH
T: (01664) 424480

Collingwood ★★★
Contact: Mrs G Young, 69 Castle
View, Amble-by-the-Sea,
Morpeth, Northumberland
NE65 0NN
T: (01665) 710303

Marina Cottage ★★★★
Contact: Mr D Black, Marina
Cottage, The Wynd, Amble-by-
the-Sea, Morpeth,
Northumberland NE65 0HH
T: (01665) 711019
F: (01665) 711019

BALDERSDALE
Durham

Clove Lodge Cottage ★★★
Contact: Mrs A Heys, Clove
Lodge Farm, Baldersdale,
Barnard Castle, County Durham
DL12 9UP
T: (01833) 650030
E: heys70.freeserve.co.uk

**The Old Chapel and Bluebell
Barn** ★★★★–★★★★★
Contact: Mrs J Moore, Briscoe
Farm, Baldersdale, Barnard
Castle, County Durham
DL12 9UL
T: (01833) 650822 &
07967 150320

BAMBURGH
Northumberland

Barn End ★★★★
Contact: Mr George Bruce, The
Steading, Westburn, Crawcrook,
Ryton, Tyne and Wear NE40 4EU
T: (0191) 413 2353
E: george.e.bruce@talk21.com

Bradford Country Cottages
★★★–★★★★
Contact: Mr L W Robson,
Bradford Country Cottages,
Bamburgh, Northumberland
NE70 7JT
T: (01668) 213432
F: (01668) 213891

Bridge End ★★★★
Contact: Mr and Mrs Roger and
Linda Topping, 98 Dowanhill
Street, Glasgow, G12 9EG
T: (0141) 334 4833 & 229 5517

Castle View Bungalow ★★★
Contact: Mr and Mrs I Nicol,
Springwood, South Lane,
Seahouses, Northumberland
NE68 7UL
T: (01665) 720320
F: (01665) 720146
E: ian@slatehall.freeserve.co.uk
I: www.slateridingcentre.com

The Cottage ★★★
Contact: Mrs S Turnbull, 1 Friars
Court, Bamburgh,
Northumberland NE69 7AE
T: (01668) 214494

**Dukesfield Farm Holiday
Cottages** ★★★★
Contact: Mrs Maria Eliana
Robinson, The Glebe, 16
Radcliffe Road, Bamburgh,
Northumberland NE69 7AE
T: (01668) 214456 & 214354
F: (01668) 214354
E: 101361.1343@compuserve.
com
I: www.org.uk/holidays.uk

**East Burton Farm Holiday
Cottages** ★★★★
Contact: Mrs W F Taylor, 6 East
Burton Cottages, Bamburgh,
Northumberland NE69 7AR
T: (01668) 214458

The Fairway ★★★
Contact: Mrs R S Middleton,
High Close House, Wylam,
Northumberland NE41 8BL
T: (01661) 852125
E: rsmiddleton@talk21.com

**Glebe House and Glebe
Cottage** ★★★★★
Contact: Mrs Maria Eliana
Robinson, EMR Properties, The
Glebe, 16 Radcliffe Road,
Bamburgh, Northumberland
NE69 7AE
T: (01668) 214456
F: (01668) 214354
E: 101361.1343@compuserve.
com
I: www.org.uk/holidays.uk

The Granary ★★★
Contact: Mrs P Cowen,
Thornleigh, Wetheral, Carlisle
CA4 8ES
T: (01228) 560245

The Haven ★★★★
Contact: Miss Lynn Gregory,
Earsdon Hill Farm, Morpeth,
Northumberland NE61 3ES
T: (01670) 787392
F: (01670) 787392
E: pg@africaselect.com

High Tutlaw House ★★★★★
Contact: Mrs Jane Mallen, Park
Farm House, Hulne Park,
Alnwick, Northumberland
NE66 3HZ
T: (01665) 602094 &
07774 606123
F: (01665) 608126
E: tutlaw@farming.co.uk

Hoppen Hall Farm Cottages
★★★★
Contact: Mrs J Mallen,
Northumberland Estates Holiday
Cottages, Alnwick Castle,
Alnwick, Northumberland
NE66 1NQ
T: (01665) 602094 &
07774 606123
F: (01665) 608126
E: nehc@farmline.com
I: www.alnwickcastle.
com/holidaycottages/

Inglenook Cottage ★★★★
Contact: Mrs A D Moore,
Beckstones, Carperby, Leyburn,
North Yorkshire DL8 4DA
T: (01969) 663363

Nineteen ★★★
Contact: Mr John McDougal,
Glenander, 27 Lucker Road,
Bamburgh, Northumberland
NE69 7BS
T: (01668) 214336
F: (01668) 214100
E: clem500@btinternet.com

The Old Coach House ★★★★
Contact: Country Holidays
ref:12179, Spring Mill, Earby,
Barnoldswick, Lancashire
BB18 6RN
T: 08700 723723
F: (01282) 844288
E: sales@ttgihg.co.uk
I: www.country-holidays.co.uk

**Outchester & Ross Farm
Cottages**★★★–★★★★
Contact: Shirley McKie, 1
Cragview Road, Belford,
Northumberland NE70 7NT
T: (01668) 213336
F: (01668) 219385
E: enquiry@rosscottages.co.uk
I: www.rosscottages.co.uk

Point Cottages ★★★
Contact: Mrs E Sanderson, 30
The Oval, Benton, Newcastle
upon Tyne NE12 9PP
T: (0191) 266 2800 &
(01665) 720246
F: (0191) 215 1630
E: info@bamburgh-cottages.
co.uk
I: www.bamburgh-cottages.
co.uk

Quarry Haven ★★★★
Contact: Mr & Mrs Martin and
Alison Wallace, 15 Arden Ave,
Brunton Park, Gosforth,
Newcastle upon Tyne NE3 5TS
T: (0191) 2363072 &
07710 760617

Saint Oswalds ★★
Contact: Mr Anthony Smith, 10
Aldbourne Road, London
W12 0LN
T: (020) 8248 9589
F: (020) 8248 9587
E: qsmith@cwcom.net

Smugglers Court ★★★★
Contact: Mr Gordon Begg, The
Old Granary, Smugglers Court,
Waren Mill, Belford,
Northumberland NE70 7EE
T: (01668) 214047 &
(01665) 721094
F: (01668) 214047
E: gordon@budle-bay.com
I: www.budle-bay.com

Springhill Farm Cottages
★★★★
Contact: Mrs J Gregory,
Springhill Farmhouse,
Seahouses, Northumberland
NE68 7UR
T: (01665) 720351
F: (01665) 721820
E: jygregory@aol.com
I: www.springhill.farm.co.uk

Struan ★★★
Contact: Mr C E Wilkie-Smith,
27 Ridley Place, Newcastle upon
Tyne, NE1 8LE
T: (0191) 232 8058 &
(01434) 432333
F: (0191) 222 1391
E: kerry@daviesbellreed.co.uk

Whinstone ★★★
Contact: Mrs P J Tait, Lyndale, 15
Kenton Road, Gosforth,
Newcastle upon Tyne NE3 4NE
T: (0191) 285 1363

Workshop Cottage ★★★★
Contact: Mrs V Dixon, The Friary,
Radcliffe Road, Bamburgh,
Northumberland NE69 7AE
T: (01668) 214269

Wynding Down ★★★★★
Contact: Mrs D Stanger, 6
Cottingwood Lane, Morpeth,
Northumberland NE61 1EA
T: (01670) 511162
E: distanger@hotmail.com

BARDON MILL
Northumberland

Ashcroft Cottages ★★★★
Contact: Mrs J Robson, Ashcroft
Farm, Bardon Mill, Hexham,
Northumberland NE47 7JA
T: (01434) 344409

Birkshaw Farmhouse Cottage
★★★
Contact: Mr E C Story, Birkshaw
Farmhouse, Bardon Mill,
Hexham, Northumberland
NE47 7JL
T: (01434) 344394
E: cstory2723@aol.com
I: accomodata.co.uk/201299

The Hott and Fern Cottage
★★★
Contact: Mrs N Harding, West
End Town Farm, Thorngrafton,
Bardon Mill, Hexham,
Northumberland NE47 7JJ
T: (01434) 344 258

Establishments printed in blue have a detailed entry in this guide

BARNARD CASTLE
Durham

Boot and Shoe Cottage
★★★★
Contact: Mrs R Peat, Waterside
Cottage, Wycliffe, Barnard
Castle, County Durham
DL12 9TR
T: (01833) 627200
F: (01833) 627200
E: bootandshoe@
teesdaleonline.co.uk
I: www.bootandshoecottage.
co.uk

East Briscoe Farm Cottages
★★★★
Contact: Mr & Mrs Peter & Ann
Wilson, East Cottage, East
Briscoe Farm, Baldersdale,
Barnard Castle, County Durham
DL12 9UL
T: (01833) 650087
F: (01833) 650027
E: peter@eastbriscoe.co.uk
I: www.eastbriscoe.co.uk

**Hauxwell Cottages (Bumpkin
Byre and Puddles End)** ★★★★
Contact: Mrs Penny Clark,
Hauxwell Grange, Marwood,
Barnard Castle, County Durham
DL12 8QU
T: (01833) 695022
F: (01833) 695022
E: jdclark@mail.sci-net.co.uk

Lanquitts Cottage ★
Contact: Mrs B M Kidd,
Strathmore Arms Farm,
Baldersdale, Cotherstone,
Barnard Castle, County Durham
DL12 9UR
T: (01833) 650345

66A Newgate ★★★
Contact: Dales Holiday Cottages,
Carleton Business Park, Carleton
New Road, Skipton, North
Yorkshire BD23 2AA
T: (01756) 799821 & 790919
F: (01756) 797012

Staindrop House Mews ★★★
Contact: Mrs D J Walton,
Staindrop House, 14 Front
street, Staindrop, Darlington,
County Durham DL2 3NH
T: (01833) 660951

Thorngate Coach House
Rating Applied For
Contact: Mrs Clare Terry,
Thorngate House, Thorngate,
Barnard Castle, County Durham
DL12 8PY
T: (01833) 637791 &
07949 193296
F: (01833) 637791

Woodland House Cottage
★★★
Contact: Mr C Harding,
Woodland House, Woodland,
Bishop Auckland, County
Durham DL13 5RH
T: (01388) 718659
E: woodlandcottage@onmail.
co.uk
I: www.cottageguide.
co.uk/woodlandhouse

BARNINGHAM
Durham

The Cottage ★★★
Contact: Mrs Jillian Anderson,
Far East Hope, Barningham,
Richmond, North Yorkshire
DL11 7DZ
T: (01833) 621206 &
07808 306568
E: aandersonjillian@aol.com

The Cottage ★★★★
Contact: Mrs Helen Lowes,
Wilson House, Barningham,
Richmond, North Yorkshire
DL11 7EB
T: (01833) 621218
F: (01833) 621110

Dove Cottage ★★★
Contact: Miss S Catton, Heath
House, Barningham, Richmond,
North Yorkshire DL11 7DU
T: (01833) 621374
F: (01833) 621374
E: dove@smithj90.fsnet.co.uk
I: www.cottageguide.
co.uk/dove-cottage

Forest Lodge ★★★
Contact: Sykes Cottages
Ref:518, Sykes Cottages, York
House, York Street, Chester,
Cheshire CH1 3LR
T: (01244) 345700
F: (01244) 321442
E: info@sykescottages.co.uk
I: www.sykescottages.co.uk

BARRASFORD
Northumberland

Barrasford Arms Cottage ★★
Contact: Mr T Milburn,
Barrasford Arms, Barrasford,
Hexham, Northumberland
NE48 4AA
T: (01434) 681237
F: (01434) 681237

BEADNELL
Northumberland

Annstead Farm ★★★–★★★★★
Contact: Mrs Susan Mellor,
Annstead Farm, Beadnell,
Northumberland NE67 5BT
T: (01665) 720387 &
07997 269403
F: (01665) 721494
E: susan@annstead.co.uk
I: www.annstead.co.uk

Beechley ★★★
Contact: Mrs Deborah Baker, 22
Upper Green Way, Tingley,
Wakefield, West Yorkshire
WF3 1TA
T: (0113) 218 9176
F: (0113) 218 9176
E: deb-n-ade@lineone.net

The Bothy ★★★★
Contact: Mrs Beryl Seaward-
Birchall, The Bothy, Shepherds
Cottage, Beadnell, Chathill,
Northumberland NE67 5AD
T: (01665) 720497
F: (01665) 720497
I: www.shepherdscottage.ntb.
org.uk

The Dells ★★★
Contact: Mr & Mrs Iain and
Andrea Slater, 25
Northumberland Gardens,
Jesmond, Newcastle upon Tyne
NE2 1HA
T: (0191) 239 9934 & 0797 144
0085
F: 07967 161515
E: andreaslater@beadnell.fsnet.
co.uk

Dune View ★★★
Contact: Sykes Cottages Ref:
688, Sykes Cottages, York House,
York Street, Chester, Cheshire
CH1 3LR
T: (01244) 345700
F: (01244) 321442
E: info@sykescottages.co.uk
I: www.sykescottages.co.uk

Low Dover Beadnell Bay
★★★★
Contact: Kath & Bob Thompson,
Low Dover Beadnell Bay,
Harbour Road, Beadnell,
Chathill, Northumberland
NE67 5BJ
T: (01665) 720291 &
07971 444070
F: (01665) 720291
E: kathandbob@lowdover.co.uk
I: www.lowdover.co.uk

Oar Cottage ★★★★
Contact: Sykes Cottages
Ref:595, Sykes Cottages, York
House, York Street, Chester,
Cheshire CH1 3LR
T: (01244) 345700
F: (01244) 321442
E: info@sykescottages.co.uk
I: www.sykescottages.co.uk

The Rowans ★★★
Contact: Mr T J Trotter, South
Cottage, Pasture Hill, Seahouses,
Northumberland NE68 7UU
T: (01665) 720891
E: thomasjtrotter@supanet.com

Sandylands & Windrush ★★★
Contact: Sykes Cottages Ref:
665,689, Sykes Cottages, York
House, York Street, Chester,
Cheshire CH1 3LR
T: (01244) 345700
F: (01244) 321442
E: info@sykescottages.co.uk
I: www.sykescottages.co.uk

Torwoodlee & Shorestone
Rating Applied For
Contact: Dales Hol Cot
Ref:1892,1893, Dales Holiday
Cottages, Carleton Business
Park, Carleton New Road,
Skipton, North Yorkshire
BD23 2AA
T: (01756) 799821 & 790919
F: (01756) 797012
E: info@dalesholcot.com
I: www.dalesholcot.com

Town Farm ★★★
Contact: Mr & Mrs P Thompson,
South Lodge, Swarland,
Morpeth, Northumberland
NE65 9JA
T: (01670) 787864 & 786188
F: (01670) 787336
E: pault@marishal.co.uk
I: www.
northumberland-holidays.com

Town House Farm ★★★
Contact: Mr & Mrs Newbon, 86
Weetwood Lane, Leeds, West
Yorkshire LS16 5NR
T: (0113) 275 7393
F: (0113) 275 7393
E: ian@bonnew.freeserve.co.uk

BEAL
Northumberland

Bee Hill Properties
★★★★–★★★★★★
Contact: Mrs Jackie Nesbitt, Bee
Hill Properties, Beal, Berwick-
upon-Tweed, Northumberland
TD15 2PB
T: (01289) 381102 &
07768 496266
F: (01289) 381418
E: info@beehill.co.uk
I: www.beehill.co.uk

BEAMISH
Durham

**Chapel House Studio
Apartments** ★★★
Contact: Mr J MacLennan,
Chapel House, Causey Row,
Marley Hill, Stanley, County
Durham NE16 5EJ
T: (01207) 290992

BELFORD
Northumberland

Belford Court ★★★★
Contact: Mr Paul Shirley, Blue
Bell Hotel, Market Place, Belford,
Northumberland NE70 7NE
T: (01668) 213543
F: (01668) 213787
E: bluebel@globalnet.co.uk
I: www.belfordcourt.com

Fenham-le-Moor Cottage
★★★
Contact: Mrs K Burn, Fenham-
le-Moor, Belford,
Northumberland NE70 7PN
T: (01668) 213247
F: (01668) 213247

Hollyhock House ★★★★
Contact: Miss Alison Turnbull,
95 St Matthews Road, London
SW2 1NE
T: (0207) 733 4904 &
07990 972196
E: ali_turnbull@hotmail.com
I: www.highstreetbelford.
freeserve.co.uk

Orchard House
Rating Applied For
Contact: Mrs Roslyn Reay,
Elwick Farm, Belford,
Northumberland NE70 7EL
T: (01668) 213242
F: (01668) 213783
E: w.r.reay@talk21.com

Owls Rest ★★★★
Contact: Ms Christine Brown,
The Old Manse, New Road,
Chatton, Alnwick,
Northumberland NE66 5PU
T: (01668) 215343
E: chattonbb@aol
I: www.oldmansechatton.ntb.
org.uk

Shepherds Cottage ★★★★
Contact: Mrs Iris Oates,
Easington Farm, Belford,
Northumberland NE70 7EG

Establishments printed in blue have a detailed entry in this guide

BELLINGHAM
Northumberland

Buteland Bothy ★★
Contact: Mrs M A Williams,
Buteland House, Bellingham,
Hexham, Northumberland
NE48 2EX
T: (01434) 220389
F: (01434) 220389
E: buteland@aol.com

Castle Hill View ★★★
Contact: Mr & Mrs Batey,
Highsteads, Front Street,
Bellingham, Hexham,
Northumberland NE48 2AA
T: (01434) 220263

Conheath Cottage ★★★★
Contact: Mrs Zaina Riddle,
Blakelaw Farm, Bellingham,
Hexham, Northumberland
NE48 2EF
T: (01434) 220250
F: (01434) 220250
E: stay@conheath.co.uk
I: www.conheath.co.uk

Riverdale Apartments ★★★
Contact: Mrs C Morris, Riverdale
Hall Hotel, Bellingham, Hexham,
Northumberland NE48 2JT
T: (01434) 220254
F: (01434) 220457
E: iben@riverdalehall.demon.
co.uk
I: www.riverdalehall.demon.
co.uk

BERWICK-UPON-TWEED
Northumberland

Felkington Farm Cottages
★★-★★★★
Contact: Mrs M J Martin,
Felkington Farm, Berwick-upon-
Tweed, Northumberland
TD15 2NR
T: (01289) 387220
F: (01289) 387220
E: martin@felkington.freeserve.
co.uk

Gorse Bungalow ★★★
Contact: Dales Hol Cot Ref:2310,
Dales Holiday Cottages, Carleton
Business Park, Carleton New
Road, Skipton, North Yorkshire
BD23 2AA
T: (01756) 799821 & 790919
F: (01756) 797012
E: info@dalesholcot.com
I: www.dalesholcot.com

**Honeysuckle Cottage and
Bluebell Cottage** ★★★★
Contact: Mr Robert Whitten,
West Longridge Farm, Berwick-
upon-Tweed, Northumberland
TD15 2JX
T: (01289) 331112
F: (01289) 304591

Ivy Cottage ★★
Contact: Proprietor, Ivy Cottage,
11 Coxons Lane, Berwick-upon-
Tweed, TD15 1DD

Kingsway Cottage ★★★★
Contact: Mrs Judith King, East
Ord Farmhouse, East Ord,
Berwick-upon-Tweed,
Northumberland TD15 2NS
T: (01289) 306228 & 0798 980
0996

Lark Rise ★★★★
Contact: Mrs Deirdre Dickson,
Crosby House, Crosby-on-Eden,
Carlisle, Cumbria CA6 4QZ
T: (01228) 573239 & 573337
F: (01228) 573338
E: enquires@norbyways.demon.
co.uk
I: www.northumbria-byways.
com/larkrise

Marshall Meadows ★★
Contact: Mr & Mrs J Fairbairn,
Marshall Meadows Farm,
Berwick-upon-Tweed,
Northumberland TD15 1UT
T: (01289) 307375

Mill Lane Apartments ★★★★
Contact: Mr John Haswell, 2
Palace Street East, Berwick-
upon-Tweed, TD15 1HT
T: (01289) 304492
E: john@milllane.plus.com
I: www.milllane.plus.com

**No 1 Gainslawhill Farm
Cottage**
Rating Applied For
Contact: Mrs Susan Wight,
Gainslawhill Farm, Berwick-
upon-Tweed, TD15 1SZ
T: (01289) 386210

The Old Barn ★★★★
Contact: Mr and Mrs Richard &
Susan Persse, High Letham
Farmhouse, High Letham,
Berwick-upon-Tweed,
Northumberland TD15 1UX
T: (01289) 306585
F: (01289) 304194
I: www.ntb.org.uk

6 Palace Green
Rating Applied For
Contact: Mr Louis Heward-Mills,
73 Bengeo Street, Hertford,
Hertfordshire SG14 3ET
T: (01992) 534828 &
07973 727865
F: (01992) 534858
E: louis@cctr-london.demon.
co.uk

57 Ravensdowne
Rating Applied For
Contact: Mrs June Cadzow,
Inland Pasture, Berwick-upon-
Tweed, TD15 2RJ
T: (01289) 306072 &
07977 046302
F: (01289) 306070
E: junecadzow@aol.com

Trevone ★★★
Contact: Mr Peter Herdman,
Devonia, 13 Bankhill, Berwick-
upon-Tweed, Northumberland
TD15 1BE
T: (01289) 307524

West Kyloe Cottages
★★-★★★★
Contact: Mrs T M Smalley,
Garden Cottage, 1 West Kyloe,
Berwick-upon-Tweed,
Northumberland TD15 2PG
T: (01289) 381279 & 0797 141
1625
F: (01289) 381279
E: info@westkyloe.co.uk
I: www.lindisfarne.org.
uk/west-kyloe-farm

West Ord Cottages
★★★-★★★★
Contact: Mrs Carol Lang, West
Ord Cottages, West Ord Farm,
Berwick-upon-Tweed,
Northumberland TD15 2XQ
T: (01289) 386631
F: (01289) 386800
E: sandy.lang@vigin.net
I: www.westord.co.uk

BISHOP AUCKLAND
Durham

Five Gables Cottage ★★★★
Contact: Mr & Mrs P&J Weston,
Five Gables Guest House, Five
Gables, Binchester, Bishop
Auckland, County Durham
DL14 8AT
T: (01388) 608204
F: (01388) 663092
E: book.in@fivegables.co.uk
I: www.fivegables.co.uk

Gill Bank Farm Cottage ★★★
Contact: Mr & Mrs A Marley, Gill
Bank Farm, Butterknowle,
Bishop Auckland, County
Durham DL13 5QF
T: (01388) 718614

Meadow View ★★
Contact: Dales Hol Cot Ref:1462,
Dales Holiday Cottages, Carleton
Business Park, Carleton New
Road, Skipton, North Yorkshire
BD23 2AA
T: (01756) 799821 & 790919
F: (01756) 797012
E: info@dalesholcot.com
I: www.dalesholcot.com

The Old Sunday School
★★★★
Contact: Mrs Pat Blayney, The
Old Sunday School, Bridge End,
Frosterley, Bishop Auckland,
County Durham DL13 2SN
T: (01388) 528913
E: pablayney@aol.com

BLANCHLAND
Northumberland

Bail Hill ★★★
Contact: Mrs J Graham,
Allenshields, Blanchland,
Consett, County Durham
DH8 9PP
T: (01434) 675274

Boltsburn Holiday Cottages
★★
Contact: Mr C E Davison, Bolts
Brae, 10 Watergate Road,
Consett, County Durham
DH8 9QS
T: (01207) 583076 & 506194

Boltslaw Cottage ★★★
Contact: Mrs N Smith, 6
Selborne Avenue, Gateshead,
Tyne and Wear NE9 6ET
T: (0191) 487 9456
F: (01670) 510300
E: asmith6000@aol.com
I: www.oas.
co.uk/ukcottages/boltslaw

BOWES
Durham

Number 1 Unicorn Cottages
★★★
Contact: Mr & Mrs Mathew Hill,
Church Lodge, York Road,
Shiptonthorpe, York YO43 3PH
T: (01430) 872560 &
(01904) 432266
E: anne.mat@ic24.net

BRANTON
Northumberland

Breamish Valley Cottages
★★★★-★★★★★
Contact: Mrs Michele Moralee,
Breamish Valley Cottages,
Branton West Side, Powburn,
Alnwick, Northumberland
NE66 4LW
T: (01665) 578263
F: (01665) 578263
E: peter@breamishvalley.co.uk
I: www.breamishvalley.co.uk

BUTTERKNOWLE
Durham

Folly Cottage ★★★
Contact: Dales Hol Cot Ref:2112,
Dales Holiday Cottages, Carleton
Business Park, Carleton New
Road, Skipton, North Yorkshire
BD23 2AA
T: (01756) 799821 & 790919
F: (01756) 797012
E: info@dalesholcot.com
I: www.dalesholcot.com

BYRNESS
Northumberland

Carter View ★★★
Contact: Mr Colin Bell, 24 Kay
Street, Stanley, County Durham
DH9 0PE
T: (01207) 283304 & (0191) 515
1122
F: (0191) 515 1055
E: colinbellstanley@hotmail.
com

Catcleugh Farm
Rating Applied For
Contact: Mr Walter Nieuwkoop,
P O Box 83, Morpeth,
Northumberland NE61 4YY
T: (01670) 772607 &
07850 983128
F: (01670) 772607
E: catcleugh@hotmail.com
I: www.catcleugh.com

The Old School House ★★★★
Contact: Dales Holiday
Cottages, Carleton Business
Park, Carleton New Road,
Skipton, North Yorkshire
BD23 2DG
T: (01756) 799821
F: (01756) 797012

CALLALY
Northumberland

Dene Cottage ★★★★
Contact: Mrs M P Winn, Dene
House, Callaly, Alnwick,
Northumberland NE66 4TA
T: (01665) 574513

CARLTON IN CLEVELAND
Tees Valley

The Coachman's Cottage
★★★
Contact: Dales Hol Cot Ref:1075,
Dales Holiday Cottages, Carleton
Business Park, Carleton New
road, Skipton, North Yorkshire
BD23 2AA
T: (01756) 799821 & 790919
F: (01756) 797012
E: info@dalesholcot.com
I: www.dalesholcot.com

Stables Cottage ★★★
Contact: Dales Hol Cot Ref:2697,
Dales Holiday Cottages, Carleton
Business Park, Carleton New
road, Skipton, North Yorkshire
BD23 2AA
T: (01756) 799821 & 790919
F: (01756) 797012
E: info@dalesholcot.com
I: www.dalesholcot.com

CARRVILLE
Durham

62 Wantage Road ★★
Contact: Mr & Mrs N Walker, 62
Wantage Road, Carrville,
Durham DH1 1LR
T: (0191) 386 2290
I: www.cottageguide.
co.uk/carrville

CASTLESIDE
Durham

**The Cottage and The Dairy
★★-★★★**
Contact: Mr & Mrs Elliot, The
Cottage and The Dairy, Derwent
Grange Farm, Castleside,
Consett, County Durham
DH8 9BN
T: (01207) 508358
E: ekelliot@aol.com

**Manor Park Cottage (Manor
Park Ltd)★★**
Contact: Mr Brian Elstrop,
Broadmeadows, Rippon Burn,
Castleside, Consett, County
Durham DH8 9HD
T: (01207) 501000 & 509308
F: (01207) 509271

Willerby Grange ★★★
Contact: Mr & Mrs Gavin &
Patricia Jopling, Willerby
Grange, Pemberton Road,
Allensford, Consett, County
Durham DH8 9BA
T: (01207) 508752 &
07974 884227
F: (01207) 508752

CAWBURN
Northumberland

Rowan Cottage ★★★★
Contact: Mrs Margaret Swallow,
Rowan Cottage, High Edges
Green, Cawburn, Haltwhistle,
Northumberland NE49 9PP
T: (01434) 320352
F: (01434) 320352
E: swallow@rowan78.freeserve.
co.uk
I: www.rowan78.freeserve.co.uk

CHATHILL
Northumberland

**The Lodge and Head
Gardener's House★★★★**
Contact: Mrs J S Burnie, The
Lodge and Head Gardener's
House, Doxford Hall, Chathill,
Alnwick, Northumberland
NE67 5DN
T: (01665) 589499
F: (01665) 589499
E: burnieclan@doxford.
freeserve.co.uk

Newstead Cottage ★★
Contact: Mrs M Riddell,
Newstead Farm, Chathill,
Northumberland NE67 5LH
T: (01665) 589263

Shepherds Cottage ★★★
Contact: Country Holidays
ref:10176, Spring Mill, Earby,
Barnoldswick, Lancashire
BB18 6RN
T: 08700 723723
F: (01282) 844288
E: sales@ttgihg.co.uk
I: www.country-holidays.co.uk

Tower Cottage ★★
Contact: Mrs S Cresswell,
Preston Tower, Chathill,
Northumberland NE67 5DH
T: (01665) 589227

CHESTER-LE-STREET
Durham

**The Old Stables
Rating Applied For**
Contact: Mr and Mrs A J Cutter,
Hollycroft, 11 The Parade,
Chester-le-Street, County
Durham DH3 3LR
T: (0191) 388 7088 &
07932 675069
E: cutter@hollycroft11.
freeserve.co.uk

Plawsworth Mews ★★★★
Contact: Mr Harry Johnson,
Plawsworth Hall Farm,
Plawsworth, Chester-le-Street,
County Durham DH2 3LD
T: (0191) 371 0251 & 371 1529
F: (0191) 371 2101

CHILLINGHAM
Northumberland

Chillingham Castle ★★★
Contact: The Administrator,
Chillingham Castle, Chillingham,
Alnwick, Northumberland
NE66 5NJ
T: (01668) 215359
F: (01668) 215463
E: enquiries@
chillingham-castle.com
I: www.chillingham-castle.com

**Herd's House & Homildon
House
Rating Applied For**
Contact: Dales Hol Cot
Ref:1577,1578, Dales Holiday
Cottages, Carleton Business
Park, Carleton New Road,
Skipton, North Yorkshire
BD23 2AA
T: (01756) 799821 & 790919
F: (01756) 797012
E: info@dalesholcot.com
I: www.dalesholcot.com

CHOPWELL
Tyne and Wear

High Pasture Cottage ★★★★
Contact: Mr Allan Low, Bowser
Hill Farm, Chopwell, Newcastle
upon Tyne NE17 7AY
T: (01207) 560881
E: alow@btinternet.com

COANWOOD
Northumberland

Mill Hill Farmhouse ★★★
Contact: Mrs S Wigham, Hargill
House, Coanwood, Haltwhistle,
Northumberland NE49 0PQ
T: (01434) 320256
E: millhill@fsmail.net
I: www.cottageguide.
co.uk/millhill

COCKFIELD
Durham

New Cottage ★★★
Contact: Mrs Margaret
Partridge, New Cottage, Law
One, Hollymoor Farm, Cockfield,
Bishop Auckland, County
Durham DL13 5HF
T: (01388) 718567 & 718260
F: (01388) 718567

Rose Cottage ★★★
Contact: Mrs M E Elstob, Rose
Cottage, Highlands, Cockfield,
Bishop Auckland, County
Durham DL13 5BG
T: (01388) 718941

**Stonecroft and Swallows Nest
★★★★**
Contact: Mrs A Tallentire, Low
Lands Farm, Cockfield, Bishop
Auckland, County Durham
DL13 5AW
T: (01388) 718251
F: (01388) 718251
E: info@farmholidaysuk.com
I: www.farmholidaysuk.com

CORBRIDGE
Northumberland

April Cottage ★★★
Contact: Mrs K E Dean, 21
Woodland Close, Chelford,
Macclesfield, Cheshire SK11 9BZ
T: (01625) 861718
E: toria_dean@hotmail.com

The Forge Cottage ★★★★
Contact: Mr & Mrs P&C Black,
Tamarisk, High Horse Close,
Rowlands Gill, Tyne and Wear
NE39 1AN
T: (01207) 542713
F: (01207) 542713
E: pandc@fsmail.net
I: www.forgecottage.ntb.org.uk

The Hayes ★★
Contact: Mrs M J Matthews, The
Hayes, Newcastle Road,
Corbridge, Northumberland
NE45 5LP
T: (01434) 632010
F: (01434) 632010
E: mjct@mmatthews.fsbusiness.
co.uk
I: www.hayes-corbridge.co.uk

Nosbor Cottage ★★★
Contact: Mrs V Robson, 7
Runnymede Road, Darras Hall,
Ponteland, Newcastle upon Tyne
NE20 9HE
T: (01661) 871135
F: (01661) 871135
E: nosboruk@yahoo.co.uk

Oswald Cottage ★★★
Contact: Mrs H K Harriman,
Swarden House, Kyloe House
Farm, Eachwick, Newcastle upon
Tyne, Northumberland
NE18 0BB
T: (01661) 852909
F: (01661) 854106
E: pwh@littonproperties.co.uk

Riversbank ★★★★
Contact: Dr J R Backhurst,
Uplands, Newcastle Road,
Corbridge, Northumberland
NE45 5LN
T: (01434) 632073

Riverview ★★★
Contact: Mrs E Lonsdale, 13
Market Place, Corbridge,
Northumberland NE45 5AW
T: (01434) 633027
F: (01434) 633027
E: d.lons@virgin.net
I: www.objectivegroup.
com/riverview

**Wallhouses South Farm
Cottage ★★★★**
Contact: Mrs E Lymburn, South
Farm, Military Road, Corbridge,
Northumberland NE45 5PU
T: (01434) 672388
E: loraip@aol.com

West Fell Cottage ★★★
Contact: E J Smith, West Fell
House, Corbridge,
Northumberland NE45 5RZ
T: (01434) 632044

CORNHILL-ON-TWEED
Northumberland

**Herds Hoose, Cherry Cottage
★★★**
Contact: Mrs Diana Tweedie,
Tithe Hill, Cornhill-on-Tweed,
Northumberland TD12 4QD
T: (01890) 850286

Jasmine Cottage ★★★
Contact: Dales Hol Cot Ref:2257,
Dales Holiday Cottages, Carleton
Business Park, Carleton New
Road, Skipton, North Yorkshire
BD23 2AA
T: (01756) 799821 & 790919
F: (01756) 797012
E: info@dalesholcot.com
I: www.dalesholcot.com

Melkington Lodge ★★★★★
Contact: Mrs Veronica Barber,
Melkington Lodge, Cornhill-on-
Tweed, Northumberland
TD12 4UP
T: (01890) 882313 &
07773 012016
F: (01890) 882300
E: barber@melkington.demon.
co.uk
I: www.melkington.co.uk

Orchard Cottage ★★★
Contact: Mrs L Carroll, Old
Egypt, Tiptoe, Cornhill-on-
Tweed, Northumberland
TD12 4XD
T: (01890) 882177 &
07974 416692
F: (01890) 883060
E: orchardcottage@tiptoe.
totalserve.co.uk
I: www.flyfishing.fsbusiness.
co.uk/wildside/tiptoe1.htm

The Stables ★★★★
Contact: Mrs M Buckle, The
Stables, Cornhill-on-Tweed,
Northumberland TD12 4QA
T: (01890) 882390
F: (01890) 883778
E: david.buckle@btinternet.com
I: www.the stables.cornhill.
btinternet.co.uk/

Tillmouth Cottage ★★★★
Contact: Mrs J A Binnie,
Tillmouth Farm, Cornhill-on-
Tweed, Northumberland
TD12 4XA
T: (01289) 382482
F: (01289) 342482

Establishments printed in blue have a detailed entry in this guide

COTHERSTONE
Durham

Berriman Cottage ★
Contact: Dales Hol Cot Ref:562, Dales Holiday Cottages, Carleton Business Park, Carleton New Road, Skipton, North Yorkshire BD23 2AA
T: (01756) 799821 & 790919
F: (01756) 797012
E: info@dalesholcot.com
I: www.dalesholcot.com

Farthings ★★★
Contact: Mr C J Bainbridge, Glen Leigh, Cotherstone, Barnard Castle, County Durham DL12 9QW
T: (01833) 650331

Thwaite Hall ★★★
Contact: Mrs A Wickham, Hillcrest, Front Street, Whitburn, Tyne and Wear SR6 7JD
T: (0191) 529 3793 & (01833) 650782
F: (0191) 529 2362

COWSHILL
Durham

Dales Farm Cottage ★★★
Contact: Dales Hol Cot Ref:1322, Dales Holiday Cottages, Carleton Business Park, Carleton New Road, Skipton, North Yorkshire BD23 2AA
T: (01756) 799821 & 790919
F: (01756) 797012
E: info@dalesholcot.com
I: www.dalesholcot.com

CRASTER
Northumberland

Craster Pine Lodges ★★★★
Contact: Mr & Mrs M Robson, 9 West End, Craster, Alnwick, Northumberland NE66 3TS
T: (01665) 576286
F: (01665) 576286
E: pinelodges@barkpots.co.uk
I: www.barkpots.co.uk

Driftwood Cottage
Rating Applied For
Contact: Dales Hol Cot Ref:2659, Dales Holiday Cottages, Carleton Business Park, Carleton New Road, Skipton, North Yorkshire BD23 2AA
T: (01756) 799821 & 790919
F: (01756) 797012
E: info@dalesholcot.com
I: www.dalesholcot.com

Ebor ★★★
Contact: Mr W Mawhinney, 7 Harley Terrace, Gosforth, Newcastle upon Tyne, NE3 1UL
T: (0191) 284 6294
E: whbmawhinney@netscapeonline.co.uk

Proctor's Stead Cottages ★★★
Contact: Mr R W Davidson, Proctor's Stead, Craster, Alnwick, Northumberland NE66 3TF
T: (01665) 576613
F: (01665) 576311
I: www.proctorsstead.ntb.org.uk

Seahaven ★★★
Contact: Mrs M A Imrie, 1 Malvern Road, Preston Grange, North Shields, Tyne and Wear NE29 9DY
T: (0191) 258 0187

CROOKHAM
Northumberland

Askew Cottage ★★★★
Contact: Mrs H Pentland, 32 Crookham Village, Cornhill-on-Tweed, Northumberland TD12 4SY
T: (01890) 820201
F: (01890) 820201
E: hjpentland@waitrose.com

CULLERCOATS
Tyne and Wear

Everitt House Holiday Flats ★★★
Contact: Mr & Mrs Steve and Carole Bradley, Everitt House Holiday Flats, 46 Beverley Terrace, Cullercoats, North Shields, Tyne and Wear NE30 4NU
T: (0191) 252 1568
F: (0191) 252 2340
E: everittflats@aol.com

DARLINGTON
Durham

High House Farm Cottages ★★★★
Contact: Mr & Mrs Harry and Peggy Wood, High House Farm Cottages, High House Farm, Houghton Le Side, Darlington, County Durham DL2 2UU
T: (01388) 834879
F: (01388) 834879

Pegasus Cottage ★★★
Contact: Mr & Mrs Stuart and Denise Chapman, 4 Tees View, Hurworth Place, Darlington, County Durham DL2 2DH
T: (01325) 722542
F: (01325) 722542
I: www.pegasuscottage.co.uk

DETCHANT
Northumberland

Longstone Cottage ★★★★
Contact: Country Holidays ref:10683, Spring Mill, Earby, Barnoldswick, Lancashire BB94 0AA
T: (01282) 445096
F: (01282) 844288
E: sales@ttgihg.co.uk
I: www.country-holidays.co.uk

DIPTON
Durham

Westlea ★★★★
Contact: Mrs A C Watson, Evergreen, Hilltop Road, Dipton, Stanley, County Durham DH9 9JY
T: (01207) 570072 & 07798 717767
F: (01207) 570072
E: westlea@connect4free.net
I: www.country.holidays

DUDDO
Northumberland

Smithy Cottage ★★
Contact: Mr & Mrs Alison and Nigel Chandler, 37 Moorside South, Fenham, Newcastle upon Tyne NE4 9BD
T: (0191) 273 5003 & 272 2100
F: (0191) 272 2100

DURHAM
Durham

26a and 26b Hallgarth Street ★★
Contact: Ms Sue Pitts, 27 Hallgarth Street, Durham, DH1 3AT
T: (0191) 384 1611

Arbour House Bungalow and Cottage ★★★
Contact: Mrs R Hunter, Arbour House Bungalow and Cottage, Arbour House Farm, Crossgate Moor, Durham DH1 4TQ
T: (0191) 384 2418
F: (0191) 386 0738
E: enquiries@arbourhouse.co.uk
I: www.arbourhouse.ntb.co.uk

Baxter Wood Cottages ★★★★
Contact: Mr & Mrs Jones, Baxter Wood Farm, Crossgate Moor, Durham, DH1 4TG
T: (0191) 386 5820
F: (0191) 386 5820

Dove Cottage & Fern Cottage ★★★★
Contact: Mrs E M Woods, 25 Orchard Drive, Durham, County Durham DH1 1LA
T: (0191) 386 4176 & 372 1810
F: (0191) 372 2864
E: durhamcottages@aol.com
I: www.durhamcottages.com

Jubilee House ★★
Contact: Mrs C Reay, Jubilee House, 9 Sidegate, Durham, DH1 5SY
T: (0191) 384 4894

The Old Power House ★★★★
Contact: Mrs Anne Hall, Garden Cottage, Southill Hall, Plawsworth, Chester-le-Street, County Durham DH3 4EQ
T: (0191) 387 3001 & 222 0626
F: (0191) 389 3569
E: g.s.hall@talk21.com

Sands Cottage ★★★
Contact: Mrs G Hodgson, Sands House, The Sands, Durham, County Durham DH1 1JY
T: (0191) 384 4731

EAGLESCLIFFE
Tees Valley

Aislaby Grange Farm Cottages ★★★
Contact: Mr A W Hutchinson, Aislaby Grange Farm Cottages, Aislaby Grange, Aislaby, Eaglescliffe, Stockton-on-Tees, Cleveland TS16 0QP
T: (01642) 782170
F: (01642) 782170

EBCHESTER
Durham

Lane Head Farm ★★★
Contact: Mrs P Proctor, Lane Head Farm, Ebchester, Consett, County Durham DH8 0SR
T: (01207) 562686
F: (01207) 562686
E: lanehead@btinternet.com

EDLINGHAM
Northumberland

Briar, Rose And Clematis Cottage ★★★★
Contact: Mrs Helen Wyld, New Moor House, Edlingham, Alnwick, Northumberland NE66 2BT
T: (01665) 574638
E: newmoorhouse@aol.com
I: www.newmoorhouse.co.uk

Hazelnuthouse ★★★★
Contact: Ms Hazel Bennett, 61 Portsmouth Road, Guildford, Surrey GU2 4BS
T: (01483) 569346 & 07966 141895
F: (01483) 569346
E: hazel.bennett@dial.pipex.com
I: www.bigfoot.com/~hazelnuthouse

Lumbylaw & Garden Cottages ★★★★
Contact: Mrs S A Lee, Lumbylaw Farm, Edlingham, Alnwick, Northumberland NE66 2BW
T: (01665) 574277
F: (01665) 574277
E: holidays@lumbylaw.co.uk
I: www.lumbylaw.ntb.org.uk

EGGLESTON
Durham

The Cottage ★★★
Contact: Dales Hol Cot Ref:2353, Dales Holiday Cottages, Carleton Business Park, Carleton New Road, Skipton, North Yorkshire BD23 2AA
T: (01756) 799821 & 790919
F: (01756) 797012
E: info@dalesholcot.com
I: www.dalesholcot.com

The Granary ★★★
Contact: Mrs R Gray, The Cottage, Eggleston Hall, Eggleston, Barnard Castle, County Durham DL12 0AG
T: (01833) 650403
F: (01833) 650378

Helm Cottage ★★★
Contact: Dales Hol Cot Ref:3024, Dales Holiday Cottages, Carleton Business Park, Carleton New road, Skipton, North Yorkshire BD23 2AA
T: (01756) 799821 & 790919
F: (01756) 797012
E: info@dalesholcot.com
I: www.dalesholcot.com

Stable Court ★★★★
Contact: Mrs J D Broughton, Bell Farm, Swanton Novers, Melton Constable, Norfolk NR24 2NW
T: (01263) 860258
F: (01263) 861174

The Stobbs ★★★
Contact: Mrs D Bainbridge, East Carnigill, Baldersdale, Barnard Castle, County Durham DL12 9UX
T: (01833) 650472

EGLINGHAM
Northumberland

Stable Cottage ★★★★
Contact: Mr N McRoberts, Ogle House, Eglingham, Alnwick, Northumberland NE66 2TZ
T: (01665) 578264
F: (01665) 578145

ELLINGHAM
Northumberland

Glebe Court ★★★
Contact: Country Holidays
ref:10898, Spring Mill, Earby,
Barnoldswick, Lancashire
BB18 6RN
T: 08700 723723
F: (01282) 844288
E: sales@ttgihg.co.uk
I: www.country-holidays.co.uk

ELLINGTON
Northumberland

Rose Cottage ★★★
Contact: Dales Hol Cot Ref:1035,
Dales Holiday Cottages, Carleton
Business Park, Carleton New
Road, Skipton, North Yorkshire
BD23 2AA
T: (01756) 799821 & 790919
F: (01756) 797012
E: info@dalesholcot.com
I: www.dalesholcot.com

ELSDON
Northumberland

Dunns Farm & Bilsmoorfoot
★★★-★★★★
Contact: Mrs M Carruthers,
Dunns Farm, Elsdon, Newcastle
upon Tyne NE19 1AL
T: (01669) 640219
I: www.dunnsfarm.ntb.org.uk

EMBLETON
Northumberland

20 Christon Bank ★★★★
Contact: Country Holidays
ref:9144, Spring Mill, Earby,
Barnoldswick, Lancashire
BB94 0AA
T: 08700 723723
F: (01282) 844288
E: sales@ttgihg.co.uk
I: www.country-holidays.co.uk

Cra-na-ge ★★★
Contact: Sykes Cottages Ref:
694, Sykes Cottages, York House,
York Street, Chester, Cheshire
CH1 3LR
T: (01244) 345700
F: (01244) 321442
E: info@sykescottages.co.uk
I: www.sykescottages.co.uk

Dairy Cottage ★★★★
Contact: Mrs Tiernan, Longbank
Farm House, Swinton, Duns,
Berwickshire TD11 3HY
T: (01890) 840342
E: ktiernan@waitrose.com
I: www.ntb.org.uk

Doxford Farm Cottages
★★-★★★★
Contact: Mrs Sarah Shell,
Doxford Farm, Chathill,
Northumberland NE67 5DY
T: (01665) 579348 & 579477
F: (01665) 579331
E: doxfordfarm@hotmail.com
I: www.doxfordfarmcottages.
com

**Dunstanburgh Castle
Courtyard Cottages** ★★★
Contact: Mr Paul Thompson,
Heritage Coast Holidays, South
Lodge, Swarland, Morpeth,
Northumberland NE65 9JD
T: (01670) 787864 & 786188
F: (01670) 787336
E: pault@marishal.co.uk
I: www.
northumberland-holidays.com

Dunstanburgh View ★★★★
Contact: Mrs B R Astbury, 9
Sunnybrae Cottages, Embleton,
Alnwick, Northumberland
NE66 3UU
T: (01665) 576509
F: (01665) 576509
E: dunstanburgh_view@
hotmail.com
I: www.dunstanburghview.ntb.
org.uk

Eider ★★★★
Contact: Mrs J Straughan,
Croft's Green, Riverside, Lesbury,
Alnwick, Northumberland
NE66 3SG
T: (01665) 830032

2A Front Street ★★
Contact: Mrs Mary Axelby, 86
Crimicar Lane, Sheffield, S10 4FB
T: (0114) 230 5090
F: (0114) 230 5090

Glebe Cottage ★★★
Contact: Mrs S Goldthorpe,
Glebe Farmhouse, Embleton,
Alnwick, Northumberland
NE66 3UX
T: (01665) 576465

Moorin Cottage
Rating Applied For
Contact: Dales Hol Cot Ref:1629,
Dales Holiday Cottages, Carleton
Business Park, Carleton New
Road, Skipton, North Yorkshire
BD23 2AA
T: (01756) 799821 & 790919
F: (01756) 797012
E: info@dalesholcot.com
I: www.dalesholcot.com

**Northumbrian Holiday
Cottages** ★★★★
Contact: Mr & Mrs Chris Seal, 1
Westfield, Gosforth, Newcastle
upon Tyne NE3 4YE
T: (0191) 285 6930 &
07711 066584
E: seal@
northumbrian-holiday-cottages.
co.uk
I: www.
northumbrian-holiday-cottages.
co.uk

FELTON
Northumberland

Garden House ★★★
Contact: Dales Hol Cot Ref:1788,
Dales Holiday Cottages, Carleton
Business Park, Carleton New
Road, Skipton, North Yorkshire
BD23 2AA
T: (01756) 799821 & 790919
F: (01756) 797012
E: info@dalesholcot.com
I: www.dalesholcot.com

FOREST-IN-TEESDALE
Durham

Laneside
Rating Applied For
Contact: Mr Greenside, Upper
Teesdale Estate, Raby Estates
Office, Middleton-in-Teesdale,
Barnard Castle, County Durham
DL12 0QH
T: (01833) 640209
F: (01833) 640963
E: teesdaleestate@rabycastle.
com
I: www.rabycastle.com

FOURSTONES
Northumberland

Frankham Lea ★★★★
Contact: Mrs Diane Allison,
Frankham Cottage, Fourstones,
Hexham, Northumberland
NE47 5DL
T: (01434) 674496
F: (01768) 867575
E: hsacommunications@
btinternet.com

FROSTERLEY
Durham

The Cottage ★★
Contact: Mrs C Grant, 3 The
Villettes, Houghton Road,
Newbottle, Houghton-le-Spring,
Tyne and Wear DH4 4EQ
T: (0191) 584 8103

Roseli Court ★★★★
Contact: Mrs Vivian Rayne, 68
Front Street, Frosterley, Bishop
Auckland, County Durham
DL13 2QS
T: (01388) 526488
F: (01388) 526488

GAINFORD
Durham

**Corner Cottage & Barn House
Mews** ★★
Contact: Dales Hol Cot
Ref:1283/1285, Dales Holiday
Cottages, Carleton Business
Park, Carleton New road,
Skipton, North Yorkshire
BD23 2AA
T: (01756) 799821 & 790919
F: (01756) 797012
E: info@daleshocot.com
I: www.daleshocot.com

East Greystone Farm Cottages
Rating Applied For
Contact: Mrs Sue Hodgson, East
Greystone Farm, Gainford,
Darlington, County Durham
DL2 3BL
T: (01325) 730236
F: (01325) 730236

Hollin Hall Cottage ★★★
Contact: Mrs J Hodgson, Hollin
Hall West, Gainford, Darlington,
County Durham DL2 3EX
T: (01325) 730808

GLANTON
Northumberland

Chestnut Cottage ★★★
Contact: Mr T Johnson, 21 West
Turnpike, Glanton, Alnwick,
Northumberland NE66 4AN
T: (01665) 578220

Coniston Cottage ★★★
Contact: Mrs J Mossman,
Coniston House, Glanton,
Alnwick, Northumberland
NE66 4AS
T: (01665) 578305

The Farmhouse ★★★★
Contact: Mrs Jackie Stothard,
Northfield Farm, Glanton,
Alnwick, Northumberland
NE66 4AG
T: (01665) 578203 & 0798 012
9386
F: (01665) 578203
E: jackie@lowalwinton.co.uk

Holly Cottage ★★★
Contact: Mr Robert Johnston &
Miss G Hibbert, Crag View
Cottage, Glanton, Alnwick,
Northumberland NE66 4AU
T: (01665) 578200 & 578336
F: (01665) 578336
E: g_hibbert@talk21.com

Thorne Cottage ★★★★
Contact: Mr & Mrs Clough,
3 High View, Darras Hall,
Ponteland, Newcastle upon Tyne
NE20 9ET
T: (01661) 822662
F: (01661) 820864
E: johnc@eaga.co.uk

GREENHAUGH
Northumberland

Bought-Hill Mill ★★★★
Contact: Mrs A Cowan, Bimmer-
Hill, Tarset, Hexham,
Northumberland NE48 1PG
T: (01434) 240373

HALTWHISTLE
Northumberland

**Bracken & Meadow View
Cottage** ★★
Contact: Mrs M Dawson,
Riverway House, 4 Wydon
Avenue, Haltwhistle,
Northumberland NE49 0AS
T: (01434) 320378

Farglow Farm ★★★★
Contact: Mrs C S Maclean, High
Edge Cottage, Moss Kennels,
Haydon Bridge, Hexham,
Northumberland NE47 8JP
T: 07765 001005 &
(01434) 344155
F: (01434) 344155

Kellah Cottages ★★★
Contact: Mrs Lesley Teasdale,
Kellah Cottages, Kellah Farm,
Haltwhistle, Northumberland
NE49 0JL
T: (01434) 320816
E: teasdale@ukonline.co.uk
I: web.ukonline.co.uk/teasdale

HAMSTERLEY
Durham

Diddridge Farm Cottage
★★★★
Contact: Ms Sheila Petch,
Diddridge Farm, Diddridge Lane,
Hamsterley, Bishop Auckland,
County Durham DL13 3PG
T: (01388) 488520
E: diddridge@tinyworld.co.uk

Edge Knoll Farm Cottages
★★★
Contact: Mr M G Edmonds, Edge
Knoll Farm, Hamsterley, Bishop
Auckland, County Durham
DL13 3PF
T: (01388) 488537
E: vacationfarm@hotmail.com

Hoppyland House ★★★
Contact: Mr & Mrs Bainbridge,
Church View, 22 Front Street,
Staindrop, Darlington, County
Durham DL2 3NH
T: (01833) 660430 &
07714 328073

Jasmine Cottage ★★★
Contact: Mrs A Roberts,
Jessamine House, Hamsterley,
Bishop Auckland, County
Durham DL13 3QF
T: (01388) 488630

1 South View Cottage ★★★
Contact: Dales Hol Cot Ref:2893,
Dales Holiday Cottages, Carleton
Business Park, Carleton New
Road, Skipton, North Yorkshire
BD23 2AA
T: (01756) 799821 & 790919
F: (01756) 797012
E: info@dalesholcot.com
I: www.dalesholcot.com

West Hoppyland Cabins ★★
Contact: Mrs C J Atkinson, West
Hoppyland Cabins, Hamsterley,
Bishop Auckland, County
Durham DL13 3NP
T: (01388) 488196 &
07802 413923

HARBOTTLE
Northumberland

Hillview ★★★★
Contact: Mrs Deirdre Dickson,
Crosby House, Crosby-on-Eden,
Carlisle, Cumbria CA6 4QZ
T: (01228) 573239 & 573337
F: (01228) 573338
E: enquires@norbyways.demon.
co.uk
I: www.northumbria-byways.
com/hillview

Honeysuckle Cottage ★★
Contact: Mrs J Bickmore,
Wayside, Harbottle, Morpeth,
Northumberland NE65 7DQ
T: (01669) 650348
I: www.rothbury.
co.uk/Accommodation/
Harbottle/Honeysuckle/
Honeysuckle.htm

HARPERLEY
Durham

**Bushblades Farm Cottage
★★★**
Contact: Mrs P Gibson,
Bushblades Farm, Harperley,
Stanley, County Durham
DH9 9UA
T: (01207) 232722

HARWOOD
Durham

**Honey Pot Cottage & Frog Hall
★**
Contact: Mr N J Liddle, Upper
Teesdale Estate, Raby Estates
Office, Middleton-in-Teesdale,
Barnard Castle, County Durham
DL12 0QH
T: (01833) 640209
F: (01833) 640963
E: teesdaleestate@rabycastle.
com
I: www.rabycastle.com

HAYDON BRIDGE
Northumberland

**Hadrian's Wall Country
Cottages ★★-★★★**
Contact: Mrs Lyn Murray,
Hadrian's Wall Country
Cottages, Hindshield Moss,
North Road, Haydon Bridge,
Hexham, Northumberland
NE47 6NF
T: (01434) 688688
F: (01434) 684867
E: cottages@hadrianswall.co.uk
I: www.hadrianswall.co.uk

**Holiday Cottage
Rating Applied For**
Contact: Mrs Cynthia Bradley,
Edenholme, John Martin Street,
Haydon Bridge, Hexham,
Northumberland NE47 6AA
T: (01434) 684622
E: edenholme@btinternet.com

HEBBURN
Tyne and Wear

**26 Hazelmoor
Rating Applied For**
Contact: Mr P Goodall, 18
Coleridge Square, Hebburn, Tyne
and Wear NE31 1QD
T: (0191) 428 6180 &
07941 611551

HEDDON-ON-THE-WALL
Northumberland

2 East Town House ★★★
Contact: Mr & Mrs C&B Amos, 1
East Town House, Heddon-on-
the-Wall, Newcastle upon Tyne
NE15 0DR
T: (01661) 852277 & 852913
F: (01661) 853063

HEPPLE
Northumberland

The Barn ★★★★
Contact: Country Holidays
ref:4166, Spring Mill, Earby,
Barnoldswick, Lancashire
BB94 0AA
T: 08700 723723
F: (01282) 844288
E: sales@ttgihg.co.uk
I: www.country-holidays.co.uk

HEXHAM
Northumberland

Brokenheugh Lodge ★★★★
Contact: Mrs R Jamieson,
Brokenheugh Lodge,
Brokenheugh Hall, Hexham,
Northumberland NE47 6JT
T: (01434) 684206 & 684557
F: (01434) 684557
E: stay@brokenheugh.co.uk
I: www.brokenheugh.co.uk

**Hexham Holiday Cottages
★★★★**
Contact: Mr & Mrs Roy & Cath
Dawson, 19 Shaftoe Leazes,
Hexham, Northumberland
NE46 3DW
T: (01434) 600114
E: cathandroy@aol.com

Moorgair Cottage ★★★★
Contact: Mrs V Ridley, Moorgair
Cottage, Slaley, Hexham,
Northumberland NE47 0AN
T: (01434) 673473
E: g_ridley@lineone.net
I: www.moorgair.co.uk

North Ashes ★★★★
Contact: Dales Hol Cot Ref:2657,
Dales Holiday Cottages, Carleton
Business Park, Carleton New
Road, Skipton, North Yorkshire
BD23 2AA
T: (01756) 799821 & 790919
F: (01756) 797012
E: info@dalesholcot.com
I: www.dalesholcot.com

Old Byre ★★★★
Contact: Mrs Elizabeth Courage,
Rye Hill Farm, Slaley, Hexham,
Northumberland NE47 0AH
T: (01434) 673259
F: (01434) 673259
E: enquiries@consult-courage.
co.uk
I: www.ryehillfarm.co.uk
🔊

Sammy's Place ★★★★★
Contact: Mr Roger McKechnie,
Dilston House, Corbridge,
Northumberland NE45 5RH
T: (01434) 633653 &
07768 365343
F: (01434) 6344640
E: roger@dilstonhouse.
freeserve.co.uk
I: www.sammyshideaways.com

Stotsfold Hall ★★★
Contact: Mrs A Soens, Stotsfold
Hall, Steel, Hexham,
Northumberland NE47 0HP
T: (01434) 673270
E: alisonsoensatstotsfoldhall@
compuserve.com

HOLY ISLAND
Northumberland

**Farne Court Cottages, Farne
View Cottage★★★**
Contact: Mrs A J Batty, Orchard
Gap, Aydon Raod, Corbridge,
Northumberland NE45 5EJ
T: (01434) 632691
F: (01434) 634170

The Haven ★★★
Contact: Mr C Souter, 30
Brandling Place South, Jesmond,
Newcastle upon Tyne, NE2
NE2 4RU
T: (0191) 281 7421 & 212 0500
F: (0191) 212 0600

Winn Cottage ★★
Contact: Mrs K M Winn, 11
Newtons Croft Crescent,
Barlborough, Chesterfield,
Derbyshire S43 4WA
T: (01246) 810767
F: (01246) 810767
E: michael.winn@which.net

HOWICK
Northumberland

South Cottage ★★
Contact: Sykes Cottages
Ref:625, Sykes Cottages, York
House, York Street, Chester,
Cheshire CH1 3LR
T: (01244) 345700
F: (01244) 321442
E: info@sykescottages.co.uk
I: www.sykescottages.co.uk

HUMSHAUGH
Northumberland

East Farm Cottage ★★★
Contact: Mrs G A Dodds, East
Farm House, Humshaugh,
Hexham, Northumberland
NE46 4AT
T: (01434) 689150
E: 101454.1266@compuserve.
com

ILDERTON
Northumberland

**Coach House & Coach House
Cottage ★★★**
Contact: Mrs M Sale, Ilderton
Glebe, Ilderton, Alnwick,
Northumberland NE66 4YD
T: (01668) 217293

INGRAM
Northumberland

**The Old Rectory
★★★★-★★★★★**
Contact: Mrs T Stephenson, The
Old Rectory, Ingram, Alnwick,
Northumberland NE66 4LT
T: (01665) 578236
E: trysha@
cheviotholidaycottages.co.uk
I: www.cheviotholidaycottages.
co.uk

IRESHOPEBURN
Durham

**High Barnes Holiday Cottage
★★★★**
Contact: Mr & Mrs J&F Wilson,
High Barnes Holiday Cottage,
High Barnes, Ireshopeburn,
Bishop Auckland, County
Durham DL13 1PY
T: (01388) 537556

Hillview Cottage ★★★
Contact: Miss Rachel O'Halleron,
1 Collindale Road, South Ferring,
Steyning, West Sussex BN12 3JF
T: (01903) 245345 & 245345
E: racmarglen@hotmail.com

KIELDER
Northumberland

**Kielder Lodges
★★★★-★★★★★★**
Contact: Hoseasons Holidays
Limited, Sunway House,
Lowestoft, Suffolk NR32 3LT
T: (01502) 500500
F: (01502) 584962
E: kielder.water@nwl.co.uk
I: www.kielder.org

KIELDER WATER
Northumberland

Calvert Trust Kielder ★★★★
Contact: Miss Rachel Cowper,
Calvert Trust Kielder, Kielder
Water, Hexham,
Northumberland NE48 1BS
T: (01434) 250232
F: (01434) 250015
E: enquiries@calvert-kielder.
com
I: www.calvert-trust.org.uk
🔊

KIRKNEWTON
Northumberland

Hillview Cottage ★★★★
Contact: Dales Hol Cot Ref:2043,
Dales Holiday Cottages, Carleton
Business Park, Carleton New
Road, Skipton, North Yorkshire
BD23 2AA
T: (01756) 799821 & 790919
F: (01756) 797012
E: info@dalesholcot.com
I: www.dalesholcot.com

KIRKWHELPINGTON
Northumberland

Herdsman Cottage ★★★★
Contact: Mrs Lorna Thornton,
Cornhills Farmhouse, Cornhills,
Kirkwhelpington, Newcastle
upon Tyne NE19 2RE
T: (01830) 540232
F: (01830) 540388
E: cornhills@farming.co.uk
I: www.
northumberlandfarmhouse.
co.uk

LANCHESTER
Durham

Browney Cottage & Browney Close ★★★
Contact: Mrs Ann Darlington, Hall Hill Farm, Lanchester, Durham, County Durham DH7 0TA
T: (01388) 730300 &
(01207) 521476
F: (01388) 730300
E: hhf@freenetname.co.uk
I: www.hallhillfarm.co.uk

LESBURY
Northumberland

Lesbury Glebe Cottage ★★★★★
Contact: Mrs D G Brunton, Lesbury Glebe, Lesbury, Alnwick, Northumberland NE66 3AU
T: (01665) 830 732

LOFTUS
Tees Valley

Liverton Lodge ★★
Contact: Dales Hol Cot Ref:1778, Dales Holiday Cottages, Carleton Business Park, Carleton New Road, Skipton, North Yorkshire BD23 2AA
T: (01756) 799821 & 790919
F: (01756) 797012
E: info@dalesholcot.com
I: www.dalesholcot.com

LONGFRAMLINGTON
Northumberland

Dene House Farm Cottages Poppy, Bluebell, Primrose, Buttercup
Rating Applied For
Contact: Mrs P Wilson, Dene House Farm Cottages Poppy, Bluebell, Primrose, Buttercup, Dene House, Smalldene, Longframlington, Morpeth, Northumberland NE65 8EE
T: (01665) 570549
F: (01665) 570549

LONGHORSLEY
Northumberland

Beacon Hill Farm Holidays ★★★★-★★★★★
Contact: Mr A B Moore, Beacon Hill House, Longhorsley, Morpeth, Northumberland NE65 8QW
T: (01670) 780900
F: (01670) 780901
E: alun@beaconhill.co.uk
I: www.beaconhill.co.uk

Cartwheel Cottage ★★★
Contact: Mr & Mrs James & Sarah Chisholm, Westerheugh Farm, Longhorsley, Morpeth, Northumberland NE65 8RH
T: (01665) 570661
E: sarah@cartwheelcottage.com

Green Yard Cottage ★★★
Contact: Mr and Mrs G Lowes, Todburn West Farm, Longhorsley, Morpeth, Northumberland NE65 8QZ
T: (01670) 788416

LONGHOUGHTON
Northumberland

Harlaw Hill Farm Cottage ★★★
Contact: Mr & Mrs A&J Pringle, Harlow Hill, Longhoughton, Alnwick, Northumberland NE66 3AA
T: (01665) 577215

Pipers Cottage ★★★
Contact: Mr & Mrs K J Dawson, Linden, Pipers Field, Longhirst Colliery, Morpeth, Northumberland NE61 3LS
T: (01670) 790300 &
07929 895429

Rose Cottage & Croft Cottage ★★-★★★
Contact: Mrs M Forsyth, Low Steads, Longhoughton, Alnwick, Northumberland NE66 3AL
T: (01665) 577227
I: www.lowsteads.co.uk

LOWICK
Northumberland

Barmoor Ridge Cottage ★★★★
Contact: Mrs Patricia Adrienne Reavley, Barmoor Ridge, Lowick, Berwick-upon-Tweed, Northumberland TD15 2QD
T: (01289) 388226
F: (01289) 388226
E: jimpyr@hotmail.com

Barmoor South Moor ★★★
Contact: Mrs A Gold, Barmoor South Moor, Lowick, Berwick-upon-Tweed TD15 2QF
T: (01289) 388205
E: barrgold@farming.co.uk

Black Bull Cottage ★★★
Contact: Mrs A Grundy, Black Bull Hotel, Main Street, Lowick, Berwick-upon-Tweed, Northumberland TD15 2UA
T: (01289) 388228
F: (01289) 388395
E: tom@blackbullowick.freeserve.co.uk
I: www.secretkingdom.com/black/bull.htm

Garland Cottage ★★★
Contact: Mrs G M Jones, The School House, Bowsden, Berwick-upon-Tweed, Northumberland TD15 2TW
T: (01289) 388459
F: (01289) 388459

Heather Cottage ★★★
Contact: Miss M Nesbit, Hetton North Farm, Lowick, Berwick-upon-Tweed, Northumberland TD15 2UL
T: (01289) 388609 & 388232
E: mnesbit@farming.co.uk
I: www.heathercottage.ntb.org.uk

LUCKER
Northumberland

Lucker Hall Steading ★★★★-★★★★★
Contact: Mrs J Mallen, Northumberland Estates Holiday, Cottages, Alnwick, Northumberland NE66 1NQ
T: (01665) 602094 &
07774 606123
F: (01665) 608126
E: nehc@farmline.com
I: www.alnwickcastle.com/holidaycottages

Lucker Mill ★★★★★
Contact: Mrs J Mallen, Northumberland Estates Holiday Cottages, Alnwick Castle, Alnwick, Northumberland NE66 1NQ
T: (01665) 602094 &
0375 606123
F: (01665) 608126
E: nehc@farmline.com
I: www.alnwickcastle.com/holidaycottages/

MARSKE-BY-THE-SEA
Tees Valley

21 Chapel Street ★★
Contact: Mrs Atherley, 19 Firrigg Drive, Marske-by-the-Sea, Redcar, Cleveland TS11 6BT
T: (01642) 487946

4 Church Street ★★★
Contact: Mrs B R Mosey, 27 The Avenue, Billericay, Essex CM12 9HG
T: (01277) 652778
E: brmosey@yahoo.co.uk

White Rose Cottage ★★★
Contact: Mr & Mrs Phillips, 21 Church Howle Crescent, Marske-by-Sea, Redcar, Cleveland TS11 7EJ
T: (01642) 481064
F: (01642) 481064
E: phillipspcp@aol.com

MEDOMSLEY
Durham

Grange Farm Cottage ★★★★
Contact: Mr W Beaumont, Medomsley Grange Farm, Medomsley, Consett, County Durham DH8 6PP
T: (01207) 562 767 & (0191) 383 5163

MELKRIDGE
Northumberland

Common House Farm ★★★
Contact: Mr and Mrs R Goodchild, Common House Farm, Melkridge, Haltwhistle, Northumberland NE49 9PF
T: (01434) 321680
E: stay@commonhousefarm.com
I: www.commonhousefarm.com

MICKLETON
Durham

Blackthorn Cottage ★★★
Contact: Mrs D Garrett, 26 St Lawrence Road, Upminster, Essex RM14 2UW
T: (01708) 225107 &
07710 530411
E: coldigar@btinternet.com
I: www.teesdalecottages.co.uk

West Tofts ★★★★
Contact: Mrs I Stoddart, Wemmergill Hall Farm, Lunedale, Middleton-in-Teesdale, Barnard Castle, County Durham DL12 0PA
T: (01833) 640379 &
(01244) 345700
F: (01833) 640379
E: wemmergill@freenet.co.uk
I: www.sykescottages.co.uk

MIDDLETON-IN-TEESDALE
Durham

The Barn ★★★
Contact: Mrs A Whitfield, Garden House, Low Side, Mickleton, Barnard Castle, County Durham DL12 0JR
T: (01833) 640759

Beverley Cottage ★★
Contact: Dales Hol Cot Ref:2088, Dales Holiday Cottages, Carleton Business Park, Carleton New Road, Skipton, North Yorkshire BD23 2AA
T: (01756) 799821 & 790919
F: (01756) 797012
E: info@dalesholcot.com
I: www.dalesholcot.com

Brock Scar Cottage ★★★★
Contact: Mrs Winfred Gargate, Brock Scar Farm, Middleton-in-Teesdale, Barnard Castle, County Durham DL12 0PW
T: (01833) 640495 & 0798 924 4786
F: (01833) 640495
E: wyngargate@barclays.net
I: www.brockscar.co.uk

Castle Cottage ★★★
Contact: Mrs J Lynch, Pikestone House, Holwick, Middleton-in-Teesdale, Barnard Castle, County Durham DL12 0NR
T: (01833) 640474

The Coach House ★★★★
Contact: Mrs J A Finn, Belvedere House, 54 Market Place, Middleton-in-Teesdale, Barnard Castle, County Durham DL12 0QH
T: (01833) 640884
F: (01833) 640884
E: info@thecoachhouse.net
I: www.thecoachhouse.net

Country Cottage ★★
Contact: Mr R B Burman, Fairlawn, 1 Thorn Road, Bramhall, Stockport, Cheshire SK7 1HG
T: (0161) 439 5435 & 860 7123
E: familyburman@cwctv.net

Firethorn Cottage ★★★
Contact: Mrs J Thompson, Cutbush Farmhouse, Hardingham Road, Hingham, Norwich NR9 4LY
T: (01953) 850 364

Green Acres, Pennine View & Meadow's Edge ★★★
Contact: Mrs G Scott, Low Way Farm, Holwick, Middleton-in-Teesdale, County Durham DL12 0NJ
T: (01833) 640506

Establishments printed in blue have a detailed entry in this guide

Hush Cottage ★★
Contact: Mrs V Mulholland, Knapp Cottage, Corton, Warminster, Wiltshire BA12 0SZ
T: (01985) 850450 & 850182
E: mul.cort@btinternet.com

Hyland View and Annexe ★★★
Contact: Mrs Kathryn Guy, 21 Laburnum Grove, Richmond, North Yorkshire DL10 5AR
T: (01748) 825640

North Wythes Hill ★★★
Contact: Mrs June Dent, Laneside, Middleton-in-Teesdale, Barnard Castle, County Durham DL12 0RY
T: (01833) 640573
E: wytheshill@teesdaleonline. co.uk

Rosedale ★★
Contact: Mrs Mary Wilkinson, Ladnek, School Road, Kirkby-in-Furness, Cumbria LA17 7TF
T: (01229) 889420
F: (01229) 889766

Shepherd's Cottage ★★★
Contact: Mrs G Scott, Lowway Farm, Holwick, Middleton-in-Teesdale, Barnard Castle, County Durham DL12 0NJ
T: (01833) 640506

Snaisgill Farm Cottage ★★★
Contact: Mrs S Parmley, Snaisgill Farm Cottage, Middleton-in-Teesdale, Barnard Castle, County Durham DL12 0RP
T: (01833) 640343

Summerville Cottage ★★★
Contact: Mr M B Fletcher, Friar House Farm, Newbiggin-in-Teesdale, Barnard Castle, County Durham DL12 0XG
T: (01833) 622202

Sunnyplace Bungalow ★★★★
Contact: Dales Hol Cot Ref:2172, Dales Holiday Cottages, Carleton Business Park, Carleton New Road, Skipton, North Yorkshire BD23 2AA
T: (01756) 799821 & 790919
F: (01756) 797012
E: info@dalesholcot.com
I: www.dalesholcot.com

Town View Cottage ★★★
Contact: Mrs R Marshall, The Bungalow, The Green, Headlam, Darlington, County Durham DL2 3HA
T: (01325) 730989
F: (01325) 730989

Westfield Cottage ★★★
Contact: Mrs Doreen Scott, Westfield House, Laithkirk, Middleton-in-Teesdale, Barnard Castle, County Durham DL12 0PN
T: (01833) 640942

MILFIELD
Northumberland

Barley Hill Cottage ★★★
Contact: Mr David Bell, 20 Balmoral Terrace, Gosforth, Newcastle upon Tyne, Northumberland NE3 1YH
T: (0191) 285 2526
E: RoseDaveBell@Yahoo.co.uk

Milfield Hill Cottage ★★★★
Contact: Dr R Craig, Milfield Hill House, Milfield, Wooler, Northumberland NE71 6JE
T: (01668) 216338
F: (01668) 216338
E: craig@milfield1.freeserve. co.uk
I: www.milfield1.freeserve.co.uk

MINDRUM
Northumberland

Bowmont Cottage ★★
Contact: Mr & Mrs S Orpwood, Bowmont Hill, Mindrum, Northumberland TD12 4QW
T: (01890) 852266
F: (01890) 850245
E: s.orpwood@farmline.com
I: www.cottageguide. co.uk/bowmonthill

The Longknowe ★★★
Contact: Mr Michael Andrews, Littleworth Farm Cottage, Littleworth Lane, Esher, Surrey KT10 9PF
T: (01372) 469751 & 464284
F: (01372) 460715
E: postmaster@littlane.demon. co.uk

MOORSHOLM
Tees Valley

Sherburn ★★★
Contact: Alison Dent, Whitby Holiday Cottages, 47 Flowergate, Whitby, North Yorkshire YO21 3BB
T: (01947) 603010
F: (01947) 821133
E: enquiries@whitby-cottages. co.uk
I: www.whitby-cottages.co.uk

MORPETH
Northumberland

Barnacre
Rating Applied For
Contact: Mrs Linda Rudd, Warren Cottage, Longhirst Village, Morpeth, Northumberland NE61 3LX
T: (01670) 790116
E: linda@mrudd.fslife.co.uk

5 Copper Chare ★★★
Contact: Mr G M Gagie, Hillside Cottage, Wood Lane, Uttoxeter, Staffordshire ST14 8JR
T: (01889) 562838

25 Hillgate ★★★
Contact: Mr Edward Quant, 41 Delaval Terrace, Gosforth, Newcastle upon Tyne NE3 4RT
T: (0191) 2130536

Netherwitton Hall Cottages ★★★
Contact: Mrs Jane Trevelyan, Netherwitton Hall Cottages, Netherwitton Hall, Morpeth, Northumberland NE61 4NW
T: (01670) 772219
F: (01670) 772332

Old Barn Cottages ★★★
Contact: Mrs J Mancey, Old Barn Cottages, Benridge Hagg, Morpeth, Northumberland NE61 3SB
T: (01670) 518507
I: benridge_cottages_uk.tripod. com

NEWBROUGH
Northumberland

Prudhamstone House Cottage ★★★
Contact: Dales Hol Cot Ref:794, Dales Holiday Cottages, Carleton Business Park, Carleton New Road, Skipton, North Yorkshire BD23 2AA
T: (01756) 799821 & 790919
F: (01756) 797012
E: info@dalesholcot.com
I: www.dalesholcot.com

NEWCASTLE UPON TYNE
Tyne and Wear

135 Audley Road ★★★
Contact: Miss Linda Wright, 137 Audley Road, South Gosforth, Newcastle upon Tyne NE3 1QH
T: (0191) 285 6374
E: lkw@audleyender.fsnet.co.uk

Walbottle House ★★★★★
Contact: Mrs S E Kent, Walbottle House, Walbottle, Newcastle upon Tyne NE15 8JD
T: (0191) 264 1108

NEWTON-BY-THE-SEA
Northumberland

3A & 3B Coastguard Cottages ★★★
Contact: Mr & Mrs M Cottam, 13 St Georges Crescent, Monkseaton, Whitley Bay, Tyne and Wear NE25 8BJ
T: (0191) 251 2506 & 251 2506
F: (0191) 222 1017
E: mark&alisoncottam@ hotmail.com
I: www.geocities. com/coastguardcottages

Link House Farm ★★★★
Contact: Mrs Jayne Hellmann, The Granary, Link House Farm, Newton-by-the-Sea, Alnwick, Northumberland NE66 3DF
T: (01665) 576820 & (01670) 860373
F: (01665) 576820

Newton Hall Cottages ★★★★
Contact: Mrs S A Patterson, Newton Hall, Newton-by-the-Sea, Alnwick, Northumberland NE66 3DZ
T: (01665) 576239
F: (01665) 576900
E: ian.patterson@newtonhall. prestel.co.uk
I: www.commercepark. co.uk/newtonhall

Seawinds ★★★
Contact: Miss J Park, Low Buston Hall, Warkworth, Morpeth, Northumberland NE65 0XY
T: (01665) 714805
F: (01665) 711345
E: jopark@farming.co.uk
I: www.seawinds.ntb.org.uk

NEWTON-ON-THE-MOOR
Northumberland

Clough Cottage ★★★
Contact: Mr M Prentice, Parkside Farm, Stonygate, Houghton-le-Spring, Tyne and Wear DH4 4NN
T: (0191) 528 0233
I: www.kirkstones. co.uk/clough_cottage/index.htm

NORHAM
Northumberland

The Boathouse ★★★
Contact: Mr G J Crabtree & Mrs Chantler, Great Humphries Farm, Grafty Green, Maidstone, Kent ME17 2AX
T: (01622) 859672

Boathouse Cottage ★★★★
Contact: Mrs Susan Dalgety, The Columns, Norham, Berwick-upon-Tweed TD15 2JZ
T: (01289) 382300
F: (01289) 382334
E: alexdalgety@compuserve. com
I: www.boathouse.ntb.org.uk

Broadstone Cottage ★★★
Contact: Mr E D Chantler, Broadstone Farm, Grafty Green, Maidstone, Kent ME17 2AT
T: (01622) 850207
F: (01233) 506299

Foggy Bumble ★★★
Contact: Mrs Joan Firth, Lowood, 3 Eagle Drive, Longridge, Berwick-upon-Tweed, TD15 2YU
T: (01289) 331882
F: (01289) 331882
E: firthj@zoom.co.uk

5 Grievestead Cottages
Rating Applied For
Contact: Mrs Maragaret Wright, 19 Houghton Avenue, Cullercoats, North Shields, Tyne and Wear NE30 3NQ
T: (0191) 252 0627 & 0778 0974929
F: (0191) 297 1984

Tweed Cottage and Teviot Cottage ★★★
Contact: Mrs K Curry, West Newbiggin, Norham, Berwick-upon-Tweed, Northumberland TD15 2NL
T: (01289) 382200
F: (01289) 382200

NORTH SUNDERLAND
Northumberland

Longstone Properties ★★★
Contact: Mrs Judy Oxley, Longstone House Hotel, 182 Main Street, Seahouses, Northumberland NE68 7UA
T: (01665) 720212

OAKENSHAW
Durham

Stockley Fell Farm Cottages ★★★★
Contact: Mrs J Carter, Stockley Fell Farm, Oakenshaw, Crook, County Durham DL15 0TN
T: (01388) 745938
F: (01388) 745938

OTTERBURN
Northumberland

Otterburn Hall Farm ★★★★
Contact: Mrs Susan Campbell, 1 Cairn View, Longframlington, Morpeth, Northumberland NE65 8JT
T: (01665) 570810
T: (01727) 844573
E: stcmcquay@compuserve.com

Rowan Cottage ★★★★
Contact: Mr & Mrs John and Jill
Wilson, Rowan Cottage,
Whitelee Farm, Byrness,
Otterburn, Northumberland
NE19 1TJ
T: (01830) 520530 &
0771 681509
F: (01830) 520888
E: john.wilson@ncl.ac.uk

Woodhill
Rating Applied For
Contact: Mrs Corrinne Knight,
Woodhill, Otterburn, Newcastle
upon Tyne NE19 1JX
T: (01830) 520657 & (0191) 232
2155

OUSTON
Durham

Katie's Cottage ★★★★
Contact: Mrs H Johnson, Low
Urpeth Farm House, Ouston,
Chester-le-Street, County
Durham DH2 1BD
T: (0191) 410 2901
F: (0191) 410 0088
E: lowurpeth@hotmail.com
I: www.lowurpeth.co.uk

OVINGTON
Durham

Village Green Cottage ★★★★
Contact: Mrs M J Green,
Ovington, Richmond, North
Yorkshire DL11 7BW
T: (01833) 627331

OVINGTON
Northumberland

Appletree Cottage ★★★★
Contact: Mrs L A Rowell,
Appletree Cottage, Ovington
Hall Farm, Ovington,
Northumberland NE42 6ED
T: (01661) 832355

Westgarth Cottage ★★★★
Contact: Mrs C Graham,
Stonecroft, Ovington,
Northumberland NE42 6EB
T: (01661) 832202

PIERCEBRIDGE
Durham

The Bungalow ★★★
Contact: Mrs J Lowe, The
Bungalow, Bolam Grange,
Piercebridge, Darlington, County
Durham DL2 3UL
T: (01388) 832779

POWBURN
Northumberland

Threestoneburn House ★★★★
Contact: Mrs Linda Bankier, The
Granary, Grindonrigg, Duddo,
Berwick-upon-Tweed TD15 2PT
T: (01289) 382025 & 330044
E: stuart.bankier@jcmr.u-net.
com

REDCAR
Tees Valley

Dove House ★★★
Contact: Mrs C McGovern, 13
Kirkleatham Lane, Redcar,
Cleveland TS10 1NS
T: (01642) 479311

Sea Mews Holiday Cottage
★★★
Contact: Mr A Hunter, 21 Hurst
Park, Redcar, Cleveland TS10 2JQ
T: (01642) 474609

RIDSDALE
Northumberland

Ridd Cottage ★★★★★
Contact: Mr David Surtees, 146
Whitley Road, Whitley Bay, Tyne
and Wear NE26 2NA
T: (0191) 258 5286 & 253 3714
F: (0191) 251 0614
E: davidsurtees@msn.com
I: www.
northumberlandcottageholidays.
co.uk

ROMALDKIRK
Durham

Jesmond Cottage ★★★★
Contact: Mrs D West, Yew Trees,
Lartington, Barnard Castle,
County Durham DL12 9BP
T: (01833) 650454
E: john@westcotts.demon.co.uk

**Romaldkirk Self Catering
Cottages ★★-★★★★**
Contact: Mrs Gwen Wall, Kleine
Cottage, Romaldkirk, Barnard
Castle, County Durham
DL12 9ED
T: (01833) 650794
I: www.cottageguide.
co.uk/romaldkirk

Sycamore Cottage ★★★★
Contact: Dales Hol Cot Ref:698,
Dales Holiday Cottages, Carleton
Business Park, Carleton New
Road, Skipton, North Yorkshire
BD23 2AA
T: (01756) 799821 & 790919
F: (01756) 797012
E: info@dalesholcot.com
I: www.dalesholcot.com

ROTHBURY
Northumberland

**Alexandra House Mews
Cottage ★★★**
Contact: Mrs L Nicholls,
Alexandra House, High Street,
Rothbury, Morpeth,
Northumberland NE65 7TE
T: (01669) 621463
E: lucy@alexandrahouse.fsnet.
co.uk
I: www.alex-house.co.uk

Black Brae Cottage ★★★★★
Contact: Mrs Amanda France,
Bickerton, Rothbury, Morpeth,
Northumberland NE65 7LW
T: (01669) 640335
E: amandafrance@netscape.net

Coquetdale House ★★★
Contact: Mrs Judith Quayle, Rye
Bank, West Hepple, Rothbury,
Morpeth, Northumberland
NE65 7LJ
T: (01669) 640242

The Cottage ★★★
Contact: Mrs I A Wilbie-Chalk,
Well Close, Townfoot, Rothbury,
Morpeth, Northumberland
NE65 7NZ
T: (01669) 620430 &
07974 716041
F: (01669) 621234
E: visitors@esoterics.org
I: www.rothbury.co.uk

Garden Cottage ★★★★★
Contact: Mrs J Hewison,
Silverton Lodge, Silverton Lane,
Rothbury, Morpeth,
Northumberland NE65 7RJ
T: (01669) 620144
F: (01669) 621920
E: silverton.lodge@btinternet.
com
I: www.silvertonlodge.co.uk

**Low Alwinton Holiday
Cottages ★★★★**
Contact: Mrs Jackie Stothard,
Northfield Farm, Glanton,
Alnwick, Northumberland
NE66 4AG
T: (01665) 578203
E: jackie@lowalwinton.co.uk
I: www.lowalwinton.co.uk

**The Old Telephone Exchange
Rating Applied For**
Contact: Ms Susan Doncaster, 1
Hibberd Road, Malin Bridge,
Sheffield, S6 4RE
T: (0114) 233 1018 &
07947 508135
E: cottage@danum.club24.co.uk

The Pele Tower ★★★★★
Contact: Mr & Mrs J D Malia, The
Pele Tower, Whitton, Rothbury,
Northumberland NE65 7RL
T: (01669) 620410
F: (01669) 621006
E: davidmalia@aol.com
I: www.thepeletower.com

Phoenix Cottage ★★★
Contact: Dales Hol Cot Ref:1956,
Dales Holiday Cottages, Carleton
Business Park, Carleton New
Road, Skipton, North Yorkshire
BD23 2AA
T: (01756) 799821 & 790919
F: (01756) 797012
E: info@dalesholcot.com
I: www.dalesholcot.com

Riverside Lodge ★★★★
Contact: Mr Eric Jensen,
Edgecombe, Hillside Road,
Rothbury, Morpeth,
Northumberland NE65 7PT
T: (01669) 620464 & (0191) 259
2300
F: (0191) 259 2360
E: info@theriversidelodge.com
I: www.theriversidelodge.com

Simonside Apartment ★★★
Contact: Country Holidays
RN:752, Holiday Cottages Group
Owner Services Dept, Spring
Mill, Earby, Barnoldswick,
Lancashire BB18 6RN
T: 0870 444 6603
F: (01282) 841539
E: sales@ttgihg.co.uk
I: www.country-holidays.co.uk

Tosson Tower Farm
★★★-★★★★★
Contact: Mrs Ann Foggin,
Tosson Tower Farm, Great
Tosson, Morpeth,
Northumberland NE65 7NW
T: (01669) 620228
F: (01669) 620228
E: ann@tossontowerfarm.com
I: www.tossontowerfarm.com

Whitton Lodge ★★★
Contact: Mr R E Thorn, Whitton
Grange, Rothbury, Morpeth,
Northumberland NE65 7RL
T: (01669) 620929
F: (01669) 620929

RUSHYFORD
Durham

West Cottage ★★★★
Contact: Mrs E Wilkinson,
Carrsides Farm, Rushyford,
Ferryhill, County Durham
DL17 0NJ
T: (01388) 720252
F: (01388) 720252
E: carrsides@farming.co.uk

ST JOHN'S CHAPEL
Durham

Burnbrae ★★★★
Contact: Dales Hol Cot Ref:2125,
Dales Holiday Cottages, Carleton
Business Park, Carleton New
Road, Skipton, North Yorkshire
BD23 2AA
T: (01756) 799821 & 790919
F: (01756) 797012
E: info@dalesholcot.com
I: www.dalesholcot.com

SALTBURN-BY-THE-SEA
Tees Valley

York Cottage ★★★
Contact: Dales Hol Cot Ref:2912,
Dales Holiday Cottages, Carleton
Business Park, Carleton New
Road, Skipton, North Yorkshire
BD23 2AA
T: (01756) 799821 & 790919
F: (01756) 797012
E: info@dalesholcot.com
I: www.dalesholcot.com

The Zetland ★★★
Contact: Mrs Joan Carter, 1
Hawthorn Grove, Yarm,
Cleveland TS15 9EZ
T: (01642) 782507
E: graham@howard95.
freeserve.co.uk
I: www.carter-steel.co.uk

Zetland Apartment ★★★★
Contact: Mr K Kelly, Apartment
25, The Zetland, Marine Parade,
Saltburn-by-the-Sea, Cleveland
TS12 1BU
T: (01287) 624390
F: (01287) 625780
E: kenkelly@xlnt-properties.
com
I: www.xlnt-properties.com

SCREMERSTON
Northumberland

The Lodge ★★★
Contact: Mr & Mrs T E Nesbitt,
41 Sunderland Road Villas,
Heworth, Gateshead, Tyne and
Wear NE10 8HB
T: (0191) 469 6434

SEAHOUSES
Northumberland

2 Archway Cottages ★★★
Contact: Mrs A K Riley, 1 The
Croft, South Lane, North
Sunderland, Seahouses,
Northumberland NE68 7XA
T: (01665) 720325

Brockburn ★★★★
Contact: Mrs P Thompson,
Highfield House, Woodhill Farm,
Ponteland, Newcastle upon Tyne
NE20 0JA
T: (01661) 860165

Establishments printed in blue have a detailed entry in this guide

Cliff House Cottages ★★★
Contact: Mr S Holford, 88A
Fenham Hall Drive, Newcastle
upon Tyne, NE4 9XA
T: (0191) 275 0854 &
(01665) 720326
F: (0191) 261 4948
E: cliffhousecottage@talk21.
com

Dairy Cottage ★★
Contact: Mr & Mrs Smith, 4
Mayfair Road, Jesmond,
Newcastle upon Tyne NE2 3DP
T: (0191) 281 8277
E: carol.smith4@virgin.net
I: www.dreamwater.
com/biz/dairycottage

Dalfaber and Lynbank ★★★
Contact: Mrs Louise Donaldson,
4 Broad Road, Seahouses,
Northumberland NE68 7UP
T: (01665) 721066 &
07889 855968
F: (01665) 721066
I: www.dalfaber-lynbank.ntb.
org.uk

Driftwood Cottage ★★★★
Contact: Mr Ian Longstaff, 15
Quarryfield, Seahouses,
Northumberland NE68 7TB
T: (01665) 720835 &
(01289) 303222

Fahren House ★★★★
Contact: Ms Caroline Shiel, The
Bield, 37 St Aidans, Seahouses,
Northumberland NE68 7SS
T: (01665) 721375 & 720308
F: (01665) 721375
E: carolinebryan@ukonline.
co.uk
I: www.farne-islands.com

Farne Court ★★★★
Contact: Mr David Donaldson,
Farne Court, St Aidans,
Seahouses, Northumberland
NE68 7SS
T: (01665) 720530

Fisherlasses Flat ★★★
Contact: Mrs Karen Wilkin,
Fisherlasses Flat, 2 South Street,
Swallow Fish Ltd, Seahouses,
Northumberland NE68 7RB
T: (01665) 721052
F: (01665) 721177
E: wilkin@swallowfish.co.uk
I: www.swallowfish.co.uk

Fishermans Mid Cottage ★★★★
Contact: Mrs D Jackson, Bilton
Barns, Alnmouth, Alnwick,
Northumberland NE66 2TB
T: (01665) 830427
F: (01665) 830063
E: dorothy@biltonbarns.co.uk
I: www.biltonbarns.co.uk

Harbour Rest ★★★
Contact: Ms Caroline Lamond,
15 Beatty Avenue, High West
Jesmond, Newcastle upon Tyne,
NE2 3QN
T: (0191) 285 7777
F: (0191) 284 8505

Juniper Cottage ★★★★
Contact: Mrs B J Purvis, Fynder,
3 Dovecote Steadings, Clifton,
Morpeth, Northumberland
NE61 6DN
T: (0191) 482 3416 &
07885 213488
E: fenwickagencies@btinternet.
com
I: www.castle-cottages.co.uk

Kipper Cottage ★★★
Contact: Mr and Mrs J A Forsyth,
East Cottage, Fenwicks Close
Farm, Earsdon, Whitley Bay,
Northumberland NE25 9TQ
T: (0191) 297 1115 & 261 2235
E: jf@theforsyths.com
I: www.kippercottage.co.uk

Kittiwake ★★★★
Contact: Mr and Mrs J&A
Nicholson, Mayfield House, 33
Main Street, Seahouses,
Northumberland NE68 7RE
T: (01665) 720491
F: (01665) 720491
E: aj.nicholson@btinternet.com

Quarry Cottage ★★★
Contact: Mrs M Alston,
Woodlea, 36 St Aidans,
Seahouses, Northumberland
NE68 7SS
T: (01665) 720235
F: (01665) 720235
E: george.alston@ic24.net

Sanderlings ★★★
Contact: Mr and Mrs CR&J
Scott, 9 Alexandra Terrace,
Stocksfield, Northumberland
NE43 7LA
T: (01661) 843127 &
07702 105094
E: chris@crscott.freeserve.co.uk

The Cottage ★★★★
Contact: Mrs Seymour, High
Wells Interiors, 46 Front Street
North, Trimdon, Trimdon
Station, County Durham
TS29 6PG
T: (01429) 880276 &
07702 156312
F: (01429) 880276
E: mary@highwells.freeserve.
co.uk
I: www.highwells.f9.co.uk

The Granary ★★★
Contact: Mr & Mrs J S Edgoose,
Todds House Farm, Sedgefield,
Stockton-on-Tees, Cleveland
TS21 3EL
T: (01740) 620244
F: (01740) 620244
E: edgoosej@aol.com
I: www.toddshousefarm.co.uk

Sprucely Farm Cottage ★★
Contact: Mr S R Harris, Sprucely
Farm, Sedgefield, Stockton-on-
Tees, Cleveland TS21 2BD
T: (01740) 620378
E: barbara@sprucely.fsnet.co.uk
I: sprucely.fsnet.co.uk

The Granary ★★★★★
Contact: Ms Mandy Lance and
Mr George Snaith, Charity Hall
Farm, Sharperton, Morpeth,
Northumberland NE65 7AG
T: (01669) 650219
F: (01669) 650219
E: mandy@charityhallfarm.com
I: www.charityhallfarm.com

**North Sharperton Farm
Cottage ★★★**
Contact: Ms C M Banks, North
Sharperton Farm Cottage,
Sharperton, Morpeth,
Northumberland NE65 7AE
T: (01669) 650321

Sycamore Cottage ★★
Contact: Mrs Janet Brewis,
Sycamore Cottage, Woodhouse,
Shilbottle, Alnwick,
Northumberland NE66 2HR
T: (01665) 575222

Barn Cottage ★★★★
Contact: Dales Hol Cot Ref:1816,
Dales Holiday Cottages, Carleton
Business Park, Carleton New
Road, Skipton, North Yorkshire
BD23 2AA
T: (01756) 799821 & 790919
F: (01756) 797012
E: info@dalesholcot.com
I: www.dalesholcot.com

**Bastle House
Rating Applied For**
Contact: Mrs Deirdre
Pepperdine, Greenhaugh Farm,
Slaggyford, Carlisle CA8 7NW
T: (01434) 381123
F: (01434) 381124
E: kpepperdine@aol.com

Clairmont Cottage ★★★★
Contact: Mrs E Allsop,
Clairmont, Slaley, Hexham,
Northumberland NE47 0AD
T: (01434) 673686
F: (01434) 673921
E: david.allsop4@which.net
I: www.clairmontslaley.
freeserve.co.uk

Combhills Farm ★★★
Contact: Mrs M A Ogle,
Combhills Farm, Slaley, Hexham,
Northumberland NE47 0AQ
T: (01434) 673475
E: m.ogle@lineone.net

The Strothers ★★★★
Contact: Mrs E K Hardy, The
Strothers, Slaley, Hexham,
Northumberland NE47 0AA
T: (01434) 673417 &
07720 720079
F: (01434) 673417
E: edna.hardy@the-strothers.
co.uk
I: www.the-strothers.co.uk

**52 Commercial Road
Rating Applied For**
Contact: Mr John Thomson, 54
Braemar Drive, South Shields,
Tyne and Wear NE34 7TZ
T: (0191) 454 2212
I: www.southshields.co.uk

38 Eccleston Road ★★★
Contact: Mrs K Cole, 9 Sea Way,
South Shields, Tyne and Wear
NE33 2NQ
T: (0191) 456 1802

Elmverne ★★★
Contact: Mrs V Peterson, 10 Elm
Avenue, South Shields, Tyne and
Wear NE34 8AF
T: (0191) 427 0949

**27 Marlborough Street North
Rating Applied For**
Contact: Mrs P Capps, Staircase
Cottage, Main Street,
Sicklinghall, Wetherby, West
Yorkshire LS22 4AU
T: (01937) 582097 &
07703 868346

**Sandhaven Beach Chalets
Rating Applied For**
Contact: Mrs Christine Rowell,
Sandhaven Beach Chalets, South
Promenade, Sea Road, South
Shields, Tyne and Wear
NE33 2LD
T: (0191) 455 8319 &
07702 962884
F: (0191) 455 8319
E: crowell@btconnect.com
I: www.sandhavenchalets.co.uk

**Isaac's and Hannah's Cottages
★★★**
Contact: Mrs Heather Robson,
Allenheads Farm, Allenheads,
Hexham, Northumberland
NE47 9HJ
T: (01434) 685312

**Highview Country House
–Apartment
Rating Applied For**
Contact: Mr J Thompson,
Highview Country House,
Kirkmerrington, Spennymoor,
County Durham DL16 7JT
T: (01388) 811006

21 Billendean Terrace ★★
Contact: Mrs M J Ingham, 8
Burnaby Crescent, Chiswick,
London W4 3LH
T: (020) 8747 0425

Whiteadder Cottage ★★★
Contact: Mr I Willcox,
Whiteadder Cottage, 101 Main
Street, Spittal, Berwick-upon-
Tweed, Northumberland
TD15 1RP
T: (01289) 306183

Establishments printed in blue have a detailed entry in this guide

STANHOPE
Durham

Primrose Cottage ★★★
Contact: Mrs D P Dickson, Northumbria Byways, Crosby House, Crosby-on-Eden, Carlisle, Cumbria CA6 4QZ
T: (01228) 573337 & 573338
F: (01228) 573338
E: enquiries@northumbria-byways.com
I: www.northumbria-byways.com

STOCKSFIELD
Northumberland

The Granary and Stable Cottage ★★★
Contact: Country Holidays ref:32,682, Spring Mill, Earby, Barnoldswick, Lancashire BB94 0AA
T: 08700 723723
F: (01282) 844288
E: sales@ttgigh.co.uk
I: www.country-holidays.co.uk

Mount Flaggon ★★★
Contact: Mrs Bridget Smith, North View House, Hedley on the Hill, Stocksfield, Northumberland NE43 7SW
T: (01661) 843867
F: (01661) 844097
E: gsmith9@compuserve.com

The Old Bakery Cottages ★★★★
Contact: Mr & Mrs W R Bolton, Greencroft, 56 New Ridley Road, Stocksfield, Northumberland NE43 7EE
T: (01661) 843217
F: 07974 910970

Old Ridley Hall ★★
Contact: Mrs J R Aldridge, Old Ridley Hall, Stocksfield, Northumberland NE43 7RU
T: (01661) 842816
E: oldridleyhall@talk21.com

Tithe Cottage & Wash House Cottage ★★★
Contact: Mrs C A Harrison, Eltringham Farm, Mickley, Stocksfield, Northumberland NE43 7DF
T: (01661) 842833

SUNDERLAND
Tyne and Wear

45 Poplar Drive ★★
Contact: Mrs M B Farrar, 50 Beechhill Road, Eltham, London SE9 1HH
T: (020) 8850 4863
E: cass.farrar@virginnet.co.uk

SWARLAND
Northumberland

3 The Square ★★★
Contact: Country Holidays ref:4939, Spring Mill, Earby, Barnoldswick, Lancashire BB18 6RN
T: 08700 723723
F: (01282) 844288
E: sales@ttgihg.co.uk
I: www.country-holidays.co.uk

SWINHOE
Northumberland

3, 4 and 5 Swinhoe Cottages ★★★
Contact: Mrs V Nixon, Swinhoe Farm House, Belford, Northumberland NE70 7LJ
T: (01668) 213370
E: valerie@swinhoecottages.co.uk
I: www.swinhoecottages.co.uk

TARSET
Northumberland

Highfield Farm Cottage ★★
Contact: Mrs M Tweddle, Highfield Farm, Tarset, Hexham, Northumberland NE48 1RT
T: (01434) 240219

The Stables ★★★★★
Contact: Mr and Mrs J Morrison-Bell, Newton, Tarset, Hexham, Northumberland NE48 1PD
T: (01434) 240535
F: (01434) 240330
E: morrisonbell@msn.com

THROPTON
Northumberland

Mordue's Cottage ★★★
Contact: Mrs Helen Farr, Lorbottle West Steads, Thropton, Morpeth, Northumberland NE65 7JT
T: (01665) 574672 & 07833 392966
F: (01665) 574672
E: Helen.Farr@farming.co.uk
I: www.cottageguide.co.uk/lorbottle.html

Physic Cottage ★★★
Contact: Mr and Mrs Andrew and Helen Duffield, Riverview, Physic Lane, Thropton, Morpeth, Northumberland NE65 7HU
T: (01669) 620450 & 07860 319237

TOW LAW
Durham

Greenwell Farm Cottages ★★★
Contact: Mrs Linda Vickers, Greenwell Farm Cottages, Greenwell Farm, Wolsingham, Tow Law, County Durham DL13 4PH
T: (01388) 527248
F: (01388) 526735
E: greenwell@farming.co.uk
I: www.greenwellfarm.co.uk

Pennine View ★★★★
Contact: Mrs M Farrow, Bracken Hill Weardale, Thornley, Tow Law, Bishop Auckland, County Durham DL13 4PQ
T: (01388) 731329
E: enquiries@bracken-hill.com
I: www.bracken-hill.com

TYNEMOUTH
Tyne and Wear

Graham House Holiday Cottages ★★★
Contact: Mr R Graham, Graham House Holiday Cottages, 5-12 Percy Gardens Cottages, Tynemouth, North Shields, Tyne and Wear NE30 4EP
T: (0191) 296 1029

WALL
Northumberland

High Barns Cottage ★★★
Contact: Country Holidays ref:N875, Spring Mill, Earby, Barnoldswick, Lancashire BB18 6RN
T: 08700 723723
F: (01282) 844288
E: sales@ttgihg.co.uk
I: www.country-holidays.co.uk

WAREN MILL
Northumberland

Eider Cottage ★★★★
Contact: Mrs S Turnbull, 1 Friars Court, Bamburgh, Northumberland NE69 7AE
T: (01668) 214494
E: theturnbulls2k@btinternet.com

Waren Lea Hall ★★★★★
Contact: Country Holidays ref:14111, Holiday Cottages Group Ltd, Spring Mill, Earby, Barnoldswick, Lancashire BB94 0AA
T: 08700 723723
F: (01282) 844288
E: sales@ttgihg.co.uk
I: www.country-holidays.co.uk

WARENFORD
Northumberland

Etive Cottage ★★★
Contact: Mr & Mrs David and Jan Thompson, The Cott, Warenford, Belford, Northumberland NE70 7HZ
T: (01668) 213233 & (01890) 820252

WARK
Northumberland

Coachmans and Stable Cottages ★★★
Contact: Mr & Mrs B D Napier, Coachmans and Stable Cottages, The Old Rectory, Wark, Hexham, Northumberland NE48 3PP
T: (01434) 230223

The Green and the Cottage ★★-★★★
Contact: Sykes Cottages Ref: 683,707, Sykes Cottages, York House, York Street, Chester, Cheshire CH1 3LR
T: (01244) 345700
F: (01244) 321442
E: info@sykescottages.co.uk
I: www.sykescottages.co.uk

Riverside Cottage ★★★
Contact: Mrs S Jackson, 16 Moss Side, Wrekenton, Gateshead, Tyne and Wear NE9 7UU
T: (0191) 487 6531
E: jimandstella@wrekenton.fsbusiness.co.uk

WARKWORTH
Northumberland

Birling Vale ★★★
Contact: Mrs Janet Brewis, Woodhouse, Shilbottle, Alnwick, Northumberland NE66 2HR
T: (01665) 575222

Buston Farm Holiday Cottages ★★★★
Contact: Miss J Park, Low Buston Hall, Warkworth, Morpeth, Northumberland NE65 0XY
T: (01665) 714805
F: (01665) 711345
E: jopark@farming.co.uk
I: www.bustonfarm.ntb.org.uk

Coquet Cottage ★★★★
Contact: Mrs Barbara Jean Purvis, Fynder, 3 Dovecote Steadings, Clifton, Morpeth, Northumberland NE61 6DN
T: (0191) 482 3416
F: (0191) 482 4288
E: fenwickagencies@btinternet.com
I: www.castle-cottages.co.uk

The Green House ★★★
Contact: Mrs Helen Cutts, The Green House, 21 Dial Place, Warkworth, Morpeth, Northumberland NE65 0XQ
T: (01665) 712322 & 713221
E: hcutts@aol.com

The Loft ★★★★
Contact: Mrs Marie Wraith, The Loft, Albion House, 21 Morwick Road, Warkworth, Morpeth, Northumberland NE65 0TG
T: (01665) 711389
E: mariewraith@hotmail.com

Mains Cottage, Magdelene House and Clydesdale Cottage ★★★-★★★★
Contact: Sykes Cottages R:469,670,671, Sykes Cottages, York House, York Street, Chester, Cheshire CH1 3LR
T: (01244) 345700
F: (01244) 321442
E: info@sykescottages.co.uk
I: www.sykescottages.co.uk

Old Barns Farmhouse Holiday Cottage ★★★★
Contact: Mrs J Wilkes, Old Barns Farmhouse Holiday Cottage, Old Barns Farmhouse, Morwick Road, Warkworth, Morpeth, Northumberland NE65 0TH
T: (01665) 713427
E: scott.wilkes@virgin.net
I: www.oldbarnsholidaycottage.co.uk

Southmede ★★★★
Contact: Mr & Mrs M H Smith, Southmede, Beal Bank, Warkworth, Morpeth, Northumberland NE65 0T
T: (01665) 711360 & 0771 304 1797
E: info@southmede.co.uk
I: www.southmede.co.uk

Southside Cottage ★★-★★★
Contact: Mr A G Bell, Southside Farm, Warkworth, Morpeth, Northumberland NE65 0YD
T: (01665) 575636

Establishments printed in blue have a detailed entry in this guide

WEARHEAD
Durham

Little Allercleugh ★★★★
Contact: Mr J H Rowe, Phillippa
Ross & Co, 1G Castle Gardens,
Stanhope, Bishop Auckland,
County Durham DL13 2FJ
T: (01388) 526111
F: (01388) 526333
E: jeremy@wearri.demon.co.uk
I: www.wearri.demon.co.uk/la1.
htm

WEST WOODBURN
Northumberland

The Hollow ★★★
Contact: Mrs Marlene Robson,
East Lodge, Nunnykirk,
Netherwitton, Morpeth,
Northumberland NE61 4PB
T: (01670) 772580 & 772246

Noble Cottage ★★★
Contact: Dales Holiday Cottages,
Ref:737, Carleton
Business Park, Carleton New
Road, Skipton, North Yorkshire
BD23 2AA
T: (01756) 799821 & 790919
F: (01756) 797012
E: info@dalesholcot.com
I: www.dalesholcot.com

WESTGATE-IN-WEARDALE
Durham

Dalehead Cottages ★★★
Contact: Mrs EMC Rountree,
Dalehead, Westgate-in-
Weardale, Bishop Auckland,
County Durham DL13 1PG
T: (01388) 517661 & 537592
F: (01388) 517661
E: tasco@enta.net

Ingoe Cottage
Rating Applied For
Contact: Mrs Carey Turnbull, Hill
House Cottage, Westgate-in-
Weardale, Bishop Auckland,
County Durham DL13 1NU
T: (01388) 517464

The Old Barn ★★★★
Contact: Mrs Angela Hackett,
High Kitty Crag, Westgate-in-
Weardale, Bishop Auckland,
County Durham DL13 1LF
T: (01388) 517562 & 528555
F: (01388) 526122
E: matthackett@talk21.com

Rowan Cottage ★★★
Contact: Mrs A C Telfer, Carfrae,
Sidehead, Westgate-in-
Weardale, County Durham
DL13 1LE
T: (01388) 517364
F: (01388) 517364
E: allison_telfer@hotmail.com

WHITBURN
Tyne and Wear

Seawynds ★★★
Contact: Mrs C E Whincop, 12
Nicholas Avenue, Whitburn,
Sunderland SR6 7DB
T: (0191) 529 3578

WHITTINGHAM
Northumberland

The Lodge ★★★
Contact: CH ref:3971,9053,
Spring Mill, Earby, Barnoldswick,
Lancashire BB18 6RN
T: 08700 723723
F: (01282) 844288
E: sales@ttgihg.co.uk
I: www.country-holidays.co.uk

WIDDRINGTON
Northumberland

Seaspray Cottage ★★★
Contact: Mrs Carole Wood,
Tudor House, Parkway,
Wilmslow, Cheshire SK9 1LS
T: (01625) 525857

WINSTON
Durham

Highcliffe Waters ★★★★
Contact: Mr & Mrs Hodson,
Highcliffe Farm, Winston,
Darlington, County Durham
DL2 3PJ
T: (01325) 730427
F: (01325) 730740
E: mrshodson@aol.com
I: www.countryholidays.co.uk

Rose Cottage ★★
Contact: Country Holidays
ref:5044, Spring Mill, Earby,
Barnoldswick, Lancashire
BB18 6RN
T: 08700 723723
F: (01282) 844288
I: www.country-holidays.co.uk

WITTON-LE-WEAR
Durham

Carrs Terrace ★★★★
Contact: Miss Merlyn Law,
93-99 Upper Richmond Road,
London SW15 2TG
T: (020) 8780 1084
F: (020) 8789 9199
E: merlynlaw@aol.com

Old Joiner's Shop ★★★★
Contact: Dales Hol Cot Ref:2630,
Dales Holiday Cottages, Carleton
Business Park, Carleton New
road, Skipton, North Yorkshire
BD23 2AA
T: (01756) 799821 & 790919
F: (01756) 797012
E: info@dalesholcot.com
I: www.dalesholcot.com

WOLSINGHAM
Durham

Ardine Cottage ★★★
Contact: Mrs M Gardiner, 3
Melbourne Place, Wolsingham,
Bishop Auckland, County
Durham DL13 3EQ
T: (01388) 527538

**Bradley Burn Holiday Cottages
★★★**
Contact: Mrs J A Stephenson,
Bradley Burn Holiday Cottages,
Bradley Burn Farm, Wolsingham,
Bishop Auckland, County
Durham DL13 3JH
T: (01388) 527285
F: (01388) 527285
E: jas@bradleyburn.co.uk
I: www.bradleyburn.co.uk

High Doctor Pasture
Rating Applied For
Contact: Mr & Mrs R J Painter,
High Doctor Pasture,
Wolsingham, Bishop Auckland,
County Durham DL13 3LR
T: (01388) 526354 &
(01642) 631715
F: (01388) 526583
E: barbara.painter@eggconnect.
net

Sandycarr Farm Cottage
★★★★
Contact: Mrs M Love, Holywell
Farm, Wolsingham, Bishop
Auckland, County Durham
DL13 3HB
T: (01388) 527249

Whitfield House Cottage
★★★
Contact: Mrs M E Shepheard, 25
Front Street, Wolsingham,
Bishop Auckland, County
Durham DL13 3DF
T: (01388) 527466
E: enquiries@whitfieldhouse.
clara.net
I: www.whitfieldhouse.clara.net

Whitfield Place Cottage
★★★★
Contact: Mrs Susan Oates, 27
Whitfield Place, Wolsingham,
Bishop Auckland, County
Durham DL13 3DF
T: (01388) 527127

WOOLER
Northumberland

Byram House ★★
Contact: Mrs C Easton, Byram
House, High Humbleton, Wooler,
Northumberland NE71 6SU
T: (01668) 281647

Castle Hill Cottage ★★★
Contact: Mr James Nall-Cain,
Waterend House,
Wheathampstead, St Albans,
Hertfordshire AL4 8EP
T: (01582) 831083
F: (01582) 831081
E: manussj@aol.com

The Castle Tower
Rating Applied For
Contact: Dales Hol Cot Ref:1636,
Dales Holiday Cottages, Carleton
Business Park, Carleton New
Road, Skipton, North Yorkshire
BD23 2AA
T: (01756) 799821 & 790919
F: (01756) 797012
E: info@dalesholcot.com
I: www.dalesholcot.com

Coldgate Mill ★★★★
Contact: Mr & Mrs A Stone,
Coldgate Mill, North Middleton,
Wooler, Northumberland
NE71 6QZ
T: (01668) 217259
E: triskellhouse@email.msn.com

Cresswell Wing ★★★★
Contact: Ms Alison Wrangham,
Cresswell Wing, Harehope Hall,
Alnwick, Northumberland
NE66 2DP
T: (01668) 217329 & 217129
F: (01668) 217346
E: ali.wrangham@farming.co.uk

The Croft ★★★
Contact: Mrs Joan Renner,
Lilburn Grange, West Lilburn,
Alnwick, Northumberland
NE66 4PP
T: (01668) 217274

Fenton Hill Farm Cottages
★★★★
Contact: Mrs Margaret Logan,
Fenton Hill, Wooler,
Northumberland NE71 6JJ
T: (01668) 216228
F: (01668) 216169
E: stay@fentonhillfarm.co.uk
I: www.fentonhillfarm.co.uk

**Firwood Bungalow &
Humphrey House**
★★★-★★★★
Contact: Mrs S E Armstrong,
North Charlton Farm, Chathill,
Alnwick, Northumberland
NE67 5HP
T: (01665) 579443
F: (01665) 579407
E: ncharlton1@agricplusnet
I: www.cottageguide.
co.uk/firwood

Hayloft & Yearle Tower
★★★★
Contact: CH ref:N377,N376,
Spring Mill, Earby, Barnoldswick,
Lancashire BB94 0AA
T: 08700 723723
F: (01282) 844288
E: sales@ttgihg.co.uk
I: www.country-holidays.co.uk

Herd's Cottage ★★★
Contact: Mrs M C Logan, Way-
To-Wooler Farm, Wooler,
Northumberland NE71 6AQ
T: (01668) 281640 & 282281
F: (01668) 282091
E: mary@w-t-w.freeserve.co.uk

Kimmerston Riding Centre ★★
Contact: Mr R Jeffreys,
Kimmerston Riding Centre,
Kimmerston Farm, Wooler,
Northumberland NE71 6JH
T: (01668) 216283
E: jane@kimmerston.com
I: www.kimmerston.com

Peth Head Cottage ★★★
Contact: Mr and Mrs J O'Malley,
Eaver Cottage, Rothbury Road,
Longframlington, Morpeth,
Northumberland NE65 8AE
T: (01665) 570381
E: info@pethhead.co.uk
I: www.pethhead.co.uk

Rose Cottage ★★★
Contact: Mrs Christine Andrews,
1 Littleworth Lane, Esher, Surrey
KT10 9PF
T: (01372) 464284
F: (01372) 467715
E: andreas@playfactors.demon.
co.uk

Westnewton Estate ★★★
Contact: Mrs Jean Davidson,
Westnewton Estate,
Westnewton, Wooler,
Northumberland NE71 6XL
T: (01668) 216077

Whitsun View ★★★
Contact: Sykes Cottages Ref:
781, Sykes Cottages, York House,
York Street, Chester, Cheshire
CH1 3LR
T: (01244) 345700
F: (01244) 321442
E: info@sykescottages.co.uk
I: www.sykescottages.co.uk

YARROW
Northumberland

Curlew Cottage ★★★
Contact: Mr and Mrs A Fellows,
101 Edgemount, Killingworth,
Newcastle upon Tyne, Tyne and
Wear NE12 6GQ
T: (0191) 268 0366
F: (0191) 268 0366
E: sscl@supanet.com

ABBEYSTEAD◦
Lancashire

Higher Lee ★★★★
Contact: Hoseasons Cottages,
Sunway House, Lowestoft,
Suffolk NR32 2LW

ACCRINGTON
Lancashire

**Low Moorside Farm Cottage
★★★**
Contact: Mr and Mrs C&E
Hallworth, Elcliffe Cottage,
Burnley Road, Clayton-le-Moors,
Accrington, Lancashire BB5 5UG
T: (01254) 237053

ALTHAM
Lancashire

The Courtyard ★★★
Contact: Mr Martin McShane,
Red Rose Cottages, 6 King
Street, Clitheroe, Lancashire
BB7 2EP
T: (01200) 420101
F: (01200) 420103
E: info@redrosecottages.co.uk
I: www.redrosecottages.co.uk

ARKHOLME
Lancashire

Redwell Fisheries ★★★
Contact: Mrs D Campbell-Barker
& Mr Hall, Redwell Fisheries,
Mere House, Kirkby Lonsdale
Road, Arkholme, Carnforth,
Lancashire LA6 1BQ
T: (015242) 21979
E: kendi603@netscapeonline.
co.uk

BACUP
Lancashire

Oakenclough Farm ★★★
Contact: Mr E Taylor, Red Rose
Cottages, 6 King Street,
Clitheroe, Lancashire BB7 2EP
T: (01200) 420101
E: info@redrosecottages.co.uk
I: www.redrosecottages.co.uk

BARROWFORD
Lancashire

Toll House ★★★
Contact: Country Holidays
ref:13226, Spring Mill, Earby,
Barnoldswick, Lancashire
BB94 0AA
T: 08700 723723
F: (01282) 844288
E: sales@ttgihg.co.uk
I: www.country-holidays.co.uk

BASHALL EAVES
Lancashire

The Coach House ★★★★
Contact: Mrs Jane Backhouse,
The Coach House, Clough
Bottom, Bashall Eaves, Clitheroe,
Lancashire BB7 3NA
T: (01254) 826285
F: (01254) 826015
E: focus.training@btinternet.
com

BILLINGTON
Lancashire

Croft View ★★★★
Contact: Mr Martin McShane,
Red Rose Cottages, 6 King
Street, Clitheroe, Lancashire
BB7 2EP
T: (01200) 420101
F: (01200) 420103
E: info@redrosecottages.co.uk
I: www.redrosecottages.co.uk

Riverview ★★★★
Contact: Red Rose Cottages, 6
King Street, Clitheroe,
Lancashire BB7 2EP
T: (01200) 420101
F: (01200) 420103
E: info@redrosecottages.co.uk
I: www.redrosecottages.co.uk

BISPHAM
Lancashire

**Queens Mansions Holiday
Apartments
Rating Applied For**
Contact: Mr H Conrad, Queens
Mansions Holiday Apartments,
224 Queens Promenade,
Bispham, Blackpool FY2 9HP
T: (01253) 355689

BLACKPOOL
Lancashire

**Abingdon Holiday Apartments
★★**
Contact: Mr Douglas Nelson,
Abingdon Holiday Apartments,
33 Holmfield Road, Blackpool,
FY2 9TB
T: (01253) 356181
I: www.
accommodation-blackpool.co.uk

**The Coach House at Ribby Hall
Holiday Village★★★★**
Contact: Mr Mark Partington,
Ribby Hall Holiday Village, Ribby
Road, Wrea Green, Preston,
Lancashire PR4 2PR
T: (01772) 671111
F: (01772) 673113
E: enquiries@ribbyhall.co.uk
I: www.ribbyhall.co.uk

Crystal Lodge ★-★★
Contact: Mr & Mrs R B
Robinson, Crystal Lodge, 10-12
Crystal Road, Blackpool, FY1 6BS
T: (01253) 346691
F: (01253) 346691

Donange ★★-★★★
Contact: Mrs Myra Hasson,
Donange, 29 Holmfield Road,
Blackpool, Lancashire FY2 9TB
T: (01253) 355051
E: donange@bushinternet.com
I: www.de-zineuk.co.uk/donange

**The Grand Hotel Holiday Flats
★★**
Contact: Mr M A Smith, The
Grand Hotel Holiday Flats,
Station Road, Blackpool,
FY4 1EU
T: (01253) 343741
F: (01253) 408228
E: max@grandholidaysflats.
co.uk
I: www.grandholidayflats.co.uk

**Monarchs Court Apartments
★★★**
Contact: Mr & Mrs Smith,
Monarchs Court Apartments,
332-334 Queens Promenade,
Norbreck, Blackpool, FY2 9AB
T: (01253) 351927

**Rayann and Avon Apartments
★★**
Contact: Mrs E Wright, Rayann
and Avon Apartments, 12-14
Havelock Street, Blackpool,
FY1 4BN
T: (01253) 292288 & 622854
E: ewright@quista.net
I: www.holidays-blackpool.com

**Ribby Hall Holiday Village
★★★**
Contact: Miss Helen Larkin,
Ribby Hall Holiday Village, Ribby
Road, Wrea Green, Preston
PR4 2PA
T: (01772) 671111
F: (01772) 673113
E: enquiries@ribbyhall.co.uk
I: www.ribbyhall.co.uk

**San Remo Holiday Flats,
Apartments and Bungalow★★**
Contact: Mrs P Crowe, San
Remo Holiday Flats, Apartments
and Bungalow, 7 Empress Drive
North, Blackpool, Lancashire
FY2 9SE
T: (01253) 353487 & 884238

Sea Cote Holiday Flats ★★
Contact: Mrs Anne Cunningham,
Sea Cote Holiday Flats, 172
Queens Promenade, Blackpool,
FY2 9JN
T: (01253) 354435

**Somerset House Holiday Flats
★★**
Contact: Mr C Midgley,
Somerset House Holiday Flats,
33 Lonsdale Road, Blackpool,
FY1 6EE
T: (01253) 346465

**Stratford Apartments
★★-★★★**
Contact: Mr and Mrs W L
Williams, 36-38 Empress Drive,
Blackpool, Lancashire FY2 9SD
T: (01253) 500150
F: (01253) 357967

**Thorncliffe Holiday Flats
★★-★★★**
Contact: Mr & Mrs R J Jackson,
Thorncliffe Holiday Flats, 1
Holmfield Road, Gynn Square,
Blackpool, FY2 9SL
T: (01253) 357561 & 357561
F: (01253) 405671
E: enquiries@
thorncliffeholidayflats.co.uk

BOLTON-BY-BOWLAND
Lancashire

Springhead Cottage ★★★★
Contact: Mr Martin McShane,
Red Rose Cottages, 6 King
Street, Clitheroe, Lancashire
BB7 2EP
T: (01200) 420101
F: (01200) 420103
E: info@redrosecottages.co.uk
I: www.redrosecottages.co.uk

BOLTON-LE-SANDS
Lancashire

Bankside Cottage ★★★
Contact: Mrs Addy, Bankside
Cottage, 21 Whin Grove, Bolton-
le-Sands, Carnforth, Lancashire
LA5 8DD
T: (01524) 735078
E: d.k.addy02@tinyworld.co.uk

46 Main Road, Flat 2 ★★★
Contact: Mrs L Clarke, 351
Heysham Road, Heysham,
Lancashire LA3 2BP
T: (01524) 411150

Salt-Pie Cottage ★★★★
Contact: Mrs Allison Wardle,
Cobblers Cottage, 12 The Nook,
Bolton-le-Sands, Carnforth,
Lancashire LA5 8LG
T: (01524) 824692 &
07866 955927

BOSLEY
Cheshire

The Old Byre ★★★
Contact: Mrs D Gilman, Pedley
House Farm, Pedley Lane,
Congleton, Cheshire CW12 3QD
T: (01260) 273650
F: (01260) 297115

BRINSCALL
Lancashire

Moors View Cottage ★★★
Contact: Mrs Sheila Smith, Four
Seasons Guest House, 9
Cambridge Road, Cleveleys,
Blackpool FY5 1EP
T: (01253) 853537 &
07715 816281
F: (01624) 662190

BURROW
Lancashire

River Bank Cottage ★★★★
Contact: Dales Hol Cot Ref:3074,
Dales Holiday Cottages, Carleton
Business Park, Carleton New
Road, Skipton, North Yorkshire
BD23 2AA
T: (01756) 799821 & 790919
F: (01756) 797012
E: info@daleshol.com
I: www.daleshol.com

BURTON
Cheshire

Honeysuckle Cottage ★★★★
Contact: Mr & Mrs C Nevett,
Honeysuckle Cottage, Warren
House Farm, Burton Lane,
Burton, Tarporley, Cheshire
CW6 0ES
T: (01829) 781178 & 0771 480
4696
E: barbara nevett@bt.com

CARNFORTH
Lancashire

Hazelnut Cottage ★★★
Contact: Mrs Hazel Wilson,
Chimneys Cottage, 37 Bradshaw
Road, Tottington, Bury,
Lancashire BL8 3PW
T: (01204) 882580 & 364914
E: joe@wilson882.freeserve.
co.uk

Establishments printed in blue have a detailed entry in this guide

Mansergh Farm House Cottages ★★★★
Contact: Mrs M J Morphy, Mansergh Farm House Cottages, Borwick, Carnforth, Lancashire LA6 1JS
T: (01524) 732586

No 60 Lakeside Lodge ★★★
Contact: Mrs J A Jennings, Auchmar, Cocker Hill, Foulridge, Colne, Lancashire BB8 7LW
T: (01282) 865866 &
07713 189874

Pine Lake Lodges 66 & 67 ★★★★
Contact: Mr David Hogarth, Cumbrian Cottages, 7 The Crescent, Carlisle, CA1 1QW
T: (01228) 599960
F: (01228) 599970
E: enquiries@cumbrian-cottages.co.uk
I: www.cumbrian-cottages.co.uk

CATON
Lancashire

Marybank Barn ★★
Contact: Mrs Julie Fisher, Marybank Barn, Caton Green, Caton, Lancaster LA2 9JG
T: (01524) 770339

CHAIGLEY
Lancashire

Waddicor Hall ★★★★
Contact: Mr Martin McShane, Red Rose Cottages, 6 King Street, Clitheroe, Lancashire BB7 2EP
T: (01200) 420101
F: (01200) 420103
E: info@redrosecottages.co.uk
I: www.redrosecottages.co.uk

CHESTER
Cheshire

Cheshire Country Cottages Rating Applied For
Contact: Mr & Mrs R G Menzies, Poplar House, Sandy Lane, Tarvin Sands, Chester, Cheshire CH3 8JQ
T: (01829) 740732 &
07860 113678
F: (01829) 740722

The City Apartment & 14 Quarry Close★★★★
Contact: Mrs Moira Martland, Upton Lodge, Wealstone Lane, Upton, Chester, CH2 1HD
T: (01244) 372091
F: (01244) 374779
E: chesterhols@clara.co.uk
I: www.chesterholidays.co.uk

Domini Mews & Romana Court ★★★
Contact: Mr and Mrs K&P Massey, 46 York Road, Connah's Quay, Deeside, Clwyd CH5 4YE
T: (01244) 815664 &
07831 855552
F: (01244) 815664

24 Elizabeth Crescent ★★-★★★
Contact: Mrs Lillian Maddock, 24 Elizabeth Crescent, Queens Park, Chester, Cheshire CH4 7AZ
T: (01244) 676141

Handbridge Village Rating Applied For
Contact: Mr R A Owen, 18 Eaton Road, Handbridge, Chester, Chester, Cheshire CH4 7EN
T: (01244) 616159

Ivy Cottage Rating Applied For
Contact: Mr & Mrs Joseph & Sonia Barry, Woodsorrel, 18 Dee Fords Avenue, Chester, Cheshire CH3 5UP
T: (01244) 403630 &
07973 211582
F: (01244) 403699
E: rmd.heritage@btconnect.com
I: rmd-heritage.co.uk

Jasmine Cottage ★★★★★
Contact: Mrs Karen Buchan, Auchmacoy House, Llanfair Road, Abergele, Conwy LL22 8DH
T: (01745) 825880 &
07831 580280
F: (01745) 825880
E: k.buchan@btinternet.com
I: www.chesterholidaycottages.com

Joesam Cottage Rating Applied For
Contact: Mrs Joan Hughes, 36A Chester Road, Sandycroft, Deeside, Clwyd CH5 2QN
T: (01244) 530312
E: johughes19@aol.co.uk

Kingswood Coach House ★★★
Contact: Mrs Caroline Perry, Kingswood Coach House, Kingswood, Parkgate Road, Saughall, Chester, Cheshire CH1 6JS
T: (01244) 851204
F: (01244) 851244
E: caroline.mcvey@psmconsulting.co.uk

Little Mayfield ★★
Contact: Mr M J Cullen, Little Mayfield, Mayfield House, Warrington Road, Hoole Village, Chester CH2 4EX
T: (01244) 300231
F: (01244) 300231

3 The Mount ★★★
Contact: Mrs Henderson, 4 Lancaster Drive, Chester, Cheshire CH3 5JW
T: (01244) 326890

3 Northgate Avenue ★★★
Contact: Mrs Sue Byrne, Walnut Cottage, Rake Lane, Chester, CH2 4DB
T: (01244) 379824 &
07801 045272
E: k.byrne@chestercc.gov.uk

Park Farm Cottage ★★★
Contact: Mrs Davies, Park Farm, Guilden Sutton Lane, Guilden Sutton, Chester, Cheshire CH3 7EX
T: (01244) 300284

Stapleford Hall Cottage ★★★
Contact: Mrs M J Winward, Stapleford Hall Cottage, Stapleford Hall, Tarvin, Chester CH3 8HH
T: (01829) 740202
F: (01829) 740202
E: staplefordcottage@hotmail.com
I: www.staplefordhallcottage.com

Tattersall Gate ★★★
Contact: Mrs R A Randle, PO Box 247, Chester, CH1 2WA
T: (01244) 401591 &
07714 457940
F: (01244) 401591
E: rosrandle@cs.com
I: www.woodbank.co.uk/thatch

York House ★★★
Contact: Mrs P K Davies, Plex Cottage, Tarporley Road, Clotton, Tarporley, Cheshire CW6 0EH
T: (01829) 781457 & 261601

CHIPPING
Lancashire

Fell View ★★★★
Contact: Mr Martin McShane, Red Rose Cottages, 6 King Street, Clitheroe, Lancashire BB7 2EP
T: (01200) 420101
F: (01200) 420103
E: info@redrosecottages.co.uk
I: www.redrosecottages.co.uk

Little Blacksticks Barn ★★★★
Contact: Mr Martin McShane, Red Rose Cottages, 6 King Street, Clitheroe, Lancashire BB7 2EP
T: (01200) 420101
F: (01200) 420103
E: info@redrosecottages.co.uk
I: www.redrosecottages.co.uk

Pale Farm Cottage ★★★★
Contact: Mr Martin McShane, Red Rose Cottages, 6 King Street, Clitheroe, Lancashire BB7 2EP
T: (01200) 420101
E: info@redrosecottages.co.uk
I: www.redrosecottages.co.uk

Rakefoot Barn ★★★-★★★★
Contact: Mrs P M Gifford, Rakefoot Barn, Rakefoot Farm, Chaigley, Clitheroe, Lancashire BB7 3LY
T: (01995) 61332 &
07889 279063
F: (01995) 61332

CLAYTON LE DALE
Lancashire

Whiteholme Studio ★★★★
Contact: Mr Graham Gardner-Boyes, Whiteholme, Ribchester Road, Clayton Le Dale, Blackburn BB1 9EY
T: (01254) 245893
E: gardnerboyes@hotmail.com

CLITHEROE
Lancashire

Chestnut Cottage ★★★★
Contact: Mr Martin McShane, Red Rose Cottages, 6 King Street, Clitheroe, Lancashire BB7 2EP
T: (01200) 420101
F: (01200) 420103
E: info@redrosecottages.co.uk
I: www.redrosecottages.co.uk

Dairy Cottage ★★★
Contact: Mr Martin McShane, Red Rose Cottages, 6 King Street, Clitheroe, Lancashire BB7 2EP
T: (01200) 420101
F: (01200) 420103
E: info@redrosecottages.co.uk
I: www.redrosecottages.co.uk

Five Fells Cottage ★★★
Contact: Mr & Mrs R Hailwood, Albion House, Kirkmoor Road, Clitheroe, Lancashire BB7 2DU
T: (01200) 424240
E: roland.hailwood@talk21.com

Greenbank Cottages ★★★★
Contact: Mr Gordon Greenwood, Greenbank Cottages, Greenbank Farm, Whalley Road, Sabden, Clitheroe, Lancashire BB7 9DT
T: (01254) 823064
F: (01254) 822314
E: gordon.greenwood@ntlworld.com

Higher Gills Farm ★★★★
Contact: Mrs Freda Pilkington, Higher Gills Farm, Rimington, Clitheroe, Lancashire BB7 4DA
T: (01200) 445370
E: pilko@highergills.co.uk
I: www.highergills.co.uk

Hydes Farm Holiday Cottages ★★★
Contact: Mrs Jean Howard, Hydes Farm, Newton-in-Bowland, Clitheroe, Lancashire BB7 3DY
T: (01200) 446353

Number 10 ★★★
Contact: Mrs C M Newhouse, 18 Church Street, Slaidburn, Clitheroe, Lancashire BB7 3ER
T: (01200) 446620
F: (01200) 446620

Owl and Hawk Cottages ★★★★
Contact: Red Rose Cottages, 6 King Street, Clitheroe, Lancashire BB7 2EP
T: (01200) 420101
F: (01200) 420103
E: info@redrosecottages.co.uk
I: www.redrosecottages.co.uk

Painter's Cottage ★★★★
Contact: Mr Martin McShane, Red Rose Cottages, 6 King Street, Clitheroe, Lancashire BB7 2EP
T: (01200) 420101
F: (01200) 420103
E: info@redrosecottages.co.uk
I: www.redrosecottages.co.uk

Ribble Cottage ★★★
Contact: Mr Martin McShane,
Red Rose Cottages, 6 King
Street, Clitheroe, Lancashire
BB7 2EP
T: (01200) 420101
F: (01200) 420103
E: info@redrosecottages.co.uk
I: www.redrosecottages.co.uk

COCKERHAM
Lancashire

**Near Moss Farm Holidays
★★★**
Contact: Mr P Sutcliffe, Near
Moss Farm Holidays, Gulf Lane,
Cockerham, Lancaster LA2 0ER
T: (01253) 790504
F: (01253) 790043
I: www.nearmossfarmholidays.
com

Patty's Barn ★★★★
Contact: Mr Christopher Parry,
Hillam Lane Farm, Cockerham,
Lancaster LA2 0DY
T: (01524) 751285 &
07957 888048
F: (01524) 751285
E: c.parry@farmline.com

CREWE BY FARNDON
Cheshire

**Meadow View Farm Cottage
★★**
Contact: Mrs P Mobbs, Meadow
View Farm Cottage, Crewe Lane
South, Crewe by Farndon,
Chester, Cheshire CH3 6HP
T: (01829) 271005

CROSTON
Lancashire

Cockfight Barn ★★★★
Contact: Mr Martin McShane,
Red Rose Cottages, 6 King
Street, Clitheroe, Lancashire
BB7 2EP
T: (01200) 420101
F: (01200) 420103
E: info@redrosecottages.co.uk
I: www.redrosecottages.co.uk

DELAMERE
Cheshire

**Wicken Tree Farm
Rating Applied For**
Contact: Mrs E Appleton, Wicken
Tree Farm, Blakemere Lane,
Norley, WA6 6NW
T: (01928) 788355
F: (01928) 788507
E: ches@williamj99.freeserve.
co.uk
I: www.wickentreefarm.co.uk

DISLEY
Cheshire

**Plattwood Farm Cottage
★★★★**
Contact: Mrs Jill Emmott,
Plattwood Farm, Lyme Park,
Disley, Stockport, Cheshire
SK12 2NT
T: (01625) 872738
F: (01625) 872738
E: plattwoodfarm@talk21.com
I: www.peakdistrictfarmhols.
co.uk

EATON
Cheshire

The Old Shippon ★★★★
Contact: Mr and Mrs L Syson,
Church House, Eaton,
Congleton, Cheshire CW12 2NH
T: (01260) 274331
E: les.syson@ukonline.co.uk

GARSTANG
Lancashire

**Arkwright Farm Cottages
Rating Applied For**
Contact: Mr Martin McShane,
Red Rose Cottages, 6 King
Street, Clitheroe, Lancashire
BB7 2EP
T: (01200) 420101
F: (01200) 420103
E: info@redrosecottages.co.uk
I: www.redrosecottages.co.uk

GISBURN
Lancashire

Twyn Ghyll Lodge ★★★
Contact: Mrs B Palmer, Twyn
Ghyll Caravan Park, Paythorne,
Clitheroe, Lancashire BB7 4JD
T: (01200) 445465 & 445721
E: bpalmer@genie.co.uk
I: www.twingill.co.uk

GREAT BARROW
Cheshire

**Hawthorn Cottage
Rating Applied For**
Contact: Mrs E M Pratt,
Woodlea, 44 Guilden Sutton
Lane, Chester, CH3 7EY
T: (01244) 317287

GREENFIELD
Greater Manchester

Clifton Cottage ★★★
Contact: Mrs J Wood, 113 Chew
Valley Road, Greenfield, Oldham
OL3 7JJ
T: (01457) 872098
F: (01457) 870760
E: ced117@aol.com
I: members.aol.
com/ajb1912/ajbutterworthltd.
html

GRESSINGHAM
Lancashire

Garden Cottage ★★★
Contact: Mrs M Burrow, Garden
Cottage, High Snab,
Gressingham, Lancaster LA2 8LS
T: (01524) 221347
E: gardencottage@highsnab.
freeserve.co.uk
I: www.highsnab.freeserve.co.uk

HALTON
Lancashire

**Pine Lodge, Rosewood
Rating Applied For**
Contact: Mr Martin McShane,
Red Rose Cottages, 6 King
Street, Clitheroe, Lancashire
BB7 2EP
T: (01200) 420101
F: (01200) 420103
E: info@redrosecottages.co.uk
I: www.redrosecottages.co.uk

HARROP FOLD
Lancashire

**Bradley House, The Granary &
Manor House Cottage
Rating Applied For**
Contact: Dales Hol Cot Ref:333,
Dales Holiday Cottages, Carleton
Business Park, Carleton New
Road, Skipton, North Yorkshire
BD23 2AA
T: (01756) 799821 & 790919
F: (01756) 797012
E: info@dalesholcot.com
I: www.dalesholcot.com

HOLLINGWORTH
Greater Manchester

**Hollingworth Hall Holiday
Cottages★–★★**
Contact: Mr Parker,
Hollingworth Hall Holiday
Cottages, Hobson Moor Road,
Hollingworth, Hyde, Cheshire
SK14 6SG
T: (01457) 766188 &
0793 718585

HORTON
Lancashire

The Lodge ★★★★
Contact: Mrs Edith Ann Thwaite,
The Lodge, Horton Hall Farm,
Horton, Skipton, North Yorkshire
BD23 3JT
T: (01200) 445300
E: ediththwaite@hotmail.com

HOYLAKE
Merseyside

**North Villa Apartments
★★★–★★★**
Contact: Mrs Sandra Verkade, 33
Cable Road, Hoylake, Wirral,
Merseyside CH47 2AY
T: (0151) 632 3982
E: sandra.verkade@btinternet.
com

HURST GREEN
Lancashire

Hunters Rest ★★★★
Contact: Mr Martin McShane,
Red Rose Cottages, 6 King
Street, Clitheroe, Lancashire
BB7 2EP
T: (01200) 420101
F: (01200) 420103
E: info@redrosecottages.co.uk
I: www.redrosecottages.co.uk

KELSALL
Cheshire

**Northwood Hall Courtyard
Cottages ★★★**
Contact: Mrs C Nock,
Northwood Hall Courtyard
Cottages, Northwood Hall, Dog
Lane, Kelsall, Tarporley, Cheshire
CW6 0RP
T: (01829) 752569
F: (01829) 751157
E: enquiries@northwood-hall.
co.uk
I: www.northwoodhall-cottages.
co.uk

LANCASTER
Lancashire

Dilling Properties ★★★
Contact: Mrs Janet Walton,
Walnut Bank Lodge, Stodday,
Lancaster LA2 0AG
T: (01524) 33863
F: (01524) 845299
E: kwalton@ntlworld.com

Rose Cottage ★★★
Contact: Mr Martin McShane,
Red Rose Cottages, 6 King
Street, Clitheroe, Lancashire
BB7 2EP
T: (01200) 420101
F: (01200) 420103
E: info@redrosecottages
I: www.redrosecottages

The Stables ★★★
Contact: Mr and Mrs R Quinn,
The Stables, Conder Green
Cottage, Conder Green,
Lancaster, LA2 0BG
T: (01524) 751568
F: (01524) 751568
E: mquinn5@compuserve.com

32 Torrisholme Road ★★★
Contact: Ms C Salisbury,
Whiteholme, Ribchester Road,
Clayton Le Dale, Blackburn,
Lancashire BB1 9EY
T: (01254) 245893 &
07899 761667
F: (01254) 382849
E: chrissiesalisbury@hotmail.
com

LIVERPOOL
Merseyside

**Premier Apartments –
Liverpool
Rating Applied For**
Contact: Mr Richard Howard,
Premier Apartments, Suite 309,
Hatton Gardens, Liverpool,
L3 2HP
T: (0151) 227 9467
F: (0151) 227 9468
I: www.premgroup.com

The Waterfront ★★★★
Contact: Mr and Mrs RG&M
Simpson, Foldend, Sineacre
Lane, Bickerstaffe, Ormskirk,
West Lancashire L39 0HR
T: (01695) 727877 &
07860 351684
E: rod+muir@foldend.fsnet.
co.uk

LYMM
Cheshire

21 Ridgeway Gardens ★★★
Contact: Mr Neil Stockdale, 36
Eagle Brow, Lymm, Cheshire
WA13 0LY
T: (01925) 756931
F: (01925) 756931
E: paulchapman@ridgeway-res.
co.uk
I: www.ridgeway-res.co.uk

LYTHAM ST ANNES
Lancashire

**The Chymes Holiday Flats
★★★**
Contact: Mrs L Winstanley, The
Chymes Holiday Flats, 21
Fairhaven Road, Lytham St
Annes, Lancashire FY8 1NN
T: (01253) 726942
F: (01253) 726942

MACCLESFIELD
Cheshire

Mill House Farm Cottage ★★
Contact: Mrs L Whittaker, Mill
House Farm, Bosley,
Macclesfield, Cheshire SK11 0NZ
T: (01260) 226265
E: lynne-whittaker@yahoo.
co.uk

Establishments printed in blue have a detailed entry in this guide

The Teachers Cottage ★★★
Contact: Peak Cottages,
Strawberry Lee Lane, Totley
Bents, Sheffield, S17 3BA
T: (0114) 262 0777 & 262 0666
F: (0114) 262 2066
E: enquiries@peakcottages.com
I: www.peakcottages.com

MALPAS
Cheshire

Orchard Cottage ★★★★
Contact: Mrs Carol Bierley, Fir
Villa, Old Castle Lane,
Threapwood, Malpas, Cheshire
SY14 7AY
T: (01948) 770683

MANCHESTER
Greater Manchester

**La Suisse Self-catering
Apartments ★★★**
Contact: Mr and Mrs Phillips,
444 Bury Old Road, Prestwich,
Manchester M25 1PQ
T: (0161) 796 0545 &
07711 200551
F: (0161) 796 0545
E: reservations@lasuisse.co.uk
I: www.lasuisse.co.uk

**Premier Apartments –
Manchester
Rating Applied For**
Contact: Mr Richard Howard, L3
Apartments, Hatton Gardens,
Liverpool, L3 2HP
T: (0151) 227 9467
F: (0151) 227 9468
E: ukapartments@premgroup.
com
I: www.premgroup.com

MARPLE
Greater Manchester

Top Lock Bungalow ★★★
Contact: Country Holidays
ref:10561, Spring Mill, Earby,
Barnoldswick, Lancashire
BB94 0AA
T: 08700 723723
F: (01282) 844288
I: www.country-holidays.co.uk

MORECAMBE
Lancashire

**Eden Vale Luxury Holiday Flats
★★-★★★**
Contact: Mr & Mrs June and
Maurice Donnelly, Eden Vale
Luxury Holiday Flats, 338 Marine
Road, Morecambe, Lancashire
LA4 5AB
T: (01524) 415544

Inglemead ★
Contact: Mrs A A Foster,
Inglemead, 87 Balmoral Road,
Morecambe, Lancashire LA3 1BH
T: (01524) 417797
E: inglemead@aol.com

**Lakeland View Holiday Flat
★★**
Contact: Mr D F Morgan, 79
South Road, Bare, Morecambe,
Lancashire LA4 6JR
T: (01524) 831355 & 401291
F: (01524) 831244

Langdale ★★
Contact: Mrs P A Armer,
Haresnape Farm, Moss Lane,
Thurnham, Lancaster LA2 0AX
T: (01524) 751142 &
07714 210178

Lynwood Holiday Flats ★★
Contact: Mr & Mrs R Shirbon,
Lynwood Holiday Flats, 61-63
Albert Road, Morecambe,
Lancashire LA4 4HY
T: (01524) 831636

May Cottage ★
Contact: Mrs M Chell, May
Cottage, 28 Bare Lane,
Morecambe, Lancashire LA4 6DF
T: (01524) 424497

Mountfield Holiday Flats ★★
Contact: Mrs Janet Mayers,
Mountfield Holiday Flats, 67
Balmoral Road, Morecambe,
Lancashire LA4 4JS
T: (01524) 423518

Northumberland House ★★
Contact: Mr Neil Briggs,
Northumberland House, 42
Northumberland Street,
Morecambe, Lancashire LA4 4BA
T: (01524) 855512
E: j.s.shaw@tesco.net

Rydal Mount ★
Contact: Mrs S Holmes, Rydal
Mount, 361 Marine Road East,
Morecambe, Lancashire LA4 5AQ
T: (01524) 411858

Sandown Holiday Flats ★★
Contact: Mr & Mrs Matthews,
367 Marine Road East,
Morecambe, Lancashire LA4 5AQ
T: (01524) 410933

NANTWICH
Cheshire

Bank Farm Cottages ★★★
Contact: Mrs A Vaughan, Bank
Farm Cottages, Newcastle Road,
Hough, Crewe CW2 5JG
T: (01270) 841809 & 841253
F: (01270) 841253

Fields Farm ★★
Contact: Mr D W Heys, Fields
Farm, Off Queens Drive,
Edleston, Nantwich, Cheshire
CW5 5JL
T: (01270) 625769
F: (01270) 625769

NESTON
Cheshire

Tumblehome ★★★
Contact: Mr J Kennedy, 4
Woodlands Road, Parkgate,
South Wirral, Cheshire CH64 6RT
T: (0151) 336 1597
F: (0151) 353 1806

NETHER KELLET
Lancashire

The Apartment ★★★
Contact: Mr S Richardson, 10
Meadowcroft, Nether Kellet,
Carnforth, Lancashire LA6 1HN
T: (01524) 734969 & 736331

ORMSKIRK
Lancashire

**Tristrams Farm Holiday
Cottages ★★★**
Contact: Mr David Swift,
Tristrams Farm Holiday
Cottages, Tristrams Farm,
Narrow Lane, Halsall, Ormskirk,
Lancashire L39 8RL
T: (01704) 840323 &
07885 842023

OVER KELLET
Lancashire

Lime Tree Cottage ★★
Contact: Mrs Greaves, Lime Tree
Cottage, Over Kellet, Carnforth,
Lancashire LA6 1DA
T: (01524) 732165

POULTON
Cheshire

The Kymin ★★
Contact: Mrs M Walker, Wallets
Farm, Straight Mile, Poulton,
Chester, Cheshire CH4 9EQ
T: (01244) 570435
F: (01244) 570435
E: wallpoul@bytecraft.net

POULTON–LE–FYLDE
Lancashire

Swans Rest ★★★★
Contact: Mrs Irene O'Connor,
Swans Rest, Garstang Road East,
Singleton, Poulton-le-Fylde
FY6 8LX
T: (01253) 886617
F: (01253) 892563
E: swansrest@btconnect.com
I: www.swansrest.co.uk

PRESTON
Lancashire

Cloggers Cottage ★★★★
Contact: Mr Martin McShane,
Red Rose Cottages, 6 King
Street, Clitheroe, Lancashire
BB7 2EP
T: (01200) 420101
F: (01200) 420103
E: info@redrosecottages.co.uk
I: www.redrosecottages.co.uk

**University of Central
Lancashire ★★**
Contact: Miss Maria Dominguez,
University of Central Lancashire,
Hospitality Services, Marsh
Building, Preston, Lancashire
PR1 2HE
T: (01772) 892650 & 892653
F: (01772) 892977
E: hospitalityservices@uclan.ac.
uk
I: www.uclan.ac.uk

QUERNMORE
Lancashire

Daisy Bank Cottage ★★★
Contact: Mrs Janette Callon,
Daisy Bank Cottage, The
Bungalow, Daisy Bank,
Quernmore, Lancaster LA1 3JN
T: (01524) 35493 &
07710 240082
E: janette.callon@virgin.net

Lodge View Cottages ★★★
Contact: Mr David Gardner, Far
Lodge, Quernmore, Lancaster
LA2 9EF
T: (01524) 63109 &
07974 785744
E: djkagardner@ukgateway.net

RIBCHESTER
Lancashire

Hazlewood ★★★★
Contact: Country Hols
ref:1572,5840, Spring Mill,
Earby, Barnoldswick, Lancashire
BB94 0AA
T: 08700 723723
F: (01282) 844288
E: sales@ttgihg.co.uk
I: www.country-holidays.co.uk

RIMINGTON
Lancashire

Raikes Barn ★★★★
Contact: Mrs E A Robinson,
Beckside Farm, Cross Hill Lane,
Rimington, Clitheroe, Lancashire
BB7 4EE
T: (01200) 445287
F: (01200) 445287
E: beckside@talk21.com
I: www.btclickforbusiness.com

ROCHDALE
Greater Manchester

The Gatehouse ★★★★
Contact: Mrs J Hirst, 46 Ashfield
Lane, Milnrow, Rochdale,
Lancashire OL16 4EW
T: (01706) 643432 & 633342
F: (01706) 354890
E: gatehouse@faxvia.net

SADDLEWORTH
Greater Manchester

The Barn Grove Farm★★★
Contact: Mrs V Stocker, The Barn
Grove Farm, Harrop Court,
Diggle, Oldham OL3 5LN
T: (01457) 870573
E: val@fishnet.co.uk

Friar Lodge ★★★
Contact: Mrs E Burke, Friar
Lodge, Lodge Lane, Delph,
Oldham OL3 5HG
T: (01457) 872718

SILVERDALE
Lancashire

Coppernob ★★★★
Contact: Mr David Hogarth,
Cumbrian Cottages, 7 The
Crescent, Carlisle, CA1 1QW
T: (01228) 599960 & 599950
F: (01228) 599970
E: enquiries@
cumbrian-cottages.co.uk
I: www.cumbrian-cottages.co.uk

**Old Waterslack Farmhouse
Caravan Cottages★★★**
Contact: Mrs N Hevey, Old
Waterslack Farmhouse Caravan
Cottages, Old Waterslack
Farmhouse, Silverdale,
Carnforth, Lancashire LA5 0UH
T: (01524) 701108
F: (01524) 844280
E: n.hevey@oldwaterslackfarm.
ukf.net
I: www.oldwaterslackfarm.ukf.
net

Pheasant Field ★★★
Contact: Sykes Cottages Ref:
684, Sykes Cottages, York House,
York Street, Chester, CH1 3LR
T: (01244) 345700
F: (01244) 321442
E: info@sykescottages.co.uk
I: www.sykescottages.co.uk

The Stables ★★★
Contact: Mrs C M Ranford, The
Stables, Lindeth House, Lindeth
Road, Silverdale, Carnforth,
Lancashire LA5 0TT
T: (01524) 702121
F: (01524) 702226
E: conquerors.maryk@virgin.net

Swallows End ★★
Contact: Dales Hol Cot Ref:1644, Dales Holiday Cottages, Carleton Business Park, Carleton New Road, Skipton, North Yorkshire BD23 2AA
T: (01756) 799821 & 790919
F: (01756) 797012
E: info@dalesholcot.com
I: www.dalesholcot.com

Wolf House Cottage ★★★
Contact: Mrs Denise Dowbiggin, Wolf House Cottage, Gibraltar, Silverdale, Carnforth, Lancashire LA5 0TX
T: (01524) 701405
F: (01524) 701405
E: denise@wolfhouse-gallery. co.uk
I: ww.wolfhouse-gallery.co.uk

SLAIDBURN
Lancashire

Burn Fell View ★★★
Contact: Red Rose Cottages, 6 King Street, Clitheroe, Lancashire BB7 2EP
T: (01200) 420101
F: (01200) 420103
E: info@redrosecottages.co.uk
I: www.redrosecottages.co.uk

Goldhill Cottage ★★★
Contact: Mr Martin McShane, Red Rose Cottages, 6 King Street, Clitheroe, Lancashire BB7 2EP
T: (01200) 420101
F: (01200) 420103
I: info@redrosecottages. co.ukwww.redrosecottages.co.uk

The Olde Stables ★★★★
Contact: Mrs Margaret Robinson, The Olde Stables, Wood House Gate Farm, Slaidburn, Clitheroe, Lancashire BB7 3AQ
T: (01200) 446240 & 446412
F: (01200) 446412

SOUTHPORT
Merseyside

Barford House Apartments ★★★
Contact: Mr Graham Watson, Barford House Apartments, 32 Avondale Road, Southport, Merseyside PR9 0ND
T: (01704) 548119
F: (01704) 530735
E: graham@barfordhouse.co.uk
I: www.barfordhouse.co.uk

Beaucliffe Holiday Flats ★★
Contact: Mrs L Lewis and Mr Allen, Beaucliffe Holiday Flats, 9 Leicester Street, Southport, Merseyside PR9 0ER
T: (01704) 537207

Castle Mews ★★★
Contact: Mr Graham Watson, Barford House Apartments, 32 Avondale Road, Southport, Merseyside PR9 0ND
T: (01704) 548119
F: (01704) 530735
E: graham@barfordhouse.co.uk
I: barfordhouse.co.uk

Martin Lane Farmhouse Holiday Cottages★★★
Contact: Mrs Stubbs, Martin Lane Farmhouse Holiday Cottages, Martin Lane Farmhouse, Burscough, Ormskirk, Lancashire L40 8JH
T: (01704) 893527 & 07803 049128
F: (01704) 893527
E: martinlanefarmhouse@ btinternet.com
I: www.martinlanefarmhouse. btinternet.co.uk

Sandcroft Holiday Flats ★
Contact: Mr & Mrs E&R Best, Sandcroft Holiday Flats, 13 Albany Road, Southport, Merseyside PR9 0JF
T: (01704) 537497
F: (01704) 537497

Sandy Brook Farm ★★★
Contact: Mr W Core, Sandy Brook Farm, 52 Wyke Cop Road, Scarisbrick, Southport, Merseyside PR8 5LR
T: (01704) 880337
F: (01704) 880337

STOCKPORT
Greater Manchester

Lake View ★★★
Contact: Mrs M Sidebottom, Shire Cottage, Benches Lane, Marple Bridge, Stockport, Cheshire SK6 5RY
T: (01457) 866536 & 07720 305281

STONYHURST
Lancashire

Alden Cottage ★★★★
Contact: Mr & Mrs P&B Carpenter, Alden Cottage, Kemple End, Birdy Brow, Stonyhurst, Clitheroe, Lancashire BB7 9QY
T: (01254) 826468
E: carpenter@aldencottage.f9. co.uk

TARPORLEY
Cheshire

Woodworth Lodge ★★
Contact: Mr F J Dykes, Woodworth House, Birds Lane, Bunbury, Tarporley, Cheshire CW6 9PU
T: (01829) 260581

TARVIN
Cheshire

Cheese Makers Cottage Rating Applied For
Contact: Mrs E Sherwin, Cross Lanes Farm, Broomheath Lane, Tarvin, Chester, Cheshire CH3 8HE
E: jc.em.sherwin@ agricontractors.fsnet.co.uk

THORNLEY
Lancashire

Thornley Hall ★★★
Contact: Mrs G Airey, Thornley Hall, Thornley, Preston PR3 2TN
T: (01995) 61243

THORNTON
Lancashire

Tarantara ★★★★
Contact: Country Holidays ref:7407, Spring Mill, Earby, Barnoldswick, Lancashire BB94 0AA
T: 08700 723723
F: (01282) 844288
I: www.country-holidays.co.uk

TOSSIDE
Lancashire

Lower Gill Farmhouse ★★★★
Contact: Holiday Cottages (Yorkshire) Ltd, Water Street, Skipton, North Yorkshire BD23 4SJ
T: (01756) 700510
F: (01756) 701678
E: info@holidaycotts.demon. co.uk

Primrose Cottage ★★★★
Contact: Holiday Cottages (Yorkshire), Water Street, Skipton, North Yorkshire BD23 1PB
T: (01756) 700510

WENNINGTON
Lancashire

Easter Cottage ★★★★
Contact: Mrs Jenny Herd, Mill Farm, Wennington, Lancaster LA2 8NU
T: (015242) 21690

WESTHOUSE
Lancashire

Hillcrest ★★
Contact: Mrs Irene Brown, Thorney Croft, Westhouse, Ingleton, Carnforth, Lancashire LA6 3PA
T: (015242) 41331

WILDBOARCLOUGH
Cheshire

Lower House Cottage ★★
Contact: Mrs F Waller, Blaze Farm, Wildboarclough, Macclesfield, Cheshire SK11 0BL
T: (01260) 227229

WILLINGTON
Cheshire

Delamere Cottage ★★★★
Contact: Mr and Mrs Sidebotham, Delamere Cottage, Willington Road, Willington, Tarporley, Cheshire CW6 0ND
T: (01829) 751628
E: jhs@sebden.com

WINCLE
Cheshire

Clough Brook Cottage ★★★★
Contact: Mr John Henshall, Clough Brook Cottage, Almeadows Farm, Wincle, Macclesfield, Cheshire SK11 0QJ
T: (01260) 227209 & 227313
F: (01260) 227209
E: henshalls@btinternet.com
I: www.allmeadows.co.uk

WISWELL
Lancashire

New Row Cottage ★★★
Contact: Mr Martin McShane, Red Rose Cottages, 6 King Street, Clitheroe, Lancashire BB7 2EP
T: (01200) 420101
F: (01200) 420103
E: info@redrosecottages.co.uk
I: www.redrosecottages.co.uk

YEALAND CONYERS
Lancashire

Stable Cottage ★★★
Contact: Dales Hol Cot Ref:1810, Dales Holiday Cottages, Carleton Business Park, Carleton New Road, Skipton, North Yorkshire BD23 2AA
T: (01756) 799821 & 790919
F: (01756) 797012
E: info@dalesholcot.com
I: www.dalesholcot.com

YEALAND REDMAYNE
Lancashire

Brackenthwaite Holiday Cottages ★★★
Contact: Mrs A S Clarke, Brackenthwaite Holiday Cottages, Brackenthwaite Farm, Yealand Redmayne, Carnforth, Lancashire LA5 9TE
T: (015395) 63276
F: (015395) 63276

YORKSHIRE

ADDINGHAM
West Yorkshire

The Cottage ★★★
Contact: Mr R Wales, Holiday Cottages (Yorkshire) Ltd, Water Street, Skipton, North Yorkshire BD23 1PB
T: (01756) 700510

Number Nine ★★★★
Contact: Mr & Mrs Francis, The Counting House, Old Lane, Low Mill Village, Addingham, Ilkley, West Yorkshire LS29 0SA
T: (01943) 831254

AIKE
East Riding of Yorkshire

The Old Chapel ★★
Contact: Sykes Cottages Ref:323, Sykes Cottages, York House, York Street, Chester, CH1 3LR
T: (01244) 345700
F: (01244) 321442
E: info@sykescottages.co.uk
I: www.sykescottages.co.uk

AINTHORPE
North Yorkshire

The B's Nest ★★★
Contact: Dales Hol Cot Ref:2583, Dales Holiday Cottages, Carleton Business Park, Carleton New Road, Skipton, North Yorkshire BD23 2AA
T: (01756) 799821 & 790919
F: (01756) 797012
E: info@dalesholcot.com
I: www.dalesholcot.com

Establishments printed in blue have a detailed entry in this guide

AIRTON
North Yorkshire

Kiln Hill Cottage ★★★
Contact: Mr R Wales, Holiday Cottages (Yorkshire) Ltd, Water Street, Skipton, North Yorkshire BD23 1PB
T: (01756) 700510

Scosthrop Old School House
Rating Applied For
Contact: Dales Hol Cot Ref:1741, Dales Holiday Cottages, Carleton Business Park, Carleton New Road, Skipton, North Yorkshire BD23 2AA
T: (01756) 799821 & 790919
F: (01756) 797012
E: info@dalesholcot.com
I: www.dalesholcot.com

AISKEW
North Yorkshire

The Courtyard ★★★★
Contact: Mr & Mrs J Cartman, The Courtyard, The Nurseries, Aiskew, Bedale, North Yorkshire DL8 1BN
T: (01677) 423689
F: (01677) 425762
E: jill@courtyard.ndirect.co.uk
I: www.courtyard.ndirect.co.uk

Groom Cottage and Tack Cottage★★★
Contact: Mrs Adele Thompson, Whitby Holiday Cottages, 47 Flowergate, Whitby, North Yorkshire YO21 3BB
T: (01947) 603010
F: (01947) 821133
E: enquiries@whitby-cottages. co.uk
I: www.whitby-cottages.co.uk

Low Newbiggin House ★★★–★★★★
Contact: Mrs Charlotte Etherington, Low Newbiggin House, Aislaby, Pickering, North Yorkshire YO21 1TQ
T: (01947) 811811
E: holidays@lownewbiggin. co.uk
I: www.lownewbiggin.co.uk

40 Main Road ★★
Contact: Mrs Adele Thompson, Whitby Holiday Cottages, 47 Flowergate, Whitby, North Yorkshire YO21 3BB
T: (01947) 603010
F: (01947) 821133
E: enquiries@whitby-cottages. co.uk
I: www.whitby-cottages.co.uk

ALDBROUGH
North Yorkshire

Greencroft Cottage ★★★
Contact: Mrs M C Baxter, Greencroft, Aldbrough St John, Richmond, North Yorkshire DL11 7TJ
T: (01325) 374550
E: ray.baxter@which.net
I: www.greencroft.org.uk

Lilac Cottage ★★★★
Contact: Mrs Helen Stubbs, 19 Seaside Road, Aldbrough, Hull HU11 4RX
T: (01964) 527645 & 0797 197 8611
E: helen@seasideroad.freeserve. co.uk
I: www.aer96.dial.pipex. com/lilac-cottage

ALDFIELD
North Yorkshire

Trips Cottage ★★★
Contact: Mrs S V Leeming, Trips Cottage, Bay Tree Farm, Aldfield, Ripon, North Yorkshire HG3 4BE
T: (01765) 620394

ALLERSTON
North Yorkshire

The Old Station ★★★★
Contact: Mr & Mrs Mark & Carol Benson, The Old Station, Main Street, Allerston, Pickering, North Yorkshire YO18 7PG
T: (01723) 859024
E: mcrbenson@aol.com

Rains Farm ★★★★
Contact: Mrs & Miss L J M Allanson, Rains Farm, Allerston, Pickering, North Yorkshire YO18 7PQ
T: (01723) 859333
E: allan@rainsfarm.freeserve. co.uk
I: www.rains-farm-holidays. co.uk

ALLERTHORPE
East Riding of Yorkshire

The Old Gravel Pits ★★★★
Contact: Dr & Mrs E F Moll, Old Gravel Pits, Allerthorpe, York YO42 4RW
T: (01759) 302192

AMPLEFORTH
North Yorkshire

Beckside Cottage ★★★
Contact: Dales Hol Cot Ref:2474, Dales Holiday Cottages, Carleton Business Park, Carleton New Road, Skipton, North Yorkshire BD23 2AA
T: (01756) 799821 & 790919
F: (01756) 797012
E: info@dalesholcot.com
I: www.dalesholcot.com

Brook House ★★★★
Contact: Mrs Mary Sturges, Brook House Cottage, West End, Ampleforth, York YO6 4DY
T: (01439) 788563
F: (01439) 788563
E: ykf31@dial.pipex.com

2 Carmel Cottage ★★★
Contact: Miss C Jennings, Carmel Cottage, Ampleforth, York YO62 4DU
T: (01439) 788467
F: (01439) 788467
E: carmelcott@onetel.net.uk

Hillside Cottage ★★★★
Contact: Mrs P Noble, Hillside, West End, Ampleforth, York YO62 4DY
T: (01439) 788303 & 07941 687018
F: (01439) 788303
E: hillsidecottage@ westend-ampleforth.co.uk
I: www.cottageguide. co.uk/hillsidecottage

APPERSETT
North Yorkshire

The Coach House ★★★
Contact: Mr W Head, The Coach House, Rigg House, High Abbotside, Appersett, Hawes, North Yorkshire DL8 3LR
T: (01969) 667375
F: (01969) 667375
E: walterhead@rigghouse. freeserve.co.uk

APPLETON–LE–MOORS
North Yorkshire

Darley Cottage ★★★★
Contact: Mr & Mrs J R Brooke, The Pottery, Appleton-le-Moors, York, North Yorkshire YO62 6TE
T: (01751) 417514
E: jbrooke@potteryl.fsnet.co.uk

Hamley Hagg Cottage ★★★
Contact: Mrs J Feaster, Hamley Hagg Cottage, Hamley Hagg Farm, Appleton-le-Moors, York, North Yorkshire YO62 6TG
T: (01751) 417413
E: mbliveries@appletonlemoors. fsnet.co.uk
I: www.appletonlemoors.fsnet. co.uk

Three Faces Cottage ★★★
Contact: Mrs B Firth, 4 West End Lane, Horsforth, Leeds LS18 5JP
T: (0113) 258 8940

APPLETREEWICK
North Yorkshire

Fellside ★★★
Contact: Mrs M Murphy, Three Peaks, 5 Barns Close, Kirby Muxloe, Leicester LE9 2BA
T: (0116) 239 5713
T: (0116) 239 5713
E: murphyjane@hotmail.com

ARKENGARTHDALE
North Yorkshire

Low Eskeleth Cottage ★★
Contact: Mrs M Barningham, Low Eskeleth Farm, Arkengarthdale, Richmond, North Yorkshire DL11 6RW
T: (01748) 884639

Low Faggergill Cottage ★★★
Contact: Mrs G M Atkinson, Low Faggergill Cottage, Arkengarthdale, Richmond, North Yorkshire DL11 6RS
T: (01244) 345700 & (01748) 884550
F: (01244) 321442

Low Lock Slack Cottage ★★★
Contact: Sykes Cottages Ref:62, Sykes Cottages, York House, York Street, Chester, CH1 3LR
T: (01244) 345700
F: (01244) 321442
E: info@sykescottages.co.uk
I: www.sykescottages.co.uk

The Old School House ★
Contact: Sykes Cottages Ref:279, Sykes Cottages, York House, York Street, Chester, CH1 3LR
T: (01244) 345700
F: (01244) 321442
E: info@sykescottages.co.uk
I: www.sykescottages.co.uk

Yew Tree House ★★
Contact: Mr R Wales, Holiday Cottages (Yorkshire) Ltd, Water Street, Skipton, North Yorkshire BD23 1PB
T: (01756) 700510

ARNCLIFFE
North Yorkshire

Green Farm Cottage
Rating Applied For
Contact: Dales Hol Cot Ref:1523, Dales Holiday Cottages, Carleton Business Park, Carleton New Road, Skipton, North Yorkshire BD23 2AA
T: (01756) 799821 & 790919
F: (01756) 797012
E: info@dalesholcot.com
I: www.dalesholcot.com

ASKHAM BRYAN
Yorkshire

The Gardeners Cottage ★★★
Contact: Country Holidays ref:12248, Holiday Cottages Group, Spring Mill, Earby, Barnoldswick, Lancashire BB94 0AA
T: 08700 723723
F: (01282) 844288
E: sales@ttgihg.co.uk
I: www.country-holidays.co.uk

ASKRIGG
North Yorkshire

Askrigg Cottages ★★★–★★★★
Contact: Mrs Kate Empsall, Whitfield, Helm, Askrigg, Leyburn, North Yorkshire DL8 3JF
T: (01969) 650565
F: (01969) 650565
E: empsall@askrigg.yorks.net
I: www.askrigg.yorks.net

Ceri's Cottage ★★★
Contact: Mrs J E Grant, Derbyhill House, Cross o' th Hands, Turnditch, Belper, Derbyshire DE56 2LT
T: (01773) 550489
E: terry@derbyhill.co.uk
I: www.derbyhill.rapidial.co.uk

Cowlingholme Cottage ★★★★
Contact: Mrs Nadine H Bell, Country Hideaways, Margarets Cottage, West Burton, Leyburn, North Yorkshire DL8 4JN
T: (01969) 663559
F: (01969) 663559
E: nhbell@aol.com
I: www.countryhideaways.co.uk

Cringley Barn ★★★★
Contact: Sykes Cottages Ref:687, Sykes Cottages, York House, York Street, Chester, CH1 3LR
T: (01244) 345700
F: (01244) 321442
E: info@sykescottages.co.uk
I: www.sykescottages.co.uk

2 Elm Hill ★★★
Contact: Mrs M Hudson, 16 The Green, Barrow, Bury St Edmunds, Suffolk IP29 5DT
T: (01284) 810121
F: (01284) 810239
E: migith@hotmail.com

Lavender Cottage ★★★★
Contact: Sykes Cottages
Ref:729, Sykes Cottages, York
House, York Street, Chester,
CH1 3LR
T: (01244) 345700
F: (01244) 321442
E: info@sykescottages.co.uk
I: www.sykescottages.co.uk

Lukes Barn ★★★
Contact: Dales Hol Cot Ref:1675,
Dales Holiday Cottages, Carleton
Business Park, Carleton New
Road, Skipton, North Yorkshire
BD23 2AA
T: (01756) 799821 & 790919
F: (01756) 797012
E: info@dalesholcot.com
I: www.dalesholcot.com

Old Mill II ★★★
Contact: Mrs Nadine Bell,
Country Hideaways, Margarets
Cottage, West Burton, Leyburn,
North Yorkshire DL8 4JN
T: (01969) 663559
F: (01969) 663559
E: nhbell@aol.com
I: www.countryhideaways.co.uk

Rook Cottage and Minnie's
Cottage ★★★-★★★★
Contact: Sykes Cottages
Ref:686,720, Sykes Cottages,
York House, York Street, Chester,
CH1 3LR
T: (01244) 345700
F: (01244) 321442
E: info@sykescottages.co.uk
I: www.sykescottages.co.uk

School House ★★★
Contact: Mrs Nadine H Bell,
Country Hideaways, Margarets
Cottage, West Burton, Leyburn,
North Yorkshire DL8 4JN
T: (01969) 663559
F: (01969) 663559
E: nhbell@aol.com
I: www.countryhideaways.co.uk

Shaw Cote Cottage ★★★
Contact: Sykes Cottages
Ref:218, Sykes Cottages, York
House, York Street, Chester,
CH1 3LR
T: (01244) 345700
F: (01244) 321442
E: info@sykescottages.co.uk
I: www.sykescottages.co.uk

The Shippon ★★★
Contact: Mrs Nadine Bell,
Country Hideaways, Margarets
Cottage, West Burton, Leyburn,
North Yorkshire DL8 4JN
T: (01969) 663559
F: (01969) 663559
E: nhbell@aol.com
I: www.countryhideaways.co.uk

Yoredale Cottage ★★
Contact: Mrs E M Miller, The
Orchard, West Burton, Leyburn,
North Yorkshire DL8 4JN
T: (01969) 663559 & 622244
E: beth_m@hotmail.com

AUSTWICK
North Yorkshire

Hickamore Cottage ★★★
Contact: Mrs Catherine Brett,
The Drey, Townsend Mead, Corfe
Castle, Wareham, Dorset
BH20 5EU
T: (01929) 480256 &
(01202) 388888
F: (01929) 388800
E: mjbco@btinternet.com

Spoutscroft Cottage
Rating Applied For
Contact: Sykes Cottages:ref 792,
Sykes Cottages, York House,
York Street, Chester, CH1 3LR
T: (01244) 345700
F: (01244) 321442
E: info@sykescottages.co.uk
I: www.sykescottages.co.uk

Wharfe House ★★★
Contact: Mr Andrew
Brocklehurst, 35 Polwarth
Street, Glasgow, G12 9UE
T: (0141) 334 6947
E: brocklehurst@bvl.org.uk

AYSGARTH
North Yorkshire

Storey's Cottage ★★★
Contact: Dales Hol Cot Ref:2393,
Dales Holiday Cottages, Carleton
Business Park, Carleton New
Road, Skipton, North Yorkshire
BD23 2AA
T: (01756) 799821 & 790919
F: (01756) 797012
E: info@dalesholcot.com
I: www.dalesholcot.com

Yore Mews ★★
Contact: Mrs Nadine H Bell,
Country Hideaways, Margarets
Cottage, West Burton, Leyburn,
North Yorkshire DL8 4JN
T: (01969) 663559
F: (01969) 663559
E: nhbell@aol.com
I: www.countryhideaways.co.uk

BAILDON
West Yorkshire

Butler Cottage ★★★
Contact: Mr & Mrs N
Rushworth, Butler House, Butler
Lane, Baildon, Shipley, West
Yorkshire BD17 6PG
T: (01274) 581530

BAINBRIDGE
North Yorkshire

Chapel End ★★★★
Contact: Dales Hol Cot Ref:2113,
Dales Holiday Cottages, Carleton
Business Park, Carleton New
Road, Skipton, North Yorkshire
BD23 2AA
T: (01756) 799821 & 790919
F: (01756) 797012
E: info@dalesholcot.com
I: www.dalesholcot.com

BALDERSBY
North Yorkshire

Elm Cottage ★★
Contact: Dales
2557,2823,3135,3136, Dales
Holiday Cottages, Carleton
Business Park, Carleton New
Road, Skipton, North Yorkshire
BD23 2AA
T: (01756) 799821 & 790919
F: (01756) 797012
E: info@dalesholcot.com
I: www.dalesholcot.com

BARDEN
North Yorkshire

The Shippon ★★★
Contact: Dales Hol Cot Ref:2877,
Dales Holiday Cottages, Carleton
Business Park, Carleton New
Road, Skipton, North Yorkshire
BD23 2AA
T: (01756) 799821 & 790919
F: (01756) 797012
E: info@dalesholcot.com
I: www.dalesholcot.com

BARMBY MOOR
East Riding of Yorkshire

Calley Barn ★★★
Contact: Mrs L M Steel,
Kimberley House, The Green,
Barmby Moor, York YO42 4EY
T: (01759) 302514
F: (01759) 302514

Northwood Coach House
★★★★
Contact: Mrs A Gregory,
Northwood House, St Helen's
Square, Barmby Moor, York, East
Riding of Yorkshire YO42 4HF
T: (01759) 302305
E: annjgregory@hotmail.com

BARROW UPON HUMBER
North Lincolnshire

Papist Hall
Rating Applied For
Contact: Mrs Marion Dawson,
22 Lynwood Avenue, Anlaby,
Hull HU10 7DP
T: (01482) 657930
F: (01482) 657553
E: info@papisthall.co.uk
I: www.papist.hall.co.uk

BARTON-LE-WILLOWS
North Yorkshire

The Old Granary ★★★★
Contact: Mrs J R Hudson, The
Old Granary, Green Farm,
Barton-le-Willows, York
YO60 7PD
T: (01653) 618387
F: (01653) 618387
E: janet@oldgranary.com
I: www.oldgranary.com

BECKWITHSHAW
North Yorkshire

The Old Mistal ★★★★
Contact: Mrs C Williams,
Bluecoat Farm, Howhill Road,
Beckwithshaw, Harrogate, North
Yorkshire HG3 1QJ
T: (01423) 561385
F: (01423) 561385
E: c.williams@mistal.fsnet.co.uk

BEDALE
North Yorkshire

High Grange Holiday Cottages
★★★★
Contact: Mr & Mrs Trevor and
Janet Ripley, High Grange
Holiday Cottages, Exelby, Bedale,
North Yorkshire DL8 2HQ
T: (01677) 422740
F: (01677) 422740
E: highgrange@yorks.net
I: www.highgrange.yorks.net

Stabann ★★★
Contact: Mr Michael Hall,
Stabann, 16 North End, Bedale,
North Yorkshire DL8 1AB
T: (01677) 424454

BELLERBY
North Yorkshire

Boar Cottage ★★★★
Contact: Dales Hol Cot Ref:2699,
Dales Holiday Cottages, Carleton
Business Park, Carleton New
Road, Skipton, North Yorkshire
BD23 2AA
T: (01756) 799821 & 790919
F: (01756) 797012
E: info@dalesholcot.com
I: www.dalesholcot.com

Scott Cottage ★★★
Contact: Mrs A Maughan, Scott
Cottage, Bellerby, Leyburn,
North Yorkshire DL8 5QP
T: (01969) 622498
F: (01969) 622498

BEMPTON
East Riding of Yorkshire

Primrose Cottage ★★★★
Contact: Dales Hol Cot Ref:2122,
Dales Holiday Cottages, Carleton
Business Park, Carleton New
Road, Skipton, North Yorkshire
BD23 2AA
T: (01756) 799821 & 790919
F: (01756) 797012
E: info@dalesholcot.com
I: www.dalesholcot.com

BEVERLEY
East Riding of Yorkshire

Beckside Cottage ★★★
Contact: Mr M N King, Beckside
Cottage, 66 Beckside, Beverley,
North Humberside HU17 0PD
T: (01482) 872291
E: kings@three.karoo.co.uk

The Cottage ★★★★
Contact: Mr Kenneth Hearne, 25
All Hallows Road, Walkington,
Beverley, East Yorkshire
HU17 8SH
T: (01482) 868310
E: knhearne@talk21.com
I: www.AKcottage.F25.com

Foremans Cottage ★★★
Contact: Mrs H Hayward, Lane
House, Beverley Road, Bishop
Burton, Beverley, North
Humberside HU17 8QY
T: (01964) 550821 &
07850 434234
F: (01964) 550898
E: paulwhay@aol.com

Old Walkergate & The Cabin
★★-★★★
Contact: Mrs M J Abbey, 5
Laughton Road, Beverley, East
Yorkshire HU17 9JR
T: (01482) 860005 &
07703 529318
F: (01482) 860005
E: margaretabbey@
beverleyselfcatering.freeserve.
co.uk
I: www.beverleyselfcatering.
freeserve.co.uk

Rudstone Walk Country
Cottages ★★★★
Contact: Mrs L Greenwood,
Rudstone Walk Country
Cottages, Rudstone Walk, South
Cave, Brough, Beverley, East
Yorkshire HU15 2AH
T: (01430) 422230
F: (01430) 424552
E: office@rudstone-walk.co.uk
I: www.rudstone-walk.co.uk

BEWERLEY
North Yorkshire
Bewerley Hall Farm ★★★★
Contact: Mrs E J Smith,
Bewerley Hall Farm, Bewerley,
Harrogate, North Yorkshire
HG3 5JA
T: (01423) 711636 & 0780 848 0417
E: chris@farmhouseholidays.
freeserve.co.uk
I: www.bewerleyhallfarm.co.uk

Buchanty House ★★★★
Contact: Mrs Angela Durance,
Harrogate Holiday Cottages, The
Old Post Office, Kettlesing,
Harrogate, North Yorkshire
HG3 2LB
T: (01423) 772700
F: (01423) 772359
E: booking@harrogateholidays.
co.uk
I: www.harrogateholidays.co.uk

4 The Green ★★★
Contact: Mr R Wales, Holiday
Cottages (Yorkshire) Ltd, Water
Street, Skipton, North Yorkshire
BD23 1PB
T: (01756) 700510

BINGLEY
West Yorkshire
The Grange
Rating Applied For
Contact: Mrs D Skinn, The
Grange, Sconce Lane, High
Eldwick, Bingley, West Yorkshire
BD16 3BL
T: (01943) 878777
F: (01943) 878777
I: www.faweathergrange.com

BIRSTWITH
North Yorkshire
3 The Square ★★★★
Contact: Mr R Wales, Holiday
Cottages (Yorkshire) Ltd, Water
Street, Skipton, North Yorkshire
BD23 1PB
T: (01756) 700510

BISHOP MONKTON
North Yorkshire
4 Glenroyd Cottages ★★★
Contact: Mr G Widnall, 44
Jesmond Road, Harrogate, North
Yorkshire HG1 4SA
T: (01423) 887091

Hall Farm Cottage ★★★
Contact: Mrs Jennifer Barker,
Hall Farm, Boroughbridge Road,
Bishop Monkton, Harrogate,
North Yorkshire HG3 3QN
T: (01765) 677200

Park House Mill
Rating Applied For
Contact: Mrs Angela Durance,
Harrogate Holiday Cottages, The
Old Post Office, Kettlesing,
Harrogate, North Yorkshire
HG3 2LB
T: (01423) 772700
F: (01423) 772359
E: booking@harrogateholidays.
co.uk
I: www.harrogateholidays.co.uk

Yorbus Grange ★★★
Contact: Mrs Angela Durance,
Harrogate Holiday Cottages, The
Old Post Office, Kettlesing,
Harrogate, North Yorkshire
HG3 2LB
T: (01423) 770831 & 772700
F: (01423) 772359
E: bookings@harrogateholidays.
co.uk
I: www.harrogateholidays.co.uk

BISHOP THORNTON
North Yorkshire
The Courtyard at 'Dukes Place'
★★★–★★★★★
Contact: Mrs Jaki Moorhouse,
The Courtyard at 'Dukes Place',
Fountains Abbey Road, Bishop
Thornton, Harrogate, North
Yorkshire HG3 3JY
T: (01765) 620229
F: (01765) 620454
E: jakimoorhouse@onetel.net.uk

Woodfield Mill Cottages
★★★★
Contact: Mr & Mrs J D Halliday,
Woodfield Mill Cottages,
Woodfield Mill, Bishop Thornton,
Harrogate, North Yorkshire
HG3 3JB
T: (01423) 771153 & 523252
F: (01423) 523838
E: jhalliday@hcconsulting.co.uk

BISHOP WILTON
East Riding of Yorkshire
Low Callis Granary ★★★★
Contact: Mrs Jayne Helen
Stringer, Low Callis Granary, Low
Callis Wold, Bishop Wilton, York
YO42 1TD
T: (01759) 368831
E: thegranary@lowcallis.plus.
com

BOLSTERSTONE
South Yorkshire
Nook Farm Holiday Cottage
★★★
Contact: Ms C J Wainwright,
Nook Farm Holiday Cottage,
Nook Farm, Bolsterstone,
Sheffield, South Yorkshire
S36 3ST
T: (0114) 288 3335

BOLTBY
North Yorkshire
The Coach House ★★★★
Contact: Holiday Homes, PO Box
9, Thirsk, North Yorkshire
YO7 2YZ
T: (01845) 597660

High Paradise Farm Cottages
★★★
Contact: Mrs Judith Skilbeck,
High Paradise Farm Cottages,
High Paradise Farm, Boltby,
Thirsk, North Yorkshire YO7 2HT
T: (01845) 537235
F: (01845) 537033
E: info@highparadise.co.uk
I: www.highparadise.co.uk

BOLTON
East Riding of Yorkshire
Croft House ★★★★
Contact: Mrs J M Sampson,
Bolton House, Bolton,
Wilberfoss, York YO41 5QX
T: (01759) 368229

BOLTON PERCY
North Yorkshire
Manor Cottages ★★★
Contact: Mrs J Houseman,
Hornington Manor, Bolton
Percy, York YO23 7AS
T: (01937) 833157

BORROWBY
North Yorkshire
Ivy Cottage ★★
Contact: Mrs Adele Thompson,
Whitby Holiday Cottages, 47
Flowergate, Whitby, North
Yorkshire YO21 3BB
T: (01947) 603010
F: (01947) 821133
E: enquiries@whitby-cottages.
co.uk
I: www.whitby-cottages.co.uk

BRAMHAM
West Yorkshire
Chestnut Chase ★★★
Contact: Mrs P Machin,
Chestnut Chase, 9 Prospect
Bank, Bramham, Wetherby, West
Yorkshire LS23 6RS
T: (01937) 842559

BRANDSBY
North Yorkshire
Highside Cottage
Rating Applied For
Contact: Dales Hol Cot Ref:2695,
Dales Holiday Cottages, Carleton
Business Park, Carleton New
Road, Skipton, North Yorkshire
BD23 2AA
T: (01756) 799821 & 790919
F: (01756) 797012
E: info@dalesholcot.com
I: www.dalesholcot.com

BRIDLINGTON
East Riding of Yorkshire
Acorn House Holiday Flats
★★★
Contact: Mr M P Beevers, Acorn
House, 9 Belgrave Road,
Bridlington, East Riding of
Yorkshire YO15 3JP
T: (01262) 672451 &
07801 013993
F: (01262) 672451
E: meruyn@acorn-property.
freeuk.com
I: www.acorn-property.freeuk.
com

Highcliffe Holiday Apartments
★
Contact: Mrs Pat Willcocks,
Highcliffe Holiday Apartments,
19 Albion Terrace, Bridlington,
East Riding of Yorkshire
YO15 2PJ
T: (01262) 674127

Marton Manor Cottages
★★★★
Contact: Mrs Jane Waind,
Marton Manor Cottages, Marton
Manor, Bridlington, East Riding
of Yorkshire YO15 1DU
T: (01262) 672522
F: (01262) 672522
E: martonmanor@
farmersweekly.net
I: www.martonmanor.fsnet.
co.uk

Orchard Court Holiday
Cottages ★★★
Contact: Mr C Dare, Orchard
Court Holiday Cottages, 65
Jewison Lane, Sewerby,
Bridlington, East Riding of
Yorkshire YO15 1DX
T: (01262) 671829
F: (01262) 671829

Victoria Holidays ★★★★
Contact: Mr & Mrs Barry & Anne
Hatfield, c/o 25 Victoria Road,
Bridlington, East Yorkshire
YO15 2AT
T: (01262) 673871
F: (01262) 609431
E: victoria.hotel@virgin.net
I: www.victoriahotelbridlington.
co.uk

**Wild Cherry Cottage &
Weavers Cottage** ★★★
Contact: Mrs Pauline Halstead,
33 Beverley Road, Driffield,
North Humberside YO25 6RZ
T: (01377) 253985 &
0794 1141942
F: (01377) 253985
E: pauline.halstead@virgin.net

BRIGSLEY
Lincolnshire
Prospect Farm Cottages
★★★★
Contact: Mrs Janet Speight,
Prospect Farm, Waltham Road,
Brigsley, Grimsby, North East
Lincolnshire DN37 0RQ
T: (01472) 826491
E: prospectfarm@btclick.com

BUCKDEN
North Yorkshire
**Dalegarth and The Ghyll
Cottages** ★★★★
Contact: Mr & Mrs D Lusted, 9
Dalegarth, Buckden, Skipton,
North Yorkshire BD23 5JU
T: (01756) 760877
F: (01756) 760877
E: dalegarth@aol.com
I: www.dalegarth.co.uk

BURNSALL
North Yorkshire
**Bland Place and Manor
Cottage** ★★★
Contact: Ms D R Lodge, Bland
Place and Manor Cottage, High
Croft, Burnsall, Skipton, North
Yorkshire BD23 6BP
T: (01756) 720668

Mandy's Cottage ★★★
Contact: Sykes Cottages
Ref:289, Sykes Cottages, York
House, York Street, Chester,
CH1 3LR
T: (01244) 345700
F: (01244) 321442
E: info@sykescottages.co.uk
I: www.sykescottages.co.uk

Oatcroft Farm Barn Apartment
★★★
Contact: Mrs J Stockdale,
Oatcroft Farm Barn Apartment,
Oatcroft Farm, Burnsall, Skipton,
North Yorkshire BD23 6BN
T: (01756) 720268

Riverside Cottage ★★★
Contact: Sykes Cottages
Ref:214, Sykes Cottages, York
House, York Street, Chester,
CH1 3LR
T: (01244) 345700
F: (01244) 321442
E: info@sykescottages.co.uk
I: www.sykescottages.co.uk

Stable Loft ★★★
Contact: Mrs Linda Aynesworth,
Summersgill Coit, Hartlington,
Burnsall, Skipton, North
Yorkshire BD23 6BY
T: (01756) 720262

North Gate Cottage ★★★
Contact: Dales Hol Cot Ref:3045,
Dales Holiday Cottages, Carleton
Business Park, Carleton New
Road, Skipton, North Yorkshire
BD23 2AA
T: (01756) 799821 & 790916
F: (01756) 797012
E: info@dalesholcot.com
I: www.dalesholcot.com

Twaingate Cottage ★★★★
Contact: Sykes Cottages
Ref:783, Sykes Cottages, York
House, York Street, Chester,
CH1 3LR
T: (01244) 345700
F: (01244) 321442
E: info@sykescottages.co.uk
I: www.sykescottages.co.uk

**Brentwood Farm Cottages
★★★★**
Contact: Mrs Anita Taylor,
Barnoldswick Lane, Burton-in-
Lonsdale, Carnforth, Lancashire
LA6 3LZ
T: (015242) 62155
F: (015242) 62155
E: info@brentwoodfarmcottages.
co.uk
I: www.brentwoodfarmcottages.
co.uk

Riverside Cottage ★★★★★
Contact: Ms P Leverton, 1 Manor
Fold, Cottingley, Bingley, West
Yorkshire BD16 1TE
T: (01274) 560542 &
07714 491241

**Park House Holiday Cottages
★★★★**
Contact: Mr Russell Hammond,
Park House Holiday Cottages,
Park House, Station Lane, Burton
Leonard, Harrogate, North
Yorkshire HG3 3RX
T: (01765) 677387 &
07976 935705
E: mail@parkhouseholidays.
com
I: www.parkhouseholidays.com

The Granary ★★★★
Contact: Mrs Margaret Raines,
The Granary, The Hermitage,
Burythorpe, Malton, North
Yorkshire YO17 9LF
T: (01653) 658201

Ivy Cottage ★★★
Contact: Dales Hol Cot Ref:2713,
Dales Holiday Cottages, Carleton
Business Park, Carleton New
Road, Skipton, North Yorkshire
BD23 2AA
T: (01756) 799821 & 790919
F: (01756) 797012
E: info@dalesholcot.com
I: www.dalesholcot.com

**Rombalds Cottage and
Crookrise Cottage★★**
Contact: Dales Hol Cot Ref:786/
787, Dales Holiday Cottages,
Carleton Business Park, Carleton
New Road, Skipton, North
Yorkshire BD23 2AA
T: (01756) 799821 & 790919
F: (01756) 797012
E: info@dalesholcot.com
I: www.dalesholcot.com

**Coverdale Lodge Cottage
★★★★**
Contact: Mrs D J Beardsmore,
Coverdale Lodge, Carlton-in-
Coverdale, Leyburn, North
Yorkshire DL8 4BA
T: (01969) 640602

Little Hollin ★★★
Contact: Mr & Mrs Anne & Peter
Wright, 6 Garden Lane,
Southsea, Hampshire PO5 3DP
T: (023) 9273 6651
E: hollin@wright.globalnet.
co.uk
I: www.users.globalnet.
co.uk/~wright

Avalon ★★★
Contact: Country Holidays
ref:816, Holiday Cottages Group,
Spring Mill, Earby, Barnoldswick,
Lancashire BB94 0AA
T: 08700 723723
F: (01282) 844288
E: sales@ttgihg.co.uk
I: www.country-holidays.co.uk

Holly Barn ★★★★
Contact: Mr William Edward
Lawson, Holly House, Carlton
Miniott, Thirsk, North Yorkshire
YO7 4NJ
T: (01845) 522099

Barnbrook ★★★
Contact: Sykes Cottages
Ref:567, Sykes Cottages, York
House, York Street, Chester,
CH1 3LR
T: (01244) 345700
F: (01244) 321442
E: info@sykescottages.co.uk
I: www.sykescottages.co.uk

The Granary ★★★★
Contact: Dales Hol Cot Ref:1159,
Dales Holiday Cottages, Carleton
Business Park, Carleton New
Road, Skipton, North Yorkshire
BD23 2AA
T: (01756) 799821 & 790919
F: (01756) 797012
E: info@dalesholcot.com
I: www.dalesholcot.com

Pencroft Cottage ★★★
Contact: Mr D Nichol, 49
Ashfield Park, Whickham,
Newcastle upon Tyne NE16 4SQ
T: (0191) 4881519 &
07940 716339
F: (0191) 4881519

Sunnybank Cottage ★★★
Contact: Mrs D Dolphin,
Sunnybank Farm, Carperby,
Leyburn, North Yorkshire
DL8 4DR
T: (01969) 663131
F: (01969) 663131
E: mdcmadol@supanet.com

Primrose Cottage ★★★★
Contact: Mrs J Graham,
Craigower, 34 West Lane, Danby,
Whitby, North Yorkshire
YO21 2LY
T: (01287) 660248
E: june@grahamdanby.com

Bay Tree Cottage ★★
Contact: Mrs J L Hugill, Prospect
Hill Farm, Catterick Village,
Richmond, North Yorkshire
DL10 7PP
T: (01748) 811305 &
07889 279701

Fox Cottage ★★★
Contact: Mr & Mrs D J Fryer, 17
High Green, Catterick,
Richmond, North Yorkshire
DL10 7LN
T: (01748) 811772

The Cottage ★★★
Contact: Mr and Mrs C&M
Rowlands, Hilltop Cottage,
North Lane, Cawthorne,
Barnsley, South Yorkshire
S75 4AG
T: (01226) 791984 & 791317
F: (01226) 792383
E: RowlandsCM@aol.com

Manor Farm ★★★
Contact: Ms D Worsley, Manor
Farm, Cawton Hall, Cawton,
York, North Yorkshire YO62 4LW
T: (01653) 628237 & 628237

Eldin Hall ★★★
Contact: Mr Nicholas Mudd, 1
Ayton Road, Seamer,
Scarborough, North Yorkshire
YO12 4RG
T: 07740 717913 &
(01723) 864649

Netherscar ★★
Contact: Sykes Cottages
Ref:281, Sykes Cottages, York
House, York Street, Chester,
CH1 3LR
T: (01244) 345700
F: (01244) 321442
E: info@sykescottages.co.uk
I: www.sykescottages.co.uk

4 Salt Lake Cottages ★★★
Contact: Mrs H G Lees,
Barnstead, Newhouses, Horton-
in-Ribblesdale, Settle, North
Yorkshire BD24 0JE
T: (01729) 860485

Broadfields Cottage ★★★
Contact: Mrs Judith Staples,
Broadfields Cottage, Broadfields,
Chop Gate, Middlesbrough,
Cleveland TS9 7JB
T: (01642) 778384

**Lavrock Hall Farmhouse
Cottage ★★**
Contact: Mrs Jane Brack, Lavrock
Hall, Chop Gate, Middlesbrough,
Cleveland TS9 7LQ
T: (01439) 798275
F: (01439) 798337
E: info@lavrockhall.co.uk
I: www.lavrockhall.co.uk

**Low Ellermire Farm Cottage
★★★**
Contact: Dales Hol Cot Ref:3027,
Dales Holiday Cottages, Carleton
Business Park, Carleton New
Road, Skipton, North Yorkshire
BD23 2AA
T: (01756) 799821 & 790919
F: (01756) 797012
E: info@dalesholcot.com
I: www.dalesholcot.com

Coppy House Stable ★★★★
Contact: Sykes Cottages
Ref:763, Sykes Cottages, York
House, York Street, Chester,
CH1 3LR
T: (01244) 345700
F: (01244) 321442
E: info@sykescottages.co.uk
I: www.sykescottages.co.uk

Dubgarth ★★
Contact: Sykes Cottages
Ref:630, Sykes Cottages, York
House, York Street, Chester,
CH1 3LR
T: (01244) 345700
F: (01244) 321442
E: info@sykescottages.co.uk
I: www.sykescottages.co.uk

Brow Top Farm ★★★
Contact: Mrs Margaret Priestley,
Brow Top Farm, Bandwin Lane,
Clayton, Bradford, West
Yorkshire BD14 6PS
T: (01274) 882178
I: www.browtopfarm.co.uk

**Gowland Farm Cottages
★★★★**
Contact: Mr D P Martin,
Gowland Farm Cottages,
Gowland Farm, Gowland Lane,
Cloughton, Scarborough, North
Yorkshire YO13 0DU
T: (01723) 870924
I: www.gowlandfarm.co.uk

Establishments printed in blue have a detailed entry in this guide

COMMONDALE
North Yorkshire

Fowl Green Farm
Rating Applied For
Contact: Mrs Susan Muir, Fowl
Green Farm, Commondale,
Whitby, North Yorkshire
YO21 2HN
T: (01287) 660742
E: susan.muir@ukonline.co.uk
I: www.fowlgreenfarm.com

CONONLEY
North Yorkshire

Ash Cottage
Rating Applied For
Contact: Dales Hol Cot Ref:2848,
Dales Holiday Cottages, Carleton
Business Park, Carleton New
Road, Skipton, North Yorkshire
BD23 2AA
T: (01756) 799821 & 790919
F: (01756) 797012
E: info@dalesholcot.com
I: www.dalesholcot.com

The Cottage
Rating Applied For
Contact: Dales Hol Cot Ref:521,
Dales Holiday Cottages, Carleton
Business Park, Carleton New
Road, Skipton, North Yorkshire
BD23 2AA
T: (01756) 799821 & 790919
F: (01756) 797012
E: info@dalesholcot.com
I: www.dalesholcot.com

The Flat – Coates ★★
Contact: Country Holidays
ref:6654, Holiday Cottages
Group, Spring Mill, Earby,
Barnoldswick, Lancashire
BB94 0AA
T: 08700 723723
F: (01282) 844288
E: sales@ttgihg.co.uk
I: www.country-holidays.co.uk

Spring Cottage ★★★
Contact: Dales Hol Cot Ref:3196,
Dales Holiday Cottages, Carleton
Business Park, Carleton New
Road, Skipton, North Yorkshire
BD23 2AA
T: (01756) 799821 & 790919
F: (01756) 797012
E: info@dalesholcot.com
I: www.dalesholcot.com

CONSTABLE BURTON
North Yorkshire

Park Gate Cottage
Rating Applied For
Contact: Dales Hol Cot Ref:
1785, Dales Holiday Cottages,
Carleton Business Park, Carleton
New Road, Skipton, North
Yorkshire BD23 2AA
T: (01756) 799821 & 790919
F: (01756) 797012
E: info@dalesholcot.com
I: www.dalesholcot.com

COPMANTHORPE
Yorkshire

Osmondene ★★
Contact: Mr Chris Brown, Pear
Trees, 1A Merchant Way,
Copmanthorpe, York YO23 3TS
T: (01904) 702491

COTTERDALE
North Yorkshire

Cornerstones ★★★
Contact: Mrs Nadine H Bell,
Country Hideaways, Margarets
Cottage, West Burton, Leyburn,
North Yorkshire DL8 4JN
T: (01969) 663559
F: (01969) 663559
E: nhbell@aol.com
I: www.countryhideaways.co.uk

COUNTERSETT
North Yorkshire

Bee-Bole Cottage ★★★
Contact: Sykes Cottages
Ref:353, Sykes Cottages, York
House, York Street, Chester,
CH1 3LR
T: (01244) 345700
F: (01244) 321442
E: info@sykescottages.co.uk
I: www.sykescottages.co.uk

COWLING
North Yorkshire

Swallow Cottage ★★★★
Contact: Dales Hol Cot Ref:2643,
Dales Holiday Cottages, Carleton
Business Park, Carleton New
Road, Skipton, North Yorkshire
BD23 2AA
T: (01756) 799821 & 790919
F: (01756) 797012
E: info@dalesholcot.com
I: www.dalesholcot.com

CRAKEHALL
North Yorkshire

Applegarth ★★
Contact: Mr R Wales, Holiday
Cottages (Yorkshire) Ltd, Water
Street, Skipton, North Yorkshire
BD23 1PB
T: (01756) 700510

**St Edmund's Country Cottages
★★–★★★**
Contact: The Proprietor, St
Edmund's Country Cottages, St
Edmund's, The Green, Crakehall,
Bedale, North Yorkshire DL8 1HP
T: (01677) 423584
F: (01677) 427397
E: stedmundscountrycottages@
hotmail.com
I: www.crakehall.org.uk

CROPTON
North Yorkshire

Allerdale ★★★
Contact: Mrs A J Feaster,
Fernwood, Cropton, Pickering,
North Yorkshire YO18 8HL
T: (01751) 417692

Beckhouse Cottages ★★★★
Contact: Mrs P Smith,
Beckhouse Cottages, Beckhouse
Farm, Cropton, Pickering, North
Yorkshire YO18 8ER
T: (01751) 417235
F: (01751) 417218
E: beckhousecarriages@
hotmail.com

2 Corner Cottage ★★
Contact: Mrs M Rowlands, 1
Corner Cottage, Cropton,
Pickering, North Yorkshire
YO18 8HH
T: (01751) 417562

High Farm Holiday Cottages
★★★★
Contact: Mrs R M Feaster, High
Farm Holiday Cottages, High
Farm, Cropton, Pickering, North
Yorkshire YO18 8HL
T: (01751) 417461
E: highfarmcropton@aol.com

DALTON
North Yorkshire

**Badgerway Stoop Cottage
★★★**
Contact: Dales Hol Cot Ref:3119,
Dales Holiday Cottages, Carleton
Business Park, Carleton New
Road, Skipton, North Yorkshire
BD23 2AA
T: (01756) 799821 & 790919
F: (01756) 797012
E: info@dalesholcot.com
I: www.dalesholcot.com

Hilltop Cottage ★★★★
Contact: Mr R M Farr, Hilltop
Cottage, Dalton House, Dalton,
Richmond, North Yorkshire
DL11 7HU
T: (01833) 621234
F: (01833) 621092
E: hilltopcottage@rfarr.
freeserve.co.uk
I: www.hilltop-dales-cottage.
co.uk

DANBY
North Yorkshire

**Ainthorpe Farm Cottage
★★★★**
Contact: Mrs Sheila Hide,
Ainthorpe Farm House, Easton
Lane, Danby, Whitby, North
Yorkshire YO21 2JW
T: (01287) 660358

Blackmires Farm ★★★
Contact: Mrs G M Rhys,
Blackmires Farm, Danby Head,
Danby, Whitby, North Yorkshire
YO21 2NN
T: (01287) 660352

Clitherbecks Farm ★★
Contact: Mr Neil Harland,
Clitherbecks Farm, Danby,
Whitby, North Yorkshire
YO21 2NT
T: (01287) 660321
E: nharland@clitherbecks.
freeserve.co.uk
I: www.clitherbecks.freeserve.
co.uk

Margold Cottage ★★★
Contact: Dales Hol Cot Ref:2505,
Dales Holiday Cottages, Carleton
Business Park, Carleton New
Road, Skipton, North Yorkshire
BD23 2AA
T: (01756) 799821 & 790919
F: (01756) 797012
E: info@dalesholcot.com
I: www.dalesholcot.com

DARLEY
North Yorkshire

The Old Byre ★★★
Contact: Mrs L A Houseman, The
Old Byre, Fairfield Farm,
Sheepcote Lane, Darley,
Harrogate, North Yorkshire
HG3 2RN
T: (01423) 780284

Seven Springs Farm ★★
Contact: Mrs C M Kish, Seven
Springs Farm, Sheepcote Lane,
Darley, Harrogate, North
Yorkshire HG3 2RW
T: (01423) 780661
F: (01423) 780661

Southfield Cottages ★★★
Contact: Mrs A Hardcastle,
Southfield Cottages, Southfield
Farm, Darley, Harrogate, North
Yorkshire HG3 2PR
T: (01423) 780258
E: bookings@harrogateholidays.
co.uk
I: www.harrogateholidays.co.uk

DENHOLME
West Yorkshire

Blacksmith's Cottages ★★
Contact: Mrs Janet Nella
Ackroyd, Blacksmith's Cottages,
Forge End, 2 Edge Bottom,
Denholme, Bradford, West
Yorkshire BD13 4JW
T: (01274) 832850
F: (01274) 832850

DONCASTER
South Yorkshire

Debd Hill Farm ★★★★
Contact: Country Holidays
ref:13631, Holiday Cottages
Group, Spring Mill, Earby,
Barnoldswick, Lancashire
BB94 0AA
T: 08700 723723
F: (01282) 844288
I: www.country-holidays.co.uk

DORE
South Yorkshire

Pat's Cottage ★★★
Contact: Mr John Drakeford, 110
Townhead Road, Dore, Sheffield,
South Yorkshire S17 3GB
T: (0114) 236 6014 &
07850 200711
F: (0114) 236 6014
E: johnmdrakeford@hotmail.
com
I: www.patscottage.co.uk

DOWNHOLME
North Yorkshire

Coldstorms Farm ★★★
Contact: Mrs Diana Greenwood,
Walburn Hall, Downholme,
Richmond, North Yorkshire
DL11 6AF
T: (01748) 822152
F: (01748) 822152

DRINGHOUSES
Yorkshire

The Annex Cottage ★★★
Contact: Country Holidays
ref:10536, Holiday Cottages
Group, Spring Mill, Earby,
Barnoldswick, Lancashire
BB94 0AA
T: 08700 732732
F: (01282) 844288
E: sales@ttgihg.co.uk
I: www.country-holidays.co.uk

DUGGLEBY
North Yorkshire
Highbury Farm Cottage
★★★★
Contact: Mr & Mrs J Sawdon,
Highbury Farm Cottage,
Highbury Farm, Duggleby,
Malton, North Yorkshire
YO17 8BN
T: (01944) 738664
E: john.sawdon@farming.co.uk
I: www.
highbury-farm-holiday-cottage.
co.uk

DUNNINGTON
North Yorkshire
**Dunnington Lodge &
Dunnington Lodge Cottage**
Rating Applied For
Contact: Dales Hol Cot
Ref:2938/3234, Dales Holiday
Cottages, Carleton Business
Park, Carleton New Road,
Skipton, North Yorkshire
BD23 2AA
T: (01756) 799821 & 790919
F: (01756) 797012
E: info@dalesholcot.com
I: www.dalesholcot.com

DUNSLEY
North Yorkshire
Field Cottage ★★★
Contact: Mrs Yvonne Coates,
Field House, Dunsley, Whitby,
North Yorkshire YO21 3TJ
T: (01947) 893392 & 893900
F: (01947) 893900

The Shippon & The Stable
★★★
Contact: Dales Hol Cot
Ref:1988/1989, Dales Holiday
Cottages, Carleton Business
Park, Carleton New Road,
Skipton, North Yorkshire
BD23 2AA
T: (01756) 799821 & 790919
F: (01756) 797012
E: info@dalesholcot.com
I: www.dalesholcot.com

EASBY
North Yorkshire
The Old Stables ★★★★
Contact: Mrs Catherine
Hawman, Park House, Easby
Hall, Easby, Great Ayton TS9 6JQ
T: (01642) 722560
F: (01642) 722560
E: piglettoo@btinternet.com
I: www.stables.totalserve.co.uk

EASINGWOLD
North Yorkshire
Allerton Cottage
Rating Applied For
Contact: Mr & Mrs K A Thornton,
Allerton House, 34 Uppleby,
Easingwold, York, North
Yorkshire YO61 3BB
T: (01347) 821912

Greenfield Farm Cottages
★★★
Contact: Mrs Margaret Morrell &
Mr A Jeffrey, Greenfield House,
Thirsk Road, Easingwold, York
YO61 3NJ
T: (01347) 822656

Mooracres Bungalow ★★★
Contact: Dales Hol Cot Ref:753,
Dales Holiday Cottages, Carleton
Business Park, Carleton New
Road, Skipton, North Yorkshire
BD23 2AA
T: (01756) 799821 & 790919
F: (01756) 797012
E: info@dalesholcot.com
I: www.dalesholcot.com

Oak Mews ★★★
Contact: Dales Hol Cot Ref:1795,
Dales Holiday Cottages, Carleton
Business Park, Carleton New
Road, Skipton, North Yorkshire
BD23 2AA
T: (01756) 799821 & 790919
F: (01756) 797012
E: info@dalesholcot.com
I: www.dalesholcot.com

White House Farm ★★★
Contact: CH
ref:12579,14470,14700, Holiday
Cottages Group, Spring Mill,
Earby, Barnoldswick, Lancashire
BB94 0AA
T: 08700 723723
F: (01282) 844288
E: sales@ttgihg.co.uk
I: www.country-holidays.co.uk

EAST MORTON
West Yorkshire
8 The Butts ★★★
Contact: Mrs Irene Holdsworth,
Moor Cottage, The Butts, East
Morton, Keighley, West
Yorkshire BD20 5RU
T: (01274) 563985

EAST WITTON
North Yorkshire
Wayland Cottage ★★★
Contact: Dales Hol Cot Ref:2379,
Dales Holiday Cottages, Carleton
Business Park, Carleton New
Road, Skipton, North Yorkshire
BD23 2AA
T: (01756) 799821 & 790919
F: (01756) 797012
E: info@dalesholcot.com
I: www.dalesholcot.com

EASTBY
North Yorkshire
Lower Heugh Cottage
★★★★★
Contact: Country Holidays
ref:11823, Holiday Cottages
Group, Spring Mill, Earby,
Barnoldswick, Lancashire
BB94 0AA
T: 08700 723723
F: (01282) 844288
I: www.country-holidays.co.uk

EBBERSTON
North Yorkshire
**The Barn and 1 and 2 The
Stables ★★★**
Contact: CH ref:1451,1452,4262,
Holiday Cottages Group, Spring
Mill, Earby, Barnoldswick,
Lancashire BB94 0AA
T: 08700 723723
F: (01282) 841539
I: www.country-holidays.co.uk

Cliff House ★★★-★★★★
Contact: Mr Simon Morris, Cliff
House, Ebberston, Scarborough,
North Yorkshire YO13 9PA
T: (01723) 859440
F: (01723) 850005
E: cliffhouseebberston@
btinternet.com

Cow Pasture Cottage ★★★★
Contact: Mr & Mrs E&J
Hodgson, Studley House, 67
Main Street, Ebberston,
Scarborough, North Yorkshire
YO13 9NR
T: (01723) 859285
F: (01723) 859285
E: ernie@jhodgson.fsnet.co.uk
I: www.studley-house.co.uk

Nesfield Cottage ★★★★
Contact: Mrs J Wood, Nesfield
Cottage, Ingleside, Burton Road,
Ashby-de-la-Zouch,
Leicestershire LE65 2TF
T: (01530) 416094
E: chris.wood4@virgin.net

EGTON
North Yorkshire
Barn Cottages ★★★-★★★★★
Contact: Mrs B Howard, Cottage
Bank Farm, Egton, Whitby, North
Yorkshire YO21 1IQ
T: (01947) 895314
F: (01947) 895314
E: enquiries@barncottages.com
I: www.barncottages.com

Westonby Cottage ★★
Contact: Mrs Joan Flintoft,
Westonby Cottage, Westonby
Farm, Egton, Whitby, North
Yorkshire YO21 1UH
T: (01947) 895296

EMBSAY
North Yorkshire
Crag View Cottage ★★★★
Contact: The Manager, Dales
Holiday Cottages, Carleton
Business Park, Skipton, North
Yorkshire BD23 2AA
T: (01756) 799821 & 790919
F: (01756) 797012

Elm Garth Cottage ★★★
Contact: Mrs Margaret Mewies,
The Craggs, Kirk Lane, Eastby,
Skipton, North Yorkshire
BD23 6SH
T: (01756) 799188
E: m.mewies@talk21.com

17 Pasture Road ★★
Contact: Mr R Wales, Holiday
Cottages (Yorkshire) Ltd, Water
Street, Skipton, North Yorkshire
BD23 1PB
T: (01756) 700510

FADMOOR
North Yorkshire
North Farm Cottages
★★★-★★★★
Contact: Mr and Mrs David and
Gill Broadbent, North Farm,
Fadmoor, York YO62 7HY
T: (01751) 431934
F: (01751) 431934

FARNDALE
North Yorkshire
**The Old Post Office and The
Chapel★★★-★★★★★**
Contact: Sykes Cottages
Ref:657,760, Sykes Cottages,
York House, York Street, Chester,
CH1 3LR
T: (01244) 345700
F: (01244) 321442
E: info@sykescottages.co.uk
I: www.sykescottages.co.uk

FEARBY
North Yorkshire
Diggers Cottage ★★★
Contact: Country Holidays
ref:842, Holiday Cottages Group,
Spring Mill, Earby, Barnoldswick,
Lancashire BB94 0AA
T: 08700 723723
F: (01282) 844288
E: sales@ttgihg.co.uk
I: www.country-holidays.co.uk

FEIZOR
North Yorkshire
Scar Close Barn ★★★★
Contact: Dales Hol Cot Ref:2953,
Dales Holiday Cottages, Carleton
Business Park, Carleton New
Road, Skipton, North Yorkshire
BD23 2AA
T: (01756) 799821 & 790919
F: (01756) 797012
E: info@dalesholcot.com
I: www.dalesholcot.com

Stockdale Barn ★★★★
Contact: Sykes Cottages
Ref:312, Sykes Cottages, York
House, York Street, Chester,
CH1 3LR
T: (01244) 345700
F: (01244) 321442
E: info@sykescottages.co.uk
I: www.sykescottages.co.uk

FELIXKIRK
North Yorkshire
Goose Cottage ★★★★
Contact: Sykes Cottages
Ref:604, Sykes Cottages, York
House, York Street, Chester,
CH1 3LR
T: (01244) 345700
F: (01244) 321442
E: info@sykescottages.co.uk
I: www.sykescottages.co.uk

FELLBECK
North Yorkshire
**1 and 2 North Oaks Farm
Cottages★★★**
Contact: Mrs S Loveless, 1 and 2
North Oaks Farm Cottages,
North Oaks Farm, Fellbeck,
Harrogate, North Yorkshire
HG3 5EP
T: (01423) 712446 & 0780 141
4395
F: (01423) 712457
E: cottages@loveless.co.uk
I: www.loveless.co.uk

South Oaks ★★★
Contact: Mrs Angela Durance,
Harrogate Holiday Cottages, The
Old Post Office, Kettlesing,
Harrogate, North Yorkshire
HG3 2LB
T: (01423) 772700
F: (01423) 772359
E: bookings@harrogateholidays.
co.uk
I: www.harrogateholidays.co.uk

Troutbeck Cottage ★★★★
Contact: Mrs C E Nelson,
Nidderdale Lodge Farm, Fellbeck,
Harrogate, North Yorkshire
HG3 5EU
T: (01423) 711677

Establishments printed in blue have a detailed entry in this guide

FILEY
North Yorkshire

Beach Holiday Flats ★★-★★★
Contact: Mr David Tindall, Beach Holiday Flats, 9-10 The Beach, Filey, North Yorkshire YO14 9LA
T: (01723) 513178
E: anntindall@aol.com
I: www.thebeach-holidayflats.co.uk

The Cottages ★★★
Contact: Mr & Mrs David Teet, The Cottages, Muston Grange, Muston Road, Filey, North Yorkshire YO14 0HU
T: (01723) 516620
F: (01723) 516620

Glenavon ★★-★★★
Contact: Mr and Mrs L Durasamy, 25 Nettleham Road, Lincoln, Lincolnshire LN2 1XJ
T: (01522) 525679 & 545743
F: (01522) 545743

Orchard Farm Cottages ★★★
Contact: Mr & Mrs A Hunneybell, Orchard Farm Cottages, 143 Stonegate, Hunmanby, Filey, North Yorkshire YO14 0PU
T: (01723) 891582
F: (01723) 891582

Saint Kitts Self Catering Holiday Flats★★-★★★
Contact: Mr & Mrs D H Midgley, Saint Kitts Self Catering Holiday Flats, 2 The Beach, Filey, North Yorkshire YO14 9LA
T: (01723) 512141
E: dhmidgley@ukonline.co.uk

FOSTON-ON-THE-WOLDS
East Riding of Yorkshire

Wold View ★★★
Contact: Mr R Wales, Holiday Cottages (Yorkshire) Ltd, Water Street, Skipton, North Yorkshire BD23 1PB
T: (01756) 700510

FREMINGTON
North Yorkshire

Hobson's Cottage ★★★
Contact: Sykes Cottages Ref:752, Sykes Cottages, York House, York Street, Chester, CH1 3LR
T: (01244) 345700
F: (01244) 321442
E: info@sykescottages.co.uk
I: www.sykescottages.co.uk

FYLINGDALES
North Yorkshire

Browdale Cottage ★★★
Contact: Mr & Mrs M&S Earnshaw, Browdale Cottage, Thorney Brow Farm, Fylingdales, Whitby, North Yorkshire YO22 4UL
T: (01947) 880052

Swallows Cottage & The Granary ★★★
Contact: Mrs Adele Thompson, Whitby Holiday Cottages, 47 Flowergate, Whitby, North Yorkshire YO21 3BB
T: (01947) 603010
F: (01947) 821133
E: enquiries@whitby-cottages.co.uk
I: www.whitby-cottages.co.uk

FYLINGTHORPE
North Yorkshire

2 Chapel Cottages ★★★
Contact: Mrs Adele Thompson, Whitby Holiday Cottages, 47 Flowergate, Whitby, North Yorkshire YO21 3BB
T: (01947) 603010
F: (01947) 821133
E: enquiries@whitby-cottages.co.uk
I: www.whitby-cottages.co.uk

Collcot ★★★
Contact: Mrs Adele Thompson, Whitby Holiday Cottages, 47 Flowergate, Whitby, North Yorkshire YO21 3BB
T: (01947) 603010
F: (01947) 821133
E: enquiries@whitby-cottages.co.uk
I: www.whitby-cottages.co.uk

Croft Farm Cottage ★★★
Contact: Mrs Joanne Braithwaite, Croft Farm, Church Lane, Fylingthorpe, Whitby, North Yorkshire YO22 4PW
T: (01947) 880231
F: (01947) 880231

South House Farm ★★★
Contact: Mrs N Pattinson, South House Farm, Millbeck, Fylingthorpe, Whitby, North Yorkshire YO22 4UQ
T: (01947) 880243
F: (01947) 880243

GALPHAY
North Yorkshire

Harry's Hideaway ★★★
Contact: Mrs Angela Durance, Harrogate Holiday Cottages, The Old Post Office, Kettlesing, Harrogate, North Yorkshire HG3 2LB
T: (01423) 772700
F: (01423) 772359
E: bookings@harrogateholidays.co.uk
I: www.harrogateholidays.co.uk

GARGRAVE
North Yorkshire

River Place ★★★
Contact: Sykes Cottages Ref:276, 696, Sykes Cottages, York House, York Street, Chester, CH1 3LR
T: (01244) 345700
F: (01244) 321442
E: info@sykescottages.co.uk
I: www.sykescottages.co.uk

36 River Place ★★★★
Contact: Country Holidays ref:451, Spring Mill, Earby, Barnoldswick, Lancashire BB94 0AA
T: 08700 723723
F: (01282) 844288
E: sales@ttgihg.co.uk
I: www.country-holidays.co.uk

GAYLE
North Yorkshire

Aysgill Cottage ★★★
Contact: Mr and Mrs D&C Allen, Scaur Head Farm, Gayle, Hawes, North Yorkshire DL8 3SF
T: (01969) 667477

Foss Cottage ★★★
Contact: Mrs Brenda Watering, Force Head Farm, Gayle, Hawes, North Yorkshire DL8 3RZ
F: (01969) 667518

Gayle Farmhouse ★★
Contact: Dales Hol Cot Ref:636, Dales Holiday Cottages, Carleton Business Park, Carleton New Road, Skipton, North Yorkshire BD23 2AA
T: (01756) 799821 & 790919
F: (01756) 797012
E: info@dalesholcot.com
I: www.dalesholcot.com

GIGGLESWICK
North Yorkshire

Bookend Cottage ★★★
Contact: Sykes Cottages Ref:713, Sykes Cottages, York House, York Street, Chester, CH1 3LR
T: (01244) 345700
F: (01244) 321442
E: info@sykescottages.co.uk
I: www.sykescottages.co.uk

Close House Cottage Holidays ★★★★
Contact: Mr & Mrs Richard & Sue Hargreaves, Close House, Giggleswick, Settle, North Yorkshire BD24 0EA
T: (01729) 822778
F: (01729) 822778

Foxholes Lodge ★★★
Contact: Mrs L Y Scruton, Foxholes, Station Road, Giggleswick, Settle, North Yorkshire BD24 0AB
T: (01729) 823505 & 824199
F: (01729) 824088

2 Gildersleets ★★★★
Contact: Dr and Mrs Griffiths, 9 Polefield Road, Blackley, Manchester M9 6FN
T: (0161) 795 9713 & 653 8673
F: (0161) 653 6570
E: doctor.g@gconnect.com

Ivy Cottage ★★★★
Contact: Dales Hol Cot Ref:629, Dales Holiday Cottages, Carleton Business Park, Carleton New Road, Skipton, North Yorkshire BD23 2AA
T: (01756) 799821 & 790919
F: (01756) 797012
E: info@dalesholcot.com
I: www.dalesholcot.com

Rose Cottage ★★★★
Contact: Mrs M Hird, Rawlinshaw Farm, Austwick, Lancaster LA2 8DD
T: (01729) 823214

Rowan House, Willow Cottage ★★★★
Contact: Sykes Cottages Ref:398,652, Sykes Cottages, York House, York Street, Chester, CH1 3LR
T: (01244) 345700
F: (01244) 321442
E: info@sykescottages.co.uk
I: www.sykescottages.co.uk

Stanton Cottage ★★★
Contact: Mrs Alison Boswell, 3 Bankwell Close, Giggleswick, Settle, North Yorkshire BD24 0BX
T: (01729) 822400
E: pboswell@ukonline.co.uk

Sutcliffe Cottage ★★
Contact: Sykes Cottages Ref:31, Sykes Cottages, York House, York Street, Chester, CH1 3LR
T: (01244) 345700
F: (01244) 321442
E: info@sykescottages.co.uk
I: www.sykescottages.co.uk

GILLAMOOR
North Yorkshire

Gales House Farm ★★★★
Contact: Mr D Ward, Gales House Farm, Kirkby Lane, Gillamoor, York YO62 7HT
T: (01751) 431258 & 07718 532009
F: 07050 650741
E: Cottages@gillamoor.com
I: www.gillamoor.com

GILLING EAST
North Yorkshire

Sunset Cottages ★★★-★★★★★
Contact: Mr & Mrs R Kelsey, Sunset Cottages, Grimston Manor Farm, Gilling East, York YO62 4HR
T: (01347) 888654
F: (01347) 888347
E: sunset@farmersweekly.net
I: www.sunsetcottages.co.uk

GILLING WEST
North Yorkshire

Gilling Old Mill ★★★★
Contact: Mr and Mrs H Bird, Gilling Old Mill, Gilling West, Richmond, North Yorkshire DL10 5JD
T: (01748) 822771
F: (01748) 822771
E: admin@yorkshiredales-cottages.com
I: www.yorkshiredales-cottages.com

GILSTEAD
West Yorkshire

Thimble Cottage & Bobbin Cottage ★★★-★★★★
Contact: Mrs L Jean Warin, March Cote Farm, Cottingley, Bingley, West Yorkshire BD16 1UB
T: (01274) 487433 & 07889 162257
F: (01274) 561074
E: jean.warin@nevisuk.net
I: www.yorkshirenet.co.uk/accgde/marchcote

GLAISDALE
North Yorkshire

Lanes Cottage ★★
Contact: Dales Hol Cot Ref:2324, Dales Holiday Cottages, Carleton Business Park, Carleton New Road, Skipton, North Yorkshire BD23 2AA
T: (01756) 799821 & 790919
F: (01756) 797012
E: info@dalesholcot.com
I: www.dalesholcot.com

London Lodge ★★★
Contact: Dales Holiday Cottages, Carleton Business Park, Skipton, North Yorkshire BD23 2AA
T: (01756) 799821 & 790919
F: (01756) 797012
E: info@dalesholcot.com
I: www.dalesholcot.com

The Studio Flat ★★★★
Contact: Mr & Mrs John & Mary Thompson, Postgate Farm, Glaisdale, Whitby, North Yorkshire YO21 2PZ
T: (01947) 897353 & 0777 920 6347
F: (01947) 897353
E: j-m.thompson.bandb@talk21.com
I: www.eskvalley.com/postgate/postgate.html

Tailors Cottage ★★
Contact: Mr Clive Sykes, Sykes Cottages, York House, York Street, Chester, CH1 3LR
T: (01244) 345700
F: (01244) 321442
E: info@sykescottages.co.uk
I: www.sykescottages.co.uk

York Cottage ★★★
Contact: Dales Hol Cot Ref:2402, Dales Holiday Cottages, Carleton Business Park, Carleton New Road, Skipton, North Yorkshire BD23 2AA
T: (01756) 799821 & 790919
F: (01756) 797012
E: info@dalesholcot.com
I: www.dalesholcot.com

GOATHLAND
North Yorkshire

Eskholme ★★★★
Contact: Mrs J M Hodgson, Woodlands, 31 Shillbank View, Mirfield, West Yorkshire WF14 0QG
T: (01924) 498154
E: ffsjan@cs.com

Hawthorn Cottage ★★★★
Contact: Mrs J Hollingsbee, Fairacre Cottage, French Road, North Fambridge, Chelmsford CM3 6NJ
T: (01621) 742100
F: (01621) 742101
E: rhollingsb@aol.com

14 Oakfield Avenue ★★
Contact: Mrs Adele Thompson, Whitby Holiday Cottages, 47 Flowergate, Whitby, North Yorkshire YO21 3BB
T: (01947) 603010
F: (01947) 821133
E: enquiries@whitby-cottages.co.uk
I: www.whitby-cottages.co.uk

Orchard Cottage ★★★
Contact: Dales Hol Cot Ref:1418, Dales Holiday Cottages, Carleton Business Park, Carleton New Road, Skipton, North Yorkshire BD23 2AA
T: (01756) 799821 & 790919
F: (01756) 797012
E: info@dalesholcot.com
I: www.dalesholcot.com

Rosedean ★★
Contact: Mrs I S Cox, Abbot's House Farm, Goathland, Whitby, North Yorkshire YO22 5NH
T: (01947) 896270 & 896026
F: (01947) 896270
E: ivegill@enterprise.net
I: www.abbotshousefarm.totalserve.co.uk/index

The Stone Cottage ★★★
Contact: Dales Holiday Cottages, Carleton Business Park, Carleton New Road, Skipton, North Yorkshire BD23 2DG
T: (01756) 799821
F: (01756) 799821

Summerholme Cottage ★★★
Contact: Dales Hol Cot Ref:2403, Dales Holiday Cottages, Carleton Business Park, Carleton New Road, Skipton, North Yorkshire BD23 2AA
T: (01756) 799821 & 790919
F: (01756) 797012
E: info@dalesholcot.com
I: www.dalesholcot.com

Woodpecker Cottage ★★★
Contact: Dales Hol Cot Ref:3125, Dales Holiday Cottages, Carleton Business Park, Carleton New Road, Skipton, North Yorkshire BD23 2AA
T: (01756) 799821 & 790919
F: (01756) 797012
E: info@dalesholcot.com
I: www.dalesholcot.com

GRASSINGTON
North Yorkshire

The Barn ★★★★
Contact: Mrs P G Evans, 3 Delph Wood Close, Gilstead, Bingley, West Yorkshire BD16 3LQ
T: (01274) 561546
E: grassington@ukonline.co.uk
I: www.qteq.co.uk/grassington

The Coach House ★★★
Contact: Dales Hol Cot Ref:3176, Dales Holiday Cottages, Carleton Business Park, Carleton New Road, Skipton, North Yorkshire BD23 2AA
T: (01756) 799821 & 790919
.F: (01756) 797012
E: info@dalesholcot.com
I: www.dalesholcot.com

Garrs House Apartment ★★★
Contact: Mr & Mrs M&A Wadsworth, 25 Watson Road, Blackpool, Lancashire FY4 1EG
T: (01253) 404726 & 07801 450624
F: (01253) 311422

3 Garrs Lane ★★★★
Contact: Country Holidays: 582, Holiday Cottages Group, Spring Mill, Earby, Barnoldswick, Lancashire BB94 0AA
T: 08700 723723
F: (01282) 844288
E: sales@ttgihg.co.uk
I: www.country-holidays.co.uk

6a Garrs Lane ★★★
Contact: Mr P A Borrill, The Fish Shop, 6 Garrs Lane, Grassington, Skipton, North Yorkshire BD23 5AT
T: (01756) 752436 & 753260
F: (01756) 753260
E: paborrill@supanet.com

High Whisp Hill ★★★
Contact: Sykes Cottages Ref:51, Sykes Cottages, York House, York Street, Chester, CH1 3LR
T: (01244) 345700
F: (01244) 321442
E: info@sykescottages.co.uk
I: www.sykescottages.co.uk

Howard Holiday Homes ★★★
Contact: Mr & Mrs A Howard, Howard Holiday Homes, Townhead Barn, Townhead, Grassington, Skipton, North Yorkshire BD23 5BL
T: (01756) 752032 & 07803 482106
E: howard.holiday.homes@tinyworld.co.uk
I: www.dalescharactercottages.co.uk

Manna Cottage ★★★★
Contact: Mrs Sheila Carr, Moor Green Farm, Tarns Lane, Threshfield, Skipton, North Yorkshire BD23 5NR
T: (01756) 752435 & 07879 845771
F: (01756) 752345
E: carr@totalise.co.uk
I: www.yorkshirenet.co.uk/stayat/mannacottage/

3 Moor Croft ★★★
Contact: Country Holidays ref:12836, Holiday Cottages Group, Spring Mill, Earby, Barnoldswick, Lancashire BB94 0AA
T: 08700 723723
F: (01282) 844288
E: sales@ttgihg.co.uk
I: www.country-holidays.co.uk

3A Pletts Fold ★★★
Contact: Mr & Mrs J M Knowles, 5 Winthorpe Avenue, Thorpe, Wakefield, West Yorkshire WF3 3ED
T: (0113) 282 0456
E: barrie.bw.knowles@talk21.com

Riverside ★★★
Contact: Mrs Marilyn Brown, 12 Bridge End, Station Road, Grassington, Skipton, North Yorkshire BD23 5NH
T: (01756) 753886 & 752432
I: www.dales.accommodation.com

Scala Glen Barn ★★★★
Contact: Mr & Mrs C Roundhill, Beechcroft, Hardy Grange, Grassington, Skipton, North Yorkshire BD23 5AJ
T: (01756) 752011 & 07759 926931
F: (01756) 752011
E: scalaglen@aol.com
I: www.oas.co.uk/ukcottages/scalaglen

Sunnyside Cottage ★★★
Contact: Mrs Carolyn Butt, Garris Lodge, Rylstone, Skipton, North Yorkshire BD23 6LJ
T: (01756) 730391
F: (01756) 730391
E: c.butt@daelnet.co.uk
I: www.dalesaccommodation.com/sunnysidecottage

Theatre Cottage
Rating Applied For
Contact: Dales Hol Cot Ref:2214, Dales Holiday Cottages, Carleton Business Park, Carleton New Road, Skipton, North Yorkshire BD23 2AA
T: (01756) 799821 & 790919
F: (01756) 797012
E: info@dalesholcot.com
I: www.dalesholcot.com

Wellhead Cottage ★★★★
Contact: Mr & Mrs Halliday, 2 Grange Drive, Horsforth, Leeds LS18 5EQ
T: (0113) 258 4212
F: (0113) 281 9455

GREAT AYTON
North Yorkshire

Flat 2 ★★
Contact: Mrs M F Metcalfe, 89 Newton Road, Great Ayton, Middlesbrough, Cleveland TS9 6DY
T: (01642) 722935

GREAT EDSTONE
North Yorkshire

Cowldyke Farm
★★★–★★★★
Contact: Mr & Mrs J R Benton, Cowldyke Farm, Great Edstone, York YO62 6PE
T: (01751) 431242
E: info@cowldyke-farm.co.uk
I: www.cowldyke-farm.co.uk

GREAT LANGTON
North Yorkshire

Stanhow Bungalow ★★★★
Contact: Lady Mary Furness, Stanhow Farm, Great Langton, Northallerton, North Yorkshire DL7 0TJ
T: (01609) 748614
F: (01609) 748614

GREEN HAMMERTON
North Yorkshire

Wasp's Nest Holiday Cottages
★★★–★★★★
Contact: Mrs M Nixon, The Wasp's Nest, Green Hammerton, York YO26 8AE
T: (01423) 330153
F: (01423) 331204
E: waspsnest@phnixon.demon.co.uk
I: www.phnixon.demon.co.uk

GREETLAND
West Yorkshire

Lower High Trees Farm ★★★
Contact: Mrs Griffiths, Lower High Trees Farm, Greetland, Halifax, West Yorkshire HX4 8PP
T: (01422) 375205
F: (01422) 375205
E: griffs@freeuk.com
I: www.greetland.org.uk

GREWELTHORPE
North Yorkshire

Crown Cottage ★★★
Contact: Dales Hol Cot Ref:718, Dales Holiday Cottages, Carleton Business Park, Carleton New Road, Skipton, North Yorkshire BD23 2AA
T: (01756) 799821 & 790919
F: (01756) 797012
E: info@dalesholcot.com
I: www.dalesholcot.com

Fir Tree Farm Holiday Homes
★★★
Contact: Mrs Jane Simpson, Fir Tree Farm Holiday Homes, Fir Tree Farm, High Bramley, Grewelthorpe, Ripon, North Yorkshire HG4 3DL
T: (01765) 658727 & 658383

Sunnyside Cottage ★★★★
Contact: Mrs Jane Shuttleworth, 224 Bradway Road, Bradway, Sheffield S17 4PE
T: (0114) 235 2783

Establishments printed in blue have a detailed entry in this guide

GRISTHORPE
North Yorkshire

Carless Cottage ★★★
Contact: Dales Holiday Cottages, Carleton Business Park, Skipton, North Yorkshire BD23 2AA
T: (01756) 799821 & 7900919
F: (01756) 797012

Dove Cottage ★★★★
Contact: Dales Hol Cot Ref:3035, Dales Holiday Cottages, Carleton Business Park, Carleton New Road, Skipton, North Yorkshire BD23 2AA
T: (01756) 799821 & 790019
F: (01756) 797012
E: info@dalesholcot.com
I: www.dalesholcot.com

GROSMONT
North Yorkshire

East Farm Cottage ★★★
Contact: Mrs Adele Thompson, Whitby Holiday Cottages, 47 Flowergate, Whitby, North Yorkshire YO21 3BB
T: (01947) 603010
F: (01947) 821133
E: enquiries@whitby-cottages.co.uk
I: www.whitby-cottages.co.uk

George Stephenson Cottage and Sir Nigel Cresley Cottage ★★★-★★★★
Contact: Mrs Adele Thompson, Whitby Holiday Cottages, 47 Flowergate, Whitby, North Yorkshire YO21 3BB
T: (01947) 603010
F: (01947) 821133
E: enquiries@whitby-cottages.co.uk
I: www.whitby-cottages.co.uk

GUNNERSIDE
North Yorkshire

Brooklands ★★★
Contact: Country Holidays ref:10913, Spring Mill, Earby, Barnoldswick, Lancashire BB18 6RN
T: 08700 723723
F: (01282) 844288
E: sales@ttgihg.co.uk
I: www.country-holidays.co.uk

Brooklyn ★★★
Contact: Mrs S Emmott, 6 Nether Way, Darley Dale, Matlock, Derbyshire DE4 2TS
T: (01629) 734270

Croft Cottage ★★
Contact: Mrs Margaret Batty, Croft House, Gunnerside, Richmond, North Yorkshire DL11 6ND
T: (01748) 886460

Dene Holme ★★★★
Contact: Mrs Annie Porter, Oxnop Hall, Low Oxnop, Gunnerside, Richmond, North Yorkshire DL11 6JJ
T: (01748) 886253 & 886206
F: (01748) 886253

East Roof ★★★
Contact: Country Holidays ref:6652, Holiday Cottages Group, Spring Mill, Earby, Barnoldswick, Lancashire BB94 0AA
T: 08700 723723
F: (01282) 844288
E: sales@ttgihg.co.uk
I: www.country-holidays.co.uk

High Oxnop
Rating Applied For
Contact: Mrs Annie Porter, Oxnop Hall, Low Oxnop, Gunnerside, Richmond, North Yorkshire DL11 6JJ
T: (01748) 886253 & 886206
F: (01748) 886253

Len House ★★
Contact: Mrs R Marlein & Mrs G Anderson, 9 Littlethorpe Close, Strensall, York YO32 5WR
T: (01904) 490623
E: richard@marlein.freeserve.co.uk

Manfield Cottage ★★★
Contact: Dales Hol Cot Ref:3110, Dales Holiday Cottages, Carleton Business Park, Carleton New Road, Skipton, North Yorkshire BD23 2AA
T: (01756) 799821 & 790919
F: (01756) 797012
E: info@dalesholcot.com
I: www.dalesholcot.com

Roof Farm ★★★
Contact: Mr R Wales, Holiday Cottages (Yorkshire) Ltd, Water Street, Skipton, North Yorkshire BD23 1PB
T: (01756) 700510

Roof House Cottage ★★★
Contact: Dales Hol Cot Ref:1761, Dales Holiday Cottages, Carleton Business Park, Carleton New Road, Skipton, North Yorkshire BD23 2AA
T: (01756) 799821 & 790919
F: (01756) 797012
E: info@dalesholcot.com
I: www.dalesholcot.com

Satron Cottage ★★
Contact: Dales Hol Cot Ref:1505, Dales Holiday Cottages, Carleton Business Park, Carleton New Road, Skipton, North Yorkshire BD23 2AA
T: (01756) 799821 & 790919
F: (01756) 797012
E: info@dalesholcot.com
I: www.dalesholcot.com

Strands Farmhouse Cottage ★★★
Contact: Mrs R N Clarkson, Strands Farmhouse, Gunnerside, Richmond, North Yorkshire DL11 6LF
E: clarkson_neil@hotmail.com

Sundale ★★
Contact: Mr R Wales, Holiday Cottages (Yorkshire) Ltd, Water Street, Skipton, North Yorkshire BD23 1PB
T: (01756) 700510

HAINWORTH
West Yorkshire

Charlie's Cottage ★★★
Contact: Dales Hol Cot Ref:2358, Dales Holiday Cottages, Carleton Business Park, Carleton New Road, Skipton, North Yorkshire BD23 2AA
T: (01756) 799821 & 790919
F: (01756) 797012
E: info@dalesholcot.com
I: www.dalesholcot.com

HALIFAX
West Yorkshire

Cherry Tree Cottages ★★★★
Contact: Mr & Mrs Stan & Elaine Shaw, Cherry Tree Cottages, Wall Nook, Barkisland, Halifax, West Yorkshire HX4 0BL
T: (01422) 372662
F: (01422) 372662
E: cherry.tree@zen.co.uk
I: www.yorkshire-cottages.co.uk

The Fall ★★★★
Contact: Mrs P A Knight, 4 Lanes End, Shibden, Halifax, West Yorkshire HX3 7UW
T: (01422) 363346

Nina's Cottage ★★★
Contact: Mrs Susan Thomas, The Barn Moorside, Old Lindley, Halifax, West Yorkshire HX4 9DF
T: (01422) 376933

HAMBLETON
North Yorkshire

Casten Cottage ★★★
Contact: Sykes Cottages Ref:549, Sykes Cottages, York House, York Street, Chester, CH1 3LR
T: (01244) 345700
F: (01244) 321442
E: info@sykescottages.co.uk
I: www.sykescottages.co.uk

HAMPSTHWAITE
North Yorkshire

Rayners Barn ★★★★
Contact: Mrs G Metcalfe, Graystone View Farm, Grayston Plain Lane, Hampsthwaite, Harrogate, North Yorkshire HG3 2LY
T: (01423) 770324
F: (01423) 772536
E: graystonefm.freeserve.co.uk

HARMBY
North Yorkshire

1,2,3 and 4 Harmby Grange Cottages ★★★★
Contact: Dales Holiday Cottages, 12 Otley street, Skipton, North Yorkshire BD23 1DY
T: (01756) 799821
F: (01756) 790919

Hillfoot House ★★
Contact: Mrs G Jones, Hillfoot House, Harmby, Leyburn, North Yorkshire DL8 5PH
T: (01969) 623632

HARROGATE
North Yorkshire

Ashness Apartments ★★★★
Contact: Mrs B Batty and Mr J Spinlove, 15 St Mary's Avenue, Harrogate, North Yorkshire HG2 0LP
T: (01423) 526894
F: (01423) 700038

Brimham Rocks Cottages ★★★-★★★★
Contact: Mrs J M Martin, Brimham Rocks Cottages, High North Farm, Fellbeck, Harrogate, North Yorkshire HG3 5EY
T: (01765) 620284
F: (01765) 620477
E: brimham@nascr.net
I: www.brimham.co.uk

Cheltenham Apartments ★★
Contact: Mr Andrew Moss, 20 Hollins Lane, Hampsthwaite, Harrogate, North Yorkshire HG3 2EJ
T: (01423) 770864 & 0773 098 6959
F: (01423) 770864
E: andrew_moss@ic24.net

Dinmore Cottages ★★★★
Contact: Mrs Mabel Ward, Dovecote Cottage, Dinmore House, Burnt Yates, Harrogate, North Yorkshire HG3 3ET
T: (01423) 770860 & 771711
F: (01423) 770860
E: aib@dinmore-cottages.freeserve.co.uk

The Flat ★★★★
Contact: Angela Durance, Harrogate Holiday Cottages, The Old Post Office, Kettlesing, Harrogate, North Yorkshire HG3 2LB
T: (01423) 772700
F: (01423) 772359
E: booking@harrogateholidays.co.uk
I: www.harrogateholidays.co.uk

Garden Apartment ★★★
Contact: Mrs A Durance, Harrogate Holiday Cottages, The Old Post Office, Kettlesing, Harrogate, North Yorkshire HG3 2LB
T: (01423) 772700
F: (01423) 772359
E: booking@harrogateholidays.co.uk
I: www.harrogateholidays.co.uk

Harrogate Apartments ★★★★
Contact: Mr and Mrs K A Hartwell, Harrogate Apartments, Crimple Head House, Beckwithshaw, Harrogate, North Yorkshire HG3 1QU
T: (01423) 500655 & 07768 662734
E: info@harrogateapartments.com
I: www.harrogateapartments.com

Holly House Farm Cottages ★★★
Contact: Miss Mary Owen, Holly House Farm Cottages, Holly House Farm, Moorcock Lane, Darley, Harrogate, North Yorkshire HG3 2QL
T: (01423) 780266 & 07710 125298
F: (01423) 780299
E: hollyhousecottages@supanet.com

477

Moor View Cottage ★★★
Contact: Mrs H L Sweeting, 45
Kingsley Drive, Harrogate, North
Yorkshire HG1 4TH
T: (014323) 885498
E: hlsweeting@easicom.com

**Mount Pleasant Farm Holiday
Cottages★★★★**
Contact: Mrs Linda Prest, Mount
Pleasant Farm, Skipton Road,
Killinghall, Harrogate, North
Yorkshire HG3 2BU
T: (01423) 504694

4 Oak Terrace ★★★
Contact: Mrs Angela Durance,
Harrogate Holiday Cottages, The
Old Post Office, Kettlesing,
Harrogate, North Yorkshire
HG3 2LB
T: (01423) 772700
F: (01423) 772359
E: bookings@harrogateholidays.
co.uk
I: www.harrogateholidays.co.uk

3 Paradise Row ★★★
Contact: Mrs Angela Durance,
Harrogate Holiday Cottages, The
Old Post Office, Kettlesing,
Harrogate, North Yorkshire
HG3 2LB
T: (01423) 772700
F: (01423) 772359
E: booking@harrogateholidays.
co.uk
I: www.harrogateholidays.co.uk

Regent Cottage ★★★
Contact: Mr Robert Blake, 1A
Moorfield Road, Woodbridge,
Suffolk IP12 4JN
T: (01394) 382565
E: deben@btclick.com

Rudding Holiday Park ★★★
Contact: Mr Martin Hutchinson,
Rudding Holiday Park, Rudding
Park, Follifoot, Harrogate, North
Yorkshire HG3 1JH
T: (01423) 870439
F: (01423) 870859
E: holiday-park@ruddingpark.
com
I: www.rudding-park.com

34 Valley Mount ★★★
Contact: Mrs Angela Durance,
Harrogate Holiday Cottages, The
Old Post Office, Kettlesing,
Harrogate, North Yorkshire
HG3 2LB
T: (01423) 772700
F: (01423) 772359
E: bookings@harrogateholidays.
co.uk
I: www.harrogateholidays.co.uk

HARTON
North Yorkshire

W Todd & Sons ★★★
Contact: Mr & Mrs C Todd, W
Todd & Sons, Harton, York
YO60 7NP
T: (01904) 468487
F: (01904) 468487
E: colin.todd@gateway.uk
I: www.visityorkshire.com

HARTWITH
North Yorkshire

The Cottage ★★★
Contact: Mrs Sue Clarke,
Brimham Lodge, Hartwith,
Harrogate, North Yorkshire
HG3 3HE
T: (01423) 771770
F: (01423) 770370
E: neil.clarke@virgin.net

Cow Close Barn ★★★★
Contact: Mrs Diana Kitzing, Cow
Close Farm, Stripe Lane,
Hartwith, Harrogate, North
Yorkshire HG3 3EY
T: (01423) 770850
F: (01423) 770993
E: rainerkitzing@aol.com

HARWOOD DALE
North Yorkshire

Lindhead Close Cottage ★★★
Contact: Country Holidays
ref:11471, Holiday Cottages
Group, Spring Mill, Earby,
Barnoldswick, Lancashire
BB94 0AA
T: 08700 723723
F: (01282) 844288
E: sales@ttgihg.co.uk
I: www.country-holidays.co.uk

HAWES
North Yorkshire

Chapel House ★★★
Contact: Dales Hol Cot Ref:2320,
Dales Holiday Cottages, Carleton
Business Park, Carleton New
Road, Skipton, North Yorkshire
BD23 2AA
T: (01756) 799821 & 790919
F: (01756) 797012
E: info@dalesholcot.com
I: www.dalesholcot.com

Cherry Tree Cottage ★★
Contact: Mrs Nadine Bell,
Country Hideaways, Margarets
Cottage, West Burton, Leyburn,
North Yorkshire DL8 4JN
T: (01969) 663559
F: (01969) 663559
E: nhbell@aol.com
I: www.countryhideaways.co.uk

Cherry Tree End ★★
Contact: Mr Ian Gendle, 10a
Frenchgate, Richmond, North
Yorkshire DL10 4SG
T: 0780 853 0186 &
07974 6998704
E: iangendle@away4.fsbusiness.
co.uk
I: www.away4.com

Gaudy House Farm ★★
Contact: Mrs Pru Phillips, Gaudy
House Farm, Gayle, Hawes,
North Yorkshire DL8 3NA
T: (01969) 667231

Jane Ann Cottage ★★
Contact: Mrs E I Sunter,
Overdales View, Simonstone,
Hawes, North Yorkshire DL8 3LY
T: (01969) 667186
E: dales@cloud-nine.org.uk
I: www.cloud-nine.org.uk/dales

Low Shaw Barn ★★★
Contact: Dales Hol Cot Ref:2367,
Dales Holiday Cottages, Carleton
Business Park, Carleton New
Road, Skipton, North Yorkshire
BD23 2AA
T: (01756) 799821 & 790919
F: (01756) 797012
E: info@dalesholcot.com
I: www.dalesholcot.com

**Mile House Farm Country
Cottages★★★★**
Contact: Mrs Anne Fawcett, Mile
House Farm Country Cottages,
Mile House Farm, Hawes, North
Yorkshire DL8 3PT
T: (01969) 667481
F: (01969) 667425
E: milehousefarm@hotmail.com
I: www.wensleydale.uk.com

Tarney Fors ★★★
Contact: Sykes Cottages
Ref:785, Sykes Cottages, York
House, York Street, Chester,
CH1 3LR
T: (01244) 345700
F: (01244) 321442
E: info@sykescottages.co.uk
I: www.sykescottages.co.uk

Warrenville Cottage ★★★
Contact: Proprietor, Warrenville
Cottage, Town Head, Hawes,
North Yorkshire DL8 2RB

Yore View ★★★
Contact: Mrs E Pedley, Yore
House, Lunds, Sedbergh,
Cumbria LA10 5PX
T: (01969) 667358

**Yorkshire Dales Country
Cottages★★★-★★★★**
Contact: Mrs Brenda Stott,
Yorkshire Dales Country
Cottages, Shaw Ghyll, High
Shaw, Simonstone, Hawes,
North Yorkshire DL8 3LY
T: (01969) 667359
F: (01969) 667894
E: rogerstott@aol.com
I: www.yorkshirenet.
co.uk/accgde/ydcotts.htm

HAWKSWICK
North Yorkshire

Privet Cottage ★
Contact: Mrs Helen Gibson,
Francis Barn, Hawkswick,
Skipton, North Yorkshire
BD23 5QA
T: (01756) 770313

Redmire Farm ★★★★★
Contact: Mr Neil Tomlinson, 5
Aire Street, Haworth, Keighley,
West Yorkshire BD22 8LX
T: (01535) 610491 & 648791
F: (01535) 610469
E: neil@mckeighley.co.uk

HAWNBY
North Yorkshire

**Old School House Cottage
★★★**
Contact: Country Holidays
ref:11258, Holiday Cottages
Group, Spring Mill, Earby,
Barnoldswick, Lancashire
BB94 0AA
T: 08700 723723
F: (01282) 841539
E: sales@ttgihg.co.uk
I: www.country-holidays.co.uk

HAWORTH
West Yorkshire

Balcony Farm ★★★★
Contact: Mrs J Raine, Balcony
Farm, Dimples Lane, Haworth,
Keighley, West Yorkshire
BD22 8QR
T: (01535) 643627

**Bottoms Farm Cottages
★★★★**
Contact: Mr J Parr, Bottoms
Farm Cottages, Bottoms Farm,
Greystones Lane, Laycock,
Keighley, West Yorkshire
BD22 0QD
T: (01535) 607720
F: (01535) 607720

**Bronte Country Cottages
★★★-★★★★**
Contact: Ms Clare Pickles,
Bronte Country Cottages,
Westfield Farm, Tim Lane,
Haworth, Keighley, West
Yorkshire BD22 7SA
T: (01535) 644568 &
0771 597319
F: (01535) 646686
E: clare@
brontecountrycottages.co.uk
I: www.brontecountrycottages.
co.uk

**Heather, Bilberry Cottage and
Grandad's Loft★★★★**
Contact: Mrs J Milner, Heather,
Bilberry Cottage and Grandad's
Loft, Hole Farm, Dimples Lane,
Haworth, Keighley, West
Yorkshire BD22 8QT
T: (01535) 644755
F: (01535) 644755
E: janet@bronteholidays.co.uk
I: www.bronteholidays.co.uk

Heron Cottage ★★★★
Contact: Mrs Grannan, Vale
Barn, Mytholmes Lane, Haworth,
Keighley, West Yorkshire
BD22 0EE
T: (01535) 644429
F: (01535) 644429
E: hilarygrannan@hotmail.com

**Hewenden Mill Cottages
★★★★**
Contact: Miss Janet & Susan
Emanuel, Hewenden Mill
Cottages, Hewenden Mill,
Cullingworth, Bradford, West
Yorkshire BD13 5BP
T: (01535) 271834
F: (01535) 273943
E: info@hewendenmillcottages.
co.uk
I: www.hewendenmillcottages.
co.uk

Penny Cottage ★★★
Contact: Dales Hol Cot Ref:3106,
Dales Holiday Cottages, Carleton
Business Park, Carleton New
Road, Skipton, North Yorkshire
BD23 2AA
T: (01756) 799821 & 790919
F: (01756) 797012
E: info@dalesholcot.com
I: www.dalesholcot.com

September Cottage ★★★★
Contact: Mrs Joy Page, 1 Compit
Hills, Cromer, Norfolk NR27 9LJ
T: (01263) 514237 &
07880 548655

Establishments printed in blue have a detailed entry in this guide

YORKSHIRE

59 Sun Street ★★
Contact: Mr & Mrs J Redmayne,
53 Park Road, Freehold,
Lancaster, LA1 3EJ
T: (01524) 64070

HAWSKER
North Yorkshire

Ling Hill Farm ★★
Contact: Mr B Tordoff and Miss
A Trotter, Ling Hill Farm, Whitby
Laithes, Hawsker, Whitby, North
Yorkshire YO22 4JY
T: (01947) 603914

West End Farm Cottage ★★★★
Contact: Dales Hol Cot Ref:1228,
Dales Holiday Cottages, Carleton
Business Park, Carleton New
Road, Skipton, North Yorkshire
BD23 2AA
T: (01756) 799821 & 790919
F: (01756) 797012
E: info@dalesholcot.com
I: www.dalesholcot.com

HEALAUGH
North Yorkshire

Lock Heather ★★★
Contact: Mrs K Donbavand, 4
Lulworth Road, Birkdale,
Southport, Merseyside PR8 2AT
T: (01704) 566317

HEATON
West Yorkshire

Honeysuckle Cottage ★★★
Contact: Mrs Pamela Stobart, 29
Haworth Road, Heaton,
Bradford, West Yorkshire
BD9 5PB
T: (01274) 541181 &
07778 037911
F: (01274) 496169

HEBDEN
North Yorkshire

Bramble Cottage ★★★
Contact: Sykes Cottages
Ref:251, Sykes Cottages, York
House, York Street, Chester,
CH1 3LR
T: (01244) 345700
F: (01244) 321442
E: info@sykescottages.co.uk
I: www.sykescottages.co.uk

Reservoir Cottage ★★★
Contact: Sykes Cottages
Ref:209, Sykes Cottages, York
House, York Street, Chester,
CH1 3LR
T: (01244) 345700
F: (01244) 321442
E: info@sykescottages.co.uk
I: www.sykescottages.co.uk

HEBDEN BRIDGE
West Yorkshire

3 Birks Hall Cottage ★★★
Contact: Mrs H Wilkinson, 1
Birks Hall, Cragg Vale, Hebden
Bridge, West Yorkshire HX7 5SB
T: (01422) 882064 & 884509

Great Burlees Farm ★★★
Contact: Mr & Mrs B Wells,
Great Burlees Farm, Hebden
Bridge, West Yorkshire HX7 8PS
T: (01422) 843382

HELMSLEY
North Yorkshire

Beadlam Farm Cottage ★★★
Contact: Mrs J M Rooke,
Beadlam Grange, Pockley, York,
North Yorkshire YO62 7TD
T: (01439) 770303
E: marke.rooke@farming.co.uk
I: www.stayfarmnorth.co.uk

Church View ★★★★
Contact: Mrs Sally Ann Foster,
Chestnut Tree Farm, Doncaster
Road, Thrybergh, Rotherham,
South Yorkshire S65 4NS
T: (01709) 852929 & 850337
E: sally.f@ntlworld.com
I: www.foster1.force9.co.uk

Fleur-de-lys ★★★★
Contact: Mrs Pat Anderson,
Sunset Holidays, Boonhill
Cottage, Newton-on-Rawcliffe,
Pickering, North Yorkshire
YO18 8QF
T: (01751) 472172
E: fleurdelys@boonhill69.
freeserve.co.uk
I: www.swiftlink.pnc-uk.
net/sc/1236a.htm

Honeysuckle Cottage ★★★
Contact: Mrs M Stringer,
Cornfield House, Bransdale,
Kirkbymoorside, York YO62 7JW
T: (01751) 431983

Plum Tree Cottage ★★★★
Contact: Mrs T Dzierzek, 46 High
Street, Farningham, Dartford
DA4 0DB
T: (01322) 863168 & 863230
F: (01322) 863168
E: dzierzek@btinternet.com

Thyme Cottage ★★★★
Contact: Mr & Mrs R Barnes,
Country Corner, 35-37 Swan
Road, Harrogate, North
Yorkshire HG1 2SA
T: (01423) 561182
F: (01423) 561182

Townend Cottage ★★★★
Contact: Mrs M Begg, Townend
Farmhouse, High Lane, Beadlam,
Nawton, York YO62 7SY
T: (01439) 770103
E: margaret.begg@ukgateway.
net
I: www.visityorkshire.com

HELPERTHORPE
North Yorkshire

Cottage Number 1&2 ★★★★
Contact: Dales Hol Cot
Ref:3194/3195, Dales Holiday
Cottages, Carleton Business
Park, Carleton New Road,
Skipton, North Yorkshire
BD23 2AA
T: (01756) 799821 & 790919
F: (01756) 797012
E: info@dalesholcot.com
I: www.dalesholcot.com

HEPTONSTALL
West Yorkshire

5 Draper Corner ★★
Contact: Mrs S A Taylor, 4
Northfield Terrace, Hebden
Bridge, West Yorkshire HX7 7NG
T: (01422) 844323

The Hayloft Flat ★★★
Contact: Mrs H M Harrison, The
Hayloft Flat, Fields Farm,
Heptonstall, Hebden Bridge,
West Yorkshire HX7 7PD
T: (01422) 843145

HEPWORTH
West Yorkshire

Uppergate Farm
Rating Applied For
Contact: Mrs Alison Booth,
Uppergate Farm, Hepworth,
Holmfirth, Huddersfield
HD9 1TG
T: (01484) 681369
F: (01484) 687343
E: stevenal.booth@virgin.net
I: www.area5.co.uk/farm

HIGH BENTHAM
North Yorkshire

Batty Farm
Rating Applied For
Contact: Dales Hol Cot Ref:1362,
Dales Holiday Cottages, Carleton
Business Park, Carleton New
Road, Skipton, North Yorkshire
BD23 2AA
T: (01756) 799821 & 790919
F: (01756) 797012
E: info@dalesholcot.com
I: www.dalesholcot.com

Holmes Farm Cottage ★★★★
Contact: Mrs L J Story, Holmes
Farm Cottage, Holmes Farm,
Low Bentham, Lancaster
LA2 7DE
T: (015242) 61198
E: lucy@clucy.demon.co.uk

Low Ben Cottage ★★★
Contact: Dales Hol Cot Ref:587,
Dales Holiday Cottages, Carleton
Business Park, Carleton New
Road, Skipton, North Yorkshire
BD23 2AA
T: (01756) 799821 & 79019
F: (01756) 797012
E: info@dalesholcot.com
I: www.dalesholcot.com

Maidencroft ★★★
Contact: Proprietor,
Maidencroft, The Bungalow, Gas
House Lane, High Bentham,
Lancaster LA2 7HQ

Parkside & Woodside ★★★★
Contact: Mr and Mrs Thomas
and Jane Marshall, Knowe Top,
Low Bentham Road, High
Bentham, Lancaster LA2 7BN
T: (015242) 62163 &
07711 587428
F: (015242) 62163
E: riversidebentham@cs.com

HIGH HAWSKER
North Yorkshire

**Grange Farm & Century's End
Cottage** ★★★★
Contact: Dales Hol Cot
Ref:2983/2984, Dales Holiday
Cottages, Carleton Business
Park, Carleton New Road,
Skipton, North Yorkshire
BD23 2AA
T: (01756) 799821 & 790919
F: (01756) 797012
E: info@dalesholcot.com
I: www.dalesholcot.com

HIGH NORMANBY
North Yorkshire

Abbey View Farm Cottage ★★
Contact: Dales Hol Cot Ref:2148,
Dales Holiday Cottages, Carleton
Business Park, Carleton New
Road, Skipton, North Yorkshire
BD23 2AA
T: (01756) 799821 & 790919
F: (01756) 797012
E: info@dalesholcot.com
I: www.dalesholcot.com

HINDERWELL
North Yorkshire

Jasmine Cottage
Rating Applied For
Contact: Whitby Holiday
Cottages, 47 Flowergate,
Whitby, North Yorkshire
YO21 3BB
T: (01947) 603010
F: (01947) 821133
E: enquiries@whitby-cottages.
co.uk
I: www.whitby-cottages.co.uk

Newton Cottage ★★★
Contact: Dales Hol Cot Ref:1732,
Dales Holiday Cottages, Carleton
Business Park, Carleton New
Road, Skipton, North Yorkshire
BD23 2AA
T: (01756) 799821 & 790919
F: (01756) 797012
E: info@dalesholcot.com
I: www.dalesholcot.com

The Old Coach House ★★★★
Contact: Mrs Adele Thompson,
Whitby Holiday Cottages, 47
Flowergate, Whitby, North
Yorkshire YO21 3BB
T: (01947) 603010
F: (01947) 821133
E: enquiries@whitby-cottages.
co.uk
I: www.whitby-cottages.co.uk

Rhuss Cottage ★★★
Contact: Mrs C L Robson, Broom
House Farm, Ugthorpe, Whitby,
North Yorkshire YO21 2BJ
T: (01947) 840454
F: (01947) 840454
E: john@broomhse.fsnet.co.uk

HOLLOW MEADOWS
South Yorkshire

Fern Hill ★★★
Contact: Mr A Altman, Fern Hill,
Hollow Meadows, Sheffield
S6 6GH
T: (0114) 230 2737

HOLMBRIDGE
West Yorkshire

Ivy Cottage ★★
Contact: Mr I Bangham & Mrs
Joyce Carter, Ivy Cottage, Ivy
Farm, Woodhead Road,
Holmbridge, Holmfirth,
Huddersfield HD7 1NQ
T: (01484) 682561
E: bangham77@hotmail.com

HOLMFIRTH
West Yorkshire

Dal-a-fr-sa ★★★★
Contact: Mr & Mrs David
Babbings, 52 Meltham Road,
Honley, Huddersfield HD9 6HC
T: (01484) 323990 & 422150
E: davidbabbings@ntlworld.com

Fern Mount Cottage ★★★
Contact: Mr and Mrs Roger and
Sally Carrier, 36 Back Lane,
Holmfirth, Huddersfield, West
Yorkshire HD9 1HG
T: (01484) 688755
F: (01484) 689378

Old Yew Barn ★★★
Contact: Mrs D Thorpe, Old Yew,
Royd Lane, Old Yew, Holmfirth,
Huddersfield HD7 1RL
T: (01484) 682334

Pellcot ★★★★
Contact: Country Holidays
ref:1152, Holiday Cottages
Group, Spring Mill, Earby,
Barnoldswick, Lancashire
BB94 0AA
T: 08700 723723
F: (01282) 8442888
I: www.country-holidays.co.uk

**The Studio & Victoria Flats
★★★-★★★★**
Contact: Mrs J Newby, 5
Upperbridge, Huddersfield Road,
Holmfirth, Huddersfield HD9 1JP
T: (01484) 684068
F: (01484) 684068

Summerwine Cottages ★★★
Contact: Mrs Susan Meakin,
Summerwine Cottages, West
Royd Farm, Marsh Lane, Shepley,
Huddersfield HD8 8AY
T: (01484) 602147 & 609427
F: (01484) 609427
E: summerwinecottages@
lineone.co.uk
I: www.summerwinecottages.
co.uk

Underhill Cottages ★★★★
Contact: Mr & Mrs Les & Anne
Dunford, 14 Cooper Lane,
Holmfirth, Huddersfield
HD7 1BP
T: (01484) 686597
F: (01484) 686597
E: underhill@holmespun.co.uk
I: www.holmespun.co.uk

HOLTBY
Yorkshire

Garden Cottage ★★★★
Contact: Dales Hol Cot Ref:1472,
Dales Holiday Cottages, Carleton
Business Park, Carleton New
Road, Skipton, North Yorkshire
BD23 2AA
T: (01756) 799821 & 790919
F: (01756) 797012
E: info@dalesholcot.com
I: www.dalesholcot.com

HORTON-IN-RIBBLESDALE
North Yorkshire

Churchgate ★★★
Contact: Dales Hol Cot Ref:3115,
Dales Holiday Cottages, Carleton
Business Park, Carleton New
Road, Skipton, North Yorkshire
BD23 2AA
T: (01756) 799821 & 790919
F: (01756) 797012
E: info@dalesholcot.com
I: www.dalesholcot.com

**Douk Ghyll Cottage
Rating Applied For**
Contact: Mr & Mrs Teal and Mr
& Mrs Traher, Valley Hotel,
93-95 Valley Drive, Harrogate,
North Yorkshire HG2 0JP
T: (01423) 504868
F: (01423) 531940
E: valley@harrogate.com
I: www.valleyhotel.co.uk

The Flat ★★★
Contact: Country Holidays
ref:6845, Holiday Cottages
Group, Spring Mill, Earby,
Barnoldswick, Lancashire
BB94 0AA
T: 08700 723723
F: (01282) 844288
E: sales@ttgihg.co.uk
I: www.country-holidays.co.uk

Whernside Cottage ★★
Contact: Sykes Cottages Ref:93,
Sykes Cottages, York House,
York Street, Chester, CH1 3LR
T: (01244) 345700
F: (01244) 321442
E: info@sykescottages.co.uk
I: www.sykescottages.co.uk

HOVINGHAM
North Yorkshire

**Beck Cottage
Rating Applied For**
Contact: Mrs Penelope Day, Beck
Cottage, Brookside, Hovingham,
York YO62 4LG
T: (01653) 628607
E: popday@onetel.net.uk

HUBY
North Yorkshire

1 & 2 Tally Hill Cottages ★★
Contact: CH ref: 3444,3445,
Holiday Cottages Group, Spring
Mill, Earby, Barnoldswick,
Lancashire BB94 0AA
T: (01282) 445096
F: (01282) 844288
E: sales@ttgihg.co.uk
I: www.country-holidays.co.uk

Fir Tree Cottage ★★★★
Contact: Mr M Owen, Fir Tree
Cottage, Fir Tree House, Strait
Lane, Huby, Leeds LS17 0EA
T: (01423) 734817
E: mcowen@talk21.com

HUDDERSFIELD
West Yorkshire

**Ashes Farm Cottages
★★★-★★★★**
Contact: Mrs B A Lockwood,
Ashes Farm Cottages, Ashes
Common Farm, Ashes Lane,
Almondbury, Huddersfield
HD4 6TE
T: (01484) 426507
F: (01484) 426507
E: enquiries@ashesfarm.demon.
co.uk
I: www.ashesfarm.demon.co.uk

Bank End ★★
Contact: Mrs Rebecca Ng, 41
Mall Road, London W6 9DG
T: (020) 8563 1186
F: (020) 8748 1170
E: rebeccang80@hotmail.com
I: www.cottageguide.
co.uk/netherton

Elam Cottage ★★★
Contact: Mrs Anne Mullany, 49
Lowerhouses Lane,
Lowerhouses, Huddersfield,
West Yorkshire HD5 8JP
T: (01484) 431432
E: mullany@tesco.net

Swallow Cottage ★★★
Contact: Mrs M Kucharczyk,
Rockley House, High Flatts,
Huddersfield, HD8 8XU
T: (01484) 607072
F: (01484) 607072
E: swallow@care4free.net

HUGGATE
East Riding of Yorkshire

Manor House Farm ★★★
Contact: Mrs S Frumin, Manor
House Farm, The Green,
Huggate, York YO42 1YZ
T: (01377) 288368
F: (01377) 288127
E: manorhouse-huggate@
ukonline.co.uk

HULL
East Riding of Yorkshire

**England's Rose Holiday Home
★★**
Contact: Mrs C Bradley, 9
Minnies Grove, Walton Street,
Hull, HU3 6JP
T: (01482) 352733

HUNMANBY
North Yorkshire

Honeysuckle Cottage ★★★
Contact: Dales Holiday Cottages,
Carleton Business Park, Carleton
New Road, Skipton, North
Yorkshire BD23 2AA
T: (01756) 799821 & 790919
I: www.dales-holiday-cottages.
com

Keld ★★★
Contact: D Emmerson, Barf
Farm, Hunmanby, Filey, North
Yorkshire YO14 9RR
T: (01723) 890804 &
07778 898521

HURST
North Yorkshire

3 Norse Longhouse ★★★
Contact: Mrs J Frankland, 115
Franklin Road, Harrogate, North
Yorkshire HG1 5EN
T: (01423) 505151
F: (01423) 505151
E: amadeushotel@btinternet.
com

Shiney Row Cottage ★★
Contact: Dales Hol Cot Ref:2786,
Dales Holiday Cottages, Carleton
Business Park, Carleton New
Road, Skipton, North Yorkshire
BD23 2AA
T: (01756) 799821 & 790919
F: (01756) 797012
E: info@dalesholcot.com
I: www.dalesholcot.com

HUSTHWAITE
North Yorkshire

Kate's Cottage ★★
Contact: Mrs S L McClanachan,
Throstle Nest, Husthwaite, York
YO61 4PH
T: (01347) 868346 &
(01845) 526550

HUTTON BUSCEL
North Yorkshire

Laneside ★★★
Contact: Mr R Wales, Holiday
Cottages (Yorkshire) Ltd, Water
Street, Skipton, North Yorkshire
BD23 1PB
T: (01756) 700510

HUTTON-LE-HOLE
North Yorkshire

Hollyside Cottage ★★★
Contact: Mrs S E Elford,
Brookside, Hutton-le-Hole, York
YO62 6UD
T: (01751) 417267

**Moorland & Heather Cottages
★★★★**
Contact: Mrs S Dussold,
Moorland & Heather Cottages,
Byre Cottage, Hutton-le-Hole,
York YO62 6UA
T: (01751) 417743
F: (01751) 417743
E: ddussold@easynet.co.uk
♿

Waterswallow Cottage ★★★
Contact: Mrs Barbara
Grabowski, Halfway House,
Hutton-le-Hole, York YO62 6UQ
T: (01751) 431596 &
07833 398138
F: (01751) 431596

HUTTON SESSAY
North Yorkshire

**White Rose Holiday Cottages
★★★**
Contact: Ms Shirley Parker,
White Rose Holiday Cottages,
Rowan Cottage, Hutton Sessay,
Thirsk, North Yorkshire YO7 3BA
T: (01845) 501215
F: (01845) 501180

ILKLEY
West Yorkshire

**Westwood Lodge, Ilkley Moor
★★★★**
Contact: Mr Tim Edwards and
Mrs Paula Hunt, Westwood
Lodge, Wells Road, Ilkley, West
Yorkshire LS29 9SF
T: (01943) 433430
F: (01943) 433431
E: welcome@westwoodlodge.
co.uk
I: www.westwoodlodge.co.uk

ILLINGWORTH
West Yorkshire

Edge End 'Croft' ★★★★
Contact: Mr John Charles
Warne, Edge End 'Croft', Edge
End Farm, Straight Lane,
Illingworth, Halifax, West
Yorkshire HX2 8UQ
T: (01422) 247743
E: susan.warne@tinyworld.
co.uk

INGLEBY CROSS
North Yorkshire

**The Cottage, Wellington Farm
★★★**
Contact: Mrs Margaret Dickins,
The Cottage, Wellington Farm,
Wellington Farm, Ingleby Cross,
Northallerton, North Yorkshire
DL6 3JX
T: (01609) 882271

INGLEBY GREENHOW
North Yorkshire
Ingleby Manor ★★★★
Contact: Mrs C Bianco, Ingleby
Manor, Ingleby Greenhow, Great
Ayton, North Yorkshire TS9 6RB
T: (01642) 722170
F: (01642) 722170
E: christine@inglebymanor.
co.uk
I: www.inglebymanor.co.uk

INGLETON
North Yorkshire
Bank Hall ★★★
Contact: Mr Philip Angus,
Brooklyn, Ingleton, Carnforth,
Lancashire LA6 3DE
T: (015242) 41127
E: philip.angus@ukgateway.net
I: www.bankhall-ingleton.co.uk

Kingsdale Head Cottage ★★★
Contact: Mrs Stephanie Faraday,
Kingsdale Head, Westhouse,
Ingleton, Carnforth, Lancashire
LA6 3PH
T: (015242) 41393

Primrose Cottage ★★★
Contact: Mr and Mrs John and
Celia Jones, Ingleborough WMC,
Spring View, Ingleton, Carnforth,
Lancashire LA6 3HE
T: (015242) 41407
F: (015242) 41407
E: topclub.john@virgin.net

Raygill Cottage ★★★
Contact: Mr R Wales, Holiday
Cottages (Yorkshire) Ltd, Water
Street, Skipton, North Yorkshire
BD23 1PB
T: (01756) 700510

Storrs Lea ★★★
Contact: Sykes Cottages
Ref:764, Sykes Cottages, York
House, York Street, Chester,
CH1 3LR
T: (01244) 345700
F: (01244) 321442
E: info@sykescottages.co.uk
I: www.sykescottages.co.uk

KEARBY
North Yorkshire
Spring Rose Cottage ★★★★
Contact: Mrs Catherine Webb,
Springmoor Lodge Ltd, The
Riddings, Kearby With Netherby,
Wetherby, West Yorkshire
LS22 4DA
T: (0113) 288 6234
F: (0113) 288 6234
E: info@maustin.co.uk

KEARBY WITH NETHERBY
North Yorkshire
Nethercroft Cottage ★★★★
Contact: Mrs Webb, Maustin
Park Ltd, The Riddings, Kearby
with Netherby, Wetherby, West
Yorkshire LS22 4DA
T: (0113) 288 6234
F: (0113) 288 6234
E: info@maustin.co.uk
I: www.maustin.co.uk

KEIGHLEY
West Yorkshire
Dimples Cottage ★★★★
Contact: Country Holidays
ref:6024, Holiday Cottages
Group, Spring Mill, Earby,
Barnoldswick, Lancashire
BB94 0AA
T: 08700 723723
F: (01282) 844288
I: www.country-holidays.co.uk

Opal Apartment ★★
Contact: Mr David Mortimer, 5
Opal Street, Ingrow, Keighley,
West Yorkshire BD22 7BP
T: (01535) 604175
F: (01535) 611448
E: david@sweetshop.fsbusiness.
co.uk
I: www.sweetshop.fsbusiness.
co.uk/default.htm

KETTLENESS
North Yorkshire
Eastwater Cottage ★★★
Contact: Dales Hol Cot Ref:1537,
Dales Holiday Cottages, Carleton
Business Park, Carleton New
Road, Skipton, North Yorkshire
BD23 2AA
T: (01756) 799821 & 790919
F: (01756) 797012
E: info@dalesholcot.com
I: www.dalesholcot.com

KETTLEWELL
North Yorkshire
Cam Cottage
Rating Applied For
Contact: Dales Hol Cot Ref:3015,
Dales Holiday Cottages, Carleton
Business Park, Carleton New
Road, Skipton, North Yorkshire
BD23 2AA
T: (01756) 799821 & 790919
F: (01756) 797012
E: info@dalesholcot.com
I: www.dalesholcot.com

Fold Farm Cottages ★★★★
Contact: Mrs B Lambert, Fold
Farm, Kettlewell, Skipton, North
Yorkshire BD23 5RH
T: (01756) 760886
F: (01756) 760464
E: fold.farm@lineone.net
I: www.foldfarm.co.uk

Heathlands ★★★
Contact: Dales Hol Cot Ref:931,
Dales Holiday Cottages, Carleton
Business Park, Carleton New
Road, Skipton, North Yorkshire
BD23 2AA
T: (01756) 799821 & 790919
F: (01756) 797012
E: info@dalesholcot.com
I: www.dalesholcot.com

Primrose Cottage ★★★★
Contact: Dales Hol Cot Ref:2504,
Dales Holiday Cottages, Carleton
Business Park, Carleton New
Road, Skipton, North Yorkshire
BD23 2AA
T: (01756) 799821 & 790919
F: (01756) 797012
E: info@dalesholcot.com
I: www.dalesholcot.com

KILDALE
North Yorkshire
Bernard's Barn ★★★
Contact: Dales Hol Cot Ref:1566,
Dales Holiday Cottages, Carleton
Business Park, Carleton New
Road, Skipton, North Yorkshire
BD23 2AA
T: (01756) 799821 & 790919
F: (01756) 797012
E: info@dalesholcot.com
I: www.dalesholcot.com

KILHAM
East Riding of Yorkshire
**Raven Hill Holiday Farmhouse
★★★**
Contact: Mr & Mrs S J Savile,
Raven Hill Farm, Kilham,
Driffield, East Yorkshire
YO25 4EG
T: (01377) 267217
F: (01377) 267217

KIPLIN
North Yorkshire
**Maryland Cottage & Baltimore
Cottage ★★**
Contact: Ms Elaine Bird, Calvert
Cottage, Kiplin Hall, Richmond,
North Yorkshire DL10 6AT
T: (01748) 812863
F: (01748) 818178

KIRBY HILL
North Yorkshire
Manor Cottage ★★★
Contact: Mrs Diana Whitby,
Manor House, Kirby Hill,
Richmond, North Yorkshire
DL11 7JH
T: (01748) 825634

KIRBY MISPERTON
North Yorkshire
2 Rose Cottages ★★★
Contact: Mrs Kathryn
Greenwood, 95 Dyson Road,
Halifax, West Yorkshire HX1 4RL
T: (01422) 364880 &
07747 818868
E: kathryn@sillaford.com

KIRKBY FLEETHAM
North Yorkshire
Wren Cottage ★★★
Contact: Mrs J R Pybus, Old
Street House Farm, Little Holtby,
Northallerton, North Yorkshire
DL7 9LN
T: (01609) 748622
F: (01609) 748571
E: jp.st.house@farmersweekly.
net

KIRKBY MALZEARD
North Yorkshire
Alma Cottage ★★★
Contact: Mrs J E Barclay, 12 St
Stephens Road, Cold Norton,
Chelmsford CM3 6JE
T: (01621) 828576 &
(01765) 658736
F: (01621) 828539
E: janet@lbarclay.demon.co.uk
I: www.almacottage.co.uk

The Cottage
Rating Applied For
Contact: Dales Hol Cot Ref:3146,
Dales Holiday Cottages, Carleton
Business Park, Carleton New
Road, Skipton, North Yorkshire
BD23 2AA
T: (01756) 799821 & 790919
F: (01756) 797012
E: info@dalesholcot.com
I: www.dalesholcot.com

Hawsett House ★★★
Contact: Mrs Angela Durance,
Harrogate Holiday Cottages, The
Old Post Office, Kettlesing,
Harrogate, North Yorkshire
HG3 2LB
T: (01423) 772700
F: (01423) 772359
E: hhc@dial.pipex.com
I: dspace.dial.pipex.com/hhc/

The Woodpeckers ★★★
Contact: Mrs E Drewery, The
Woodpeckers, Kirkby Malzeard,
Ripon, North Yorkshire HG4 3SE
T: (01765) 658206

KIRKBYMOORSIDE
North Yorkshire
Burton House ★★★
Contact: Country Holidays
ref:13729, Spring Mill, Earby,
Barnoldswick, Lancashire
BB94 0AA
T: 08700 723723
F: (01282) 844288
E: sales@ttgihg.co.uk
I: www.country-holidays.co.uk

**Catterbridge Farm Cottage
★★★★**
Contact: Mrs Jayne Peace,
Catterbridge Farm,
Kirkbymoorside, York, North
Yorkshire YO62 6NF
T: (01751) 433271

Cherry View Cottage ★★★★
Contact: Mrs SMP Drinkel, High
Hagg Farm, Kirkbymoorside,
York YO62 7JF
T: (01751) 431714 & 433187

The Cornmill ★★★★
Contact: Mr and Mrs Jeff and
Lindsay Lee, The Cornmill, Kirby
Mills, Kirkbymoorside, York
YO62 6NP
T: (01751) 432000
F: (01751) 432300
E: cornmill@kirbymills.demon.
co.uk
I: www.kirbymills.demon.co.uk

Dale End Cottage ★★★
Contact: Mrs M Bentley, 6 The
Drive, Marple, SK6 6DR
T: (0161) 427 1942

Ellerslie ★★★
Contact: Mrs Davison, 26
Castlegate, Kirkbymoorside, York
YO62 6BJ
T: (01751) 431112

Horseshoe Cottage ★★★
Contact: Mr and Mrs David and
Susan Snowden, Hollyhock,
Brawby, Malton, North Yorkshire
YO17 6PY
T: (01653) 668470

Keldholme Cottages ★★★
Contact: Mr B Hughes,
Keldholme Cottages, Keldholme,
Kirkbymoorside, York YO62 6NA
T: (01751) 431933

Establishments printed in blue have a detailed entry in this guide

Oak Lodge ★★★
Contact: Mrs Andrea Turnbull,
Oak Lodge, Whitethorn Farm,
Rook Barugh, Kirkbymoorside,
York YO62 6PF
T: (01751) 431298

**Sinnington Common Farm
★★★-★★★★**
Contact: Mrs Felicity Wiles,
Sinnington Common Farm,
Kirkbymoorside, York YO62 6NX
T: (01751) 431719
F: (01751) 431719
E: felicity@scfarm.demon.co.uk
I: www.scfarm.demon.co.uk

**Sleightholmedale Cottages
★★★★**
Contact: Mrs R James,
Sleightholmedale Cottages,
Sleightholmedale,
Kirkbymoorside, York YO62 7JG
T: (01751) 431942

Surprise View Cottage ★★★★
Contact: Mrs S R Wass,
Sinnington Lodge, Sinnington,
York YO62 6RB
T: (01751) 431345
T: (01751) 433418
E: ruth@wass.dnx.oc.uk

West End Cottage ★★
Contact: Sykes Cottages
Ref:661, Sykes Cottages, York
House, York Street, Chester,
CH1 3LR
T: (01244) 345700
F: (01244) 321442
E: info@sykescottages.co.uk
I: www.sykescottages.co.uk

KIRKSTALL
West Yorkshire

The Tops ★★
Contact: Mr M S Miles, 21
Wadlands Drive, Farsley, Pudsey,
West Yorkshire LS28 5JS
T: (0113) 257 2197
F: (0113) 257 2197

KNARESBOROUGH
North Yorkshire

Acorn Cottage ★★★
Contact: Mrs & Mrs C&S
Webster, Oakwood Farm, Hay-A-
Park, Knaresborough, North
Yorkshire HG5 0RX
T: (01423) 863144 & 860106
F: (01423) 865375
E: acorn.cottage@virgin.net
I: www.acorn-cottage.com

**Badger Hill Properties
★★★-★★★★**
Contact: Mr M McGrath,
Dropping Well Village Ltd,
Badger Hill Properties,
Harrogate Road, Knaresborough,
North Yorkshire HG5 8DP
T: (01423) 862352
F: (01423) 868021
E: manager@badgerhill.co.uk
I: www.badgerhill.co.uk

6 Cheapside ★★
Contact: Mrs Doreen Cook, 21
Manor Road, Knaresborough,
North Yorkshire HG5 0BN
T: (01423) 862641

Garden Apartment ★★★
Contact: Mrs A Rowinski,
Garden Apartment, 3 Aspin Way,
Knaresborough, North Yorkshire
HG5 8HL
T: (01423) 860463
E: gardenapartment@hotmail.
com

The Granary ★★★
Contact: Mrs P M Thornton, The
Granary, Gibbet Farm, Farnham
Lane, Farnham, Knaresborough,
North Yorkshire HG5 9JP
T: (01423) 862065 & 862271
F: (01423) 862271

33 Kirkgate ★★★
Contact: Ms Angela Durance,
Harrogate Holiday Cottages, The
Old Post Office, Kettlesing,
Harrogate, North Yorkshire
HG3 2LB
T: (01423) 772700
F: (01423) 772359
E: bookings@harrogateholidays.
co.uk
I: www.harrogateholidays.co.uk

**Knaresborough Holiday
Apartments ★★**
Contact: Mr & Mrs C A Cheney,
2A Aspin Lane, Knaresborough,
North Yorkshire HG5 8ED
T: (01423) 862629
F: (01423) 862629

**Uncle Tom's Holiday Cabins
★★★**
Contact: Mrs Pat Ridsdale, Uncle
Tom's Holiday Cabins, 22
Waterside, Knaresborough,
North Yorkshire HG5 8DF
T: (01423) 867045 &
07831 256563
F: (01423) 867045

**Watergate Lodge Holiday
Apartments ★★★-★★★★**
Contact: Mr & Mrs Peter &
Lesley Guest, Watergate Lodge
Holiday Apartments, Watergate
Haven, Ripley Road,
Knaresborough, North Yorkshire
HG5 9BU
T: (01423) 864627
F: (01423) 861087
E: watergate.haven@virgin.net
I: business.virgin.net/watergate.
haven

LASTINGHAM
North Yorkshire

**Lastingham Holiday Cottages
★★★-★★★★**
Contact: Mrs A Cattle,
Lastingham Holiday Cottages,
Littlegarth, Lastingham, York
YO62 6TJ
T: (01751) 417223
E: robcat@cw.com.net

LAVERTON
North Yorkshire

**Laverton Holiday Cottages
★★★**
Contact: Mrs R Brassington,
Laverton Holiday Cottages,
Laverton Grange, Laverton,
Ripon, North Yorkshire HG4 3SX
T: (01765) 658262 & 658863
E: ron@brasso95.freeserve.co.uk
I: www.cottageguide.
co.uk/lavertoncottages

LEALHOLM
North Yorkshire

**Greenhouses Farm Cottages
★★★**
Contact: Mr & Mrs Nick
Eddleston, Greenhouses Farm
Cottages, Greenhouses Farm,
Lealholm, Whitby, North
Yorkshire YO21 2AD
T: (01947) 897486
F: (01947) 897486
E: n_eddleston@yahoo.com
I: www.
greenhouses-farm-cottages.
co.uk

**Poets Cottage Holiday Flat
★★**
Contact: Mrs B E Rees, 25
Roseberry Road, Norton,
Stockton-on-Tees, Cleveland
TS20 1JZ
T: (01642) 532413
E: rees@btinternet.com

Stable Cottage ★★★★
Contact: Dales Hol Cot Ref:2985,
Dales Holiday Cottages, Carleton
Business Park, Carleton New
Road, Skipton, North Yorkshire
BD23 2AA
T: (01756) 799821 & 790919
F: (01756) 797012
E: info@dalesholcot.com
I: www.dalesholcot.com

West Banks Farmhouse ★★★
Contact: Dales Hol Cot Ref:1671,
Dales Holiday Cottages, Carleton
Business Park, Carleton New
Road, Skipton, North Yorkshire
BD23 2AA
T: (01756) 799821 & 790919
F: (01756) 797012
E: info@dalesholcot.com
I: www.dalesholcot.com

LEEDS
West Yorkshire

Harman Suite ★★★★
Contact: Miss Simerpreet Kaur,
Harman Suite, 48 St Martins
Avenue, Leeds, LS7 3LG
T: (0113) 295 5886 & 262 2734
F: (0113) 295 5886
E: info@harmansuite.co.uk
I: www.harmansuite.co.uk

University of Leeds ★★
Contact: Mrs Heather Smith,
University of Leeds, Leeds,
LS2 9JT
T: (0113) 233 6100
F: (0113) 233 6107
E: confoffice@leeds.ac.uk
I: www.leeds.ac.uk/conference

LEVISHAM
North Yorkshire

**The Hopper, The Granary & The
Cottage★★-★★★★**
Contact: Mr Dales Hol Cot:2317/
1813/3171, Dales Holiday
Cottages, Carleton Business
Park, Carleton New Road,
Skipton, North Yorkshire
BD23 2AA
T: (01756) 799821 & 790919
F: (01756) 797012
E: info@dalesholcot.com
I: www.dalesholcot.com

Lilac Farm ★★★
Contact: Mrs H M Eddon, Lilac
Farm, Levisham, Pickering, North
Yorkshire YO18 7NL
T: (01751) 460281
E: heather@lilacfarm.f9.co.uk
I: www.lilacfarm.f9.co.uk

**Weathervane, Dove Cottage,
Windflower & Garden Wing
★★★**
Contact: Dales Hol Cot
Ref:1904/5/6/7, Dales Holiday
Cottages, Carleton Business
Park, Carleton New Road,
Skipton, North Yorkshire
BD23 2AA
T: (01756) 799821 & 790919
F: (01756) 797012
E: info@dalesholcot.com
I: www.dalesholcot.com

LEYBURN
North Yorkshire

Calverts of Leyburn ★★★
Contact: Mrs A Calvert, Smithy
Lane, Grove Square, Leyburn,
North Yorkshire DL8 5DZ
T: (01969) 623051 & 622364
F: (01969) 624345
E: cottages@calverts.co.uk
I: www.calverts.co.uk

2 Crown Court Cottage ★★★
Contact: Mr & Mrs R&D Terry,
Old Farm, Barden, Leyburn,
North Yorkshire DL8 5JS
T: (01969) 624448 &
07808 293378
F: (01969) 624448
E: dalescottages@sniffout.com
I: www.
yorkshiredalesholidaycottages.
co.uk

**Dales View Holiday Homes
★★-★★★**
Contact: Messrs J&M Chilton,
Dales View Holiday Homes,
Jenkins Garth, Leyburn, North
Yorkshire DL8 5SP
T: (01969) 623707 & 622808
F: (01969) 623707
E: daleshols@aol.com
I: www.daleshols.com

Eastburn Cottage ★★★★
Contact: Mrs Nadine H Bell,
Country Hideaways, Margarets
Cottage, West Burton, Leyburn,
North Yorkshire DL8 4JN
T: (01969) 663559
F: (01969) 663559
E: nhbell@aol.com
I: www.countryhideaways.co.uk

Foal Barn ★★★
Contact: Mrs O Canham, Hayloft
Suite, Foal Barn, Spennithorne,
Leyburn, North Yorkshire
DL8 5PR
T: (01969) 622580 &
07870 494162
🐾

Low Riseborough ★★
Contact: Mr John Rowntree, 95
Chiswick Village, London
W4 3BZ
T: (020) 8994 9837 & 8747 9080
F: (020) 8995 4674

Newsteads Flat ★★★
Contact: Mrs Lynn Hill, White Rose Poultry Ltd, PO Box 17, Leyburn, North Yorkshire DL8 5YS
T: (01969) 622800 & 624994
F: (01969) 622155

The Old Fire Station ★★★
Contact: Miss C Wallace-Lowell, 4 Shawl Terrace, Leyburn, North Yorkshire DL8 5DA
T: (01969) 623993

Thorney Cottages ★★★
Contact: Mrs Nadine Bell, Country Hideaways, Margarets Cottage, West Burton, Leyburn, North Yorkshire DL8 4JN
T: (01969) 663559
F: (01969) 663559
E: nhbell@aol.com
I: www.countryhideaways.co.uk

Throstlenest Cottages ★★-★★★
Contact: Mr D Ransom, 7 Throstlenest Cottages, Walk Mill Lane, Harmby Road, Leyburn, North Yorkshire DL8 5HF
T: (01969) 623694
F: (01969) 624755

LINTON
North Yorkshire

Primrose Cottage ★★★★
Contact: Mrs C M Hayes, Spiredale Beck Cottage, Skirethorns Lane, Threshfield, Skipton, North Yorkshire BD23 5NX
T: (01756) 752033
E: cmhayes@bigfoot.com

Wharfedene ★★★
Contact: Miss Liquorish, 6 Hope Street, Beeston, Nottingham NG9 1DR
T: (0115) 922 3239
E: eliquorish@learnall.net

LINTON-ON-OUSE
North Yorkshire

Nursery View & Fuchsia Cottage ★★★
Contact: Dales Hol Cot Ref:1463/1464, Dales Holiday Cottages, Carleton Business Park, Carleton New Road, Skipton, North Yorkshire BD23 2AA
T: (01756) 799821 & 790919
F: (01756) 797012
E: info@dalesholcot.com
I: www.dalesholcot.com

LITTLE OUSEBURN
North Yorkshire

Hawtree Cottage ★★★★
Contact: Mrs Anne Llewellyn, Hawtree House, Main Street, Little Ouseburn, York, North Yorkshire YO26 9TD
T: (01423) 331526 & 0780 193 1825
E: annellewellyn@yahoo.com

LITTON
North Yorkshire

Stonelands ★★★★
Contact: Mrs B Cowan, Stonelands Farm Yard Cottages, Litton, Skipton, North Yorkshire BD23 5QE
T: (01756) 770293

LOCKTON
North Yorkshire

Ashfield Cottage ★★★
Contact: Mrs Carol Fisk, Ashfield Cottage, Lockton, Pickering, North Yorkshire YO18 7PZ
T: (01751) 460397 & (01723) 352201

Barn Cottage ★★★
Contact: Mrs G Grant, East Farm, Buslingthorpe, Lincoln, Lincolnshire LN3 5AQ
T: (01673) 842283
E: james@brailsford27.freeserve.co.uk

Old Barn Cottage
Rating Applied For
Contact: Dales Hol Cot Ref:3237, Dales Holiday Cottages, Carleton Business Park, Carleton New Road, Skipton, North Yorkshire BD23 2AA
T: (01756) 799821 & 790919
F: (01756) 797012
E: info@dalesholcot.com
I: www.dalesholcot.com

LOFTHOUSE
North Yorkshire

Acorn Quality Cottages ★★★★
Contact: Mrs S Kerr, 82 Trafalgar Road, Birkdale, Southport, Merseyside PR8 2NJ
T: (01704) 568941
E: acornqualitycottages@supanet.com
I: www.acornqualitycottages.co.uk

LONG MARSTON
North Yorkshire

The Cottage ★★★
Contact: Mrs E M Gilmour, The Cottage, Old Lane, Long Marston, York YO26 7LF
T: (01904) 738535
F: (01904) 738535
E: bobgilmour@totalise.co.uk

LOTHERSDALE
North Yorkshire

Street Head Farm ★★★★★
Contact: Mrs J Gooch, Tow Top Farm, Cononley, Skipton, West Yorkshire BD20 8HY
T: (01535) 632535 & 07740 606268
E: streethead@towtop.fsnet.co.uk

LOW BENTHAM
North Yorkshire

Borrans Cottage ★★★
Contact: Sykes Cottages Ref:653, Sykes Cottages, York House, York Street, Chester, CH1 3LR
T: (01244) 345700
F: (01244) 321442
E: info@sykescottages.co.uk
I: www.sykescottages.co.uk

LOW CATTON
East Riding of Yorkshire

2 Appletree Cottages ★★★★
Contact: Mr & Mrs R Hales, Gold Cup Inn, Low Catton, York YO41 1EA
T: (01759) 371354

LOW ROW
North Yorkshire

High Smarber ★★★
Contact: Mrs Kathleen Hird, Smarber Hall, Low Row, Richmond, North Yorkshire DL11 6PX
T: (01748) 886243
E: dietzfacciolo@att.net

Oak Tree Barn ★★★
Contact: Country Holidays ref:10661, Holiday Cottages Group, Spring Mill, Earby, Barnoldswick, Lancashire BB94 0AA
T: 08700 723723
F: (01282) 844288
E: sales@ttgihg.co.uk
I: www.country-holidays.co.uk

LOWER DUNSFORTH
North Yorkshire

Blackett House ★★★
Contact: Country Holidays ref:2449, Holiday Cottages Group, Spring Mill, Earby, Barnoldswick, Lancashire BB18 6RN
T: 08700 723723
F: (01282) 844288
E: sales@ttgihg.co.uk
I: www.country-holidays.co.uk

MALHAM
North Yorkshire

The Old Barn Flat ★★★
Contact: Mr and Mrs Byron and Janet Uttley, The Old Barn Cottage, Malham, Skipton, North Yorkshire
T: (01729) 830486
F: (01729) 830486
E: byron.uttley@genie.co.uk
I: www.yorkshirenet.com

The Old School ★★★★
Contact: Mr R Wales, Holiday Cottages (Yorkshire) Ltd, Water Street, Skipton, North Yorkshire BD23 1PB
T: (01756) 700510

Waterside Cottage ★★★★
Contact: Sykes Cottages Ref:641, Sykes Cottages, York House, York Street, Chester, CH1 3LR
T: (01244) 345700
F: (01244) 321442
E: info@sykescottages.co.uk
I: www.sykescottages.co.uk

MALTON
North Yorkshire

Rowgate Cottage ★★★★
Contact: Mrs Janet Clarkson, Rowgate Farm, Thorpe Bassett, Malton, North Yorkshire YO17 8LU
T: (01944) 758277

Swans Nest Cottage ★★★
Contact: Mrs Yvonne Dickinson, Abbots Farm House, Ryton, Malton, North Yorkshire YO17 6SA
T: (01653) 694970
E: yvonnedickinson@excite.co.uk
I: www.oas.co.uk/ukcottages/swans-nest

4 Wellgarth
Rating Applied For
Contact: Mrs D Waudby, 5 Wellgarth, Swinton, Malton, North Yorkshire YO17 6SS
T: (01653) 697548

MARISHES
North Yorkshire

Bellafax Holiday Cottage ★★★★
Contact: Dales Hol Cot Ref:2798, Dales Holiday Cottages, Carleton Business Park, Carleton New Road, Skipton, North Yorkshire BD23 2AA
T: (01756) 799821 & 790919
F: (01756) 797012
E: info@dalesholcot.com
I: www.dalesholcot.com

MARRICK
North Yorkshire

Tetheran Cottage ★★★
Contact: Dales Hol Cot Ref:2045, Dales Holiday Cottages, Carleton Business Park, Carleton New Road, Skipton, North Yorkshire BD23 2AA
T: (01756) 799821 & 790919
F: (01756) 797012
E: info@dalesholcot.com
I: www.dalesholcot.com

MARTON
North Yorkshire

Orchard House ★★★
Contact: Mr & Mrs Paul Richardson, Orchard House, Main Street, Marton, Sinnington, York YO62 6RD
T: (01751) 432904
F: (01751) 430733

Wildsmith Court ★★★★
Contact: Mr and Mrs J&H Milner, Wildsmith Court, The Granary, Marton, Sinnington, York YO62 6RD
T: (01751) 431358
E: milner@wildsmithcourt.freeserve.co.uk

MARTON CUM SEWERBY
East Riding of Yorkshire

Grange Farm Cottages ★★★-★★★★
Contact: Mr R F Dibb, Ryal, Marton cum Sewerby, Bridlington, East Riding of Yorkshire YO15 1DU
T: (01262) 671137
E: richard.dibb@btclick.com

MASHAM
North Yorkshire

Barn Owl Cottage ★★★
Contact: Dales Hol Cot Ref:1178, Dales Holiday Cottages, Carleton Business Park, Carleton New Road, Skipton, North Yorkshire BD23 2AA
T: (01756) 799821 & 790919
F: (01756) 797012
E: info@dalesholcot.com
I: www.dalesholcot.com

Chapel Post House ★★★
Contact: Mrs Angela Durance,
Harrogate Holiday Cottages, The
Old Post Office, Kettlesing,
Harrogate, North Yorkshire
HG3 2LB
T: (01423) 772700
F: (01423) 772359
E: bookings@harrogateholidays.
co.uk
I: www.harrogateholidays.co.uk

Masham Cottages ★★★
Contact: Mr J B Airton, Masham
Cottages, Sunnyside, 27 Red
Lane, Masham, Ripon, North
Yorkshire HG4 4HH
T: (01765) 689327
E: airton@bronco.co.uk
I: www.mashamcottages.co.uk

MELMERBY
North Yorkshire

Field Cottage ★★★
Contact: Mrs Nadine Bell,
Country Hideaways, Margarets
Cottage, West Burton, Leyburn,
North Yorkshire DL8 4JN
T: (01969) 663559
F: (01969) 663559
E: nbell@aol.com
I: www.countryhideaways.co.uk

West Close Cottage ★★★
Contact: Mrs Nadine H Bell,
Country Hideaways, Margarets
Cottage, West Burton, Leyburn,
North Yorkshire DL8 4JN
T: (01969) 663559
F: (01969) 663559
E: nhbell@aol.com
I: www.countryhideaways.co.uk

MELTHAM
West Yorkshire

Constance Cottage ★★★★
Contact: Mr P Esposito & Ms J B
Jackman, 148 Huddersfield
Road, Meltham, Huddersfield
HD9 4AL
T: (01484) 851737 & 851811
F: (01484) 851609

Cuish Cottage ★★★★
Contact: Mrs Mairi Binns, Crepe
Corner Restaurant, 7
Huddersfield Road, Holmfirth,
Huddersfield, West Yorkshire
HD7 1JR
T: (01484) 681532
E: martin@crepes.freeserve.
co.uk

MICKLEBY
North Yorkshire

14 The Lane ★★★★
Contact: Mrs Adele Thompson,
Whitby Holiday Cottages, 47
Flowergate, Whitby, North
Yorkshire YO21 3BB
T: (01947) 603010
F: (01947) 821133
E: enquiries@whitby-cottages.
co.uk
I: www.whitby-cottages.co.uk

MIDDLEHAM
North Yorkshire

Castle Hill Cottage
Rating Applied For
Contact: Dales Hol Cot Ref:1506,
Dales Holiday Cottages, Carleton
Business Park, Carleton New
Road, Skipton, North Yorkshire
BD23 2AA
T: (01756) 799821 & 790919
F: (01756) 799012
E: info@dalesholcot.com
I: www.dalesholcot.com

The Cottage ★★★
Contact: Mrs Jacqueline Welch,
67 Saughton Road North,
Edinburgh, EH12 7JB
T: (0131) 334 3118 & 549 3691

Honeykiln Cottage ★★★
Contact: Dales Hol Cot Ref:3197,
Dales Holiday Cottages, Carleton
Business Park, Carleton New
Road, Skipton, North Yorkshire
BD23 2AA
T: (01756) 799821 & 790919
F: (01756) 797012
E: info@dalesholcot.com
I: www.dalesholcot.com

Milton House ★★★
Contact: Dales Hol Cot Ref:2680,
Dales Holiday Cottages, Carleton
Business Park, Carleton New
Road, Skipton, North Yorkshire
BD23 2AA
T: (01756) 799821 & 790919
F: (01756) 797012
E: info@dalesholcot.com
I: www.dalesholcot.com

4 North Street ★★
Contact: Mr R Wales, Holiday
Cottages (Yorkshire) Ltd, Water
Street, Skipton, North Yorkshire
BD23 1PB
T: (01756) 700510

Smithy Cottage ★★
Contact: Country Holidays
ref:741, Holiday Cottages Group,
Spring Mill, Earby, Barnoldswick,
Lancashire BB94 0AA
T: 08700 723723
F: (01282) 844288
E: sales@ttgihg.co.uk
I: www.country-holidays.co.uk

Stonecroft ★★★★
Contact: Mrs C M Wildman,
Mount Cottage, 6
Wolverhampton Road, Codsall,
Wolverhampton WV8 1PR
T: (01902) 844659

Sunnyside Cottage ★★★
Contact: Dales Hol Cot Ref:2531,
Dales Holiday Cottages, Carleton
Business Park, Carleton New
Road, Skipton, North Yorkshire
BD23 2AA
T: (01756) 799821 & 790919
F: (01756) 797012
E: info@dalesholcot.com
I: www.dalesholcot.com

Teal Cottage ★★★★
Contact: Country Holidays Ref:
15566, Holiday Cottages Group
Owner Services Dept, Spring
Mill, Earby, Barnoldswick,
Lancashire BB18 6RN
T: 0870 444 6604
F: (01281) 841539
E: sales@ttgihg.co.uk
I: www.country-holidays.co.uk

MIDDLESMOOR
North Yorkshire

Abbey Holiday Cottages
★★★★
Contact: Mrs K Holmes, Abbey
Holiday Cottages, 12 Panorama
Close, Pateley Bridge, Harrogate,
North Yorkshire HG3 5NY
T: (01423) 712062
F: (01423) 712062
E: abbeyholiday.cottages@
virgin.net

MIDDLETON
North Yorkshire

Merrylea Holiday Cottage ★★
Contact: Mrs Carole Andrews,
Manor Farm, Main Street,
Middleton, Pickering, North
Yorkshire YO18 8PA
T: (01751) 474900

MUKER
North Yorkshire

Corner Cottage ★★★
Contact: Dales Hol Cot Ref:914,
Dales Holiday Cottages, Carleton
Business Park, Carleton New
Road, Skipton, North Yorkshire
BD23 2AA
T: (01756) 799821 & 790919
F: (01756) 797012
E: info@dalesholcot.com
I: www.dalesholcot.com

MURTON
Yorkshire

Windy Ridge ★★★
Contact: Dales Hol Cot Ref:3175,
Dales Holiday Cottages, Carleton
Business Park, Carleton New
Road, Skipton, North Yorkshire
BD23 2AA
T: (01756) 799821 & 790919
F: (01756) 797012
E: info@dalesholcot.com
I: www.dalesholcot.com

MYTON-ON-SWALE
North Yorkshire

Plump House Farm Holiday
Cottages ★★★
Contact: Mrs Maxine Walker,
Plump House Farm, York Road,
Myton-on-Swale, York, North
Yorkshire YO61 2RA
T: (01423) 360650 &
(01347) 823698
F: (01347) 823184
E: plumphousefarm@aol.com

NAFFERTON
East Riding of Yorkshire

Heapfield Cottage ★★★
Contact: Dales Holiday Cottages,
Carleton Business Park, Carleton
New Road, Skipton, North
Yorkshire BD23 2AA
T: (01756) 799821 & 790919
F: (01756) 797012

NAWTON
North Yorkshire

Portholm ★★★★
Contact: Mrs Susan Hughes, The
Vicarage, The Parade, Berwick-
upon-Tweed, Northumberland
TD15 1DF
T: (01289) 306136
F: (01289) 306136
E: berwick.church@bigwig.net
I: www.bigwig.net/berwick.
church/index.htm

Valley View Lodges ★★
Contact: Mr and Mrs Harry and
June Simpson, Valley View
Lodges, Station Road, Nawton,
York YO62 7RG
T: (01439) 770555

NETHERTHONG
West Yorkshire

59 Deanbrook Road
Rating Applied For
Contact: Mr and Mrs K R
Dorman, Field House Farm,
Scotgate Road, Honley,
Huddersfield HD7 2RE
T: (01484) 661031

NEWBIGGIN
North Yorkshire

The Rowans ★★★
Contact: Dales Hol Cot Ref:210,
Dales Holiday Cottages, Carleton
Business Park, Carleton New
Road, Skipton, North Yorkshire
BD23 2AA
T: (01756) 799821 & 790919
F: (01756) 797012
E: info@dalesholcot.com
I: www.dalesholcot.com

NEWSHAM
North Yorkshire

Dyson House Barn ★★★★
Contact: Mr and Mrs R Clarkson,
Dyson House, Newsham,
Richmond, North Yorkshire
DL11 7QP
T: (01833) 627365 & 0771 444
5405

High Dalton Hall Cottage
★★★★
Contact: Mrs Elizabeth Jopling,
High Dalton Hall, York Street,
Newsham, Richmond, North
Yorkshire DL11 7RG
T: (01833) 621450
F: (01833) 621450

The Mill Cottage ★★★
Contact: Dales Hol Cot Ref:323,
Dales Holiday Cottages, Carleton
Business Park, Carleton New
Road, Skipton, North Yorkshire
BD23 2AA
T: (01756) 799821 & 790919
F: (01756) 797012
E: info@dalesholcot.com
I: www.dalesholcot.com

NEWTON-LE-WILLOWS
North Yorkshire

The Shippon ★★
Contact: Mrs V M Nelson,
Woodbine House, Newton-le-
Willows, Bedale, North Yorkshire
DL8 1TG
T: (01677) 450227
E: andrew.nelson3@virgin.net
I: business.virgin.net/andrew.
nelson3

Tykes Fold ★★★
Contact: Sykes Cottages
Ref:736, Sykes Cottages, York
House, York Street, Chester,
CH1 3LR
T: (01244) 345700
F: (01244) 321442
E: info@sykescottages.co.uk
I: www.sykescottages.co.uk

Establishments printed in blue have a detailed entry in this guide

NEWTON-ON-OUSE
North Yorkshire
Village Farm Holidays ★★★★
Contact: Mr R Wales, Holiday Cottages (Yorkshire) Ltd, Water Street, Skipton, North Yorkshire BD23 1PB
T: (01756) 700510

NEWTON-ON-RAWCLIFFE
North Yorkshire
Edgemoor Cottage ★★★
Contact: Mrs L S Wilkinson, 1096 Halifax Road, Hartshead Moor, Cleckheaton, West Yorkshire BD19 6PE
T: (01274) 877089

Hill Rise Cottage ★★★
Contact: Dales Hol Cot Ref:1617, Dales Holiday Cottages, Carleton Business Park, Carleton New Road, Skipton, North Yorkshire BD23 2AA
T: (01756) 799821 & 790919
F: (01756) 797012
E: info@dalesholcot.com
I: www.dalesholcot.com

Hillcrest Cottage ★★★★
Contact: Mrs P M Orgill, Drift Cottage, Freckenham, Bury St Edmunds, Suffolk IP28 8JG
T: (01638) 720081

Let's Holiday ★★★
Contact: Mr John Wicks, Let's Holiday, Mel House, Newton-on-Rawcliffe, Pickering, North Yorkshire YO18 8QA
T: (01751) 475396
F: (01751) 475396
E: john.wicks@letsholiday.com
I: www.letsholiday.com

Manor Farm Cottages ★★★★
Contact: Lady Kirk, Manor Farm Cottages, Manor Farm, Newton-on-Rawcliffe, Pickering, North Yorkshire YO18 8QA
T: (01751) 472601
F: (01751) 472601

Stable Cottage ★★★
Contact: Mr & Mrs P D Gardner, The Old Vicarage, Newton-on-Rawcliffe, Pickering, North Yorkshire YO18 8QD
T: (01751) 476126
E: sueashburn2007@aol.com

Sunset Cottage ★★★★
Contact: Mrs Pat Anderson, Sunset Holidays, Boonhill Cottage, Newton-on-Rawcliffe, Pickering, North Yorkshire YO18 8QF
T: (01751) 472172
E: sunset@boonhill69.freeserve.co.uk
I: www.swiftlink.pnc-uk.net/sc/1236.htm

NORTH COWTON
North Yorkshire
Millstone ★★★
Contact: Sykes Cottages Ref:613, Sykes Cottages, York House, York Street, Chester, CH1 3LR
T: (01244) 345700
F: (01244) 321442
E: info@sykescottages.co.uk
I: www.sykescottages.co.uk

NORTH STAINLEY
North Yorkshire
Sleningford Grange Cottage ★★★★
Contact: Sykes Cottages Ref:515, Sykes Cottages, York House, York Street, Chester, CH1 3LR
T: (01244) 345700
F: (01244) 321442
E: info@sykescottages.co.uk
I: www.sykescottages.co.uk

NORTHALLERTON
North Yorkshire
The Byre ★★★★
Contact: Mrs M Crowe, The Byre, Hill View Farm, Bullamoor, Northallerton, North Yorkshire DL6 3QW
T: (01609) 776072

Hill House Farm Cottages ★★★★
Contact: Mr J Griffith, Hill House Farm Cottages, Hill House Farm, Little Langton, Northallerton, North Yorkshire DL7 0PZ
T: (01609) 770643
F: (01609) 760438
E: info@hillhousefarmcottages.com

2 Summerfield Cottage ★★★
Contact: Mrs S H Holmes, Summerfield House Farm, Welbury, Northallerton, North Yorkshire DL6 2SL
T: (01609) 882393
F: (01609) 882393
E: theholmeswelbury@talk21.com

NORTON
North Yorkshire
The Cottage ★★★
Contact: Mrs P Barber, The Cottage, 69 Welham Road, Norton, Malton, North Yorkshire YO17 9DS
T: (01653) 693409
E: Patricia.barber@Btinternet.com

NORWOOD
North Yorkshire
West Wing ★★★
Contact: Country Holidays ref: 8888, Holiday Cottages Group, Spring Mill, Earby, Barnoldswick, Lancashire BB94 0AA
T: 08700 723723
F: (01282) 844288
E: sales@ttgihg.co.uk
I: www.country-holidays.co.uk

NUNNINGTON
North Yorkshire
The Cottage ★★
Contact: Dales Hol Cot Ref:200, Dales Holiday Cottages, Carleton Business Park, Carleton New Road, Skipton, North Yorkshire BD23 2AA
T: (01756) 799821 & 790919
F: (01756) 797012
E: info@dalesholcot.com
I: www.dalesholcot.com

Orchard Cottage ★★
Contact: Mr & Mrs C Foxton, Ness Farm, West Ness, Nunnington, York YO62 5XE
T: (01439) 784226

OAKWORTH
West Yorkshire
22 & 24 Rushey Hall ★★★
Contact: CH ref:4337,3133, Holiday Cottages Group, Spring Mill, Earby, Barnoldswick, Lancashire BB94 0AA
T: 08700 723723
F: (01282) 844288
I: www.country-holidays.co.uk

Moorcock Cottage ★★★
Contact: Dales Hol Cot Ref:2896, Dales Holiday Cottages, Carleton Business Park, Carleton New Road, Skipton, North Yorkshire BD23 2AA
T: (01756) 799821 & 790919
F: (01756) 797012
E: info@dalesholcot.com
I: www.dalesholcot.com

OLD BYLAND
North Yorkshire
Tylas Lodge ★★★
Contact: Mrs Jane Holmes, Tylas Farm, Old Byland, York, North Yorkshire YO62 5LH
T: (01439) 798308
F: (01439) 798461
E: holmesivan@btinternet.com

Valley View Farm ★★★★
Contact: Mrs C S Robinson, Valley View Farm, Old Byland, York, North Yorkshire YO62 5LG
T: (01439) 798221
E: salley@valleyviewfarm.com
I: www.valleyviewfarm.com

OSGODBY
North Yorkshire
Sea Views ★★★★
Contact: Mr and Mrs O'Connor, 15 Halifax Road, Brighouse, West Yorkshire HD62AA
T: (01484) 401757 & 07967 170341
E: pat@oconn100.freeserve.co.uk
I: www.sea-views-scarborough.co.uk

OSMOTHERLEY
North Yorkshire
Monk's Walk
Rating Applied For
Contact: Dales Hol Cot Ref:2041, Dales Holiday Cottages, Carleton Business Park, Carleton New Road, Skipton, North Yorkshire BD23 2AA
T: (01756) 799821 & 790919
F: (01756) 797012
E: info@dalesholcot.com
I: www.dalesholcot.com

OXENHOPE
West Yorkshire
Hawksbridge Cottage ★★★
Contact: Mrs H M Holmes, 2 Hawksbridge Lane, Oxenhope, Keighley, West Yorkshire BD22 9QU
T: (01535) 642203

Lynden Barn Cottage ★★★★
Contact: Mrs I Spencer, Lynden Barn, Sawood Lane, Oxenhope, Keighley, West Yorkshire BD22 9SP
T: (01535) 645074 & 07775 743210
E: lyndenbarn@hotmail.com
I: members.netscapeonline.co.uk/lyndenbarn/index.html

2 Mouldgreave Cottages ★★★
Contact: Mrs N Mackrell, Mouldgreave House, Oxenhope, Keighley, West Yorkshire BD22 9RT
T: (01535) 642325
F: (01535) 640370
E: mackrells@lineone.net

Royd Wood Cottage ★★★
Contact: Mrs D Kinghorn, Wild Fell, 16 South Close, Guiseley, Leeds LS20 8JD
T: (01943) 872767

Well Head Cottage ★★★★★
Contact: Mrs Nicola Binns, Well Head Barn, Hanging Gate Lane, Oxenhope, Keighley, West Yorkshire BD22 9RJ
T: (01535) 647966
E: nicola@brontecottages.co.uk
I: www.brontecottages.co.uk

Yate Cottage ★★★
Contact: Mrs Jean M M Dunn, Yate House, Yate Lane, Oxenhope, Keighley, West Yorkshire BD22 9HL
T: (01535) 643638
E: jeanandhugh@dunnyate.freeserve.co.uk
I: www.oas.co.uk/ukcottages/yatecottage

PATELEY BRIDGE
North Yorkshire
Blue Plain Cottage ★★★
Contact: Mr & Mrs J Ninness, 125 Hinckley Road, Stoke Golding, Nuneaton, Warwickshire CV13 6ED
T: (01455) 213086

Grassfield Country Cottage ★★★★
Contact: Country Holidays ref:9177, Holiday Cottages Group, Spring Mill, Earby, Barnoldswick, Lancashire BB94 0AA
T: 08700 723723
F: (01282) 844288
E: sales@ttgihg.co.uk
I: www.country-holidays.co.uk

Old Spring Wood Lodges ★★★★
Contact: Mrs A R Helme, Old Spring Wood Lodges, Helme Pasture, Hartwith Bank, Summer Bridge, Harrogate, North Yorkshire HG3 4DR
T: (01423) 780279
F: (01423) 780994
E: info@oldspringwoodlodges.co.uk
I: www.oldspringwoodlodges.co.uk
🚶

16 Park Road ★★★
Contact: Mrs A Durance, Harrogate Holiday Cottages, Kettlesing, Harrogate, North Yorkshire HG3 2LB
T: (01423) 772700
F: (01423) 772359
E: bookings@harrogateholidays.co.uk
I: www.harrogateholidays.co.uk

Rainbows End ★★★
Contact: Sykes Cottages Ref:61, Sykes Cottages, York House, York Street, Chester, CH1 3LR
T: (01244) 345700
F: (01244) 321442
E: info@sykescottages.co.uk
I: www.sykescottages.co.uk

Rolling Mill Stable ★★★
Contact: Sykes Cottages Ref:244, Sykes Cottages, York House, York Street, Chester, CH1 3LR
T: (01244) 345700
F: (01244) 321442
E: info@sykescottages.co.uk
I: www.sykescottages.co.uk

Scott House ★★★★★
Contact: Mr & Mrs M F Halliday, 2 Grange Drive, Horsforth, Leeds LS18 5EQ
T: (0113) 258 4212
F: (0113) 281 9455

PICKERING
North Yorkshire

Barker Stakes Farm ★★–★★★
Contact: Mrs S E Hardy, Barker Stakes Farm, Lendales Lane, Pickering, North Yorkshire YO18 8EE
T: (01751) 476759

Beech Farm Cottages ★★★★–★★★★★
Contact: Mr Rooney Massara, Beech Farm Cottages, Wrelton, Pickering, North Yorkshire YO18 8PG
T: (01751) 476612
F: (01751) 475032
E: holiday@beechfarm.com
I: www.beechfarm.com

Byzan Cottage ★★★
Contact: Mrs P J Roberts, Anfield, 10 Beacon Park, 1st Avenue, Pickering, North Yorkshire YO18 8AQ
T: (01751) 472077 & (01723) 863778

Costa Lodge ★★★★
Contact: Mr & Mrs G&K Hartas, Costa Lodge, Westgate Carr Road, Pickering, North Yorkshire YO18 8LZ
T: (01751) 475317

East Kingthorpe House ★★★★
Contact: Mr and Mrs G Abbott, Buckthorn House, Malton Road, Pickering, North Yorkshire YO18 8EA
T: (01751) 473848
E: geoffabbott@supanet.com
I: kingthorpe.freeservers.com/

Eastgate Cottages ★★★–★★★★
Contact: Mr and Mrs Kevin & Elaine Bedford, Eastgate Cottages, 117 Eastgate, Pickering, North Yorkshire YO18 7DW
T: (01751) 476653 & 471303
F: (01751) 471310
E: info@ northyorkshirecottages.co.uk
I: www.northyorkshirecottages.co.uk

Easthill Farm House and Gardens ★★★★
Contact: Mrs Diane Stenton, Easthill Farm House and Gardens, Wilton Road, Thornton Dale, Pickering, North Yorkshire YO18 7QP
T: (01751) 474561
E: easthill@freeuk.com
I: www.easthill-farm-holidays.co.uk

Eastside Cottage ★★★
Contact: Mrs E Evans, Eastside Farm, Newton upon Rawcliffe, Pickering, North Yorkshire YO18 8QA
T: (01751) 477204

Garden Cottage Rating Applied For
Contact: Mrs Elaine Bedford, Eastgate Cottages, 117 Eastgate, Pickering, North Yorkshire YO18 7DW
T: (01751) 476653 & 471303
F: (01751) 471310
E: info@ northyorkshirecottages.co.uk
I: www.northyorkshirecottages.co.uk

Greystones Cottage ★★★
Contact: Mr R Wales, Holiday Cottages (Yorkshire) Ltd, Water Street, Skipton, North Yorkshire BD23 1PB
T: (01756) 700510

Joiners Cottage ★★★
Contact: Mr and Mrs P&C Fisher, Farndale House, 103 Eastgate, Pickering, North Yorkshire YO18 7DW
T: (01751) 475158

Kale Pot Farmhouse ★★★
Contact: Mr & Mrs R Medd, 37 High Street, Olney, Buckinghamshire MK46 4EB
T: (01234) 240296
F: (01234) 240296
E: richard.medd@talk21.co.uk

Keld Head Farm Holiday Cottages ★★★★
Contact: Mr R Wales, Holiday Cottages (Yorkshire) Ltd, Water Street, Skipton, North Yorkshire BD23 1PB
T: (01756) 700510

Lilac Cottage ★★★
Contact: Mr & Mrs R&D Munn, Lilac Cottage, 23 Westgate, Pickering, North Yorkshire YO18 8BA
T: (01751) 472193

Lynton Cottage ★★★
Contact: Dales Hol Cot Ref:2800, Dales Holiday Cottages, Carleton Business Park, Carleton New Road, Skipton, North Yorkshire BD23 2AA
T: (01756) 799821 & 790919
F: (01756) 797012
E: info@dalesholcot.com
I: www.dalesholcot.com

New Meadows ★★★
Contact: Mrs K J Hill, New Meadows, 66 Ruffa Lane, Pickering, North Yorkshire YO18 7HT
T: (01751) 473258

Newton Cottage ★★★
Contact: Mr Tony Danks, 34 Smalewell Drive, Pudsey, West Yorkshire LS28 8HX
T: (0113) 257 7313 & 07956 658894
E: mal.danks@btinternet.com

The Old Coach House, The Tack Room ★★★★
Contact: Mr & Mrs SH&G Hackett, Bramwood Guest House, 19 Hallgarth, Pickering, North Yorkshire YO18 7AW
T: (01751) 474066

Rawcliffe House Farm ★★★★
Contact: Mrs Sheila Ducat, Rawcliffe House Farm, Stape, Pickering, North Yorkshire YO18 8JA
T: (01751) 473292
F: (01751) 473766
E: sheilarh@yahoo.com
I: www.yorkshireaccommodation.com

Rose Barn ★★★★
Contact: Mrs J Hornsby, Grindale House, Pickering, North Yorkshire YO18 7DW
T: (01751) 476636 & 07968 207948

The Sidings ★★★
Contact: Mr & Mrs L&EP Varley, 21 Redwood, Compton Acres, West Bridgeford, Nottingham, NG2 7UL
T: (0115) 945 5543
E: varleyfm@supanet.com

South View Cottages ★★★–★★★★★
Contact: Mr P Simpson, 107 Church Street, Whitby, North Yorkshire YO22 4DE
T: (01947) 604406

3 Spring Garden Cottage ★★★
Contact: Mr P Smith, Spring Gardens, Keld Head, Pickering, North Yorkshire YO18 8LJ
T: (01751) 473412 & 475177

1 Tannery Cottages ★★★
Contact: Mr and Mrs Robert and Diana Ellis, 29 Hartington Close, Dorridge, Solihull, West Midlands B93 8SU
T: (01564) 779573
F: 0870 052 5303
E: bob@ems-knowle.demon.co.uk

Town End Farm Cottage ★★
Contact: Mr P R Holmes, Town End Farm Cottage, Eastfield Road, Pickering, North Yorkshire YO18 7HU
T: (01751) 472713 & 473983

Upper Carr Chalet and Touring Park ★★★
Contact: Mr & Mrs M Harker, Upper Carr Chalet and Touring Park, Upper Carr Lane, Malton Road, Pickering, North Yorkshire YO18 7JP
T: (01751) 473115
F: (01751) 473115
E: harker@uppercarr.demon.co.uk
I: www.upercarr.demon.co.uk

White Lodge Cottage ★★★
Contact: Mrs E A Briggs, White Lodge, 54 Eastgate, Pickering, North Yorkshire YO18 7DU
T: (01751) 473897

POCKLINGTON
East Riding of Yorkshire

Greyhavens Bungalow ★★
Contact: Dales Hol Cot Ref:1960, Dales Holiday Cottages, Carleton Business Park, Carleton New Road, Skipton, North Yorkshire BD23 2AA
T: (01756) 799821 & 790919
F: (01756) 797012
E: info@dalesholcot.com
I: www.dalesholcot.com

Rosewalden ★★★
Contact: Mrs Angela Morris, 14 Barmby Road, Pocklington, York YO42 2DP
T: (01759) 306133
E: roseswalden@aol.com

PORT MULGRAVE
North Yorkshire

Haefen Cottage ★★★
Contact: Dales Hol Cot Ref:2522, Dales Holiday Cottages, Carleton Business Park, Carleton New Road, Skipton, North Yorkshire BD23 2AA
T: (01756) 799821 & 790919
F: (01756) 797012
E: info@dalesholcot.com
I: www.dalesholcot.com

PRESTON-UNDER-SCAR
North Yorkshire

Croxford Cottage ★★
Contact: Dales Hol Cot Ref:2034, Dales Holiday Cottages, Carleton Business Park, Carleton New Road, Skipton, North Yorkshire BD23 2AA
T: (01756) 799821 & 790919
F: (01756) 797012
E: info@dalesholcot.com
I: www.dalesholcot.com

Mallyan Wynd ★★
Contact: Mrs Nadine H Bell, Country Hideaways, Margarets Cottage, West Burton, Leyburn, North Yorkshire DL8 4JN
T: (01969) 663559
F: (01969) 663559
E: nhbell@aol.com
I: www.countryhideaways.co.uk

Rocky View ★★★
Contact: Mrs Nadine H Bell, Country Hideaways, Margarets Cottage, West Burton, Leyburn, North Yorkshire DL8 4JN
T: (01969) 663559
F: (01969) 663559
E: nhbell@aol.com
I: www.countryhideaways.co.uk

PRIMROSE VALLEY
North Yorkshire

Calm Waters Bungalow ★★
Contact: Dales Hol Cot Ref:2478, Dales Holiday Cottages, Carleton Business Park, Carleton New Road, Skipton, North Yorkshire BD23 2AA
T: (01756) 799821 & 790919
F: (01756) 797012
E: info@dalesholcot.com
I: www.dalesholcot.com

Establishments printed in blue have a detailed entry in this guide

RATHMELL
North Yorkshire
Layhead Farm Cottages
★★★★
Contact: Mrs H R Hyslop, Field
House, Rathmell, Settle, North
Yorkshire BD24 0LD
T: (01729) 840234
F: (01729) 840775
E: rosehyslop@layhead.co.uk
I: www.layhead.co.uk

The Old Coach House ★★★
Contact: Sykes Cottages
Ref:459, Sykes Cottages, York
House, York Street, Chester,
CH1 3LR
T: (01244) 345700
F: (01244) 321442
E: info@sykescottages.co.uk
I: www.sykescottages.co.uk

RAVENSCAR
North Yorkshire
Raven Lea ★★★★
Contact: Mrs D M Turner, Raven
Lea, Station Road, Ravenscar,
Scarborough, North Yorkshire
YO13 0LX
T: (01723) 870949

**Smugglers Rock Country
House** ★★★
Contact: Mrs S Gregson,
Smugglers Rock Country House,
Staintondale Road, Ravenscar,
Scarborough, North Yorkshire
YO13 0ER
T: (01723) 870044
E: info@smugglersrock.co.uk
I: www.smugglersrock.co.uk

REETH
North Yorkshire
**Burton House, Greystones,
Turbine House and Charlies
Stable**★★★★
Contact: Mrs P R Procter, Hill
Cottage, Reeth, Richmond,
North Yorkshire DL11 6SQ
T: (01748) 884273
E: cprocter@aol.com
I: www.uk-cottages.com

Crow Hall ★★★
Contact: Mr R Wales, Holiday
Cottages (Yorkshire) Ltd, Water
Street, Skipton, North Yorkshire
BD23 1PB
T: (01756) 700510

23 Hill Close ★★★★
Contact: Country Holidays
ref:11837, Holiday Cottages
Group, Spring Mill, Earby,
Barnoldswick, Lancashire
BB94 0AA
T: 08700 723723
F: (01282) 844288
E: sales@ttgihg.co.uk
I: www.country-holidays.co.uk

Kernot Court ★★
Contact: Mr M Hodgson, Kernot
Court, Reeth, Richmond, North
Yorkshire DL11 6SF
T: (01748) 884662

Stonegate Cottage ★★★
Contact: Country Holidays
ref:6160, Holiday Cottages
Group, Spring Mill, Earby,
Barnoldswick, Lancashire
BB94 0AA
T: 08700 723723
F: (01282) 844288
E: sales@ttgihg.co.uk
I: www.country-holidays.co.uk

Swaledale Cottages
★★★-★★★★
Contact: Mrs J T Hughes,
Swaledale Cottages,
Thiernswood Hall, Healaugh,
Richmond, North Yorkshire
DL11 6UJ
T: (01748) 884526
F: (01748) 884834

Winmaur Cottage ★★★★
Contact: Dales Hol Cot Ref:2995,
Dales Holiday Cottages, Carleton
Business Park, Carleton New
Road, Skipton, North Yorkshire
BD23 2AA
T: (01756) 799821 & 790919
F: (01756) 797012
E: info@dalesholcot.com
I: www.dalesholcot.com

Wraycroft Holiday Cottages
★★★★
Contact: Mrs F Hodgson,
Wraycroft Holiday Cottages,
Wraycroft, Reeth, Richmond,
North Yorkshire DL11 6SU
T: (01748) 884497
F: (01748) 884497

REIGHTON
North Yorkshire
Reighton Hall (The Cottage)
Rating Applied For
Contact: Ms Dawn McKie,
Reighton Hall, Church Hill,
Reighton, Filey, North Yorkshire
YO14 7RX
T: (01723) 890601
F: (01723) 890260
E: dawn@reightonhall.com
I: www.reightonhall.com

Seaton House ★★★★
Contact: Dales Hol Cot Ref:3058,
Dales Holiday Cottages, Carleton
Business Park, Carleton New
Road, Skipton, North Yorkshire
BD23 2AA
T: (01756) 799821 & 790919
F: (01756) 797012
E: info@dalesholcot.com
I: www.dalesholcot.com

RICHMOND
North Yorkshire
**Barn Owl Cottage and
Kingfisher Cottage**★★★★
Contact: Mr & Mrs G W
Fothergill, Barn Owl Cottage and
Kingfisher Cottage, Red House
Farm, Easby, Richmond, North
Yorkshire DL10 7EU
T: (01748) 822038

The Bungalow ★★★
Contact: CH ref:5527,5528,
Holiday Cottages Group, Spring
Mill, Earby, Barnoldswick,
Lancashire BB94 0AA
T: 08700 723723
F: (01282) 841539
E: sales@ttgihg.co.uk
I: www.country-holidays.co.uk

Castle View ★★★★
Contact: Country Holidays
ref:8352, Holiday Cottages
Group, Spring Mill, Earby,
Barnoldswick, Lancashire
BB94 0AA
T: 08700 723723
F: (01282) 844288
E: sales@ttgihg.co.uk
I: www.country-holidays.co.uk

Chestnut Cottage ★★★
Contact: Mr & Mrs P Donaldson,
Cowstand Farm, Catterick,
Richmond, North Yorkshire
DL10 7PP
T: (01748) 811911
E: p.donal5069@aol.com
I: www.cottageguide.
co.uk/chestnutcottage

Coach House ★★★★
Contact: Mrs M F Turnbull,
Coach House, Whashton Springs
Farm, Whashton, Richmond,
North Yorkshire DL11 7JS
T: (01748) 822884
F: (01748) 826285
E: whashton@turnbullg.
freeserve.co.uk
I: www.whashtonsprings.co.uk

16 Culloden Mews ★★★
Contact: Mrs Joanna
Newcombe, 683 Welbeck Road,
Walker, Newcastle upon Tyne
NE6 4JL
T: (0191) 263 4608
E: karl@newcombe02.fsnet.
co.uk

Dillon's Cottage ★★
Contact: Sykes Cottages
Ref:703, Sykes Cottages, York
House, York Street, Chester,
CH1 3LR
T: (01244) 345700
F: (01244) 321442
E: info@sykescottages.co.uk
I: www.sykescottages.co.uk

Fryers Cottage ★★★
Contact: Mr & Mrs O Blease, 26
Newbiggin, Richmond, North
Yorkshire DL10 4DT
T: (01748) 823344 &
07803 833675

Ingledew Cottage ★★★
Contact: Mr DJ Nichols & Miss G
Chisholm, 7 Strait Lane,
Hurworth on Tees, Darlington,
County Durham DL2 2AH
T: (01325) 721736 & 282371
E: donandgrace@aol.com
I: www.resiweb.
co.uk/richmond-self-catering

Nuns Cottage Yard ★★★
Contact: Mrs Susan Parks, 5
Hurgill Road, Richmond, North
Yorkshire DL10 4AR
T: (01748) 822809
F: (01429) 864320
E: nunscottage@richmond.org.
uk
I: richmond.org.
uk/business/nunscottage

Rose Cottage ★★★★
Contact: Mr David Hunt, 11
Richmond Road, Skeeby,
Richmond, North Yorkshire
DL10 5DR
T: (01748) 823080
E: huntsholidays@hotmail.com
I: www.huntsholidays.co.uk

Thornlea Cottage ★★★
Contact: Mr C P Sykes, Sykes
Cottages, York House, York
Street, Chester, CH1 3LR
T: (01244) 345700
F: (01244) 321442
E: info@sykesottages.co.uk
I: www.sykescottages.co.uk

3 Young's Yard ★★
Contact: Mrs K Swainston,
Millcroft, Tunstall Road,
Catterick, Richmond, North
Yorkshire DL10 7PR
T: (01748) 818410 & 812932

RILLINGTON
North Yorkshire
Thorpe-Rise ★★★
Contact: Mrs Marilyn Legard,
Thorpe-Rise, 10 High Street,
Rillington, Malton, North
Yorkshire YO17 8LA
T: (01944) 758446
E: marilyn@mlegard.freeserve.
co.uk

RIPLEY
North Yorkshire
Lilac Cottage ★★★
Contact: Mrs Sarah Rose, Lilac
Cottage, 14 Orchard Lane,
Ripley, Harrogate, North
Yorkshire HG3 3AT
T: 07740 479273
F: (01423) 771880

RIPON
North Yorkshire
5 Bondgate Green ★★★
Contact: Mrs R M Norris, Downe,
Baldersby, Thirsk, North
Yorkshire YO7 4PP
T: (01765) 640283
F: (01765) 640556
E: doronic@cs.com

**Byre Cottage & Swallow
Cottage** ★★★★
Contact: Mr & Mrs R&P
Spensley, Moor End Farm,
Knaresborough Road,
Littlethorpe, Ripon, North
Yorkshire HG4 3LU
T: (01765) 677419
E: pspensley@ukonline.co.uk
I: www.yorkshirebandb.co.uk

1a King Street ★★★
Contact: Mrs Angela Durance,
Harrogate Holiday Cottages, The
Old Post Office, Kettlesing,
Harrogate, North Yorkshire
HG3 2LB
T: (01423) 772700
F: (01423) 772359
E: bookings@harrogateholidays.
co.uk
I: www.harrogateholidays.co.uk

Lacon Hall Cottages ★★
Contact: Mr & Mrs A C Cook,
Lacon Hall Cottages, Lacon Hall,
Sawley, Ripon, North Yorkshire
HG4 3EE
T: (01765) 620658

Mallorie Bungalow ★★★
Contact: Dales Hol Cot Ref:2176,
Dales Holiday Cottages, Carleton
Business Park, Carleton New
Road, Skipton, North Yorkshire
BD23 2AA
T: (01756) 799821 & 790919
F: (01756) 797012
E: info@dalesholcot.com
I: www.dalesholcot.com

RISHWORTH
West Yorkshire

The Old Post Office ★★★★
Contact: Mr Steven Edwards,
Calder House, 264 Oldham Road,
Rishworth, Sowerby Bridge,
West Yorkshire HX6 4QB
T: (01422) 823840 &
07966 256233

ROBIN HOOD'S BAY
North Yorkshire

1 and 2 Wragby Barn ★★★★
Contact: Mrs M Fenby, 12
Prospect Fields, High Hawsker,
Whitby, North Yorkshire
YO22 4LG
T: (01947) 880719
F: (01947) 880719

Bank House Cottage ★★★
Contact: Mrs Adele Thompson,
Whitby Holiday Cottages, 47
Flowergate, Whitby, North
Yorkshire YO21 3BB
T: (01947) 603010
F: (01947) 821133
E: enquiries@whitby-cottages.
co.uk
I: www.whitby-cottages.co.uk

Brudenell Cottage ★★
Contact: Country Holidays
ref:2384, Holiday Cottages
Group, Spring Mill, Earby,
Barnoldswick, Lancashire
BB94 0AA
T: 08700 723723
F: (01282) 844288
E: sales@ttgihg.co.uk
I: www.country-holidays.co.uk

**Farsyde House Farm Cottages
★★-★★★★**
Contact: Mrs A Green, Farsyde
House Farm Cottages, Robin
Hood's Bay, Whitby, North
Yorkshire YO22 4UG
T: (01947) 880249 & 880877
F: (01947) 880877
E: farsydestud@talk21.com

Fenay Cottage ★★★
Contact: Dales Hol Cot Ref:2524,
Dales Holiday Cottages, Carleton
Business Park, Carleton New
Road, Skipton, North Yorkshire
BD23 2AA
T: (01756) 799821 & 790919
F: (01756) 797012
E: info@dalesholcot.com
I: www.dalesholcot.com

High Cliff ★★★
Contact: Country Holidays
ref:5921, Holiday Cottages
Group, Spring Mill, Earby,
Barnoldswick, Lancashire
BB94 0AA
T: 08700 723723
F: (01282) 844288
E: sales@ttgihg.co.uk
I: www.country-holidays.co.uk

Inglenook ★★★★
Contact: Mrs Lesley Abbott, 7
Goodwood Grove, York,
YO24 1ER
T: (01904) 622059 & 700164
I: www.inglenook-cottage.co.uk

Lingers Hill ★★★
Contact: Mrs F Harland, Lingers
Hill Farm, Thorpe Lane, Robin
Hood's Bay, Whitby, North
Yorkshire YO22 4TQ
T: (01947) 880608

The Loft ★★
Contact: Mrs Adele Thompson,
Whitby Holiday Cottages, 47
Flowergate, Whitby, North
Yorkshire YO21 3BB
T: (01947) 603010
F: (01947) 821133
E: enquiries@whitby-cottages.
co.uk
I: www.whitby-cottages.co.uk

Odinsfeld ★★★
Contact: Mrs Adele Thompson,
Whitby Holiday Cottages, 47
Flowergate, Whitby, North
Yorkshire YO21 3BB
T: (01947) 603010
F: (01947) 821133
E: enquiries@whitby-cottages.
co.uk
I: www.whitby-cottages.co.uk

Primrose Cottage ★★★
Contact: Country Holidays
ref:970, Holiday Cottages Group,
Spring Mill, Earby, Barnoldswick,
Lancashire BB94 0AA
T: 08700 723723
F: (01282) 844288
I: www.country-holidays.co.uk

The Robin's Nest ★★★
Contact: Mrs Adele Thompson,
Whitby Holiday Cottages, 47
Flowergate, Whitby, North
Yorkshire YO21 3BB
T: (01947) 603010
F: (01947) 821133
E: enquiries@whitby-cottages.
co.uk
I: www.whitby-cottages.co.uk

**The White Owl Holiday
Apartments ★★-★★★**
Contact: Mr David Higgins, The
White Owl Holiday Apartments,
Victoria Terrace, Robin Hood's
Bay, Whitby, North Yorkshire
YO22 4RL
T: (01947) 880879

ROSEDALE ABBEY
North Yorkshire

Coach House ★★★★
Contact: Mrs L Sugars, Coach
House, Sevenford House,
Rosedale Abbey, Pickering,
North Yorkshire YO18 8SE
T: (01751) 417283
F: (01751) 417505
E: sevenford@aol.com

**Craven Garth Holiday Cottages
★★★**
Contact: Mrs Ena Dent, Craven
Garth Holiday Cottages, Craven
Garth Farm, Rosedale Abbey,
Pickering, North Yorkshire
YO18 8RH
T: (01751) 417506
F: (01751) 417506
E: ena@cravengarth.com
I: www.cravengarth.com

Dale Cottage ★★★★
Contact: Sykes Cottages
Ref:594, Sykes Cottages, York
House, York Street, Chester,
CH1 3LR
T: (01244) 345700
F: (01244) 321442
E: info@sykescottages.co.uk
I: www.sykescottages.co.uk

**East Lodge Coach House
★★★★**
Contact: Sykes Cottages
Ref:782, Sykes Cottages, York
House, York Street, Chester,
CH1 3LR
T: (01244) 345700
F: (01244) 321442
E: info@sykescottages.co.uk
I: www.sykescottages.co.uk

10 Hill Cottage ★★★★
Contact: Deborah & Colin
Wilson, 48 Hob Hill Close,
Saltburn-by-the-Sea, Cleveland
TS12 1NB
T: (01287) 625921
F: (01287) 625921
E: wilson@csdj.freeserve.co.uk

4 Hill Houses ★★★
Contact: Mrs A Bell, 10 Rye Dale,
Pine Hills, Guisborough, North
Yorkshire TS14 8JE
T: (01287) 634152

Rowan Cottage ★★★
Contact: Dales Hol Cot Ref:2566,
Dales Holiday Cottages, Carleton
Business Park, Carleton New
Road, Skipton, North Yorkshire
BD23 2AA
T: (01756) 799821 & 790919
F: (01756) 797012
E: info@dalesholcot.com
I: www.dalesholcot.com

Stable Cottage ★★★
Contact: Mrs Christine
Ewington, Stable Cottage,
Medds Farmhouse, Thorgill,
Rosedale Abbey, Pickering,
North Yorkshire YO18 8SQ
T: (01751) 417583
E: ewington@medds.co.uk
I: www.medds.co.uk

ROSEDALE EAST
North Yorkshire

1 Hill Houses ★★★
Contact: Mrs M Harrison, 28
George Street, Driffield, East
Yorkshire YO25 6RA
T: (01377) 253042
E: mary.harrison@btinternet.
com

RUNSWICK BAY
North Yorkshire

7 Nettledale Close ★★
Contact: Mrs Adele Thompson,
Whitby Holiday Cottages, 47
Flowergate, Whitby, North
Yorkshire YO21 3BB
T: (01947) 603010
F: (01947) 821133
E: enquiries@whitby-cottages.
co.uk
I: www.whitby-cottages.co.uk

Runswick Lodge ★★★
Contact: Dales Hol Cot Ref:1647,
Dales Holiday Cottages, Carleton
Business Park, Carleton New
Road, Skipton, North Yorkshire
BD23 2AA
T: (01756) 799821 & 790919
F: (01756) 797012
E: info@dalesholcot.com
I: www.dalesholcot.com

RUSWARP
North Yorkshire

Egton Cottage ★★
Contact: Sykes Cottages
Ref:734, Sykes Cottages, York
House, York Street, Chester,
CH1 3LR
T: (01244) 345700
F: (01244) 321442
E: info@sykescottages.co.uk
I: www.sykescottages.co.uk

Esk View Cottage ★★★
Contact: Dales Hol Cot Ref:1912,
Dales Holiday Cottages, Carleton
Business Park, Carleton New
Road, Skipton, North Yorkshire
BD23 2AA
T: (01756) 799821 & 790919
F: (01756) 797012
E: info@dalesholcot.com
I: www.dalesholcot.com

Maybeck Cottage ★★★
Contact: Dales Hol Cot Ref:1674,
Dales Holiday Cottages, Carleton
Business Park, Carleton New
Road, Skipton, North Yorkshire
BD23 2AA
T: (01756) 799821 & 790919
F: (01756) 797012
E: info@dalesholcot.com
I: www.dalesholcot.com

Sowerby House ★★
Contact: Mrs Adele Thompson,
Whitby Holiday Cottages, 47
Flowergate, Whitby, North
Yorkshire YO21 3BB
T: (01947) 603010
F: (01947) 821133
E: enquiries@whitby-cottages.
co.uk
I: www.whitby-cottages.co.uk

**Turnerdale Cottage
Rating Applied For**
Contact: Mr David Haycox & Mrs
Sue Brooks, Shoreline Cottages
Ltd, PO Box 135, Leeds, West
Yorkshire LS14 3XJ
T: (0113) 289 3539 &
07801 419255
F: (0113) 289 3541
E: reservations@
shoreline-cottages.com
I: www.shoreline-cottages.com

SALTAIRE
West Yorkshire

Overlookers Cottage ★★★★
Contact: Mrs Anne Heald, 2
Victoria Road, Saltaire, Shipley,
West Yorkshire BD18 3LA
T: (01274) 774993 & 774122
F: (01274) 774464

SALTON
North Yorkshire

Dove Court ★★★★
Contact: Mrs Helen Earnshaw,
Dove Court, Sparrow Hall,
Salton, York YO62 6RW
T: (01751) 431697 &
(01642) 397832
E: helen@dovecourt.com
I: www.dovecourt.com
&

Establishments printed in blue have a detailed entry in this guide

SALTWICK BAY
North Yorkshire

Brook House Barn ★★★
Contact: Dales Hol Cot Ref:1340, Dales Holiday Cottages, Carleton Business Park, Carleton New Road, Skipton, North Yorkshire BD23 2AA
T: (01756) 799821 & 790919
F: (01756) 797012
E: info@dalesholcot.com
I: www.dalesholcot.com

SANDSEND
North Yorkshire

Garden Flat ★★
Contact: Mrs Adele Thompson, Whitby Holiday Cottages, 47 Flowergate, Whitby, North Yorkshire YO21 3BB
T: (01947) 603010
F: (01947) 821133
E: enquiries@whitby-cottages.co.uk
I: www.whitby-cottages.co.uk

Harlow Cottage
Rating Applied For
Contact: Mrs S Brooks, Shoreline Cottages Limited, PO Box 135, Leeds, LS14 3XJ
T: (0113) 289 3539
F: (0113) 289 3541
E: reservations@shoreline-cottages.com
I: www.shoreline-cottages.com

Howdale Cottage ★★★★
Contact: Mrs Adele Thompson, Whitby Holiday Cottages, 47 Flowergate, Whitby, North Yorkshire YO21 3BB
T: (01947) 603010
F: (01947) 821133
E: enquiries@whitby-cottages.co.uk
I: www.whitby-cottages.co.uk

Plovers Nest ★★★
Contact: Dales Hol Cot Ref:2785, Dales Holiday Cottages, Carleton Business Park, Carleton New Road, Skipton, North Yorkshire BD23 2AA
T: (01756) 799821 & 790919
F: (01756) 797012
E: info@dalesholcot.com
I: www.dalesholcot.com

Puzzle Corner ★★★
Contact: Dales Hol Cot Ref:1679, Dales Holiday Cottages, Carleton Business Park, Carleton New Road, Skipton, North Yorkshire BD23 2AA
T: (01756) 799821 & 790919
F: (01756) 797012
E: info@dalesholcot.com
I: www.dalesholcot.com

Ravenswood ★★★
Contact: Mrs Adele Thompson, Whitby Holiday Cottages, 47 Flowergate, Whitby, North Yorkshire YO21 3BB
T: (01947) 603010
F: (01947) 821133
E: enquiries@whitby-cottages.co.uk
I: www.whitby-cottages.co.uk

2 Sunnyside ★★★
Contact: Mrs Adele Thompson, Whitby Holiday Cottages, 47 Flowergate, Whitby, North Yorkshire YO21 3BB
T: (01947) 603010
F: (01947) 821133
E: enquiries@whitby-cottages.co.uk
I: www.whitby-cottages.co.uk

Toll Bar ★★★★
Contact: Dales Hol Cot Ref:2243, Dales Holiday Cottages, Carleton Business Park, Carleton New Road, Skipton, North Yorkshire BD23 2AA
T: (01756) 799821 & 790919
F: (01756) 797012
E: info@dalesholcot.com
I: www.dalesholcot.com

SAWLEY
North Yorkshire

Monks Way ★★★
Contact: Mrs Ziya Mactaggart, Monks Way, Green Farm, Sawley, Ripon, North Yorkshire HG4 3EQ
T: (01765) 620611 & 07960 476581
F: (01765) 620313
E: ziya@greenfarm.demon.co.uk
I: www.greenfarm.demon.co.uk/monks01.htm

Sawley Arms Cottages ★★★★
Contact: Mrs June Hawes, Sawley Arms, Sawley, Ripon, North Yorkshire HG4 3EQ
T: (01765) 620642
F: (01765) 620642

SCALBY
North Yorkshire

Away From The Madding Crowd ★★★★
Contact: Mr & Mrs Peter Ward, Spring Farm, Scalby Nabs, Scalby, Scarborough, North Yorkshire YO13 0SL
T: (01723) 360502

Barmoor Farmhouse Holiday Cottages ★★★★
Contact: Mr D A Sharp, 16 Throxenby Lane, Newby, Scarborough, North Yorkshire YO12 5HW
T: (01723) 363256 & 354835

SCARBOROUGH
North Yorkshire

Avenwood Apartments ★★
Contact: Mr D I Atkinson, Avenwood Apartments, 129 Castle Road, Scarborough, North Yorkshire YO11 1HX
T: (01723) 374640

Cresta House Flats ★★★★
Contact: Ms L S Dobie, 4 Riverside Drive, Nether Poppleton, York YO26 6JY
T: (01904) 799703
E: crestahouse@hotmail.com

East Farm Country Cottages ★★★-★★★★
Contact: Ms Janice Hutchinson, 106 Columbus Ravine, Scarborough, North Yorkshire YO12 7QZ
T: (01723) 506406
F: (01723) 507356
I: www.eastfarmcottages.co.uk

Executive Apartments ★★★
Contact: Mrs H C Alderwick, 3 Oriel Bank, Scarborough, North Yorkshire YO11 2SZ
T: (01723) 369043
I: www.s-h-a.dircon.co.uk

Forge Valley Cottages ★★★★
Contact: Mr David Beeley, Barn House, 8a Westgate, Old Malton, Malton, North Yorkshire YO17 7HE
T: (01653) 698251
F: (01653) 691962

Glaisdale Holiday Flats and Cottage ★★★
Contact: Mr M D Holliday FHCIMA, Glaisdale Holiday Flats and Cottage, 49 West Street, Scarborough, North Yorkshire YO11 2QR
T: (01723) 372728
F: (01723) 372728
E: michael.holliday@tesco.net
I: www.s-h-a.dircon.co.uk

Green Gables Hotel Holiday Flats★★-★★★
Contact: Mrs J McGovern, Green Gables Hotel Holiday Flats, West Bank, Scarborough, North Yorkshire YO12 4DX
T: (01723) 361005
E: ggables@netcomuk.co.uk

Ivy Cottage ★★★★
Contact: Mr & Mrs K Hilton, 1 Ivy Cottage, Castlegate, East Ayton, Scarborough, North Yorkshire YO13 9EJ
T: (01723) 864407 & 07711 198589

Lawnswood ★
Contact: Mr & Mrs Kevin Makepeace, 2 View Grove, Scarborough, North Yorkshire YO11 3JA
T: (01723) 363653
F: (01723) 353521
E: flats@scarborough.co.uk
I: www.scarborough-flats.co.uk

Lendal House ★★★
Contact: Mrs Petra Scott, 34 Trafalgar Square, Scarborough, North Yorkshire YO12 7PY
T: (01723) 372178
E: info@lendalhouse.co.uk
I: www.lendalhouse.co.uk

Miramar Holiday Flats ★-★★★
Contact: Mr and Mrs Martinson, Miramar Holiday Flats, 32 The Esplanade, Scarborough, North Yorkshire YO11 2AR
T: (01723) 364853
F: (01723) 364853
E: miramarflats@aol.com

Sea Vista Holiday Bungalow ★★★★
Contact: Mr & Mrs A Roper, Merlewood, Bradford Road, Bingley, West Yorkshire BD16 1TT
T: (01274) 564741
F: (01274) 548525

Spikers Hill Country Cottages ★★★
Contact: Mrs J Hutchinson, Spikers Hill Country Cottages, Spikers Hill Farm, West Ayton, Scarborough, North Yorkshire YO13 9LB
T: (01723) 862537
F: (01723) 865511
E: janet@spikershill.ndo.co.uk
I: www.spikershill.ndo.co.uk

Town Farm Cottage ★★★★
Contact: Mr & Mrs Joe Green, Town Farm, Cloughton, Scarborough, North Yorkshire YO13 0AE
T: (01723) 870278
F: (01723) 870968
E: mail@greenfarming.co.uk
I: www.greenfarming.co.uk

Villa Knockfierna ★★★★
Contact: Mrs P Pilling, Villa Knockfierna, 28 Manor Road, Scarborough, North Yorkshire YO12 7RZ
T: (01723) 500103
F: (01723) 500103

Vincent Holiday Complex ★★-★★★
Contact: Mr & Mrs Alan & Sandra Hopkins, Vincent Holiday Complex, 42-43 Sandside, Scarborough, North Yorkshire YO11 1PG
T: (01723) 500997 & 373258
E: vincents.scarborough@btinternet.com
I: www.s-h-a.dircon.co.uk

Wayside Farm Holiday Cottages ★★-★★★
Contact: Mr & Mrs Peter Halder, Wayside Farm Holiday Cottages, Whitby Road, Cloughton, Scarborough, North Yorkshire YO13 0DX
T: (01723) 870519

White Acre ★★★
Contact: Mr J G Squire, J G Squire (Holidays) Ltd, 54 Falsgrave Road, Scarborough, North Yorkshire YO12 5AX
T: (01723) 374220 & 360542
F: (01723) 366693

White Gable ★★★★
Contact: Mr J G Squire, J G Squire (Holidays) Ltd, 54 Falsgrave Road, Scarborough, North Yorkshire YO12 5AX
T: (01723) 374220 & 360542
F: (01723) 366693

The Windmill
Rating Applied For
Contact: Mr Roland Thompson, The Old Mill Hotel, Mill Street, Scarborough, North Yorkshire YO11 1SZ
T: (01723) 372735
F: (01723) 377190
E: info@windmill-hotel.co.uk
I: www.windmill-hotel.co.uk

Wrea Head Cottage Holidays
★★★★
Contact: Mr & Mrs Chris &
Andrea Wood, Wrea Head
Cottage Holidays, Wrea Head
House, Barmoor Lane, Scalby,
Scarborough, North Yorkshire
YO13 0PG
T: (01723) 375844 &
07801 384994
F: (01723) 500274
E: ytb@wreaheadcotghols.
demon.co.uk
I: www.wreaheadcotghols.
demon.co.uk

SCOTCH CORNER
North Yorkshire

5 Cedar Grove ★★★
Contact: Mr and Mrs J P Lawson,
The Close, Mill Lane, Cloughton,
Scarborough, North Yorkshire
YO13 0AB
T: (01723) 870455 & 870017

SCOTTON
North Yorkshire

The Granary ★★★★
Contact: Mrs Ann Tavanyar, Java
House, Low Hall Lane, Scotton,
Catterick Garrison, North
Yorkshire DL9 3PL
T: (01748) 835302 &
077138 752263
F: (01748) 836306
E: anntavanyar@dialstart.net

SEDBUSK
North Yorkshire

The Coach House ★★★
Contact: Dales Hol Cot Ref:2016,
Dales Holiday Cottages, Carleton
Business Park, Carleton New
Road, Skipton, North Yorkshire
BD23 2AA
T: (01756) 799821 & 790919
F: (01756) 797012
E: info@dalesholcot.com
I: www.dalesholcot.com

Jasmine Cottage ★★★★
Contact: Mrs A D Moore,
Beckstones, Carperby, Leyburn,
North Yorkshire DL8 4DA
T: (01969) 663363

Wagtail Cottage ★★★★
Contact: Mrs Shirley Smith, Old
Camms House, Kettlewell Lane,
Askrigg, Leyburn, North
Yorkshire DL8 3JJ
T: (01969) 650297
E: roger@oldcamms.fsnet.uk

West Cottage ★★
Contact: Mrs Nadine H Bell,
Country Hideaways, Margarets
Cottage, West Burton, Leyburn,
North Yorkshire DL8 4JN
T: (01969) 663559
F: (01969) 663559
E: nhbell@aol.com
I: www.countryhideaways.co.uk

SELBY
North Yorkshire

Lund Farm Cottages ★★★
Contact: Mr and Mrs Chris and
Helen Middleton, Lund Farm
Cottages, Lund Farm, Gateforth,
Selby, North Yorkshire YO8 9LE
T: (01757) 228775
F: (01757) 228775
E: chris.middleton@farmline.
com
I: www.lundfarm.co.uk
&

Poplar Cottage ★★★
Contact: Country Holidays
ref:14065, Spring Mill, Earby,
Barnoldswick, Lancashire
BB94 0AA
T: 08700 723723
F: (01282) 844288
I: www.country-holidays.co.uk

SELSIDE
North Yorkshire

The Byres ★★★–★★★★
Contact: Mrs S E Lambert,
Selside Farm, Selside, Settle,
North Yorkshire BD24 0HZ
T: (01729) 860367

Selside Farm Barn ★★★
Contact: Mr R Wales, Holiday
Cottages (Yorkshire) Ltd, Water
Street, Skipton, North Yorkshire
BD23 1PB
T: (01756) 700510

SETTLE
North Yorkshire

Devonshire Flat
Rating Applied For
Contact: Mr A Aspden,
Devonshire House, 27 Duke
Street, Settle, North Yorkshire
BD24 9DJ
T: (01729) 825781

Hazel Cottage ★★★
Contact: Country Holidays
ref:8374, Holiday Cottages
Group, Spring Mill, Earby,
Barnoldswick, Lancashire
BB94 0AA
T: 08700 723723
F: (01282) 844288
E: sales@ttgihg.co.uk
I: www.country-holidays.co.uk

Ingleborough Cottage
Rating Applied For
Contact: Mr & Mrs Jean
Needham, 9 Mayfield Close,
Holcombe Brook, Ramsbottom,
Bury, Lancashire BL0 9TL
T: (01204) 883594 &
07974 957038

Old Brew House & Brewhouse
Cottage ★★★
Contact: CH
ref:2696,3435,B4959, Holiday
Cottages Group, Spring Mill,
Earby, Barnoldswick, Lancashire
BB94 0AA
T: 08700 723723
F: (01282) 844288
E: sales@ttgihg.co.uk
I: www.country-holidays.co.uk

SEWERBY
East Riding of Yorkshire

Clematis Cottage and Hind's
Cottage ★★★★
Contact: Mr and Mrs John and
Angela Foster, Clematis Cottage
and Hind's Cottage, Field House,
Jewison Lane, Sewerby,
Bridlington, East Yorkshire
YO16 6YG
T: (01262) 674932 &
07714 726675
F: (01262) 608688
E: john.foster@farmline.com
I: www.
field-house-farm-cottages.co.uk

SHAW MILLS
North Yorkshire

Fern Bank ★★★★
Contact: Mr R Wales, Holiday
Cottages (Yorkshire) Ltd, Water
Street, Skipton, North Yorkshire
BD23 1PB
T: (01756) 700510

SHEFFIELD
South Yorkshire

The Clough ★★★★
Contact: Mrs B King & Mr N
Ritchie, The Clough, Mayfield
House, Mayfield Road, Sheffield,
S10 4PR
T: (0114) 230 1949
F: (0114) 230 2014
E: breking@hotmail.com

The Flat ★★★
Contact: Mr M J Cox, The Flat,
152 Whirlowdale Road,
Sheffield, S7 2NL
T: (0114) 221 5553

Hangram Lane Farmhouse
★★★★
Contact: Mrs J Clark, Hangram
Lane Farmhouse, Hangram Lane
Grange, Hangram Lane,
Ringinglow, Sheffield, S11 7TQ
T: (0114) 230 3570

Mill Lane Farm Cottage ★★★
Contact: Mrs G Fletcher, 19
Dobcroft Close, Sheffield,
S11 9LL
T: (0114) 236 4495 & 263 0188
F: (0114) 236 2599

Moor Royd House
★★★–★★★★
Contact: Mrs Janet Hird, Moor
Royd House, Manchester Road,
Millhouse Green, Penistone,
Sheffield S36 9FG
T: (01226) 763353
F: (01226) 763353
E: janet@moorroydhouse.
freeserve.co.uk
I: www.moorroydhouse.com

Sale Hill Lodge ★★★★
Contact: Mrs G Williams, 40
Stainton Road, Greystones Road,
Sheffield, S11 7AX
T: (0114) 267 8630
F: (0114) 267 8630
E: stayinsheff@hotmail.com

Shrewsbury Cottage ★★★
Contact: Colin MacQueen, Peak
Cottages, Strawberry Lee Lane,
Totley Bank, Sheffield, S17 3BA
T: (0114) 262 0777
F: (0114) 262 0666
E: enquiries@peakcottages.com
I: www.peakcottages.com

SHERBURN
North Yorkshire

Westfield Granary ★★★
Contact: Mr R Wales, Holiday
Cottages (Yorkshire) Ltd, Water
Street, Skipton, North Yorkshire
BD23 1PB
T: (01756) 700510

SHERIFF HUTTON
North Yorkshire

Howard's End ★★
Contact: Dales Hol Cot Ref:1862,
Dales Holiday Cottages, Carleton
Business Park, Carleton New
Road, Skipton, North Yorkshire
BD23 2AA
T: (01756) 799821 & 790919
F: (01756) 797012
E: info@dalesholcot.com
I: www.dalesholcot.com

SILSDEN
West Yorkshire

Ford Cottage ★★★
Contact: Dales Hol Cot Ref:89,
Dales Holiday Cottages, Carleton
Business Park, Carleton New
Road, Skipton, North Yorkshire
BD23 2AA
T: (01756) 799821 & 790919
F: (01756) 797012
E: info@dalesholcot.com
I: www.dalesholcot.com

Honeymans Cottage ★★★
Contact: Mr R Wales, Holiday
Cottages (Yorkshire) Ltd, Water
Street, Skipton, North Yorkshire
BD23 1PB
T: (01756) 700510

SINNINGTON
North Yorkshire

Bridge Cottage ★★★
Contact: Mrs K S Slowther, 49
Eastwood Road, Leigh-on-Sea,
Essex SS9 3AH
T: (01702) 715182 &
07966 465887
E: patrickslowther@virgin.net

Bridle Cottage ★★★
Contact: Dales Hol Cot Ref:1720,
Dales Holiday Cottages, Carleton
Business Park, Carleton New
Road, Skipton, North Yorkshire
BD23 2AA
T: (01756) 799821 & 790919
F: (01756) 797012
E: info@dalesholcot.com
I: www.dalesholcot.com

Goose End of Seven House
★★★
Contact: Dales Hol Cot Ref:1779,
Dales Holiday Cottages, Carleton
Business Park, Carleton New
Road, Skipton, North Yorkshire
BD23 2AA
T: (01756) 799821 & 790919
F: (01756) 797012
E: info@dalesholcot.com
I: www.dalesholcot.com

Sevenside Holiday Bungalow
★★★
Contact: Mrs Elizabeth Allan,
Station House, Sinnington, York
YO62 6RA
T: (01751) 431812

SKIPTON
North Yorkshire

Cawder Hall Cottages
★★★–★★★★★
Contact: Mr Graham Pearson,
Cawder Hall Cottages, Cawder
Lane, Skipton, North Yorkshire
BD23 2TD
T: (01756) 791579
F: (01756) 797036
E: info@cawderhallcottages.
co.uk
I: www.farm-holidays.co.uk
&

Dales Flat ★★
Contact: Mrs M J Little, Dale House, Skipton Road, Steeton, Keighley, West Yorkshire BD20 6PD
T: (01535) 653637 &
(01756) 791688

Dalestone ★★★
Contact: Mr & Mrs M&A Wadsworth, 25 Watson Road, Blackpool, Lancashire FY4 1EG
T: (01253) 404726 &
07801 450624
F: (01253) 311422

Garden Cottage
Rating Applied For
Contact: Mrs Barbara Anne Ross, 56 Otley Street, Skipton, North Yorkshire BD23 1ET
T: (01756) 799867

Ginnel Mews ★★★
Contact: Sykes Cottages Ref:46, Sykes Cottages, York House, York Street, Chester, CH1 3LR
T: (01244) 345700
F: (01244) 321442
E: info@sykescottages.co.uk
I: www.sykescottages.co.uk

Hallams Yard ★★★
Contact: Dales Hol Cot Ref:255, Dales Holiday Cottages, Carleton Business Park, Carleton New Road, Skipton, North Yorkshire BD23 2AA
T: (01756) 799821 & 790919
F: (01756) 797012
E: info@dalesholcot.com
I: www.dalesholcot.com

Haven Cottage & Garden Cottage
Rating Applied For
Contact: Dales Hol Cot Ref:2334/2344, Dales Holiday Cottages, Carleton Business Park, Carleton New Road, Skipton, North Yorkshire BD23 2AA
T: (01756) 799821 & 790919
F: (01756) 797012
E: info@dalesholcot.com
I: www.dalesholcot.com

The Hide ★★★
Contact: Sykes Cottages Ref:617, Sykes Cottages, York House, York Street, Chester, CH1 3LR
T: (01244) 345700
F: (01244) 321442
E: info@sykescottages.co.uk
I: www.sykescottages.co.uk

High Malsis Farmhouse ★★★
Contact: Mrs S A Fort, High Malsis Farmhouse, High Malsis, Glusburn, Keighley, West Yorkshire BD20 8DU
T: (01535) 633309

The Lodge ★★★
Contact: Dales Hol Cot Ref:1740, Dales Holiday Cottages, Carleton Business Park, Carleton New Road, Skipton, North Yorkshire BD23 2AA
T: (01756) 799821 & 790919
F: (01756) 797012
E: info@dalesholcot.com
I: www.dalesholcot.com

Low Skibeden Farm Cottage ★★★
Contact: Mrs Heather Simpson, Low Skibeden Farmhouse, Harrogate Road, Skipton, North Yorkshire BD23 6AB
T: (01756) 793849 &
07050 207787
F: (01756) 793804
E: skibhols.yorksdales@talk21.com
I: www.yorkshirenet.co.uk/accgde.lowskibeden

Maypole Cottage ★★★★
Contact: Mrs E M Gamble, Blackburn House, Thorpe, Skipton, North Yorkshire BD23 6BJ
T: (01756) 720609

None-go-Bye Farm Cottage ★★★
Contact: Mrs M A Lawn, None Go Bye Farm, Grassington Road, Skipton, North Yorkshire BD23 3LB
T: (01756) 793165

7 Pasture Road ★★★
Contact: Mr & Mrs C Lunnon, 17 Cherry Tree Way, Helmshore, Rossendale, Lancashire BB4 4JZ
T: (01706) 230653
E: j.lunnon@blackburn.ac.uk

29 Pembroke Street ★★★
Contact: Mr R P Davis, Highfield Hotel, 58 Keighley Road, Skipton, North Yorkshire BD23 2NB
T: (01756) 793182
F: (01756) 793182
I: www.highfield-hotel.co.uk

Sandywood ★★★★
Contact: Sykes Cottages Ref:693, Sykes Cottages, York House, York Street, Chester, CH1 3LR
T: (01244) 345700
F: (01244) 321442
E: info@sykescottages.co.uk
I: www.sykescottages.co.uk

Skipton Cottages ★★★
Contact: Mr and Mrs K R Dorman, Field House Farm, Scotgate Road, Honley, Huddersfield, West Yorkshire HD7 2RE
T: (01484) 661031

SKIPWITH
North Yorkshire

Applegarth ★★★
Contact: Country Holidays ref:5988, Holiday Cottages Group, Spring Mill, Earby, Barnoldswick, Lancashire BB94 0AA
T: 08700 723723
F: (01282) 844288
E: sales@ttgihg.co.uk
I: www.country-holidays.co.uk

SLEIGHTS
North Yorkshire

Groves Dyke ★★★
Contact: Mrs A Carson, Groves Bank, Woodlands Drive, Sleights, Whitby, North Yorkshire YO21 1RY
T: (01947) 811404
F: (01947) 811404
E: ranger@onyxnet.co.uk
I: slj.co.uk/clients/grovesdyke

Holly Lodge ★★★
Contact: Mrs Adele Thompson, Whitby Holiday Cottages, 47 Flowergate, Whitby, North Yorkshire YO21 3BB
T: (01947) 603010
F: (01947) 821133
E: enquiries@whitby-cottages.co.uk
I: www.whitby-cottages.co.uk

Lowdale Cottage ★★★
Contact: Mrs M Walker, Lowdale Farmhouse, Sleights, Whitby, North Yorkshire YO22 5AF
T: (01947) 810828
E: lowdale.holidaycot@mail.com

The Stable ★★★★
Contact: Dales Hol Cot Ref:2892, Dales Holiday Cottages, Carleton Business Park, Carleton New Road, Skipton, North Yorkshire BD23 2AA
T: (01756) 799821 & 790919
F: (01756) 797012
E: info@dalesholcot.com
I: www.dalesholcot.com

Underhill Cottage ★★★
Contact: Dales Hol Cot Ref:2874, Dales Holiday Cottages, Carleton Business Park, Carleton New Road, Skipton, North Yorkshire BD23 2AA
T: (01756) 799821 & 790919
F: (01756) 797012
E: info@dalesholcot.com
I: www.dalesholcot.com

SLINGSBY
North Yorkshire

The Arches ★★★
Contact: Mr & Mrs S G Prest, Castle Farm, Slingsby, York YO62 4AE
T: (01653) 628277 &
07702 587386
F: (01653) 628277
E: sgprest@farming.co.uk
I: www.holidaycottage.f9.co.uk

Dawson Cottage ★★★
Contact: Mrs Julia Snowball, Harlsey House, Railway Street, Slingsby, York YO62 4AL
T: (01653) 628136 & 628248
F: (01653) 628413
E: pwsnowball@talk21.com

Keepers Cottage Holidays ★★★
Contact: Mrs Joanna Pavey, Keepers Cottage Holidays, Keepers Cottage, Slingsby, York YO62 4AN
T: (01653) 628656

SNAINTON
North Yorkshire

Foxglove Cottage ★★★★★
Contact: Mrs Sandra Simpson, The Old Post Office, Thorpe Bassett, Malton, North Yorkshire YO17 8LU
T: (01944) 758047 & 758751
F: (01944) 758047
E: ssimpsoncottages@aol.com

SNEATON
North Yorkshire

The Annexe ★★★
Contact: Mrs Adele Thompson, Whitby Holiday Cottages, 47 Flowergate, Whitby, North Yorkshire YO21 3BB
T: (01947) 603010
F: (01947) 821133
E: enquiries@whitby-cottages.co.uk
I: www.whitby-cottages.co.uk

Bennison House Farm ★★★★
Contact: Mr & Mrs R G Thompson, Bennison House Farm, Sneaton, Whitby, North Yorkshire YO22 5HS
T: (01947) 820292

Rose Cottage ★★★
Contact: Mrs Adele Thompson, Whitby Holiday Cottages, 47 Flowergate, Whitby, North Yorkshire YO21 3BB
T: (01947) 603010
F: (01947) 821133
E: enquiries@whitby-cottages.co.uk
I: www.whitby-cottages.co.uk

SOUTH KILVINGTON
North Yorkshire

Mowbray Stable Cottages ★★★
Contact: Mrs Margaret Backhouse, Mowbray, Stockton Road, South Kilvington, Thirsk, North Yorkshire YO7 2LY
T: (01845) 522605

SOWERBY
North Yorkshire

The Old Granary
Rating Applied For
Contact: Country Holidays ref:23, Holiday Cottages Group, Spring Mill, Earby, Barnoldswick, Lancashire BB94 0AA
T: (01282) 445096
F: (01282) 844288
E: sales@ttgihg.co.uk
I: www.country-holidays.co.uk

The Old Manor House Cottage ★★★
Contact: Mrs M Jackson, The Old Manor House, 27 Front Street, Sowerby, Thirsk, North Yorkshire YO7 1JQ
T: (01845) 526642
F: (01845) 526568
I: www.theoldmanorhouse.com

SOWERBY BRIDGE
West Yorkshire

Shield Hall Holiday Cottage ★★★
Contact: Mr J R Broadbent, Shield Hall, Shield Hall Lane, Sowerby, Sowerby Bridge, West Yorkshire HX6 1NJ
T: (01422) 832165

SPAUNTON
North Yorkshire

Grange Farm Cottage ★★★★
Contact: Mrs J Bailey, Grange Farm, Spaunton, Appleton-le-Moors, York YO62 6TR
T: (01751) 417292
F: (01751) 417892
E: judi.b@btclick.com

STACKHOUSE
North Yorkshire

Woodend ★★★
Contact: Country Holidays
ref:1827, Holiday Cottages
Group, Spring Mill, Earby,
Barnoldswick, Lancashire
BB18 6RN
T: 08700 723723
F: (01282) 844288
E: sales@ttgihg.co.uk
I: www.country-holidays.co.uk

STAINTONDALE
North Yorkshire

Whitehall Farm Holiday Cottages ★★★
Contact: Mr and Mrs James and
Celia White, Whitehall Farm
Holiday Cottages, Whitehall
Farm, Staintondale,
Scarborough, North Yorkshire
YO13 0EY
T: (01723) 870234 &
077698 684644
E: celia@white66fs.business.
co.uk
I: www.whitehallcottages.co.uk

STAITHES
North Yorkshire

Beach Way Bungalow ★★★
Contact: Dales Cot Hol Ref:848,
Dales Holiday Cottages, Carleton
Business Park, Carleton New
Road, Skipton, North Yorkshire
BD23 2AA
T: (01756) 799821 & 790919
F: (01756) 797012
E: info@dalesholcot.com
I: www.dalesholcot.com

Blue Porch Cottage ★★
Contact: Country Holidays
ref:10438, Holiday Cottages
Group, Spring Mill, Earby,
Barnoldswick, Lancashire
BB18 6RN
T: 08700 723723
F: (01282) 844288
E: sales@ttgihg.co.uk
I: www.country-holidays.co.uk

Cliff Cottage ★★★
Contact: Country Holidays
ref:4635, Holiday Cottages
Group, Spring Mill, Earby,
Barnoldswick, Lancashire
BB94 0AA
T: 08700 723723
F: (01282) 844288
E: jil.o.ward@talk21.com
I: www.country-holidays.co.uk

Coastguard Cottage ★★
Contact: Country Holidays
ref:10410, Holiday Cottages
Group, Spring Mill, Earby,
Barnoldswick, Lancashire
BB94 0AA
T: 08700 723723
F: (01282) 844288
E: sales@ttgihg.co.uk
I: www.country-holidays.co.uk

The Coop ★★★
Contact: Sykes Cotttages
Ref:733, Sykes Cottages, York
House, York Street, Chester,
CH1 3LR
T: (01244) 345700
F: (01244) 321442
E: info@sykescottages.co.uk
I: www.sykescottages.co.uk

The Cottage ★★★
Contact: Mrs Adele Thompson,
Whitby Holiday Cottages, 47
Flowergate, Whitby, North
Yorkshire YO21 3BB
T: (01947) 603010
F: (01947) 821133
E: enquiries@whitby-cottages.
co.uk
I: www.whitby-cottages.co.uk

The Cottage ★★
Contact: Mrs Adele Thompson,
Whitby Holiday Cottages, 47
Flowergate, Whitby, North
Yorkshire YO21 3BB
T: (01947) 603010
F: (01947) 821133
E: enquiries@whitby-cottages.
co.uk
I: www.whitby-cottages.co.uk

11 Cowbar Cottage ★★
Contact: Country Holidays,
Spring Mill, Earby, Barnoldswick,
Lancashire BB94 0AS
T: 08700 723723
E: sales@ttgigh.co.uk
I: www.country-holidays.co.uk

21 Cowbar Cottages ★★★★
Contact: Mrs Adele Thompson,
Whitby Holiday Cottages, 47
Flowergate, Whitby, North
Yorkshire YO21 3BB
T: (01947) 603010
F: (01947) 821133
E: enquiries@whitby-cottages.
co.uk
I: www.whitby-cottages.co.uk

Glencoe ★★
Contact: Rev David Purdy, The
Vicarage, Church Street,
Kirkbymoorside, York YO62 6AZ
T: (01751) 431452

77a High Street ★★
Contact: Mrs Adele Thompson,
Whitby Holiday Cottages, 47
Flowergate, Whitby, North
Yorkshire YO21 3BB
T: (01947) 603010
F: (01947) 821133
E: enquiries@whitby-cottages.
co.uk
I: www.whitby-cottages.co.uk

Springfields ★★★
Contact: Mrs F Verrill,
Springfields, 42 Staithes Lane,
Staithes, Saltburn-by-the-Sea,
Cleveland TS13 5AD
T: (01947) 841011

STAMFORD BRIDGE
East Riding of Yorkshire

The Cottage ★★★
Contact: Mrs S M Foster, The
Cottage, High Catton Grange,
Stamford Bridge, York YO41 1EP
T: (01759) 371374
F: (01759) 371374

Sparrow Hall Holiday Cottages ★★★
Contact: Mr & Mrs Nick & Pam
Gaunt, 1 Silver Hill Cottage,
Sutton upon Derwent, York
YO14 9DF
T: (01904) 607999

STANBURY
West Yorkshire

Sarah's Cottage ★★★★
Contact: Mrs E Fuller, 101 Main
Street, Stanbury, Keighley, West
Yorkshire BD22 0HA
T: (01535) 643015
E: brian.fuller2@btinternet.com

STARBOTTON
North Yorkshire

Horseshoe Cottage ★★★
Contact: Mrs MFJ Croft, Chapel
Fold, Brooks Court, School Lane,
Addingham, Ilkley, West
Yorkshire LS29 0JF
T: (01943) 831984

STAXTON
North Yorkshire

Cuckoo Cottage ★★★★
Contact: Dales Hol Cot Ref:2991,
Dales Holiday Cottages, Carleton
Business Park, Carleton New
Road, Skipton, North Yorkshire
BD23 2AA
T: (01756) 799821 & 790919
F: (01756) 797012
E: info@dalesholcot.com
I: www.dalesholcot.com

STEETON
West Yorkshire

11 Mill Lane ★★
Contact: Mr R Wales, Holiday
Cottages (Yorkshire) Ltd, Water
Street, Skipton, North Yorkshire
BD23 1PB
T: (01756) 700510

STIRTON
North Yorkshire

Cockpit Corner ★★★
Contact: Dales Hol Cot Ref:1699,
Dales Holiday Cottages, Carleton
Business Park, Carleton New
Road, Skipton, North Yorkshire
BD23 2AA
T: (01756) 799821 & 790919
F: (01756) 797012
E: info@dalesholcot.com
I: www.dalesholcot.com

STOCKTON-ON-THE-FOREST
Yorkshire

2 Crosslands ★★
Contact: Mr R Wales, Holiday
Cottages (Yorkshire) Ltd, Water
Street, Skipton, North Yorkshire
BD23 1PB
T: (01756) 700510

STOKESLEY
North Yorkshire

Levenside ★★★★
Contact: Dales Hol Cot Ref:2156,
Dales Holiday Cottages, Carleton
Business Park, Carleton New
Road, Skipton, North Yorkshire
BD23 2AA
T: (01756) 799821 & 790919
F: (01756) 797012
E: info@dalesholcot.com
I: www.dalesholcot.com

SUMMER BRIDGE
North Yorkshire

Dove Cote Cottage ★★★
Contact: Mrs G Bray, Dove Cote
Cottage, Brimham Rocks,
Summer Bridge, Harrogate,
North Yorkshire HG3 4DW
T: (01423) 780786
F: (01423) 780786

SUTTON-ON-THE-FOREST
North Yorkshire

K M Knowlson Holiday Cottages ★★★
Contact: Mrs H Knowlson,
Thrush House, Well Lane,
Sutton-on-the-Forest, York
YO61 1ED
T: (01347) 810225
F: (01347) 810225
E: kmkholcottyksuk@aol.com

TERRINGTON
North Yorkshire

The Barn ★★★
Contact: Mrs Jo Gibson, The
Barn, Birkdale Farm, Mowthorpe,
Terrington, York YO60 6QE
T: (01653) 648301

Terrington Holiday Cottages
★★★-★★★★
Contact: Mrs S Goodrick,
Terrington Holiday Cottages, 3
Springfield Court, South Back
Lane, Terrington, York YO60 6PY
T: (01653) 648370
E: goodrick@terrington10.
freeserve.co.uk
I: www.terrington10.freeserve.
co.uk

THIRSK
North Yorkshire

The Granary ★★★★
Contact: Mrs Mary Harrison,
East Farm, Thirlby, Thirsk, North
Yorkshire YO7 2DJ
T: (01845) 597554
E: mary@thegranary36.fsnet.
co.uk

The Norton
Rating Applied For
Contact: Mrs Denise Tribe, Slade
Cottage, Sandhutton, Thirsk,
North Yorkshire YO7 4RW
T: (01845) 5777889 & 587558
E: twotribes@currantbun.com
I: www.geocities.
com/sladecottage

The Old School House ★★★
Contact: Mrs G Readman,
School House, Catton, Thirsk,
North Yorkshire YO7 4SG
T: (01845) 567308

Pasture Field House ★★
Contact: Mrs D Hunter, Pasture
Field House, Newsham Road,
Thirsk, North Yorkshire YO7 4DE
T: (01845) 587230
F: (01845) 587230

Poplars Holiday Cottages
★★★★
Contact: Mrs C M Chilton,
Poplars Holiday Cottages, The
Poplars, Carlton Miniott, Thirsk,
North Yorkshire YO7 4LX
T: (01845) 522712
F: (01845) 522712
E: the_poplars_cottages@
btopenworld.com
I: www.yorkshirebandb.co.uk

Shires Court ★★★
Contact: Mrs Judy Rennie, Shires
Court, Moor Road, Knayton,
Thirsk, North Yorkshire YO7 4BS
T: (01845) 537494

Establishments printed in blue have a detailed entry in this guide

80 St James Green ★★★
Contact: Mrs Joanna Todd, 79 St
James Green, Thirsk, North
Yorkshire YO7 1AJ
T: (01845) 523522 &
07790 055498

Duck Cottage
Rating Applied For
Contact: Dales Hol Cot Ref:992,
Dales Holiday Cottages, Carleton
Business Park, Carleton New
Road, Skipton, North Yorkshire
BD23 2AA
T: (01756) 799821 & 790919
F: (01756) 797012
E: info@dalesholcot.com
I: www.dalesholcot.com

**Mytholmbridge Studio
Cottage ★★★★**
Contact: Mrs S Clay,
Mytholmbridge Farm, Luke Lane,
Thongsbridge, Holmfirth,
Huddersfield HD9 7TB
T: (01484) 686642
E: weareclay@ukonline.co.uk

The Garden Flat ★★★
Contact: Country Holidays
ref:11178, Holiday Cottages
Group, Spring Mill, Earby,
Barnoldswick, Lancashire
BB94 0AA
T: 08700 723723
F: (01282) 844288
E: sales@ttgihg.co.uk
I: www.country-holidays.co.uk

High Green Cottage ★★★
Contact: Mr Clive Sykes, Sykes
Holiday Cottages, York House,
York Street, Chester, CH1 3LR
T: (01244) 345700
F: (01244) 321442
E: info@sykescottages.co.uk
I: www.sykescottages.co.uk

Low Green House ★★★★
Contact: Mrs Nadine H Bell,
Country Hideaways, Margarets
Cottage, West Burton, Leyburn,
North Yorkshire DL8 4JN
T: (01969) 663559
F: (01969) 663559
E: nhbell@aol.com
I: www.countryhideaways.co.uk

Meadowcroft ★★★
Contact: Mr M C Mason,
Hunters Hollow, Penmaen,
Swansea SA3 2HQ
T: (01792) 371602
F: (01792) 371602
E: mcmason@globalnet.co.uk

The Old Barn ★★★
Contact: Mrs Nadine Bell,
Country Hideaways, Margarets
Cottage, West Burton, Leyburn,
North Yorkshire DL8 4JN
T: (01969) 663559

Wayside ★★★
Contact: Sykes Cottages
Ref:435, Sykes Cottages, York
House, York Street, Chester,
CH1 3LR
T: (01244) 345700
T: (01244) 321442
E: info@sykescottages.co.uk
I: www.sykescottages.co.uk

Woodpecker Cottage ★★★★
Contact: Mrs Nadine H Bell,
Country Hideaways, Margarets
Cottage, West Burton, Leyburn,
North Yorkshire DL8 4JN
T: (01969) 663559
F: (01969) 663559
E: nhbell@aol.com
I: wwww.countryhideaways.
co.uk

Acresgreen Bungalow ★★★★
Contact: Mrs Margaret
Barraclough, Well Heads Farm,
Thornton, Bradford, West
Yorkshire BD13 3SJ
T: (01274) 834262
F: (01274) 834262
I: www.acresgreen.co.uk

Brookwood ★★★
Contact: Mrs G Balderson &
Claire Lealman, Brookwood,
Welcome Cafe, Thornton Dale,
Pickering, North Yorkshire
YO18 7RW
T: (01751) 474272 & 474218
F: (01751) 472372
E: baldersons@hotmail.com

5 Church Lane ★★★
Contact: Country Holidays
ref:1004, Holiday Cottages
Group, Spring Mill, Earby,
Barnoldswick, Lancashire
BB94 0AA
T: 08700 723723
F: (01282) 841539
E: sales@ttgihg.co.uk
I: www.country-holidays.co.uk

25 Farmanby Close ★★★
Contact: Mrs Elizabeth Barnes,
Burton Bank, Wills Grove, Mill
Hill, London NW17 1QG
T: (020) 8959 1487 & 8959 0017

Orchard House ★★★
Contact: Dales Hol Cot Ref:3118,
Dales Holiday Cottages, Carleton
Business Park, Carleton New
Road, Skipton, North Yorkshire
BD23 2AA
T: (01756) 799821 & 790919
F: (01756) 797012
E: info@dalesholcot.com
I: www.dalesholcot.com

**Summertree Granary &
Summertree Studio★★★**
Contact: Mr & Mrs B Eldridge,
Summertree Farm, High
Marishes, Malton, North
Yorkshire YO17 6UH
T: (01751) 474625
F: (01751) 474355
E: bridget.m.eldridge@talk21.
com
I: www.summertree.sagenet.
co.uk

Walks View ★★★
Contact: Dales Hol Cot Ref:1000,
Dales Holiday Cottages, Carleton
Business Park, Carleton New
Road, Skipton, North Yorkshire
BD23 2AA
T: (01756) 799821 & 790919
F: (01756) 797012
E: info@dalesholcot.com
I: www.dalesholcot.com

White Cottage ★★★
Contact: Country Holidays ref:
940, Holiday Cottages Group,
Spring Mill, Earby, Barnoldswick,
Lancashire BB18 6RN
T: 08700 723723
F: (01282) 844288
E: sales@ttgihg.co.uk
I: www.country-holidays.co.uk

The Cottage ★★★
Contact: Dales Hol Cot Ref:2166,
Dales Holiday Cottages, Carleton
Business Park, Carleton New
Road, Skipton, North Yorkshire
BD23 2AA
T: (01756) 799821 & 790919
F: (01756) 797012
E: info@dalesholcot.com
I: www.dalesholcot.com

The Old Goat House ★★★★
Contact: Mrs Annette Riley,
South View, Thornton Rust,
Leyburn, North Yorkshire
DL8 3AN
T: (01969) 663716
E: riley@oldgoathouse.
freeserve.co.uk
I: www.wensleydale.
org/accommodation/
theoldgoathouse

Outgang Cottage
Rating Applied For
Contact: Dales Hol Cot Ref:1468,
Dales Holiday Cottages, Carleton
Business Park, Carleton New
Road, Skipton, North Yorkshire
BD23 2AA
T: (01756) 799821 & 790919
F: (01756) 797012
E: info@dalesholcot.com
I: www.dalesholcot.com

The Old Post Office ★★★★
Contact: Mrs Sandra Simpson,
The Old Post Office, Thorpe
Bassett, Malton, North Yorkshire
YO17 8LU
T: (01944) 758047
F: (01944) 758047
E: ssimpsoncottages@aol.com

Brazengate ★★★
Contact: Sykes Cottages Ref:55,
Sykes Cottages, York House,
York Street, Chester, CH1 3LR
T: (01244) 345700
F: (01244) 321442
E: info@sykescottages.co.uk
I: www.sykescottages.co.uk

Dalesgate ★★
Contact: Dales Hol Cot Ref:1006,
Dales Holiday Cottages, Carleton
Business Park, Carleton New
Road, Skipton, North Yorkshire
BD23 2AA
T: (01756) 799821 & 790919
F: (01756) 797012
E: info@dalesholcot.com
I: www.dalesholcot.com

Wharfe Lodge ★★
Contact: Sykes Cottages
Ref:536, Sykes Cottages, York
House, York Street, Chester,
CH1 3LR
T: (01244) 345700
F: (01244) 321442
E: info@sykescottages.co.uk
I: www.sykescottages.co.uk

**Thwaite Farm Cottages
★★★-★★★★**
Contact: Mrs Gillian Whitehead,
Thwaite Farm, Thwaite,
Richmond, North Yorkshire
DL11 6DR
T: (01748) 886444
E: info@thwaitefarmcottages.
co.uk
I: www.thwaitefarmcottages.
co.uk

**Thwaitedale Cottages
★★★-★★★★**
Contact: Mrs Pauline Allen, Foss
Garth, Thwaite, Richmond,
North Yorkshire DL11 6DR
T: (01530) 272794 &
(01969) 667364
F: (01530) 272794
E: valerie@theturret.freeserve.
co.uk
I: www.thwaitecottages.co.uk

Turfy Gill Hall ★★★★
Contact: Mr & Mrs Keith & Ivy
Moseley, Turfy Gill Hall, Skeugh
Head, Angram, Richmond, North
Yorkshire DL11 6DT
T: (01748) 886369
F: (01748) 886593
E: info@turfygill.com
I: www.turfygill.com

Stable Cottage ★★★★
Contact: Mr M E Palmer, Village
Farm, Main Street, Tibthorpe,
Driffield, North Humberside
YO25 9LA
T: (01377) 229448 &
07703 457937
E: david.palmer@bigfoot.com
I: www.stable-cottage.com

Bridge House Cottage ★★★
Contact: Mr Peter White & Ms
Adele Wilkinson, Bridge House
Cottage, Hull Bridge House,
Weel Road, Tickton, Beverley,
East Riding of Yorkshire
HU17 9RY
T: (01964) 542355
E: alw@amj.co.uk

Ben's Cottage ★★★★
Contact: Mrs Julie Terry, Broad
Oak Farm, Tockwith, York, North
Yorkshire YO26 7QQ
T: (01423) 358304 &
(01484) 608763
E: jterry@benscottage.fsnet.
co.uk

TODMORDEN
West Yorkshire

Ashenhurst Cottage ★★★
Contact: Mrs H M Grieve,
Ashenhurst House, Ashenhurst
Road, Todmorden, Lancashire
OL14 8DS
T: (01706) 812086
F: (01706) 812693

Butterworth Cottage ★★★
Contact: Mr & Mrs Neil and
Patricia Butterworth,
Butterworth Cottage, Cinder Hill
Farm, Castle Lane, Todmorden,
Lancashire OL14 8AA
T: (01706) 813067
E: bookings@cottage-holiday.
co.uk
I: www.cottage-holiday.co.uk

The Cottage ★★★
Contact: Mr & Mrs A Bentham,
The Cottage, Causeway East
Farmhouse, Lee Bottom Road,
Todmorden, Lancashire
OL14 6HH
T: (01706) 815265
F: (01706) 815265
E: andrew@bentham5.
freeserve.co.uk

Rake Farm Barn ★★★★★
Contact: Mr and Mrs Paul and
June Hughes, Rake Farm Barn,
Cross Lee, Todmorden,
Lancashire OL14 8DG
T: (01706) 813091 &
07801 456805
E: pjh@rakefarm1560.freeserve.
co.uk

**Stannally Farm Cottage
★★★★**
Contact: Mrs Dineen Ann Brunt,
Stannally Farm, Stoney Royd
Lane, Todmorden, Lancashire
OL14 8EP
T: (01706) 813998
F: (01706) 813998
E: dineenbrunt@cs.com

**Staups Barn Holiday Cottage
★★★**
Contact: Mr & Mrs D Crabtree,
Staups Cottage, Staups Lane,
Higher Eastwood, Todmorden,
Lancashire OL14 8RU
T: (01706) 812730
F: (01706) 812730
E: staups1@supanet

**Stoodley Glen Pennine Cottage
★★★**
Contact: Mr Barry Whitehead,
11 Stoodley Glen, Todmorden,
Lancashire OL14 6DL
T: (01706) 818282

TOLLERTON
North Yorkshire

Gill Cottage ★★★★
Contact: Dales Hol Cot Ref:1977,
Dales Holiday Cottages, Carleton
Business Park, Carleton New
Road, Skipton, North Yorkshire
BD23 2AA
T: (01756) 799821 & 790919
F: (01756) 797012
E: info@dalesholcot.com
I: www.dalesholcot.com

**School Cottages
Rating Applied For**
Contact: Mrs Sue Hardy, School
Cottages, 5 School Cottages,
Main Street, Tollerton, York
YO61 1QQ
T: (01347) 830034 &
07989 333525
F: (01347) 830034

UGGLEBARNBY
North Yorkshire

**Howlet Hall Farm Cottage
★★★**
Contact: Dales Hol Cot Ref:1556,
Dales Holiday Cottages, Carleton
Business Park, Carleton New
Road, Skipton, North Yorkshire
BD23 2AA
T: (01756) 799821 & 790919
F: (01756) 797012
E: info@dalesholcot.com
I: www.dalesholcot.com

WADSWORTH
West Yorkshire

Stray Leaves ★★★
Contact: Mrs R H Ryder, Stray
Leaves, Wadsworth, Hebden
Bridge, West Yorkshire HX7 8TN
T: (01422) 842353

WAKEFIELD
West Yorkshire

Parklands Hotel Cottages ★★
Contact: Mr & Mrs Birtwistle,
Parklands Hotel Cottages, 143
Horbury Road, Wakefield, West
Yorkshire WF2 8TY
T: (01924) 377407
F: (01924) 290348
E: steve@parklands23.fsnet.
co.uk
I: www.parklandshotel.co.uk

WALSDEN
West Yorkshire

Henshaw Farm Cottage ★★★
Contact: Mr Paul Hunt, 9
Outgaits Lane, Hunmanby, Filey,
North Yorkshire YO14 0PX
T: (01723) 891826
E: paulhunt@ukonline.co.uk
I: www.cottagesdirect.
com/henshawfarm

WANSFORD
East Riding of Yorkshire

Trout Inn Cottage ★★★
Contact: Mr & Mrs Robin
Farnsworth, The White House,
Wansford, Driffield, East
Yorkshire YO25 8NX
T: (01377) 254224
F: (01377) 254224

**Watersedge Cottage
Rating Applied For**
Contact: Dales Hol Cot Ref:3301,
Dales Holiday Cottages, Carleton
Business Park, Carleton New
Road, Skipton, North Yorkshire
BD23 2AA
T: (01756) 799821 & 790919
F: (01756) 797012
E: info@dalesholcot.com
I: www.dalesholcot.com

WATH-IN-NIDDERDALE
North Yorkshire

Wickwoods ★★
Contact: Mr R Wales, Holiday
Cottages (Yorkshire) Ltd, Water
Street, Skipton, North Yorkshire
BD23 1PB
T: (01756) 700510

WELBURN
North Yorkshire

Castle View ★★★
Contact: Mr & Mrs Michael
Cockerill, West End, Welburn,
York YO60 7DX
T: (01653) 618344

WEST BURTON
North Yorkshire

Cherry Tree Cottage ★★
Contact: Mrs Nadine H Bell,
Country Hideaways, Margarets
Cottage, West Burton, Leyburn,
North Yorkshire DL8 4JN
T: (01969) 663559
F: (01969) 663559
E: nhbell@aol.com
I: www.countryhideaways.co.uk

First Floor Apartment ★★★
Contact: Mrs Nadine Bell,
Country Hideaways, Margarets
Cottage, West Burton, Leyburn,
North Yorkshire DL8 4JN
T: (01969) 663559
F: (01969) 663559
E: nhbell@aol.com
I: www.countryhideaways.co.uk

**The Garden Level Apartment
★★★**
Contact: Mrs Nadine H Bell,
Country Hideaways, Margarets
Cottage, West Burton, Leyburn,
North Yorkshire DL8 4JN
T: (01969) 663559
F: (01969) 663559
E: nhbell@aol.com
I: www.countryhideaways.co.uk

Grange House ★★★★
Contact: Mrs Z Mort, Grange
House, Walden Head, West
Burton, Leyburn, North
Yorkshire DL8 4LF
T: (01969) 663641

Green Bank ★★★
Contact: Mrs Nadine Bell,
Country Hideaways, Margarets
Cottage, West Burton, Leyburn,
North Yorkshire DL8 4JN
T: (01969) 663559
F: (01969) 663559
E: nhbell@aol.com
I: www.countryhideaways.co.uk

**The Ground Floor Apartment
★★★**
Contact: Mrs Nadine H Bell,
Country Hideaways, Margarets
Cottage, West Burton, Leyburn,
North Yorkshire DL8 4JN
T: (01969) 663559
F: (01969) 663559
E: nhbell@aol.com
I: www.countryhideaways.co.uk

Ivy Cottage ★★★
Contact: Mr R Wales, Holiday
Cottages (Yorkshire) Ltd, Water
Street, Skipton, North Yorkshire
BD23 1PB
T: (01756) 700510

New Walden Cottage ★★★
Contact: Mrs Karen Chapman,
Ryders Farm, Back Nook, West
Burton, Leyburn, North
Yorkshire DL8 4JU
T: (01969) 663121
E: ryderscoppicekc@aol.com

Penny Farthings ★★★
Contact: Mrs Nadine H Bell,
Country Hideaways, Margarets
Cottage, West Burton, Leyburn,
North Yorkshire DL8 4JN
T: (01969) 663559
F: (01969) 663559
E: nhbell@aol.com
I: www.countryhideaways.co.uk

Post Office Barn ★★★★
Contact: Mrs Nadine H Bell,
Country Hideaways, Margarets
Cottage, West Burton, Leyburn,
North Yorkshire DL8 4JN
T: (01969) 663559
F: (01969) 663559
E: nhbell@aol.com
I: www.countryhideaways.co.uk

Studio Apartment ★★
Contact: Mrs Nadine H Bell,
Country Hideaways, Margarets
Cottage, West Burton, Leyburn,
North Yorkshire DL8 4JN
T: (01969) 663559
F: (01969) 663559
E: nhbell@aol.com
I: www.countryhideaways.co.uk

WEST HESLERTON
North Yorkshire

**Whin Moor Cottage
Rating Applied For**
Contact: Dales Hol Cot Ref:1575,
Dales Holiday Cottages, Carleton
Business Park, Carleton New
Road, Skipton, North Yorkshire
BD23 2AA
T: (01756) 799821 & 790919
F: (01756) 797012
E: info@dalesholcot.com
I: www.dalesholcot.com

**Whin-Moor Farm Cottage
★★★**
Contact: Mr Dales Hol Cot Ref
1575, Dales Holiday Cottages,
Carleton Business Park, Carleton
New Road, Skipton, North
Yorkshire BD23 2AA
T: (01756) 799821 & 790919
F: (01756) 797012
E: info@dalesholcot.com
I: www.dalesholcot.com

WEST SCRAFTON
North Yorkshire

**Hill Top Farm Cottage Holidays
★★★★**
Contact: Mr & Mrs Caroline
Harrison, Hill Top Farm Cottage
Holidays, West Scrafton,
Middleham, Leyburn, North
Yorkshire DL8 4RU
T: (01969) 640663
E: holidays.scrafton@
breathemail.net
I: www.stayfarmnorth.co.uk

The Old Chapel ★★
Contact: Dales Hol Cot Ref:2664,
Dales Holiday Cottages, Carleton
Business Park, Carleton New
Road, Skipton, North Yorkshire
BD23 2AA
T: (01756) 799821 & 790919
F: (01756) 797012
E: info@dalesholcot.com
I: www.dalesholcot.com

Establishments printed in blue have a detailed entry in this guide

WEST WITTON
North Yorkshire

1 Chestnut Garth ★★★
Contact: Sykes Cottages
Ref:779, Sykes Cottages, York
House, York Street, Chester,
CH1 3LR
T: (01244) 345700
F: (01244) 321442
E: info@sykescottages.co.uk
I: www.sykescottages.co.uk

Dairy Cottage ★★★
Contact: Mrs Nadine H Bell,
Country Hideaways, Margarets
Cottage, West Burton, Leyburn,
North Yorkshire DL8 4JN
T: (01969) 663559
F: (01969) 663559
E: nhbell@aol.com
I: www.countryhideaways.co.uk

The Granary ★★
Contact: Dales Hol Cot Ref:398,
Dales Holiday Cottages, Carleton
Business Park, Carleton New
Road, Skipton, North Yorkshire
BD23 2AA
T: (01756) 799821 & 790919
F: (01756) 797012
E: info@dalesholcot.com
I: www.dalesholcot.com

Ivy Dene Cottage ★★★
Contact: Mr R Dickinson, Ivy
Dene Guest House, Main Street,
West Witton, Leyburn, North
Yorkshire DL8 4LP
T: (01969) 622785
F: (01969) 622785

**Wrang View and Garth End
★★**
Contact: Dales Hol Cot
Ref:1117/1118, Dales Holiday
Cottages, Carleton Business
Park, Carleton New Road,
Skipton, North Yorkshire
BD23 2AA
T: (01756) 799821 & 790919
F: (01756) 797012
E: info@dalesholcot.com
I: www.dalesholcot.com

WETWANG
East Riding of Yorkshire

Lilac Cottage ★★★★
Contact: Country Holidays
ref:3459, Holiday Cottages
Group, Spring Mill, Earby,
Barnoldswick, Lancashire
BB94 0AA
T: 08700 723723
F: (01282) 844288
E: sales@ttgihg.co.uk
I: www.country-holidays.co.uk

WHASHTON
North Yorkshire

Mount Pleasant Farm ★★★
Contact: Mrs A Pittaway, Mount
Pleasant Farm, Whashton,
Richmond, North Yorkshire
DL11 7JP
T: (01748) 822784
F: (01748) 822784

WHITBY
North Yorkshire

1-4 Captain Cook's Haven ★★
Contact: Mrs Adele Thompson,
Whitby Holiday Cottages, 47
Flowergate, Whitby, North
Yorkshire YO21 3BB
T: (01947) 603010
F: (01947) 821133
E: enquiries@whitby-cottages.
co.uk
I: www.whitby-cottages.co.uk

Abbey View Cottage ★★★★
Contact: Mr David Haycox & Mrs
Sue Brooks, Shoreline Cottages
Ltd, PO Box 135, Leeds, West
Yorkshire LS14 3XJ
T: (0113) 289 3539 &
07801 419255
F: (0113) 289 3541
E: reservations@
shoreline-cottages.com
I: www.shoreline-cottages.com

Ammonite Cottage ★★★★
Contact: Dales Hol Cot Ref:3038,
Dales Holiday Cottages, Carleton
Business Park, Carleton New
Road, Skipton, North Yorkshire
BD23 2AA
T: (01756) 799821 & 790919
F: (01756) 797012
E: info@dalesholcot.com
I: www.dalesholcot.com

The Anchorage ★★★
Contact: Sykes Cottages
Ref:360, Sykes Cottages, York
House, York Street, Chester,
CH1 3LR
T: (01244) 345700
F: (01244) 321442
E: info@sykescottages.co.uk
I: www.sykescottages.co.uk

1 Arundel Place ★★★
Contact: Mrs Adele Thompson,
Whitby Holiday Cottages, 47
Flowergate, Whitby, North
Yorkshire YO21 3BB
T: (01947) 603010
F: (01947) 821133
E: enquiries@whitby-cottages.
co.uk
I: www.whitby-cottages.co.uk

Asp House ★★★
Contact: Mrs P Ward, Asp
House, Asp House Farm,
Stainsacre, Whitby, North
Yorkshire YO22 4LR
T: (01947) 603997
E: asphousefarm@pward3.
fsnet.co.uk
I: www.pward3.fsnet.co.uk

Awd Tuts ★★★★
Contact: Mr and Mrs K&C
Baines, 66 Hill Crest Drive,
Molescroft, Beverley, East
Yorkshire HU17 7JL
T: (01482) 880815 &
07712 215042
F: (01482) 679762
E: ken@kbs.karoo.co.uk
I: www.kbs.karoo.net

Bakehouse Cottage ★★★★
Contact: Mr David Haycox & Mrs
Sue Brooks, Shoreline Cottages
Ltd, PO Box 135, Leeds, West
Yorkshire LS14 3XJ
T: (0113) 289 3539 &
07801 419255
F: (0113) 289 3541
E: reservations@
shoreline-cottages.com
I: www.shoreline-cottages.com

15 Borough Place ★★★
Contact: Mrs Adele Thompson,
Whitby Holiday Cottages, 47
Flowergate, Whitby, North
Yorkshire YO21 3BB
T: (01947) 603010
F: (01947) 821133
E: enquiries@whitby-cottages.
co.uk
I: www.whitby-cottages.co.uk

**Brook House Farm Holiday
Cottages ★★★★**
Contact: Mrs S White, Brook
House Farm Holiday Cottages,
Brook House Farm, Houlsyke,
Whitby, North Yorkshire
YO21 2LH
T: (01287) 660064

Broom Cottage ★★
Contact: Mrs Adele Thompson,
Whitby Holiday Cottages, 47
Flowergate, Whitby, North
Yorkshire YO21 3BB
T: (01947) 603010
F: (01947) 821133
E: enquiries@whitby-cottages.
co.uk
I: www.whitby-cottages.co.uk

12A Brunswick Street ★★★
Contact: Mrs Adele Thompson,
Whitby Holiday Cottages, 47
Flowergate, Whitby, North
Yorkshire YO21 3BB
T: (01947) 603010
F: (01947) 821133
E: enquiries@whitby-cottages.
co.uk
I: www.whitby-cottages.co.uk

2 Burns Yard ★★★
Contact: Mrs Adele Thompson,
Whitby Holiday Cottages, 47
Flowergate, Whitby, North
Yorkshire YO21 3BB
T: (01947) 603010
F: (01947) 821133
E: enquiries@whitby-cottages.
co.uk
I: www.whitby-cottages.co.uk

3 Burns Yard ★★
Contact: Mrs Adele Thompson,
Whitby Holiday Cottages, 47
Flowergate, Whitby, North
Yorkshire YO21 3BB
T: (01947) 603010
F: (01947) 821133
E: enquiries@whitby-
cottages.co.uk
I: www.whitby-cottages.co.uk.

**Captain Cook's Haven
★★★-★★★★**
Contact: Mrs Anne Barrowman,
Captain Cooks Haven, Larpool
Lane, Whitby, North Yorkshire
YO22 4NE
T: (01947) 601396 &
(01502) 500500
F: (01947) 893573
I: www.hoseasons.co.uk

113 Church Street ★★★
Contact: Mrs Adele Thompson,
Whitby Holiday Cottages, 47
Flowergate, Whitby, North
Yorkshire YO21 3BB
T: (01947) 603010
F: (01947) 821133
E: enquiries@whitby-cottages.
co.uk
I: www.whitby-cottages.co.uk

**12 Church Street
Rating Applied For**
Contact: Whitby Holiday
Cottages, 47 Flowergate,
Whitby, North Yorkshire
YO21 3BB
T: (01947) 603010
F: (01947) 821133
E: enquiries@whitby-cottages.
co.uk
I: www.whitby-cottages.co.uk

Cobble Cottage ★★★
Contact: Dales Hol Cot Ref:1808,
Dales Holiday Cottages, Carleton
Business Park, Carleton New
Road, Skipton, North Yorkshire
BD23 2AA
T: (01756) 799821 & 790919
F: (01756) 797012
E: info@dalesholcot.com
I: www.dalesholcot.com

Coble Cottage ★★★
Contact: Mrs Adele Thompson,
Whitby Holiday Cottages, 47
Flowergate, Whitby, North
Yorkshire YO21 3BB
T: (01947) 603010
F: (01947) 821133
E: enquiries@whitby-cottages.
co.uk
I: www.whitby-cottages.co.uk

Corner House ★★★
Contact: Dales Hol Cot Ref:3156,
Dales Holiday Cottages, Carleton
Business Park, Carleton New
Road, Skipton, North Yorkshire
BD23 2AA
T: (01756) 799821 & 790919
F: (01756) 797012
E: info@dalesholcot.com
I: www.dalesholcot.com

Cuddy Cottage ★★★★
Contact: Mr David Haycox & Mrs
Sue Brooks, Shoreline Cottages
Ltd, PO Box 135, Leeds, West
Yorkshire LS14 3XJ
T: (0113) 289 3539 &
07801 419255
F: (0113) 289 3541
E: reservations@
shoreline-cottages.com
I: www.shoreline-cottages.com

**Elizabeth House Holiday Flats
★-★★★★**
Contact: Mrs Rosaline Cooper,
Park View, 14 Chubb Hill Road,
Whitby, North Yorkshire
YO21 1JU
T: (01947) 604213 &
07867 618244
F: (01947) 604213
E: cooperhouse@tinyworld.
co.uk
I: www.elizabeth-house.fsnet.
co.uk

Establishments printed in blue have a detailed entry in this guide

7 Esk Terrace ★★★
Contact: Mrs Adele Thompson,
Whitby Holiday Cottages, 47
Flowergate, Whitby, North
Yorkshire YO21 3BB
T: (01947) 603010
F: (01947) 821133
E: enquiries@whitby-cottages.
co.uk
I: www.whitby-cottages.co.uk

Esk View ★★★
Contact: Mrs Adele Thompson,
Whitby Holiday Cottages, 47
Flowergate, Whitby, North
Yorkshire YO21 3BB
T: (01947) 603010
F: (01947) 821133
E: enquiries@whitby-cottages.
co.uk
I: www.whitby-cottages.co.uk

**Fayvan Holiday Apartments
★★★★**
Contact: Mrs P Moore, Fayvan
Holiday Apartments, 43 Crescent
Avenue, West Cliff, Whitby,
North Yorkshire YO21 3EQ
T: (01947) 604813
F: (01947) 604813

Fern Cottage ★★★★
Contact: Mrs Adele Thompson,
Whitby Holiday Cottages, 47
Flowergate, Whitby, North
Yorkshire YO21 3BB
T: (01947) 603010
F: (01947) 821133
E: enquiries@whitby-cottages.
co.uk
I: www.whitby-cottages.co.uk

Flat 2 ★★★
Contact: Mrs Adele Thompson,
Whitby Holiday Cottages, 47
Flowergate, Whitby, North
Yorkshire YO21 3BB
T: (01947) 603010
F: (01947) 821133
E: enquiries@whitby-cottages.
co.uk
I: www.whitby-cottages.co.uk

Flat 3 ★★★
Contact: Mrs Adele Thompson,
Whitby Holiday Cottages, 47
Flowergate, Whitby, North
Yorkshire YO21 3BB
T: (01947) 603010
F: (01947) 821133
E: enquiries@whitby-cottages.
co.uk
I: www.whitby-cottages.co.uk

Flat 3 ★★★
Contact: Mrs Adele Thompson,
Whitby Holiday Cottages, 47
Flowergate, Whitby, North
Yorkshire YO21 3BB
T: (01947) 603010
F: (01947) 821133
E: enquiries@whitby-cottages.
co.uk
I: www.whitby-cottages.co.uk

Foredeck ★★
Contact: Dales Hol Cot Ref:1695,
Dales Holiday Cottages, Carleton
Business Park, Carleton New
Road, Skipton, North Yorkshire
BD23 2AA
T: (01756) 799821 & 790919
F: (01756) 797012
E: info@dalesholcot.com
I: www.dalesholcot.com

Forget-Me-Not ★★★
Contact: Whitby Holiday
Cottages, 47 Flowergate,
Whitby, North Yorkshire
YO21 3BB
T: (01947) 603010
F: (01947) 821133
E: enquiries@whitby-cottages.
co.uk
I: www.whitby-cottages.co.uk

Glencoe – Garden Flat ★★★★
Contact: Mrs Julie Charlton,
Glencoe Holiday Flats, 18 Linden
Close, Briggs Wath, Whitby,
North Yorkshire YO21 1TA
T: (01947) 811531

Harbour View ★★★
Contact: Mrs Adele Thompson,
Whitby Holiday Cottages, 47
Flowergate, Whitby, North
Yorkshire YO21 3BB
T: (01947) 603010
F: (01947) 821133
E: enquiries@whitby-cottages.
co.uk
I: www.whitby-cottages.co.uk

**Harbour View and Church View
★★★**
Contact: Mrs Adele Thompson,
Whitby Holiday Cottages, 47
Flowergate, Whitby, North
Yorkshire YO21 3BB
T: (01947) 603010
F: (01947) 821133
E: enquiries@whitby-cottages.
co.uk
I: www.whitby-cottages.co.uk

Henrietta Cottage ★★★★
Contact: Mr David Haycox & Mrs
Sue Brooks, Shoreline Cottages
Ltd, PO Box 135, Leeds, West
Yorkshire LS14 3XJ
T: (0113) 289 3539 &
07801 419255
F: (0113) 289 3541
E: reservations@
shoreline-cottages.com
I: www.shoreline-cottages.com

Henrietta House ★★★
Contact: Dr S M Thornton,
Brookhouse, Dam Lane,
Leavening, Malton, North
Yorkshire YO17 9SF
T: (01653) 658249
E: enquiries@seasideholiday.
co.uk
I: www.seasideholiday.co.uk

7 Henrietta Street ★★
Contact: Mr William Usher, 2
Southlands Avenue, Whitby,
North Yorkshire YO21 3DY
T: (01947) 605868

**8 Horse Road
Rating Applied For**
Contact: Whitby Holiday
Cottages, 47 Flowergate,
Whitby, North Yorkshire
YO21 3BB
T: (01947) 603010
F: (01947) 821133
E: enquiries@whitby-cottages.
co.uk
I: www.whitby-cottages.co.uk

Jet Cottage ★★★
Contact: Mrs Adele Thompson,
Whitby Holiday Cottages, 47
Flowergate, Whitby, North
Yorkshire YO21 3BB
T: (01947) 603010
F: (01947) 821133
E: enquiries@whitby-cottages.
co.uk
I: www.whitby-cottages.co.uk

Kildale ★★★
Contact: Mrs Adele Thompson,
Whitby Holiday Cottages, 47
Flowergate, Whitby, North
Yorkshire YO21 3BB
T: (01947) 603010
F: (01947) 821133

Kiln Cottage ★★★★
Contact: Mr David Haycox & Mrs
Sue Brooks, Shoreline Cottages
Ltd, PO Box 135, Leeds, West
Yorkshire LS14 3XJ
T: (0113) 289 3539 &
07801 419255
F: (0113) 289 3541
E: reservations@
shoreline-cottages.com
I: www.shoreline-cottages.com

Kingfisher Cottage ★★★
Contact: Dales Hol Cot Ref:2588,
Dales Holiday Cottages, Carleton
Business Park, Carleton New
Road, Skipton, North Yorkshire
BD23 2AA
T: (01756) 799821 & 790919
F: (01756) 797012
E: info@dalesholcot.com
I: www.dalesholcot.com

Kipper Cottage ★★★★
Contact: Mrs Adele Thompson,
Whitby Holiday Cottages, 47
Flowergate, Whitby, North
Yorkshire YO21 3BB
T: (01947) 603010
F: (01947) 821133
E: enquiries@whitby-cottages.
co.uk
I: www.whitby-cottages.co.uk

The Lamp House ★★★★
Contact: Mrs Adele Thompson,
Whitby Holiday Cottages, 47
Flowergate, Whitby, North
Yorkshire YO21 3BB
T: (01947) 603010
F: (01947) 821133
E: enquiries@whitby-cottages.
co.uk
I: www.whitby-cottages.co.uk

Little Venice ★★★
Contact: Dales Hol Cot Ref:2642,
Dales Holiday Cottages, Carleton
Business Park, Carleton New
Road, Skipton, North Yorkshire
BD23 2AA
T: (01756) 799821 & 790919
F: (01756) 797012
E: info@dalesholcot.com
I: www.dalesholcot.com

Lobster Pot Cottage ★★
Contact: Mrs Adele Thompson,
Whitby Holiday Cottages, 47
Flowergate, Whitby, North
Yorkshire YO21 3BB
T: (01947) 603010
F: (01947) 821133
E: enquiries@whitby-cottages.
co.uk
I: www.whitby-cottages.co.uk

Manor Cottage ★★★★
Contact: Dales Hol Cot Ref:2448,
Dales Holiday Cottages, Carleton
Business Park, Carleton New
Road, Skipton, North Yorkshire
BD23 2AA
T: (01756) 799821 & 790919
F: (01756) 797012
E: info@dalesholcot.com
I: www.dalesholcot.com

Mariner's Cottage ★★★★
Contact: Mr David Haycox & Mrs
Sue Brooks, Shoreline Cottages
Ltd, PO Box 135, Leeds, West
Yorkshire LS14 3XJ
T: (0113) 289 3539 &
07801 419255
F: (0113) 289 3541
E: reservations@
shoreline-cottages.com
I: www.shoreline-cottages.com

New Hills ★★★
Contact: Dales Hol Cot Ref:2586,
Dales Holiday Cottages, Carleton
Business Park, Carleton New
Road, Skipton, North Yorkshire
BD23 2AA
T: (01756) 799821 & 790919
F: (01756) 797012
E: info@dalesholcot.com
I: www.dalesholcot.com

**Old Boatman's Shelter
Rating Applied For**
Contact: Ms Alison Halidu, 50
Carr Hill Lane, Briggswath,
Whitby, North Yorkshire
YO21 1RS
T: (01947) 811089

**6 Old Coastguard Cottages
★★★**
Contact: Ms J M Noble, Howdale
House, Browside, Fylingdales,
Whitby, North Yorkshire YO22
T: (01947) 881064

Penny Hedge House ★★★★
Contact: Dales Hol Cot Ref:2994,
Dales Holiday Cottages, Carleton
Business Park, Carleton New
Road, Skipton, North Yorkshire
BD23 2AA
T: (01756) 799821 & 790919
F: (01756) 797012
E: info@dalesholcot.com
I: www.dalesholcot.com

Perkins Cottage ★★★★
Contact: Mrs Adele Thompson,
Whitby Holiday Cottages, 47
Flowergate, Whitby, North
Yorkshire YO21 3BB
T: (01947) 603010
F: (01947) 821133
E: enquiries@whitby-cottages.
co.uk
I: www.whitby-cottages.co.uk

**Primrose & Bluebell Cottages
★★★**
Contact: Mr & Mrs R E Hopps,
Primrose & Bluebell Cottages,
Low Newbiggin North Farm,
Aislaby, Whitby, North Yorkshire
YO21 1TQ
T: (01947) 810948 & 811644
E: barbara@bhopps.freeserve.
co.uk
I: www.stilwell.co.uk

Establishments printed in blue have a detailed entry in this guide

Prince of Wales Cottage
Rating Applied For
Contact: Mr David Haycox & Mrs Sue Brooks, Shoreline Cottages Ltd, PO Box 135, Leeds, West Yorkshire LS14 3XJ
T: (0113) 289 3539 & 07801 419255
F: (0113) 289 3541
E: reservations@shoreline-cottages.com
I: www.shoreline-cottages.com

8 Prospect Place ★★★
Contact: Mrs Adele Thompson, Whitby Holiday Cottages, 47 Flowergate, Whitby, North Yorkshire YO21 3BB
T: (01947) 603010
F: (01947) 821133
E: enquiries@whitby-cottages.co.uk
I: www.whitby-cottages.co.uk

Quay Cottage ★★★
Contact: Mrs M A Coulson Clarke, Sheridan, 49 Meadowfields, Whitby, North Yorkshire YO21 1QG
T: (01947) 825322
E: macc_whitby@yahoo.co.uk

Quayside Cottage
Rating Applied For
Contact: Mr David Haycox & Mrs Sue Brooks, Shoreline Cottages Ltd, PO Box 135, Leeds, West Yorkshire LS14 3XJ
T: (0113) 289 3539 & 07801 419255
F: (0113) 289 3541
E: reservations@shoreline-cottages.com
I: www.shoreline-cottages.com

2 Richardson Row ★★★
Contact: Mrs Adele Thompson, Whitby Holiday Cottages, 47 Flowergate, Whitby, North Yorkshire YO21 3BB
T: (01947) 603010
F: (01947) 821133
E: enquiries@whitby-cottages.co.uk
I: www.whitby-cottages.co.uk

Rose Cottage ★★★
Contact: Mrs Adele Thompson, Whitby Holiday Cottages, 47 Flowergate, Whitby, North Yorkshire YO21 3BB
T: (01947) 603010
F: (01947) 821133
E: enquiries@whitby-cottages.co.uk
I: www.whitby-cottages.co.uk

St Joseph's Cottage ★★★★
Contact: Mr David Haycox & Mrs Sue Brooks, Shoreline Cottages Ltd, PO Box 135, Leeds, West Yorkshire LS14 3XJ
T: (0113) 289 3539 & 07801 419255
F: (0113) 289 3541
E: reservations@shoreline-cottages.com
I: www.shoreline-cottages.com

Sandfield House Farm ★★★★
Contact: Mr & Mrs Martin & Chrissie Warner, Sandfield House Farm, Sandsend Road, Whitby, North Yorkshire YO21 3SR
T: (01947) 602660
F: (01947) 606274
E: sandfieldw@aol.com

Sandglass Cottage
Rating Applied For
Contact: Mr David Haycox & Mrs Sue Brooks, Shoreline Cottages Ltd, PO Box 135, Leeds, West Yorkshire LS14 3XJ
T: (0113) 289 3539 & 07801 419255
F: (0113) 289 3541
E: reservations@shoreline-cottages.com
I: www.shoreline-cottages.com

Scoresby Cottage
Rating Applied For
Contact: Mrs Adele Thompson, Whitby Holiday Cottages, 47 Flowergate, Whitby, North Yorkshire YO21 3BB
T: (01947) 603010
F: (01947) 821133
E: enquiries@whitby-cottages.co.uk
I: www.whitby-cottages.co.uk

Seagull Cottage ★★★★
Contact: Mr David Haycox & Mrs Sue Brooks, Shoreline Cottages Ltd, PO Box 135, Leeds, West Yorkshire LS14 3XJ
T: (0113) 289 3539 & 07801 419255
F: (0113) 289 3541
E: reservations@shoreline-cottages.com
I: www.shoreline-cottages.com

Seagull Cottage ★★★
Contact: Mrs Adele Thompson, Whitby Holiday Cottages, 47 Flowergate, Whitby, North Yorkshire YO21 3BB
T: (01947) 603010
F: (01947) 821133
E: enquiries@whitby-cottages.co.uk
I: www.whitby-cottages.co.uk

Seaway & Wick Cottage
★★★–★★★★★
Contact: Dales Hol Cot Ref:2149/1974, Dales Holiday Cottages, Carleton Business Park, Carleton New Road, Skipton, North Yorkshire BD23 2AA
T: (01756) 799821 & 790919
F: (01756) 797012
E: info@dalesholcot.com
I: www.dalesholcot.com

Shackleton House
★★★–★★★★★
Contact: Dales Hol Cot Ref:3188, Dales Holiday Cottages, Carleton Business Park, Carleton New Road, Skipton, North Yorkshire BD23 2AA
T: (01756) 799821 & 790919
F: (01756) 797012
E: info@dalesholcot.com
I: www.dalesholcot.com

23 Silver Street
Rating Applied For
Contact: Mrs Adele Thompson, Whitby Holiday Cottages, 47 Flowergate, Whitby, North Yorkshire YO21 3BB
T: (01947) 603010
F: (01947) 821133
E: enquiries@whitby-cottages.co.uk
I: www.whitby-cottages.co.uk

25A Silver Street
Rating Applied For
Contact: Whitby Holiday Cottages, 47 Flowergate, Whitby, North Yorkshire YO21 3BB
T: (01947) 603010
F: (01947) 821133
E: enquiries@whitby-cottages.co.uk
I: www.whitby-cottages.co.uk

Southern Cross ★★★
Contact: Mrs Adele Thompson, Whitby Holiday Cottages, 47 Flowergate, Whitby, North Yorkshire YO21 3BB
T: (01947) 603010
F: (01947) 821133
E: enquiries@whitby-cottages.co.uk
I: www.whitby-cottages.co.uk

Speedy's Cottage ★★★
Contact: Mrs D A Elliott, The Enamel Workshop, 128 Church Street, Whitby, North Yorkshire YO22 4DE
T: (01947) 606216
F: (01947) 606216
I: www.enamelworkshop.co.uk

Spring Vale ★★★★
Contact: Mr David Haycox & Mrs Sue Brooks, Shoreline Cottages Ltd, PO Box 135, Leeds, West Yorkshire LS14 3XJ
T: (0113) 289 3539 & 07801 419255
F: (0113) 289 3541
E: reservations@shoreline-cottages.com
I: www.shoreline-cottages.com

Storm Cottage ★★
Contact: Mrs Adele Thompson, Whitby Holiday Cottages, 47 Flowergate, Whitby, North Yorkshire YO21 3BB
T: (01947) 603010
F: (01947) 821133
E: enquiries@whitby-cottages.co.uk
I: www.whitby-cottages.co.uk

Stowaway Cottage ★★
Contact: Mrs Adele Thompson, Whitby Holiday Cottages, 47 Flowergate, Whitby, North Yorkshire YO21 3BB
T: (01947) 603010
F: (01947) 821133
E: enquiries@whitby-cottages.co.uk
I: www.whitby-cottages.co.uk

Studio Flat 6 ★★★
Contact: Mrs Adele Thompson, Whitby Holiday Cottages, 47 Flowergate, Whitby, North Yorkshire YO21 3BB
T: (01947) 603010
F: (01947) 821133
E: enquiries@whitby-cottages.co.uk
I: www.whitby-cottages.co.uk

Sunnyside ★★★
Contact: Mrs Adele Thompson, Whitby Holiday Cottages, 47 Flowergate, Whitby, North Yorkshire YO21 3BB
T: (01947) 603010
F: (01947) 821133
E: enquiries@whitby-cottages.co.uk
I: www.whitby-cottages.co.uk

Swallow Holiday Cottages ★★
Contact: Mr & Mrs McNeil, Swallow Holiday Cottages, Long Lease Farm, Hawsker, Whitby, North Yorkshire YO22 4LA
T: (01947) 603790
F: (01947) 603790
I: www.swallowcottages.co.uk

Swallows Nest, The Farmhouse and Wheelhouse ★★★★
Contact: CH ref:11123,11124,14547, Holiday Cottages Group Owner Serviced Dept, Spring Mill, Earby, Barnoldswick, Lancashire BB94 0AA
T: 08700 723723
F: (01282) 844288
E: sales@ttgihg.co.uk
I: www.country-holidays.co.uk

Swan Cottage ★★★
Contact: Mrs M A Smith, Swan Farm, High Hawsker, Whitby, North Yorkshire YO22 4LH
T: (01947) 880682

Thimble Cottage, 15 Loggerhead Yard ★★
Contact: Mr P Breeze, The Barn, Gun End, Swythamley, Macclesfield, Cheshire SK11 0SJ
T: (01260) 227391

Time & Tide ★★
Contact: Mrs Adele Thompson, Whitby Holiday Cottages, 47 Flowergate, Whitby, North Yorkshire YO21 3BB
T: (01947) 603010
F: (01947) 821133
E: enquiries@whitby-cottages.co.uk
I: www.whitby-cottages.co.uk

Tyneholme ★★★
Contact: Mrs Adele Thompson, Whitby Holiday Cottages, 47 Flowergate, Whitby, North Yorkshire YO21 3BB
T: (01947) 603010
F: (01947) 821133
E: enquiries@whitby-cottages.co.uk
I: www.whitby-cottages.co.uk

West End Cottage ★★★★
Contact: Mr David Haycox & Mrs Sue Brooks, Shoreline Cottages Ltd, PO Box 135, Leeds, West Yorkshire LS14 3XJ
T: (0113) 289 3539 & 07801 419255
F: (0113) 289 3541
E: reservations@shoreline-cottages.com
I: www.shoreline-cottages.com

7 West Terrace ★★★★
Contact: Mrs Adele Thompson, Whitby Holiday Cottages, 47 Flowergate, Whitby, North Yorkshire YO21 3BB
T: (01947) 603010
F: (01947) 821133
E: enquiries@whitby-cottages.co.uk
I: www.whitby-cottages.co.uk

White Rose Holiday Cottages
★★★-★★★★
Contact: Mrs J E Roberts,
Greenacres, 5 Brook Park,
Sleights, Whitby, North
Yorkshire YO21 1RT
T: (01947) 810763
E: enquiries@www.
whiterosecottages.com
I: www.whiterosecottages.com

WHITWELL-ON-THE-HILL
North Yorkshire
The Hay Loft ★★★
Contact: Mrs Anne Polley, El
Paso, Barton Hill, Whitwell-on-
the-Hill, York YO60 7JX
T: (01653) 618324
E: anne.polley@btinternet.com

WHIXLEY
North Yorkshire
Ashwood House
Rating Applied For
Contact: Ms Julie Mett, Waters
Edge, 5 Earlsborough Terrace,
Marygate, York, YO30 7BQ
T: (01904) 644625
F: (01904) 731516
E: julie@watersedgeyork.co.uk
I: www.watersedgeyork.co.uk

WILTON
North Yorkshire
The Old Forge ★★★
Contact: Mrs Bernice Graham,
The Old Forge, Wilton, Pickering,
North Yorkshire YO18 7JY
T: (01751) 477399
F: (01751) 477464
E: theoldforge@themutual.net
I: www.forgecottages.
themutual.net/fc.html

Rose Cottage ★★★★
Contact: Dales Hol Cot Ref:2830,
Dales Holiday Cottages, Carleton
Business Park, Carleton New
Road, Skipton, North Yorkshire
BD23 2AA
T: (01756) 799821 & 790919
F: (01756) 797012
E: info@dalesholcot.com
I: www.dalesholcot.com

Sands Farm Country Cottages
★★★★
Contact: Miss M A Tomlinson,
Sands Farm Country Cottages,
Wilton, Pickering, North
Yorkshire YO18 7JY
T: (01751) 474405
F: (01751) 476866
E: sandsfarm@faxvia.net

WINKSLEY
North Yorkshire
Meadow View Cottage ★★★
Contact: Mr L Broadbent, 9
Roydscliffe Road, Heaton,
Bradford, West Yorkshire
BD9 5PT
T: (01274) 541622

WOLD NEWTON
East Riding of Yorkshire
Owl Cottage ★★★★
Contact: Mr & Mrs Richard &
Lisa Morton, 78 Queen Victoria
Road, Totley Rise, Sheffield
S17 4HU
T: (0114) 235 6463 & 266 4141
F: (0114) 266 9836
E: richard@mortonprice.demon.
co.uk

WORSBROUGH
South Yorkshire
Delf Cottage ★★★★
Contact: Mrs Julie Elmhirst, Delf
House, Houndhill Lane,
Worsbrough, Barnsley, South
Yorkshire S70 6TX
T: (01226) 282430 &
07768 766448
F: (01226) 282430
E: t.elmhirst@btinternet.com
I: www.delfcottage.co.uk

WORTON
North Yorkshire
Stoney End Holidays
★★★-★★★★★
Contact: Mrs Pamela Hague,
Stoney End, Worton, Askrigg,
Leyburn, North Yorkshire
DL8 3ET
T: (01969) 650652
F: (01969) 650077
E: stoneyendholidays@
btinternet.com
I: www.
stoneyendholidays@btinternet.
co.uk

WRELTON
North Yorkshire
Hallgarth ★★★★
Contact: Mrs Carol Marsh,
Orchard House, Wrelton,
Pickering, North Yorkshire
YO18 8PG
T: (01751) 476081

Vale Cottage ★★★★
Contact: Mr & Mrs T H Scaling,
Cliff Farm, Sinnington, York
YO62 6SS
T: (01751) 473792
F: (01751) 473792
E: jeanscaling@btinternet.com

WROOT
North Lincolnshire
Rye House Granary ★★★
Contact: Mr Robin Aconley, Rye
House, High Street, Wroot,
Doncaster, South Yorkshire
DN9 2BT
T: (01302) 770196 &
07967 003713
E: robinaconley@tinyworld.
co.uk

YEADON
West Yorkshire
Gillcroft Cottage ★★★★
Contact: Mrs I Croft, Gillcroft, 41
Gill Lane, Yeadon, Leeds
LS19 7DE
T: (0113) 250 4198
F: (0113) 250 4327

YORK
North Yorkshire
Abbeygate House ★★★★★
Contact: Mr & Mrs C Halliday, 3
Grange Drive, Horsforth, Leeds
LS18 5EQ
T: (0113) 258 9833

Apple Cottage ★★★
Contact: Mrs Jean Corrigan,
Highfields, Beckdale Road,
Helmsley, York YO62 5AS
T: (01439) 770705
F: (01439) 770705

Asgard ★★★★
Contact: Mrs Hilary Shepherd,
18 White Horse Close,
Huntington, York YO32 9GH
T: (01904) 768856
F: (01904) 768856

Baile Hill Cottage ★★★
Contact: Mr & Mrs P&S
Hodgson, Baile Hill Cottage,
Avalon, North Lane, Wheldrake,
York, North Yorkshire YO19 6AY
T: (01904) 448670
F: (01904) 448908
E: holiday.cottage@btinternet.
com
I: www.btinternet.com/~holiday.
cottage

Baille Hill House ★★★★★
Contact: Mr & Mrs M F Halliday,
2 Grange Drive, Horsforth, Leeds
LS18 5EQ
T: (0113) 258 4212
F: (0113) 281 9455

Barbican Mews ★★★
Contact: Mrs Helen Jones,
Homefinders Holidays, 11
Walmgate, York, North Yorkshire
YO1 9TX
T: (01904) 632660 & 655200
F: (01904) 615388
E: c.thomas-letters.of.york@
btinternet.com
I: www.letters.of.york.co.uk

19A Barbican Mews ★★★
Contact: Mrs Helen Jones,
Homefinders Holidays, 11
Walmgate, York, North Yorkshire
YO1 9TX
T: (01904) 632660 & 655200
F: (01904) 615388
E: c.thomas-letters.of.york.
btinternet.com
I: www.letters.of.york.co.uk

Bishopgate Pavilion ★★★★★
Contact: Mr J K Graham, 31
Falcon Way, Clippers Quay,
London E14 9UP
T: (020) 7538 8980 &
07973 857187
F: (020) 7538 8980
E: johnkgraham31@hotmail.
com
I: www.johnkgraham.com

Bishophill Holidays ★★
Contact: Mrs Lesley Shimmin, 49
Moorgate, Acomb, York
YO24 4HP
T: (01904) 796118
F: (01904) 796118
E: enquiries@bishophill.co.uk
I: www.bishophill.co.uk

1 Bishops Court ★★★
Contact: Mrs Helen Jones,
Homefinders Holidays, 11
Walmgate, York, North Yorkshire
YO1 9TX
T: (01904) 632660 & 655200
F: (01904) 651388
E: c.thomas-letters.of.york@
btinternet.com
I: www.letters.of.york.co.uk

5 Bishops Court ★★★
Contact: Mrs Anna Ives, 39
Lakeside, Acaster Malbis, York
YO23 2TY
T: (01904) 700457

Bishops Hotel Apartment
★★★★
Contact: Mr & Mrs Magson,
Bishops Hotel, 135 Holgate
Road, Holgate, York, YO24 4DF
T: (01904) 628000
F: (01904) 628181
E: bishops@ukonline.co.uk
I: www.bishopshotel.co.uk

**Bootham Park View Holiday
Apartments** ★★-★★★
Contact: Miss S D Wilson,
Bootham Park View Holiday
Apartments, 20 Grosvenor
Terrace, Bootham, York,
YO30 7AG
T: (01904) 631011
E: shelagh@wilsons14.fsnet.
co.uk
I: www.boothamparkview.co.uk

Centre York Cottages
★★-★★★
Contact: Mr William Richardson,
Catton Park, Wilberfoss, York
YO41 5QA
T: (01759) 388280
F: (01759) 388280
E: william@
centre-yorkcottages.fsnet.co.uk
I: www.centre.yorkcottages.
fsnet.co.uk

Classique ★★-★★★
Contact: Mrs P Inns, 21
Larchfield, Stockton Lane, York,
YO31 1JS
T: (01904) 421339
F: (01904) 421339

Cloisters Walk ★★★
Contact: Mr S Burrows, 1 St
Marys, York, York YO30 7DD
T: (01904) 638915

1 Cloisters Walk ★★★
Contact: Mrs Helen Jones,
Homefinders Holidays, 11
Walmgate, York, North Yorkshire
YO1 9TX
T: (01904) 632660 & 655200
F: (01904) 651388
E: c.thomas-letters.of.york@
btinternet.com
I: www.letters.of.york.co.uk

2 Cloisters Walk ★★★
Contact: Mrs D Preece & Mrs D
Widdicombe, York Holiday
Homes, 53 Goodramgate, York,
North Yorkshire YO1 7LS
T: (01904) 641997
F: (01904) 613453
I: www.yorkshirenet.
co.uk/accgde/yorkholidayhomes

4 Cloisters Walk ★★★
Contact: Mr Jack Mawson, 5
Castle Garth, Sewerby,
Bridlington, East Riding of
Yorkshire YO15 1EJ
T: (01262) 602912

Colonia Holidays ★★★
Contact: Mrs M R Booth,
'Kenilworth', Hutton Street,
Hutton Wandesley, York, North
Yorkshire YO26 7ND
T: (01904) 738579

Establishments printed in blue have a detailed entry in this guide

Five Pennies ★★★★
Contact: Mrs M B Wilson, Five
Pennies, Broad Lane, Appleton
Roebuck, York, North Yorkshire
YO23 7DS
T: (01904) 744562
F: (01904) 744562
E: nosliw90@hotmail.com

**Flat 24 Middleton House
★★★★**
Contact: Mrs Carole Bowes,
Melrose House Farm, Sutton
Road, Thirsk, North Yorkshire
YO7 2ES
T: (01845) 597334

Forget Me Nots ★★★★
Contact: Mrs Helen Jones,
Homefinders Holidays, 11
Walmgate, York, North Yorkshire
YO1 9TX
T: (01904) 632660 & 655200
F: (01904) 615388
E: c.thomas-letters.of.york@
btinternet.com
I: www.letters.of.york.co.uk

Garden Cottage ★★★
Contact: Mrs Katy Harvey, Moat
View House, 28 Lord Mayor's
Walk, York, North Yorkshire
YO31 7HA
T: (01904) 623329
E: katy.harvey@amserve.net

6 Hunt Court ★★★
Contact: Mrs D Preece & Mrs D
Widdicombe, York Holiday
Homes, 53 Goodramgate, York,
YO1 7LS
T: (01904) 641997
F: (01904) 613453
I: www.yorkshirenet.
co.uk/accgde/yorkholidayhomes

Hyrst Mews ★★
Contact: Mrs D Jones, Sand
Hutton Manor, Upper Helmsley
Road, Sand Hutton, York
YO41 1JZ
T: (01904) 468698

**Knowle House Apartments
★★**
Contact: Mr Graham Harrand,
Hedley House, 3 Bootham
Terrace, York, YO30 7DH
T: (01904) 637404
F: (01904) 639774
E: h.h@mcmail.com
I: www.hedleyhouse.com

Merricote Cottages ★★★
Contact: Mr Andrew Williamson,
Merricote Cottages, Malton
Road, Stockton-on-the-Forest,
York YO32 9TL
T: (01904) 400256 &
07939 522748
E: merricote@hotmail.com

12 Monkbridge Court ★★★★
Contact: Mrs Angela Bush,
Burtonfields Hall, Stamford
Bridge, York YO41 1SA
T: (01759) 371308 &
07710 474338
F: (01759) 371308
E: abhols@hotmail.com

45 Monkgate ★★-★★★
Contact: Mrs D Preece & Mrs D
Widdicombe, York Holiday
Homes, 53 Goodramgate, York,
North Yorkshire YO1 7LS
T: (01904) 641997
F: (01904) 613453
I: www.yorkshirenet.
co.uk/accgde/yorkholidayhomes

**12 Monkgate Cloisters
★★★★**
Contact: Mrs D Preece & Mrs D
Widdicombe, York Holiday
Homes, 53 Goodramgate, York,
YO1 7LS
T: (01904) 641997
F: (01904) 613453
I: www.yorkshirenet.
co.uk/accgde/yorkholidayhomes

**13 Monkgate Cloisters
★★★★**
Contact: Mrs D Preece & Mrs D
Widdicombe, York Holiday
Homes, 53 Goodramgate, York,
North Yorkshire YO1 7LS
T: (01904) 641997
F: (01904) 613453
I: www.yorkshirenet.
co.uk/accgde/yorkholidayhomes

Owl Cottage ★★
Contact: Mrs R Fletcher, Owl
Cottage, Long Acres, The Village,
Osbaldwick, York YO10 3NP
T: (01904) 410438 & 414404
F: (01904) 414404
E: rjf@cfga.co.uk

9 Pear Tree Court ★★★
Contact: Mrs D Preece & Mrs D
Widdicombe, York Holiday
Homes, 53 Goodramgate, York,
YO1 7LS
T: (01904) 641997
F: (01904) 613453
I: www.yorkshirenet.
co.uk/accgde/yorkholidayhomes

Priory Cottage ★★★
Contact: Mrs Helen Jones,
Homefinders Holidays, 11
Walmgate, York, North Yorkshire
YO1 9TX
T: (01904) 632660 & 655200
F: (01904) 615388
E: c.thomas-letters.of.york.
btinternet.com
I: www.letters.of.york.co.uk

29 Richardson Street ★★★
Contact: Mrs Helen Jones,
Homefinders Holidays, 11
Walmgate, York, North Yorkshire
YO1 9TX
T: (01904) 632660 & 655200
F: (01904) 651388
E: c.thomas-letters.of.york@
btinternet.com
I: www.letters.of.york.co.uk

River Haven ★★★★
Contact: Mrs Hilary Kernohan,
Duncanne House, Roecliffe Lane,
Boroughbridge, York YO51 9LN
T: (01423) 325417 &
07710 147665
E: hilarysholidayhomes@
btconnect.com
I: www.hilarysholidayhomes.
co.uk

Riverside Holiday Flat ★★★★
Contact: Mr P A Jackson, 17
Great Close, Cawood, Selby,
North Yorkshire YO8 3UG
T: (01757) 268207 &
07885 921691
F: (01757) 268122
E: pajack@lineone.net
I: www.yorkriversideholidayflat.
co.uk

Riverside House ★★★★
Contact: Mrs B Harris, 258
Tadcaster Road, York, YO24 1ES
T: (01904) 633044 & 0780 101
7477
E: tio.pep@virgin.net

**Shambles Holiday Apartments
★★★★**
Contact: Mr and Mrs Fletcher,
Shambles Holiday Apartments,
The Art Shop, 27-27a Shambles,
York, North Yorkshire YO1 7LX
T: (01904) 623898
F: (01904) 671283
E: shamblesholiday-york@
tinyworld.co.uk

**Stakesby Holiday Flats
Rating Applied For**
Contact: Mr Anthony Bryce,
Stakesby Holiday Flats, 4 St
George's Place, Mount Vale,
Tadcaster Road, York, YO24 1DR
T: (01904) 611634 &
07831 218504

Swallow Hall ★★★
Contact: Mrs C Scutt, Swallow
Hall, Crockey Hill, York
YO19 4SG
T: (01904) 448219
E: christine_scutt@hotmail.com

5 Thomas Street ★★★
Contact: Mrs C Howarth, 17
Westbury Road, Crumpsall,
Manchester M8 5RX
T: (0161) 795 2614

Turks Head Court ★★★
Contact: Mrs D Preece & Mrs D
Widdicombe, York Holiday
Homes, 53 Goodramgate, York,
North Yorkshire YO1 7LS
T: (01904) 641997
F: (01904) 613453
I: www.yorkshirenet.
co.uk/accgde/yorkholidayhomes

**York Holiday Apartments
★★★**
Contact: Mr Malcolm Bradley,
Mulberry Farm, Lumby, South
Milford, Leeds, West Yorkshire
LS25 5JA
T: (01977) 683499 &
07770 533553
F: (01977) 680110
E: malcolmrbradley@
farmersweekly.net
I: www.yorkholidayapartments.
co.uk

**York Lakeside Lodges
★★★★-★★★★★**
Contact: Mr N Manasir, York
Lakeside Lodges, Moor Lane,
York, YO24 2QU
T: (01904) 702346 &
07831 885824
F: (01904) 701631
E: neil@yorklakesidelodges.
co.uk
I: www.yorklakesidelodges.co.uk

HEART OF ENGLAND

ABBERLEY
Worcestershire

Hill Farm ★★★
Contact: Mr & Mrs M&E Reece,
Hill Farm, Wynniatts Way,
Abberley, Worcester WR6 6BZ
T: (01299) 896415

Old Yates Cottages ★★★
Contact: Mr & Mrs R M
Goodman, Old Yates Farm,
Abberley, Worcester WR6 6AT
T: (01299) 896500
F: (01299) 896065
E: oldyates@aol.com
I: www.oldyatescottages.co.uk

ALCESTER
Warwickshire

**Dorset House Cottage and
Dorset House★★★★**
Contact: Mrs G Plummer, Dorset
House, Church Street, Alcester,
Warwickshire B49 5AJ
T: (01789) 762856
F: (01789) 766165

HeronView ★★★★
Contact: Mr & Mrs Heather and
Mike Bosworth, HeronView,
Cross Guns Cottage, Mill Lane,
Oversley Green, Alcester,
Stratford-upon-Avon,
Warwickshire B49 6LF
T: (01789) 766506 &
07966 201505
F: (01789) 400851
E: heather@heronview.
freeserve.co.uk
I: www.heronview.freeserve.
co.uk

Establishments printed in blue have a detailed entry in this guide

ALDERTON
Gloucestershire
Rectory Farm Cottages
★★★-★★★★★
Contact: Mr & Mrs M A Burton, Rectory Farm Cottages, Alderton, Tewkesbury, Gloucestershire GL20 8NW
T: (01242) 620455
F: (01242) 620455
E: prburton@talk21.com
I: www.rectoryfarmcottages.co.uk

ALDERWASLEY
Derbyshire
Church View ★★★
Contact: Mr S Mihulka, Knob Cottage, Alderwasley, Belper, Derbyshire DE56 2RA
T: (01629) 823728
F: (01629) 823728

ALDSWORTH
Gloucestershire
Aldsworth Place ★★★
Contact: Mr & Mrs Munson-Kingham, Aldsworth Place, Aldsworth, Cheltenham, Gloucestershire GL54 3RE
T: (01451) 844461
F: (01451) 844871

ALDWARK
Derbyshire
The Old Coach House ★★★★
Contact: Mr Nigel John Smith, 94 Northwood Lane, Darley Dale, Matlock, Derbyshire DE4 2HR
T: (01629) 733114

ALFORD
Lincolnshire
Manor Farm Cottage ★★
Contact: Mrs R A Farrow, Manor Farm Cottage, Manor Farm, Strubby, Alford, Lincolnshire LN13 0LW
T: (01507) 450228

Woodthorpe Country Cottages
★★★★
Contact: Mrs J Stubbs, Woodthorpe Country Cottages, Woodthorpe, Alford, Lincolnshire LN13 0DD
T: (01507) 450294
F: (01507) 450294
E: secretary@woodthorpehall.com
I: www.woodthorpehall.co.uk

ALFRETON
Derbyshire
The Coach House ★★★★
Contact: Mr & Mrs D M Whitaker, The Old Vicarage, 136 Derby Road, Swanwick, Alfreton, Derbyshire DE55 1AD
T: (01773) 605116
F: (01773) 528703
E: pwhitaker@dial.pipex.com

ALKMONTON
Derbyshire
The Looseboxes Dairy House Farm ★★★★
Contact: Mr A Harris, The Looseboxes Dairy House Farm, Alkmonton, Longford, Ashbourne, Derbyshire DE6 3DG
T: (01335) 330359
F: (01335) 330359
E: b&b@dairyhousefarm.forceq.co.uk
I: www.digitalpages.co.uk/looseboxes

ALMELEY
Herefordshire
The Old Granary ★★
Contact: CH Ref:6241, Country Holidays Group Owner Services Dept, Spring Mill, Earby, Barnoldswick, Lancashire BB18 6RN
T: 0870 444 6603
F: (01282) 841539
E: sales@ttgihg.co.uk
I: www.country-holidays.co.uk

ALSOP-EN-LE-DALE
Derbyshire
Church Farm Cottages ★★★★
Contact: Mrs Christine Duffell, Church Farm, Alsop-en-le-Dale, Ashbourne, Derbyshire DE6 1QP
T: (01335) 390216
F: (01335) 390216
E: churchfarmcottages.alsop@virgin.net
I: www.cressbrook.co.uk/ashborn/churchfarm

ALSTONEFIELD
Staffordshire
Church Farm Cottage ★★★★
Contact: Mrs S Fowler, Church Farm, Stanshope, Ashbourne, Derbyshire DE6 2AD
T: (01335) 310243
F: (01335) 310243
E: sue@fowler89.fsnet.co.uk
I: www.dovedalecottages.co.uk

The Gables ★★★
Contact: Mr R McKee, Timewell Estates Plc, P O Box 15, Hoylake, Wirral, Merseyside CH48 1QQ
T: (0151) 6253264
F: (0151) 6256853
E: timewell@btconnect.com
I: www.dovedale.org.uk

Gateham Grange Cottage & The Coach House
★★★-★★★★
Contact: Mrs T Flower, Gateham Grange Cottage & The Coach House, Alstonefield, Ashbourne, Derbyshire DE6 2FT
T: (01335) 310349
E: gateham.grange@btinternet.com
I: www.peakdistrictfarmhols.co.uk

Hope Marsh Cottage
Rating Applied For
Contact: Peak Cottages, Strawberry Lee Lane, Totley Bents, Sheffield, S17 3BA
T: (0114) 262 0777
F: (0114) 262 0666
E: enquries@peakcottages.com
I: www.peakcottages.com

Kitchen Cottage ★★★★
Contact: Ms C Osborne, The Old Vicarage, Alstonefield, Ashbourne, Derbyshire DE6 2FX
T: (01335) 310453
F: (01335) 310459
E: carrieosborne@compuserve.com

ALTON
Staffordshire
Fox House Cottages ★★★★
Contact: Mr & Mrs R Aston, Fox House, Tithe Barn, Alton, Stoke-on-Trent ST10 4AZ
& (01538) 702910

Foxglove Cottage ★★★★
Contact: Country Hols Ref: 11949, Country Holidays, Spring Mill, Earby, Barnoldswick, Lancashire BB18 6RN
T: 0870 444 6603
F: (01282) 884288
E: sales@ttgigh.co.uk
I: www.country-holidays.co.uk

The Homesteads ★★★
Contact: Mrs A Smith, 24 Dove Lane, Rocester, Uttoxeter, Staffordshire ST14 5LA
T: (01889) 590062

Jasmine Cottage ★★★
Contact: Mrs M Ward, Jasmine Cottage, Tithe Barn, Alton, Stoke-on-Trent, Staffordshire ST10 4AZ
T: (01538) 702633

The Raddle Inn ★★
Contact: Mr P Wilkinson, The Raddle Inn, Quarry Bank, Hollington, Stoke-on-Trent ST10 4HQ
T: (01889) 507278 & 507568
F: (01889) 507355
E: peter@logcabin.co.uk
I: www.logcabin.co.uk

Rock Lea ★★★★
Contact: Country Holidays ref: 14147, Country Holidays Sales, Spring Mill, Earby, Barnoldswick, Lancashire BB94 0AA
T: 08700 723723
F: (01282) 844288
E: sales@ttgihg.co.uk
I: www.country-holidays.co.uk

ALVELEY
Shropshire
Shropshire Views
Rating Applied For
Contact: Mr & Mrs J Braithwaite, Hill Fields Farm, Shatterford, Kidderminster, Worcestershire DY12 1RA
T: (01299) 861253 & 861344
F: (01299) 861275

ALVESTON
Warwickshire
Tods Earth ★★★★
Contact: Mr & Mrs V Selby, 88 Old Town Mews, Stratford-upon-Avon, Warwickshire CV37 6GR
T: (01789) 414626

AMBERLEY
Gloucestershire
The Culver House ★★
Contact: Mrs M Shiner, The Culver House, Amberley, Stroud, Gloucestershire GL5 5BA
T: (01453) 873337
F: (01453) 872126

The Squirrels ★★★
Contact: Mrs V G Bowen, The Squirrels, Theescombe, Amberley, Stroud, Gloucestershire GL5 5AU
T: (01453) 836940
E: valeriebowen@thesquirrels.fsbusiness.co.uk

ARNOLD
Nottinghamshire
The Grannary ★★★
Contact: Mrs P A Lamin, The Grannary, Top House Farm, Mansfield Road, Arnold, Nottingham NG5 8PH
T: (0115) 926 8330

ASFORDBY
Leicestershire
Amberley Gardens Self-catering ★★★
Contact: Mr Bruce Brotherhood, Amberley Gardens Self-catering, 4 Church Lane, Asfordby, Melton Mowbray, Leicestershire LE14 3RU
T: (01664) 812314
F: (01664) 813740
E: doris@amberleygardens.net
I: www.amberleygardens.net

Stable Cottage ★★★★
Contact: Ms S M Gregson-Murray, The Old Rectory, Church Lane, Asfordby, Melton Mowbray, Leicestershire LE14 3RU
T: (01664) 813679
F: (0115) 9242450

ASHBOURNE
Derbyshire
Alstonefield Holiday Homes
★★★
Contact: Mr & Mrs E R Allen, Alstonefield Holiday Homes, Post Office House, Alstonefield, Ashbourne, Derbyshire DE6 2FX
T: (01335) 310201
F: (01335) 310201

Ashfield And Dove Cottages
★★★
Contact: Mr A Tatlow, Ashfield Farm, Calwich, Ashbourne, Derbyshire DE6 2EB
T: (01335) 324279 & 324443

Borrowdale Cottage ★★★
Contact: Mrs W Parratt, 24 Weydon Lane, Farnham, Surrey GU9
T: (01252) 712562

Callow Top Cottages 1 and 2
★★★
Contact: Mrs Sue Deane, Callow Top Cottages 1 and 2, Callow Top Holiday Park, Buxton Road, Ashbourne, Derbyshire DE6 2AQ
T: (01335) 344020
F: (01335) 344020
E: callotop@talk21.com
I: www.callotop.co.uk

The Coach House Ashley Cottages ★★★
Contact: Country Holidays ref: 10915 Sales, Holiday Cottages Group Limited, Spring Mill, Earby, Barnoldswick, Lancashire BB94 0AA
T: 08700 723723
F: (01282) 841539
E: sales@ttgigh.co.uk
I: www.country-holidays.co.uk

Fiddlers Barn ★★★★
Contact: Mrs E J Hopkin, Brook Cottage, Kniveton, Ashbourne, Derbyshire DE6 1JN
T: (01335) 342243

The Grooms Quarters
Rating Applied For
Contact: Mr and Mrs R J Thompson, The Grooms Quarters, The Old Coach House, Hall Lane, Wootton, Ashbourne, Derbyshire DE6 2GW
T: (01335) 324549

Establishments printed in blue have a detailed entry in this guide

Haifa
Rating Applied For
Contact: Mr David Dudley, 8
Esher Court, The Arbours,
Northampton, NN3 3RN
T: (01604) 403625 &
07778 290429
F: (01604) 403646

Hillside Croft ★ ★ ★ ★ ★
Contact: Mrs Pat Walker,
Offcote Grange, Offcote,
Ashbourne, Derbyshire DE6 1JQ
T: (01335) 344795 &
07808 899493
F: (01335) 348358
E: cottages@hillsidecroft.co.uk
I: www.hillsidecroft.co.uk

Home Farm Cottages Limited
★ ★ ★ ★ – ★ ★ ★ ★ ★
Contact: Mrs P Longley, Home
Farm Cottages Limited, Hall
Lane, Wootton, Ashbourne,
Derbyshire DE6 2GW
T: (01335) 324433
E: homefarm@hipp.demon.
co.uk
I: www.hipp.demon.co.uk

Moore's Cottage Farm
★ ★ ★ – ★ ★ ★ ★
Contact: Mr David Restrick and
Janet Watson, Moore's Cottage
Farm, Slack Lane, Upper
Mayfield, Ashbourne, Derbyshire
DE6 2JX
T: (01335) 346121 &
07932 159895
F: (01335) 300668
E: janetwatson@waitrose.com

The Old Farmhouse ★ ★ ★ ★
Contact: Mrs H Quicke, Roystone
Grange, Pikehall, Matlock,
Derbyshire DE4 2PQ
T: (01335) 390288
F: (01335) 390382
E: roystone@msn.com

Old Miller's Cottage ★ ★ ★
Contact: Mrs P M Hewitt, 45
Portway Drive, Tutbury, Burton
upon Trent, Staffordshire
DE13 9HU
T: (01283) 815895

The Orchards ★ ★ ★
Contact: Mrs Vanessa Holland,
Rushley Farm, Ilam, Ashbourne,
Derbyshire DE6 2BA
T: (01538) 308205
E: rushley.farm@talk21.com
I: www.peakdistrict-tourism.gov.
uk/peakdistrict/accomm/
theorchards/

Slade House Farm ★ ★ ★ ★
Contact: Mr & Mrs A T Philp,
Slade House Farm, Ilam,
Ashbourne, Derbyshire DE6 2BB
T: (01538) 308123
F: (01538) 308777
E: alanphilp@sladehousefarm.
co.uk
I: www.sladehousefarm.co.uk

2 Smiths Yard
Contact: Mr and Mrs P Ellis, 57
Longfield Drive, Amersham,
Buckinghamshire HP6 5HE
T: (01494) 728926 & 864225
F: (01494) 868008
E: peter@wwe.co.uk

Thorpe Cloud View ★ ★ ★ ★ ★
Contact: Mr Philip Ramsbottom,
Thorpe House, Thorpe,
Ashbourne, Derbyshire DE6 2AW
T: (01335) 350215 &
07801 839661
E: phil@ramsbottomp.fsnet.
co.uk

Woodhead Farm ★ ★
Contact: Mrs Norma Short,
Woodhead Farm, Agnes
Meadow Lane, Kniveton,
Derbyshire DE6 1JR
T: (01335) 342274

Yeldersley Hall
★ ★ ★ ★ – ★ ★ ★ ★ ★
Contact: Mr Andrew Bailey,
Yeldersley Hall, Ashbourne,
Derbyshire DE6 1LS
T: (01335) 343432
E: joanbailey@yeldersleyhall.
freeserve.co.uk

6 Bath Lane ★ ★ ★
Contact: Mrs Doreen Gasson, 13
Babelake Street, Packington,
Ashby-de-la-Zouch,
Leicestershire LE65 1WD
T: (01530) 412012

Upper Rectory Farm Cottages
★ ★ ★ ★ ★
Contact: Mrs Jean Corbett,
Cottage Farm, Norton-Juxta-
Twycross, Atherstone,
Warwickshire CV9 3QH
T: (01827) 880448
E: w.corbett@farmline.com

Churchdale Holidays
★ ★ ★ ★ ★
Contact: Mrs Sarah Winkworth-
Smith, Churchdale Holidays,
Churchdale Farm, Ashford in the
Water, Bakewell, Derbyshire
DE45 1NX
T: (01629) 640269
F: (01629) 640608
E: info@churchdaleholidays.
co.uk
I: www.churchdaleholidays.co.uk

Corner Cottage ★ ★ ★ ★ ★
Contact: Mrs Margaret Smith,
Peak District Holidays, Bar End,
Bar Road, Baslow, Bakewell,
Derbyshire DE45 1SF
T: (01246) 582140 &
07711 457744

End Cottage ★ ★ ★ ★
Contact: Mrs L Wright, Stancil
House, Barn Furlong, Great
Longstone, Bakewell, Derbyshire
DE45 1TR
T: (01629) 640136 &
07762 083674

Foxglove Cottage ★ ★ ★ ★
Contact: Mr C MacQueen, Peak
Cottages, Strawberry Lee Lane,
Totley Bents, Sheffield, S17 3BA
T: (0114) 262 0777
F: (0114) 262 0666

Green Gates ★ ★ ★
Contact: Mr C MacQueen, Peak
Cottages, Strawberry Lee Lane,
Totley Bents, Sheffield, S17 3BA
T: (0114) 2620777
F: (0114) 2620666
E: enquiries@peakcottages.com
I: www.peakcottages.com

Gritstone Cottage ★ ★ ★
Contact: Mrs Ann Lindsay,
Gritstone House, Greaves Lane,
Ashford in the Water, Bakewell,
Derbyshire DE45 1QH
T: (01629) 813563
F: (01629) 813563

Little Batch ★ ★ ★ ★ ★
Contact: Mrs J Stephens, 1 Hall
End Lane, Ashford in the Water,
Bakewell, Derbyshire DE45 1QJ
T: (01629) 813909
F: (01629) 813909

Thorpe Cottage ★ ★ ★ ★
Contact: Mrs Sheila Newman, 14
Pool Drive, Bessacarr, Doncaster,
South Yorkshire DN4 6UX
T: (01302) 536763
F: (01302) 536763

Underwood ★ ★ ★ ★
Contact: Mrs P E Hollingworth,
Brushfield House, Church Street,
Ashford in the Water, Bakewell,
Derbyshire DE45 1QB
T: (01629) 812128

Berrow Farm Cottage ★ ★ ★ ★
Contact: Mrs P M Barter, Berrow
Farm, Ashleworth, Gloucester
GL19 4JW
T: (01452) 700323

Little Manor ★ ★ ★ ★
Contact: Mrs S M Barnes,
Ashleworth Manor, Ashleworth,
Gloucester GL19 4LA
T: (01452) 700350 & 700350
F: (01452) 700350
E: rjb@ashleworthmanor.fsnet.
co.uk

Holestone Moor Barns
★ ★ ★ – ★ ★ ★ ★
Contact: Mr & Mrs Clemerson,
Holestone Moor Barns,
Holestone Moor Farm,
Holestone Moor, Ashover,
Chesterfield, Derbyshire S45 0JS
T: (01246) 591263 & 590923
F: (01246) 591263
E: enquiries@hmbarns.co.uk
I: www.hmbarns.co.uk

Stone House ★ ★ ★
Contact: Ms Shirley Mason,
Stone House, Ashton,
Leominster, Herefordshire
HR6 0DN
T: (01584) 711461

Vale Farm House ★ ★ ★ ★
Contact: Mrs E Zanotto, Vale
Farm House, Stoke Road,
Ashton, Northampton NN7 2JN
T: (01604) 863696 &
07802 417701
F: (01604) 862859

The Cider House ★ ★ ★ ★
Contact: Mr & Mrs B Bunn,
Windy Ridge, Cottons Lane,
Ashton-under-Hill, Evesham,
Worcestershire WR11 6SS
T: (01386) 881009
E: cider.house@virgin.net.
I: freespace.virgin.net/brian.
bunn/index.htm

Workshop Cottage ★ ★ ★ ★
Contact: Mr & Mrs A Cole,
Martins, Temple Road, Aslackby,
Sleaford, Lincolnshire NG34 0HJ
T: (01778) 440113 &
07885 561780
F: (01778) 440920

Aslockton Grange Cottage
★ ★ ★
Contact: Mrs Thompson,
Aslockton Grange Cottage,
Aslockton Grange, Aslockton,
Nottingham, Nottinghamshire
NG13 9AJ
T: (01949) 850204 &
07860 599946

The Granary ★ ★ ★ ★
Contact: Mrs L Morgan, Rowton
Grange, Aston-on-Clun, Craven
Arms, Shropshire SY7 0PA
T: (01588) 660227
F: (01588) 660227
E: all@rowtongrange.freeserve.
co.uk

Hipsley Farm Cottages ★ ★ ★ ★
Contact: Mrs A Prosser, Waste
Farm, Hurley, Atherstone,
Warwickshire CV9 2LR
T: (01827) 872437
F: (01827) 872437
E: ann@hipsley.co.uk
I: www.hipsley.co.uk

Hillview ★ ★ ★
Contact: Mrs M Justice, Hillview,
Staythorpe Road, Averham,
Newark, Nottinghamshire
NG23 5RA
T: (01636) 702874
F: (01636) 702874

Poulton Court ★ ★ ★
Contact: Mr and Mrs M
MacFarlane, Poulton Court,
Poulton Court Farm, Awre,
Newnham-on-Severn,
Gloucestershire GL14 1ES
T: (01594) 510249
F: (01594) 510249

The Bungalow ★ ★ ★
Contact: Mr & Mrs T Price,
Sussex Acres, Lower Lye,
Aymestrey, Leominster,
Herefordshire HR6 9TA
T: (01568) 770582 &
07980 094289

Cordwainer Cottage ★ ★ ★
Contact: Mrs M Buckle,
Cordwainer Cottage, Stoney
Villa Farm, Salters Well, Bagnall,
Stoke-on-Trent, Staffordshire
ST9 9JY
T: (01782) 302575
F: (01782) 302575

BAKEWELL
Derbyshire

Anne Cottage ★★★★★
Contact: Mrs Margaret Smith, Peak District Holidays, Bar End, Bar Road, Baslow, Bakewell, Derbyshire DE45 1SF
T: (01246) 582140 &
07711 457744

Bakewell Holiday Cottages (Coach Cottage and Brew House)★★★★
Contact: Mrs Caroline Hinchliffe, Bakewell Holiday Cottages Avondale, Haddon Road, Bakewell, Derbyshire DE45 1EP
T: (01629) 814102
F: (01629) 815077
E: coachcott@aol.com
I: www.bakewellcottages.co.uk

Ball Cross Farm Cottages ★★★★
Contact: Mrs J Edwards, Ball Cross Farm Cottages, Chatsworth Estate, Bakewell, Derbyshire DE45 1PE
T: (01629) 815215
E: info@ballcrossfarm.com
I: www.ballcrossfarm.com

The Barn ★★★★
Contact: Mr G J Raymont, 44 Newland Lane, Ash Green, Coventry, CV7 9BA
T: (024) 76644173 &
0774 8543829

Bay Tree Cottage
Rating Applied For
Contact: Mrs P Green, 81 Belmont Road, Kirkby-in-Ashfield, Nottingham NG17 9DY
T: (01623) 754617
E: rdg3@lineone.net

Bolehill Farm Holiday Cottages ★★–★★★
Contact: Mr A J Staley, Bolehill Farm Holiday Cottages, Monyash Road, Bakewell, Derbyshire DE45 1QW
T: (01629) 812359
F: (01629) 812359
E: tonystaley@hotmail.com
I: www.bolehillfarmcottages.co.uk

Burton Cottage ★★
Contact: Mr & Mrs R Bosett, Lane Side, Duck Row, Pilsley Village, Bakewell, Derbyshire DE45 1UJ
T: (01246) 583545
F: (01246) 583075
E: bosettr@supanet.com

Carter's Mill Cottage ★★★★
Contact: Mrs S J Marsden, Mill Farm, Haddon Grove, Over Haddon, Bakewell, Derbyshire DE45 1JF
T: (01629) 812013
F: (01629) 814734

Cosy Cottage
Rating Applied For
Contact: Peak Cottages, Strawberry Lee Lane, Totley Bents, Sheffield, S17 3BA
T: (0114) 262 0777
F: (0114) 262 0666
E: enquiries@peakcottages.com
I: www.peakcottages.com

The Cottage ★★★★
Contact: Mrs L Wright, Stancil House, Barn Furlong, Great Longstone, Bakewell, Derbyshire DE45 1TR
T: (01629) 640136 &
07762 083674

Dale End Farm ★★★
Contact: Mrs E M Hague, Dale End Farm, Gratton Dale, Youlgreave, Bakewell, Derbyshire DE45 1LN
T: (01629) 650453
E: john.elizabeth.hague@talk21.com

Dale View Farm
Rating Applied For
Contact: Mrs Janet Frost, Dale View Farm, Gratton, Bakewell, Derbyshire DE45 1LN
T: (01629) 650670

East View ★★★★
Contact: Mr & Mrs F Dickinson, Meadow View, Coombes Road, Bakewell, Derbyshire DE45 1AQ
T: (01629) 812961 &
07967 265072

Edge View ★★★★
Contact: Mrs G P Rogers, Penylan, Monyash Road, Bakewell, Derbyshire DE45 1FG
T: (01629) 813336
F: (01629) 813336

Endcliff Cottage ★★★
Contact: Mrs S J Marriott, Endcliff House, The Orchard, Stanedge Road, Bakewell, Derbyshire DE45 1DG
T: (01629) 813687
E: mike.marriott@btinternet.com

Four Winds ★★★
Contact: Mr C Sykes, Sykes Cottages, York House, York Street, Chester, CH1 3LR
T: (01244) 345700
F: (01244) 321442
E: info@sykescottages.co.uk
I: www.sykescottages.co.uk

Haddon Grove Farm Cottages ★★★
Contact: Mr J H Boxall, Haddon Grove Farm Cottages, Haddon Grove Farm, Monyash Road, Bakewell, Derbyshire DE45 1JF
T: (01629) 813551
F: (01629) 815684

Harthill Hall Country House Cottages★★★★–★★★★★
Contact: Mrs Nicola Bunting, Harthill Hall Country House Cottages, Alport, Bakewell, Derbyshire DE45 1LH
T: (01629) 636190 &
07703 126635
F: (01629) 636967
E: nicola@harthillhall.co.uk
I: www.harthillhall.co.uk

Limestone Cottage ★★★
Contact: Mrs V Hartley, 1 Church Street, Ashford in the Water, Bakewell, Derbyshire DE45 1QB
T: (01629) 813230
E: b&b@hartleycons.co.uk

Mannerswood View ★★★★
Contact: Mrs Kathleen Sheldon, 47 Drabbles Road, Matlock, Derbyshire DE4 3LD
T: (01629) 55163

Meadows
Rating Applied For
Contact: Peak Cottages, Strawberry Lee Lane, Totley Bents, Sheffield, S17 3BA
T: (0114) 262 0777
F: (0114) 262 0666
E: enquiries@peakcottages.com
I: www.peakcottages.com

1 Milford Bungalow ★★★
Contact: Country Holidays ref: 8694 Sales, Holiday Cottages Group Limited, Spring Mill, Earby, Barnoldswick, Lancashire BB94 0AA
T: 08700 723723
F: (01282) 844288
I: www.country-holidays.co.uk

The Penthouse ★★★★★
Contact: Mrs E Buxton, Bearda Mill, Swythamley, Macclesfield, Cheshire SK11 0RE
T: (01260) 227276 &
(01270) 766421
F: (01270) 768912

Puddle Dux Cottage ★★★★
Contact: Mr Colin MacQueen, Peak Cottages, Strawberry Lee Lane, Totley Bents, Sheffield, S17 3BA
T: (0114) 2620777
F: (0114) 2620666
E: enquiries@peakcottages.com
I: www.peakcottages.com

Riverside Apartment ★★★★
Contact: Mr Colin MacQueen, Peak Cottages, Strawberry Lee Lane, Totley Bents, Sheffield, S17 3BA
T: (0114) 2620777
F: (0114) 2620666
E: enquiries@peakcottages.com
I: www.peakcottages.com

Rozel ★★★★
Contact: Mr Colin MacQueen, Peak Cottages, Strawberry Lee Lane, Totley Bents, Sheffield, S17 3BA
T: (0114) 2620777
F: (0114) 2620666
E: enquiries@peakcottages.com
I: www.peakcottages.com

Shutts Farm ★★★★
Contact: Mr and Mrs Corbridge, Orchard Close, The Shutts, Bakewell, Derbyshire DE45 1JA
T: (01629) 813639 &
07866 821305

Spout Farm ★★★
Contact: Mrs Ena Patterson, The Bungalow, Elton, Matlock, Derbyshire DE4 2BY
T: (01629) 650358

Yuletide Cottage ★★★
Contact: Mr & Mrs D Figg, c/o Hollands Butcher's Shop, Church Street, Youlgrave, Bakewell, Derbyshire DE45 1UR
T: (01629) 636234

BALLIDON
Derbyshire

Rachels Croft ★★★★
Contact: Mrs Alison Edge, Oldfield House, Ballidon, Ashbourne, Derbyshire DE6 1QX
T: (01335) 390587

BAMFORD
Derbyshire

Derwent View ★★★★
Contact: Mr & Mrs P Mannion, 12 Ashopton Drive, Bamford, Hope Valley, Derbyshire S33 0BU
T: (01433) 651637 &
07773 701737

Shatton Hall Farm ★★★★
Contact: Mrs A H Kellie, Shatton Hall Farm, Bamford, Hope Valley S33 0BG
T: (01433) 620635
F: (01433) 620689
E: a.j.kellie@virgin.net
I: freespace.virgin.net/a.j.kellie/home.htm

Thornhill View ★★★
Contact: Mrs Joyce Fairbairn, Thornhill View, Hope Road, Bamford, Hope Valley, Derbyshire S33 0AL
T: (01433) 651823 &
07790 814173

Thornseat Cottage ★★★
Contact: Mr Colin MacQueen, Peak Cottages, Strawberry Lee Lane, Totley Bents, Sheffield, S17 3BA
T: (0114) 2620777
F: (0114) 2620666
E: enquiries@peakcottages.com
I: www.peakcottages.com

Wesley Cottage ★★★
Contact: Mr Colin MacQueen, Peak Cottages, Strawberry Lee Lane, Totley Bents, Sheffield, S17 3BA
T: (0114) 2620777
F: (0114) 2620666
E: enquiries@peakcottages.com
I: www.peakcottages.com

BARBER BOOTH
Derbyshire

The Old Stable ★★★
Contact: Colin MacQueen, Peak Cottages, Paddock Cottage, Strawberry Lee Lane, Totley Bents, Sheffield, S17 3BA
T: (0114) 2620777
F: (0114) 2620666

BARFORD
Warwickshire

The Barn ★★★★
Contact: Mrs M Peirson, The Barn, 46 Church Street, Barford, Warwick CV35 8EN
T: (01926) 624145
E: marypeirson@compuserve.co.uk

Harvest Barn ★★★★
Contact: Mr & Mrs Bottomley, Harvest Barn, 15 Chestnut Grove, Barley Fields, Main Street, Moreton Morrell, Warwick, Warwickshire CV35 9DG
T: (01926) 651669

BARLASTON
Staffordshire
Wedgwood Memorial College ★★
Contact: Ms Elaine Heather, Wedgwood Memorial College, Station Road, Barlaston, Stoke-on-Trent, Staffordshire ST12 9DG
T: (01782) 372105 & 373427
F: (01782) 372393
E: wedgwood.college@staffordshire.gov.uk
I: www.aredu.org.uk/wedgwoodcollege

BARLOW
Derbyshire
Heron Lodge ★★★★
Contact: Mrs P Moffatt, Heron Lodge, Oxton Rakes Hall Farm, Barlow, Derbyshire S18 7SE
T: (0114) 2899290
F: (0114) 2899260
E: bookings@heron-lodge.hypermart.net
I: heron-lodge.hypermart.net

Mill Farm Cottage ★★-★★★
Contact: Mrs O M Ward, Mill Farm Cottage, Mill Farm, Barlow, Dronfield S18 7TJ
T: (0114) 289 0543
E: cottages@barfish.fsnet.co.uk
I: www.barlowlakes.co.uk

BARROW UPON SOAR
Leicestershire
Kingfisher Cottage ★★★★
Contact: Mr J Matthews, 114 Main Street, Woodhouse Eaves, Loughborough, Leicestershire LE12 8RZ
T: (01509) 890244
E: nikkidavid@aol.com
I: www.englishcottages.com

BASLOW
Derbyshire
Corner Cottage ★★★★
Contact: Peak Cottages, Strawberry Lee Lane, Totley Bents, Sheffield, S17 3BA
T: (0114) 2620777
F: (0114) 2620666
E: enquiries@peakcottages.com
I: www.peakcottages.com

Goose Green Apartment ★★★★
Contact: Mr D W Bailey, Goose Green Apartment, c/o Goose Green Tearooms, Nether End, Baslow, Bakewell, Derbyshire DE45 1SR
T: (01246) 583000
E: mail@goosegreen-tearooms.co.uk
I: www.goosegreen-tearooms.co.uk

Goose Green Cottage ★★★★★
Contact: Ms Margaret Smith, Peak District Holidays, Bar End, Bar Road, Baslow, Bakewell, Derbyshire DE45 1SF
T: (01246) 582140

**Hall Cottage
Rating Applied For**
Contact: Mr & Mrs R W Griffiths, Beechcroft, School Lane, Baslow, Bakewell, Derbyshire DE45 1RZ
T: (01246) 582900
F: (01246) 583675
E: hallcottage@btinternet.com

**Tom's Cottage
Rating Applied For**
Contact: Ms Hazel Bell, Nether Croft, Eaton Place, Baslow, Bakewell, Derbyshire DE45 1RW
T: (01246) 583564
E: nethercroftBandB@aol.com

Wrose Cottage ★★★
Contact: Mrs J Cartledge, Bramley Court, Waterside, Calver Road, Baslow, Bakewell, Derbyshire DE45 1RR
T: (01246) 583131
F: (01246) 583131

BAUMBER
Lincolnshire
Gathman's Cottage ★★★
Contact: Mrs W Harrison, Manor Farm, Hemingby, Horncastle, Lincolnshire LN9 5QF
T: (01507) 578352
F: (01507) 578352
E: gathmans@freenetname.co.uk
I: www.gathmanscottage.co.uk

BAYTON
Worcestershire
The Mill House ★★
Contact: Mrs J Chance, The Mill House, Bayton, Clows Top, Kidderminster, Worcestershire DY14 9LP
T: (01299) 832608
F: (01299) 832137
E: janechnc@aol.com
I: www.themillhouse-bayton.co.uk

BEELEY
Derbyshire
Brookside Cottage ★★★
Contact: Country Hols Ref: 1118, Country Holidays Group Owner Services Dept, Spring Mill, Earby, Barnoldswick, Lancashire BB18 6RN
T: 0870 444 6603
F: (01282) 844288
I: www.country-holidays.co.uk

BELMESTHORPE
Rutland
Elder Flower Cottage ★★★
Contact: Mr and Mrs Wilkinson, Meadow View, Shepherds Walk, Belmesthorpe, Stamford, Lincolnshire PE9 4JG
T: (01780) 757188 & 07711 533204
F: (01780) 757188

BELPER
Derbyshire
Chevin Green Farm ★★★
Contact: Mr C A Postles, Chevin Green Farm, Chevin Road, Belper, Derby DE56 2UN
T: (01773) 822328
F: (01773) 822328
E: spostles@globalnet.co.uk
I: chevingreenfarm.co.uk

**Chevin House Farm Cottages
Chevin House Farm ★★★★**
Contact: Mr & Mrs M Jordan, Chevin House Farm Cottages Chevin House Farm, Chevin Road, Belper, Derby DE56 2UN
T: (01773) 823144
F: (01773) 823144
E: jordan@chevinhousefarm.co.uk

The Sheiling ★★★
Contact: Country Holidays ref: 12853 Sales, Holidays Cottages Group Limited, Spring Mill, Earby, Barnoldswick, Lancashire BB94 0AA
T: 08700 723723
F: (01282) 844288
E: sales@ttgihg.co.uk
I: www.country-holidays.co.uk

Wiggonlea Stable ★★★★
Contact: Mrs SR Spendlove, Wiggonlea Stable, Wiggonlea Farm, Alderwasley, Belper, Derbyshire DE56 2RE
T: (01773) 852344
E: ruth@wiggonlea.fsnet.co.uk
I: www.wiggonlea.fsnet.co.uk

BERRY HILL
Gloucestershire
South View House ★★
Contact: Mrs Mandy Crook, 12 Machen Road, Broadwell, Coleford, Gloucestershire GL16 7BU
T: (01594) 835557

BEWDLEY
Worcestershire
The Brant ★★★★
Contact: Mrs Helen Robson, Chapel House, Heightington, Bewdley, Worcestershire DY12 2XY
T: (01299) 825603
F: (01299) 825603

Painsmore Cottage ★★
Contact: Mrs S J Drummy, Dowles House, Bewdley, Worcestershire DY12 3AA
T: (01299) 403137

Peacock Coach House ★★★★
Contact: Mrs P Hall, Peacock House, Lower Park, Bewdley, Worcestershire DY12 2DP
T: (01299) 400149 & 07788 416439
F: (01299) 401082
E: priscahall@hotmail.com

Riverview Cottage ★★★
Contact: Mr & Mrs J Giles, The Lodge, Station Road, Bewdley, Worcestershire DY12 1BT
T: (01299) 403481 & 402546

Severn Valley Properties ★★★
Contact: Mr & Mrs G Parker, Severn Valley Properties, Elm House, Kidderminster Road, Wribbenhall, Bewdley, Worcestershire DY12 1LJ
T: (01299) 402030
F: (01299) 266900

The White Cottage Garden Flat ★★★★
Contact: Mrs S A Tallents, The White Cottage, Kinlet, Bewdley, Worcestershire DY12 3BD
T: (01299) 841238
F: (01299) 841482
E: sallytallents@talk21.com

BIBURY
Gloucestershire
Bibury Holiday Cottages Coln Court★★★
Contact: Mr A R Binns, Cotswold Heritage Ltd, Coln Cottage, Arlington, Bibury, Cirencester, Gloucestershire GL7 5NL
T: (01285) 740314
F: (01285) 740314

Cotteswold House Cottages ★★★★
Contact: Mrs Judith Underwood, Cotteswold House, Arlington, Bibury, Cirencester, Gloucestershire GL7 5ND
T: (01285) 740609
F: (01285) 740609
E: cotteswold.house@btclick.com
I: home.btclick.com/cotteswold.house

Hartwell Farm Cottages ★★★-★★★★★
Contact: Mrs E C Mann, Hartwell Farm, Ready Token, Cirencester, Gloucestershire GL7 5SY
T: (01285) 740210
F: (01285) 740210

BIRCH VALE
Derbyshire
Hallishaw Cote ★★★★
Contact: Mrs Jennifer Hallam, Cold Harbour Farm, New Mills, High Peak, Derbyshire SK22 4QJ
T: (01663) 746155 & 749953
F: (01663) 743299
E: george.hallam@ic24.net
I: www.hallishawcote.co.uk

BIRCHOVER
Derbyshire
Birchover Cottages ★★★
Contact: Mr C MacQueen, Peak Cottages, Strawberry Lee Lane, Totley Bents, Sheffield, S17 3BA
T: (0114) 262 0777
F: (0114) 262 0666

Robin's Rest ★★
Contact: Mr C MacQueen, Peak Cottages, Strawberry Lee Lane, Totley Bents, Sheffield, S17 3BA
T: (0114) 262 0777
F: (0114) 262 0666

Uppertown Hayloft ★★★
Contact: Mr Colin MacQueen, Peak Cottages, Strawberry Lee Lane, Totley Bents, Sheffield, S17 3BA
T: (0114) 2620777
F: (0114) 2620666
E: enquiries@peakcottages.com
I: www.peakcottages.com

BIRMINGHAM
West Midlands
Sandon Apartment ★★★
Contact: Ms V Price, Sandon Apartment, 385 Hagley Road, Edgbaston, Birmingham B17 8DL
T: (0121) 420 2301
F: (0121) 429 5155

BIRTLEY
Shropshire
Hinds Cottage ★★★★
Contact: Mrs H Newby, White House Farm, Deerfold, Birtley, Bucknell, Shropshire SY7 0EF
T: (01568) 770242
E: geof.newby@lycos.com
I: www.hindscottage.co.uk

BISHOP'S CASTLE
Shropshire

Apple Tree Cottage ★ ★ ★ ★
Contact: Mrs J Brickett, Apple Tree, White Gritt, Minsterley, Shrewsbury, Shropshire SY5 0JN
T: (01588) 650331
E: JJ@331appletree.freeserve. co.uk
I: www.cottageguide. co.uk/appletree

Claremont ★ ★ ★
Contact: Mrs A Price, Claremont, Bishop's Castle, Shropshire SY9 5BW
T: (01588) 638170
F: (01588) 638170
E: price@claremontcottages. freeserve.co.uk
I: www.priceclaremont.co.uk

The Firs ★ ★ ★
Contact: Mr Sykes, Sykes Cottage, York House, York Street, Chester, CH1 3LR
T: (01244) 345700
F: (01244) 321442
E: info@sykescottages.co.uk
I: www.sykescottages.co.uk

Mount Cottage ★ ★ ★ ★
Contact: Mr P Roberts, 2 Bastick House, Bull Lane, Bishop's Castle, Shropshire SY9 5DA
T: (01588) 638281

Walkmill Cottage ★ ★ ★
Contact: Mr B Preston, Walkmill Cottage, Wentnor, Bishop's Castle, Shropshire SY9 5DZ
T: (01588) 650671

BISHOP'S CLEEVE
Gloucestershire

Northgate ★ ★ ★ ★
Contact: Mr & Mrs R J Warner, The Skerries, Station Road, Woodmancote, Cheltenham, Gloucestershire GL52 9HR
T: (01242) 676143

BISHOPS FROME
Herefordshire

The Chapel ★ ★ ★
Contact: Mrs D Harrison, Cheyney Park, Bishops Frome, Worcester WR6 5AS
T: (01531) 640846
F: (01531) 640846

BISLEY
Gloucestershire

Coopers Cottage ★ ★ ★
Contact: Mr & Mrs M G Flint, Wells Cottage, Bisley, Stroud, Gloucestershire GL6 7AG
T: (01452) 770289

Rose Cottage ★ ★ ★ ★
Contact: Mr James Meyer, 14a Hesper Mews, London SW5 0HH
T: (0207) 835 0444
E: lindaycamp@aol.com
I: www.rosecottage.co.uk

BITTERLEY
Shropshire

Angel House ★ ★ ★
Contact: Mr & Mrs Henry John Mears, Angel House, Angel Bank, Bitterley, Ludlow, Shropshire SY8 3HT
T: (01584) 890 755
F: (01584) 890 755

BLACKBROOK
Staffordshire

Nags Head Farm Cottages ★ ★ ★
Contact: Mr D Leathem, Nags Head Farm, Nantwich Road, Blackbrook, Newcastle-under-Lyme, Staffordshire ST5 5EH
T: (01782) 680334
E: dave.nagsheadfarm.@ breathenet
I: www. holidaycottagesstaffordshire. co.uk

BLAKENEY
Gloucestershire

Orchard Cottage ★ ★ ★
Contact: Mrs S Thomas, Orchard Cottage, C/O Gable Cottage, Furnace Valley, Blakeney, Gloucestershire GL15 4DH
T: (01594) 510537
F: (01594) 516336

BLANKNEY
Lincolnshire

Blankney Golf Club ★ ★ ★
Contact: Mr D Priest, Blankney Golf Club, Blankney, Lincoln LN4 3AZ
T: (01526) 320263
F: (01526) 322521

BLOCKLEY
Gloucestershire

Brookdale ★ ★ ★
Contact: Mrs A Taylor, The Stables, Mill Lane, Broom, Alcester, Warwickshire B50 4HS
T: (01789) 778674

Buttercup Cottage ★ ★ ★ ★
Contact: Mrs C Bromley, Richard David Automobiles Ltd, PO Box 125, Leamington Spa, Warwickshire CV32 6RY
T: (01926) 420202 & 424683

Cinquefoil Cottage ★ ★ ★
Contact: Mrs Patricia Hinksman, 45 Brookmans Avenue, Brookmans Park, Hatfield, Hertfordshire AL9 7QH
T: (01707) 652485

Honeysuckle Cottage ★ ★ ★
Contact: Miss P Street, Field House, Bibsworth Lane, Broadway, Worcestershire WR12 7LW
T: (01386) 858667
E: pamakin@talk21.com

Julianas Court ★ ★ ★ ★
Contact: Mr T R Lomas, The Cedars, 92 Prestbury Road, Macclesfield, Cheshire SK10 3BN
T: (01625) 613701
E: emlomas@hotmail.com

Lower Farm Cottages ★ ★ ★–★ ★ ★ ★
Contact: Mrs K Batchelor, Lower Farm Cottages, Lower Farmhouse, Blockley, Moreton-in-Marsh, Gloucestershire GL56 9DP
T: (01386) 700237
F: (01386) 700237
I: www.lower-farm.co.uk

BOCKLETON
Worcestershire

1 Grafton Cottage ★ ★
Contact: Mrs S Thomas, Grafton Farm, Bockleton, Tenbury Wells, Worcestershire WR15 8PT
T: (01568) 750602
E: grafton.farm@btinternet.com

BODENHAM
Herefordshire

The Forge ★ ★ ★–★ ★ ★ ★
Contact: Mrs M E Timmer, The Forge, Bodenham, Hereford HR1 3JZ
T: (01568) 797144
E: andy-timmer@bodenham. freeserve.co.uk
I: www.bodenhamforge.co.uk

BONSALL
Derbyshire

Croft Cottage ★ ★ ★ ★
Contact: Mr Colin MacQueen, Peak Cottages Ltd, Strawberry Lee Lane, Totley Bents, Sheffield, S17 3BA
T: (0114) 2620777
F: (0114) 2620666
E: enquiries@peakcottages.com
I: www.peakcottages.com

Hollies Cottage ★ ★ ★
Contact: Mrs J Mountney, 38 High Street, Bonsall, Matlock, Derbyshire DE4 2AR
T: (01629) 823162 & 823909

Old School House Cottage ★ ★ ★
Contact: Mr Colin MacQueen, Peak Cottages, Strawberry Lee Lane, Totley Bents, Sheffield, S17 3BA
T: (0114) 2620777
F: (0114) 2620666
E: enquiries@peakcottages.com
I: www.peakcottages.com

BOSTON
Lincolnshire

The Lodge at Pinewood ★ ★ ★
Contact: Ms Sylvia Kilshaw, Pinewood, Ralphs Lane, Frampton West, Boston, Lincolnshire PE20 1QZ
T: (01205) 723739
F: (01205) 723739
E: skilshaw@pinewood99. demon.co.uk

BOURTON–ON–THE–WATER
Gloucestershire

Annes Cottage ★ ★ ★ ★
Contact: Mrs A Oakes, White Rails Farm, Atch Lench, Evesham, Worcestershire WR11 5SP
T: (01386) 870727 & 07712 112998
F: (01386) 870727
E: deborah.oakes@ persona-mgt.co.uk

Bobble Cottage ★ ★ ★
Contact: Country Holidays reference: 15430, Spring Mill, Barnoldswick, Lancashire BB94 0AS
T: 08700 723 723
F: (01281) 841539
E: sales@ttgihg.co.uk
I: www.country-holidays.co.uk

Captains Cabin and Crows Nest ★ ★ ★ ★
Contact: CH ref: 11214,12028, Country Holidays Group Owner Services Dept, Spring Mill, Earby, Barnoldswick, Lancashire BB18 6RN
T: 0870 444 6603
F: (01282) 841539
E: sales@ttgihg.co.uk
I: www.country-holidays.co.uk

**The Chesters
Rating Applied For**
Contact: Miss Wendy Ratcliffe, Avalon, Rissington Road, Bourton-on-the-Water, Cheltenham, Gloucestershire GL54 2DX
T: (01451) 821014

The Coach House of the Dower House ★ ★
Contact: Mrs P Adams, The Dower House, Bourton-on-the-Water, Cheltenham, Gloucestershire GL54 2AP
T: (01451) 820629

Cotswold Cottage Company ★ ★ ★ ★
Contact: Mrs Deirdre Boyle, Cotswold Cottage Company, Wells Head, Temple Guiting, Cheltenham, Gloucestershire GL54 5RR
T: (01451) 850560
F: (01451) 850241
E: cotscoto@email.msn.com
I: www.cotswoldcottage.co.uk

Farncombe Apartment ★ ★ ★
Contact: Mrs J M Wright, Farncombe Apartment, Clapton, Bourton-on-the-Water, Cheltenham, Gloucestershire GL54 2LG
T: (01451) 820120 & 07714 701142
F: (01451) 820120
E: jwrightbb@aol.com
I: www.SmoothHound. co.uk/hotels/farncombe.html

Florries Cottage ★ ★ ★
Contact: Country Holidays - 1362 Sales, Holiday Cottages Group Limited, Spring Mill, Earby, Barnoldswick, Lancashire BB94 0AA
T: 08700 723723
F: (01282) 844288
E: sales@ttgihg.co.uk
I: www.country-holidays.co.uk

Greenleighs ★ ★ ★ ★
Contact: Mrs J Tombs, The Old Forge, Tytherington, Wotton-under-Edge, Gloucestershire GL12 8UH
T: (01454) 419760

Little Baines Cottage, Bow Cottage and Well Cottage ★ ★ ★ ★
Contact: Mrs J Fracasso, Home Farm House, Little Rissington, Cheltenham, Gloucestershire GL54 2NA
T: (01451) 820691

Establishments printed in blue have a detailed entry in this guide

Magnolia Cottage Apartment
★★★★
Contact: Mr & Mrs M Cotterill,
Magnolia Cottage, Lansdowne,
Bourton-on-the-Water,
Cheltenham, Gloucestershire
GL54 2AR
T: (01451) 821841
F: (01451) 821841
E: kgrist@glos.businesslink.
co.uk
I: www.cottageguide.
co.uk/magnolia

Oxleigh Cottages ★★★★
Contact: Mrs B Smith, Dairy
House Farm, Croxton Lane,
Middlewich, Cheshire CW10 9LA
T: (01606) 833245 &
0773 474108
F: (01606) 837139
E: bsmith_croxton@yahoo.
co.uk

Pear Tree Cottage
Rating Applied For
Contact: Mrs J Farace, 27 Park
Road, Chipping Norton,
Oxfordshire OX7 5PA
T: (01608) 644737

Pheasant Walk ★★★★
Contact: Mrs P Avery, Pheasant
Walk, Grove Farm, Cold Aston,
Cheltenham, Gloucestershire
GL54 3BJ
T: (01451) 810942
F: (01451) 810942
E: grovefarm@coldaston.fsnet.
co.uk

Southview and Courtyard
Cottages ★★★-★★★★
Contact: Mr and Mrs Nando &
Joyce Fracasso, Southview and
Courtyard Cottages, c/o Home
Farm House, Little Rissington,
Bourton-on-the-Water,
Cheltenham, Gloucestershire
GL54 2NA
T: (01451) 820691

Tagmoor Hollow Apartment
★★★★
Contact: Mrs G Bennett,
Tagmoor Hollow, Marshmouth
Lane, Bourton-on-the-Water,
Cheltenham, Gloucestershire
GL54 2EE
T: (01451) 821307

Well Cottage ★★★★
Contact: Mr & Mrs J Roberts,
Wayside Cottage, Letch Lane,
Bourton-on-the-Water,
Cheltenham, Gloucestershire
GL54 2DG
T: (01451) 824059
F: (01451) 810940

BRACKLEY
Northamptonshire

Iletts Courtyard ★★★★
Contact: Mrs S Bellingham, Iletts
Farm, Whitfield, Brackley,
Northamptonshire NN13 7TY
T: (01280) 703244 &
07714 689206
F: (01280) 703244
E: iletts@clara.co.uk
I: home.clara.net/iletts

BRADLEY
Derbyshire

Briar, Primrose and Bluebell
Cottages ★★★
Contact: Mrs J Hinds, Yeldersley
Old Hall Farm, Yeldersley Lane,
Bradley, Ashbourne, Derbyshire
DE6 1PH
T: (01335) 344504
F: (01335) 344504
E: janethindsfarm@yahoo.co.uk
I: www.
ashbourne-accommodation.
co.uk

Coppice Farm ★★★★
Contact: Country Holidays ref:
967 Sales, Holiday Cottages
Group Limited, Spring Mill,
Earby, Barnoldswick, Lancashire
BB94 0AA
T: 08700 723723
F: (01282) 844288
E: sales@ttgihg.co.uk
I: www.country-holidays.co.uk

Shepherds Folly ★★★★
Contact: Mrs Kathy Cowley,
Shepherds Folly, Bradley,
Ashbourne, Derbyshire DE6 1LL
T: (01335) 343315 &
(0114) 2620777

BRADNOP
Staffordshire

The Coach House ★★★★★
Contact: Mr E J Torr, Brook Farm,
Bradnop, Leek, Staffordshire
ST13 7NQ
T: (01538) 383113

Millstones ★★★
Contact: Mrs J Edwards,
Millstones, Ashbourne Road,
Bottomhouse, Bradnop, Leek,
Staffordshire ST13 7NZ
T: (01538) 304548

School House ★★★★★
Contact: Mr C Sykes, Sykes
Cottages, York House, York
Street, Chester, CH1 3LR
T: (01244) 345700
F: (01244) 321442
E: info@sykescottages.co.uk
I: www.sykescottages.co.uk

BRADWELL
Derbyshire

Bridge End Barn ★★★★
Contact: Mrs G Gascoyne,
Bridge End Barn, Brough,
Bradwell, Hope Valley S33 9HG
T: (01433) 621258

The Croft and Edge View
★★★-★★★★
Contact: Mr Sykes, Sykes
Cottage, York House, York
Street, Chester, CH1 3LR
T: (01244) 345700
F: (01244) 321442
E: info@sykescottages.co.uk
I: www.sykescottages.co.uk

Derwent Cottage ★★★
Contact: Mr Mark Gilbertson,
124 Cranbrook Road, Chiswick,
London W4 2LJ
& (020) 8747 9450
E: markanddoona@hotmail.com

Smalldale
Rating Applied For
Contact: Mr C Sykes, Sykes
Cottages, York House, York
Street, Chester, CH1 3LR
T: (01244) 345700
F: (01244) 321442
E: info@sykescottages.co.uk
I: www.sykescottages.co.uk

BRAILES
Warwickshire

Mill Holm Cottage and Mill
Flat ★★★
Contact: Mr R M Case,
Whichford Mill, Cherington,
Shipston-on-Stour,
Warwickshire CV36 5JB
T: (01608) 686537
E: RODCASE29@HOTMAIL.COM
I: WWW.COTTAGEGUIDE.CO.
UK/WHICHFORDMILL

BRAILSFORD
Derbyshire

The Cottage ★★★★
Contact: Mrs C Phillips, The
Cottage, Culland Mount Farm,
Brailsford, Ashbourne,
Derbyshire DE6 3BW
T: (01335) 360313
E: carolphillips@Farmersweekly.
net

BRAMPTON BRYAN
Herefordshire

Hicks Farm Holidays ★★★★
Contact: Mrs S Bywater, Hicks
Farm, Boresford, Presteigne,
Powys LD8 2NB
T: (01544) 260237
E: holidays@hicksfarm.
fsbusiness.co.uk

BRASSINGTON
Derbyshire

Ivy Cottage ★★★
Contact: Mrs PM Potter,
Highfields, Pounder Lane,
Bonsall, Matlock, Derbyshire
DE4 2AT
T: (01629) 823018
E: ivy.cottage@ukgateway.net

Jack's Cottage ★★★★
Contact: Mr C MacQueen, Peak
Cottages, Strawberry Lee Lane,
Totley Bents, Sheffield, S17 3BA
T: (0114) 262 0777
F: (0114) 262 0666

BREDON
Worcestershire

The Moretons
★★★★-★★★★★
Contact: Mr & Mrs A Soutar, The
Moretons, Bredon, Tewkesbury,
Gloucestershire GL20 7EN
T: (01684) 772294
F: (01684) 772262
E: moretonsbredon@msn.com
I: www.worcs.com/moretons

BRIDGNORTH
Shropshire

The Barn ★★★★★
Contact: Mr K Hazelwood, Bay
Horse Farm, Drakelow Lane,
Wolverley, Kidderminster,
Worcestershire DY11 5RY
T: (01562) 850671 &
07850 287209

Bulls Head Cottages ★★★
Contact: Mr D Baxter, The Bulls
Head, Chelmarsh, Bridgnorth,
Shropshire WV16 6BA
T: (01746) 861469
F: (01746) 862646
E: dave@bullshead.fsnet.co.uk
I: www.stargate-uk.
co.uk/bullshead
🏃

The Cottage ★★★
Contact: Mrs S Jennison,
Sandward Guesthouse, 47
Cartway, Bridgnorth, Shropshire
WV16 4BG
T: (01746) 765913

Eudon Burnell Cottages ★★★
Contact: Mrs M A Crawford
Clarke, Eudon Burnell,
Bridgnorth, Shropshire
WV16 6UD
T: (01746) 789235
F: (01746) 789550
E: eudonburnell@
virtual-shropshire.co.uk
I: www.stargate-uk.
co.uk/eudon-burnell-cottages

The Gatehouse
Rating Applied For
Contact: Mrs B Cash, Upton
Cressett Hall, Bridgnorth,
Shropshire WV16 6UH
T: (01746) 714307
F: (01746) 714506

The Granary ★★★
Contact: Mrs Sarah Allen, The
Granary, The Old Vicarage,
Ditton Priors, Bridgnorth,
Shropshire WV16 6SQ
T: (01746) 712272 & 712288
F: (01746) 712288
E: allens@oldvicditton.
freeserve.co.uk

Lobby Stables ★★★★
Contact: Mrs Helen Danks,
Lobby Farm, Oldfield, Bridgnorth,
Shropshire WV16 6AQ
T: (01746) 789218
E: lobby-farm@lineone.net
I: cottageguide.co.uk/lobbyfarm

The Loosebox Ellerdine★★★★
Contact: Mr & Mrs G J Higgins,
Ellerdine, Occupation Lane,
Chelmarsh, Bridgnorth,
Shropshire WV16 6BE
T: (01746) 861397
F: (01746) 861397

No.1 & 2 Coachmans Cottage
★★★★
Contact: Mrs Helen Turner,
Severn House, Lower Forge,
Eardington, Bridgnorth,
Shropshire WV16 5LQ
T: (01746) 768197 &
07778 807413
F: (01746) 768847

The Old Stables ★★★
Contact: Mr K A Owen, 3 St
Johns Street, Lowtown,
Bridgnorth, Shropshire
WV15 6AG
T: (01746) 765476 &
07971 185722
F: (01746) 767344

Severn Rest ★★★
Contact: Miss J Cartwright, 8
Riverside, Bridgnorth,
Shropshire WV16 4BH
T: (01746) 768242
E: jacky.cartwright@virgin.net

Tudor Cottage ★★
Contact: Mrs J B Henshaw, The White Cottage, 17 High Street, Claverley, Bridgnorth, Shropshire WV5 7DR
T: (01746) 710262

BRIGSTOCK
Northamptonshire

The Gable End ★★★
Contact: Mrs H Clarke, The Gables, 2 Benefield Road, Brigstock, Kettering, Northamptonshire NN14 3ES
T: (01536) 373674
F: (01536) 373674
E: Marcus@Clarke.1999.co.uk

BRILLEY
Herefordshire

Fern Hall Cottage ★★★
Contact: Country Hols ref: 9384, Country Holidays Group Owner Services Dept, Spring Mill, Earby, Barnoldswick, Lancashire BB18 6RN
T: 0870 444 6603
F: (01282) 844288
E: sales@ttgihg.co.uk
I: www.country-holidays.co.uk

BRIMFIELD
Herefordshire

Weathervane ★★★★
Contact: Mrs M Sims, Brimfield Cottage, Brimfield, Ludlow, Shropshire SY8 4NE
T: (01584) 711208
F: (01584) 711208
E: simsbrimfield@netscapeonline.co.uk

BRIMPSFIELD
Gloucestershire

Brimpsfield Farmhouse Annexe ★★★
Contact: Country Holidays ref: 1463 Sales, Country Holidays, Spring Mill, Earby, Barnoldswick, Lancashire BB94 0AA
T: 08700 723723
F: (01282) 844288
I: www.country-holidays.co.uk

BROAD CAMPDEN
Gloucestershire

Lion Cottage ★★★
Contact: Mrs B L Rawcliffe, Lion Cottage, Broad Campden, Chipping Campden, Gloucestershire GL55 6UR
T: (01386) 840077

BROADWAY
Worcestershire

1-2 Lower Mill Cottages ★★★★
Contact: Mr A Scott, Crown and Trumpet Inn, Church Street, Broadway, Worcestershire WR12 7AE
T: (01386) 853202 & 087000 750500
E: ascott@cotswoldholidays.co.uk
I: www.cotswoldholidays.co.uk

Broadway Court ★★-★★★
Contact: Ms M Davis, Broadway Court, 89-93 High Street, Broadway, Worcestershire WR12 7AL
T: (01386) 852237 & 859493
E: bookings@cotswold-inns-hotels.co.uk
I: www.thecotswoldcottages.co.uk

Hesters House ★★★
Contact: Mrs L Dungate, Inglenook, Brokengate Lane, Denham, Uxbridge, Middlesex UB9 4LA
T: (01895) 834357
F: (01895) 832904
E: pdungate@aol.com

Skylark ★★★★
Contact: Mrs D Simon, Gazeley View, Tally Ho, Hawling, Cheltenham, Gloucestershire GL54 5SX
T: 07977 974592
E: info@skylarkholidays.com
I: www.cotswolds-broadway.co.uk

BROADWELL
Warwickshire

Little Biggin ★★★
Contact: Mr and Mrs Adrian & Linda Denham, Broadwell House Farm, Broadwell, Rugby, Warwickshire CV23 8HF
T: (01926) 812347
F: (01926) 812347
E: broadwellhouse@ntlworld.com

BROCKTON
Shropshire

Old Quarry Cottage Apartment Rating Applied For
Contact: Mrs N Thorpe, Old Quarry Cottage, Brockton, Much Wenlock, Shropshire TF13 6JR
T: (01746) 785596
E: rod@brockton.fsbusiness.co.uk

BROMSBERROW HEATH
Gloucestershire

Honeysuckle Cottage ★★★★
Contact: Mrs W S Hooper, Greenlands, Bromsberrow Heath, Ledbury, Herefordshire HR8 1PG
T: (01531) 650360 & 07831 358585

BROMSGROVE
Worcestershire

East View Apartment ★★★
Contact: Mrs A Westwood, Little Shortwood, Brockhill Lane, Tardebigge, Bromsgrove, Worcestershire B60 1LU
T: (01527) 63180
F: (01527) 63180
E: westwoodja@hotmail.com

BROMYARD
Herefordshire

The Coach House ★★★
Contact: Country Holidays ref: 7471 Sales, Holiday Cottages Group Limited, Spring Mill, Earby, Barnoldswick, Lancashire BB94 0AA
T: 08700 723723
F: (01282) 844288
I: www.country-holidays.co.uk

BROSELEY
Shropshire

Aynsley Cottages ★★★
Contact: Mrs E M Elcock, Shalimar, Fox Lane, Broseley, Shropshire TF12 5LR
T: (01952) 882695

BROUGH
Derbyshire

Brough House Barn ★★★★
Contact: Mrs Dorothy Nustedt, The Stables Brough House Barn, Brough, Bradwell, Hope Valley, Derbyshire S33 9HG
T: (01433) 621553 & (0114) 262 0777

BROWN EDGE
Staffordshire

Ladymoor View Cottage Rating Applied For
Contact: Mrs M E Adams, Ladymoor View, Hill Top, Brown Edge, Stoke-on-Trent ST6 8UB
T: (01782) 504668

BUCKLAND
Gloucestershire

Hillside Cottage and The Bothy ★★★★
Contact: Mr C Edmondson, Burhill, Buckland, Broadway, Worcestershire WR12 7LY
T: (01386) 858842
F: (01386) 853900

BUCKNELL
Shropshire

Weston Cottage ★★★★
Contact: Mrs K Bevan, The Mews, 18 Keepers Lane, The Wergs, Wolverhampton, West Midlands WV6 8UA
T: (01902) 752442
E: kbevan@allcomm.co.uk
I: westoncottage.co.uk

BURGH-LE-MARSH
Lincolnshire

The Chestnut Farm and Country Cottages ★★★
Contact: Mrs J M Mackinder, The Chestnut Farm and Country Cottages, Wainfleet Road, Burgh-le-marsh, Skegness, Lincolnshire PE24 5AH
T: (01754) 810904
F: (01754) 810904
E: mack@freenetname.co.uk
I: www.thechestnutsfarm.co.uk

Sycamore Fishing Lakes Rating Applied For
Contact: Mrs Joy Giraldez, Sycamore Fishing Lakes, Skegness Road, Burgh-le-Marsh, Skegness, Lincolnshire PE24 5LN
T: (01754) 811411
I: www.sycamorelakes.co.uk

BURGHILL
Herefordshire

Manor Barn Rating Applied For
Contact: Mr AN Christie, Manor Barn, Burghill Manor, Burghill, Hereford HR4 7RX
T: (01432) 761447
F: (01432) 761447
E: enquiries@herefordshire-cottages.com
I: www.country-holidays.co.uk

BURLEY GATE
Herefordshire

Holly Lodge ★★★
Contact: Mr B C Lawrence, Holly Tree Cottage, Burley Gate, Hereford HR1 3QS
T: (01432) 820493
E: lawrence3@supanet.com
I: www.cottageguide.co.uk/hollylodge.html

BURLTON
Shropshire

The Stables and The Granary ★★★
Contact: Country Holidays - 2638, 2642 Sales, Country Holidays, Spring Mill, Earby, Barnoldswick, Lancashire BB94 0AA
T: 08700 723723
F: (01282) 844288
I: www.country-holidays.co.uk

BURMINGTON
Warwickshire

Hazelwood Manor Farm ★★★
Contact: Ms S A Parker, Hazelwood Manor Farm, Burmington, Shipston-on-Stour, Warwickshire CV36 5AR
T: (01608) 664224 & 07710 836744
F: (01608) 664224
E: shirley_parker@hotmail.com

BURWARTON
Shropshire

The Wicket ★★★★
Contact: Mrs J M Millard, Brown Clee Holidays Estate Office, Burwarton, Bridgnorth, Shropshire WV16 6QQ
T: (01746) 787207 & 787422
E: millard@burwarton-estates.co.uk

BUTTERTON
Staffordshire

Croft Head Farm Cottages ★★★-★★★★
Contact: Mr M Clark, Croft Head Farm Cottages, Croft Head Farm, Butterton, Leek, Staffordshire ST13 7TD
T: (01538) 304347
F: (01538) 304347
E: manon@lineone.net
I: www.farmholidays.co.uk

Swainsley Farm ★★★★★
Contact: Mr & Mrs C J Snook, Swainsley Farm, Butterton, Leek, Staffordshire ST13 7SS
T: (01298) 84530
♿

BUXTON
Derbyshire

Barn House ★★★
Contact: Mr & Mrs M Jury, Barn House, Litton Mill, Buxton, Derbyshire SK17 8SW
T: (01298) 872751
F: (01298) 872751

The Bungalow at Litton Mill ★★★-★★★★
Contact: Mr Marcus Milton, 7 Mountlands, Hardwick Square South, Buxton, Derbyshire SK17 6QD
T: (01298) 27778 & 27446
F: (01298) 73045
E: hoe@litton-mill.clara.net
I: www.litton-mill.clara.net
🎣

Cavendish Apartment Rating Applied For
Contact: Mr John Limer, Cavendish Apartment, Apartment 1, 3 Cavendish Villas, Buxton, Derbyshire SK17 6JE
T: (01298) 78827
E: jblimer@compuserve.com

The Coach House ★★★
Contact: Mr C MacQueen, Peak Cottages, Strawberry Lee Lane, Totley Bents, Sheffield, S17 3BA
T: (0114) 2620777
F: (0114) 2620666
E: enquiries@peakcottages.com
I: www.peakcottages.com

The Garden Flat ★★★★
Contact: Mrs H Butler, Manor House, 9 Manchester Road, Buxton, Derbyshire SK17 6SE
T: (01298) 22959
F: (01298) 22959

Glen Apartment
Rating Applied For
Contact: Peak Cottages, Strawberry Lee Lane, Totley Bents, Sheffield, S17 3BA
T: (0114) 262 0777
F: (0114) 262 0666
E: enquiries@peakcottages.com
I: www.peakcottages.com

Green Farm Holiday Flats ★★
Contact: Mrs S A Williams, Green Farm Holiday Flats, Green Farm, King Sterndale, Buxton, Derbyshire SK17 9SF
T: (01298) 70141

Harefield ★★★★
Contact: Mr & Mrs G Hardie, Harefield, 15 Marlborough Road, Buxton, Derbyshire SK17 6RD
T: (01298) 24029
F: (01298) 24029
E: hardie@harefield1.freeserve.co.uk
I: www.harefield1.freeserve.co.uk

Hargate Hall ★★★
Contact: Mr Jackson, Hargate Hall, Wormhill, Buxton, Derbyshire SK17 8TA
T: (01298) 872591
I: www.hargate-hall.co.uk

Ivy House ★★★
Contact: Ms Sheila Stubbs, 1 Lodgewood Cottages, Taxal, Whaley Bridge, Stockport, High Peak SK23 7DU
T: (01663) 733875

Lake View ★★★
Contact: Mr C MacQueen, Peak Cottages, Strawberry Lee Lane, Totley Bents, Sheffield, S17 3BA
T: (0114) 262 0777
F: (0114) 262 0666
E: enquiries@peakcottages.com
I: www.peakcottages.com

Meadow Barn Cottage
Rating Applied For
Contact: Peak Cottages, Strawberry Lee Lane, Totley Bents, Sheffield, S17 3BA
T: (0114) 262 0777
F: (0114) 262 0666
E: enquries@peakcottages.com
I: www.peakcottages.com

The Old Coach House ★★★★
Contact: Mr C Sykes, Sykes Cottages, York House, York Street, Chester, CH1 3LR
T: (01244) 345700
F: (01244) 321442
E: info@sykescottages.co.uk
I: www.sykescottages.co.uk

The Old Stables ★★★
Contact: Mr & Mrs T B Cowlishaw, 136 Green Lane, Buxton, Derbyshire SK17 9DQ
T: (01298) 71086 & 71086
F: (01298) 77678
E: jackie@cowlishawtravel.co.uk

Outlow ★★★
Contact: Mr Colin MacQueen, Peak Cottages, Strawberry Lee Lane, Totley Bents, Sheffield, S17 3BA
T: (0114) 262 0777
F: (0114) 262 0666
E: enquiries@peakcottages.com
I: www.peakcottages.com

Peak Forest Country Cottages ★★★
Contact: Mr & Mrs Baker, Peak Forest Country Cottages, Greenhead Farm, Old Dam Lane, Peak Forest, Buxton, Derbyshire SK17 8EW
T: (01298) 26308 & (01629) 814967
F: (01629) 814967
E: stevebaker@peakforest.fsbusiness.co.uk

Priory Lea Holiday Flats ★★-★★★
Contact: Mrs G Taylor, Priory Lea Holiday Flats, 50 White Knowle Road, Buxton, Derbyshire SK17 9NH
T: (01298) 23737

5 Silverlands Bungalow ★★★
Contact: Mrs N Oldfield, Oldfield Guest House, 8 Macclesfield Road, Buxton, Derbyshire SK17 9AH
T: (01298) 24371
E: info@buxtonlet.com
I: www.buxtonlet.com

1 Silverlands Cottage ★★★
Contact: Mrs N Oldfield, 8 Macclesfield Road, Buxton, Derbyshire SK17 9AH
T: (01298) 24371
E: info@buxtonlet.com
I: www.buxtonlet.com

Sittinglow Farm ★★★
Contact: Mrs Ann S Buckley, Sittinglow Farm, Dove Holes, Buxton, Derbyshire SK17 8DA
T: (01298) 812271

1a Spencer Road ★★★★
Contact: Mrs M Swain, 1 Spencer Road, Buxton, Derbyshire SK17 9DX
T: (01298) 25451

Spencer Road Holiday Apartment
Rating Applied For
Contact: Ms Mary Glover, Cotterill Farm, Biggin-by-Hartington, Buxton, Derbyshire SK17 0DJ
T: (01298) 84447
F: (01298) 84664
E: patrick@skemp.u-net.com
I: www.skemp.u-net.com

Thorn Heyes ★★
Contact: Ms Sylvia Hicken & Mr Melvyn Hadfield, Thorn Heyes, 137 London Road, Buxton, Derbyshire SK17 9NW
T: (01298) 23539
E: syl.mel@hartingtonhotel.co.uk
I: www.hartingtonhotel.co.uk

Waterdell Apartment ★★
Contact: Mrs E D Dillon, Waterdell House, Burlington Road, Buxton, Derbyshire SK17 9AR
T: (01298) 26746 & 28393
E: ddillon@globalnet.co.uk

CALLOW
Herefordshire

Cross In Hand Farm Cottage ★★★★
Contact: Dr J Thornton, Cross In Hand Farm, Callow, Hereford HR2 8EF
T: (01981) 540957 & 07778 307719

The Loft at Cold Nose ★★★★
Contact: Mr John Evans, Cottage Life, Cold Nose Cottage, Callow, Hereford, Herefordshire HR2 8DE
T: (01432) 340954
E: john@cottagelife.freeserve.co.uk

CALVER
Derbyshire

Knouchley Cottage ★★★★
Contact: Peak Cottages, Paddock Cottage, Strawberry Lee Lane, Totley Bents, Sheffield, S17 3BA
T: (0114) 2620777
F: (0114) 2620666
E: enquries@peakcottages.com
I: www.peakcottages.com

Sunnyside ★★★
Contact: Peak Cottages, Strawberry Lee Lane, Totley Bents, Sheffield, S17 3BA
T: (0114) 262 0777
F: (0114) 262 0666
E: enquiries@peakcottages.com
I: www.peakcottages.com

CARDINGTON
Shropshire

The Kennels Holding ★★★
Contact: Mrs R Jones, The Kennels Holding, Plaish, Cardington, Church Stretton, Shropshire SY6 7HX
T: (01694) 771549

CAREBY
Lincolnshire

Linnet Cottage ★★★
Contact: Mr & Mrs B Cooper, Maazledene, Careby, Stamford, Lincolnshire PE9 4EA
T: (01780) 410580
F: (01780) 410580
E: haresleap@supanet.com

CAREY
Herefordshire

Carey Dene and Rock House ★★★
Contact: Mrs R M Price, Folly Farm, Holme Lacy, Hereford HR2 6LS
T: (01432) 870259
F: (01432) 870259
E: ritamprice@aol.com

The Stable ★★★★
Contact: Mrs J McDonnell, Mews Cottage, Carey, Hereford, Herefordshire HR2 6NF
T: (01432) 840463
E: Jan@Mcdonnellfamily.com
I: www.cottageguide.co.uk/thestable

CARSINGTON
Derbyshire

Breach Farm
Rating Applied For
Contact: Mrs Michelle Wilson, Breach Farm, Carsington, Matlock, Derbyshire DE4 4DD
T: (01629) 540265

Knockerdown Holiday Cottages ★★★-★★★★★
Contact: Ms Cathy Lambert, Knockerdown Holiday Farm, Knockerdown, Ashbourne, Derbyshire DE6 1NQ
T: (01629) 540525
F: (01629) 540525
E: cathy@knockerdown-cottages.co.uk
I: www.derbyshireholidaycottages.co.uk

Owslow
Rating Applied For
Contact: Mr Peter Oldfield, Owslow, Owslow Farm, Carsington, Matlock, Derbyshire DE4 4DD
T: (01629) 540510 & 540254
F: (01629) 540445
E: poldfield@owslow.co.uk

CASTLETON
Derbyshire

Cave End Cottage ★★★★
Contact: Mr Colin MacQueen, Peak Cottages, Strawberry Lee Lane, Totley Bents, Sheffield, S17 3BA
T: (0114) 2620777
F: (0114) 2620666
E: enquiries@peakcottages.com
I: www.peakcottages.com

Eastry Cottage ★★★★
Contact: Mrs P J Webster, Hillside House, Pindale Road, Castleton, Hope Valley S33 8WU
T: (01433) 620312
F: (01433) 620312

High View Cottage ★★★
Contact: Mr C MacQueen, Peak Cottages, Strawberry Lee Lane, Totley Bents, Sheffield, S17 3BA
T: (0114) 262 0777
F: (0114) 262 0666
E: enquiries@peakcottages.com
I: www.peakcottages.com

Millbridge Cottage ★★★★
Contact: Mrs Cutts, Millbridge House, Millbridge, Castleton, Hope Valley S33 8WR
T: (01433) 621556

Trickett Gate Barn ★★★★
Contact: Mrs L Woollacott, Trickett Gate Barn, Castleton, Hope Valley S33 8WR
T: (01433) 620007
E: lesleywoollacott@hotmail.com

CHAPEL-EN-LE-FRITH
Derbyshire

The Coach House ★★★
Contact: Country Holidays ref: 6163 Sales, Holiday Cottages Group Limited, Spring Mill, Earby, Barnoldswick, Lancashire BB94 0AA
T: 08700 723723
F: (01282) 844288
I: www.country-holidays.co.uk

Hawthorn Cottage ★★★
Contact: Mrs Olive Fraser, Rose Cottage, Bagshaw, Chapel-en-le-Frith, High Peak SK23 0QU
T: (01298) 813294

Herb View at Newlyn ★★★
Contact: Mr & Mrs Mike & Helen Cullen, Newlyn, Crossings Road, Chapel-en-le-Frith, High Peak SK23 9RY
T: (01298) 814775 &
07765 196296

Keepers Cottage ★★★
Contact: Mrs Mary Hayward, Slack Hall Farm, Castleton Road, Chapel-en-le-Frith, High Peak, Derbyshire SK23 0QS
T: (01298) 812845

Ridge Hall ★★★★★
Contact: Mrs J Franklin, Ridge Hall, Chapel-en-le-Frith, High Peak SK23 9UD
T: (01298) 815862 & 813130
F: (01298) 815862
E: ridgehall@aol.com
I: www.ridge-hall.com

Sweetpiece Cottage ★★★★
Contact: Mr Colin MacQueen, Peak Cottages, Strawberry Lee Lane, Totley Bents, Sheffield, S17 3BA
T: (0114) 2620777
F: (0114) 2620666
E: enquiries@peakcottages.com
I: www.peakcottages.com

CHARLTON KINGS
Gloucestershire

Coxhorne Farm ★★★
Contact: Mr & Mrs J Close, Coxhorne Farm, London Road, Charlton Kings, Cheltenham, Gloucestershire GL52 6UY
T: (01242) 236599

CHATSWORTH
Derbyshire

Cherry Tree Cottage and Fox View Cottage★★★★
Contact: Mr & Mrs Phillip & Jane Meakin, Cherry Tree Cottage and Fox View Cottage, Cherry Tree Farm, Darley Road, Stonedge, Ashover, Chesterfield, Derbyshire S45 0LW
T: (01246) 591000 & 591111
F: (01246) 591111
E: jane@cherrytreecottages.freeserve.co.uk
I: www.cherrytreecottages.freeserve.co.uk

CHEADLE
Staffordshire

The Barn ★★★★
Contact: Mr S Kendrick, The Barn, Woodhouse Farm, Lockwood Road, Kingsley Holt, Cheadle, Staffordshire ST10 4QU
T: (01538) 754250
E: ask@woodhousefarm.net
I: www.woodhousefarm.net

Hermitage Lodge ★★★
Contact: Mrs W Barlow, Hermitage Farm, Froghall, Cheadle, Staffordshire Moorlands ST10 2HQ
T: (01538) 266515
F: (01538) 266155
E: wilma@hermitagefarm.co.uk
I: www.hermitagefarm.co.uk

Marmadukes Folly ★★★★
Contact: Mrs R Harrison, Threapwood Farm, Cheadle, Stoke-on-Trent ST10 4RB
T: (01538) 753268

CHEDDLETON
Staffordshire

Cheddleton Grange Farm ★★★★
Contact: Mr & Mrs J Goodwin, Cheddleton Grange Farm, Cheddleton, Leek, Staffordshire ST13 7HN
T: (01538) 360344

CHEDWORTH
Gloucestershire

Hill Farm Cottage ★★★
Contact: Mrs E R Edelsten, Hill Farm House, Chedworth, Cheltenham, Gloucestershire GL54 4AG
T: (01285) 720421

Laines Farm Barn ★★★★
Contact: Miss S Callard, Laines Farm, Chedworth, Cheltenham, Gloucestershire GL54 4NS
T: (01285) 720468

Tiddley Dyke ★★★★
Contact: Mrs Jenny Bull, Buffers, School Lane, Chedworth, Cheltenham, Gloucestershire GL54 4AJ
T: (01285) 720673

CHELMARSH
Shropshire

Duck, Drake & Cart Cottages ★★★
Contact: Mrs M Roberts, Dinney Farm, Chelmarsh, Bridgnorth, Shropshire WV16 6AU
T: (01746) 861070
F: (01746) 861002
I: www.smoothhound.co.uk/hotels/dinney.html

Little Dinney Barn ★★★
Contact: Mr & Mrs W Palmer, Little Dinney Barn, The Common, Chelmarsh, Bridgnorth, Shropshire WV16 6BG
T: (01746) 862297
E: littledinney@stargate-uk.co.uk
I: www.virtual-shropshire.co.uk/little-dinney-barn

CHELMORTON
Derbyshire

Dale Grange Cottage ★★
Contact: Mrs M Wheeldon, Dale Grange Farm, Chelmorton, Buxton, Derbyshire SK17 9SG
T: (01298) 85206

The Hall ★★★
Contact: Mrs L F Marsden, Town End Farm, Chelmorton, Buxton, Derbyshire SK17 9SH
T: (01298) 85249
E: charles.marsden@nottingham.ac.uk

School Farm ★★★
Contact: Country Holidays ref: 8461 sales, Holiday Cottages Group Limited, Spring Mill, Earby, Barnoldswick, Lancashire BB94 0AA
T: 08700 723723
F: (01282) 841539
I: www.country-holidays.co.uk

CHELTENHAM
Gloucestershire

Amaray – Selkirk Gardens ★★
Contact: Mr & Mrs W P Hastelow, Hamilton Cottage, 66 Duke Street, Cheltenham, Gloucestershire GL52 6BP
T: (01242) 580005 &
(01452) 830456

The Annexe ★★★
Contact: Mrs P Corbett, 11 Oldfield Crescent, St Marks, Cheltenham, Gloucestershire GL51 7BB
T: (01242) 524608

Balcarras Farm Holiday Cottages ★★★
Contact: Mr & Mrs D Ballinger, Balcarras Farm, London Road, Charlton Kings, Cheltenham, Gloucestershire GL52 6UT
T: (01242) 584837
E: ballinger@bfhc.fsnet.co.uk

The Courtyard ★★★★
Contact: Mrs Jane Reynolds, The Courtyard, 22 Montpellier Spa Road, Cheltenham, Gloucestershire GL50 1UL
T: (01242) 517412 &
07966 251486
F: (01242) 517412
E: breynolds@phoenixint.com

The Garden Flat ★★★★
Contact: Ms Jenny Wardle, Change Forum Ltd, 20 Lansdown Parade, Cheltenham, Gloucestershire GL50 2LH
T: (01242) 577450
F: (01242) 527151
E: jennyw@changeforum.co.uk

The Garden Studio ★★★★
Contact: Mrs I Ellams, The Garden Studio, 53 Gratton Road, Cheltenham, Gloucestershire GL50 2BZ
T: (01242) 575572

Harrys Cottage ★★★
Contact: Mr P Smith, 1 Church Row, Shipton Oliffe, Cheltenham, Gloucestershire GL54 4JD
T: (01242) 820598
E: paulsmith@helenchurch.freeserve.uk

Holmer Cottages ★★★★
Contact: Mrs Jill Collins, Holmer Cottages, Haines Orchard, Woolstone, Cheltenham, Gloucestershire GL52 9RG
T: (01242) 672848
F: (01242) 672848
E: holmercottages@talk21.com

Oakfield Rise ★★★★
Contact: Mr T Russell, Oakfield Rise, Ashley Road, Battledown, Cheltenham, Gloucestershire GL52 6NU
T: (01242) 222220 &
07932 081826
I: www.oakfieldrise.com

Old Rectory Cottages ★★★–★★★★
Contact: Ms Karen Fesemeyer, Old Rectory, Woolstone, Cheltenham, Gloucestershire GL52 9RG
T: (01242) 673766
F: (01242) 677011
E: fesey@aol.com
I: www.theoldrectory.com

Priory Cottage ★★★
Contact: Mr T S Mant, Church Gate, Southam Lane, Southam, Cheltenham, Gloucestershire GL52 3NY
T: (01242) 584693
F: (01242) 584693
E: iansmant@hotmail.com

Regency Maisonette ★★★★
Contact: Mrs J Reynolds, 22 Montpellier Spa Road, Cheltenham, Gloucestershire GL50 1UL
T: (01242) 517412 &
07966 251486
F: (01242) 517412
E: breynolds@phoenixint.com

Ullenwood Court Cottages ★★★★
Contact: Mrs P J Cuttell, Ullenwood Court Cottages, Ullenwood Court, Ullenwood, Cheltenham, Gloucestershire GL53 9QS
T: (01242) 236770
F: (01242) 254680

Upper Coberley Farm ★★★
Contact: Mrs A Allen, Upper Coberley Farm, Upper Coberley, Cheltenham, Gloucestershire GL53 9RB
T: (01242) 870306
E: allen@uppercoberley.freeserve.co.uk

The Vergus ★★★
Contact: Mrs R M Preen, Ashley, Staverton Village, Cheltenham, Gloucestershire GL51 0TW
T: (01242) 680511 &
07973 419613
E: ritapreen@aol.com

Willoughby House Hotel and Apartments
Rating Applied For
Contact: Mrs S Lloyd-Gillespie, Willoughby House Hotel, 1 Suffolk Square, Cheltenham, Gloucestershire GL50 2DR
T: (01242) 522798
E: bookings@willoughbyhouse.com
I: www.willoughbyhouse.com

Wimble Cottage ★★
Contact: Mrs H J Beardsell, Crane Hill, Oxenton, Cheltenham, Gloucestershire GL52 4SE
T: (01242) 673631
F: (01242) 673631

CHESTERFIELD
Derbyshire

Faversham House ★★★
Contact: Mrs M McIntyre, 31 Beverley Gardens, Wembley, Middlesex HA9 9RD
T: (020) 8908 4807 & 8908 4050
F: (020) 8908 2684

49 Parkhouse Road ★★★
Contact: Mrs Tina Cave, 51 Parkhouse Road, Lower Pilsley, Chesterfield, Derbyshire S45 8DG
T: (01246) 853467
E: chryslinash@aol.com

Pear Tree Cottage ★★★
Contact: Mrs C Beckett,
Laburnum Cottage, 46 Hardstoft
Road, Pilsley, Chesterfield,
Derbyshire S45 8BL
T: (01773) 872767 &
(01246) 850311

Ploughmans Cottage ★★★★
Contact: Mr and Mrs W G Fry,
Ploughmans Cottage, Low Farm,
Main Road, Marsh Lane,
Sheffield, Derbyshire S21 5RH
T: (01246) 435328
F: (01246) 435328

CHINLEY
Derbyshire

The Cottage ★★★
Contact: Ms J Stocks, The
Cottage, Naze House,
Maynestone Road, Chinley, High
Peak SK23 6AH
T: (01663) 750314
E: jstocks@nildram.co.uk

Fernbank ★★★
Contact: Mrs J Storer, 33
Rowton Grange Road, Chapel-
en-le-Frith, High Peak,
Derbyshire SK23 0LD
T: (01298) 813458

Monks Meadow Cottage ★★★★
Contact: Mrs P M Gill, Monks
Meadow Farm, Hayfield Road,
Chinley Head, High Peak,
SK23 6AL
T: (01663) 750329
E: monksmeadow@yahoo.com

CHIPPING CAMPDEN
Gloucestershire

Bank Cottage ★★★★
Contact: Mr R Hutsby, Middle
Hill Farm, Charlecote, Warwick,
CV35 9EH
T: (01789) 841525 &
07778 153180
F: (01789) 841523
E: robert.hutsby@btinternet.
com
I: www.broadway-cotswolds.
co.uk/bank.html

Barnstones ★★★★★
Contact: Mr & Mrs F J Jones,
Barnstones, Aston Road,
Chipping Campden,
Gloucestershire GL55 6HR
T: (01386) 840975
F: (01386) 840975
E: frank_jones@oxfe.ac.uk

Box Tree Cottage ★★★
Contact: Mr R Hutsby, Middle
Hill Farm, Charlecote, Warwick,
CV35 9EH
T: (01789) 841525 &
07778 153180
F: (01789) 841523
E: robert.hutsby@btinternet.
com
I: www.broadway-cotswolds.
co.uk/boxtree.html

Chapter Cottage ★★★★
Contact: Mr P Revers, The
Tyning, Blind Lane, Chipping
Campden, Gloucestershire
GL55 6ED
T: (01386) 841450 &
07866 887495
E: prpco@dircon.co.uk
I: www.perpetuare.com

Cowfair ★★★
Contact: Mrs J V Whitehouse,
Weston Park Farm, Dovers Hill,
Chipping Campden,
Gloucestershire GL55 6UW
T: (01386) 840835
E: jane_whitehouse@hotmail.
com

Dragon House ★★★★
Contact: Country Holidays ref:
8386 Sales, Holiday Cottages
Group Limited, Spring Mill,
Earby, Barnoldswick, Lancashire
BB94 0AA
T: 08700 723723
F: (01282) 844288
E: sales@country-holidays.co.uk
I: www.country-holidays.co.uk

Grafton Mews ★★★★
Contact: Ms Sheila Rolland,
Campden Cottages, Folly
Cottage, Paxford, Chipping
Campden, Gloucestershire
GL55 6XG
T: (01386) 593315
F: (01386) 593057
E: campdencottages@
btinternet.com
I: www.campdencottages.co.uk

Honey Pot ★★★★
Contact: Mrs Dorothy Brook, Tod
Cot, Noel Court, Calf Lane,
Chipping Campden,
Gloucestershire GL55 6BS
T: (01386) 841127
E: dotbrook@easicom.com
I: www.stratford-upon-avon.
co.uk/honeypot.htm

Little Thatch ★★★★
Contact: Mrs D Gadsby,
'Hillsdown', Aston Road,
Chipping Campden,
Gloucestershire GL55 6PL
T: (01386) 840234

Lychgate Cottage ★★★★
Contact: Mr R Hutsby, Middle
Hill Farm, Charlecote, Warwick,
CV35 9EH
T: (01789) 841525 &
07778 153180
F: (01789) 841523
E: robert.hutsby@btinternet.
com
I: www.broadway-cotswolds.
co.uk/lychgate.html

Merlin Cottage ★★★★
Contact: Miss S Rolland,
Campden Cottages, Folly
Cottage, Paxford, Chipping
Campden, Gloucestershire
GL55 6XG
T: (01386) 593315
F: (01386) 593057
E: campdencottages@
btinternet.com
I: www.campdencottages.co.uk

2 Noel Court ★★★★
Contact: Country Holidays ref:
13449 Sales, Holiday Cottages
Group Limited, Spring Mill,
Earby, Barnoldswick, Lancashire
BB94 0AA
T: 08700 723723
F: (01282) 844288
E: sales@ttgihg.co.uk
I: www.country-holidays.co.uk

10 Sheep Street ★★★
Contact: Mr and Mrs T J Ayres,
Glydestones, Guthries Bridge,
Chipping Campden,
Gloucestershire GL55 6BU
T: (01386) 841942 &
07775 713275
E: tjayres@talk21.com

Shepherd's Cottage ★★★★
Contact: Miss S Rolland,
Campden Cottages, Folly
Cottage, Paxford, Chipping
Campden, Gloucestershire
GL55 6XG
T: (01386) 593315
F: (01386) 593057
E: campdencottages@
btinternet.com
I: www.campdencottages.co.uk

Whistlers Corner ★★★★
Contact: Mr R Hutsby, Middle
Hill Farm, Charlecote, Warwick
CV35 9EH
T: (01789) 841525 &
07778 153180
F: (01789) 841523
E: robert.hutsby@btinternet.
com
I: www.broadway-cotswolds.
co.uk/whistlers.html

CHRISTCHURCH
Gloucestershire

East View
Rating Applied For
Contact: Country Holidays ref:
6242 Sales, Country Holidays,
Spring Mill, Earby, Barnoldswick,
Lancashire BB94 0AA
T: 08700 723723
F: (01282) 844288
E: sales@ttgihg.co.uk
I: www.country-holidays.co.uk

Glenwood ★★★
Contact: Mr & Mrs K Harvey,
Glenwood, Christchurch,
Coleford, Gloucestershire
GL16 7NR
T: (01594) 833128
F: (01594) 833128

CHURCH LANGTON
Leicestershire

The Courtyard Cottages ★★★★
Contact: Mr A Tripp, The
Courtyard Cottages, Home Farm,
Church Langton, Market
Harborough, Leicestershire
LE16 7SY
T: (01858) 545184
F: (01858) 545876
E: jo@home.farm.freeuk.com

CHURCH STRETTON
Shropshire

The Acorn ★★★
Contact: Mrs J E Follows,
Oaklands, Marshbrook, Church
Stretton, Shropshire SY6 6RQ
T: (01694) 781448
F: (01694) 781372

The Barn, Daisy's Place and Goose Yard ★★★★
Contact: Mr Sykes, Sykes
Cottage, York House, York
Street, Chester, CH1 3LR
T: (01244) 345700
F: (01244) 321442
E: info@sykescottages.co.uk
I: www.sykescottages.co.uk

Berry's Coffee House ★★★★
Contact: Mr J Gott, Berry's
Coffee House, 17 High Street,
Church Stretton, Shropshire
SY6 6BU
T: (01694) 724452
E: all@berryscoffeehouse.co.uk
I: www.berryscoffeehouse.co.uk

Botvyle Farm ★★★
Contact: Mr & Mrs G
Bebbington, Botvyle Farm, All
Stretton, Church Stretton,
Shropshire SY6 7JN
T: (01694) 722869

Brook House Farm ★★★★
Contact: Mrs Joan Egerton,
Brook House Farm, Wall-under-
Heywood, Church Stretton,
Shropshire SY6 7DS
T: (01694) 771308

Broome Farm Cottages ★★★★★
Contact: Mr M Cavendish,
Broome Farm Cottages, Broome
Farm, Chatwall, Church Stretton,
Shropshire SY6 7LD
T: (01694) 771776 &
07968 057873
F: (01694) 771784
E: mark@broome-farm.co.uk
I: broome-farm.co.uk

The Crispen Cottage ★★★
Contact: Mr & Mrs C&M Jones,
The Crispen, Stone Acton Road,
Wallbank, Church Stretton,
Shropshire SY6 7HL
T: (01694) 771319
🐾

Fairway ★★★★
Contact: Mrs R Powell, Oaker, 43
Shrewsbury Road, Church
Stretton, Shropshire SY6 6EU
T: (01694) 723159
I: rosemary@oaker.freeserve.
co.uk

Granary Cottage ★★★★
Contact: Mr & Mrs J Kirkwood,
Lower Day House, Church Preen,
Church Stretton, Shropshire
SY6 7LH
T: (01694) 771521
E: jim@lowerdayhouse.
freeserve.co.uk

Jasleigh ★★★
Contact: Mrs W Lewis, 31
Church Street, Church Stretton,
Shropshire SY6 6DQ
T: (01694) 723173 & 751212
F: (01694) 723173

Longmynd Hotel ★★★
Contact: Mr M Chapman,
Longmynd Hotel, Cunnery Road,
Church Stretton, Shropshire
SY6 6AG
T: (01694) 722244
F: (01694) 722718
E: reservations@longmynd.
co.uk
I: www.longmynd.co.uk

Mill House ★★★★
Contact: Mr & Mrs D M Betton,
Marsh Mill, Marshbrook, Church
Stretton, Shropshire SY6 6RQ
T: (01694) 781274
F: (01694) 781274

Parkgate Cottages ★★★
Contact: Mrs Audrey Hill,
Parkgate Farmhouse,
Pulverbatch, Shrewsbury,
Shropshire SY5 8DH
T: (01694) 751303
E: park-gate@lineone.net
I: www.shropshiretourism.com

Redwood Heights ★★★
Contact: Mrs M Bond, Redwood
Heights, Watling Street South,
Church Stretton, Shropshire
SY6 7BJ
T: (01694) 724332 &
07703 413132
E: maureen@redwoodheights.
freeserve.co.uk

The Retreat ★★★
Contact: Mr & Mrs J L Bennett,
The Retreat, 72 Watling Street
South, Church Stretton,
Shropshire SY6 7BH
T: (01694) 723370

Spring End ★★★★★
Contact: Mrs E M Parker, 87
Watling Street South, Church
Stretton, Shropshire SY6 7BH
T: (01694) 723645
E: lizparker@stretton.ndo.co.uk

Ye Olde Stables at Jinlye ★★★★
Contact: Miss K Tory, Ye Olde
Stables at Jinlye, Jinlye, Castle
Hill, All Stretton, Church
Stretton, Shropshire SY6 6JP
T: (01694) 723243
F: (01694) 723243
E: info@jinlye.co.uk
I: www.jinlye.co.uk

CHURCHDOWN
Gloucestershire

Chosen Hill House ★★★★
Contact: Country Holidays -
8392 Sales, Holiday Cottages,
Spring Mill, Earby, Barnoldswick,
Lancashire BB94 0AA
T: 08700 723723
F: (01282) 844288
I: www.country-holidays.co.uk

CINDERFORD
Gloucestershire

Rose Cottage ★★★
Contact: Mrs Elizabeth O'Shea,
Highpoint, Durfold Hill, Dorking
Road, Warnham, Horsham, West
Sussex RH12 3RZ
T: (01403) 243464

CIRENCESTER
Gloucestershire

16 Coxwell Street
Rating Applied For
Contact: Mr Barry Giles,
'Cottesmore', 1 Saxon Road,
Cirencester, Gloucestershire
GL7 1AX
T: (01285) 651876

Glebe Farm Holiday Lets ★★★★
Contact: Mrs P Handover, Glebe
Farm Holiday Lets, Glebe Farm,
Barnsley Road, Cirencester,
Gloucestershire GL7 5DY
T: (01285) 659226
F: (01285) 642622

The Malthouse Granary ★★★★
Contact: Mrs B O'Leary, The
Malthouse, Poulton, Cirencester,
Gloucestershire GL7 5HN
T: (01285) 850006 & 850433
F: (01285) 850437
E: bernie.oleary@btinternet.com

Mayfield Cottage ★★
Contact: Mrs J I Hutson,
Mayfield House, Cheltenham
Road, Perrotts Brook,
Cirencester, Gloucestershire
GL7 7BH
T: (01285) 831301
F: (01285) 831301
E: jhutson@btclick.com

Old Mill Cottages ★★★★
Contact: Mrs Catherine Hazell,
Ermin House Farm, Syde,
Cheltenham, Gloucestershire
GL53 9PN
T: (01285) 821255 &
07799 420020
F: (01285) 821531
E: catherine@oldmillcottages.
fsnet.co.uk
I: www.oldmillcottages.co.uk

The Tallet Cottage ★★★★★
Contact: Mrs V J Arbuthnott, The
Tallet, Calmsden, Cirencester,
Gloucestershire GL7 5ET
T: (01285) 831437
F: (01285) 831437
E: vanessa@thetallet.demon.
co.uk
I: www.thetallet.co.uk

Warrens Gorse Cottages ★★
Contact: Mrs N Randall, Home
Farm, Warrens Gorse,
Cirencester, Gloucestershire
GL7 7JD
T: (01285) 831261

Westley Farm ★★-★★★
Contact: Mr J Usborne, Westley
Farm, Chalford, Stroud,
Gloucestershire GL6 8HP
T: (01285) 760262
F: (01285) 760262
E: westleyfarm@cs.com
I: www.westleyfarm.co.uk

CLAXBY
Lincolnshire

The Coach House ★★★
Contact: Mrs Elizabeth Wilson,
Claxby Manor, Claxby, Alford,
Lincolnshire LN13 0HJ
T: (01507) 466374

CLEARWELL
Gloucestershire

Stank Farm ★★★
Contact: Mr S Clarke, Stank
Farm, Lower Cross, Clearwell,
Coleford, Gloucestershire
GL16 8LD
T: (01594) 832203

4 Temperance Cottages ★★
Contact: Mrs J S Bond, 3 Post
Office Lane, Wantage,
Oxfordshire OX12 8DR
T: (01235) 767577

CLEE ST MARGARET
Shropshire

Titchbourne Cottage ★★★★
Contact: Country Holidays ref:
9882 Sales, Holiday Cottages
Group Limited, Spring Mill,
Earby, Barnoldswick, Lancashire
BB94 0AA
T: 08700 723723
F: (01282) 844288
E: sales@ttgih.co.uk
I: www.country-holidays.co.uk

CLEEVE HILL
Gloucestershire

The Old Dairy ★★★★
Contact: Mr & Mrs Rickie &
Jenny Gauld, Slades Farm,
Bushcombe Lane, Cleeve Hill,
Cheltenham, Gloucestershire
GL52 3PN
T: (01242) 676003
F: (01242) 676003
E: rickieg@btinternet.com
I: www.btinternet.
com/~cotswoldcottages

CLEEVE PRIOR
Worcestershire

Top Farm Cottage ★★★
Contact: Country Hols Ref:
11842, Country Holidays Group
Owner Services Dept, Spring
Mill, Earby, Barnoldswick,
Lancashire BB18 6RN
T: 0870 444 6603
F: (01282) 844288
E: sales@ttgih.co.uk
I: www.country-holidays.co.uk

CLEOBURY MORTIMER
Shropshire

Hop Barn ★★★★
Contact: Mrs B A Jones, Neen
Court, Neen Sollars, Cleobury
Mortimer, Kidderminster,
Worcestershire DY14 0AH
T: (01299) 271204 &
07787 525436
F: (01299) 271930
E: birgintanne@aol.com
I: thehopbarn.topaties.com

Prescott Mill ★★★
Contact: Mrs W Etchells,
Prescott Mill, Stottesdon,
Cleobury Mortimer, Shropshire
DY14 8RR
T: (01746) 718721
F: (01746) 718718
E: brown15@virgin.net or
mail@prescott-mill-cottage.
co.uk
I: www.prescott-mill-cottage.
co.uk

The White Cottage ★★★
Contact: Mrs B Edwards, The
White Cottage, Hopton Bank,
Cleobury Mortimer,
Kidderminster, Worcestershire
DY14 0QF
T: (01584) 890768

CLIFTON
Derbyshire

Strawberry Cottage
Rating Applied For
Contact: Peak Cottages,
Strawberry Lee Lane, Totley
Bents, Sheffield, S17 3BA
T: (0114) 262 0777
F: (0114) 262 0666
E: enquries@peakcottages.com
I: www.peakcottages.com

CLIFTON UPON TEME
Worcestershire

Hopeway Cottage ★★★★★
Contact: Mr & Mrs C&E White,
Hope Wynd, The Village, Clifton
upon Teme, Worcester WR6 6EN
T: (01886) 812496
F: (01886) 812429
E: countryways@hopeway.co.uk
I: www.hopeway.co.uk

CLUN
Shropshire

Dick Turpin Cottage at
Cockford Hall ★★★★★
Contact: Mr Roger Wren, Dick
Turpin Cottage at Cockford Hall,
Cockford Hall, Cockford Bank,
Clun, Craven Arms, Shropshire
SY7 8LR
T: (01588) 640327
F: (01588) 640881
E: cockford.hall@virgin.net
I: www.find-a-place.
co.uk/dickturpincottage

The Duck Barn ★★★
Contact: Mrs Suzanne
Donaldson, The Duck Barn, 4
Church Street, Clun, Craven
Arms, Shropshire SY7 8JW
T: (01588) 640926
F: (01588) 640926

The Lodge ★★★★
Contact: Country Hols ref: 5517,
Country Holidays Group Owner
Services Dept, Spring Mill, Earby,
Barnoldswick, Lancashire
BB18 6RN
T: 0870 444 6603
F: (01282) 841539
E: ownerservices@ttgih.co.uk
I: www.country-holidays.co.uk

The Miller's House ★★★★
Contact: Ms G Della Casa,
Birches Mill, Birches Mill, Clun,
Craven Arms, Shropshire
SY7 8NL
T: (01588) 640409
F: (01588) 640409
E: gill@birchesmill.fsnet.co.uk
I: www.virtual-shropshire.
co.uk/birchesmill

The Thatch ★★★
Contact: Dr H Suckling, 93
Ribblesdale Avenue, London
N11 3AQ
T: (01588) 640206 &
(020) 83686130
E: heathers@doctors.org.uk

Wagtail Cottage ★★★★
Contact: Mrs J Williams, Wagtail
Cottage, Hurst Mill Farm, Clun,
Craven Arms, Shropshire
SY7 0JA
T: (01588) 640224
F: (01588) 640224
E: hurstmillholidays@tinyworld.
co.uk
I: www.hurstmillholidays

Woolbury Barn ★★★★
Contact: Mrs F Morris, Woolbury
Barn, Hollybush Farm,
Woodside, Clun, Craven Arms,
Shropshire SY7 0JB
T: (01588) 640481

Establishments printed in blue have a detailed entry in this guide

CLUNTON
Shropshire

Kingfisher Apartment ★★★
Contact: Mrs S A Pittam,
Kingfisher Apartment, Tawny
Cottage, Clunton, Craven Arms,
Shropshire SY7 0HP
T: (01588) 660327

COALBROOKDALE
Shropshire

**Coalbrookdale, Tea Kettle Row
Cottages★★★-★★★★**
Contact: Mrs M Jones, 34 Darby
Road, Coalbrookdale, Telford,
Shropshire TF8 7EW
T: (01952) 433202
E: mary@teakettlecottages.
co.uk
I: www.teakettlecottages.co.uk

COLEFORD
Gloucestershire

Coach House Cottage ★★★
Contact: Mrs A Richards,
Buckstone Lodge, Staunton,
Coleford, Gloucestershire
GL16 8PD
T: (01594) 833122 &
07767 425755

**Firtrees Holiday Bungalow
★★★**
Contact: Mr & Mrs P A Brain,
Asgard House, 84 Park Road,
Christchurch, Coleford,
Gloucestershire GL16 7AZ
T: (01594) 832576 &
07885 615359

Melrose Cottage ★★
Contact: Mrs J S Bond, 3 Post
Office Lane, Wantage,
Oxfordshire OX12 8DR
T: (01235) 767577

32 Tudor Walk ★★★
Contact: Mrs S J Beale, 82 Park
Road, Christchurch, Coleford,
Gloucestershire GL16 7AZ
T: (01594) 832061 & 832549

Woodside Cottage ★★★
Contact: Mrs Helen Evans,
Peacked Rocks Cottage, The
Rocks, Joys Green, Lydbrook,
Gloucestershire GL17 9RS
T: (01594) 823408 & 861119
F: (01594) 823408

COLESHILL
Warwickshire

Castle-Green ★★★★
Contact: Mr & Mrs Hancocks,
Castle-Green, Nunwode Lea,
Nuneaton Road, Over Whitacre,
Coleshill, Birmingham B46 2NP
T: (01675) 481518
E: castlegreen@btinternet.com

COLWALL
Herefordshire

Threshing Barn ★★★★
Contact: Mr R Coates, Lower
House Farm, Evendine Lane,
Colwall, Malvern, Worcestershire
WR13 6DT
T: (01684) 540284 &
07973 721809
E: robincoates@compuserve.
com

COMBS
Derbyshire

Pyegreave Cottage ★★★★
Contact: Mr N C Pollard,
Pyegreave Farm, Combs, High
Peak SK23 9UX
T: (01298) 813444
F: (01298) 815381
E: n.pollard@allenpollard.co.uk
I: www.holidayapartments.org

COMPTON ABDALE
Gloucestershire

**Spring Hill Stable Cottages
★★★**
Contact: Mrs M L Smail, Spring
Hill Stable Cottages, Spring Hill,
Compton Abdale, Cheltenham,
Gloucestershire GL54 4DU
T: (01242) 890263
E: springhillcottages@yahoo.
co.uk

CORSE LAWN
Gloucestershire

The Lodge ★★★★★
Contact: Mrs E Gardner, Little
Manor, Corse Lawn, Gloucester
GL19 4LU
T: (01452) 780363
F: (01452) 780363
E: ch@lkywhite.demon.co.uk
I: www.holidaybank.co.uk

Plough's End ★★★
Contact: Mr Arthur Cooke,
Plough's End, Corse Lawn,
Gloucester GL19 4LZ
T: (01452) 780120

COSTOCK
Nottinghamshire

**Costock Manor Luxury
Cottages ★★★★★**
Contact: Mr and Mrs D Simblet,
Costock Manor Luxury Cottages,
The Manor, Church Lane,
Costock, Loughborough,
Nottinghamshire LE12 6UZ
T: (01509) 852250 & 853337
F: (01509) 853337
E: simblet@costock-manor.
co.uk
I: www.costock-manor.co.uk

COUND
Shropshire

The Cottage ★★★
Contact: Mr & Mrs J A Willetts,
Severnside, Cound, Shrewsbury
SY5 6AF
T: (01952) 510352

COWLEY
Gloucestershire

**Pixwold Farm Cottages
Rating Applied For**
Contact: Mr and Mrs Sylvia and
Joe Vick, Pixwold Farm Cottages,
Cockleford, Cowley, Cheltenham,
Gloucestershire GL53 9NW
T: (01242) 870426
E: cottages@pixwold.freeserve.
co.uk

CRANHAM
Gloucestershire

Woodside Farm ★★★
Contact: Mr & Mrs T H Spencer
Cox, Woodside Farm, Cranham,
Gloucester GL4 8HB
T: (01452) 812699

CRASWALL
Herefordshire

Rose Cottage ★★★
Contact: Mrs M J Howard, The
Three Horse Shoes, Craswall,
Hereford HR2 0PL
T: (01981) 510631

CRAVEN ARMS
Shropshire

Gwynfa ★★★
Contact: Mrs D M Wall, The
Balkans, Longmeadow End,
Craven Arms, Shropshire
SY7 8ED
T: (01588) 673375

**Halford Holiday Homes
★★★-★★★★**
Contact: Mr & Mrs E James,
Halford Holiday Homes, Halford
Farm, Craven Arms, Shropshire
SY7 9JG
T: (01588) 672382
I: www.go2.co.uk/halford

Malt House ★★★★★
Contact: Mrs M J Mellings, Long
Meads, Lower Barns Road,
Ludford, Ludlow, Shropshire
SY8 4DS
T: (01584) 873315 &
07970 076942
E: jean@mellings.freeserve.
co.uk
I: www.mellings.freeserve.co.uk

Orchard Cottage ★★★★
Contact: Mrs P Webb, Strefford
House, Strefford, Craven Arms,
Shropshire SY7 8DE
T: (01588) 673340
F: (01588) 673340
E: webb.streffordhouse@
virginnet

**Swallows Nest and Robin's
Nest ★★★★**
Contact: Mrs C Morgan,
Strefford Hall, Strefford, Craven
Arms, Shropshire SY7 8DE
T: (01588) 672383

**Upper Onibury Cottages
★★★★**
Contact: Mrs V S Hickman,
Upper Onibury Cottages, Upper
Onibury, Craven Arms,
Shropshire SY7 9AW
T: (01584) 856206 & 856236
F: (01584) 856236
E: oniburycottages@yahoo.com

CRESSAGE
Shropshire

Jasmine Lodge ★★★
Contact: Ms Kate Hogwood,
Jasmine Lodge, Wood Lane,
Cressage, Shrewsbury SY5 6DY
T: (01952) 510375
F: (01952) 510350
E: shrop.mus@lineone.net
I: www.accomodata.
co.uk/270699.htm

CRESSBROOK
Derbyshire

**Apartment
Rating Applied For**
Contact: Mrs Wendy Hicks,
Chert Cottage, Main Road, Great
Longstone, Bakewell, Derbyshire
DE45 1TG
T: (01629) 640410

Badger Cottage ★★★★
Contact: Mrs J Watkins, Trinity
House, Cressbrook, Buxton,
Derbyshire SK17 8SX
T: (01298) 872927
F: (01298) 872927
E: janwatkins@cosycotts.
freeserve.co.uk
I: www.cosycotts.freeserve.co.uk

**Cressbrook Hall Cottages
★★★**
Contact: Mrs B H Bailey,
Cressbrook Hall Cottages Ltd,
Cressbrook Hall, Cressbrook,
Buxton, Derbyshire SK17 8SY
T: (01298) 871289
F: (01298) 871845
E: stay@cressbrookhall.co.uk
I: www.cressbrookhall.co.uk

Monsal View ★★★
Contact: Mr C MacQueen, Peak
Cottages, Strawberry Lee Lane,
Totley Bents, Sheffield, S17 3BA
T: (0114) 262 0777
F: (0114) 262 0666
E: enquiries@peakcottages.com
I: www.peakcottages.com

CRESWELL
Derbyshire

Dukes Cottages ★★★★
Contact: Mrs G Bateman, Dukes
Cottages, 46 Sheffield Road,
Creswell, Worksop,
Nottinghamshire S80 4HW
T: (01909) 722769
F: (01909) 722769
E: cottages@waywender.com

CRICH
Derbyshire

**Avista Property Partnership
★★★★**
Contact: Mr Keith William
Bendon, Avista Property
Partnership, Penrose, Sandy
Lane, Crich, Matlock, Derbyshire
DE4 5DE
T: (01773) 852625 &
077 12633309
E: keith@avista.freeserve.co.uk
I: www.s-h-systems.
co.uk/hotels/avista.html

Clover Stable ★★★★
Contact: Mr Colin MacQueen,
Peak Cottages, Strawberry Lee
Lane, Totley Bents, Sheffield,
S17 3BA
T: (0114) 2620777
F: (0114) 2620666
E: enquiries@peakcottages.com
I: www.peakcottages.com

**Holly Bank
Rating Applied For**
Contact: Country Holidays ref:
9769 Sales, Country Holidays,
Spring Mill, Earby, Barnoldswick,
Lancashire BB94 0AA
T: 08700 723723
F: (01282) 844288
E: sales@ttgihg.co.uk
I: www.country-holidays.co.uk

Ivy Dene Cottage ★★★
Contact: Mrs M Holtam, Market
Place, Crich, Matlock, Derbyshire
DE4 5DD
T: (01773) 852416

Primrose Cottage ★★★
Contact: Mrs P Dwyer, 101 Ripley Road, Heage, Belper, Derbyshire DE56 2HU
T: (01773) 857964

CROMFORD
Derbyshire

1 High Peak Cottages ★★★
Contact: Country Holidays - 3969 Sales, Holiday Cottages Group Limited, Spring Mill, Earby, Barnoldswick, Lancashire BB94 0AA
T: 08700 723723
F: (01282) 844288
E: sales@ttgihg.co.uk
I: www.country-holidays.co.uk

Kinrara ★
Contact: Mr E Traska, 5 Burnwood Drive, Wollaton, Nottingham NG8 2DJ
T: (01159) 282640 & 252698
E: etraska@aol.com

The Lock Up
Rating Applied For
Contact: Mrs Angela Ash, The Old Printing Works, Scarthin, Cromford, Matlock, Derbyshire DE4 3QF
T: (01629) 822541

CROPWELL BISHOP
Nottinghamshire

Corner Cottage ★★★
Contact: Ms Hilary Hawkins, The Weekend Company Ltd, 66 London Road, Nottingham, NG2 3AW
T: (0115) 985 1775
F: (0115) 985 1795
E: hilary@weekendco.com
I: weekendco.com

CROWLAND
Lincolnshire

Abbey Walk Cottage ★★★★
Contact: Mr R Agate, Green View, Leofric Close, Crowland, Peterborough PE6 0NW
T: (01733) 211628 & 210217
E: abbeycottage@yahoo.co.uk

CUBBINGTON
Warwickshire

Briarley ★★★
Contact: Mr R Adams, 20 Queen Street, Cubbington, Leamington Spa, Warwickshire CV32 7NA
T: (01926) 429949

CURBAR
Derbyshire

Upper Barn and Lower Barn ★★★
Contact: Mr and Mrs M J Pierce, Upper Barn and Lower Barn, Orchard House, Curbar, Calver, Hope Valley S32 3YJ
T: (01433) 631885 & 07831 297356
F: (0114) 2903309
E: mp@nbvickers.co.uk
I: www.bvickers.co.uk

CUTTHORPE
Derbyshire

Cow Close Farm Cottages ★★★
Contact: Mr & Mrs S E Gaskin, Cow Close Farm, Overgreen, Cutthorpe, Chesterfield, Derbyshire S42 7BA
T: (01246) 232055

DAGLINGWORTH
Gloucestershire

Corner Cottage ★★★★
Contact: Mrs V M Bartlett, Brook Cottage, 23 Farm Court, Daglingworth, Cirencester, Gloucestershire GL7 7AF
T: (01285) 653478
F: (01285) 653478

DARLEY DALE
Derbyshire

Housekeepers Cottage ★★★★★
Contact: Mrs L Rudkin, The Winnatts, Long Hill, Darley Dale, Matlock, Derbyshire DE4 2HE
T: (01629) 733270 & 07836 633753
F: (01629) 733270
E: housekeeperscottage@hotmail.com

Nether End c/o Nether Hall ★★★★
Contact: Mrs L Wilson, Nether End c/o Nether Hall, Hallmoor Road, Darley Dale, Matlock, Derbyshire DE4 2HF
T: (01629) 732 131 & 07970 900017
⚓

DENSTONE
Staffordshire

Keepers Cottage ★★★★
Contact: Mr C Ball, Manor House Farm, Denstone, Prestwood, Uttoxeter, Staffordshire ST14 5DD
T: (01889) 590415 & (01335) 343669
F: (01335) 342198
E: cm_ball@yahoo.co.uk
I: 4posteraccom.com

DERBY
Derbyshire

Bank Cottage ★★★
Contact: Mrs P K Pym, 2 The Hollow, Mickleover, Derby DE3 5DG
T: (01332) 515607

Home Farm House ★★★
Contact: Country Holidays - 11910 Sales, Holiday Cottages Group Limited, Spring Mill, Earby, Barnoldswick, Lancashire BB94 0AA
T: 08700 723723
F: (01282) 844288
E: sales@ttgihg.co.uk
I: www.country-holidays.co.uk

DIDDLEBURY
Shropshire

Goosefoot Barn Cottages ★★★★
Contact: Mrs Sally Loft, Goosefoot Barn Cottages, Pinstones, Diddlebury, Craven Arms, Shropshire SY7 9LB
T: (01584) 861326
E: sally@goosefoot.freeserve.co.uk

DILHORNE
Staffordshire

Birchenfields Farm ★★★
Contact: Mr & Mrs P Edge, Birchenfields Farm, Dilhorne, Stoke-on-Trent, Staffordshire ST10 2PX
T: (01538) 753972

DORRINGTON
Lincolnshire

Dorrington Cottages ★★★
Contact: Ms Crafer, Dorrington Cottages, 12 Church Lane, Timberland, Lincoln LN4 3SB
T: (01526) 378222

Netley Hall Holidays Ltd ★★★★★
Contact: Mr S Lilley, Netley Hall Holidays Ltd c/o Steve Lilley Racing Ltd, 4 Windmill Bank, Wombourne, Wolverhampton, WV5 9JD
T: (01743) 718339
T: (01743) 718272
E: holidays@netleyhall.co.uk
I: www.netleyhall.co.uk

DORSINGTON
Warwickshire

Windmill Grange Cottage ★★★★
Contact: Mrs L Hollis, Windmill Grange, Dorsington, Stratford-upon-Avon, Warwickshire CV37 8BQ
T: (01789) 720866 & 07836 799039
F: (01789) 721872
E: lornah_windmillgrange@hotmail.com
I: www.windmillgrange.co.uk

DOVEDALE
Derbyshire

3 Orchard View ★★★
Contact: Mrs H E Rees, The Cottage, 37 Back Lane, Chellaston, Derby DE73 1TN
T: (01332) 701026

DRAYCOTT-IN-THE-CLAY
Staffordshire

Granary Court Holiday Cottages★★★★
Contact: Mrs Lynne Statham, Granary Court Holiday Cottages, Stubby Lane, Draycott-in-the-Clay, Ashbourne, Derbyshire DE6 5BU
T: (01283) 820917
F: (01283) 820917
E: webmaster@granarycourt.demon.co.uk
I: www.granarycourt.demon.co.uk

DRONFIELD
Derbyshire

Oxton Rakes Farm ★★★
Contact: Ann and Hugo McGhee, Oxton Rakes Farm, Oxton Rakes, Barlow, Dronfield, S18 7TH
T: (0114) 289 0367
F: (0114) 289 0379

DUNTISBOURNE ABBOTS
Gloucestershire

The Old Cottage
Rating Applied For
Contact: Mrs G Simpson, Church Barn, Hawling, Cheltenham, Gloucestershire GL54 5TA
T: (01451) 850118
F: (01451) 850118
E: paul.gill@btinternet.com
I: www.cottageguide.co.uk/cotswold-cottages

DUNTISBOURNE ROUSE
Gloucestershire

Swallow Barns
Rating Applied For
Contact: Mr & Mrs Anthony & Jean Merrett, Swallow Barns, Rectory Farm, Duntisbourne Rouse, Cirencester, Gloucestershire GL7 7AP
T: (01285) 651031
I: www.cottageinthecountry.co.uk

DURSLEY
Gloucestershire

Two Springbank ★★★
Contact: Mrs F A Jones, 32 Everlands, Cam, Dursley, Gloucestershire GL11 5NL
T: (01453) 543047
E: philippa.charters@care4free.net

EAGLE
Lincolnshire

Eagle and Thorpe Crossing Cottage ★★★
Contact: Mr Patrick Britton, 95 Lauriston Road, Victoria Park, London E9 7HJ
T: (020) 8986 5601 & 0777 5927916
F: (020) 8986 5601
E: p.j.britton@amserve.net

EARDISLEY
Herefordshire

Arboyne House ★★★
Contact: Mr & Mrs C Bysouth, Arboyne House, Church Road, Eardisley, Hereford HR3 6NH
T: (01544) 327058
E: arboyne.house@lineone.net
I: www.arboyne.co.uk

EARL STERNDALE
Derbyshire

Jerusalem Cottage ★★★★
Contact: Country Holidays - 9603,10847,48,49 Sales, Country Holidays, Spring Mill, Earby, Barnoldswick, Lancashire BB94 0AA
T: 08700 723723
F: (01282) 844288
E: sales@ttgihg.co.uk
I: www.country-holidays.co.uk

Wheeldon Trees Farm Holiday Cottages★★★★
Contact: Country Hols ref: 5941/3/5/7, Country Holidays Group Owner Services Dept, Spring Mill, Earby, Barnoldswick, Lancashire BB18 6RN
T: 0870 444 6603
F: (01282) 844288
E: @ttgihg.co.uk
I: www.country-holidays.co.uk

EAST HADDON
Northamptonshire

East Haddon Grange ★★★★
Contact: Mr & Mrs G Pike, East Haddon Grange, East Haddon, Northampton NN6 8DR
T: (01604) 770368
F: (01604) 770368
E: ged.pike@u.genie.co.uk

Establishments printed in blue have a detailed entry in this guide

Mulberry Cottage ★★★★★
Contact: Mr & Mrs M Smerin,
Lane Cottage, St Andrews Road,
East Haddon, Northampton
NN6 8DE
T: (01604) 770244 &
(01327) 844822
F: (01327) 844822
E: liz@smerin.freeserve.co.uk

**Rye Hill Country Cottages
★★★★**
Contact: Mr and Mrs M R
Widdowson, Rye Hill Country
Cottages, Holdenby Road, East
Haddon, Northampton NN6 8JR
T: (01604) 770990
F: (01604) 770237
E: ryehills@compuserve.com
I: www.ryehillcottages.co.uk
🚶

EASTMOOR
Derbyshire

Bilberry Lodge ★★★
Contact: Mrs J Gill, Nether Rod
Knowle Farm, Eastmoor,
Chesterfield, Derbyshire
S42 7DB
T: (01246) 566151 &
(0114) 2620777
E: enquiries@peakcottages.com
I: www.peakcottages.com

EASTON ON THE HILL
Northamptonshire

The Old Bakery ★★★
Contact: Mrs M Yogasundram,
The Old Bakery, 25 West Street,
Easton on the Hill, Stamford,
Lincolnshire PE9 3LS
T: (01780) 753898
E: yogiandmel@theoldbakery25.
freeserve.co.uk

EBRINGTON
Gloucestershire

Pump Cottage ★★★
Contact: Mr R Hutsby, Middle
Hill Farm, Charlecote, Warwick
CV35 9EH
T: (01789) 841525 &
07778 153180
F: (01789) 841523
E: robert.hutsby@btinternet.
com
I: www.broadway-cotswolds.
co.uk/pump.html

ECCLESHALL
Staffordshire

**Cadbury Cottage
Rating Applied For**
Contact: Mrs Margaret
Housiaux, Cadbury Cottage, The
Old Creamery, Pershall,
Eccleshall, Stafford ST21 6NE
T: (01785) 851402

ECKINGTON
Worcestershire

Nafford House ★★★
Contact: Mrs J E Wheatley,
Nafford House, Eckington,
Pershore, Worcestershire
WR10 3DJ
T: (01386) 750233

EDALE
Derbyshire

Carr Bank Cottages ★★
Contact: Holiday Cottages
(Yorkshire) Limited, Water
Street, Skipton, North Yorkshire
BD23 1PB
T: (01756) 700510

Grindslow House ★★★
Contact: Mrs S Crook, c/o Meller
Braggins, The Estate Office,
Rostherne, Knutsford, Cheshire
WA16 6SW
T: (01565) 830395
F: (01565) 830241

**Hathaway and Heath Cottages
★★★**
Contact: Mrs S Gee, Cotefield
Farm, Ollerbrook, Edale, Hope
Valley, Derbyshire S33 2ZG
T: (01433) 670273
F: (01433) 670273

Skinners' Hall ★★★★
Contact: Mrs Susan Favell,
Skinners' Hall, Edale, Hope Valley
S33 7ZE
T: (01433) 670 281
F: (01433) 670 481
E: sue@skinnershall.freeserve.
co.uk
I: www.skinnershall.freeserve.
co.uk

EDITH WESTON
Rutland

**Edith Weston Cottage
Holidays ★★★-★★★**
Contact: Mrs Jayne Barber, Edith
Weston Cottage Holidays, Brake
Spinney, St Mary's Close, Edith
Weston, Rutland LE15 8HF
T: (0115) 9373201 &
(01780) 720081
E: ewch@rutnet.co.uk
I: www.rutnet.co.uk

EDLASTON
Derbyshire

Church Farm Cottages ★★★
Contact: Mrs Lois Blake, Church
Farm, Edlaston, Ashbourne,
Derbyshire DE6 2DQ
T: (01335) 300328
E: adeblake@aol.com
I: www.churchfarm-holidays.
freeserve.co.uk

ELKINGTON
Northamptonshire

Manor Farm ★★★★
Contact: Mr & Mrs Michael and
Hilary Higgott, Manor Farm,
Elkington, Northampton
NN6 6NH
T: (01858) 575245 &
07711 322163
F: (01858) 575213

ELKSTONE
Gloucestershire

The Dolls House ★★★
Contact: Mrs M Cooch, Enfield
Farm, Elkstone, Cheltenham,
Gloucestershire GL53 9PB
T: (01242) 870244

Stable Cottage ★★★
Contact: Mrs V Lawrenson,
Grove House, Elkstone, Buxton,
Derbyshire SK17 0LU
T: (01538) 300487 &
07790 754155
E: elkstones@talk21.com

ELLESMERE
Shropshire

Colemere Farm Cottages ★★★
Contact: Mrs S Livermore,
Colemere Farm, Ellesmere,
Shropshire SY12 0QL
T: (01939) 270846

The Pool House ★★
Contact: Mr C Sykes, Sykes
Cottages, York House, York
Street, Chester, CH1 3LR
T: (01244) 345700
F: (01244) 321442

ELMLEY CASTLE
Worcestershire

**The Cottage Manor Farm
House★★**
Contact: Mr & Mrs B D Lovett,
Manor Farm House, Main Street,
Elmley Castle, Pershore,
Worcestershire WR10 3HS
T: (01386) 710286
F: (01386) 710112

ELTON
Derbyshire

Barncroft ★★★
Contact: Mr and Mrs R G
Durgan, Barncroft, Well Street,
Elton, Matlock, Derbyshire
DE4 2BY
T: (01629) 650645 &
07977 570019
E: rogerdurgan@compuserve.
com

The Stable ★★★★
Contact: Mrs Jean Carson, The
Stable, Homestead Farm, Main
Street, Elton, Matlock,
Derbyshire DE4 2BW
T: (01629) 650359

EMPINGHAM
Rutland

2 Walnut Close ★★★
Contact: Mrs Pat Stevens, Mill
Cottage, Crown Street, Oakham,
Rutland LE15 6AE
T: (01572) 724155

ENGLISH BICKNOR
Gloucestershire

Dryslade Farm ★★★
Contact: Mrs D Gwilliam,
Dryslade Farm, English Bicknor,
Coleford, Gloucestershire
GL16 7PA
T: (01594) 860259 &
07801 732778
F: (01594) 860259
E: dryslade@agriplus.net
I: www.fweb.org.uk/dryslade
🚶

Upper Tump Farm ★★★
Contact: Mrs M Merrett, Upper
Tump Farm, Tump Lane,
Eastbach, English Bicknor,
Coleford, Gloucestershire
GL16 7EU
T: (01594) 860072

EPPERSTONE
Nottinghamshire

The Loft House ★★★★
Contact: Mrs J Esam, Criftin
Farm, Epperstone, Nottingham
NG14 6AT
T: (0115) 965 2039
F: (0115) 965 5490
E: jennyesam@compuserve.com
I: www.nottsfarmtourism.co.uk

The Mews ★★★
Contact: Mrs Susan Santos,
Eastwood Farm, Hagg Lane,
Epperstone, Nottingham
NG14 6AX
T: (0115) 966 3018
E: santosthemews@hotmail.
com

The Mistal ★★★★
Contact: Mr and Mrs Peake,
Ricketwood Farm, Chapel Lane,
Epperstone, Nottingham
NG14 6AR
T: (0115) 965 2086

EVESHAM
Worcestershire

10 Abbey Quay ★★★
Contact: Mr J Payne, Hampton
Mill, Corn Mill Road, Evesham,
Worcestershire WR11 6LL
T: (01386) 442902 &
07973 166196
F: (01386) 423509

Nubarn Cottage ★★★★
Contact: Mrs P Taylor, Anvil
House, 9a Badsey Road,
Evesham, Worcestershire
WR11 5DS
T: (01386) 442787

Thatchers End ★★★★
Contact: Mr & Mrs Wilson, 60
Pershore Road, Evesham,
Worcestershire WR11 6PQ
T: (01386) 446269 &
07710 006949
F: (01386) 446269
E: trad.accom@virgin.net
I: freespace.virgin.net/trad.
accom

EYAM
Derbyshire

**Dalehead Court Cottages
★★★★**
Contact: Mrs D M Neary,
Laneside Farm, Hope, Hope
Valley, Derbyshire S33 6RR
T: (01433) 620214
F: (01433) 620214
E: laneside@lineone.net
I: www.laneside.fsbusiness.co.uk

**Fern and Brosterfield Cottage
Brosterfield Hall★★★★**
Contact: Mrs J Vickers, Fern and
Brosterfield Cottage Brosterfield
Hall, Bakewell Road, Foolow,
Eyam, Hope Valley, Derbyshire
S32 5QB
T: (01433) 631254 &
07836 382834
F: (01433) 631254
E: rcv@bvickers.co.uk
I: www.peak-cottages.com

Jonas House ★★★★
Contact: Mr & Mrs G Richards,
12 Kingsway, Scunthorpe, South
Humberside DN17 1BL
T: (01724) 870711 & 280397
F: (01724) 280397

Lark Cottage ★★★★★
Contact: Mrs M Smith, Peak
District Holidays, Bar End, Bar
Road, Baslow, Bakewell,
Derbyshire DE45 1SF
T: (01246) 582140 &
07711 457744

1 Lydgate Cottages ★★★★
Contact: Mrs S P Harrop,
Townfield House, Townfield
Lane, Warburton, Lymm,
Cheshire WA13 9SR
T: (01925) 752118
E: sandraharrop@
townfieldhouse.freeserve.co.uk

Merrill House & Cottage ★★★
Contact: Ms Jane Hill, Eagle Tor
Farm, Birchover, Matlock,
Derbyshire DE4 2LY
T: (01629) 650555

513

Rowan Cottage
Rating Applied For
Contact: Country Holidays ref: 9412 Sales, Holiday Cottages Group Limited, Spring Mill, Earby, Barnoldswick, Lancashire BB94 0AA
T: 08700 723723
F: (01282) 844288
I: www.country-holidays.co.uk

The Trap House
Rating Applied For
Contact: Peak Cottages, Strawberry Lee Lane, Totley Bents, Sheffield, S17 3BA
T: (0114) 262 0777
F: (0114) 262 0666
E: enquiries@peakcottages.com
I: www.peakcottages.com

Watchmakers Cottage ★★★★
Contact: Mrs N J Carmichael, Croft View Cottage, Foolow, Eyam, Hope Valley S32 5QA
T: (01433) 630711
E: carmichaelat@hotmail.com

EYDON
Northamptonshire

Crockwell Farm ★★★★
Contact: Mrs L Pellerin, Crockwell Farm, Eydon, Daventry, Northamptonshire NN11 3QA
T: (01327) 361358 &
0771 4218285
F: (01327) 361573
E: info@crockwellfarm.co.uk
I: www.crockwellfarm.co.uk

FAIRFORD
Gloucestershire

The Cottage, East End House ★★★★★
Contact: Mrs D Ewart, East End House, Fairford, Gloucestershire GL7 4AP
T: (01285) 713715
F: (01285) 713505
E: eastendho@cs.com
I: www.eastendhouse.co.uk

FAR FOREST
Worcestershire

Manor Holding ★★★
Contact: Mr & Mrs N Dobson-Smyth, 32 Church Street, Hagley, Stourbridge, West Midlands DY9 0NA
T: 07970 260010 &
(01562) 883609
E: nds@landscapeconsultancy.freeserve.co.uk

FENNY BENTLEY
Derbyshire

Swallows Cottage ★★★
Contact: Country Holidays ref: 9995 Sales, Holiday Cottages Group Limited, Spring Mill, Earby, Barnoldswick, Lancashire BB94 0AA
T: 08700 723723
F: (01282) 844288
E: sales@ttgihg.co.uk
I: www.country-holidays.co.uk

FLASH
Staffordshire

Northfield Farm ★★-★★★
Contact: Mrs E Andrews, Northfield Farm, Flash, Quarnford, Buxton, Derbyshire SK17 0SW
T: (01298) 22543
F: (01298) 27849
E: northfield@btinternet.com

FLORE
Northamptonshire

Brewer's Cottage ★★★★
Contact: Mrs A Loasby, The Old Baker's Arms, Kings Lane, Flore, Northampton NN7 4LQ
T: (01327) 349737
F: (01327) 349747
E: BrewersCottage@homeinflore.fsnet.co.uk

FOOLOW
Derbyshire

Sycamore Cottage ★★★
Contact: Mrs M S Norton, The Rest, Foolow, Eyam, Hope Valley, Derbyshire S32 5QR
T: (01433) 630186

FORD
Shropshire

Longmore Cottage ★★★★
Contact: Mrs M Powell, Home Farm, Rowton, Halfway House, Shrewsbury, Shropshire SY5 9EN
T: (01743) 884201
F: (01743) 884201

FORTHAMPTON
Gloucestershire

The South Wing ★★★★
Contact: Mrs K I Yeaman, The Dower House, Forthampton, Gloucester GL19 4QW
T: (01684) 298498
F: (01684) 298498

FOWNHOPE
Herefordshire

Birds Farm Cottage ★★★
Contact: Mrs J Edwards, White House, How Caple, Hereford HR1 4SR
T: (01989) 740644
F: (01989) 740388
E: birdscottage@yahoo.com

FRAMPTON MANSELL
Gloucestershire

Twissells Mill ★★
Contact: Mr & Mrs Daphne & Martin Neville, Bakers Mill, Frampton Mansell, Stroud, Gloucestershire GL6 8JH
T: (01285) 760234
F: martin.neville@ukgateway.net

FRAMPTON-ON-SEVERN
Gloucestershire

Clair Cottage ★★★★
Contact: Mrs A Cullen, Church Court Cottage, Church End, Frampton-on-Severn, Gloucester GL2 7EH
T: (01452) 740289
E: claircottage@waitrose.com

Old Priest Cottage and Old Stable Cottage ★★★★-★★★★★
Contact: Mr and Mrs M R Williams, Tan House Farm, Frampton-on-Severn, Gloucester GL2 7EH
T: (01452) 741072
F: (01452) 741072
E: tanhouse.farm@lineone.net

FRITCHLEY
Derbyshire

Top Hat ★★★
Contact: Holiday Cottages (Yorkshire) Limited, Water Street, Skipton, North Yorkshire BD23 1PB
T: (01756) 700510

FROCESTER
Gloucestershire

Kestrel Cottage
Rating Applied For
Contact: Mr FJ Holpin, F J Holpin & Sons Ltd, 1 Leaze Close, Berkeley, Gloucestershire GL13 9BZ
T: (01453) 810486

FRODESLEY
Shropshire

The Haven ★★★
Contact: Mrs J Pickard, The Haven, Frodesley, Dorrington, Shrewsbury SY5 7EY
T: (01694) 731672
E: the-haven@frodesley.fsnet.co.uk
I: www.cottageguide.co.uk/the-haven

The Wendy House ★★★
Contact: Mrs W Brown & Mr Leach, The Wendy House, 1 Old Frodesley Barns, Frodesley, Shrewsbury, Shropshire SY5 7HD
T: (01694) 731798
F: (01694) 731798
E: the-wendy-house@faxvia.com
I: www.the-wendy-house.com

FROGHALL
Staffordshire

Foxtwood Cottages ★★★★
Contact: Mr C Worrall, Foxtwood Cottages, Foxt Road, Froghall, Stoke-on-Trent ST10 2HJ
T: (01538) 266160
E: clive@foxtwood.fsnet.co.uk

FULBECK
Lincolnshire

Toad Hall
Rating Applied For
Contact: Mrs Margaret Farnsworth, St Helier, South Heath Lane, Fulbeck, Grantham, Lincolnshire NG32 3HX
T: (01400) 272682

FULLETBY
Lincolnshire

High Beacon Cottage ★★★★
Contact: Mr & Mrs A Walker, High Beacon Cottage, High Beacon Farm, Fulletby, Horncastle, Lincolnshire LN9 6LB
T: (01507) 534009 &
07977 077337
F: (01507) 534009
E: beacon.cottage@virgin.net
I: www.highbeaconcottage.co.uk

GATCOMBE
Gloucestershire

Oatfield Farmhouse & Cottages ★★★★-★★★★★
Contact: Mr J & Mrs P Berrisford, Oatfield Farmhouse & Cottages, Etloe, Blakeney, Gloucestershire GL15 4AY
T: (01594) 510372
F: (01594) 510372
I: www.oatfieldfarm.co.uk

GAYDON
Warwickshire

The Wagon House ★★★★
Contact: Miss G A Malsbury, Manor Farm, Gaydon, Warwick, Warwickshire CV35 0HB
T: (01926) 640232 &
07773 152140
F: (01926) 640232

GLOSSOP
Derbyshire

Hillside Cottage ★★★
Contact: Country Holidays - 975 Sales, Holiday Cottages Group Limited, Spring Cottage, Earby, Barnoldswick, Lancashire BB94 0AA
T: 08700 723723
F: (01282) 844288
E: sales@ttgihg.co.uk
I: www.country-holidays.co.uk

GLOUCESTER
Gloucestershire

Norfolk House
Rating Applied For
Contact: Mrs P J Jackson, 3 Wood Street, Higham Ferrers, Wellingborough, Northamptonshire NN9 8DL
T: (01933) 316062

Number Ten ★★★
Contact: Mr M A Lampkin, Number Ten, 10 Albion Street, Gloucester, Gloucestershire GL1 1UE
T: (01452) 304402 & 528815
E: lampkinternet.com@bushinternet.com

The Vineary ★★★
Contact: Mrs A Snow, Vinetree Cottage, Solomons Tump, Huntley, Gloucester GL19 3EB
T: (01452) 830006

GOTHERINGTON
Gloucestershire

Bakery Cottage ★★★
Contact: Mrs Weller, Wortheal House, Southam Lane, Southam, Cheltenham, Gloucestershire GL52 3NY
T: (01242) 236765

Barn Cottages ★★★★
Contact: Mr Paul Tilley, Moat Farm, 34 Malleson Road, Gotherington, Cheltenham, Gloucestershire GL52 9ET
T: (01242) 672055 & 676807
F: 07050 665639
E: jo@moatfarm.free-online.co.uk
I: www.moatfarm.free-online.co.uk

GRANGEMILL
Derbyshire

Chapelgate Cottage ★★★★
Contact: Mrs Mary Lomas,
Chapelgate Cottage, Lydgate
Farm, Aldwark, Grangemill,
Matlock, Derbyshire DE4 4HW
T: (01629) 540250
F: (01629) 540250
E: joy.lomas@btinternet.com

GRANTHAM
Lincolnshire

Appletree Cottage ★★★★
Contact: Elizabeth Puxty, Stone
House, 4 Church Lane, Ropsley,
Grantham, Lincolnshire
NG33 4DA
T: (01476) 585620

Granary Cottage ★★★★
Contact: Miss Pepper, Granary
Cottage, The Farmhouse, Little
Humby, Grantham, Lincolnshire
NG33 4HW
T: (01476) 585311

GREAT CARLTON
Lincolnshire

Willow Farm ★★
Contact: Mr J Clark, Willow
Farm, Great Carlton, Louth,
Lincolnshire LN11 8JP
T: (01507) 338540

GREAT COMBERTON
Worcestershire

The Granary ★★★★
Contact: Mr & Mrs J Newbury,
Tibbitts Farm, Great Comberton,
Pershore, Worcestershire
WR10 3DT
T: (01386) 710210
F: (01386) 710210

GREAT HALE
Lincolnshire

The Old Stable ★★★★
Contact: Mr & Mrs N E
Redmond, The Old Stable, The
Old Vicarage, 9 Church Street,
Great Hale, Sleaford,
Lincolnshire NG34 9LF
T: (01529) 460307
E: c.redmond@virgin.net

GREAT HUCKLOW
Derbyshire

Burrs Cottage ★★★
Contact: Mr C Sykes, Sykes
Cottages, York House, York
Street, Chester, CH1 3LR
T: (01244) 345700
F: (01244) 321442
E: info@sykescottages.co.uk
I: www.sykescottages.co.uk

The Hayloft ★★★
Contact: Mrs Margot Darley,
Stanley House Farm, Great
Hucklow, Buxton, Derbyshire
SK17N 8R
T: (01298) 871044
I: peakdistrictfarmhols.co.uk

**Kates Cottage and Martins
Cottage★★★★**
Contact: Mr & Mrs H Johnson,
Stanley Moor Farm, Great
Hucklow, Buxton, Derbyshire
SK17 8RL
T: (01298) 871506
E: katesmartinscotts@
btinternet.co.uk

South View Cottage ★★★★
Contact: Mrs M Waterhouse,
Holme Cottage, Windmill, Great
Hucklow, Buxton, Derbyshire
SK17 8RE
T: (01298) 871440 &
07785 791193
F: (01298) 871440

West End Lodge ★★★★
Contact: Ms Janet Persey, West
End, Great Hucklow, Buxton,
Derbyshire SK17 8RF
T: (01298) 871593 &
07775 597833
F: (01298) 871593
E: hucklow@aol.com

GREAT LONGSTONE
Derbyshire

Applehoe Cottage ★★★★
Contact: Mr M Scawen,
Fieldsview, Station Road, Great
Longstone, Bakewell, Derbyshire
DE45 1TS
T: (01629) 640593
F: 0870 0568861
E: mikes@ga-memik.demon.
co.uk
I: www.ga-memik.demon.co.uk

Netherdale ★★
Contact: Country Hols ref: 8134,
Country Holidays Group Owner
Services Dept, Spring Mill, Earby,
Barnoldswick, Lancashire
BB18 6RN
T: 0870 444 6603
F: (01282) 841539

Two Bears Cottage ★★★★
Contact: Mr & Mrs V Squire, 185
Crimicar Lane, Sheffield,
S10 4EH
T: (0114) 2303274

GREAT RISSINGTON
Gloucestershire

The Dairy Barn ★★★★
Contact: Mrs G M Agg, The Dairy
Barn, Rectory Lane, Great
Rissington, Cheltenham,
Gloucestershire GL54 2LL
T: (01451) 810649 & 821034

GREAT STURTON
Lincolnshire

Old Barn Cottages ★★★
Contact: Mr Dan Dobson, Old
Barn Cottages, Beech House,
Great Sturton, Horncastle,
Lincolnshire LN9 5NX
T: (01507) 578435
F: (01507) 578435
E: danandko@dobson78.
freeserve.co.uk
I: www.dobson78.freeserve.
co.uk

GRINDLEFORD
Derbyshire

Middle Cottage ★★★
Contact: Peak Cottages, Paddock
Cottage, Strawberry Lane, Totley
Bents, Sheffield, South Yorkshire
S17 3BA
T: (0114) 262 0777
F: (0114) 262 0666
I: www.peakcottages.com

GRINSHILL
Shropshire

**Barleycorn Barns
Rating Applied For**
Contact: Mr Neil Lewis & Ms
Kerry Taylor, Barleycorn Cottage,
Grinshill, Shrewsbury,
Shropshire SY4 3BH
T: (01939) 220333 &
(01952) 608274
F: (01952) 608275
E: booking@barleycornbarns.
com

HADNALL
Shropshire

Freshfields ★★★
Contact: Mrs I Brisbourne,
Freshfields, Painsbrook, Hadnall,
Shrewsbury SY4 4BA
T: (01939) 210214
F: (01939) 210688

HAGWORTHINGHAM
Lincolnshire

Holly Cottage ★★★★
Contact: Mrs L Barley, Lyons Hill,
Chapel Lane, Toynton All Saints,
Spilsby, Lincolnshire PE23 5AF
T: (01790) 753000
F: (01790) 752405

HALLINGTON
Lincolnshire

**The Paddy House and
Blacksmiths Shop★★★★**
Contact: Mrs H Canter, The
Paddy House and Blacksmiths
Shop, Hallington Farming
Company, Home Farm,
Hallington, Louth, Lincolnshire
LN11 9QX
T: (01507) 605864 &
(01472) 356143
F: (01472) 250365
E: canter.hallington@virginnet.
co.uk
I: freespace.virginnet.
co.uk/canter.hallington/index.
htm

HALLOW
Worcestershire

The New Cottage ★★★★
Contact: Mrs D F Jeeves, The
New Cottage, Bridles End House,
Greenhill Lane, Hallow,
Worcester WR2 6LG
T: (01905) 640953
E: jeeves@thenewcottage.co.uk
I: www.thenewcottage.co.uk

HALSE
Northamptonshire

Hill Farm ★★★★
Contact: Mr J Robinson, Hill
Farm, Halse, Brackley,
Northamptonshire NN13 6DT
T: (01280) 703300 &
07860 865146

HAMBLETON
Rutland

Home Farm Mews ★★★
Contact: Mrs S Brown, 12
Westland Road, Cottesmore,
Oakham, Leicestershire LE15 7DT
T: (01572) 813242

HANDLEY
Derbyshire

Ridgewell Farm ★★★★
Contact: Mrs Ann Kerry,
Ridgewell Farm, Handley Lane,
Handley, Clay Cross,
Chesterfield, Derbyshire S45 9AT
T: (01246) 590698
F: (01246) 590698

HANLEY SWAN
Worcestershire

Little Merebrook ★★★★
Contact: Mr A Bishop, Little
Merebrook, Hanley Swan,
Worcester WR8 0EH
T: (01684) 310899
F: (01684) 310899

HARBY
Leicestershire

New Farm Cottage ★★★
Contact: Mrs J Stanley, New
Farm, Waltham Road, Harby,
Melton Mowbray, Leicestershire
LE14 4DB
T: (01949) 860640
F: (01949) 861165

HARTINGTON
Derbyshire

Beech Cottage ★★★
Contact: Mrs L Birch, Dale
House, Hartington, Buxton,
Derbyshire SK17 0AS
T: (01298) 84532
E: lesley@beechcottage99.
freeserve.co.uk
I: www.beechcottage99.
freeserve.co.uk

The Chapel ★★★-★★★★
Contact: CH ref: 11839, Holiday
Cottages Group Owner Services
Dept, Spring Mill, Earby,
Barnoldswick, Lancashire
BB18 6RN
T: 0870 444 6603
F: (01282) 844288
E: sales@ttgihg.co.uk
I: www.country-holidays.co.uk

Church View ★★★
Contact: Miss K Bassett, Digmer,
Hartington, Buxton, Derbyshire
SK17 0AQ
T: (01298) 84660

**Cotterill Farm Cottages
★★★★**
Contact: Mrs Frances Skemp,
Cotterill Farm Cottages, Cotterill
Farm, Biggin-by-Hartington,
Buxton, Derbyshire SK17 0DJ
T: (01298) 84447
F: (01298) 84664
E: patrick@skemp.u-net.com
I: www.skemp.u-net.com

**Cruck and Wolfscote Cottage
★★★★**
Contact: Mrs Jane Gibbs,
Wolfscote Grange Farm,
Hartington, Buxton, Derbyshire
SK17 0AX
T: (01298) 84342
E: wolfscote@btinternet.com
I: www.cottageguide.
co.uk/wolfscote

Establishments printed in blue have a detailed entry in this guide

Dove Barns ★★★★
Contact: Mr Colin MacQueen,
Peak Cottages, Strawberry Lee
Lane, Totley Bents, Sheffield,
S17 3BA
T: (0114) 2620777
F: (0114) 2620666
E: enquiries@peakcottages.com
I: www.peakcottages.com

Hartington Cottages ★★
Contact: Mr Colin MacQueen,
Peak Cottages, Strawberry Lee
Lane, Totley Bents, Sheffield,
S17 3BA
T: (0114) 2620777
F: (0114) 2620666
E: enquiries@peakcottages.com
I: www.peakcottages.com

Old House Farm Cottage ★★★
Contact: Mrs S Flower, Old
House Farm Cottage, Newhaven,
Hartington, Buxton, Derbyshire
SK17 0DY
T: (01629) 636268
F: (01629) 636268
E: s.flower1@virgin.net
I: freespace.virgin.net/s.flowers1

**1 Staley Cottage and Victoria
House★★★-★★★★**
Contact: Mr and Mrs J Oliver,
Carr Head Farm, Penistone,
Sheffield S36 7GA
T: (01226) 762387

HATHERSAGE
Derbyshire

Oaks Farm ★★★
Contact: Mrs P M Bardwell, Oaks
Farm, Highlow, Hathersage,
Hope Valley, Derbyshire S32 1AX
T: (01433) 650494
E: oaksfarm@fsbdial.co.uk
I: ukonline.
co.uk/oaksfarm/index.html

St.Michael's Cottage ★★★
Contact: Miss H Turton, Saint
Michael's Environmental
Education Centre, Main Road,
Hathersage, Hope Valley
S32 1BB
T: (01433) 650309
F: (01433) 650089
E: stmichaels@education.
nottscc.gov.uk

Topcroft ★★★
Contact: Mr C MacQueen, Peak
Cottages, Strawberry Lee Lane,
Totley Bents, Sheffield, S17 3BA
T: (0114) 262 0777
F: (0114) 262 0666

HATTON
Lincolnshire

The Cottage ★★★
Contact: Mrs Frances von
Hidegh-Pichler, The Summer
House, Hatton, Wragby,
Lincolnshire LN8 5QG
T: (01673) 858835

The Gables ★★★★
Contact: Mrs J L Merivale, The
Gables, Hatton Hall Farm,
Hatton, Market Rasen,
Lincolnshire LN8 5QG
T: (01673) 858862 &
07702 271041
E: jmerivale@aol.com
I: www.thegables-nation.co.uk

HATTON
Warwickshire

The Dairy ★★★
Contact: Mrs L Baker, Green
Gates Farm, Station Road,
Hatton, Warwick, Warwickshire
CV35 7LJ
T: (01926) 842438
E: greengatesfarm@hotmail.
com

HAWLING
Gloucestershire

The Bothy ★★★★
Contact: Mrs S Watters,
Brocklehurst, Hawling,
Cheltenham, Gloucestershire
GL54 5TA
T: (01451) 850772
E: hawling@aol.com

Middle Farm Cottages ★★★★
Contact: Mr & Mrs N J
Woollacott, Middle Farm
Cottages, Middle Farm, Hawling,
Cheltenham, Gloucestershire
GL54 5SZ
T: (01451) 850744
E: nigel.woollacott@ukonline.
co.uk

HAYFIELD
Derbyshire

**Bowden Bridge Cottage
★★★★**
Contact: Mrs Margrith Easter,
Bowden Bridge Cottage, Kinder,
Hayfield, High Peak, Derbyshire
SK22 2LH
T: (01663) 743975
F: (01663) 743812
E: j_easter@talk21.com

HENLEY-IN-ARDEN
Warwickshire

Irelands Farm ★★★★
Contact: Mr & Mrs Williams,
Irelands Farm, Irelands Lane,
Henley-in-Arden, Solihull, West
Midlands B95 5SA
T: (01564) 792476
F: (01564) 792476
E: stephanie.williams1@
btinternet.com

HENNOR
Herefordshire

**Hennor House
Rating Applied For**
Contact: Mrs Sally Hall, Hennor
Holidays, Hennor House,
Hennor, Leominster,
Herefordshire HR6 0QR
T: (01568) 760665
F: (01568) 760665
E: salihall@aol

HEREFORD
Herefordshire

Anvil Cottage ★★★★
Contact: Mrs Jennie Layton,
Grafton Villa Farm House,
Grafton, Hereford HR2 8ED
T: (01432) 268689
F: (01432) 268689
E: jennielayton@ereal.net
I: www.s-h-system.
@uk/hotels/graftonv.html
🖼

Breinton Court ★★★
Contact: Mrs G Hands, Breinton
Court, Lower Breinton, Hereford,
HR4 7PG
T: (01432) 268156 &
(01443) 687057
F: (01432) 265134

**Home From Home Holidays
★★**
Contact: Mr & Mrs Bill & Maggie
Matthews, 16 St Martins
Avenue, Hereford, Herefordshire
HR2 7RQ
T: (01432) 272259
E: bandm@prospectpl.fsnet.
co.uk

Longwood Cottage ★★★
Contact: Mrs V Harris, S L C
(Services) Limited, Ashfield
House, Sollers Hope, Hereford,
HR1 4RL
T: (01989) 740248
F: (01989) 740214
E: kenverharris@aol.com

New Fairfield ★★★
Contact: Mrs H White, New
Fairfield, Hampton Bishop,
Hereford, HR1 4JP
T: (01432) 277285 & 370759
E: hcwhite1@yahoo.com

Rushford ★★★
Contact: Mrs M W Roberts,
Rushford, 7 Belle Bank Avenue,
Holmer, Hereford HR4 9RL
T: (01432) 273380
F: (01432) 273380

HIMBLETON
Worcestershire

The Granary ★★★
Contact: Mrs P A Havard, The
Granary, Phepson Farm,
Himbleton, Droitwich,
Worcestershire WR9 7JZ
T: (01905) 391205
F: (01905) 391338
E: harvard@globalnet.co.uk
I: www.phepsonfarm.co.uk

HINCKLEY
Leicestershire

**Crossways Country Holidays
★★★★**
Contact: Mr and Mrs John Mac
and Carol Mac, Crossways
Country Holidays, Crossways
Farm, Lutterworth Road,
Burbage, Hinckley, Leicestershire
LE10 3AH
T: (01455) 239261 &
07946 421123
F: (01445) 633889
E: user@burbage60.fsnet.co.uk
I: www.crossways-holidays.
co.uk

HOARWITHY
Herefordshire

Aspen Cottage ★★★
Contact: Mr & Mrs Mike or Val
Gardner, Aspen House,
Hoarwithy, Hereford,
Herefordshire HR2 6QP
T: (01432) 840353 &
07796 671449
F: (01432) 840353
E: hoarwithy@aol.com

Old Mill Cottage ★★★
Contact: Mrs Carol Probert, Old
Mill, Hoarwithy, Hereford
HR2 6QH
T: (01432) 840602
F: (01432) 840602

HOLBEACH
Lincolnshire

Poachers Den ★★★
Contact: Mr B Flynn, 34 Fen
Road, Holbeach, Spalding,
Lincolnshire PE12 8QA
T: (01406) 423625
F: (01406) 423625
E: MFlynn8748@aol.com
I: www.SmoothHound.
co.uk/hotels/poachers.html

HOLLINGTON
Staffordshire

**Rowan Cottage
Rating Applied For**
Contact: Mrs A Campbell,
Camwood Croft, Great Gate
Road, Winnoth Dale, Tean,
Stoke-on-Trent, Staffordshire
ST10 4HB
T: (01538) 722031

HOLLOWAY
Derbyshire

**Florence Nightingale Chapel
Rating Applied For**
Contact: Mrs S Metcalf, 14
Chapel Lane, Holloway, Matlock,
Derbyshire DE4 5AU
T: (01629) 534652
F: (01629) 534977
E: pmetcalf@lineone.net

HOLYMOORSIDE
Derbyshire

Millclose Cottage ★★★
Contact: Mr and Mrs A Stockton,
Millclose Cottage, Millclose
Farm, Nether Loads,
Holymoorside, Chesterfield,
Derbyshire S42 7HW
T: (01246) 567624
F: (01246) 567624
E: allan.stockton@btinternet.
com

HOPE
Derbyshire

Aston Cottages ★★★★
Contact: Mrs R Morley, Aston
Cottages, The Dimings, Aston
Lane, Hope Valley, S33 6RA
T: (01433) 621619 &
07974 465758
E: rmorley@dimings.freeserve.
co.uk
I: www.sallydog.
co.uk/astoncottages/

**Farfield Farm Cottages
★★★★**
Contact: Mrs G Elliott, Farfield
Farm Cottages, Farfield Farm,
Hope, Hope Valley, Derbyshire
S33 6RA
T: (01433) 620640
F: (01433) 620640
E: gill@farfield.gemsoft.co.uk
I: www.farfield.gemsoft.co.uk

Keepers Lodge ★★★★★
Contact: Mrs C Bell, Spring
House Farm, Castleton, Hope
Valley, Derbyshire S33 8WB
T: (01433) 620962
E: thebells@btinternet.com
I: www.
peak-district-holiday-cottages.
co.uk

Establishments printed in blue have a detailed entry in this guide

Laneside Farm Cottages
★★★★
Contact: Mrs D M Neary,
Laneside Farm, Hope, Hope
Valley S33 6RR
T: (01433) 620214
F: (01433) 620214
E: laneside@lineone.net
I: www.laneside.fs.business.
co.uk

Oaker Farm Holiday Cottage
★★★
Contact: Mrs Julie Ann Hadfield,
Oaker Farm, Off Edale Road,
Hope, Hope Valley, Derbyshire
S33 6RF
T: (01433) 621955
E: juliehadfield@care4free.net

The Old Bell and Ebenezer Barn
★★★
Contact: Mr M Davis, Bennet
Grange, Jefferys Green,
Sheffield, S10 4PA
T: (0114) 230 3463
F: (0114) 2722265

Twitchill Farm Cottages
★★★-★★★★
Contact: Mrs S Atkin, Twitchill
Farm Cottages, Edale Road,
Hope, Hope Valley S33 6RF
T: (01433) 621426 &
07721 429657
E: sarahatkin@aol.com
I: www.oas.
co.uk/ukcottages/twitchill

HOPESAY
Shropshire

Hesterworth Holidays
★★-★★★
Contact: Mr & Mrs R B Davies,
Hesterworth Holidays, Hopesay,
Craven Arms, Shropshire
SY7 8EX
T: (01588) 660487
F: (01588) 660487
E: hesterworth@go2.co.uk
I: www.hesterworth.co.uk

HOPTON
Derbyshire 𝒪

Peakside ★★★
Contact: Mr C MacQueen, Peak
Cottages, Strawberry Lee Lane,
Totley Bents, Sheffield, S17 3BA
T: (0114) 2620777
F: (0114) 2620666
E: enquiries@peakcottages.com
I: www.peakcottages.com

HOPTON CASTLE
Shropshire

Oaks View Barn ★★★★
Contact: Mrs D M Williams,
Upper House Farm, Hopton
Castle, Craven Arms, Shropshire
SY7 0QF
T: (01547) 530319
I: www.go2.co.uk/upperhouse

HORNCASTLE
Lincolnshire

Coach House ★★★
Contact: Holiday Cottages Ref:
11456, Holiday Cottages Group
Owner Services Dept, Spring
Mill, Earby, Barnoldswick,
Lancashire BB18 6RN
T: 0870 444 6603
F: (01282) 841539
E: sales@ttgihg.co.uk
I: www.country-holidays.co.uk

Southolme Cottage ★★★
Contact: Mr David Gresham, 38
Woodlands Road, Moseley,
Birmingham B11 4HE
T: (0121) 449 5666
F: (0121) 246 2929
E: 106561.2222@compuserve.
com
I: www.southolmecottage.
freeserve.co.uk

HORSINGTON
Lincolnshire

Wayside Cottage ★★★
Contact: Mr & Mrs I G
Williamson, 72 Mill Lane,
Woodhall Spa, Lincolnshire
LN10 6QZ
T: (01526) 353101 &
07967 520289
E: WILL@williamsoni.freeserve.
co.uk
I: www.skegness.
net/woodhallspa.htm

HORSLEY WOODHOUSE
Derbyshire

Amber Court ★★★-★★★★
Contact: Mr Nicholas Mitchell,
Linkwood Farm, Wood Lane,
Horsley Woodhouse, Ilkeston,
Derbyshire DE7 6BN
T: (01332) 880283 & 883030
F: (01332) 883002
E: nicholas@ambercourt.co.uk
I: www.ambercourt.com

HOW CAPLE
Herefordshire

Falcon Field ★★★
Contact: Mrs ME Glover, Falcon
Field, How Caple, Hereford
HR1 4TF
T: (01989) 740680
E: glover@ukonline.co.uk
I: holidaybank.
co.uk/neuk/h0639.htm

HULME END
Staffordshire

East & West Cawlow Barn
★★★★
Contact: Mr Clive Sykes, Sykes
Cottages, York House, York
Street, Chester, CH1 3LR
T: (01244) 345700
F: (01244) 321442
E: info@sykescottages.co.uk
I: www.sykescottages.co.uk

The Old Dairy ★★★
Contact: Mrs M Grayson, The
Old Dairy, Endon House Farm,
Beresford Lane, Hulme End,
Buxton, Derbyshire SK17 0HG
T: (01298) 84515
F: (01298) 84476
E: mariannechalcraft@
endonhouse.fsnet.co.uk

ILAM
Staffordshire

**Beechenhill Cottage and The
Cottage by the Pond**★★★★
Contact: Mrs S Prince,
Beechenhill Cottage and The
Cottage by the Pond,
Beechenhill Farm, Ilam,
Ashbourne, Derbyshire DE6 2BD
T: (01335) 310274
F: (01335) 310274
E: beechenhill@btinternet.com
I: www.beechenhill.co.uk

Throwley Hall Farm
★★★-★★★★★
Contact: Mrs M A Richardson,
Throwley Hall Farm, Ilam,
Ashbourne, Derbyshire DE6 2BB
T: (01538) 308202 & 308243
F: (01538) 308243
E: throwleyhall@talk21.com
I: throwleyhallfarm.co.uk

ILMINGTON
Warwickshire

Featherbed Cottage ★★★★
Contact: Mr S D Price,
Featherbed Lane, 8 Nellands
Close, Ilmington, Shipston-on-
Stour, Warwickshire CV36 4NF
T: (01608) 682215
E: featherbedcottage@hotmail.
com

IPSTONES
Staffordshire

Brookhays ★★
Contact: Mrs A Lomas, High
Meadows, Windmill Lane,
Ashbourne, Derbyshire DE6 1JA
T: (01335) 344132

Coach House Stables ★★★
Contact: Mrs S Wyncoll, Coach
House Stables, The Noggin,
Ipstones, Stoke-on-Trent
ST10 2LQ
T: (01538) 266579
E: susan@the-noggin.freeserve.
co.uk

Glenwood House Farm ★★
Contact: Mrs A Elliott, Glenwood
House Farm, Ipstones, Stoke-on-
Trent ST10 2JP
T: (01538) 266294

Greenhills Cottage ★★★
Contact: Mr C Sykes, Sykes
Cottages, York House, York
Street, Chester, CH1 3LR
T: (01244) 345700
F: (01244) 321442
E: info@sykescottages.co.uk
I: www.sykescottages.co.uk

Meadow Place ★★★★
Contact: Mr C Sykes, Sykes
Cottages, York House, York
Street, Chester, CH1 3LR
T: (01244) 345700
F: (01244) 321442
E: info@sykescottages.co.uk
I: www.sykescottages.co.uk

Old Hall Farm Cottages ★★
Contact: Mr & Mrs D R Glover,
Old Hall Farm Cottages, Old Hall
Farm, Church Lane, Ipstones,
Stoke-on-Trent ST10 2LF
T: (01538) 266465

The Stables & The Cart Shed
Rating Applied For
Contact: Mr & Mrs Hilary &
Michael Hall, Clough Head Farm,
Shay Lane, Ipstones, Stoke-on-
Trent ST10 2LZ
T: (01538) 266259

IRONBRIDGE
Shropshire

Abbaca Apartments ★★★
Contact: Mrs P Taylor, Cambus
House, 29 High Street, Broseley,
Shropshire TF12 5EZ
T: (01952) 882313

Bottom End Cottage ★★★★
Contact: Mr P A Ottley, 8
Ladywood, Ironbridge, Telford,
Shropshire TF8 7JR
T: (01952) 883770 & 433086
F: 07967 052275
E: bottomendcottage@
theironbridge.co.uk
I: www.theironbridge.co.uk

21 Buildwas Road ★★★
Contact: Country Holidays ref:
2740 Sales, Country Holidays,
Spring Mill, Earby, Barnoldswick,
Lancashire BB94 0AA
T: 08700 723723
F: (01282) 844288
I: www.country-holidays.co.uk

Dale End Cottages
Rating Applied For
Contact: Mr D W Gibson, St
Lukes House, St Lukes Road,
Doseley, Telford, Shropshire
TF4 3BD
T: (01952) 507107

Eleys of Ironbridge
★★★-★★★★
Contact: Ms Jayne Mountford,
Eleys of Ironbridge, 13 Tontine
Hill, Ironbridge, Telford,
Shropshire TF8 7AL
T: (01952) 684249 &
07966 534539
F: (01952) 684249
E: jayne@eleys-ironbridge.co.uk

Ivy Cottage ★★★
Contact: Mrs R Crofts, 36
Coneybury View, Broseley,
Shropshire TF12 5AX
T: (01952) 882203
E: ruthcrofts@aol.com

Martha's Cottage ★★★
Contact: Mr B A Richards,
Thorpe House, High Street,
Coalport, Telford, Shropshire
TF8 7HP
T: (01952) 586789
F: (01952) 586789

Paradise House ★★
Contact: Mrs M Gilbride,
Paradise House, 3 Paradise,
Coalbrookdale, Telford,
Shropshire TF8 7NR
T: (01952) 433379

Pine Cottage ★★★★
Contact: Country Holidays -
12405 Sales, Holiday Cottages
Group Limited, Spring Mill,
Earby, Barnoldswick, Lancashire
BB94 0AA
T: 08700 723723
F: (01282) 844288
I: www.country-holidays.co.uk

KENILWORTH
Warwickshire

Castle Cottages ★★★★
Contact: Mrs S A Tomalin, 7
Castle Green, Kenilworth,
Warwickshire CV8 1NE
T: (01926) 852204
E: sheilatomalin@tinyonline.
co.uk

Jackdaw Cottage ★★★★
Contact: Mrs L Grierson, The
White Bungalow, 6 Canterbury
Close, Kenilworth, Warwickshire
CV8 2PU
T: (01926) 855616 &
07970 792131
F: (01926) 513189
E: kgrierson@ukonline.co.uk

Establishments printed in blue have a detailed entry in this guide

The Little Barn ★★★
Contact: Mrs J Oliver, Crewe
Farm Barns, Crewe Lane,
Kenilworth, Warwickshire
CV8 2LA
T: (01926) 850692

KENLEY
Shropshire

No 1 & 2 Courtyard Cottages
★★★★
Contact: Mrs A Gill, No 1 & 2
Courtyard Cottages, Lower
Springs Farm, Kenley,
Shrewsbury SY5 6PA
T: (01952) 510841
E: a-gill@lineone.net

KERSALL
Nottinghamshire

Rose and Sweetbriar Cottages
★★★
Contact: Mrs B Wood, Rose and
Sweetbriar Cottages, Hill Farm,
Kersall, Newark,
Nottinghamshire NG22 OBJ
T: (01636) 636274

KETTERING
Northamptonshire

The Villiers Suite Cranford Hall
★★★
Contact: Mrs P Sneddon, The
Villiers Suite Cranford Hall,
Cranford, Kettering,
Northamptonshire NN14 4AL
T: (01536) 330248
F: (01536) 330203
E: cranford@farmline.com
I: cranfordhall.co.uk

KIDDERMINSTER
Worcestershire

**Strawberry and Pear Tree
Cottage** ★★★
Contact: Mr and Mrs SA Betts,
Strawberry and Pear Tree
Cottage, C/o Stepping Stones,
Kidderminster, Worcestershire
DY14 9UG
T: (01299) 266359 & 269063

KING'S STANLEY
Gloucestershire

Rectory Cottage ★★★★
Contact: Country Holidays ref:
9131 Sales, Holiday Cottages
Group Limited, Spring Mill,
Earby, Barnoldswick, Lancashire
BB94 0AA
T: 08700 723723
F: (01282) 844288
E: sales@ttgihg.co.uk
I: www.country-holidays.co.uk

KINGS CAPLE
Herefordshire

Ruxton Mill ★★★★
Contact: Mrs M Slater, Ruxton
Farm, Kings Caple, Hereford
HR1 4TX
T: (01432) 840493
F: (01432) 840493

KINGSLEY
Staffordshire

Old Nurses Cottage ★★★
Contact: Mrs L Salmon, Newhall
Farmhouse, Hazels Cross Road,
Kingsley, Stoke-on-Trent,
Staffordshire ST10 2AY
T: (01538) 754762 &
07855 584790
E: newhall@kingsley7.freeserve.
co.uk

KINGTON
Herefordshire

Newburn Cottage ★★★
Contact: Mr I W Laurie,
Newburn Farm, Kington,
Herefordshire HR5 3HD
T: (01544) 230176
F: (01544) 230176
E: laurie@click.kc3.co.uk

KINNERSLEY
Herefordshire

Upper Newton Farmhouse
★★★★
Contact: Mr & Mrs Jon and Pearl
Taylor, Upper Newton
Farmhouse, Upper Newton
Farmhouse, Kinnersley, Hereford
HR3 6QB
T: (01544) 327727
F: (01544) 327727
E: jtaylor@click.kc3.co.uk
I: www.uppernewton.
herefordshire.com

KINWARTON
Warwickshire

The Granary ★★★
Contact: Mrs S Kinnersley, Glebe
Farm, Kinwarton, Alcester,
Warwickshire B49 6HB
T: (01789) 762554
F: (01789) 762554
E: johnandsusan@kinnersley.
fsworld.co.uk

KIRK IRETON
Derbyshire

**Bluebell, Buttercup and Clover
Barn** ★★★★
Contact: Mr & Mrs K Pollard,
Alton Nether Farm, Tinkerley
Lane, Kirk Ireton, Ashbourne,
Derbyshire DE6 3LF
T: (01335) 370270
F: (01335) 370270
E: ben@redpepperpictures.
freeserve.co.uk
I: www.peakcottages.co.uk

Grange Holidays ★★★★
Contact: Mr M Race, Grange
Holidays, Tinkerley Lane, Kirk
Ireton, Ashbourne, Derbyshire
DE6 3LF
T: (01335) 370880
E: malcolm@malcolmrace.fsnet.
co.uk
I: www.
ashbourne-accommodation.
co.uk

**Hillside Farm
Rating Applied For**
Contact: Ms Lynne Phillips,
Hillside Farm, Field Lane, Kirk
Ireton, Ashbourne, Derbyshire
DE6 3JT
T: (01335) 370038

Ivy Cottage ★★★
Contact: Peak Cottages Ltd,
Strawberry Lee Lane, Totley
Bents, Sheffield, S17 3BA
T: (0114) 262 0777
F: (0114) 262 0666

Waterside Cottages ★★★
Contact: Mr Victor Sellers, Mill
Farm, Mill Lane, Brailsford,
Ashbourne, Derbyshire DE6 3BB
T: (01335) 361429
E: juss.vicatvirginnet.co.uk

KIRK LANGLEY
Derbyshire

The Cart Hovel ★★★★
Contact: Mrs S Gibbs, Brun Farm
View, Brun Lane, Kirk Langley,
Ashbourne, Derbyshire DE6 4LU
T: (01332) 824214 &
07790 398547

KIRKLINGTON
Nottinghamshire

The Gatehouse ★★
Contact: Mr & Mrs S Crane, The
Gatehouse, Belle Eau Park,
Kirklington, Newark,
Nottinghamshire NG22 8TX
T: (01623) 871605 & 411103
F: (01623) 411103
E: gatehouse@belleeau.
freeserve.co.uk
I: www.belleeau.freeserve.co.uk

KNIGHTCOTE
Warwickshire

Knightcote Farm Cottages
★★★★★
Contact: Mrs F Walker, The Bake
House, Knightcote, Leamington
Spa, Warwickshire CV47 2EF
T: (01295) 770637
F: (01295) 770135
E: fionawalkerfarmcottages.
com
I: www.farmcottages.com

KNIVETON
Derbyshire

The Nook ★★★★
Contact: Mrs S E Osborn,
Barracca, Ivydene Close, Earl
Shilton, Leicester LE9 7NR
T: (01455) 842609
E: susan.osborn@virgin.net
I: www.come.to/thenook

Willow Bank ★★★
Contact: Mrs ME Vaughan,
Willow Bank, Kniveton,
Ashbourne, Derbyshire DE6 1JJ
T: (01335) 343308 &
07977 563093
E: maryvaughan@compuserve.
com
I: www.vaughan77.fsnet.co.uk

LAMBLEY
Nottinghamshire

Dickman's Cottage ★★★
Contact: Mrs Rosamond J
Marshall Smith, Springsyde,
Birdcage Walk, Otley, West
Yorkshire LS21 3HB
T: (01943) 462719
F: (01943) 850925
E: marshallsmithuk@hotmail.
com

LEA
Derbyshire

Coach House ★★★
Contact: Mr and Mrs Hobson,
Coach House, Main Road, Lea,
Matlock, Derbyshire DE4 5GJ
T: (01629) 534346
F: (01629) 534346
I: www.coachhouselea.co.uk

The Mill House ★★★★
Contact: Country Hols ref: 5035,
Country Holidays Group Owner
Services Dept, Spring Mill, Earby,
Barnoldswick, Lancashire
BB18 6RN
T: 0870 444 6603
F: (01282) 841539
E: sales@ttgihg.co.uk
I: www.country-holidays.co.uk

Moorlands ★★★
Contact: Mrs J White, Moors
Farm, Lea, Ross-on-Wye,
Herefordshire HR9 7JY
T: (01989) 750230

Nightingale Holiday Cottage
★★★
Contact: Mr and Mrs P S
Waterfall, 3 The Row, Lea,
Matlock, Derbyshire DE4 5GJ
T: (01629) 534546
F: (01629) 534546

LEAMINGTON SPA
Warwickshire

Barn Owl Cottage ★★★★
Contact: Mrs B Norman,
Fosseway Barns, Fosse Way,
Offchurch, Leamington Spa,
Warwickshire CV33 9BQ
T: (01926) 614647
F: (01926) 614647
E: bnorman@fossebarn.prestel.
co.uk

Blackdown Farm Cottages ★
Contact: Mr & Mrs R Solt,
Blackdown Farm, Sandy Lane,
Leamington Spa, Warwickshire
CV32 6QS
T: (01926) 422522
F: (01926) 450996

Furzen Hill Farm ★★★
Contact: Mrs C M Whitfield,
Furzen Hill Farm, Cubbington
Heath, Leamington Spa,
Warwickshire CV32 7UJ
T: (01926) 424791
F: (01926) 424791

The Lodge ★★★
Contact: Mr & Mrs G Hayward,
The Lodge, 20 Avenue Road,
Leamington Spa, Warwickshire
CV31 3PQ
T: (01926) 422721
F: (01926) 888863
E: accommodation@
the-lodge-leamington-spa.co.uk
I: www.
the-lodge-leamington-spa.co.uk

LEATON
Shropshire

Vicarage Cottage ★★★★★
Contact: Mrs J Mansell-Jones,
The Old Vicarage, Leaton,
Shrewsbury, Shropshire SY4 3AP
T: (01939) 290989
F: (01939) 290989
E: m-j@oldvicleaton.com
I: www.oldvicleaton.com

LECHLADE
Gloucestershire

**Morley House Cottage
Rating Applied For**
Contact: Ms Diana Lock & Mr
Micheal Hackett, Morley House
Cottage, Market Place, Lechlade,
Gloucestershire GL7 3AA
T: (01367) 252794 &
07946 586724
E: dianalock@supanet.com

LEDBURY
Herefordshire

**Coach House Apartment
Rating Applied For**
Contact: Mr M Williams, Leadon
House Hotel, Ross Road,
Ledbury, Herefordshire HR8 2LP
T: (01531) 631199
F: (01531) 631476
E: leadon.house@amserve.net
I: www.leadonhouse.co.uk

Establishments printed in blue have a detailed entry in this guide

Fairoaks Farm Cottages
★★★-★★★★
Contact: Mrs G D Lodge, Rudge
House Farm, Weston-under-
Penyard, Ross-on-Wye,
Herefordshire HR9 5TP
T: (01989) 750268
F: (01989) 750603

Heathfield House ★★★★
Contact: Mrs B Miller, Heathfield
House, Ross Road, Ledbury,
Herefordshire HR8 2LE
T: (01531) 632829
F: (01531) 632829
I: www.SmoothHound.
co.uk/hotels/heathf.html

Homend Bank Cottage ★★★
Contact: Mrs E F Hughes, R H &
R W Clutton The Estate Office,
Leighton Court, Ledbury,
Herefordshire HR8 2UN
T: (01531) 640262
F: (01531) 640719
E: mail@elizabethhughes.
freeon-line.co.uk

Mooloolaba ★★★★
Contact: Mrs L M Ward,
Mooloolaba, 4 Biddulph Way,
Ledbury, Herefordshire HR8 2HN
T: (01531) 633646

Netherhall Cottage ★★★
Contact: Mrs P M Harrison,
Netherhall, Church Street,
Ledbury, Herefordshire HR8 1DJ
T: (01531) 632748 & 632976
F: (01531) 631011
E: patriciaharrison@
compuserve.com

The Old Kennels Farm
★★-★★★★
Contact: Mrs J Wilce, The Old
Kennels Farm, Bromyard Road,
Ledbury, Herefordshire HR8 1LG
T: (01531) 635024 &
07909 584542
F: (01531) 635241
I: www.ledbury.org.
uk/oldkennels/

Priors Court ★★★★
Contact: Mrs C Holmes, Priors
Court, Hollow Lane, Staplow,
Ledbury, Herefordshire HR8 1NQ
T: (01531) 640250
I: www.priorscourthols.co.uk

The Studio ★★★
Contact: Mr & Mrs D Riley, The
Studio, Kynaston Place,
Kynaston, Ledbury,
Herefordshire HR8 2PD
T: (01531) 670321
E: david@criley56.freeserve.
co.uk

White House Cottages
★★★-★★★★
Contact: Mrs Marianne Hills, The
White House, Aylton, Ledbury,
Herefordshire HR8 2RQ
T: (01531) 670349
F: (01531) 670057

LEEK
Staffordshire

Bank End Farm Cottages
★★★-★★★★
Contact: Mrs B Robinson, Bank
End Farm Cottages, Leek Old
Road, Longsdon, Stoke-on-
Trent, Staffordshire ST9 9QJ
T: (01538) 383638

Blackshaw Grange
★★★-★★★★
Contact: Mr & Mrs K Williams,
Blackshaw Grange, Blackshaw
Moor, Leek, Staffordshire
ST13 8TL
T: (01538) 300165
E: kevwilliams@btinternet.com
I: website.lineone.
net/~blackshawgrange

Broomyshaw Country Cottages
Lower Broomyshaw Farm
★★★
Contact: Mr & Mrs G T Saul,
Broomyshaw Country Cottages
Lower Broomyshaw Farm,
Winkhill, Leek, Staffordshire
ST13 7QZ
T: (01538) 308298

Candy Cottage ★★★★
Contact: Mrs S G Plant, Upper
Cadlow Farm, Winkhill, Leek,
Staffordshire ST13 7QX
T: (01538) 266243
E: splanuppercadlow@hotmail.
com
I: www.cottageguide.
co.uk/candycottage/

Ford Coach House Cottage
★★★★
Contact: Mrs C Tomlinson, Ford
Hall Farm, Ford, Leek,
Staffordshire ST13 7RW
T: (01538) 304342

Larks Rise ★★★
Contact: Ms L Melland, Larks
Rise, New House Farm, Bottom
House, Leek, Staffordshire
ST13 7PA
T: (01538) 304350 &
07850 183208
F: (01538) 304338
E: newhousefarm@btinternet.
com

Overton Bank Cottage
Rating Applied For
Contact: Mr C Sykes, Sykes
Cottages, York House, York
Street, Chester, CH1 3LR
T: (01244) 345700
F: (01244) 321442
E: info@sykescottages.co.uk
I: www.sykescottages.co.uk

Rosewood ★★★
Contact: Mr T A & Mrs E Mycock,
Rosewood, Lower Berkhamsytch
Farm, Bottom House, Leek,
Staffordshire ST13 7QP
T: (01538) 308213
F: (01538) 308213

LEICESTER
Leicestershire

Romany ★★
Contact: Mrs E Harris, 86 Station
Lane, Scraptoft, Leicester,
LE7 9UF
T: (0116) 2927161
E: romany1@talk21.com

LEINTHALL STARKES
Herefordshire

Brooklyn ★★★
Contact: Mrs V Morgan,
Marlbrook Hall, Elton, Ludlow,
Shropshire SY8 2HR
T: (01568) 770230

LEINTWARDINE
Herefordshire

Badgers Bluff Holiday
Cottages ★★★★
Contact: Mr R Norton, The
Todding Farmhouse,
Leintwardine, Craven Arms,
Shropshire SY7 0LX
T: (01547) 540648
F: (01547) 540648

Oak Cottage ★★★
Contact: Mrs Vivienne Faulkner,
24 Watling Street, Leintwardine,
Craven Arms, Shropshire
SY7 0LW
T: (01547) 540629
F: (01547) 540442
E: fmjones@axismundi.co.uk
I: www.oakenash.co.uk

Oaklands Farm ★-★★
Contact: Mrs Sally Ann Swift,
Oaklands Farm, Kinton,
Leintwardine, Craven Arms,
Shropshire SY7 0LT
T: (01547) 540635
E: mrpaswift@netscapeonline.
co.uk

LEOMINSTER
Herefordshire

Ashton Court Farm ★★★
Contact: Mrs P Edwards, Ashton
Court Farm, Ashton, Leominster,
Herefordshire HR6 0DN
T: (01584) 711245

The Buzzards ★★★★
Contact: Ms E Povey, The
Buzzards, Kingsland, Leominster,
Herefordshire HR6 9QE
T: (01568) 708941
E: booking@bakerpovey.co.uk
I: www.bakerpovey.co.uk

Eaton Cottage ★★★
Contact: Mrs Audrey Pritchard,
Eaton Farm, Stoke Prior Road,
Leominster, Herefordshire
HR6 0NA
T: (01568) 612095

Mill House Flat ★★★
Contact: Mrs E M Thomas,
Woonton Court Farm, Leysters,
Leominster, Herefordshire
HR6 0HL
T: (01568) 750232
F: (01568) 750232
E: thomas.woontoncourt@
famousweekly.net

LINCOLN
Lincolnshire

Bight House ★★★★
Contact: Mr M S Sharpe, Bight
House, 17 East Bight, Lincoln,
LN2 1QH
T: (01522) 534477

The Cobbles ★★
Contact: Mr JM Scott,
Sunnyside, Lincoln Road,
Brattleby, Lincoln, Lincolnshire
LN1 2SQ
T: (01522) 730561 & 754904
F: (01522) 513995

22 The Crown Windmill ★★★
Contact: Mr J C Griffin, 22 The
Crown Windmill, Princess Street,
Lincoln, LN5 7QD
T: (01522) 533562 &
07966 461887
F: (01522) 519691
E: windymillers@btinternet.com

9 Dorron Court ★★★
Contact: Mr Barry Dean, Cedar
Lodge, Thackers Lane, Branston,
Lincoln LN4 1LT
T: (01522) 791442 & 525132
F: (01522) 523067

The Flat ★★★
Contact: Mrs E A Slingsby, 3
Greestone Place, Lincoln,
LN2 1PP
T: (01522) 560880 & 524984
F: (01522) 535600
E: auction@thos-mawer.co.uk
I: www.greestoneplacelincoln.
co.uk

Howard Cottage ★★★★
Contact: Mrs G Bateman,
Wickens, High Street, Scampton,
Lincoln LN1 2SE
T: (01522) 730811
F: (01522) 730027

Lilac Cottage ★★★
Contact: Mrs V Verner, 1B Danes
Terrace, Lincoln, LN2 1LP
T: (01522) 533347

Manor Farm Cottage ★★★★
Contact: Mrs R M Marris, Manor
Farm Cottage, Brattleby, Lincoln
LN1 2SQ
T: (01522) 730475
E: rae.marris@farming.co.uk

Martingale Cottage ★★★
Contact: Mrs P A Pate, 19 East
Street, Nettleham, Lincoln
LN2 2SL
T: (01522) 751795
E: patsy.pate@ntlworld.com

Old Vicarage Cottage ★★★★
Contact: Mrs S Downs, The Old
Vicarage, East Street, Nettleham,
Lincoln, Lincolnshire LN2 2SL
T: (01522) 750819
F: (01522) 750819
E: susan@oldvic.net

Pingles Cottage ★★★
Contact: Mrs P A Sutcliffe,
Pingles Cottage, Grange Farm,
Broxholme, Lincoln LN1 2NG
T: (01522) 702441

St Clements ★★★
Contact: Mrs G Marshall, St
Clements, Langworth Gate,
Lincoln, Lincolnshire LN2 4AD
T: (01522) 538087
F: (01522) 560642
E: jroywood@aol.com

Tennyson Court
Rating Applied For
Contact: Mr Andrew Carnell,
Tennyson Court, Tennyson
House, 3 Tennyson Street,
Lincoln, LN1 1LZ
T: (01522) 569892 &
0800 9805408
F: (01522) 887997
E: andrew@tennyson-court.
co.uk
I: www.tennyson-court.co.uk

Witham View ★★★★
Contact: Miss S Reynolds, 43
Mons Road, Lincoln, LN1 3UF
T: (01522) 851631

LINGEN
Herefordshire

Home Farm ★★★
Contact: Mrs A Thomas, The
Paddocks, Lingen, Bucknell,
Shropshire SY7 0DZ
T: (01544) 267271

LITTLE DEWCHURCH
Herefordshire

The Granary ★★★★
Contact: Mrs K Tibbetts, The
Granary, Henclose Farm, Little
Dewchurch, Hereford HR2 6PP
T: (01432) 840826
F: (01432) 840826

LITTLE HEREFORD
Herefordshire

Fairview ★★★
Contact: Holiday Cottages
Group Limited, Spring Mill,
Earby, Barnoldswick, Lancashire
BB18 6RN
T: 08700 723723
F: (01282) 844288
E: sales@ttgihg.co.uk
I: www.country-holidays.co.uk

LITTLE HUCKLOW
Derbyshire

Glider View Cottage ★★★★
Contact: English Country
Cottages Ref:RBN, Glider View
Cottage, Little Hucklow, Buxton,
Derbyshire
T: (01246) 591207 &
0870 5851155

**The Parlour and The Dairy
★★★★**
Contact: Mrs W Mycock, The
Parlour and The Dairy, Forest
Lane Farm, Little Hucklow,
Buxton, Derbyshire SK17 8JE
T: (01298) 871226 &
07974 181699
F: (01298) 871226

LITTLE LONGSTONE
Derbyshire

**The Lodge and Dove Cottage
★★★-★★★★**
Contact: Mrs A Davey, Chestnut
House, Little Longstone,
Bakewell, Derbyshire DE45 1NN
T: (01629) 640542
F: (01629) 640542
E: annie@littlelongstone.
freeserve.co.uk

**Orrs Barn
Rating Applied For**
Contact: Peak Cottages,
Strawberry Lee Lane, Totley
Bents, Sheffield, S17 3BA
T: (0114) 262 0777
F: (0114) 262 0666
E: enquires@peakcottages.com
I: www.peakcottages.com

LITTON
Derbyshire

Ashleigh Cottage ★★★
Contact: Mrs S A Maxted,
Ashleigh, Litton, Buxton,
Derbyshire SK17 8QU
T: (01298) 872505 &
07778 753853

2 Cross View ★★★
Contact: Ms C Rowan, 44
Burnham Road, St Albans,
Hertfordshire AL1 4QW
T: (01727) 844169
E: rowan@olive.u-net.com
I: www.peakdistrict-tourism.gov.
uk/peakdistrict/page2a.htm

The Hillock ★★★
Contact: L G Burrows, The
Hillock, Litton, Buxton,
Derbyshire SK17 8QU
T: (01298) 871018

LLANGROVE
Herefordshire

Wisteria Cottage ★★★
Contact: Mr and Mrs F Powell,
Prospect Place, Ross-on-Wye,
Herefordshire HR9 6ET
T: (01989) 770596 & 770159
E: Prospectplacehr96et@
btinternet.com

LLANYBLODWEL
Shropshire

The Coach House ★★★★
Contact: Mr and Mrs S Perks,
Huntsmans Lodge, Llanyblodwel,
Oswestry, Shropshire SY10 8NF
T: (01691) 828038

LOBTHORPE
Lincolnshire

Old Moat Barn ★★★
Contact: Mrs S Grindal, Hall
Farm, Lobthorpe, Grantham,
Lincolnshire NG33 5LS
T: (01476) 860350
F: (01476) 861724
E: grindal@freeuk.com

LONG BUCKBY
Northamptonshire

The Old Tollhouse ★★★
Contact: Country Hols Ref:
1056, Country Holidays Group
Owner Services Dept, Spring
Mill, Earby, Barnoldswick,
Lancashire BB18 6RN
T: 0870 444 6603
F: (01282) 841539
E: sales@ttgihg.co.uk
I: www.country-holidays.co.uk

LONGBOROUGH
Gloucestershire

Cottage Barn ★★★★
Contact: Mr and Mrs R William-
Ellis, Cottage Barn, Sunnybank,
Chapel Lane, Longborough,
Moreton-in-Marsh,
Gloucestershire GL56 0QR
T: (01451) 830695
F: (01451) 830695
E: rupert.williams-ellis@talk21.
com

Hope Cottage ★★★★
Contact: Mrs J Gooding,
Garnons Chase, Collin Close,
Willersey, Broadway,
Worcestershire WR12 7PP
T: (01386) 853718
F: (01386) 853795
E: jgooding@clara.co.uk
I: www.hopecottage.com

LONGDEN
Shropshire

Oak Villa Barn ★★★★
Contact: Mr & Mrs J E Jones, Oak
Villa, Lower Common, Longden,
Shrewsbury, Shropshire
SY5 8HG
T: (01743) 718323
E: gwenjones@lineone.net

LONGNOR
Staffordshire

Bank Top Farm ★
Contact: Mrs L Slack, Lower
Redfern, Edgeside Farm,
Longnor, Buxton, Derbyshire
SK17 0RB
T: (01298) 83402

Manifold Apartments ★★
Contact: Miss Jeanette Naden,
Manifold Apartments, Manifold
Fish & Chip Shop and Tearoom,
The Market Square, Longnor,
Buxton, Derbyshire SK17 0NS
T: (01298) 83317 & 25537

Manifold View ★★★
Contact: Mrs J Dickinson, Top
Farm, Longnor, Buxton,
Derbyshire SK17 0PR
T: (01298) 83271 & 28453
E: darryl.d@virgin.net
I: www.
peak-life-leisure/manifoldview.
co.uk

Vincent Cottage ★★★★
Contact: Mr Colin MacQueen,
Peak Cottages, Strawberry Lee
Lane, Totley Bents, Sheffield,
S17 3BA
T: (0114) 2620777
F: (0114) 2620666
E: enquiries@peakcottages.com
I: www.peakcottages.com

LOUGHBOROUGH
Leicestershire

The Woodlands ★★★
Contact: Mr & Mrs J Grudgings,
14 Beacon Drive, Loughborough,
Leicestershire LE11 2BD
T: (01509) 214596
E: thewoodlands@bushinternet.
com

LOUTH
Lincolnshire

**Ashwater House
★★★-★★★★**
Contact: Mrs H Mapletoft,
Ashpot Cottage, Willow Drive,
Louth, Lincolnshire LN11 0AH
T: (01507) 609295
F: (01507) 354624
E: robnholly@tesco.net
I: www.ashwaterhouse.co.uk

**Canal Farm Cottages
★★★-★★★★**
Contact: Mr & Mrs Richard
Drinkel, Canal Farm Cottages,
Canal Farm, Austen fen,
Grainthorpe, Louth, Lincolnshire
LN11 0NX
T: (01472) 388825 &
07831 400051
F: (01472) 388825
E: canalfarm@ukhome.net
I: www.oas.
co.uk/ukcottages/canalfarm

**10 Founders Way
Rating Applied For**
Contact: Holiday Cottages Ref:
12800, Holiday Cottages Group
Owner Services Dept, Spring
Mill, Earby, Barnoldswick,
Lancashire BB18 6RN
T: 0870 444 6603
F: (01282) 844288
E: ownerservices@ttgihg.co.uk
I: www.country-holidays.co.uk

Mill Lodge ★★★
Contact: Mrs P Cade, Mill Lodge,
Benniworth House Farm,
Donington on Bain, Louth,
Lincolnshire LN11 9RD
T: (01507) 343265

**Waingrove Farm Country
Cottages ★★★★**
Contact: Mrs S Smith,
Waingrove Farm, Fulstow, Louth,
Lincolnshire LN11 0XQ
T: (01507) 363704 &
07778 163992
F: (01507) 363704
E: macandstephanie@
waingrove.demon.co.uk
I: www.lincolnshirecottages.com

LOWER BENEFIELD
Northamptonshire

Granary Cottage ★★★
Contact: Mrs R C Singlehurst,
Brook Farm, Lower Benefield,
Peterborough PE8 5AE
T: (01832) 205215

LOWER LEMINGTON
Gloucestershire

Court Farm Cottage ★★★★
Contact: Country Holidays -
1182 Sales, Holiday Cottages
Group Limited, Spring Mill,
Earby, Barnoldswick, Lancashire
BB94 0AA
T: 08700 723723
F: (01282) 844288
E: sales@ttgihg.co.uk
I: www.country-holidays.co.uk

LOWER SLAUGHTER
Gloucestershire

**The Burrows and Sloe Trees
★★★**
Contact: CH ref: 10192,10193,
Country Holidays Group Owner
Services Deptartment, Spring
Mill, Earby, Barnoldswick,
Lancashire BB18 6RN
T: 0870 444 6603
F: (01282) 841539
E: sales@ttgihg.co.uk

Malt House Cottage ★★★★
Contact: Mrs CE Hutsby, Little
Hill Farm, Wellesbourne,
Warwick, CV35 9EB
T: (01789) 840261
F: (01789) 842270
E: charhutsby@talk21.com
I: www.accomodata.
co.uk/06099.htm

LUDLOW
Shropshire

The Avenue Flat ★★★★
Contact: Mr R E Meredith, The
Avenue Flat, The Avenue,
Ashford Carbonell, Ludlow,
Shropshire SY8 4DA
T: (01584) 831616
E: ronmeredithavenue@talk21.
com

The Bakery Apartment ★★★
Contact: Mrs Deborah Cook, 7
Beech Close, Ludlow, Shropshire
SY8 2PD
T: (01584) 877042 & 872815

Bribery Cottage ★★★
Contact: Mr & Mrs R Caithness,
2 Dinham, Ludlow, Shropshire
SY8 1EJ
T: (01584) 872828
F: (01584) 872828
E: richard.caithness@virgin.net
I: www.virtual-shropshire.
co.uk/bribery-cottage

Establishments printed in blue have a detailed entry in this guide

Cariad House and Cariad Cottage ★★★
Contact: Mrs C Fitzmaurice, 16 Morden Road, Newport, Gwent NP19 7EU
T: (01633) 666732
F: (01633) 666732
E: carol.fitzmaurice@ntlworld.com

Casa Dona Marcella ★★★★
Contact: Mrs M Mills-Pereira, Middlewood Stables, Lowerwood Road, Ludlow, Ludlow, Shropshire SY8 2JG
T: (01584) 856401
F: (01584) 856629
E: marrob065@aol.com
I: www.southshropshire.org.uk/casadona

Church Bank ★★
Contact: Mrs K R Laurie, Church Bank, Burrington, Ludlow, Shropshire SY8 2HT
T: (01568) 770426
E: laurie2502@lineone.net

Elm Lodge Apartment ★★★
Contact: Country Holidays Ref: 12971 Holiday Cottages Group Limited, Spring Mill, Earby, Barnoldswick, Lancashire BB18
T: 08700 723723
F: (01282) 844258
E: sales@ttgihg.co.uk
I: www.country-holidays.co.uk

Garden Apartment Rating Applied For
Contact: Ms Sue Walsh, Holloway Farm, Hungerford, Craven Arms, Shropshire SY7 9HG
T: (01584) 841225
F: (01584) 841225
E: suewalsh@tesco.net
I: www.virtual-shropshire.co.uk/greenwich

Garden Cottage ★★★★
Contact: Mr N Pash, Hideaways, Chapel House, Luke Street, Berwick St John, Shaftesbury, Dorset SP7 0HQ
T: (01747) 828170 & 828000
F: (01747) 829090
E: enq@hideaways.co.uk
I: www.hideaways.co.uk/property2.cfm?ref=H182

1 Glencoe Terrace ★★★
Contact: Mrs L M Pearce, 3 The Crossings, Stanton Lacy, Ludlow, Shropshire SY8 2BY
T: (01584) 856384

The Granary ★★★
Contact: Mr & Mrs R Mercer, Tana Leas Farm, Clee St Margaret, Craven Arms, Shropshire SY7 9DZ
T: (01584) 823272
F: (01584) 823272
E: r.mercer@tinyworld.co.uk

Grazers Cottage, Calvers Cottage and Threshers Cottage ★★★★
Contact: Mr & Mrs N Tudge, Ashford Farm, Ashford Carbonell, Ludlow, Shropshire SY8 4DB
T: (01584) 831243
F: (01584) 831243
E: ashfordfarms@aol.com
I: www.ashfordfarms.co.uk

Haldon Cottage ★★★
Contact: Mrs H Richardson, Haldon, 6 Corve Street, Ludlow, Shropshire SY8 1DA
T: (01584) 876763 & 07801 690776
F: (01584) 872830
E: HR@SEAMCO.DEMON.CO.UK

Hazel Cottage ★★★
Contact: Mrs R E Sanders, Duxmoor Farm, Onibury, Craven Arms, Shropshire SY7 9BQ
T: (01584) 856342

Horseshoe Cottage ★★★★
Contact: Mr & Mrs T R Gill, 3 Fosse Close, Sharnford, Hinckley, Leicestershire LE10 3PQ
T: (01455) 272874
F: (01455) 272874
E: trgill@btinternet.com

Lilac Cottage ★★★
Contact: Mrs Elizabeth Grant, Wheelers Hope Cottage Farm, Easthope, Much Wenlock, Shropshire TF13 6DN
T: (01746) 785564
I: www.cottagefarm@farmersweekly.uk

Limebrook Annexe ★★★
Contact: Mrs M Poole, Limebrook Annexe, Limebrook, Leinthall Starkes, Ludlow, Shropshire SY8 2HP
T: (01568) 770243

Mocktree Barns Holiday Cottages ★★–★★★
Contact: Mr & Mrs Clive & Cynthia Prior, Mocktree Barns, Leintwardine, Ludlow, Shropshire SY7 0LY
T: (01547) 540441

2 Mortimer Court ★★★
Contact: Mr & Mrs S A Chilton, Plot 5, Friars Gardens, Lower Galderford, Ludlow, Shropshire SY8 1RX
T: (01584) 877293
F: (01584) 877293
E: schilton@schilton.freeserve.co.uk

The Old Vicarage Holiday Cottages ★★★
Contact: Mr & Mrs J Deplae, The Old Vicarage, Downton-on-the-Rock, Ludlow, Shropshire SY8 2HX
T: (01584) 856385
E: langdownton@btinternet.com
I: www.freezone.co.uk/langdownton/

Post Horn Cottage ★★
Contact: Ms H Davis, 32 Leamington Drive, Chilwell, Beeston, Nottingham
T: (0115) 922 2383

Ravenscourt Manor ★★★★
Contact: Mrs Elizabeth Purnell, Ravenscourt Manor, Woofferton, Ludlow, Shropshire SY8 4AL
T: (01584) 711905
F: (01584) 711905
I: www.virtual-shropshire.co.uk/ravencourt-manor

Sutton Court Farm Cottages ★★★★
Contact: Mr & Mrs S J Cronin, Sutton Court Farm, Little Sutton, Stanton Lacy, Ludlow, Shropshire SY8 2AJ
T: (01584) 861305
F: (01584) 861441
E: suttoncourtfarm@go2.co.uk
I: www.go2.co.uk/suttoncourtfarm

19 Titterstone Cottages ★★★
Contact: Mr & Mrs W Longrigg, 22 Vardens Road, London SW11 1RH
T: (020) 7203 5000 & 7350 1435
F: (020) 7350 1435

Toad Hall ★★★
Contact: Mrs Jean Taylor, Lindisfarne, 12 Toll Gate Road, Ludlow, Shropshire SY8 1TQ
T: (01584) 874161
F: (01584) 874161

1 Whitcliffe Cottages ★★★★
Contact: Ms H Murphy, Period Properties (Ludlow) Ltd, 9 Lower Broad Street, Ludlow, Ludlow, Shropshire SY8 1PQ
T: (01584) 876931

The Wool Shop ★★
Contact: Mr & Mrs R Mercer, Tana Leas Farm, Clee St Margaret, Craven Arms, Shropshire SY7 9DZ
T: (01584) 823272
F: (01584) 823272
E: v.mercer@tinyworld.co.uk

LULLINGTON Derbyshire

Aubrietia Cottage ★★★★
Contact: Mrs R Cooper, The Grange, Lullington, Swadlincote, Derbyshire DE12 8ED
T: (01827) 373219 & 07774 885596
F: (01283) 515885

LYDBROOK Gloucestershire

Beggars Roost ★★★
Contact: Mr & Mrs T Akester, Moorwood Farmhouse, Lydbrook, Gloucestershire GL17 9SU
T: (01594) 860685
F: (01594) 861333
E: tim@moorwood.demon.co.uk

LYDNEY Gloucestershire

2 Arlin Cottages ★★★★
Contact: Mrs S Freeman, 1 Arlin Cottages, Lower Road, Yorkley, Lydney, Gloucestershire GL15 4TH
T: (01594) 562187
F: (01594) 562187

Bream Cross Farm ★★★
Contact: Mr & Mrs G Reeks, Bream Cross Farm, Lydney, Gloucestershire GL16 6EU
T: (01594) 562208
F: (01594) 564399

Highbury Coach House ★★★
Contact: Mr A R Midgley, Highbury Coach House, Bream Road, Lydney, Gloucestershire GL15 5JH
T: (01594) 842339
F: (01594) 844948
E: midgleya1@aol.com

Wisteria Cottage ★★★★
Contact: Mrs E Rye, Rose Cottage, Church Walk, Viney Hill, Lydney, Gloucestershire GL15 4NY
T: (01594) 510435
E: ericarye@onetel.net.uk

MADELEY Shropshire

Fletcher House ★★★★★
Contact: Mrs Moira Shean, Fletcher House, The Old Vicarage, Church Street, Madeley, Telford, Shropshire TF7 5BN
T: (01952) 525522 & 525524
F: (01952) 525524
E: houseoffletcher@aol.com
I: www.fletcherhouse.co.uk

MADLEY Herefordshire

Canon Bridge House ★★★★
Contact: Mrs A Anscomb, Canon Bridge House, Canon Bridge, Madley, Hereford HR2 9JF
T: (01981) 251104
F: (01981) 251412
E: timothy.anscomb4@virgin.net
I: www.oas.co.uk/ukcottages

Chilstone Cross ★
Contact: Mrs F J Griffiths, Chilstone Farm, Madley, Hereford HR2 9JR
T: (01981) 250210
F: (01981) 250286

MAESBROOK Shropshire

Black Horse Cottages ★★★
Contact: CH ref: 12408,12409, Country Holidays Group Owner Services Dept, Spring Mill, Earby, Barnoldswick, Lancashire BB18 6RN
T: 0870 444 6603 & (01743) 884284
F: (01282) 844288
I: www.country-holidays.co.uk

MALTBY LE MARSH Lincolnshire

Yew Tree Cottage ★★★
Contact: Mrs Ann Graves, Grange Farm, Maltby le Marsh, Alford, Lincolnshire LN13 0JP
T: (01507) 450267
F: (01507) 450180

MALVERN Worcestershire

Annexe to Blue Cedars ★★★
Contact: Mrs P M Longmire, Blue Cedars, Peachfield Close, Malvern Wells, Malvern, Worcestershire WR14 4AN
T: (01684) 566689
E: pml@peachfield.freeserve.co.uk

April Cottage ★★★
Contact: Mrs P M Longmire, 2 Peachfield Close, Malvern, Worcestershire WR14 4AN
T: (01684) 566689
E: pml@peachfield.freeserve.co.uk

The Coach House ★★★
Contact: Mrs J Jones, 58 North Malvern Road, Malvern, Worcestershire WR14 4LX
T: (01684) 569562

The Cottages at Westwood House ★★★★
Contact: Mrs J Wright and Mrs J Staddon, The Cottages at Westwood House, Park Road, West Malvern, Malvern, Worcestershire WR14 4DS
T: (01684) 892308 & 578004
F: (01684) 892882
E: DavidWrightTrans@cs.com
I: www.oas.
co.uk/ukcottages/westwood

The Dell ★★★-★★★★
Contact: Mrs D Knight, The Dell House, 2 Green Lane, Malvern Wells, Malvern, Worcestershire WR14 4HU
T: (01684) 564448
F: (01684) 893974
E: diana@dellhouse.co.uk
I: www.dellhouse.co.uk

End Cottage ★★★
Contact: Mr & Mrs Wight, The Rectory, Fish House Lane, Stoke Prior, Bromsgrove, Worcestershire B60 4JT
T: (01527) 832501
E: dennis.wight@tesco.net

Farmhouse Cottage ★★★
Contact: Mrs S Stringer, Cowleigh Park Farm, Cowleigh Road, Malvern, Worcestershire WR13 5HJ
T: (01684) 566750
F: (01684) 566750
E: cowleighparkfarm@talk21.com

Four Seasons ★★★
Contact: Mr M E James, Four Seasons, 7 Newtown Road, Malvern, Worcestershire WR14 1PD
T: (01684) 575045
E: james@markeric.freeserve.co.uk

Greenbank House Garden Flat ★★★
Contact: Mrs S M Matthews, Greenbank House Garden Flat, 236 West Malvern Road, West Malvern, Malvern, Worcestershire WR14 4BG
T: (01684) 567328

Hidelow House Cottages ★★★★-★★★★★
Contact: Mrs P Diplock, Hidelow House, Acton Beauchamp, Worcester WR6 5AH
T: (01886) 884547
F: (01886) 884060
E: accommodation@hidelow.co.uk
I: www.hidelow.co.uk

Holywell Cottage ★★★★
Contact: Mrs M E Humm, Thornbury House Hotel, 16 Avenue Road, Great Malvern, Malvern, Worcestershire WR14 4LE
T: (01684) 572278
F: (01684) 577042
E: thornburyhousehotel@compuserve.com

Myrtle Cottage ★★★
Contact: Country Holidays Ref: 15093, Country Holidays, Springmill, Earby, Barnoldswick, Lancashire BB94 4OA
T: 08700 723723

The Old Bakery ★★★
Contact: Mrs J Aldridge, West End House, Lower Dingle, West Malvern, Malvern, Worcestershire WR14 4BQ
T: (01684) 566044
F: (01684) 566044
E: westendhouse@btinternet.com

25 Queens Drive ★★★
Contact: Mrs A Jeffs, 25 Queens Drive, Malvern, Worcestershire WR14 4RE
T: (01684) 561337
F: (01684) 562526

Whitewells Farm Cottages ★★★★
Contact: Mr & Mrs D Kavanagh, Whitewells Farm Cottages, Whitewells Farm, Ridgeway Cross, Malvern, Worcestershire WR13 5JS
T: (01886) 880607
F: (01886) 880360
E: whitewells.farm@btinternet.com

MANSFIELD
Nottinghamshire

Blue Barn Cottage ★★★
Contact: Mrs J Ibbotson, Blue Barn Farm, Nether Langwith, Mansfield, Nottinghamshire NG20 9JD
T: (01623) 742248 & 07885 485346
F: (01623) 742248
E: ibbotsonbluebarn@netscapeonline.co.uk

MARDEN
Herefordshire

Vauld House Farm ★★★
Contact: Mrs J Wells, Vauld House Farm, Marden, Hereford, Herefordshire HR1 3HA
T: (01568) 797347
F: (01568) 797366
E: wellsthevauld@talk21.com

MARKET DRAYTON
Shropshire

The Old Smithy Holiday Cottages ★★★★
Contact: Mrs Carmel Simpson, The Old Smithy Holiday Cottages, The Lightwoods, Market Drayton, Shropshire TF9 3JU
T: (01630) 661661

MARKET HARBOROUGH
Leicestershire

The Bluebell Wood ★★
Contact: Mrs Sylvia Hughes, Greenfields, Bowden Road, Thorpe Langton, Market Harborough, Leicestershire LE16 7TP
T: (01858) 545320

Short Lodge ★★★
Contact: Ms J E Durham, Short Lodge, Arthingworth, Market Harborough, Leicestershire LE16 8LB
T: (01858) 525323

MARKET RASEN
Lincolnshire

Papermill Cottages ★★★-★★★★★
Contact: Mr & Mrs Peter & Joyce Rhodes, Vale Farm, Caistor Lane, Tealby, Market Rasen, Lincolnshire LN8 3XN
T: (01673) 838010
F: (01673) 838127
E: peter.rhodes1@btinternet.com
I: www.irac.org.uk/pmc

Pelham Arms Farm ★★★
Contact: Mr & Mrs T Henderson, Pelham Arms Farm, Claxby Moor, Market Rasen, Lincolnshire LN8 3YP
T: (01673) 828261
E: pelhamarms.farm@btinternet.com

MARSH LANE
Derbyshire

Fold Farm ★★★
Contact: Mr and Mrs F W Ryan, 10 Hawkshead Avenue, Dronfield Woodhouse, Dronfield, S18 8NB
T: (01246) 415143
E: foldfarm@fwryan.freeserve.co.uk
I: www.fwryan.freeserve.co.uk

MARTON
Shropshire

Highgate Cottage ★★★
Contact: Mr Sykes, Sykes Cottage, York House, York Street, Chester, CH1 3LR
T: (01244) 345700
F: (01244) 321442
E: info@sykescottages.co.uk
I: www.sykescottages.co.uk

MATLOCK
Derbyshire

Ashmore House Garden Apartment ★★★★
Contact: Mr M H Thomas, Ashmore House, Ashover Road, Littlemoor, Ashover, Chesterfield, Derbyshire S45 0BL
T: (01246) 590343
F: (01246) 861494

The Byre & The Hayloft ★★★★
Contact: Mr & Mrs J P Walden, The Byre & The Hayloft, Cuckoostone Grange Farm, Cuckoostone Lane, Matlock, Derbyshire DE4 5LF
T: (01629) 581777

Carsington Cottages ★★★
Contact: Mrs Valerie Riach, Carsington Cottages, Swiers Farm, Carsington, Matlock, Derbyshire DE4 4DE
T: (01629) 540513 & 07971 868838
F: (01629) 540513
E: enquiries@carsingtoncottags.co.uk
I: www.carsingtoncottages.co.uk

The Coach House ★★★
Contact: Mrs Dorothy Kingsbury, The Rise Cottage, Church Street, Holloway, Matlock, Derbyshire DE4 5AY
T: (01629) 534462
F: (01629) 531634
E: chkings@netcomuk.co.uk
I: www.chkingsbury.co.uk

Coach House ★★★
Contact: Country Holidays - 3351 Sales, Country Holidays, Spring Mill, Earby, Barnoldswick, Lancashire BB94 0AA
T: 08700 723723
F: (01282) 844288
I: www.country-holidays.co.uk

Croft Edge ★★★
Contact: Mr Colin MacQueen, Peak Cottages, Strawberry Lee Lane, Totley Bents, Sheffield, S17 3BA
T: (0114) 2620777
F: (0114) 2620666
E: enquiries@peakcottages.com
I: www.peakcottages.com

Darwin Lake ★★★★
Contact: Ms Cath Lambert, Gainsborough Leisure Holiday Cottages, Knockerdown Farm, Knockerdown, Ashbourne, Derbyshire DE6 1NQ
T: (01629) 540525 & 735859
F: (01629) 540525
E: cathy@knockerdown-cottages.co.uk
I: www.derbyshireholidaycottages.co.uk

Dene Cottage
Rating Applied For
Contact: Ms A Latham, 11 The Charters, Lichfield, Staffordshire WS13 7LX
T: (01543) 319440 & 07970 940841
F: (01543) 319441
E: amanda@threespires.net
I: www.peakdistrictcottage.co.uk

Eagle Cottage ★★★★
Contact: Mrs M E Prince, Haresfield House, Birchover, Matlock, Derbyshire DE4 2BL
T: (01629) 650634
E: maryprince@msn.com
I: www.cressbrook.co.uk/youlgve/eagle/

The Flat ★★★★
Contact: Mrs A P Baker, Ernest Bailey House, Butts Drive, Matlock, Derbyshire DE4 3DJ
T: (01629) 760615
E: ebh@talk21.com

The Fold ★★★★
Contact: Mr J Hinman, The Old Post Office, 31 Main Road, Darley Bridge, Matlock, Derbyshire DE4 2JY
T: (01629) 734333

Hadfield House ★★
Contact: Mrs M Evans, Christ Church Vicarage, Doncaster Road, Ardsley, Barnsley, South Yorkshire S71 5EF
T: (01226) 203784
E: rgrevans@compuserve.com

Honeysuckle and Clematis Cottages ★★★★
Contact: Mrs Linda Lomas, Middle Hills Farm, Grangemill, Derby DE4 4HY
T: (01629) 650368
F: (01629) 650368
E: l.lomas@btinernet.com
I: www.peakdistrictfarmhols.co.uk

Establishments printed in blue have a detailed entry in this guide

Ivonbrook Grange Farm Cottage ★★★
Contact: Mr Sykes, Sykes Cottage, York House, York Street, Chester, CH1 3LR
T: (01244) 345700
F: (01244) 321442
E: info@sykescottages.co.uk
I: www.sykescottages.co.uk

Masson Leys Farm ★★★★
Contact: Mrs B Dawes, Masson Leys Farm, Salters Lane, Matlock, Derbyshire DE4 2PA
T: (01629) 582944

Mooredge Barns ★★★★-★★★★★
Contact: Mr C MacQueen, Peak Cottages, Strawberry Lee Lane, Totley Bents, Sheffield, S17 3BA
T: (0114) 262 0777
F: (0114) 262 0666
E: enquiries@peakcottages.com
I: www.peakcottages.com

Primrose Cottage ★★
Contact: Holiday Cottages (Yorkshire) Limited, Water Street, Skipton, North Yorkshire BD23 1PB
T: (01756) 700510

Warren Carr Hayloft ★★★★
Contact: Mrs Cherry Armishaw, Warren Carr Hayloft, Warren Carr Barn, Near Stanton Lees, Matlock, Derbyshire DE4 2LN
T: (01629) 733856 &
07790 592527
E: cherry@warrencarrbarn.freeserve.co.uk
I: www.cressbrook.co.uk/matlock/warrencarrbarn/index.html

Wayside Farm Holidays ★★★
Contact: Mrs Janet Hole, Wayside Farm Holidays, Wayside Farm, Matlock Moor, Matlock, Derbyshire DE4 5LZ
T: (01629) 582967 &
07971 415510

14 Wellfield Court ★★★
Contact: Holiday Cottages (Yorkshire) Limited, Water Street, Skipton, North Yorkshire BD23 1PB
T: (01756) 700510

Wingate Barn ★★★
Contact: Mr & Mrs J P Smith, Wingate House, Bent Lane, Darley Hillside, Matlock, Derbyshire DE4 2HN
T: (01629) 735621
E: holidays@wingatehouse.fsnet.co.uk

MATLOCK BATH
Derbyshire

Derwent View ★★★
Contact: Mr T Heathcote, 3 Wellington House, Waterloo Road, Matlock Bath, Matlock, Derbyshire DE4 3PH
T: (01629) 57473
F: (01629) 57473

Nonsuch Apartment ★★★★
Contact: Mr Dennis Smith, Wilson Lane Farm House, Main Street, Heath Village, Chesterfield, Derbyshire S44 5SA
T: (01246) 851421

Rambler Cottage ★★★
Contact: Mr Colin MacQueen, Peak Cottages, Strawberry Lee Lane, Totley Bents, Sheffield, S17 3BA
T: (0114) 262 0777
F: (0114) 262 0666
E: enquiries@peakcottages.com
I: www.peakcottages.com

MAY HILL
Gloucestershire

The Folly ★★★
Contact: Country Hols ref:8060, Country Holidays Group Owner Services Dept, Spring Mill, Earby, Barnoldswick, Lancashire BB18 6RN
T: 0870 444 6603
F: (01282) 844288
E: ownerservices@ttgihg.co.uk
I: www.country-holidays.co.uk

MELTON MOWBRAY
Leicestershire

Stables Annexe Dovecote House★★★★
Contact: Mrs A Meek, Dovecote House, Thorpe Arnold, Melton Mowbray, Leicestershire LE14 4RU
T: (01664) 563384
F: (01664) 563384
E: ameek64872@aol.com

MEOLE BRACE
Shropshire

Stable Cottage ★★
Contact: Mrs U Baugh, Glebe House, Vicarage Road, Meole Brace, Shrewsbury SY3 9EZ
T: (01743) 236914
E: s.baugh@virgin.net

MIDDLE DUNTISBOURNE
Gloucestershire

Flowers Barn ★★★★
Contact: Mrs Tina Barton, Manor Farm, Middle Duntisbourne, Cirencester, Gloucestershire GL7 7AR
T: (01285) 658145 &
07866 450417
F: (01285) 651504
E: tina.barton@farming.co.uk
I: www.SmoothHound.co.uk/hotels/manorfar.html

MIDDLETON-BY-YOULGREAVE
Derbyshire

Chapel Cottage ★★★
Contact: Mrs Jenny Aston, Chapel House, Middleton-by-Youlgreave, Derby DE45 1LS
T: (01629) 636665
F: (01629) 636665
E: JASTON3000@aol.com

Curlew Cottage, Abbot's Flight & Monks Rest★★★★
Contact: Mrs Carole Brister, Lowfield Farm, Middleton-by-Youlgreave, Bakewell, Derbyshire DE45 1LR
T: (01629) 636180
F: (01629) 636815
E: brister@quista.net

Holly Homestead Cottage ★★★★
Contact: Mr & Mrs D W Edge, Ridgeway House, Hillcliff Lane, Turnditch, Belper, Derbyshire DE56 2EA
T: (01773) 550754
F: (01773) 550754
E: daveedge@turnditch82.freeserve.co.uk

MIDDLETON SCRIVEN
Shropshire

Harry's House ★★★★
Contact: Mrs P Round, Coates Farm, Middleton Scriven, Bridgnorth, Shropshire WV16 6AG
T: (01746) 789224

MILLER'S DALE
Derbyshire

Bank Top Cottage ★★★
Contact: Mrs A Lee-Overton, Bank Top Cottage, Meadow Lane, Miller's Dale, Buxton, Derbyshire SK17 8SN
T: (01298) 872462
F: (01298) 872461
E: ALICE.LEE-OVERTON@VIRGIN.NET

Kingfisher Cottage ★★★★
Contact: Mr & Mrs E Cawthorne, 8 Curzon Terrace, Litton Mills, Miller's Dale, Buxton, Derbyshire SK17 8SR
T: (01298) 871948
E: cawthorneEF@btinternet.com

Miller's Dale Cottages & Monks Retreat★★★-★★★★
Contact: Mrs P Wilkson, Monks Dale Farm, Miller's Dale, Buxton, Derbyshire SK17 8SN
T: (01298) 871306
F: (01298) 871306
E: pamwilkson@hotmail.com
I: www.cressbrook.co.uk/tidza/monksdale

MILLTOWN
Derbyshire

Greenfield Barn ★★★★
Contact: Mr & Mrs T Page, Greenfield House, Oakstedge Lane, Milltown, Ashover, Derbyshire S45 0HA
T: (01246) 590119

MILWICH
Staffordshire

Summerhill Farm ★★★★
Contact: Mrs P A Milward, Summerhill Farm, Milwich, Stafford, Staffordshire ST18 0EL
T: (01889) 505546
F: (01889) 505692
E: p.milward@btinternet.com

MINCHINHAMPTON
Gloucestershire

Long Acre Cottage ★★★★
Contact: Mr D Govier, Long Acre, Nags Head Lane, Minchinhampton, Stroud, Gloucestershire GL6 9AY
T: (01453) 882914
F: (01453) 882914
I: www.users.globalnetco.uk/~goves

Vine House Flat ★★★★
Contact: Mrs V M Finn, Vine House, Friday Street, Minchinhampton, Stroud, Gloucestershire GL6 9JL
T: (01453) 884437

The Woolsack ★★★★
Contact: Mrs E Hayward, The Woolsack, Hyde Wood House, Cirencester Road, Minchinhampton, Stroud, Gloucestershire GL6 8PE
T: (01453) 885504
F: (01453) 885504
E: info@hydewoodhouse.co.uk
I: www.hydewoodhouse.co.uk

MININGSBY
Lincolnshire

Stamford Farmhouse ★★
Contact: Mrs Morris, Stamford Farmhouse, Miningsby, Lincolnshire PE22 7NW
T: (01507) 588682

MINSTERLEY
Shropshire

Brookland ★★★
Contact: Country Hols ref: 1744, Country Holidays Group Owner Services Deptartment, Spring Mill, Earby, Barnoldswick, Lancashire BB18 6RN
T: 0870 444 6603
F: (01282) 844288
I: www.country-holidays.co.uk

Hill Cottage ★★★★
Contact: Mrs Rachel Lawton, Ritton Place, Pennerley, Minsterley, Shrewsbury, Shropshire SY5 0NE
T: (01743) 791918 &
07788 594057
F: (01743) 791918
E: rachel-lawton@hill-cottage.freeserve.co.uk
I: www.virtual-shropshire.co.uk/hill-cottage

Luckley Cottage ★★★★
Contact: Mr M Johnson, Oakern, Bromlow, Minsterley, Shrewsbury, Shropshire SY5 0ED
T: (01743) 891469

Ovenpipe Cottage ★★★
Contact: Mr A B & Mrs P Thornton, Tankerville Lodge, Stiperstones, Minsterley, Shrewsbury, Shropshire SY5 0NB
T: (01743) 791401
F: (01743) 791401
E: tankervillelodge@supanet.com

Upper House Farm Cottage ★★★★
Contact: Mrs K Stanhope, Upper House Farm, Minsterley, Shrewsbury SY5 0AA
T: (01743) 792831 &
07968 652370
F: (01743) 792831
E: k.stanhope@ukonline.co.uk

Establishments printed in blue have a detailed entry in this guide

MISERDEN
Gloucestershire
Sudgrove Cottages ★★★
Contact: Mr M G Ractliffe,
Sudgrove Cottages, Miserden,
Stroud, Gloucestershire GL6 7JD
T: (01285) 821322
F: (01285) 821322
E: enquiries@sudgrovecottages.
co.uk
I: www.sudgrovecottages.co.uk

MITCHELDEAN
Gloucestershire
The Granary ★★★★
Contact: Mrs A Frost, Green
Farm, Jubilee Road, Abenhall,
Mitcheldean, Gloucestershire
GL17 0EE
T: (01594) 544622
E: gary.frostl@virgin.net

MONSAL DALE
Derbyshire
**Heron Cottage Upperdale Farm
★★★**
Contact: Mr & Mrs J Clarke,
Heron Cottage Upperdale Farm,
Upperdale, Monsal Dale, Buxton,
Derbyshire SK17 8SZ
T: (01629) 640536

**Riversdale Farm Holiday
Cottages ★★★★**
Contact: Mrs M A Jackson,
Riversdale Farm Holiday
Cottages, Riversdale, Monsal
Dale, Buxton, Derbyshire
SK17 8SZ
T: (01629) 640500
E: mick@riversdalefarm.co.uk
I: www.riversdalefarm.co.uk

MONTFORD BRIDGE
Shropshire
Mytton Mill Flat ★★★
Contact: Mrs P Minshall, Mytton
Mill House, Forton Heath,
Montford Bridge, Shrewsbury
SY4 1HA
T: (01743) 850497

MONYASH
Derbyshire
The Barn ★★★★
Contact: Mr A J Staley, Bolehill
Farm, Monyash Road, Bakewell,
Derbyshire DE45 1QW
T: (01629) 812359
F: (01629) 812359
E: tonystaley@hotmail.com
I: www.bolehillfarmcottages.
co.uk

Rose Cottage ★★★
Contact: Brian & Heather Read,
20 Church Street, Monyash,
Bakewell, Derbyshire DE45 1JH
T: (01629) 813629

Sheldon Cottages ★★★
Contact: Mr and Mrs R Tyler,
Sheldon House, Chapel Street,
Monyash, Bakewell, Derbyshire
DE45 1JJ
T: (01629) 813067
F: (01629) 813067
E: sheldonhouse@lineone.net

MORETON-IN-MARSH
Gloucestershire
Cosy Cottage ★★★★
Contact: Mrs J Gingell, 18
Nursery Close, Mickleton,
Chipping Campden,
Gloucestershire GL55 6TX
T: (01386) 438808
E: peter@gingell.net

The Cottage ★★★
Contact: Mrs R M Warriner,
Broadmoor Farm, Little Wolford,
Shipston-on-Stour,
Warwickshire CV36 5LZ
T: (01608) 684223
F: (01608) 684261
E: rozwarriner@cs.com
🖾

The Flat ★★★★
Contact: Ms Sheila Rolland,
Campden Cottages, Folly
Cottage, Paxford, Chipping
Campden, Gloucestershire
GL55 6XG
T: (01386) 593315
F: (01386) 593057
E: campdencottages@
btinternet.com
I: www.campdencottages.co.uk

Hayloft ★★★
Contact: Mrs J Wright,
Twostones, Evenlode, Moreton-
in-Marsh, Gloucestershire
GL56 0NY
T: (01608) 651104

The Laurels ★★★
Contact: Mrs S I Billinger, Blue
Cedar House, Stow Road,
Moreton-in-Marsh,
Gloucestershire GL56 0DW
T: (01608) 650299
E: gandisb@dialstart.net

**Little Pinners
Rating Applied For**
Contact: Mrs Miriam Gilbert,
Country House Interiors, High
Street, Moreton-in-Marsh,
Gloucestershire GL56 0AT
T: (01608) 650007
F: (01608) 650007

Magellan House Flat ★★★
Contact: Mr & Mrs B Benson,
Magellan House, Bourton Road,
Moreton-in-Marsh,
Gloucestershire GL56 0BD
T: (01608) 650781
F: (01608) 652074

Michaelmas Cottage ★★★★
Contact: Mr M J Gaffney,
Wavertree Cottage, Shrubbs Hill
Lane, Sunningdale, Ascot,
Berkshire SL5 0LD
T: (01344) 624833
F: (01344) 624693
E: michael@spoonerco.com
I: www.country-cottages.org.uk

**Michaelmas Daisy Cottage
★★★**
Contact: Mrs H Fewtrell, Almond
Lodge, Wyck Rissington,
Cheltenham, Gloucestershire
GL54 2PN
T: (01451) 822027
F: (01451) 822027
E: letty@gl54.freeserve.co.uk

2 Rose Terrace ★★★
Contact: Ms A Richards, Manor
Cottages, Priory Mews, 33A
Priory Lane, Burford, Oxford
OX18 4SG
T: (01993) 824252
F: (01993) 824443
E: manorcott@netcomuk.co.uk
I: welcome.to/manorcottages

The Trees ★★★
Contact: Mrs R Ward, 15
Gisborough Way, Bailey's
Meadow, Loughborough,
Leicestershire LE11 4FU
T: (01509) 646135

Twinkle Toes Cottage ★★★★
Contact: Mrs Christine Gowing,
Barley Cottage, Churchill,
Chipping Norton, Oxfordshire
OX7 6NW
T: (01608) 658579
E: kcgowing@talk21.com

MORTON BAGOT
Warwickshire
**Manor Farm Cottages Royland
Farms Ltd★★★★**
Contact: Mrs P Green, Manor
Farm, Morton Bagot, Studley,
Warwickshire B80 7ED
T: (01527) 852219
F: (01527) 852219
E: roylands@farmers weekly.net
I: www.manorfarmcottages.
co.uk

MORVILLE
Shropshire
Hurst Farm Cottage ★★★★
Contact: Mr & Mrs D Brick, Hurst
Farm, Morville, Bridgnorth,
Shropshire WV16 4TF
T: (01746) 714375
F: (01746) 714375
E: hurstfarm@talk21.com

MOUNTSORREL
Leicestershire
Stonehurst Lodge ★★★
Contact: Mrs Marilyn Duffin,
Stonehurst Lodge, Stonehurst
Farm, 141 Loughborough Road,
Mountsorrel, Loughborough,
Leicestershire LE12 7AR
T: (01509) 413216 &
07885 639457
I: www.farm18.fsnet.co.uk

MUCH BIRCH
Herefordshire
The Coach House ★★★
Contact: Mr Jon Norris,
Whitewells, Much Birch,
Hereford, Herefordshire
HR2 8HZ
T: (01981) 540061
E: jon@herefordshire.com
I: www.herefordshire.
com/coach-house

MUCH COWARNE
Herefordshire
**Cowarne Hall Cottages
★★★-★★★★**
Contact: Mr & Mrs M Bradbury,
Cowarne Hall, Much Cowarne,
Bromyard, Herefordshire
HR7 4JQ
T: (01432) 820317
F: (01432) 820093
E: rm@cowarnehall.freeserve.
co.uk

Old Bridgend Cottage ★★★
Contact: Mrs A M Morgan, 32
Chestnut Grove, New Malden,
Surrey KT3 3JN
T: (020) 8942 0702
F: (020) 8949 4950

MUCH MARCLE
Herefordshire
Wolton Brook ★★★★
Contact: Mrs A Putley, Lower
Wolton Farm, Much Marcle,
Ledbury, Herefordshire HR8 2NY
T: (01531) 660429
F: (01531) 660429

MUCH WENLOCK
Shropshire
The Coach House ★
Contact: Mrs K.V. Dower, The
Grange, Much Wenlock,
Shropshire TF13 6DD
T: (01952) 727152
E: roy.dower@virgin.net
I: www.country-holidays.co.uk

Plum Cottage ★★★
Contact: Mrs J Hazell-Jackson,
11 Barrow Street, Much
Wenlock, Shropshire TF13 6EN
T: (01952) 728134

The Priory ★★★
Contact: Mrs A Croft, The Priory,
Bull Ring, Much Wenlock,
Shropshire TF13 6HS
T: (01952) 728280 &
0797 1911914
E: ahc1@supanet.com

Priory Cottage ★★★
Contact: Mrs J Cumberland,
Priory Cottage, Bull Ring, Much
Wenlock, Shropshire TF13 6HS
T: (01952) 727386

3 Queen Street ★★★
Contact: Mrs E A Williams, 68
Church Hill, Penn,
Wolverhampton, West Midlands
WV4 5JD
T: (01902) 341399
E: williams_letting@hotmail.
com

18 Sheinton Street ★★★★
Contact: Country Holidays ref:
8371 Sales, Holiday Cottages
Group Limited, Spring Mill,
Earby, Barnoldswick, Lancashire
BB94 0AA
T: 08700 723723
F: (01282) 844288
E: sales@ttgihg.co.uk
I: www.country-holidays.co.uk

Stokes Cottage ★★★
Contact: Mrs Suzanne Hill,
Stokes Cottage, Newtown House
Farm, Much Wenlock,
Shropshire TF13 6DB
T: (01952) 728380 & 727293
F: (01952) 728130
E: ChrisHill@farmersweekly.net

NAUNTON
Gloucestershire
Bake House ★★★
Contact: Ms Joan Timmins, The
Littons, Main Square, Naunton,
Cheltenham, Gloucestershire
GL54 3AT
T: (01451) 850443

Mill Barn Cottage ★★
Contact: Mrs M Hindley, Mill
Barn Cottage, Mill Barn,
Naunton, Cheltenham,
Gloucestershire GL54 3AF
T: (01451) 850417
F: (01451) 850196

Yew Tree House ★★★★
Contact: Mrs P Smith, White
Gables, Woodcote Park Road,
Epsom, Surrey KT18 7EX
T: (01372) 723166 & 813472
F: (01372) 813472
E: patriciasmith43@hotmail.
com
I: www.yewtreehouse.
free-online.co.uk

NEEN SOLLARS
Shropshire

Live and Let Live ★★★
Contact: Mr and Mrs C&I
Ferguson, Live and Let Live, Neen
Sollars, Kidderminster,
Worcestershire DY14 9AB
T: (01299) 832391 & 832981

NETHERSEAL
Staffordshire

Grangefields
Rating Applied For
Contact: Mrs Rita Hill & Mrs
Alison Hill, Grangefields,
Netherseal, Swadlincote,
Derbyshire DE12 8BT
T: (01827) 373253 &
(01283) 761445

NEW MILLS
Derbyshire

Shaw Farm ★★★
Contact: Mrs Nicky Burgess,
Shaw Farm, Shaw Marsh, New
Mills, High Peak SK22 4QE
T: (0161) 4271841
E: nicky.burgess@talk21.com

NEWARK
Nottinghamshire

The Stables Ashdene★★★★
Contact: Mrs G Herbert, The
Stables Ashdene, Radley Road,
Halam, Newark,
Nottinghamshire NG22 8AH
T: (01636) 812335

NEWCASTLE-UNDER-LYME
Staffordshire

Slaters Country Inn ★★★
Contact: Mrs Karen Slater,
Slaters Country Inn, Stone Road,
Baldwins Gate, Newcastle-
under-Lyme, Staffordshire
ST5 5ED
T: (01782) 680052
F: (01782) 680136
I: www.slaterscountryinn.co.uk

NEWHAVEN
Derbyshire

Bank Top Barn ★★★
Contact: Mrs Sandra Lowndes,
Bank Top Cottage, Newhaven,
Buxton, Derbyshire SK17 0DS
T: (01335) 390274
E: nlowndes@hotmail.com

NEWLAND
Gloucestershire

Birchamp Coach House
★★★★
Contact: Mrs Karen Davies,
Birchamp Coach House,
Birchamp House, Newland,
Coleford, Gloucestershire
GL16 8NP
T: (01594) 833143 &
07714 703028
F: (01594) 836775
E: birchamp.1@virgin.net

NEWTON GRANGE
Derbyshire

New Hanson Bungalow ★★★
Contact: Mrs L A Bonsall, New
Hanson Grange Farm, Newton
Grange, Ashbourne, Derbyshire
DE6 1NN
T: (01335) 310258
F: (01335) 310258
E: NHGFarmHoliday@tinyworld.
co.uk
I: www.ashbourne-town.
com/accom/new-hanson

NORBURY
Staffordshire

Oulton House Farm ★★★★
Contact: Mrs Judy Palmer,
Oulton House Farm, Norbury,
Stafford ST20 0PG
T: (01785) 284264
F: (01785) 284264
E: judy@oultonhousefarm.co.uk
I: www.oultonhousefarm.co.uk

NORMANTON-ON-TRENT
Nottinghamshire

East Gate Cottage ★★★
Contact: Country Holidays -
10524 Sales, Holiday Cottages
Group Limited, Spring Mill,
Earby, Barnoldswick, Lancashire
BB94 0AA
T: 08700 723723
F: (01282) 844288
E: sales@ttgihg.co.uk
I: www.country-holidays.co.uk

NORTH PIDDLE
Worcestershire

Humblebee Hall ★★★★★
Contact: Mr & Mrs Neil Pykett,
Humblebee Hall, North Piddle,
Grafton Flyford, Worcester
WR7 4PF
T: (01905) 381127
F: (01905) 380020

NORTHAMPTON
Northamptonshire

The Long Barn ★★★★★
Contact: Mrs L Carter,
Broombank, Upper Harlestone,
Northampton, NN7 4EL
T: (01604) 583237
E: longbarn_uk@yahoo.co.uk

Mill Barn Cottage ★★★
Contact: Mr Roger Wolens, Mill
Barn Cottage, The Mill House,
Mill Lane, Earls Barton,
Northampton, Northants
NN6 0NR
T: (01604) 810507
F: (01604) 810507
E: roger@themillbarn.
free-online.co.uk
I: www.themillbarn.free-online.
co.uk

NORTON CANON
Herefordshire

Havercroft ★★★
Contact: Mrs C M McNair,
Pencombe House Cottage,
Pencombe, Bromyard,
Herefordshire HR7 4RW
T: (01885) 400667 &
07710 267656
E: calandpeacock@hotmail.com

NORTON IN HALES
Shropshire

Gardeners Cottage ★★★★
Contact: Mrs Sara Smith,
Gardeners Cottage, Bellaport
Home Farm, Norton in Hales,
Market Drayton, Shropshire
TF9 4AZ
T: (01630) 653023
F: (01630) 653023

NYMPSFIELD
Gloucestershire

Crossways ★★★
Contact: Mr & Mrs F J Bowen,
Crossways, Tinkley Lane,
Nympsfield, Stonehouse,
Gloucestershire GL10 3TU
T: (01453) 860309

OAKAMOOR
Staffordshire

Dimmingsdale Chalet ★
Contact: Mrs Maggie Wheeler,
Dimmingsdale Chalet, Old
Furnace Farm, Greendale,
Oakamoor, Stoke-on-Trent
ST10 3AP
T: (01538) 702442
F: (01538) 702981
E: oldfurnace@aol.com

Tenement Farm ★★★
Contact: Mrs Joyce Miller & Mr
Stan Leese, Tenement Farm,
Three Lows, Ribden, Oakamoor,
Stoke-on-Trent ST10 3BW
T: (01538) 702333 & 703603
F: (01538) 703603
E: stanleese@aol.com
I: www.touristnetuk.
com/wm/tenement-farm

OCLE PYCHARD
Herefordshire

Ocle Court Cottage ★★★★
Contact: Mr M E Oliver, Ocle
Court Cottage, Ocle Court, Ocle
Pychard, Hereford HR1 3RD
T: (01432) 820280 &
07850 335001
F: (01432) 820569
I: theolivers.org.uk

ODDINGTON
Gloucestershire

Lower Court Cottages
★★★-★★★★
Contact: Mrs Juliet Pauling,
Lower Court Farm, Chadlington,
Oxford OX7 3NQ
T: (01608) 676422 &
07976 883175
F: (01608) 676422
E: jpauling@lineone.net

OLD BRAMPTON
Derbyshire

Chestnut Cottage and Willow
Cottage ★★★
Contact: Mrs Patricia Green,
Priestfield Grange, Old
Brampton, Chesterfield,
Derbyshire S42 7JH
T: (01246) 566159

OLD SOMERBY
Lincolnshire

Post Office Cottage
Rating Applied For
Contact: Mrs Christine Grocock,
Post Office Cottage, Old Post
Office, Old Somerby, Grantham,
Lincolnshire NG33 4AB
T: (01476) 563897

OLDBURY
Shropshire

Greensted Cottage ★★
Contact: Mrs S Amos, Greensted,
Oldbury, Bridgnorth, Shropshire
WV16 5EE
T: (01746) 763125

OLDCROFT
Gloucestershire

Cider Press Cottage ★★★★
Contact: Mr & Mrs S Hinton,
Cider Press Cottage, 1 Westleigh
Villa, St Swithens Road, Oldcroft,
Lydney, Gloucestershire
GL15 4NF
T: (01594) 510285
F: (01594) 510285

OMBERSLEY
Worcestershire

Pope's Cottage ★★
Contact: Ms C Davies, Border
County Cottages, Bear Lanes,
Newtown, Powys SY16 2QZ
T: (01686) 625000
F: (01686) 622465
E: info@wales-holidays.co.uk
I: www.wales-holidays.co.uk

ONECOTE
Staffordshire

Moorland House Holiday
Cottages ★★★
Contact: Mrs E M Luckett,
Moorland House, Onecote, Leek,
Staffordshire ST13 7RU
T: (01538) 304380

ORCOP
Herefordshire

The Burnett Farmhouse
★★★★
Contact: Mr and Mrs M A
Gooch, The Burnett Farmhouse,
Orcop, Hereford HR2 8SF
T: (01981) 540 999
F: (01981) 540 999
E: burnett.farmhouse@talk21.
com

Bury Farm ★★
Contact: Mrs G Goodwin, Old
Kitchen Farm, Garway Hill,
Hereford HR2 0DE
T: (01981) 240383

OSWESTRY
Shropshire

Canalside Cottage ★★
Contact: Mr C Sykes, Sykes
Cottages, York House, York
Street, Chester, CH1 3LR
T: (01244) 345700
F: (01244) 321442

The Cross Keys ★★★
Contact: Mr & Mrs P J Rothera,
The Cross Keys, Selattyn,
Oswestry, Shropshire SY10 7DH
T: (01691) 650247

Hinsdale ★★
Contact: Mrs B M Roberts,
Hinsdale, Twmpath Lane,
Gobowen, Oswestry, Shropshire
SY10 7AH
T: (01691) 650408

The Old Rectory Cottage ★★
Contact: Mrs Maggie Barnes,
The Old Rectory Cottage,
Selattyn, Oswestry, Shropshire
SY10 7DH
T: (01691) 659708

Underhill House ★★★★
Contact: Mr G Hughes, Underhill House, Racecourse Road, Oswestry, Shropshire SY10 7PN
T: (01691) 661660 &
07801 590103

OUNDLE
Northamptonshire

The Bolt Hole ★★★★
Contact: Mrs Anita Spurrell, Rose Cottage, 70 Glapthorne Road, Oundle, Peterborough PE8 4PT
T: (01832) 273521 & 272298
F: (01832) 275409

13 Cotterstock Road ★★★
Contact: Mr & Mrs J S J Czwortek, 13 Cotterstock Road, Oundle, Peterborough PE8 4PN
T: (01832) 273371

Oundle Cottage Breaks ★★★-★★★★
Contact: Mr and Mrs Simmonds, Oundle Cottage Breaks, 30 Market Place, Oundle, Peterborough PE8 4BE
T: (01832) 273531
F: (01832) 274938
E: richard@SimmondsatOundle. co.uk
I: www.oundlecottagebreaks. co.uk

OVER HADDON
Derbyshire

Burton Manor Barns ★★★★
Contact: Mr C MacQueen, Peak Cottages, Strawberry Lee Lane, Totley Bents, Sheffield, S17 3BA
T: (0114) 2620777
F: (0114) 2620666

OWLPEN
Gloucestershire

Owlpen Manor ★★★-★★★★
Contact: Ms Julia Webb, Owlpen Manor, Owlpen, Uley, Dursley, Gloucestershire GL11 5BZ
T: (01453) 860261
F: (01453) 860819
E: sales@owlpen.com
I: www.1travel.com/owlpen

OXTON
Nottinghamshire

Wesley Farm Cottage ★★★★
Contact: Mrs H Palmer, Windmill Farm, Forest Road, Oxton, Southwell, Nottinghamshire NG25 0SZ
T: (0115) 9652043 &
07976 975038
E: enquiries@wesleycottage. com
I: wesleycottage.com

PAINSWICK
Gloucestershire

1 Hambutts Cottages ★★★★
Contact: Mr G A Hawkins, Bath Place, Birdlip, Gloucester, Gloucestershire GL4 8JH
T: (01452) 863140 &
07720 748261
E: godfrey.hawkins@btinternet. com

Verlands Retreats ★★★★★
Contact: Mrs and Mr M Young, Verlands, Vicarage Street, Painswick, Stroud, Gloucestershire GL6 6XP
T: (01452) 812099
F: (01452) 814215
E: accommodation@painswick. com
I: www.painswick.com

PARKEND
Gloucestershire

The Coach House ★★★★
Contact: Mrs C Yeatman, Deanfield, Royal Forest of Dean, Parkend, Lydney, Gloucestershire GL15
T: (01594) 562256

PARWICH
Derbyshire

Brook Cottage ★★★
Contact: Mr & Miss Terry & Nicola Pickard, Brook House, Parwich, Ashbourne, Derbyshire DE6 1QL
T: (01335) 390360 & (01335
) 300589
F: (01335) 300589

Croft Cottage ★★★★
Contact: Mrs S Tallis, The Croft, Creamery Lane, Parwich, Ashbourne, Derbyshire DE6 1QB
T: (01335) 390440 &
07798 587754
F: (01335) 390440
E: enquiries@croftcottage.co.uk
I: www.croftcottage.co.uk

Curlew Wheatear and Redstart Cottages★★★
Contact: Mr Colin McQueen, Peak Cottages, Paddock Cottage, Strawberry Lane, Totley Bents, Sheffield, S17 3BA
T: (0114) 262 0777
F: (0114) 262 0666

PAXFORD
Gloucestershire

Fox Cottage ★★★★
Contact: Miss S Rolland, Campden Cottages, Folly Cottage, Paxford, Chipping Campden, Gloucestershire GL55 6XG
T: (01386) 593315
F: (01386) 593057
E: campdencottages@ btinternet.com
I: www.campdencottages.co.uk

PEMBRIDGE
Herefordshire

The Cottage ★★★
Contact: Mr P & Mrs H S Jones, Park Cottage, 113 West Street, Warwick, CV34 6AH
T: (01926) 410319 &
07803 976052
F: (01926) 410319
E: parkcott@aol.com

The Granary and The Dairy ★★★
Contact: Mrs N Owens, The Granary and The Dairy, The Grove, Pembridge, Leominster, Herefordshire HR6 9HP
T: (01544) 388268
F: (01544) 388154
E: nancy@grovedesign.co.uk

Orchard Lodge & Tippet's Lodge Tibhall Lodges★★★
Contact: Mr & Mrs J Gwatkin, Tibhall Lodge, Tibhall, Pembridge, Leominster, Herefordshire HR6 9JR
T: (01544) 388428

Rowena Cottage ★
Contact: Mrs D Malone, The Cottage, Holme, Newark, Nottinghamshire NG23 7RZ
T: (01636) 672914

PERSHORE
Worcestershire

Court Close Farm ★★★
Contact: Mrs Eileen Fincher, Court Close Farm Manor Road, Eckington, Pershore, Worcestershire WR10 3BH
T: (01386) 750297
F: (01386) 750297
E: fincher@ukonline.co.uk

Treaford ★★★
Contact: Mrs L Bailey, The Grange, Little Comberton, Pershore, Worcestershire WR10 3EH
T: (01386) 710331
E: treaford@talk21.com
I: www.stratford-upon-avon. co.uk.treaford.htm

PICKLESCOTT
Shropshire

Bank Farm Cottage ★★★★
Contact: Mrs Alison Lucas, Bank Farm Cottage, Bank Farm, Picklescott, Church Stretton, Shropshire SY6 6NT
T: (01694) 751219
E: a-lucas@lineone.net

PILLERTON HERSEY
Warwickshire

Roman Acres Cottage ★★★
Contact: Mrs R Williams, Roman Acres, Oxhill Bridle Road, Pillerton Hersey, Warwick CV35 0QB
T: (01789) 740360
E: ros@romanacres.freeuk.com

PLUNGAR
Leicestershire

The Old Wharf ★★★★★
Contact: Mrs Elaine Pell, Grange Farm, Granby Lane, Plungar, Nottingham NG13 0JJ
T: (01949) 860630

PRESTBURY
Gloucestershire

Home Farm ★★★★
Contact: Mr C M Banwell, Home Farm, Mill Street, Prestbury, Cheltenham, Gloucestershire GL52 3BG
T: (01242) 583161
F: (01242) 224161
I: www.homefarm.clara.net/

PRESTON
Gloucestershire

The Tallet ★★★
Contact: Mrs Susan Spivey, The Tallet, The Old Farmhouse, Preston, Cirencester, Gloucestershire GL7 5PR
T: (01285) 653405
F: (01285) 653405

The Thatched Cottage ★★★★
Contact: Miss C Emmett, Windmill, Barrowden Road, Morcott, Oakham, Leicestershire LE15 9DQ
T: (01572) 747373
F: (01572) 737581

PRESTON WYNNE
Herefordshire

The Cyder Barn and Stables ★★★★
Contact: Mrs J R Rogers & Rachael Rogers, New House Farm, Preston Wynne, Hereford HR1 3PE
T: (01432) 820621
F: (01432) 820621
E: rachael@themail.co.uk
I: freespace.virgin.net/rogers. newhousefarm

Wisteria Cottage ★★★
Contact: Mrs Jenni Maund, Lower Town, Preston Wynne, Hereford HR1 3PB
T: (01432) 820608
F: (01432) 820608

PRESTWOOD
Staffordshire

Swallows Loft ★★★★
Contact: Mrs Joyce Beeson, Swallows Loft, Brook Cottage, Quixhill Lane, Prestwood, Uttoxeter, Staffordshire ST14 5DD
T: (01889) 590464
F: (01335) 342808
E: bookings@swallows-loft. fsnet.co.uk
I: www.swallows-loft.fsnet.co.uk

PRINCETHORPE
Warwickshire

Stretton Lodge Barns ★★★
Contact: Mrs E Best, Stretton Lodge, Oxford Road, Princethorpe, Rugby, Warwickshire CV23 9QD
T: (01926) 632351 &
07778 632351
F: (01926) 317868
E: c.best@btinternet.com

PULVERBATCH
Shropshire

2 Holly Grove Cottages ★★★★
Contact: Mrs S M Morris, Holly Grove Farm, Pulverbatch, Shrewsbury SY5 8DD
T: (01743) 718300
E: pulverbatch@farmersweekly. net
I: www.virtual-shropshire. co.uk/holly

QUARNFORD
Derbyshire

Black Clough Farmhouse ★★-★★★
Contact: Mrs A Brocklesby, 4 St Georges Square, London SW1V 2HP
T: (020) 730 1117 &
07976 547717
E: edwina@globalnet.co.uk

Establishments printed in blue have a detailed entry in this guide

Colshaw Cottage ★★★
Contact: Country Holidays ref:
5291 Sales, Holiday Cottages
Group Limited, Spring Mill,
Earby, Barnoldswick, Lancashire
BB94 0AA
T: 08700 723723
F: (01282) 844288
E: sales@ttgihg.co.uk
I: www.country-holidays.co.uk

Greens Farm ★★★
Contact: Mrs A Gould, Flash
Head, Quarnford, Buxton,
Derbyshire SK17 0TE
T: (01298) 25172

New Colshaw Farm ★★★
Contact: Mr J Belfield, Lower
Colshaw Farm, Hollinsclough,
Quarnford, Buxton, Derbyshire
SK17 0SL
T: (01298) 73266 & 23423

RANDWICK
Gloucestershire

Beulah ★★
Contact: Mrs M Davis, Beulah,
The Lane, Randwick, Stroud,
Gloucestershire GL6 6HL
T: (01453) 757577

REDMARLEY
Gloucestershire

**Playley Green Cottages
★★★★**
Contact: Mr A McKechnie,
Playley Green Cottages, Playley
Green Farm, Redmarley,
Gloucester GL19 3NB
T: (01531) 650309
F: (01531) 650375
E: playley-cottages@lineone.net

REEPHAM
Lincolnshire

Refaim Lodge ★★★★
Contact: Mrs Marie-Louise
Papworth, Clayton Consulting
Partners, Refaim Lodge, The Old
Vicarage, Reepham, Lincoln
LN3 4DQ
T: (01522) 753577 & 751749
F: (01522) 753577
E: marie-louise@
claytonconsultants.fsnet.co.uk

RICHARDS CASTLE
Shropshire

The Barn ★★★★
Contact: Mrs and Mr S Plant,
Ryecroft, Richards Castle,
Ludlow, Shropshire SY8 4EU
T: (01584) 831224
F: (01584) 831224
E: ryecroftbarn@hotmail.com
I: www.ludlow.org.u.k./ryecroft

ROCK
Worcestershire

The Barn ★★★★
Contact: Mr M S Deall, Chinook,
Bliss Gate, Rock, Kidderminster,
Worcestershire DY14 9YE
T: (01299) 266047

The Little Houses ★★
Contact: Mrs S Ward, Organs Hill
Farm, Rock, Kidderminster,
Worcestershire DY14 9SS
T: (01299) 266435

ROSS-ON-WYE
Herefordshire

The Ashe ★★★
Contact: Mrs M Ball, The Ashe,
Bridstow, Ross-on-Wye,
Herefordshire HR9 6QA
T: (01989) 563336
E: Holidaycottages.the.ashe@
ukgateway.net
I: www.burnett24.freeserve.
co.uk

**Barn House and Oaklands
★★-★★★**
Contact: Mrs A Farr, Southwell
Court, Broad Oak, Hereford,
Herefordshire HR2 8RA
T: (01600) 750333
E: farrcottages@yahoo.com
I: farrsouthwell.fsnet.co.uk

Browns Cottage ★★★★
Contact: Country Holidays ref:
67504 Sales, Country Holidays,
Spring Mill, Earby, Barnoldswick,
Lancashire BB94 0AA
T: 08700 723723
F: (01282) 844288
I: www.country-holidays.co.uk

Columbine Cottage ★★★
Contact: Mrs S J Wall, Radcliffe
House, Wye Street, Ross-on-
Wye, Herefordshire HR9 7BS
T: (01989) 563895

Coughton House ★★★
Contact: Mrs Balchin, Coughton
House, Coughton, Ross-on-Wye,
Herefordshire HR9 5SF
T: (01989) 562612 & 567322
F: (01989) 567322
E: chasewood@bigwig.net

**The Game Larders and The Old
Bakehouse★★-★★★**
Contact: Mr McIntyre and Miss
A McIntyre, The Game Larders
and, Old Bakehouse, Wythall,
Walford, Ross-on-Wye,
Herefordshire HR9 5SD
T: (01989) 562688
F: (01989) 768269
E: wythall@globalnet.co.uk

**Mainoaks Farm Cottages
★★★-★★★★**
Contact: Mrs P A Unwin, Hill
House, Chase End, Bromsberrow,
Ledbury, Herefordshire HR8 1SE
T: (01531) 650448
E: mainoaks@hotmail.com

Man of Ross House ★★
Contact: Mr D Campkin, 8
Maitland Road, Reading, Berks
RG1 6NL
T: (0118) 9572561
F: (0118) 9594867

Mill Cottage ★★★★
Contact: Mrs H J Gammond,
Rudhall Farm, Ross-on-Wye,
Herefordshire HR9 7TL
T: (01989) 780240

New Court ★★★
Contact: Mrs Jill Bailey, New
Court, Marstow, Ross-on-Wye,
Herefordshire HR9 6HF
T: (01600) 890465
F: (01600) 890465
E: newcourtfarms.wyenet.co.uk
I: www.wyenet.co.uk

Old Cider House ★★★★
Contact: Mrs H A Jackson,
Lowcop, Glewstone, Ross-on-
Wye, Herefordshire HR9 6AN
T: (01989) 562827
F: (01989) 563877
E: man.of.ross.ltd@farming.
co.uk

Old Forge Cottage ★★★
Contact: Mrs J S Jennings, The
Tower House, Priory Road,
Dodford, Bromsgrove,
Worcestershire B61 9DF
T: (01527) 833880
F: (01527) 833880

The Old Hall ★★★
Contact: Mr & Mrs G Lovett, The
Old Hall, 7 Hom Green, Ross-on-
Wye, Herefordshire HR9 7TG
T: (01989) 567864
F: (01989) 567869

The Olde House ★★★
Contact: P J & J Fray, Keepers
Cottage, Upton Bishop, Ross-
on-Wye, Herefordshire HR9 7UE
T: (01989) 780383
F: (01989) 780383
E: peter@pjfray.co.uk
I: www.oldehouse.com

Orchard View ★★★
Contact: Mr & Mrs G Powell,
Underhill Farm, Foy, Ross-on-
Wye, Herefordshire HR9 6RD
T: (01989) 567950

Paddocks Farm ★★★★★
Contact: Ms Catherine Gaskell,
Paddocks Farm, Deep Dean,
Ross-on-Wye, Herefordshire
HR9 5SQ
T: (01989) 768699
F: (01989) 768699
E: info@pakkocksfarm.co.uk
I: www.paddocksfarm.co.uk

Perrystone Cottages ★★★
Contact: Mrs J Sanders,
Woodlands Farm, Little
Dewchurch, Hereford, HR2 6QD
T: (01432) 840488
F: (01432) 840700
E: upperhouse@hotmail.com

River View ★★
Contact: Country Holidays ref:
8216 Sales, Holiday Cottages
Group Limited, Spring Mill,
Earby, Barnoldswick, Lancashire
BB94 0AA
T: 08700 723723
F: (01282) 844288
I: www.country-holidays.co.uk

Riverview Apartment ★★★
Contact: Ms Jane Roberts,
Riverview Apartment, Edde
Cross House, Edde Cross Street,
Ross-on-Wye, Herefordshire
HR9 7BZ
T: (01989) 563299 &
07931 561553
E: river.wye-view@virgin.net
I: freespace.virgin.net/river.
wye-view

**Watchmaker's Cottage
★★★★**
Contact: Mrs J Clark, Daffaluke
House, Glewstone, Ross-on-
Wye, Herefordshire HR9 6BB
T: (01989) 770369
F: (01989) 770369
E: watchmakerscottage@
madasafish.com

**Wharton Lodge Cottages
★★★★★**
Contact: Mrs N Cross, Wharton
Lodge Cottages, Weston-under-
Penyard, Ross-on-Wye,
Herefordshire HR9 7JX
T: (01989) 750140
F: (01989) 750140
E: ncross@whartonlodge.co.uk
I: www.whartonlodge.co.uk

Willows ★★★★
Contact: Ms J G Taylor,
Cavendish Cottage, Buckcastle
Hill, Bridstow, Ross-on-Wye,
Herefordshire HR9 6QF
T: (01989) 562619
F: (01989) 563304

Y Crwys ★★★
Contact: Mr & Mrs Colin and
Angie Fuller, 3 The Square,
Goodrich, Ross-on-Wye,
Herefordshire HR9 6HX
T: (01600) 890799
E: rosiekeegan@yahoo.co.uk

ROSTON
Derbyshire

**Derbyshire Dales Holidays
★★★★**
Contact: Mrs Beryl Wheeler,
Town End Farm, Roston,
Ashbourne, Derbyshire DE6 2EH
T: (01335) 324062
F: (01335) 324062

ROWSLEY
Derbyshire

Bluebell Cottage ★★★★
Contact: Mr & Mrs M
Henderson, 67 Dalewood
Avenue, Beauchief, Sheffield,
S8 0EG
T: (0114) 2817217 &
07713 165328
F: (0114) 2817217
E: jane97@blueyonder.co.uk

New Falling Cottage ★★★★
Contact: Mrs Mona Haylock,
New Falling Cottage, New
Falling Farm, Rowsley, Matlock,
Derbyshire DE4 2NN
T: (01629) 734936

RUARDEAN
Gloucestershire

Horlicks ★★★
Contact: Mrs R Huggins, True
Blue House, Ruardean,
Gloucestershire GL17 9TP
T: (01594) 542144

RUGBY
Warwickshire

Lawford Hill Farm ★★★★
Contact: Mr & Mrs Susan Moses,
Lawford Hill Farm, Lawford
Heath Lane, Rugby,
Warwickshire CV23 9HG
T: (01788) 542001
F: (01788) 537880
E: lawford.hill@talk21.com
I: www.lawfordhill.co.uk

RUSCOMBE
Gloucestershire

Rosevine Cottage ★★★
Contact: Mr & Mrs C Denton,
Cedar Cottage, Ludlow Green,
Ruscombe, Stroud,
Gloucestershire GL6 6DH
T: (01453) 755988
F: (01453) 755988
E: David.Denton@tesco.net

RUSHBURY
Shropshire

Lilywood Cottage ★★★★
Contact: Mrs R Lole, Lilywood Barn, Lilywood Lane, Rushbury, Church Stretton, Shropshire SY6 7EA
T: (01694) 771286

RUSHTON SPENCER
Staffordshire

Cosy Nook ★★★★★
Contact: Mrs J C Matravers, Ivydene, Rushton Spencer, Macclesfield, Cheshire SK11 0QU
T: (01260) 226570 & (0161) 927 7491
F: (01260) 226570
E: 106366.3376@compuserve.com
I: www.cottageguide.co.uk/cosynook

Deepdale Cottage ★★★★
Contact: Country Holidays ref: 10648, Country Holidays Group Owner Services Dept, Spring Mill, Earby, Barnoldswick, Lancashire BB18 6RN
T: 0870 444 6603
F: (01282) 841539
E: sales@ttgihg.co.uk
I: www.country-holidays.co.uk

RYTON
Shropshire

Fairfield Bungalow ★★★
Contact: Country Hols ref: 10994, Country Holidays Group Owner Services Dept, Spring Mill, Earby, Barnoldswick, Lancashire BB18 6RN
T: 0870 444 6603
F: (01282) 844288
I: www.country-holidays.co.uk

ST BRIAVELS
Gloucestershire

The Cottage ★★★
Contact: Mr M Mullin, 54 Priory Gardens, Highgate, London N6 5QS
T: (020) 8340 6716
E: mullin@edit54.freeserve.co.uk

The Cottage ★★★
Contact: Mr M Mullin, 54 Priory Gardens, Highgate, London N6 5QS
T: (020) 8340 6716
E: mullin@edit54.freeserve.co.uk

1 Townsend Cottage ★★★
Contact: Mrs G Dougan, Hanley Farm, Stroat, Chepstow, Gwent NP16 7NA
T: (01291) 625287

1 Townsend Cottage ★★★
Contact: Mrs G Dougan, Hanley Farm, Stroat, Chepstow, Gwent NP16 7NA
T: (01291) 625287

SEAGRAVE
Leicestershire

**Swan Cottage
Rating Applied For**
Contact: Mr Robert Miller, Miller Services, 43 Swan Street, Seagrave, Loughborough, Leicestershire LE12 7NL
T: (01509) 812037
F: (01509) 812037

SEDGEBERROW
Worcestershire

The Calf Pen ★★★★
Contact: Mr and Mrs M Pilling, The Dower House, Barn Lane, Sedgeberrow, Evesham, Worcestershire WR11 6UR
T: (01386) 882095 & 07957 461391
E: calfpen_pilling@btinternet.com

Hall Farm Country Holidays ★★★-★★★★
Contact: Mrs D Stow, Lower Portway Farm, Sedgeberrow, Evesham, Worcestershire WR11 6UB
T: (01386) 881298
F: (01386) 881298

SELSTON
Nottinghamshire

Cottages in the Square ★★★-★★★★
Contact: Mr Keith Hill, Cottages in the Square, 62 Nottingham Road, Selston, Nottingham NG16 6DE
T: (01773) 812029
F: (01623) 559849
E: cottages2000@yahoo.com
I: www.cottages2000.com

Kinnaird ★★★
Contact: Mrs Karen Barton, 10 Searwood Avenue, Kirkby-in-Ashfield, Nottingham, Nottinghamshire NG17 8HL
T: (01623) 441278 & 07950 130967
F: (01623) 441278

SHARDLOW
Derbyshire

The Old Workshop ★★★★
Contact: Mrs D Hansen, 24 Mill Green, The Wharf, Shardlow, Derby DE72 2WE
T: (01332) 799820 & (0115) 9742234

SHAWBURY
Shropshire

Sowbath Farm ★★★★
Contact: Mrs S Griffiths, Sowbath Farm, Sowbath Farm, Shawbury, Shrewsbury SY4 4ES
T: (01939) 250064
F: (01939) 250064

SHEEN
Staffordshire

Bank Top Lodge ★★★★
Contact: Mrs N Birch, Bank Top Farm, Sheen, Buxton, Derbyshire SK17 0HN
T: (01298) 84768

Ferny Knowle ★★★★★
Contact: Mr G Grindon, Ferny Knowle, Sheen, Buxton, Derbyshire SK17 0ER
T: (01298) 83264

SHEEPSCOMBE
Gloucestershire

Catkins ★★
Contact: Mrs J M French, Catkins, Hazelhanger, Far End, Sheepscombe, Stroud, Gloucestershire GL6 7RL
T: (01452) 812040

SHELDON
Derbyshire

Lower Farm Cottage ★★★
Contact: Mr Colin MacQueen, Peak Cottages, Strawberry Lee Lane, Totley Bents, Sheffield, S17 3BA
T: (0114) 2620777
F: (0114) 2620666
E: enquiries@peakcottages.com
I: www.peakcottages.com

Townend Cottage ★★★
Contact: Mrs Ethel Plumtree, Townend Cottage, Sheldon, Bakewell, Derbyshire DE45 1QS
T: (01629) 813 322

SHIFNAL
Shropshire

The Flat ★★★
Contact: Mr and Mrs R Wild, The Flat, 4 Church Street, Shifnal, Shropshire TF11 9AA
T: (01952) 461136

Silvermere Mews ★★★
Contact: Mrs S E Blake, Hawkshutt Farm, Stretton, Stafford, Staffordshire ST19 9QU
T: (01785) 840808
I: www.silvermere.co.uk

SHIPSTON-ON-STOUR
Warwickshire

Little Barn ★★★★
Contact: Mrs K Lawrence, Acorns, Ascott, Shipston-on-Stour, Warwickshire CV36 5PP
T: (01608) 684240
E: johnandkaren.lawrence@ic24.net
I: www.littlebarn@members.easyspace.com/index.htm

Springfield Cottage ★★★
Contact: Mrs I Pinfold, Pine Tree Cottage, Whichford, Shipston-on-Stour, Warwickshire CV36 5PE
T: (01608) 684352

SHIRLAND
Derbyshire

Park Farm Cottages ★★★
Contact: Mrs J Pursglove, Park Farm Cottages, Shirland Park Farm Cottage, Park Lane, Shirland, Alfreton, Derbyshire DE55 6AX
T: (01773) 830011
F: (01773) 836593
E: parklane@parklane.plus.com

SHIRLEY
Derbyshire

Shirley Hall Farm ★★★
Contact: Mrs Sylvia Foster, Shirley Hall Farm, Shirley, Ashbourne, Derbyshire DE6 3AS
T: (01335) 360346 & 360820
F: (01335) 360346
E: shirleyhallfarm.com
I: www.sylviafoster@shirleyhallfarm.com

SHREWSBURY
Shropshire

**The Apartment
Rating Applied For**
Contact: Mr Grant Pennington, The Cornhouse Restaurant, 59A Wyle Cop, Shrewsbury, SY1 1XJ
T: (01743) 231991
F: (01743) 358893

Benjay Cottage ★★★★
Contact: Country Holidays ref: 12324, Country Holidays Owners Services Dept, Spring Mill, Earby, Barnoldswick, Lancashire BB94 0AA
T: 0870 444 6603 & (01743) 703685
F: (01282) 841 539

Cross Hill ★★★
Contact: Mrs E A Williams, 68 Church Hill, Penn, Wolverhampton, West Midlands WV4 5JD
T: (01902) 341399
E: williams_letting@hotmail.com

Inglenook ★★
Contact: Mrs J M Mullineux, Fach-Hir, Brooks, Welshpool, Powys SY21 8QP
T: (01686) 650361

89 Longden Coleham ★★★
Contact: Mrs J Connor, Willow House, Crescent Lane, Town Walls, Shrewsbury, SY1 1TR
T: (01743) 355047 & 07966 507027

Mill House Farm ★★★
Contact: Mrs C L Burton, Mill House Farm, Cruckmeole, Shrewsbury, SY5 8JN
T: (01743) 860325

Newton Meadows Holiday Cottages ★★★★
Contact: Country Holidays ref: 14127, 28, 29 Sales, Holiday Cottages Group Limited, Spring Mill, Earby, Barnoldswick, Lancashire BB94 0AA
T: (01282) 445096
F: (01282) 844288
I: www.country-holidays.co.uk

Ryton Farm Holiday Cottages ★★-★★★
Contact: Mrs A Cartwright, Ryton Farm, Ryton, Dorrington, Shrewsbury SY5 7LY
T: (01743) 718449
F: (01743) 718870
I: www.rytonfarm.co.uk

SIBBERTOFT
Northamptonshire

Brook Meadow Holiday Chalets ★★★-★★★★
Contact: Mrs M J Hart, Brook Meadow Holiday Chalets, The Wrongs, Welford Road, Sibbertoft, Market Harborough, Leicestershire LE16 9UJ
T: (01858) 880886 & 07802 543806
F: (01858) 880485
E: brookmeadow@farmline.com
I: www.brookmeadow.co.uk

SKEGNESS
Lincolnshire

Lyndene Holiday Apartments ★-★★
Contact: Mr M Bailey, 11A St Margarets Avenue, Skegness, Lincolnshire PE25 2LX
T: (01754) 766108 & 610413
E: info@lyndene-uk.com
I: www.lyndene-uk.com

Springfield & Island Holiday Apartments★-★★★
Contact: Mr & Mrs Haines, Springfield & Island Holiday Apartments, 30-32 Scarborough Avenue, Skegness, Lincolnshire PE25 2TA
T: (01754) 762660
E: carol@springfield-island. fsnet.co.uk
I: www.skegness-resort. co.uk/springfield/

SLAD
Gloucestershire
Woodbine Cottage ★★★
Contact: Mrs Helene Moore, The New House, Friday Street, Painswick, Stroud, Gloucestershire GL6 6QJ
T: (01452) 813923 &
07775 715970
F: (01452) 814612
E: helene@etchats.freeserve. co.uk

SNAILBEACH
Shropshire
The Blessing ★★★
Contact: Mr & Mrs M J Dennis, 3 Farm Cottages, Snailbeach, Shrewsbury, Shropshire SY5 0LP
T: (01743) 791489

SNELSTON
Derbyshire
Owls Roost ★★★★
Contact: Mrs M Kay, Brook Farm, Snelston, Ashbourne, Derbyshire DE6 2GP
T: (01335) 324602 &
(0114) 2620777

SOMERCOTES
Derbyshire
Chestnut Cottage ★★★
Contact: Country Hols ref: 7126, Country Holidays Group Owner Services Dept, Spring Mill, Earby, Barnoldswick, Lancashire BB18 6RN
T: 0870 444 6603
F: (01282) 841539
I: www.country-holidays.co.uk

SOMERSAL HERBERT
Derbyshire
Somersal Farm Barn Conversions
Rating Applied For
Contact: Mrs Bridget Noakes, G R & B L Noakes, Bromley Park Farm, Abbots Bromley, Rugeley, Staffordshire WS15 3AJ
T: (01283) 585265 &
07802 768899

SOUDLEY
Gloucestershire
The Cottage ★★★
Contact: Mrs Helen Evans, Peaked Rocks Cottage, The Rocks, Joys Green, Lydbrook, Gloucestershire GL17 9RF
T: (01594) 861119 & 823408
F: (01594) 823408

SOUTH CERNEY
Gloucestershire
12 and 13 The Willows ★★★★
Contact: Mrs R S Holiday, 27 North Lodge, Epsom College, Epsom, Surrey KT17 4JH
T: (01372) 821227 &
(01285) 862898
F: (01372) 821227
E: rosalynholiday@hotmail.com

Lodge 62, Spring Lakes ★★★
Contact: Mrs J Cooke, 23 Copse End, Camberley, Surrey GU15 2BP
T: (01276) 25540

The Watermark Club ★★★-★★★★★
Contact: Ms Sharon Godsall, The Watermark Club, Isis Lake, South Cerney, Cirencester, Gloucestershire GL7 5TL
T: (01285) 862288 & 869181
F: (01285) 862488
E: enquiries@watermarkclub. co.uk
I: www.watermarkclub.co.uk

SOUTH LUFFENHAM
Rutland
Country View Holiday Home ★★★★
Contact: Mr Terry Langley or Jamie Langley, Birch House, The Row, Sutton, Ely, Cambridgeshire CB6 2PD
T: (01353) 777762
F: (01353) 777762

SOUTHWELL
Nottinghamshire
The Nest ★★★
Contact: Mrs Diana Dawes, The Nest, Cooks Lane, Morton-Cum-Fiskerton, Southwell, Nottinghamshire NG25 0XQ
T: (01636) 830140

SPARROWPIT
Derbyshire
Daisy Bank Cottage and Hope Cottage★★★
Contact: Mrs H Batterbee, Daisy Bank, Sparrowpit, Buxton, Derbyshire SK17 8ET
T: (01298) 813027

Whitelee Cottage ★★★★
Contact: Mr Colin MacQueen, Peak Cottages, Strawberry Lee Lane, Totley Bents, Sheffield, S17 3BA
T: (0114) 262 0777
F: (0114) 262 0666
E: enquiries@peakcottages.com
I: www.peakcottages.com

SPILSBY
Lincolnshire
Northfields Farm Cottages ★★★
Contact: Mrs C A Miller, Northfields Farm Cottages, Northfields Farm, Mavis Enderby, Spilsby, Lincolnshire PE23 4EW
T: (01507) 588251 &
07720 046868
F: (01507) 588251
E: patrick.miller@talk21.com
I: www.lineone. net/~holidaycottages/

Owl Barn ★★★★
Contact: Mr D T Neal, Owl Barn, Serena Lodge, Stonepit Lane, Skendleby, Spilsby, Lincolnshire PE23 4QB
T: (01754) 890244
E: owlbreak@supanet.com

SPROXTON
Leicestershire
Appletree Cottage ★★★
Contact: Mrs C Slack, Appletree Cottage, The Green, 19 Main Street, Sproxton, Melton Mowbray, Leicestershire LE14 4QS
T: (01476) 860435
F: (01476) 860435

STAFFORD
Staffordshire
Soapsuds Cottage ★★★★
Contact: Mrs J Bristow, The Mount, Chebsey, Stafford, Staffordshire ST21 6JU
T: (01785) 760208
T: (01785) 760731
E: bobb@cla.org.uk

STAMFORD
Lincolnshire
Palm Cottage ★★★
Contact: Mrs P A Webster, Palm House, The Green, Ketton, Stamford, Lincolnshire PE9 3RA
T: (01780) 721499

STANFORD BRIDGE
Worcestershire
The Riseling ★★★★
Contact: Mrs J W Lane, The Rise, Stanford Bridge, Worcester WR6 6SP
T: (01886) 853438

STANLEY
Derbyshire
Yew Tree Farm ★★★★
Contact: Mrs Gail Newman, Yew Tree Farm, Morley Lane, Stanley Village, Ilkeston, Derbyshire DE7 6EZ
T: (0115) 932 9803 &
07977 222587
E: gailnewman@ yewtreefarm94.freeserve.co.uk

STANSHOPE
Staffordshire
Damgate Barns, Reuben's Roost, Bremen's Barn, Hope's Hideaway
Rating Applied For
Contact: Peak Cottages, Strawberry Lee Lane, Totley Bents, Sheffield, S17 3BA
T: (0114) 262 0777
F: (0114) 262 0666
E: enquiries@peakcottages.com
I: www.peakcottages.com

STANTON
Gloucestershire
Charity Cottage ★★★
Contact: Mrs V Ryland, Charity Farm, Stanton, Broadway, Worcestershire WR12 7NE
T: (01386) 584339
F: (01386) 584270
E: kennethryland@ukonline. co.uk
I: www.myrtle-cottage. co.uk/ryland.htm

Stanton Court Cottages ★★★★
Contact: Mrs S Campbell, Stanton Court Cottages, Stanton Court, Stanton, Broadway, Worcestershire WR12 7NE
T: (01386) 584527
F: (01386) 584682
E: sales@stantoncourt.co.uk
I: www.stantoncourt.co.uk

STANTON IN PEAK
Derbyshire
Lathkill Cottage ★★★
Contact: Country Hols ref: 4504, Country Holidays Group Owner Services Dept, Spring Mill, Earby, Barnoldswick, Lancashire BB18 6RN
T: 0870 444 6603
F: (01282) 844288
E: sales@ttgihg.co.uk
I: www.country-holidays.co.uk

STANTON-ON-THE-WOLDS
Nottinghamshire
Foxcote Cottage ★★★★
Contact: Mrs Joan Hinchley, Foxcote Cottage, Hill Farm (Foxcote), Melton Road, Stanton-on-the-Wolds, Keyworth, Nottinghamshire NG12 5PJ
T: (0115) 937 4337
F: (0115) 937 4337
E: BJHinchley@aol.com

STARKHOLMES
Derbyshire
Hazel Cottage ★★★★
Contact: Mr Colin MacQueen, Peak Cottages, Strawberry Lee Lane, Totley Bents, Sheffield, S17 3BA
T: (0114) 2620777
F: (0114) 2620666
E: enquiries@peakcottages.com
I: www.peakcottages.com

STIPERSTONES
Shropshire
The Old Granary Cottages ★★
Contact: Mrs A Wyke, Middle Farm, Shelve, Minsterley, Shrewsbury SY5 0JF
T: (01743) 891268

The Resting Hill
Rating Applied For
Contact: Mrs M Rowson, Resting Hill, 46 Snailbeach, Minsterley, Shrewsbury, Shropshire SY5 0LT
T: (01743) 791219

STOKE BRUERNE
Northamptonshire
3 Canalside ★★★
Contact: Mr Trevor Morley, 29 Main Road, Shutlanger, Towcester, Northamptonshire NN12 7RU
T: (01604) 862107 &
07850 922176
F: (01604) 864098
E: stokebruerneboats.co.uk

STOKE-ON-TRENT
Staffordshire
Bank End Farm Cottages ★★★
Contact: Mr & Mrs K&E Meredith, Bank End Farm, Hammond Avenue, Brown Edge, Stoke-on-Trent ST6 8QU
T: (01782) 502160
E: pjmeredith@btinternet.com

Janwin ★★★
Contact: Mrs & Mr K J Simpson, WaterfallCross, Winkhill, Leek, Staffordshire ST13 7PX
T: (01538) 308539 &
07970 273295

Jay's Barn
Rating Applied For
Contact: Mrs C Babb, Rest Cottage, Bradley in the Moor, Stoke-on-Trent, ST10 4DF
T: (01889) 507444

Lockwood Hall Farm ★★★
Contact: Mrs R Sherratt, Lockwood Hall Farm, Lockwood Road, Kingsley Holt, Stoke-on-Trent, ST10 2DH
T: (01538) 752270
F: (01538) 752270
E: sherratt@lockwoodhall.freeserve.co.uk

Low Roofs ★★★
Contact: Mrs L Malkin, 62 Albert Terrace, Wolstanton, Newcastle-under-Lyme, Staffordshire ST5 8AY
T: (01782) 627087
F: (01782) 627087

STONEHOUSE
Gloucestershire

Pound Cottage ★★★
Contact: Country Hols ref: 11602, Country Holidays Group Owner Services Dept, Spring Mill, Earby, Barnoldswick, Lancashire BB18 6RN
T: 0870 444 6603
F: (01282) 841539
E: sales@ttgihg.co.uk
I: www.country-holidays.co.uk

STOURPORT-ON-SEVERN
Worcestershire

Winnall House Cottage and Caravan Park★★★-★★★★★
Contact: Mrs Sheila Wilson, Winnall House Cottage and Caravan Park, Winnall House, Lincomb, Stourport-on-Severn, Worcestershire DY13 9RG
T: (01299) 250389

STOW-ON-THE-WOLD
Gloucestershire

Broad Oak Cottages
★★★★-★★★★★
Contact: Mrs M Wilson, The Counting House, Stow-on-the-Wold, Cheltenham, Gloucestershire GL54 1AL
T: (01451) 830794 & 830794
F: (01451) 830794
E: rafw@aol.com

Broom Cottage ★★★★
Contact: Mrs B Russell, Little Broom, Maugersbury, Stow-on-the-Wold, Cheltenham, Gloucestershire GL54 1HP
T: (01451) 830510
E: davidandbrenda@talk21.com
I: www.accofind.com/

Carters Cottage ★★
Contact: Mr & Mrs R Howard, Rookery Farm, Ab Lench, Evesham, Worcestershire WR11 4UP
T: (01386) 462230
F: (01386) 462230

Cotswold Cottages ★★★
Contact: Mr K Spiers, Forest Gate, Frog Lane, Milton-under-Wychwood, Oxford OX7 6JZ
T: (01993) 831495
F: (01993) 831095
E: info@cottageinthecountry.co.uk
I: www.cottageinthecountry.co.uk

Foden Lodge ★★★
Contact: Mr & Mrs L Gypps, 77 Park Lane, Waltham Cross, Hertfordshire EN8 8AD
T: (01992) 301800
E: thefodenlodge@hotmail.com
I: www.come.to/fodenlodge

Horseshoe Cottage ★★★★
Contact: Mr & Mrs M R McHale, Forge House, Lower Oddington, Moreton-in-Marsh, Gloucestershire GL56 0UP
T: (01451) 831556

Johnston Cottage ★★★
Contact: Mrs Yvonne Johnston, Fosse Manor Hotel, Stow-on-the-Wold, Cheltenham, Gloucestershire GL54 1JX
T: (01451) 830354 & (01608) 650816
F: (01451) 832486

Luckley Holidays ★★★★
Contact: Mr Robert Wharton, Luckley Holidays, Longborough, Moreton-in-Marsh, Gloucestershire GL56 0RD
T: (01451) 870885 & 07931 567525
F: (01541) 831481
E: luckleyholidays@talk21.com
I: www.luckley-holidays.co.uk

Maugersbury Manor ★★★
Contact: Mr C S Martin, Maugersbury Manor, Stow-on-the-Wold, Cheltenham, Gloucestershire GL54 1HP
T: (01451) 830581
F: (01451) 870902
E: karen@manorholidays.co.uk
I: www.manorholidays.co.uk

Old Corner Cottage ★★★★
Contact: Mrs Cathy Terry, St. Helens Vicarage, St. Helens Gardens, London W10 6LP
T: (0208) 960 5067
F: (0208) 965782
E: cathy.terry@cornercottage23.fsbusiness.co.uk

3 The Old Shop ★★★★
Contact: Mrs Norma Marfell, Hillside Cottage, Broadwell, Moreton-in-Marsh, Gloucestershire GL56 0UA
T: (01451) 830617
F: (01451) 830617

Park Farm Holiday Cottages
★★★★
Contact: Mrs J C Ricketts, Park Farm, Maugersbury, Cheltenham, Gloucestershire GL54 1HP
T: (01451) 830227
F: (01451) 870568
E: parkfarm.cottages@virgin.net

Park House Cottage ★★★
Contact: Mr & Mrs G Sutton, Park House, 8 Park Street, Stow-on-the-Wold, Cheltenham, Gloucestershire GL54 1AQ
T: (01451) 830159
F: (01451) 870809
E: info@parkhousecottage.co.uk
I: www.parkhousecottage.co.uk

Rose's Cottage ★★★★
Contact: Mr & Mrs R Drinkwater, Rose's Cottage, The Green, Broadwell, Moreton-in-Marsh, Gloucestershire GL56 0UF
T: (01451) 830007 & 870228

Stable Cottage ★★★★
Contact: Mrs M Hill, Spring Barn, Upper Swell, Stow-on-the-Wold, Cheltenham, Gloucestershire GL54 1EW
T: (01451) 830198 & 07710 281030

Valley View
Rating Applied For
Contact: Mr & Mrs P J Craddock, 25 Avenue Road, Dorridge, Solihull, West Midlands B93 8LD
T: (01564) 770143

Vintners Cottage ★★★★★
Contact: Mrs P D Taylor, 12 Dale Bank, Oakdale, Harrogate, North Yorkshire HG1 2LP
T: (01423) 502355

Weavers Cottage ★★★
Contact: Country Holidays ref: 9400 Sales, Country Holidays, Spring Mill, Earby, Barnoldswick, Lancashire BB94 0AA
T: 08700 723723
F: (01282) 844288
E: sales@ttgihg.co.uk
I: www.country-holidays.co.uk

STRATFORD-UPON-AVON
Warwickshire

20-21 Bancroft Place ★★★★
Contact: Mrs Stella Carter, Park View, 57 Rother Street, Stratford-upon-Avon, Warwickshire CV37 6LT
T: (01789) 266839
F: (01789) 266839

Anne's House
Rating Applied For
Contact: Mrs K Cauvin, 34 Evesham Place, Stratford-upon-Avon, Warwickshire CV37 6HT
T: (01789) 550197
F: (01789) 295322
E: karenc@anneshouse.com
I: www.anneshouse.com

As You Like It ★★★
Contact: Mrs J Reid, Inwood House, New Road, Alderminster, Stratford-upon-Avon, Warwickshire CV37 8PE
T: (01789) 450266 & 07956 692015
F: (01789) 450266

Bard Cottage ★★★★
Contact: Mrs M Hicks, 2 Beech Court, Stratford-upon-Avon, Warwickshire CV37 7UQ
T: (01789) 205039
F: (01789) 261386
E: Maureen.Hicks@btinternet.com
I: www.stratford-upon-avon.co.uk/bardcott.htm

Carpenter Barn ★★★★
Contact: Mr K Roberts, 5 Sunbury Cottages, Church Road, Northfield, Birmingham B31 2LB
T: 07957 856626 &
(0121) 4767450
F: (0121) 4767450

Charlecote Cottage 2 Willicote Pastures★★★★
Contact: Mr J Lea, 6 Oak Wharf Mews, Birchdale Road, Appleton, Warrington, Cheshire WA4 5AS
T: (01925) 604106 &
(0151) 4952099
F: (0151) 4246785
E: jplea@aol.com

Chestnut Cottage ★★★
Contact: Mrs J Rush, Gospel Oak House, Pathlow, Stratford-upon-Avon, Warwickshire CV37 0JA
T: (01789) 292764

1 College Mews ★★★★
Contact: Mr I R Reid, Inwood House, New Road, Alderminster, Stratford-upon-Avon, Warwickshire CV37 8PE
T: (01789) 450266 & 07956 602915
F: (01789) 450266

The Cottage at Fosbroke House ★★★
Contact: Mr & Mrs Newbury, Fosbroke House, 4 High Street, Bidford-on-Avon, Alcester, Warwickshire B50 4BU
T: (01789) 772327

Ely Street ★★★
Contact: Mr N Pash, Hideaways, Chapel House, Luke Street, Berwick St John, Shaftesbury, Dorset SP7 0HQ
T: (01747) 828170
F: (01747) 829090
E: enq@hideaways.co.uk
I: www.hideaways.co.uk/property2.cfm?ref=H180Stratford- upon-Avon

Flower Court ★★★★
Contact: Mrs R Liddell, Settlestones, Hidcote Boyce, Chipping Campden, Gloucestershire GL55 6LT
T: (01386) 438833 &
(01789) 731382
E: stratfordtic@shakespeare-country.co.uk
I: www.stratford-upon-avon.co.uk

Grey Mill Farm Piggery Cottages ★★★★
Contact: Mrs J M Ingram, Grey Mill Farm, Alcester Road, Wootton Wawen, Stratford-upon-Avon, Warwickshire B95 6HL
T: (01564) 792582
F: (01564) 792582
E: tony@greymillfarm.co.uk
I: www.greymillfarm.co.uk

Establishments printed in blue have a detailed entry in this guide

Guild Court
Rating Applied For
Contact: Mr John Hookman,
Guild Court, 3 Guild Street,
Stratford-upon-Avon,
Warwickshire CV37
T: (01789) 293007
F: (01789) 296301
E: enquiries@guildcourt.co.uk
I: www.guildcourt.co.uk

39 Heritage Mews ★★★
Contact: Country Holidays ref:
13450 Sales, Country Holidays,
Spring Mill, Earby, Barnoldswick,
Lancashire BB18 6RN
T: 08700 723723
F: (01282) 844288
E: sales@ttgihg.co.uk
I: www.country-holidays.co.uk

Kingzett ★★★★
Contact: Country Holidays ref:
10858 Sales, Holiday Cottages
Group Limited, Spring Mill,
Earby, Barnoldswick, Lancashire
BB18 6RN
T: 08700 723723
F: (01282) 844288
E: sales@ttgihg.co.uk
I: www.country-holidays.co.uk

Loaf Cottage ★★★★
Contact: Sir William Lawrence,
The Knoll, Walcote, Alcester,
Warwickshire B49 6LZ
T: (01789) 488303 &
07836 636932
F: 0797 1434810
E: cottage@
cottageinthecountry.co.uk
I: www.cottageinthecountry.
co.uk

The Mill House ★★★–★★★★
Contact: Mrs Sheila Greenwood,
The Mill House, Mill Lane,
Welford-on-Avon, Stratford-
upon-Avon, Warwickshire
CV37 8EW
T: (01789) 750267

42 Shakespeare Street ★★★
Contact: Mr K D Field, Avon
House, Mulberry Street,
Stratford-upon-Avon,
Warwickshire CV37 6SD
T: (01789) 298141
F: (01789) 262272

61 Waterside ★★★★
Contact: Mrs V Lewis, 65
Longdon Close, Redditch,
Worcestershire B98 7UZ
T: (01527) 527407
E: valerie@lewis2730.freeserve.
co.uk

Woodcote ★★★★★
Contact: Mr & Mrs W A Lucas,
Tanglewood, Park Close,
Wilmcote, Stratford-upon-Avon,
Warwickshire CV37 9XE
T: (01789) 293932
F: (01789) 261855
E: lucasstratford@aol.com
I: www.lucasstratford.co.uk

STRATTON
Gloucestershire

Rose Cottage
Rating Applied For
Contact: Mrs B Bemmet, 9
Albion Street, Stratton,
Cirencester, Gloucestershire
GL7 2HT
T: (01285) 654893

STRETTON
Staffordshire

Anvil Cottage ★★★★
Contact: Mrs S Blake, Hawkshutt
Farm, Stretton, Stafford
ST19 9QU
T: (01785) 840808 &
07973 109499
I: WWW.SILVERMERE.CO.UK

STRETTON ON FOSSE
Warwickshire

Woodfield Cottage ★★★
Contact: Mrs A Best, 4 Bear
Close, Henley-in-Arden, Solihull,
West Midlands B95 5HS
T: (01564) 793354
E: john.best@talk21.com

STROUD
Gloucestershire

Folly Acres ★★
Contact: Mr R Sanders, 11
Shepherds Croft, Stroud,
Gloucestershire GL5 1US
T: (01453) 766822

**Whitminster House Cottages
★★–★★★**
Contact: Mrs A R Teesdale,
Whitminster House,
Whitminster, Gloucestershire
GL2 7PN
T: (01452) 740204
F: (01452) 740204
E: whitminster@mcmail.com
I: www.
whitminsterhousecottages.
mcmail.com
⌨

The Yew Tree ★★★★
Contact: Mrs E Peters, The Yew
Tree, Walls Quarry, Brimscombe,
Stroud, Gloucestershire GL5 2PA
T: (01453) 887594 &
07879 400352
F: (01453) 883428
E: elizabeth.peters@tesco.net
I: www.holidaycottages-uk.
com/gloucestershire

SUCKLEY
Worcestershire

Tundridge Mill ★★★★
Contact: Mrs P J Beard,
Tundridge Mill, Suckley,
Worcester WR6 5DP
T: (01886) 884478
F: (01886) 884478

SUTTERTON
Lincolnshire

Somercotes ★★★
Contact: Dr J V Sharp, Inish Fail,
Orchard Close, East Hendred,
Wantage, Oxfordshire OX12 8JJ
T: (01235) 833367
F: (01235) 833367
E: j.v.sharp@btinternet.com

SUTTON ON THE HILL
Derbyshire

The Chop House ★★★★
Contact: Mr and Mrs Lennard,
Windle Hill Farm, Sutton on the
Hill, Ashbourne, Derbyshire
DE6 5JH
T: (01283) 732377
F: (01283) 732377
E: windlehill@btinternet.com
I: www.windlehill.btinternet.
co.uk

SUTTON ST JAMES
Lincolnshire

**Foremans Bridge Caravan Park
★★★★**
Contact: Mrs Alison Strahan,
Foreman's Bridge Caravan Park,
Sutton Road, Sutton St James,
Spalding, Lincolnshire PE12 0HU
T: (01945) 440346
F: (01945) 440346
E: FOREMANSBRIDGE@
BTINTERNET.COM
I: www.foremans.bridge.co.uk

SWAYFIELD
Lincolnshire

Greystones Lodge ★★★★
Contact: Mrs C Stanley,
Greystones, Overgate Road,
Swayfield, Grantham,
Lincolnshire NG33 4LG
T: (01476) 550985
F: (01476) 550989
E: jslog@mcmail.com

SYMONDS YAT
Herefordshire

Old Court Farm ★★★★
Contact: Mrs Edwina Gee, Old
Court Farm, Symonds Yat, Ross-
on-Wye, Herefordshire HR9 6DA
T: (01600) 890316
F: (01600) 890316
E: teddy.gee@breathemail.net
I: www.holidaybank.
co.uk/uk/heuk/ho587.htm

SYMONDS YAT WEST
Herefordshire

The Snuggle ★★★
Contact: Mr & Mrs Simich, 21
Vaga Crescent, Wye Croft Park,
Ross-on-Wye, Herefordshire
HR9 7RQ
T: (01989) 769258 &
07941 495650
F: (01989) 769258
E: simich@onetel.net.uk

Woodlands ★★
Contact: Mrs C Blows, 14
Honeycroft Hill, Uxbridge,
Middlesex UB10 9NH
T: (01895) 236227

TADDINGTON
Derbyshire

Ash Barn
Rating Applied For
Contact: Ms J Hawley, Ash Barn,
Taddington, Buxton, Derbyshire
SK17 9UB
T: (01298) 85453 &
07760 466395
E: jah@ashtreebarn.fsnet.
co.uk/ashtreebarn@ukonline.
co.uk

**Burfoot Cottage and Fiddlers
Folly★★★★**
Contact: Miss Nichola Mews,
Lower Farm, Brushfield,
Taddington, Buxton, Derbyshire
SK17 9UQ
T: (01298) 85521

Lodley View Farm ★★★★
Contact: Mr & Mrs Nicholas,
Adagio Ltd, Hollybank, Lumb
Lane, Darley Dale, Matlock,
Derbyshire DE4 2HP
T: (01629) 732151
F: (01629) 735002
I: www.peakcottages.co.uk

**Middle Farm Holiday Cottages
★★★★**
Contact: Mr and Mrs B Mullan,
Middle Farm Holiday Cottages,
Middle Farm, Brushfield,
Taddington, Buxton, Derbyshire
SK17 9UQ
T: (01298) 85787
E: bmullan1@aol.com
I: www.cressbrook.
co.uk/tidza/brushfield

Town End House
Rating Applied For
Contact: Mr C MacQueen, Peak
Cottages, Paddock Cottage,
Strawberry Lee Lane, Totley
Bents, Sheffield, S17 3BA
T: (0114) 262 0777
F: (0114) 262 0666

TANSLEY
Derbyshire

Blakelow Cottages ★★★★
Contact: Mr Colin MacQueen,
Peak Cottages, Strawberry Lee
Lane, Totley Bents, Sheffield,
S17 3BA
T: (0114) 2620777
F: (0114) 2620666
E: enquiries@peakcottages.com
I: www.peakcottages.com

TEAN
Staffordshire

Old School Cottage ★★★
Contact: Country Holidays ref:
11351, Country Holidays Group
Owner Services Dept, Spring
Mill, Earby, Barnoldswick,
Lancashire BB18 6RN
T: 0870 444 6603
F: (01282) 841539
E: sales@ttgihg.co.uk
I: www.country-holidays.co.uk

The Rockery ★★★★
Contact: Mrs D Rushton, The
Rockery, Abbey View Cottage,
Quarry Road,, Hollington, Stoke-
on-Trent ST10 4HP
T: (01889) 507434

TELFORD
Shropshire

Church Farm Cottages ★★★
Contact: Mrs V I Evans, Church
Farm Cottages, Rowton,
Wellington, Telford, Shropshire
TF6 6QY
T: (01952) 770381
F: (01952) 770381
E: churchfarm@bigfoot.com
I: www.
virtual-shropshire/churchfarm
⌨

Jasmine Barn ★★★
Contact: Mrs E L Broadbent,
Jasmine Cottage, Sleapford,
Long Lane, Telford, Shropshire
TF6 6HQ
T: (01952) 256252

Old Stables Cottage ★★★
Contact: Mrs M Ferriday, 4
Laburnum Drive, Madeley,
Telford, Shropshire TF7 5SE
T: (01952) 684238
E: ferriday@madeley6.freeserve.
co.uk

7 Pool View ★★★
Contact: Country Hols ref: 4385,
Country Holidays Group Owner
Services Dept, Spring Mill, Earby,
Barnoldswick, Lancashire
BB18 6RN
T: 0870 444 6603
F: (01282) 841539
E: sales@ttgihg.co.uk
I: www.country-holidays.co.uk

Witchwell Cottage ★★★★
Contact: Mrs R Carter, Wenboro
Cottage, Church Lane, Little
Wenlock, Telford, Shropshire
TF6 5BB
T: (01952) 505573
E: rcarter@wenboro.freeserve.
co.uk
I: www.witchwellcottage.co.uk

TEMPLE GUITING
Gloucestershire

The Furrow ★★★★
Contact: Mrs V Hughes, The
Furrow, The Ploughmans
Cottage, Temple Guiting,
Cheltenham, Gloucestershire
GL54 5RW
T: (01451) 850733
F: (01451) 850733

Springbank ★★★★
Contact: Mr Kate Mather,
Landgate House, Colman,
Temple Guiting, Cheltenham,
Gloucestershire GL54 5RT
T: (01451) 850571
F: (01451) 850614
E: landgatemathers@tesco.net

**The Tallett and The Hayloft
★★★**
Contact: Ms L Andrews, Stone
Cottage, Jubilee Lane, Milton-
under-Wychwood, Oxford
OX7 6EW
T: (01993) 832067

TEMPLE NORMANTON
Derbyshire

Rocklea Private House ★★★
Contact: Mr and Mrs R Stirling,
8 Ranworth Road, Bramley,
Rotherham, South Yorkshire
S66 2SN
T: (01709) 543108 &
07810 320992

TENBURY WELLS
Worcestershire

**Colleybatch Pine Lodges
★★★★**
Contact: Mr & Mrs R&E Tebbett,
Colleybatch Pine Lodges,
Colleybatch, Boraston Bank,
Tenbury Wells, Worcestershire
WR15 8LQ
T: (01584) 810153 &
(01299) 823158
F: (01299) 827011

3 Park Terrace ★★★★
Contact: Mrs Hambelton,
Weavers, Rochford, Tenbury
Wells, Worcestershire WR15 8FL
T: (01584) 781767
E: david@tascomms.demon.
co.uk

TETBURY
Gloucestershire

Folly Farm Cottages ★★★
Contact: Mr J Benton, Folly
Farm, Tetbury, Gloucestershire
GL8 8XA
T: (01666) 502475
F: (01666) 502358
E: info@gtb.co.uk
I: www.gtb.co.uk

TETFORD
Lincolnshire

**Cornerways and The Garth
★★★★-★★★★★**
Contact: Holiday Cotts
Ref:6656/13241, Holiday
Cottages Group Owner Services
Dept, Spring Mill, Earby,
Barnoldswick, Lancashire
BB18 6RN
T: 0870 444 6603
F: (01282) 841539
E: sales@ttgigh.co.uk
I: www.country-holidays.co.uk

Grange Farm Cottages ★★★
Contact: Mr & Mrs Downes,
Grange Farm, Salmonby,
Horncastle, Lincolnshire
LN9 6QS
T: (01507) 534101
F: (01507) 534101

TETNEY
Lincolnshire

Beech Farm Cottages ★★★★
Contact: Mr & Mrs N L Smith,
Beech Farm Cottages, Beech
Farm, Station Road, Tetney,
Grimsby, North East Lincolnshire
DN36 5HX
E: norman@beechfarm.fsworld.
co.uk
I: www.beechfarmcottages.co.uk

TEWKESBURY
Gloucestershire

**Abbey Antiques Holiday Flat
★★★**
Contact: Mrs S Brazdys, Abbey
Antiques Bed and Breakfast, 62
Church Street, Tewkesbury,
Gloucestershire GL20 5RZ
T: (01684) 298145

Cavaliers Cottage ★★★
Contact: Mr C R Willis, 70
Blenhiem Drive, Bredon,
Tewkesbury, Gloucestershire
GL20 7QQ
T: (01684) 773127 & 773254
F: (01684) 773264
I: www.cwgroup@btconnect

**Courtyard Cottages
★★★-★★★★**
Contact: Mr H W Herford, Upper
Court, Kemerton, Tewkesbury,
Gloucestershire GL20 7HY
T: (01386) 725351
F: (01386) 725472
E: sales@ttgihg.co.uk
I: www.country-holidays.co.uk

**The Stable Rose Hill Farm
★★★**
Contact: Mrs E M Collinson,
Rose Hill Farm, Stokes Lane,
Bushley, Tewkesbury,
Gloucestershire GL20 6HS
T: (01684) 293598

THEDDLETHORPE ALL SAINTS
Lincolnshire

Horsleys Cottage ★★
Contact: Mrs J W Stringer,
Horsleys, Theddlethorpe All
Saints, Mablethorpe,
Lincolnshire LN12 1PE
T: (01507) 338797
F: (01507) 338797

THORPE
Derbyshire

**Dove Mount Holiday Lets
Rating Applied For**
Contact: Mrs Jackie Perkins,
Dove Mount Holiday Lets, Dove
Mount Farm, Spend Lane,
Thorpe, Ashbourne, Derbyshire
DE6 2TR
T: (01335) 350473
F: (01335) 350118
E: info@dovemountfarm.co.uk
I: www.dovemountfarm.co.uk

Hawthorn Studio ★★★
Contact: Mrs Suzanne Walton,
Hawthorn Cottage, Church Lane,
Thorpe, Ashbourne, Derbyshire
DE6 2AW
T: (01335) 350494

Paxtons Studio ★★★
Contact: Mrs M Wilford, Paxtons
Studio, Paxtons, Thorpe,
Ashbourne, Derbyshire DE6 2AW
T: (01335) 350302
I: www.derbyshire-online.co.uk

THREEKINGHAM
Lincolnshire

**Laundon Cottage
Rating Applied For**
Contact: Holiday Cottages Ref:
4090, Holiday Cottages Group
Owner Services Dept, Spring
Mill, Earby, Barnoldswick,
Lancashire BB18 6RN
T: 0870 444 6603
F: (01282) 844288
E: salesttgihg.co.uk
I: www.country-holidays.co.uk

TIBSHELF
Derbyshire

Raven House Farm ★★★
Contact: Mr P A Rowlands, 0700
4 a Holiday, Ashtrees, The
Causeway, Mark, Highbridge,
Somerset TA9 4QF
T: 0700 4246543 & 0707 424
6543
F: 0700 4246543
E: Paul@ravenhousefarm.
freeserve.co.uk
I: www.07004aholiday.com

TIDESWELL
Derbyshire

Butterfield Cottage ★★★★
Contact: Mrs J Watkins, Trinity
House, Cressbrook, Buxton,
Derbyshire SK17 8SX
T: (01298) 872927
F: (01298) 872927
E: janwatkins@cosycotts.
freeserve.co.uk
I: www.cosycotts.freeserve.co.uk

2 Church Street ★★★
Contact: Mrs Brenda Allen, 2
Church Street, Tideswell, Buxton,
Derbyshire SK17 8PE
T: (01298) 871446

Cornerstones Cottage ★★★
Contact: Country Holidays ref:
10955 Sales, Holiday Cottages
Group Limited, Spring Mill,
Earby, Barnoldswick, Lancashire
BB94 0AA
T: 08700 723723
F: (01282) 844288
E: sales@ttgihg.co.uk
I: www.country-holidays.co.uk

Geil Torrs ★★
Contact: Ms J Buttle, Geil Torrs,
Buxton Road, Tideswell, Buxton,
Derbyshire SK17 8QJ
T: (01298) 871302

Goldstraws ★★★
Contact: Mr & Mrs D J
Sutherland, 2 Curzon Terrace,
Litton Mill, Buxton, Derbyshire
SK17 8SR
T: (01298) 871100
F: (01298) 871641
E: eng@goldstrawshouse.co.uk
I: www.goldstrawshouse.co.uk

Lane End Cottage ★★★
Contact: Mr John Snowden, 6
Winterbank Close, Sutton in
Ashfield, Nottinghamshire
NG17 1LS
T: (01623) 557279

**Markeygate Cottage and Barn
★★★★**
Contact: Mr Colin MacQueen,
Peak Cottages, Strawberry Lee
Lane, Totley Bents, Sheffield,
S17 3BA
T: (0114) 2620777
F: (0114) 2620666
E: enquiries@peakcottages.com
I: www.peakcottages.com

Stanley Barn ★★★
Contact: Mrs Jean Hopkins,
Stanley Barn, Stanley House,
Sherwood Road, Tideswell,
Buxton, Derbyshire SK17 8HJ
T: (01298) 872327

Stone Cottage ★★★
Contact: Mrs S Oates, Vicarage
Cottage, High Street, Tideswell,
Buxton, Derbyshire SK17 8LD
T: (01298) 871921 & (0114) 268
0200

TIRLEY
Gloucestershire

Town Street Cottage ★★★
Contact: Country Holidays ref:
737 Sales, Holiday Cottages
Group Limited, Spring Mill,
Earby, Barnoldswick, Lancashire
BB94 0AA
T: 08700 723723
F: (01282) 844288
E: sales@ttgihg.co.uk
I: www.country-holidays.co.uk

TODENHAM
Gloucestershire

**Applegate
Rating Applied For**
Contact: Mrs C F Crump,
Applegate, The Retreat,
Springbank, Todenham,
Moreton-in-Marsh,
Gloucestershire GL56 9PA
T: (01608) 651307

TREFONEN
Shropshire
Little Barn ★★★★
Contact: Mrs Sue Batley,
Wulfruna Cottage, Old Post
Office Lane, Trefonen, Oswestry,
Shropshire SY10 9DL
T: (01691) 653387
E: info@little-barn.co.uk
I: www.little-barn.co.uk

TURNDITCH
Derbyshire
The Stables ★★★★
Contact: Mrs J Grant, The
Stables, Derbyhill House, Cross
O'th Hands, Turnditch, Belper,
Derbyshire DE56 2LT
T: (01773) 550489
E: terry@derbyhill.co.uk
I: www.derbyhill.co.uk

TWO DALES
Derbyshire
Piggery ★★★
Contact: Mr Colin MacQueen,
Peak Cottages, Strawberry Lee
Lane, Totley Bents, Sheffield,
S17 3BA
T: (0114) 2620777
F: (0114) 2620666
E: enquiries@peakcottages.com
I: www.peakcottages.com

Tree Tops ★★★★
Contact: Peak Cottages, Paddock
Cottage, Strawberry Lee Lane,
Totley Rise, Sheffield S17 3BA
T: (0114) 262 0777
F: (0114) 262 0666

UFTON
Warwickshire
Wood Farm ★★★★
Contact: Mr Derek Hiatt, Wood
Farm, Ufton, Leamington Spa,
Warwickshire CV33 9PH
T: (01926) 612270 &
07831 111312

ULEY
Gloucestershire
Blacknest Cottage ★★★★
Contact: Mr D Grindley,
Blacknest Cottage, Owlpen, Uley,
Dursley, Gloucestershire
GL11 5BZ
T: (01453) 860034
F: (01453) 860034
E: enquiries@blacknestcottage.
co.uk
I: www.blacknestcottage.co.uk

Coopers Cottage ★★★★
Contact: Mrs D Griffiths, 48
Orchard Leaze, Cam, Dursley,
Gloucestershire GL11 6HX
T: (01453) 542861

ULLINGSWICK
Herefordshire
Acorn Annex ★★★
Contact: Mr R H Wadley, Acorn
Annex, The Oaks, Ullingswick,
Hereford HR1 3JG
T: (01432) 820371 &
07790 360844
E: robwad@quista.net

UPPER HULME
Staffordshire
The Barn and The Stable ★★★
Contact: Country Holidays ref:
13775/13376 Sales, Country
Holidays, Spring Mill, Earby,
Barnoldswick, Lancashire
BB94 0AA
T: 08700 723723
F: (01282) 844288
I: www.country-holidays.co.uk

**Paddock Farm Holiday
Cottages ★★★★**
Contact: Mr & Mrs M Barlow,
Paddock Farm, Upper Hulme,
Leek, Staffordshire ST13 8TY
T: (01538) 300345 & 300145

UPPER MAYFIELD
Derbyshire
Green Acres ★★★
Contact: Mr Clive Mycock, Back
of the Brook, Waterfall,
Waterhouses, Stoke-on-Trent
ST10 3JA
T: (01538) 308236

UPPER QUINTON
Warwickshire
1 Meon View ★★★★
Contact: Mrs A Rimell, 1 Meon
View, Taylors Lane, Upper
Quinton, Stratford-upon-Avon,
Warwickshire CV37 8LG
T: (01789) 720080

**Winton House Cottage
★★★★**
Contact: Mrs G Lyon, Winton
House, The Green, Upper
Quinton, Stratford-upon-Avon,
Warwickshire CV37 8SX
T: (01789) 720500 &
07831 485483
E: gail@wintonhouse.com
I: www.wintonhouse.com

UPPER SLAUGHTER
Gloucestershire
Home Farm Stable ★★★★★
Contact: Mrs M A Bayetto,
Home Farmhouse, Upper
Slaughter, Cheltenham,
Gloucestershire GL54 2JF
T: (01451) 820487 &
07901 684664
E: maureen.bayetto@virgin.net
I: www.home-farm-stable.co.uk

UPPINGHAM
Rutland
The Stables Apartment ★★
Contact: Mr and Mrs R M Peach,
The Old Rectory New Road,
Belton in Rutland, Oakham,
Rutland LE15 9LE
T: (01572) 717279
F: (01572) 717343
E: bb@stablemate.demon.co.uk

4 Stockerston Road ★★★
Contact: Mr or Mrs Lloyd, 4
Stockerston Road, Uppingham,
Oakham, Rutland LE15 9UD
T: (01572) 823478 & 823955
F: (01572) 823955

UPTON ST LEONARDS
Gloucestershire
Hill Farm Cottages ★★
Contact: Mrs M McLellan, Hill
Farm Cottages, Hill Farm, Upton
Hill, Upton St Leonards,
Gloucester GL4 8DA
T: (01452) 614081

UPTON-UPON-SEVERN
Worcestershire
Whitehall Barn ★★★-★★★★
Contact: Mr & Mrs R Staines,
Whitehall, Brotheridge Green,
Hanley Castle, Worcester
WR8 0BB
T: (01684) 310376

UPTON WARREN
The Durrance ★★★★
Contact: Mrs Helen Hirons, The
Durrance, Berry Lane, Upton
Warren, Bromsgrove,
Worcestershire B61 9EL
T: (01562) 777533
F: (01562) 777533
E: helenhirons@thedurrance.
fsnet.co.uk

UTTOXETER
Staffordshire
Chestnut Cottage ★★★
Contact: Mrs Susan Tania
Sketchley, Chestnut Cottage,
Marston Bank, Marston
Montgomery, Uttoxeter,
Staffordshire ST14 5BT
T: (01889) 590736
F: (01889) 590736

VOWCHURCH
Herefordshire
The Front Dore ★★★
Contact: Mrs M Layton, The
Front Dore, Ponty Pinna Farm,
Vowchurch, Hereford HR2 0QE
T: (01981) 550266

WADDINGWORTH
Lincolnshire
Redhouse Cottage ★★★★
Contact: Mr & Mrs A Pritchard,
Redhouse Farm, Waddingworth,
Woodhall Spa, Lincolnshire
LN10 5EE
T: (01507) 578285 &
07702 678241
F: (01507) 578285

WARMINGTON
Northamptonshire
Papley Farm Cottages ★★★★
Contact: Mrs J Lane, Slade
House, Papley Farm,
Warmington, Peterborough
PE8 6UU
T: (01832) 272583
F: (01832) 272583

WARSLOW
Staffordshire
**Shay Side Barn and Cottage
★★★★**
Contact: Mr Sykes, Sykes
Cottage, York House, York
Street, Chester, CH1 3LR
T: (01244) 345700
F: (01244) 321442
E: info@sykescottages.co.uk
I: www.sykescottages.co.uk

WARWICK
Warwickshire
Copes Flat ★★★
Contact: Mrs E Draisey, Forth
House, 44 High Street, Warwick,
CV34 4AX
T: (01926) 401512
F: (01926) 490809
E: info@forthhouseuk.co.uk
I: www.forthhouseuk.co.uk

Whitley Elm Cottages ★★★★
Contact: Mr & Mrs C Bevins,
Whitley Elm Cottages, Case
Lane, Mousley End, Rowington,
Warwickshire CV35 7JE
T: (01926) 484577
F: (01926) 484577
E: clive.bevins@btclick.com

WATERHOUSES
Staffordshire
Broadhurst Farm ★★★★
Contact: Mrs P Mycock,
Broadhurst Farm, Waterhouses,
Stoke-on-Trent ST10 3LQ
T: (01538) 308261

**Greenside and Greenside
Cottage ★★★-★★★★**
Contact: Mr Sykes, Sykes
Cottage, York House, York
Street, Chester, CH1 3LR
T: (01244) 345700
F: (01244) 321442
E: info@sykescottages.co.uk
I: www.sykescottages.co.uk

Limestone View Cottage ★★★
Contact: Mrs Wendy Webster,
Limestone View Farm, Stoney
Lane, Cauldon, Waterhouses,
Stoke-on-Trent, Staffordshire
ST10 3EP
T: (01538) 308288
E: wendywebster@
limestoneviewfarm.freeserve.
co.uk
I: www.peakdistrictfarmhols.
co.uk

WELFORD-ON-AVON
Warwickshire
Church View ★★★★
Contact: Mrs Barbara Stovell,
Hawkswood, Barton Road,
Welford-on-Avon, Stratford-
upon-Avon, Warwickshire
CV37 8EZ
T: (01789) 750187
F: (01789) 751034
E: stovell@mgowners_club.net

The Granary ★★★★
Contact: Mr & Mrs B E Spink,
The Granary, Rumer Hall
Cottage, Welford-on-Avon,
Stratford-upon-Avon,
Warwickshire CV37 8AF
T: (01789) 750752 &
07961 815286
F: (01789) 750752
E: maria.spink@lineone.net

WELLAND
Worcestershire
**Mutlows Farm Cottages
★★★★**
Contact: Mrs P J Lewis, Mutlows
Farm Cottages, Drake Street,
Welland, Malvern,
Worcestershire WR13 6LP
T: (01684) 310878
F: (01684) 310878
E: alan.lewis4@btinternet.com

WELLESBOURNE
Warwickshire
Walton Hall ★★★
Contact: Mr Brian Bradley,
Walton Hall Members Ltd,
Walton Hall, Walton,
Wellesbourne, Warwick
CV35 9HU
T: (01789) 842424
F: (01789) 470418
E: enquiries@waltonhall.co.uk
I: www.waltonhall.co.uk

WELLINGTON
Shropshire
The Coach House ★★★★
Contact: Mrs M M Fellows, Old
Vicarage, Wrockwardine,
Wellington, Telford, Shropshire
TF6 5DG
T: (01952) 244859 & (0121) 212
2131
F: (0121) 212 1249

WELLOW
Nottinghamshire
Foliat Cottages ★★★
Contact: Mr and Mrs Carr,
Jordan Castle Farm, Wellow,
Newark, Nottinghamshire
NG22 0EL
T: (01623) 861088
F: (01623) 861088
E: janet.carr@farmline.com
I: www.
sherwoodforestholidaycottages.
com

WEM
Shropshire
Soulton Hall Cottages ★★
Contact: Mrs A P Ashton,
Soulton Hall Cottages, Soulton
Hall, Wem, Shrewsbury SY4 5RS
T: (01939) 232786
F: (01939) 234097

WENSLEY
Derbyshire
Ivy Cottage ★★★
Contact: Mr Sykes, Sykes
Cottage, York House, York
Street, Chester, CH1 3LR
T: (01244) 345700
F: (01244) 321442
E: info@sykescottages.co.uk
I: www.sykescottages.co.uk

WESSINGTON
Derbyshire
Dell Farm ★★★
Contact: Mr and Mrs T Anthony,
Dell Farm, Wessington, Alfreton,
Derbyshire DE55 6DU
T: (01773) 832889
F: (01773) 832889
I: www.cottageguide.
co.uk/dellfarm

WEST FELTON
Shropshire
Rectory Cottage ★★★
Contact: Country Holidays Ref:
12096, Country Holidays Owner
Services Department, Spring
Mill, Earby, Barnoldswick,
Lancashire BB18 6RN
T: 08700 723726
F: (01282) 844288
I: www.mocro-plus-web.
net/cgale/cottage

WESTBURY
Shropshire
Garden Cottage ★★★
Contact: Mrs C W Halliday,
Garden Cottage, Whitton Hall,
Westbury, Shrewsbury,
Shropshire SY5 9RD
T: (01743) 884270
F: (01743) 884158
E: whittonhall@btinternet.com

WESTBURY-ON-SEVERN
Gloucestershire
Gatwick Cottage ★★
Contact: Mrs M Andrews, Rock
Farm, Rock Lane, Westbury-on-
Severn, Gloucestershire
GL14 1QJ
T: (01452) 760210

WESTON ON AVON
Warwickshire
**March Font and Hurnberry
Cottages★★★★**
Contact: Mr & Mrs R Bluck,
Weston Farm, Weston on Avon,
Stratford-upon-Avon,
Warwickshire CV37 8JY
T: (01789) 750688

WESTON RHYN
Shropshire
Gledstone ★
Contact: Mr Derek Stone,
Gledstone, 4 Yew Tree Cottages,
Rhoswiel, Weston Rhyn,
Oswestry, Shropshire SY10 7TB
T: (01691) 773993
F: (01691) 773993

Mill Cottage ★★★
Contact: Mr & Mrs H Brannick,
Mill Cottage, Mill House, The
Wern, Weston Rhyn, Oswestry,
Shropshire SY10 7ER
T: (01691) 659738

WESTON SUBEDGE
Gloucestershire
Buff's Cottage ★★★
Contact: Mrs C Nelson, The Old
Baptist Manse, Sheep Street,
Stow-on-the-Wold,
Cheltenham, Gloucestershire
GL54 1AA
T: (01451) 870813
E: caroline.nelson@virgin.net

WESTON UNDERWOOD
Derbyshire
**Brook Cottage and
Honeysuckle Cottage★★★**
Contact: Mrs L Adams, Parkview
Farm, Weston Underwood,
Ashbourne, Derbyshire DE6 4PA
T: (01335) 360352
F: (01335) 360352
E: parkviewfarm@hotmail.com
I: parkviewfarm.co.uk

WETTON
Staffordshire
Manor Barn ★★★
Contact: Mr Colin MacQueen,
Peak Cottages, Strawberry Lee
Lane, Totley Bents, Sheffield,
S17 3BA
T: (0114) 2620777
F: (0114) 2620666
E: enquiries@peakcottages.com
I: www.peakcottages.com

Old Sunday School
Rating Applied For
Contact: Peak Cottages,
Strawberry Lee Lane, Totley
Bents, Sheffield, S17 3BA
T: (0114) 262 0777
F: (0114) 262 0666
E: enquries@peakcottages.com
I: www.peakcottages.com

Stable Barn ★★★
Contact: Mrs H Higton, The Old
Post Office, Wetton, Ashbourne,
Derbyshire DE6 2AP
T: (01335) 310312

Wetton Barns
★★★★-★★★★★
Contact: Mr M P Jackson,
Wetton Barns Holiday Cottages
c/o Riversdale, Monsal Dale,
Buxton, Derbyshire SK17 8SZ
T: (01629) 640187
F: (01629) 640187
E: mick@riversdale-farm.
freeserve.co.uk

WHALEY BRIDGE
Derbyshire
Cloud Cottage ★★★★
Contact: Country Holidays -
9405 Sales, Country Holidays,
Spring Mill, Earby, Barnoldswick,
Lancashire BB94 0AA
T: 08700 723723
F: (01282) 844288
I: www.country-holidays.co.uk

Cote Bank Cottages ★★★★
Contact: Mrs P Broadhurst, Cote
Bank Cottages, Buxworth,
Whaley Bridge, High Peak,
Derbyshire SK23 7NP
T: (01663) 750566
F: (01663) 750566
E: cotebank@btinternet.com
I: www.peakdistrictfarmhols.
co.uk

**Shallcross Hall Cottage
★★★★**
Contact: Country Holidays refL
11737 Sales, Holiday Cottages
Group Limited, Spring Mill,
Earby, Barnoldswick, Lancashire
BB94 0AA
T: 08700 723723
F: (01282) 844288
I: www.country-holidays.co.uk

WHATELEY
Staffordshire
33 Rosemary Cottage ★★★
Contact: Mrs V E Coles, 31 Old
Forge Cottage, Whateley,
Tamworth, Staffordshire
B78 2ET
T: (01827) 280826

WHATSTANDWELL
Derbyshire
Smithy Forge Cottages ★★★
Contact: Mr C R Buxton, End
Cottage, 32 Station Road,
Denby, Ripley, Derbyshire
DE5 8ND
T: (01332) 881758 & 780232
F: (01332) 780232
E: chris@certificateframing.
co.uk

WHICHFORD
Warwickshire
Hillside Cottage ★★★★
Contact: Mrs J R Haines, Ascott
House Farm, Whichford, Long
Compton, Shipston-on-Stour,
Warwickshire CV36 5PP
T: (01608) 684655
F: (01608) 684539
E: dp.hainesfarms@farmline.
com
I: www.touristnetuk.
com/wm/ascotthouse/index.htm

**The Hops and The Vines
★★★★**
Contact: Mrs C Garner, The Hops
and The Vines, The Norman
Knight, Whichford, Shipston-
on-Stour, Warwickshire
CV36 5PE
T: (01608) 684621
F: (01608) 684621
E: carole@thenormanknight.
co.uk
I: www.thenormanknight.co.uk

Horseshoe Cottage ★★★
Contact: Mrs S Gore, Holly
Cottage, The Green, Whichford,
Shipston-on-Stour,
Warwickshire CV36 5PE
T: (01608) 684310
F: (01608) 684310
E: suevaudin@community.co.uk

WHITBOURNE
Herefordshire
**The Barn, The Coach House and
The Potting Shed**
★★★★-★★★★★
Contact: Mr & Mrs Gilly and Cliff
Poultney, The Olde Rectory, Boat
Lane, Whitbourne, Worcester
WR6 5RS
T: (01886) 82 2000
F: (01886) 82 2100
E: stay@olde-rectory.co.uk
I: www.olde-rectory.co.uk

Crumplebury Farmhouse ★★★
Contact: Mrs A Evans, Dial
House, Whitbourne, Worcester,
Herefordshire WR6 5SG
T: (01886) 821534
F: (01886) 821534
🏃

Elcocks Cottage ★★★
Contact: Mr & Mrs M R Hogg, 61
Pereira Road, Harborne,
Birmingham, B17 9JB
T: (0121) 427 1395
E: mikehogguk@aol.com

Keepers Cottage ★★★★
Contact: Country Holidays Sales,
Country Holidays, Spring Mill,
Earby, Barnoldswick, Lancashire
BB94 0AA
T: 08700 723723
F: (01282) 844288
E: sales@ttgihg.co.uk
I: www.country-holidays.co.uk

WHITCHURCH
Shropshire
Combermere Abbey Cottages
★★★★-★★★★
Contact: Ms Pugh, Combermere
Abbey Cottages, Combermere,
Whitchurch, Shropshire SY13
T: (01948) 871637
F: (01948) 871293
E: cottages@combermereabbey.
co.uk
I: www.combermereabbey.co.uk

Establishments printed in blue have a detailed entry in this guide

The Granary ★★★
Contact: Mrs Maggie White, The Old Rectory, Calverhall, Whitchurch, Shropshire SY13 4PE
T: (01948) 890696
E: magalan@awhite62. freeserve.co.uk

Holiday Cottage ★★★★
Contact: Mr and Mrs A Wright, The Park, Tilstock, Whitchurch, Shropshire SY13 3NL
T: (01948) 880 669 &t (01432) 840287
F: (01270) 629603
E: lettings@sfc.co.uk

WHITECROFT
Gloucestershire

The Sidings ★★★
Contact: Mrs V Long, Fiddlers Green, Mitchel Troy Common, Monmouth, Gwent NP25 4JQ
T: (01600) 714464
F: (01600) 714464
E: glong4464@aol.com

WHITESHILL
Gloucestershire

The Coach House ★★★★
Contact: Mr T Searby, Noble House, The Plain, Whiteshill, Stroud, Gloucestershire GL6 6AA
T: (01453) 765441
F: (01453) 752595
E: watertalks@cwcom.net
I: www.trevorsearby.co.uk

WHITTINGTON MOOR
Derbyshire

20 Sanforth Street ★★★
Contact: Mr & Mrs B Armstrong, Holmedene, Ashford Road, Bakewell, Derbyshire DE45 1GL
T: (01629) 813448
E: bernard-armstrong@lineone. net

WHITTLEBURY
Northamptonshire

Dolly's Cottage ★★
Contact: Mrs P Clapp, 6 High Street, Whittlebury, Northamptonshire NN12 8XJ
T: (01327) 857896
F: (01327) 857896
E: patal@cwcom.net

WILLERSEY
Gloucestershire

Ninds Farm Cottage ★★★
Contact: Country Holidays ref: 11001 Sales, Holiday Cottages Group Limited, Spring Mill, Earby, Barnoldswick, Lancashire BB94 0AA
T: 08700 723723
F: (01282) 844288
I: www.country-holidays.co.uk

Rex Cottage ★★
Contact: Mrs P Baldwin, Rex House, Willersey, Broadway, Worcestershire WR12 7PJ
T: (01386) 852365

WILLOUGHBY
Warwickshire

The Saddlery ★★★★★
Contact: Mrs E Heckford, Manor Farm, Brooks Close, Willoughby, Rugby, Warwickshire CV23 8BY
T: (01788) 890256
E: thesaddlery@heckford. fsbusiness.co.uk

WILTON
Herefordshire

Benhall Farm ★★★
Contact: Mrs Carol Brewer, Benhall Farm, Benhall Farm, Wilton, Ross-on-Wye, Herefordshire HR9 6AG
T: (01989) 563900 &t 07900 264612
I: carol_m_brewer@hotmail. com

WINCHCOMBE
Gloucestershire

Briar Cottage ★★★★
Contact: Mrs D Parker, The Olde Bakehouse, Castle Street, Winchcombe, Cheltenham, Gloucestershire GL54 5JA
T: (01242) 602441
F: (01242) 602441
E: deniseparker@onetel-net.uk

Cockbury Court Cottages ★★★★
Contact: Mr & Mrs J Charlton, Cotswold Cottages Limited, Rowan Lodge, Neata Farm, Greet, Cheltenham, Gloucestershire GL54 5BL
T: (01242) 604806
F: (01242) 604806
E: john@rowan-lodge.demon. co.uk
I: www.cotswoldcottagesltd. co.uk/bookings

Dunbar Cottage
Rating Applied For
Contact: Ms Linda Andrews, 53 Gloucester Street, Winchcombe, Cheltenham, Gloucestershire GL54 5LX
T: (01242) 604946

2 Enfield Cottages
Rating Applied For
Contact: Mr & Mrs Jennifer McCoach, 34 Lime Avenue, Lillington, Leamington Spa, Warwickshire CV32 7DF
T: (01926) 339030 & 773402
E: jmccoach@fish.co.uk

Manor Farm ★★★★
Contact: Mr & Mrs R Day, Manor Farm, Greet, Winchcombe, Cheltenham, Gloucestershire GL54 5BJ
T: (01242) 602423 &t 0777 1732307
F: (01242) 602423
E: janet@dickandjanet

The Old Stables ★★★
Contact: Miss Jane Eayrs, Hill View, Farmcote, Winchcombe, Cheltenham, Gloucestershire GL54 5AU
T: (01242) 603860 &t 07703 126521
F: (01242) 603860

Orchard Cottage ★★★
Contact: Mrs S M Rolt, Stanley Pontlarge, Winchcombe, Cheltenham, Gloucestershire GL54 5HD
T: (01242) 602594

Styche Cottage ★★★★
Contact: Mrs Anne Bayston, 276A Myton Road, Warwick, CV34 6PT
T: (01926) 831508
E: stychecottage@bayston.f9. co.uk
I: styche-cottage.co.uk

Sudeley Castle Country Cottages ★★★
Contact: Mrs N Dyke, Sudeley Castle, Winchcombe, Cheltenham, Gloucestershire GL54 5JD
T: (01242) 602308
F: (01242) 602959
E: natalie.dyke@sudeley.org.uk

Traditional Accommodation ★★★★–★★★★★
Contact: Mr & Mrs Wilson, 60 Pershore Road, Evesham, Worcestershire WR11 6PQ
T: (01386) 446269 &t 07710 006949
F: (01386) 446269
E: trad.accom@virgin.net
I: freespace.virgin.net/trad. accom

Tythe Barn Holiday Cottages ★★★★
Contact: Mr & Mrs D Gould, The Old Schoolhouse, Gretton Road, Gotherington, Cheltenham, Gloucestershire GL52 9EP
T: (01242) 677122
F: (01242) 677122
E: tythebarn@aol.com
I: www.tythebarncottages.co.uk

WINKHILL
Staffordshire

Alma Cottage
Rating Applied For
Contact: Mrs Diana Cope, Alma Cottage, Little Paradise Farm, Blackbrook, Winkhill, Leek, Staffordshire ST13 7QR
T: (01538) 308909 & 308859
F: (01538) 308910

WINSTER
Derbyshire

Briar Cottage ★★★★
Contact: Mrs A Walters, Heathcote House, Main Street, Winster, Matlock, Derbyshire DE4 2DJ
T: (01629) 650342

Gingerbread Cottage ★★★★
Contact: Mrs Jill Wild, Gingerbread Cottage, September Cottage, East Bank, Winster, Matlock, Derbyshire DE4 2DT
T: (01629) 650071
E: gingerbread@envirobiz.net
I: www.wildgray.fsnet.co.uk

The Headlands Fold ★★★
Contact: Mrs Janet Shiers, The Headlands Fold, The Headlands, Winster, Matlock, Derbyshire DE4 2DS
T: (01629) 650523
E: jan@familyshiers.org.uk
I: homepagestesconet/ ~janetshiers

WIRKSWORTH
Derbyshire

Bull Close Cottage
Rating Applied For
Contact: Country Hols ref: 11215, Country Holidays Group Owner Services Dept, Spring Mill, Earby, Barnoldswick, Lancashire BB18 6RN
T: 0870 444 6603
F: (01282) 844288
I: www.country-holidays.co.uk

The Cottage
Rating Applied For
Contact: Mrs N Hagger, The Cottage, Durhamhouse, 42 North End, Wirksworth, Derby DE4 4FG
T: (01629) 826159

Hillside Cottage ★★★
Contact: Mrs A Simons, 4 Tippendell Lane, Chiswell Green, St Albans, Hertfordshire AL2 3HL
T: (01727) 852684

Hopton Estates ★★★★
Contact: Mr & Mrs Bill & Eddy Brogden, Hopton Estates, Hopton Hall, Hopton, Wirksworth, Derby, Derbyshire DE4 4DF
T: (01629) 540458 &t 07774 705716
T: (01629) 540712
E: h.e@saqnet.co.uk
I: www.hoptonhall.co.uk

Snuffless Dip ★★★
Contact: Mrs M Doxey, Chandlers, West End, Wirksworth, Matlock, Derbyshire DE4 4EG
T: (01629) 824466

WITCOMBE
Gloucestershire

Witcombe Park Holiday Cottages ★★★
Contact: Mrs Hicks-Beach, Witcombe Farm, Great Witcombe, Gloucester GL3 4TR
T: (01452) 863591
F: (01452) 863591

WITHINGTON
Gloucestershire

Ballingers Farmhouse Cottages ★★★★
Contact: Mrs Judith Pollard, Fairhaven Holiday Cottages, Derby House, 123 Watling Street, Gillingham, Kent ME7 2YY
T: (01242) 890335
E: pollardfam@compuserve. com
I: www.smoothhound. co.uk/hotels/ball.html

WOODCHESTER
Gloucestershire

The Coach House ★★★★
Contact: Mrs C Walsh, The Firs, Selsley Road, Woodchester, Stroud, Gloucestershire GL5 5NQ
T: (01453) 873088
F: (01453) 873053
E: cwalsh3088@aol.com

WOODHALL SPA
Lincolnshire

Cuckoo Land ★★★
Contact: Mr and Mrs Coates, 16 The Broadway, Woodhall Spa, Lincolnshire LN10 6ST
T: (01526) 353336
E: cuckoo.land@ic24.net
I: www.cuckoo-land.co.uk

Mill Lane Cottage ★★
Contact: Mr & Mrs I G
Williamson, 72 Mill Lane,
Woodhall Spa, Lincolnshire
LN10 6QZ
T: (01526) 353101 &
07967 520289
E: WILL@williamsoni.freeserve.
co.uk
I: www.skegness.
net/woodhallspa.htm

WOODMANCOTE
Gloucestershire

25 Chapel Lane ★★★★
Contact: Mrs D A Taylor, 23
Chapel Lane, Woodmancote,
Cheltenham, Gloucestershire
GL52 4HT
T: (01242) 676685
E: taylor@danskin80.fsnet.co.uk

WORCESTER
Worcestershire

Honeysuckle Cottages ★★★
Contact: Mr R J Gilchrist, 32
Barbourne Road, Knights Rest,
Worcester, WR1 1HU
T: (01905) 24257 &
07939 178786
F: (01905) 26202

**Little Lightwood Farm
★★-★★★**
Contact: Mrs V A Rogers, Little
Lightwood Farm, Lightwood
Lane, Cotheridge, Worcester
WR6 5LT
T: (01905) 333236
F: (01905) 333236
E: lightwood.holidaysatvirgin.
net

**Maybury and Malvern View
★★★**
Contact: Mr & Mrs R Houghton,
Upper Lightwood Farm, Lower
Broadheath, Worcester,
WR2 6RL
T: (01905) 333202
E: jph6@hotmail.com

Mill Cottage ★★★★
Contact: Mrs V Baylis, Mill
Cottage, Mildenham Mill, Egg
Lane, Claines, Worcester
WR3 7SA
T: (01905) 451554

Noken Farm Cottage ★
Contact: Mrs M E Pritchard,
Noken Farm, Sinton Green,
Hallow, Worcester WR2 6NW
T: (01905) 640531
F: (01905) 640531

**Stildon Manor Cottage
★★★★**
Contact: Mr & Mrs P Wilding-
Davies, Stildon Manor, Menith
Wood, Worcester, WR6 6UL
T: (01299) 832720
F: (01299) 832720

WORMELOW
Herefordshire

Old Forge Cottage ★★★
Contact: Mrs S Wheeler, Old
Forge Cottage, Lyston Smithy,
Wormelow, Hereford HR2 8EL
T: (01981) 540625

WORTHEN
Shropshire

Hawthorn Cottage ★★★
Contact: Mr Sykes, Sykes
Cottage, York House, York
Street, Chester, CH1 3LR
T: (01244) 345700
F: (01244) 321442
E: info@sykescottages.co.uk
I: www.sykescottages.co.uk

WOTTON-UNDER-EDGE
Gloucestershire

The Burrow ★★★
Contact: Country Hols
ref:B5831, Country Holidays
Group Owner Services Dept,
Spring Mill, Earby, Barnoldswick,
Lancashire BB94 0AA
T: 0870 4446604
F: (01282) 841539

Hill Mill Cottage ★★★★
Contact: Mrs P Nash, Hill Mill
House, Ozleworth, Wotton-
under-Edge, Gloucestershire
GL12 7QR
T: (01453) 842401
F: (01453) 842401
E: pnash@cupoftea21.freeserve.
co.uk

WRANGLE
Lincolnshire

Auraceria House Farm ★★
Contact: Holiday Cottages Ref:
10616, Holiday Cottages Group
Owner Services Dept, Spring
Mill, Earby, Barnoldswick,
Lancashire BB18 6RN
T: 0870 444 6603
F: (01282) 844288
E: sales@ttgihg.co.uk
I: www.country-holidays.co.uk

WYRE PIDDLE
Worcestershire

Peaceavon ★★★★
Contact: Mr & Mrs N Price, 20
Cosby Road, Littlethorpe,
Leicester LE9 5HP
T: (116) 2862891
E: pricenr@aol.com

WYTHALL
Worcestershire

Inkford Court Cottages ★★★
Contact: Mr J S Bedford, Inkford
Court Cottages, Alcester Road,
Wythall, Birmingham B47 6DL
T: (01564) 822304 &
07831 462451
F: (01564) 829618

YARDLEY GOBION
Northamptonshire

The Stable ★★
Contact: Mr Alan Paine, The
Stable, Old Wharf Farm, The
Wharf, Yardley Gobion,
Towcester, Northamptonshire
NN12 7UE
T: (01908) 542293 &
07850 772370
F: (01908) 542293

YARPOLE
Herefordshire

West End Cottage ★★
Contact: Mrs C Niblett,
Brookhouse Farm, Yarpole,
Leominster, Herefordshire
HR6 0BB
T: (01568) 780269
F: (01568) 780269
E: cordelia@cniblett.fsnet.co.uk

YORKLEY
Gloucestershire

**Shap House Cottages
Rating Applied For**
Contact: Country Holidays -
10802, 10807 Sales, Country
Holidays, Spring Mills, Earby,
Barnoldswick, Lancashire
BB94 0AA
T: (01282) 445096
F: (01282) 844288
I: www.country-holidays.co.uk

YOULGREAVE
Derbyshire

Appletree Cottage ★★★
Contact: Mr C MacQueen, Peak
Cottages, Strawberry Lee Lane,
Totley Bents, Sheffield, S17 3BA
T: (0114) 262 0777
F: (0114) 262 0666

April Cottage ★★★
Contact: Mrs A Naybour,
Christmas Cottage, Church
Street, Youlgreave, Bakewell,
Derbyshire DE45 1WL
T: (01629) 636151
F: (01629) 636151
E: anaybour@talk21.com

Easter Cottage ★★★
Contact: Country Holidays -
13178 Sales, Holiday Cottages
Group Limited, Spring Mill,
Earby, Barnoldswick, Lancashire
BB18 6RN
T: 08700 723723
F: (01282) 844288
E: sales@ttgihg.co.uk
I: www.country-holidays.co.uk

Linden Cottage ★★★
Contact: Country Hols Ref:
5103, Country Holidays Group
Owner Services Dept, Spring
Mill, Earby, Barnoldswick,
Lancashire BB18 6RN
T: 0870 444 6603
F: (01282) 844288
I: www.country-holidays.co.uk

The Old Grocers Shop ★★★★
Contact: Mr C MacQueen, Peak
Cottages, Strawberry Lee Lane,
Totley Bents, Sheffield, S17 3BA
T: (0114) 2620777
F: (0114) 2620666
E: enquiries@peakcottages.com
I: www.peakcottages.com

Rockhaven ★★★
Contact: Mr and Mrs J W
Sutcliffe, 32 Coalmoor Lane,
Telford, Shropshire TF4 3QB
T: (01952) 506186

Rose Cottages ★★★★
Contact: Mr & Mrs J Upton, Rose
Cottages, Copper Pot, Conksbury
Lane, Youlgreave, Bakewell,
Derbyshire DE45 1WR
T: (01629) 636487
E: john@upton68.fsnet.co.uk

Sage Cottage ★★★★
Contact: Mr C MacQueen, Peak
Cottages, Strawberry Lee Lane,
Totley Bents, Sheffield, S17 3BA
T: (0114) 2620777 & 2620666
E: enquiries@peakcottages.com
I: www.peakcottages.com

Sunnyside ★★★
Contact: Ms J Steed, Falkland
House, 10 New Road,
Youlgreave, Bakewell, Derbyshire
DE45 1WP
T: (01629) 636195

Tempus Cottage ★★★
Contact: Mr and Mrs A
Thornelow, Tempus Cottage, 67
Ingle Road, Chatham, Kent
ME4 5SD
T: (01634) 401479

Thimble Cottage ★★★
Contact: Mr Colin MacQueen,
Peak Cottages, Strawberry Lee
Lane, Totley Bents, Sheffield,
S17 3BA
T: (0114) 2620777
F: (0114) 2620666
E: enquiries@peakcottages.com
I: www.peakcottages.com

Thyme Cottage ★★★★
Contact: Mrs S A MacDonald,
Hardanger, Main Street,
Youlgrave, Bakewell, Derbyshire
DE45 1UW
T: (01629) 636472
F: (01629) 636472
E: lm@maccolour.co.uk

Establishments printed in blue have a detailed entry in this guide

EAST OF ENGLAND

ACLE
Norfolk

Station Cottage ★★★★
Contact: Mr David Harris,
Station Cottage, Station Road,
Acle, Norwich NR13 3BZ
T: (01493) 751136
F: (01493) 752930
E: broadsman@lineone.net
I: www.oas.
co.uk/ukcottages/station

ALDEBURGH
Suffolk

Aldeburgh Court ★★★
Contact: Mr & Mrs Oliver &
Susie Hayward, 62 Hill Rise,
Richmond, Surrey TW10 6UB
T: (020) 8940 3750 & 8948 8835
E: susie@okhayward.demon.
co.uk

Braid House ★★★
Contact: Mrs Anney Lewis, Tree
House, Church Street, Ticehurst,
Wadhurst, East Sussex TN5 7DL
T: (01580) 200342
E: anney.lewis@btinternet.com

8 Coastguard Court ★★★
Contact: Mr & Mrs J Mauger,
Mount Pleasant Farmhouse,
Redisham, Beccles, Suffolk
NR34 8LU
T: (01502) 575896
F: (01502) 575896
E: john.mauger@eggconnect.
net
I: www.blythweb.
co.uk/coastguard-court

Cosy Corner ★★★
Contact: Mrs B A Fryer, Cosy
Corner, 41 Mariners Way,
Aldeburgh, Suffolk IP15 5QH
T: (01728) 453121

The Cottage ★★★
Contact: Mrs J Alexander, The
Old Rectory, Old Church Road,
Melton, Woodbridge, Suffolk
IP13 6DH
T: (01394) 383822 &
(01728) 830123

Crabbe Cottage ★★★
Contact: Mr Roger Williams, The
Court House, Tostock Place, Bury
St Edmunds, Suffolk IP30 9PG
T: (01359) 270444
F: (01359) 271226
E: roger@ss100.com
I: www.aldeburgh.suffolk.co.uk

Cragside ★★★★
Contact: Mrs L Valentine,
Rookery Farm, Cratfield,
Halesworth, Suffolk IP19 0QE
T: (01986) 798609
F: (01986) 798609
E: j.r.valentine@btinternet.com

Dial Flat ★
Contact: Mrs P D Harrison, Dial
House, 5 Dial Lane, Aldeburgh,
Suffolk IP15 5AG
T: (01728) 453212
E: pam@harpd.freeserve.co.uk

The Dutch House Flat ★★★
Contact: Mr Christopher Bacon,
Dodnash Priory Farm, Bentley,
Ipswich, Suffolk IP9 2DF
T: (01473) 310682 &
07836 731821
F: (01473) 311131
E: cbacon@freeuk.com

290 High Street ★★★
Contact: Mrs Vanessa Gorst, 12a
Eton Avenue, London NW3 3EH
T: (020) 74355552 &
(01728) 452676

38 Lee Road ★★★★
Contact: Mrs E M Wagener,
Fairfield, Silver Street, Stansted,
Essex CM24 8HE
T: (01279) 813182
F: (01279) 647128
E: jrwagener@aol.com

Magenta ★★★
Contact: Mrs Vanessa Gorst, 12a
Eton Avenue, London NW3 3EH
T: (020) 7435 5552 &
(01728) 452377
F: (020) 7435 5552

May Lodge ★★★★
Contact: Mr & Mrs Richard &
Wendy Pither, Suffolk Secrets, 7
Frenze Road, Diss, IP22 3PA
T: (01379) 651297
F: (01379) 641555
E: holidays@suffolk-secrets.
co.uk
I: www.suffolk-secrets.co.uk

Mermaid Cottage ★★★★
Contact: Mrs Jacqueline Collier,
Clopton Hall, Clopton,
Woodbridge, Suffolk IP13 6QB
T: (01473) 735004 &
07788 885082
E: jmicollier@cs.com

Orlando ★★★
Contact: Mr Peter Hatcher,
Martlesham Hall, Church Lane,
Martlesham, Woodbridge,
Suffolk IP12 4PQ
T: (01394) 382126 & 274321
F: (01394) 382126
E: peter@hatcher.co.uk

Pebble Beach ★★★
Contact: Mrs M M Orr, 33 The
Terrace, Aldeburgh, Suffolk
IP15 5HJ
T: (01728) 453489
F: (01728) 454871
E: michaelorr@supanet.com

**Telegraph Cottage and Barn
★★★**
Contact: Mr Richard John Balls,
Gorse Hill, Leiston Road,
Aldeburgh, Suffolk IP15 5QD
T: (01728) 452162 &
07855 390185
F: (01728) 452162
E: gorse40@hotmail.com
I: www.selfcateringsuffolk.co.uk

ALRESFORD
Essex

Creek Lodge ★★★
Contact: Mrs Patricia Mountney,
Creek Lodge, Ford Lane,
Alresford, Colchester, Essex
CO7 8BE
T: (01206) 825411

ASHDON
Essex

**Whitensmere Farm Cottages
★★★★-★★★★★**
Contact: Mrs Susan Ford,
Whitensmere Farm, Ashdon,
Saffron Walden, Essex CB10 2JQ
T: (01799) 584244 &
07798 750351
F: (01799) 584244
E: gford@lineone.net
I: www.
holidaycottagescambridge.co.uk

AYLMERTON
Norfolk

The Bungalow ★★★
Contact: Mr Nigel Ripley,
Aylmerton House, Holt Road,
Aylmerton, Norwich NR11 8QA
T: (01263) 837445

Moorland Park ★★★
Contact: Mrs Elaine Field,
Moorland Park, Holt Road,
Aylmerton, Norwich NR11 8QA
T: (01263) 837508
F: (01263) 837508
E: garycromertravel@btclick.
com

**Thyme Untied
Rating Applied For**
Contact: Mr A Mackay, 70
Cromer Road, Sheringham,
Norfolk NR26 8RT
T: (01263) 824955
F: (01263) 824955

AYLSHAM
Norfolk

Holly Cottage ★★★
Contact: Mr & Mrs R M Burr,
Burgh House, Burgh Road,
Aylsham, Norwich, Norfolk
NR11 6AT
T: (01263) 733567

BABRAHAM
Cambridgeshire

The Granary ★★★
Contact: Mrs Gill Kotschy, The
Granary, Chalk Farm, High
Street, Babraham, Cambridge
CB2 4AG
T: (01223) 837783 & 834900
F: (01223) 834113
E: kotschy@dial.pipex.com
I: www.granaryvisit.co.uk

BACTON
Norfolk

Swiss Cottage ★★★★
Contact: Mrs Linda Weinberg,
Buehl Str 6, 8113 Boppelsen,
Switzerland, 8113
T: 00 411 844 2222
F: 00 411 840 0222
E: swissonthebeach@cs.com

BALE
Norfolk

Chapel Field Cottage ★★★
Contact: Mrs Judith Everitt,
Wheelcroft, Field Dalling Road,
Bale, Fakenham, Norfolk
NR21 0QS
T: (01328) 878419

BANHAM
Norfolk

Olde Farm Cottage ★★★
Contact: Mrs K Girling, Olde
Farm Cottage, Olde Farm, New
Buckenham Road, Banham,
Norwich NR16 2DA
T: (01953) 860023
F: (01953) 860023
E: pgreystoke@aol.com
I: www.greystokegraphics.co.uk

BANNINGHAM
Norfolk

Bridge Bungalow ★★★
Contact: Mrs Jane Shulver,
Norfolk Country Cousins, Point
House, Ridlington, North
Walsham, Norfolk NR28 9TY
T: (01692) 650286
F: (01692) 650180
E: norfolk.cousins@netcom.
co.uk
I: www.norfolk-cottages.co.uk

BARNEY
Norfolk

The Stables ★★★
Contact: Mrs Christine
Blackman, London House, The
Street, Barney, Fakenham,
Norfolk NR21 0AD
T: (01328) 878204

BARTON TURF
Norfolk

Gunns Cottage ★★★
Contact: Mrs Jane Shulver,
Norfolk Country Cousins, Point
House, Ridlington, North
Walsham, Norfolk NR28 9TY
T: (01692) 650286
F: (01692) 650180
E: norfolk.cousins@netcom.
co.uk
I: www.norfolk-cottages.co.uk

BAWDESWELL
Norfolk

Jotts Cottage ★★★★
Contact: Mr & Mrs John Clarke,
Jasmine house, Dereham road,
Bawdeswell, East Dereham,
Norfolk NR20 4AA
T: (01362) 688444 &
0778 726279
F: (01362) 688172
E: clarkes.jasmine@virgin.net

BAYLHAM
Suffolk

**Baylham House Annexe &
Baylham House Flat
★★-★★★**
Contact: Mrs Ann Storer,
Baylham House Farm, Mill Lane,
Baylham, Ipswich, Suffolk
IP6 8LG
T: (01473) 830264
F: (01473) 830264
E: ann@baylham-house-farm.
co.uk
I: www.baylham-house-farm.
co.uk

BEACHAMWELL
Norfolk

Carole Wilsons Rectory Holidays ★★★
Contact: Mrs C Wilson, Carole Wilsons Rectory Holidays, The Old Rectory, Beachamwell, Swaffham, Norfolk PE37 8BE
T: (01366) 328628
E: rectoryholidays@talkgas.net

BECCLES
Suffolk

9 The Maltings ★★★
Contact: Mrs Brenda Lanchester & Mr Birch, Brick Kiln Barn, Kings Lane, Weston, Beccles, Suffolk NR34 8TG
T: (01502) 717362 & 711888
F: (01502) 711888
E: bircharch@aol.com

Redisham Hall ★★★★
Contact: Country Holidays, Spring Mill, Earby, Barnoldswick, Lancashire BB94 0AA
T: 08700 723723
I: www.country-holidays.co.uk

BEESTON
Norfolk

Holmdene Farm ★★★
Contact: Mrs J S Davidson, Holmdene Farm, Beeston, King's Lynn, Norfolk PE32 2NJ
T: (01328) 701284
I: www.northnorfolk.co.uk/holmdenefarm

BEESTON REGIS
Norfolk

29 Abbey Park ★★
Contact: Mrs Joan Munday, Keys Holidays, 18 Station Road, Sheringham, Norfolk NR26 8RE
T: (01263) 823010
F: (01263) 821449
E: info@keys-holidays.co.uk
I: www.keys-holidays.co.uk

BELCHAMP ST PAUL
Essex

Colefair Cottage ★★★★
Contact: Mr Kirk Forrest, Suffolk & Norfolk Country Cottages, Hillside Orchard, Rectory Farm Lane, Orwell, Royston, Hertfordshire SG8 5RB
T: (01223) 207946
F: (01223) 208893
E: admin@suffolkandnorfolkcottages.co.uk
I: www.suffolkandnorfolkcottages.co.uk

BERKHAMSTED
Hertfordshire

Holly Tree & Jack's Cottage ★★★
Contact: Mrs D Barrington, 20 & 21 Ringshall, Little Gaddesden, Berkhamsted, Hertfordshire HP4 1ND
T: (01442) 843464
F: (01442) 842051
E: RBBarrington@aol.com

BEYTON
Suffolk

The Coach House ★★
Contact: Mrs Barbara Jeffery, Sideways Cottage, The Green, Beyton, Bury St Edmunds, Suffolk IP30 9AD
T: (01359) 270219

---

1 The Cottages ★★★
Contact: Mrs A Self, Eastgate Post Office, 19 Eastgate Street, Bury St Edmunds, Suffolk IP33 1XX
T: (01284) 752763
E: terry.self@lineone.net

Dibolds ★★★
Contact: Mrs J Smith, Dibolds, Thurston Road, Beyton, Bury St Edmunds, Suffolk IP30 9AE
T: (01359) 270467
E: john@noble80.freeserve.co.uk

Manorflat ★★★★
Contact: Mr & Mrs Kay and Mark Dewsbury, Manorhouse, The Green, Beyton, Bury St Edmunds, Suffolk IP30 9AF
T: (01359) 270960
E: manorhouse@beyton1.com
I: www.beyton1.com

BILDESTON
Suffolk

Friar's Cottage ★★★★★
Contact: Mrs P Sewell, 21 High Street, Bildeston, Ipswich, Suffolk IP7 7EX
T: (01449) 741108
F: (01449) 741108
E: patricia@pmsewell.fsnet.co.uk
I: www.friarscottage.co.uk

Minto Cottage ★★★
Contact: Mr & Mrs A Cox, Minto House, 74 High Street, Bildeston, Ipswich, Suffolk IP7 7EA
T: (01449) 744988
F: (01449) 740086
E: andycox@eidosnet.co.uk
I: www.mintoholidays.co.uk

BILLERICAY
Essex

The Pump House Apartment ★★★★★
Contact: Mrs E R Bayliss, Pump House, Church Street, Great Burstead, Billericay, Essex CM11 2TR
T: (01277) 656579
F: (01277) 631160
E: john.bayliss@willmottdixon.co.uk

BILLINGTON
Bedfordshire

Brewery Cottage ★★★
Contact: Mrs Angie Leach & Mrs J Franlin, Lets Unlimited, Town Farm, Ivinghoe, Leighton Buzzard, Bedfordshire LU7 9EZ
T: (01296) 668455 & 660279
F: (01296) 668455
E: w.h.leach.and.sons@farmline.com
I: members.farmline.com/angie

BINHAM
Norfolk

4 Abbey House ★★★★
Contact: Mrs Val Rivers, Lion House, Church Street, North Creake, Fakenham, Norfolk NR21 9AD
T: (01328) 730596 & 730825

Betty's Cottage & Bob's Cottage ★★★★
Contact: Ms Fiona Thompson, Betty's Cottage & Bob's Cottage, Field House, Walsingham Road, Binham, Fakenham, Norfolk NR21 0BU
T: (01328) 830639

Fairfield Cottage ★★★
Contact: Mrs Sheila Thornton, Apple Acre, Bleasby Road, Thurgarton, Nottingham NG14 7FW
T: (01636) 830395
F: (0115) 9878011

BISHOP'S STORTFORD
Hertfordshire

Cedar Court Apartment ★★★
Contact: Mrs J M Windus, Anglesey House, 16 Grailands, Bishop's Stortford, Hertfordshire CM23 2RG
T: (01279) 653614
E: jeanwindus@aol.com
I: www.stortford.co.uk

BITTERING
Norfolk

Dairy Farmhouse ★★★-★★★
Contact: Mrs M White, Dairy Farmhouse, Rawhall Lane, Bittering, Dereham, Norfolk NR19 2QU
T: (01362) 687687
F: (01362) 687687

BLAKENEY
Norfolk

Cottage Holidays Blakeney ★★
Contact: Mrs Ann Farrow, 45 Swafield Rise, North Walsham, Norfolk NR28 0DG
T: (01692) 403369 & 405188
F: (01692) 405188

Currie's Cottage ★★★
Contact: Dr & Mrs Fogarty, 202 Unthank Road, Norwich, Norfolk NR2 2AH
T: (01603) 502007
E: curriescottage@cs.com

The Friary ★★★
Contact: Mrs D Cooke, 31 Bracondale, Norwich, NR1 2AT
T: (01603) 624827
E: cookehd@paston.co.uk

Greencroft ★★★
Contact: Mrs B D Joice, High House Farm, Litcham, King's Lynn, Norfolk PE32 2RY
T: (01328) 701266
F: (01328) 701345

Janda ★
Contact: Mrs Joan Munday, Keys Holidays, 18 Station Road, Sheringham, Norfolk NR26 8RE
T: (01263) 823010
F: (01263) 821449
E: info@keys-holidays.co.uk
I: www.keys-holidays.co.uk

Loades Cottage ★★★
Contact: Holiday Cottages Ref: 13152, Holiday Cottages Group Owner Services Dept, Spring Mill, Earby, Barnoldswick, Lancashire BB18 6RN
T: (01282) 445096
F: (01282) 844288
E: owners@ttgihg.co.uk
I: www.country-holidays.co.uk

Mariners Hill Cottages ★★★
Contact: Mrs B Pope, The Lodge, Back Lane, Blakeney, Holt, Norfolk NR25 7NR
T: (01263) 740477
F: (01263) 741356

Quayside Cottages ★★-★★★
Contact: Mrs V Álvarez, New Wellbury Farmhouse, Wellbury Park, Hitchin, Hertfordshire SG5 3BP
T: (01462) 768627
F: (01462) 768320
E: veronicaAlvarez@compuserve.com
I: www.blakeneycottages.co.uk

Roslyn ★★
Contact: Mrs Brenda Eke, Bermuda House, 169 Fakenham Road, Melton Constable, Norfolk NR24 2DN
T: (01263) 860111 & 860263

The Seagulls ★★★★
Contact: ECC Ref: CEU, English Country Cottages, Stoney Bank, Earby, Barnoldswick, Lancashire BB94 0AA
T: 0870 5851100 & 5851177
F: 0870 5851150
E: owners@ttgihg.co.uk

The Stable Court and Apartments ★★★
Contact: Mr & Mrs Peter Darling, Langham Hall, Langham, Holt, Norfolk NR25 7BX
T: (01328) 830375
F: (01328) 830775
E: peter.darling1@btinternet.com
I: www.ukcoastalholidays.com/go/langhamhall

BLAXHALL
Suffolk

Willows ★★
Contact: Mrs Elizabeth Simmonds, 54 St Augustines Road, Bedford, MK40 2NA
T: (01234) 214686

BLYTHBURGH
Suffolk

Whitehouse Barns Rating Applied For
Contact: Mrs Penelope Roskell-Griffiths, 61 Benthal Road, London N16 7AR
T: (020) 8806 5969
E: peneloperoskell@yahoo.co.uk

BRADWELL
Norfolk

Aardvark House ★★
Contact: Mr Alex Brown, 2 Avington, Great Holm, Milton Keynes MK8 9DQ
T: (01908) 569628
I: www.alex.brown.hemscott.net

BRAINTREE
Essex

1 Red Lion Cottages ★
Contact: Mrs M McKellar Ratcliffe, 2 Red Lion Cottages, Lanham Green Road, Cressing, Braintree, Essex CM7 8DR
T: (01376) 584043
F: (01376) 584043
E: redlion@eurasian-nation.demon.co.uk
I: www.stilwell.co.uk

Establishments printed in blue have a detailed entry in this guide

BRAMFIELD
Suffolk
Japonica House ★★★
Contact: Mr Richard Pither,
Suffolk Secrets, 7 Frenze Road,
Diss, IP22 4PA
T: (01379) 651297
F: (01379) 641555
E: holidays@suffolk-secrets.
co.uk
I: www.suffolk-secrets.co.uk

BRANCASTER
Norfolk
11 Anchorage View ★★★
Contact: Mrs Sandra Hohol,
Norfolk Holiday Homes, 62
Westgate, Hunstanton, Norfolk
PE36 5EL
T: (01485) 534267 & 534560
F: (01485) 535230
E: shohol@
birdsnorfolkholidayhomes.co.uk
I: www.
norfolkholidayhomes-birds.
co.uk

Dunlin ★
Contact: Mrs Sandra Hohol,
Norfolk Holiday Homes, 62
Westgate, Hunstanton, Norfolk
PE36 5EL
T: (01485) 534267
F: (01485) 535230
E: shohol@
birdsnorfolkholidayhomes.co.uk
I: www.
norfolkholidayhomes-birds.
co.uk

Russett Lodge ★★★
Contact: Mrs Sandra Hohol,
Norfolk Holiday Homes, 62
Westgate, Hunstanton, Norfolk
PE36 5EL
T: (01485) 534267
F: (01485) 535230
E: shohol@
birdsnorfolkholidayhomes.co.uk
I: www.
norfolkholidayhomes-birds.
co.uk

Thompson Brancaster Farms
★★★
Contact: Mrs Sue Lane, 4
Stiffkey Road, Warham, Wells-
next-the-Sea, Norfolk NR23 1NP
T: 07885 269538
F: (01328) 710144
E: sue@rsdlane.freeserve.co.uk
I: www.tbfholidayhomes.co.uk

BRANCASTER STAITHE
Norfolk
Crows Nest & Crowfoot ★★★
Contact: Mr David Langley, Crow
Green, Middlegate Road,
Frampton, Boston, Lincolnshire
PE20 1AR
T: (01205) 722547
F: (01205) 722547
E: langley@crowgreen.
freeserve.co.uk

21 Dale End ★★★★
Contact: Mrs Debbie Clark, Stone
House, 19 Main Street, Seaton,
Oakham, Leicestershire
LE15 9HU
T: (01572) 747389
F: (01572) 747693
E: debbie@courtneycampbell.
com
I: www.hemingwayclark.
com/norfolk

Island Cottage ★
Contact: Mrs Sandra Hohol,
Norfolk Holiday Homes, 62
Westgate, Hunstanton, Norfolk
PE36 5BU
T: (01485) 534267
F: (01485) 535230
E: shohol@
birdsnorfolkholidayhomes.co.uk
I: www.
norfolkholidayhomes-birds.
co.uk

Vista & Carpenters Cottages
★★★
Contact: Mrs G J Smith, Dale
View, Brancaster Staithe, King's
Lynn, Norfolk PE31 8BY
T: (01485) 210497
F: (01485) 210497

Westbourne ★★★
Contact: Mrs Sandra Hohol,
Norfolk Holiday Homes, 62
Westgate, Hunstanton, Norfolk
PE36 5EL
T: (01485) 534267
F: (01485) 535230
E: shohol@
birdsnorfolkholidayhomes.co.uk
I: www.
norfolkholidayhomes-birds.
co.uk

BRANDON
Suffolk
Deacons Cottage ★★
Contact: Mrs B D Deacon,
Deacons Cottage, South Street,
Hockwold, Thetford, Norfolk
IP26 4JG
T: (01842) 828023 & 878739

Poplar Hall ★★★★
Contact: Mrs Anna Garwood,
Poplar Hall, Frostenden Corner,
Frostenden, Wangford, Suffolk
NR34 7JA
T: (01502) 578549
I: www.southwold.
co.uk/poplar-hall/

BRAUGHING
Hertfordshire
Edwinstree Chapel ★★★★
Contact: Mrs Pamela Bradley,
Edwinstree Chapel, Edwinstree,
Dassels, Braughing, Ware,
Hertfordshire SG11 2RR
T: (01763) 289509 &
07719 485815

BRISLEY
Norfolk
Church Farm Cottages
★★★-★★★★
Contact: Mrs G V Howes, Church
Farm Cottages, Brisley, Dereham,
Norfolk NR20 5LL
T: (01362) 668332 &
07747 877375
F: (01362) 668332

The Old Stable Annexe ★★
Contact: Mrs J B Gaymer, The
Old Stable Annexe, School Road,
Brisley, East Dereham, Norfolk
NR20 5LH
T: (01362) 668793

BRISTON
Norfolk
Swallows Way ★★★
Contact: Mrs Pauline Milham,
Thyrnegate, The Street,
Gasthorpe, Diss, Norfolk
IP22 2TL
T: (01953) 681779

BROCKDISH
Norfolk
The Olde Coach House ★★★★
Contact: Mr & Mrs J Spooner,
The Olde Coach House, The
Street, Brockdish, Diss, Norfolk
IP21 4JY
T: (01379) 668146

BRUISYARD
Suffolk
Bruisyard Hall ★★★★
Contact: Mr R C Rous,
Dennington Hall, Woodbridge,
Suffolk IP13 8AU
T: (01728) 638712
F: (01728) 638712
E: Dennington@farmline.com
I: www.bruisyardhall.co.uk

BRUNDALL
Norfolk
Idle Hours ★★★
Contact: Mrs E Rowntree, 1
Howards Thickett, Gerrards
Cross, Buckinghamshire SL9 7NT
T: (01753) 885163
F: (01753) 891317
E: rowntree@dial.pipex.com

BUNGAY
Suffolk
**Garden Cottage & Courtyard
Cottage** ★★★★
Contact: Mr & Mrs P W Slater,
Manor Farm House, Bungay,
Suffolk NR35 1PQ
T: (01986) 896895 &
07976 693506
F: (01986) 896840

BUNTINGFORD
Hertfordshire
Southfields Cottages ★★
Contact: Mrs I A Murchie,
Southfields Cottages,
Southfields Farm, Throcking,
Buntingford, Hertfordshire
SG9 9RD
T: (01763) 281224 & 0777 557
1258
F: (01763) 281224
E: lamurchie@hotmail.com

BURGH NEXT AYLSHAM
Norfolk
The Lodge ★★★★
Contact: Mrs Isabel Newton,
North Farm, Burgh next
Aylsham, Aylsham, Norwich
NR11 6TW
T: (01603) 279800
F: (01603) 278187
E: isabel.n@virgin.net

BURNHAM MARKET
Norfolk
Burnham Hall ★★★★
Contact: Mrs Jane Shulver,
Norfolk Country Cousins, Point
House, Ridlington, North
Walsham, Norfolk NR28 9TY
T: (01692) 650286
F: (01692) 650180
E: norfolk.cousins@netcom.
co.uk
I: www.norfolk-cottages.co.uk

Foundry Barn ★★★★
Contact: Mr & Mrs P Benson,
Badgers Croft, Nottwood Lane,
Stoke Row, Henley-on-Thames,
Oxfordshire RG9 5PU
T: (01491) 681644
F: (01491) 681644

4 The Maltings ★★★★
Contact: Ms Anne Silverman,
131 Gilbert Road, Cambridge,
CB4 3PA
T: (01223) 364367 & 425168
F: (01223) 424826
E: info@bmcottage.fsnet.co.uk
I: www.bmcottage.fsnet.co.uk

3 The Maltings Cottages ★★
Contact: Mr & Mrs Poll,
Birkwood, Station Road,
Burnham Market, King's Lynn,
Norfolk PE31
T: (01328) 738840

Stable Cottage ★★★★
Contact: Mrs Anne Cringle,
Stable Cottage, The Old Black
Horse, Burnham Market, King's
Lynn, Norfolk PE31 8HD
T: (01328) 738456
E: pmcringle@aol.com

BURNHAM-ON-CROUCH
Essex
38 Petticrow Quays ★★★★
Contact: Mr Paul Ayling, 19
Maple Avenue, Leigh-on-Sea,
Essex SS9 1PR
T: (01702) 715144 &
0771 1231129
F: (01702) 714881

BURNHAM OVERY STAITHE
Norfolk
Dolphins ★★★
Contact: Mrs Camilla Warner,
The Cottage, Wendens Ambo,
Saffron Walden, Essex CB11 4JX
T: (01799) 540247
T: (01799) 542101
E: dolphins@wambo.co.uk

BURNHAM OVERY TOWN
Norfolk
Mill House Annexe ★★★
Contact: Mrs Anthea Moore Ede,
16 Victoria Grove, London
W8 5RW
T: (0207) 5848826 &
(01328) 730384
F: (0207) 5818694
E: antheamooreede@zoom.
co.uk

BURY ST EDMUNDS
Suffolk
Brook Villa ★★★
Contact: Mr David Manning,
Brook Villa, Rushbrooke Lane,
Bury St Edmunds, Suffolk
IP33 2RR
T: (01284) 764387

**The Court & The Granary
Suites** ★★-★★★★
Contact: Mrs Roberta Truin, The
Court & The Granary Suites,
Melford Road, Lawshall, Bury St
Edmunds, Suffolk IP29 4PX
T: (01284) 830385 &
07711 829546
F: (01284) 830385
E: brighthousefarm@supanet.
com
I: www.brighthousefarm.fsnet.
co.uk

Garden Corner ★★★★
Contact: Mr J D Stemp, Garden
Corner, 91a Kings Road, Bury St
Edmunds, Suffolk IP33 3DT
T: (01284) 702848

Kitchen Flat ★★★
Contact: Mrs Eileen Storey, 15 Northgate Street, Bury St Edmunds, Suffolk IP33 1HP
T: (01284) 755744
F: (01284) 755744

The Manse ★★★★★
Contact: Pat, Sturgeons Hall, The Green, Hartest, Bury St Edmunds, Suffolk IP29 4DH
T: (01284) 830690
F: (01284) 830228
E: gig_manning@lineone.net
I: www.themanse.uk.com

BUXTON
Norfolk

Birds Place Farm Kosy Cottage ★★★
Contact: Mr & Mrs W J Catchpole, Birds Place Farm, Back Lane, Buxton, Norwich NR10 5HD
T: (01603) 279585

BYLAUGH
Norfolk

Meadowview ★★★
Contact: Mrs Jenny Lake, Meadowview, Park Farm, Bylaugh, East Dereham, Norfolk NR20 4QE
T: (01362) 688584
E: lakeparkfm@aol.com

CALIFORNIA
Norfolk

Bella Vista ★★★★
Contact: Mr & Mrs N J Sampson, Beachside Holidays, Wakefield Court, Rottenstone Lane, California, Great Yarmouth, Norfolk NR29 3QT
T: (01493) 730279 &
07752 811572
F: (01493) 730279
E: beachside@fsbdial.co.uk
I: www.beachside-holidays.co.uk

CAMBRIDGE
Cambridgeshire

Brooklands Court ★★★★
Contact: Mr & Mrs Oliver Digney, 9a Cambridge Road, Great Shelford, Cambridge CB2 5JE
T: (01223) 841294
F: (01223) 841294
E: sdigney@clarencehouse.fsnet.co.uk
I: www.clarencehouse.org.uk

Clarence House ★★★★
Contact: Mr & Mrs Oliver Digney, 9a Cambridge Road, Great Shelford, Cambridge CB2 5JE
T: (01223) 841294
F: (01223) 841294
E: sdigney@clarence.house.fsnet.co.uk
I: ww.clarencehouse.org.uk

The Cottage ★★
Contact: Mrs S May, The Cottage, Lower Farm, Hadstock, Cambridge CB1 6PF
T: (01223) 891566

Glebe Cottage ★★
Contact: Mrs F M Key, Glebe Cottage, 44 Main Street, Hardwick, Cambridge CB3 7QS
T: (01954) 212895
E: fm.key@btinternet.com

Home From Home Apartments ★★★
Contact: Mrs E Fasano, Bungalow rear of, 78 Milton Road, Cambridge, CB4 1LA
T: (01223) 323555 &
07740 594306
F: (01223) 563509
E: homefromhome@tesco.net
I: www.smoothhound.co.uk/hotels/homefrom.html

Victoria Apartment ★★★★
Contact: Mrs Maria Fasano, Victoria, 57 Arbury Road, Cambridge, CB4 2JB
T: (01223) 350086 &
07803 906619
F: (01223) 350086
E: vicmaria@globalnet.co.uk
I: www.victoriaguesthouse.co.uk

CASTLE ACRE
Norfolk

Cherry Tree Cottage ★★★★
Contact: Mr & Mrs C J Boswell, Wellington House, Back Lane, Castle Acre, King's Lynn, Norfolk PE32 2AR
T: (01760) 755000
F: (01760) 755000
E: boswell@paston.co.uk

The Cottage
Rating Applied For
Contact: Mrs Jane Famous, 45 Hawthorn Avenue, Palmers Green, London N13 4JS
T: (020) 8442 3186 & 8886 0800
F: (020) 8442 3091
E: jfamous@staff.conel.ac.uk

Friars Croft ★★★
Contact: Mrs E McGrath, Hillside, Mill Road, Shipdham, Thetford, Norfolk IP25 7LU
T: (01362) 820408

Peddars Cottage ★★★
Contact: Mrs Angela Swindell, St Saviour's Rectory, St Saviour, Jersey, Channel Islands JE2 7NP
T: (01534) 727480 & 736679
F: (01534) 727480
E: jsyedu71@localdial.com

1 Sandles Court ★★
Contact: Mrs J B Wood, 9 Brancaster Way, Swaffham, Norfolk PE37 7RY
T: (01760) 722455 &
07930 892506
E: j.wood1@tinyonline.co.uk

CASTLE HEDINGHAM
Essex

Rosemary Farm ★★★-★★★★
Contact: Mr Garry Ian Henderson, Rosemary Farm, Rosemary Lane, Castle Hedingham, Halstead, Essex CO9 3AJ
T: (01787) 461653 & 370399

CASTOR
Cambridgeshire

The Wrens Nest ★★★
Contact: Mrs PJ Huckle, Cobnut Cottage, 45 Peterborough Road, Castor, Peterborough PE5 7AX
T: (01733) 380745
F: (01733) 380745
E: huckle.cobnut@talk21.com

CATFIELD
Norfolk

Double Dutch ★★★
Contact: Mrs Patricia Lovell, 29 Edgebury, Chislehurst, Kent BR7 6JL
T: (0208) 8578173

CAWSTON
Norfolk

Brandiston Barn Cottage ★★★
Contact: Holiday Cottages Ref: 3088, Holiday Cottages Group Owner Services Dept, Spring Mill, Earby, Barnoldswick, Lancashire BB18 6RN
T: (01282) 445444 &
07778 755168
F: (01282) 841539
E: sales@ttgohg.co.uk
I: www.country-holidays.co.uk

CHARSFIELD
Suffolk

Rosehill Cottage ★★★★
Contact: Ms Di Janus, 33 Freegrove Road, London N7 9JG
T: (0207) 6096610 & 6072133
F: (0207) 6871070
E: di@dijanus.freeserve.co.uk
I: www.suffolk-cottage.co.uk

CHEDGRAVE
Norfolk

Barn Owl Holidays ★★★
Contact: Mrs R Beattie, Barn Owl Holidays, Bryons Green, Big Back Lane, Chedgrave, Norwich NR14 6HB
T: (01508) 528786
F: (01508) 528698
E: rosemarybeatties@hotmail.com

CHELMONDISTON
Suffolk

Alma Cottage ★★★
Contact: Mr John Pugh, Culver End, Amberley, Stroud, Gloucestershire GL5 5AG
T: (01453) 872551
F: (01453) 843225
E: john.pugh@talk21.com

CHELMSFORD
Essex

Bury Barn Cottage ★★★★
Contact: Mr Richard Morris, Bury Barn Cottage, Bury Road, Pleshey, Chelmsford, Essex CM3 1HB
T: (01245) 237372 & 237372
F: (01245) 237327
E: rmorris@richardmorrisfurniture.com
I: www.richardmorrisfurniture.com

CLARE
Suffolk

Grannys Cottage ★★★★
Contact: Mrs Margaret Chapman, Eastcotts Farm, Calford Green, Sturmer, Haverhill, Suffolk CB9 7UN
T: (01440) 702897

CLEY NEXT THE SEA
Norfolk

Archway Cottage ★★★
Contact: Mrs V Jackson, 3A Brickendon Lane, Brickendon, Hertford SG13 8NU
T: (01992) 511303 & 503196
F: (01992) 511303

Dolphin Cottage ★★★
Contact: Mr & Mrs Ian Mashiter, 11 Branksome Close, Norwich, Norfolk NR4 6SP
T: (01603) 457560 &
07889 559181
E: nicola.mashiter@lineone.net

Thurn Cottage ★★★
Contact: Mr & Mrs Chris & Carol Smith, 15 South Hanningfield Way, Runwell, Wickford, Essex SS11 7DR
T: (01268) 769801 &
(01708) 722179
E: cjcksmith@btinternet.com

Tickers ★★★★
Contact: Mrs Nicola Arrowsmith-Brown, Forge Cottage, The Street, South Walsham, Norwich, Norfolk NR13 6DQ
T: (01603) 270457
E: arrows270@aol.com
I: www.cottageguide.co.uk/tickers

Woodbine Cottage
Rating Applied For
Contact: Mr & Mrs Fraser & Louise Wibberley, Old Town Hall House Coast Road, Cley next the Sea, Holt, Norfolk NR25 7RZ
T: (01263) 740284
I: www.oldtownhallhouse.co.uk

COCKFIELD
Suffolk

Old Hall Farm Stables ★★★
Contact: Mr & Mrs Jamieson, Old Hall Farm, Old Hall Lane, Cockfield, Bury St Edmunds, Suffolk IP30 0LQ
T: (01284) 827093
F: (01284) 827053

COLCHESTER
Essex

Castle Heights ★★★★
Contact: Mrs J Wright & Mrs J Egerton, Excelsis Rentals, 20 Wavell Avenue, Colchester, Essex CO2 7HR
T: (01206) 522661 & 504301
E: j.egerton@ntlworld.com

Castle Road Cottages ★★★★-★★★★
Contact: Mrs Patsie Ford, 19 High Street, Nayland, Colchester CO6 4JG
T: (01206) 262210
F: (01206) 262210

The Laurels ★★★★
Contact: Mrs M Morgan, 5 St Johns Close, Colchester, Essex CO4 4HP
T: (01206) 842646
F: (01206) 842646
E: morgan.landywood@tesco.net
I: w

Mundy ★★★
Contact: Mrs Jan Blackwell, Grebe House, The Crescent, West Bergholt, Colchester CO6 3DA
T: (01206) 240910

50 Rosebery Avenue ★★★
Contact: Mrs K Webb, 51 Rosebery Avenue, Colchester, Essex CO1 2UP
T: (01206) 866888
E: katowebb@ntlworld.com

Establishments printed in blue have a detailed entry in this guide

The Tea House ★★★★
Contact: Mr Nicholas
Charrington, Layer Marney
Tower, Layer Marney, Colchester
CO5 9US
T: (01206) 330784
F: (01206) 330784
E: nicholas@layermarney.
demon.co.uk
I: layermarneytower.com

COLKIRK
Norfolk

**Saddlery and Hillside Cottage
★★★**
Contact: Mrs Catherine Joice,
Colkirk Hall, Colkirk, Fakenham,
Norfolk NR21 7ND
T: (01328) 862261
F: (01328) 856464
E: charles.joice@btinternet.com

COOKLEY
Suffolk

Bucks Farm ★★★★
Contact: Mr J Bradshaw, Bucks
Farm, Cookley, Halesworth,
Suffolk IP19 0LX
T: (01986) 784216 &
(017771) 677294
F: (01986) 784216
E: jo@bucksfarm-holidays.co.uk
I: www.bucksfarm-holidays.
co.uk

COPDOCK
Suffolk

**The Briars & Mansard Cottage
★★★★**
Contact: Mrs R Steward, High
View, Back Lane, Washbrook,
Ipswich IP8 3JA
T: (01473) 730494
E: rosanna.steward@virgin.net

COTTON
Suffolk

Coda Cottages ★★★★
Contact: Mrs Kate Sida-Nicholls,
Coda Cottages, Poplar Farm,
Dandy Corner, Cotton,
Stowmarket, Suffolk IP14 4QX
T: (01449) 780076
F: (01449) 780280
E: codacottages@dandycorner.
co.uk

CRANMER
Norfolk

Home Farm ★★★★
Contact: Mrs Lynne & John
Johnson, Home Farm, Cranmer,
Fakenham, Norfolk NR21 9HY
T: (01328) 823135
E: bookings@
homefarmcranmer.co.uk
I: www.homefarmcranmer.co.uk

CRANWORTH
Norfolk

**The Old Gamebird Cottages
★★★★**
Contact: Mr & Mrs Lenk, The Old
Gamebird Cottages, The
Courtyard, Cranworth, Thetford,
Norfolk NR19 7TB
T: (01362) 820097
F: (01362) 821333
E: gamebird@azsualpacas.com

CRATFIELD
Suffolk

Cherry Trees ★★★
Contact: Mrs Chris Knox, Cherry
Trees, Cratfield Hall, Cratfield,
Halesworth, Suffolk IP19 0DR
T: (01379) 586709
F: (01349) 586709
E: j.l.knox@farming.co.uk

School Farm Cottages ★★★★
Contact: Mrs Claire Sillett,
School Farm, Cratfield,
Halesworth, Suffolk IP19 0BU
T: (01986) 798844
F: (01986) 798394
E: schoolfarmcotts@aol.com

CROMER
Norfolk

**61 & 150 Kings Chalet Park
★★**
Contact: Mr & Mrs Cole, 201
Roughton Road, Cromer, Norfolk
NR27 9LN
T: (01263) 513932
E: pmcole@talk21.com

All Stay-a-While ★–★★
Contact: Mr J Andrews,
Lausanne, 215 Holt Road,
Cromer, Norfolk NR27 9JN
T: (01263) 514505 & 512641

Avenue Holiday Flats ★★★
Contact: Mr John Bradley, Flat 1,
24 Cliff Avenue, Cromer, Norfolk
NR27 0AN
T: (01263) 513611
F: (01263) 515009

**Beverley House Holiday
Apartments ★–★★**
Contact: Mr & Mrs P R Day,
Beverley House Holiday
Apartments, 17 Alfred Road,
Cromer, Norfolk NR27 9AN
T: (01263) 512787
F: (01263) 512787

Cliff Hollow ★★
Contact: Miss L M Willins, Cliff
Haven, 35 Overstrand Road,
Cromer, Norfolk NR27 0AL
T: (01263) 512447
F: (01263) 512447

15 Clifton Park ★★★
Contact: Norfolk Country
Cottage, Carlton House, Market
Place, Reepham, Norwich
NR10 4JJ
T: (01603) 871872
F: (01603) 870304

Drift Barn Cottage ★★★
Contact: Mr T Payne, Drift
Cottage Farm, Felbrigg, Norwich
NR11 8PL
T: (01263) 513765

2 The Gangway ★★
Contact: Mrs B L Price,
Misterton, Kendal Avenue,
Epping, Essex CM16 4PN
T: (01992) 572672

**Greenwood Holiday Cottage
★★★**
Contact: Mrs J L Hemming, The
Lookout, 11 Cliff Drive, Cromer,
Norfolk NR27 0AW
T: (01263) 514139

The Grove ★★★
Contact: Mrs A Graveling, The
Grove, 95 Overstrand Road,
Cromer, Norfolk NR27 0DJ
T: (01263) 512412
F: (01263) 513416
E: thegrove@barclays.net
I: www.thegrovecromer.co.uk

Kings Chalet Park ★★
Contact: Mrs V Bateman,
Stenson, 32 Overstrand Road,
Cromer, Norfolk NR27 0AJ
T: (01263) 511308

Kings Chalet Park ★★
Contact: Mr & Mrs Horner-
Glister, 42 Springfield Close,
Burton-on-the-Wolds,
Loughborough, Leicestershire
LE12 5AN
T: (01509) 880032

110 King's Chalet Park ★★
Contact: Mrs I Scoltock,
Shangri-La, Little Cambridge,
Duton Hill, Dunmow, Essex
CM6 3QU
T: (01371) 870482

68 Kings Chalet Park ★★
Contact: Mrs J M Beck, The
Flintstones, 9 Salmons Way,
Fakenham, Norfolk NR21 8NG
T: (01328) 863947

**Northrepps Holiday Properties
★★–★★**
Contact: Mrs Gill Sargent,
Northrepps Holiday Properties,
Northrepps Hall, Cromer,
Norfolk NR27 0JW
T: (01263) 512236 & 513969
F: (01263) 515588
E: estate.office@gurney.co.uk

Shelly House ★★
Contact: Mr Steven Ballantyne,
5 Whites Row, Bishopsgate,
London E1 7NF
T: (020) 73750184
F: (020) 73750553
E: draxballantyne@aol.com

Suncourt Holiday Flats ★★
Contact: Mr & Mrs A R Hams,
The Officers House, Walcott
Road, Bacton, Norfolk NR12 0HB
T: (01692) 650022 &
07790 522229
E: suncourtflats@email.com

CROXLEY GREEN
Hertfordshire

22 Longmans Close ★★★★
Contact: Mr & Mrs Anthony
Barulis, 98 New Road, Croxley
Green, Rickmansworth,
Hertfordshire WD3 3EP
T: (01923) 775277

DALLINGHOO
Suffolk

Robins Nest ★★★★
Contact: Mr Robert Blake, 1a
Moorfield Road, Woodbridge,
Suffolk IP12 4JN
T: (01394) 382565 &
(01473) 736220
E: deben@btclick.com

DARSHAM
Suffolk

The Granary ★★★
Contact: Mrs S Bloomfield, The
Granary, Priory Farm, Darsham,
Saxmundham, Suffolk IP17 3QD
T: (01728) 668459

Rolletts Marsh ★★★
Contact: Mr & Mrs Richard &
Wendy Pither, Suffolk Secrets, 7
Frenze Road, Diss, IP22 4PA
T: (01379) 651297
F: (01379) 641555
E: holidays@suffolk-secrets.
co.uk
I: www.suffolk-secrets.co.uk

DENVER
Norfolk

Denver Windmill ★★★
Contact: Denver Windmill, Sluice
Road, Denver, Downham Market,
Norfolk PE38 0EG
T: (01366) 384009
F: (01366) 384009

**West Hall Farm Holidays and
Lakeside Fisheries★★★**
Contact: Mrs S J Riches-Florido,
West Hall Farm Holidays and
Lakeside Fisheries, West Hall
Farm, Sluice Road, Denver,
Downham Market, Norfolk
PE38 0DZ
T: (01366) 387074 & 383291
F: (01366) 387074
E: west_hall_farm_holidays@
yahoo.com
I: www.west-hall-farm-holidays.
co.uk

DERSINGHAM
Norfolk

Hillside ★★★
Contact: Mr Lindsay Harmer,
Hillside, Hawthorn Drive,
Dersingham, King's Lynn,
Norfolk PE31 6QQ
T: (01485) 544043 &
(01895) 676824
E: harmer@globalnet.co.uk

The Oaks Cottage ★★★★
Contact: Mr & Mrs Ben
Mullarkey, 46 Chapel Road,
Dersingham, King's Lynn,
Norfolk PE31 6PN
T: (01485) 540761
E: jb.mullarkey@eidosnet.co.uk
I: www.oakscottage.co.uk

The Old Forge ★★★★
Contact: Mr Webb & Ms Oakes, 4
Manor Road, Dersingham, King's
Lynn, Norfolk PE31 6LD
T: (01485) 544410
F: (01485) 544410
E: the.old.forge@talk21.com

DILHAM
Norfolk

Dairy Farm Cottages ★★★★
Contact: Mr & Mrs James &
Annabel Paterson, Rumford
Limited, Manor Farm, Dilham,
North Walsham, Norfolk
NR28 9PZ
T: (01692) 535178 & 536883
F: (01692) 536723
E: japdilman@farmline.com

DISS
Norfolk

Honey Bee Cottage ★★★
Contact: Mrs Rachel Davy,
Honey End, Upper Street,
Billingford, Diss, Norfolk
IP21 4HR
T: (01379) 741449
F: (01379) 741449
E: chrisjdavy@freenetname.
co.uk
I: www.honeybeecott.co.uk

541

Old Mill Farm ★★★
Contact: Mrs Pauline Ward, Old Mill Farm, Hopton Road, Garboldisham, Diss, Norfolk IP22 2RJ
T: (01953) 681350
F: (01953) 681752
I: www.oldmillfarm.co.uk

Shelfanger Hall ★★★
Contact: Mrs D Butler, Shelfanger Hall, Shelfanger, Diss IP22 2DE
T: (01379) 642094
🅰

Walcot Green Farm Cottage ★★★★
Contact: Mrs Nannette Catchpole, Walcot Green Farm, Diss, Norfolk IP22 5SU
T: (01379) 652806
F: (01379) 652806
E: n.catchpole.wgf@virgin.net
I: website.lineone.net/~walcotgreenfarm

DOCKING
Norfolk

Colbridge Cottage ★★
Contact: Country Hols Ref: 1392, Holiday Cottages Group, Spring Mill, Earby, Barnoldswick, Lancashire BB94 0AA
T: (01282) 445096
F: (01282) 844288
E: sales@ttgihg.co.uk
I: www.country-holidays.co.uk

Courtyard Cottage & Norfolk House★★★★★
Contact: Mr Alan Witley, Cherry Tree Cottage, 17 Peddars Way South, Ringstead, Hunstanton, Norfolk PE36 5LF
T: (01485) 525341 & 532543
F: (01485) 532715
E: holidays@witleypress.co.uk

Honeysuckle Cottage ★★★★
Contact: Miss Amanda Cox, The Lodge, White Road, Methwold, Thetford, Norfolk IP26 4PA
T: (01366) 727384

Mill House ★★★
Contact: Mr Harry Hammond, The Tutors House, G Social, Radley College, Abingdon, Oxfordshire

Muffin Cottage ★★★
Contact: Mrs Sandra Hohol, Norfolk Holiday Homes, 62 Westgate, Hunstanton, Norfolk PE36 5EL
T: (01485) 534267 & 534560
F: (01485) 535230
E: shohol@birdsnorfolkholidayhomes.co.uk
I: www.norfolkholidayhomes-birds.co.uk

1 Oddfellows Row ★★
Contact: Mrs Anne Smith, Folgate Farm, Folgate Road, Heacham, King's Lynn, Norfolk PE31 7BE
T: (01485) 572015

Paradise Cottage ★★★
Contact: Mrs Ann Firth, The Homestead, High Street, Docking, King's Lynn, Norfolk PE31 8NH
T: (01485) 518930
F: (01485) 518940
E: ranthony.firth@btinternet.com

Rose Cottage ★★★
Contact: Mrs Rick and Sue Tunnard, Keepers Cottage, Little Lane, Docking, King's Lynn, Norfolk PE31 8NT
T: (01485) 518000

DUDDENHOE END
Essex

Cosh Cottage ★★★★
Contact: Mrs D R Perks, The Cosh, Duddenhoe End, Saffron Walden, Essex CB11 4UX
T: (01763) 838880 & 07767 886637
E: susan.perks@virgin.net

DUNWICH
Suffolk

Cliff House Holiday Park ★★★
Contact: Mr Hay & Mr S Johnson, Cliff House (Dunwich), Minsmere Road, Dunwich, Saxmundham, Suffolk IP17 3DQ
T: (01728) 648282
E: enquiries@cliffhouseholidays.co.uk
I: www.cliffhouseholidays.co.uk

Tinkers Cottage ★★
Contact: Mr & Mrs Richard Pither, Suffolk Secrets, 7 Frenze Road, Diss, IP22 4PA
T: (01379) 641297
F: (01379) 641555
E: holidays@suffolk-secrets.co.uk
I: www.suffolk-secrets.co.uk

EAST BERGHOLT
Suffolk

Woodstock Wing ★★★
Contact: Mr & Mrs Keith & Janet Alcoe, Woodstock Wing, Woodstock, Gaston Street, East Bergholt, Colchester CO7 6SD
T: (01206) 298724

EAST HARLING
Norfolk

Berwick Cottage ★★★
Contact: Mr W G Tickner, 25 Webbscroft Road, Dagenham, Essex RM10 7NL
T: (020) 8595 7056
♿

Dolphin Lodge ★★★★
Contact: Mrs E Jolly, Dolphin Lodge, Roudham Farm, East Harling, Norwich NR16 2RJ
T: (01953) 717126
F: (01953) 718593
E: jolly@roudhamfarm.co.uk
I: www.farmstayanglia.co.uk

EAST RAYNHAM
Norfolk

Blossom Cottages ★★
Contact: Mrs Susan Panter, Clebar, Colkirk Road, East Raynham, Fakenham, Norfolk NR21 7EJ
T: (01328) 855118
F: (01328) 855118
E: susan@clebar.freeserve.co.uk

EAST RUDHAM
Norfolk

Rose Cottage Annex ★★
Contact: Mrs E M Mawby, Rose Cottage, Bagthorpe Road, East Rudham, King's Lynn, Norfolk PE31 8RA
T: (01485) 528274

EAST RUNTON
Norfolk

Mallards Rest ★★★
Contact: Mrs Nicola Thompson, Mallards Rest, Ravenna, Lower Common, East Runton, Cromer, Norfolk NR27 9PG
T: (01263) 512496

Poplars Caravan and Chalet Park ★★-★★★
Contact: Mr & Mrs K Parfitt, Poplars Caravan and Chalet Park, Brick Lane, East Runton, Cromer, Norfolk NR27 9PL
T: (01263) 512892

EDGEFIELD
Norfolk

Flintstones ★★★
Contact: Holiday Cottages Ref: 10881, Holiday Cottages Group Owner Services Dept, Spring Mill, Earby, Barnoldswick, Lancashire BB18 6RN
T: (01282) 445096
F: (01282) 844288
E: sales@ttgihg.co.uk
I: www.country-holidays.co.uk

ELMSTEAD MARKET
Essex

Birds Farm ★★★-★★★★
Contact: Mrs Joanna Burke, Birds Farm, Elmstead Market, Colchester CO7 7EY
T: (01206) 823838

ELMSWELL
Suffolk

Kiln Farm ★★★
Contact: Mrs Susan Knights, Kiln Farm, Kiln Lane, Elmswell, Bury St Edmunds, Suffolk IP30 9QR
T: (01359) 240442 & 242604
E: barry-sue@kilnfarm.fsnet.co.uk

Oak Farm ★★★★★
Contact: Mr & Mrs D Dyball, Willow Farm, Ashfield Road, Elmswell, Bury St Edmunds, Suffolk IP30 9HG
T: (01359) 240263
F: (01359) 240263

ELSWORTH
Cambridgeshire

Meadow Farm Cottage ★★★★
Contact: Mr & Mrs A Taylor, Meadow Farm, Broad End, Elsworth, Cambridge CB3 8JD
T: (01954) 268042
F: (01954) 268044

ELY
Cambridgeshire

Hill House Farm Cottage ★★★★
Contact: Mrs H E Nix, Hill House Farm Cottage, 9 Main Street, Coveney, Ely, Cambridgeshire CB6 2DJ
T: (01353) 778369
E: hill_house@madasafish.com

ERISWELL
Suffolk

Church Cottage ★★★★★
Contact: Ms Yoland Goode, Elveden Farms Ltd, Estate Office, Elveden, Thetford, Norfolk I
T: (01638) 533318
E: elveden@farmline.com

Cranhouse ★★★★★
Contact: Ms Yoland Goode, Elveden Farms Ltd, Estate Office, Elveden, Thetford, Norfolk I
T: (01638) 533318
E: elveden@farmline.com

ERPINGHAM
Norfolk

Grange Farm ★★★
Contact: Mrs Jane Bell, The Grange, Erpingham, Norwich, Norfolk NR11 7QX
T: (01263) 761241
F: (01263) 761241
E: jane@bellkitchen.freeserve.co.uk
I: www.grangefarmholidays.fsnet.co.uk

Keepers Cottage ★★★
Contact: Mrs M D Daniels, Woodbine Cottage, Blacksmith Lane, Erpingham, Norwich, Norfolk NR11 7QF
T: (01263) 761724

EYE
Suffolk

Manor House Cottages ★★★-★★★★
Contact: Mr David Mason, Manor House Cottages, Yaxley Manor House, Mellis Road, Yaxley, Eye, Suffolk IP23 8DG
T: (01379) 788181 & 07860 797874
F: (01379) 788422
E: david@dmenterprises.demon.co.uk
I: www.manorhousecottages.co.uk

FAKENHAM
Norfolk

Manor Farm ★★★★
Contact: Mr Abram, Manor Farm, Oxwick, Fakenham, Norfolk NR21 7HZ
T: (01328) 700300
F: (01328) 700755

The Paddocks ★★★★
Contact: Mrs & Mr Tessa & Tony Gent, The Paddocks, Little Barney, Fakenham, Norfolk NR21 0NL
T: (01328) 878803
F: (01328) 878802

Rosings Cottage ★★★
Contact: Mrs Denise Perchard, 23 Kingsbury Avenue, St Albans, Hertfordshire AL3 4TA
T: (01727) 843227 & 856527
F: (01727) 843193
E: perchards@aol.com

Stables Cottage and Oxford Barn ★★★
Contact: Mr & Mrs J Matthews, The Greyhound, West Raynham, Fakenham, Norfolk NR21 7EZ
T: (01328) 838509
F: (01328) 838814
E: greyhound@cottage84.freeserve.co.uk

Establishments printed in blue have a detailed entry in this guide

Vere Lodge ★★★–★★★★
Contact: Mrs Bowlby, Vere Lodge, South Raynham, Fakenham, Norfolk NR21 7HE
T: (01328) 838261 & 838262
F: (01328) 838300
E: major@verelodge.fsnet.co.uk

FELIXSTOWE
Suffolk

Fairlight Detached Bungalow ★★★
Contact: Mrs D Knights, Priory View, 127 High Road East, Old Felixstowe, Felixstowe, Suffolk IP11 9PS
T: (01394) 277730

Flat 2 ★★★
Contact: Mrs Gwen Lynch, Cedar House, 20 The Close, Tattingstone, Ipswich, Suffolk IP9 2PD
T: (01473) 328729

Honeypot Cottage ★★★
Contact: Mrs Theresa Adams, Deben Lodge, Falkenham, Ipswich, Suffolk IP10 0RA
T: (01394) 448564
F: (01394) 448564
E: adams99@talk21.com

Kimberley Holiday Flats ★★
Contact: Mrs Valerie Reed, Kimberley Holiday Flats, 105-107 Undercliff Road, Felixstowe, Suffolk IP11 2AF
T: (01394) 672157

Sea View Holiday Flat ★★★★
Contact: Mrs S Brady, 50 St Georges Road, Felixstowe, Suffolk IP11 9PN
T: (01394) 274231
E: suembrady@talk21.com

30A Undercliff Road West ★★
Contact: Mrs Doris Bloomfield, 30 Undercliff Road West, Felixstowe, Suffolk IP11 2AJ
T: (01394) 284749

FIELD DALLING
Norfolk

Oak Barn ★★★★
Contact: Mrs Angela Harcourt, Hard Farm House, Little Marsh Lane, Field Dalling, Holt, Norfolk NR25 7LL
T: (01328) 830655
F: (01328) 830257
E: harcog@farming.co.uk

FILBY
Norfolk

Wychwood ★★★
Contact: Norfolk Country Cottages, Carlton House, Market Place, Reepham, Norwich, Norfolk NR10 4JJ
T: (01603) 871872
F: (01603) 870304
E: cottages@paston.co.uk
I: www.norfolkcottages.co.uk

FOXLEY
Norfolk

Moor Farm Stable Cottages ★★–★★★
Contact: Mr P Davis, Moor Farm, Foxley, Dereham, Norfolk NR20 4QN
T: (01362) 688523
F: (01362) 688523
E: moorfarm@aol.com

FRAMLINGHAM
Suffolk

Boundary Farm ★★★
Contact: Mrs Susan Seabrook, Boundary Farm, Saxtead Road, Framlingham, Woodbridge, Suffolk IP13 9PZ
T: (01728) 621026

Wood Lodge ★★★
Contact: Mr Tim Kindred, Wood Lodge, High House Farm, Cransford, Woodbridge, Suffolk IP13 9PD
T: (01728) 663461
F: (01728) 663409
E: kindred@highhousefarm.co.uk

FRESSINGFIELD
Suffolk

Mount Pleasant ★★★
Contact: Mr T Eastoe, Mount Pleasant, New Street, Fressingfield, Eye, Suffolk IP21 5PG
T: (01379) 588258

FRINTON-ON-SEA
Essex

Quartette ★★★
Contact: Mr Robert Bucke, 73 Connaught Avenue, Frinton-on-Sea, Essex CO13 9PP
T: 07010 716013
F: 0870 765 3746
E: ipsw@btinternet.com
I: www.ipsw.btinternet.co.uk/quartette.htm

GARBOLDISHAM
Norfolk

Burnside ★★★★
Contact: Mrs Connie Atkins, Burnside, Alderwood, Hopton Road, Garboldisham, Diss, Norfolk IP22 2RQ
T: (01953) 688376
F: (01953) 681743
E: douconatkins@waitrose.com

Squirrels at Ingleneuk Lodge ★★★
Contact: Mrs Jean Stone, Ingleneuk Lodge, Hopton Road, Garboldisham, Diss, Norfolk IP22 2RQ
T: (01953) 681541
F: (01953) 681138
E: ingleneuk.lodge@virgin.net

GATELEY
Norfolk

Honeysuckle Cottage ★★★
Contact: Mr & Mrs Colin Gatenby, 38 Wheeler Avenue, Oxted, Surrey RH8 9LE
T: (01883) 714113
E: colin@jazzfans.co.uk

GAYTON
Norfolk

Field View ★★★
Contact: Mr & Mrs S Watkinson, St Winifreds, Lynn Road, Gayton, King's Lynn, Norfolk PE32 1QJ
T: (01553) 636629
F: (01553) 636629
E: fieldviewcottage@hotmail.com

Willow Cottage ★★★
Contact: Mr Michael Pooley, West Hall Farm, Winch Road, Gayton, King's Lynn, Norfolk PE32 1QP
T: (01553) 636519
F: (01553) 636519
E: mike@westhallfarm.co.uk
I: www.westhallfarm.co.uk

GOLDHANGER
Essex

Vaulty Manor ★★–★★★
Contact: Ms T Ward, Vaulty Manor, Goldhanger Road, Goldhanger, Essex CM9 8BQ
T: (01621) 855628

GORLESTON-ON-SEA
Norfolk

Avondale Road
Rating Applied For
Contact: Mr Paul Martin, Flat 10, 150 Randolph Avenue, Maida Vale, London W9 1PG
T: (020) 72861644 & 07930 533929
E: paulm@evanston22.freeserve.co.uk

GREAT DUNMOW
Essex

The Granary ★★★★
Contact: Mr & Mrs J P Burton, The Granary, Moor End Farm, Broxted, Dunmow, Essex CM6 2EL
T: (01371) 870821 & 870821
I: www.moorendfarm.com

Old Piggeries ★★★
Contact: Mr J Kirby, Old Piggeries, Grange Farm, Little Dunmow, Dunmow, Essex CM6 3HY
T: (01371) 820205
F: (01377) 820205

GREAT FRANSHAM
Norfolk

The Dog House ★★★★
Contact: Mr B Williams, Kennels Farm, Station Road, Great Fransham, East Dereham, Norfolk NR19 2JB
T: (01362) 687315
E: frances@kennelsfarm.freeserve.co.uk

GREAT HOCKHAM
Norfolk

Old School Cottage ★★★★
Contact: Mr & Mrs Colin & Karin Titley, Beechwood House, Wretham Road, Great Hockham, Thetford, Norfolk IP24 1NY
T: (01953) 498277

GREAT MASSINGHAM
Norfolk

Primrose Cottage ★★★
Contact: Mrs C A Riches, 21 Weasenham Road, Great Massingham, King's Lynn, Norfolk PE32 2EY
T: (01485) 520216

GREAT PLUMSTEAD
Norfolk

Windfalls ★★★
Contact: Mrs Jane Jones, Hall Farm, Middle Road, Great Plumstead, Norwich, Norfolk NR13 5EF
T: (01603) 720235 & 07801 689144
F: (01603) 722008
E: hall.farm@brinternet.com

GREAT SNORING
Norfolk

Home Cottage ★★★
Contact: Mr A Rivett, Windmill Farm, Wood Norton, East Dereham, Norfolk NR20 5BN
T: (01263) 860462 & 07778 819965

Rose Cottage ★★★★
Contact: Mrs Gilly Paramor, 4 Hall Farm Cottages, Pedlars Lane, Fulmodestone, Fakenham, Norfolk NR21 0NH
T: (01328) 878867 & 07990 661383
F: (01328) 878867
E: gilly@gparamor.freeserve.co.uk
I: www.clevencycottages.freeserve.co.uk

Valentine Cottage ★★★★
Contact: Ms Susie Dormer, 5 Westgate Street, Blakeney, Holt, Norfolk NR25 7NQ
T: (01263) 741777
F: (01263) 741666
E: ccottages@dialstart.net

GREAT WIGBOROUGH
Essex

Honeysuckle Cottage ★★★★
Contact: Mr K M Benner, Mistletoe Cottage, Great Wigborough, Colchester CO5 7RH
T: (01206) 735282

GREAT YARMOUTH
Norfolk

Kenwood Holiday Flats
Rating Applied For
Contact: Mr D J Allen, 31 Crosstead, Great Yarmouth, Norfolk NR30 4AP
T: (01493) 852740

GRESHAM
Norfolk

Astalot and Avalon Cottages ★★
Contact: Mrs J J Murray, Mariners Hard High Street, Cley, Holt, Norfolk NR25 7RX
T: (01263) 740404 & 740801
F: (01263) 740404

The Little Place ★★
Contact: Mr & Mrs Paul Hill, Loke End Cottage, The Loke, Gresham, Norwich NR11 8RJ
T: (01263) 577344

Threeways ★★★
Contact: Mrs Joan Munday, Keys Holidays, Keys Estate Agents, 18 Station Road, Sheringham, Norfolk NR26 8RE
T: (01263) 823010
F: (01263) 821449
E: info@keys-holidays.co.uk
I: www.keys-holidays.co.uk

HADLEIGH
Suffolk

Chip Cottage ★★★★★
Contact: Mrs Sheila Jenkins, 21 Nodens Way, Lydney, Gloucestershire GL15 5NP
T: (01594) 841371
E: chipcottage@btinternet.com

Stable Cottages ★★★★
Contact: Mrs Margaret Langton,
Stable Cottages, The Granary,
Chattisham Place, Chattisham,
Ipswich IP8 3QD
T: (01473) 652210
F: (01473) 652210
E: margaret.langton@talk21.
com
I: www.farmstayanglia.
co.uk/chattisham

Sulleys Manor Farm Cottages
★★★
Contact: Mr John Reid, Sulleys
Manor Farm, Lower Raydon,
Ipswich, Suffolk IP7 5QQ
T: (01473) 310718 & 828150
F: (01473) 828150

HAINFORD
Norfolk

Four Sticks ★★★
Contact:, Norfolk Country
Cousins, Point House,
Ridlington, North Walsham,
Norfolk NR28 9TY
T: (01692) 650286
F: (01692) 650180
E: norfolk.cousins@netcom.
co.uk
I: www.norfolk-cottages.co.uk

HALSTEAD
Essex

The Coach House ★★★★
Contact: Mr & Mrs K Bradley,
The Coach House, White House,
High Street, Halstead, Essex
CO9 2AP
T: (01787) 476641 &
07703 894047
F: (01787) 476641

Gainsford Hall ★★★★
Contact: Mr Chris Barnard & Ms
Archer, Houghtons Farm,
Gainsford End, Toppesfield,
Halstead, Essex CO9 4EH
T: (01787) 237334

HAPPISBURGH
Norfolk

3 Grubb Street Cottages
★★★★
Contact: Holiday Cottages Ref:
3762, Holiday Cottages Group
Owner Services Dept, Spring
Mill, Earby, Barnoldswick,
Lancashire BB18 6RN
T: (01282) 445444
F: (01282) 841539
E: sales@ttgihg.co.uk
I: wwwcountry-holiday.co.uk

HARLESTON
Norfolk

Hall Farm Cottage ★★★
Contact: Mr John Sanderson,
South Elmham Hall, St Cross,
Harleston, Norfolk IP20 0PZ
T: (01986) 782526 &
07958 798298
F: (01986) 782203
E: enquiries@southelmham.
co.uk
I: www.southelmham.co.uk

HARPLEY
Norfolk

Rosedene ★★★★
Contact: Mr Roger Osborne,
Duryard, 22 Westgate Green,
Hevingham, Norwich, Norfolk
NR10 5RF
T: (01603) 754349
F: 0870 1383280
E: rogero@pobox.com
I: www.pobox.com/~rogero

HARROLD
Bedfordshire

Ouse View ★★★
Contact: Mrs R Northern, The
Priory, Priory Farm, High Street,
Harrold, Bedford MK43 7EE
T: (01234) 720293
F: (01234) 720292
E: ros.northern@farmline.com

Priory Farm Chalet ★★
Contact: Mrs R Northern, The
Priory, Priory Farm, High Street,
Harrold, Bedford MK43 7EE
T: (01234) 720293
F: (01234) 720292
E: ros.northern@farmline.com

HARTEST
Suffolk

Crown Cottage ★★★
Contact: Holiday Cottages Ref:
10981, Holiday Cottages Group
Owner Services Dept, Spring
Mill, Earby, Barnoldswick,
Lancashire BB18 6RN
T: (01282) 445444
F: (01282) 841539
E: sales@ttgihg.co.uk
I: www.country-holidays.co.uk

HAUGHLEY
Suffolk

The Cottage ★★★
Contact: Mrs Mary Noy, Red
House Farm, Station Road,
Haughley, Stowmarket, Suffolk
IP14 3QP
T: (01449) 673323
F: (01449) 675413

HAVERHILL
Suffolk

Windswept ★★★
Contact: Mrs J R Notley, The
Chestnuts, Withersfield,
Haverhill, Suffolk CB9 7RY
T: (01440) 704582
F: (01440) 704582
E: jane@ikidunot.freeserve.
co.uk
I: www.geocities.
com/thetropics/core/2353

HAWSTEAD
Suffolk

The Old Stables ★★★★
Contact: Mrs Lesley Carey,
Church Farm House, Hawstead,
Bury St Edmunds, Suffolk
IP29 5NT
T: (01284) 386132
F: (01284) 386134
E: theoldstables@aol.com

HEACHAM
Norfolk

Cedar Springs ★★-★★★
Contact: Mrs A Howe, Owl
Lodge, Jubilee Road, Heacham,
King's Lynn, Norfolk PE31 7AR
T: (01485) 570609

Cedar Springs Chalets ★
Contact: Mr & Mrs Michael
Chestney, 35 West Raynham,
Fakenham, Norfolk NR21 7EY
T: (01328) 838341

**Cheney Hollow Guest Cottage
& Cheney Hollow Garden
Cottage**★★★-★★★★
Contact: Mrs Thelma Holland,
Cheney Hollow, 3-5 Cheney Hill,
Heacham, King's Lynn, Norfolk
PE31 7BX
T: (01485) 572625 &
07767 796410
F: (01485) 572625
E: thelma@cheneyhollow.co.uk
I: www.cheneyhollow.co.uk

11 The Drift ★★★★
Contact: Mrs Rachel Holliday, 15
Wilson Drive, East Winch, King's
Lynn, Norfolk PE32 1NX
T: (01553) 842134

Holly Cottage ★★★
Contact: Mrs n O'Callaghan, The
Hermitage, Wilton Road,
Heacham, King's Lynn, Norfolk
PE31 7AD
T: (01485) 571838
F: (01485) 571838

The Lookout ★★
Contact: Mrs Sandra Hohol,
Norfolk Holiday Homes, 62
Westgate, Hunstanton, Norfolk
PE36 5EL
T: (01485) 534267 & 534560
F: (01485) 535230
E: shohol@
birdsnorfolkholidayhomes.co.uk
I: www.
norfolkholidayhomes-birds.
co.uk

Manor Farm Cottage ★★★
Contact: Mrs C Wallace, Manor
Farm, Heacham, King's Lynn,
Norfolk PE31 7JX
T: (01485) 570567 &
07974 406221
F: (01485) 570567
E: carolewallace@talk21.com

3 New Row ★★★
Contact: Holiday Cottages Ref:
30264, Holiday Cottages Group
Owner Services Dept, Spring
Mill, Earby, Barnoldswick,
Lancashire BB18 6RN
T: (01282) 445096
F: (01282) 844288
E: sales@ttgihg.co.uk
I: www.country-holidays.co.uk

**The Old Station Waiting
Rooms** ★★★
Contact: Mr & Mrs Clay, The Old
Station Waiting Rooms, 97
Station Road, Heacham, King's
Lynn, Norfolk PE31 7AW
T: (01485) 570712
E: clay@oldstation.fsnet.co.uk

Painters Corner ★★★★
Contact: Mrs N J O'Callaghan,
The Hermitage, 2 Wilton Road,
Heacham, King's Lynn, Norfolk
PE31 7AD
T: (01485) 571838
F: (01485) 571838
E: sunnymeadholpark@aol.com
I: www.sunnymead-holidays.
co.uk

4 Pretoria Cottages ★★★
Contact: Mrs H Barnes, 58 High
Drive, New Malden, Surrey
KT3 3UB
T: (020) 8942 6675 &
(01376) 331645

2 Retreat Cottage ★★
Contact: Mrs I J Rooth, 32
Church Green, Hunstanton
Road, Heacham, King's Lynn,
Norfolk PE31 7HH
T: (01485) 572072 & 571438
E: clare@clarerooth.demon.
co.uk

Robin Hill ★★
Contact: Mrs D M Gidney, Robin
Hill, Hunstanton Road,
Heacham, King's Lynn, Norfolk
PE31 7JX
T: (01485) 570309

The Roost & The Hayloft ★★★
Contact: Mrs n O'Callaghan, The
Hermitage, Wilton Road,
Heacham, King's Lynn, Norfolk
PE31 7AD
T: (01485) 571838
F: (01485) 571838

Tawny Cottage ★★★★
Contact: Ms Irene Alexander,
Norfolk Country Cottages,
Carlton House, Market Place,
Reepham, Norwich NR10 4JJ
T: (01603) 871872
F: (01603) 870304
E: cottages@paston.co.uk

Turret House ★★★★
Contact: Mrs Laurice Jarman,
The Great Escape Holiday
Company Limited, The Granary,
Station Road, Docking, King's
Lynn, Norfolk PE31 8LY
T: (01485) 518717
F: (01485) 518937
E: holidays@greatescapes.
demon.co.uk

HEMPTON
Norfolk

Claire's Cottage ★★★
Contact: Mr Trevor Land,
Beechwood, 9 Station Road,
Digswell, Welwyn, Hertfordshire
AL6 0DU
T: (01438) 715166
F: (01438) 712372
E: trevor.land@btinternet.com

HESSETT
Suffolk

Wilwyn & Chapel Cottages
★★★
Contact: Mr & Mrs Chris & Nicky
Glass, Alwyd Cottage, The Street,
Hessett, Suffolk IP30 9AZ
T: (01359) 270736 &
07860 352739
F: (01359) 270736
E: chrisglass@hessettgrain.
co.uk
I: www.cottageguide.
co.uk/hessett

HICKLING
Norfolk

Old Chapel Cottage ★★★
Contact: Mrs C Brown,
Hollingbery, Guilt Cross,
Kenninghall, Norwich NR16 2LJ
T: (01953) 681314
F: (01953) 681681

Establishments printed in blue have a detailed entry in this guide

HIGH KELLING
Norfolk
The Annexe ★★★
Contact: Mrs Joan Munday, Keys Holidays, 18 Station Road, Sheringham, Norfolk NR26 8RE
T: (01263) 823010
F: (01263) 821449
E: info@keys-holidays.co.uk
I: www.keys-holidays.co.uk

HILLINGTON
Norfolk
The Old Rectory ★★-★★★
Contact: Mrs Sarah & Christopher Thompsett, The Old Rectory, Station Road, Hillington, King's Lynn, Norfolk PE31 6DE
T: (01485) 600177

HINDOLVESTON
Norfolk
Lavender Cottage ★★★★
Contact: Ms Jacqui Rose & Mr Phillip Archer, Thatches, Nedging Road, Nedging Tye, Ipswich, Suffolk IP7 7HL
T: (01449) 741396 & (0207) 2147047
E: philarcher_uk@yahoo.co.uk

Pine Cottage ★★★
Contact: Mr & Mrs Scammell, 61 Ladbrooke Drive, Potters Bar, Hertfordshire EN6 1QW
T: (0207) 493 6151 & (01707) 651734

HINGHAM
Norfolk
The Granary ★★★★
Contact: Mrs C Dunnett, College Farm, Hingham, Norwich NR9 4PP
T: (01953) 850596
F: (01953) 851364
E: christine.dunnett@lineone.net

Pearce's Farmhouse ★★★
Contact: Mrs Judy Watson, Sea Mere, Hingham, Norwich, Norfolk NR9 4LP
T: (01953) 850217
F: (01953) 851628
E: judywatson@compuserve.com

HITCHAM
Suffolk
The Bakery, Lily Cottage and Franz Cottage★★-★★★
Contact: Ms Melanie Rieger, The Bakery, Lily Cottage and Franz Cottage, c/o Mill House, Water Run, Hitcham, Ipswich, Suffolk IP7 7LN
T: (01449) 740315 & 07767 304762
F: (01449) 740315
E: hitcham@aol.com
I: millhouse-hitcham.co.uk

HOCKWOLD
Norfolk
Lilac Barns ★★★★
Contact: Hoseasons Country Cottages, Sunway House, Lowestoft, Suffolk NR32 2LW
T: (01502) 501515
I: www.hoseasons.co.uk

HOLLESLEY
Suffolk
The Sandlings Centre
Rating Applied For
Contact: Mr M J Adams, The Sandlings Centre, Lodge Road, Hollesley, Woodbridge, Suffolk IP12 3RR
T: (01394) 411422
F: (01394) 411422
E: mja@sandlings.co.uk
I: www.sandlings.co.uk

HOLME NEXT THE SEA
Norfolk
9 Barnwell Cottages ★★★
Contact: Mrs S Sadler, 7 Malthouse Court, Green Lane, Thornham, Hunstanton, Norfolk PE36 6NW
T: (01485) 512085
F: (01485) 512085

Beach Cottage ★★★★
Contact: Mrs S Jones, Beach House, Beach Road, Holme next the Sea, Hunstanton, Norfolk PE36 6LG
T: (01485) 525201
E: robertjones@samphire1.demon.co.uk

Brook Bungalow ★★★
Contact: Mrs J A Whitsed, 8 Holme Close, Ailsworth, Peterborough PE5 7AQ
T: (01733) 380028
F: (01733) 380028
E: john@jwhitsed.freeserve.co.uk
I: www.cottageguide.co.uk

Eastgate Barn ★★★
Contact: Mrs S Simeone, Eastgate Barn, Eastgate Road, Holme next the Sea, Hunstanton, Norfolk PE36 6LL
T: (01485) 525218

Rose Cottage ★★★★
Contact: Mrs Stephanie Hedge, 34 Rampton Road, Cottenham, Cambridge, Cambridgeshire CB4 8LK
T: (01954) 250470 & 07790 336263
F: (01954) 250667

Sunnymead Corner ★★★-★★★★
Contact: Mrs Nicola O'Callaghan, The Hermitage, Wilton Road, Heacham, King's Lynn, Norfolk PE31 7AD
T: (01485) 571838
E: mail@sunnymead-holidays.co.uk
I: www.sunnymead-holidays.co.uk

Swift Cottage ★★★
Contact: Mr R G Simmonds, Oundle Cottage Breaks, 30 Market Place, Oundle, Peterborough PE8 4BE
T: (01832) 273531
F: (01832) 274938
E: richard@simmondsatoundle.co.uk
I: www.oundlecottagebreaks.co.uk

Whitegates ★★★★
Contact: Mr & Mrs K Felgate, 51 Kirkgate Street, Holme next the Sea, Hunstanton, Norfolk PE36 6LH
T: (01485) 525556
E: kevin.felgate@talk21.com

Wissens Cottage
Rating Applied For
Contact: Mr & Mrs Kevin & Caroline Felgate, Wissens Cottage, 57 Kirkgate Street, Holme next the Sea, Hunstanton, Norfolk PE36 6LH
T: (01485) 525556
E: kevin.felgate@talk21.uk

HOLT
Norfolk
17 Albert Street
Rating Applied For
Contact: Mrs Helen North, Eldon House, Eldon Lane, Braishfield, Romsey, Hampshire SO51 0PT
T: (01794) 368864

Brock Cottage ★★★★
Contact: Mrs Laurice Jarman, The Great Escape Holiday Company Limited, The Granary, Station Road, Docking, King's Lynn, Norfolk PE31 8LY
T: (01485) 518717
F: (01485) 518937
E: holidays@greatescapes.demon.co.uk

6 Carpenters Cottage ★★★
Contact: Mrs S M Beament, Higher Moorlake, Moorlake Cross, Crediton, Devon EX17 5EL
T: (01363) 773789
E: justinbeament@beeb.net

Cherry Tree Cottage ★★★
Contact: Mrs Judy Everitt, Wheelcroft, Field Dalling Road, Bale, Fakenham, Norfolk NR21 0QS
T: (01328) 878419

1 Crowlands Cottage ★★★
Contact: Mrs Julie Pell, 11 Birch Grove, Spalding, Lincolnshire PE11 2HL
T: (01775) 725126
F: (01775) 725126
E: julie.pell@talk21.com

Half-Acre ★★
Contact: Mrs Joan Munday, Keys Holidays, 18 Station Road, Sheringham, Norfolk NR26 8RE
T: (01263) 823010
F: (01263) 821449
E: info@keys-holidays.co.uk
I: www.keys-holidays.co.uk

Hidden Talents
Rating Applied For
Contact: Mr & Mrs Barker, The Anchor, 19 Quay Street, Woodbridge, Suffolk IP12 1BX
T: (01394) 582649 & 610212
F: (01394) 610212

Honeysuckle Cottage ★★★
Contact: Miss E I Allison, Orchard House, Withers Close, Holt, Norfolk NR25 6NH
T: (01263) 712457

Mansall House ★★
Contact: Mrs Joan Munday, Keys Holidays, 18 station Road, Sheringham, Norfolk NR26 8RE
T: (01263) 823010
F: (01263) 821449
E: info@keys-holidays.co.uk
I: www.keys-holidays.co.uk

Sunnyside Cottage ★★★
Contact: Mr Michael Drake, Broadland House, Station New Road, Brundall, Norwich NR13 5PQ
T: (01603) 712524
F: (01603) 712524
E: michael.drake@ukgateway.net

Wood Farm Cottages ★★★-★★★★
Contact: Mrs Diana Elsby, Wood Farm Cottages, Wood Farm, Plumstead Road, Edgefield, Melton Constable, Norfolk NR24 2AQ
T: (01263) 587347
F: (01263) 587347
E: info@wood-farm.com
I: www.wood-farm.com
🐾

HORHAM
Suffolk
Alpha Cottages ★★★
Contact: Mr & Mrs Brian Cooper, Lodge Farm, The Street, Horham, Eye, Suffolk IP21 5DX
T: (01379) 384424
F: (01379) 384424
♿

HORNING
Norfolk
Bure House ★★★★
Contact: Norfolk Country Cottages, Carlton House, Market Place, Reepham, Norwich, Norfolk NR10 4JJ
T: (01603) 871872
F: (01603) 870304
E: cottages@paston.co.uk
I: www.norfolkcottages.co.uk

Hall Farm Cottages ★★★★
Contact: Mrs & Mr Linda & Ivor Hudson, Hall Farm Cottages, Hall Farm, Horning, Norwich, Norfolk NR12 8NJ
T: (01692) 630385 & 07050 101746
F: (01692) 630385
E: cottages@hallfarm.com
I: www.hallfarm.com
♿

Horning Lodges 1,2,3, Kates & Lady Lodge & Eagle Cottage ★★★
Contact: Mr Robert King, King Line Cottages, Ferry View Estate, Horning, Norwich NR12 8PT
T: (01692) 630297 & 630030
F: (01692) 630498
E: kingline@norfolk-broads.co.uk
I: www.norfolk-broads.co.uk

Little River View ★★★
Contact: Mrs V J Free, 7 Magwitch Close, Newlands Spring, Chelmsford, Essex CM1 4YE
T: (01245) 441981
E: victoria@littleriverview.co.uk
I: www.littleriverview.co.uk

545

Premiere Marina Cottages
★★★
Contact: Ms Lynne Clarke, Ferry
Road, Horning, Norwich,
NR12 8PS
T: (01692) 630392 & 631040
E: lynne@ferry-marina.co.uk
I: www.ferry-marina.co.uk

HORNINGTOFT
Norfolk

The Old Stables ★★★
Contact: Mr Ivan Baker, The Old
Stables, Church Farm,
Horningtoft, East Dereham,
Norfolk NR20 5DX
T: (01328) 700496 & 700262

HOVETON
Norfolk

Navigators ★★★
Contact: Mrs Jane Shulver,
Norfolk Country Cousins, Point
House, Ridlington, North
Walsham, Norfolk NR28 9TY
T: (01692) 650286
F: (01692) 650180
E: norfolk.cousins@netcom.
co.uk
I: www.norfolk-cotages.co.uk
I: www.norfolk-cottages.co.uk

HUNSTANTON
Norfolk

Albert House ★★★
Contact: Mr & Mrs Edward
Flanagan, 13 Whernside Road,
Woodthorpe, Nottingham
NG5 4LD
T: (0115) 9262 999 &
07855 115723
I: web.ukonline.co.uk/albert.
house/

Altera ★★★
Contact: Mrs J H Larman, 64
Hillview Road, Hatch End,
Pinner, Middlesex HA5 4PE
T: (020) 8421 3815
E: jeanlarman@tinyworld.co.uk

Ashdale House ★★★★
Contact: Mrs Sandra Hohol,
Norfolk Holiday Homes, 62
Westgate, Hunstanton, Norfolk
PE36 5EL
T: (01485) 534267
F: (01485) 535230
E: shohol@
birdsnorfolkholidayhomes.co.uk
I: www.
norfolkholidayhomes-birds.
co.uk

Beeches
Rating Applied For
Contact: Mr & Mrs I D Judd,
Hunstanton Holidays, 64 Tudor
Road, Godmanchester,
Huntingdon, Cambridgeshire
PE29 2DW
T: (01480) 411509
F: (01480) 411509
E: hunstanton_hols@onetel.net.
uk
I: www.hunstantonholidays.
co.uk

Belle Vue Apartments ★★★
Contact: Mrs Sandra Bowman,
Belle Vue Apartments, 28 St
Edmunds Avenue, Hunstanton,
Norfolk PE36 6BW
T: (01485) 532826 & 532156

Brincliffe ★★★
Contact: Mrs Sandra Hohol,
Norfolk Holiday Homes, 62
Westgate, Hunstanton, Norfolk
PE36 5EL
T: (01485) 534267 & 534560
F: (01485) 535230
E: shohol@
birdsnorfolkholidayhomes.co.uk
I: www.
norfolkholidayhomes-birds.
co.uk

The Bungalow ★★
Contact: Mrs P M Harris, Karivil,
3 Ratby Meadow Lane, St Johns,
Narborough, Leicester LE9 5BN
T: (0116) 286 2943

Chalet 4 ★
Contact: Mr & Mrs Michael
Chestney, 35 West Raynham,
Fakenham, Norfolk NR21 7EY
T: (01328) 838341

Cleeks ★★★
Contact: Mrs Sandra Hohol,
Birds Norfolk Holiday Homes, 62
Westgate, Hunstanton, Norfolk
PE36 5EL
T: (01485) 534267 & 534560
F: (01485) 535230
E: shohol@
birdsnorfolkholidayhomes.co.uk
I: www.
norfolkholidayhomes-birds.
co.uk

70 Cliff Parade ★★
Contact: Mrs Sandra Hohol,
Norfolk Holiday Homes, 62
Westgate, Hunstanton, Norfolk
PE36 5EL
T: (01485) 534267
F: (01485) 535230
E: shohol@
birdsnorfolkholidayhomes.co.uk
I: www.
norfolkholidayhomes-birds.
co.uk

Coach House ★★★★★
Contact: Mr John Osborne,
Coach House, 24 Homefields
Road, Hunstanton, Norfolk
PE36 5HJ
T: (01485) 535859
F: (01485) 532388
E: info@oriellodge.co.uk
I: www.oriellodge.co.uk

40 Collingwood Road ★★★
Contact: Mrs Sandra Hohol,
Norfolk Holiday Homes, 62
Westgate, Hunstanton, Norfolk
PE36 5EL
T: (01485) 534267
F: (01485) 535230
E: shohol@
birdsnorfolkholidayhomes.co.uk
I: www.
norfolkholidayhomes-birds.
co.uk

End of the Road ★★
Contact: Mrs Sandra Hohol,
Birds Norfolk Holiday Homes, 62
Westgate, Hunstanton, Norfolk
PE36 5EL
T: (01485) 534267 & 534560
F: (01485) 535230
E: shohol@
birdsnorfolkholidayhomes.co.uk
I: www.
norfolkholidayhomes-birds.
co.uk

Flat 11 ★★
Contact: Mrs Sandra Hohol,
Norfolk Holiday Homes, 62
Westgate, Hunstanton, Norfolk
PE36 5EL
T: (01485) 534267 & 534560
F: (01485) 535230
E: shohol@
birdsnorfolkholhomes.co.uk
I: www.
norfolkholidayhomes-birds.
co.uk

Flat 12 ★★
Contact: Mrs Sandra Hohol,
Norfolk Holiday Homes, 62
Westgate, Hunstanton, Norfolk
PE36 5EL
T: (01485) 534267 & 534560
F: (01485) 535230
E: shohol@
birdsnorfolkholidayhomes.co.uk
I: www.
norfolkholidayhomes-birds.
co.uk

Ground Floor Flat ★★★
Contact: Mrs Sandra Hohol,
Norfolk Holiday Homes, 62
Westgate, Hunstanton, Norfolk
PE36 5EL
T: (01485) 534267 & 534560
F: (01485) 535230
E: shohol@
birdsnorfolkholidayhomes.co.uk
I: www.
norfolkholidayhomes-birds.
co.uk

32 Hunstanton Road ★★
Contact: Mrs Sandra Hohol,
Norfolk Holiday Homes, 62
Westgate, Hunstanton, Norfolk
PE36 5EL
T: (01485) 534267
F: (01485) 535230
E: shohol@
birdsnorfolkholidayhomes.co.uk
I: www.
norfolkholidayhomes-birds.
co.uk

Jaskville ★★★
Contact: Mr & Mrs John & Ann
Smith, Jaskville, 11 Nene Road,
Hunstanton, Norfolk PE36 5BZ
T: (01485) 533404

1 Lower Lincoln Street ★★★
Contact: Mr M J Emsden, Sutton
House Hotel, 24 Northgate,
Hunstanton, Norfolk PE36 6AP
T: (01485) 532552
E: mikeemsden@totalise.co.uk
I: www.hotelshunstanton.co.uk

Minna Cottage ★★★
Contact: Mr T Cassie, 21 The
Green, Hunstanton, Norfolk
PE36 5AH
T: (01485) 532448
E: cassie@globalnet.co.uk

No 2, 39 South Beach Road
★★
Contact: Mrs Sandra Hohol,
Birds Norfolk Holiday Homes, 62
Westgate, Hunstanton, Norfolk
PE36 5EL
T: (01485) 534267
F: (01485) 535230
E: sholhol@
birdsnorfolkholidayhomes.co.uk
I: www.
norfolkholidayhomes-birds.
co.uk

Number 14 ★★★
Contact: Mr G King, 8 Keble
Close, North Wootton, King's
Lynn, Norfolk PE30 3RU
T: (01553) 675696

Osborne Cottage ★
Contact: Mrs Sandra Hohol,
Norfolk Holiday Homes, 62
Westgate, Hunstanton, Norfolk
PE36 5EL
T: (01485) 534267 & 534560
F: (01485) 535230
E: shohol@
birdsnorfolkholidayhomes.co.uk
I: www.
norfolkholidayhomes-birds.
co.uk

Roundstones ★★★
Contact: Mrs Sandra Hohol,
Birds Norfolk Holiday Homes, 62
Westgate, Hunstanton, Norfolk
PE38 5EL
T: (01485) 534267
F: (01485) 535230
E: shohol@
birdsnorfolkholidayshomes.co.uk
I: www.
norfolkholidayhomes-birds.
co.uk

Saint Crispin ★★★
Contact: Mrs Lesley Poore, Saint
Crispin, 3 Wodehouse Road, Old
Hunstanton, Hunstanton,
Norfolk PE36 6JD
T: (01485) 534036
E: st.crispins@dial.pipex.com
I: www.cobblers.cottage@dial.
pipex.com

Sandpiper Cottage ★★★
Contact: Mrs Sandra Hohol,
Norfolk Holiday Homes, 62
Westgate, Hunstanton, Norfolk
PE36 5EL
T: (01485) 534267 & 534560
F: (01485) 535230
E: shohol@
birdsnorfolkholidayhomes.co.uk
I: www.
norfolkholidayhomes-birds.
co.uk

44 Sea Lane ★★
Contact: Mrs Sandra Hohol,
Norfolk Holiday Homes, 62
Westgate, Hunstanton, Norfolk
PE36 5EL
T: (01485) 534267
F: (01485) 535230
E: shohol@
birdsnorfolkholidayhomes.co.uk
I: www.
norfolkholidayhomes-birds.
co.uk

Sea View ★★
Contact: Mr Jeremy Roberts, 51
Park Road, Peterborough,
PE1 2TH
T: (01733) 342172 & 576144

Spindrift ★★★
Contact: Mrs Sandra Hohol,
Norfolk Holiday Homes, 62
Westgate, Hunstanton, Norfolk
PE36 5EL
T: (01485) 534267 & 534560
F: (01485) 535230
E: shohol@
birdsnorfolkholidayhomes.co.uk
I: www.
norfolkholidayhomes-birds.
co.uk

Establishments printed in blue have a detailed entry in this guide

Upper & Lower Fieldsend ★★★
Contact: Mrs S Tweedy Smith,
Upper & Lower Fieldsend,
Homefields Road, Hunstanton,
Norfolk PE36 5HL
T: (01485) 532593
F: (01485) 532593

West Lodge ★★★
Contact: Mrs G Tibbs, Cole Green
Cottage, Cole Green, Sedgeford,
Hunstanton, Norfolk PE36 5LS
T: (01485) 571770 &
07711 569388
F: (01485) 571770

Westgate Flat ★
Contact: Mrs Jean Chilleystone,
27 Clarence Road, Hunstanton,
Norfolk PE36 6HQ
T: (01485) 533646 & 532279

HUNTINGDON
Cambridgeshire

The Forge White Gates★★★
Contact: Mr Robert Pickard, The
Estate Office, Grange Farm,
Huntingdon, Cambridgeshire
PE28 2PH
T: (01487) 773555 &
07860 210890
F: (01487) 773545
E: admin@arfco.co.uk

HUNWORTH
Norfolk

Green Farm Barn ★★★★
Contact: Mrs Patricia Hoskison,
Green Farm Barn, The Green,
Hunworth, Melton Constable,
Norfolk NR24 2AA
T: (01263) 713177
F: (01263) 710083
E: alan.tagsy@freeserve.co.uk

Spink's Nest ★★
Contact: Mrs Angela Hampshire,
River Bank, King Street,
Hunworth, Melton Constable,
Norfolk NR24 2EH
T: (01263) 713891

IKEN
Suffolk

The Old Stable ★★★★
Contact: Mrs Gunilla Hailes, The
Anchorage, Church Lane, Iken,
Woodbridge, Suffolk IP12 2ES
T: (01728) 688263
F: (01728) 688262

INGOLDISTHORPE
Norfolk

Goldcrest ★★★
Contact: Ms Lorraine Pearson,
Goldcrest, Sandy Lane,
Ingoldisthorpe, King's Lynn,
Norfolk PE31 6NN
T: (01485) 544681 &
07950 028858
F: (01485) 544681
I: www.goldcrestproperty.com

Swan Cottage ★★★★
Contact: Mr A A Swan, 56 Hill
Road, Ingoldisthorpe, King's
Lynn, Norfolk PE31 6NZ
T: (01485) 543882 &
07904 387317
E: swans.norfolk@virgin.net

Timekeepers Cottage ★★★
Contact: Mrs Lyn Storry
Leathersich, Homefield, 32
Manor Road, Dersingham, King's
Lynn, Norfolk PE31 6LD
T: (01485) 540700
E: lynsl@supanet.com

IPSWICH
Suffolk

**Mockbeggars Flat
Rating Applied For**
Contact: Mrs Priscilla Clayton-
Mead, Mockbeggars Hall,
Claydon, Ipswich IP6 0AH
T: (01473) 830239
F: (01473) 832989
E: pru@mockbeggars.co.uk
I: www.mockbeggars.co.uk

IXWORTH
Suffolk

**Cobwebs
Rating Applied For**
Contact: Mrs Claire Ivory,
Riverside Paddocks, Stow Road,
Ixworth, Bury St Edmunds,
Suffolk IP31 2JB
T: (01359) 231798

KELLING
Norfolk

The Plough Wheel ★★★
Contact: Mrs Jane Shulver,
Norfolk Country Cousins, Point
House, Ridlington, North
Walsham, Norfolk NR28 9TY
T: (01692) 650286
F: (01692) 650180
E: norfolk.cousins@netcom.
co.uk
I: www.norfolk-cottages.co.uk

Rose Cottage ★★★
Contact:, Norfolk Country
Cousins, Point House,
Ridlington, North Walsham,
Norfolk NR28 9TY
T: (01692) 650286
F: (01692) 650180
E: norfollk-cousins@netcom.
co.uk
I: www.norfolk-cottages.co.uk

KESSINGLAND
Suffolk

Church Road ★★★
Contact: Mr James Rayment, 28
Woollards Lane, Great Shelford,
Cambridge CB2 5LZ
T: (01223) 843048

74 The Cliff ★★
Contact: Mrs Saunders, 22
Wanstead Park Avenue, London
E12 5EN
T: (020) 8989 5636 &
07957 195839

East Lee ★★★
Contact: Mrs Marilyn Burgoyne,
East Lee, c/o Ocean View,
Coastguard Lane, Kessingland,
Lowestoft, Suffolk NR33 7RE
T: (01502) 740095

Holiday Cottage ★★
Contact: Mr & Mrs G Smith, 5
Bassett Way, Greenford,
Middlesex UB6 9DG
T: (020) 8578 8965
F: (020) 8578 8965

**Kessingland Cottages 11
kessingland Cottages★★**
Contact: Mr John Ryan, 17 The
Byway, Potters Bar,
Hertfordshire EN6 2LN
T: (01707) 643511

Kew Cottage ★★★
Contact: Mrs J Gill, 46 St
Georges Avenue, Northampton,
NN2 6JA
T: (01604) 717301 & 791424
F: (01604) 791424
E: b.s.g.@btinternet.com

Knights Holiday Homes ★
Contact: Mr Michael Knights,
198 Church Road, Kessingland,
Lowestoft, Suffolk NR33 7SF
T: (01502) 588533
E: knights@bligh77.freeserve.
co.uk

KETTLEBASTON
Suffolk

The Rector's Retreat ★★★
Contact: Mr & Mrs Peter
Gutteridge, The Rector's Retreat,
The Old Convent, The Street,
Kettlebaston, Ipswich IP7 7QA
E: holidays@kettlebaston.fsnet.
co.uk
I: www.kettlebaston.fsnet.co.uk/
⟰

KETTLESTONE
Norfolk

91 & 93A The Street ★★★
Contact: Holiday Cott
Ref:11583/11584, Holiday
Cottages Group Owner Services
Dept, Spring Mill, Earby,
Barnoldswick, Lancashire
BB18 6RN
T: (01282) 44544
F: (01282) 841539
E: sales@ttgihg.co.uk
I: www.country-holidays.co.uk

KING'S LYNN
Norfolk

Granery ★★★
Contact: Mrs Ann Jones, Manor
House, Churchgate Way,
Terrington St Clement, King's
Lynn, Norfolk PE34 4LZ
T: (01553) 828700

KNAPTON
Norfolk

Cornerstone Cottage ★★★★
Contact: Mr & Mrs Eves,
Cornerstone House, The Street,
Knapton, North Walsham,
Norfolk NR28 0AD
T: (01263) 722884 &
07780 612254
I: www.broadland.
com/cornerstone

The Cottage ★★
Contact: Mrs A R Michaels, 23
Lauradale Road, Fortis Green,
London N2 9LT
T: (020) 8444 7678
E: armichaels@aol.com

**High House Cottage
Rating Applied For**
Contact: Mr B W Hall, High
House, Hall Lane, Knapton,
Norfolk NR28 0SG
T: (01263) 721827

**Stable Court
Rating Applied For**
Contact: Mrs J Lloyd, The New
House, Knapton, North
Walsham, Norfolk NR28 0RX
T: (01263) 722119

White House Farm ★★★
Contact: Mr & Mrs C Goodhead,
White House Farm, Knapton,
North Walsham, Norfolk
NR28 0RX
T: (01263) 721344
E: goodhead@whfarm.
swinternet.co.uk
I: www.geocities.
com/whitehousefarmnorfolk

KNODISHALL
Suffolk

Forget-Me-Not ★★★
Contact: Mr & Mrs Richard &
Wendy Pither, Suffolk Secrets, 7
Frenze Road, Diss, IP22 4PA
T: (01379) 651297
F: (01379) 641555
E: holiday@suffolk-secrets.
co.uk
I: www.suffolk-secrets.co.uk

Meadowcroft ★★★★
Contact: Mrs H C Laws-Smith,
Rosendale, School Road,
Knodishall, Saxmundham,
Suffolk IP17 1UD
T: (01728) 830533
F: (01728) 830533

LANGHAM
Norfolk

Redfern Cottage ★★
Contact: Mrs Laurice Jarman,
The Great Escape Holiday
Company Limited, The Granary,
Station Road, Docking, King's
Lynn, Norfolk PE31 8LY
T: (01485) 518717
F: (01485) 518937
E: holidays@greatescapes.
demon.co.uk

Sunnyside Cottage ★★★★
Contact: Mr & Mrs T E Shephard,
11 Faire Road, Glenfield,
Leicester LE3 8EE
T: (0116) 2872739

LAVENHAM
Suffolk

86 Church Street ★★★★
Contact: Mrs Jill Price, 50 Bear
Street, Nayland, Colchester,
Suffolk CO6 4HX
T: (01206) 263944 &
07776 293733
F: (01206) 263693
E: jill.price@lavenham.f2s.com
I: www.lavenham.f2s.com

**Daffodil Cottage
Rating Applied For**
Contact: Mrs M Hussey, Brett
Farm, The Common, Lavenham,
Sudbury, Suffolk CO10 9PG
T: (01787) 248533

Glebe Cottage ★★★★
Contact: Mrs Klair Bauly,
Malting Farm, Hessett, Bury St
Edmunds, Suffolk IP30 9BJ
T: (01359) 271528 &
07050 233520
F: (01359) 271528
E: kbauly@waitrose.com

The Grove ★★★★
Contact: Mr & Mrs Mark Scott &
Stefanie Wege, The Grove, Priory
Green, Edwardstone, Lavenham,
Sudbury, Suffolk CO10 5PP
T: (01787) 211115
F: (01787) 211220
E: stefanie@edwardstone.
demon.co.uk
I: www.grove-cottages.co.uk

Establishments printed in blue have a detailed entry in this guide

The Hayloft ★★★★★
Contact: Mrs Annabel Jackson, Market House, Market Place, Lavenham, Sudbury, Suffolk CO10 9QZ
T: (01787) 249129 & 249122
F: (01787) 249122
E: annabeljjackson@hotmail.com
I: www.thehayloft.net

Lavender Cottage ★★★★
Contact: Mrs Joyce Taylor, Birches, Bray Road, Maidenhead, Berkshire SL6 1UQ
T: (01628) 627741 & 07880 916563

Lavenham Cottages ★★★★★
Contact: Mrs D Sowerby, Washmere Cottage, Washmere Green, Great Waldingfield, Sudbury, Suffolk CO10 0TE
T: (01787) 249149
F: (01787) 249149

Old Wetherden Hall ★★★
Contact: Mrs J Elsden, Old Wetherden Hall, Hitcham, Ipswich, IP7 7PZ
T: (01449) 740574 & 07798 728406
F: (01449) 740574
E: farm@weatherdenhall.force9.co.uk

Quakers Yard ★★★
Contact: Mr David Aldous, Two A's Hoggards Green, Stanningfield, Bury St Edmunds, Suffolk IP29 4RG
T: (01284) 827271

12 Ropers Court ★★★
Contact: Mr Roger Arnold, Queen's House, Church Square, Bures, Suffolk CO8 5AB
T: (01787) 227760 & 07802 841448
F: (01787) 227082
E: rogerarnold1@compuserve.com
I: website.lineone.net/~elizabeth_arnold

The Loosebox & The Old Stables★★★
Contact: Mr & Mrs John & Jane Reeve, Laxfield Leisure Ltd, High Street, Laxfield, Woodbridge, Suffolk IP13 8DU
T: (01986) 798019
F: (01986) 798019
E: laxfieldleisure@talk21.com

Abbey View Lodge ★★★
Contact: Mrs L Stobbart, Orchard House, 105 Abbey Road, Leiston, Suffolk IP16 4TA
T: (01728) 830350 & 831128
E: info@abbeyview.co.uk
I: www.abbeyview.co.uk

Micawbers ★★★★
Contact: Mrs Joan Hockley, Piggotts Farm, Albury End, Ware, Hertfordshire SG11 2HS
T: (01279) 771281 & 759042
F: (01279) 771517
E: hockley@globalnet.co.uk

The Studio ★★★
Contact: Mr & Mrs Richard & Wendy Pither, Suffolk Secrets, 7 Frenze Road, Diss, IP22 4PA
T: (01379) 651297
F: (01379) 641555
E: holidays@suffolk-secrets.co.uk
I: www.suffolk-secrets.co.uk

4 Canaan Row ★★★
Contact: Mr David Court, Norfolk Country Cottages, Carlton House, Market Place, Reepham, Norwich NR10 4JJ
T: (01603) 871872
F: (01603) 870304
E: cottages@paston.co.uk
I: www.norfolkcottages.co.uk/litcham.htm

The Old Farmhouse ★★★
Contact: Mrs J Archer, Chalk Farm, Druids Lane, Litcham, King's Lynn, Norfolk PE32 2YA
T: (01328) 701331
F: (01328) 701331
E: judiarcher@aol.com

Horseshoes ★★★
Contact: Mrs Julie Abbs, Anchor Farm Cottage, Wood Lane, Little Ellingham, Attleborough, Norfolk NR17 1JZ
T: (01953) 454514 & 07775 517515
E: edward@eabbs.fsnet.co.uk

Stable Cottage ★★★★
Contact: Mrs Kate Muskett, Little Henham Hall, Little Henham, Saffron Walden, Essex CB11 3XR
T: (01279) 850228
F: (01279) 850397

Green Farm Barn ★★★★
Contact: Rev & Mrs D P Pritchard, The Rectory, Hart Street, Henley-on-Thames, Oxfordshire RG9 2AU
T: (01491) 572134

The White House Cottage & Barn Lodge★★★
Contact: Mrs C Lee, The White House, The Street, Little Snoring, Fakenham, Norfolk NR21 0AJ
T: (01328) 878789 & 878103

Orchard View Numbers 1 – 4 ★★★
Contact: Mrs Maureen Chapman-Barker, Little Bowsers Farm, Bowsers Lane, Little Walden, Saffron Walden, Essex CB10 1XQ
T: (01799) 527315
F: (01799) 527315
E: sales@farmerkit.co.uk
I: www.farmerkit.co.uk

The Old Coach House ★★★★
Contact: Mr & Mrs Geoff & Julia Holloway, Bramble Cottage, Helmingham Road, Otley, Ipswich, Suffolk IP6 9NS
T: (020) 85878400 & (01473) 890035
E: theoldcoach.house@btinternet.com
I: www.theoldcoach.house.btinternet.co.uk

Caves Farm Barns ★★★
Contact: Mr Stephen Kerridge, Caves Farm Barns, Caves Farm, 25 Hale Fen, Littleport, Ely, Cambridgeshire CB6 1EJ
T: (01353) 861423 & 00787 505180
F: (01353) 861423
E: cb6steve@aol.com

4 Church Walk ★★
Contact: Mr M A Thomas, 33 Patshull Road, Kentish Town, London NW5 2JX
T: (01787) 310066 & (020) 7267 3653
F: (01932) 568933
E: thomasm@rmc-group.com

Hope Cottage ★★★★
Contact: Ms S Jamil, 219 Parkwood Drive, Sudbury, Suffolk CO10 1LX
T: (01787) 310199 & 07970 808701
F: (01787) 310199
E: sns.jam@tesco.net
I: www.hope-cottage-suffolk.co.uk

The Roost ★★★
Contact: Mr & Mrs C K Entwistle, Brick Kiln Farmhouse, Sustead Road, Lower Gresham, Norwich, Norfolk NR11 8RE
T: (01263) 577388
E: enthome@compuserve.com
🅰

1B Watermill Close ★★★
Contact: Mrs Joan Munday, Keys Holidays, 18 Station Road, Sheringham, Norfolk NR26 8RE
T: (01263) 823010
F: (01263) 821449
E: info@keys-holidays.co.uk
I: www.keys-holidays.co.uk

Pier View Holiday Apartments ★★-★★★
Contact: Mrs Pam Cross, 3 Mill Road, Mutford, Beccles, Suffolk NR34 7UR
T: (01502) 476280 & 0771 3862704
F: (01502) 476280

Suffolk Seaside & Broadlands ★★★
Contact: Mr B Smith, 2 Pound Farm Drive, Oulton, Lowestoft, Suffolk NR32 4RG
T: (01502) 508711

Tides Reach Holiday Flats ★★
Contact: Mrs M Tallamy, Brindle Bay, Borrow Road, Oulton Broad, Lowestoft, Suffolk NR32 3PW
T: (01502) 573853

16 Wilson Road ★★★
Contact: Mr & Mrs Murray, 24 Maltese Road, Chelmsford, Essex CM1 2PA
T: (01245) 266018
F: (01245) 287000

Holly Cottage & Rowan Cottage ★★-★★★
Contact: Mr Thomas, Collin Green Farm, Lyng, Norwich NR9 5LH
T: (01603) 880158
F: (01603) 881228

Old School Lodge ★★★★
Contact: Holiday Cottages Ref: 11815, Holiday Cottages Group Owner Services Dept, Spring Mill, Earby, Barnoldswick, Lancashire BB18 6RN
T: (01282) 445096
F: (01282) 844288
E: sales@ttgihg.co.uk
I: www.country-holidays.co.uk

Wensum Cottage ★★★
Contact: Mrs Jane Shulver, Norfolk Country Cousins, Point House, Ridlington, North Walsham, Norfolk NR28 9TY
T: (01692) 650286
F: (01692) 650180
E: norfolk.cousins@netcom.co.uk
I: www.norfolk-cottages.co.uk

Little Wintersleet Farm ★★★
Contact: Mrs Merie Keeble, Little Wintersleet Farm, Little Wintersleet, London Road, Maldon, Essex CM9 6LJ
T: (01621) 856354

Field House ★★★
Contact: Mr N Pash, Hideaways, Chapel House, Luke Street, Berwick St John, Shaftesbury, Dorset SP7 0HQ
T: (01747) 828170
F: (01747) 829090
E: enq@hideaways.co.uk
I: www.hideaways.co.uk/property2.cfm?ref=H704Marsworth

Greenside Cottage ★★★
Contact: Mrs B I Dyball, Greenside, 30 The Green, Martham, Great Yarmouth, Norfolk NR29 4PA
T: (01493) 740375

Wayfarers Cottage ★★★★
Contact: Mr & Mrs Gogle, Old Hall Farm, Old Hal Road, Mattishall, East Dereham, Norfolk NR20 3PA
T: (01362) 850214 & 07785 935354

Establishments printed in blue have a detailed entry in this guide

MIDDLETON
Norfolk
The Cottage ★★★
Contact: Holiday Cottages Ref: 7416, Holiday Cottages Group Owner Services Dept, Spring Mill, Earby, Barnoldswick, Lancashire BB18 6RN
T: (01282) 445444
F: (01282) 841539
E: sales@ttgihg.co.uk
I: www.country-holidays.co.uk

Rose Farm Barns ★★★★
Contact: Mrs Janet Maricic, Rose Farm, Middleton, Saxmundham, Suffolk IP17 3NG
T: (01728) 648456 &
07885 194945
&

MUCH HADHAM
Hertfordshire
Blackcroft Farmhouse ★★★
Contact: Mrs Gill Trundle, Blackcroft Farmhouse, Kettle Green, Much Hadham, Hertfordshire SG10 6AD
T: (01279) 843832 & 0775 981 8932
E: trundle@freenet.co.uk

MUNDESLEY
Norfolk
The Croft ★★★
Contact: Mr R W Hams, Tower House, 21 Paston Road, Mundesley, Norwich, Norfolk NR11 8BN
T: (01263) 720351 &
0786 6908381

Holiday Properties (Mundesley) Ltd ★-★★★
Contact: Mr & Mrs Mark & Nadine Gray, Holiday Properties (Mundesley) Ltd, 6A Paston Road, Mundesley, Norwich NR11 8BN
T: (01263) 720719 & 722646
E: holidayproperties@tesco.net
I: www.holidayprops.freeuk.com

Overcliff Lodge ★★★
Contact: Mr Jill Sneyd, Overcliff Lodge, 46 Cromer Road, Mundesley, Norwich NR11 8DB
T: (01263) 720016
F: (01263) 720016
E: overclifflodge@btinternet.co
I: www.broadland.com/overclifflodge/

Sunshine Cottages ★★★★
Contact: Mr & Mrs GD Fiske, The Old House, 28 High Street, Mundesley, Norwich, Norfolk NR11 8LH
T: (01263) 722342
F: (01263) 722342
E: bookings@fiskies.co.uk
I: www.fiskies.co.uk

MUNDON
Essex
Wayside Annexe ★★★★
Contact: Mrs Vivien Clark, Wayside, Main Road, Mundon, Maldon, Essex CM9 6NU
T: (01621) 740374
E: peter.clark@care4free.net

NARBOROUGH
Norfolk
Church Farm Holiday Homes ★★★★
Contact: Mrs Nicky St Lawrence, Church Farm Holiday Homes, Church Farm, Narborough, King's Lynn, Norfolk PE32 1TE
T: (01760) 337696 &
07801 641570
F: (01760) 337858
E: nickystlawrence@ouvip.com
I: www.churchfarmholidayhomes.com

NAYLAND
Suffolk
Gladwins Farm ★★★★-★★★★★
Contact: Mrs Pauline Dossor, Harpers Hill, Nayland, Colchester CO6 4NU
T: (01206) 262261
F: (01206) 263001
E: gladwinsfarm@compuserve.co.uk
I: www.gladwinsfarm.co.uk
&

NEWMARKET
Suffolk
La Hogue Cottage ★★★★
Contact: Mr & Mrs J M Tilbrook, La Hogue Hall, Chippenham, Ely, Cambridgeshire CB7 5PZ
T: (01638) 750433 & 712253
F: (01638) 712833
E: r.tilbrook@farming.co.uk

Swallows Rest ★★★★
Contact: Mrs Gill Woodward, Swallows Rest, 6 Ditton Green, Woodditton, Newmarket, Suffolk CB8 9SQ
T: (01638) 730823
F: (01638) 731767

NORTH CREAKE
Norfolk
Harvest Cottage ★★★
Contact: Mrs Hilary Bagley, Church Lane Cottage, Off Cross Street, Salthouse, Holt, Norfolk NR25 7XH
T: 07771 887436 & (020) 7976 6791
F: (020) 7828 7133

Lavender Cottage ★★★
Contact: Mr & Mrs D Maund, Field House, 15 Church Street, North Creake, Fakenham, Norfolk NR21 9JN
T: (01328) 730460

NORTH ELMHAM
Norfolk
Blackhall Barn ★★★★
Contact: Mrs Helen Howell, Tower Farm, Bintree, East Dereham, Norfolk NR20 5NQ
T: (01362) 683527
🏕

NORTH WALSHAM
Norfolk
The Wolery ★★★★
Contact: Hoseasons Holidays Ltd, Sunway House, Lowestoft, Suffolk NR32 2LW
T: (01502) 502614
🏕

NORTHREPPS
Norfolk
Flint Cottage ★★★
Contact: Mr & Mrs Peter & Jill Breeze, Fairview, Madams Lane, Northrepps, Cromer, Norfolk NR27 0LP
T: (01263) 579699

Torridon & Yeomans Cottage ★★★★
Contact: Mrs A Youngman, Shrublands Farm, Northrepps, Cromer, Norfolk NR27 0AA
T: (01263) 579297
F: (01263) 579297
E: youngman@farming.co.uk
I: www.broadland.com/torridon

Woodland House ★★★
Contact: Mrs Louise Strong, Woodland House, Cromer Road, Northrepps, Cromer, Norfolk NR27 0JY
T: (01263) 579736
E: stephen.strong@virgin.net

NORWICH
Norfolk
The Hideaway & Pondside ★★★-★★★★
Contact: Mrs C B Reilly, Heath Bungalow, Woodbastwick Road, Blofield Heath, Norwich, NR13 4AB
T: (01603) 715052
E: pondside@talk21.com
I: www.norfolkbroads.com/thehideaway
🏕

30 Kingsley Road ★★★
Contact: Miss Sally Clarke, 3 Kingsley Road, Norwich, NR1 3RB
T: (01603) 615819
F: (01603) 615819
E: kingsley@paston.co.uk

Sommersby ★★★
Contact: Miss D Jackson, 31 Guycook Close, Great Cornard, Sudbury, Suffolk CO10 0JX
T: (01787) 372903

33 St Stephens Square ★★★
Contact: Holiday Cottages Ref: 10882, Holiday Cottages Group Owner Services Dept, Spring Mill, Earby, Barnoldswick, Lancashire BB18 6RN
T: (01282) 445444
F: (01282) 841539
E: sales@ttgihg.co.uk
I: www.country-holidays.co.uk

ORFORD
Suffolk
41 Daphne Road ★★★
Contact: Mrs Phyllida Flint, Green Lane House, Castle Green, Orford, Woodbridge, Suffolk IP12 2NF
T: (01394) 450159
F: (01394) 450827

47 Daphne Road ★★★
Contact: Mrs Sheila Hitchcock, Church Farm Cottage, Sudbourne, Woodbridge, Suffolk IP12 2BP
T: (01394) 450714
F: (01394) 450714
E: barryhitchcock@compuserve.com

Vesta Cottage ★★★
Contact: Mrs Penny Kay, 74 Broad Street, Orford, Woodbridge, Suffolk IP12 2NQ
T: (01394) 450652
F: (01394) 450097
E: kaysorford@compuserve.com
I: www.oas.co.uk/uk.cottages/vesta/

OULTON
Norfolk
Willowbank Cottage ★★★
Contact: Mrs Deborah Evans, 55 Soame Close, Aylsham, Norwich NR11 6JF
T: (01263) 735183
F: (01223) 358222
E: info@smartex.com

OULTON BROAD
Suffolk
156 Bridge Road ★★★
Contact: Mrs Sandra Dyer, Barnstable House, Blundeston Road, Corton, Lowestoft, Suffolk NR32 5DD
T: (01502) 730716 & 562111

7 Holly Road ★★
Contact: Mrs T Moore, 97A Normanston Drive, Oulton Broad, Lowestoft, Suffolk NR32 2PX
T: (01502) 563868

Maltings Holiday Accommodation ★★★
Contact: Ivy House Farm Hotel, Ivy Lane, Oulton Broad, Lowestoft, Suffolk NR33 8HY
T: (01502) 501353
F: (01502) 501539
E: maltings@ivyhousefarm.co.uk

White House Farm ★★★
Contact: Mr & Mrs Andrew Hughes, White House Farm, Burnt Hill Lane, Oulton Broad, Lowestoft, Suffolk NR33 8HU
T: (01502) 564049
E: mail@whitehousefarm.org.uk
I: www.whitehousefarm.org.uk

OVERSTRAND
Norfolk
Buckthorns ★★★★
Contact: Mrs Anthea Carver, 10 Stevenage Road, London SW6 6ES
T: (020) 7736 6764
F: (020) 7736 1218

1 Golf Cottage ★★★
Contact: Mrs Joan Munday, Keys Holidays, 18 Station Road, Sheringham, Norfolk NR26 8RE
T: (01263) 823010
F: (01263) 821449
E: info@keys-holidays.co.uk
I: www.keys-holidays.co.uk

Poppyland Holiday Cottages ★★★-★★★★
Contact: Mrs T Riches, Poppyland Holiday Cottages, 21 Regent Street, Wickmere, Norwich, Norfolk NR11 7ND
T: (01263) 577473
F: (01265) 570087
E: poppyland@totalise.co.uk
I: www.broadland.com/poppyland

Establishments printed in blue have a detailed entry in this guide

Summersville ★★★
Contact: Mr J C Laidlow, 19 High Street, Overstrand, Cromer, Norfolk NR27 0AB
T: (01263) 579368 &
07773 651850
E: john.laidlow@lineone.net

OXBOROUGH
Norfolk

Hythe Cottage ★★★
Contact: Dr Barbara Sommerville, 23 Portugal Place, Cambridge, CB5 8AF
T: (01223) 740444
E: bas@flora-garden-tours.co.uk

OXNEAD
Norfolk

Keepers Cottage ★★★
Contact: Norfolk Country Cottages, Carlton House, Market Place, Reepham, Norwich, Norfolk NR10 4JJ
T: (01603) 871872
F: (01603) 870304
E: cottages@paston.co.uk

PAKEFIELD
Suffolk

Cliff Cottage ★★★
Contact: Mrs Thelma Bruce, Fishermans Cottage, Pakefield Street, Pakefield, Lowestoft NR33 0JS
T: (01502) 501955 &
07747 891372

Holiday Cottage ★★★★
Contact: Mrs V J Mead, 15 Walmer Road, Pakefield, Lowestoft, Suffolk NR33 7LE
T: (01502) 515414 &
07767 853065

PELDON
Essex

Rose Barn Cottage ★★★★
Contact: Mrs A Everett, Rose Barn, Mersea Road, Peldon, Colchester CO5 7QJ
T: (01206) 735317
F: (01206) 735311
E: everettaj@aol.com

PENTNEY
Norfolk

Nar Valley Holiday Cottages
Rating Applied For
Contact: Ms Rosemary De Bootman, Nar Valley Holiday Cottages, Great Ketlam Farm, Low Road, Pentney, King's Lynn, Norfolk PE32 1JF
T: (01760) 338797
E: narvalleycottages@tinyonline.co.uk

PLAYFORD
Suffolk

The Olde Post Office ★★
Contact: Mr & Mrs G C Booker, Glenham, Hill Farm Road, Playford, Ipswich IP6 9DU
T: (01473) 624939 & 410115
E: glenham@tesco.net
I: www.glenham.hypermart.net

POLSTEAD
Suffolk

Granary Cottage and Dairy Cottage ★★★
Contact: CHols Ref:14775/ Blakes B5376, Country Holidays Owner Services Dept, Spring Mill, Earby, Barnoldswick, Lancashire BB94 0AA
T: (01282) 445444
F: (01282) 841539
I: www.country-holidays.co.uk

The Stables ★★★
Contact: Mr & Mrs Richard English, Sprotts Farm, Holt Road, Polstead, Colchester CO6 5BT
T: (01787) 210368
E: R.J.English@btinternet.com

POTTER HEIGHAM
Norfolk

Herbert Woods
Rating Applied For
Contact: Ms Carmen Wright, Herbert Woods, Broads Haven, Potter Heigham, Great Yarmouth, Norfolk NR29 5JD
T: (01692) 670711
F: (01692) 670734
E: carmen@broads.co.uk
I: www.broads.co.uk

RATTLESDEN
Suffolk

The Dower House ★★★★
Contact: Mrs H M Voysey, The Dower House, Clopton Green, Rattlesden, Bury St Edmunds, Suffolk IP30 0RN
T: (01449) 736 332
E: all@voysey.freeserve.co.uk

REDBOURN
Hertfordshire

The Beeches ★★★
Contact: Mrs J Surridge, The Beeches, Hemel Hempstead Road, Redbourn, St Albans, Hertfordshire AL3 7AG
T: (01582) 792638

REEPHAM
Norfolk

Manor Farm Cottage ★★★★
Contact: Country Holidays:12450, Spring Mill, Earby, Barnoldswick, Lancashire BB18
T: (01282) 445096
F: (01282) 844288
E: sales@ttgihg.co.uk
I: www.country-holidays.co.uk

Rookery Farm ★★★
Contact: Mrs Jan Ashford, Rookery Farm, Church Street, Reepham, Norwich NR10 4JW
T: (01603) 871847

RENDHAM
Suffolk

The Cottage ★★
Contact: Mrs E M Spinney, The Old Vicarage, Rendham, Saxmundham, Suffolk IP17 2AF
T: (01728) 663656
F: (01728) 663656
E: elizabethspinney@eggconnect.net

REYDON
Suffolk

The Ark ★★★
Contact: Mr & Mrs Richard Pither, Suffolk Secrets, 7 Frenze Road, Diss, IP22 4PA
T: (01379) 651297
F: (01379) 641555
E: holidays@suffollk.secrets.co.uk
I: www.suffolk-secrets.co.uk

Quay House Chalet ★★
Contact: Mrs Claire Guppy, Olde Banke House, 69 High Street, Southwold, Suffolk IP18 6DS
T: (01502) 723323 & 725273
F: (01502) 723323
E: chalets@southwold-quayhouse.co.uk
I: www.southwold-quayhouse.co.uk

Richmond ★★★
Contact: Mr Richard Pither, Suffolk Secrets, 7 Frenze Road, Diss, IP22 4PA
T: (01379) 651297
F: (01379) 641555
E: holidays@suffolk-secrets.co.uk
I: www.suffolk-secrets.co.uk

Whimbrel Cottage ★★★
Contact: Mr & Mrs Richard & Wendy Pither, Suffolk Secrets, 7 Frenze Road, Diss, IP22 4PA
T: (01379) 651297
F: (01379) 641555
E: holidays@suffolk-secrets.co.uk
I: www.suffolk-secrets.co.uk

RICKINGHALL
Suffolk

Chestnut View ★★★
Contact: Albion Rose Properties Ltd, Priory Lane, Royston, Hertfordshire SG8 9DU
T: (01379) 898663 &
(01763) 249999
F: (01763) 247793

RINGSTEAD
Norfolk

Brew House Barn ★★★★
Contact: Mrs M Harmes, Brew House Barn, Gin Trap Inn, Ringstead, Hunstanton, Norfolk PE36 5JU
T: (01485) 525264
E: margaret@gintrap.co.uk
I: www.gintrap.co.uk

Crossways ★
Contact: Mrs Sandra Hohol, Norfolk Holiday Homes, 62 Westgate, Hunstanton, Norfolk PE36 5EL
T: (01485) 534267
T: (01485) 535230
E: shohol@birdsnorfolkholidayhomes.co.uk
I: www.norfolkholidayhomes-birds.co.uk

7 Langford Cottages ★★★★
Contact: Mr Douglas Hill, Woodstock, Shootersway Lane, Berkhamsted, Hertfordshire HP4 3NW
T: (01442) 864387 & (020) 7250 2086
F: (01442) 871589
E: djbhill@waitrose.com

Lindsey Cottage ★★★
Contact: Mrs Jane Shulver, Norfolk Country Cousins, Point House, Ridlington, North Walsham, Norfolk NR28 9TY
T: (01692) 650286
F: (01692) 650180
E: norfolk.cousins@netcom.co.uk
I: www.norfolk-cotages.co.uk

ROUGHTON
Norfolk

Nora Blogg's Cottage ★★
Contact: Mr H W Varden, Chalden Cottage, Felbrigg Road, Roughton, Cromer, Norfolk NR11 8PA
T: (01263) 513353

RUNCTON HOLME
Norfolk

Thorpland Manor Barns ★★★★
Contact: Mrs Mary Caley, Thorpland Manor Barns, Downham Road, Runcton Holme, King's Lynn, Norfolk PE33 0AD
T: (01553) 810409
F: (01553) 811831

SAFFRON WALDEN
Essex

The Barn ★★
Contact: Mr John Goose, Burntwood End, Little Walden, Saffron Walden, Essex CB10 1XE
T: (01799) 523202 &
(01638) 730518
E: john.goose@aventis.com

Bayley Cottage ★★★
Contact: Mrs A Petty, 4 Museums Street, Saffron Walden, Essex CB10 1BN
T: (01799) 528885 &
07790 990525

The Byre ★★★
Contact: Mrs T Westerhuis, The Byre, Rockells Farm, Duddenhoe End, Saffron Walden, Essex CB11 4UY
T: (01763) 838053

Newhouse Farm ★★★★
Contact: Mrs Emma Redcliffe, Newhouse Farm, Walden Road, Radwinter, Saffron Walden, Essex CB10 2SP
T: (01799) 599211
F: (01799) 599967
E: emmaredcliffe@hotmail.com

ST ALBANS
Hertfordshire

21 Cathedral Court ★★★★
Contact: Ms Margot Choo, Monworth Limited, 12 Wyton, Welwyn Garden City, Hertfordshire AL7 2PF
T: (01707) 327977 &
07930 581746
E: margot_monworth@hotmail.com
I: www.btinternet.com/~monworth/home

Clarence Cottage
Rating Applied For
Contact: Mr & Mrs Paul McGoohan, 12 Richard Stagg Close, St Albans, Hertfordshire AL1 5AT
T: (01727) 762345 &
07801 365600
F: (01727) 762345

Establishments printed in blue have a detailed entry in this guide

The Hollies ★★★★
Contact: Mrs Anne Newbury,
The Hollies, 11 Spencer Place,
Sandridge, St Albans,
Hertfordshire AL4 9DW
T: (01727) 859845
E: martin.newbury@ntlworld.
co.uk

ST OSYTH
Essex

Park Hall Holiday Cottages ★★★★★
Contact: Mrs Trisha Ford, Park
Hall Holiday Cottages, Park
Farm, St Osyth, Colchester
CO16 8HG
T: (01255) 820922
I: www.
parkhall-holidaycottages.com

SALLE
Norfolk

Coachman's Cottage ★★★
Contact: Mrs Glynis Pratt, Walk
Gates Cottages, Salle, Norwich,
Norfolk NR10 4SF
T: (01603) 870417 & (020) 7584
5047

Lodge Cottage ★★★
Contact: Mr Chris Penn, Salle
Moor Hall Farm, Salle, Norwich
NR10 4SB
T: (01603) 879046
F: (01603) 879047
E: chris@sallemoorhallfm.u-net.
co

SALTHOUSE
Norfolk

Dun Cow Public House ★★★
Contact: Mrs Kay Groom, Public
House, Coast Road, Salthouse,
Holt, Norfolk NR25 7XG
T: (01263) 740467

SANDRINGHAM
Norfolk

Folk on the Hill ★★★★
Contact: Mrs L Skerritt, Mill
Cottage, Mill Road, Dersingham,
King's Lynn, Norfolk PE31 6HY
T: (01485) 544411 &
07798 946334
E: lili@skerritt-euwe.freeserve.
co.uk

SAXMUNDHAM
Suffolk

Flora Cottage ★★★★
Contact: Mr & Mrs Richard &
Wendy Pither, Suffolk Secrets, 7
Frenze Road, Diss, IP22 4PA
T: (01379) 651297
F: (01379) 641555
E: holidays@suffolk-secrets.
co.uk
I: www.suffolk-secrets.co.uk

Harvey's Mill ★★★★
Contact: Mrs CE Baker, Harvey's
Mill, Benstead, Main Road,
Kelsale, Saxmundham, Suffolk
IP17 2RD
T: (01728) 603212 &
07831 260733
E: mail@bensteadhouse.
freeserve.co.uk
I: www.blythweb.
co.uk/harveysmill

Snape Maltings ★★-★★★
Contact: Ms Dawn Hannan,
Snape Maltings, Snape,
Saxmundham, Suffolk IP17 1SR
T: (01728) 688303
F: (01728) 688930
E: dawn@snapemaltings.co.uk
I: www.snapemaltings.co.uk

SCULTHORPE
Norfolk

Bay House ★★★
Contact: Holiday Cottages Ref:
883, Holiday Cottages Group
Owner Services Dept, Spring
Mill, Earby, Barnoldswick,
Lancashire BB18 6RN
T: (01282) 445444
F: (01282) 841539
E: sales@ttgihg.co.uk
I: www.country-holidays.co.uk

The Cottage ★★★
Contact: Mrs M Chapman, 30
Lambert Cross, Saffron Walden,
Essex CB10 2DP
T: (01799) 527287

Greenacre Bungalow ★★
Contact: Mrs J Tuddenham,
Greenacre Bungalow, 1 The
Street, Sculthorpe, Fakenham,
Norfolk NR21 9QD
T: (01328) 862858

SEA PALLING
Norfolk

Marlow Cottage ★★★
Contact: Mrs Jane Shulver,
Norfolk Country Cousins, Point
House, Ridlington, North
Walsham, Norfolk NR28 9TY
T: (01692) 650286
F: (01692) 650180
E: norfolk.cousins@netcom.
co.uk
I: www.norfolk-cottages.co.uk

Vi La Vaer ★★★
Contact: Mrs Jane Shulver,
Norfolk Country Cousins, Point
House, Ridlington, North
Walsham, Norfolk NR28 9TY
T: (01692) 650286
F: (01692) 650180
E: norfolk.cousins@netcom.
co.uk
I: www.norfolk-cottages.co.uk

SEDGEFORD
Norfolk

Lavender Cottage ★★★★
Contact: Mr & Mrs Martin
Kennedy-Hill, 9 Wheatfields,
Hillington, King's Lynn, Norfolk
PE31 6BH
T: (01485) 600850
E: mkh@tinyonline.co.uk
I: www.lavendercottage.co.uk

SHARRINGTON
Norfolk

Gable Cottage ★★
Contact: Miss M Lakey, Ash Yard,
Sharrington, Melton Constable,
Norfolk NR24 2PH
T: (01263) 860459 & 860393

Hunt Cottage and The Dairy ★★★★
Contact: 11140 Country
Holidays:10584 /, Spring Mill,
Earby, Barnoldswick, Lancashire
BB18
T: (01282) 445096
F: (011282) 844288
E: sales@ttgihg.co.uk
I: www.country-holidays.co.uk

Stone Cottage ★★★
Contact: Mrs Jane Shulver,
Norfolk Country Cousins, Point
House, Ridlington, North
Walsham, Norfolk NR28 9TY
T: (01692) 650286
F: (01692) 650180

SHEERING
Hertfordshire

No 4 The Plashets ★★★
Contact: Mrs Maureen Mills, 15
Thorley Hill, Bishop's Stortford,
Hertfordshire CM23 3ND
T: (01279) 655508
E: ian.mills.@macconvilles.com

SHELLEY
Suffolk

Ivy Tree Cottage Annexe ★★★
Contact: Mrs H Lock, Ivy Tree
Cottage, Shelley, Ipswich
IP7 5RE
T: (01473) 827632

SHERINGHAM
Norfolk

4 & 5 Seaview ★★★
Contact: Mrs Joan Munday, Keys
Holidays, 18 Station Road,
Sheringham, Norfolk NR26 8RE
T: (01263) 823010
F: (01263) 821449
E: info@keys-holidays.co.uk
I: www.keys-holidays.co.uk

The Annexe ★★
Contact: Mrs Joan Munday, Keys
Holidays, Keys Estate Agents, 18
Station Road, Sheringham,
Norfolk NR26 8RE
T: (01263) 823010
F: (01263) 821449
E: info@keys-holidays.co.uk
I: www.keys-holidays.co.uk

Augusta ★★★
Contact: Mr Trevor Claydon,
Owlet House, Laurel Drive, Holt,
Norfolk NR25 6JR
T: (01263) 713998
E: dynamictrev@
netscapeonline.co.uk
I: www.broadland.
com/selcate/shering/augusta.
html

1 The Avenue ★★★
Contact: Mrs Joan Munday, Keys
Holidays, Keys Estate Agents, 18
Station Road, Sheringham,
Norfolk NR26 8RE
T: (01263) 823010
F: (01263) 821449
E: info@keys-holidays.co.uk
I: www.keys-holidays.co.uk

Aylestone Cottage ★★★
Contact: Mrs Joan Munday, Keys
Holidays, 18 Station Road,
Sheringham, Norfolk NR26 8RE
T: (01263) 823010
F: (01263) 821449
E: info@keys-holidays.co.uk
I: www.keys-holidays.co.uk

70 Barford Road ★★
Contact: Mrs Joan Munday, Keys
Holidays, 18 Station Road,
Sheringham, Norfolk NR26 8RE
T: (01263) 823010
F: (01263) 821449
E: info@keys-holidays.co.uk
I: www.keys-holidays.co.uk

Bethel Cottage ★★★
Contact: Mrs Joan Munday, Keys
Holidays, 18 Station Road,
Sheringham, Norfolk NR26 8RE
T: (01263) 823010
F: (01263) 821449
E: info@keys-holidays.co.uk
I: www.keys-holidays.co.uk

8 Church Street ★★
Contact: Mrs Joan Munday, Keys
Holidays, 18 Station Road,
Sheringham, Norfolk NR26 8RE
T: (01263) 823010
F: (01263) 821449
E: info@keys-holidays.co.uk
I: www.keys-holidays.co.uk

23 Cremer Street ★★
Contact: Mrs Joan Munday, Keys
Holidays, 18 Station Road,
Sheringham, Norfolk NR26 8RE
T: (01263) 823010
F: (01263) 821449
E: info@keys-holidays.co.uk
I: www.keys-holidays.co.uk

10 Cromer Road ★★
Contact: Mrs Joan Munday, Keys
Holidays, 18 Station Road,
Sheringham, Norfolk NR26 8RE
T: (01263) 823010
F: (01263) 821449
E: info@keys-holidays.co.uk
I: www.keys-holidays.co.uk

1 Driftway Court ★★
Contact: Mrs Joan Munday, Keys
Holidays, Keys Estate Agents, 18
Station Road, Sheringham,
Norfolk NR26 8RE
T: (01263) 823010
F: (01263) 821449
E: info@keys-holidays.co.uk
I: www.keys-holidays.co.uk

7 Driftway Court ★★★
Contact: Mrs Joan Munday, Keys
Holidays, 18 Station Road,
Sheringham, Norfolk NR26 8RE
T: (01263) 823010
F: (01263) 821449
E: info@keys-holidays.co.uk
I: www.keys-holidays.co.uk

The Duncan ★★★
Contact: Mr & Mrs R Wolsey,
The Duncan, Burlington House,
No 2 The Esplanade,
Sheringham, Norfolk NR26 8LG
T: (01263) 821267

**Fisherman's Cottage &
Fisherman's Hyde Cottage ★★-★★★**
Contact: Mrs Bernadette
Bennett, 35 Sandilands Road,
London SW6 2BD
T: (020) 7381 0771
F: (020) 7371 0883

Flat 2 ★★
Contact: Mrs V L Muggridge,
Laburnham, 8 Warren Close,
High Kelling, Holt, Norfolk
NR25 6QX
T: (01263) 712688

Flat 3, 7 Westcliff ★★★
Contact: Mrs Joan Munday, Keys
Holidays, 18 Station Road,
Sheringham, Norfolk NR26 8RE
T: (01263) 823010
F: (01263) 821449
E: info@keys-holidays.co.uk
I: www.keys-holidays.co.uk

Flint Cottage ★★★
Contact: Mrs Joan Munday, Keys
Holidays, G A Key, 18 Station
Road, Sheringham, Norfolk
NR26 8RE
T: (01263) 823010
F: (01263) 821449
E: info@keys-holidays.co.uk
I: www.keys-holidays.co.uk

Glendalough ★★★
Contact: Mrs J Teather, 8 Cromer
Road, Sheringham, Norfolk
NR26 8RR
T: (01263) 825032
E: janetandbrian@telinco.co.uk
I: www.broadland.
com/glendalough

Hall Cottage ★★★
Contact: Mrs Jane Shulver,
Norfolk Country Cousins, Point
House, Ridlington, North
Walsham, Norfolk NR28 9TY
T: (01692) 650286
F: (01692) 650180
E: norfolk.cousins@netcom.
co.uk
I: www.norfolk-cottages.co.uk

The Haven ★★★
Contact: Mrs P Pilkington, 2
Moorgreen, Newthorpe,
Nottingham NG16 2FB
T: (01773) 763010

High Lee ★★
Contact: Mr & Mrs M J Nelson,
519 Galleywood Road,
Chelmsford, Essex CM2 8AA
T: (01245) 262436

Ivydene ★★★
Contact: Mrs Joan Munday, Keys
Holidays, 18 Station Road,
Sheringham, Norfolk NR26 8RE
T: (01263) 823010
F: (01263) 821449
E: info@keys-holidays.co.uk
I: www.keys-holidays.co.uk

Jasmine Cottage ★★★
Contact: Mrs Joan Munday, Keys
Holidays, 18 Station Road,
Sheringham, Norfolk NR26 8RE
T: (01263) 823010
F: (01263) 821449
E: info@keys-holidays.co.uk
I: www.keys-holidays.co.uk

5 Jubilee Drive ★★
Contact: Mrs Joan Munday, Keys
Holidays, 18 Station Road,
Sheringham, Norfolk NR26 8RE
T: (01263) 823010
F: (01263) 821449
E: info@keys-holidays.co.uk
I: www.keys-holidays.co.uk

Kungshallen ★★★
Contact: Mrs Joan Munday, Keys
Holidays, 18 Station Road,
Sheringham, Norfolk NR26 8RE
T: (01263) 823010
F: (01263) 821449
E: info@keys-holidays.co.uk
I: www.keys-holidays.co.uk

Marine Cottage ★★
Contact: Mrs Joan Munday, Keys
Holidays, Keys Estate Agents, 18
Station Road, Sheringham,
Norfolk NR26 8RE
T: (01263) 823010
F: (01263) 821449
E: info@keys-holidays.co.uk
I: www.keys-holidays.co.uk

Mussel Cottage & Sea Chest ★★★
Contact: Mrs Isabel Randall, 11
Whitehall Yard, Wyndham
Street, Sheringham, Norfolk
NR26 8BB
T: (01263) 820321
F: 08701 286505
E: millglade@hotmail.com

1 The Old Boathouse ★★
Contact: Mrs Joan Munday, Keys
Holidays, 18 Station Road,
Sheringham, Norfolk NR26 8RE
T: (01263) 823010
F: (01263) 821449
E: info@keys-holidays.co.uk
I: www.keys-holidays.co.uk

Old Schoolyard Cottage ★★
Contact: Mrs Joan Munday, Keys
Holidays, 18 Station Road,
Sheringham, Norfolk NR26 8RE
T: (01263) 823010
F: (01263) 821449
E: info@keys-holidays.co.uk
I: www.keys-holidays.co.uk

**Pinecones
Rating Applied For**
Contact: Mrs P Harvey,
Pinecones, 70 Cromer Road,
Sheringham, Norfolk NR26 8RT
T: (01263) 824955
F: (01263) 824955

Poppy Cottage ★★★
Contact: Mr Peter Crook, 10
Hallgate, Thorpe End, Norwich,
NR13 5DQ
T: (01603) 300324
F: (01603) 633638
E: jacqui.peter@virginnet.co.uk

8 Seaview ★★★
Contact: Mrs Joan Munday, Keys
Holidays, 18 Station Road,
Sheringham, Norfolk NR26 8RE
T: (01263) 823010
F: (01263) 821449
E: info@keys-holidays.co.uk
I: www.keys-holidays.co.uk

Spring Cottage ★★★
Contact: Mrs Joan Munday, Keys
Holidays, 18 Station Road,
Sheringham, Norfolk NR26 8RE
T: (01263) 823010
F: (01263) 821449
E: info@keys-holidays.co.uk
I: www.keys-holidays.co.uk

48 Station Road ★★★
Contact: Mrs Barbara Barker, 50
Station Road, Sheringham,
Norfolk NR26 8RG
T: (01638) 716933 &
07979 366555

Victoria Court ★★★★
Contact: Mr Graham Simmons,
Camberley, 62 Cliff Road,
Sheringham, Norfolk NR26 8BJ
T: (01263) 823101
F: (01263) 821433

10 Vista Court ★★★
Contact: Mrs Joan Munday, Keys
Holidays, 18 Station Road,
Sheringham, Norfolk NR26 8RE
T: (01263) 823010
F: (01263) 821449
E: info@keys-holidays.co.uk
I: www.keys-holidays.co.uk

4 Vista court ★★★
Contact: Mrs Joan Munday, Keys
Holidays, 18 Station Road,
Sheringham, Norfolk NR26 8RE
T: (01263) 823010
F: (01263) 821449
E: info@keys-holidays.co.uk
I: www.keys-holidays.co.uk

8 Vista Court ★★★
Contact: Mrs Joan Munday, Keys
Holidays, 18 Station Road,
Sheringham, Norfolk NR26 8RE
T: (01263) 823010
F: (01263) 821449
E: info@keys-holidays.co.uk
I: www.keys-holidays.co.uk

16 Wyndham Street ★★★
Contact: Mrs Joan Munday, Keys
Holidays, 18 Station Road,
Sheringham, Norfolk NR26 8RE
T: (01263) 823010
F: (01263) 821449
E: info@keys-holidays.co.uk
I: www.keys-holidays.co.uk

SHIPMEADOW
Suffolk

Cherry Tree Farm ★★★
Contact: Mr & Mrs Peter
Harrison, Cherry Tree Farm, Low
Road, Shipmeadow, Beccles,
Suffolk NR34 8HP
T: (01502) 711706
F: (01502) 715611
E: woodton@lineone.net
I: www.cherrytreehomepage.
com

SIBLE HEDINGHAM
Essex

Brickwall Farm ★★★★
Contact: Mrs Jean Fuller,
Brickwall Farm, Sible
Hedingham, Halstead, Essex
CO9 3RH
T: (01787) 460329 &
07885 359714
F: (01787) 460329
E: brickwallfarm@btinternet.
com

SIBTON
Suffolk

Bluebell, Bonny, Buttercup & Bertie ★★★★
Contact: Mrs Margaret Gray,
Park Farm, Sibton,
Saxmundham, Suffolk IP17 2LZ
T: (01728) 668324
F: (01728) 668564
E: margaret.gray@btinternet.
com
I: www.farnstayanglia.
co.uk/parkfarm
🏃

**Faith Cottage
Rating Applied For**
Contact: Mr & Mrs Belton,
Cardinal House, Pouy Street,
Sibton, Saxmundham, Suffolk
IP17 2JH
T: (01728) 660111

SLOLEY
Norfolk

Piggery Cottage and Hewitts Cottage★★★★
Contact: Mrs Ann Jones, Piggery
Cottage and Hewitts Cottage,
Sloley Farm, Sloley, Norwich
NR12 8HJ
T: (01692) 536281
F: (01692) 535162
E: sloley@farmhotel.u-net.com
I: www.norfolkbroads.
co.uk/sloleyfarm

SNAPE
Suffolk

The Granary ★★★★
Contact: Mrs Sally Gillett, Croft
Farm, Snape, Saxmundham,
Suffolk IP17 1QU
T: (01728) 688254
E: e.r.gillett@btinternet.com

Smithy Cottage ★★★★
Contact: Mr Richard Pither,
Suffolk Secrets, 7 Frenze Road,
Diss, IP22 4PA
T: (01379) 651297
F: (01379) 641555
E: holidays@suffolk-secrets.
co.uk
I: www.suffolk-secrets.co.uk

Valley Farm Barns ★★★★
Contact: C Nicholson, Valley
Farm Barns, Aldeburgh Road,
Snape, Saxmundham, Suffolk
IP17 1QH
T: (01728) 689071
E: chrisvalleyfarm@aol.com

Whitewalls ★★
Contact: Mr Richard Pither,
Suffolk Secrets, 7 Frenze Road,
Diss, IP22 4PA
T: (01379) 651297
F: (01379) 641555
E: holidays@suffolk-secrets.
co.uk
I: www.suffolk-secrets.co.uk

SNETTISHAM
Norfolk

Carpenters Lodge ★★★
Contact: Mr N Madgett,
Carpenters Bungalow, 6 Norton
Hill, Snettisham, King's Lynn,
Norfolk PE31 7LZ
T: (01485) 541580
E: nmmadgett@hotmail.com
I: www.carpenterslodge.co.uk

The Coach House ★★★
Contact: Mrs Marion Peters-
Loader, The Coach House,
Snettisham House, St Thomas's
Lane, Snettisham, King's Lynn,
Norfolk PE31 7RZ
T: (01485) 544902 &
07850 878095
F: (01485) 542734
E: cliveloader@hotmail.com

Cobbe Court ★★★
Contact: Mr & Mrs James
Douglas, Cobbe Court,
Snettisham House, Snettisham,
Norfolk PE31 7RZ
T: (01485) 543986

Establishments printed in blue have a detailed entry in this guide

4 The Courtyard ★★★
Contact: Mrs Jennifer Overson, 9 Fakenham Chase, Holbeach, Spalding, Lincolnshire PE12 7QU
T: (01406) 422569 &
07715 054355
E: jennyoverson@
norfolkholidaycottages.co.uk
I: www.norfolkholidaycottages.
co.uk

Cursons Cottage ★★★
Contact: Mrs A Campbell, Craven House, Lynn Road, Snettisham, King's Lynn, Norfolk PE31 7LW
T: (01485) 541179 & 535678
F: (01485) 543259
E: ian.averilcampbell@
btinternet.com

Ethelville ★★
Contact: Mrs Sandra Hohol, Birds Norfolk Holiday Homes, 62 Westgate, Hunstanton, Norfolk PE36 5EL
T: (01485) 534267
F: (01485) 535230
E: shohol@
birdsnorfolkholidayhomes.co.uk
I: www.
norfolkholidayhomes-birds.
co.uk

Hollies Cottage ★★★★
Contact: Mrs E Aldridge, The Hollies, 12 Lynn Road, Snettisham, King's Lynn, Norfolk PE31 7LS
T: (01485) 541294 &
07798 827485
F: (01485) 541294

Lancaster Lodge ★★★
Contact: Mrs Sandra Hohol, Birds Norfolk Holiday Homes, 62 Westgate, Hunstanton, Norfolk PE36 5EL
T: (01485) 534267 & 534560
F: (01485) 535230
E: shohol@
birdsnorfolkholidayshomes.co.uk
I: www.
norfolkholidayhomes-birds.
co.uk

Lavender Cottage ★★★
Contact: Mrs R Barry, 10 Jubilee Gardens, Snettisham, King's Lynn, Norfolk PE31 7RN
T: (01485) 541280

The Old Farm House Cottage ★★★
Contact: Mrs Jacqueline Sandy, The Old Farm House, Bircham Road, Snettisham, King's Lynn, Norfolk PE31 7NG
T: (01485) 543106 &
07767 868119
E: LandJSandy@ukonline.co.uk

The Smithy ★★★
Contact: Mrs Sandra Hohol, Norfolk Holiday Homes, 62 Westgate, Hunstanton, Norfolk PE36 5EL
T: (01485) 534267 & 534560
F: (01485) 535230
E: shohol@
birdsnorfolkholidayhomes.co.uk
I: www.
norfolkholidayhomes-birds.
co.uk

SOHAM
Cambridgeshire

Netherhall Manor Lodge ★★★
Contact: Holiday Cottages Ref: 50311, Holiday Cottages Group Owner Services Dept, Spring Mill, Earby, Barnoldswick, Lancashire BB18 6RN
T: (01282) 445096
F: (01282) 844288
E: sales@ttgihg.co.uk
I: www.country-holidays.co.uk

SOUTH ACRE
Norfolk

Peddars Way Cottage Holidays ★★★
Contact: Ms Sian Larrington, Peddars Way Cottage Holidays, Church Farm House, South Acre, King's Lynn, Norfolk PE32 2AD
T: (01760) 755129 &
07884 267764
E: sian@
peddarswaycottgeholidays.co.uk

SOUTH BENFLEET
Essex

Alice's Place ★★★
Contact: Mr & Mrs S Millward, 43 Danesfield, South Benfleet, Essex SS7 5EE
T: (01268) 756283
E: stevemillward@supanet.com

SOUTH CREAKE
Norfolk

Stoneycott Cottage ★★
Contact: Mrs M Haw, Fir Tree Cottage, Station Road, Brundall, Norwich NR13 5LA
T: (01603) 715588

SOUTH MIMMS
Hertfordshire

The Black Swan ★★-★★★
Contact: Mr W A Marsterson, The Black Swan, 62-64 Blanche Lane, South Mimms, Potters Bar, Hertfordshire EN6 3PD
T: (01707) 644180
F: (01707) 642344

SOUTH WOOTTON
Norfolk

Pixie Wood ★★★★
Contact: Holiday Cottages Ref: 10575, Holiday Cottages Group Owner Services Dept, Spring Mill, Earby, Barnoldswick, Lancashire BB18 6RN
T: (01282) 44544
F: (01282) 841539
E: sales@ttgihg.co.uk
I: www.country-holidays.co.uk

SOUTHBURGH
Norfolk

Chestnut Barn Annexe ★★★★
Contact: Miss Debbie Newson, New Cottage, 12 Chapel Street, Hingham, Norwich, Norfolk NR9 4JH
T: (01953) 851042
F: (01953) 850874
E: debbie.newson@btinternet.com
⛺

SOUTHEND-ON-SEA
Essex

Royal Apartments ★★★
Contact: Mrs P Monk, Royal Apartments, 12 Royal Terrace, Southend-on-Sea, SS1 1DY
T: (01702) 345323
F: (01702) 390415
E: pat@french-property.com

SOUTHMINSTER
Essex

Avonmore ★★★★
Contact: Mr & Mrs I Bull, Rose House, Poole Street, Cavendish, Sudbury, Suffolk CO10 8BD
T: (01787) 280063 & 282617
F: (01787) 282617
E: mrd@teambull.co.uk

SOUTHREPPS
Norfolk

Clipped Hedge Cottages ★★★
Contact: Mr A Blyth, 2 Vicarage Road, Sheringham, Norfolk NR26 8NH
T: (01263) 822817

SOUTHWOLD
Suffolk

Blackshore Corner ★★★★
Contact: Mr Richard Pither, Suffolk Secrets, 7 Frenze Road, Diss, IP22 4PA
T: (01379) 651297
F: (01379) 641555
E: holidays@suffolk-secrets.co.uk
I: www.suffolk-secrets.co.uk

Blackshore Cottage ★★★
Contact: Mr & Mrs Richard & Wendy Pither, Suffolk Secrets, 7 Frenze Road, Diss, IP22 4PA
T: (01379) 651297
F: (01379) 641555
E: holidays@suffolk-secrets.co.uk
I: www.suffolk-secrets.co.uk

The Blue House ★★★
Contact: Mr & Mrs Richard Pither, Suffolk Secrets, 7 Frenze Road, Diss, IP22 4PA
T: (01379) 651297
F: (01379) 641555
E: holidays@suffolk-secrets.co.uk
I: www.suffolk-secrets.co.uk

The Bolt Hole ★★★
Contact: Mr Richard Pither, Suffolk Secrets, 7 Frenze Road, Diss, IP22 4PA
T: (01379) 651297
F: (01379) 641555
E: holidays@suffolk-secrets.co.uk
I: www.suffolk-secrets.co.uk

Cherry Trees ★★★★
Contact: Mr Richard Pither, Suffolk Secrets, 7 Frenze Road, Diss, IP22 4PA
T: (01379) 651297
F: (01379) 641555
E: holidays@suffolk-secrets.co.uk
I: www.suffolk-secrets.co.uk

The Cottage ★★★★
Contact: Mr T Thomas, 2 Pier Court, Pier Avenue, Southwold, Suffolk IP18 6BL
T: (01502) 723561

Devon House ★★★
Contact: Mr & Mrs Richard & Wendy Pither, Suffolk Secrets, 7 Frenze Road, Diss, IP22 4PA
T: (01379) 651297
F: (01379) 641555
E: holidays@suffolk-secrets.co.uk
I: www.suffolk-secrets.co.uk

Fern Cottage ★★★
Contact: Mr Richard Pither, Suffolk Secrets, 7 Frenze Road, Diss, IP22 3PA
T: (01379) 651297
F: (01379) 641555
E: holidays@suffolk-secrets.co.uk
I: www.suffolk-secrets.co.uk

Harbour Cottage ★★★
Contact: Mrs S E Harris, 2 Ullswater, Carlton Colville, Lowestoft, Suffolk NR33 8WG
T: (01502) 513658 &
07860 426559

Horseshoe Cottage ★★
Contact: Debbie & Jennifer Frost & Tallon, Acanthus Property Letting Services, 9 Trinity Street, Southwold, Suffolk IP18 6JH
T: (01502) 724033 & 722806
F: (01502) 725168
E: sales@southwold-holidays.co.uk
I: www.southwold-holidays.co.uk

The Little Blue House ★★
Contact: Mrs Diana Wright, The Kiln, The Folley, Layer-de-la-Haye, Colchester CO2 0HZ
T: (01206) 738003

33 Marlborough Road ★★★
Contact: Mrs S Rawstron, 5 High Street, Watlington, Oxford, Oxfordshire OX49 5PZ
T: (01491) 613108
E: jrrawstron@attglobal.net

The Old Rope House ★★★★
Contact: Mrs Sian Mortlock, The Moorings, 16 Jermyns Road, Reydon, Southwold, Suffolk IP18 6QB
T: (01502) 724769 &
07957 613749
E: vince@vmortlovk.fsnet.co.uk
I: www.theoldropehouse.co.uk

15 Pier Avenue ★★★
Contact: Mr & Mrs Richard & Wendy Pither, Suffolk Secrets, 7 Frenze Road, Diss, IP22 4PA
T: (01379) 651297
F: (01379) 641555
E: holidays@suffolk-secrets.co.uk
I: www.suffolk-secrets.co.uk

Red Roofs ★★
Contact: Mr Richard Pither, Suffolk Secrets, 7 Frenze Road, Diss, IP22 4PA
T: (01379) 651297
F: (01379) 641555
E: holidays@suffolk-secrets.co.uk
I: www.suffolk-secrets.co.uk

Rosemary Cottage ★★★
Contact: Mr & Mrs Richard &
Wendy Pither, Suffolk Secrets, 7
Frenze Road, Diss, IP22 4PA
T: (01379) 651297
F: (01379) 641555
E: holidays@suffolk-secrets.
co.uk
I: www.suffolk-secrets.co.uk

Saltings ★★
Contact: Mr & Mrs Richard &
Wendy Pither, Suffolk Secrets, 7
Frenze Road, Diss, IP22 4PA
T: (01379) 651297
F: (01379) 641555
E: holidays@suffolk-secrets.
co.uk
I: www.suffolk-secrets.co.uk

The Shed ★★
Contact: Mr & Mrs Richard &
Wendy Pither, Suffolk Secrets, 7
Frenze Road, Diss, IP22 3PA
T: (01379) 651297
F: (01379) 641555
E: holidays@suffolk-secrets.
co.uk
I: www.suffolk-secrets.co.uk

Shell House ★★★★
Contact: Mrs Elisabeth Fairs,
Home Farm, Heveningham,
Halesworth, Suffolk IP19 0EL
T: (01986) 798250 & 798240
F: (01986) 798754

Solely Southwold ★★-★★★
Contact: Miss Kathy Oliver, 1
Sawyers Cottage, Norfolk Road,
Wangford, Southwold, Suffolk
NR34 8RE
T: (01502) 578383
F: (01502) 578383
E: kathy@solely-southwold.
co.uk
I: www.solely-southwold.co.uk

20 St James Green ★★
Contact: Mrs Doris Burley, 8
Long Marsh Close, Reydon,
Southwold, Suffolk IP18 6RS
T: (01502) 724096

Suffolk House
Rating Applied For
Contact: Mrs Betty Freeman,
Suffolk House, 18 Dunwich
Road, Southwold, Suffolk
IP18 6LJ
T: (01502) 723742

Suton Cottage ★★
Contact: Mr & Mrs Richard &
Wendy Pither, Suffolk Secrets, 7
Frenze Road, Diss, IP22 4PA
T: (01379) 651297
F: (01379) 641555
E: holidays@suffolk-secrets.
co.uk
I: www.suffolk-secrets.co.uk

SPEXHALL
Suffolk

Rose Cottage ★★★
Contact: Mrs S Hammond,
South Lodge, Redisham Hall,
Beccles, Suffolk NR34 8LZ
T: (01502) 575894

SPIXWORTH
Norfolk

**Spixworth Hall Cottages
★★★-★★★★**
Contact: Mrs Sheelah Jane Cook,
Grange Farm, Buxton Road,
Spixworth, Norwich NR10 3PR
T: (01603) 898190 & 898272
F: (01603) 897176
E: hallcottages@btinterent.com
I: www.hallcottages.co.uk
&

SPROWSTON
Norfolk

Holme ★★
Contact: Mrs P Guyton, 2
Recreation Ground Road,
Sprowston, Norwich NR7 8EN
T: (01603) 465703

STALHAM
Norfolk

144 Broadside Chalet Park ★★
Contact: Mr J J Crawford, 5
Collingwood Avenue, Surbiton,
Surrey KT5 9PT
T: (020) 8241 0658 & 8337 4487
F: (020) 8241 0658
E: crawfcall@compuserve.com
I: www.norfolkholiday.co.uk

**Teasel Stalham Yacht Services
Ltd★★★★**
Contact: Mrs J N Simpson,
Stalham Yacht Services Ltd, The
Staithe, Stalham, Norwich
NR12 9DA
T: (01692) 580288
F: (01692) 582636
E: boats@rivercraft.fsnet.co.uk
I: www.broadland.com/rivercraft

STANFIELD
Norfolk

Mangreen Farm
Rating Applied For
Contact: Mrs Moore, Mangreen
Farm, Stanfield, East Dereham,
Norfolk NR20 4HZ
T: (01328) 700272

STANHOE
Norfolk

The Barn ★★★
Contact: Holiday Cottages Ref:
2937, Holiday Cottages Group
Owner Services Dept, Spring
Mill, Earby, Barnoldswick,
Lancashire BB18 6RN
T: (01282) 445444
F: (01282) 841539
E: sales@ttging.co.uk
I: www.country-holidays.co.uk

Cherry Tree Cottage ★★★★
Contact: Mrs Warren, Cedar
House, Sharrington Road,
Brinton, Melton Constable,
Norfolk NR24 2QG
T: (01263) 862292

Fuschia Cottage ★★★
Contact: Mr M R Tinsley,
Bramble Cottage, 6 The Green,
Stanhoe, King's Lynn, Norfolk
PE31 8QE
T: (01485) 518896
F: 518896
E: tinsley@bushinternet.com

4 The Green ★★★
Contact: Mrs Priscilla Ash, New
Farm House, Moat Road,
Terrington St Clement, King's
Lynn, Norfolk PE34 4PN
T: (01553) 827157 & 810253
F: (01553) 827410

Ivy Cottage ★★★
Contact: Holiday Cottages
Ref:2289, Holiday Cottages
Group Owner Services Dept,
Spring Mill, Earby, Barnoldswick,
Lancashire BB18 6RN
T: (01282) 445096
F: (01282) 844288
E: sales@ttgihg.co.uk
I: www. country-holidays.co.uk

STANSTED MOUNTFITCHET
Essex

Walpole Farm House ★★★
Contact: Mrs Jill Walton,
Walpole Farm House, Cambridge
Road, Stansted Mountfitchet,
Stansted, Essex CM24 8TA
T: (01279) 812265
F: (01279) 812098

STIFFKEY
Norfolk

Harbour House ★★★★
Contact: Mr K R Bindley, Hill
House, 20 Hill House Road,
Norwich, Norfolk NR1 4BQ
T: (01603) 270637

Hawthorns ★★
Contact: Mrs M C Hickey-Smith,
18 Poplar Road, Histon,
Cambridge CB4 9LN
T: (01223) 572316
E: hawthorns_norfolk@
hotmail.com

Mount Tabor ★★★
Contact: Mrs P E Norris, 30
Cotswold Drive, Royton,
Oldham, Lancashire OL2 5HD
T: (0161) 6336834 &
(01263) 823320
E: roger@stiffkeycottage.fsnet.
co.uk

Primrose Cottage ★★★
Contact: Mrs T E Pearson, High
Gables, Wells Road, Stiffkey,
Wells-next-the-Sea, Norfolk
NR23 1AJ
T: (01328) 830303

Primrose Cottage ★★★
Contact: Mr N Fell, 40 Church
Street, Fordham, Ely,
Cambridgeshire CB7 5NJ
T: (01638) 721248

2 Red Lion Cottages ★★★
Contact: Ms Jane Whitaker, 8
Hollybank Cottages, The Avenue,
Comberbach, Northwich,
Cheshire CW9 6HT
T: (01606) 892368
E: jane.pathways@virgin.net

STODY
Norfolk

Glaven Cottage ★★★★
Contact: Mr & Mrs Weston,
Glaven, Brinton Road, Stody,
Melton Constable, Norfolk
NR24 2ED
T: (01263) 860222
I: www.connect.to/glaven

STOKE-BY-NAYLAND
Suffolk

**Jums Cottage and Cobbs
Cottage ★★**
Contact: Mr H Engleheart, The
Priory, Stoke-by-Nayland,
Colchester CO6 4RL
T: (01206) 262216

STOWMARKET
Suffolk

Barn Cottages ★★★★
Contact: Mrs M Tydeman,
Goldings, East End Lane,
Stonham Aspal, Stowmarket,
Suffolk IP14 6AS
T: (01449) 711229
E: maria@barncottages.co.uk
I: www.barncottages.co.uk

Woodlands ★★★★
Contact: Country Holidays Ref
7148, Spring Mill, Earby,
Barnoldswick, Lancashire BB18
T: (01282) 445096 & 844288
F: (01282) 841539
E: sales@ttgihg.co.uk
I: www.country-holidays.co.uk

STRADBROKE
Suffolk

**Water Meadow Cottages
★★★★**
Contact: Mr & Mrs David & Beryl
Johnson, The Lilacs Neavers
Lane, Stradbroke, Eye, Suffolk
IP21 5HY
T: (01379) 384407
F: (01379) 384407

STRATFORD ST ANDREW
Suffolk

Toad Hall Flat ★★★
Contact: Mr & Mrs P J Hunt,
Stratford Lodge, Stratford St
Andrew, Saxmundham, Suffolk
IP17 1LJ
T: (01728) 603463
F: (01728) 604501
E: peregrine.hunt@btinternet.
com

STRUMPSHAW
Norfolk

The Garden Wing ★★★★
Contact: Holiday Cottages Ref:
13925, Holiday Cottages Group
Owner Services Department,
Spring Mill, Earby, Barnoldswick,
Lancashire BB18 6RN
T: (01282) 445444
F: (01282) 844288
E: sales@ttgihg.co.uk
I: www.country-holidays.co.uk

SUDBURY
Suffolk

Putts ★★★
Contact: Mr & Mrs T E
Humphreys, Howe House, Gt
Hickbush, Gt Henny, Sudbury,
Suffolk CO10 7LU
T: (01787) 269507
E: howehouse@lineone.net

SURLINGHAM
Norfolk

Twitchers Rest ★★★
Contact: Mrs Janet Howes,
Kenmare House, Bramerton
Road, Surlingham, Norwich,
Norfolk NR14 7DE
T: (01508) 537031

SWAFFHAM
Norfolk

Hall Barn Cottages ★★★
Contact: Mr P Lawrence, Hall
Barn Cottages, Old Hall Lane,
Beechamwell, Swaffham,
Norfolk PE37 8BG
T: (01366) 328794
F: (01366) 328794

Establishments printed in blue have a detailed entry in this guide

SWANTON ABBOT
Norfolk

Magnolia Cottage
Rating Applied For
Contact: Mrs Christine Nockolds,
Hill Farm House, Swanton Hill,
Swanton Abbot, Norwich,
Norfolk NT10
T: (01692) 538481

SWANTON MORLEY
Norfolk

Teal and Heron Cottage ★★★
Contact: Mrs Sally Marsham,
Waterfall Farm, Worthing Road,
Swanton Morley, East Dereham,
Norfolk NR20 4QD
T: (01362) 637300 &
0797 4395571
F: (01362) 637300

SWANTON NOVERS
Norfolk

Danesway
Rating Applied For
Contact: Ms Eileen Summerlee,
18 Station Road, Thursford,
Fakenham, Norfolk NR21 0BG
T: (01263) 712062 &
(01328) 878407
E: summerleecottage@aol.com

SYDERSTONE
Norfolk

Jasmine Cottage ★★
Contact: Mrs Sandra Hohol,
Norfolk Holiday Homes, 62
Westgate, Hunstanton, Norfolk
PE36 5EL
T: (01485) 534267 & 534560
F: (01485) 535230
E: shohol@
birdsnorfolkholidayshomes.co.uk
I: www.
norfolkholidayhomes-birds.
co.uk

Nightingale Cottage ★★★
Contact: Mrs Gail Gordon, Tudor
House, High Street, Tittleshall,
King's Lynn, Norfolk PE32 2PJ
T: (01328) 700492
E: gail4steve@aol.com

TATTERSETT
Norfolk

Tat Valley Holiday Cottages
★★★–★★★★
Contact: Mr T W Hurn, Tat Valley
Holiday Cottages, Lower Farm,
Tattersett, King's Lynn, Norfolk
PE31 8RT
T: (01485) 528506
E: enquiries@
norfolkholidayhomes.co.uk
I: www.norfolkholidayhomes.
co.uk

TERRINGTON ST CLEMENT
Norfolk

Northgate Lodge Flat ★★★
Contact: Mrs J Howling,
Northgate Lodge Flat, Northgate
Lodge, 21 Northgateway,
Terrington St Clement, King's
Lynn, Norfolk PE34 4LG
T: (01553) 828428
E: jbh@interads.co.uk

THAXTED
Essex

Thaxted Holiday Cottages
★★★★
Contact: Mrs Yolanda De Bono,
Thaxted Holiday Cottages,
Totmans Farm, Dunmow Road,
Thaxted, Dunmow, Essex
CM6 2LU
T: (01371) 830233
E: enquiries@
thaxtedholidaycottages.co.uk
I: www.thaxtedholidaycottages.
co.uk

THEBERTON
Suffolk

The Stables ★★★
Contact: Mr Richard Pither,
Suffolk Secrets, 7 Frenze Road,
Diss, IP22 4PA
T: (01379) 651297
F: (01379) 641555
E: holidays@suffolk-secrets.
co.uk
I: www.suffolk-secrets.co.uk

Tea Pot Hall ★★★★★
Contact: Mr & Mrs Richard &
Wendy Pither, Suffolk Secrets, 7
Frenze Road, Diss, IP22 4PA
T: (01379) 651297
F: (01379) 641555
E: holidays@suffolk-secrets.
co.uk
I: www.suffolk-secrets.co.uk

Woodpecker Cottage ★★★
Contact: Mr & Mrs Richard &
Wendy Pither, Suffolk Secrets, 7
Frenze Road, Diss, IP22 4PA
T: (01379) 651297
F: (01379) 641555
E: holidays@suffolk-secrets.
co.uk
I: www.suffolk-secrets.co.uk

THORNAGE
Norfolk

Daisy Lodge ★★
Contact: Mrs Melanie Hickling,
Primrose Farm Barns, Back Lane,
Roughton, Norwich, Norfolk
NR11 8QR
T: (01263) 761705 &
0789 9032436

THORNHAM
Norfolk

Bay Tree Cottage ★★★
Contact: Mrs J B Wilson, Bay
Tree Cottage, High Street,
Thornham, Hunstanton, Norfolk
PE36 6LY
T: (01485) 512204

Linzel Cottage ★★★★
Contact: Mrs K Charnley, Birds
Norfolk Holiday Homes, 62
Westgate, Hunstanton, Norfolk
PE36 5EL
T: (01485) 534267
F: (01485) 535230
E: shohol@
birdsnorfolkholidayhomes.co.uk
I: www.
norfolkholidayhomes-birds.
co.uk

1 Malthouse cottages
Rating Applied For
Contact: Mrs L K Rigby, Brindle
cottage, 6 Church Hill, Castor,
Peterborough, PE5 7AU
T: (01733) 380399
F: (01733) 380399
E: leslierigby@castor.freeserve.
co.uk

8 Malthouse Court ★★★
Contact: Sue Sadler, 7
Malthouse Court, Thornham,
Hunstanton, Norfolk PE36 6NW
T: (01485) 512085
F: (01485) 512085

Manor Cottage ★★
Contact: Mrs Sandra Hohol,
Norfolk Holiday Homes, 62
Westgate, Hunstanton, Norfolk
PE36 5EL
T: (01485) 534267 & 534560
F: (01485) 535230
E: shohol@
birdsnorfolkholidayhomes.co.uk
I: www.
norfolkholidayhomes-birds.
co.uk

Manor Farm Cottages
★★★–★★★★
Contact: Mr/Mrs M Goddard,
Manor Farm House, Thornham,
Hunstanton, Norfolk PE36 6NB
T: (01485) 512272 &
07836 685266
F: (01485) 512241

Oyster Cottage ★★★
Contact: Mrs G Tibbs, Cole Green
Cottage, Sedgeford, Hunstanton,
Norfolk PE36 5LS
T: (01485) 571770 &
07711 569388
F: (01485) 571770

Rushmeadow Studio ★★★
Contact: Mr M Wyett,
Rushmeadow Studio, Main
Road, Thornham, Hunstanton,
Norfolk PE36 6LZ
T: (01485) 512372

21 Shepherds Pightle ★★★★
Contact: Mrs S Sadler, 7
Malthouse Court, Green Lane,
Thornham, Hunstanton, Norfolk
PE36 6NW
T: (01485) 512085
F: (01485) 512085

The Studio ★★★
Contact: Mrs Sandra Hohol,
Norfolk Holiday Homes, 62
Westgate, Hunstanton, Norfolk
PE36 5EL
T: (01485) 534267 & 534560
F: (01485) 535230
E: shohol@
birdsnorfolkholidayhomes.co.uk
I: www.
norfolkholidayhomes-birds.
co.uk

Sunrise ★★★★
Contact: Country Holidays REf
6048, Spring Mill, Earby,
Barnoldswick, Lancashire BB18
T: (01282) 445096
F: (01282) 844288
E: sales@ttgihg.co.uk
I: www.country-holidays.co.uk

Swiss Cottage ★★★
Contact: Mrs Sandra Hohol,
Birds Norfolk Holiday Homes, 62
Westgate, Hunstanton, Norfolk
PE36 5EL
T: (01485) 534267 & 534560
F: (01485) 535230
E: shohol@
birdsnorfolkholidayhomes.co.uk
I: www.
norfolkholidayhomes-birds.
co.uk

1 West End Cottages ★★
Contact: Mr & Mrs J K Hardy, 23
Kings Grove, Barton, Cambridge,
Cambridgeshire CB3 7AZ
T: (01223) 263859 & 207382

THORNHAM PARVA
Suffolk

Chandos Barns ★★
Contact: Mrs & Mr Judy & Kevin
O'Keefe, Chandos Barns,
Chandos Farmhouse, Thornham
Parva, Eye, Suffolk IP23 8ES
T: (01379) 783791

THORPE MARKET
Norfolk

**Poppyland Cottage &
Puddleduck Cottage**
★★★–★★★★
Contact: Mr & Mrs John & Gill
Smith, Poppyland Cottage, The
Green, Thorpe Market, Norwich,
Norfolk NR11 8AJ
T: (01263) 833219 &
07860 600489
I: www.poppyland.org.uk

THORPENESS
Suffolk

The Country Club Apartments
★★★★
Contact: Reception, Thorpeness
Golf Club and Hotel Limited, The
Golf Club, Thorpeness, Leiston,
Suffolk IP16 4NH
T: (01728) 452176
F: (01728) 453868
E: info@thorpeness.co.uk
I: www.thorpeness.co.uk

Hope Cove Cottage ★★★
Contact: Mrs Irene Pearman,
Piggotts Farm, Albury End, Ware,
Hertfordshire SG11 2HS
T: (01920) 822781
F: (01279) 771517
E: hockley@globalnet.co.uk

The House in the Clouds ★★★
Contact: Mrs S Le Comber, The
House in The Clouds, 4 Hinde
House, 14 Hinde Street, London
W1U 3BG
T: (0207) 2243615 & 0771 845
5988
F: (020) 7224 3615

7 The Uplands ★★★
Contact: Mrs Diane Holmes, 2
Red House Cottage, Uplands
Road, Thorpeness, Leiston,
Suffolk IP16 4NG
T: (01728) 454648

THROCKING
Hertfordshire
Bluntswood Hall Cottages
★★★
Contact: Mrs Sally Smyth,
Bluntswood Hall Cottages,
Bluntswood Hall, Throcking,
Buntingford, Hertfordshire
SG9 9RN
T: (01763) 281204 &
07850 425557
F: (01763) 281204
E: smyth14@hotmail.com

THURLEIGH
Bedfordshire
Scald Farm ★
Contact: Mr Reg Towler, C V
Towler & Sons, Scald Farm,
Thurleigh, Bedford MK44 2DP
T: (01234) 771996 & 772775
F: (01234) 771996
E: scaldendfarm@tesco.net

THURSFORD
Norfolk
Hayloft ★★★
Contact: Mrs Ann Green, Old
Coach House, Thursford,
Fakenham, Norfolk NR21 0BD
T: (01328) 878273

TITCHWELL
Norfolk
Parker Farm Cottages
★★★–★★★★
Contact: Mrs S Howell, 8 White
City, Titchwell, King's Lynn,
Norfolk PE31 8BD
T: (01485) 210831

TOLLESBURY
Essex
Fernleigh ★★★
Contact: Mrs Gillian Willson,
Fernleigh, 16 Woodrolfe Farm
Lane, Tollesbury, Maldon, Essex
CM9 8SX
T: (01621) 868245
F: (01621) 868245
E: gillwillson@ntlworld.com

TRIMINGHAM
Norfolk
Church Farm Cottage ★★
Contact: Mrs T M Turner, Church
Farm Cottage, Church Lane,
Trimingham, Norwich NR11 8AL
T: (01263) 833269

Poppy Cottage ★★★
Contact: Mrs Sue Bacon, Walnut
Cottage, Aylmerton, Norwich,
Norfolk NR11 8AN
T: (01263) 837672

TRIMLEY
Suffolk
Treacle Pot Cottage ★★★
Contact: Mr Richard Borley, 69
Grimston Lane, Trimley,
Felixstowe, Suffolk IP11 0SA
T: (01394) 275367

TRIMLEY ST MARTIN
Suffolk
Gemini ★★★
Contact: Mr Stephen Olden,
Gemini, 256 High Road, Trimley
St Martin, Felixstowe, Suffolk
IP11 0RG
T: (01394) 214093

TRUNCH
Norfolk
**South Cottage and Briar
Cottage ★★★**
Contact: Mr & Mrs P Lomax,
Malthouse Cottage, Mundesley
Road, Trunch, North Walsham,
Norfolk NR28 0QB
T: (01263) 721973
E: ronbet@fdn.co.uk

TUNSTALL
Suffolk
**Knoll Cottage
Rating Applied For**
Contact: Mrs J L Robinson,
Timbertop Farm, Ashfield,
Stowmarket, Suffolk IP14 6NA
T: (01728) 685084 &
07968 792321
F: (01728) 685492
E: jill@timbertop.co.uk

WALBERSWICK
Suffolk
Shrublands ★★★★
Contact: Mr & Mrs Richard
Pither, Suffolk Secrets, 7 Frenze
Road, Diss, IP22 4PA
T: (01379) 651297
F: (01379) 641555
E: holidays@suffolk-secrets.
co.uk
I: www.suffolk-secrets.co.uk

WALSHAM-LE-WILLOWS
Suffolk
Bridge Cottage ★★
Contact: Mrs H M Russell, The
Beeches, Walsham-le-Willows,
Bury St Edmunds, Suffolk
IP31 3AD
T: (01359) 259227
F: (01359) 258206

WANGFORD
Suffolk
15 Elms Lane ★★★
Contact: Mr David Weight, 4
Long Marsh Close, Reydon,
Southwold, Suffolk IP18 6RS
T: (01502) 724705
E: weight@onetel.net.uk

Strickland Cottage ★★★
Contact: Mr & Mrs Richard &
Wendy Pither, Suffolk Secrets, 7
Frenze Road, Diss, IP22 4PA
T: (01379) 651297
F: (01379) 641555
E: holidays@suffolk-secrets.
co.uk
I: www.suffolk-secrets.co.uk

WASHBROOK
Suffolk
Stebbings Cottage ★★★
Contact: Mrs Caroline Fox,
Stebbings, Back Lane,
Washbrook, Ipswich, Suffolk
IP8 3JA
T: (01473) 730216 & 0798 906
1088
E: carolinefox@netscapeonline.
co.uk

WATFORD
Hertfordshire
Banbury Terrace ★★★
Contact: Ms Beverley Gurr,
Grover Accommodations, 32
Manorville Road, Apsley, Hemel
Hempstead, Herfordshire
HP3 0AP
T: 07092 013752 &
07968 491164
F: 07092 013752
E: beverley@bravoh.freeserve.
co.uk
I: www.groveraccommodations.
co.uk

WELLS-NEXT-THE-SEA
Norfolk
Annie's ★★★
Contact: Mrs M E Musk-Rolph,
Valley Farm, East Tuddenham,
Dereham, Norfolk NR20 3NE
T: (01603) 880253

Barnacles ★★★★
Contact: Mr Andrew Wace,
Eastgate Farm, Great
Walsingham, Norfolk NR22 6AB
T: (01328) 820028 &
07768 951102
F: (01328) 821100
E: waceptnrs@farming.co.uk
I: wellstown@fsnet.co.uk

Chantry ★★★
Contact: Mrs V Jackson, 3A
Brickendon Lane, Brickendon,
Hertford SG13 8NU
T: (01992) 511303 & 503196
F: (01992) 511303

7 Chapel Yard ★★★★
Contact: Mrs Elizabeth Buxton,
Barn House, Hempstead, Holt,
Norfolk NR25 6TP
T: (01263) 714082
E: elizabethbuxton@tinyworld.
co.uk

Fisherman's Cottage ★★★
Contact: Ms Lesley Whitby, 170
Leighton Road, London
NW5 2RE
T: (020) 7679 9477 & 7485 0573
E: i.whitby@ucl.ac.uk

Gabriel Cottage ★★★★
Contact: Dr & Mr M Strong,
Saltings, East Quay, Wells-next-
the-Sea, Norfolk NR23 1LE
T: (01328) 710743

Hillside ★★★
Contact: Ms Carol Goulding,
Hillside, Plummers Hill, Wells-
next-the-Sea, Norfolk NR23 1ES
T: (01328) 710037 &
07720 588042

Holly Tree Cottage ★★★★
Contact: Mr Graham Wild, West
End House, 26 Dogger Lane,
Wells-next-the-Sea, Norfolk
NR23 1BE
T: (01328) 711190 &
(01603) 476276
E: wildatwestend@ukf.net

Honeypot Cottage ★★★
Contact: Mrs Joan Price,
Shingles, Southgate Close,
Wells-next-the-Sea, Norfolk
NR23 1HG
T: (01328) 711982
F: (01328) 711982
E: walker.al@talk21.com
I: members.tripod.
com/honeypothouse

Poppy Cottage ★★★
Contact: Mrs Christine Curtis,
Ship Cottage, East Quay, Wells-
next-the-Sea, Norfolk NR23 1LE
T: (01328) 710395

Ranters Cottage ★★★
Contact: Mrs Hilary Marsden, St
Phillips, 22 Charles Street,
Berkhamsted, Hertfordshire
HP4 3DF
T: (01442) 872486
E: george.marsden@publicis.
co.uk

5 Standard Cottages ★★★
Contact: Mrs Bridget Jones,
Appletree Cottage, 48 Dychurch
Lane, Bozeat, Wellingborough,
Northamptonshire NN29 7JP
T: (01933) 663257
E: bridget.jones@ukgateway.net
I: www.bridget.jones.ukgateway.
net

Swallow Cottage ★★★
Contact: Mrs Sue Court, Orchard
House, 11 Chapel Yard, Wells-
next-the-Sea, Norfolk NR23 1BJ
T: (01328) 711467

Swamp Cottage ★★
Contact: Mr S G Haggett, 27
Wedon Way, Bygrave, Baldock,
Hertfordshire SG7 5DX
T: (01462) 895237

Wagtails ★★★
Contact: Ms Frances Poulton, 46
Waveney Close, Wells-next-the-
Sea, Norfolk NR23 1HT
T: (01328) 710014

WELNEY
Norfolk
Biangi Bungalow ★★★
Contact: Holiday Cottages Ref:
10907, Holiday Cottages Group
Owner Services Dept, Spring
Mill, Earby, Barnoldswick,
Lancashire BB18 6RN
T: (01282) 445444
F: (01282) 841539
E: sales@ttgihg.co.uk
I: www.country-holidays.co.uk

WELWYN
Hertfordshire
**Gamekeeper's Lodge & Shire
Barn ★★★–★★★★**
Contact: Mr & Mrs Marinus
Buisman, Welwyn Home Farm
Enterprises Ltd, Lockley Farm,
Welwyn, Hertfordshire AL6 0BL
T: (01438) 718641
F: (01438) 714238
E: lockley.farm@virgin.net
I: www.lockleyfarm.co.uk

WENDENS AMBO
Essex
The Chapel (Cottage) ★★
Contact: Mrs R J Barratt, 35
Rudall Crescent, London
NW3 1RR
T: (020) 7435 1126

WENHASTON
Suffolk
**The Buntings
Rating Applied For**
Contact: Mr L E Freeman,
Halcyon House, Blyford Lane,
Wenhaston, Halesworth, Suffolk
IP19 9BS
T: (01502) 478677
F: (01502) 478677

Myrtles ★★
Contact: Mr & Mrs Richard &
Wendy Pither, Suffolk Secrets, 7
Frenze Road, Diss, IP22 4PA
T: (01379) 651297
F: (01379) 650116
E: holidays@suffolk-secrets.
co.uk
I: www.suffolk-secrets.co.uk

WEST BECKHAM
Norfolk

Flint Farm Cottages
★★-★★★
Contact: Mrs J Wilson, Flint
Farm Cottages, Chestnut Farm,
West Beckham, Holt, Norfolk
NR25 6NX
T: (01263) 822241
F: (01263) 822243
E: john@mcneil-wilson.
freeserve.co.uk

WEST MERSEA
Essex

The Oysters ★★★★
Contact: Mrs Teresa Cox,
Orchard House, 35 Empress
Avenue, West Mersea,
Colchester, Essex CO5 8EX
T: (01206) 384427
E: teresacox@aol.com

WEST RAYNHAM
Norfolk

Pollywiggle Cottage ★★★
Contact: Mrs Marilyn Farnham-
Smith, 79 Earlham Road,
Norwich, Norfolk NR2 3RE
T: (01603) 471990 & 612221
F: (01603) 612221
E: marilynfs@cwcom.net
I: www.pollywigglecottage.co.uk

24 The Street ★★
Contact: Mrs A M Hook, 19
Northolme Road, Highbury,
London N5 2UZ
T: (020) 7226 9640
F: (020) 7226 9640
E: ammlon@aol.com

WEST RUDHAM
Norfolk

North, Bertie's Cottages ★★
Contact:, Blakes, Stoney Bank
Road, Earby, Barnoldswick,
Lancashire BB94 0BL
T: 08700 708090

WEST RUNTON
Norfolk

Beacon Hill ★★
Contact: Mrs Justina Morris,
Beacon Hill, Sandy Lane, West
Runton, Cromer, Norfolk
NR27 9NB
T: (01263) 838162

Brens ★★★
Contact: Mrs Joan Munday, Keys
Holidays, G A Key, 18 Station
Road, Sheringham, Norfolk
NR26 8RE
T: (01263) 823010
F: (01263) 821449
E: info@keys-holidays.co.uk
I: www.keys-holidays.co.uk

Cove Cottage ★★★
Contact: Mrs Joan Munday, Keys
Holidays, 18 Station Road,
Sheringham, Norfolk NR26 8RE
T: (01263) 823010
F: (01263) 821449
E: info@keys-holidays.co.uk
I: www.keys-holidays.co.uk

Fursecroft ★★★
Contact: Mrs Joan Munday, Keys
Holidays, 18 Station Road,
Sheringham, Norfolk NR26 8RE
T: (01263) 823010
F: (01263) 821449
E: info@keys-holidays.co.uk
I: www.keys-holidays.co.uk

Hurlingham House ★★★
Contact: Mrs Jane Shulver,
Norfolk Country Cousins, Point
House, Ridlington, North
Walsham, Norfolk NR28 9TY
T: (01692) 650286
F: (01692) 650180
E: norfolk.cousins@netcom.
co.uk
I: www.norfolk-cottages.co.uk

Old Farm Cottage ★★★
Contact: Mrs J A Hack, 1 Abbey
Road, Sheringham, Norfolk
NR26 8HH
T: (01263) 824729
F: (01263) 825239

Roman Camp Brick Chalets
★★★
Contact: Mr J N Julian, Roman
Camp Caravan Park, West
Runton, Cromer, Norfolk
NR27 9ND
T: (01263) 837256

Roseacre Country House
★-★★
Contact: Mr & Mrs Lunken,
Roseacre Country House, West
Runton, Cromer, Norfolk
NR27 9QS
T: (01263) 837221

8 Travers Court ★★★
Contact: Mrs C L Oliver, Maple
Cottage, Arkesden Road,
Clavering, Saffron Walden, Essex
CB11 4QU
T: (01799) 550265

Woodacre 1 & 2 ★-★★
Contact: Mrs Joan Munday, Keys
Holidays, 18 Station Road,
Sheringham, Norfolk NR26 8RE
T: (01263) 823010
F: (01263) 821449
E: info@keys-holidays.co.uk
I: www.keys-holidays.co.uk

WESTCLIFF-ON-SEA
Essex

**Thames Estuary Holiday
Apartments**★★★
Contact: Mr Donald Watson, 83
Vardon Drive, Leigh-on-Sea,
Essex SS9 3SJ
T: (01702) 477255

**Thames Estuary Holiday
Apartments**
Rating Applied For
Contact: Mr & Mrs Moxon, 30
Aberdeen Gardens, Leigh-on-
Sea, Essex SS9 3RH
T: (01702) 555155 &
07905 235155
E: mandy@amoxon.freeserve.
co.uk

WESTLETON
Suffolk

Apple Tree Cottage ★★★
Contact: Mr Richard Pither,
Suffolk Secrets, 7 Frenze Road,
Diss, IP22 3PA
T: (01379) 651297
F: (01379) 641555
E: holidays@suffolk-secrets.
co.uk
I: www.suffolk-secrets.co.uk

Easter Cottage ★★★
Contact: Mr & Mrs Richard &
Wendy Pither, Suffolk Secrets, 7
Frenze Road, Diss, IP22 4PA
T: (01379) 651297
F: (01379) 641555
E: holidays@suffolk-secrets.
co.uk
I: www.suffolk-secrets.co.uk

**Ebenezer House, 1&3&5
Ebenezer Row** ★★
Contact: Mr Richard Pither,
Suffolk Secrets, 7 Frenze Road,
Diss, IP22 4PA
T: (01379) 651297
F: (01379) 641555
E: holidays@suffolk-secrets.
co.uk
I: www.suffolk-secrets.co.uk

Eversley Cottage
Rating Applied For
Contact: Welcome Cottage
Holidays, Embsay Mills, Embsay,
Skipton, North Yorkshire
BD23 6QF
T: (01756) 799999

1 Sunnyside ★★★
Contact: Mr & Mrs Richard &
Wendy Pither, Suffolk Secrets, 7
Frenze Road, Diss, IP22 4PA
T: (01379) 651297
F: (01379) 641555
E: holidays@suffolk-secrets.
co.uk
I: www.suffolk-secrets.co.uk

The Weavers ★★★
Contact: Mr & Mrs Richard &
Wendy Pither, Suffolk Secrets, 7
Frenze Road, Diss, IP22 4PA
T: (01379) 651297
F: (01379) 641555
E: holidays@suffolk-secrets.
co.uk
I: www.suffolk-secrets.co.uk

WEYBOURNE
Norfolk

Bolding Way Holiday Cottages
★★★-★★★★
Contact: Mr Charlie Harrison,
Bolding Way Holiday Cottages,
The Stables, Bolding Way,
Weybourne, Holt, Norfolk
NR25 7SW
T: (01263) 588666
F: (01263) 588666
E: holidays@boldingway.co.uk
I: www.boldingway.co.uk

The Coach House ★★★
Contact: Mr & Mrs Charles
Lacoste, Rosedale Farm
Guesthouse, Holt Road,
Weybourne, Holt, Norfolk
NR25 7ST
T: (01263) 588778 &
07760 493538
E: rosedale.lacostes@tinyworld.
co.uk
I: www.sheringham-network.
co.uk/rosedale

Home Farm Cottage ★★★
Contact: Mrs Sally Middleton,
Home Farm Cottage, Home
Farm, Holt Road, Weybourne,
Holt, Norfolk NR25 7ST
T: (01263) 588334

Lower Byre
Rating Applied For
Contact: Ms Valerie James, 5
Birch Grove, Spalding,
Lincolnshire PE11 2HL
T: (01775) 760938
T: (01775) 762856
E: val@5birchgrove.co.uk

The Old Stables ★★★
Contact: Mr Hudson, Field
House, Sheringham Road,
Weybourne, Holt, Norfolk
NR25 7EY
T: (01263) 588231
F: (01263) 588231

Trailer Cottage ★★★
Contact: Mrs Joan Munday, Keys
Holidays, 18 Station Road,
Sheringham, Norfolk NR26 8RE
T: (01263) 823010
F: (01263) 821449
E: info@keys-holidays.co.uk
I: www.keys-holidays.co.uk

The Treehouse ★★
Contact: Mrs Sharon Moss, Ash
Tree Cottage, Mill Road, Thorpe
Abbotts, Diss, Norfolk IP21 4HX
T: (01379) 668225

Well Cottage ★★★
Contact: Mrs J A Pinnington,
Well Cottage, Springs, Sandy Hill
Lane, Weybourne, Holt, Norfolk
NR25 7HW
T: (01263) 588276
I: www.exploring.co.uk

Weybourne Forest Lodges
Rating Applied For
Contact: Mr & Mrs Chris & Sue
Tansley, Weybourne Forest
Lodges, Sandy Hill Lane,
Weybourne, Holt, Norfolk
NR25 7HW
T: (01263) 588440
F: (01263) 588588

Weybourne Holiday Homes
★★★
Contact: Mrs S M Lawson,
Weybourne Holiday Homes,
Weybourne Hall Holiday Park,
Weybourne, Holt, Norfolk
NR25 7EX
T: (01263) 588356
E: weyholhome@aol.com

WHEPSTEAD
Suffolk

Rowney Cottage ★★★
Contact: Mrs Kati Turner,
Rowney Farm, Whepstead, Bury
St Edmunds, Suffolk IP29 4TQ
T: (01284) 735842 &
07957 758848
F: (01284) 735842

WHISSONSETT
Norfolk

No 2 Sunnyside ★★★
Contact: Mrs T J Rand, The
Dibblers, Gormans Lane, Colkirk,
Fakenham, Norfolk NR21 7NP
T: (01328) 855960
F: (01328) 864745
E: teresa.rand@virgin.net

WICKHAM SKEITH
Suffolk
The Netus ★★★
Contact: Mrs Joy Homan, Street
Farm, Wickham Skeith, Eye,
Suffolk IP23 8LP
T: (01449) 766275

WICKMERE
Norfolk
Swallow Cottages (Poppyland
Holiday Cottages)★★★★
Contact: Mr & Mrs Riches, 21
Regent Street, Wickmere,
Norwich, Norfolk NR11 7ND
T: (01263) 577473
F: (01263) 570087
E: poppyland@totalise.co.uk
I: www.broadland.
com/poppyland

WIGHTON
Norfolk
Malthouse ★★★
Contact: Mrs Linden Green,
Whey Curd Farm, Copys Green,
Wighton, Wells-next-the-Sea,
Norfolk NR23 1NY
T: (01328) 820204 & 820175
F: (01328) 820175
I: t.b.green@lineone.net

WILBURTON
Cambridgeshire
Florrie's Holiday Cottage
Rating Applied For
Contact: Mr & Mrs Roy &
Barbara Griffiths, 1 Station
Cottages, Station Road,
Wilburton, Ely, Cambridgeshire
CB6 3PZ
T: (01353) 740101
E: info@florries.co.uk
I: www.florries.co.uk

WINGFIELD
Suffolk
Keeley's Farm ★★★
Contact: Mrs Gloria Elsden,
Keeley's Farm, Solomon Place,
Syleham, Eye, Suffolk IP21 4LT
T: (01379) 668409 & 586382

WINTERTON-ON-SEA
Norfolk
Transacre Ltd ★★★★
Contact: Mrs Penny Beard,
Transacre Ltd, Burnley Hall, East
Somerton, Great Yarmouth,
Norfolk NR29 4DZ
T: (01493) 393206
F: (01493) 393745
E: penny@burnleyhall.co.uk

WISBECH
Cambridgeshire
Common Right Barns ★★★★
Contact: Mrs T M Fowler,
Common Right Barns, Common
Right Farm, Plash Drove,
Wisbech St Mary, Wisbech,
Cambridgeshire PE13 4SP
T: (01945) 410424
F: (01945) 410424
E: teresa@commonrightbarns.
co.uk
I: www.commonrightbarns.co.uk

WIVETON
Norfolk
Laneway Cottage ★★★★
Contact: Mrs Catherine Joice,
Colkirk Hall, Colkirk, Fakenham,
Norfolk NR21 7ND
T: (01328) 862261
F: (01328) 856464
E: charles.joice@btinternet.com

WOOD NORTON
Norfolk
The Small Barn ★★★
Contact: Miss M J Lister, The
Small Barn, Severals Grange,
Holt Road, Wood Norton, East
Dereham, Norfolk NR20 5BL
T: (01362) 684206

WOODBRIDGE
Suffolk
Colston Hall Cottage ★★★
Contact: Mr J Bellefontaine,
Colston Hall Cottage, Colston
Hall, Badingham, Woodbridge,
Suffolk IP13 8LB
T: (01728) 638375 &
07850 869744
F: (01728) 638084

The Cottage ★★★
Contact: Mr & Mrs Andrew
Brown, 7A Catherine Road,
Woodbridge, Suffolk IP12 4JP
T: (01394) 384355 & 382732

Easton Farm Park ★★★★
Contact: Mr Mark Clixby, Easton
Farm Park, Easton, Woodbridge,
Suffolk IP13 0EQ
T: (01728) 746475
F: (01728) 747861
E: easton@eastonfarmpark.
co.uk
I: www.eastonfarmpark.co.uk

Mousehole Cottage ★★★
Contact: Mr John Hammond, 34
Seckford Street, Woodbridge,
Suffolk IP12 4LY
T: (01394) 386253
F: (01394) 384007
E: john_hammond@talk21.com.
uk
I: www.cottageguide.
co.uk/mousehole

Quayside Cottage ★★★
Contact: Mr Richard Leigh,
Quayside, The Quay,
Waldringfield, Woodbridge,
Suffolk IP12 4QZ
T: (01473) 736724
E: quayside@waldringfield.org.
uk

Sampsons Mill ★★★
Contact: Mrs S Turner,
Sampsons Mill, 21 Mill Lane,
Wickham Market, Woodbridge,
Suffolk IP13 0SF
T: (01728) 746791
F: (01728) 746791
E: sampsons.mill@virgin.net

WOOLPIT
Suffolk
The Bothy ★★★★
Contact: Mrs Kathryn Parker,
Grange Farm, Woolpit Green,
Woolpit, Bury St Edmunds,
Suffolk IP30 9RG
T: (01359) 241143
F: (01359) 244296
E: grangefarm@btinternet.com
I: www.farmstayanglia.
co.uk/grangefarm/

WORTHAM
Suffolk
Ivy House Farm
★★★–★★★★
Contact: Mr & Mrs Paul Bradley,
Ivy House Farm, Wortham, Diss,
Norfolk IP22 1RD
T: (01379) 898395
E: prjsbrad@aol.com
I: wwwholidaycottagesnorfolk.
go.uk

Olde Tea Shop Apartment
★★★★
Contact: Mrs A P Dumbell, Post
Office Stores, Wortham, Diss,
Norfolk IP22 1PP
T: (01379) 783210
E: teashop@wortham.freeserve.
co.uk

WORTHING
Norfolk
Mill Stream Cottages ★★★
Contact: HC Ref: 13153/4/5/6/7,
Holiday Cottages Group Owner
Services Dept, Spring Mill, Earby,
Barnoldswick, Lancashire
BB18 6RN
T: (01282) 445096
F: (01282) 844288
E: sales@ttgihg.co.uk
I: www.country-holidays.co.uk

WRENTHAM
Suffolk
Rose Cottage ★★★
Contact: Mrs Marion Hall, White
House Farm, West End,
Wrentham, Beccles, Suffolk
NR34 7NE
T: (01502) 675271 & 675694
E: marion@whitehouse52.
freeserve.co.uk
I: www.crosswinds.freeserve.
co.uk

Summer Cottage ★★★
Contact: Mrs Meades, 47 Cotmer
Road, Oulton Broad, Lowestoft,
Suffolk NR33 9PS
T: (01502) 568122

WROXHAM
Norfolk
Daisy Broad Lodges ★★★★
Contact: Mr Daniel Thwaites,
Barns Brinkcraft, Riverside Road,
Wroxham, Norwich, Norfolk
NR12 8UD
T: (01603) 782625 & 782333
F: (01603) 784072
E: daniel@barnesbrinkcraft.
co.uk
I: www.barnesbrinkcraft.co.uk

Kingfisher Lodge ★★★★
Contact: Mrs D Campling,
Fineway Cruises, Riverside Road,
Wroxham, Norwich NR12 8UD
T: (01603) 782309
F: (01603) 784838
E: steve@fineway.freeserve.
co.uk
I: www.finewayleisure.co.uk

Peninsula Cottages and Leisure
Centre★★★
Contact: Mrs S Pollock,
Peninsula Cottages and Leisure
Centre, Moore and Co,
Staitheway Road, Wroxham,
Norwich NR12 8RX
T: (01603) 783311
F: (01603) 784295
E: mooresboats@aol.com

Whitegates Apartment ★★★
Contact: Mrs CM Youd,
Whitegates Apartment, 181
Norwich Road, Wroxham,
Norwich NR12 8RZ
T: (01603) 781037

Establishments printed in blue have a detailed entry in this guide

SOUTH WEST

ABBOTSBURY
Dorset

The Cottage ★★★
Contact: Mrs Val Dredge, The
Cottage, Grove Lane,
Abbotsbury, Weymouth, Dorset
DT3 4JH
T: (01305) 871462
E: val@thecottage-abbotsbury.
co.uk
I: www.thecottage-abbotsbury.
co.uk

**Elworth Farmhouse Cottage
★★★★**
Contact: Mrs C Wade, Elworth
Farmhouse, West Elworth,
Abbotsbury, Weymouth, Dorset
DT3 4HF
T: (01305) 871693
E: jdwade@aol.com
I: www.elworth.supanet.com

**Gorwell Farm Cottages
★★★★★**
Contact: Mrs J M Pengelly, M J
Pengelly Ltd, Gorwell Farm,
Abbotsbury, Weymouth, Dorset
DT3 4JX
T: (01305) 871401
F: (01305) 871441
E: mary@gorwellfarm.co.uk
I: www.gorwellfarm.co.uk

The Old Coastguards ★★★★
Contact: Mrs Cheryl Varley, The
Old Coastguards, Abbotsbury,
Weymouth, Dorset DT3 4LB
T: (01305) 871335
F: (01305) 871766
E: reception@oldcoastguards.
com
I: www.oldcoastguards.com

ABBOTSHAM
Devon

Bowood Farm ★★★★
Contact: Toad Hall Cottages,
Elliot House, Church Street,
Kingsbridge, Devon TQ7 1BY
T: (01548) 521366
F: (01548) 853086
E: thc@toadhallcottages.com
I: www.toadhallcottages.com

ABBOTSKERSWELL
Devon

3 Elm Cottages ★★★
Contact: Mrs Buckpitt, 3 Elm
Cottages, Abbotskerswell,
Newton Abbot, Devon TQ12
T: (01626) 334053

ADSBOROUGH
Somerset

**Adsborough Farm Barn
★★★★**
Contact: CH ref: 851, Holiday
Cottages Group, Spring Mill,
Earby, Barnoldswick, Lancashire
BB18 6RN
T: (01282) 445096
F: (01282) 844299
E: ch.sales@ttgihg.co.uk
I: www.country-holidays.co.uk

ADVENT
Cornwall

Aldermoor ★★★-★★★★★
Contact: Mrs H Golding,
Aldermoor, Advent, Camelford,
Cornwall PL32 9QQ
T: (01840) 213366
F: (01840) 213366

Little Parkwalls ★★★★
Contact: Mr & Mrs Bowater,
Helpful Holidays, Mill Street,
Chagford, Newton Abbot, Devon
TQ13 8AW
T: (01647) 433593
F: (01647) 433694
E: help@helpfulholidays.com
I: www.helpfulholidays.com

ALCOMBE
Somerset

Flat 4 Bhairab ★★★
Contact: Mr T R Brewer, Flat 4
Bhairab, 17 Manor Road,
Alcombe, Minehead, Somerset
TA24 6EH
T: (01643) 706790

ALHAMPTON
Somerset

The Truckle ★★★★
Contact: Dr M Labanowska, The
Truckle, Langford Farmhouse,
Alhampton, Shepton Mallet,
Somerset BA4 6PY
T: (01749) 860611
F: (01749) 860342
E: margy@thetruckle.co.uk
I: www.thetruckle.co.uk

ALLERFORD
Somerset

**Lynch Country House Holiday
Apartments★★★★**
Contact: Mr and Mrs B Tacchi,
Lynch Country House Holiday
Apartments, Allerford,
Minehead, Somerset TA24 8HJ
T: (01643) 862800
F: (01643) 862800
E: admin@lynchcountryhouse.
co.uk
I: www.lynchcountryhouse.co.uk

The Pack Horse ★★★
Contact: Mr & Mrs Garner, The
Pack Horse, Allerford, Minehead,
Somerset TA24 8HW
T: (01643) 862475
F: (01643) 862475
E: holidays@thepackhorse.
freewire.co.uk
I: www.thepackhorse.net

AMESBURY
Wiltshire

The Stables ★★★★
Contact: Mrs A Thatcher, Ivy
Cottage, Netheravon, Salisbury,
SP4 9QW
T: (01980) 670557
F: (01980) 670557
E: athatcher@bigfoot.com
I: www.oas.
co.uk/ukcottages/thestables

APPLEDORE
Devon

**Appledown
Rating Applied For**
Contact: Appledore Holiday
Letting Agency, 20 Market
Street, Appledore, Bideford,
Devon EX39 1PW
T: (01237) 476191
F: (01237) 479621
E: enquiries@appledore-letting.
co.uk
I: www.appledore-letting.co.uk

Bosuns Haven ★★
Contact: Appledore Holiday
Letting Agency Agency, 20
Market Street, Appledore,
Bideford, Devon EX39 1PW
T: (01237) 476191
F: (01237) 479621
E: enquiries@appledore-letting.
co.uk
I: www.appledore-letting.co.uk

Cobble Cottage ★★
Contact: Appledore Holiday
Letting Agency Agency, 20
Market Street, Appledore,
Bideford, Devon EX39 1PW
T: (01237) 476191
F: (01237) 479621
E: enquiries@appledore-letting.
co.uk
I: www.appledore-letting.co.uk

Cockle Cottage ★★★
Contact: Mrs Marilyn Hughes,
20 Francis Drive, Westward Ho!,
Bideford, Devon EX39 1XE
T: (01237) 425574
E: cocklecottage@littlenaze.
freeserve.co.uk
I: www.littlenaze.freeserve.
co.uk/cocklecottage/

Dolls House ★★
Contact: Appledore Holiday
Letting Agency, 20 Market
Street, Appledore, Bideford,
Devon EX39 1PW
T: (01237) 476191
F: (01237) 479621
E: enquiries@appledore-letting.
co.uk
I: www.appledore-letting.co.uk

Gannets Nest ★★★
Contact: Appledore Holiday
Letting Agency Agency, 20
Market Street, Appledore,
Bideford, Devon EX39 1PW
T: (01237) 476191
F: (01237) 479621
E: enquiries@appledore-letting.
co.uk
I: www.appledore-letting.co.uk

5 Hillcliffe Terrace ★★★
Contact: Appledore Holiday
Letting Agency Agency, 20
Market Street, Appledore,
Bideford, Devon EX39 1PW
T: (01237) 476191
F: (01237) 479621
E: enquiries@appledore-letting.
co.uk
I: www.appledore-letting.co.uk

Honeymoon Cottage ★★★
Contact: Appledore Holiday
Letting Agency, 20 Market
Street, Appledore, Bideford,
Devon EX39 1PW
T: (01237) 476191
F: (01237) 479621
E: enquiries@appledore-letting.
co.uk
I: www.appledore-letting.co.uk

2 Ibex Court ★★
Contact: Appledore Holiday
Letting Agency, 20 Market
Street, Appledore, Bideford,
Devon EX39 1PW
T: (01237) 476191
F: (01237) 479621
E: enquiries@appledore-letting.
co.uk
I: www.appledore-letting.co.uk

131 Irsha Street ★★
Contact: Appledore Holiday
Letting Agency Agency, 20
Market Street, Appledore,
Bideford, Devon EX39 1PW
T: (01237) 476191
F: (01237) 479621
E: enquiries@appledore-letting.
co.uk
I: www.appledore-letting.co.uk

71 Irsha Street ★★★
Contact: Appledore Holiday
Letting Agency, 20 Market
Street, Appledore, Bideford,
Devon EX39 1PW
T: (01237) 476191
F: (01237) 479621
E: enquiries@appledore-letting.
co.uk
I: www.appledore-letting.co.uk

2 The Maltings ★★
Contact: Appledore Holiday
Letting Agency Agency, 20
Market Street, Appledore,
Bideford, Devon EX39 1PW
T: (01237) 476191
F: (01237) 479621
E: enquiries@appledore-letting.
co.uk
I: www.appledore-letting.co.uk

38 Market Street ★★★
Contact: Appledore Holiday
Letting Agency, 20 Market
Street, Appledore, Bideford,
Devon EX39 1PW
T: (01237) 476191
F: (01237) 479621
E: enquiries@appledore-letting.
co.uk
I: www.appledore-letting.co.uk

**Meander, Bimbo's and Two
Rivers ★★★**
Contact: Mr Peter Morris, Farm
& Cottage Holidays, Victoria
House, 12 Fore Street, Northam,
Bideford, Devon EX39 1AW
T: (01237) 479146
F: (01237) 421512
E: farmcott@cix.co.uk
I: www.farmcott.co.uk

31 Meeting Street ★★
Contact: Appledore Holiday
Lertting Agency Agency, 20
Market Street, Appledore,
Bideford, Devon EX39 1PW
T: (01237) 476191
F: (01237) 479621
E: enquiries@appledore-letting.
co.uk
I: www.appledore-letting.co.uk

Old Coastguards ★
Contact: Appledore Holiday
Letting Agency Agency, 20
Market Street, Appledore,
Bideford, Devon EX39 1PW
T: (01237) 476191
F: (01237) 479621
E: enquiries@appledore-letting.
co.uk
I: www.appledore-letting.co.uk

Puffin ★★★★
Contact: Mrs Rita Skinner,
Manor Cottage, Cot Manor,
Landkey Road, Newport,
Barnstaple, Devon EX32 9BL
T: (01271) 342929
F: (01271) 342929
E: Rita@adhoc.force9.co.uk

Quay House ★★
Contact: Appledore Holiday
Letting Agency Agency, 20
Market Street, Appledore,
Bideford, Devon EX39 1PW
T: (01237) 476191
F: (01237) 479621
E: enquiries@appledore-letting.
co.uk
I: www.appledore-letting.co.uk

Quayside Cottage
Rating Applied For
Contact: Appledore LHoliday
Letting Agency Agency, 20
Market Street, Appledore,
Bideford, Devon EX39 1PW
T: (01237) 476191
F: (01237) 479621
E: enquiries@appledore-letting.
co.uk
I: www.appledore-letting.co.uk

Sailmakers ★★
Contact: Mrs S A Palmer,
Marlheath, 179 Old Woking
Road, Maybury, Woking, Surrey
GU22 8HP
T: (01483) 761982

Sandridge ★★
Contact: Appledore Holiday
Letting Agency Agency, 20
Market Street, Appledore,
Bideford, Devon EX39 1PW
T: (01237) 476191
F: (01237) 479621
E: enquiries@appledore-letting.
co.uk
I: www.appledore-letting.co.uk

Trinity Cottage ★★★
Contact: Appledore Holiday
Letting Agency, 20 Market
Street, Appledore, Bideford,
Devon EX39 1PW
T: (01237) 476191
F: (01237) 479621
E: enquiries@appledore-letting.
co.uk
I: www.appledore-letting.co.uk

Tunnel Cottage ★★★
Contact: Appledore Holiday
Letting Agency, 20 Market
Street, Appledore, Bideford,
Devon EX39 1PW
T: (01237) 476191
F: (01237) 479621
E: enquiries@appledore-letting.
co.uk
I: www.appledore-letting.co.uk

The Waterfront ★★★★★
Contact: Mr Peter Morris, Farm
& Cottage Holidays, Victoria
House, 12 Fore Street, Northam,
Bideford, Devon EX39 1AW
T: (01237) 479146
F: (01237) 421512
E: farmcott@cix.co.uk
I: www.farmcott.co.uk

APPLEY
Somerset

Stone Barn Cottage ★★★
Contact: Mrs A Champion,
Appley Court Farm, Appley, Nr
Wellington, Somerset TA21 0HJ
T: (01823) 673263
F: (01823) 673287
E: goappleycourt@aol.com

ASHBRITTLE
Somerset

The Old Dairy ★★★★
Contact: Mr & Mrs CR Buswell,
Chackeridge Farm, Ashbrittle,
Wellington, Somerset TA21 0LT
T: (01823) 672757

ASHBURTON
Devon

Stares Nest Cottage ★★
Contact: Mrs Anne Mortimore,
Hazelwood, Holne, Ashburton,
Devon TQ13 7SJ
T: (01364) 631235

Wooder Manor Holiday Homes
★★-★★★
Contact: Mrs Angela Bell,
Wooder Manor Holiday Homes,
Widecombe-in-the-Moor,
Newton Abbot, Devon TQ13 7TR
T: (01364) 621391
F: (01364) 621391
E: angelabell@woodermanor.
co.uk
I: www.woodermanor.co.uk

Wren & Robin Lodges ★★★
Contact: Mrs Margaret Phipps,
Wren & Robin Lodges, New Cott
Farm, Poundsgate, Ashburton,
Newton Abbot, Devon TQ13 7PD
T: (01364) 631421
I: www.newcott-farm.co.uk

ASHCOTT
Somerset

Huckham Cottage ★★★
Contact: CH ref: 8862, Holiday
Cottages Group Owner Services
Dept, Spring Mill, Earby,
Barnoldswick, Lancashire
BB18 6RN
T: (01282) 445096
F: (01282) 844299
E: ch.sales@ttgihg.co.uk
I: www.country-holidays.co.uk

ASHFORD
Devon

Ashford Holt Cottage ★★
Contact: Toad Hall Cottages,
Elliot House, Church Street,
Kingsbridge, Devon TQ7 1BY
T: (01548) 521366
F: (01548) 853086
E: thc@toadhallcottages.com
I: www.toadhallcottages.com

Helliers Farm ★★★★
Contact: Mr & Mrs Bowater,
Helpful Holidays, Mill Street,
Chagford, Newton Abbot, Devon
TQ13 8AW
T: (01647) 433593
F: (01647) 433694
E: help@helpfulholidays.com
I: www.helpfulholidays.com

Incledon Barn ★★★
Contact: Marsden's Cottage
Holidays, 2 The Square,
Braunton, Devon EX33 2JB
T: (01271) 813777
F: (01271) 813664
E: holidays@marsdens.co.uk
I: www.marsdens.co.uk

Luscott Barton ★★★
Contact: CH ref: 9289, Holiday
Cottages Group Owner Services
Dept, Spring Mill, Earby,
Barnoldswick, Lancashire
BB94 0AA
T: (01282) 445096
F: (01282) 844299
E: ch.sales@ttgihg.co.uk
I: www.country-holidays.co.uk

ASHPRINGTON
Devon

The Shippon ★★★
Contact: Mr & Mrs Bowater,
Helpful Holidays, Mill Street,
Chagford, Newton Abbot, Devon
TQ13 8AW
T: (01647) 433593
F: (01647) 433694
E: help@helpfulholidays.com
I: www.helpfulholidays.com

ASHREIGNEY
Devon

Colehouse Farm ★★★★
Contact: Mr Peter Morris, Farm
& Cottage Holidays, Victoria
House, 12 Fore Street, Northam,
Bideford, Devon EX39 1AW
T: (01237) 479146
F: (01237) 421512
E: farmcott@cix.co.uk
I: www.farmcott.co.uk

Northcott Barton Farm
Holiday Cottage ★★★
Contact: Mrs S J Gay, Northcott
Barton Farm Holiday Cottage,
Northcott Barton, Ashreigney,
Chulmleigh, Devon EX18 9PR
T: (01769) 520259
I: www.bigwig.
net/northcott_farm

ASHTON
Cornwall

Veronica Cottage ★★★
Contact: CH ref: 11330, Holiday
Cottages Group Owner Services
Dept, Spring Mill, Earby,
Barnoldswick, Lancashire
BB18 6RN
T: (01282) 445096
F: (01282) 844299
E: ch.sales@ttgihg.co.uk
I: www.country-holidays.co.uk

ASHWATER
Devon

Blagdon Farm Country
Holidays ★★★★-★★★★★
Contact: Mr and Mrs A W Blight,
Blagdon Farm Country Holidays,
Ashwater, Beaworthy, Devon
EX21 5DF
T: (01409) 211509 &
07768 666139
F: (01409) 211510
E: Blagfarm@Netcomuk.co.uk
♿

Braddon Cottages ★★★
Contact: Mr & Mrs George &
Anne Ridge, Braddon Cottages,
Ashwater, Beaworthy, Devon
EX21 5EP
T: (01409) 211350
F: (01409) 211350
I: www.braddoncottages.co.uk

ASKERSWELL
Dorset

Court Farm Cottages
★★★★-★★★★★
Contact: Mrs Rebecca Bryan,
Court Farm Cottages, Askerswell,
Dorchester, Dorset DT2 9EJ
T: (01308) 485668
F: (01308) 485074
E: courtfarmcottages@eclipse.
co.uk
I: www.eclipse.
co.uk/courtfarmcottages/
webpg2

Little Court ★★★★
Contact: Mr L A Vickery, The
Barn House, Moens Farm,
Uploders, Bridport, Dorset
DT6 4PH
T: (01308) 421933
E: vicklen@tesco.net

Little Grey Cottage ★★★
Contact: Mrs M Machin, Little
Grey Cottage, Askerswell,
Dorchester, Dorset DT2 9EL
T: (01308) 485317
E: mmachin@mmachin.
eurobell.co.uk
I: www.users.globalnet.
co.uk/~ahcltd/
littlegreybrochure.htm

West Hembury Farm ★★★★
Contact: Dr & Mrs A Hunt, West
Hembury Farm, Askerswell,
Dorchester, Dorset DT2 9EN
T: (01308) 485289
F: (01308) 485041
E: hunt@westhembury.com
I: www.westhembury.com

Establishments printed in blue have a detailed entry in this guide

AWLISCOMBE
Devon

Godford Farm ★★★
Contact: Mrs S Lawrence,
Godford Farm, Otter Holt and
Owl Hayes, Awliscombe,
Honiton, Devon EX14 3PW
T: (01404) 42825
F: (01404) 42825
E: lawrencesally@hotmail.com
I: www.devon-farm-holidays.
co.uk

**Wessington Farm Cottage
★★★**
Contact: Mr Peter Morris, Farm
& Cottage Holidays, Victoria
House, 12 Fore Street, Northam,
Bideford, Devon EX39 1AW
T: (01237) 479146
F: (01237) 421512
E: farmcott@cix.co.uk
I: www.farmcott.co.uk

AXMINSTER
Devon

**Furzeleigh House Country
Cottages
Rating Applied For**
Contact: Mr & Mrs Rob & Shirley
Blatchford, Furzeleigh House
Country Cottages, Lyme Road,
Axminster, Devon EX13 5SW
T: (01297) 34448

Hilltop ★★★
Contact: Mrs A Morris,
Townshayne Farm, Northleigh,
Colyton, Devon EX24 6BU
T: (01404) 831714

**Symondsdown Cottages
★★-★★★**
Contact: Mr and Mrs S Hynds,
Symondsdown Cottages,
Woodbury Lane, Woodbury
Cross, Axminster, Devon
EX13 5TL
T: (01297) 32385

AXMOUTH
Devon

**Combe Farm Cottages
★★-★★★**
Contact: CH Ref: 13901, 2,3,
Country Holidays, Spring Mill,
Earby, Barnoldswick, Lancashire
BB18 6RN
T: (01282) 445096
F: (01282) 844299
E: ch.sales@ttgihg.co.uk
I: www.country-holidays.co.uk

Herons ★★★
Contact: CH Ref: 15246, Holiday
Cottages Group, Spring Mill,
Earby, Barnoldswick, Lancashire
BB18 6RN
T: (01282) 445096
F: (01282) 844299
E: ch.sales@ttgihg.co.uk
I: www.country-holidays.co.uk

Stepps Barn ★★★★★
Contact: Jean Bartlett Cottage
Holidays, Fore Street, Beer,
Seaton, Devon EX12 3JB
T: (01297) 23221
F: (01297) 23303
E: jeanb@netbreaks.com
I: www.netbreaks.com/jeanb

AYLESBEARE
Devon

Alpine Park Cottages ★★★
Contact: Mrs W Atkin, Alpine
Park Cottages, Sidmouth Road,
Aylesbeare, Exeter EX5 2JW
T: (01395) 233619

BABBACOMBE
Devon

The Beeches ★★
Contact: Holiday Homes &
Cottages South West, 365a
Torquay Road, Paignton, Devon
TQ3 2BT
T: (01803) 663650
F: (01803) 664037
E: holcotts@aol.com
I: www.swcottages.co.uk

Sunnybank ★★★
Contact: Holiday Homes &
Cottages South West, 365A
Torquay Road, Paignton, Devon
TQ3 2BT
T: (01803) 663650
F: (01803) 664037
E: holcotts@aol.com
I: www.swcottages.co.uk

Willow Cottage ★★★
Contact: Holiday Homes &
Cottages South West, 365A
Torquay Road, Paignton, Devon
TQ3 2BT
T: (01803) 663650
F: (01803) 664037
E: holcotts@aol.com
I: www.swcottages.co.uk

BAMPTON
Devon

Glenlyn ★★★
Contact: Mr & Mrs M Van Riel,
Glenlyn, Shillingford Road,
Bampton, Tiverton, Devon
EX16 9AD
T: (01398) 331432
F: (01398) 331432
E: vanriel_glenlnuk@brnet.net

Three Gates Farm ★★★★
Contact: Mrs Alison Spencer,
Three Gates Farm, Huntsham,
Tiverton, Devon EX16 7QH
T: (01398) 331280

Veltham Cottages ★★★
Contact: Mrs Pauline Krombas,
Veltham Cottages, Veltham
House, Morebath, Tiverton,
Devon EX16 9AL
T: (01398) 331465 &
(01392) 274039
F: (01392) 425529

Westbrook House ★★★
Contact: Mrs Patricia Currie,
Westbrook House, Bampton,
Tiverton, Devon EX16 9HU
T: (01398) 331418
F: (01398) 331418
E: brian@currie.co.uk
I: www.westbrookhouse.co.uk

Wonham Barton ★★★
Contact: Mrs A McLean
Williams, Wonham Barton,
Bampton, Tiverton, Devon
EX16 9JZ
T: (01398) 331312
F: (01398) 331312
E: anne@devonfarms.co.uk
I: www.devonfarms.co.uk

BARBROOK
Devon

Florries Cottage ★★★★
Contact: Marsden's Cottage
Holidays, 2 The Square,
Braunton, Devon EX33 2JB
T: (01271) 813777
F: (01271) 813664
E: holidays@marsdens.co.uk
I: www.marsdens.co.uk

New Mill Farm ★★★
Contact: Mr R J Bingham,
Outovercott Riding Stables,
Barbrook, Lynton, Devon
EX35 6JR
T: (01598) 753341

West Lyn Farm ★★★
Contact: Mrs Barber, West Lyn
Farm, Barbrook, Lynton, Devon
EX35 6LD
T: (01598) 753618

Woodside ★★★
Contact: Mrs Sally Gunn,
Woodside, Barbrook, Lynton,
Devon EX35 6PD
T: (01598) 753298
E: woodside@salian.fsnet.co.uk

BARNSTAPLE
Devon

Country Ways ★★★★
Contact: Mrs Kate Price, Country
Ways, Little Knowle Farm, High
Bickington, Umberleigh, Devon
EX37 9BJ
T: (01769) 560503
F: (01769) 560503
E: kate.price@virgin.net
I: www.devon-holiday.co.uk

Humes Farm Cottages ★★★
Contact: Marsden's Cottage
Holidays, 2 The Square,
Braunton, Devon EX33 2JB
T: (01271) 813777
F: (01271) 813664
E: holidays@marsdens.co.uk
I: www.marsdens.co.uk

North Hill Cottages ★★★
Contact: Mrs Nicky Hann, Best
Leisure, North Hill, Shirwell,
Barnstaple, Devon EX31 4LG
T: (01271) 850611
F: (01271) 850693
I: www.bestleisure.co.uk

Willesleigh Farm ★★★★
Contact: Mr & Mrs C&A
Esmond-Cole, Willesleigh Farm,
Goodleigh, Barnstaple, Devon
EX32 7NA
T: (01271) 343763

BARTON ST. DAVID
Somerset

Mill House ★★★★
Contact: Mrs Rita Knight, Mill
House, Mill Road, Barton St.
David, Somerton, Somerset
TA11 6DF
T: (01458) 851215
F: (01458) 851372
E: KnightsMillHouse@aol.com
I: www.smoothhound.
co.uk/hotels/millhouse3.html

BATCOMBE
Somerset

**The Coach House at Boords
Farm★★★★**
Contact: Mr & Mrs Michael &
Anne Page, Boords The Coach
House at Farm, Batcombe,
Shepton Mallet, Somerset
BA4 6HD
T: (01749) 850372
F: (01749) 850372
E: boordsfarm@michaelp.
demon.co.uk

BATH
Bath and North East Somerset

31 Alexandra Road ★★★
Contact: Mr and Mrs David
Barnett, 32 Alexandra Road,
Bath, BA
T: (01225) 429296
F: (01225) 429296

**Bath Centre Stay Holidays
★★★**
Contact: Mr Gerald Davey, Bath
Centre Stay Holidays, 16 Great
Pulteney Street, Bath, BA2 4BR
T: (01225) 313205 &
07974 106823
F: (01225) 313205
E: holidays@bathcentrestay.
freeserve.co.uk

**Bath City Breaks
Rating Applied For**
Contact: Mrs Maggie Davis, Bath
City Breaks, 17 Pulteney Road,
Barnard Villas, Bath, BA2 4EZ
T: (01225) 466776

**Bath Spa University College
★★**
Contact: Ms Rebecca Webb,
Bath Spa University College Ltd,
6 Somerset Place, Bath, BA1 5SF
T: (01225) 875574 & 875620
F: (01225) 875627
E: conferencing@bathspa.ac.uk

**The Beeches Farmhouse
★★★★★**
Contact: Mr & Mrs Kevin and
Sharon Gover, The Beeches
Farmhouse, Holt Road,
Bradford-on-Avon, Wiltshire
BA15 1TS
T: (01225) 863475 &
07774 607417
F: (01225) 863996
E: beeches-farmhouse@
netgates.co.uk
I: www.beeches-farmhouse.
co.uk

Calverley Wing ★★★★
Contact: Mrs Jenny John,
Calverley Wing, South Stoke
Hall, South Stoke, Bath,
Somerset BA2 7DL
T: (01225) 833387
F: (01225) 833387
E: tandjjohn@aol.com

Church Farm Cottages ★★★★
Contact: Mrs Trish Bowles,
Church Farm, Winsley, Bradford-
on-Avon, Wiltshire BA15 2JH
T: (01225) 722246 &
07768 543027
F: (01225) 722246
E: stay@churchfarmcottages.
com
I: www.churchfarmcottages.com

The Coach House (Bath)
★★★★
Contact: Mr R Quiggen, The
Coach House (Bath), Stoneleigh
Lodge, Lansdown Road, Bath,
BA1 5TJ
T: (01225) 332213 &
07747 686165
F: (01225) 332213
E: cj@bathselfcatering.demon.
co.uk
I: www.bathselfcatering.demon.
co.uk

Courtyard Apartment
Rating Applied For
Contact: Dr J Wilk, Courtyard
Apartment, Bath Vacations
Rentals, 101 Sydney Place, Bath,
BA2 6NE
T: 0770 2416846

2 Devonshire Villas ★★★
Contact: Mr & Mrs D Wall, 2
Devonshire Villas, Wellsway,
Bath, BA2 4SX
T: (01225) 331539
E: ionawall106301.142@
compuserve.com

3 Devonshire Villas ★★★
Contact: Mr Gina Avant-Patel, 3
Devonshire Villas, Garden Flat,
Wellsway, Bath, BA2 4SX
T: (01225) 482053

Flat 2 ★★★★★
Contact: Mrs Clare Margaret
Travers, 9 Prior Park Buildings,
Bath, BA2 4NP
T: (01225) 312011
E: traversa@aol.com
I: www.bathbreaks.co.uk

Georgian Apartment ★★★
Contact: Mrs Susanne Marie
Cragg, Renting Places,
Summerhaze, 2 Ludwells
Orchard, Paulton, Bristol
BS39 7XW
T: (01761) 415655 & 418034
E: rentingplaces@btinternet.
com

Greyfield Farm Cottages
★★★★-★★★★★
Contact: Mrs J Merry, Greyfield
Farm Cottages, Greyfield Road,
High Littleton, Bristol BS39 6YQ
T: (01761) 471132
E: jurie@greyfieldfarm.com
I: www.greyfieldfarm.com

Luxury Apartments of Bath
★★★★★
Contact: Ms M Benghauser, 19
Lansdown Crescent, Bath,
BA1 5EX
T: (01225) 311101 &
07980 818446
E: margaret@
luxuryapartmentsofbath.co.uk
I: www.luxuryapartmentsofbath.
co.uk

2 Margaret's Buildings
Rating Applied For
Contact: Mr N Pash, Hideaways,
Luke Street, Berwick St John,
Shaftesbury, Dorset SB7 0HQ
T: (01747) 828170
F: (01747) 829090
E: enq@hideaways.co.uk

Riverside Apartment ★★★
Contact: Mr Graham Wilson,
Riverside Apartment, 1 Norfolk
Buildings, Bath, BA1 2BP
T: (01225) 337968
E: wilson.g@talk21.com

Riverside Cottage ★★
Contact: Mr Barrie & Valerie
Trezise, Riverside Cottage, 1
High Street, Wick, Bristol
BS30 5QJ
T: (0117) 9372304

Saint Enogat Garden
Apartment ★★★
Contact: Mr & Mrs Steve
Clewley, Saint Enogat Garden
Apartment, 38 Milton Avenue,
Bath, BA2 4QZ
T: (01225) 313568 &
(01453) 763611
E: hjclewley@hotmail.com
I: www.st-enogat.co.uk

Second Floor Flat ★★★★
Contact: Mrs L C Bishop, Oddley
House, 15 Heatherdale Road,
Camberley, Surrey GU15 2LR
T: (01276) 29033

Spring Farm Holiday Cottages
★★★-★★★★
Contact: Mrs Sue Brown, Spring
Farm Holiday Cottages,
Carlingcott, Bath, BA2 8AP
T: (01761) 435524 &
07710 904216
F: (01761) 439461
E: suebrown@
springfarmcottages.co.uk
I: www.springfarmcottages.
co.uk

1st Let ★
Contact: Mr Ralph Hodges, 1st
Let, 13 Victoria Road, Bath,
BA2 3QY
T: (01225) 448252 & 460009
F: (01225) 442375
E: rebecca@1st-let.com
I: www.lst-let.com

125 Wells Road ★★
Contact: Ms Maggie Dixon, 125
Wells Road, Bath, BA2 3AN
T: (01225) 317059

BATHEALTON
Somerset
Woodlands Farm ★★★
Contact: Mrs Joan Greenway,
Woodlands Farm, Bathealton,
Taunton, Somerset TA4 2AH
T: (01984) 623271 & 624696

BEAMINSTER
Dorset
34 Church Street
Rating Applied For
Contact: Mrs Janet Stockdale,
Crossways, Aston Street, Aston
Tirrold, Didcot, Oxfordshire
OX11 9DQ
T: (01235) 850297
F: (01235) 536982

Greens Cross Farm ★★★
Contact: Mr DG Baker, Greens
Cross Farm, Stoke Road,
Beaminster, Dorset DT8 3JL
T: (01308) 862661
F: (01308) 863800

Juniper Cottage X3456
★★★★
Contact: Lyme Bay Holidays,
Boshouse, 44 Church Street,
Lyme Regis, Dorset DT7 3DA
T: (01297) 443363
F: (01297) 445576
E: email@lymebayholidays.
co.uk
I: www.lymebayholidays.co.uk

Lewesdon Farm Holidays
★★★★
Contact: Mr & Mrs Smith,
Lewesdon Farm Holidays,
Lewesdon Farm, Stoke Abbott,
Beaminster, Dorset DT8 3JZ
T: (01308) 868270

The Lodge Holiday Cottage
★★★
Contact: Mr & Mrs Ian & Valerie
Spacie, The Lodge Holiday
Cottage, Beaminster House,
Tunnel Road, Beaminster, Dorset
DT8 3BQ
T: (01308) 863468
F: (01308) 863468
E: iv.spacie@virgin.net

Orchard End ★★★
Contact: Mrs P M Wallbridge,
Watermeadow House, Bridge
Farm, Hooke, Beaminster, Dorset
DT8 3PD
T: (01308) 862619
F: (01308) 862619
E: enquiries@
watermeadowhouse.co.uk
I: www.watermeadowhouse.
co.uk

Stable Cottage ★★★★
Contact: Mrs Diana Clarke,
Meerhay Manor, Beaminster,
Dorset DT8 3SB
T: (01308) 862305
F: (01308) 863977
E: meerhay@aol.com
I: www.meerhay.co.uk

BEER
Devon
The Admirals View ★★★★
Contact: Jean Bartlett Cottage
Holidays, Fore Street, Beer,
Seaton, Devon EX12 3JB
T: (01297) 23221 & 20973
F: (01297) 23303
E: jeanb@netbreaks.com
I: www.netbreaks.com/jeanb

Beer View and Nookies
★★-★★★★
Contact: Mrs Jean Forbes-
Harriss, Beer View and Nookies,
Berry House, Berry Lane, Beer,
Seaton, Devon EX12 3JS
T: (01297) 20096
F: (01297) 20096
E: forbesh@globalnet.co.uk

Brooksyde ★★
Contact: Jean Bartlett Cottage
Holidays, Fore Street, Beer,
Seaton, Devon EX12 3JB
T: (01297) 23221
F: (01297) 23303
E: jeanb@netbreaks.com
I: www.netbreaks.com/jeanb

Cider Cottage ★★★
Contact: Jean Bartlett Cottage
Holidays, Fore Street, Beer,
Seaton, Devon EX12 3JB
T: (01297) 23221
F: (01297) 23303
E: jeanb@netbreaks.com
I: www.netbreaks.com/jeanb

Dairy Flat ★★★
Contact: Jean Bartlett Cottage
Holidays, Fore Street, Beer,
Seaton, Devon EX12 3JB
T: (01297) 23221
F: (01297) 23303
E: jeanb@netbreaks.com
I: www.netbreaks.com/jeanb

Hardergraft ★★★
Contact: Jean Bartlett Cottage
Holidays, Fore Street, Beer,
Seaton, Devon EX12 3JB
T: (01297) 23221
F: (01297) 23303
E: jeanb@netbreaks.com
I: www.netbreaks.com/jeanb

Hollyhocks ★★★
Contact: Jean Bartlett Cottage
Holidays, Fore Street, Beer,
Seaton, Devon EX12 3JB
T: (01297) 23221
F: (01297) 23303
E: jeanb@netbreaks.com
I: www.netbreaks.com/jeanb

Hope Cottage and Creole
Cottage ★★★★
Contact: Jean Bartlett Cottage
Holidays, Fore Street, Beer,
Seaton, Devon EX12 3JB
T: (01297) 23221
F: (01297) 23303
E: jeanb@netbreaks.com
I: www.netbreaks.com/jeanb

The Lilacs ★★★
Contact: Jean Bartlett Cottage
Holidays, Fore Street, Beer,
Seaton, Devon EX12 3JB
T: (01297) 23221 & 20973
F: (01297) 23303
E: jeanb@netbreaks.com
I: www.netbreaks.com/jeanb

Marine House Apartments &
Twyford Cottage
★★★★-★★★★★
Contact: Jean Bartlett Cottage
Holidays, Fore Street, Beer,
Seaton, Devon EX12 3JB
T: (01297) 23221
F: (01297) 23303
E: jeanb@netbreaks.com
I: www.netbreaks.com/jeanb

The Meadows ★★★★
Contact: Jean Bartlett Cottage
Holidays, Fore Street, Beer,
Seaton, Devon EX12 3JB
T: (01297) 23221
F: (01297) 23303
E: jeanb@netbreaks.com
I: www.netbreaks.com/jeanb

Purley ★★★
Contact: Jean Bartlett Cottage
Holidays, Fore Street, Beer,
Seaton, Devon EX12 3JB
T: (01297) 23221
F: (01297) 23303
E: jeanb@netbreaks.com
I: www.netbreaks.com/jeanb

Ramblers ★★★
Contact: Jean Bartlett Cottage
Holidays, Fore Street, Beer,
Seaton, Devon EX12 3JB
T: (01297) 23221
F: (01297) 23303
E: jeanb@netbreaks.com
I: www.netbreaks.com/jeanb

Rattenbury Lodge ★★★
Contact: Jean Bartlett Cottage
Holidays, Fore Street, Beer,
Seaton, Devon EX12 3JB
T: (01297) 23221
F: (01297) 23303
E: jeanb@netbreaks.com
I: www.netbreaks.com/jeanb

Syringa ★★
Contact: Jean Bartlett Cottage
Holidays, Fore Street, Beer,
Seaton, Devon EX12 3JB
T: (01297) 23221
F: (01297) 23303
E: jeanb@netbreaks.com
I: www.netbreaks.com/jeanb

Tanglewood ★★★
Contact: Ms Kate Bartlett, Jean
Bartlett Cottage Holidays The
Old Dairy, Fore Street, Beer,
Seaton, Devon EX12 3JB
T: (01297) 23221 & 20973
F: (01297) 23303
E: jeanb@netbreaks.com
I: www.netbreaks.com/jeamb

1 West View ★★
Contact: Jean Bartlett Cottage
Holidays, Fore Street, Beer,
Seaton, Devon EX12 3JB
T: (01297) 23221
F: (01297) 23303
E: jeanb@netbreaks.com
I: www.netbreaks.com/jeanb

Westview Cottage ★★★
Contact: Jean Bartlett Cottage
Holidays, Fore Street, Beer,
Seaton, Devon EX12 3JB
T: (01297) 23221
F: (01297) 23303
E: jeanb@netbreaks.com
I: www.netbreaks.com/jeanb

BEESON
Devon

Andryl ★★★
Contact: Ms BER Wotton,
Andryl, Lower Farm, Beeson,
Kingsbridge, Devon TQ7 2HW
T: (01548) 580527

BELSTONE
Devon

1 Church Cottages ★★★
Contact: Mr and Mrs R S
Kingwell, St Annes House, 7
Vicar Street, Wymondham,
Norfolk NR18 OPL
T: (01953) 601271
E: mandrkingwell@btinternet.
com

BERRYNARBOR
Devon

Adventure Cottage ★★★★
Contact: Marsden's Cottage
Holidays, 2 The Square,
Braunton, Devon EX33 2JB
T: (01271) 813777
F: (01271) 813664
E: holidays@marsdens.co.uk
I: www.marsdens.co.uk

Beech Leigh ★★★★★
Contact: Marsden's Cottage
Holidays, 2 The Square,
Braunton, Devon EX33 2JB
T: (01271) 813777
F: (01271) 813664
E: holidays@marsdens.co.uk
I: www.marsdens.co.uk

Cobwebs Cottage ★★★
Contact: Mr & Mrs Ian &
Christine Smith, Mill Park House,
Mill Lane, Berrynarbor,
Ilfracombe, Devon EX34 9SH
T: (01271) 882990
F: (01271) 882682
E: ian_smith@millparkhouse.
freeserve.co.uk
I: www.millparkhouse.freeserve.
co.uk

Glebe House & Coach House
★★★★
Contact: Marsden's Cottage
Holidays, 2 The Square,
Braunton, Devon EX33 2JB
T: (01271) 813777
F: (01271) 813664
E: holidays@marsdens.co.uk
I: www.marsdens.co.uk

Ropes End ★★★
Contact: Mrs B Y Davey, Ropes
End, Newberry Hill, Berrynarbor,
Ilfracombe, Devon EX34 9SS
T: (01271) 883476

Smythen Farm Coastal Holiday
Cottages★★★–★★★★
Contact: Mr & Ms Thompson &
Elstone, Smythen Farm Coastal
Holiday Cottages, Smythen,
Sterridge Valley, Berrynarbor,
Ilfracombe, Devon EX34 9TB
T: (01271) 882875

BERWICK ST JAMES
Wiltshire

Rose Cottage
Rating Applied For
Contact: Mrs N E Barker, The Old
Byre, Primrose Lane, Woodfalls,
Salisbury SP5 2NA
T: (01725) 511085

BETTISCOMBE
Dorset

Conway Bungalow ★★★
Contact: Mrs M A Smith,
Conway Bungalow, Bettiscombe,
Bridport, Dorset DT6 5NT
T: (01308) 868313
F: (01308) 868313
E: conway@wdi.co.uk
I: www.wdi.co.uk/conway
🚶

BIDDESTONE
Wiltshire

Barn End ★★★★
Contact: Mrs F J Davis, Barn End,
The Barn, Manor Farm,
Biddestone, Chippenham,
Wiltshire SN14 7DH
T: (01249) 712104
E: jennyandbob@biddestone.
demon.co.uk

BIDEFORD
Devon

Coachmans Cottage ★★★
Contact: Mr and Mrs T M
Downie, Staddon House,
Monkleigh, Bideford, Devon
EX39 5JR
T: (01805) 623670

Fir Tree Cottage ★★
Contact: Mr Peter Morris, Farm
& Cottage Holidays, Victoria
House, 12 Fore Street, Bideford,
Devon EX39 1AW
T: (01237) 479146
F: (01237) 421512
E: farmcott@cix.co.uk
I: www.farmcott.co.uk

Pillhead Farm ★★★–★★★★
Contact: Mr Richard Hill,
Pillhead Farm, Old Barnstaple
Road, Bideford, Devon EX39 4NF
T: (01237) 479337 &
0774 8877195
F: (01237) 479337
E: hill@pillheadfarm.fsnet.co.uk

BIGBURY-ON-SEA
Devon

Apartment 2 ★★★★★
Contact: Helpful Holidays, Mill
Street, Chagford, Newton Abbot,
Devon TQ13 8AW
T: (01647) 433593
F: (01647) 433694
E: help@helpfulholidays.com
I: www.helpfulholidays.com

Apartment 29 ★★★★★
Contact: Mr & Mrs Bowater,
Helpful Holidays, Mill Street,
Chagford, Newton Abbot, Devon
TQ13 8AW
T: (01647) 433593
F: (01647) 433694
E: help@helpfulholidays.com
I: www.helpfulholidays.com

Apartment 5 ★★★★★
Contact: Mr J Davies, 10 Queens
Road, London W5 2SA
T: (020) 89910876

Apartment 6 ★★★★★
Contact: Mr & Mrs Bowater,
Helpful Holidays, Mill Street,
Chagford, Newton Abbot, Devon
TQ13 8AW
T: (01647) 433593
F: (01647) 433694
E: help@helpfulholidays.com
I: www.helpfulholidays.com

Beachdown ★★
Contact: Mr W S Menzies,
Beachdown Holiday Bungalows,
Challaborough Bay,
Challaborough, Kingsbridge,
Devon TQ7 4JB
T: (01548) 810089
F: (01548) 810089
E: beachdown@yahoo.com

Ferrycombe ★★★★
Contact: Mrs Juliet Fooks, Little
Grassington, The Spinneys,
Heathfield, East Sussex
TN21 8YN
T: (01435) 863045 &
0705 0030231

Sea View ★★★
Contact: Mrs P Southgate, Sea
View, Parker Road, Bigbury-on-
Sea, Kingsbridge, Devon TQ7 4AT
T: (01548) 810191
F: (01548) 810191

1 Sharpland Crest ★★★
Contact: Mrs A Hough, 7 Oriole
Drive, Pennsylvania, Exeter,
Devon EX4 4SJ
T: (01392) 438234

Thornbury ★★★★
Contact: Mrs J M Tagent,
Challaborough Cottage,
Ringmore, Kingsbridge, Devon
TQ7 4HW
T: (01548) 810520
E: met@cix.co.uk

BINEGAR
Somerset

Spindle Cottage ★★★★
Contact: CH ref: 5975, Holiday
Cottages Group Owner Services
Dept, Spring Mill, Earby,
Barnoldswick, Lancashire
BB18 6RN
T: (01282) 445096
F: (01282) 844299
E: ch.sales@ttgihg.co.uk
I: www.country-holidays.co.uk

BISHOP'S NYMPTON
Devon

Canon Cottage ★★★
Contact: Toad Hall Cottages,
Elliot House, Church Street,
Kingsbridge, Devon TQ7 1BY
T: (01548) 521366
F: (01548) 853086
E: thc@toadhallcottages.com
I: www.toadhallcottages.com

Crosse Farm ★★★
Contact: Mrs D A Verney, Crosse
Farm, Wing of Farmhouse,
Bishop's Nympton, South
Molton, Devon EX36 4PB
T: (01769) 550288

Knowle Down Cottage ★★★
Contact: Mrs G M Huckle,
Knowle Down, Avercombe,
Bishop's Nympton, South
Molton, Devon EX36 4EA
T: (01769) 550702
E: gillian_huckle@barclays.net

BISHOP'S TAWTON
Devon

Horswell Farm Cottages
★★★★
Contact: Mr Roger Stanbury,
Horswell Farm Cottages,
Horswell Cottages, Bishop's
Tawton, Barnstaple, Devon
EX32 0ED
T: (01271) 343505
F: (01271) 326393
E: horswellfarm@hotmail.com
I: www.horswell-cottages.co.uk

May Cottage ★★★★
Contact: Mr Peter Morris, Farm
& Cottage Holidays, Victoria
House, 12 Fore Street, Northam,
Bideford, Devon EX39 1AW
T: (01237) 479146
F: (01237) 421512
E: farmcott@cix.co.uk
I: www.farmcott.co.uk

BISHOPS HULL
Somerset

1 Old School Cottages ★★
Contact: Mrs Randle, Shute
Cottage, Shutewater Hill,
Bishops Hull, Taunton, Somerset
TA1 5EQ
T: (01823) 331189
E: fp10000@cus.cam.ac.uk

BITTON
Gloucestershire

The Gate House ★★
Contact: Mr P Stone, The Gate House, Green Gables, Redfield Hill, Bitton, Bristol BS30 6NX
T: (0117) 932 5303
F: (0117) 932 5303
E: gatehouse@houseofstone.co.uk

BLACK TORRINGTON
Devon

Kingsley Mill ★★★★
Contact: Mr Peter Morris, Farm & Cottage Holidays, Victoria House, 12 Fore Street, Northam, Bideford, Devon EX39 1AW
T: (01237) 479146
F: (01237) 421512
E: farmcott@cix.co.uk
I: www.farmcott.co.uk

BLACKAWTON
Devon

1 Below Chapel ★★
Contact: Mrs S Wills, 2 Below Chapel, Blackawton, Totnes, Devon TQ9 7BN
T: (01803) 712409

Chuckle Too ★★★
Contact: Jill Hanlon, Chuckle Cottage, Main Street, Blackawton, Totnes, Devon TQ9 7BG
T: (01803) 712455
F: (01803) 712455

BLACKBOROUGH
Devon

Bodmiscombe Farm ★★★
Contact: Mrs B M Northam, Bodmiscombe Farm, Blackborough, Cullompton, Devon EX15 2HR
T: (01884) 266315
F: (01884) 266315

BLACKDOWN
Dorset

The Grooms Quarters W4183 ★★★
Contact: Lyme Bay Holidays, Boshouse, 44 Church Street, Lyme Regis, Dorset DT7 3DA
T: (01297) 443363
F: (01297) 445576
E: email@lymebayholidays.co.uk
I: www.lymebayholidays.co.uk

BLACKWATER
Cornwall

Grove Farm Cottage ★★★
Contact: CH ref: 11801, Holiday Cottages Group Owner Services Department, Spring Mill, Earby, Barnoldswick, Lancashire BB18 6RN
T: (01282) 445096
F: (01282) 844299
E: ch.sales@ttgihg.co.uk
I: www.country-holidays.co.uk

BLATCHBRIDGE
Somerset

Mill Cottage ★★★★
Contact: Mrs Thelma Morris, Mill Cottage, Blatchbridge, Frome, Somerset BA11 5EJ
T: (01373) 464784

BLISLAND
Cornwall

Bridge Pool Cottage ★★★★
Contact: Mrs & Mr Kathryn & Trevor Sobey, Higher Trevartha Farm, Pengover, Liskeard, Cornwall PL14 3NJ
T: (01579) 343382

Lavethan ★★★
Contact: Mr & Mrs Bowater, Helpful Holidays, Mill Street, Chagford, Newton Abbot, Devon TQ13 8AW
T: (01647) 433593
F: (01647) 433694
E: help@helpfulholidays.com
I: www.helpfulholidays.com

BLUE ANCHOR
Somerset

Huntingball Lodge ★★★★
Contact: Mr D Murray, Huntingball Lodge, Blue Anchor, Minehead, Somerset TA24 6JP
T: (01984) 640076

Primrose Hill Holidays ★★★
Contact: Mr M Babb, Primrose Hill Holidays, Wood Lane, Blue Anchor, Minehead, Somerset TA24 6LA
T: (01643) 821200
E: martyn.babb@virgin.net

BODMIN
Cornwall

Lanjew Park ★★★★
Contact: Mrs E Biddick, Lanjew Park, Lanjew Farm, Withiel, Bodmin, Cornwall PL30 5PB
T: (01726) 890214
F: (01726) 890214

Mennabroom Farm ★★★
Contact: Mrs J G Lucas, Mennabroom Farm, Warleggan, Mount, Bodmin, Cornwall PL30 4HE
T: (01208) 821272
F: (01208) 821555
E: lucas@nmadial.co.uk

Tor View ★★★★
Contact: Mr & Mrs Rob & Helen Watson, Tor View, Trebell Green, Lanivet, Bodmin, Cornwall PL30 5HR
T: (01208) 831472
F: (01208) 831472

BODREAN
Cornwall

Apple Orchard Bungalow ★★★
Contact: Mr Peter Morris, Farm & Cottage Holidays, Victoria House, 12 Fore Street, Bideford, Devon EX39 1AW
T: (01237) 479146
F: (01237) 421512
E: farmcott@cix.co.uk
I: www.farmcott.co.uk

BOLVENTOR
Cornwall

Trezibbett Farm Flat ★★★
Contact: Mr Peter Morris, Farm & Cottage Holidays, Victoria House, 12 Fore Street, Northam, Bideford, Devon EX39 1AW
T: (01237) 479146
F: (01237) 421512
E: farmcott@cix.co.uk
I: www.farmcott.co.uk

BOSCASTLE
Cornwall

Anneth Lowen ★★★★
Contact: Mrs K M Dougan, Kernow Holidays, 7 Oaks Road, Woking, Surrey GU21 1DU
T: (01483) 765446 & 0870 3214657
F: 0870 3214658
E: kay.dougan@kernowholidays.co.uk
I: www.kernowholidays.co.uk

The Boathouse ★★★★
Contact: Mrs T E Webster, Seagulls, The Harbour, Boscastle, Cornwall PL35 0AG
T: (01840) 250413 & 250374
I: www.businessthisiscornwall.co.uk/boathouse/

Cargurra Cottage ★★★★
Contact: Mrs Elson, Hennett, St Juliot, Boscastle, Cornwall PL35 0BT
T: (01840) 261206
F: (01840) 261206
E: gillian@cargurra.co.uk
I: www.cargurra.co.uk

Courtyard Farm and Cottages ★★★
Contact: Mr Compton, Courtyard Farm and Cottages, Lesnewth, Boscastle, Cornwall PL35 0HR
T: (01840) 261256
F: (01840) 261794
E: courtyard.farm@virgin.net
I: www.cornwall-online.co.uk/courtyard-farm-cottages

Glenthorn ★★
Contact: CH Ref: 14441, Holiday Cottages Group, Spring Mill, Earby, Barnoldswick, Lancashire BB18 6RN
T: (01282) 445096
F: (01282) 844299
E: ch.sales@ttgihg.co.uk
I: www.country-holidays.co.uk

Hillside Cottage ★★★★
Contact: Mr & Mrs J&Y Harman, 46 Gill Crescent, Taunton, Somerset TA1 4NS
T: (01823) 284736 & 363040

Paradise Farm Cottage ★★★
Contact: Mrs D M Hancock, Paradise Farm Cottage, Boscastle, Cornwall PL35 0BL
T: (01840) 250528

Reddivallen Farm
Rating Applied For
Contact: Ms L Brewer, Reddivallen Farm, Trevalga, Boscastle, Cornwall PL35 0EE
T: (01840) 250854

Shepherd's Cottage ★★★
Contact: Ms Carol Jenkins, Endellion House, Parc Road, Llangybi, Usk, Monmouthshire NP15 1NL
T: (01633) 450417
E: carol@choicecornishcottages.com
I: www.choicecornishcottages.com

Westerings ★★★
Contact: Mrs S A Wakelin, Westerings, Forrabury, Boscastle, Cornwall PL35 0DJ
T: (01840) 250314
E: shirley@westeringsholidays.co.uk
I: www.westeringsholidays.co.uk

BOVEY TRACEY
Devon

Lower Elsford Farm
Rating Applied For
Contact: Mrs EH Miller, Lower Elsford Farm, Bovey Tracey, Newton Abbot, Devon TQ13 9NY
T: (01647) 277563

Stickwick Farm ★★★
Contact: Mrs L Harvey, Frost Farm, Bovey Tracey, Newton Abbot, Devon TQ13 9PP
T: (01626) 833266
E: linda@frostfarm.co.uk

Warmhill Farm ★★★★
Contact: Mr W B Marnham, Warmhill Farm, Hennock, Bovey Tracey, Newton Abbot, Devon TQ13 9QH
T: (01626) 833229
E: warmhill@dial.pipex.com

BOWDEN
Devon

Higher Bowden ★★★★
Contact: Mrs & Mr Monica & Paul Khosla, Higher Bowden, Bowden, Dartmouth, Devon TQ6 0LH
T: (01803) 770745
F: (01803) 770262
E: cottages@higherbowden.com
I: www.higherbowden.com

BOX
Wiltshire

Oakleaf and Acorn Cottage ★★★
Contact: CH ref: 8602,8603, Country Holidays Group Owner Services Dept, Spring Mill, Earby, Barnoldswick, Lancashire BB94 0AA
T: (01282) 445096
F: (01282) 844299
E: ch.sales@ttgihg.co.uk
I: www.country-holidays.co.uk

BRADFORD-ON-AVON
Wiltshire

The Barton ★★★
Contact: Ms Rosemary Harding, The Haven, London Road, Pewsham, Chippenham, Wiltshire SN15 3RW
T: (01249) 655401
F: (01249) 655401

The Flat Martins★★
Contact: Mrs D Young, The Flat Martins, Whitehill, Bradford-on-Avon, Wiltshire BA15 1SQ
T: (01225) 863253
F: (01225) 863253
E: diana.young@ukonline.co.uk

Greystone Cottage ★★★
Contact: Mrs Gillian Mary Patel, 19 Church Street, Bradford-on-Avon, Wiltshire BA15 1LN
T: (01225) 868179 & 0771 4494006
F: (01225) 867084
E: vivandgill@yahoo.co.uk

Establishments printed in blue have a detailed entry in this guide

The Loft ★★★★
Contact: Mrs Helen Rawlings, Great Ashley Farm, Ashley Lane, Bradford-on-Avon, Wiltshire BA15 2PP
T: (01225) 864563
F: (01225) 864563
E: greatashleyfarm@farmersweekly.net

The Moorings Lodges ★★★
Contact: Ms Joanna Heap, Old Farm, Widbrook, Bradford-on-Avon, Wiltshire BA15 1UD
T: (01225) 862608
F: (01225) 867900

BRADNINCH
Devon

Highdown Farm ★★★★
Contact: Mrs S Vallis, Highdown Farm, Bradninch, Exeter EX5 4LJ
T: (01392) 881028
F: (01392) 881272
E: svallis@highdownfarm.co.uk
I: www.highdownfarm.co.uk

Park Bungalow & Five Elms ★★★
Contact: Mrs Eileen Persey, Park Farm, Bradninch, Exeter EX5 4RD
T: (01392) 881526
F: (01392) 881249
E: persey.park@bt.internet.com
I: www.btinternet.com/persey.park/holidays

BRADWORTHY
Devon

Jubilee Cottage ★★★★
Contact: Holiday Cottages Group, Spring Mill, Earby, Barnoldswick, Lancashire BB18 6RN
T: (01282) 445096
F: (01282) 844299
E: ch.sales@ttgihg.co.uk
I: www.country-holidays.co.uk

Lake House Holiday Cottages ★★★
Contact: Mr & Mrs Peter & Lesley Lewin, Lake House Holiday Cottages, Lake Villa, Bradworthy, Holsworthy, Devon EX22 7SQ
T: (01409) 241962
E: lesley@lakevilla.co.uk
I: www.lakevilla.co.uk

Lympscott Farm Holidays ★★★★
Contact: Mrs Caroline Furse, Lympscott Farm Holidays, Bradworthy, Holsworthy, Devon EX22 7TR
T: (01409) 241607
F: (01409) 241607

Wagtail Cottage ★★★
Contact: Mr Paul Batten, Brexworthy Farm, Bradworthy, Holsworthy, Devon EX22 7TR
T: (01409) 241488

BRANSCOMBE
Devon

Little Scotshays ★★★
Contact: Jean Bartlett Cottage Holidays, Fore Street, Beer, Seaton, Devon EX12 3JB
T: (01297) 23221
F: (01297) 23303
E: jeanb@netbreaks.com
I: www.netbreaks.com/jeanb

The Old Sunday School ★★★★
Contact: Jean Bartlett Cottage Holidays, Fore Street, Beer, Seaton, Devon EX12 3JB
T: (01297) 23221
F: (01297) 23303
E: jeanb@netbreaks.com
I: www.netbreaks.com/jeanb

Sellerswood ★★
Contact: Jean Bartlett Cottage Holidays, Fore Street, Beer, Seaton, Devon EX12 3JB
T: (01297) 23221
F: (01297) 23303
E: jeanb@netbreaks.com
I: www.netbreaks.com/jeanb

BRATTON
Somerset

Woodcombe Lodges ★★★★
Contact: Mrs N Hanson, Woodcombe Lodges, Bratton Lane, Minehead, Somerset TA24 8SQ
T: (01643) 702789 & 07974 844914
F: (01643) 702789
E: nicola@woodcombelodge.co.uk
I: www.woodcombelodge.co.uk

BRATTON CLOVELLY
Devon

Jersey Cottage ★★★
Contact: Mr R J Williamson, Jersey Cottage, Headson Farm, Bratton Clovelly, Okehampton, Devon EX20 4JP
T: (01837) 871417 & 871508
F: (01837) 871417
E: bob@rjwilliamson.fsnet.co.uk

BRATTON FLEMING
Devon

Bluebell & Snowdrop Cottages ★★★
Contact: Mr & Mrs S Lyons, Lower Knightacott, Bratton Fleming, Barnstaple, Devon EX31 4SF
T: (01598) 710507

Bracken Roost ★★★★
Contact: Mr Lawrie Scott, Bracken Roost, Bracken House, Bratton Fleming, Barnstaple, Devon EX31 4TG
T: (01598) 710320
F: (01598) 710115
E: lawrie@brackenhousehotel.com
I: www.brackenhousehotel.com

Bratton Mill Cottage ★★★★
Contact: Bratton Mill Cottage, Bratton Mill, Bratton Fleming, Barnstaple, Devon EX31 4RU

Capelands Farm ★★★
Contact: Toad Hall Cottages, Elliot House, Church Street, Kingsbridge, Devon TQ7 1BY
T: (01548) 521366
F: (01548) 853086
E: thc@toadhallcottages.com
I: www.toadhallcottages.com

Hunnacott ★★★
Contact: Marsden's Cottage Holidays, 2 The Square, Braunton, Devon EX33 2JB
T: (01271) 813777
F: (01271) 813664
E: holidays@marsdens.co.uk
I: www.marsdens.co.uk

Thornlea ★★★
Contact: Mrs Marion Ridd-Jones, North Thorne, Bratton Fleming, Barnstaple, Devon EX31 4SL
T: (01598) 763297
F: (01598) 763297
E: royandmarion@northorne.freeserve.co.uk

Wallover Barton Cottages ★★★
Contact: Marsden's Cottage Holidays, 2 The Square, Braunton, Devon EX33 2JB
T: (01271) 813777
F: (01271) 813664
E: holidays@marsdens.co.uk
I: www.marsdens.co.uk

BRAUNTON
Devon

Bloomfield ★★★
Contact: Marsden's Cottage Holidays, 2 The Square, Braunton, Devon EX33 2JB
T: (01271) 813777
F: (01271) 813664
E: holidays@marsdens.co.uk
I: www.marsdens.co.uk

Broadlands ★★★★
Contact: Marsden's Cottage Holidays, 2 The Square, Braunton, Devon EX33 2JB
T: (01271) 813777
F: (01271) 813664
E: holidays@marsdens.co.uk
I: www.marsdens.co.uk

Buckland Cottage ★★★
Contact: Marsden's Cottage Holidays, 2 The Square, Braunton, Devon EX33 2JB
T: (01271) 813777
F: (01271) 813664
E: holidays@marsdens.co.uk
I: www.marsdens.co.uk

Buckland Mews ★★★
Contact: Marsden's Cottage Holidays, 2 The Square, Braunton, Devon EX33 2JB
T: (01271) 813777
F: (01271) 813664
E: holidays@marsdens.co.uk
I: www.marsdens.co.uk

Casquets ★★★★
Contact: Marsden's Cottage Holidays, 2 The Square, Braunton, Devon EX33 2JB
T: (01271) 813777
F: (01271) 813664
E: holidays@marsdens.co.uk
I: www.marsdens.co.uk

1 Cottage Close ★★★
Contact: Miss J Elson, 47 Beechwood Avenue, Greenford, Middlesex UB6 9UD
T: (020) 8578 8984

Farmhouse Cottage ★★★
Contact: Marsden's Cottage Holidays, 2 The Square, Braunton, Devon EX33 2JB
T: (01271) 813777
F: (01271) 813664
E: holidays@marsdens.co.uk
I: www.marsdens.co.uk

The Garden Flat ★★★
Contact: Marsden's Cottage Holidays, 2 The Square, Braunton, Devon EX33 2JB
T: (01271) 813777
F: (01271) 813664
E: holidays@marsdens.co.uk
I: www.marsdens.co.uk

Goadgates ★★★
Contact: Marsden's Cottage Holidays, 2 The Square, Braunton, Devon EX33 2JB
T: (01271) 813777
F: (01271) 813664
E: holidays@marsdens.co.uk
I: www.marsdens.co.uk

Hylands ★★★★
Contact: Marsden's Cottage Holidays, 2 The Square, Braunton, Devon EX33 2JB
T: (01271) 813777
F: (01271) 813664
E: holidays@marsdens.co.uk
I: www.marsdens.co.uk

Incledon Farmhouse ★★★
Contact: Marsden's Cottage Holidays, 2 The Square, Braunton, Devon EX33 2JB
T: (01271) 813777
F: (01271) 813664
E: holidays@marsdens.co.uk
I: www.marsdens.co.uk

Landfall ★★★
Contact: Marsden's Cottage Holidays, 2 The Square, Braunton, Devon EX33 2JB
T: (01271) 813777
F: (01271) 813664
E: holidays@marsdens.co.uk
I: www.marsdens.co.uk

Leacroft ★★★
Contact: Marsden's Cottage Holidays, 2 The Square, Braunton, Devon EX33 2JB
T: (01271) 813777
F: (01271) 813664
E: holidays@marsdens.co.uk
I: www.marsdens.co.uk

Lime Tree Nursery ★★★★
Contact: Marsden's Cottage Holidays, 2 The Square, Braunton, Devon EX33 2JB
T: (01271) 813777
F: (01271) 813664
E: holidays@marsdens.co.uk
I: www.marsdens.co.uk

Little Comfort Farm ★★★
Contact: Mrs JH Milsom, Little Comfort Farm, Braunton, Devon EX33 2NJ
T: (01271) 812414
F: (01271) 812414
E: jackie.milsom@bkclick.com
I: www.littlecomfortfarm.co.uk

1 Millhouse Cottage ★★★
Contact: Marsden's Cottage Holidays, 2 The Square, Braunton, Devon EX33 2JB
T: (01271) 813777
F: (01271) 813664
E: holidays@marsdens.co.uk
I: www.marsdens.co.uk

2 Millhouse Cottage ★★★
Contact: Marsden's Cottage Holidays, 2 The Square, Braunton, Devon EX33 2JB
T: (01271) 813777
F: (01271) 813664
E: holidays@marsdens.co.uk
I: www.marsdens.co.uk

The Old Byre ★★★★
Contact: Marsden's Cottage
Holidays, 2 The Square,
Braunton, Devon EX33 2JB
T: (01271) 813777
F: (01271) 813664
E: holidays@marsdens.co.uk
I: www.marsdens.co.uk

The Old Mill House ★★★★
Contact: Marsden's Cottage
Holidays, 2 The Square,
Braunton, Devon EX33 2JB
T: (01271) 813777
F: (01271) 813664
E: holidays@marsdens.co.uk
I: www.marsdens.co.uk

Orchard House ★★★
Contact: Marsden's Cottage
Holidays, 2 The Square,
Braunton, Devon EX33 2JB
T: (01271) 813777
F: (01271) 813664
E: holidays@marsdens.co.uk
I: www.marsdens.co.uk

Park Villa ★★★
Contact: Marsden's Cottage
Holidays, 2 The Square,
Braunton, Devon EX33 2JB
T: (01271) 813777
F: (01271) 813664
E: holidays@marsdens.co.uk
I: www.marsdens.co.uk

Ramblers Return ★★★
Contact: Marsden's Cottage
Holidays, 2 The Square,
Braunton, Devon EX33 2JB
T: (01271) 813777
F: (01271) 813664
E: holidays@marsdens.co.uk
I: www.marsdens.co.uk

Waverley ★★★★
Contact: Marsden's Cottage
Holidays, 2 The Square,
Braunton, Devon EX33 2JB
T: (01271) 813777
F: (01271) 813664
E: holidays@marsdens.co.uk
I: www.marsdens.co.uk

Well Cottage ★★★★
Contact: Mr & Mrs Peter & Janet
Cornwell, Marsden's Cottage
Holidays, 2 The Square,
Braunton, Devon EX33 2JB
T: (01271) 815266 &
07776 075981
F: (01271) 813664
E: holidays@marsdens.co.uk
I: www.marsdens.co.uk

Willoways ★★★
Contact: Marsden's Cottage
Holidays, 2 The Square,
Braunton, Devon EX33 2JB
T: (01271) 813777
F: (01271) 813664
E: holidays@marsdens.co.uk
I: www.marsdens.co.uk

Windspray ★★★
Contact: Marsden's Cottage
Holidays, 2 The Square,
Braunton, Devon EX33 2JB
T: (01271) 813777
F: (01271) 813664
E: holidays@marsdens.co.uk
I: www.marsdens.co.uk

BRAYFORD
Devon

Kedworthy
Rating Applied For
Contact: Mr Peter Morris, Farm
& Cottage Holidays, Victoria
House, 12 Fore Street, Northam,
Bideford, Devon EX39 1AW
T: (01237) 479146
F: (01237) 421512
E: farmcott@cix.co.uk
I: www.farmcott.co.uk

Lydcott Barton ★★★★
Contact: Marsden's Cottage
Holidays, 2 The Square,
Braunton, Devon EX33 2JB
T: (01271) 813777
F: (01271) 813664
E: holidays@mardens.co.uk
I: www.marsdens.co.uk

Muxworthy Cottage ★★
Contact: Mrs G M Bament,
Muxworthy Farm, Brayford,
Barnstaple, Devon EX32 7QP
T: (01598) 710342

Rockley Farmhouse ★★★
Contact: Mrs Renee Dover,
Rockley Farmhouse, Brayford,
Barnstaple, Devon EX32 7QR
T: (01598) 710429
F: (01598) 710429
E: rockley@hicon.co.uk
I: www.hicon.co.uk/rockley

BREAGE
Cornwall

Goose Cottage ★★★★
Contact: Cornish Cottage
Holidays, The Old Turnpike Dairy,
Godolphin Road, Helston,
Cornwall TR13 8GL
T: (01326) 573808
F: (01326) 564992
E: enquiry@
cornishcottageholidays.co.uk
I: www.cornishcottageholidays.
co.uk

Pump House ★★★★
Contact: Cornish Cottage
Holidays, Godolphin Road,
Helston, Cornwall TR13 8AA
T: (01326) 573808
F: (01326) 564992
E: enquiry@
cornishcottageholidays.co.uk
I: www.cornishcottageholidays.
co.uk

BREAN
Somerset

Gadara Bungalow ★★
Contact: Mr T M Hicks, Gadara
Bungalow, Diamond Farm,
Weston Road, Brean, Burnham-
on-Sea, Somerset TA8 2RL
T: (01278) 751263
E: feelfreetoemailme@
diamondfarm42.freeserve.co.uk
I: www.diamondfarm.co.uk

BRENT KNOLL
Somerset

Dairy View ★★
Contact: Mrs S Frost, Applewithy
Cottage, Ham Road, Brent Knoll,
Highbridge, Somerset TA9 4BJ
T: (01278) 785994
E: sfrost3277@aol.com

West Croft Farm Dairy Cottage
★★★
Contact: Mrs J Harris, West Croft
Farm Dairy Cottage, Brent
Street, Brent Knoll, Highbridge,
Somerset TA9 4BE
T: (01278) 760259

BRENTOR
Devon

Smithy Cottage ★★★
Contact: Mrs S Wetherbee,
Thorn Cottage, Burn Lane,
Brentor, Tavistock, Devon
PL19 0ND
T: (01822) 810285

BRIDESTOWE
Devon

Knole Farm ★★★
Contact: Mrs Mavis Bickle, Knole
Farm, Bridestowe, Okehampton,
Devon EX20 4HA
T: (01837) 861241
F: (01837) 861241

Pieck and Embleton Cottages
★★★
Contact: CH ref: 4265,5487,
Country Holidays Group Owner
Services Dept, Spring Mill, Earby,
Barnoldswick, Lancashire
BB18 6RN
T: (01282) 445096
F: (01282) 844299
E: ch.sales@ttgihg.co.uk
I: www.country-holidays.co.uk

BRIDFORD
Devon

Hole Farm Cottage ★★★
Contact: Mr & Mrs Bowater,
Helpful Holidays, Mill Street,
Chagford, Newton Abbot, Devon
TQ13 8AW
T: (01647) 433593
F: (01647) 433694
E: help@helpfulholidays.com
I: www.helpfulholidays.com

BRIDGWATER
Somerset

Grange Barn ★★★★★
Contact: Mr Matthew Wheeler,
Grange Barn, Cannington,
Bridgwater, Somerset TA5 2LD
T: (01278) 652216
F: (01278) 653611
E: grangehols@aol.com
I: www.grangehols.co.uk

BRIDPORT
Dorset

Coniston Holiday Apartments
★★★
Contact: Mrs Jackie Murphy,
Coniston Holiday Apartments,
Coniston House, Victoria Grove,
Bridport, Dorset DT6 3AE
T: (01308) 424049
F: (01308) 424049

Fern Down Farm ★★★
Contact: Mrs S Solly, Fern Down
Farm, Shatcombe Lane, Wynford
Eagle, Dorchester, Dorset
DT2 0EZ
T: (01300) 320810
E: pdnsolly@hotmail.com

Granary Cottage ★★★
Contact: Granary Cottage,
Washing Pool Farm, Bridport,
Dorset DT6

Hayday ★★★
Contact: Mr Michael Pegg,
Hayday, 29 Howard Road,
Bridport, Dorset DT6 4SG
T: (01308) 424438

**Holiday Cottages Numbers 1
and 3 Stanley Place ★★**
Contact: Mrs B Barford,
Bowood, Post Lane, Cotleigh,
Honiton, Devon EX14 9HZ
T: (01404) 861566

Jessops Avenue W4272 ★★★
Contact: Lyme Bay Holidays,
Boshouse, 44 Church Street,
Lyme Regis, Dorset DT7 3DA
T: (01297) 443363
F: (01297) 445576
E: email@lymebayholidays.
co.uk
I: www.lymebayholidays.co.uk

Lancombes House ★★★
Contact: Mr and Mrs Mansfield,
Lancombes House, West Milton,
Bridport, Dorset DT6 3TN
T: (01308) 485375
I: www.lancombeshouse.co.uk

Rudge Farm ★★★★
Contact: Mrs S Diment, Rudge
Farm, Chilcombe, Bridport,
Dorset DT6 4NF
T: (01308) 482630
F: (01308) 482635
E: sue@rudgefarm.co.uk
I: www.rudgefarm.co.uk

Strongate Farm ★★★
Contact: Mrs Sandra Huxter,
Strongate Farm, Salwayash,
Bridport, Dorset DT6 5JD
T: (01308) 488295

Sunnyside Farm ★★★
Contact: Major and Mrs M A
Everitt, Sunnyside Farm,
Loscombe, Bridport, Dorset
DT6 3TL
T: (01308) 488481
F: (01308) 488136

Sunset ★★★
Contact: Mr C D Walker,
Eypeleaze, 117 West Bay Road,
Bridport, Dorset DT6 4EQ
T: (01308) 423363
F: (01308) 420228
E: cdan@walker42.freeserve.
co.uk

30 Victoria Grove ★★
Contact: Mr & Mrs J&W Brook,
30 Victoria Grove, Bridport,
Dorset DT6 3AD
T: (01308) 424605

West Bay Road X3460 ★★★
Contact: Lyme Bay Holidays,
Boshouse, 44 Church Street,
Lyme Regis, Dorset DT7 3DA
T: (01297) 443363
F: (01297) 445576
E: email@lymebayholidays.
co.uk
I: www.lymebayholidays.co.uk

Wooth Manor Cottage ★★★
Contact: Mrs G Martelli, The Old
Workhouse, Netherbury,
Bridport, Dorset DT6 5LW
T: (01308) 488348 &
07773 749675

BRISTOL

Avonside ★★★
Contact: Mrs D M Ridout,
Avonside, 19 St Edyth's Road,
Sea Mills, Bristol BS9 2EP
T: (0117) 968 1967

16 Ferrymans Court ★★★★★
Contact: Mr Pete Hodges, 16
Ferrymans Court, Queen Street,
Bristol, BS2 0JB
T: 07710 207953
E: pete.hodges@virginnet.co.uk
I: www.watersidebristol.co.uk

Redland Flat ★★★
Contact: Mr H I Jones, Flat 1,
Elm Lodge, Elm Grove, London,
London NW2 3AE
T: (020) 8450 6761
E: redlandflat.btc@ondigital.
com

BRIXHAM
Devon

29 Berry Head Road ★★★
Contact: Holiday Homes &
Cottages South West, 365A
Torquay Road, Paignton, Devon
TQ3 2BT
T: (01803) 663650
F: (01803) 664037
E: holcotts@aol.com
I: www.swcottages.co.uk

Blue Chip Vacations ★★★★★
Contact: Mrs S Cutting, Blue
Chip Vacations, Moorings Reach,
Brixham, Devon TQ5 9HA
T: (01803) 855282

Captain's Quarters ★★★★★
Contact: Mrs G E Tricker, The Hill
House, 23 St Peter's Hill,
Brixham, Devon TQ5 9TE
T: (01803) 857937
F: (01803) 857937
E: gtricker@aol.com
I: www.captainsquarters.co.uk

11 The Close ★★★
Contact: Holiday Homes &
Cottages South West, 365A
Torquay Road, Paignton, Devon
TQ3 2BT
T: (01803) 663650
F: (01803) 664037
E: holcotts@aol.com
I: www.swcottages.co.uk

Devoncourt Holiday Flats ★★
Contact: Mr Robin Hooker,
Devoncourt Holiday Flats, Berry
Head Road, Brixham, Devon
TQ5 9AB
T: (01803) 853748 &
07050 338889
F: (01803) 855775
E: devoncourt@devoncoast.com
I: www.devoncourt.net

10 Fishcombe Cove ★★★
Contact: Holiday Homes &
Cottages South West, 365A
Torquay Road, Paignton, Devon
TQ3 2BT
T: (01803) 663650
F: (01803) 664037
E: holcotts@aol.co.uk
I: www.swcottages.co.uk

The Harbour's Edge ★★★
Contact: Mr & Mrs C Booth, 24
The Close, Brixham, Devon
TQ5 8RF
T: (01803) 859859

8 Heath Court ★★★
Contact: Mr CH ref: 10318,
Holiday Cottages Group Owner
Services Dept, Spring Mill, Earby,
Barnoldswick, Lancashire
BB18 6RN
T: (01282) 445096
F: (01282) 844299
E: ch.sales@ttgihg.co.uk
I: www.country-holidays.co.uk

Mudberry House ★★★
Contact: Holiday Homes &
Cottages South West, 365A
Torquay Road, Paignton, Devon
TQ3 2BT
T: (01803) 663650
F: (01803) 664037
E: holcotts@aol.com
I: www.swcottages.co.uk

173 Northfields Lane ★★★
Contact: Holiday Homes &
Cottages South West, 365A
Torquay Road, Paignton, Devon
TQ3 2BT
T: (01803) 663650
F: (01803) 664037
E: holcotts@aol.com
I: www.swcottages.co.uk

17 Ocean View Drive ★★★★
Contact: Holiday Homes &
Cottages South West, 365A
Torquay Road, Paignton, Devon
TQ3 2BT
T: (01803) 663650
F: (01803) 664037
E: holcotts@aol.com
I: www.swcottages.co.uk

The Quarterberth ★★
Contact: Mr Ian Butterworth,
Holiday Homes & Cottages
South West, 365A Torquay Road,
Paignton, Devon TQ3 2BT
T: (01803) 663650

Sailor's Haunt ★★★★
Contact: Mr Richard Haycock,
Beaumont House, 25 Siston
Common, Warmley, Bristol
BS15 4NY
T: (0117) 9676659
F: (0117) 9676659
E: beaumont.cottages@virgin.
net
I: www.beaumont.cottages.co.uk

Seacat Cottage
Rating Applied For
Contact: Holiday Homes &
Cottages South West, 365A
Torquay Road, Paignton, Devon
TQ3 2BT
T: (01803) 663650
F: (01803) 664037
E: holcotts@aol.com
I: www.swcottages.co.uk

BROADHEMBURY
Devon

Garden Lodge ★★★
Contact: Mrs Anne Barons,
Garden Lodge, Stafford Barton,
Broadhembury, Honiton, Devon
EX14 3LU
T: (01404) 841403
F: (01404) 841403
E: anne@staffordbarton.
devonfarms.co.uk

BROADMAYNE
Dorset

Holcombe Valley Cottages
★★★
Contact: Mr & Mrs Peter & Jane
Davies, Holcombe Valley
Cottages, Chalky Road,
Broadmayne, Dorchester, Dorset
DT2 8PW
T: (01305) 852817
F: (01305) 854539
E: holvalcots@aol.com
I: www.holcombe-cottages.co.uk

BROADOAK
Dorset

Stoke Mill Farm ★★-★★★
Contact: Mrs Anthea Bay, Stoke
Mill Farm, Broadoak, Bridport,
Dorset DT6 5NR
T: (01308) 868036
I: www.stokemillholidays.20m.
com

BROADSANDS
Devon

86 Brunel Road ★★★
Contact: Holiday Homes &
Cottages South West, 365A
Torquay Road, Paignton, Devon
TQ3 2BT
T: (01803) 663650
F: (01803) 664037
E: holcotts@aol.com
I: www.swcottages.co.uk

BROMHAM
Wiltshire

The Byres ★★
Contact: Mr and Mrs G B Myers,
The Byres, Mead View, 84
Westbrook, Bromham,
Chippenham, Wiltshire
SN15 2EE
T: (01380) 850557

Farthings ★★★
Contact: Mrs G Steed, Farthings,
The Cottage, West Brook,
Bromham, Chippenham,
Wiltshire SN15 2EE
T: (01380) 850255
E: RJSteed@cottage16.
freeserve.co.uk

BROMPTON RALPH
Somerset

Oddwell Cottage ★★★
Contact: CH ref: 68023, Country
Holidays Group Owner Services
Dept, Spring Mill, Earby,
Barnoldswick, Lancashire
BB18 6RN
T: (01282) 445096
F: (01282) 844299
E: ch.sales@ttgihg.co.uk
I: www.country-holidays.co.uk

BROMPTON REGIS
Somerset

Brookside ★★★
Contact: Marsden's Cottage
Holidays, 2 The Square,
Braunton, Devon EX33 2JB
T: (01271) 813777
F: (01271) 813664
E: holidays@marsdens.co.uk
I: www.marsdens.co.uk

Weatherham Farm Cottages
★★★★
Contact: Mrs Anne Caldwell,
Weatherham Farm Cottages,
Weatherham Farm, Brompton
Regis, Dulverton, Somerset
TA22 9LG
T: (01398) 371303
F: (01398) 371104
E: Acaldwell@weatherham.
freeserve.co.uk
I: www.exmoortourism.
org/weatherhamfarm.htm

BRYHER
Cornwall

**Atlanta Holiday
Accommodation** ★★★
Contact: Mrs G R Langdon,
Atlanta Holiday
Accommodation, Bryher, Isles of
Scilly TR23 0PR
T: (01720) 422823

Glenhope ★★★
Contact: Mr R E Langdon,
Glenhope, Bryher, Isles of Scilly
TR23 0PR
T: (01720) 423136
F: (01720) 423166
E: glenhope@ukonline.co.uk

**Hebe, Fernside & Shippen
Cottage** ★★★
Contact: Mrs K Taylor, Veronica
Farm, Bryher, Isles of Scilly
TR23 0PR
T: (01720) 422862

Hillside Farm ★★★-★★★★
Contact: Mrs Ruth Jenkins,
Hillside Farm, Bryher, Isles of
Scilly TR23 0PR
T: (01720) 423156

South Hill ★★★
Contact: Mrs M Bennett,
Firmans, Bryher, Isles of Scilly
TR23
T: (01720) 422411
E: marianbennett@excite.co.uk

The White House Flat ★★★
Contact: Mr R F Bushell, The
White House, Bryher, Isles of
Scilly TR23 0PR
T: (01720) 422010
F: (01720) 422010

BUCKFASTLEIGH
Devon

Mill Cottage ★★★
Contact: Mr & Mrs Bowater,
Helpful Holidays, Mill Street,
Chagford, Newton Abbot, Devon
TQ13 8AW
T: (01647) 433593
F: (01647) 433694
E: help@helpfulholidays.com
I: www.helpfulholidays.com

BUCKLAND BREWER
Devon

Adipit ★★★★
Contact: Powell's Cottage
Holidays, High Street,
Saundersfoot, Dyfed SA69 9EJ
T: (01834) 812791
F: (01834) 811731
E: info@powells.co.uk
I: www.powells.co.uk

Millstones ★★★
Contact: Mr Peter Morris, Farm
& Cottage Holidays, Victoria
House, 12 Fore Street, Northam,
Bideford, Devon EX39 1AW
T: (01237) 479146
F: (01237) 421512
E: farmcott@cix.co.uk
I: wwww.farmcott.co.uk

BUCKLAND IN THE MOOR
Devon

The Pine Lodge ★★★
Contact: Holiday Homes &
Cottages South West, 365A
Torquay Road, Paignton, Devon
TQ3 2BT
T: (01803) 663650
F: (01803) 664037
E: holcotts@aol.com
I: www.swcottages.co.uk

BUCKLAND NEWTON
Dorset

Domineys Cottages ★★★★
Contact: Mrs J D Gueterbock,
Domineys Cottages, Domineys
Yard, Buckland Newton,
Dorchester, Dorset DT2 7BS
T: (01300) 345295
F: (01300) 345596

BUCKLAND ST MARY
Somerset

The Apartment ★★★★
Contact: Mr Roy Harkness,
Hillside, Buckland St Mary,
Chard, Somerset TA20 3TQ
T: (01460) 234599 &
07703 633770
F: (01460) 234599
E: royandmarge@hillsidebsm.
freeserve.co.uk

Leveret Cottage ★★★
Contact: Mrs S M Float, Leveret
Cottage, Hare House,
Blackwater, Buckland St Mary,
Chard, Somerset TA20 3LE
T: (01460) 234638
E: info@leverecottage.co.uk

BUDE
Cornwall

Atlantic View Bungalows
★★★
Contact: Mr & Mrs Chris &
Brenda Raven, Atlantic View
Bungalows, Marine Drive,
Widemouth Bay, Bude, Cornwall
EX23 0AG
T: (01288) 361716 &
07989 433078
E: enquiries@atlanticview.co.uk
I: www.atlanticview.co.uk

Broomhill Manor Country
Estate★★★★
Contact: Mr C B Mower,
Broomhill Manor Country
Estate, Broomhill Manor, Bude,
Cornwall EX23 9HA
T: (01288) 352940
F: (01288) 356526
E: chris@broomhillmanor.co.uk
I: www.broomhillmanor.co.uk

Downlands ★★★
Contact: Mr Clive Bloy,
Downlands, Maer Lane, Bude,
Cornwall EX23 9EE
T: (01288) 356920
E: sonia@downlands.net
I: www.downlands.net

The Falcon Hotel ★★★
Contact: Mr & Mrs T Browning,
The Falcon Hotel, Breakwater
Road, Bude, Cornwall EX23 8SD
T: (01288) 352005
F: (01288) 356359
E: reception@falconhotel.com
I: www.falconhotel.com

Forda Lodges
★★★★-★★★★★
Contact: Mr & Mrs J Chibbett,
Forda Lodges, Kilkhampton,
Bude, Cornwall EX23 9RZ
T: (01288) 321413
F: (01288) 321413
E: forda.lodges@virgin.net
I: www.fordalodges.co.uk

Glebe House Cottages Limited
★★★★
Contact: Mr and Mrs James
Varley, Glebe House Cottages
Limited, Bridgerule, Holsworthy,
Devon EX22 7EW
T: (01288) 381272
E: holidays@
glebehousecottages.freeserve.
co.uk
I: www.glebehousecottages.
co.uk

Houndapitt Farm Cottages
★★★
Contact: Mr A Heard,
Houndapitt Farm Cottages,
Sandymouth Bay, Stibb, Bude,
Cornwall EX23 9HW
T: (01288) 355455
E: anthony@houndapitt.co.uk
I: www.houndapitt.co.uk

Ivyleaf Barton Cottages
★★-★★★★★
Contact: Mr & Mrs P McIntyre,
Ivyleaf Barton, Ivyleaf Hill, Bude,
Cornwall EX23 9LD
T: (01288) 321237
F: (01288) 321937
E: ivyleafbarton@hotmail.com

Kennacott Court ★★★★★
Contact: Mr & Mrs R H Davis,
Kennacott Court, Widemouth
Bay, Bude, Cornwall EX23 0ND
T: (01288) 361766 & 361683
F: (01288) 361434
E: maureen@kennacottcourt.
co.uk
I: www.kennacottcourt.co.uk

Langfield Manor ★★★
Contact: Mr & Mrs Keith &
Christa Freestone, Langfield
Manor, Broadclose, Bude,
Cornwall EX23 8DP
T: (01288) 352415
F: (01288) 353416
E: freestone.langfield@virgin.
net
I: www.bude.co.uk/langfield

Manby ★★★
Contact: Mrs L Hoole, 54
Western Road, Oxford, OX1 4LG
T: (01865) 245268 &
07980 137360
E: hoole@patrol.i-way.co.uk

Mornish Holiday Apartments
★★★★
Contact: Mr & Mrs John & Julia
Hilder, Mornish Holiday
Apartments, 20 Summerleaze
Crescent, Bude, Cornwall
EX23 8HJ
T: (01288) 352972
F: (01288) 352972
E: johnhilder@classicfm.net
I: www.bude.
co.uk/mornish-apartments

Penhalt Farm and Aalsmeer
★★★
Contact: Mr & Mrs D Marks,
Penhalt Farm, Widemouth Bay,
Poundstock, Bude, Cornwall
EX23 0DG
T: (01288) 361210
F: (01288) 361210
I: www.holidaybank.co.uk/
penhaltfarm

Wild Pigeon Holidays ★★★
Contact: Mrs Anne Longley, Wild
Pigeon Holidays, 8 Breakwater
Road, Bude, Cornwall EX23 8LQ
T: (01288) 353839

Woolstone Manor Farm
★★★★
Contact: Mr MJ Wright,
Woolstone Manor Farm, Bude,
Cornwall EX23 0NB
T: (01288) 361639

BUDLEIGH SALTERTON
Devon

Lufflands ★★★★
Contact: Mr & Mrs C Goode,
Lufflands, Yettington, Budleigh
Salterton, Devon EX9 7BP
T: (01395) 568422
F: (01395) 568810
E: lufflands@compuserve.com
I: www.lufflands.co.uk

BUDOCK WATER
Cornwall

Higher Kergilliack ★★★
Contact: Mr & Mrs Bowater,
Helpful Holidays, Mill Street,
Chagford, Newton Abbot, Devon
TQ13 8AW
T: (01647) 433593
F: (01647) 433694
E: help@helpfulholidays.com
I: www.helpfulholidays.com

BUGFORD
Devon

Quarry Lake Farm ★★★
Contact: Mr Peter Morris, Farm
& Cottage Holidays, Victoria
House, 12 Fore Street, Northam,
Bideford, Devon EX39 1AW
T: (01237) 479146
F: (01237) 421512
E: farmcott@cix.co.uk
I: www.farmcott.co.uk

BUGLE
Cornwall

Higher Menadew ★★★★
Contact: Ms A Higman, Higher
Menadew, Bugle, St Austell,
Cornwall PL26 8QW
T: (01726) 850310

BURLAWN
Cornwall

Wren Cottage ★★★
Contact: Harbour Holidays,
Estuary House, Rock Road, Rock,
Wadebridge, Cornwall
PL27 6NW
T: (01208) 862424
F: (01208) 862218
E: rockhols@aol.com
I: www.rockholidays.com

BURNHAM-ON-SEA
Somerset

8 Allandale Road ★
Contact: Ms M J Mayo,
Maeswalter, Heol Senni, Brecon,
Powys LD3 8SU
T: (01874) 636629
E: maeswalter@talk21.com

Beachside Apartment ★★★
Contact: Mr Richard Hingston,
Beachside Apartment, 1 The
Colony, Berrow Road, Burnham-
on-Sea, Somerset TA8 2HA
T: (01278) 784571
F: (01278) 784571
E: hingston@globalnet.co.uk

Glenlora ★★
Contact: Mrs S Street, Glenlora,
44 Cross Street, Burnham-on-
Sea, Somerset TA8 1PF
T: (01278) 786597

36 Gloucester Road ★★
Contact: Mr and Mrs D Duke, 10
Main Road, West Huntspill,
Highbridge, Somerset TA9 3DN
T: (01278) 781846

Hurn Farm ★★★
Contact: Mrs O R Holdom, Hurn
Farm, Hurn Lane, Berrow,
Burnham-on-Sea, Somerset
TA8 2QT
T: (01278) 751418
E: hurnfarm@
hurnfarmcottages.co.uk
I: www.hurnfarmcottages.co.uk

Prospect Farm ★★★
Contact: Mrs Gillian Wall,
Prospect Farm, Strowlands, East
Brent, Highbridge, Somerset
TA9 4JH
T: (01278) 760507

Stable Cottage and Coach
House ★★
Contact: Mr & Mrs Bigwood,
Brean Farm, Brean Down, Brean,
Burnham-on-Sea, Somerset
TA8 2RR
T: (01278) 751055
F: (01278) 751055

Stoddens Farm Holiday
Cottages ★★★
Contact: Mrs Sandra Tipling,
Stoddens Farm, Stoddens Road,
Burnham-on-Sea, Somerset
TA8 2DE
T: (01278) 782505
F: (01278) 792221
E: stoddens-cottages@
netgates.co.uk

BURROWBRIDGE
Somerset

Hillview ★★★
Contact: Mrs Rosalind Griffiths,
Hillview, Stanmoor Road,
Burrowbridge, Bridgwater,
Somerset TA7 0RX
T: (01823) 698308
F: (01823) 698308

Establishments printed in blue have a detailed entry in this guide

BURSTOCK
Dorset

Whetham Farm The Flat ★★
Contact: Mrs Curtis, Whetham Farm The Flat, Burstock, Beaminster, Dorset DT8 3LH
T: (01308) 868293

BURTON BRADSTOCK
Dorset

Graston Farm Cottage ★★★
Contact: Mrs S J Bailey, Graston Farm Cottage, Annings Lane, Burton Bradstock, Bridport, Dorset DT6 4NG
T: (01308) 897603
F: (01308) 897016
E: graston@ukgateway.net

Pebble Beach Lodge ★★★
Contact: Mr and Mrs Bruce and Jan Hemingway, Pebble Beach Lodge, Coast Road, Burton Bradstock, Bridport, Dorset DT6 4RJ
T: (01308) 897428
F: (01308) 897428

BUTCOMBE
North Somerset

Butcombe Farm ★★★
Contact: Mr Barry Harvey, Butcombe Farm, Aldwick Lane, Butcombe, North Somerset BS40 7UW
T: (01761) 462380
F: (01761) 462300
E: info@butcombe-farm. demon.co.uk
I: www.butcombe-farm.demon. co.uk

BUTLEIGH WOOTTON
Somerset

Little Broadway ★★
Contact: Mrs Mary Butt, Proprietor, Broadway Farm, Butleigh Wootton, Glastonbury, Somerset BA6 8TX
T: (01458) 442824
F: (01458) 442824

CADBURY
Devon

Fursdon Estate ★★★-★★★★★
Contact: Mrs Catriona Fursdon, Fursdon Estate, Fursdon House, Cadbury, Exeter, Devon EX5 5JS
T: (01392) 860860
F: (01392) 860126
E: enquiries@fursdon.co.uk
I: www.fursdon.co.uk

CALLINGTON
Cornwall

Cadson Manor Farm ★★★★
Contact: Mr B Crago, Cadson Manor Farm, Callington, Cornwall PL17 7HW
T: (01579) 383969
F: (01579) 383969
E: greenstock@callington. swinternet.co.uk
I: www.chcor.co.uk. cottages/cadson-manor

Venterdon House Barn ★★★★
Contact: Mr & Mrs Bowater, Helpful Holidays, Mill Street, Chagford, Newton Abbot, Devon TQ13 8AW
T: (01647) 433593
F: (01647) 433694
E: help@helpfulholidays.com
I: www.helpfulholidays.com

CALNE
Wiltshire

Riversbrook Cottages ★★★
Contact: Mr Steve Harding, Hayle Farm Hotel and Restaurant, Quemerford, Calne, Wiltshire SN11 8UJ
T: (01249) 813275
F: (01249) 813275
E: hayle-farm@eclipse.co.uk
I: www.eclipse.co.uk/hayle-farm

CAMELFORD
Cornwall

Helsbury Park ★★★★★
Contact: Mr & Mrs Pluess, Helsbury Park, Camelford, Cornwall PL32 9RH
T: (01840) 212220

Kenningstock Cottage ★★★
Contact: Mrs I L Austin-Smith, Kenningstock Mill, Advent, Camelford, Cornwall PL32 9QP
T: (01840) 213538 & 213761
F: (01840) 213394
E: austinsmith100@aol

Vilnius ★★★
Contact: CH ref: 66068, Holiday Cottages Group Owner Services Dept, Spring Mill, Earby, Barnoldswick, Lancashire BB18 6RN
T: (01282) 445096
F: (01282) 844299
E: ch.sales@ttgihg.co.uk
I: www.country-holidays.co.uk

Warmington House ★★★
Contact: Mr & Mrs Peter & Pauline Inns, 38 Egloshayle Road, Wadebridge, Cornwall PL27 6AE
T: (01208) 813003
E: inns@barclays

CAPE CORNWALL
Cornwall

Nanpean Barn Holiday Flats ★★★
Contact: CH ref: 2131-2133, Holiday Cottages Group Owner Services Dept, Spring Mill, Earby, Barnoldswick, Lancashire BB18 6RN
T: (01282) 445096
F: (01282) 844299
E: ch.sales@ttgihg.co.uk
I: www.country-holidays.co.uk

CARBIS BAY
Cornwall

61 Laity Lane ★★★
Contact: CH ref: 10704, Holiday Cottages Group Owner Services Dept, Spring Mill, Earby, Barnoldswick, Lancashire BB18 6RN
T: (01282) 445096
F: (01282) 844299
E: ch.sales@ttgihg.co.uk
I: www.country-holidays.co.uk

Rotorua Apartments ★★★★
Contact: Mrs Linda Roach, Rotorua Apartments, Trencrom Lane, Carbis Bay, St Ives, Cornwall TR26 2TD
T: (01736) 795419
F: (01736) 795419
E: rotoruaapt@aol.com
I: www.stivesapartments.com

CARDINHAM
Cornwall

Muckle Byre Cottage ★★★
Contact: Mr & Mrs Steve & Viv Clemens, Muckle Byre Cottage, Welltown, Cardinham, Bodmin, Cornwall PL30 4EG
T: (01208) 821477
E: stevclem@aol.com

CASTLE CARY
Somerset

Clanville Manor Tallet ★★★★
Contact: Mrs S P Snook, Clanville Manor, Castle Cary, Somerset BA7 7PJ
T: (01963) 350124 & 07966 512732
F: (01963) 350313
E: clanville@aol.com
I: www.somerset-farm-holiday. co.uk/tallet-home-page.htm

Cockhill Old Barn ★★★★
Contact: Mrs A Peppin, Lower Cockhill Farm, Castle Cary, Somerset BA7 7NZ
T: (01963) 351288
F: (01963) 351840
E: bookings@cockhill.co.uk

Orchard Farm Cottages ★★★
Contact: Mr and Mrs R D Boyer, Orchard Farm, Cockhill, Castle Cary, Somerset BA7 7NY
T: (01963) 350418
F: (01963) 350418
E: boyer@talk21.com
I: www. leisurehuntcom/ adhmlcockhillfarm

CATTISTOCK
Dorset

Little Greystones ★★★
Contact: Mr & Mrs A&J Fletcher, Greystones, Cattistock, Dorchester, Dorset DT2 0JB
T: (01300) 320477
E: j_f.fletcher@virgin-net.uk

4 The Rocks ★★★★
Contact: Mr A P Stockwell, The Old Vicarage, Yarcombe, Honiton, Devon EX14 9BD
T: (01404) 861594
F: (01404) 861594

Upshalls ★★★
Contact: Mr J G Walmsley, Castle Hill Cottage, Duck Street, Cattistock, Dorchester, Dorset DT2 0JH
T: (01300) 320550
F: (01300) 320550

CAUNDLE MARSH
Dorset

Marsh Court Home Farm ★★
Contact: Ms S Fox-Pitt, I 4 Top Albany, Piccadilly, London W1J 0AX
T: (0207) 4342808 & 07951 118461

CERNE ABBAS
Dorset

Gingerfox Cottage ★★★
Contact: Mr & Mrs John & Clare Killinger, 5 Duck Street, Cerne Abbas, Dorchester, Dorset DT2 7LA
T: (01300) 341718
F: (01300) 341718
E: clare.killinger@which.net

Old Gaol Cottage ★★★★★
Contact: Ms Nicky Willis, Lamperts Cottage, 10 Dorchester Road, Sydling St Nicholas, Dorchester, Dorset DT2 9NU
T: (01300) 341659
F: (01300) 341699
E: nickywillis@f1racing.co

CHAGFORD
Devon

Gibhouse ★★★★-★★★★★
Contact: Mr & Mrs Bowater, Helpful Holidays, Mill Street, Chagford, Newton Abbot, Devon TQ13 8AW
T: (01647) 433593
F: (01647) 433694
E: help@helpfulholidays.com
I: www.helpfulholidays.com

10 Greystones Cottage ★★★
Contact: Mr & Mrs Bowater, Helpful Holidays, Mill Street, Chagford, Newton Abbot, Devon TQ13 8AW
T: (01647) 433593
F: (01647) 433694
E: help@helpfulholidays.com
I: www.helpfulholidays.com

Moorlands Hotel ★★★
Contact: Dr & Mrs David Spear, Moorlands Hotel, 26-28 Mill Street, Chagford, Newton Abbot, Devon TQ13 8AW
T: (01647) 432214
F: (01647) 432214
E: woof@mail.eclipse.co.uk
I: www.eclipse. co.uk/~052096/rehome.htm

Springfield Cottage ★★★★
Contact: Mr & Mrs Bowater, Helpful Holidays, Mill Street, Chagford, Newton Abbot, Devon TQ13 8AW
T: (01647) 433593
F: (01647) 433694
E: help@helpfulholidays.com
I: www.helpfulholidays.com

Throwleigh Manor Gamekeepers/Coach House & Pear Tree ★★★
Contact: Mrs J Smitheram, Throwleigh Manor Gamekeepers/Coach House & Pear Tree, Throwleigh, Okehampton, Devon EX20 2JF
T: (01647) 231630
F: (01647) 231630

Yelfords ★★★★★
Contact: Mrs G Cain, Yelfords, Chagford, Newton Abbot, Devon TQ13 8ES
T: (01647) 432546

CHALLACOMBE
Devon

Home Place Farm Cottages ★★★
Contact: Mr Mark Ravenscroft, Home Place Farm Cottages, Challacombe, Barnstaple, Devon EX31 4TS
T: (01598) 763283
F: (01598) 763283
E: markandsarah@ holidayexmoor.co.uk
I: www.holidayexmoor.co.uk

Town Tenement ★★★
Contact: Mrs S M Yendell, Town Tenement, Challacombe, Barnstaple, Devon EX31 4TS
T: (01598) 763320

Whitefield Barton ★★★
Contact: Mrs Rosemarie Kingdon, Whitefield Barton, Challacombe, Barnstaple, Devon EX31 4TU
T: (01598) 763271
I: www.exmoorholidays.co.uk

2 Yelland Cottages ★★
Contact: Mrs M J Kingdon, West Whitefield, Challacombe, Barnstaple, Devon EX31 4TU
T: (01598) 763433

CHAPEL AMBLE
Cornwall

Ambledown ★★★★★
Contact: Mr & Mrs T J Gorringe, Ambledown, Chapel Amble, Wadebridge, Cornwall PL27 6EP
T: (01208) 841380
F: (01208) 841464

Carclaze Farm ★★★★
Contact: Mrs J Nicholls, Carclaze Farm, Chapel Amble, Wadebridge, Cornwall PL27 6EP
T: (01208) 813886
E: enquires@carclaze.dabsol.co.uk
I: www.carclaze.co.uk

Coombe Mill ★★★
Contact: Harbour Holidays - Rock, Estuary House, Rock Road, Rock, Wadebridge, Cornwall PL27 6NW
T: (01208) 862424
F: (01208) 862218
E: rockhols@aol.com
I: www.rockholidays.com

Homeleigh Farm ★★★★
Contact: Mrs A J Rees, Homeleigh Farm, Chapel Amble, Wadebridge, Cornwall PL27 6EU
T: (01208) 812411
F: (01208) 815025
E: homeleigh@eclipse.co.uk
I: www.eclipse.co.uk/homeleigh

The Olde House ★★★
Contact: Mr and Mrs A Hawkey, The Olde House, Chapel Amble, Wadebridge, Cornwall PL27 6EN
T: (01208) 813219 & 815230
F: (01208) 815689
E: info@theoldhouse.co.uk
I: www.theoldehouse.co.uk

Rooke Country Cottages ★★★★★
Contact: Mrs Gill Reskelly, Rooke Country Cottages, Rooke Farm, Chapel Amble, Wadebridge, Cornwall PL27 6ES
T: (01208) 880368
F: (01208) 880600
E: info@rookecottages.com
I: www.rookecottages.com

Rooke Mill ★★★★
Contact: Diana Bullivant Holidays, South Winds, Trebell Green, Lanivet, Bodmin, Cornwall PL30 5HR
T: (01208) 831336
F: (01208) 831336
E: diana@dbullivant.fsnet.co.uk
I: www.cornwall-online.co.uk/diana-bullivant

CHARD
Somerset

Yew Tree Cottage ★★★★
Contact: Mr & Mrs Viv & Phillip Hopkins, Yew Tree Cottage, Hornsbury Hill, Chard, Somerset TA20 3DB
T: (01460) 64735
F: (01460) 66163
E: ytcottage@aol.com
I: www.yewtreecottage.org.uk

CHARDSTOCK
Devon

Barn Owls Cottage ★★★★
Contact: Mrs J Hafner, Barn Owls Cottage, Chardstock, Axminster, Devon EX13 7BY
T: (01460) 220475
F: (01460) 220475
E: barnowls@hafner.fsbusiness.co.uk

CHARLTON MUSGROVE
Somerset

Pigsty, Cowstall & Bullpen Cottages ★★★
Contact: Mrs B C Chilcott, Pigsty, Cowstall & Bullpen Cottages, Barrow Lane Farm, Charlton Musgrove, Wincanton, Somerset BA9 8HJ
T: (01963) 33217
F: (01963) 31449
E: chrischilcott@farmersweekly.net

CHARMINSTER
Dorset

Meadow Cottage ★★★
Contact: Mrs E Hanson, 2 Swarthmore Road, Birmingham, B29 4JR
T: (0121) 4751196

CHARMOUTH
Dorset

5 Barneys Close L4225 ★★★
Contact: Lyme Bay Holidays, Boshouse, 44 Church Street, Lyme Regis, Dorset DT7 3DA
T: (01297) 443363
F: (01297) 445576
E: email@lymebayholidays.co.uk
I: www.lymebayholidays.co.uk

Barney's Close L4226 ★★★
Contact: Lyme Bay Holidays, Boshouse, 44 Church Street, Lyme Regis, Dorset DT7 3DA
T: (01297) 443363
F: (01297) 445576
E: email@lymebayholidays.co.uk
I: www.lymebayholidays.co.uk

Befferlands Farm
Rating Applied For
Contact: Mr & Mrs R S Andrews, Befferlands Farm, Betterlands Farm, Charmouth, Bridport, Dorset DT6
T: (01297) 560203

Bridge House ★★★
Contact: Mrs M Warren, Bridge House, Bridge Road, Charmouth, Bridport, Dorset DT6 6QP
T: (01297) 560609

Bridge House K4271 ★★★
Contact: Lyme Bay Holidays, Bos House, 44 Church Street, Lyme Regis, Dorset DT7 3DA
T: (01297) 443363
F: (01297) 445576
E: email@lymebayholidays.co.uk
I: www.lymebayholidays.co.uk

Charleston Holiday Cottages ★★★
Contact: Mrs Kim Wood, Grosvenor Cottage, The Street, Charmouth, Bridport, Dorset DT6
T: (01297) 560053

Coach House Flat J4175 ★★★★
Contact: Lyme Bay Holidays, Boshouse, 44 Church Street, Lyme Regis, Dorset DT7 3DA
T: (01297) 443363
F: (01297) 445576
E: email@lymebayholidays.co.uk
I: www.lymebayholidays.co.uk

Dolphin Leap ★★★
Contact: The Proprietor, Dolphin Leap, Charmouth, Bridport, Dorset

Double Common K4229 ★★★★
Contact: Lyme Bay Holidays, Boshouse, 44 Church Street, Lyme Regis, Dorset DT7 3DA
T: (01297) 443363
F: (01297) 445576
E: email@lymebayholidays.co.uk
I: www.lymebayholidays.co.uk

Flat 10 Seahorse K4143 ★★★
Contact: Lyme Bay Holidays, Boshouse, 44 Church Street, Lyme Regis, Dorset DT7 3DA
T: (01297) 443363
F: (01297) 445576
E: email@lymebayholidays.co.uk
I: www.lymebayholidays.co.uk

Fleur K4243 ★★★
Contact: Lyme Bay Holidays, Boshouse, 44 Church Street, Lyme Regis, Dorset DT7 3DA
T: (01297) 443363
F: (01297) 445576
E: email@lymebayholidays.co.uk
I: www.lymebayholidays.co.uk

7 Hammonds Mead ★★
Contact: Lyme Bay Holiday Cottages, Boshouse, 44 Church Street, Lyme Regis, Dorset DT7 3DA
T: (01297) 443363
E: email@lymebayholidays.co.uk

Lias Lea L3501 ★★★
Contact: Lyme Bay Holidays, Boshouse, 44 Church Street, Lyme Regis, Dorset DT7 3DA
T: (01297) 443363
F: (01297) 445576
E: email@lymebayholidays.co.uk
I: www.lymebayholidays.co.uk

Little Catherston Farm ★★
Contact: Mr R J White, Little Catherston Farm, Charmouth, Bridport, Dorset DT6 6LZ
T: (01297) 560550

Little Melbourne J4268 ★★★
Contact: Lyme Bay Holidays, Boshouse, 44 Church Street, Lyme Regis, Dorset DT7 3DA
T: (01297) 443363
F: (01297) 445576
E: email@lymebayholidays.co.uk
I: www.lymebayholidays.co.uk

Manor Farm Holiday Centre ★★
Contact: Mr Robin Loosmore, Manor Farm Holiday Centre, Charmouth, Bridport, Dorset DT6 6QL
T: (01297) 560226
F: (01297) 560429
E: enq@manorfarmholidaycentre.co.uk
I: www.manorfarmholidaycentre.co.uk

2 Meads Cottages ★★
Contact: 2 Meads Cottages, Charmouth, Bridport, Dorset DT6

Miskyns K3557 ★★★
Contact: Lyme Bay Holiday Cottages, Boshouse, 44 Church Street, Lyme Regis, Dorset DT7 3DA
T: (01297) 443363
E: email@lymebayholidays.co.uk
I: www.lymebayholidays.co.uk

No 1 Double Common L4221 ★★★★
Contact: Lyme Bay Holidays, Boshouse, 44 Church Street, Lyme Regis, Dorset DT7 3DA
T: (01297) 443363
F: (01297) 445576
E: email@lymebayholidays.co.uk
I: www.lymebayholidays.co.uk

No 11 Double Common L4222 ★★★★
Contact: Lyme Bay Holidays, Boshouse, 44 Church Street, Lyme Regis, Dorset DT7 3DA
T: (01297) 443363
F: (01297) 445576
E: email@lymebayholidays.co.uk
I: www.lymebayholidays.co.uk

No 3 Double Common L4223 ★★★★
Contact: Lyme Bay Holidays, Boshouse, 44 Church Street, Lyme Regis, Dorset DT7 3DA
T: (01297) 443363
F: (01297) 445576
E: email@lymebayholidays.co.uk
I: www.lymebayholidays.co.uk

Old Coach House ★★★
Contact: Jean Bartlett Cottage Holidays, Fore Street, Beer, Seaton, Devon EX12 3JB
T: (01297) 23221
F: (01297) 23303
E: jeanb@netbreaks.com
I: www.netbreaks.com/jeanb

Penderel L3958 ★★★
Contact: Lyme Bay Holidays, Boshouse, 44 Church Street, Lyme Regis, Dorset DT7 3DA
T: (01297) 443363
F: (01297) 445576
E: email@lymebayholidays.co.uk
I: www.lymebayholidays.co.uk

Establishments printed in blue have a detailed entry in this guide

The Poplars ★★★
Contact: Mrs Jane Pointing,
Wood Farm Caravan and
Camping Park, Axminster Road,
Charmouth, Bridport, Dorset
DT6 6BT
T: (01297) 560697
E: holiday@woodfarm.co.uk
I: www.woodfarm.co.uk

Portland House K4129 ★★★
Contact: Lyme Bay Holidays,
Boshouse, 44 Church Street,
Lyme Regis, Dorset DT7 3DA
T: (01297) 443363
F: (01297) 445576
E: email@lymebayholidays.co.uk
I: www.lymebayholidays.co.uk

Riverside Cottage K4263 ★★★★
Contact: Lyme Bay Holidays,
Boshouse, 44 Church Street,
Lyme Regis, Dorset 01297
T: (01297) 443363
F: (01297) 445576
E: email@lymebayholidays.co.uk
I: www.lymebayholidays.co.uk

Rosern K4064 ★★★
Contact: Lyme Bay Holidays,
Boshouse, 44 Church Street,
Lyme Regis, Dorset DT7 3DA
T: (01297) 443363
F: (01297) 445576
E: email@lymebayholidays.co.uk
I: www.lymebayholidays.co.uk

Sarum L4240 ★★★
Contact: Lyme Bay Holidays,
Boshouse, 44 Church Street,
Lyme Regis, Dorset DT7 3DA
T: (01297) 443363
F: (01297) 445576
E: email@lymebayholidays.co.uk
I: www.lymebayholidays.co.uk

The Shoe and Stocking ★★★
Contact: The Shoe and Stocking,
The Street, Charmouth, Bridport,
Dorset DT6

Smiths Farm ★★★
Contact: Mr & Mrs Alan & Susan
Russell, Smiths Farm, Axminster
Road, Penn, Charmouth,
Bridport, Dorset DT6 6BY
T: (01297) 560167
F: (01297) 560478
E: sales@kitchenmate.co.uk
I: www.smithsfarm.co.uk

The Stone House N3911 ★★★★★
Contact: Lyme Bay Holidays,
Boshouse, 44 Church Street,
Lyme Regis, Dorset DT7 3DA
T: (01297) 443363
F: (01297) 445576
E: email@lymebayholidays.co.uk
I: www.lymebayholidays.co.uk

Thalatta M3988 ★★
Contact: Lyme Bay Holidays,
Boshouse, 44 Church Street,
Lyme Regis, Dorset DT7 3DA
T: (01297) 443363
F: (01297) 445576
E: email@lymebayholidays.co.uk
I: www.lymebayholidays.co.uk

Tillicum M3927 ★★★
Contact: Lyme Bay Holidays,
Boshouse, 44 Church Street,
Lyme Regis, Dorset DT7 3DA
T: (01297) 443363
F: (01297) 445576
E: email@lymebayholidays.co.uk
I: www.lymebayholidays.co.uk

Upper Flat ★★
Contact: Upper Flat, Greystones,
Off The Street, Charmouth,
Bridport, Dorset DT6

Willows K3909 ★★★
Contact: Lyme Bay Holidays,
Boshouse, 44 Church Street,
Lyme Regis, Dorset DT7 3DA
T: (01297) 443363
F: (01297) 445576
E: email@lymebayholidays.co.uk
I: www.lymebayholidays.co.uk

CHEDDAR
Somerset

Applebee (South) Barn Cottage ★
Contact: Mrs K W Richardson,
Applebee (South) Barn Cottage,
The Hayes, Cheddar, Somerset
BS27 3AN
T: (01934) 743146 &
07721 579593
F: (01934) 743146

Cheddar Lodge ★★★
Contact: Mr Jon Rawlings,
Cheddar Lodge, Old Cheddar
Cottage, Draycott Road,
Cheddar, Somerset BS27 3RP
T: (01934) 743859 &
07974 579070
F: (01934) 741550
E: jon@1rawlings.freeserve.co.uk

Home Farm Cottages ★★★-★★★★★
Contact: Mrs Christine Marlow,
Home Farm Cottages, Home
Farm, Barton, Winscombe,
Cheddar, Somerset BS25 1DX
T: (01934) 842078
E: chris@homefarmcottages.co.uk
I: www.homefarmcottages.co.uk

Millyard Cottage ★★★★
Contact: Mr Stuart Fisher,
Millhaven, Stoke Street, Rodney
Stoke, Cheddar, Somerset
BS27 3UP
T: (01749) 870962
E: stuartfisher2@compuserve.com
I: www.stuarts-holidays.bc1.net

Orchard Court & Bungalow ★★★★
Contact: Mrs Carol Roberts,
Orchard Lodge, Tweentown,
Cheddar, Somerset BS27 3HY
T: (01934) 742116

Spring Cottages ★★★
Contact: Mrs Jennifer Buckland,
Spring Cottages, Venns Gate,
Cheddar, Somerset BS27 3LW
T: (01934) 742493
F: (01934) 742493
E: buckland@springcottages.co.uk
I: www.springcottages.co.uk

Sungate Holiday Apartments ★★
Contact: Miss A Fieldhouse,
Market Cross Hotel, Church
Street, Cheddar, Somerset
BS27 3RA
T: (01934) 742264 & 842273
F: (01934) 741411

CHEDZOY
Somerset

Nelson Cottage ★★★★
Contact: Mr & Mrs S Robbins,
Nelson Lodge, Chedzoy Lane,
Chedzoy, Bridgwater, Somerset
TA7 8QR
T: (01278) 453492

CHELDON
Devon

Cheldon Barton ★
Contact: Mrs Susannah Mudge,
The Vicars Stalls, Chulmleigh,
Devon EX18 7DD
T: (01769) 580298
F: (01769) 580298
E: susannahmudge@hotmail.com

CHELSTON
Devon

Summerdyne Apartments ★★★
Contact: Mr & Mrs Dale &
Mandy Tanner, Summerdyne
Apartments, Greenway Road,
Chelston, Torquay, Devon
TQ2 6JE
T: (01803) 605439
F: (01803) 607441
I: www.summerdyne.co.uk

CHERITON BISHOP
Devon

Horselake Farm ★★★
Contact: CH Ref: 14493/6,
Holiday Cottages Group Owner
Services Department, Spring
Mill, Earby, Barnoldswick,
Lancashire BB94 0AA
T: (01282) 445096
F: (01282) 844299
E: ch.sales@ttgihg.co.uk
I: www.country-holidays.co.uk

CHEW MAGNA
Bath and North East Somerset

Chew Hill Farm ★★★
Contact: Mrs S Lyons, Chew Hill
Farm, Chew Magna, Bristol
BS40 8QP
T: (01275) 332496 &
07831 117186
F: (01275) 332037

Woodbarn Farm Cottages ★★★-★★★★
Contact: Mrs Judi Hasell,
Woodbarn Farm, Denny Lane,
Chew Magna, Bristol BS40 8SZ
T: (01275) 332599
F: (01275) 332599
E: woodbarnfarm@hotmail.com

CHIDEOCK
Dorset

Acorn Cottage ★★★★
Contact: Mr Grant Roberts, 20
Eastland Road, Thornbury,
Bristol BS35 1DS
T: (01454) 415140 & 413056
F: (01454) 415140
E: grant@robe87.freeserve.co.uk

Ash Cottage ★★★
Contact: Mr SJ Dixon, Ash
Cottage, 26 Dartmouth Place,
Chiswick, London W4 2RH
T: (0208) 995 6529
E: simon.dixon@htb.org.uk

The Coach House ★★★
Contact: Mr & Mrs Eric/Denise
Tweddle, Warren House Bed &
Breakfast, Chideock, Bridport,
Dorset DT6 6JW
T: (01297) 489704
F: (01297) 489704

Guard House Cottage ★★★
Contact: Mrs Joyce Whittaker,
Seatown House, Seatown,
Chideock, Bridport, Dorset
DT6 6JU
T: (01297) 489417 & 489856
F: (01297) 489151

Willowhayne Cottages ★★★★
Contact: Mr & Mrs RJ Pavitt,
Rakes Holt, 11 St Georges Hall,
Haye Lane, Lyme Regis, Dorset
DT7 3NT
T: (01297) 444471 &
07966 176082
F: (01297) 444471
E: willowhayne.cottages@virgin.net
I: www.willowhaynecottages.com

CHILLA
Devon

Eastlake Farm ★★★-★★★★
Contact: Country Hols Ref:9145,
Holiday Cottages Group Limited,
Spring Mill, Barby, Barnoldswick,
Lancashire BB94 0AA
T: (01282) 445096
F: (01282) 844288
I: www.country-holidays.co.uk

CHILLINGTON
Devon

Friends Cottage ★★★
Contact: Powell's Cottage
Holidays, High Street,
Saundersfoot, Dyfed SA69 9EJ
T: (01834) 812791
F: (01834) 811731
E: info@powells.co.uk
I: www.powells.co.uk

Tanpits Cottage ★★★★
Contact: Mr & Mrs Bowater,
Helpful Holidays, Mill Street,
Chagford, Newton Abbot, Devon
TQ13 8AW
T: (01647) 433593
F: (01647) 433694
E: help@helpfulholidays.com
I: www.helpfulholidays.com

CHILSWORTHY
Devon

Parnacott Barn ★★★
Contact: Mr & Mrs Bowater,
Helpful Holidays, Mill Street,
Chagford, Newton Abbot, Devon
TQ13 8AW
T: (01647) 433593
F: (01647) 433694
E: help@helpfulholidays.com
I: www.helpfulholidays.com

CHILTON POLDEN
Somerset

Goose Lane Farmhouse & Cottages★★★★
Contact: Mr & Mrs Jeff & Beverley Poole, Goose Lane Farmhouse & Cottages, Goose Lane, Chilton Polden, Bridgwater, Somerset TA7 9ED
T: (01278) 722955
F: (01278) 722955
E: jbkpoole@cs.com

CHILTON TRINITY
Somerset

Chilton Farm ★★★★
Contact: Mr Peter Morris, Farm & Cottage Holidays, Victoria House, 12 Fore Street, Northam, Bideford, Devon EX39 1AW
T: (01237) 479146
F: (01237) 421512
E: farmcott@cix.co.uk
I: www.farmcott.co.uk

CHIPPENHAM
Wiltshire

Nut Tree Cottage ★★★
Contact: Mrs M D Payne, Nut Tree Cottage, Long Dean, Chippenham, Wiltshire SN14 7EX
T: (01249) 782354

The Parlour ★★★
Contact: Mrs C J Miles, Middle Farm, Stanley, Chippenham, Wiltshire SN15 3RF
T: (01249) 650339

Roward Farm ★★★★
Contact: Mr David Humphrey, Roward Farm, Roward Farm, Draycot Cerne, Chippenham, Wiltshire SN15 4SG
T: (01249) 758147
F: (01249) 758149
E: d.humphrey@roward.demon.co.uk

Swallow Cottage ★★★★
Contact: Mrs Suzanne Candy, Olivemead Farm, Olivemead Lane, Dauntsey, Chippenham, Wiltshire SN15 4JQ
T: (01666) 510205
F: (01666) 510205
E: olivemead@farming.co.uk

CHIPPING SODBURY
South Gloucestershire

Tan House Farm Cottage ★★★
Contact: Mrs C E James, Tan House Farm Cottage, Tan House Farm, Yate, Bristol, South Gloucestershire BS37 7QL
T: (01454) 228280
F: (01454) 228777

CHITTLEHAMHOLT
Devon

Grange Cottage ★★★★
Contact: Marsden's Cottage Holidays, 2 The Square, Braunton, Devon EX33 2JB
T: (01271) 813777
F: (01271) 813664
E: holidays@mardens.co.uk
I: www.marsdens.co.uk

Higher Ditchaton Water ★★★★
Contact: Mrs Anne Thorne, Higher Ditchaton Water, Chittlehamholt, Umberleigh, Devon EX37 9HB
T: (01769) 540389

Simmons Farm Cottage ★★★
Contact: Marsden's Cottage Holidays, 2 The Square, Braunton, Devon EX33 2JB
T: (01271) 813777
F: (01271) 813664
E: holidays@marsdens.co.uk
I: www.marsdens.co.uk

CHITTLEHAMPTON
Devon

Lower Langaton ★★★★
Contact: Mr Peter Morris, Farm & Cottage Holidays, Victoria House, 12 Fore Street, Northam, Bideford, Devon EX39 1AW
T: (01237) 479146
F: (01237) 421512
E: farmcott@cix.co.uk
I: www.farmcott.co.uk

CHUDLEIGH
Devon

Coombeshead Farm ★★★
Contact: Mr & Mrs R Smith, Coombeshead Farm, Coombeshead Cross, Chudleigh, Newton Abbot, Devon TQ13 0NQ
T: (01626) 853334
E: anne-coombeshead@supanet.com

Farmborough House ★★★
Contact: Mrs Deirdre Aldridge, Farmborough House, Old Exeter Road, Chudleigh, Newton Abbot, Devon TQ13 0DR
T: (01626) 853258
F: (01626) 853258
E: holidays@farmborough-house.com
I: www.farmborough-house.com

Saddleback Cottage ★★★
Contact: Mrs Jenny Brandon, Church House, Chudleigh Knighton, Newton Abbot, Devon TQ13 0HE
T: (01626) 852123
F: (01626) 852123
E: brandon@churchhouse100.freeserve.co.uk
I: www.inthecountry.co.uk/saddleback

Silver Cottage ★★★
Contact: Mr E J Gardner, 75 Old Exeter Street, Chudleigh, Newton Abbot, Devon TQ13 0JX
T: (01626) 854571
F: (01626) 854571

CHULMLEIGH
Devon

Beech Grove Bungalow ★★★★
Contact: Mrs J Middleton, East Westacott, Riddlecombe, Chulmleigh, Devon EX18 7PF
T: (01769) 520210
F: (01769) 520210
I: www.beechgroveholidaycottage.co.uk

Bridleway Cottages ★★★
Contact: Mrs Fiona Lincoln-Gordon, Bridleway Cottages, Golland Farm, Golland Lane, Burrington, Umberleigh, Devon EX37 9JP
T: (01769) 520263
F: (01769) 520263
E: golland@btinternet.com
I: www.golland.btinternet.co.uk

Deer Cott ★★★★
Contact: Mr & Mrs George & Mary Simpson, Deer Cott, Middle Garland, Chulmleigh, Devon EX18 7DU
T: (01769) 580461
F: (01769) 580461
E: deercott@sosi.net
I: www.sosi.net/users/deercott

Wembworthy Down ★★★
Contact: CH ref:6188,11495,15181, Holiday Cottages Group Owner Services Dept, Spring Mill, Earby, Barnoldswick, Lancashire BB18 6RN
T: (01282) 445096
F: (01282) 844299
E: ch.sales@ttgihg.co.uk
I: www.country-holidays.co.uk

CHURCHINFORD
Somerset

South Cleeve Bungalow, Beeches and Hoemoor ★★★–★★★★
Contact: CH ref: 50219,11897,50185, Holiday Cottages Group Owner Services Dept, Spring Mill, Earby, Barnoldswick, Lancashire BB18 6RN
T: (01282) 445096
F: (01282) 844299
E: ch.sales@ttgihg.co.uk
I: www.country-holidays.co.uk

CHURCHSTOW
Devon

Thatchers End
Rating Applied For
Contact: Mrs J P Stevens, 25 Station Road, Keyham, Plymouth PL2 1NF
T: (01752) 563532

CLAWTON
Devon

The Old Vicarage
Rating Applied For
Contact: Mrs C Pix, Chapel Farm, St Dominick, Saltash, Cornwall PL12 6SL
T: (01579) 351660

CLENCH
Wiltshire

Stable Cottage ★★★★
Contact: Mrs Clarissa Roe, Clench Farmhouse, Clench, Marlborough, Wiltshire SN8 4NT
T: (01672) 810264 & 07774 784601
F: (01672) 811458
E: clarissaroe@btinternet.com
I: www.stablecottage&clench.co.uk

CLOVELLY
Devon

Lower Waytown
Rating Applied For
Contact: Mrs & Mr Annette & Colin Penny, Lower Waytown, Horn's Cross, Clovelly, Bideford, Devon EX39 5DN
T: (01237) 451787 & 07974 567328
F: (01237) 451787
E: aircp@penny26.freeserve.co.uk

Old Burscott ★★★
Contact: Mrs S Hancock, Lashbrook, 119 Burscott, Higher Clovelly, Clovelly, Bideford, Devon EX39 5RR
T: (01237) 431502 & (020) 7388 7627
F: (020) 7209 5869
E: rayca@easynet.co.uk
I: ownerservice@ttgihg.co.uk

CLUTTON
Bath and North East Somerset

Cholwell Hall ★★★
Contact: Mr I Kealey, Cholwell Hall, Clutton, BS39 5TE
T: (01761) 452380
I: www.cholwellhall.co.uk

COLERNE
Wiltshire

Thickwood House (Garden Cottages) ★★★
Contact: Mr C Agombar, Thickwood House, Thickwood Lane, Colerne, Chippenham, Wiltshire SN14 8BN
T: (01225) 744377
F: (01225) 742329

COLYFORD
Devon

Whitwell Farm Cottages ★★★★★
Contact: Mr Mike Williams, Whitwell Farm Cottages, Colyford, Colyton, Devon EX24 6HS
T: 0800 0902419 & (01297) 552566
F: (01297) 552911
E: 100755.66@compuserve.com
I: www.a5star.co.uk

COLYTON
Devon

Barritshayes Farm ★★★
Contact: Mr & Mrs D Clarke, Barritshayes Farm, Northleigh Road, Colyton, Devon EX24 6DU
T: (01297) 552485
F: (01297) 553730
E: barritshayes@btinternet.com

Coles House ★★★★
Contact: Jean Bartlett Cottage Holidays, Fore Street, Beer, Seaton, Devon EX12 3JB
T: (01297) 23221
F: (01297) 23303
E: jeanb@netbreaks.com
I: www.netbreaks.com/jeanb

65 Govers Meadow ★★★
Contact: Jean Bartlett Cottage Holidays, Fore Street, Beer, Seaton, Devon EX12 3JB
T: (01297) 23221
F: (01297) 23303
E: jeanb@netbreaks.com
I: www.netbreaks.com/jeanb

Lovehayne Farm Cottages ★★★★
Contact: Mrs Philippa Bignell, Lovehayne Farm, Southleigh, Colyton, Devon EX24 6JE
T: (01404) 871216
F: (01404) 871216
E: cottages@fairway.globalnet.co.uk
I: www.lovehayne.co.uk

Establishments printed in blue have a detailed entry in this guide

Michaelmas Cottage ★★★
Contact: CH ref: 9785, Country
Holidays Group Owner Services
Dept, Spring Mill, Earby,
Barnoldswick, Lancashire
BB18 6RN
T: (01282) 445096
F: (01282) 844299
E: ch.sales@ttgihg.co.uk
I: www.country-holidays.co.uk

Smallicombe Farm ★★★★
Contact: Mrs M A Todd,
Smallicombe Farm, Northleigh,
Colyton, Devon EX24 6BU
T: (01404) 831310
F: (01404) 831431
E: maggie_todd@yahoo.com
I: www.smallicombe.com

COMBE MARTIN
Devon

Beech Cottage ★★★★
Contact: Marsden's Cottage
Holidays, 2 The Square,
Braunton, Devon EX33 2JB
T: (01271) 813777
F: (01271) 813664
E: holidays@marsdens.co.uk
I: www.marsdens.co.uk

The Cottage ★★
Contact: Mr Gurr, The Cottage,
Combe Martin, Devon

Coulscott ★★★★
Contact: Ms Trish Twigger,
Coulscott, Nutcombe Hill,
Combe Martin, Ilfracombe,
Devon EX34 0PQ
T: (01271) 883339
F: (01271) 883723
E: stay@coulscott.co.uk
I: www.coulscott.co.uk

Ebrington Holiday Cottage
★★★
Contact: Mr H Irwin, Glen Lyn,
Borough Road, Combe Martin,
Ilfracombe, Devon EX34 0AN
T: (01271) 882292
F: (01271) 882391
E: vincent.irwin@virgin.net

Elmdene Cottage ★★★★
Contact: Marsden's Cottage
Holidays, 2 The Square,
Braunton, Devon EX33 2JB
T: (01271) 813777
F: (01271) 813664
E: holidays@marsdens.co.uk
I: www.marsdens.co.uk

Lee Down Farm Cottage ★★★
Contact: Marsden's Cottage
Holidays, 2 The Square,
Braunton, Devon EX33 2JB
T: (01271) 813777
F: (01271) 813664
E: holidays@marsdens.co.uk
I: www.marsdens.co.uk

Mill Cottage ★★★
Contact: Mr and Mrs Martin and
Margaret Wolverson, Stag
Cottage, Holdstone Down,
Combe Martin, Ilfracombe,
Devon EX34 0PF
T: (01271) 882449 &
07831 118676

Pretoria ★★★★
Contact: Mrs Heather Trueman,
6 Cross Mead, Lynton, Devon
EX35 6DG
T: (01598) 753517
E: russ@crown-inn.freeserve.
co.uk

Sea Breezes & Fairwind ★★★
Contact: Marsden's Cottage
Holidays, 2 The Square,
Braunton, Devon EX33 2JB
T: (01271) 813777
F: (01271) 813664
E: holidays@marsdens.co.uk
I: www.marsdens.co.uk

1 Stattens Cottages ★★★
Contact: Mrs Peggy Crees, 47
Kingcup Drive, Bisley, Woking,
Surrey GU24 9HH
T: (01483) 488790 &
(01276) 24660
F: (01932) 562638
E: fullspur.cam@btinternet.com
I: www.romseyassoc.
com/holidayhomes

Wheel Farm Country Cottages
★★★★
Contact: Mr & Mrs John
Robertson, Wheel Farm Country
Cottages, Berry Down, Combe
Martin, Ilfracombe, Devon
EX34 0NT
T: (01271) 882100
F: (01271) 883120

Widmouth Farm Cottages
★★-★★★
Contact: Mrs Elizabeth Sansom,
Widmouth Farm Cottages,
Watermouth, Ilfracombe, Devon
EX24 9RX
T: (01271) 863743
F: (01271) 866479
E: holidays@
widmouthfarmcottages.co.uk
I: www.widmouthfarmcottages.
co.uk

Wood Sorrell ★★★
Contact: Marsden's Cottage
Holidays, 2 The Square,
Braunton, Devon EX33 2JB
T: (01271) 813777
F: (01271) 813664
E: holidays@marsdens.co.uk
I: www.marsdens.co.uk

Yetland Farm Cottages ★★★
Contact: Marsden's Cottage
Holidays, 2 The Square,
Braunton, Devon EX33 2JB
T: (01271) 813777
F: (01271) 813664
E: holidays@marsdens.co.uk
I: www.marsdens.co.uk

COMBEINTEIGNHEAD
Devon

Fairways ★★★★
Contact: Holiday Homes &
Cottages South West, 365a
Torquay Road, Paignton, Devon
TQ3 2BT
T: (01803) 663650
F: (01803) 664037
E: holcotts@aol.com
I: www.swcottages.co.uk

The Old Bakery ★★
Contact: Holiday Homes &
Cottages South West, 365A
Torquay Road, Paignton, Devon
TQ3 2BT
T: (01803) 663650
F: (01803) 664037
E: holcotts@aol.com
I: ww.swcottages.co.uk

Pilgrim Cottage ★★★
Contact: Mrs Deane, Taplow
Cottage, Combeinteignhead,
Newton Abbot, Devon TQ12 4RE
T: (01626) 873567

Westborough Cottage & Little
Westborough ★★★-★★★★
Contact: Holiday Homes &
Cottages South West, 365A
Torquay Road, Paignton, Devon
TQ3 2BT
T: (01803) 663650
F: (01803) 664037
E: holcotts@aol.com
I: www.swcottages.co.uk

COMPTON DUNDON
Somerset

Castlebrook Holiday Cottages
★★★
Contact: Mr JRE Hunt,
Castlebrook Holiday Cottages,
Castlebrook, Compton Dundon,
Somerton, Somerset TA11 6PR
T: (01458) 841680
F: (01458) 441680

Wisteria Cottage ★★★★
Contact: Mrs Georgina Baston,
The Old Farmhouse, Compton
Dundon, Somerton, Somerset
TA11 6PS
T: (01458) 442848

COMPTON MARTIN
Bath and North East Somerset

Wrangle Cottage ★★★
Contact: Mrs Gill Mayers,
Wrangle Cottage, Compton
Martin, Bristol BS40 6LB
T: (01761) 221279 & 221162
F: (01761) 221162
E: gillandjohn@lineone.net

CONSTANTINE
Cornwall

Anneth Lowen ★★★★
Contact: Cornish Cottage
Holidays, Godolphin Road,
Helston, Cornwall TR13 8AA
T: (01326) 573808
F: (01326) 564992
E: enquiry@
cornishcottageholidays.co.uk
I: www.cornishcottageholidays.
co.uk

Carvinack ★★★★
Contact: Mr & Mrs Davies,
Greendale, Constantine,
Falmouth, Cornwall TR11
T: (01326) 340889

The Fuchsia's ★★★
Contact: Cornish Traditional
Cottages, Blisland, Bodmin,
Cornwall PL30 4HS
T: (01208) 821666

Graelyn ★★★★
Contact: Cornish Cottage
Holidays, The Old Turnpike Dairy,
Godolphin Road, Helston,
Cornwall TR13 8AA
T: (01326) 573808
F: (01326) 564992
E: enquiry@
cornishcottageholidays.co.uk
I: www.cornishcottageholidays.
co.uk

Gwavas ★★★★
Contact: Cornish Cottage
Holidays, The Old Turnpike Dairy,
Godolphin Road, Helston,
Cornwall TR13 8AA
T: (01326) 573808
F: (01326) 564992
E: enquiry@
cornishcottageholidays.co.uk
I: www.cornishcottageholidays.
co.uk

Jackdaw Cottage ★★★★
Contact: Mrs JP Castling,
Chatelain House, High Street,
Little Chesterford, Saffron
Walden, Essex CB10 1TS
T: (01799) 531231 &
(01209) 860642
E: jill.castling@tesco.net
I: www.cornwall-online.co.uk

Napheane ★★★★
Contact: Cornish Cottage
Holidays, Godolphin Road,
Helston, Cornwall TR13 8AA
T: (01326) 573808
F: (01326) 564992
E: enquriy@
cornishcottageholidays.co.uk
I: www.cornishcottageholidays.
co.uk

Pella Barn ★★★★
Contact: Cornish Cottage
Holidays, The Old Turnpike Dairy,
Godolphin Road, Helston,
Cornwall TR13 8AA
T: (01326) 573808
F: (01326) 564992
E: enquiry@
cornishcottageholidays.co.uk
I: www.cornishcottageholidays.
co.uk

Swallow Barn ★★★★
Contact: Cornish Cottage
Holidays, Godolphin Road,
Helston, Cornwall TR13 8AA
T: (01326) 573808
F: (01326) 564992
E: enquiry@
cornishcottageholidays.co.uk
I: www.cornishcottageholidays.
co.uk

CONSTANTINE BAY
Cornwall

Brambles ★★★
Contact: Mr & Mrs Bowater,
Helpful Holidays, Mill Street,
Chagford, Newton Abbot, Devon
TQ13 8AW
T: (01647) 433593
F: (01647) 433694
E: help@helpfulholidays.com
I: www.helpfulholidays.com

Kalundu ★★★★
Contact: Cornish Horizons,
Higher Trehemborne, St Merryn,
Padstow, Cornwall PL28 8JU
T: (01841) 520889 & 521333
F: (01841) 521523
E: cottages@cornishhorizons.
co.uk
I: www.cornishhorizons.co.uk

Kittiwake ★★★★
Contact: Cornish Horizons,
Higher Trehemborne, St Merryn,
Padstow, Cornwall PL28 8JU
T: (01841) 520889 & 521333
F: (01841) 521523
E: cottages@cornishhorizons.
co.uk
I: www.cornishhorizons.co.uk

Lees Nook
Rating Applied For
Contact: Mrs J Stuttaford, Lees
Nook, Constantine Bay,
Padstow, Cornwall PL28 8JJ
T: (01841) 520344

Porth Clyne ★★★★
Contact: Cornish Horizons
Holiday Cottages, Higher
Trehemborne, St Merryn,
Padstow, Cornwall PL28 8JU
T: (01841) 520889 & 521333
F: (01841) 521523
E: cottages@cornishhorizons.
co.uk
I: www.cornishhorizons.co.uk

Stone's Throw ★★★
Contact: Mr & Mrs Temple,
Whytegates, East Gores Road,
Coggeshall, Colchester CO6 1RZ
T: (01376) 561265
F: 0870 132 5817
E: iantemple@bigfoot.com
I: www.northcornwall.fsnet.
co.uk

Treless ★★★★
Contact: Cornish Horizons,
Higher Trehemborne, St Merryn,
Padstow, Cornwall PL28 8JU
T: (01841) 520889 & 521333
F: (01841) 521523
E: cottages@cornishhorizons.
co.uk
I: www.cornishhorizons.co.uk

COOMBE
Cornwall

Lanyons ★★★
Contact: Mr Peter Morris, Farm
& Cottage Holidays, Victoria
House, 12 Fore Street, Northam,
Bideford, Devon EX39 1AW
T: (01237) 479146
F: (01237) 421512
E: farmcott@cix.co.uk
I: www.farmcott.co.uk

COOMBE BISSETT
Wiltshire

Cross Farm Cottage ★★
Contact: Mrs S Kittermaster,
Cross Farm Cottage, Cross Farm,
Coombe Bissett, Salisbury,
Wiltshire SP5 4LY
T: (01722) 718293
F: (01722) 718665

COPPLESTONE
Devon

Sandford-Ash Farm ★★★
Contact: Mrs Cleverdon,
Sandford-Ash Farm,
Copplestone, Crediton, Devon
EX17 5NZ
T: (01363) 84264

CORNTOWN
Devon

Frog Cottage
Rating Applied For
Contact: Mrs A Wotton, Great
Stert Farm, Cornwood, Ivybridge,
Devon PL21
T: (01752) 837788

CORNWOOD
Devon

Middle Rook Farmhouse ★★★
Contact: Mr & Mrs Dollard, East
Rooke, Cornwood, Ivybridge,
Devon PL2 9RF
T: (01752) 837605 & 837711
F: (01752) 837888
E: gavvo@msn.com
I: www.delamore.com

CORSHAM
Wiltshire

Linleys Farm Cottages
Rating Applied For
Contact: Ms Harriet Warr,
Linleys Farm Cottages, Linleys
Farm, Linley, Corsham, Wiltshire
SN13 9PG
T: (01249) 745578

Wadswick Barns ★★★★★
Contact: Mr & Mrs Tim &
Carolyn Barton, Wadswick
Barns, Wadswick, Corsham,
Wiltshire SN13 8JB
T: (01225) 810733
F: (01225) 810307
E: barns@wadswick.co.uk
I: www.wadswick.co.uk

COTLEIGH
Devon

Authers Cottage ★★★
Contact: Milkbere Cottage
Holidays, Milkbere House, 14
Fore Street, Seaton, Devon
EX12 2LA
T: (01297) 20729 & 22925
F: (01297) 24831
E: info@milkbere.com
I: www.milkbere.com

Little Leywood ★★★★
Contact: Mrs M A Morgan,
Leywood Cottage, Post Lane,
Cotleigh, Honiton, Devon
EX14 9HZ
T: (01404) 861351

COVERACK
Cornwall

**Applewood & Swallows Rest
★★★★**
Contact: Cornish Cottage
Holidays, Godolphin Road,
Helston, Cornwall TR13 8AA
T: (01326) 573808
F: (01326) 564992
E: enquiry@
cornishcottageholidays.
co.uk
I: www.cornishcottageholidays.
co.uk

**Coverack Headland Flat 17
★★★★**
Contact: Cornish Cottage
Holidays, Godolphin Road,
Helston, Cornwall TR13 8AA
T: (01326) 573808
F: (01326) 564992
E: enquiry@
cornishcottageholidays.
co.uk
I: www.cornishcottageholidays.
co.uk

**Coverack Headland Flat 7
★★★★**
Contact: Cornish Cottage
Holidays, Godolphin Road,
Helston, Cornwall TR13 8AA
T: (01326) 573808
F: (01326) 564992
E: enquiry@
cornishcottageholidays.
co.uk
I: www.cornishcottageholidays.
co.uk

Fernleigh ★★★
Contact: Cornish Cottage
Holidays, Godolphin Road,
Helston, Cornwall TR13 8AA
T: (01326) 573808
F: (01326) 564992
E: enquiry@
cornishcottageholidays.
co.uk
I: www.cornishcottageholidays.
co.uk

Gloster Cottage ★★
Contact: Cornish Cottage
Holidays, Godolphin Road,
Helston, Cornwall TR13 8AA
T: (01326) 573808
F: (01326) 564992
E: enquiry@
cornishcottageholidays.co.uk
I: www.cornishcottageholidays.
co.uk

Harbour Cottage ★★
Contact: Mrs Parr, The Beach
House, Coverack, Helston,
Cornwall TR12 6TE
T: (01326) 280621

Lower Landfall ★★★
Contact: Cornish Cottage
Holidays, The Old Turnpike Dairy,
Godolphin Road, Helston,
Cornwall TR13 8AA
T: (01326) 573808 & 564992
E: enquiry@
cornishcottageholidays.co.uk
I: www.cornishcottageholidays.
co.uk

North Cottage ★★★
Contact: Cornish Cottage
Holidays, Godolphin Road,
Helston, Cornwall TR13 8AA
T: (01326) 573808
F: (01326) 564992
E: enquiry@
cornishcottageholidays.co.uk
I: www.cornishcottageholidays.
co.uk

South Cottage ★★★
Contact: Cornish Cottage
Holidays, The Old Turnpike Dairy,
Godolphin Road, Helston,
Cornwall TR13 8AA
T: (01326) 573808
F: (01326) 564992
E: enquiry@
cornishcottageholidays.co.uk
I: www.cornishcottageholidays.
co.uk

Swallows Rest
Rating Applied For
Contact: Cornish Cottage
Holidays, The Old Turnpike Dairy,
Godolphin Road, Helston,
Cornwall TR13 8AA
T: (01326) 573808
F: (01326) 564992
E: enquiry@
cornishcottageholidays.co.uk
I: www.cornishcottageholidays.
co.uk

Tremorvah ★★★
Contact: Cornish Cottage
Holidays, The Old Turnpike Dairy,
Godolphin Road, Helston,
Cornwall TR13 8AA
T: (01326) 573808
F: (01326) 564992
E: enquiry@
cornishcottageholidays.co.uk
I: www.cornishcottageholidays.
co.uk

**Upper Mellan and Lower
Mellan Barn ★★★**
Contact: Cornish Cottage
Holidays, The Old Turnpike Dairy,
Godolphin Road, Helston,
Cornwall TR13 8AA
T: (01326) 573808
F: (01326) 564992
E: enquiry@
cornishcottageholidays.co.uk
I: www.cornishcottageholidays.
co.uk

COXLEY
Somerset

The Potting Shed ★★★★
Contact: Mr & Mrs J Van
Bergen-Henegouwen, Potting
Shed Holidays, Harters Hill
Cottage, Pillmoor Lane, Coxley,
Wells, Somerset BA5 1RF
T: (01749) 672857
E: cjvbhhol@aol.com
I: www.pottingshedholidays.
co.uk

CRACKINGTON HAVEN
Cornwall

**The Old School Holiday
Cottages ★★**
Contact: Mrs Pat Preller,
Broomhill, Rosecare, St Gennys,
Bude, Cornwall EX23 OBE
T: (01840) 230310
F: (01840) 230612

**Rosecare Farm Cottages
★★★★-★★★★★**
Contact: Mr and Mrs John
Stone, Rosecare Farm Cottages,
Rosecare, St Gennys, Bude,
Cornwall EX23 OBE
T: (01840) 230375
E: gilljohn@rosecare.freeserve.
co.uk
I: www.cottageguide.
co.uk/rosecare

CRAPSTONE
Devon

Midway ★★★
Contact: Mrs S Eggins, Leigh
Farm, Roborough, Plymouth,
Devon PL6 7BS
T: (01752) 733221 &
(01822) 852225

CREDITON
Devon

Eastacott Farm ★★★
Contact: Farm & Cottage
Holidays, Victoria House, 12 Fore
Street, Bideford, Devon
EX39 1AW
T: (01237) 479698
F: (01237) 421512
E: farmcott@cix.co.uk
I: www.farmcott.co.uk

**White Witches and Stable
Lodge ★★★-★★★★**
Contact: Mrs Gillbard, Hele
Barton, Black Dog, Crediton,
Devon EX17 4QJ
T: (01884) 860278
F: (01884) 860278
E: gillbard@eclipse.co.uk
I: www.eclipse.co.uk/helebarton

CREECH ST MICHAEL
Somerset

Northend Farm ★★★★
Contact: Mrs J Tutill, Northend
Farm, Creech St Michael,
Taunton, Somerset TA3 5ED
T: (01823) 442380

CREWKERNE
Somerset

**Higher Easthams Farm
★★★★**
Contact: Mr & Mrs M&J
Stockton, Higher Easthams
Farm, Crewkerne, Somerset
TA18 7QQ
T: (01460) 76216 & 78271

Establishments printed in blue have a detailed entry in this guide

CROWCOMBE
Somerset

Poundisford Cottage ★★★★
Contact: Mrs M Baxter,
Cannicott Cottage, Curland,
Taunton, Somerset TA3 5SA
T: (01823) 480675 &
07968 137038
F: (01823) 480675
E: chrisbaxter007@aol.com

CROWCOMBE HEATHFIELD
Somerset

The Cottage ★★★★
Contact: Mr & Mrs Bowater,
Helpful Holidays, Mill Street,
Chagford, Newton Abbot, Devon
TQ13 8AW
T: (01647) 433593
F: (01647) 433694
E: help@helpfulholidays.com
I: www.helpfulholidays.com

CROWLAS
Cornwall

Cuckoo Cottage ★★★
Contact: Mrs H Jackman,
Mowshurst Farmhouse, Swan
Lane, Edenbridge, Kent TN8 6AH
T: (01732) 862064

CROYDE
Devon

The Apartment ★★★
Contact: Marsden's Cottage
Holidays, 2 The Square,
Braunton, Devon EX33 2JB
T: (01271) 813777
F: (01271) 813664
E: holidays@marsdens.co.uk
I: www.marsdens.co.uk

Blue Haze ★★★
Contact: Marsden's Cottage
Holidays, 2 The Square,
Braunton, Devon EX33 2JB
T: (01271) 813777
F: (01271) 813664
E: holidays@marsdens.co.uk
I: www.marsdens.co.uk

Bramleys ★★★
Contact: Marsden's Cottage
Holidays, 2 The Square,
Braunton, Devon EX33 2JB
T: (01271) 813777
F: (01271) 813664
E: holidays@marsdens.co.uk
I: www.marsdens.co.uk

The Bungalow ★★★★
Contact: Marsden's Cottage
Holidays, 2 The Square,
Braunton, Devon EX33 2JB
T: (01271) 813777
F: (01271) 813664
E: holidays@marsdens.co.uk
I: www.marsdens.co.uk

Chestnut Cottage ★★★★
Contact: Marsden's Cottage
Holidays, 2 The Square,
Braunton, Devon EX33 2JB
T: (01271) 813777
F: (01271) 813664
E: holidays@marsdens.co.uk
I: www.marsdens.co.uk

Chuggs Farm ★★★
Contact: The Proprietor, Chuggs
Farm, Croyde, Braunton, Devon

Cockleshell ★★★
Contact: Marsden's Cottage
Holidays, 2 The Square,
Braunton, Devon EX33 2JB
T: (01271) 813777
F: (01271) 813664
E: holidays@marsdens.co.uk
I: www.marsdens.co.uk

**Croyde Bay Lodge Apartments
1 & 2 ★★★★**
Contact: Mrs J Penny, Croyde
Bay House Hotel, Moor Lane,
Croyde, Braunton, Devon
EX33 1PA
T: (01271) 890270

Cubbies Corner ★★★
Contact: Marsden's Cottage
Holidays, 2 The Square,
Braunton, Devon EX33 2JB
T: (01271) 813777
F: (01271) 813664
E: holidays@marsdens.co.uk
I: www.marsdens.co.uk

**Denham Farm Country House
★★★**
Contact: Mrs J Barnes, Denham
Farm Country House, North
Buckland, Braunton, Devon
EX33 1HY
T: (01271) 890297
F: (01271) 890297

Dunehaven ★★★★
Contact: Marsden's Cottage
Holidays, 2 The Square,
Braunton, Devon EX33 2JB
T: (01271) 813777
F: (01271) 813664
E: holidays@marsdens.co.uk
I: www.marsdens.co.uk

The Dunes ★★★★
Contact: Marsden's Cottage
Holidays, 2 The Square,
Braunton, Devon EX33 2JB
T: (01271) 813777
F: (01271) 813664
E: holidays@marsdens.co.uk
I: www.marsdens.co.uk

Embleton ★★★★
Contact: Marsden's Cottage
Holidays, 2 The Square,
Braunton, Devon EX33 2JB
T: (01271) 813777
F: (01271) 813664

Fir Tree Cottage ★★★
Contact: Marsden's Cottage
Holidays, 2 The Square,
Braunton, Devon EX33 2JB
T: (01271) 813777
F: (01271) 813664
E: holidays@marsdens.co.uk
I: www.marsdens.co.uk

Hillview ★★★★
Contact: Marsden's Cottage
Holidays, 2 The Square,
Braunton, Devon EX33 2JB
T: (01271) 813777
F: (01271) 813664
E: holidays@marsdens.co.uk
I: www.marsdens.co.uk

Honeycott ★★★
Contact: Marsdens Cottage
Holidays 2 The square, Braunton,
North Devon, Braunton, Devon
EX33 2JB
T: (01271) 813777 & 813664
E: holidays@marsdens.co.uk
I: www.marsdens.co.uk

Keats Lodge ★★★★
Contact: Marsden's Cottage
Holidays, 2 The Square,
Braunton, Devon EX33 2JB
T: (01271) 813777
F: (01271) 813664
E: holidays@marsdens.co.uk
I: www.marsdens.co.uk

Little Doone ★★★★
Contact: Marsden's Cottage
Holidays, 2 The Square,
Braunton, Devon EX33 2JB
T: (01271) 813777
F: (01271) 813664
E: holidays@marsdens.co.uk
I: www.marsdens.co.uk

Lorna Doone View ★★★
Contact: Marsden's Cottage
Holidays, 2 The Square,
Braunton, Devon EX33 2JB
T: (01271) 813777
F: (01271) 813664
E: holidays@marsdens.co.uk
I: www.marsdens.co.uk

Lundy Lodge ★★★★
Contact: Marsden's Cottage
Holidays, 2 The Square,
Braunton, Devon EX33 2JB
T: (01271) 813777
F: (01271) 813664
E: holidays@marsdens.co.uk
I: www.marsdens.co.uk

The Mallows ★★★
Contact: Marsden's Cottage
Holidays, 2 The Square,
Braunton, Devon EX33 2JB
T: (01271) 813777
F: (01271) 813664
E: holidays@marsdens.co.uk
I: www.marsdens.co.uk

Montana ★★★
Contact: MarstCottottage
Holidays 2 The Square,
Braunton, North Devon,
Braunton, Devon EX33 2JB
T: (01271) 813664 & 813664
E: holidays@marsdens.co.uk
I: www.marsdens.co.uk

Moorhurst Lea ★★★
Contact: Marsden's Cottage
Holidays, 2 The Square,
Braunton, Devon EX33 2JB
T: (01271) 813777
F: (01271) 813664
E: holidays@marsdens.co.uk
I: www.marsdens.co.uk

Myrtle Cottage ★★★★
Contact: Marsden's Cottage
Holidays, 2 The Square,
Braunton, Devon EX33 2JB
T: (01271) 813777
F: (01271) 813664
E: holidays@marsdens.co.uk
I: www.marsdens.co.uk

Oceanside ★★★
Contact: Mr & Mrs D Scarlett, 7
Glebe Lane, Long Street,
Hanslope, Buckinghamshire
MK19 7DD
T: (01908) 516444
F: (01908) 516174
E: mail@oceansidecroyde.co.uk
I: www.oceansidecroyde.co.uk

Oceanus & Poseidon ★★★
Contact: Marsden's Cottage
Holidays, 2 The Square,
Braunton, Devon EX33 2JB
T: (01271) 813777
F: (01271) 813664
E: holidays@marsdens.co.uk
I: www.marsdens.co.uk

**Old Coastguards Cottage
★★★**
Contact: Marsden's Cottage
Holidays, 2 The Square,
Braunton, Devon EX33 2JB
T: (01271) 813777
F: (01271) 813664
E: holidays@marsdens.co.uk
I: www.marsdens.co.uk

Outer Bias ★★★★
Contact: Marsden's Cottage
Holidays, 2 The Square,
Braunton, Devon EX33 2JB
T: (01271) 813777
F: (01271) 813664
E: holidays@marsdens.co.uk
I: www.marsdens.co.uk

Oyster Falls ★★★★
Contact: Marsden's Cottage
Holidays, 2 The Square,
Braunton, Devon EX33 2JB
T: (01271) 813777
F: (01271) 813664
E: holidays@marsdens.co.uk
I: www.marsdens.co.uk

The Paddocks ★★★
Contact: Marsden's Cottage
Holidays, 2 The Square,
Braunton, Devon EX33 2JB
T: (01271) 813777
F: (01271) 813664
E: holidays@marsdens.co.uk
I: www.marsdens.co.uk

Ramblers ★★★★
Contact: Marsden's Cottage
Holidays, 2 The Square,
Braunton, Devon EX33 2JB
T: (01271) 813777
F: (01271) 813664
E: holidays@marsdens.co.uk
I: www.marsdens.co.uk

Rose Villa ★★★★
Contact: Marsden's Cottage
Holidays, 2 The Square,
Braunton, Devon EX33 2JB
T: (01271) 813777
F: (01271) 813664
E: holidays@marsdens.co.uk
I: www.marsdens.co.uk

Sands End ★★★★
Contact: Marsden's Cottage
Holidays, 2 The Square,
Braunton, Devon EX33 2JB
T: (01271) 813777
F: (01271) 813664
E: holidays@marsdens.co.uk
I: www.marsdens.co.uk

Seahaven ★★★★
Contact: Marsden's Cottage
Holidays, 2 The Square,
Braunton, Devon EX33 2JB
T: (01271) 813777
F: (01271) 813664
E: holidays@marsdens.co.uk
I: www.marsdens.co.uk

Sennen Cottage ★★★
Contact: Marsden's Cottage Holidays, 2 The Square, Braunton, Devon EX33 2JB
T: (01271) 813777
F: (01271) 813664
E: holidays@marsdens.co.uk
I: www.marsdens.co.uk

Summerdyne ★★★
Contact: Marsden's Cottage Holidays, 2 The Square, Braunton, Devon EX33 2JB
T: (01271) 813777
F: (01271) 813664
E: holidays@marsdens.co.uk
I: www.marsdens.co.uk

Summerfield ★★★
Contact: Marsden's Cottage Holidays, 2 The Square, Braunton, Devon EX33 2JB
T: (01271) 813777
F: (01271) 813664
E: holidays@marsdens.co.uk
I: www.marsdens.co.uk

Sunny Skies ★★★★
Contact: Marsden's Cottage Holidays, 2 The Square, Braunton, Devon EX33 2JB
T: (01271) 813777
F: (01271) 813664
E: holidays@marsdens.co.uk
I: www.marsdens.co.uk

Sunnyside ★★★★
Contact: Marsden's Cottage Holidays, 2 The Square, Braunton, Devon EX33 2JB
T: (01271) 813777
F: (01271) 813664
E: holidays@marsdens.co.uk
I: www.marsdens.co.uk

Sunset View ★★★
Contact: Marsden's Cottage Holidays, 2 The Square, Braunton, Devon EX33 2JB
T: (01271) 813777
F: (01271) 813664
E: holidays@marsdens.co.uk
I: www.marsdens.co.uk

Suntana & Little Suntana ★★★
Contact: Marsden's Cottage Holidays, 2 The Square, Braunton, Devon EX33 2JB
T: (01271) 813777
F: (01271) 813664
E: holidays@marsdens.co.uk
I: www.marsdens.co.uk

Tara ★★★
Contact: The Proprietor, Tara, 20 Moor Lane, Croyde, Braunton, Devon

Wayside ★★★
Contact: Marsden's Cottage Holidays, 2 The Square, Braunton, Devon EX33 2JB
T: (01271) 813777
F: (01271) 813664
E: holidays@marsdens.co.uk
I: www.marsdens.co.uk

Westside ★★★
Contact: Marsden's Cottage Holidays, 2 The Square, Braunton, Devon EX33 2JB
T: (01271) 813777
F: (01271) 813664
E: holidays@marsdens.co.uk
I: www.marsdens.co.uk

Withyside ★★★★
Contact: Marsden's Cottage Holidays, 2 The Square, Braunton, Devon EX33 2JB
T: (01271) 813777
F: (01271) 813664
E: holidays@marsdens.co.uk
I: www.marsdens.co.uk

CROYDE BAY
Devon

Braemar ★★★
Contact: Mr Peter Morris, Farm & Cottage Holidays, Victoria House, 12 Fore Street, Northam, Bideford, Devon EX39 1AW
T: (01237) 479146
F: (01237) 421512
E: farmcott@cix.co.uk
I: www.farmcott.co.uk

Lane Head Bungalow ★★★
Contact: Mr Ian MacDermott, 13 Swallow Close, Barnstaple, Devon EX31
T: (01271) 325284

CUCKLINGTON
Somerset

Hale Farm ★★
Contact: Mrs P David, Hale Farm, Cucklington, Wincanton, Somerset BA9 9PN
T: (01963) 33342

CURY
Cornwall

Chestnut Cottage ★★★
Contact: Mullion Holiday Cottages, Churchtown, Mullion, Helston, Cornwall TR12 7HN
T: (01326) 240315
F: (01326) 241090

Merries Barn ★★★★
Contact: Mr P C Moore, Merries Barn, Cury Cross Lanes, Helston, Cornwall TR12 7RA
T: (01326) 241356

Treloskan Farm ★★★
Contact: Mrs M Lane, Treloskan Farm, Cury, Helston, Cornwall TR12
T: (01326) 240493

CUSGARNE
Cornwall

Hope Cottage ★★★
Contact: Cornish Cottage Holidays, The Old Turnpike Dairy, Godolphin Road, Helston, Cornwall TR13 8AA
T: (01326) 573808
F: (01326) 564992
E: enquiry@cornishcottageholidays.co.uk
I: www.cornishcottageholidays.co.uk

Killigrew Barn ★★★★
Contact: Cornish Cottage Holidays, Godolphin Road, Helston, Cornwall TR13 8AA
T: (01326) 573808
F: (01326) 564992
E: enquiry@cornishcottageholidays.co.uk
I: www.cornishcottageholidays.co.uk

DARTINGTON
Devon

Billany ★★★
Contact: Mr Peter Morris, Farm & Cottage Holidays, Victoria House, 12 Fore Street, Bideford, Devon EX39 1AW
T: (01237) 479146
F: (01237) 421512
E: farmcott@cix.co.uk
I: www.farmcott.co.uk

DARTMEET
Devon

The Barn ★★★
Contact: Mr & Mrs Bowater, Helpful Holidays, Mill Street, Chagford, Newton Abbot, Devon TQ13 8AW
T: (01647) 433593
F: (01647) 433694
E: help@helpfulholidays.com
I: www.helpfulholidays.com

DARTMOUTH
Devon

Barrington House ★★★★★
Contact: Mrs E Baldwin, Barrington House, Mount Boone, Dartmouth, Devon TQ6 9HZ
T: (01803) 835545

33 Clarence Hill ★★★★
Contact: Mrs Sally Pool, Lansdown, Magpie Lane, Coleshill, Amersham, Buckinghamshire HP7 0LS
T: (01494) 727687

Little Coombe Cottage ★★★★★
Contact: Mr & Mrs Unitt, Little Coombe Farm, Dittisham, Dartmouth, Devon TQ6 0JB
T: (01803) 722599
F: (01803) 722599

Lower Swannaton Farm ★★
Contact: Mr Peter Morris, Farm & Cottage Holidays, Victoria House, 12 Fore Street, Northam, Bideford, Devon EX39 1AW
T: (01237) 479146
F: (01237) 421512
E: farmcott@cix.co.uk
I: www.farmcott.co.uk

The Old Bakehouse ★★–★★★
Contact: Mrs S R Ridalls, The Old Bakehouse, 7 Broadstone, Dartmouth, Devon TQ6 9NR
T: (01803) 834585 & 07909 680884
F: (01803) 834585

Slippery Causeway ★★★★
Contact: Mrs Alexandra Walker, Higher Dart Cottage, Manor Street, Dittisham, Dartmouth, Devon TQ6 0EX
T: (01803) 722261
E: higher.dart@tinyonline.co.uk
I: www.slipperycauseway.co.uk

DAVIDSTOW
Cornwall

Meadowcourt ★★★★
Contact: Powell's Cottage Holidays, High Street, Saundersfoot, Dyfed SA69 9EJ
T: (01834) 812791
F: (01834) 811731
E: info@powells.co.uk
I: www.powells.co.uk

DAWLISH
Devon

Cofton Country Cottage Holidays ★★★★
Contact: Mr & Mrs W G Jeffery, Cofton Country Cottage Holidays, Starcross, Nr Dawlish, Exeter, Devon EX6 8RP
T: (01626) 890111
F: (01626) 891572
E: enquiries@cofton-holidays-devon.co.uk
I: www.cofton-holidays-devon.co.uk

Flat 29 Rockstone Rating Applied For
Contact: Holiday Homes & Cottages South West, 365a Torquay Road, Paignton, Devon TQ3 2BT
T: (01803) 663650
F: (01803) 664037
E: holcotts@aol.com
I: www.swcottages.co.uk

Mustard House ★★★
Contact: Holiday Homes & Cottages South West, 365A Torquay Road, Paignton, Devon TQ3 2BT
T: (01803) 663650
F: (01803) 664037
E: holcotts@aol.com
I: www.swcottages.co.uk

Shell Cove House ★★★★
Contact: Ms L Jameson, Shell Cove House, Old Teignmouth ROad, Dawlish, Devon EX7 0NJ
T: (01626) 862523
F: (01626) 862523
E: shellcovehouse@btclick.com

The White House ★★
Contact: Mrs Sarah Long, The White House, 32 Westcliff, Dawlish, Devon EX7 9DN
T: (01626) 862494
F: (01626) 862494
E: sarahlong@westcountryholiday.com
I: westcountryholiday.com

DAWLISH WARREN
Devon

17 Devondale Court ★★
Contact: Holiday Homes & Cottages South West, 365a Torquay Road, Paignton, Devon TQ3 2BT
T: (01803) 663650
F: (01803) 664037
E: holcotts@aol.com
I: www.swcottages.co.uk

32 Devondale Court ★★★
Contact: Holiday Homes & Cottages South West, 365a Torquay Road, Paignton, Devon TQ3 2BT
T: (01803) 663650
F: (01803) 664037
E: holcotts@aol.com
I: www.swcottages.co.uk

Eastdon Estate ★★★★
Contact: Mrs V Jeffery, Cofton Country Holidays, Dawlish, Devon EX6 8RP
T: (01626) 890111
F: (01626) 891572
E: enquiries@cofton-holidays-devon.co.uk
I: www.cofton-holidays-devon.co.uk

Establishments printed in blue have a detailed entry in this guide

DELABOLE
Cornwall

Rough Park Farmhouse ★★★
Contact: Mr & Mrs Bowater,
Helpful Holidays, Mill Street,
Chagford, Newton Abbot, Devon
TQ13 8AW
T: (01647) 433593
F: (01647) 433694
E: help@helpfulholidays.com
I: www.helpfulholidays.com

DERRY HILL
Wiltshire

Willow Cottage ★★★
Contact: Mrs Elizabeth McNally,
Orchard House, Tyneholm,
Pencaitland, Tranent, East
Lothian EH34 5DJ
T: (01875) 340494 & 340000

DEVIZES
Wiltshire

The Derby ★★★
Contact: Mrs D Tyler, The Derby,
Home Farm, Heddington, Calne,
Wiltshire SN11 0PL
T: (01380) 850523
F: (01380) 850523
E: W.S.Tyler@farmline.com

2 Eastfield Cottages ★★★
Contact: Mr & Mrs David and
Nina Lamb, Eastfield House,
London Road, Devizes, Wiltshire
SN10 2DW
T: (01380) 721562
F: (01380) 721562
E: david@devizes.force9.co.uk

The Gate House ★★★★
Contact: Mrs L Stratton, The
Gate House, Wick Lane, Devizes,
Wiltshire SN10 5DW
T: (01380) 725283
F: (01380) 722382
E: laura@gatehouse-b-and-b.
freeserve.co.uk

Owls Cottage ★★★★
Contact: Mrs G C Whittome,
Owls Cottage, 48 White Street,
Easterton, Devizes, Wiltshire
SN10 4PA
T: (01380) 818804
F: (01380) 818804
E: gill_whittome@yahoo.co.uk

**Rendells Farm Holiday
Cottages ★★★**
Contact: Mr & Mrs Keith & Sue
Roper & Baron, The Barn,
Rendells Farm, All Cannings,
Devizes, Wiltshire SN10 3PA
T: (01380) 860243 &
07778 355873
F: (01895) 270708
E: sroper@waitrose.com
I: www.rendellsfarmcottages.
com

DEVORAN
Cornwall

Tinners ★★★
Contact: Mrs Margie Lumby,
Special Places, Poachers Reach,
Feock, Truro, Cornwall TR3 6SQ
T: (01872) 864400
F: (01872) 864400
E: office@
specialplacescornwall.co.uk
I: www.specialplacescornwall.
co.uk

DEWLISH
Dorset

Ashbank ★★★
Contact: Messrs J/M Bissell,
Lower Dairy House, Crawthorne
Farm, Crawthorne, Dorchester,
Dorset DT2 7NG
T: (01258) 837788

DIDWORTHY
Devon

Didworthy House ★★★★
Contact: Mr & Mrs Reg & Jill
Tavendale & Hamilton,
Didworthy House, Didworthy,
South Brent, Devon TQ10 9EF
T: (01364) 72655
F: (01364) 73022
E: didworthhouse@aol.com

DIPTFORD
Devon

The Old Stables ★★★
Contact: Mrs Tregelles, Stert
Barton, Diptford, Totnes, Devon
T: (01548) 821256

DITTISHAM
Devon

Browns Farm ★★★★
Contact: Mrs Carol Fraenkel,
Browns Farm, Capton,
Dittisham, Dartmouth, Devon
TQ6 0JE
T: (01803) 712556
F: (01803) 712556

Cobwebs ★★★★
Contact: Dart Valley Cottages,
East Cornworthy Cottage, East
Cornworthy, Totnes, Devon
TQ9 7HQ
T: (01803) 722561
F: (01803) 722561
E: enquiries@
dartvalleycottages.co.uk
I: www.dartvalleycottages.co.uk

Sarah Elliots ★★★★
Contact: Dart Valley Cottages,
East Cornworthy Cottage, East
Cornworthy, Totnes, Devon
TQ9 7HQ
T: (01803) 722561
F: (01803) 722561
E: enquiries@
dartvalleycottages.co.uk
I: www.dartvalleycottages.co.uk

DODDISCOMBSLEIGH
Devon

Perry Farm Cottage ★★★
Contact: Mr & Mrs Bowater,
Helpful Holidays, Mill Street,
Chagford, Newton Abbot, Devon
TQ13 8AW
T: (01647) 433593
F: (01647) 433694
E: help@helpfulholidays.com
I: www.helpfulholidays.com

DOLTON
Devon

Ham Farm ★★★★–★★★★★
Contact: Mr and Mrs Cobbledick,
Hebron, Calf Street, Torrington,
Devon EX38 8EG
T: (01805) 624000
F: (01805) 623058

DORCHESTER
Dorset   ∘

Damers Cottage ★★★
Contact: Mrs Rosemary Hodder,
Damers Cottage, East Chaldon,
Dorchester, Dorset DT2 8DN
T: (01305) 852829
F: (01305) 852025
E: RH@cottage-holidays-dorset.
co.uk
I: www.cottage-holidays-dorset.
co.uk

25 Frome Terrace ★★★
Contact: Mr & Mrs D E James, 10
Diggory Crescent, Dorchester,
Dorset DT1 2SP
T: (01305) 257512

**Greenwood Grange Farm
Cottages ★★★★–★★★★★**
Contact: Mrs Jayne O'Brien,
Greenwood Grange Farm
Cottages, Higher Bockhampton,
Dorchester, Dorset DT2 8QH
T: (01305) 268874 & 260212
F: (01305) 268874
E: enquiries@
greenwoodgrange.co.uk
I: www.greenwoodgrange.co.uk

**Hardy Country Holidays
★★★–★★★★**
Contact: Mrs Frances Carroll,
Hardy Country Holidays, Rew
Manor, Rew, Dorchester, Dorset
DT2 9HB
T: (01305) 889222

**Higher Waterston Farm
Cottages ★★★**
Contact: Mr Peregrine Pole-
Carew, Higher Waterston Farm
Cottages, Higher Waterston
Farm, Piddlehinton, Dorchester,
Dorset DT2 7SW
T: (01305) 848208
F: (01305) 848208
E: ppc@silverdirect.demon.
co.uk/waterston
I: www.silverdirect.demon.
co.uk/waterston
♿

The Laurels Cottage ★★
Contact: Mrs RC Lester, The
Laurels Cottage, 7A Church Hill,
Piddlehinton, Dorchester, Dorset
DT2 7TB
T: (01300) 348366

**Lower Wrackleford Farm
Rating Applied For**
Contact: Mrs & Mr Caroline &
Steve Foot, Lower Wrackleford
Farm, Dorchester, Dorset
DT2 9SN
T: (01305) 265390 &
07811 284104
E: wrackle.ford@virgin.net

8 Maiden Castle Road ★★★
Contact: Mr & Mrs T Kolodynski,
8 Maiden Castle Road,
Dorchester, Dorset.DT1 2ER
T: (01305) 257211
F: 0870 056 1547
E: tk@mailmatic.demon.co.uk

Manor Farm ★★★–★★★★★
Contact: Mrs Jackie Kind, Hardy
Cottage, Manor Farm, Frampton,
Dorchester, Dorset DT2 9ND
T: (01300) 320197
F: (01935) 891761
E: dhjfootltd@aol.comm

The Stables ★★★★
Contact: Mrs Elizabeth Peckover,
The Barn, Pallington, Dorchester,
Dorset DT2 8QU
T: (01305) 849344
E: stables@epeckover.fsnet.
co.uk

2 Trinity Cottages ★★★
Contact: Mrs J R Bunce, 13 The
Old Barns, Fordington Dairy,
Athelstan Road, Dorchester,
Dorset DT1 1FD
T: (01305) 250456

Wolfeton Lodge ★★★
Contact: Mrs K Thimbleby,
Wolfeton House, Dorchester,
Dorset DT2 9QN
T: (01305) 263500
F: (01305) 265090

DOULTING
Somerset

Brottens Lodge ★★★★
Contact: Mrs Caroline Gent,
Brottens Lodge, Doulting,
Shepton Mallet, Somerset
BA4 4RB
T: (01749) 880601
E: brottens@ukgateway.net

DOWLISH FORD
Somerset

**Number 3 New Buildings
★★★**
Contact: Mrs Hillary Mead,
Greenclose Cottage, Knowle St
Giles, Chard, Somerset TA20 4AX
T: (01460) 61996

DOWN THOMAS
Devon

Bayfield ★★★
Contact: CH ref: 10143, Holiday
Cottages Group, Spring Mill,
Earby, Barnoldswick, Lancashire
BB18 6RN
T: (01282) 445096
F: (01282) 844299
E: ch.sales@ttgihg.co.uk
I: www.country-holidays.co.uk

DRAYCOTT
Somerset

The Hollies ★★★★
Contact: Mrs Claire Curlewis,
The Hollies, School Lane,
Draycott, Cheddar, Somerset
BS27 3SD
T: (01934) 742301 &
07703 954159
E: andrew.curlewis@
holliescottage.co.uk
I: www.travelengland.org.
uk/home_fr.htm

Martindale ★★★
Contact: CH ref: 10687, Holiday
Cottages Group Owner Services
Dept, Spring Mill, Earby,
Barnoldswick, Lancashire
BB18 6RN
T: (01282) 445096
F: (01282) 844299
E: ch.sales@ttgihg.co.uk
I: www.country-holidays.co.uk

DREWSTEIGNTON
Devon

East Underdown ★★★★★
Contact: Mr & Mrs Bowater,
Helpful Holidays, Mill Street,
Chagford, Newton Abbot, Devon
TQ13 8AW
T: (01647) 433593
F: (01647) 433694
E: help@helpfulholidays.com
I: www.helpfulholidays.com

Michaelmas & Gardeners
★★★★
Contact: Mr & Mrs Thomas,
Netherton Vine, Drewsteignton,
Exeter EX6 6RB
T: (01647) 281602

Netherton House ★★★★
Contact: Mr & Mrs Bowater,
Helpful Holidays, Mill Street,
Chagford, Newton Abbot, Devon
TQ13 8AW
T: (01647) 433593
F: (01647) 433694
E: help@helpfulholidays.com
I: www.helpfulholidays.com

DRIMPTON
Dorset

Little Brookfield ★★★
Contact: Mrs J Angold,
Brookfield, Chard Road,
Drimpton, Beaminster, Dorset
DT8 3RF
T: (01308) 867058
F: (01308) 867080

DULVERTON
Somerset

Anstey Mills Cottage ★★★★
Contact: Mrs D Braukmann-
Pugsley, Anstey Mills Cottage,
East Liscombe, Dulverton,
Somerset TA22 9RZ
T: (01398) 341329
E: doris@b-pugsley.freeserve.
co.uk
I: www.b-pugsley.freeserve.
co.uk

Ashway Cottage ★★★
Contact: Mr George Vellacott,
Ashway Cottage, Ashway Farm,
Dulverton, Somerset TA22 9QD
T: (01398) 323577

Draydon Cottages Exmoor
★★★★
Contact: Ms K Bennett, 12 St
Anthony's Close, Ottery St Mary,
Devon EX11 1EN
T: (01392) 433524
E: kate@draydon.co.uk
I: www.draydon.co.uk

Mead Cottage ★★★
Contact: Mrs Abigail Humphrey,
Mead Cottage, Highercombe
Farm, Dulverton, Somerset
TA22 9PT
T: (01398) 323616
F: (01398) 323616
E: abigal@highercombe.demon.
co.uk
I: www.highercombe.demon.
co.uk

Northmoor House & Lodge
★★★★
Contact: Mr Tim Tarling,
Northmoor, Dulverton, Somerset
TA22 9QF
T: (01398) 323720
E: timtarling@northmoor.fsnet.
co.uk
I: www.northmoorhouse.co.uk
🐾

Paddons ★★★
Contact: Mrs Mary McMichael,
Paddons, Northmoor Road,
Dulverton, Somerset TA22 9PW
T: (01398) 323514
F: (01398) 324283
E: marymm@bscd.org.uk

Page House ★★
Contact: Mrs S Doggrell, Toomer
Farm, Henstridge, Templecombe,
Somerset BA8 0PH
T: (01963) 250237
F: (01963) 250237

DUNKERTON
Bath and North East Somerset

The Barn ★★★★
Contact: Mrs M Weeks, The
Barn, Clover Cross Farm,
Dunkerton, Bath BA2 8BU
T: (01225) 835159 &
07973 190541
F: (01225) 835159
E: dajaweeks@aol.com

DUNSFORD
Devon

Poppy Cottage ★★★
Contact: Miss Hazel Cant, 23 Fox
Brook, Wootton Bassett,
Swindon SN4 8QD
T: (01793) 850555
E: hazel@hcant.freeserve.co.uk

DUNSTER
Somerset

Castle View ★★★★
Contact: Mrs R Neville, Castle
View, 30 High Street, Dunster,
Minehead, Somerset TA24 6SG
T: (01643) 821528

5 Chapel Row ★★★
Contact: Mr EJ Hall, 12 Rue
Gabriel Faure, 78290 Croissy-
sur-Seine, France
T: 00331 3053 6730
E: familydavidmhall@
compuserve.com

Duddings Country Holidays
★★★-★★★★
Contact: Mr Richard Tilke,
Duddings Country Holidays,
Duddings, Timberscombe,
Minehead, Somerset TA24 7TB
T: (01643) 841123
F: (01643) 841165
E: richard@duddings.co.uk
I: www.duddings.co.uk

Grooms Cottage ★★★★
Contact: Ms P Disney, Grooms
Cottage, Knowle Lane, Dunster,
Minehead, Somerset TA24 6TX
T: (01643) 821497

Little Quarme Cottages
★★★★-★★★★★
Contact: Mrs Tammy Cody-
Boutcher, Little Quarme
Cottages, Wheddon Cross,
Minehead TA24 7EA
T: (01643) 841249
F: (01643) 841249
E: 106425.743@compuserve.
com
I: www.littlequarme-cottages.
co.uk

The Old Priory Cottage
★★★★
Contact: Miss Jane Forshaw, The
Old Priory Cottage, The Old
Priory, Dunster, Minehead,
Somerset TA24 6RY
T: (01643) 821540

Pound ★★★
Contact: Mrs S M Sherrin, The
Bungalow, Orchard Road,
Carhampton, Minehead,
Somerset TA24 6NW
T: (01643) 821366
F: (01643) 821366

The Studio and Courtyard Flats
★★★
Contact: Mrs G C Harwood, 1
Church Street, Dunster,
Minehead, Somerset TA24 6SH
T: (01643) 821485

DURRINGTON
Wiltshire

Hengelow ★★★
Contact: Mr and Mrs Derrick/
Anna Foord, 32 Stonehenge
Road, Durrington, Salisbury,
Wiltshire SP4 8BP
T: (01980) 653709
F: (01980) 653709

EAST ALLINGTON
Devon

Flear Farm Cottages
★★★★-★★★★★
Contact: Mrs Julie Ford, Flear
Farm Cottages, Flear Farm, East
Allington, Totnes, Devon
TQ9 7RF
T: (01548) 521227
F: (01548) 521600
E: flearfarm@btinternet.com
I: www.flearfarm.co.uk

Homeleigh ★★★
Contact: Miss Jennifer Tibbs, 24
Fairlop Close, Calcot, Reading,
Berkshire RG31 7EF
T: (0118) 9412889
F: (0118) 9412889
E: j.tibbs@mail.excite.com

Pitt Farm ★★★-★★★★
Contact: Mr & Mrs C&D Bates,
Pitt Farm, Green Lane, East
Allington, Totnes, Devon
TQ9 7QD
T: (01548) 521234
F: (01548) 521518
E: christopher.bates@ukonline.
co.uk
I: www.ukonline.
co.uk/christopher.bates/

EAST BRENT
Somerset

Knoll Farm ★★★
Contact: Mrs Jeanne Champion,
Knoll Farm, Jarvis Lane, East
Brent, Highbridge, Somerset
TA9 4HS
T: (01278) 760227

EAST CHINNOCK
Somerset

Weston House ★★★★
Contact: Mrs Susan Gliddon,
Weston House, East Chinnock,
Yeovil, Somerset BA22 9EL
T: (01935) 863712
E: westonhouseuk@
netscapeonline.co.uk

EAST COKER
Somerset

Little Prymleigh ★★★★
Contact: Mrs C Williams,
Prymleigh, Yeovil Road, East
Coker, Yeovil, Somerset
BA22 9HW
T: (01935) 863313

EAST HUNTSPILL
Somerset

Cote Farm ★★
Contact: Mr & Mrs M J Elsworth,
Cote Farm, Haggetts Lane, East
Huntspill, Highbridge, Somerset
TA9 3PD
T: (01278) 786790

Withy Grove Farm ★★
Contact: Mr & Mrs Lionel &
Wendy Baker, Withy Grove Farm,
East Huntspill, Highbridge,
Somerset TA9 3NP
T: (01278) 784471
I: www.withygrovefarm.co.uk

EAST PORTLEMOUTH
Devon

Two West Waterhead ★★★★
Contact: Mr and Mrs I Stokes, 12
Elmcroft Cres, Horfield, Bristol
BS7 9NF
T: (0117) 951 6333

EASTERTON
Wiltshire

Stable End ★★★
Contact: CH Ref: 64003, Holiday
Cottages Groups Owner Services
Department, Spring Mill, Earby,
Barnoldswick, Lancashire
BB18 6RN
T: (01282) 445096
F: (01282) 844299
E: ch.sales@ttgihg.co.uk
I: www.country-holidays.co.uk

EDINGTON
Wiltshire

Cheam House
Rating Applied For
Contact: Cheam House, 17
Greatwoods, Greater Lane,
Edington, Westbury, Wiltshire
BA13 4QA
T: (01380) 830631

Greengrove Cottage ★★★★
Contact: CH Ref: CE19, Holiday
Cottages Group, Spring Mill,
Earby, Barnoldswick, Lancashire
BB18 6RN
T: (01282) 445096
F: (01282) 8442999
E: ch.sales@ttgihg.co.uk
I: www.country-holidays.co.uk

Establishments printed in blue have a detailed entry in this guide

EDMONTON
Cornwall
Quarryman's Cottages No 20 & No 1 ★★
Contact: Mrs Carol Jenkins, Endellion House, Parc Road, Llangybi, Usk, Gwent NP15 1NL
T: (01633) 450417
E: carol@choicecornishcottages.com
I: www.choicecornishcottages.com

ENMORE
Somerset
The Cotte ★★★
Contact: Mr Peter Morris, Farm & Cottage Holidays, Victoria House, 12 Fore Street, Northam, Bideford, Devon EX39 1AW
T: (01237) 479146
F: (01237) 421512
E: farmcott@cix.co.uk
I: www.farmcott.co.uk

ETCHILHAMPTON
Wiltshire
Heath Knapp Cottage ★★
Contact: Mr John Blake, Heath Knapp Cottage, Etchilhampton, Devizes, Wiltshire SN10 3JU
T: (01380) 860000 & 860304
F: (01380) 860111

EXBOURNE
Devon
Easterbrook Farm Cottages ★★★
Contact: Mr M A Pryce, Easterbrook Farm, Exbourne, Okehampton, Devon EX20 3QY
T: (01837) 851674 & 07831 588183
E: pryce.easterbrook@btinternet.com

EXETER
Devon
Coach House Farm ★★★★★
Contact: Mr J Bale, Coach House Farm, Moor Lane, Broadclyst, Exeter, EX5 3JH
T: (01392) 461254
F: (01392) 460931
E: meadowview@mpprops.fsnet.co.uk
♿

Fairwinds Holiday Bungalow ★★★★
Contact: Mrs W Price, Fairwinds Hotel, Kennford, Exeter, Devon EX6 7UD
T: (01392) 832911

EXFORD
Somerset
Bailiffs Cottage ★★★
Contact: Mr Martin Burnett, Bailiffs Cottage, Muddicombe Lane, Exford, Minehead, Somerset TA24 7NH
T: (01643) 831342
E: burnettjfx@altavista.com

Court Farm ★★★
Contact: Mrs Horstmann, Court Farm, Exford, Minehead, Somerset TA24 7LY
T: (01643) 831207
F: (01643) 831207
E: beth@courtfarm.co.uk
I: www.courtfarm.co.uk

Riscombe Farm Holiday Cottages and Stabling ★★★★
Contact: Mr & Mrs Brian & Leone Martin, Riscombe Farm Holiday Cottages and Stabling, Exford, Minehead, Somerset TA24 7NH
T: (01643) 831480
F: (01643) 831480
E: info@riscombe.co.uk
I: www.riscombe.co.uk

Rocks Bungalow ★★★★
Contact: Mrs Kathryn Tucker, Stetfold Rocks Farm, Exford, Minehead, Somerset TA24 7NZ
T: (01643) 831213
E: tucker@exfordfsbusiness.co.uk

Stilemoor Bungalow ★★★
Contact: Mrs Joan Atkins, 2 Edgcott Cottages, Exford, Minehead, Somerset TA24 7QG
T: (01643) 831564
F: (01643) 831564
E: j_atkins@altavista.com
I: www.homepage.attavista.com/stilemoor

Westermill Farm ★★-★★★★
Contact: Mrs Jackie Edwards, Westermill Farm, Exford, Minehead, Somerset TA24 7NJ
T: (01643) 831238
F: (01643) 831660
E: holidays@westermill-exmoor.co.uk
I: www.exmoorcamping.co.uk
♿

EXMINSTER
Devon
Berrybrook House ★★★★
Contact: Mr & Mrs Mike Williams, Hillside, Exminster Hill, Exminster, Exeter EX6 8DW
T: (01392) 832319
F: (01392) 832319

EXMOUTH
Devon
1,2,3,4 Channel View ★★★
Contact: Mr Messrs Lenn, St Andrews Holiday Homes, Channel View, The Esplanade, Exmouth, Devon EX8 2AZ
T: (01395) 222555
F: (01395) 270766
E: st-andrews@lineone.net

25 Bicton Street ★★
Contact: Holiday Havens Of Devon, 13b Albion Street, Exmouth, Devon EX8 1JL
T: (01395) 275223
F: (01395) 275223
E: graham@havensrentals.fsnet.co.uk

4 Crossingfields House ★★★
Contact: Holiday Havens Of Devon, 13b Albion Street, Exmouth, Devon EX8 1JL
T: (01395) 275223
F: (01395) 275223
E: graham@havensrentals.fsnet.co.uk

43 Egremont Road ★★
Contact: Holiday Havens Of Devon, 13b Albion Street, Exmouth, Devon EX8 1JL
T: (01395) 275223
F: (01395) 275223
E: graham@havensrentals.fsnet.co.uk

Flat 1 ★★★
Contact: Holiday Havens Of Devon, 13b Albion Street, Exmouth, Devon EX8 1JL
T: (01395) 275223
F: (01395) 275223
E: graham@havensrentals.fsnet.co.uk

The Mews Cottage ★★★
Contact: Mrs A Loveridge, The Mews Cottage, The Mews, Knappe Cross, Brixington Lane, Exmouth, Devon EX8 5DL
T: (01395) 272198

Pilot Cottage ★★★★
Contact: Mr and Mrs Woods, The Kerans Hotel, The Esplanade, Exmouth, Devon EX8 1DS
T: (01395) 222882
E: seahorse@xmouth.co.uk
I: www.xmouth.co.uk

EXTON
Somerset
Oakley Lodge ★★★
Contact: Mrs A Pantall, Upper House, Staunton on Wye, Hereford HR4 7LW
T: (01981) 500249
E: anne.pantall@amserve.net
I: www.oakley-lodge.co.uk

EYPE
Dorset
Highlands End Holiday Park ★★★
Contact: Mr Martin Cox, Highlands End Holiday Park, Eype, Bridport, Dorset DT6 6AR
T: (01308) 422139
F: (01308) 425672
E: holidays@wdlh.co.uk
I: www.wdlh.co.uk

FALMOUTH
Cornwall
Baywatch ★★★
Contact: Cornish Cottage Holidays, Godolphin Road, Helston, Cornwall TR13 8AA
T: (01326) 573808
F: (01326) 564992
E: enquiry@cornishcottageholidays.co.uk
I: www.cornishcottageholidays.co.uk

Captains Corner & Sunrise ★★★-★★★★
Contact: Mrs Margie Lumby, Special Places, Poachers Reach, Feock, Truro, Cornwall TR3 6SQ
T: (01872) 864400
F: (01872) 864400
E: office@specialplacescornwall.co.uk
I: www.specialplacescornwall.co.uk

The Charthouse ★★★
Contact: Mrs Margie Lumby, Special Places, Poachers Reach, Feock, Truro, Cornwall TR3 6SQ
T: (01872) 864400
F: (01872) 864400
E: office@specialplacescornwall.co.uk
I: www.specialplacescornwall.co.uk

Dolphin Cottage ★★★
Contact: Cornish Cottage Holidays, Godolphin Road, Helston, Cornwall TR13 8AA
T: (01326) 573808
F: (01326) 564992
E: enquiry@cornishcottageholidays.co.uk
I: www.cornishcottageholidays.co.uk

The Foredeck ★★★
Contact: Cornish Cottage Holidays, The Old Turnpike Dairy, Godolphin Road, Helston, Cornwall TR13 8AA
T: (01326) 573808
F: (01326) 564992
E: enquiry@cornishcottageholidays.co.uk
I: www.cornishcottageholidays.co.uk

Parklands ★★★
Contact: Mrs J A Simmons, 215a Perry Street, Billericay, Essex CM12 0NZ
T: (01277) 654425
E: steve@simmo58.freeserve.co.uk

Pendra Loweth Holiday Village Rating Applied For
Contact: Mr J Hick, Pendra Loweth Holiday Village, Maen Valley, Falmouth, Cornwall TR11 5BJ
T: (01326) 312689

Pennant Cottage ★★★★
Contact: Cornish Cottage Holidays, The Old Turnpike Dairy, Godolphin Road, Helston, Cornwall TR13 8AA
T: (01326) 573808
F: (01326) 564992
E: enquiry@cornishcottageholidays.co.uk
I: www.cornishcottageholidays.co.uk

The Retreat ★★★★
Contact: Cornish Cottage Holidays, The Old Turnpike Dairy, Godolphin Road, Helston, Cornwall TR13 8AA
T: (01326) 573808
F: (01326) 564992
E: enquiry@cornishcottageholidays.co.uk
I: www.cornishcottageholidays.co.uk

Seaworthy ★★★★
Contact: Cornish Cottage Holidays, The Old Turnpike Dairy, Godolphin Road, Helston, Cornwall TR13 8AA
T: (01326) 573808
F: (01326) 564992
E: enquiry@cornishcottageholidays.co.uk
I: www.cornishcottageholidays.co.uk

Stable Cottage ★★★
Contact: Mrs Margie Lumby, Special Places, Poachers Reach, Feock, Truro, Cornwall TR3 6SQ
T: (01872) 864400
F: (01872) 864400
E: office@specialplacescornwall.co.uk
I: www.specialplacescornwall.co.uk

Tall Ships ★★★★★
Contact: Mr M Couldry, 8
Campbeltown Way, Port
Pendennis, Falmouth, Cornwall
TR11 3YE
T: (01326) 311440
F: (01326) 316781
E: mike.couldry@virgin.net
I: www.cornwall-online.
co.uk/tallships

**Toldeen Waterside Studio
★★★**
Contact: Mrs Margie Lumby,
Special Places, Poachers Reach,
Feock, Truro, Cornwall TR3 6SQ
T: (01872) 864400
F: (01872) 864400
E: office@
specialplacescornwall.co.uk
I: www.specialplacescornwall.
co.uk

Turnaround Cottage ★★★★
Contact: Cornish Cottage
Holidays, The Old Turnpike Dairy,
Godolphin Road, Helston,
Cornwall TR13 8AA
T: (01326) 573808
F: (01326) 564992
E: enquiry@
cornishcottageholidays.co.uk
I: www.cornishcottageholidays.
co.uk

FARMBOROUGH
Bath and North East Somerset

Barrow Croft ★★★★
Contact: Mrs Cherilyn Langley,
Barrow Vale Farm, Farmborough,
Bath BA3 1BL
T: (01761) 470300
E: cherilynlangley@hotmail.com
I: www.visitbath.co.uk

FAULKLAND
Somerset

The Green Farm ★★★★★
Contact: Mrs A Gatley, The
Green Farm House, Faulkland,
Bath BA3 5UY
T: (01373) 834331
F: (01373) 834331

Lime Kiln Farm ★★★★★
Contact: Mrs M J Kendall, Lime
Kiln Farm, Faulkland, Bath
BA3 5XE
T: (01373) 834305
E: limekiln@btinternet.com

FENNY BRIDGES
Devon

Skinners Ash Farm ★★★★
Contact: Mrs Jill Godfrey,
Skinners Ash Farm, Fenny
Bridges, Honiton, Devon
EX14 3BH
T: (01404) 850231
I: www.cottageguide.
co.uk/skinnersash/

FENTON PITTS
Cornwall

Penvivian Cottage ★★★
Contact: Mrs Jane Hoskin,
Penvivian Cottage, Penvivian
Farm, Fenton Pitts, Bodmin,
Cornwall PL30 5HT
T: (01208) 831632
E: penvivian@penvivian.
freeserve.co.uk
I: www.cottageguide.
co.uk/penvivan

FEOCK
Cornwall

Brambles ★★★
Contact: Cornish Cottage
Holidays, The Old Turnpike Dairy,
Godolphin Road, Helston,
Cornwall TR13 8AA
T: (01326) 573808
F: (01326) 564992
E: enquiry@
cornishcottageholidays.co.uk
I: www.cornishcottageholidays.
co.uk

Pebble Cottage ★★★
Contact: Mrs Margie Lumby,
Special Places, Poachers Reach,
Feock, Truro, Cornwall TR3 6SQ
T: (01872) 864400
F: (01872) 864400
E: office@
specialplacescornwall.co.uk
I: www.specialplacescornwall.
co.uk

Seaview Farm Cottage ★★
Contact: Mrs Margie Lumby,
Special Places, Poachers Reach,
Feock, Truro, Cornwall TR3 6SQ
T: (01872) 864400
F: (01872) 864400
E: office@
specialplacescornwall.co.uk
I: www.specialplacescornwall.
co.uk

FIVE LANES
Cornwall

The Little Barn ★★★★
Contact: Ms Sheila Taylor, The
Little Barn, Thorn Cottage, Five
Lanes, Launceston, Cornwall
PL15 7RX
T: (01566) 86689
F: (01566) 86936
E: sheilataylor@littlebarn.
demon.co.uk
I: www.littlebarn.demon.co.uk

FLUSHING
Cornwall

Make-an-Mend ★★★★
Contact: Cornish Cottage
Holidays, The Old Turnpike Dairy,
Godolphin Road, Helston,
Cornwall TR13 8AA
T: (01326) 573808
F: (01326) 564992
E: enquiry@
cornishcottageholidays.co.uk
I: www.cornishcottageholidays.
co.uk

Pitick House ★★★★
Contact: Mrs Margie Lumby,
Special Places, Poachers Reach,
Feock, Truro, Cornwall TR3 6SQ
T: (01872) 864400
F: (01872) 864400
E: office@
specialplacescornwall.co.uk
I: www.specialplacescornwall.
co.uk

Quay Cottage ★★★
Contact: Mrs Margie Lumby,
Special Places, Poachers Reach,
Feock, Truro, Cornwall TR3 6SQ
T: (01872) 864400
F: (01872) 864400
E: office@
specialplacescornwall.co.uk
I: www.specialplacescornwall.
co.uk

Tradewinds ★★★
Contact: Cornish Cottage
Holidays, The Old Turnpike Dairy,
Godolphin Road, Helston,
Cornwall TR13 8AA
T: (01326) 573808
F: (01326) 564992
E: enquiry@
cornishcottageholidays.co.uk
I: www.cornishcottageholidays.
co.uk

FORD
Wiltshire

Ivy Cottage ★★★
Contact: Mrs R Helps, 3 The
Dene, Ford, Chippenham,
Wiltshire SN14 8RR
T: (01249) 782008
F: (01249) 782398
E: r-helps@tinyworld.co.uk

FOWEY
Cornwall

Chester House ★★★★
Contact: Estuary Cottages,
Estuary House, Fore Street,
Fowey, Cornwall PL23 1AH
T: (01726) 832965
F: (01726) 832866
E: info@estuarycottages.co.uk
I: www.estuarycottages.co.uk

Chy Vounder ★★
Contact: Fowey Harbour
Cottages (W Hill & Son), 3 Fore
Street, Fowey, Cornwall
PL23 1AH
T: (01726) 832211
F: (01726) 832901

**Crow's Nest & West Wing
★★★★**
Contact: Estuary Cottages,
Estuary House, Fore Street,
Fowey, Cornwall PL23 1AH
T: (01726) 832965 & 832299
F: (01726) 832866
E: info@estuarycottages.co.uk
I: www.estuarycottages.co.uk

3 Dolphin Houses ★★★
Contact: Estuary Cottages,
Estuary House, Fore Street,
Fowey, Cornwall PL23 1AH
T: (01726) 832965 & 832299
F: (01726) 832866
E: info@estuarycottages.co.uk
I: www.estuarycottages.co.uk

The Dolphins ★★★
Contact: Estuary Cottages,
Estuary House, Fore Street,
Fowey, Cornwall PL23 1AH
T: (01726) 832965
F: (01726) 832866
E: info@estuarycottages.co.uk
I: www.estuarycottages.co.uk

Ferrymans Cottage ★★★★
Contact: Estuary Cottages,
Estuary House, Fore Street,
Fowey, Cornwall PL23 1AH
T: (01726) 832965
F: (01726) 832866
E: info@estuarycottages.co.uk
I: www.estuarycottages.co.uk

2 Harbour Cottages ★★★
Contact: Estuary Cottages,
Estuary House, Fore Street,
Fowey, Cornwall PL23 1AH
T: (01726) 832965 & 832299
F: (01726) 832866
E: info@estuarycottages.co.uk
I: www.estuarycottages.co.uk

Little Quoin ★★★★
Contact: Estuary Cottages,
Estuary House, Fore Street,
Fowey, Cornwall PL23 1AH
T: (01726) 832965 & 832299
F: (01726) 832866
E: info@estuarycottages.co.uk
I: www.estuarycottages.co.uk

Palm Trees ★★
Contact: W J B Hill & Son, 3 Fore
Street, Fowey, Cornwall PL23
T: (01726) 832211
F: (01726) 832901
E: hillandson@talk21.com

Penventinue Farm ★★★
Contact: Mr/Miss D/S Bence/
Blacker, Penventinue Farm,
Fowey, Cornwall PL23 1JT
T: (01726) 832516 &
07767 650119
F: (01726) 832504
E: sueblacker@talk21.com

Refuge Court ★★★★
Contact: Estuary Cottages,
Estuary House, Fore Street,
Fowey, Cornwall PL23 1AH
T: (01726) 832965 & 832299
F: (01726) 832866
E: info@estuarycottages.co.uk
I: www.estuarycottages.co.uk

River Watch ★★★
Contact: Estuary Cottages,
Estuary House, Fore Street,
Fowey, Cornwall PL23 1AH
T: (01726) 832965 & 832299
F: (01726) 832866
E: info@estuarycottages.co.uk
I: www.estuarycottages.co.uk

Rose Cottage ★★★
Contact: Estuary Cottages,
Estuary House, Fore Street,
Fowey, Cornwall PL23 1AH
T: (01726) 832965
F: (01726) 832866
E: info@estuarycottages.co.uk
I: www.estuarycottages.co.uk

The Square Rig ★★★★
Contact: Ms Clare Adams,
Square Rig Holidays, Steps
House, 10 St Johns Street,
Bromsgrove, Worcestershire
B61 8QY
T: (01527) 575929
F: (01527) 833466
E: members.aol.com/sqrighol

17a St Finbarrus Road ★★
Contact: Fowey Harbour
Cottages, 3 Fore Street, Fowey,
Cornwall PL23 1AH
T: (01726) 832211
F: (01726) 832901
E: hillandson@talk21.com

Star Cottage ★★★★
Contact: Estuary Cottages,
Estuary House, Fore Street,
Fowey, Cornwall PL23 1AH
T: (01726) 832965 & 832299
F: (01726) 832866
E: info@estuarycottages.co.uk
I: www.estuarycottages.co.uk

Tamara ★★★
Contact: Estuary Cottages,
Estuary House, Fore Street,
Fowey, Cornwall PL23 1AH
T: (01726) 832965 & 832299
F: (01726) 832866
E: info@estuarycottages.co.uk
I: www.estuarycottages.co.uk

Establishments printed in blue have a detailed entry in this guide

Tide House ★★★
Contact: Estuary Cottages,
Estuary House, Fore Street,
Fowey, Cornwall PL23 1AH
T: (01726) 832965
F: (01726) 832866
E: info@estuarycottages.co.uk
I: www.estuarycottages.co.uk

Trenython Manor Hotel and Country Club ★★★★
Contact: Miss Miriam Hopper,
Trenython Manor Hotel and
Country Club, Tywardreath, Par,
Cornwall PL24 2TS
T: (01726) 814797
F: (01726) 817030
E: info@trenython.co.uk

Trevannion ★★★
Contact: Estuary Cottages,
Estuary House, Fore Street,
Fowey, Cornwall PL23 1AH
T: (01726) 832965
F: (01726) 832866
E: info@estuarycottages.co.uk
I: www.estuarycottages.co.uk

The Trustees ★★★
Contact: Estuary Cottages,
Estuary House, Fore Street,
Fowey, Cornwall PL23 1AH
T: (01726) 832965
F: (01726) 832866
E: info@estuarycottages.co.uk
I: www.estuarycottages.co.uk

Waterfront Apartment ★★★★
Contact: Estuary Cottages,
Estuary House, Fore Street,
Fowey, Cornwall PL23 1AH
T: (01726) 832965 & 832299
F: (01726) 832866
E: info@estuarycottages.co.uk
I: www.estuarycottages.co.uk

Westcliffe ★★
Contact: Estuary Cottages,
Estuary House, Fore Street,
Fowey, Cornwall PL23 1AH
T: (01726) 832965 & 832299
F: (01726) 832866
E: info@estuarycottages.co.uk
I: www.estuarycottages.co.uk

FREMINGTON
Devon

Lower Yelland Farm ★★★
Contact: Mr Peter Day, Lower
Yelland Farm, Fremington,
Barnstaple, Devon EX31 3EN
T: (01271) 860101 &
07803 933642
F: (01271) 860101
E: pday@loweryellandfarm.co.uk
I: www.loweryellandfarm.co.uk

FRESHFORD
Bath and North East Somerset

The Barton Cottage ★★★
Contact: Mrs C Foster, 57
Hillcrest Drive, Southdown, Bath
BA2 1HD
T: (01225) 429756

Dolphin Cottage ★★★★★
Contact: Mrs Rowena Wood,
Dolphin House, Freshford, Bath
BA2 7UQ
T: (01225) 722100 &
07808 402975
F: (01225) 723741
E: rowena_wood@compuserve.com

FRITHELSTOCK
Devon

Honeysuckle Cottage ★★★★
Contact: Mrs R G Hunkin, East
Ash Farm, Frithelstockstone,
Torrington, Devon EX38 8JS
T: (01805) 623412 &
07967 751781
E: roghunkin@ukonline.co.uk
I: www.tarka-country.co.uk/honeysuckle

FROME
Somerset

Bollow Hill Farm
Rating Applied For
Contact: Mr & Ms Emma or
Mark Kaye, Bollow Hill Farm,
Friggle Street, Frome, Somerset
BA11 5LJ
T: (01373) 463007
F: (01373) 463030

Executive Holidays ★★★★–★★★★★
Contact: Mr R A Gregory,
Executive Holidays, Whitemill
Farm, Iron Mills Lane, Oldford,
Frome, Somerset BA11 2NR
T: (01373) 452907 &
07860 147525
F: (01373) 453253
E: info@executiveholidays.co.uk
I: www.executiveholidays.co.uk

Hill View ★★
Contact: Mrs M House, Forest
View, Gare Hill, Frome, Somerset
BA11 5EZ
T: (01985) 844276
E: wells@packsaddle11.freeserve.co.uk

St Katharine's Lodge ★★★★
Contact: Mrs Tania Maynard, St
Katharine's Cottage, East
Woodlands, Frome, Somerset
BA11 5LQ
T: (01373) 471434 & 474411
F: (01373) 474499
E: roger@stkaths.com

GALMPTON
Devon

1-2 Weymouth Cottages ★★
Contact: Mrs A E Rossiter,
Burton Farm, Galmpton,
Kingsbridge, Devon TQ7 3EY
T: (01548) 561210
F: (01548) 561210
E: anne@burtonfarm.co.uk
I: www.burtonfarm.co.uk

Georgia ★★
Contact: Holiday Homes &
Cottages South West, 365A
Torquay Road, Paignton, Devon
TQ3 2BT
T: (01803) 663650
F: (01803) 664037
E: holcotts@aol.com
I: www.swcottages.co.uk

GARA BRIDGE
Devon

Gara Cottages ★★★
Contact: Mr & Mrs Bowater,
Helpful Holidays, Mill Street,
Chagford, Newton Abbot, Devon
TQ13 8AW
T: (01647) 433593
F: (01647) 433694
E: help@helpfulholidays.com
I: www.helpfulholidays.com

GEORGE NYMPTON
Devon

East Trayne Cottage ★★★★
Contact: Marsden's Cottage
Holidays, 2 The Square,
Braunton, Devon EX33 2JB
T: (01271) 813777
F: (01271) 813664
E: holidays@marsdens.co.uk
I: www.marsdens.co.uk

GEORGEHAM
Devon

Appletree Cottage ★★★
Contact: Marsden's Cottage
Holidays, 2 The Square,
Braunton, Devon EX33 2JB
T: (01271) 813777
F: (01271) 813664
E: holidays@marsdens.co.uk
I: www.marsdens.co.uk

Burver Cottage ★★★★
Contact: Marsden's Cottage
Holidays, 2 The Square,
Braunton, Devon EX33 2JB
T: (01271) 813777
F: (01271) 813664
E: holidays@marsdens.co.uk
I: www.marsdens.co.uk

Callum Cottage ★★★
Contact: Marsden's Cottage
Holidays, 2 The Square,
Braunton, Devon EX33 2JB
T: (01271) 813777
F: (01271) 813664
E: holidays@marsdens.co.uk
I: www.marsdens.co.uk

16 David's Hill ★★★
Contact: Marsden's Cottage
Holidays, 2 The Square,
Braunton, Devon EX33 2JB
T: (01271) 813777
F: (01271) 813664
E: holidays@marsdens.co.uk
I: www.marsdens.co.uk

Denre ★★★
Contact: Marsden's Cottage
Holidays, 2 The Square,
Braunton, Devon EX33 2JB
T: (01271) 813777
F: (01271) 813664
E: holidays@marsdens.co.uk
I: www.marsdens.co.uk

Pickwell Barton Cottages ★★–★★★
Contact: Mrs S Cook, Pickwell
Barton Cottages, Georgeham,
Braunton, Devon EX33 1LA
T: (01271) 890987 & 890994
F: (01271) 890987

Rock Cottage ★★
Contact: Marsden's Cottage
Holidays, 2 The Square,
Braunton, Devon EX33 2JB
T: (01271) 813777
F: (01271) 813664
E: holidays@marsdens.co.uk
I: www.marsdens.co.uk

GERMANSWEEK
Devon

Northcombe Farm ★★–★★★
Contact: CH ref: 1535,1760,
Country Holidays Group Owner
Services Dept, Spring Mill, Earby,
Barnoldswick, Lancashire
BB18 6RN
T: (01282) 445096
F: (01282) 844299
E: ch.sales@ttgihg.co.uk
I: www.country-holidays.co.uk

GERMOE
Cornwall

The Old Barn ★★★
Contact: Cornish Home
Holidays, 12 Parade Street,
Penzance, Cornwall TR18 4BU
T: (01736) 368575
F: (01736) 351943
E: chh@chh.co.uk
I: www.chh.co.uk

Treweeth ★★★
Contact: Cornish Cottage
Holidays, The Old Turnpike Dairy,
Godolphin Road, Helston,
Cornwall TR13 8AA
T: (01326) 573808
F: (01326) 564992
E: enquiry@cornishcottageholidays.co.uk
I: www.cornishcottageholidays.co.uk

GERRANS
Cornwall

Casita ★★★
Contact: Cornish Cottage
Holidays, The Old Turnpike Dairy,
Godolphin Road, Helston,
Cornwall TR13 8AA
T: (01326) 573808
F: (01326) 564992
E: enquiry@cornishcottageholidays.co.uk
I: www.cornishcottageholidays.co.uk

GITTISHAM
Devon

Westgate Cottage ★★★★
Contact: Jean Bartlett Cottage
Holidays, Fore Street, Beer,
Seaton, Devon EX12 3JB
T: (01297) 23221
F: (01297) 23303
E: jeanb@netbreaks.com
I: www.netbreaks.com/jeanb

GLASTONBURY
Somerset

60 Bove Town ★★
Contact: Mrs C Robertson,
Treventon, Well Lane, St
Keverne, Helston, Cornwall
TR12 6LZ
T: (01326) 280514
E: losowek.herbs@btinternet.com

Cordis Mundi ★★★
Contact: Mr & Mrs Neil & Alison
Stevenson, Cordis Mundi,
Bovetown, Glastonbury,
Somerset BA6 8JG
T: (01458) 830590
F: (01458) 830580
E: alisonspco@ukonline.co.uk

In-B-Tween Cottage ★★★★
Contact: Mr & Mrs J Van
Bergen-Henegouwen, Potting
Shed Holidays, Harters Hill
Cottage, Pillmoor Lane, Coxley,
Wells, Somerset BA5 1RF
T: (01749) 672857
E: cjvbhhol@aol.com
I: www.pottingshedholidays.co.uk

The Lightship ★★
Contact: Ms R Rose, The
Lightship, 82 Bove Town,
Glastonbury, Somerset BA6 8JG
T: (01458) 833698

Magdalene House Trust ★★
Contact: Ms Anne Stallybrass,
Magdalene House Trust, 38
Magdalene Street, Glastonbury,
Somerset BA6 9EJ
T: (01458) 835235

Michaelmas Cottage ★★★★
Contact: Mrs J E Sale,
Michaelmas House, West
Pennard, Glastonbury, Somerset
BA6 8NS
T: (01458) 835293

**Middlewick Farm Holiday
Cottages ★★★★**
Contact: Mr & Mrs Roy and Avril
Coles, Middlewick Farm Holiday
Cottages, Middlewick Farm,
Wick Lane, Glastonbury,
Somerset BA6 8JW
T: (01458) 832351
F: (01458) 832351

St Edmunds Cottage ★★★★
Contact: Mrs Jeannette
Heygate-Browne, St Edmunds
Cottage, 26 Wells Road,
Glastonbury, Somerset BA6 9BS
T: (01458) 830461
E: rheygatebrowne@aol.com
I: www.members.aol.
com/rheygatebrowne/
stedmundscottage/homepage.
html

Victoria Farm ★★
Contact: Mr & Mrs ILE Rands,
Victoria Farm, Bradley Lane,
Glastonbury, Somerset BA6 8LW
T: (01458) 850509

Ynysbach ★★
Contact: Mr Peter Townhill, 5
Wick Hollow, Glastonbury,
Somerset BA6 8JQ
T: (01458) 831458

GODNEY
Somerset

Swallow Barn ★★★★
Contact: Mrs H J Millard,
Double-Gate Farm, Godney,
Wells, Somerset BA5 1RX
T: (01458) 832217
F: (01458) 835612
E: hilary@doublegate.demon.
co.uk
I: www.somerset-farm-holiday.
co.uk/
old_cart_house_phhome_page.
htm
⊛

**Tor View & Church Cottages
★★★**
Contact: Mr & Mrs Michael &
Jenny Churches, Godney Farm
Holiday Cottages, Godney, Wells,
Somerset BA5 1RX
T: (01458) 831141
F: (01458) 831141
E: michael+jenny@godneyfarm.
freeserve.co.uk

GOLANT
Cornwall

**Church Meadow
Rating Applied For**
Contact: Mrs R Varco, Church
Meadow, Penquite Farm, Golant,
Fowey, Cornwall PL23 1LB
T: (01726) 833319
F: (01726) 833319
E: varco@farmersweekly.net
I: www.cornwall-online.
co.uk/churchmeadow

GOLDSITHNEY
Cornwall

Chrystle ★★★
Contact: Cornish Cottage
Holidays, The Old Turnpike Dairy,
Godolphin Road, Helston,
Cornwall TR13 8AA
T: (01326) 573808
F: (01326) 564992
E: enquiry@
cornishcottageholidays.co.uk
I: www.cornishcottageholidays.
co.uk

GOODLEIGH
Devon

The Haven ★★★★
Contact: Marsden's Cottage
Holidays, 2 The Square,
Braunton, Devon EX33 2JB
T: (01271) 813777
F: (01271) 813664
E: holidays@marsdens.co.uk
I: www.marsdens.co.uk

The Old Granary ★★★★
Contact: Marsden's Cottage
Holidays, 2 The Square,
Braunton, Devon EX33 2JB
T: (01271) 813777
F: (01271) 813664
E: holidays@marsdens.co.uk
I: www.marsdens.co.uk

GOODRINGTON
Devon

**Ashdene Holiday Apartments
★★-★★★**
Contact: Mrs & Mr Jill & David
Beckett, Ashdene Holiday
Apartments, Cliff Park Road,
Goodrington, Paignton, Devon
TQ4 6NB
T: (01803) 558397
F: (01803) 558397
E: ashdene.apts@goodrington.
fsbusiness.co.uk
I: www.paigntondevon.
co.uk/ashdene.htm

GORRAN HAVEN
Cornwall

Seamew and Haven ★★★
Contact: Cornish Cottage
Holidays, Godolphin Road,
Helston, Cornwall TR13 8AA
T: (01326) 573808
F: (01326) 564992
E: enquiry@
cornishcottageholidays.co.uk
I: www.cornishcottageholidays.
co.uk

Tregillan ★★★
Contact: Mr and Mrs K Pike,
Tregillan, Trewollock Lane,
Gorran Haven, St Austell,
Cornwall PL26 6NT
T: (01726) 842452
E: tregillan-hol-apts@talk21.
com

GREAT CHEVERELL
Wiltshire

Downswood ★
Contact: Mrs Ros Shepherd,
Downswood, Great Cheverell,
Devizes, Wiltshire SN10 5TW
T: (01380) 813304

GRITTENHAM
Wiltshire

**Orchard View
Rating Applied For**
Contact: Mr & Mrs P Cary,
Orchard View, Grittenham,
Chippenham, Wiltshire SN15 4JX
T: (01666) 510747

GUNWALLOE
Cornwall

Hingey Farm ★★★★
Contact: Cornish Cottage
Holidays, The Old Turnpike Dairy,
Godolphin Road, Helston,
Cornwall TR13 8AA
T: (01326) 573808
F: (01326) 564992
E: enquiry@
cornishcottageholidays.co.uk
I: www.cornishcottageholidays.
co.uk

GURNEY SLADE
Somerset

**Sunnyside House and Cottage
★★-★★★**
Contact: Mrs J Bridges, Mendip
Holiday Homes, Hylands,
Binegar, Shepton Mallet,
Somerset BA3 4TP
T: (01749) 840592 &
(01761) 419337
F: (01749) 840592

GWEEK
Cornwall

Corner Cottage ★★★
Contact: Cornish Cottage
Holidays, Godolphin Road,
Helston, Cornwall TR13 8AA
T: (01326) 573808
F: (01326) 564992
E: enquiry@
cornishcottageholidays.co.uk
I: www.cornishcottageholidays.
co.uk

HALWILL
Devon

Anglers Paradise ★★★★
Contact: Mr Zyg Gregorek,
Anglers Paradise, The Gables,
Winsford, Halwill, Beaworthy,
Devon EX21 5XT
T: (01409) 221559
F: (01409) 221559
I: www.anglers-paradise.co.uk
⊛

HARBOURNEFORD
Devon

Hilly Field Cottages ★★★
Contact: Mrs J Tinkler, Hilly Field
Farm, Harbourneford, South
Brent, Devon TQ10 9DT
T: (01364) 72513
F: (01364) 73808
E: ken.tinkler@hemscott.net

HARCOMBE
Devon

Chapel Cottage ★★★
Contact: Jean Bartlett Cottage
Holidays The Old Dairy, Fore
Street, Beer, Seaton, Devon
EX12 3JB
T: (01297) 23221 & 20973
F: (01297) 23303
E: jeanb@netbreaks.com
I: www.netbreaks.com/jeanb

Harcombe House ★★★★
Contact: Mr Dave Matthews,
Lyme Bay Holiday Cottages,
Boshouse, 44 Church Street,
Lyme Regis, Dorset DT7 3DA
T: (01297) 443363

HARDINGTON MANDEVILLE
Somerset

Stable Cottage ★★★
Contact: Mr Peter Morris, Farm
& Cottage Holidays, Victoria
House, 12 Fore Street, Northam,
Bideford, Devon EX39 1AW
T: (01237) 479146
F: (01237) 421512
E: farmcott@cix.co.uk
I: www.farmcott.co.uk

HARLYN BAY
Cornwall

Harlyn Farmhouse ★★★
Contact: Mrs Hazel Perry, 35
Westbury Hill, Westbury-on-
Trym, Bristol BS9 3AG
T: (0117) 9624831
F: (0117) 9624831
E: hazel@sperry1.demon.co.uk

**No 1 Harlyn Bay Cottages
Rating Applied For**
Contact: Mrs Sally Albright, 10
Trewithan Parc, Lostwithiel,
Cornwall PL22 OBD
T: (01208) 873856
F: (01208) 873856
E: trewithan@hotmail.com

HARTLAND
Devon

Corner Cottage ★★★
Contact: Mr & Mrs DH&E O'Dell,
Corner Cottage, End Cottage,
Elmscot, Hartland, Bideford,
Devon EX39 6ES
T: (01237) 441620

Ford Hill Cottage ★★
Contact: Marsden's Cottage
Holidays, 2 The Square,
Braunton, Devon EX33 2JB
T: (01271) 813777
F: (01271) 813664
E: holidays@marsdens.co.uk
I: www.marsdens.co.uk

Lower Elmscott Farm ★★★
Contact: Mr Peter Morris, Farm
& Cottage Holidays, Victoria
House, 12 Fore Street, Northam,
Bideford, Devon EX39 1AW
T: (01237) 479146
F: (01237) 421512
E: farmcott@cix.co.uk
I: www.farmcott.co.uk

Rosedown Cottages ★★★★
Contact: Miss Michelle du Toit,
Rosedown Cottages, Rosedown
Farm, Hartland, Bideford, Devon
EX39 6AH
T: (01237) 441333
E: michelle@rosedown.co.uk
I: www.rosedown.co.uk

Yapham Cottages ★★★
Contact: Mrs J Young, Yapham
Farm, Hartland, Bideford, Devon
EX39 6AN
T: (01237) 441916
E: jane.yapham@virgin.net

Establishments printed in blue have a detailed entry in this guide

HAWKCHURCH
Devon

Angel Farm Apartment (X4277) ★★★
Contact: Lyme Bay Holidays, Boshouse, 44 Church Street, Lyme Regis, Dorset DT7 3DA
T: (01297) 443363
F: (01297) 445576
E: email@lymebayholidays.co.uk
I: www.lymebayholidays.co.uk

Castle House Cottage W4210 ★★★
Contact: Lyme Bay Holidays, Boshouse, 44 Church Street, Lyme Regis, Dorset DT7 3DA
T: (01297) 443363
F: (01297) 445576
E: email@lymebayholidays.co.uk
I: www.lymebayholidays.co.uk

Northay Farm ★★★
Contact: Mrs D Olof, Northay Farm, Hawkchurch, Axminster, Devon EX13 5UU
T: (01297) 678591

HAWKRIDGE
Somerset

West Hollowcombe Cottages ★★★
Contact: Mr Peter Morris, Farm & Cottage Holidays, Victoria House, 12 Fore Street, Northam, Bideford, Devon EX39 1AW
T: (01237) 479146
F: (01237) 421512
E: farmcott@cix.co.uk
I: www.farmcott.co.uk

HAYLE
Cornwall

Kernow ★★
Contact: Holiday Homes & Cottages South West, 365A Torquay Road, Paignton, Devon TQ3 2BT
T: (01803) 663650
F: (01803) 664037
E: holcotts@aol.com
I: www.swcottages.co.uk

Manor House & Corn Barn ★★★★
Contact: Powell's Cottage Holidays, High Street, Saundersfoot, Dyfed SA69 9EJ
T: (01834) 812791
F: (01834) 811731
E: info@powells.co.uk
I: www.powells.co.uk

Nankervis ★★★
Contact: Cornish Cottage Holidays, The Old Turnpike Dairy, Godolphin Road, Helston, Cornwall TR13 8AA
T: (01326) 573808
F: (01326) 564992
E: enquiry@cornishcottageholidays.co.uk
I: www.cornishcottageholidays.co.uk

Truthwall Farm ★★★
Contact: Mrs S Goldsworthy, Truthwall Farm, Leedstown, Hayle, Cornwall TR27 5EU
T: (01736) 850266

HEANTON
Devon

Grange House ★★★★
Contact: Marsden's Cottage Holidays, 2 The Square, Braunton, Devon EX33 2JB
T: (01271) 813777
F: (01271) 813664
E: holidays@marsdens.co.uk
I: www.marsdens.co.uk

HEDDINGTON
Wiltshire

Harley Bungalow ★★
Contact: Mrs M Fox, Harley Bungalow, Harley Farm, Heddington, Calne, Wiltshire SN11 0PS
T: (01380) 850214
F: (01380) 850214

HELE
Devon

Hele Payne Farm Cottages ★★★★
Contact: Mrs S A Maynard, Hele Payne Farm Cottages, Hele Payne Farm, Hele, Exeter, Devon EX5 4PH
T: (01392) 881356 & 881530
F: (01392) 881530
E: hele-payne@tinyworld.co.uk

HELFORD
Cornwall

Christmas Cottage ★★★
Contact: Cornish Cottage Holidays, Godolphin Road, Helston, Cornwall TR13 8AA
T: (01326) 573808
F: (01326) 564992
E: enquiry@cornishcottageholidays.co.uk
I: www.cornishcottageholidays.co.uk

Chy an Treth ★★
Contact: Helford River Holidays, The Boat House, Helford Passage, Falmouth, Cornwall TR11 5LB
T: (01326) 250278
F: (01326) 251102
E: enquiries@holidaycornwall.co.uk
I: www.holidaycornwall.co.uk

Courtyard 9c ★★★
Contact: Helford River Holidays, The Boat House, Helford Passage, Falmouth, Cornwall TR11 5LB
T: (01326) 250278
F: (01326) 251102
E: enquiries@holidaycornwall.co.uk
I: www.holidaycornwall.co.uk

1 Demelza ★★★
Contact: Helford River Holidays, The Boat House, Helford Passage, Falmouth, Cornwall TR11 5LB
T: (01326) 250278
F: (01326) 251102
E: enquiries@holidaycornwall.co.uk
I: www.holidaycornwall.co.uk

2 Demelza ★★★
Contact: Helford River Holidays, The Boat House, Helford Passage, Falmouth, Cornwall TR11 5LB
T: (01326) 250278
F: (01326) 251102
E: enquiries@holidaycornwall.co.uk
I: www.holidaycornwall.co.uk

3 Demelza ★★★
Contact: Helford River Holidays, The Boat House, Helford Passage, Falmouth, Cornwall TR11 5LB
T: (01326) 250278
F: (01326) 251102
E: enquiries@holidaycornwall.co.uk
I: www.holidaycornwall.co.uk

4 Demelza ★★★
Contact: Helford River Holidays, The Boat House, Helford Passage, Falmouth, Cornwall TR11 5LB
T: (01326) 250278
F: (01326) 251102
E: enquiries@holidaycornwall.co.uk
I: www.holidaycornwall.co.uk

Pirates Den ★★★
Contact: Helford River Holidays, The Boat House, Helford Passage, Falmouth, Cornwall TR11 5LB
T: (01326) 250278
F: (01326) 251102
E: enquiries@holidaycornwall.co.uk
I: www.holidaycornwall.co.uk

Riverside ★★★★
Contact: Helford River Holidays, The Boat House, Helford Passage, Falmouth, Cornwall TR11 5LB
T: (01326) 250278
F: (01326) 251102
E: enquiries@holidaycornwall.co.uk
I: www.holidaycornwall.co.uk

Strand ★★★
Contact: Helford River Holidays, The Boat House, Helford Passage, Falmouth, Cornwall TR11 5LB
T: (01326) 250278
F: (01326) 251102
E: enquiries@holidaycornwall.co.uk
I: www.holidaycornwall.co.uk

Treath Vean ★★★
Contact: Helford River Holidays, The Boat House, Helford Passage, Falmouth, Cornwall TR11 5LB
T: (01326) 250278
F: (01326) 251102
E: enquiries@holidaycornwall.co.uk
I: www.holidaycornwall.co.uk

HELSTON
Cornwall

Chy-an-Ity Bras ★★★
Contact: Ms C Bordeaux, Carne Haven, Gillan Cove, Manaccan, Helston, Cornwall TR12 6HF
T: (01326) 231668

Seagulls ★★★
Contact: Cornish Cottage Holidays, The Old Turnpike Dairy, Godolphin Road, Helston, Cornwall TR13 8AA
T: (01326) 573808
F: (01326) 564992
E: enquiry@cornishcountryholidays.co.uk
I: www.cornishcottageholidays.co.uk

Tregevis Farm ★★★★
Contact: Mrs J A Bray, Tregevis Farm, St Martin, Helston, Cornwall TR12 6DN
T: (01326) 231265

HELSTONE
Cornwall

Mayrose Farm ★★★
Contact: Mr Clive Ahrens, Mayrose Farm, Helstone, Camelford, Cornwall PL32 9RN
T: (01840) 213509 & 213507
F: (01840) 213509
E: mayrosefarm@hotmail.com

HEMYOCK
Devon

Chapel Cottage ★★★
Contact: Mrs Anthea Edwards, Chapel Farm, Culm Davy, Hemyock, Cullompton, Devon EX15 3UR
T: (01823) 680430

HENSTRIDGE
Somerset

The Coach House ★★★★★
Contact: HIB CH22, Holiday Cottages Group, Spring Mill, Earby, Barnoldswick, Lancashire BB94 0AA
T: (01282) 445096
F: (01282) 844299
E: ch.sales@ttgihg.co.uk
I: www.country-holidays.co.uk

Quiet Corner Cottage and Cartshed Cottage ★★★★
Contact: Mr and Mrs B Thompson, Quiet Corner Farm, Henstridge, Somerset BA8 0RA
T: (01963) 363045
F: (01963) 363045

HENTON
Somerset

The Coach House ★★★
Contact: CH ref: 11120, Holiday Cottages Group Owner Services Dept, Spring Mill, Earby, Barnoldswick, Lancashire BB18 6RN
T: (01282) 445096
F: (01282) 844299
E: ch.sales@ttgihg.co.uk
I: www.country-holidays.co.uk

HERODSFOOT
Cornwall

Coombe Farm Holiday Cottages ★★★★
Contact: Mrs Claire Trevelyan, Coombe Farm Holiday Cottages, Coombe Farm, Herodsfoot, Liskeard, Cornwall PL14 4RS
T: (01579) 320548 & 321789
F: (01579) 321789
E: trevelyan@coombe-farm.co.uk
I: www.coombe-farm.co.uk

HEYWOOD
Wiltshire

Pine Lodge ★
Contact: Mrs Mary Prince, Lea Cottage, 12 Church Road, Heywood, Westbury, Wiltshire BA13 4LP
T: (01373) 822949
E: Pinelodgex@aol.com

HIGH BICKINGTON
Devon

Yelland Farm ★★★★
Contact: Mrs P Woollacott, Yelland Farm, High Bickington, Umberleigh, Devon EX37 9BX
T: (01769) 560666
F: (01769) 560666
E: holiday@yellandfarm.co.uk
I: www.yellandfarm.co.uk

HIGHAMPTON
Devon

Legge Farm Coarse Fishery ★★
Contact: Mrs & Mr Rosemary & Graham Hall, Legge Farm Coarse Fishery, Church Road, Highampton, Beaworthy, Devon EX21 5LF
T: (01409) 231464

HIGHBRIDGE
Somerset

164 Burnham Road ★★
Contact: Mrs Carolyn Boley, 5 Charlestone Road, Burnham-on-Sea, Somerset TA8 2AP
T: (01278) 788265 & 787177

HILFIELD
Dorset

Good Hope Studio Flat ★★★
Contact: Mrs Caroline Frew, The Good Hope, Hillfield, Dorchester, Dorset DT2 7BD
T: (01963) 210551
E: caroline@thegoodhope.co.uk
I: www.thegoodhope.co.uk

HILPERTON
Wiltshire

Ashton Lodge Cottage ★★★
Contact: Mrs D F Richards, Ashton Lodge Cottage, Ashton Lodge, Ashton Road, Hilperton, Trowbridge, Wiltshire BA14 7QY
T: (01225) 751420
F: 0870 130 7729
E: dfrichards@ashtonlodge. freeserve.co.uk

HINTON ST GEORGE
Somerset

Old Farm ★★★
Contact: Mr & Mrs Khan-Davis, Old Farm, Hinton St George, Somerset TA17 8SA
T: (01460) 72553
E: khandavis@btinternet.com

**Summer Hill Cottage
Rating Applied For**
Contact: Mr L Farris, Summer Hill Cottage, Niddons House, Green Street, Hinton St George, Somerset TA17 8SQ
T: (01460) 74475

○ HOLBETON
Devon

The Laurels (Apartment) ★★★
Contact: Yealm Holidays, 8 Whittingham Road, Collaton, Yealmpton, Plymouth, Devon PL8 2NF
T: (01752) 872712
F: (01752) 873173
E: info@yealm-holidays.co.uk
I: www.yealm-holidays.co.uk

HOLCOMBE ROGUS
Devon

Whipcott Heights ★★★★
Contact: Mrs S M Gallagher, Whipcott Heights, Holcombe Rogus, Wellington, Somerset TA21 0NA
T: (01823) 672339
F: (01823) 672339
E: whipcott@aol.com

HOLSWORTHY
Devon

Beech House ★★★★
Contact: Mrs M Heard, Thorne Park, Chilsworthy, Holsworthy, Devon EX22 7BL
T: (01409) 253339
F: (01409) 253339

Hole Farm ★★★
Contact: Mr Peter Morris, Farm & Cottage Holidays, Victoria House, 12 Fore Street, Northam, Bideford, Devon EX39 1AW
T: (01237) 479146
F: (01237) 421512
E: farmcott@cix.co.uk
I: www.farmcott.co.uk

Leworthy Cottage ★★★
Contact: Mrs Patricia Jennings, Leworthy Cottage, Leworthy Farmhouse, Lower Leworthy, Pyworthy, Holsworthy, Devon EX22 6SJ
T: (01409) 259469

Thorne Manor Farm ★★
Contact: Mr & Mrs SW Graham, Thorne Manor Farm, Holsworthy, Devon EX22 7JD
T: (01409) 253685 & 0797 038059

Yellowlands Farm ★★★★
Contact: Mr & Mrs Bowater, Helpful Holidays, Mill Street, Chagford, Newton Abbot, Devon TQ13 8AW
T: (01647) 433593
F: (01647) 433694
E: help@helpfulholidays.com
I: www.helpfulholidays.com

HOLYWELL BAY
Cornwall

Pennasville Holidays ★★★–★★★★
Contact: Mrs S M Penna, Pennasville Holidays, c/o Nantewynn House, Holywell Bay, Newquay, Cornwall TR8 5PP
T: (01637) 830447
F: (01637) 830447

HONITON
Devon

Treaslake Holiday Cottages ★★★★–★★★★★
Contact: Mr & Mrs Paul & Julia Hardy, Treaslake Holiday Cottages, Buckerell, Honiton, Devon EX14 3EP
T: (01404) 850292
F: (01404) 850292
E: devoncottage@breathe.com
I: www.devoncottage.com

HOPE COVE
Devon

Blue Bay Apartments ★★★
Contact: Mrs J H Moon, Little Orchard, Kellaton, Kingsbridge, Devon TQ7 2ES
T: (01548) 511400
F: (01548) 511400
E: bbayapts@aol.co.uk

Hope Barton Barns ★★★★
Contact: Mike & Judy Tromans, Hope Barton Barns, Bolberry Road, Hope Cove, Kingsbridge, Devon TQ7 3HT
T: (01548) 561393
F: (01548) 560938
E: info@hopebarton.co.uk
I: www.hopebarton.co.uk

Ocean View ★★★★
Contact: Mrs Cuming, Atlantic Lodge, Hope Cove, Kingsbridge, Devon TQ7 3HH
T: (01548) 561873

Seascape ★★★
Contact: Mrs H Kolb, 57 The Whiteway, Cirencester, Gloucestershire GL7 2HQ
T: (01285) 654781
F: (01285) 654781
E: kolbe@btinternet.com
I: www.englishholidayhouses. co.uk

Thornlea Mews Holiday Cottages★★★
Contact: Mr & Mrs John & Ann Wilton, Thornlea Mews Holiday Cottages, Hope Cove, Salcombe, Devon TQ7 3HB
T: (01548) 561319
F: (01548) 561319
E: thornleamews@rdplus.net

HORN'S CROSS
Devon

The Cottage ★★★
Contact: Mr PM Morris, Farm & Cottage Holidays, Victoria House, 12 Fore Street, Northam, Bideford, Devon EX39 1AW
T: (01237) 479146
F: (01237) 421512
E: farmcott@cix.co.uk
I: www.farmcott.co.uk

HORSINGTON
Somerset

Lois Barns ★★★
Contact: Mr and Mrs P Constant, Lois Barns, Lois Farm, Horsington, Templecombe, Somerset BA8 0EW
T: (01963) 370496
F: (01963) 370496
E: p.constant@talk21.com
I: www.somerset-farm-holiday. co.uk

HORTON
Gloucestershire

Bridle Path Cottage ★★★
Contact: Mr Clive Sykes, Sykes Cottages, York House, York Street, Chester, CH1 3LR
T: (01244) 345700
F: (01244) 321442
E: info@sykescottages.co.uk
I: www.sykescottages.co.uk

HUISH CHAMPFLOWER
Somerset

The Cottage ★★★
Contact: Mrs Mary Reynolds, Manor Farmhouse, Huish Champflower, Taunton, Somerset TA4 2EY
T: (01984) 624915
F: (01984) 624915
E: reynolds@aol.com

HUNTSHAW
Devon

Twitchen Farmhouse ★★★★
Contact: Ms Debby Appleby, Twitchen Farmhouse, Twitchen Farm, Huntshaw, Torrington, Devon EX38 7HQ
T: (01271) 858507 & 07808 494860
F: (01271) 858625
E: twitchenfarm@aol.com
I: www.twitchen-farm.co.uk

HUXHAM
Devon

Bussells Farm ★★★★
Contact: Mr & Mrs RS Downey, Bussells Farm, Huxham, Exeter, Devon EX5 4EN
T: (01392) 841238
F: (01392) 841345
E: rob.downey@bussellsfarm. co.uk
I: www.bussellsfarm.co.uk

IDEFORD
Devon

George House Studio ★★★
Contact: Mrs J L Dunford, George House Studio, Fore Street, Ideford, Chudleigh, Newton Abbot, Devon TQ13 0AY
T: (01626) 853483
F: (01626) 853483
E: bdunfo557@aol.com

Well Barn ★★★
Contact: Mrs L J Tolley, Well Barn, Olchard, Sandygate, Newton Abbot, Devon TQ12 3GX
T: (01626) 853830 & 07879 430044

ILFRACOMBE
Devon

The Admirals House ★★★★
Contact: Miss D Marshall, The Ilfracombe Carlton Hotel, Runnacleave Road, Ilfracombe, Devon EX34 8AR
T: (01271) 862446 & 863711
F: (01271) 865379

Benricks ★★
Contact: Marsden's Cottage Holidays, 2 The Square, Braunton, Devon EX33 2JB
T: (01271) 813777
F: (01271) 813664
E: holidays@marsdens.co.uk
I: www.marsdens.co.uk

Establishments printed in blue have a detailed entry in this guide

Butterfly Farmhouse ★★★
Contact: Mr & Mrs S Ellis, Bunch of Grapes, 36 High Street, Ilfracombe, Devon EX34 9DA
T: (01271) 863276

Cheyne Flat ★★★
Contact: Marsden's Cottage Holidays, 2 The Square, Braunton, Devon EX33 2JB
T: (01271) 813777
F: (01271) 813664
E: holidays@marsdens.co.uk
I: www.marsdens.co.uk

Coastguards Cottage ★★★
Contact: Marsden's Cottage Holidays, 2 The Square, Braunton, Devon EX33 2JB
T: (01271) 813777
F: (01271) 813664
E: holidays@marsdens.co.uk
I: www.marsdens.co.uk

Colesbourne House ★★–★★★
Contact: Mrs P M Lawson, Colesbourne House, Crofts Lea Park, Ilfracombe, Devon EX34 9PN
T: (01271) 863126

Cornmill Cottage ★★★★
Contact: Marsden's Cottage Holidays, 2 The Square, Braunton, Devon EX33 2JB
T: (01271) 813777
F: (01271) 813664
E: holidays@marsdens.co.uk
I: www.marsdens.co.uk

The Dell ★★★
Contact: Marsden's Cottage Holidays, 2 The Square, Braunton, Devon EX33 2JB
T: (01271) 813777
F: (01271) 813664
E: holidays@marsdens.co.uk
I: www.marsdens.co.uk

Farthings Nest ★★★
Contact: Marsden's Cottage Holidays, 2 The Square, Braunton, Devon EX33 2JB
T: (01271) 813777
F: (01271) 813664
E: holidays@marsdens.co.uk
I: www.marsdens.co.uk

Horne Cottage & Horne House ★★★
Contact: Marsden's Cottage Holidays, 2 The Square, Braunton, Devon EX33 2JB
T: (01271) 813777
F: (01271) 813664
E: holidays@marsdens.co.uk
I: www.marsdens.co.uk

Lantern Cottage ★★★
Contact: Lantern Cottage, Old Coastguard Cottage, Ilfracombe, Devon EX34

The Lodge, Stables & Paddocks ★★★
Contact: Marsden's Cottage Holidays, 2 The Square, Braunton, Devon EX33 2JB
T: (01271) 813777
F: (01271) 813664
E: holidays@marsdens.co.uk
I: www.marsdens.co.uk

The Mill House ★★★★
Contact: Marsden's Cottage Holidays, 2 The Square, Braunton, Devon EX33 2JB
T: (01271) 813777
F: (01271) 813664
E: holidays@marsdens.co.uk
I: www.marsdens.co.uk

Mimosa Cottage ★★★
Contact: Marsden's Cottage Holidays, 2 The Square, Braunton, Devon EX33 2JB
T: (01271) 813777
F: (01271) 813664
E: holidays@marsdens.co.uk
I: www.marsdens.co.uk

Mostyn ★★★
Contact: Marsden's Cottage Holidays, 2 The Square, Braunton, Devon EX33 2JB
T: (01271) 813777
F: (01271) 813664
E: holidays@marsdens.co.uk
I: www.marsdens.co.uk

Norwood Holiday Flats ★★★
Contact: Mrs B Bulled, Norwood Holiday Flats, Highfield Road, Ilfracombe, Devon EX34 9LH
T: (01271) 862370

The Round House ★★★★
Contact: Marsden's Cottage Holidays, 2 The Square, Braunton, Devon EX33 2JB
T: (01271) 813777
F: (01271) 813664
E: holidays@marsdens.co.uk
I: www.marsdens.co.uk

The Stables ★★★
Contact: Marsden's Cottage Holidays, 2 The Square, Braunton, Devon EX33 2JB
T: (01271) 813777
F: (01271) 813664
E: holidays@marsdens.co.uk
I: www.marsdens.co.uk

White Pebbles ★★★
Contact: Mrs J M Foreshew, White Pebbles, The Torrs, Torrs Walk Avenue, Ilfracombe, Devon EX34 8AU
T: (01271) 864579

ILLOGAN
Cornwall

Carn Vista ★★★★
Contact: Cornish Cottage Holidays, The Old Turnpike Dairy, Godolphin Road, Helston, Cornwall TR13 8AA
T: (01326) 573808
F: (01326) 564992
E: enquiry@cornishcottageholidays.co.uk
I: www.cornishcottageholidays.co.uk

ILMINSTER
Somerset

Myrtle House ★★★★
Contact: Mr & Mrs G Denman, 16 Challis Green, Barrington, Cambridge CB2 5RJ
T: (01223) 871294
E: gordon.denman@earthling.net
I: www.appleorchard.freeserve.co.uk

ILSINGTON
Devon

The Old Forge ★★★★
Contact: Powell's Cottage Holidays, High Street, Saundersfoot, Dyfed SA69 9EJ
T: (01834) 812791
F: (01834) 811731
E: info@powells.co.uk
I: www.powells.co.uk

INSTOW
Devon

Garden House ★★★★
Contact: Marsden's Cottage Holidays, 2 The Square, Braunton, Devon EX33 2JB
T: (01271) 813777
F: (01271) 813664
E: holidays@marsdens.co.uk
I: www.marsdens.co.uk

Inglenook Cottage ★★★★
Contact: Marsden's Cottage Holidays, 2 The Square, Braunton, Devon EX33 2JB
T: (01271) 813777
F: (01271) 813664
E: holidays@marsdens.co.uk
I: www.marsdens.co.uk

The Old Dairy ★★★★
Contact: Marsden's Cottage Holidays, 2 The Square, Braunton, Devon EX33 2JB
T: (01271) 813777
F: (01271) 813664
E: holidays@marsdens.co.uk
I: www.marsdens.co.uk

Orchard Farm ★★★
Contact: Mr Gordon Steer, Orchard Farm, Instow, Bideford, Devon EX39 4LR
T: (01271) 860517

IPPLEPEN
Devon

Bulleigh Park ★★★
Contact: Mrs Angela Dallyn, Bulleigh Park, Bulleigh Park Farm, Ipplepen, Newton Abbot, Devon TQ12 5UA
T: (01803) 872254
F: (01803) 872254
E: bulleigh@lineone.net

ISLES OF SCILLY

3 & 4 Well Cross ★
Contact: Mr A M Perry, Treboeth Guest House, St Mary's, Isles of Scilly TR21 0HX
T: (01720) 422548

An Oberva ★★
Contact: Mrs J Berryman, Chy an Mor, 4 Fore Street, Porthleven, Helston, Cornwall TR13 9HQ
T: (01326) 574113

Boswartreth ★★★
Contact: Island Properties Holidays Lettings & Management, Porthmellon, St Mary's, Isles of Scilly TR21 0JY
T: (01720) 422082
F: (01720) 422211
E: enquiries@islesofscillyholidays.com
I: www.islesofscillyholidays.com

Green Farm Cottage ★★★
Contact: Mr D Wright, Green Farm, St Mary's, Isles of Scilly TR21 0NX
T: (01720) 422324
F: (01720) 423406
E: wright.d@btconnect.com
I: www.scillybulbs.co.uk

Harbour View ★★★
Contact: Mrs L Hopkins, Harbour View, Bryher, Isles of Scilly TR23 0PR
T: (01720) 422222

Holy Vale Holiday Houses ★★★
Contact: Mr & Mrs JR&K Banfield, Holy Vale Holiday Houses, Holy Vale Farmhouse, St Mary's, Isles of Scilly TR21 0NT
T: (01720) 422429
F: (01720) 422429
E: johnkayholyvale@lineone.net

Leumeah House ★★
Contact: Island Properties, Porthmellon, St Mary's, Isles of Scilly
T: (01720) 422082
F: (01720) 422211
E: enquiries@islesofscillyholidays.com
I: www.islesofscillyholidays.com

Moonrakers Holiday Flats ★★★
Contact: Mr R J Gregory, Moonrakers Holiday Flats, St Mary's, Isles of Scilly TR21 0JF
T: (01720) 422717
E: gregory@moonrakersholidayflats.fsnet.co.uk
I: www.moonrakersholidayflats.fsnet.co.uk

Mount Flagon ★★★–★★★★
Contact: Mr & Mrs R&J Crawford, Mount Flagon, Harry's Walls, St Mary's, Isles of Scilly TR21 0NE
T: (01720) 422598
F: (01720) 422529

Pednbrose ★★★
Contact: Miss E H Astbury, 23 Wonford Road, Exeter, EX2 4LH
T: (01392) 250050

Puffin Burrow ★★★★
Contact: Mrs Carol Sargeant, Willow Tree House, Kingstone Winslow, Swindon, Wiltshire SN6 8NG
T: (01793) 710062
F: (01793) 710387

Seaways Flower Farm & Standing Stone ★★★–★★★★
Contact: Mrs Juliet May, Seaways Flower Farm & Standing Stone, Porth Low, St Mary's, Isles of Scilly TR21 0NF
T: (01720) 422845
F: (01720) 423224

Trefoil 1 Godolphin House ★★★
Contact: Mr A C Terry, School Bungalow, St Martin's, Isles of Scilly TR25 0QL
T: (01720) 422329

IVYBRIDGE
Devon

Almora ★★★★
Contact: Powell's Cottage
Holidays, High Street,
Saundersfoot, Dyfed SA69 9EJ
T: (01834) 812791
F: (01834) 811731
E: info@powells.co.uk
I: www.powells.co.uk

Beacon Cottage ★★★
Contact: Mrs S Edwards,
Moorhedge Farm, David's Lane,
Ivybridge, Devon PL21 0DP
T: (01752) 894820
F: (01752) 894820

JACOBSTOW
Cornwall

Pinestone Cottage ★★★
Contact: Mrs B Knight,
Pinestone Cottage, The Owl
House, Southcott, Jacobstow,
Bude, Cornwall EX23 0BP
T: (01840) 230364
F: (01840) 230364

KENTISBURY FORD
Devon

Friars Cottages ★★★★
Contact: Mr & Mrs Malcolm &
Janet Tate, Friars Farm,
Kentisbury Ford, Barnstaple,
Devon EX31 4ND
T: (01271) 882207

KENTON
Devon

1 Devon Cottage ★★★★★
Contact: Ms Judith Dickinson,
P.O. Box 2182, East Hampton,
New York 11937, USA
T: (01626) 891702

KEWSTOKE
North Somerset

Norton Court Farm ★★★
Contact: CH ref: 11376, Holiday
Cottages Group Owner Services
Dept, Spring Mill, Earby,
Barnoldswick, Lancashire
BB18 6RN
T: (01282) 445096
F: (01282) 844299
E: ch.sales@ttgihg.co.uk
I: www.country-holidays.co.uk

KILLIVOSE
Cornwall

The Old Barn ★★★★
Contact: Cornish Cottage
Holidays, The Old Turnpike Dairy,
Godolphin Road, Helston,
Cornwall TR13 8AA
T: (01326) 573808
F: (01326) 564992
E: enquiry@
cornishcottageholidays.co.uk
I: www.cornishcottageholidays.
co.uk

KILMINGTON
Devon

Little Thatch ★★★★
Contact: Lyme Bay Holidays,
Boshouse, 44 Church Street,
Lyme Regis, Dorset DT7 3DA
T: (01297) 443363
F: (01297) 445576
E: email@lymebayholidays.
co.uk
I: www.lymebayholidays.co.uk

Orfield ★★★
Contact: Milkbere Cottage
Holidays, Milkbere House, 14
Fore Street, Seaton, Devon
EX12 2LA
T: (01297) 20729
F: (01297) 24831
E: info@milkbere.com
I: www.milkbere.com

KING'S NYMPTON
Devon

Venn Farm Holidays ★★★
Contact: Mrs I Martin, Venn
Farm Holidays, Venn Farm,
King's Nympton, Umberleigh,
Devon EX37 9TR
T: (01769) 572448
E: isla@bmvenn.demon.co.uk
I: www.bmvenn.demon.co.uk

KINGSBRIDGE
Devon

**The Laurels, Coach House &
Coachmans Lodge
★★★–★★★★**
Contact: Mrs B J Baker, South
Allington House, Chivelstone,
Kingsbridge, Devon TQ7 2NB
T: (01548) 511272
F: (01548) 511421
E: barbara@sthallingtonbnb.
demon.co.uk
I: www.sthallingtonbnb.demon.
co.uk

**Malston Mill Farm Holiday
Cottages ★★★★**
Contact: Mr and Mrs Tony and
Linda Gresham, Malston Mill
Farm Holiday Cottages,
Kingsbridge, Devon TQ7 2DR
T: (01548) 852518
F: (01548) 854084
E: gresham@malstonmill.fsnet.
co.uk
I: www.webmachine.
co.uk/malstonmill

North Upton Barns ★★★
Contact: Mr and Mrs W T
Gunning, North Upton,
Bantham, Kingsbridge, Devon
TQ7 3AB
T: (01548) 560508 & 562114

Reads Farm ★★★
Contact: Mrs A Pethybridge,
Reads Farm, Loddiswell,
Kingsbridge, Devon TQ7 4RT
T: (01548) 550317
F: (01548) 550317

Sloop Inn ★★★★
Contact: Mr N Girling, Sloop Inn,
Bantham, Kingsbridge, Devon
TQ7 3AJ
T: (01548) 560489 & 560215
F: (01548) 561940

Swan Cottage ★★★
Contact: Mr & Mrs Bowater,
Helpful Holidays, Mill Street,
Chagford, Newton Abbot, Devon
TQ13 8AW
T: (01647) 433593
F: (01647) 433694
E: help@helpfulholidays.com
I: www.helpfulholidays.com

**Trouts Holiday Apartments
★★★**
Contact: Mrs Jill Norman,
Prospect Cottage Trouts Holiday
Apartments, South Hallsands,
Kingsbridge, Devon TQ7 2EY
T: (01548) 511296
F: (01548) 511296
E: troutshallsands@
netscapeonline.co.uk
I: www.troutsholidays.co.uk

KINGSDON
Somerset

The Lodge ★★★
Contact: Mrs Jo Furneaux, The
Lodge, Kingsdon, Somerton,
Somerset TA11 7LE
T: (01935) 841194

KINGSHEANTON
Devon

Huish Cottage ★★★
Contact: Marsden's Cottage
Holidays, 2 The Square,
Braunton, Devon EX33 2JB
T: (01271) 813777
F: (01271) 813664
E: holidays@marsdens.co.uk
I: www.marsdens.co.uk

The Welkin ★★★★
Contact: Marsden's Cottage
Holidays, 2 The Square,
Braunton, Devon EX33 2JB
T: (01271) 813777
F: (01271) 813664
E: holidays@marsdens.co.uk
I: www.marsdens.co.uk

KINGSTEIGNTON
Devon

Plumb Corner ★★★★
Contact: Holiday Homes &
Cottages South West, 365A
Torquay Road, Paignton, Devon
TQ3 2BT
T: (01803) 663650
F: (01803) 664037
E: holcotts@aol.com
I: www.swcottages.co.uk

KINGSTON ST MARY
Somerset

Rose Cottage ★★★
Contact: CH ref: 6152, Holiday
Cottages Group Owner Services
Department, Spring Mill, Earby,
Barnoldswick, Lancashire
BB18 6RN
T: (01282) 445096
F: (01282) 844299
E: ch.sales@ttgihg.co.uk
I: www.country-holidays.co.uk

KINGSWEAR
Devon

1 Agra Villas ★★★
Contact: Holiday Homes &
Cottages South West, 365a
Torquay Road, Paignton, Devon
TQ3 2BT
T: (01803) 663650
F: (01803) 664037
E: holcotts@aol.com
I: www.swcottages.co.uk

**Number 5
Rating Applied For**
Contact: CH Ref: 12809, Holiday
Cottages Group Owner Services
Department, Spring Mill, Earby,
Barnoldswick, Lancashire
BB94 0AA
T: (01282) 445096
F: (01282) 844299
E: ch.sales@ttgihg.co.uk
I: www.country-holidays.co.uk

KNOWLE
Devon

Lee Ford ★★★–★★★★
Contact: Mr N Lindsay-Fynn, Lee
Ford, White/Lodge Cottages,
Studio Apartment, Knowle,
Budleigh Salterton, Devon
EX9 7AJ
T: (01395) 445894
F: (01395) 446219
E: crescent@leeford.co.uk

LACOCK
Wiltshire

**Cyder House and Cheese House
★★★★**
Contact: Mr and Mrs Philip &
Susan King, Cyder House and
Cheese House, Wick Farm, Wick
Lane, Lacock, Chippenham,
Wiltshire SN15 2LU
T: (01249) 730244 &
07957 417915
F: (01249) 730072
E: kingsilverlands2@btinternet.
com

**The Paddocks Whitehall
Garden Centre★★★**
Contact: CH Ref: 13672, Country
Holidays, Spring Mill, Earby,
Barnoldswick, Lancashire
BB18 6RN
T: (01282) 844284

LADOCK
Cornwall

Higher Hewas ★★★★
Contact: Mrs Pamela Blake,
Lower Hewas, Ladock, Truro,
Cornwall TR2 4QH
T: (01726) 882318

LAMORNA COVE
Cornwall

Sunnyvale No 1 ★★
Contact: Mr Simon Blunt, 7
Sea-View Terrace, Church Street,
Helston, Cornwall TR13 8NL
T: (01736) 763608

LAMYATT
Somerset

Hillside Cottage ★★★★
Contact: Miss J Candy, 15
Banksia Close, Tiverton, Devon
EX16 6TT
T: (01749) 813451 &
(01884) 243377
E: janet@j-candy.demon.co.uk
I: www.hillside-cottage.com

LANDRAKE
Cornwall

The Coach House ★★★★
Contact: Mrs N Walker, The
Coach House, Lantallack Farm,
Landrake, Saltash, Cornwall
PL12 5AE
T: (01752) 851281
F: (01752) 851281
E: Lantallack@ukgateway.net
I: www.lantallack.co.uk

Establishments printed in blue have a detailed entry in this guide

LANEAST
Cornwall

Trewithen Lodge ★★★
Contact: CH REF: 9489, C/O
Country Holidays Group Owner
Services Dept (ETB), Spring Mill,
Earby, Barnoldswick, Lancashire
BB18 6RN
T: (01282) 445400
F: (01566) 86343
E: sales@ttgihg.co.uk

LANGLEY BURRELL
Wiltshire

Cedarwood ★★★
Contact: Mrs Helen Miflin, Grove
Farm, Sutton Lane, Langley
Burrell, Chippenham, Wiltshire
SN15 4LW
T: (01249) 721500 & 720413
F: (01249) 720413

LANGLEY MARSH
Somerset

Vickery View
Rating Applied For
Contact: Mrs Mariella Hopkins,
Vickery View, The Three
Horseshoes, Langley Marsh,
Taunton, Somerset TA4 2UL
T: (01984) 623763
E: m.hopkins@uk.gateway.net

LANGPORT
Somerset

2 Bow Cottage ★★
Contact: CH ref: 10997, Holiday
Cottages Group Owner Services
Dept, Spring Mill, Earby,
Barnoldswick, Lancashire
BB18 6RN
T: (01282) 445096
F: (01282) 844299
E: ch.sales@ttgihg.co.uk
I: www.country-holidays.co.uk

Drayton Manor Cottage ★★★
Contact: Mrs Sheila Beresford,
Drayton Manor, Drayton,
Langport, Somerset TA10 0LL
T: (01458) 253796
E: peter@celfus.freeserve.co.uk

Hay Loft & Stables ★★★
Contact: Mrs Pauline Pickard,
Hay Loft & Stables, Dairy House
Farm, Muchelney Ham,
Langport, Somerset TA10 0DJ
T: (01458) 253113

Muchelney Ham Farm
★★★-★★★★★
Contact: Mrs Ann Woodborne,
Muchelney Ham Farm,
Muchelney, Langport, Somerset
TA10 0DJ
T: (01458) 250737
F: (01458) 250737
I: www.muchelneyhamfarm.
co.uk

LANGRIDGE
Bath and North East Somerset

Langridge Studio ★★★★
Contact: Mr Brian Shuttleworth,
Langridge House, Langridge,
Bath BA1 9BX
T: (01225) 338874
F: (01225) 338874
E: info@langridge-studio.co.uk
I: www.langridge-studio.co.uk

LANGTON HERRING
Dorset

3 Lower Farm, Chelsea
Cottage, The Brambles, The
Sycamores,★★★★
Contact: Mrs A E Mayo, Higher
Farm, Rodden, Weymouth,
Dorset DT3 4JE
T: (01305) 871347 & 871187
F: (01305) 871347
E: jane@mayo.fsbusiness.co.uk

LANGTREE
Devon

2 Moors View ★★★
Contact: Mr Peter Morris, Farm
& Cottage Holidays, Victoria
House, 12 Fore Street, Northam,
Bideford, Devon EX39 1AW
T: (01237) 479146
F: (01237) 421512
E: farmcott@cix.co.uk
I: www.farmcott.co.uk

LANHYDROCK
Cornwall

Lanhydrock Farm Cottages
★★★-★★★★
Contact: Mrs Chalotte Barrow,
Lanhydrock Farm Cottages
Treffry Farm House, Lanhydrock,
Bodmin, Cornwall PL30 5AF
T: (01208) 75819

LANNER
Cornwall

Little Shalom ★★★
Contact: Powell's Cottage
Holidays, High Street,
Saundersfoot, Dyfed SA69 9EJ
T: (01834) 812791
F: (01834) 811731
E: info@powells.co.uk
I: www.powells.co.uk

LANREATH-BY-LOOE
Cornwall

The Old Rectory ★★★
Contact: Mr and Mrs C Duncan,
The Old Rectory, Lanreath-by-
Looe, Looe, Cornwall PL13 2NU
T: (01503) 220247
F: (01503) 220108
E: ask@oldrectory-lanreath.
co.uk
I: www.oldrectory-lanreath.
co.uk

Oversteps ★★★★
Contact: Cornish Cottage
Holidays, The Old Turnpike Dairy,
Godolphin Road, Helston,
Cornwall TR13 8AA
T: (01326) 573808
F: (01326) 564992
E: enquiry@
cornishcottageholidays.co.uk
I: www.cornishcottageholidays.
co.uk

LANSALLOS
Cornwall

West Kellow Farmhouse
★★★★
Contact: Mrs E Julian, West
Kellow Farmhouse, Lansallos,
Looe, Cornwall PL13 2QL
T: (01503) 272089

LATCHLEY
Cornwall

The Apple Loft ★★★★
Contact: Ms Margaret Blake, The
Apple Loft, Old Solomons Farm,
Latchley, Gunnislake, Cornwall
PL18 9AX
T: (01822) 833242
E: info@oldsolomonsfarm.co.uk
I: www.oldsolomonsfarm.co.uk

LAUNCESTON
Cornwall

Bamham Farm Cottages
★★★-★★★★
Contact: Mrs J A Chapman,
Bamham Farm Cottages, Higher
Bamham Farm, Launceston,
Cornwall PL15 9LD
T: (01566) 772141
F: (01566) 775266
E: jackie@bamhamfarm.co.uk
I: www.cottages-cornwall.co.uk

Langdon Farm Cottage
★★-★★★★★
Contact: Mrs F Rawlinson,
Langdon Farm, Boyton,
Launceston, Cornwall PL15 8NW
T: (01566) 785389
E: g.f.rawlinson@btinternet.com

Swallows ★★★
Contact: Mrs Kathryn Broad,
Lower Dutson Farm, Launceston,
Cornwall PL15 9SP
T: (01566) 776456
F: (01566) 776456
E: francis.broad@btclick.com

Ta Mill ★★★-★★★★★
Contact: Mrs Helen Harvey, Ta
Mill, St Clether, Launceston,
Cornwall PL15 8PS
T: (01840) 261797 &
07778 961819
F: (01840) 261381
E: helen@tamill.co.uk
I: www.tamill.co.uk

Trevadlock Farm Cottages Platt
and Trotters Cottages★★★★
Contact: Mrs Barbara Sleep,
Trevadlock Farm Cottages Platt
and Trotters Cottages,
Trevadlock Farm, Congdon's
Shop, Launceston, Cornwall
PL15 7PW
T: (01566) 782239
F: (01566) 782239
E: trevadlockfarm@compuserve.
com
I: www.trevadlock.co.uk

Wheatley Cottage and Barn
★★★★
Contact: Mrs V Griffin, Wheatley
Cottage and Barn, Wheatley
Farm, Maxworthy, Launceston,
Cornwall PL15 8LY
T: (01566) 781232
F: (01566) 781232
E: wheatfrm@compuserve.com
I: www.chycor.
co.uk/cottages/wheatley

LEE
Devon

Crowness Cottage ★★★
Contact: The Proprietor,
Crowness Cottage, Lee,
Ilfracombe, Devon

Ivy Bank ★★
Contact: Mrs M E Race, Ivy Bank,
Lee, Ilfracombe, Devon EX34 8LN
T: (01271) 862453
F: (01271) 864732

Lincombe House ★★★
Contact: Mr & Mrs Ian & Cynthia
Stuart, Lincombe House, Lee,
Ilfracombe, Devon EX34 8LL
T: (01271) 864834
F: (01271) 864834
E: stuart.lincombehouse@
btinternet.com
I: www.lincombehouse.co.uk

Lower Campscott Farm ★★★
Contact: Mrs M Cowell, Lower
Campscott Farm, Lee,
Ilfracombe, Devon EX34 8LS
T: (01271) 863479
F: (01271) 867639
E: setaside@msn.com

LEIGH
Dorset

1 Church Farm Cottages ★★★
Contact: CH ref: 11740, Holiday
Cottages Group Owner Services
Dept, Spring Mill, Earby,
Barnoldswick, Lancashire
BB18 6RN
T: (01282) 445096
F: (01282) 844299
E: ch.sales@ttgihg.co.uk
I: www.country-holidays.co.uk

LERRYN
Cornwall

Puddleduck Cottage ★★★★
Contact: Estuary Cottages,
Estuary House, Fore Street,
Fowey, Cornwall PL23 1AH
T: (01726) 832965 & 832299
F: (01726) 832866
E: info@estuarycottages.co.uk
I: www.estuarycottages.co.uk

LEWANNICK
Cornwall

Trevadlock Manor & Cottages
★★★
Contact: Mr & Mrs PR Hall,
Trevadlock Manor & Cottages,
Trevadlock Manor, Lewannick,
Launceston, Cornwall PL15 7PW
T: (01566) 782227
E: aspenpartners@trevadlock.
fsnet.co.uk

LEWDOWN
Devon

Lion's Den ★★★
Contact: Mrs Barbara Dawkins,
Lion's Den, Lion Cottage,
Lewdown, Okehampton, Devon
EX20 4BU
T: (01566) 783437 &
(01626) 852770

LEZANT
Cornwall

East Penrest Barn ★★★★★
Contact: Mrs J Rider, East
Penrest Barn, East Penrest,
Lezant, Launceston, Cornwall
PL15 9NR
T: (01579) 370186
F: (01579) 370477
E: jorider@eastpenrest.
freeserve.co.uk
I: www.eastpenrest.freeserve.
co.uk

Trevallen ★★★
Contact: Powell's Cottage
Holidays, High Street,
Saundersfoot, Dyfed SA69 9EJ
T: (01834) 812791
F: (01834) 811731
E: info@powells.co.uk
I: www.powells.co.uk

LIFTON
Devon

The Cider House ★★★
Contact: Mrs Anthea
Sandercock, Dingle's Steam
Village, Milford, Lifton, Devon
PL16 0AT
T: (01566) 783425
F: (01566) 783584

LISKEARD
Cornwall

Beechleigh Cottage ★★★★
Contact: Mrs S Rowe,
Beechleigh Cottage, Tregondale
Farm, Menheniot, Liskeard,
Cornwall PL14 3RG
T: (01579) 342407
F: (01579) 342407
E: tregondale@connectfree.
co.uk
I: www.tregondalefarm.co.uk

Lodge Barton ★★★
Contact: Mrs R Hodin, Lodge
Barton, Lamellion, Liskeard,
Cornwall PL14 4JX
T: (01579) 344432
F: (01579) 344432
E: lodgebart@aol.com
I: www.selectideas.
co.uk/lodgebarton

Lower Trengale Farm ★★★★
Contact: Mrs L Kidd, Lower
Trengale Farm, Liskeard,
Cornwall PL14 6HF
T: (01579) 321019
F: (01579) 321432
E: lkidd@eurobell.co.uk
I: www.trengaleholidaycottages.
co.uk

Wadham Court ★★★★
Contact: Mr & Mrs Bowater,
Helpful Holidays, Mill Street,
Chagford, Newton Abbot, Devon
TQ13 8AW
T: (01647) 433593
F: (01647) 433694
E: help@helpfulholidays.com
I: www.helpfulholidays.com

LITTLE PETHERICK
Cornwall

Pine Lodge ★★★★
Contact: Cornish Horizons,
Higher Trehemborne, St Merryn,
Padstow, Cornwall PL28 8JU
T: (01841) 520889 & 521333
F: (01841) 521523
E: cottages@cornishhorizons.
co.uk
I: www.cornishhorizons.co.uk

Westcreek ★★★★
Contact: Cornish Cottage
Holidays, The Old Turnpike Dairy,
Godolphin Road, Helston,
Cornwall TR13 8AA
T: (01326) 573808
F: (01326) 564992
E: enquiry@
cornishcottageholidays.co.uk
I: www.cornishcottageholidays.
co.uk

LITTLE TORRINGTON
Devon

**Torridge House Cottages
★★-★★★**
Contact: Mrs B Terry, Torridge
House Cottages, Little
Torrington, Torrington, Devon
EX38 8PS
T: (01805) 622542
F: (01805) 622360
I: www.torridgehouse.co.uk

LITTLEHAM
Devon

**Cuckoo's Nest & Robins Nest
★★★★**
Contact: Mr Peter Morris, Farm
& Cottage Holidays, Victoria
House, 12 Fore Street, Bideford,
Devon EX39 1AW
T: (01237) 479146
F: (01237) 421512
E: farmcott@cix.co.uk
I: www.farmcott.co.uk

**Robin Hill Farm Cottages
★★★★**
Contact: Ref:FAD,FKH,FAR,FKJ,
English Country Cottages,
Holiday Cottages Group Owner
Services Department, Spring
Mill, Earby, Barnoldswick,
Lancashire BB94 0AA
T: 0870 5851155

LITTON CHENEY
Dorset

**Baglake Barn and Brewery
Cottage ★★★★-★★★★★**
Contact: Mrs and Mr L Barbour,
Baglake Barn and Brewery
Cottage, Baglake Farm, Litton
Cheney, Dorchester, Dorset
DT2 9AD
T: (01308) 482222

Wheelwrights Cottage ★★★★
Contact: Mrs D C Spicer, 1 Litton
Hill, Litton Cheney, Dorchester,
Dorset DT2 9AN
T: (01308) 482617

LIVERTON
Devon

**Lookweep Farm Cottages
★★★**
Contact: Mrs Helen Griffiths,
Lookweep Farm Cottages,
Lookweep Farm, Liverton,
Newton Abbot, Devon TQ12 6HT
T: (01626) 833277
F: (01626) 834412
I: www.lookweep.co.uk

**Moor Copse Farm Cottages
★★★**
Contact: Mr & Mrs P Cross,
Moor Copse Farm Cottages,
Moor Copse Farm, Liverton,
Newton Abbot, Devon TQ12 6HT
T: (01626) 833920
F: (01626) 833920

LOBB
Devon

**South Lobb Cottage and House
★★★**
Contact: Mr Peter Morris, Farm
& Cottage Holidays, Victoria
House, 12 Fore Street, Northam,
Bideford, Devon EX39 1AW
T: (01237) 479146
F: (01237) 421512
E: farmcott@cix.co.uk
I: www.farmcott.co.uk

LODDISWELL
Devon

**Woolston Lodge
Rating Applied For**
Contact: Mr & Mrs Bowater,
Helpful Holidays, Mill Street,
Chagford, Newton Abbot, Devon
TQ13 8AW
T: (01647) 433593
F: (01647) 433694
E: help@helpfulholidays.com
I: www.helpfulholidays.com

LONDON APPRENTICE
Cornwall

The Gables ★★★
Contact: Mrs L McGuffie, The
Gables, Spindrift, London
Apprentice, St Austell, Cornwall
PL26
T: (01726) 69316

LONG ROCK
Cornwall

Tolver Dairy ★★★★
Contact: Cornish Cottage
Holidays, The Old Turnpike Dairy,
Godolphin Road, Helston,
Cornwall TR13 8AA
T: (01326) 573808
F: (01326) 564992
E: enquiry@
cornishcottageholidays.co.uk
I: www.cornishcottageholidays.
co.uk

LONGBRIDGE DEVERILL
Wiltshire

Copperfield ★★★
Contact: Mr Peter Morris, Farm
& Cottage Holidays, Victoria
House, 12 Fore Street, Northam,
Bideford, Devon EX39 1AW
T: (01237) 479146
F: (01237) 421512
E: farmcott@cix.co.uk
I: www.farmcott.co.uk

Sturgess Farmhouse ★★★★
Contact: Mr A Ramsay, Sturgess
Farmhouse, Longbridge Deverill,
Warminster, Wiltshire BA12 7EA
T: (01985) 840329
E: info@sturgessbarns.co.uk
I: www.sturgessbarns.co.uk

LONGDOWN
Devon

**Perridge House, Fordlands
Farmhouse & Cottage
★★★-★★★★★**
Contact: Mr & Mrs Bowater,
Helpful Holidays, Mill Street,
Chagford, Newton Abbot, Devon
TQ13 8AW
T: (01647) 433593
F: (01647) 433694
E: help@helpfulholidays.com
I: www.helpfulholidays.com

LOOE
Cornwall

Alices Cottage ★★★★
Contact: Cornish Cottage
Holidays, Godolphin Road,
Helston, Cornwall TR13 8AA
T: (01326) 573808
F: (01326) 564992
E: enquiry@
cornishcottageholidays.co.uk
I: www.cornishcottageholidays.
co.uk

**Badham Farm Holiday
Cottages ★★★**
Contact: Mr & Mrs R&J Brown,
Badham Farm Holiday Cottages,
St Keyne, Liskeard, Cornwall
PL14 4RW
T: (01579) 343572
F: (01579) 343572

**Barclay House Cottages
★★★★★**
Contact: Mr Barclay, Barclay
House, The Hotel, Restaurant &
Luxury Cottages, St Martin's
Road, Looe, Cornwall PL13 1LP
T: (01503) 262929
F: (01503) 262632
E: info@barclayhouse.co.uk
I: www.barclayhouse.co.uk

**Bocaddon Holiday Cottages
★★★★**
Contact: Mrs Alison Maiklem,
Bocaddon, Lanreath, Looe,
Cornwall PL13 2PG
T: (01503) 220192 & 220245
F: (01503) 220245
E: bocaddon@aol.com

**Bucklawren Farm
★★★★-★★★★★**
Contact: Mrs J Henly,
Bucklawren Farm, St Martins,
Looe, Cornwall PL13 1NZ
T: (01503) 240738
F: (01503) 240481
E: bucklawren@compuserve.
com
I: www.cornwallexplore.
co.uk/bucklawren

Chy-an-Nor ★★★
Contact: Mrs J Mickleburgh, 85
Carey Park, Killigarth, Polperro,
Looe, Cornwall PL13 2JP
T: (01503) 272349
E: rmick@eurobell.co.uk

Crylla Valley Cottages ★★★★
Contact: Mrs M Walsh, Crylla
Valley Cottages, Notter Bridge,
Saltash, Cornwall PL12 4RN
T: (01752) 851133
F: (01752) 851666
E: sales@cryllacottages.co.uk
I: www.cryllacottages.co.uk

**Lemain Garden Apartments
★★★**
Contact: Mr & Mrs Alan & Dee
Palin, Lemain Garden
Apartments, Portuan Road, West
Looe, Looe, Cornwall PL13 2DR
T: (01503) 262073 & 264574
F: (01503) 265288
E: sales@lemain.com
I: www.lemain.com

Penvith Cottages ★★★★
Contact: Mr & Mrs P Windle,
Aysgarth, Horsham Road,
Cranleigh, Surrey GU6 8DY
T: (01483) 277894
E: beatrix@talk21.com
I: www.cornwall-online.
co.uk/penvith

Establishments printed in blue have a detailed entry in this guide

Plaidy Beach Holiday Apartments ★ ★ - ★ ★ ★
Contact: Mr & Mrs Colin Keating, Plaidy Beach Holiday Apartments, Plaidy Park Road, Plaidy, Looe, Cornwall PL13 1LG
T: (01503) 262044
E: keating@easynet.co.uk

Rivercroft Hotel and Apartments ★ ★ ★
Contact: Mrs J M Cairns, Rivercroft Hotel & Apartments, Station Road, East Looe, Looe, Cornwall PL13 1HL
T: (01503) 262251
F: (01503) 265494
E: rivercroft.hotel@virgin.net
I: www.rivercrofthotel.co.uk

Rock Towers Apartments ★ ★ ★ ★
Contact: Mr Clive Dixon, Cornish Collection, 73 Bodrigan Road, Barbican, East Looe, Looe, Cornwall PL13 1EH
T: (01503) 262736 &
07768 752936
F: (01503) 262736
E: cornishcol@aol.com
I: www.cornishcollection.co.uk

Summercourt Coastal Cottages ★ ★ ★ ★
Contact: Mrs B Slingsby, Summercourt Coastal Cottages, Bodigga Cliff, St Martin, Looe, Cornwall PL13 1NZ
T: (01503) 263149

Tredinnick Farm
Rating Applied For
Contact: Mrs A E Barrett, Tredinnick Farm, Duloe, Liskeard, Cornwall PL14 4PJ
T: (01503) 262997
F: (01503) 265554

LOOE
Cornwall

Well Meadow Cottage ★ ★ ★ ★
Contact: Mrs Kaye Chapman, Coldrinnick Farm, Duloe, Liskeard, Cornwall PL14 4QF
T: (01503) 220251 &
07977 378916
E: kaye@coldrinnick.fsnet.co.uk

LOSCOMBE
Dorset

Garden Cottage ★ ★ ★
Contact: Major J L Poe, Pear Tree Farm, Loscombe, Bridport, Dorset DT6 3TL
T: (01308) 488223
E: poe@loscombe.freeserve.co.uk

LOSTWITHIEL
Cornwall

Hartswheal Barn ★ ★ ★
Contact: Mrs W Jordan, Hartswell Farm, St Winnow, Lostwithiel, Cornwall PL22 0RB
T: (01208) 873419
F: (01208) 873419
E: hartswheal@connexions.co.uk
I: www.connexions.co.uk/hartswheal/index.htm

Lanwithan Manor, Farm & Waterside Cottages ★ ★ ★ - ★ ★ ★ ★
Contact: Mr H F Edward-Collins, Lanwithan Cottages, Lostwithiel, Cornwall PL22 0LA
T: (01208) 872444
F: (01208) 872444
E: HEC@ukgateway.net

Newham Farm Cottages ★ ★ ★ ★
Contact: Mrs P Bolsover, Newham Farm Cottages, Lostwithiel, Cornwall PL22 0LD
T: (01208) 872262
F: (01208) 873401

The Roundhouse ★ ★ ★ ★
Contact: CH Ref: 11106, Holiday Cottages Group Owner Services Department, Spring Mill, Earby, Barnoldswick, Lancashire BB18 6RN
T: (01282) 445096
F: (01282) 844299
E: ch.sales@ttgihg.co.uk
I: www.country-holidays.co.uk

Tredethick Farm Cottages ★ ★ ★ ★
Contact: Mr & Mrs Tim & Nicky Reed, Tredethick Farm Cottages, Little Bakes, Tredethick, Lostwithiel, Cornwall PL22 0LE
T: (01208) 873618
F: (01208) 873618
E: holidays@tredethick.co.uk
I: www.tredethick.co.uk

LOWER ODCOMBE
Somerset

The Cottage ★ ★ ★
Contact: Mrs N C Worledge, The Cottage, Old Dairy House, Lower Odcombe, Yeovil, Somerset BA22 8TX
T: (01935) 862874
E: john.worledge@lineone.net

LUDGVAN
Cornwall

Yellow Blossom Cottage ★ ★
Contact: Cornish Cottage Holidays, The Old Turnpike Dairy, Godolphin Road, Helston, Cornwall TR13 8AA
T: (01326) 573808
F: (01326) 564992
E: enquiry@cornishcottageholidays.co.uk
I: www.cornishcottageholidays.co.uk

LUSTLEIGH
Devon

Lustleigh Mills ★ ★ ★ - ★ ★ ★ ★
Contact: Mrs J A Rowe, Lustleigh Mills, Lustleigh, Newton Abbot, Devon TQ13 9SS
T: (01647) 277357
E: lustleighmills@ukgateway.net
I: www.lustleighmills.btinternet.co.uk

Rockvale Stable Cottage & Barn Cottage ★ ★ ★ ★
Contact: Mrs Janet Ploog, Rockvale Stable Cottage & Barn Cottage, Lustleigh, Newton Abbot, Devon TQ13 9TH
T: (01647) 277264
F: (01647) 277512

LUXBOROUGH
Somerset

The Old Granary ★ ★ ★ ★
Contact: Mrs A Simpson, The Old Granary, Luxborough, Watchet, Somerset TA23 0SJ
T: (01984) 640909
E: simpstheoldgranary@talk21.com

LYDEARD ST LAWRENCE
Somerset

Oaklea House ★ ★ ★ ★
Contact: Mrs Peta-Elaine Barker, Oaklea House, Tolland Rocks, Lydeard St Lawrence, Taunton, Somerset TA4 3PW
T: (01984) 667373
F: (01984) 667373
E: Barker@Oakleahouse.fsnet.co.uk

LYDFORD
Devon

Mucky Duck Inn ★ ★ ★
Contact: Mr & Mrs B&M Payne, Mucky Duck Inn, Lydford Gorge, Lydford, Okehampton, Devon EX20 4BL
T: (01822) 820208
F: (01822) 820208

LYME REGIS
Dorset

2/3 Ozone Terr. B4036 4036/3 ★ ★ ★
Contact: Lyme Bay Holiday Cottages, Boshouse, 44 Church Street, Lyme Regis, Dorset DT7 3DA
T: (01297) 443363
E: email@lymebayholidays.co.uk
I: www.lymebayholidays.co.uk

Alwyns B4002 ★ ★ ★
Contact: Lyme Bay Holidays, Boshouse, 44 Church Street, Lyme Regis, Dorset DT7 3DA
T: (01297) 443363
F: (01297) 445576
E: email@lymebayholidays.co.uk
I: www.lymebayholidays.co.uk

Appletrees ★ ★ ★
Contact: Mr & Mrs Charles & Liz Teall, Salford Mill, Mill Cottage, Salford, Chipping Norton, Oxfordshire OX7 5YQ
T: (01608) 641304 & 642849
F: (01608) 644442
E: teall@compuserve.com

Aquae Sulis
Rating Applied For
Contact: Lyme Bay Holiday Cottages, Boshouse, 44 Church Street, Lyme Regis, Dorset DT7 3DA
T: (01297) 443363
E: email@lymebayholidays.co.uk
I: www.lymebayholidays.co.uk

The Arched House ★ ★ ★
Contact: Lyme Bay Holidays, Boshouse, 44 Church Street, Lyme Regis, Dorset DT7 3DA
T: (01297) 443363
F: (01297) 445576
E: email@lymebayholidays.co.uk
I: www.lymebayholidays.co.uk

Banff B4109 ★ ★ ★
Contact: Lyme Bay Holidays, Boshouse, 44 Church Street, Lyme Regis, Dorset DT7 3DA
T: (01297) 443363
F: (01297) 445576
E: email@lymebayholidays.co.uk
I: www.lymebayholidays.co.uk

Bay View Court C3950 ★ ★
Contact: Lyme Bay Holidays, Boshouse, 44 Church Street, Lyme Regis, Dorset DT7 3DA
T: (01297) 443363
F: (01297) 445576
E: email@lymebayholidays.co.uk
I: www.lymebayholidays.co.uk

Benwick B4232 ★ ★ ★ ★
Contact: Lyme Bay Holidays, Boshouse, 44 Church Street, Lyme Regis, Dorset DT7 3DA
T: (01297) 443363
F: (01297) 445576
E: email@lymebayholidays.co.uk
I: www.lymebayholidays.co.uk

Blacksmith Cottage ★ ★ ★ ★
Contact: Mrs S Jolley, Westward, Loves Lane, Morcombelake, Bridport, Dorset DT6 6DZ
T: (01297) 489778
E: su@westward.fsbusiness.co.uk

The Boat House B4081 ★ ★ ★
Contact: Lyme Bay Holidays, Boshouse, 44 Church Street, Lyme Regis, Dorset DT7 3DA
T: (01297) 443363
F: (01297) 445576
E: email@lymebayholidays.co.uk
I: www.lymebayholidays.co.uk

Brightwater Apartment ★ ★
Contact: Mr Royson Davies, Fairfield Cottage, Charmouth Road, Lyme Regis, Dorset DT7 3HH
T: (01297) 445362

Broad Street Apartment C4049 ★ ★ ★
Contact: Lyme Bay Holidays, Boshouse, 44 Church Street, Lyme Regis, Dorset DT7 3DA
T: (01297) 443363
F: (01297) 445576
E: email@lymebayholidays.co.uk
I: www.lymebayholidays.co.uk

1 Channel View ★ ★
Contact: Mrs D R Postles, 1 Channel View, The Cobb, Lyme Regis, Dorset DT7 3JT
T: (01297) 442563

Church Cliff
Rating Applied For
Contact: Lyme Bay Holiday Cottages, Boshouse, 44 Church Street, Lyme Regis, Dorset DT7 3DA
T: (01297) 443363
E: email@lymebayholidays.co.uk
I: www.lymebayholidays.co.uk

Church Street B4270 ★★★
Contact: Lyme Bay Holidays,
Boshouse, 44 Church Street,
Lyme Regis, Dorset 01297
T: (01297) 443363
F: (01297) 445576
E: email@lymebayholidays.
co.uk
I: www.lymebayholidays.co.uk

Clappentail Apartment B4142 ★★★
Contact: Lyme Bay Holidays,
Boshouse, 44 Church Street,
Lyme Regis, Dorset DT7 3DA
T: (01297) 443363
F: (01297) 445576
E: email@lymebayholidays.
co.uk
I: www.lymebayholidays.co.uk

5 Clappentail Court B4141 ★★★★
Contact: Lyme Bay Holidays,
Boshouse, 44 Church Street,
Lyme Regis, Dorset DT7 3DA
T: (01297) 443363
F: (01297) 445576
E: email@lymebayholidays.
co.uk
I: www.lymebayholidays.co.uk

Cleeve House B3437 ★★★
Contact: Lyme Bay Holidays,
Boshouse, 44 Church Street,
Lyme Regis, Dorset DT7 3DA
T: (01297) 443363
F: (01297) 445576
E: email@lymebayholidays.
co.uk
I: www.lymebayholidays.co.uk

Cliff Cottage ★★★
Contact: Mrs Sue Rose, Brantfell
House, 55 New Road, Whitehill,
Bordon, Hampshire GU35 9AX
T: (01420) 472512 &
(02392) 811444

Cobb House ★★
Contact: Jean Bartlett Cottage
Holidays, Fore Street, Beer,
Seaton, Devon EX12 3JB
T: (01297) 23221
F: (01297) 23303
E: jeanb@netbreaks.com
I: www.netbreaks.com/jeanb

Cockwell Cross Cottage ★★★★
Contact: Lyme Bay Holidays,
Boshouse, 44 Church Street,
Lyme Regis, Dorset DT7 3DA
T: (01297) 443363
F: (01297) 445576
E: email@lymebayholidays.
co.uk
I: www.lymebayholidays.co.uk

Coombe Hayes Farm Cottage ★★★
Contact: Mrs R Duffin, Coombe
Hayes Farm Cottage, Wadley
Hill, Uplyme, Lyme Regis, Dorset
DT7 3SU
T: (01297) 445744
E: rozduffin@excite.co.uk
I: www.lymeregis.com

Coombe House Flat ★★★
Contact: Mrs D Duncan, Coombe
House, 41 Coombe Street, Lyme
Regis, Dorset DT7 3PY
T: (01297) 443849
F: (01297) 443849
E: duncs@hugduncan.freeserve.
co.uk

Coombe Street B4278 ★★★
Contact: Lyme Bay Holidays,
Boshouse, 44 Church Street,
Lyme Regis, Dorset DT7 3DA
T: (01297) 443363
F: (01297) 445576
E: email@lymebayholidays.
co.uk
I: www.lymebayholidays.co.uk

Coram Tower Holidays ★★★
Contact: Mr & Mrs John &
Margaret McLaren, Coram Tower
Holidays, Pound Road, Lyme
Regis, Dorset DT7 3HX
T: (01297) 442012
E: jmmclaren@tesco.net

Crystal ★★★
Contact: Miss Bridget Horner,
Littlemead, Lyme Road, Yawl,
Lyme Regis, Dorset DT7 3UZ
T: (01297) 442231
E: bridge.horner@talk21.com
I: www.lymeregis.com/crystal

3 Dolphin Cottages ★★
Contact: Mrs D E Lindfield,
Sunnyside, Itchingfield,
Horsham, West Sussex
RH13 7NX
T: (01403) 791258

Fairfield Cottage ★★★
Contact: Mr R S Davies, Fairfield
Cottage, Charmouth Road, Lyme
Regis, Dorset DT7 3HH
T: (01297) 445362

Farwest ★★★
Contact: Jean Bartlett Cottage
Holidays, Fore Street, Beer,
Seaton, Devon EX12 3JB
T: (01297) 23221
F: (01297) 23303
E: jeanb@netbreaks.com
I: www.netbreaks.com/jeanb

Flat 1 Pyne House★★
Contact: Ms Sue Dare, 117
Leander Road, London SW2 2NB
T: (020) 86718587 &
07971 242257

Flat 2 Woodville B4059 ★★
Contact: Lyme Bay Holidays,
Boshouse, 44 Church Street,
Lyme Regis, Dorset DT7 3DA
T: (01297) 443363
F: (01297) 445576
E: email@lymebayholidays.
co.uk
I: www.lymebayholidays.co.uk

The Gables Holiday Apartments ★★
Contact: Mr & Mrs Alan &
Christine Simpson, The Gables
Holiday Apartments, Church
Street, Lyme Regis, Dorset
DT7 3BX
T: (01297) 442536

Green House & Stable Cottage ★★-★★★★
Contact: Mr William Prescott,
Green House & Stable Cottage,
Colway Lane, Lyme Regis, Dorset
DT7 3UB
T: (01297) 443787
E: prescott@williamsind.demon.
co.uk

Greystones Apartment ★★★★
Contact: Mrs J B Gollop,
Greystones, View Road, Lyme
Regis, Dorset DT7 3AA
T: (01297) 443678 & 0771 825
3557
F: (01297) 443678
E: greystones@callnetuk.com
I: www.greystones-lymeregis.
com

Hadleigh Villas B3520 ★★★
Contact: Lyme Bay Holidays,
Boshouse, 44 Church Street,
Lyme Regis, Dorset DT7 3DA
T: (01297) 443363
F: (01297) 445576
E: email@lymebayholidays.
co.uk
I: www.lymebayholidays.co.uk

Harbour House Flats ★★★
Contact: Mrs Jill Baker, The
Cedars, Stoke St Mary, Taunton,
Somerset TA3 5DE
T: (01823) 442395 & 364779

Harmony Cottage ★★★
Contact: Harmony Cottage,
26-27 Church Street, Lyme
Regis, Dorset DT7

The Haven D4096 ★★★
Contact: Lyme Bay Holidays,
Boshouse, 44 Church Street,
Lyme Regis, Dorset DT7 3DA
T: (01297) 443363
F: (01297) 445576
E: email@lymebayholidays.
co.uk
I: www.lymebayholidays.co.uk

Haverings B4242 ★★★
Contact: Lyme Bay Holidays, Bos
House, 44 Church Street, Lyme
Regis, Dorset DT7 3DA
T: (01297) 443363
F: (01297) 445576
E: email@lymebayholidays.
co.uk
I: www.lymebayholidays.co.uk

Haye Farm Bungalow, Stables, Hayloft & Dairy★★★
Contact: Mr & Mrs Bob & Grace
Anderson, Haye Farm, Haye
Lane, Lyme Regis, Dorset
DT7 3UD
T: (01297) 442400
F: (01297) 442745

Ilex House ★★★
Contact: Mr Royson Davies,
Fairfield Cottage, Charmouth
Road, Lyme Regis, Dorset
DT7 3HH
T: (01297) 445362

Iverna ★★
Contact: Iverna, Colway Lane,
Lyme Regis, Dorset DT7

Jasper B4108 ★★★
Contact: Lyme Bay Holidays,
Boshouse, 44 Church Street,
Lyme Regis, Dorset DT7 3DA
T: (01297) 443363
F: (01297) 445576
E: email@lymebayholidays.
co.uk
I: www.lymebayholidays.co.uk

Kamloops and Nanaimo ★★★
Contact: Mr D W Sweet, Grove
Cottage, Hollybush Lane, Stoke
Bishop, Bristol BS9 1BH
T: (0117) 968 1866

Kippir Cottage ★★★
Contact: Mr Royson Davies,
Fairfield Cottage, Charmouth
Road, Lyme Regis, Dorset
DT7 3HH
T: (01297) 445362

La Casa ★★★
Contact: Mr Royson Davies,
Fairfield Cottage, Charmouth
Road, Lyme Regis, Dorset
DT7 3HH
T: (01297) 445362

Lea Croft B4250 ★★★
Contact: Lyme Bay Holidays,
Boshouse, 44 Church Street,
Lyme Regis, Dorset DT7 3DA
T: (01297) 443363
F: (01297) 445576
E: email@lymebayholidays.
co.uk
I: www.lymebayholidays.co.uk

Lentons C4260 ★★★★
Contact: Lyme Bay Holidays,
Boshouse, 44 Church Street,
Lyme Regis, Dorset DT7 3DA
T: (01297) 443363
F: (01297) 445576
E: email@lymebayholidays.
co.uk
I: www.lymebayholidays.co.uk

Little Cleve ★★★★
Contact: Mr Alister Mackenzie,
Carters Cottage, Smithams Hill,
East Harptree, Bristol BS40 6BZ
T: (01761) 221554

Little Clovelly A3602 ★★★★
Contact: Lyme Bay Holidays,
Boshouse, 44 Church Street,
Lyme Regis, Dorset DT7 3DA
T: (01297) 443363
F: (01297) 445576
E: email@lymebayholidays.
co.uk
I: www.lymebayholidays.co.uk

Little Jordan C4300 ★★★★
Contact: Lyme Bay Holidays,
Boshouse, 44 Church Street,
Lyme Regis, Dorset DT7 3DA
T: (01297) 443363
F: (01297) 445576
E: email@lymebayholidays.
co.uk
I: www.lymebayholidays.co.uk

Little Thatch C3439 ★★★
Contact: Lyme Bay Holidays,
Boshouse, 44 Church Street,
Lyme Regis, Dorset DT7 3DA
T: (01297) 443363
F: (01297) 445576
E: email@lymebayholidays.
co.uk
I: www.lymebayholidays.co.uk

Lucerne ★★★
Contact: Mr O Lovell, Lucerne,
View Road, Lyme Regis, Dorset
DT7 3AA
T: (01297) 443752
E: OwenLucerne@lineone.net

Lym Close B4253 ★★★
Contact: Lyme Bay Holidays,
Boshouse, 44 Church Street,
Lyme Regis, Dorset DT7 3DA
T: (01297) 443363
F: (01297) 445576
E: email@lymebayholidays.
co.uk
I: www.lymebayholidays.co.uk

Establishments printed in blue have a detailed entry in this guide

23 Lym Close C4179 ★★★
Contact: Lyme Bay Holidays,
Boshouse, 44 Church Street,
Lyme Regis, Dorset DT7 3DA
T: (01297) 443363
F: (01297) 445576
E: email@lymebayholidays.
co.uk
I: www.lymebayholidays.co.uk

3 Lymbrook ★★
Contact: Mrs MV Thompson, 42
Havil Street, Camberwell,
London SE5 7RS
T: (020) 7703 7977 &
(01243) 574279

4 Lymbrook Cottages ★★★
Contact: Mrs K E Start, Monks
Hall, Bowsers Lane, Little
Walden, Saffron Walden, Essex
CB10 1XQ
T: (01799) 522096

Malden Cottage B4265 ★★
Contact: Lyme Bay Holidays,
Boshouse, 44 Church Street,
Lyme Regis, Dorset DT7 3DA
T: (01297) 443363
F: (01297) 445576
E: email@lymebayholidays.
co.uk
I: www.lymebayholidays.co.uk

**Mermaid Cottage C4281
★★★★**
Contact: Lyme Bay Holidays,
Boshouse, 44 Church Street,
Lyme Regis, Dorset 01297
T: (01297) 443363
F: (01297) 445576
E: email@lymebayholidays.
co.uk
I: www.lymebayholidays.co.uk

Mill Green (Ref: B4003) ★★★
Contact: Lyme Bay Holidays,
Boshouse, 44 Church Street,
Lyme Regis, Dorset DT7 3DA
T: (01297) 443363
F: (01297) 445576
E: email@lymebayholidays.
co.uk
I: www.lymebayholidays.co.uk

Monmouth Cottage ★
Contact: Mrs W R Fisk, 28
Station Road, Crewkerne,
Somerset TA18 8AJ
T: (01460) 73878

None Go By A4279 ★★★
Contact: Lyme Bay Holidays,
Boshouse, 44 Church Street,
Lyme Regis, Dorset DT7 3DA
T: (01297) 443363
F: (01297) 445576
E: email@lymebayholidays.
co.uk
I: www.lymebayholidays.co.uk

Okanagen B4107 ★★★
Contact: Lyme Bay Holidays,
Boshouse, 44 Church Street,
Lyme Regis, Dorset DT7 3DA
T: (01297) 443363
F: (01297) 445576
E: email@lymebayholidays.
co.uk
I: www.lymebayholidays.co.uk

2 Ozone Terrace A3603 ★★★
Contact: Lyme Bay Holidays,
Boshouse, 44 Church Street,
Lyme Regis, Dorset DT7 3DA
T: (01297) 443363
F: (01297) 445576
E: email@lymebayholidays.
co.uk
I: www.lymebayholidays.co.uk

Queen Ann's Lodge ★★★★
Contact: Mr Royson Davies,
Fairfield Cottage, Charmouth
Road, Lyme Regis, Dorset
DT7 3HH
T: (01297) 445362

**River View
Rating Applied For**
Contact: Lyme Bay Holiday
Cottages, Boshouse, 44 Church
Street, Lyme Regis, Dorset
DT7 3DA
T: (01297) 443363
E: email@lymebayholidays.
co.uk
I: www.lymebayholidays.co.uk

**Rose and Honeysuckle
Cottages ★★★★**
Contact: Mr Matthew Strong,
Braden Chartered Surveyors,
Laverstoke Grange, Whitchurch,
Hampshire RG28 7PF
T: (01256) 896444
F: (01256) 896555
E: braden@andover.co.uk

St Agnes A3601 ★★★
Contact: Lyme Bay Holidays,
Boshouse, 44 Church Street,
Lyme Regis, Dorset DT7 3DA
T: (01297) 443363
F: (01297) 445576
E: email@lymebayholidays.
co.uk
I: www.lymebayholidays.co.uk

**St Andrews Holiday Flats
★★★**
Contact: Mrs Cynthia Wendy
McHardy, St Andrews Holiday
Flats, Uplyme Road, Lyme Regis,
Dorset DT7 3LP
T: (01297) 445495
F: (01297) 445495

Sea Tree House ★★★★
Contact: Mr David Parker, Sea
Tree House, 18 Broad Street,
Lyme Regis, Dorset DT7 3QE
T: (01297) 442244
F: (01297) 442244
E: seatree.house@ukonline.
co.uk
I: www.lymeregis.
com/seatreehouse

Sea View ★★★
Contact: Jean Bartlett Cottage
Holidays, Tree Street, Beer,
Seaton, Devon EX12 3JB
T: (01297) 23221
F: (01297) 23303
E: jeanb@netbreaks.com
I: www.netbreaks.com/jeanb

Seaward B4280 ★★★★
Contact: Lyme Bay Holidays,
Boshouse, 44 Church Street,
Lyme Regis, Dorset DT7 3DA
T: (01297) 443363
F: (01297) 445576
E: email@lymebayholidays.
co.uk
I: www.lymebayholidays.co.uk

Sherborne Lane B4241 ★★
Contact: Lyme Bay Holidays,
Boshouse, 44 Church Street,
Lyme Regis, Dorset DT7 3DA
T: (01297) 443363
F: (01297) 445576
E: email@lymebayholidays.
co.uk
I: www.lymebayholidays.co.uk

**22a Sherborne Lane C4197
4197★★★**
Contact: Lyme Bay Holidays,
Boshouse, 44 Church Street,
Lyme Regis, Dorset DT7 3DA
T: (01297) 443363
F: (01297) 445576
E: email@lymebayholidays.
co.uk
I: www.lymebayholidays.co.uk

**35 Sherborne Lane C4266
★★★**
Contact: Lyme Bay Holidays,
Boshouse, 44 Church Street,
Lyme Regis, Dorset DT7 3DA
T: (01297) 443363
F: (01297) 445576
E: email@lymebayholidays.
co.uk
I: www.lymebayholidays.co.uk

57a Silver Street ★★★
Contact: Ms Rhoda Elwick,
Thatch, Uplyme Road, Lyme
Regis, Dorset DT7 3LP
T: (01297) 442212
F: (01297) 443485
E: thethatch@lineone.net
I: www.holidaycottages-uk.com

Silver Street A4273 ★★★
Contact: Lyme Bay Holidays,
Boshouse, 44 Church Street,
Lyme Regis, Dorset DT7 3DA
T: (01297) 443363
F: (01297) 445576
E: email@lymebayholidays.
co.uk
I: www.lymebayholidays.co.uk

Skagen Lodge ★★
Contact: Skagen Lodge, Lyme
Regis, Dorset DT7

Skagen Lodge B3440 ★★★
Contact: Lyme Bay Holidays,
Boshouse, 44 Church Street,
Lyme Regis, Dorset DT7 3DA
T: (01297) 443363
F: (01297) 44576
E: email@lymebayholidays.
co.uk
I: www.lymebayholidays.co.uk

Stable Cottage ★★★★
Contact: Mrs Penny Jones, The
Coach House, Haye Lane, Lyme
Regis, Dorset DT7 3NQ
T: (01297) 442656
F: (01297) 442656

**Stonehaven Holiday
Apartments ★★**
Contact: Mr & Mrs Cross,
Stonehaven Holiday
Apartments, 33 Silver Street,
Lyme Regis, Dorset DT7 3HS
T: (01297) 443809

The Studio ★★★
Contact: Ms K Fitzroy, The
Studio, 52 Broad Street, Lyme
Regis, Dorset DT7 3QF
T: (01297) 442616 & 442653
E: katie.fitzroy@btinternet.com
I: www.lymeregis.com

Sunnybank C3442 ★★★★
Contact: Lyme Bay Holidays,
Boshouse, 44 Church Street,
Lyme Regis, Dorset DT7 3DA
T: (01297) 443363
F: (01297) 445576
E: email@lymebayholidays.
co.uk
I: www.lymebayholidays.co.uk

Swallow House B4249 ★★★
Contact: Lyme Bay Holidays,
Boshouse, 44 Church Street,
Lyme Regis, Dorset DT7 3DA
T: (01297) 443363
F: (01297) 445576
E: email@lymebayholidays.
co.uk
I: www.lymebayholidays.co.uk

Talbot Road C4267 ★★★
Contact: Lyme Bay Holidays,
Boshouse, 44 Church Street,
Lyme Regis, Dorset 01297
T: (01297) 443363
F: (01297) 445576
E: email@lymebayholidays.
co.uk
I: www.lymebayholidays.co.uk

Top Flat ★★★
Contact: Lyme Bay Holiday
Cottages, Boshouse, 44 Church
Street, Lyme Regis, Dorset
DT7 3DA
T: (01297) 443363
E: email@lymebayholidays.
co.uk
I: www.lymebayholidays.co.uk

View House D4100 ★★★★
Contact: Lyme Bay Holidays,
Boshouse, 44 Church Street,
Lyme Regis, Dorset DT7 3DA
T: (01297) 443363
F: (01297) 445576
E: email@lymebayholidays.
co.uk
I: www.lymebayholidays.co.uk

The Walk C4006 ★★★
Contact: Lyme Bay Holidays,
Boshouse, 44 Church Street,
Lyme Regis, Dorset DT7 3DA
T: (01297) 443363
F: (01297) 445576
E: email@lymebayholidays.
co.uk
I: www.lymebayholidays.co.uk

Waltham House ★★★
Contact: Mr D Matthews, Lyme
Bay Holidays, Bos House, 44
Church Street, Lyme Regis,
Dorset DT7 3DA
T: (01297) 443363
F: (01297) 445576

Water Cottage ★★
Contact: Mrs Claire Laven-
Morris, 67 Montholme Road,
London SW11 6HX
T: (020) 7924 6194
F: (020) 7228 6779

1 Wellhayes ★★★
Contact: Mrs P Boyland, Barn
Park Farm, Stockland Hill, Nr
Cotleigh, Honiton, Devon
EX14 9JA
T: (01404) 861297
F: (01404) 861297

Establishments printed in blue have a detailed entry in this guide

The Wellhouse V4133 ★★★★
Contact: Lyme Bay Holidays, Boshouse, 44 Church Street, Lyme Regis, Dorset DT7 3DA
T: (01297) 443363
F: (01297) 445576
E: email@lymebayholidays.co.uk
I: www.lymebayholidays.co.uk

Westover Farm Cottages ★★★
Contact: Mrs Debby Snook, Westover Farm Cottages, Westover Farm, Wootton Fitzpaine, Bridport, Dorset DT6 6NE
T: (01297) 560451 &
07887 752755
E: wfcottages@aol.com

17 Woodmead Road C4069 ★★★
Contact: Lyme Bay Holiday Cottages, Boshouse, 44 Church Street, Lyme Regis, Dorset DT7 3DA
T: (01297) 443363
F: (01297) 445576
E: email@lymebayholidays.co.uk
I: www.lymebayholidays.co.uk

LYMPSHAM
Somerset

Dulhorn Farm Caravan Park ★★
Contact: Mr and Mrs J E Bowden, Dulhorn Farm Caravan Park, Weston Road, Lympsham, Weston-super-Mare BS24 0JQ
T: (01934) 750298
F: (01934) 750913

Lower Wick Farm ★★-★★★
Contact: Mrs C H Young, Lower Wick Farm, Wick Lane, Lympsham, Somerset BS24 0HG
T: (01278) 751333

LYMPSTONE
Devon

Ventnor Cottage ★★★
Contact: Mr CH ref: 4420, Holiday Cottages Group Owner Services Dept, Spring Mill, Earby, Barnoldswick, Lancashire BB18 6RN
T: (01282) 445444
F: (01282) 841539
E: sales@ttgihg.co.uk
I: www.country-holidays.co.uk

LYNMOUTH
Devon

Cheswood ★★★
Contact: Mr & Mrs M&S Moore & Taylor-Moore, Horseshoe Cottage, Emery Down, Lyndhurst, Hampshire SO43 7EB
T: (023) 8028 3253 & 8028 3225
F: (023) 8028 3217

Clooneavin Holidays ★★★
Contact: Mr and Mrs Davidson, Clooneavin Holidays, Clooneavin Path, Lynmouth, Devon EX35 6EE
T: (01598) 753334
I: www.northdevon.co.uk/clooneavin.htm

Countisbury Lodge ★★★
Contact: Marsden's Cottage Holidays, 2 The Square, Braunton, Devon EX33 2JB
T: (01271) 813777
F: (01271) 813664
E: holidays@marsdens.co.uk
I: www.marsdens.co.uk

Shan Lea ★★★
Contact: Mrs JM Berry, Berrys Way, Lydiate Lane, Lynton, Devon EX35 6HE
T: (01598) 752352 & 753983

Water's Edge Cottage ★★★★
Contact: Mr M Wolverson, Stag Cottage, Holdstone Down, Combe Martin, Ilfracombe, Devon EX34 0PF
T: (01271) 882449 &
07831 118676

Wilrose Cottage ★★★
Contact: Mr & Mrs Garry Carr, 18 Stanhope Road, Weston-super-Mare, North Somerset BS23 4LP
T: (01934) 623019
F: (01934) 644606
E: gcarr62401@aol.com

LYNTON
Devon

Buttershaw Cottage ★★★★
Contact: Marsden's Cottage Holidays, 2 The Square, Braunton, Devon EX33 2JB
T: (01271) 813777
F: (01271) 813664
E: holidays@marsdens.co.uk
I: www.marsdens.co.uk

Honeypot Cottage ★★★
Contact: Mr D Woodlands, Rockvale Hotel, Lee Road, Lynton, Devon EX35 6HW
T: (01598) 752279

Lyn House ★★
Contact: Mrs S Richards, Lyn House, Sinai Hill, Lynton, Devon EX35 6AX
T: (01598) 752229

Nettlecombe Cottage ★★★
Contact: Marsden's Cottage Holidays, 2 The Square, Braunton, Devon EX33 2JB
T: (01271) 813777
F: (01271) 813664
E: holidayds@marsdens.co.uk
I: www.marsdens.co.uk

Puffin Cottage
Rating Applied For
Contact: Marsden's Cottage Holidays, 2 The Square, Braunton, Devon EX33 2JB
T: (01271) 813777
F: (01271) 813664
E: holidays@marsdens.co.uk
I: www.marsdens.co.uk

Royal Castle Lodge ★★★★
Contact: Mr M Wolverson, Prime Spot Holiday Cottages, Stag Cottage, Holdstone Down, Combe Martin, Ilfracombe, Devon EX34 0PF
T: (01271) 882449 &
0777 9861643

West Ilkerton Farm ★★★
Contact: Mrs V Eveleigh, West Ilkerton Farm, Lynton, Devon EX35 6QA
T: (01598) 752310
F: (01598) 752310
E: west.ilkerton@mailandnews.com
I: www.exmoortourism.org/west.ilkertonfarm.htmlwww.ilkerton.exmoor-holiday.co.uk

Wringcliffe, Sillery ★★★-★★★★★
Contact: Mr P Shimwell, Wringcliffe, Sillery, Burlington House, 11 Lee Road, Lynton, Devon EX35 6HW
T: (01598) 753352
F: (01598) 753352
E: art@gunnsgallery.freeserve.co.uk

MAENPORTH
Cornwall

Crags 15 ★★★
Contact: Helford River Holidays, The Boat House, Helford Passage, Falmouth, Cornwall TR11 5LB
T: (01326) 250278
F: (01326) 251102
E: enquiries@holidaycornwall.co.uk
I: www.holidaycornwall.co.uk

Crags 18 ★★★★
Contact: Helford River Holidays, The Boat House, Helford Passage, Falmouth, Cornwall TR11 5LB
T: (01326) 250278
F: (01326) 251102
E: enquiries@holidaycornwall.co.uk
I: www.holidaycornwall.co.uk

63 Lower Maen Cottage ★★★★
Contact: Helford River Holidays, The Boat House, Helford Passage, Falmouth, Cornwall TR11 5LB
T: (01326) 250278
F: (01326) 251102
E: enquiries@holidaycornwall.co.uk
I: www.holidaycornwall.co.uk

66 Lower Maen Cottage ★★★★
Contact: Helford River Holidays, The Boat House, Helford Passage, Falmouth, Cornwall TR11 5LB
T: (01326) 250278
F: (01326) 251102
E: enquiries@holidaycornwall.co.uk
I: www.holidaycornwall.co.uk

36 Lower Stables ★★★★
Contact: Helford River Holidays, The Boat House, Helford Passage, Falmouth, Cornwall TR11 5LB
T: (01326) 250278
F: (01326) 251102
E: enquiries@holidaycornwall.co.uk
I: www.holidaycornwall.co.uk

Maenporth Ridge No. 2 ★★★★
Contact: Helford River Holidays, The Boat House, Helford Passage, Falmouth, Cornwall TR11 5LB
T: (01326) 250278
F: (01326) 251102
E: enquiries@holidaycornwall.co.uk
I: www.holidaycornwall.co.uk

61 Monterey ★★★★
Contact: Helford River Holidays, The Boat House, Helford Passage, Falmouth, Cornwall TR11 5LB
T: (01326) 250278
F: (01326) 251102
E: enquiries@holidaycornwall.co.uk
I: www.holidaycornwall.co.uk

59 Monterey Cottage ★★★★
Contact: Helford River Holidays, The Boat House, Helford Passage, Falmouth, Cornwall TR11 5LB
T: (01326) 250278
F: (01326) 251102
E: enquiries@holidaycornwall.co.uk
I: www.holidaycornwall.co.uk

Ridges 11 ★★★
Contact: Helford River Holidays, The Boat House, Helford Passage, Falmouth, Cornwall TR11 5LB
T: (01326) 250278
F: (01326) 251102
E: enquiries@holidaycornwall.co.uk
I: www.holidaycornwall.co.uk

55 Upper Maen Cottage ★★★★
Contact: Helford River Holidays, The Boat House, Helford Passage, Falmouth, Cornwall TR11 5LB
T: (01326) 250278
F: (01326) 251102
E: enquiries@holidaycornwall.co.uk
I: www.holidaycornwall.co.uk

45 Upper Stables ★★★★
Contact: Helford River Holidays, The Boat House, Helford Passage, Falmouth, Cornwall TR11 5LB
T: (01326) 250278
F: (01326) 251102
E: enquiries@holidaycornwall.co.uk
I: www.holidaycornwall.co.uk

46 Upper Stables ★★★★
Contact: Helford River Holidays, The Boat House, Helford Passage, Falmouth, Cornwall TR11 5LB
T: (01326) 250278
F: (01326) 251102
E: enquiries@holidaycornwall.co.uk
I: www.holidaycornwall.co.uk

Establishments printed in blue have a detailed entry in this guide

50 Upper Stables ★★★★
Contact: Helford River Holidays, The Boat House, Helford Passage, Falmouth, Cornwall TR11 5LB
T: (01326) 250278
F: (01326) 251102
E: enquiries@holidaycornwall.co.uk
I: www.holidaycornwall.co.uk

51 Upper Stables ★★★★
Contact: Helford River Holidays, The Boat House, Helford Passage, Falmouth, Cornwall TR11 5LB
T: (01326) 250278
F: (01326) 251102
E: enquiries@holidaycornwall.co.uk
I: www.holidaycornwall.co.uk

MAIDEN NEWTON
Dorset
Lancombe Country Cottages ★★★★
Contact: Mr S A Banks, Lancombe Country Cottages, Lancombe Country Cottages, Lancombe Farm, Maiden Newton, Dorchester, Dorset DT2 0HU
T: (01300) 320562
F: (01300) 320562
E: lancombe@talk21.com
I: www.lancombe.co.uk

MAIDENCOMBE
Devon
Langley Manor ★★★
Contact: Holiday Homes & Cottages South West, 365A Torquay Road, Paignton, Devon TQ3 2BT
T: (01803) 663650
F: (01803) 664037
E: holcotts@aol.com
I: www.swcottages.co.uk

Parkfield Luxury Holiday Apartments ★★★
Contact: Mr & Mrs Roy & June Lewis, Parkfield Luxuray Holiday Apartment, Claddon Lane, Maidencombe, Torquay TQ1 4TB
T: (01803) 328952
F: (01803) 328952
E: enquiries@parkfieldapartments.co.uk
I: www.parkfieldapartments.co.uk

MALBOROUGH
Devon
Bolberry House Farm ★★★★
Contact: Mr & Mrs Bowater, Helpful Holidays, Mill Street, Chagford, Newton Abbot, Devon TQ13 8AW
T: (01647) 433593
F: (01647) 433694
E: help@helpfulholidays.com
I: www.helpfulholidays.com

Dairy Court ★★★★
Contact: Mr Kevin Pamphlion, c/o The Lodge, Malborough, Kingsbridge, Devon TQ7 3RN
T: (01548) 561405
F: (01548) 561111
E: accom@compuserve.com
I: www.ourworld.compuserve.com/homepages/accom

Portlemore View ★★★
Contact: Mr Andrew Cannon, 23 Malborough Park, Malborough, Kingsbridge, Devon TQ7 3SR
T: (01548) 560929 & 07941 196210
F: (01548) 562183
E: portlemoreview@aol.com

Withymore Cottage ★★★
Contact: Mrs J Hocking, Withymore Farm, Malborough, Kingsbridge, Devon TQ7 3ED
T: (01548) 561275
F: (01548) 561275
I: www.devonfarms.co.uk

MALMESBURY
Wiltshire
Cow Byre and Bull Pen ★★★
Contact: Mrs Edna Edwards, Cow Byre and Bull Pen, Stonehill Farm, Charlton, Malmesbury, Wiltshire SN16 9DY
T: (01666) 823310
F: (01666) 823310
E: johnedna@stonehillfarm.fsnet.co.uk

MALPAS
Cornwall
Curlews
Rating Applied For
Contact: Ms Margie Lumby, Special Places In Cornwall, Poachers Reach, Feock, Truro, Cornwall TR3 6SQ
T: (01872) 864400
F: (01872) 864400
E: office@specialplacescornwall.co.uk
I: www.specialplacescornwall.co.uk

Trelowthas ★★★★
Contact: Mr C Churm, 2 The Rookery, Tythby Road, Cropwell Butler, Nottingham NG12 3AA
T: (0115) 9334707 & 07774 278635

MANACCAN
Cornwall
Chy Pyth ★★★★
Contact: Cornish Cottage Holidays, The Old Turnpike Dairy, Godolphin Road, Helston, Cornwall TR13 8AA
T: (01326) 573808
F: (01326) 564992
E: enquiry@cornishcottageholidays.co.uk
I: www.cornishcottageholidays.co.uk

Discovery ★★★
Contact: Cornish Cottage Holidays, Godolphin Road, Helston, Cornwall TR13 8AA
T: (01326) 573808
F: (01326) 564992
E: enquiry@cornishcottageholidays.co.uk
I: www.cornishcottageholidays.co.uk

Foxes Barn ★★★
Contact: Mr Fone, Parc An Fox, Tregarne, Manaccan, Helston, Cornwall
T: (01326) 280150

Hallowarren Barn ★★
Contact: Cornish Cottage Holidays, The Old Turnpike Dairy, Godolphin Road, Helston, Cornwall TR13 8AA
T: (01326) 573808
F: (01326) 564992
E: enquiry@cornishcottageholidays.co.uk
I: www.cornishcottageholidays.co.uk

Hallowarren Cottage ★★★★
Contact: Cornish Cottage Holidays, The Old Turnpike Dairy, Godolphin Road, Helston, Cornwall TR13 8AA
T: (01326) 573808
F: (01326) 564992
E: enquiry@cornishcottageholidays.co.uk
I: www.cornishcottageholidays.co.uk

Hillside Cottage ★★★
Contact: Cornish Cottage Holidays, The Old Turnpike Dairy, Godolphin Road, Helston, Cornwall TR13 8AA
T: (01326) 573808
F: (01326) 564992
E: enquiry@cornishcottageholidays.co.uk
I: www.cornishcottageholidays.co.uk

Mandalay ★★★
Contact: Cornish Cottage Holidays, The Old Turnpike Dairy, Godolphin Road, Helston, Cornwall TR13 8AA
T: (01326) 573808
F: (01326) 564992
E: enquiry@cornishcottageholidays.co.uk
I: www.cornishcottageholidays.co.uk

Minster Farm ★★★★
Contact: Cornish Cottage Holidays, Godolphin Road, Helston, Cornwall TR13 8AA
T: (01326) 573808
F: (01326) 564992
E: enquiry@cornishcottageholidays.co.uk
I: www.cornishcottageholidays.co.uk

Myrtle Cottage ★★★
Contact: Mrs B Williams, Addiscombe, St Keverne, Helston, Cornwall TR12
T: (01326) 280013

Penjoy ★★
Contact: Cornish Cottage Holidays, The Old Turnpike Dairy, Godolphin Road, Helston, Cornwall TR13 8AA
T: (01326) 573808
F: (01326) 564992
E: enquiry@cornishcottageholidays.co.uk
I: www.cornishcottageholidays.co.uk

Tregithy Barn ★★★
Contact: Cornish Cottage Holidays, The Old Turnpike Dairy, Godolphin Road, Helston, Cornwall TR13 8AA
T: (01326) 573808
F: (01326) 564992
E: enquiry@cornishcottageholidays.co.uk
I: www.cornishcottageholidays.co.uk

MANATON
Devon
Homer Heales ★★
Contact: Mrs A Moreton, Great Houndtor, Manaton, Newton Abbot, Devon TQ13 9UW
T: (01647) 221202

Wingstone Farm Cottage ★★★
Contact: Mrs Rich, Wingstone Farm, Manaton, Newton Abbot, Devon TQ13
T: (01647) 221215
E: julietterich@ukgateway.net

MANNINGFORD ABBOTS
Wiltshire
The Old Tulip Barn ★★★
Contact: Mrs Margot Andrews, Huntlys, Manningford Abbots, Pewsey, Wiltshire SN9 6HZ
T: (01672) 563663
F: (01672) 851249

MARAZION
Cornwall
Polgew ★★★★
Contact: Mrs Diane Hickman, Paddock Wood, Crenver Corner, Camborne, Cornwall TR14 0PE
T: (01209) 831740
F: (01209) 832007
E: polgew1@ntlworld.com
I: www.westcornwallholidays.co.uk

St Aubyn Estates ★★★-★★★★★
Contact: Mrs Mary St Aubyn, St Aubyn Estates, The Manor Office, Marazion, Cornwall TR17 0EF
T: (01736) 710233
F: (01736) 711544
E: godolphin@manor-office.co.uk
I: www.staubynestates.co.uk

Tregew Vean ★★
Contact: Mrs J H Pool, Tregew, Rose Hill, Marazion, Cornwall TR17 0HB
T: (01736) 710247

The White House, Courtyard Cottage and Courtyard Mews Flat★★★
Contact: Ms Jo Sewell, Exmoor House, Porlock, Minehead, Somerset TA24 8EY
T: (01643) 863155
F: (01643) 863371
E: cornishcottages@its-fts.com

MARHAMCHURCH
Cornwall
Marhayes ★★★
Contact: Mr Peter Morris, Farm & Cottage Holidays, Victoria House, 12 Fore Street, Northam, Bideford, Devon EX39 1AW
T: (01237) 479146
F: (01237) 421512
E: farmcott@cix.co.uk
I: www.farmcott.co.uk

MARK
Somerset
Dutch Court Farm ★★
Contact: Mrs Margaret Jean Hares, Dutch Court Farm, Dutch Road, Mark, Highbridge, Somerset TA9 4QR
T: (01278) 783474

Pear Tree Cottage ★★★
Contact: Mrs Susan Slocombe,
Pear Tree Cottage, Northwick
Road, Mark, Highbridge,
Somerset TA9 4PG
T: (01278) 641228
E: northwickfarm@breathemail.
net

Yardwall House ★★★
Contact: Mrs Lynne Smith,
Yardwall House, Yardwall Road,
Mark, Highbridge, Somerset
TA9 4QE
T: (01278) 641453
F: (01278) 641673
E: yardwall@tesco.net

MARKET LAVINGTON
Wiltshire

Hazel Cottage ★★★★
Contact: Mrs J M Hodgkinson, 5
Parsonage Lane, Market
Lavington, Devizes, Wiltshire
SN10 4AA
T: (01380) 813516
F: (01380) 813516
E: okasan@waitrose.com

MARSTON
Wiltshire

**Barn Cottage & Stable Cottage
★★★★**
Contact: Mrs Joy Reardon, Barn
Cottage & Stable Cottage, Home
Farm, Close Lane, Marston,
Devizes, Wiltshire SN10 5SN
T: (01380) 725484

MARTINHOE
Devon

**Hollowbrook Lodge & Cottage
★★★★**
Contact: Marsden's Cottage
Holidays, 2 The Square,
Braunton, Devon EX33 2JB
T: (01271) 813777
F: (01271) 813664
E: holidays@marsdens.co.uk
I: www.marsdens.co.uk

Ivy Cottage ★★★
Contact: Marsden's Cottage
Holidays, 2 The Square,
Braunton, Devon EX33 2JB
T: (01271) 813777
F: (01271) 813664
E: holidays@marsdens.co.uk
I: www.marsdens.co.uk

MARWOOD
Devon

The Tallett ★★★
Contact: Marsden's Cottage
Holidays, 2 The Square,
Braunton, Devon EX33 2JB
T: (01271) 813777
F: (01271) 813664
E: holidays@marsdens.co.uk
I: www.marsdens.co.uk

MAWGAN PORTH
Cornwall

Trelawns ★★★★
Contact: Cornish Cottage
Holidays, The Old Turnpike Dairy,
Godolphin Road, Helston,
Cornwall TR13 8AA
T: (01326) 573808
F: (01326) 564992
E: enquiry@
cornishcottageholidays.co.uk
I: www.cornishcottageholidays.
co.uk

Trelyn ★★★
Contact: Cornish Cottage
Holidays, The Old Turnpike Dairy,
Godolphin Road, Helston,
Cornwall TR13 8AA
T: (01326) 573808
F: (01326) 564992
E: enquiry@
cornishcottageholidays.co.uk
I: www.cornishcottageholidays.
co.uk

MELKSHAM
Wiltshire

**Moorlands Self Catering
Holiday Homes★★★★**
Contact: Mrs Jackie Moore,
Moorlands Self Catering Holiday
Homes, The Coach House,
Station Approach, Melksham,
Wiltshire SN12 8BN
T: (01225) 702155 &
07900 056546
F: (01225) 702155
E: moorlands@aol.com
I: www.moorlandsuk.co.uk

MELPLASH
Dorset

Binghams Farm ★★★
Contact: Mr & Mrs Roy and
Barbara Philpott, Binghams
Farm, Melplash, Bridport, Dorset
DT6 3TT
T: (01308) 488234
E: binghamsfarm@hotmail.com
I: www.binghamsfarm.co.uk

Vine Cottage ★★★★
Contact: Lyme Bay Holidays,
Boshouse, 44 Church Street,
Lyme Regis, Dorset DT7 3DA
T: (01297) 443363
F: (01297) 445576
E: email@lymebayholidays.
co.uk
I: www.lymebayholidays.co.uk

MEMBURY
Devon

Goodmans House ★★★★
Contact: Mr Patricia Spencer,
Goodmans House, Furley,
Axminster, Devon EX13 7TU
T: (01404) 881690

MENHENIOT
Cornwall

**Hayloft Courtyard Cottages
★★★–★★★★**
Contact: Mr & Mrs Hore,
Hoseasons Country Cottages,
Lowestoft, Suffolk NR32 2LW
T: (01502) 501515
I: www.hoseasons.co.uk

Trewint Farm ★★★–★★★★
Contact: Mrs Elizabeth Rowe,
Trewint Farm, Menheniot,
Liskeard, Cornwall PL14 3RE
T: (01579) 347155
F: (01579) 347155
I: www.geocities.
com/trewint_2000

MERE
Wiltshire

Brookside Holiday Cottage ★★
Contact: Mrs E K Savage,
Waterside, Burton, Mere,
Warminster, Wiltshire BA12 6BR
T: (01747) 860079 & 860541
F: (01747) 860079
E: brookside@inker.com
I: www.stillwell.co.uk

2 Chance Cottages ★★★★
Contact: Mr & Mrs N B White,
Chance Cottage, Shaftesbury
Road, Mere, Warminster,
Wiltshire BA12 6BW
T: (01747) 861401 &
07977 035814
F: (01747) 861401
E: chancecottage@btinternet

Lower Mere Park Farm ★★★
Contact: Mrs Nicky Mitchell,
Lower Mere Park Farm, Mere,
Warminster, Wiltshire BA12 6AD
T: (01747) 830771

Mallard Lodge ★★★★
Contact: Mrs C Campbell,
Whistley Waters, Milton-on-
Stour, Gillingham, Dorset
SP8 5PT
T: (01747) 840666
F: (01747) 840666
E: campbell.whistley@virgin.net

Primrose Cottage ★★★
Contact: Mrs J Bristow, Castle
View, The Fields, Mere,
Warminster, Wiltshire BA12 6EA
T: (01747) 860103

MEVAGISSEY
Cornwall

Albatross ★★★
Contact: Mr & Mrs Bowater,
Helpful Holidays, Mill Street,
Chagford, Newton Abbot, Devon
TQ13 8AW
T: (01647) 433593
F: (01647) 433694
E: help@helpfulholidays.com
I: www.helpfulholidays.com

Lerryn and Pink ★★★
Contact: Holiday Homes &
Cottages South West, 365A
Torquay Road, Paignton, Devon
TQ3 2BT
T: (01803) 663650
F: (01803) 664037
E: holcotts@aol.com
I: www.swcottages.co.uk

**Treleaven Farm Cottages
★★★★**
Contact: Mr L Hennah, Treleaven
Farm Cottages, Treleaven Farm,
Mevagissey, St Austell, Cornwall
PL26 6RZ
T: (01726) 843558 & 842413
F: (01726) 843558
E: linda.hennah@btinternet.
com
I: www.treleavenfarm.co.uk

**Treloen Holiday Apartments
★★★**
Contact: Mr and Mrs C J
Seamark, Treloen Holiday
Apartments, Dept E, Polkirt Hill,
Mevagissey, St Austell, Cornwall
PL26 6UX
T: (01726) 842406
F: (01726) 842406
E: holidays@treloen.co.uk
I: www.treloen.co.uk

MICHAELSTOW
Cornwall

**48 Michaelstow Holiday
Village ★★**
Contact: Mr & Mrs Sevier, The
Chestnuts, Trevarren, St Columb,
Cornwall TR6 6PJ
T: (01726) 860227
E: jmsevier@globalnet.co.uk
I: www.users.globalnet.co.uk.
jmsevier/
michaelstow%20no%2048.htm

MIDDLE MARWOOD
Devon

Primrose House ★★★★
Contact: Marsden's Cottage
Holidays, 2 The Square,
Braunton, Devon EX33 2JB
T: (01271) 813777
F: (01271) 813664
E: holidays@marsdens.co.uk
I: www.marsdens.co.uk

MIDDLEMARSH
Dorset

White Horse Farm ★★★
Contact: Mr David Wilding,
White Horse Farm, Middlemarsh,
Sherborne, Dorset DT9 5QN
T: (01963) 210222
F: (01963) 210222
E: enquiries@whitehorsefarm.
co.uk
I: www.whitehorsefarm.co.uk

MILLBROOK
Cornwall

The Retreat/The Studio ★★★
Contact: Mr Peter Morris, Farm
& Cottage Holidays, Victoria
House, 12 Fore Street, Northam,
Bideford, Devon EX39 1AW
T: (01237) 479146
F: (01237) 421512
E: farmcott@cix.co.uk
I: www.farmcott.co.uk

MILLENDREATH
Cornwall

Lavernock Holidays ★★
Contact: Mr & Mrs C B Mathias,
34 Pen-nant Road, Felinfoel,
Llanelli, Carms SA14 8ES
T: (01554) 751037

MILTON ABBOT
Devon

Coriander ★★★
Contact: Mr I Prout, Coriander,
Milton Abbot, Tavistock, Devon
PL19 0QP
T: (01822) 870217

MILTON DAMEREL
Devon

The Coach House ★★★
Contact: CH ref: 8394, Holiday
Cottages Group Owner Services
Dept, Spring Mill, Earby,
Barnoldswick, Lancashire
BB94 0AA
T: (01282) 445096
F: (01282) 844299
E: ch.sales@ttgihg.co.uk
I: www.country-holidays.co.uk

Northtown Farm ★★★
Contact: Farm & Cottage
Holidays, 12 Fore Street,
Northam, Bideford, Devon EX39
T: (01409) 261389

MILVERTON
Somerset
Turnpike Cottage ★★
Contact: Mr Peter Cowling,
Kirazli, Turnpike, Milverton,
Taunton, Somerset TA4 1LF
T: (01823) 400492

MINEHEAD
Somerset
Anchor Cottage ★★★★
Contact: Dr J C Malin, 3 The
Courtyard, Bancks Street,
Minehead, Somerset TA24 5DJ
T: (01643) 707529
F: (01643) 708712

Combe Cottages ★★★★
Contact: Mrs B D Parks, Mead
House, 104 Periton Lane,
Minehead, Somerset TA24 8DZ
T: (01643) 704939

Dome Flat ★★★★
Contact: Mr J Lowin, 176A
Harefield Road, Uxbridge,
Middlesex UB8 1PP
T: (01895) 236972

Dove Cottage ★★★
Contact: Mr B B Waterman, 38
Fernleigh Road, Winchmore Hill,
London N21 3AL
T: (020) 8882 4920

Eversleigh ★★
Contact: Mrs S J Downing,
Eversleigh, Flat 2, The Esplanade,
Minehead, Somerset TA24 5QS
T: (01643) 705796

Fishermans Cottages ★★★
Contact: Mrs PDR Martin, 57
Quay Street, Minehead,
Somerset TA24 5UL
T: (01643) 704263

Fox Cottage ★★★
Contact: Mr RCS Frost, Old
Stone, 13 Park Street, Dunster,
Minehead, Somerset TA24 6SR
T: (01643) 822193

Harbour Cottage ★★
Contact: Mrs J M Medland,
Heatherbank, Glebelands,
Minehead, Somerset TA24 8DH
T: (01643) 702893

The Haven Holiday Flats ★★
Contact: Mrs P Thorpe, The
Haven Holiday Flats, 41
Blenheim Road, Minehead,
Somerset TA24 5QA
T: (01643) 705167

Higher Rodhuish Farm ★★★
Contact: Mrs J Thomas, Higher
Rodhuish Farm, Minehead,
Somerset TA24 6QL
T: (01984) 640253
F: (01984) 640253

Hindon Farm ★★★-★★★★
Contact: Mrs Webber, Hindon
Farm, Minehead, Somerset
TA24 8SH
T: (01643) 705244
F: (01643) 705244

The Hopcott ★★★
Contact: CH ref: 7445,10920,
Holiday Cottages Group Owner
Services Dept, Spring Mill, Earby,
Barnoldswick, Lancashire
BB94 0AA
T: (01282) 445096
F: (01282) 844299
E: ch.sales@ttgihg.co.uk
I: www.country-holidays.co.uk

Jaycroft ★★★
Contact: The Proprietor,
Jaycroft, 29 Glenmore Road,
Minehead, Somerset TA24 5BQ

La Mer ★★★★
Contact: Mrs A Bowden, 4 Tides
Reach, The Harbour, Minehead,
Somerset TA24 5UL
T: (01643) 704405 & 705235

Little Barn Cottage ★★★★
Contact: Mrs Marian Padgett,
Little Barn Cottage, Selworthy,
Minehead, Somerset TA24 8TL
T: (01643) 862303

Luxury Flat ★★
Contact: Mr & Mrs D J Coward,
28 Parks Lane, Minehead,
Somerset TA24 8BT
T: (01643) 705634

Old Black Boy Cottage ★★★
Contact: Mr & Mrs Harvey, 42
Bampton Street, Minehead,
Somerset TA24 5TT
T: (01643) 705016

Parkside ★★
Contact: Mrs Janet Bond,
Parkside, 31 Blenheim Road,
Minehead, Somerset TA24 5PZ
T: (01643) 703720
I: www.travel.to/parkside

Peake Cottage ★★★
Contact: Mr H J Davies, 5 West
Park Close, Minehead, Somerset
TA24 8BB
T: (01643) 704634

Pella ★★★
Contact: Mrs H C Yendole, Pella,
Western Lane, Minehead,
Somerset TA24 8BZ
T: (01643) 703277

Rosanda House ★★★
Contact: Mr & Mrs Richard &
Lorna Robbins, Rosanda House,
2 Northfield Road, Minehead,
Somerset TA24 5QQ
T: (01643) 704958 &
07867 501910
E: enquiries@rosanda.co.uk
I: www.rosanda.co.uk

Seagate Cottage ★★★★
Contact: Dr & Mr M&R Eaton &
Ball, 'Applegarth', Middle
Chinnock, Crewkerne, Somerset
TA18 7PW
T: (01935) 881436
E: megan.eaton@ukonline.co.uk

Waters Edge ★★★
Contact: CH Ref: 15296,
Holidays Cottages Group, Owner
Services Dept, Spring Mill, Earby,
Barnoldswick, Lancashire
BB18 6RN
T: (01282) 445096
F: (01282) 844299
E: ch.sales@ttgihg.co.uk
I: www.country-holidays.co.uk

MINIONS
Cornwall
Trewalla Farm ★★★★
Contact: Fiona Cotter, Trewalla
Farm, Minions, Liskeard,
Cornwall PL14 6ED
T: (01579) 342385
F: (01579) 342385

MITHIAN
Cornwall
Miner's Retreat ★★★
Contact: Cornish Cottage
Holidays, The Old Turnpike Dairy,
Godolphin Road, Helston,
Cornwall TR13 8AA
T: (01326) 573808
F: (01326) 564992
E: enquiry@
cornishcottageholidays.co.uk
I: www.cornishcottageholidays.
co.uk

MODBURY
Devon
**Oldaport Farm Cottages
★★★★**
Contact: Miss C M Evans,
Oldaport Farm Cottages,
Modbury, Ivybridge, Devon
PL21 0TG
T: (01548) 830842
F: (01548) 830998
E: cathy.evans@dial.pipex.com
I: www.oldaport.dial.pipex.com

Pinewood Lodge ★★★★
Contact: Mrs Fiona Dukes, 188
Solihull Road, Shirley, Solihull,
West Midlands B90 3LG
T: (0121) 7441162 &
07778 263827
F: (0121) 7441162
E: fdukes@globalnet.co.uk

MONKTON COMBE
Bath and North East Somerset
Spring Cottage ★★★
Contact: Mr & Mrs Arnold,
Riverside Lodge, 78 High Street,
Brandon, Suffolk IP27 0AU
T: (01842) 811236 &
07720 906480
F: (01842) 811236

MONTACUTE
Somerset
Abbey Farm ★★★
Contact: Mrs J R Jenkins, Abbey
Farm, Montacute, Somerset
TA15 6UA
T: (01935) 823572
F: (01935) 823572
E: xxe70@dial.pipex.com
I: www.dial.pipex.com

Woodhouse Cottage ★★★★
Contact: Mr and Mrs G
Baggesen, Woodhouse Cottage,
Woodhouse Lane, Montacute,
Somerset TA15 6XL
T: (01935) 824487
F: (01935) 823720
E: patricia.baggesen@tesco.net

MORCHARD BISHOP
Devon
Fern Cottage ★★★
Contact: Mr and Mrs Sparke,
Tyonalanga, 66 Lampton Road,
Long Ashton, Bristol BS41 9AQ
T: (01275) 393626

MORCOMBELAKE
Dorset
Norchard Farmhouse ★★★
Contact: Mrs M Ollard, Norchard
Farmhouse, Morcombelake,
Bridport, Dorset DT6 6EP
T: (01297) 489263
F: (01297) 489661

Prospect ★★
Contact: Mrs E Holford,
Prospect, Morcombelake,
Bridport, Dorset DT6 6DJ
T: (01297) 489637

MORETONHAMPSTEAD
Devon
Budleigh Farm ★★-★★★★
Contact: Mrs J Harvey, Budleigh
Farm, Moretonhampstead,
Newton Abbot, Devon TQ13 8SB
T: (01647) 440835 & 440436
E: swharvey@budleighfarm.
co.uk
I: www.budleighfarm.co.uk

Great Doccombe Farm ★★★★
Contact: Mr and Mrs D G Oakey,
Great Doccombe Farm,
Doccombe, Moretonhampstead,
Newton Abbot, Devon TQ13 8SS
T: (01647) 440694

**Narramore Farm Cottages
★★★★**
Contact: Mrs Sue Horn,
Narramore Farm Cottages,
Narramore Farm,
Moretonhampstead, Newton
Abbot, Devon TQ13 8QT
T: (01647) 440455
F: (01647) 440031
E: narramore@btinternet.com
I: www.narramorefarm.co.uk

Yarningale ★★★
Contact: Mrs Sarah Radcliffe,
Yarningale, Exeter Road,
Moretonhampstead, Newton
Abbot, Devon TQ13 8SW
T: (01647) 440560
F: (01647) 440560
E: sally.radcliffe@virgin.net

MORTEHOE
Devon
Combesgate House ★★★
Contact: Mr & Mrs Sprason,
Ferndale Leisure, 36 Ferndale
Park, Stourbridge, West
Midlands DY9 0RB
T: (01562) 883038
F: (01562) 886592
E: ferndale.leisure@virgin.net
I: www.freespace.virgin.
net/keith.sprason/ferndale/

Crows Nest ★★★
Contact: Marsden's Cottage
Holidays, 2 The Square,
Braunton, Devon EX33 2JB
T: (01271) 813777
F: (01271) 813664
E: holidays@marsdens.co.uk
I: www.marsdens.co.uk

**Mailscot & Wykeham
★★-★★★**
Contact: Marsden's Cottage
Holidays, 2 The Square,
Braunton, Devon EX33 2JB
T: (01271) 813777
F: (01271) 813664
E: holidays@marsdens.co.uk
I: www.marsdens.co.uk

MORVAL
Cornwall
**Wringworthy Holiday Cottages
★★★★**
Contact: Mr Peter Morris, Farm
& Cottage Holidays, Victoria
House, 12 Fore Street, Northam,
Bideford, Devon EX39 1AW
T: (01237) 479146
F: (01237) 421512
E: farmcott@cix.co.uk
I: www.farmcott.co.uk

SOUTH WEST

MORWENSTOW
Cornwall

**Gooseham Barton Cottages
Rating Applied For**
Contact: Miss D Hamilton,
Gooseham Barton Cottages,
Gooseham Barton, Morwenstow,
Bude, Cornwall EX23 9PG
T: (01288) 331204

MOSTERTON
Dorset

Riverside ★★
Contact: Mrs Young, 61 Clifton
Road, Southampton, SO15 4GY
T: (023) 8077 1729

MOTHECOMBE
Devon

**The Flete Estate Holiday
Cottages★★★-★★★★★**
Contact: Miss J Webb, The Flete
Estate Holiday Cottages,
Mothecombe, Holbeton,
Plymouth PL8 1LA
T: (01752) 830253
F: (01752) 830500
E: cottages@flete.co.uk
I: www.flete.co.uk

MOUNT HAWKE
Cornwall

Wayside ★★
Contact: Cornish Cottage
Holidays, Godolphin Road,
Helston, Cornwall TR13 8AA
T: (01326) 573808
F: (01326) 564992
E: enquiry@
cornishcottageholidays.co.uk
I: www.cornishcottageholidays.
co.uk

MOUSEHOLE
Cornwall

The Barn ★★★
Contact: Cornish Cottage
Holidays, Godolphin Road,
Helston, Cornwall TR13 8AA
T: (01326) 573808
F: (01326) 564992
E: enquiry@
cornishcottageholidays.co.uk
I: www.cornishcottageholidays.
co.uk

Coastpath Cottage ★★★
Contact: Cornish Cottage
Holidays, Godolphin Road,
Helston, Cornwall TR13 8AA
T: (01326) 573808
F: (01326) 564992
E: enquiry@
cornishcottageholidays.co.uk
I: www.cornishcottageholidays.
co.uk

Fern Cottage ★★★
Contact: Mr & Mrs Phillip &
Melanie Stephens, Churleys
Cottage, Fore Street, Mousehole,
Penzance, Cornwall TR19 6TQ
T: (01736) 731363
E: stephens@churleys.freeserve.
co.uk

Harbour Lights ★★★
Contact: Cornish Cottage
Holidays, The Old Turnpike Dairy,
Godolphin Road, Helston,
Cornwall TR13 8AA
T: (01326) 573808
F: (01326) 564992
E: enquiry@
cornishcottageholidays.co.uk
I: www.cornishcottageholidays.
co.uk

Harbourside Cottage ★★★★
Contact: Ms Jo Sewell, Exmoor
House, Porlock, Minehead,
Somerset TA24 8EY
T: (01643) 863155
F: (01643) 863371

2 The Old Standard ★★★
Contact: Mr & Mrs J Underhill,
The Old Vicarage, Collingbourne
Kingston, Marlborough,
Wiltshire SN8 3SE
T: (01264) 850234
F: (01264) 850703

Sarahs Cottage ★★
Contact: CH ref: 1672, Country
Holidays Group Owner Services
Dept, Spring Mill, Earby,
Barnoldswick, Lancashire
BB18 6RN
T: (01282) 445096
F: (01282) 844299
E: ch.sales@ttgihg.co.uk
I: www.country-holidays.co.uk

Tide's Reach ★★★★
Contact: Mr & Mrs S Hall,
Exmoor House, Porlock,
Minehead, Somerset TA24 8EY
T: (01643) 863155
F: (01643) 863371
E: cornishcottages@its-fts.com

Tregarron ★★★
Contact: Mrs Beryl Matthews,
'Cair-Kinan', 4 Gwelenys Road,
Mousehole, Penzance, Cornwall
T: (01736) 731202

MUCHELNEY
Somerset

**Gothic House (The Old Dairy)
★★★**
Contact: Mrs Joy Thorne, Gothic
House (The Old Dairy),
Muchelney, Langport, Somerset
TA10 0DW
T: (01458) 250626
E: joy-thorne@totalserve.co.uk

MUCHELNEY HAM
Somerset

South Ham Barn ★★★
Contact: Mrs Elizabeth
Nightingale, South Ham Farm,
Muchelney Ham, Langport,
Somerset TA10 0DJ
T: (01458) 250816
F: (01458) 250816
E: p.nightingale@btinternet.
com

MUDDIFORD
Devon

Ashtree Cottage ★★★★
Contact: Marsden's Cottage
Holidays, 2 The Square,
Braunton, Devon EX33 2JB
T: (01271) 813777
F: (01271) 813664
E: holidays@marsdens.co.uk
I: www.marsdens.co.uk

MUDGLEY
Somerset

Hayloft Cottage ★★★
Contact: Mr Hugh Tucker,
Hayloft Cottage, Court Farm,
Mudgley, Wedmore, Somerset
BS28 4TY
T: (01934) 712367 &
07974 467229
E: htucker@courtfarmcottages.
co.uk
I: www.courtfarmcottages.co.uk/

MULLACOTT CROSS
Devon

**The Stable and Farmhouse
★★★**
Contact: Mrs M Furnifer, The
Stable and Farmhouse, Higher
Mullacott Farm, Mullacott Cross,
Ilfracombe, Devon EX34 8NA
T: (01271) 866594

MULLION
Cornwall

**Higher Predannack Farmhouse
★★★★**
Contact: Cornish Cottage
Holidays, Godolphin Road,
Helston, Cornwall TR13 8AA
T: (01326) 573808
F: (01326) 564992
E: enquiry@
cornishcottageholidays.co.uk
I: www.cornishcottageholidays.
co.uk

Mullion Mill Cottage ★★★
Contact: Mrs Lane, Treloskan
Farm, Cury, Helston, Cornwall
TR12
T: (01326) 240493

Nythfa ★★★
Contact: Cornish Cottage
Holidays, The Old Turnpike Dairy,
Godolphin Road, Helston,
Cornwall TR13 8AA
T: (01326) 573808
F: (01326) 564992
E: enquiry@
cornishcottageholidays.co.uk
I: www.cornishcottageholidays.
co.uk

Ogo-Dour ★★★
Contact: Cornish Cottage
Holidays, The Old Turnpike Dairy,
Godolphin Road, Helston,
Cornwall TR13 8AA
T: (01326) 573808
F: (01326) 564992
E: enquiry@
cornishcottageholidays.co.uk
I: www.cornishcottageholidays.
co.uk

Predannack Farmhouse ★★★
Contact: Cornish Cottage
Holidays, The Old Turnpike Dairy,
Godolphin Road, Helston,
Cornwall TR13 8AA
T: (01326) 573808
F: (01326) 564992
E: enquiry@
cornishcottageholidays.co.uk
I: www.cornishcottageholidays.
co.uk

Predannack Manor ★★★
Contact: Cornish Cottage
Holidays, The Old Turnpike Dairy,
Godolphin Road, Helston,
Cornwall TR13 8AA
T: (01326) 573808
F: (01326) 564992
E: enquiry@
cornishcottageholidays.co.uk
I: www.cornishcottageholidays.
co.uk

Tregonning ★★★
Contact: Cornish Cottage
Holidays, The Old Turnpike Dairy,
Godolphin Road, Helston,
Cornwall TR13 8AA
T: (01326) 573808
F: (01326) 564992
E: enquiry@
cornishcottageholidays.co.uk
I: www.cornishcottageholidays.
co.uk

Trenance Farm Cottages ★★★
Contact: Mr & Mrs Richard &
Jennifer Tyler Street, Trenance
Farm Cottages, Trenance Farm,
Mullion, Helston, Cornwall
TR12 7HB
T: (01326) 240639
F: (01326) 240639
E: trenancefarm@cwcom.net
I: www.trenancefarmholidays.
co.uk

**Trewenna & Scrumpy Cottage
★★★★**
Contact: Mr Peter Morris, Farm
& Cottage Holidays, Victoria
House, 12 Fore Street, Northam,
Bideford, Devon EX39 1AW
T: (01237) 479146
F: (01237) 421512
E: farmcott@cix.co.uk
I: www.farmcott.co.uk

MULLION COVE
Cornwall

**Polpeor Holiday Apartments
and Cottages★★★-★★★★**
Contact: Mr M Raftery, Mullion
Cottages, Churchtown, Mullion,
Helston, Cornwall TR12 7HN
T: (01326) 240315
F: (01326) 241090
E: bookings@mullioncottages.
com
I: www.mullioncottages.com

MUSBURY
Devon

Green Meadows ★★★
Contact: Milkbere Cottage
Holidays, 14 Fore Street, Seaton,
Devon EX12 2LA
T: (01297) 20729
F: (01297) 24831
E: info@milkbere.com
I: www.milkbere.com

MYLOR
Cornwall

Albion House Cottages ★
Contact: Mrs P Polglase, Mylor,
Falmouth, Cornwall TR11 5SQ
T: (01872) 870570

Establishments printed in blue have a detailed entry in this guide

NANSTALLON
Cornwall

Stables Cottage ★★★★
Contact: Mr Hinde, Stables Cottage, Lower Mulberry Farm, Nanstallon, Bodmin, Cornwall PL30 5LJ
T: (01208) 831636
E: hind831636@aol.com
I: www.members.aol.com/hind831636

Tregarthen Cottages ★★★★★
Contact: Mrs Margaret Bealing, Tregarthen Cottages, Nanstallon, Bodmin, Cornwall PL30 5LB
T: (01208) 831570 &
(01841) 533147
F: (01208) 831570
E: enquiries@tregarthencottages.co.uk
I: www.tregarthencottages.co.uk

NETHERHAY
Dorset

The Lodge ★★★★
Contact: Mr & Mrs Gibbs, The Lodge, The Old Barn, Netherhay, Beaminster, Dorset DT8 3RH
T: (01308) 867597
E: shirley@drimpton1964.freeserve.co.uk

NETTLECOMBE
Dorset

Wren Cottage ★★★★
Contact: Mrs Eirlys Johnson, 9 The Berkeleys, Fetcham, Leatherhead, Surrey KT22 9DW
T: (01372) 378907
E: eirlys.johnson@tinyworld.co.uk

NEW POLZEATH
Cornwall

Atlantic View & Annexe ★★★–★★★★★★
Contact: Harbour Holidays, Estuary House, Rock Road, Rock, Wadebridge, Cornwall PL27 6NW
T: (01208) 862424
F: (01208) 862218
E: rockhols@aol.com
I: www.rockholidays.com

Hilcote ★★★
Contact: Harbour Holidays - Rock, Estuary House, Rock Road, Rock, Wadebridge, Cornwall PL27 6LD
T: (01208) 862424
F: (01208) 862218
E: rockhols@aol.com
I: www.rockholidays.com

Treheather ★★★
Contact: Dr E Mayall, Osmond House, Stoke Canon, Exeter EX5 4AA
T: (01392) 841219

Veronica Cottage ★★★
Contact: Harbour Holidays - Rock, Estuary House, Rock Road, Rock, Wadebridge, Cornwall PL27 6NW
T: (01208) 862424
F: (01208) 862218
E: rockhols@aol.com
I: www.rockholidays.com

NEWBRIDGE
Cornwall

Bostrase Stables ★★★
Contact: CH Ref:13843, Holiday Cottages Group Owner Services Dept, Spring Mill, Earby, Barnoldswick, Lancashire BB18 6RN
T: (01282) 445096
F: (01282) 844299
E: ch.sales@ttgihg.co.uk
I: www.country-holidays.co.uk

NEWLYN
Cornwall

Bryn ★★★
Contact: Cornish Cottage Holidays, The Old Turnpike Dairy, Godolphin Road, Helston, Cornwall TR13 8AA
T: (01326) 573808
F: (01326) 564992
E: enquiry@cornishcottageholidays.co.uk
I: www.cornishcottageholidays.co.uk

Chywoone Farm ★★★
Contact: CH ref: 8803,8804,8805, Holiday Cottages Group Owner Services Dept, Spring Mill, Earby, Barnoldswick, Lancashire BB18 6RN
T: (01282) 445096
F: (01282) 844299
E: ch.sales@ttgihg.co.uk
I: www.country-holidays.co.uk

Shamaal ★★★★
Contact: Cornish Cottage Holidays, The Old Turnpike Dairy, Godolphin Road, Helston, Cornwall TR13 8AA
T: (01326) 573808
F: (01326) 564992
E: enquiry@cornishcottageholidays.co.uk
I: www.cornishcottageholidays.co.uk

NEWQUAY
Cornwall

Manuels Farm ★★★
Contact: Mr and Mrs A Wilson, Manuels Farm, Quintrell Downs, Newquay, Cornwall TR8 4NY
T: (01637) 878300
F: (01637) 878300
E: james@manuelsfarm.co.uk
I: www.manuelsfarm.co.uk

NEWTON ABBOT
Devon

Chipley Mill
Rating Applied For
Contact: Mr L Coleman, Chipley Mill, Chipley Mill, Bickington, Newton Abbot, Devon TQ12 6JW
T: (01626) 821681
F: (01626) 821681
E: mswift@btconnect.com
I: www.chipleymill.co.uk

NEWTON FERRERS
Devon

Anchor Cottage ★★★★
Contact: Yealm Holidays, 8 Whittingham Road, Collaton, Yealmpton, Plymouth, Devon PL8 2NF
T: (01752) 872712
F: (01752) 873173
E: info@yealm-holidays.co.uk
I: www.yealm-holidays.co.uk

Flat 1 Crown Yealm ★★
Contact: Yealm Holidays, 8 Whittingham Road, Collaton, Yealmpton, Plymouth, Devon PL8 2NF
T: (01752) 872712
F: (01752) 873173
E: info@yealm-holidays.com
I: www.yealm-holidays.com

Glen Cottage ★★★
Contact: Yealm Holidays, 8 Whittingham Road, Collaton, Yealmpton, Plymouth, Devon PL8 2NF
T: (01752) 872712
F: (01752) 873173
E: infor@yealm-holidays.co.uk
I: www.yealm-holidays.co.uk

Upwood ★★★
Contact: Mrs A M Stackhouse, Upwood, Court Road, Newton Ferrers, Plymouth, Devon PL8 1DA
T: (01752) 872286
E: aline@upwood54.freeserve.co.uk

Yealm Harbourside Apartments ★★
Contact: Yealm Holidays, 8 Whittingham Road, Collaton, Yealmpton, Plymouth, Devon PL8 2NF
T: (01752) 872712
F: (01752) 873173
E: info@yealm-holidays.co.uk
I: www.yealm-holidays.co.uk

29 Yealm Road ★★★★
Contact: Mr & Mrs Bowater, Helpful Holidays, Mill Street, Chagford, Newton Abbot, Devon TQ13 8AW
T: (01647) 433593
F: (01647) 433694
E: help@helpfulholidays.com
I: www.helpfulholidays.com

NEWTON ST PETROCK
Devon

Church Gate Cottage ★★
Contact: Mr Peter Morris, Farm & Cottage Holidays, Victoria House, 12 Fore Street, Northam, Bideford, Devon EX39 1AW
T: (01237) 479146
F: (01237) 421512
E: farmcott@cix.co.uk
I: www.farmcott.co.uk

NORTH BARROW
Somerset

Richmond House Holiday Accommodation ★★★
Contact: Mrs Penny Trott, Barrow Farm, North Barrow, Yeovil, Somerset BA22 7LZ
T: (01963) 240543 &
07760 193174
F: (01963) 240543
E: rhholidays@netscape.online.co.uk
I: www.rhholidays.co.uk

NORTH BREWHAM
Somerset

Horseshoe Farm Cottage ★★★
Contact: CH ref: 77, Holiday Cottages Group Owner Services Dept, Spring Mill, Earby, Barnoldswick, Lancashire BB94 0AA
T: (01282) 445096
F: (01282) 844299
E: ch.sales@ttging.co.uk
I: www.country-holidays.co.uk

NORTH CHIDEOCK
Dorset

Hell Barn Cottages Hell Farmhouse ★★★
Contact: Mr and Mrs Diana and Shigeaki Takezoe, Hell Farmhouse, Hell Lane, North Chideock, Bridport, Dorset DT6 6LA
T: (01297) 489589
F: (01297) 489043
E: diana@hellbarn.co.uk
I: www.hellbarn.co.uk

NORTH CURRY
Somerset

Wisteria Cottage ★★
Contact: The Proprietor, Wisteria Cottage, Church Road, North Curry, Taunton, Somerset TA3 6LL

NORTH HILL
Cornwall

The Granary ★★★★
Contact: Ms Jill Goodman, Challs, Landreyne, North Hill, Launceston, Cornwall PL15 7LZ
T: (01566) 782573
E: eastgate@landreyne.freeserve.co.uk
I: www.eastgatebarn.co.uk

NORTH MOLTON
Devon

Bampfylde Cottage ★★★★★
Contact: Marsden's Cottage Holidays, 2 The Square, Braunton, Devon EX33 2JB
T: (01271) 813777
F: (01271) 813664
E: holidays@marsdens.co.uk
I: www.marsdens.co.uk

The Byre ★★★★
Contact: Mr C R Fade, The Byre, Limeslake, North Molton, South Molton, Devon EX36 3LY
T: (01598) 740494
E: fade@limeslake.freeserve.co.uk

Lambscombe Farm Cottages ★★★★
Contact: Mr & Mrs R Boulter, Lambscombe Farm Cottages, North Molton, South Molton, Devon EX36 3JT
T: (01598) 740558
E: richardboulter@supanet.com
I: www.lambscombefarm.co.uk

Pitt Farm ★★★★
Contact: Mrs G M Ayre, Pitt Farm, North Molton, South Molton, Devon EX36 3JR
T: (01598) 740285
I: www.devonfarms.co.uk

West Millbrook Farm ★★–★★★
Contact: Mrs R J Courtney, West Millbrook Farm, West Millbrook, Twitchen, South Molton, Devon EX36 3LP
T: (01598) 740382
I: www.north.molton.co.uk

NORTH PETHERWIN
Cornwall

Castle Milford Mill ★★★★
Contact: Mr Peter Morris, Farm
& Cottage Holidays, Victoria
House, 12 Fore Street, Northam,
Bideford, Devon EX39 1AW
T: (01237) 479146
F: (01237) 421512
E: farmcott@cix.co.uk
I: www.farmcott.co.uk

Waterloo Farm ★★★★
Contact: Mr Peter Morris, Farm
& Cottage Holidays, Victoria
House, 12 Fore Street, Northam,
Bideford, Devon EX39 1AW
T: (01237) 479146
F: (01237) 421512
E: farmcott@cix.co.uk
I: www.farmcott.co.uk

NORTH TAMERTON

Tamar Valley Cottages ★★★
Contact: Mr & Mrs Stephen
Rhodes, Tamar Valley Cottages,
North Tamerton House, North
Tamerton, Holsworthy, Devon
EX22 6SA
T: (01409) 271284
F: (01409) 271110
E: karinmoncrieff@ukgateway.
com.uk
I: tamarvalleycottages.com.uk

NORTH TAWTON
Devon

**East Hill Bungalow Farm
★★★**
Contact: Mr & Mrs Bowater,
Helpful Holidays, Mill Street,
Chagford, Newton Abbot, Devon
TQ13 8AW
T: (01647) 433593
F: (01647) 433694
E: help@helpfulholidays.com
I: www.helpfulholidays.com

NORTH WHILBOROUGH
Devon

Long Barn ★★★★★
Contact: Mr and Mrs John and
Ann Stocks, Long Barn, North
Whilborough, Newton Abbot,
Devon TQ12 5LP
T: (01803) 875044
F: (01803) 813842
E: longbarn@tinyworld.co.uk
I: www.ruralretreats.co.uk

NORTHAM
Devon

Bay View Maisonette ★★★
Contact: Mr Peter Morris, Farm
& Cottage Holidays, Victoria
House, 12 Fore Street, Bideford,
Devon EX39 1AW
T: (01237) 479146
F: (01237) 421512
E: farmcott@cix.co.uk
I: www.farmcott.co.uk

NORTON
Devon

West Norton Barn ★★★★
Contact: Mr Peter Morris, Farm
& Cottage Holidays, Victoria
House, 12 Fore Street, Northam,
Bideford, Devon EX39 1AW
T: (01237) 479146
F: (01237) 421512
E: farmcott@cix.co.uk
I: www.farmcott.co.uk

NORTON SUB HAMDON
Somerset

Bagnell Cottage ★★★
Contact: Eileen McCawley,
Bagnell Cottage, Little Norton,
Norton Sub Hamdon, Stoke sub
Hamdon, Somerset TA14 6TF
T: (01935) 862802
F: (01935) 862802
E: kevin.mccawley1@btinternet.
com

Little Norton Mill ★★★★
Contact: Mrs Lynn Hart, Little
Norton Mill, Little Norton,
Norton Sub Hamdon, Stoke sub
Hamdon, Somerset TA14 6TE
T: (01935) 881337
F: (01935) 881337
E: tom.hart@dial.pipex.com
I: www.priory.com/life/normi/01.
htm

The Stable ★★★★
Contact: Mr & Mrs John Fisher,
Brook House, Norton Sub
Hamdon, Stoke sub Hamdon,
Somerset TA14 6SR
T: (01935) 881789
F: (01935) 881789

NOSS MAYO
Devon

Linhay ★★★★
Contact: Hoseasons Country
Cottages, Sunway House,
Lowestoft, Suffolk NR32 2LN
T: (01502) 502615
F: (01502) 514298
E: cottages@hoseasons.co.uk

Mallards ★★★
Contact: Yealm Holidays, 8
Whittingham Road, Collaton,
Yealmpton, Plymouth, Devon
PL8 2NF
T: (01752) 872712
F: (01752) 873173
E: info@yealm-holidays.co.uk
I: www.yealm-holidays.co.uk

**Netton Farm Holiday Cottages
★★★**
Contact: Mrs Edwards, 4 Butts
Park, Newton Ferrers, Plymouth
PL8 1HY
T: (01752) 872235

**The Post House & The Galley
★★★★**
Contact: Yealm Holidays, 8
Whittingham Road, Collaton,
Yealmpton, Devon PL8 2NF
T: (01752) 872712
F: (01752) 873173
E: info@yealm-holidays.co.uk
I: www.yealm-holidays.co.uk

Wentworth Place ★★★★
Contact: Wentworth Place,
Revelstoke Road, Noss Mayo,
Plymouth PL8 1EA

NUNNEY
Somerset

Columbine Cottage ★★★
Contact: Mr & Mrs Anne & Ian
Robson, White House, Leigh
Street, Leigh Upon Mendip,
Somerset BA3 5QP
T: (01373) 812879
F: (01373) 813385
E: annejanrob@breathemail.net

OAKFORD
Devon

Apple Tree Cottage ★★★★
Contact: Ms C Booth, 47 Bradley
Gardens, Ealing, London
W13 8HE
T: (020) 8997 8028 & 7330 4955
F: (020) 8997 3633
E: claire@appletreeoakford.
fsnet.co.uk
I: www.appletree-oakford.co.uk

Coombe Cottage ★★★★
Contact: Mrs Mary Reed,
Coombe House, Oakford,
Tiverton, Devon EX16 9HF
T: (01398) 351281
F: (01398) 351211
E: coombehse@aol.com
I: www.exmoor-holiday-cottage.
co.uk

Pykes ★★★★★
Contact: Mr & Mrs Bowater,
Helpful Holidays, Mill Street,
Chagford, Newton Abbot, Devon
TQ13 8AW
T: (01647) 433593
F: (01647) 433694
E: help@helpfulholidays.com
I: www.helpfulholidays.com

OAKSEY
Wiltshire

Woodpecker Cottage ★★★
Contact: Mr & Mrs Martin & Ann
Shewry-Fitzgerald, Manby's
Farm, Oaksey, Malmesbury,
Wiltshire SN16 9SA
T: (01666) 577399
F: (01666) 577241
E: manbys@oaksey.junglelink.
co.uk
I: www.manbysfarm.com

OKEHAMPTON
Devon

Beer Farm ★★★★
Contact: Mr & Mrs R&S Annear,
Beer Farm, Okehampton, Devon
EX20 1SG
T: (01837) 840265
F: (01837) 840245
E: beerfarm.oke@which.net
I: www.beerfarm.co.uk

Fowley House ★★★
Contact: Mr Peter Morris, Farm
& Cottage Holidays, Victoria
House, 12 Fore Street, Northam,
Bideford, Devon EX39 1AW
T: (01237) 479146
F: (01237) 421512
E: farmcott@cix.co.uk
I: www.farmcott.co.uk

Little Bidlake Barns ★★★★
Contact: Mrs J Down, Little
Bidlake Barns, Bridestowe,
Okehampton, Devon EX20 4NS
T: (01837) 861233
F: (01837) 861233
E: bidlakefrm@aol.com
I: www.littlebidlakefarm.com

**Week Farm Country Holidays
★★★★**
Contact: Mrs Margaret
Hockridge, Week Farm Country
Holidays, Week Farm,
Bridestowe, Okehampton, Devon
EX20 4HZ
T: (01837) 861221
F: (01837) 861221
E: accom@weekfarmonline.com
I: www.weekfarmonline.com

OSMINGTON
Dorset

The Old Dairy ★★★★★
Contact: Mrs Karent Lee-Knott,
The Old Dairy, Halls Farm,
Church Lane, Osmington,
Weymouth, Dorset DT3 6EW
T: (01305) 837068 &
07747 803317
F: (01305) 837068

OTHERY
Somerset

**Middlefield Farm Cottage
★★★**
Contact: Mrs A S Winslade,
Elmgrove Bungalow, Middlefield
Farm, Holloway Road, Othery,
Bridgwater, Somerset TA7 0QF
T: (01823) 698368
F: (01823) 698368

OTTERHAM
Cornwall

Old Newham Farm ★★★
Contact: Mrs Mary Purdue, Old
Newham Farm, Otterham,
Camelford, Cornwall PL32 9SR
T: (01840) 230470
F: (01840) 230303
E: cottages@old-newham.co.uk
I: www.old-newham.co.uk

OTTERTON
Devon

Honeysuckle Cottage ★★★
Contact: Holiday Cottages
Group, Spring Mill, Earby,
Barnoldswick, Lancashire
BB18 6RN
T: (01282) 445096
F: (01282) 844299
E: ch.sales@ttgihg.co.uk
I: www.country-holidays.co.uk

OTTERY ST MARY
Devon

**Deblins Brook Farm Cottage
★★★★**
Contact: Mr GC Butler, Deblins
Brook Farm Cottage, Sandgate
Lane, Wiggaton, Ottery St Mary,
Devon EX11 1PX
T: (01404) 811331
F: (01404) 811331

Haven Cottage ★★★
Contact: Mr Tony Harwood,
Paradise Cottage, Chapel Lane,
Ottery St Mary, Devon EX11 1HQ
E: tonyharwood@email.com

OWERMOIGNE
Dorset

Jasmine Cottage ★★
Contact: Mrs J Lawton, 9
Moreton Road, Owermoigne,
Dorchester, Dorset DT2 8HT
T: (01305) 854457

PADSTOW
Cornwall

Alexandra House ★★★★
Contact: Mrs Moreen Williams,
Alexandra House, 30 Dennis
Road, Padstow, Cornwall
PL28 8DE
T: (01841) 532503

Bayside ★★★
Contact: Mr Eric Dawe, The Post
Office, St Merryn, Padstow,
Cornwall PL28 8NA
T: (01841) 520444
F: (01841) 520284
E: edawe@freeuk.com
I: www.cornwall.online.
co.uk/padstow-pride

Establishments printed in blue have a detailed entry in this guide

Beau Vista ★★★★
Contact: Mr P Haseldine, 12 Lanadwell Street, Padstow, Cornwall PL28 8AN
T: (01841) 533270 &
07767 405550
F: (01841) 533270
E: beauvista@padstow.uk.com
I: www.padstow.uk.com/beauvista

10 Broad Street, 2 Mill Road, 5 Mill Road★★-★★★
Contact: Mrs Susan Farr, Sheepcombe Farm, Washingpool Hill, Tockington, Bristol BS32 4NZ
T: (01454) 614861 & 613252
F: (01454) 613252

Broomleaf Cottage ★★★
Contact: Mr & Mrs Osborne, Cornish Horizions, Higher Trehemborne, St Merryn, Padstow, Cornwall PL28 8JU
T: (01841) 520889
F: (01841) 521523
E: cottages@cornishhorizons.co.uk
I: www.cornishhorizons.co.uk

Elmwood Cottages ★★★-★★★★★
Contact: Mrs Sandra Powell, Elmwood Cottages, Towan, St Merryn, Padstow, Cornwall PL28 8PJ
T: (01841) 520823
F: (01841) 520823

Fisherman's Cottage ★★
Contact: Mr & Mrs S&H Angelinetta, 18 Church Street, Banwell, North Somerset BS29 6EA
T: (01934) 822688
F: (01934) 822688

Fuchsia Cottage ★★★
Contact: Mrs N Lumley, Magnolia Cottage, 1 College Mews, Stokesley, Middlesbrough, Cleveland TS9 5DJ
T: (01642) 710732
E: lumley@magnolia1.fsnet.co.uk
I: www.fuchsiacottage.co.uk

Fulmar ★★★★
Contact: Mrs W A Richards, 24 Lancaster Crescent, Annington Parc, St Eval, Wadebridge, Cornwall PL27 7TP
T: (01841) 541296 &
07796 138516
E: w.a.richards@btinternet.com

Harbour View Holiday Flats ★★★
Contact: Mrs T Oliver, Harvest Moon, Leatherhead Road, Oxshott, Leatherhead, Surrey KT22 0HG
T: (01372) 842122 &
(01841) 532328
E: beach.hols@dial.pipex.com

Holly Cottage ★★★
Contact: Mr Brian Miller, 16 Hunts Road, Stratford-upon-Avon, Warwickshire CV37 7JJ
T: (01789) 299826
E: brian@bubbly2000.freeserve.co.uk

Hollyhocks ★★★★
Contact: Mr C Riddle, Molesworth House, Royal Cornwall Showground, Wadebridge, Cornwall PL27 7JE
T: (01208) 812183
F: (01208) 812713
E: rcaa@btinternet.com

The Laurels Holiday Park ★★★-★★★★
Contact: Mr A D Nicholson, The Laurels, Padstow Road, Whitecross, Wadebridge, Cornwall PL27 7JQ
T: (01208) 813341
F: (01208) 813341
E: anicholson@thelaurels-park.freeserve.co.uk
I: www.thelaurels-park.freeserve.co.uk

Little Dolphins ★★★
Contact: Mr & Mrs Osborne, Cornish Horizions, Higher Trehemborne, St Merryn, Padstow, Cornwall PL28 8JU
T: (01841) 520889
F: (01841) 521523
E: cottages@cornishhorizons.co.uk
I: www.cornishhorizions.co.uk

**The Lobster Pot
Rating Applied For**
Contact: 'Holidays', 101 Coventry Road, Coleshill, Birmingham B46 3EX
T: 0870 4423684
F: 0870 4423685

Market Square Holiday Apartments ★★★-★★★★
Contact: Mrs M Higgins, Tregolds, Whitecross, Wadebridge, Cornwall PL27 7JB
T: (01208) 813379

Marwood ★★★
Contact: Mr Eric Dawe, The Post Office, St Merryn, Padstow, Cornwall PL28 8NA
T: (01841) 520444
F: (01841) 520284
E: edawe@freeuk.com
I: www.cornwall-online.co.uk/padstow-pride

14 Mill Road ★★★★
Contact: Mrs L McCall, Poldark, St Merryn, Padstow, Cornwall PL28 8QA
T: (01841) 520998

The Old Bakery ★★★★
Contact: Mr Anthony Tippett, T W Properties, 6 Cross Street, Padstow, Cornwall PL28 8AT
T: (01841) 532885
F: (01841) 873517
E: tony.twproperties@virgin.net

12 The Old Boatyard ★★★
Contact: Mrs L McCall, Poldark, St Merryn Village, Padstow, Cornwall PL28 8QA
T: (01841) 520998 &
07977 190865

The Old Mill ★★★★
Contact: CH ref: 12054, Holiday Cottages Group Owner Services Dept, Spring Mill, Earby, Barnoldswick, Lancashire BB94 0AA
T: (01282) 445096
F: (01282) 844299
E: ch.sales@ttgihg.co.uk
I: www.country-holidays.co.uk

The Old Tailor's Shop ★★★
Contact: 'Holidays', 101 Coventry Road, Coleshill, Birmingham B46 3EX
T: 0870 4423684
F: 0870 4423685
E: heather@holidays-cornwall.com
I: www.holidays-cornwall.com

Overcliff ★★★
Contact: Mr & Mrs John & Gillian Hammond, The Mount Farm, Foxton, Market Harborough, Leicestershire LE16 7RD
T: (0116) 2517171 &
(01858) 545386
F: (01858) 545950
E: pjh@pjh.u-net.com

Padstow Holiday Cottages ★★★
Contact: Mrs Pat Walker, 1 Sarah's Gate, Little Petherick, Wadebridge, Cornwall PL27 7QT
T: (01841) 541180
E: info@padstow-selfcatering.co.uk
I: www.padstow-selfcatering.co.uk

Parnalls ★★
Contact: Mrs Howells, 1 Lanadwell Street, Padstow, Cornwall PL28 8AN
T: (01841) 532257

Primrose House ★★★★
Contact: Cornish Horizons Cottage Holidays Agent, Higher Trehemborne, St Merryn, Padstow, Cornwall PL28 8JU
T: (01841) 520889 & 521333
F: (01841) 521523
E: cottages@cornishhorizons.co.uk
I: www.cornishhorizons.co.uk

Redlands & Coachhouse ★★★★-★★★★★
Contact: Mr & Mrs Bowater, Helpful Holidays, Mill Street, Chagford, Newton Abbot, Devon TQ13 8AW
T: (01647) 433593
F: (01647) 433694
E: help@helpfulholidays.com
I: www.helpfulholidays.com

St Ervan Country Cottages ★★★
Contact: Mrs Carole Swain, St Ervan Country Cottages, The Old Rectory, St Ervan, Wadebridge, Cornwall PL27 7TA
T: (01841) 540255 &
07767 687457
F: (01841) 541002

13 Sarah's View ★★★
Contact: Mrs Tina Evans, 32 Dennis Road, Padstow, Cornwall PL28 8DE
T: (01841) 532814 &
07970 861748
F: (01841) 533480
E: buttfish@tinyworld.co.uk

The School House ★★★★
Contact: Mr & Mrs MJ Wilson, Coldharbour Farm, Coldharbour Lane, Hildenborough, Tonbridge, Kent TN11 9JX
T: (01732) 832085
F: (01732) 832228
E: hg.letting@virgin.net
I: www.holiday-rentals.co.uk

Shore Lodge ★★★★★
Contact: Mrs G Vivian, Gambia, 4 St Saviours Lane, Padstow, Cornwall PL28 8BD
T: (01841) 533791
E: gill.price2@virgin.net
I: www.holiday-padstow.co.uk

The Slate House ★★★★
Contact: Mrs Jane Sampson, Kingsdown House, High Street, Meysey Hampton, Cirencester, Gloucestershire GL7 5JP
T: (01285) 851703
F: (01285) 851703

**Squirrels
Rating Applied For**
Contact: Mr & Mrs Osborne, Cornish Horizons Holiday Cottages, Higher Trehemborne, St Merryn, Padstow, Cornwall PL28 8JU
T: (01841) 520889
F: (01841) 521523
E: cottages@cornishhorizons.co.uk
I: www.cornishhorizons.co.uk

Stable Cottage, Bay Cottage & Clover Cottage★★★★
Contact: Mrs J Hagley, Trevethan farm, Sarah's Lane, Padstow, Cornwall PL28 8LE
T: (01841) 532874
F: (01841) 532874
I: www.padstowcottages.co.uk

**Stone Cottage
Rating Applied For**
Contact: Dr J Richardson, 45A Cassiobury Park Avenue, Watford, WD18 7LD
T: (01923) 226218
F: (01923) 226218
E: jrichardson09@aol.com

Sunbeam Cottage ★★★★
Contact: Ms Wendy Gidlow, Sunbeam Cottage, 39 Duke Street, Padstow, Cornwall PL28 8AD
T: (01841) 533634
F: (01841) 532271
E: wendy@wgidlow-fsnet.co.uk
I: www.sunbeam_cottage.co.uk

Sunday & Sunrise Cottage ★★★★★
Contact: Mrs D E Hoe, 14 The Green, Snitterfield, Stratford-upon-Avon, Warwickshire CV37 0JG
T: (01789) 730223
F: (01789) 730199
E: mail@sundaycottage.co.uk
I: www.sundaycottage.co.uk

Tregirls ★★★
Contact: Mrs Watson Smyth, Tregirls, Padstow, Cornwall PL28 8RR
T: (01841) 532648

Tremorvah ★★
Contact: 'Holidays', 101 Coventry Road, Coleshill, Birmingham B46 3EX
T: 0870 4423684
F: 0870 4423685
E: heather@holidays-cornwall.com
I: www.holidays-cornwall.com

Trenoder ★★★
Contact: Mr & Mrs Osborne, Cornish Horizons, Higher Trehemborne, St Merryn, Padstow, Cornwall PL28 8JU
T: (01841) 520889
F: (01841) 521523
E: cottages@cornishhorizons. co.uk

Trevorrick Farm ★★★
Contact: Mrs & Mr Melanie & Mike Topliff & Benwell, Trevorrick Farm, St Issey, Wadebridge, Cornwall PL27 7QH
T: (01841) 540574
F: (01841) 540574
E: info@trevorrick.co.uk
I: www.trevorrick.co.uk

Valerian ★★★
Contact: Mrs G Vivian, Gambia, 4 St Saviours Lane, Padstow, Cornwall PL28 8BD
T: (01841) 533791
E: gill.price2@virgin.net
I: www.holiday-padstow.co.uk

Zefyros ★★★
Contact: Mrs JM Harris, The Pheasantry, East Hope, Much Wenlock, Shropshire TF13 6DN
T: (01746) 785504

't Sandt ★★★
Contact: Cornish Horizons, Higher Trehemborne, St Merryn, Padstow, Cornwall PL28 8JU
T: (01841) 520889 & 521333
F: (01841) 521523
E: cottages@cornishhorizons. co.uk
I: www.cornishhorizons.co.uk

PAIGNTON
Devon

Astor House ★★★
Contact: The Proprietor, Astor House, 54 Old Torquay Road, Preston, Paignton, Devon TQ

Bosuns Cottage
Rating Applied For
Contact: Holiday Homes & Cottages South West, 365A Torquay Road, Paignton, Devon TQ3 2BT
T: (01803) 663650
F: (01803) 664037
E: holcotts@aol.co.uk
I: www.swcottages.co.uk

The Conifers ★★
Contact: Holiday Homes & Cottages South West, 365A Torquay Road, Paignton, Devon TQ3 2BT
T: (01803) 663650
F: (01803) 664037
E: holcotts@aol.com
I: www.swcottages.co.uk

Cranmore Lodge ★★★
Contact: Mr Deryck Edwards, Cranmore Lodge, 45 Marine Drive, Paignton, Devon TQ3 2NS
T: (01803) 556278 & 07714 497302
F: (01803) 665797

81 Dolphin Crescent ★★★
Contact: Holiday Homes & Cottages South West, 365a Torquay Road, Paignton, Devon TQ3 2BT
T: (01803) 663650
F: (01803) 664037
E: holcotts@aol.com
I: www.swcottages.co.uk

Fortescue ★★★
Contact: Holiday Homes & Cottages South West, 365A Torquay Road, Paignton, Devon TQ3 2BT
T: (01803) 663650
F: (01803) 664037
E: holcotts@aol.com
I: www.swcottages.co.uk

Glencoe Holiday Flats ★★★
Contact: Mrs P J Ayles, Glencoe Holiday Flats, Seafront, 7 Esplanade Road, Paignton, Devon TQ4 6EB
T: (01803) 557727
F: (01803) 666512

Harwood Lodge ★★★★
Contact: Mr & Mrs Holgate, Harwood Lodge, 4 Roundham Road, Paignton, Devon TQ4 6DN
T: (01803) 401357
I: www.harwoodlodge.co.uk

15 Hennock Road ★★★★
Contact: Holiday Homes & Cottages South West, 365A Torquay Road, Paignton, Devon TQ3 2BT
T: (01803) 663650
F: (01803) 664037
E: holcotts@aol.com
I: www.swcottages.co.uk

23 James Avenue ★★★★
Contact: Mr & Mrs Saunders, 182 Blatchcombe Road, Paignton, Devon TQ3 2JP
T: (01803) 526132

Little Spinney ★★★
Contact: Holiday Homes & Cottages South West, 365A Torquay Road, Paignton, Devon TQ3 2BT
T: (01803) 663650
F: (01803) 664037
E: holcotts@aol.com
I: www.swcottages.co.uk

152 Penwill Way ★★★★
Contact: Holiday Homes & Cottages South West, 365A Torquay Road, Paignton, Devon TQ3 2BT
T: (01803) 663650
F: (01803) 664037
E: holcotts@aol.com
I: www.swcottages.co.uk

103 Preston Down Road ★★★
Contact: Holiday Homes & Cottages South West, 365A Torquay Road, Paignton, Devon TQ3 2BT
T: (01803) 663650
F: (01803) 664037
E: holcotts@aol.com
I: www.swcottages.co.uk

66 Primley Park ★★★
Contact: Holiday Homes & Cottages South West, 365A Torquay Road, Paignton, Devon TQ3 2BT
T: (01803) 663650
F: (01803) 664037
E: holcotts@aol.com
I: www.swcottages.com

Sea View ★★★
Contact: Holiday Homes & Cottages South West, 365A Torquay Road, Paignton, Devon TQ3 2BT
T: (01803) 663650
F: (01803) 664037
E: holcotts@aol.com
I: www.swcottages.co.uk

Torbay Holiday Motel ★-★★
Contact: Mr G P Booth, Torbay Holiday Motel, Totnes Road, Paignton, Devon TQ4 7PP
T: (01803) 558226
F: (01803) 663375
E: enquiries@thm.co.uk
I: www.thm.co.uk

PARRACOMBE
Devon

The Pines ★★★
Contact: Mr & Mrs Bowater, Helpful Holidays, Mill Street, Chagford, Newton Abbot, Devon TQ13 8AW
T: (01647) 433593
F: (01647) 433694
E: help@helpfulholidays.com
I: www.helpfulholidays.com

Voley Farm ★★★★
Contact: Ms Judith Killen, Voley Farm, Parracombe, Barnstaple, Devon EX31 4PG
T: (01598) 763315
F: (01598) 763660
E: voleyfarm@tesco.net
I: www.voleyfarm.com

PAUL
Cornwall

Bob's House ★★★
Contact: Mrs S Giles, Kerris Farmhouse, Kerris, Paul, Penzance, Cornwall TR19 6UY
T: (01736) 731309
E: susangiles@btconnect.com
I: www.cornwall-online. co.uk/kerris-farm

PAULTON
Bath and North East Somerset

The Coach House ★★★★
Contact: Mrs Jenny Ahlberg, The Coach House, Hanham House, Hanham Lane, Paulton, Bristol BS39 7PF
T: (01761) 413121
F: (01761) 413121
E: jennyahlberg@aol.com

PEDWELL
Somerset

Higher Nythe Farm ★★★
Contact: Mrs M Coombes, Higher Nythe Farm, Pedwell, Bridgwater, Somerset TA7 9BN
T: (01458) 210271

PENDEEN
Cornwall

Kerenza ★★
Contact: Cornish Cottage Holidays, Godolphin Road, Helston, Cornwall TR13 8AA
T: (01326) 573808
F: (01326) 564992
E: enquiry@ cornishcottageholidays.co.uk
I: www.cornishcottageholidays. co.uk

Maitland House ★★
Contact: Cornish Cottage Holidays, The Old Turnpike Dairy, Godolphin Road, Helston, Cornwall TR13 8AA
T: (01326) 573808
F: (01326) 564992
E: enquiry@ cornishcottageholidays.co.uk
I: www.cornishcottageholidays. co.uk

Sunset Cottage ★★★
Contact: Mrs S Russell, 29 Fennel Way, Brympton, Yeovil, Somerset BA22 8SA
T: (01935) 414470
E: sunset@cottage9910. freeserve.co.uk
I: www.cornwall-online.co.uk

Trewellard Manor Farm ★★★-★★★★
Contact: Mrs M Bailey, Trewellard Manor Farm, Pendeen, Penzance, Cornwall TR19 7SU
T: (01736) 788526
F: (01736) 788526

PENHALLOW
Cornwall

Nutmeg & Peppercorn ★★★★
Contact: Cornish Cottage Holidays, The Old Turnpike Dairy, Godolphin Road, Helston, Cornwall TR13 8AA
T: (01326) 573808
F: (01326) 564992
E: enquiry@ cornishcottageholidays.co.uk
I: www.cornishcottageholidays. co.uk

PENSILVA
Cornwall

Meadow Lea ★★★★
Contact: CH ref: 7388, Holiday Cottages Group Owner Services Dept, Spring Mill, Earby, Barnoldswick, Lancashire BB18 6RN
T: (01282) 445096
F: (01282) 844299
E: ch.sales@ttgihg.co.uk
I: www.country-holidays.co.uk

PENTEWAN
Cornwall

Crofters End ★★★
Contact: Mr and Mrs Radmore, Higher Penrose, Tregony, Truro, Cornwall TR2 5SS
T: (01872) 501269
F: (01872) 501269

PENWITHICK
Cornwall

Poolside ★★★
Contact: Mr G McGhee, 21 Queen Street, Lostwithiel, Cornwall PL22 0AD
T: (01208) 873086
E: gerrymcghee@hotmail.com

PENZANCE
Cornwall

Aston Cottage ★★★
Contact: Mr & Mrs Bowater, Helpful Holidays, Mill Street, Chagford, Newton Abbot, Devon TQ13 8AW
T: (01647) 433593
F: (01647) 433694
E: help@helpfulholidays.com
I: www.helpfulholidays.com

Gweal Brooth ★★★
Contact: Cornish Cottage
Holidays, Godolphin Road,
Helston, Cornwall TR13 8AA
T: (01326) 573808
F: (01326) 564992
E: enquiry@
cornishcottageholidays.co.uk
I: www.cornishcottageholidays.
co.uk

The Old Farmhouse ★★★★
Contact: Mrs Vivienne Hall, The
Old Farmhouse, Chegwidden
Farm, St Levan, Penzance,
Cornwall TR19 6LP
T: (01736) 810516 &
07831 834013
F: (01736) 810516
E: halls@chegwidden.fsnet.
co.uk
I: www.chegwidden.fsnet.co.uk

Rainbow's End ★★★★
Contact: Hoseasons Holidays,
Lowestoft, Suffolk NR32 2LW
T: (01502) 500505
F: (01502) 514298
E: mail@hoseasons.co.uk

Rospannel Farm ★★★
Contact: Mr GB Hocking,
Rospannel Farm, Crows-an-Wra,
Penzance, Cornwall TR19 6HS
T: (01736) 810262
E: gbernard@thefreeinternet.
co.uk

Saint Pirans Cottages ★★★
Contact: Mrs Caroline Gresswell,
The White House, Micheldever,
Winchester, Hampshire
SO21 3AJ
T: (01962) 774379

Slipway Cottage ★★★
Contact: CH ref: 11201, Holiday
Cottages Group Owner Services
Dept, Spring Mill, Earby,
Barnoldswick, Lancashire
BB18 6RN
T: (01282) 445096
F: (01282) 844299
E: ch.sales@ttgihg.co.uk
I: www.country-holidays.co.uk

Summer Breeze ★★★
Contact: Mrs L Roberts, The
Barn, Trewarveneth Vean,
Tredaude Lane, Newlyn,
Penzance, Cornwall TR18 5DL
T: (01736) 351949

Trevenen ★★★★
Contact: Cornish Cottage
Holidays, The Old Turnpike Dairy,
Godolphin Road, Helston,
Cornwall TR13 8AA
T: (01326) 573808
F: (01326) 564992
E: enquiry@
cornishcottageholidays.co.uk
I: www.cornishcottageholidays.
co.uk

PERRANPORTH
Cornwall

4 Eureka Vale ★★★
Contact: Mr and Mrs J A Cuthill,
27 St George's Hill, Perranporth,
Cornwall TR6 0JS
T: (01872) 573624

PERRANWELL STATION
Cornwall

The Barn ★★★
Contact: Mrs Margie Lumby,
Special Places, Poachers Reach,
Feock, Truro, Cornwall TR3 6SQ
T: (01872) 864400
F: (01872) 864400
E: office@
specialplacescornwall.co.uk
I: www.specialplacescornwall.
co.uk

Greenwith Cottage ★★★
Contact: Mrs Margie Lumby,
Special Places, Poachers Reach,
Feock, Truro, Cornwall TR3 6SQ
T: (01872) 864400
F: (01872) 864400
E: office@
specialplacescornwall.co.uk
I: www.specialplacescornwall.
co.uk

Lymington Cottage ★★★★
Contact: Mrs Margie Lumby,
Special Places, Poachers Reach,
Feock, Truro, Cornwall TR3 6SQ
T: (01872) 864400
F: (01872) 864400
E: office@
specialplacescornwall.co.uk
I: www.specialplacescornwall.
co.uk

Postbox Cottage ★★★★
Contact: Mrs Margie Lumby,
Special Places, Poachers Reach,
Feock, Truro, Cornwall TR3 6SQ
T: (01872) 864400
F: (01872) 864400
E: office@
specialplacescornwall.co.uk
I: www.specialplacescornwall.
co.uk

The Studio
Rating Applied For
Contact: Ms Margie Lumby,
Special Places In Cornwall,
Poachers Reach, Feock, Truro,
Cornwall TR3 6SQ
T: (01872) 864400
F: (01872) 864400
E: office@
specialplacescornwall.co.uk
I: www.specialplacescornwall.
co.uk

PETER TAVY
Devon

Moorview Cottage ★★★★
Contact: Mr Peter Morris, Farm
& Cottage Holidays, Victoria
House, 12 Fore Street, Northam,
Bideford, Devon EX39 1AW
T: (01237) 479146
F: (01237) 421512
E: farmcott@cix.co.uk
I: www.farmcott.co.uk

Old Sowtontown ★★★
Contact: Mr Christopher
Boswell, Old Sowtontown, Peter
Tavy, Tavistock, Devon PL19 9JR
T: (01882) 810687
E: chrisboswe@aol.com
I: www.dartmoorholidays.co.uk

PETROCKSTOW
Devon

Deer Park ★★★★
Contact: Mr & Mrs Bowater,
Helpful Holidays, Mill Street,
Chagford, Newton Abbot, Devon
TQ13 8AW
T: (01647) 433593
F: (01647) 433694
E: help@helpfulholidays.com
I: www.helpfulholidays.com

PHILLACK
Cornwall

An Egarag ★★
Contact: Mrs Julie Petterson, An
Egarag, 11 Riviere Towans,
Phillack, Hayle, Cornwall
TR27 5AF
T: (01736) 753775 & 752717

PHILLEIGH
Cornwall

Ardevora Farm ★★★
Contact: Mr David Edgerton,
Ardevora Farm, Philleigh, Truro,
Cornwall TR2 5LZ
T: (01872) 501680
E: ardevora@lineone.net

Lemon Cottage ★★★★
Contact: Mrs A L Thomas,
Polmenna Farm, Philleigh, Truro,
Cornwall TR2 5ND
T: (01872) 580406
E: andythomaspolmenna@
hotmail.com

PIDDLEHINTON
Dorset

Hawthorn Cottage ★★★★
Contact: Brenda Turley, 9
Kinross Close, Spinney Hill,
Northampton, NN3 6BP
T: (01604) 644050

PIDDLETRENTHIDE
Dorset

Coach House ★★★
Contact: Mr & Mrs AMR Drewe,
Coach House, Lackington
Farmhouse, Piddletrenthide,
Dorchester, Dorset DT2 7QU
T: (01300) 348253
F: (01300) 348222
E: rdrewe@dinst.free-online.
co.uk

PILLATON
Cornwall

Upalong & Downalong
★★★★
Contact: Mrs Barnicoat,
Trefenton, Pillaton, Saltash,
Cornwall PL12 6QX
T: (01579) 350141

PLAIN-AN-GWARRY
Cornwall

Tregurtha Barn ★★★
Contact: Cornish Home
Holidays, 12 Parade Street,
Penzance, Cornwall TR18 4BU
T: (01736) 368575
F: (01736) 351493
E: chh@chh.co.uk
I: www.chh.co.uk

PLAYING PLACE
Cornwall

Kernewek ★★★
Contact: Cornish Cottage
Holidays, The Old Turnpike Dairy,
Godolphin Road, Helston,
Cornwall TR13 8AA
T: (01326) 573808
F: (01326) 564992
E: enquiry@
cornishcottageholidays.co.uk
I: www.cornishcottageholidays.
co.uk

PLYMOUTH
Devon

The Cobbles Flat 5 ★★★★
Contact: Yealm Holidays, 8
Whittingham Road, Collaton,
Yealmpton, Plymouth, Devon
PL8 2NF
T: (01752) 872712
F: (01752) 873173
E: info@yealm-holidays.co.uk
I: www.yealm-holidays.com

Coombe Farm ★★★
Contact: Mrs S J MacBean,
Coombe Farm, Wembury Road,
Wembury, Plymouth PL9 ODE
T: (01752) 401730
F: (01752) 401730

Haddington House Apartments
★★★★
Contact: Mrs A Budd, 20 Pearn
road, Higher Compton,
Plymouth, PL3 5JF
T: (01752) 767730 &
07808 015126
F: (01752) 767048
E: abudd@talk21.com
I: www.abudd.co.uk

Hideaway ★★★★
Contact: Yealm Holidays, 8
Whittingham Road, Collaton,
Yealmpton, Devon PL8 2NF
T: (01752) 872712
F: (01752) 873173
E: info@yealm-holidays.co.uk
I: www.yealm-holidays.co.uk

Hoeside Holiday Flats ★★★
Contact: Mrs D Seymour, The
Old Rectory, 20 Penlee Way,
Stoke, Plymouth PL3 4AW
T: (01752) 563504
F: (01752) 563504
E: hoeside.dsfs@virgin.net

PLYMTREE
Devon

Talehead Cottage ★★★
Contact: CH ref: 50308, Holiday
Cottages Group Owner Services
Dept, Spring Mill, Earby,
Barnoldswick, Lancashire
BB18 6RN
T: (01282) 445096
F: (01282) 844299
E: ch.sales@ttgihg.co.uk
I: www.country-holidays.co.uk

POLPERRO
Cornwall

Beville and Hael-A-Gwynt
Cottages ★★
Contact: Mrs N J Blake,
Sunways, The Coombes,
Polperro, Looe, Cornwall
PL13 2RQ
T: (01503) 272485 &
(01579) 344151

Brent House ★★
Contact: Mrs R Bristowe, Brent House, Talland Hill, Polperro, Looe, Cornwall PL13 2RY
T: (01503) 272495

Classy Cottages
★★★★–★★★★★
Contact: Mrs & Mr Fiona & Martin Nicolle, Blanches Windsor, Polperro, Looe, Cornwall PL13 2PT
T: 07000 423000
E: nicolle@classycottages.co.uk
I: www.classycottages.co.uk

Crumplehorn Cottages
★★★–★★★★
Contact: Mr M Collings, Crumplehorn Cottages, The Anchorage, Portuan Road, Hannafore, Looe, Cornwall PL13 2DN
T: (01503) 262523
F: (01503) 262523
E: gloria@crumplehorncottages.co.uk
I: www.crumplehorncottage.co.uk

Little Laney and Polhaven ★★★★
Contact: Mrs Tegan Cornish, 8 The Queensway, Austenwood Common, Gerrards Cross, Buckinghamshire SL9 8NF
T: (01753) 882482
F: (01753) 882546
E: martin.cornish@lineone.net
I: www.cornish-cottage.com

POLRUAN-BY-FOWEY
Cornwall

Peppercorn Cottage ★★
Contact: W J B Hill & Son, 3 Fore Street, Fowey, Cornwall PL23 1AH
T: (01726) 832211
F: (01726) 832901
E: hillandson@talk21.com

2 Providence Place ★★★★
Contact: Estuary Cottages, Estuary House, Fore Street, Fowey, Cornwall PL23 1AH
T: (01726) 832965 & 832299
F: (01726) 832866
E: info@estuarycottages.co.uk
I: www.estuarycottages.co.uk

Puckles Place ★★
Contact: W J B Hill & Son, 3 Fore Street, Fowey, Cornwall PL23 1AH
T: (01726) 832211
F: (01726) 832901
E: hillandson@talk21.com

Rose Villa ★★
Contact: W J B Hill & Son, 3 Fore Street, Fowey, Cornwall PL23 1AH
T: (01726) 832211
F: (01726) 832901
E: hillandson@talk21.com

Tremaine Cottage ★★★
Contact: W J B Hill & Son, 3 Fore Street, Fowey, Cornwall PL23 1AH
T: (01726) 832211
F: (01726) 832901
E: hillandson@talk21.com

POLWHELE
Cornwall

Orchard Bungalow ★★★
Contact: Mrs Thomas, Calerick Farm, Polwhele, Truro, Cornwall TR4 9AE
T: (01872) 272937

POLYPHANT
Cornwall

Darkes Court Cottages ★★★
Contact: Mr Richard Sowerby, Darkes Court Cottages, Polyphant, Launceston, Cornwall PL15 7PS
T: (01566) 86598
F: (01566) 86795

Tregarth ★★★
Contact: Mr Peter Morris, Farm & Cottage Holidays, Victoria House, 12 Fore Street, Northam, Bideford, Devon EX39 1AW
T: (01237) 479146
F: (01237) 421512
E: farmcott@cix.co.uk
I: www.farmcott.co.uk

POLZEATH
Cornwall

The Lookout ★★★
Contact: Harbour Holidays - Rock, Estuary House, Rock Road, Rock, Wadebridge, Cornwall PL27 6NW
T: (01208) 862424
F: (01208) 862218
E: rockhols@aol.com
I: www.rockholidays.com

Marmarra ★★★
Contact: Harbour Holidays - Rock, Estuary House, Rock Road, Rock, Wadebridge, Cornwall PL27 6NW
T: (01208) 862424
F: (01208) 862218
E: rockhols@aol.com
I: www.rockholidays.com

1 Pentire View
Rating Applied For
Contact: Diana Bullivant Holidays, South Winds, Trebell Green, Lanivet, Bodmin, Cornwall PL30 5HR
T: (01208) 831336
F: (01208) 831336
E: diana@dbullivant.fsnet.co.uk
I: www.cornwall-online.co.uk/diana-bullivant

2 Pentire View ★★
Contact: Diana Bullivant Holidays, South Winds, Trebell Green, Lanivet, Bodmin, Cornwall PL30 5HR
T: (01208) 831336
F: (01208) 831336
E: diana@dbullivant.fsnet.co.uk
I: www.cornwall-online.co.uk/diana-bullivant

Seaview ★★★
Contact: Diana Bullivant Holidays, South Winds, Trebell Green, Lanivet, Bodmin, Cornwall PL30 5HR
T: (01208) 831336
F: (01208) 831336
E: diana@d.bullivant.fsnet.co.uk
I: www.cornwall-online.co.uk/diana-bullivant

Stonechat ★★★
Contact: 'Holidays', 101 Coventry Road, Coleshill, Birmingham B46 3EX
T: 0870 4423684
F: 0870 4423685
E: heather@holidays-cornwall.com
I: www.holidays-cornwall.com

Trecreege Barn ★★★
Contact: Harbour Holidays - Rock, Estuary House, Rock Road, Rock, Wadebridge, Cornwall PL27 6NW
T: (01208) 862424
F: (01208) 862218
E: rockhols@aol.com
I: www.rockholidays.com

PORKELLIS
Cornwall

Ivy's Cabin ★★★
Contact: Cornish Cottage Holidays, Godolphin Road, Helston, Cornwall TR13 8AA
T: (01326) 573808
F: (01326) 564992
E: enquiry@cornishcottageholidays.co.uk
I: www.cornishcottageholidays.co.uk

PORLOCK
Somerset

Church Farm ★★★★
Contact: Toad Hall Cottages, Elliot House, Church Street, Kingsbridge, Devon TQ7 1BY
T: (01548) 521366
F: (01548) 853086
E: thc@toadhallcottages.com
I: www.toadhallcottages.com

East Cottage ★★★
Contact: Mrs Sue Gannon, 17 Wedlakes, Watchet, Somerset TA23 OJL
T: (01984) 633495
F: (01984) 633495

Green Chantry ★★★★
Contact: M Payton, Home Farm, Burrowbridge, Bridgwater, Somerset TA7 ORF
T: (01823) 698330
F: (01823) 698169
E: maggie_payton@hotmail.com

Hartshanger Holidays ★★★★
Contact: Mrs Anna Edward, Hartshanger Holidays, Hartshanger, Toll Road, Porlock, Minehead, Somerset TA24 8JH
T: (01643) 862700
F: (01643) 862700
E: hartshanger@lineone.net
I: www.hartshanger.com

Hunters Rest ★★★
Contact: Mr B West, Hunters Rest, Mill Lane, Hawkcombe, Porlock, Minehead, Somerset TA24 8QW
T: (01643) 862349
F: (01643) 863295
E: porlock@ratio.org.uk

Woodside Cottage ★★
Contact: Mr & Ms Lawrence & Daley, 41 Princes Road, Tivoli, Cheltenham, Gloucestershire GL50 2TX
T: (01242) 261435
E: woodside_cottage@hotmail.com

PORT GAVERNE
Cornwall

Green Door Cottages
★★★–★★★★
Contact: Mrs M Ross, Green Door Cottages, Port Gaverne, Port Isaac, Cornwall PL29 3SQ
T: (01208) 880244 & 0500 657867
F: (01208) 880151
E: pghotel@telinco.co.uk
I: www.chycor.co.uk/hotels/port-gaverne

PORT ISAAC
Cornwall

Atlanta ★★
Contact: Harbour Holidays, Estuary House, Rock Road, Rock, Wadebridge, Cornwall PL27 6NW
T: (01208) 862424
F: (01208) 862218
E: rockhols@aol.com
I: www.rockholidays.com

Trelanic ★★
Contact: 'Holidays', 101 Coventry Road, Coleshill, Birmingham B46 3EX
T: 0870 4423684
F: 0870 4423685
E: heather@holidays-cornwall.com
I: www.holidays-cornwall.com

Trevathan Farm
★★★–★★★★
Contact: Mrs J Symons, Trevathan Farm, St Endellion, Port Isaac, Cornwall PL29 3TT
T: (01208) 880248
F: (01208) 880248
E: symons@trevathanfarm.com
I: www.trevethanfarm.com

The White House
Rating Applied For
Contact: Dr AT Hambly, Bodrean Manor, St Clements, Truro, Cornwall TR4 9AG
T: (01872) 264400
F: (01872) 264400
E: anthonyhambly@hotmail.com
I: www.cornishholidays.uk.com

PORTESHAM
Dorset

Sleepers ★★★
Contact: Mrs S Northover, Gorselands Caravan Park, West Bexington, Dorchester, Dorset DT2 9DJ
T: (01308) 897232
F: (01308) 897239

PORTHALLOW
Cornwall

Bank Cottage ★★★
Contact: Cornish Cottage Holidays, Godolphin Road, Helston, Cornwall TR13 8AA
T: (01326) 573808
F: (01326) 564992
E: enquiry@cornishcottageholidays.co.uk
I: www.cornishcottageholidays.co.uk

Establishments printed in blue have a detailed entry in this guide

Cockle Island Cottage ★★★★
Contact: Cornish Cottage Holidays, The Old Turnpike Dairy, Godolphin Road, Helston, Cornwall TR13 8AA
T: (01326) 573808
F: (01326) 564992
E: enquiry@cornishcottageholidays.co.uk
I: www.cornishcottageholidays.co.uk

PORTHCURNO
Cornwall

Rospletha Farm ★★★★
Contact: Mrs P Thomas, Bosistow Farm, St Levan, Penzance, Cornwall TR19
T: (01736) 871254

Stargazey ★★★★
Contact: Ms E Trenary, Treeve Moor House, Sennen, Penzance, Cornwall TR19 7AE
T: (01736) 871284 &
07771 914660
F: (020) 8783 2788
E: info@firstandlastcottages.co.uk
I: www.firstandlastcottages.co.uk

PORTHLEVEN
Cornwall

An-Mordros ★★★★
Contact: Cornish Cottage Holidays, The Old Turnpike Dairy, Godolphin Road, Helston, Cornwall TR13 8GL
T: (01326) 573808
F: (01326) 564992
E: inquirey@cornishcottageholidays.co.uk
I: www.cornishcottageholidays.co.uk

Atlantic Cottage ★★★
Contact: Cornish Cottage Holidays, Godolphin Road, Helston, Cornwall TR13 8AA
T: (01326) 573808
F: (01326) 564992
E: enquiry@cornishcottageholidays.co.uk
I: www.cornishcottageholidays.co.uk

Crabpot Cottage ★★
Contact: Cornish Cottage Holidays, Godolphin Road, Helston, Cornwall TR13 8AA
T: (01326) 573808
F: (01326) 564992
E: enquiry@cornishcottageholidays.co.uk
I: www.cornishcottageholidays.co.uk

Flagstaffe House ★★★
Contact: Cornish Cottage Holidays, Godolphin Road, Helston, Cornwall TR13 8AA
T: (01326) 573808
F: (01326) 564992
E: enquiry@cornishcottageholidays.co.uk
I: www.cornishcottageholidays.co.uk

Harbour View ★★★
Contact: Cornish Cottage Holidays, Godolphin Road, Helston, Cornwall TR13 8AA
T: (01326) 573808
F: (01326) 564992
E: enquiry@cornishcottageholidays.co.uk
I: www.cornishcottageholidays.co.uk

The Haven ★★★★
Contact: Cornish Cottage Holidays, The Old Turnpike Dairy, Godolphin Road, Helston, Cornwall TR13 8AA
T: (01326) 573808
F: (01326) 564992
E: enquiry@cornishcottageholidays.co.uk
I: www.cornishcottageholidays.co.uk

Iemanja ★★★
Contact: Mrs Molloy-Davey, Iemanja, 8 Chapel Terrace, Porthleven, Helston, Cornwall TR13 9DT
T: (01326) 573637

Mounts Bay Cottage ★★★★
Contact: Cornish Cottage Holidays, Godolphin Road, Helston, Cornwall TR13 8AA
T: (01326) 573808
F: (01326) 564992
E: enquiry@cornishcottageholidays.co.uk
I: www.cornishcottageholidays.co.uk

Mounts Bay Villa ★★★
Contact: Mrs Lewin, An Mordros Hotel, Peverell Terrace, Porthleven, Helston, Cornwall TR13
T: (01326) 562236

Pegs ★★★
Contact: Cornish Cottage Holidays, The Old Turnpike Dairy, Godolphin Road, Helston, Cornwall TR13 8AA
T: (01326) 573808
F: (01326) 564992
E: enquiry@cornishcottageholidays.co.uk
I: www.cornishcottageholidays.co.uk

Peverell ★★
Contact: Cornish Cottage Holidays, The Old Turnpike Dairy, Godolphin Road, Helston, Cornwall TR13 8AA
T: (01326) 573808
F: (01326) 564992
E: enquiry@cornishcottageholidays.co.uk
I: www.cornishcottageholidays.co.uk

Rock Pools ★★★
Contact: Cornish Cottage Holidays, The Old Turnpike Dairy, Godolphin Road, Helston, Cornwall TR13 8AA
T: (01326) 573808
F: (01326) 564992
E: enquiry@cornishcottageholidays.co.uk
I: www.cornishcottageholidays.co.uk

Seagull Cottage ★★★
Contact: Country Hols Ref:11559, Holiday Cottages Group Limited, Spring Mill, Earby, Barnoldswick, Lancashire BB94 0AA
T: (01282) 445096
F: (01282) 844288
I: www.country-holidays.co.uk

Tye Rock Hotel & Apartments ★★★
Contact: Ms Judy Fordree, Tye Rock Country House Hotel, Loe Bar Road, Porthleven, Helston, Cornwall TR13 9EW
T: (01326) 572695
F: (01326) 572695

PORTHTOWAN
Cornwall

Beachside Court ★★★★
Contact: Cornish Cottage Holidays, Godolphin Road, Helston, Cornwall TR13 8AA
T: (01326) 573808
F: (01326) 564992
E: enquiry@cornishcottageholidays.co.uk
I: www.cornishcottageholidays.co.uk

PORTLAND
Dorset

Inglis Cottage ★★★★
Contact: Mr & Mrs Nigel & Judith Shaw, 145 Wakeham, Portland, Dorset DT5 1HR
T: (01305) 821042 &
07850 837367
E: nigelshaw@seeshaws.freeserve.co.uk
I: www.seeshaws.freeserve.co.uk

Lilac Cottage ★★★
Contact: Mrs Gill Morris, 1 Mermaid Cottages, Wakeham, Portland, Dorset DT5 1HS
T: (01305) 823359
E: portmorris@aol.com

The Old Higher Lighthouse ★★★★
Contact: Mrs F E Lockyer, The Old Higher Lighthouse, Portland Bill, Portland, Dorset DT5 2JT
T: (01305) 822300
E: f.lockyer@talk21.com
I: www.heartofdorset.easynet.com

PORTREATH
Cornwall

The Barnyard ★★★★
Contact: CH ref: 2994-3000, Holiday Cottages Group, Spring Mill, Earby, Barnoldswick, Lancashire BB18 6RN
T: (01282) 445096
F: (01282) 844299
E: ch.sales@ttgihg.co.uk
I: www.country-holidays.co.uk

Cliff View ★★★
Contact: Powell's Cottage Holidays, High Street, Saundersfoot, Dyfed SA69 9EJ
T: (01834) 812791
F: (01834) 811731
E: info@powells.co.uk
I: www.powells.co.uk

Cober Cay ★★★
Contact: CH ref: 50293, Holiday Cottages Group Owner Services Department, Spring Mill, Earby, Barnoldswick, Lancashire BB94 0AA
T: (01282) 445096
F: (01282) 844299
E: ch.sales@ttgihg.co.uk
I: www.country-holidays.co.uk

The Moorings ★★★
Contact: Powell's Cottage Holidays, High Street, Saundersfoot, Dyfed SA69 9EJ
T: (01834) 812791
F: (01834) 811731
E: info@powells.co.uk
I: www.powells.co.uk

Trengove Farm Cottages ★★★
Contact: Mrs Lindsey Richards, Trengove Farm, Cot Road, Illogan, Redruth, Cornwall TR16 4PU
T: (01209) 843008
F: (01209) 843682
E: richards@farming.co.uk

PORTWRINKLE
Cornwall

Treliske ★★★★
Contact: Mrs J E Cadwallader, 6 Cross Park, Crafthole, Torpoint, Cornwall PL11 3BH
T: (01503) 230933

POSTBRIDGE
Devon

Clapper Cottage ★★
Contact: Mr A Smerdon, 1 Forestry House, Bellever, Postbridge, Yelverton, Devon PL20 6SY
T: (01822) 880244

POTTERNE
Wiltshire

Abbotts Ball Farm ★★★
Contact: CH ref: 12707, Holiday Cottages Group, Spring Mill, Earby, Barnoldswick, Lancashire BB94 0AA
T: (01282) 445096
F: (01282) 844299
E: ch.sales@ttgihg.co.uk
I: www.country-holidays.co.uk

Stroud Hill Farm Holidays ★★★
Contact: Mrs Helen Straker, Stroud Hill Farm, Potterne Wick, Potterne, Devizes, Wiltshire SN10 5QR
T: (01380) 720371

POUGHILL
Cornwall

Moor Farm
Rating Applied For
Contact: Mr Peter Morris, Farm & Cottage Holidays, Victoria House, 12 Fore Street, Northam, Bideford, Devon EX39 1AW
T: (01237) 479146
F: (01237) 421512
E: farmcott@cix.co.uk
I: www.farmcott.co.uk

Establishments printed in blue have a detailed entry in this guide

POUNDISFORD
Somerset
Old Mapp's Cottage ★★★
Contact: Mrs C A Bartlett, Old
Mapp's Cottage, Corner House,
Poundisford, Taunton, Somerset
TA3 7AE
T: (01823) 421197
F: (01823) 421737

POUNDSGATE
Devon
Bramblemoor Cottage ★★★★
Contact: Mrs Helen Hull,
Bramblemoor Cottage, Leusdon,
Poundsgate, Newton Abbot,
Devon TQ13 7NU
T: (01364) 631410
E: helen.hull@eclipse.co.uk

Rogues Roost ★
Contact: Mrs Susan Booty,
Rogues Roost, Poundsgate,
Newton Abbot, Devon TQ13 7PS
T: (01364) 631223
E: sue@roguesroost.co.uk
I: www.roguesroost.co.uk

POUNDSTOCK
Cornwall
Pegsdown ★★★
Contact: Powell's Cottage
Holidays, High Street,
Saundersfoot, Dyfed SA69 9EJ
T: (01834) 812791
F: (01834) 811731
E: info@powells.co.uk
I: www.powells.co.uk

PRAA SANDS
Cornwall
Bre An Mor ★★★
Contact: Cornish Cottage
Holidays, Godolphin Road,
Helston, Cornwall TR13 8AA
T: (01326) 573808
F: (01326) 564992
E: enquiry@
cornishcottageholidays.co.uk
I: www.cornishcottageholidays.
co.uk

**Sea Meads Holiday Homes
★★★**
Contact: Miss Nicky Hann, Best
Leisure, North Hill, Shirwell,
Barnstaple, Devon EX31 4LG
T: (01271) 850611
F: (01271) 850693

PRESTON
Devon
3 Deers Leap Close ★★★
Contact: Holiday Homes &
Cottages South West, 365a
Torquay Road, Paignton, Devon
TQ3 2BT
T: (01803) 663650
F: (01803) 664037
E: holcotts@aol.com
I: www.swcottages.co.uk

PRINCETOWN
Devon
**Huccaby Farm
Rating Applied For**
Contact: Mr Peter Morris, Farm
& Cottage Holidays, Victoria
House, 12 Fore Street, Northam,
Bideford, Devon EX39 1AW
T: (01237) 479146
F: (01237) 421512
E: farmcott@cix.co.uk
I: www.farmcott.co.uk

PUDDINGTON
Devon
Corner Cottage ★★★
Contact: Marsden's Cottage
Holidays, 2 The Square,
Braunton, Devon EX33 2JB
T: (01271) 813777
F: (01271) 813664
E: holidays@marsdens.co.uk
I: www.marsdens.co.uk

PUDDLETOWN
Dorset
7 Athelhampton Road ★★
Contact: Mrs J Stephens, Zoar
House, Puddletown, Dorchester,
Dorset DT2 8SR
T: (01305) 848498

Idlicote ★★★
Contact: Mr P Silvester, Cote
Holdings, 6 Coombe Road,
Puddletown, Dorchester, Dorset
DT2 8RZ
T: (01305) 848140
F: (01305) 849531
E: philsilvester@compuserve.
com

**Weatherbury Cottages
★★★★**
Contact: Mr and Mrs D C Howes,
Rendalls Row, 7A High Street,
Puddletown, Dorchester, Dorset
DT2 8RT
T: (01305) 848358
E: weatherbury@onetel.net.uk

PUNCKNOWLE
Dorset
Daisy Down Cottage ★★★★
Contact: Ms Susan Ikin,
Puncknowle Manor Farmhouse,
Puncknowle, Dorchester, Dorset
DT2 9BJ
T: (01308) 897692
F: (01308) 898022
E: gtice@
puncknowlemanorfarm.com

PUTSBOROUGH
Devon
11 Clifton Court ★★★★
Contact: Marsden's Cottage
Holidays, 2 The Square,
Braunton, Devon EX33 2JB
T: (01271) 813777
F: (01271) 813664
E: holidays@marsdens.co.uk
I: www.marsdens.co.uk

17 Clifton Court ★★★★
Contact: Marsden's Cottage
Holidays, 2 The Square,
Braunton, Devon EX33 2JB
T: (01271) 813777
F: (01271) 813664
E: holidays@marsdens.co.uk
I: www.marsdens.co.uk

19 Clifton Court ★★★★
Contact: Mr & Mrs Peter & Janet
Cornwell, Marsden's Cottage
Holidays, 2 The Square,
Braunton, Devon EX33 2JB
T: (01271) 813777
F: (01271) 813664
E: holidays@marsdens.co.uk
I: www.marsdens.co.uk

25 Clifton Court ★★★★
Contact: Marsden's Cottage
Holidays, 2 The Square,
Braunton, Devon EX33 2JB
T: (01271) 813777
F: (01271) 813664
E: holidays@marsdens.co.uk
I: www.marsdens.co.uk

Flat 1 Clifton Court ★★★★
Contact: Marsden's Cottage
Holidays, 2 The Square,
Braunton, Devon EX33 2JB
T: (01271) 813777
F: (01271) 813664
E: holidays@marsdens.co.uk
I: www.marsdens.co.uk

Flat 10 Clifton Court ★★★★
Contact: Marsden's Cottage
Holidays, 2 The Square,
Braunton, Devon EX33 2JB
T: (01271) 813777
F: (01271) 813664
E: holidays@marsdens.co.uk
I: www.marsdens.co.uk

Flat 18 Clifton Court ★★★★
Contact: Marsden's Cottage
Holidays, 2 The Square,
Braunton, Devon EX33 2JB
T: (01271) 813777
F: (01271) 813664
E: holidays@marsdens.co.uk
I: www.marsdens.co.uk

Flat 22 Clifton Court ★★★★
Contact: Marsden's Cottage
Holidays, 2 The Square,
Braunton, Devon EX33 2JB
T: (01271) 813777
F: (01271) 813664
E: holidays@marsdens.co.uk
I: www.marsdens.co.uk

Flat 24 Clifton Court ★★★★
Contact: Marsden's Cottage
Holidays, 2 The Square,
Braunton, Devon EX33 2JB
T: (01271) 813777
F: (01271) 813664
E: holidays@marsdens.co.uk
I: www.marsdens.co.uk

Flat 32 Clifton Court ★★★★
Contact: Marsden's Cottage
Holidays, 2 The Square,
Braunton, Devon EX33 2JB
T: (01271) 813777
F: (01271) 813664
E: holidays@marsdens.co.uk
I: www.marsdens.co.uk

Flat 7 Clifton court ★★★★
Contact: Marsden's Cottage
Holidays, 2 The Square,
Braunton, Devon EX33 2JB
T: (01271) 813777
F: (01271) 813664
E: holidays@marsdens.co.uk
I: www.marsdens.co.uk

Vention ★★★★
Contact: Marsden's Cottage
Holidays, 2 The Square,
Braunton, Devon EX33 2JB
T: (01271) 813777
F: (01271) 813664
E: holidays@marsdens.co.uk
I: www.marsdens.co.uk

PYLLE
Somerset
4 Lockswell Cottages ★★★★
Contact: Mrs S Maidment,
Purbeck House, Bath Road,
Beckington, Frome BA11 6SJ
T: (01373) 830729

RAME
Cornwall
Polhawn Fort ★★★
Contact: Mr & Mrs Bowater,
Helpful Holidays, Mill Street,
Chagford, Newton Abbot, Devon
TQ13 8AW
T: (01647) 433593
F: (01647) 433694
E: help@helpfulholidays.com
I: www.helpfulholidays.com

RATTERY
Devon
**Craven Cottage & The Barn
★★★-★★★★**
Contact: CH ref: 10769, Holiday
Cottages Group, Spring Mill,
Earby, Barnoldswick, Lancashire
BB18 6RN
T: (01282) 445096
F: (01282) 844299
E: ch.sales@ttgihg.co.uk
I: www.country-holidays.co.uk

RESTRONGUET
Cornwall
Regatta Cottage ★★★★
Contact: Mrs Margie Lumby,
Special Places, Poachers Reach,
Feock, Truro, Cornwall TR3 6SQ
T: (01872) 864400
F: (01872) 864400
E: office@
specialplacescornwall.co.uk
I: www.specialplacescornwall.
co.uk

RIDDLECOMBE
Devon
Manor Farm ★★★
Contact: Mrs E Gay, Manor
Farm, Riddlecombe, Chulmleigh,
Devon EX18 7NX
T: (01769) 520335
F: (01769) 520335

RINGSTEAD
Dorset
The Creek ★★
Contact: Mrs F Fisher, The Creek,
Ground Floor Flat, Ringstead,
Dorchester, Dorset DT2 8NG
T: (01305) 852251
F: (01305) 852251
E: michaelandfredafisher@
btinternet.com

Upton Farm ★★★★★
Contact: Mr and Mrs A Davis,
Upton Farm, Ringstead,
Dorchester, Dorset DT2 8NE
T: (01305) 853970

ROADWATER
Somerset
Briar Cottage ★★★★
Contact: Mr Neil Hedges, Briar
Cottage, The Old Mineral Line,
Roadwater, Watchet, Somerset
TA23 0RJ
T: (01984) 640020

Tacker Street Cottage ★★
Contact: Mrs A J Thomas, Higher
Rodhuish Farm, Rodhuish,
Minehead, Somerset TA24 6QL
T: (01984) 640253
F: (01984) 640253

Establishments printed in blue have a detailed entry in this guide

Timwood Combe Cottage ★★★★
Contact: Mrs V A Liddiard,
Timwood Combe Cottage,
Comberow Lane, Roadwater,
Watchet, Somerset TA23 0QR
T: (01984) 641040
I: www.exmoorholidaycottage.
com

ROBOROUGH
Devon

Little Meadows ★★★
Contact: Powell's Cottage
Holidays, High Street,
Saundersfoot, Dyfed SA69 9EJ
T: (01834) 812791
F: (01834) 811731
E: info@powells.co.uk
I: www.powells.co.uk

ROCK
Cornwall

Cant Cove ★★★★★
Contact: Mr Sleeman, The
Cottage, Cant Farm, Rock,
Wadebridge, Cornwall PL27 6RL
T: (01208) 862841
F: (01208) 862142
E: info@cantcove.co.uk
I: www.cantcove.co.uk

Ferryside ★★
Contact: Harbour Holidays,
Estuary House, Rock Road, Rock,
Wadebridge, Cornwall PL27 6LD
T: (01208) 862424
F: (01208) 862218
E: rockhols@aol.com
I: www.rockholidays.com

Gullway ★★★★★
Contact: Diana Bullivant
Holidays, South Winds, Trebell
Green, Lanivet, Bodmin,
Cornwall PL30 5HR
T: (01208) 831336
F: (01208) 831336
E: diana@dbullivant.fsnet.co.uk
I: www.cornwall-online.
co.uk/diana-bullivant

Gybe-O ★★★
Contact: Diana Bullivant
Holidays, South Winds, Trebell
Green, Lanivet, Bodmin,
Cornwall PL30 5HR
T: (01208) 831336
F: (01208) 831336
E: diana@dbullivant.fsnet.co.uk
I: www.cornwall-online.
co.uk/diana-bullivant

Little Riggs ★
Contact: Diana Bullivant
Holidays, South Winds, Trebell
Green, Lanivet, Bodmin,
Cornwall PL30 5HR
T: (01208) 831336
F: (01208) 831336
E: diana@dbullivant.fsnet.co.uk
I: www.cornwall-online.
co.uk/diana-bullivant

**The Mariners Hotel
★★-★★★★**
Contact: Mrs Annette Miller, The
Mariners Hotel, The Slipway,
Rock, Wadebridge, Cornwall
PL27 6LD
T: (01208) 862312
F: (01208) 863827
E: amiller767@aol.com
I: www.chycor.co.uk/mariners

Meadowside ★★★★★
Contact: Diana Bullivant
Holidays, South Winds, Trebell
Green, Lanivet, Bodmin,
Cornwall PL30 5HR
T: (01208) 831336
F: (01208) 831336
E: diana@dbullivant.fsnet.co.uk
I: www.cornwall-online.
co.uk/diana-bullivant

Mullets ★★★★
Contact: Diana Bullivant
Holidays, South Winds, Trebell
Green, Lanivet, Bodmin,
Cornwall PL30 5HR
T: (01208) 831336
F: (01208) 831336
E: diana@d.bullivant.fsnet.co.uk
I: www.cornwall-online.
co.uk/diana-bullivant

Porthilly Cottage ★★★
Contact: Harbour Holidays -
Rock, Estuary House, Rock Road,
Rock, Wadebridge, Cornwall
PL27 6NW
T: (01208) 862424
F: (01208) 862218
E: rockhols@aol.com
I: www.rockholidays.com

ROCOMBE
Devon

**Sunshine Cottage V4132
★★★**
Contact: Lyme Bay Holidays,
Boshouse, 44 Church Street,
Lyme Regis, Dorset DT7 3DA
T: (01297) 443363
F: (01297) 445576
E: email@lymebayholidays.
co.uk
I: www.lymebayholidays.co.uk

RODNEY STOKE
Somerset

**Maytree Barn
Rating Applied For**
Contact: CH ref: 10080,13036,
Holiday Cottages Group Owner
Services Dept, Spring Mill, Earby,
Barnoldswick, Lancashire
BB18 6RN
T: (01282) 445096
F: (01282) 844299
E: ch.sales@ttgihg.co.uk
I: www.country-holidays.co.uk

ROSE ASH
Devon

**Nethercott Manor Farm
★★-★★★**
Contact: Mrs Carol Woollacott,
Nethercott Manor Farm, Rose
Ash, South Molton, Devon
EX36 4RE
T: (01769) 550483
F: (01769) 550483

ROSUDGEON
Cornwall

Bosvean ★★★
Contact: Cornish Home
Holidays, 12 Parade Street,
Penzance, Cornwall TR18 4BU
T: (01736) 368575
F: (01736) 351943
E: chh@chh.co.uk
I: www.chh.co.uk

ROUSDON
Devon

The Gables ★★★★
Contact: Jean Bartlett Cottage
Holidays, Fore Street, Beer,
Seaton, Devon EX12 3JB
T: (01297) 23221
F: (01297) 23303
E: jeanb@netbreaks.com
I: www.netbreaks.com/jeanb

RUAN HIGH LANES
Cornwall

Chy Tyak ★★★★
Contact: Mrs P Carbis, Trenona
Farm, Ruan High Lanes, Truro,
Cornwall TR2 5JS
T: (01872) 501339 &
07775 698953
F: (01872) 501339
E: pamelacarbis@cs.com
I: www.connexions.
co.uk/chytyak
♿

**Lower Penhallow Farm
★★★★**
Contact: Ms & Mr Deborah &
Johan Raper & Balster, Lower
Penhallow Farm, Ruan High
Lanes, Truro, Cornwall TR2 5LS
T: (01872) 501105
F: (01872) 501105
E: 106346.444@compuserve.
com
I: www.ourworld.compuserve.
com/homepages/balslev_raper

Trelagossick Farm ★★★
Contact: Mrs Rachel Carbis,
Trelagossick Farm, Ruan High
Lanes, Truro, Cornwall TR2 5JU
T: (01872) 501338

RUAN MINOR
Cornwall

**Valley View
Rating Applied For**
Contact: Mrs Williams,
Addiscombe, St Keverne,
Helston, Cornwall TR12
T: (01326) 280013

RYALL
Dorset

Castle View ★★
Contact: Mrs Pat Weeks, Castle
View, Castle View Farm, Ryall,
Bridport, Dorset DT6 6EN
T: (01297) 489725

Hit n Miss ★★
Contact: Jean Bartlett Cottage
Holidays, Fore Street, Beer,
Seaton, Devon EX12 3JB
T: (01297) 23221
F: (01297) 23303
E: jeanb@netbreaks.com
I: www.netbreaks.com/jeanb

ST AGNES
Cornwall

Croft Cottage ★★★★
Contact: Mrs J Sawle, Croft
Cottage, Beacon Cottage Farm,
Beacon Drive, St Agnes,
Cornwall TR5 0NU
T: (01872) 552347 & 553381

Gothic Cottages ★★
Contact: Mrs G Willson, 6
Norfolk Lodge, 114 Richmond
Hill, Richmond, Surrey TW10 6RJ
T: (020) 8948 0691
E: g.rolls-willson@kingston.ac.
uk
I: www.waitrose.com/~gwillson

Marna Cottage ★★★
Contact: Cornish Cottage
Holidays, The Old Turnpike Dairy,
Godolphin Road, Helston,
Cornwall TR13 8AA
T: (01326) 573808
F: (01326) 564992
E: enquiry@
cornishcottageholidays
I: www.cornishcottageholidays.
co.uk

Periglis Cottage ★★★
Contact: Mr J A Paget-Brown,
Periglis Cottage, St Agnes, Isles
of Scilly TR22 0PL
T: (01720) 422366

The Porthvean ★★★
Contact: Mr & Mrs Bowater,
Helpful Holidays, Mill Street,
Chagford, Newton Abbot, Devon
TQ13 8AW
T: (01647) 433593
F: (01647) 433694
E: help@helpfulholidays.com
I: www.helpfulholidays.com

Sea Thatch ★★★★
Contact: Cornish Cottage
Holidays, The Old Turnpike Dairy,
Godolphin Road, Helston,
Cornwall TR13 8AA
T: (01326) 573808
F: (01326) 564992
E: enquiry@
cornishcottageholidays.co.uk
I: www.cornishcottageholidays.
co.uk

ST AUSTELL
Cornwall

**Bosinver Farm Cottages
★★-★★★★**
Contact: Mrs Pat Smith,
Bosinver Farm Cottages,
Bosinver Farm, Trelowth, St
Austell, Cornwall PL26 7DT
T: (01726) 72128
F: (01726) 72128
E: bosinver@holidays2000.
freeserve.co.uk
I: www.bosinver.co.uk

Greenlane Barn ★★★
Contact: Mr and Mrs Barnecut,
Bodinnick Farm, St Stephens, St
Austell, Cornwall PL25 7LL
T: (01726) 882421

Nanjeath Farm ★★★★
Contact: Mrs J Sandercock,
Nanjeath Farm, Lanjeth, St
Austell, Cornwall
T: (01726) 70666 &
07810 005636
I: www.nanjeath.co.uk

Poltarrow Farm ★★★★
Contact: Mrs J D Nancarrow,
Poltarrow Farm, St Mewan, St
Austell, Cornwall PL26 7DR
T: (01726) 67111
F: (01726) 67111
E: enquire@poltarrow.co.uk
I: www.poltarrow.co.uk
♿

Southfield ★★★
Contact: Mrs Pamela Treleaven,
Trevissick Farm, Trenarren, St
Austell, Cornwall PL26 6BQ
T: (01726) 75819
F: (01726) 68052

Tregongeeves Farm Holiday Cottages★★★-★★★★
Contact: Mr and Mrs R J Clemo, Tregongeeves Farm Holiday Cottages, St Austell, Cornwall PL26 7DS
T: (01726) 68202
F: (01726) 68202
E: johnclemo@aol.com
I: www.cornwall-holidays.co.uk

ST BREWARD
Cornwall

Darrynane Cottages ★★★
Contact: Mrs A Clark, Darrynane, St Breward, Bodmin, Cornwall PL30 4LZ
T: (01208) 850885
E: darrynane@eclipse.co.uk
I: www.darrynane.co.uk

Meadowside Cottage ★★★★
Contact: Mr & Mrs Feasey, Meadowside Cottage, Mellon Farm, St Breward, Bodmin, Cornwall PL30 4PL
T: (01208) 851497
F: (01208) 851497
E: feaseymellon@aol.com
I: www.mellonfarm.co.uk

ST BURYAN
Cornwall

Treverven House
★★★-★★★★★
Contact: Mrs C A Ryan, Treverven House, St Buryan, Penzance, Cornwall TR19 6DL

ST CLETHER
Cornwall

Treven Farmhouse ★★★
Contact: Mr Peter Morris, Farm & Cottage Holidays, Victoria House, 12 Fore Street, Northam, Bideford, Devon EX39 1AW
T: (01237) 479146
F: (01237) 421512
E: farmcott@cix.co.uk
I: www.farmcott.co.uk

Wagonners Rest ★★★★
Contact: Cornish Cottage Holidays, The Old Turnpike Dairy, Godolphin Road, Helston, Cornwall TR13 8AA
T: (01326) 573808
F: (01326) 564992
E: enquiry@cornishcottageholidays.co.uk
I: www.cornishcottageholidays.co.uk

ST COLUMB MAJOR
Cornwall

Forget Me Not Cottage ★★
Contact: Mr & Mrs E Johnson, 106 Frederick Street, Waddesdon, Aylesbury, Buckinghamshire HP18 0LX
T: (01296) 651722 & 651603
F: (01296) 655649

ST ERTH
Cornwall

Trenedros Green ★★★
Contact: Cornish Cottage Holidays, The Old Turnpike Dairy, Godolphin Road, Helston, Cornwall TR13 8AA
T: (01326) 573808
F: (01326) 564992
E: enquiry@cornishcottageholidays.co.uk
I: www.cornishcottageholidays.co.uk

ST EVAL
Cornwall

Trelorna
Rating Applied For
Contact: Ms Laura Knott, Trelorna, St Eval, Wadebridge, Cornwall PL27 7UJ
T: (01841) 520992

ST GENNYS
Cornwall

Brevean ★★★★
Contact: Mr & Mrs Batchelor, Small Hill Barton, St Gennys, Bude, Cornwall EX23 0BQ
T: (01840) 230230
F: (01840) 230539
E: wildbrooks@aol.com

Penrowan Farmhouse ★★★★
Contact: Mr Peter Morris, Farm & Cottage Holidays, Victoria House, 12 Fore Street, Northam, Bideford, Devon EX39 1AW
T: (01237) 479146
F: (01237) 421512
E: farmcott@cix.co.uk
I: www.farmcott.co.uk

ST GILES ON THE HEATH
Devon

Downicary Farm ★★★
Contact: Mr & Mrs Bowater, Helpful Holidays, Mill Street, Chagford, Newton Abbot, Devon TQ13 8AW
T: (01647) 433593
F: (01647) 433694
E: help@helpfulholidays.com
I: www.helpfulholidays.com

ST HILARY
Cornwall

Stone Cottage ★★★
Contact: Cornish Home Holidays, 12 Parade Street, Penzance, Cornwall TR18 4BU
T: (01736) 368575
F: (01736) 351493
E: chh@chh.co.uk
I: www.chh.co.uk

ST ISSEY
Cornwall

Blable Farm Barns ★★★★★
Contact: Mr & Mrs Mike & Alison Roberts, Blable Farm Barns, St Issey, Wadebridge, Cornwall PL27 7RF
T: (01208) 815813
E: blablefarm@btclick.com

Cannalidgey Villa ★★★
Contact: Mr D J Old, Cannalidgey Villa Farm, St Issey, Wadebridge, Cornwall PL27 7RB
T: (01208) 812276 & (01841) 540212

Hawksland Mill ★★★★
Contact: Mr Richard Jenkins, Henry J Clare Limited, Hawksland Mill, St Issey, Wadebridge, Cornwall PL27 7RG
T: (01208) 815404
F: (01208) 816831
E: hjc@hawkslandmill.idps.co.uk
I: www.hawkslandmill.co.uk

The Manor House ★
Contact: Mr Simon Zeal, The Manor House, Churchtown, St Issey, Wadebridge, Cornwall PL27 7QB
T: (01841) 540346
F: (01841) 540346
E: groups@holiday-adventure.com
I: www.holiday-adventure.com

ST IVES
Cornwall

Ayr Holiday Homes ★★★
Contact: Mr A R Baragwanath, Ayr Holiday Homes, Ayr Holiday Park, Ayr, St Ives, Cornwall TR26 1EJ
T: (01736) 795855
F: (01736) 798797
E: recept@ayrholidays.co.uk
I: www.ayrholidaypark.co.uk

Carrack Widden ★★★★
Contact: Mrs C Perry, Tros-an-Mor, Treloyhan Manor Drive, St Ives, Cornwall TR26 2AS
T: (01736) 793370

Casa Bella ★★★★
Contact: Mrs C Perry, Tros-an-Mor, Treloyhan Manor Drive, St Ives, Cornwall TR26 2AS
T: (01736) 793370

Chy Mor and Premier Apartments ★★★
Contact: Mr M Gill, Beach House, The Wharf, St Ives, Cornwall TR26 1QA
T: (01736) 798798 & 07887 653165
F: (01736) 796831
E: mgill@stivesharbour.com
I: www.stivesharbour.com

Sea Echoes Holiday House ★★★
Contact: Mr & Mrs Gordon & Pamela Mitchell, Seaforth, Skidden Hill, St Ives, Cornwall TR26 2DU
T: (01736) 798625 & 07768 334825
F: (01736) 798625
E: flashkiwi@aol.com
I: www.surfviewapartments.com

The Studio ★★★
Contact: Mrs Carol Holland, Little Parc Owles, Carbis Bay, St Ives, Cornwall TR26 2RQ
T: (01736) 793015
F: (01736) 793258

Tregenna Castle Self-Catering Tregenna Castle Hotel ★★-★★★★
Contact: Mrs T Bannister, Tregenna Castle, Treloyan Avenue, St Ives, Cornwall TR26 2DE
T: (01736) 759254 & 795588
F: (01736) 796066
E: tregenna-castle.demon.co.uk

Trevalgan Holiday Farm ★★★★
Contact: Mrs J S Osborne, Trevalgan Holiday Farm, Trevalgan Farm, St Ives, Cornwall TR26 3BJ
T: (01736) 796433
F: (01736) 796433
I: www.trevalgan.co.uk

ST JOHN
Cornwall

Greenmantle ★★★★
Contact: Mrs Tanner, Greenmantle, Bungalow, St John, Torpoint, Cornwall PL11 3AR
T: (01752) 823118

ST JUST-IN-PENWITH
Cornwall

Casple Cottage
Rating Applied For
Contact: Mr & Mrs KR Smith, Higher House, Higherland, Stoke Climsland, Callington, Cornwall PL17 8LD
T: (01579) 370608

Nanquidno Vean ★★★
Contact: Mrs P M Gildea, 4 Tyer Street, Stratford-upon-Avon, Warwickshire CV37 6TY
T: (01789) 299338

Seascape ★★★★★
Contact: Mrs Marilyn Daly, Kenython, Kenython Lane, St Just-in-Penwith, Penzance TR19 7PT
T: (01736) 786678 & 07747 770701
F: (01736) 786726
E: justred44@hotmail.com
I: www.seascape-stjust.co.uk

Swallows End ★★★★
Contact: Mr & Mrs Richens, Swallows End, Kelynack Moor Farmhouse, Bosworlas, St Just-in-Penwith, Penzance, Cornwall TR19 7RQ
T: (01736) 787011

ST JUST IN ROSELAND
Cornwall

Carrick View ★★★★
Contact: Mrs Margie Lumby, Special Places, Poachers Reach, Feock, Truro, Cornwall TR3 6SQ
T: (01872) 864400
F: (01872) 864400
E: office@specialplacescornwall.co.uk
I: www.specialplacescornwall.co.uk

ST KEVERNE
Cornwall

East End Cottage ★★★★
Contact: Cornish Cottage Holidays, Godolphin Road, Helston, Cornwall TR13 8AA
T: (01326) 573808
F: (01326) 564992
E: enquiry@cornishcottageholidays.co.uk
I: www.cornishcottageholidays.co.uk

Eden House Wing ★★★
Contact: Cornish Cottage Holidays, Godolphin Road, Helston, Cornwall TR13 8AA
T: (01326) 573808
F: (01326) 564992
E: enquiry@cornishcottageholidays.co.uk
I: www.cornishcottageholidays.co.uk

Fatty Owls ★★★★
Contact: Ms Y Cole, Trenoweth, St Keverne, Helston, Cornwall TR12 6QQ
T: (01326) 280199
E: trenoweth@compuserve.com

Establishments printed in blue have a detailed entry in this guide

Higher Roskorwell Cottage ★★★★
Contact: Mrs Jenny Crowther, 18 Greenhill, Sutton, Surrey SM1 3LG
T: (020) 8644 5357
F: (020) 8644 3005
I: www.higher.
roskorwell@appleonline.net

Old Valley Mill ★★★
Contact: Cornish Cottage Holidays, The Old Turnpike Dairy, Godolphin Road, Helston, Cornwall TR13 8AA
T: (01326) 573808
F: (01326) 564992
E: enquiry@
cornishcottageholidays.co.uk
I: www.cornishcottageholidays.
co.uk

Penrose Farm Cottage ★★★
Contact: Cornish Cottage Holidays, The Old Turnpike Dairy, Godolphin Road, Helston, Cornwall TR13 8AA
T: (01326) 573808
F: (01326) 564992
E: enquiry@
cornishcottageholidays.co.uk
I: www.cornishcottageholidays.
co.uk

Roskorwell Cottage ★★★
Contact: Cornish Cottage Holidays, The Old Turnpike Dairy, Godolphin Road, Helston, Cornwall TR13 8AA
T: (01326) 573808
F: (01326) 564992
E: enquiry@
cornishcottageholidays.co.uk
I: www.cornishcottageholidays.
co.uk

Tarragon ★★★★
Contact: Cornish Cottage Holidays, The Old Turnpike Dairy, Godolphin Road, Helston, Cornwall TR13 8AA
T: (01326) 573808
F: (01326) 564992
E: enquiry@
cornishcottageholidays.co.uk
I: www.cornishcottageholidays.
co.uk

Tregoning Manor Cottages ★★★
Contact: Mr & Mrs Bowater, Helpful Holidays, Mill Street, Chagford, Newton Abbot, Devon TQ13 8AW
T: (01647) 433593
F: (01647) 433694
E: help@helpfulholidays.com
I: www.helpfulholidays.com

Trenoweth Mill ★★★★
Contact: Cornish Cottage Holidays, The Old Turnpike Dairy, Godolphin Road, Helston, Cornwall TR13 8AA
T: (01326) 573808
F: (01326) 564992
E: enquiry@
cornishcottageholidays.co.uk
I: www.cornishcottageholidays.
co.uk

Trenoweth Valley Farm Cottages ★
Contact: Mrs Rosemary Peters, Trenoweth Valley Farm Cottages, St Keverne, Helston, Cornwall TR12 6QQ
T: (01326) 280910
F: (01326) 281079
E: lpta@lizardpeninsula.
freeserve.co.uk
I: www.lizard-peninsula.co.uk

Trevallack Farmhouse ★★★
Contact: Cornish Cottage Holidays, Godolphin Road, Helston, Cornwall TR13 8AA
T: (01326) 573808
F: (01326) 564992
E: enquiry@
cornishcottageholidays.co.uk
I: www.cornishcottageholidays.
co.uk

ST KEW
Cornwall

**The Barn House
Rating Applied For**
Contact: Mr & Mrs Janet Chancellor, Ashley, Forty Green Road, Beaconsfield, Buckinghamshire HP9 1XL
T: (01494) 670696
E: jeremy.chancellar@which.net

The Granary ★★★★
Contact: Mr & Mrs J&S Whitten, Hale Farmhouse, St Kew, Bodmin, Cornwall PL30 3HE
T: (01208) 880836 & 0771 224 2299
F: (01208) 880836
E: hale@rmplc.co.uk
I: www.cornwall.online

Paget & Every ★★★
Contact: Harbour Holidays - Rock, Estuary House, Rock Road, Rock, Wadebridge, Cornwall PL27 6NW
T: (01208) 862424
F: (01208) 862218
E: rockhols@aol.com
I: www.rockholidays.com

Treharrock Farm Cottages ★★★★
Contact: Mrs Emerald Quinn, Treharrock Farm, Pendoggett, St Kew, Bodmin, Cornwall PL29 3TA
T: (01208) 880517
F: (01208) 880517
E: treharrockfarmcottages@
btinternet.com

ST LEVAN
Cornwall

Chyreen ★★★
Contact: Cornish Cottage Holidays, The Old Turnpike Dairy, Godolphin Road, Helston, Cornwall TR13 8AA
T: (01326) 573808
F: (01326) 564992
E: enquiry@
cornishcottageholidays.co.uk
I: www.cornishcottageholidays.
co.uk

ST MABYN
Cornwall

Elderbush Cottage ★★★
Contact: Elderbush Cottage, St Mabyn, Bodmin, Cornwall PL30 3BY

ST MARTIN
Cornwall

The Bull House ★★★★
Contact: Cornish Cottage Holidays, Godolphin Road, Helston, Cornwall TR13 8AA
T: (01326) 573808
F: (01326) 564992
E: enquiry@
cornishcottageholidays.co.uk
I: www.cornishcottageholidays.
co.uk

Summercourt House ★★★
Contact: Cornish Cottage Holidays, Godolphin Road, Helston, Cornwall TR13 8AA
T: (01326) 573808
F: (01326) 564992
E: enquiry@
cornishcottageholidays.co.uk
I: www.cornishcottageholidays.
co.uk

Trecoose Summer Studio★★★
Contact: Cornish Cottage Holidays, The Old Turnpike Dairy, Godolphin Road, Helston, Cornwall TR13 8GL
T: (01326) 573808
F: (01326) 564992
E: enquiry@
cornishcottageholidays.co.uk
I: www.cornishcottageholidays.
co.uk

ST MARTIN'S
Cornwall

Carron Farm ★★★
Contact: Mrs J M Walder, Carron Farm, St Martin's, Isles of Scilly TR25 0QL
T: (01720) 422893

Churchtown Farm ★★★★
Contact: Mr A Julian, Churchtown Farm, St Martin's, Isles of Scilly TR25 0QL
T: (01720) 422169
F: (01720) 422800
E: info@
churchtownfarmholidays.co.uk

Connemara Farm ★★★
Contact: Mr T A Perkins, 2 Coastguard Cottages, Higher Town, St Martin's, Isles of Scilly TR25 0QL
T: (01720) 422814
F: (01720) 422814

Daymark Holidays ★★★
Contact: Mrs S Daly, Daymark Holidays, Breakaway Farm, St Martin's, Isles of Scilly TR25 0QL
T: (01720) 422872
F: (01720) 422872

Grans Cottage and The Stable ★★★★
Contact: Mrs A C Humphries, Grans Cottage and The Stable, Middle Town, St Martin's, Isles of Scilly TR25 0QN
T: (01720) 422810
F: (01720) 422810
E: ahscilly@talk21.com

Signal Row Cottages ★★
Contact: Mrs DIJ Perkins, Signal Row Cottages, Signal Row, St Martin's, Isles of Scilly TR25 0QL
T: (01720) 422863

The Stables ★★★
Contact: Mr John Boyle, Sunset, Salt Cellar Hill, Porthleven, Helston, Cornwall TR13 9DP
T: (01326) 563811
F: (01326) 563811
E: john@sharkbayfilms.demon.
co.uk

ST MARY'S
Isles of Scilly

Ajax ★★★
Contact: Island Properties Holiday Lettings & Management, Porthmellon, St Mary's, Isles of Scilly TR21 0JY
T: (01720) 422082
F: (01720) 422211
E: enquiries@
islesofscillyholidays.com
I: www.islesofscillyholidays.com

Albany Flats ★★★
Contact: Mrs Isabel Trenear, Albany Flats, Church Street, St Mary's, Isles of Scilly TR21 0JT
T: (01720) 422601

Allwinds ★★
Contact: Mrs S P Lewis, Henhurst Farm, Foots lane, Burwash Weald, Etchingham, East Sussex TN19 7LE
T: (01435) 883239
F: (01435) 883252
E: johnl@henhurst.demon.co.uk

Anchor Cottage ★★★
Contact: Island Properties Holiday Lettings & Management, Porthmellon, St Mary's, Isles of Scilly TR21 0JY
T: (01720) 422082
F: (01720) 422211
E: enquiries@
islesofscillyholidays.com
I: www.islesofscillyholidays.com

1 and 2 Quay House ★★★
Contact: Island Properties Holidays Lettings & Management, Porthmellon, St Mary's, Isles of Scilly TR21 0JY
T: (01720) 422082
F: (01720) 422211
E: enquiries@
islesofscillyholidays.com
I: www.islesofscillyholidays.com

Anglesea House ★★★★
Contact: Island Properties Holiday Lettings & Management, Porhtmellon, St Mary's, Isles of Scilly TR21 0JY
T: (01720) 422082
F: (01720) 422211
E: enquiries@
islesofscillyholidays.com
I: www.islesofscillyholidays.com

Apartment Two Four Seasons ★★★
Contact: Mrs S D Jones, 44 Boverton Drive, Brockworth, Gloucester, GL3 4DA
T: (01452) 618619 & 07887 550222

Ardwyn ★★★★
Contact: Mrs G M Osborne, The Withies, Old Town, St Mary's, Isles of Scilly TR21 0PA
T: (01720) 422986

Armorel Cottage ★★★
Contact: Island Properties
Holiday Lettings & Management,
Porthmellon, St Mary's, Isles of
Scilly TR21 0JY
T: (01720) 422082
F: (01720) 422211
E: enquiries@
islesofscillyholidays.com
I: www.islesofscillyholidays.com

Bar Escapade ★★★
Contact: Island Properties,
Church Street, St Mary's, Isles of
Scilly
T: (01720) 422082
F: (01720) 422111
E: enquiries@
islesofscillyholidays.com
I: www.islesofscillyholidays.com

The Barn ★★★
Contact: Island Properties
Holiday Lettings & Management,
Porthmellon, St Mary's, Isles of
Scilly TR21 0JY
T: (01720) 422082
F: (01720) 422211
E: enquiries@
islesofscillyholidays.com
I: www.islesofscillyholidays.com

3 Bay View ★★★
Contact: Island Properties
Holiday Lettings & Management,
Porthmellon, St Mary's, Isles of
Scilly TR21 0JY
T: (01720) 422082
F: (01720) 422211
E: enquiries@
islesofscillyholidays.com
I: www.islesofscillyholidays.com

Beach House Flat ★★★
Contact: Island Properties
Holiday Lettings & Management,
Porthmellon, St Mary's, Isles of
Scilly TR21 0JY
T: (01720) 422082
F: (01720) 422211
E: enquiries@
islesofscillyholidays.com
I: www.islesofscillyholidays.com

Beach Mooring Flat 1, Smugglers Ride★★★★
Contact: Mrs Susan Eccles,
Orchard Meadow, Well Lane,
Gerrans, Portscatho, Truro,
Cornwall TR2 5EG
T: (01872) 580997

Beachside Maisonette Above Co-op★★★
Contact: Island Properties
Holiday Lettings & Management,
Porthmellon, St Mary's, Isles of
Scilly TR21 0JY
T: (01720) 422082
F: (01720) 422211
E: enquiries@
islesofscillyholidays.com
I: www.islesofscillyholidays.com

Beggars Roost ★★
Contact: Mr K E Peay, 19 Langley
Avenue, Surbiton, Surrey
KT6 6QN
T: (020) 8399 8364

Bounty Ledge ★★
Contact: Mr RT Jackman,
Scillonian Estate Agency, 8
Lower Strand, St Mary's, Isles of
Scilly TR21 0PS
T: (01720) 422124

Bylet Holiday Homes ★★★
Contact: Mr D Williams, Bylet
Holiday Homes, The Bylet,
Church Road, St Mary's, Isles of
Scilly TR21 0NA
T: (01720) 422479
F: (01720) 422479
E: thebylet@bushinternet.com
I: www.geocities.
com/bylet_holidays/

The Cabin ★★★
Contact: Mr & Mrs Parsons, The
Cabin 2 Bank Cottage, St Mary's,
St Mary's, Isles of Scilly
TR21 0HY
T: (01720) 422393
F: (01720) 422393

The Cabin ★
Contact: Dr & Mrs Raymond,
Low Green, Lindale, Grange-
over-Sands, Cumbria LA11 6ND
T: (015395) 34780 &
07980 981825
F: (015395) 34780
E: gwyn.raymond@talk21.com

The Captains Cabin ★★★
Contact: Mrs P A Rowe, The
Captains Cabin, Marine House,
Church Street, Hugh Town, St
Mary's, Isles of Scilly TR21 0JT
T: (01720) 422966
E: peggy@rowe55.freeserve.
co.uk

Christmas House ★★★
Contact: Mr J E Chiverton,
Kistvan, St Mary's, Isles of Scilly
TR21 0JE
T: (01720) 422002

Church Hall Cottage ★★★★
Contact: Mr D E Townend,
Trelawney Guest House, Church
Street, St Mary's, Isles of Scilly
TR21 0JT
T: (01720) 422377 &
0790 0016113
F: (01720) 422377
E: dtownend@netcomuk.co.uk

Clemys Cottage ★★
Contact: Mr and Mrs P Cattran,
Tregarthen Farm, Zennor, St Ives,
Cornwall TR26 3BP
T: (01736) 794970 & 796977
F: (01736) 794970
E: petche@cwcom.net

The Corner House ★★★
Contact: Island Properties
Holiday Lettings & Management,
Porthmellon, St Mary's, Isles of
Scilly TR21 0JY
T: (01720) 422082
F: (01720) 422211
E: enquiries@
islesofscillyholidays.com
I: www.islesofscillyholidays.com

Cornerways ★★★★
Contact: Mr and Mrs H D
Pritchard, Cornerways, Jacksons
Hill, St Mary's, Isles of Scilly
TR21 0JZ
T: (01720) 422757
F: (01720) 422757

The Crow's Nest ★★★
Contact: Mrs Stella Carter, The
Old Bakehouse, Winterborne
Road, Abingdon, Oxfordshire
OX14 1AJ
T: (01235) 520317 & 527495
F: (01235) 527495
E: stella@bakehouse.supanet.
com

Dolphins ★★★★
Contact: Island Properties
Holiday Lettings & Management,
Porthmellon, St Mary's, Isles of
Scilly TR21 0JY
T: (01720) 422082
F: (01720) 422211
E: enquiries@
islesofscillyholidays.com
I: www.islesofscillyholidays.com

Dunmallard, Lower Flat ★★★
Contact: Mr and Mrs W S Elliot,
2 Greenhill Mead, Pesters Lane,
Somerton, Somerset TA11 7AB
T: (01458) 272971

Eastbank ★★★
Contact: Mrs Linda Roberts,
Rose Cottage Nurseries, Acomb
Common, Hatfield, Doncaster,
South Yorkshire DN7 6ET
T: (01302) 737160 & 841856
F: (01302) 846909
E: linda@rosecott.force9.co.uk
I: www.rosecott.force9.co.uk

Ebor Cottage ★★★
Contact: Island Properties
Holiday Lettings & Management,
Porthmellon, St Mary's, Isles of
Scilly TR21 0JY
T: (01720) 422082
F: (01720) 422211
E: enquiries@
islesofscillyholidays.com
I: www.islesofscillyholidays.com

Escallonia ★★★★
Contact: Mrs S J Quinton, 31
Forest Ridge, Keston, Kent
BR2 6EG
T: (01689) 850216

The Flat ★★★★
Contact: Mrs Jill May, The Flat,
The Sandpiper Shop, Hugh
Town, St Mary's, Isles of Scilly
TR21 0HY
T: (01720) 422189 & 422122
F: (01720) 422398

Flat 2 Kenwyn
Rating Applied For
Contact: The Proprietor, Flat 2
Kenwyn, Church Street, St
Mary's, Isles of Scilly TR21

Flat 2 Madura ★★★
Contact: Mrs W A Davis, 40
Hawkwell Chase, Hockley, Essex
SS5 4NH
T: (01702) 203515
E: fredadavis@lineone.net

Flat 3 Rosevean ★★★
Contact: Mrs E Talbot, 35
Barracks Lane, Macclesfield,
Cheshire SK10 1QJ
T: (01625) 427059

Flat 4 Kenwyn ★★★
Contact: Mrs P M Vian,
Southmead, Telegraph, St
Mary's, Isles of Scilly TR21 0NR
T: (01720) 423100
E: vian@btinternet.com

Flats 3 & 4 ★★
Contact: Island Properties
Holiday Lettings & Management,
Porthmellon, St Mary's, Isles of
Scilly TR21 0JY
T: (01720) 422082
F: (01720) 422211
E: enquiries@
islesofscillyholidays.com
I: www.islesofscillyholidays.com

Garrison Holidays ★★★
Contact: Mr and Mrs E W
Moulson, Garrison Holidays, St
Mary's, Isles of Scilly TR21 0LS
T: (01720) 422670 &
07774 604556
F: (01720) 422670
E: tedmoulson@compuserve.
com
I: ourworld.compuserve.
com/homepages/tedmoulson
I: www.isles-of-scilly.co.ukwww.
ourworld.compuserve.
com/homepages/tedmoulson

Glandore Apartments ★★★★
Contact: Mrs Stephen Morris,
Glandore Apartments, Glandore
Apartments, Porthloo, St Mary's,
Isles of Scilly TR21 0NE
T: (01720) 422535
E: apartments@glandore.co.uk

6 Godolphin House & 8 Buzza Street ★★★
Contact: Mrs A S Hogg, 92
Brinklow Road, Coventry,
CV3 2HY
T: (024) 7645 0455

1 Golden Bay Mansions ★★★
Contact: Mrs M H Barnes, Three
Gables, MacFarlands Down, St
Mary's, Isles of Scilly TR21 0NS
T: (01720) 423141

Greystones ★★
Contact: Mr Jackman, Scillonian
Estate Agency, 8 Lower Strand,
St Mary's, Isles of Scilly
TR21 0PS
T: (01720) 422124
F: (01720) 422124

Gunner Rock
Rating Applied For
Contact: Mr J Heslin, Gunner
Rock, Jackson's Hill, St Mary's,
Isles of Scilly TR21 0JZ
T: (01720) 422595

Harbour Lights with Smugglers Ride ★★★
Contact: Mr T C Clifford, The
Glen, Trolver Croft, Feock, Truro,
Cornwall TR3 6RT
T: (01872) 863537
F: (01872) 863537
E: tcclif@globalnet.co.uk
I: www.users.globalnet.
co.uk/~tcclif/

5 Harbour View Mansions
Rating Applied For
Contact: Mrs Sheila Thomas,
Auriga Guest House, 7
Portheressa Road, St Mary's,
Isles of Scilly TR21 0JL
T: (01720) 422637

Harbour Walls ★★★
Contact: Island Properties
Holiday Lettings & Management,
Porthmellon, St Mary's, Isles of
Scilly TR21 0JY
T: (01720) 422082
F: (01720) 422211
E: enquiries@
islesofscillyholidays.com
I: www.islesofscillyholidays.com

Establishments printed in blue have a detailed entry in this guide

Haycocks ★★★
Contact: Island Properties
Holiday Lettings & Management,
Porthmellon, St Mary's, Isles of
Scilly TR21 0JY
T: (01720) 422082
F: (01720) 422211
E: enquiries@
islesofscillyholidays.com
I: www.islesofscillyholidays.com

Inglenook ★★★
Contact: Mr J White, 4 Wray
Park Road, Reigate, Surrey
RH2 0DD
T: (01737) 248890
F: (01737) 242770
E: jon@holidayinglenook.co.uk
I: www.holidayinglenook.co.uk

**Isles of Scilly Steamship
Company Limited★★★**
Contact: Ms J Marks, Isles of
Scilly Steamship Company
Limited, Hugh Town, St Mary's,
Isles of Scilly TR21 0LJ
T: (01720) 422357 & 422358

Jasmine Cottage ★★★
Contact: Claire Harvey, Bank
House, The Bank, St Mary's, Isles
of Scilly TR21 0HY
T: (01720) 422111

Katrine ★★★
Contact: Mrs P A Hayden, 2
Buzza Street, St Mary's, Isles of
Scilly TR21 0HX
T: (01720) 422178

Kingston House ★★★
Contact: Island Properties
Holiday Lettings & Management,
Porthmellon, St Mary's, Isles of
Scilly TR21 0JY
T: (01720) 422082
F: (01720) 422211
E: enquiries@
islesofscillyholidays.com
I: www.islesofscillyholidays.com

Kirklees Holiday Flat ★★★
Contact: Mr & Mrs P&G
Coldwell, Kirklees, Porthcressa,
St Mary's, Isles of Scilly TR21 0JL
T: (01720) 422623

Kistvaen ★★
Contact: Mrs Chiverton,
Kistvaen, Sally Port, St Mary's,
Isles of Scilly TR21 0JE
T: (01720) 422002
F: (01720) 422002
E: chivy002@aol.com

Lea View ★★★
Contact: Island Properties
Holiday Lettings & Management,
Porthmellon, St Mary's, Isles of
Scilly TR21 0JY
T: (01720) 422082
F: (01720) 422211
E: enquiries@
islesofscillyholidays.com
I: www.islesofscillyholidays.com

The Lighthouse ★★★
Contact: Island Properties
Holiday Lettings & Management,
Porthmellon, St Mary's, Isles of
Scilly TR21 0JY
T: (01720) 422082
F: (01720) 422211
E: enquiries@
islesofscillyholidays.com
I: www.islesofscillyholidays.com

Lower Ganilly Flat ★★★
Contact: Island Properties,
Church Street, St Mary's, Isles of
Scilly TR21 0JY
T: (01720) 422082
F: (01720) 422211
E: enquiries@
islesofscillyholidays.com
I: www.islesofscillyholidays.com

**Lunnon Cottage, The Quillet,
Medlar★★★**
Contact: Mrs P Rogers, Lunnon
Cottage, The Quillet, Medlar,
Lunnon, St Mary's, Isles of Scilly
TR21 0NZ
T: (01720) 422422

Madura I ★★★
Contact: Island Properties
Holiday Lettings & Management,
Porthmellon, St Mary's, Isles of
Scilly TR21 0JY
T: (01720) 422082
F: (01720) 422211
E: enquiries@
islesofscillyholidays.com
I: www.islesofscillyholidays.com

Manilla Flats ★★★
Contact: Mrs F Grottick,
Burgundy House, Ram's Valley,
St Mary's, Isles of Scilly
TR21 0JX
T: (01720) 422424

**Maypole, Upper & Lower Flats
★★★**
Contact: Island Properties
Holiday Lettings & Management,
Porthmellon, St Mary's, Isles of
Scilly TR21 0JY
T: (01720) 422082
F: (01720) 422211
E: enquiries@
islesofscillyholidays.com
I: www.islesofscillyholidays.com

Minalto Holiday Flats ★★★
Contact: Mr Richard Vaughan,
Minalto Holiday Flats, Church
Street, St Mary's, Isles of Scilly
TR21 0JT
T: (01720) 423159

Minmow Holiday Flats ★★★
Contact: Mr D K Simpson,
Stoneraise, Old Town, St Mary's,
Isles of Scilly TR21 0NH
T: (01720) 422561

The Moos ★★-★★★
Contact: Mrs S B Williams,
Polmennor, Pelistry, St Mary's,
Isles of Scilly TR21 0NX
T: (01720) 422605

Morgelyn ★★★
Contact: Mrs J Lishman,
Morgelyn, McFarlands Down, St
Mary's, Isles of Scilly TR21 0NS
T: (01720) 422897
E: info@morgelyn.co.uk
I: www.morgelyn.co.uk

The Mount ★★★★
Contact: Mrs PEM Loxton,
Glendale, Jerusalem Terrace, St
Mary's, Isles of Scilly TR21 0JH
T: (01720) 422484

Mount Todden Farm ★★★
Contact: Miss Anna Ebert,
Mount Todden Farm, St Mary's,
Isles of Scilly TR21 0NY
T: (01720) 422311

4 Myrtle Cottages ★★★
Contact: Island Properties
Holiday Lettings & Management,
Porthmellon, St Mary's, Isles of
Scilly TR21 0JY
T: (01720) 422082
F: (01720) 422211
E: enquiries@
islesofscillyholidays.com
I: www.islesofscillyholidays.com

5 Myrtle Cottages ★★★
Contact: Island Properties
Holiday Letings & Management,
Porthmellon, St Mary's, Isles of
Scilly TR21 0JY
T: (01720) 422082
F: (01720) 422211
E: enquiries@
islesofscillyholidays.com
I: www.islesofscillyholidays.com

6 Myrtle Cottages ★★★
Contact: Mrs A J Guy, Longstone
Farm, St Mary's, Isles of Scilly
TR21 0NW
T: (01720) 422895

Newfort House ★★★★
Contact: Island Properties
Holiday Lettings & Management,
Porthmellon, St Mary's, Isles of
Scilly TR21 0JY
T: (01720) 422082
F: (01720) 422211
E: enquiries@
islesofscillyholidays.com
I: www.islesofscillyholidays.com

No. 3 Godolphin House ★★★
Contact: Island Properties
Holiday Lettings & Management,
Porthmellon, St Mary's, Isles of
Scilly TR21 0JY
T: (01720) 422082
F: (01720) 422211
E: enquiries@
islesofscillyholidays.com
I: www.islesofscillyholidays.com

No 3 Bungalow ★★
Contact: Mrs M Sherris, Content
Farm, St Mary's, Isles of Scilly
TR21 0NS
T: (01720) 422496

The Old Cottage ★★
Contact: Mrs P E Lethbridge, The
Old Cottage, Garrison Hill, St
Mary's, Isles of Scilly TR21 0HY
T: (01720) 422630

The Palms ★★
Contact: Mrs J Lethbridge, The
Palms, Maypole, St Mary's, Isles
of Scilly TR21 0NU
T: (01720) 422404

Peacehaven ★★
Contact: Mr PA Bennett,
Borough Farm, St Mary's, Isles of
Scilly TR21
T: (01720) 422326

Pelistry Cottage ★★★
Contact: Mrs Brenda Ashford,
Tean, Hugh Street, St Mary's,
Isles of Scilly TR21 0LL
T: (01720) 422059

Pengarriss ★★★
Contact: Mrs A Walker, 4 Copse
View Cottages, Redenham,
Andover, Hampshire SP11 9AT
T: (01264) 772758

Pennlyon ★★
Contact: Mrs M Feast, Sole
Agent, Bryher Cottage,
Whitemoor Lane, Sambourne,
Redditch B96 6NT
T: (01527) 893619 &
(01720) 422082

Perran ★★★
Contact: Island Properties
Holiday Lettings & Management,
Church Street, St Mary's, Isles of
Scilly TR21 0JY
T: (01720) 422082
F: (01720) 422211
E: enquiries@
islesofscillyholidays.com
I: www.islesofscillyholidays.com

Pharmacy Flat ★★★
Contact: Mrs J A Douglas,
Pharmacy Flat, St Mary's
Pharmacy, St Mary's, Isles of
Scilly TR21 0LG
T: (01720) 422533

Pilots Gig Flat ★★★★
Contact: Mrs J H Holliday, The
White House, Staverton,
Daventry, Northamptonshire
NN11 6JH
T: (01327) 871053

Plumb Cottage ★★★★
Contact: Island Properties
Holiday Lettings & Management,
Porthmellon, St Mary's, Isles of
Scilly TR21 0JY
T: (01720) 422082
F: (01720) 422211
E: enquiries@
islesofscillyholidays.com
I: www.islesofscillyholidays.com

9 Porthcressa Road ★★★
Contact: Mr J W Phillips, 4 The
Strand, St Mary's, Isles of Scilly
TR21 0PT
T: (01720) 422078
F: (01720) 422078
E: rosecottage@infinnet.co.uk

2 Porthcressa View ★★★
Contact: Mrs Diana Peat, 39
Garrick Close, Walton-on-
Thames, Surrey KT12 5NZ
T: (01932) 222644 & 707196
F: (01932) 707196
E: cpeat@aol.com

Porthlow Farm ★-★★★
Contact: Mrs A P Mawer,
Porthlow Farm, St Mary's, Isles
of Scilly TR21 0NF
T: (01720) 422636

Porthmellon House ★★★
Contact: Mrs Rosemary Clifton,
Porthmellon House,
Porthmellon, St Mary's, Isles of
Scilly TR21 0JY
T: (01720) 422748

The Retreat ★★★
Contact: Island Properties
Holiday Lettings & Management,
Porthmellon, St Mary's, Isles of
Scilly TR21 0JY
T: (01720) 422082
F: (01720) 422211
E: enquiries@
islesofscillyholidays.com
I: www.islesofscillyholidays.com

Rillston ★★★★
Contact: Mrs M C Lorenz, Four
Winds, Telegraph, St Mary's, Isles
of Scilly TR21 0NR
T: (01720) 422522

Rockside Cottage ★★★
Contact: Mrs J May, Peninnis House, Peninnis, St Mary's, Isles of Scilly TR21 0NA
T: (01720) 422122
F: (01720) 422122

Rocky Hill Chalets ★★
Contact: Mrs DK Edwards, Rocky Hill Chalets, Rocky Hill, St Mary's, Isles of Scilly TR21 0NE
T: (01720) 422955

1 Rosevean
Rating Applied For
Contact: Dr & Mrs Raymond, Low Green Farm, Lindale, Grange-over-Sands, Cumbria LA11 6ND
T: (015395) 34780 &
07980 981825
F: (015395) 34780
E: gwyn.raymond@talk21.com

4 Rosevean House ★★★
Contact: Mr Mark Littleford, Halangy, McFarland's Down, St Mary's, Isles of Scilly TR21 0NS
T: (01720) 423102

The Round House ★★
Contact: Island Properties Holiday Lettings & Management, Porthmellon, St Mary's, Isles of Scilly TR21 0JY
T: (01720) 422082
F: (01720) 422211
E: enquiries@
islesofscillyholidays.com
I: www.islesofscillyholidays.com

Sailcheck ★★★
Contact: Miss E A Hodges, The White House, Northfield Road, Tring, Hertfordshire HP23 5QW
T: 07776 308068

Sallakee Farm ★★
Contact: Mrs P A Mumford, Sallakee Farm, St Mary's, Isles of Scilly TR21 0NZ
T: (01720) 422391

22 Sally Port ★★
Contact: Mr J A Hyde, 30A St Peters Hill, Newlyn, Penzance, Cornwall TR18 5EH
T: (01736) 366199

Shamrock Self Catering ★
Contact: Miss Tracey Guy, Shamrock Self Catering, Shamrock, St Mary's, Isles of Scilly TR21 0NW
T: (01720) 423269 &
07768 190106

Shipwrights Cottage
Maisonettes ★★★★
Contact: Mrs M C Lorenz, Four Winds, Telegraph, St Mary's, Isles of Scilly TR21 0NR
T: (01720) 422522

14 Silver Street ★★★
Contact: Island Properties Holiday Lettings & Management, Porthmellon, St Mary's, Isles of Scilly TR21 0JY
T: (01720) 422082
F: (01720) 422211
E: enquiries@
islesofscillyholidays.com
I: www.islesofscillyholidays.com

12 Silver Street and 1 Porthcressa★★★
Contact: Mrs L J Mills, 6 Highclere Drive, Longdean Park, Hemel Hempstead, Hertfordshire HP3 8BT
T: (01442) 262871

Spanish Ledge Holiday Flats ★★★
Contact: Mr and Mrs J Humphreys, Spanish Ledge Holiday Flats, The Parade, St Mary's, Isles of Scilly TR21 0LP
T: (01720) 422338
F: (01720) 423507
E: spanishledge@ic24.net

1 Springfield Court ★★
Contact: Island Properties, Porthmellon, St Mary's, Isles of Scilly TR21 0JY
T: (01720) 422082
F: (01720) 422211
E: enquiries@
islesofscillyholidays.com
I: www.islesofscillyholidays.com

7 Springfield Court ★★
Contact: Island Properties Holiday Lettings & Management, Porthmellon, St Mary's, Isles of Scilly TR21 0JY
T: (01720) 422082
F: (01720) 422211
E: enquiries@
islesofscillyholidays.com
I: www.islesofscillyholidays.com

9 Springfield Court ★★★
Contact: Island Properties Holiday Lettings & Management, Porthmellon, St Mary's, Isles of Scilly TR21 0JY
T: (01720) 422082
F: (01720) 422211
E: enquiries@
islesofscillyholidays.com
I: www.islesofscillyholidays.com

Spy Hole ★★★
Contact: Island Properties Holiday Lettings & Management, Porthmellon, St Mary's, Isles of Scilly TR21 0JY
T: (01720) 422082
F: (01720) 422211
E: enquiries@
islesofscillyholidays.com
I: www.islesofscillyholidays.com

10 The Strand ★★★★
Contact: Mrs P Murray, The Barn, Westcott, Tremaine, Launceston, Cornwall PL15 8SA
T: (01566) 781270
E: cottage@madnmap.com
I: www.madnmap.com

Sunny Creek ★★
Contact: Island Properties Holiday Lettings & Management, Porthmellon, St Mary's, Isles of Scilly TR21 0JY
T: (01720) 422082
F: (01720) 422211
E: enquiries@
islesofscillyholidays.com
I: www.islesofscillyholidays.com

Sunnyside Flats ★★
Contact: Mr M W Brown, Sunnyside Flats, Rosemary Cottage, St Mary's, Isles of Scilly TR21 0NW
T: (01720) 422903

The Tardis ★★★
Contact: Mrs M Williams, The Tardis, C/O Briar Lea, Pelistry, St Mary's, Isles of Scilly TR21 0NX
T: (01720) 422209

2 Telegraph Bungalows ★
Contact: Mrs S Mumford, Newford Farm, St Mary's, Isles of Scilly TR21 0NS
T: (01720) 422650

Tolman House ★★★★
Contact: Mrs Rita Trotman, Tolman House, Old Town, St Mary's, Isles of Scilly TR21 0NH
T: (01720) 422967
F: (01720) 422967
E: tolhouse@hotmail.com

Top Flat ★★★
Contact: Mrs Christine Hosken, Top Flat, Trenoweth Farm, St Mary's, Isles of Scilly TR21 0NS
T: (01720) 422666

Tredavoe Cottage ★★★
Contact: Mrs Isobel Brown, Penventon, Porthcressa, St Mary's, Isles of Scilly TR21 0JQ
T: (01720) 422914
F: (01720) 422914
E: tredavoe.cottage@virgin.net
I: www.freespace.virgin.net/tredavoe.cottage/

Treglesyn ★★★
Contact: Mrs M Holden, 11 Hurst Lane, Cumnor, Oxford OX2 9PR
T: (01865) 864022

Tremelethen Farm ★★★
Contact: Mrs S Hale, Tremelethen Farm, St Mary's, Isles of Scilly TR21 0NZ
T: (01720) 422436
F: (01720) 423226

Trevessa ★★★★
Contact: Mrs PA Browning, Wingletang Guest House, The Parade, St Mary's, Isles of Scilly TR21 0LP
T: (01720) 422381

Upper Flat, Dunmallard ★★★
Contact: Mr & Mrs D J Poynter, 17 Braybrooke Road, Wargrave, Reading RG10 8DU
T: (0118) 940 3539

Verona ★★★
Contact: Island Properties Holiday Lettings & Management, Porthmellon, St Mary's, Isles of Scilly TR21 0JY
T: (01720) 422082
F: (01720) 422211
E: enquiries@
islesofscillyholidays.com
I: www.islesofscillyholidays.com

Warleggan Holiday Flats ★★★
Contact: Mrs C F Hiron, Warleggan Holiday Flats, Church Street, St Mary's, Isles of Scilly TR21 0JT
T: (01720) 422563
F: (01720) 422563
E: terry.hiron@virgin.net

The White Cottage ★★★
Contact: Mr RT Jackman, Scillonian Estate Agency, 8 Lower Street, St Mary's, Isles of Scilly TR21 0PS
T: (01720) 422124

Wisteria Cottage ★★★★
Contact: Claire Harvey, 1 Bank Flats, Bank House, St Mary's, Isles of Scilly TR21
T: (01720) 422111

1 Wras ★★★
Contact: Island Properties Holiday Lettings & Management, Porthmellon, St Mary's, Isles of Scilly TR21 0JY
T: (01720) 422082
F: (01720) 422211
E: enquiries@
islesofscillyholidays.com
I: www.islesofscillyholidays.com

2 The Wrasse ★★
Contact: Mr and Mrs K W Symons, 22 Ennor Close, St Mary's, Isles of Scilly TR21 0NL
T: (01720) 422210

'Avoca Holiday Homes' ★★★★
Contact: Mr & Mrs Elizabeth & Colin Ridsdale, 'Avoca Holiday Homes', 'Avoca', Hospital Lane, St Mary's, Isles of Scilly TR21 0LQ
T: (01720) 422656
F: (01720) 422656

ST MARYCHURCH
Devon

11 Rowley Road ★★
Contact: Holiday Homes & Cottages South West, 365A Torquay Road, Paignton, Devon TQ3 2BT
T: (01803) 663650
F: (01803) 664037
E: holcotts@aol.com
I: www.swcottages.co.uk

ST MAWES
Cornwall

Captain's Cottage ★★★
Contact: Mrs Margie Lumby, Special Places, Poachers Reach, Feock, Truro, Cornwall TR3 5SQ
T: (01872) 864400
F: (01872) 864400
E: office@
specialplacescornwall.co.uk
I: www.specialplacescornwall.co.uk

Coppers ★★★★
Contact: Mrs Margie Lumby, Special Places, Poachers Reach, Feock, Truro, Cornwall TR3 6SQ
T: (01872) 864400
F: (01872) 864400
E: office@
specialplacescornwall.co.uk
I: www.specialplacescornwall.co.uk

Dolphins ★★★
Contact: Mrs Margie Lumby, Special Places, Poachers Reach, Feock, Truro, Cornwall TR3 6SQ
T: (01872) 864400
F: (01872) 864400
E: office@
specialplacescornwall.co.uk
I: www.specialplacescornwall.co.uk

Establishments printed in blue have a detailed entry in this guide

The Gingerbread House
★★★★
Contact: Mrs Margie Lumby,
Special Places, Poachers Reach,
Feock, Truro, Cornwall TR3 6SQ
T: (01872) 864400
F: (01872) 864400
E: office@
specialplacescornwall.co.uk
I: www.specialplacescornwall.
co.uk

Little Hill ★★★
Contact: Cornish Cottage
Holidays, Godolphin Road,
Helston, Cornwall TR13 8AA
T: (01326) 573808
F: (01326) 564992
E: enquiry@
cornishcottageholidays.co.uk
I: www.cornishcottageholidays.
co.uk

Lower Fountain ★★★★
Contact: Mrs Margie Lumby,
Special Places, Poachers Reach,
Feock, Truro, Cornwall TR3 6SQ
T: (01872) 864400
F: (01872) 864400
E: office@
specialplacescornwall.co.uk
I: www.specialplacescornwall.
co.uk

Mariners ★★★★
Contact: Ms Margie Lumby,
Special Places, Poachers Reach,
Feock, Truro, Cornwall TR3 6SQ
T: (01872) 864400
F: (01872) 864400
E: office@
specialplacescornwall.co.uk
I: www.specialplacescornwall.
co.uk

Penlee ★★★
Contact: Mrs Margie Lumby,
Special Places, Poachers Reach,
Feock, Truro, Cornwall TR3 6SQ
T: (01872) 864400
F: (01872) 864400
E: office@
specialplacescornwall.co.uk
I: www.specialplacescornwall.
co.uk

Seaward ★★★★
Contact: Mrs Margie Lumby,
Special Places, Poachers Reach,
Feock, Truro, Cornwall TR3 6SQ
T: (01872) 864400
F: (01872) 864400
E: office@
specialplacescornwall.co.uk
I: www.specialplacescornwall.
co.uk

Starboard, Rocklee & Prydes
★★★-★★★★
Contact: Mrs Margie Lumby,
Special Places, Poachers Reach,
Feock, Truro, Cornwall TR3 6SQ
T: (01872) 864400
F: (01872) 864400
E: office@
specialplacescornwall.co.uk
I: www.specialplacescornwall.
co.uk

Sunnybanks ★★★★
Contact: Ms Margie Lumby,
Special Places In Cornwall,
Poachers Reach, Feock, Truro,
Cornwall TR3 6SQ
T: (01872) 864400
F: (01872) 864400
E: office@
specialplacescornwall.co.uk
I: www.specialplacescornwall.
co.uk

ST MAWGAN
Cornwall

Polgreen Manor ★★★
Contact: Mrs J A Wake, NDD,
Polgreen Manor, St Mawgan,
Newquay, Cornwall TR8 4AG
T: (01637) 860700
F: (01637) 875165

Retorrick Mill ★★-★★★
Contact: Ms Jenny Bertoli,
Retorrick Mill, St Mawgan,
Newquay, Cornwall TR8 4BH
T: (01637) 860460
E: www.
selfcateringbungalowscornwall.
com

ST MERRYN
Cornwall

Camelot ★★★
Contact: Mrs Tozer, Pine Trees,
Kilhallon, Par, Cornwall
PL24 2RL
T: (01726) 813318
F: (01726) 817440
E: keith@tozerhome.freeserve.
co.uk

Chalet 83 ★
Contact: Elizabeth Kerry, Church
Cottage, Chiseldon, Swindon,
Wiltshire SN4 0NJ
T: (01793) 740284 &
07778 792859

Little Lancarrow ★★★
Contact: Mr & Mrs Osborne,
Cornish Horizons Holiday
Cottages, Higher Trehemborne,
St Merryn, Padstow, Cornwall
PL28 8JU
T: (01841) 520889
F: (01841) 521523
E: cottages@cornishhorizons.
co.uk
I: www.cornishhorizons.co.uk

Lower Trevorgus ★★★★
Contact: Cornish Horizons,
Higher Trehemborne, St Merryn,
Padstow, Cornwall PL28 8JU
T: (01841) 520889 & 521333
F: (01841) 521523
E: cottages@cornishhorizons.
co.uk
I: www.cornishhorizons.co.uk

St Hilary ★★
Contact: Cornish Horizons,
Higher Trehemborne, St Merryn,
Padstow, Cornwall PL28 8JU
T: (01841) 520889 & 521333
F: (01841) 521523
E: cottages@cornishhorizons.
co.uk
I: www.cornishhorizons.co.uk

Trebrumble ★★★
Contact: Cornish Horizons
Holiday Cottages Agent, Higher
Trehemborne, St Merryn,
Padstow, Cornwall PL28 8JU
T: (01841) 520889 & 521333
F: (01841) 521523
E: cottages@cornishhorizons.
co.uk
I: www.cornishhorizons.co.uk

ST MINVER
Cornwall

April Cottage ★★★★★
Contact: Harbour Holidays,
Estuary House, Rock Road, Rock,
Wadebridge, Cornwall
PL27 6NW
T: (01208) 862424
F: (01208) 862218
E: rockhols@aol.com
I: www.rockholidays.co.uk

The Blandings ★★★★
Contact: Harbour Holidays,
Estuary House, Rock Road, Rock,
Wadebridge, Cornwall
PL27 6NW
T: (01208) 862424
F: (01208) 862218
E: rockhols@aol.com
I: www.rockholidays.com

The Bothy ★★★★
Contact: Harbour Holidays -
Rock, Estuary House, Rock Road,
Rock, Wadebridge, Cornwall
PL27 6NW
T: (01208) 862424
F: (01208) 862218
E: rockhols@aol.com
I: www.rockholidays.com

Brae Cottage ★★★★
Contact: Harbour Holidays -
Rock, Estuary House, Rock Road,
Rock, Wadebridge, Cornwall
PL27 6NW
T: (01208) 862424
F: (01208) 862218
E: rockhols@aol.com
I: www.rockholidays.com

Bunkers Cottage ★★★★
Contact: Harbour Holidays -
Rock, Estuary House, Rock Road,
Rock, Wadebridge, Cornwall
PL27 6NW
T: (01208) 862424
F: (01208) 862218
E: rockhols@aol.com
I: www.rockholidays.com

Caldarvan ★★★★
Contact: Harbour Holidays -
Rock, Estuary House, Rock Road,
Rock, Wadebridge, Cornwall
PL27 6NW
T: (01208) 862424
F: (01208) 862218
E: rockhols@aol.com
I: www.rockholidays.com

Casa Piedra Cottage ★★★★
Contact: Harbour Holidays -
Rock, Estuary House, Rock Road,
Rock, Wadebridge, Cornwall
PL27 6NW
T: (01208) 862424
F: (01208) 862218
E: rockhols@aol.com
I: www.rockholidays.com

Cowrie ★★★★
Contact: Harbour Holidays,
Estuary House, Rock Road, Rock,
Wadebridge, Cornwall
PL27 6NW
T: (01208) 862424
F: (01208) 862218
E: rockhols@aol.com
I: www.rockholidays.com

The Farmhouse Roserrow
★★★★
Contact: Harbour Holidays,
Estuary House, Rock Road, Rock,
Wadebridge, Cornwall
PL27 6NW
T: (01208) 862424
F: (01208) 862218
E: rockhols@aol.com
I: www.rockholidays.com

Gearys ★★★★
Contact: Harbour Holidays -
Rock, Estuary House, Rock Road,
Rock, Wadebridge, Cornwall
PL27 6NW
T: (01208) 862424
F: (01208) 862218
E: rockhols@aol.com
I: www.rockholidays.com

Gwella ★★★★
Contact: Harbour Holidays -
Rock, Estuary House, Rock Road,
Rock, Wadebridge, Cornwall
PL27 6NW
T: (01208) 862424
F: (01208) 862218
E: rockhols@aol.com
I: www.rockholidays.com

Idle Rocks ★★★★
Contact: Harbour Holidays -
Rock, Estuary House, Rock Road,
Rock, Wadebridge, Cornwall
PL27 6NW
T: (01208) 862424
F: (01208) 862218
E: rockhols@aol.com
I: www.rockholidays.com

Janners Retreat ★★★
Contact: Harbour Holidays -
Rock, Estuary House, Rock Road,
Rock, Wadebridge, Cornwall
PL27 6NW
T: (01208) 862424
F: (01208) 862218
E: rockhols@aol.com
I: www.rockholidays.com

Keepers ★★★★
Contact: Harbour Holidays -
Rock, Estuary House, Rock Road,
Rock, Wadebridge, Cornwall
PL27 6NW
T: (01208) 862424
F: (01208) 862218
E: rockhols@aol.com
I: www.rockholidays.com

Mayfield ★★★★
Contact: Harbour Holidays -
Rock, Estuary House, Rock Road,
Rock, Wadebridge, Cornwall
PL27 6NW
T: (01208) 862424
F: (01208) 862218
E: rockhols@aol.com
I: www.rockholidays.com

The Millhouse ★★★★
Contact: Harbour Holidays -
Rock, Estuary House, Rock Road,
Rock, Wadebridge, Cornwall
PL27 6NW
T: (01208) 862424
F: (01208) 862218
E: rockhols@aol.com
I: www.rockholidays.com

Molvenny ★★★★
Contact: Harbour Holidays -
Rock, Estuary House, Rock Road,
Rock, Wadebridge, Cornwall
PL27 6NW
T: (01208) 862424
F: (01208) 862218
E: rockhols@aol.com
I: www.rockholidays.com

The Nineteenth ★★★★
Contact: Harbour Holidays,
Estuary House, Rock Road, Rock,
Wadebridge, Cornwall
PL27 6NW
T: (01208) 862424
F: (01208) 862218
E: rockhols@aol.com
I: www.rockholidays.com

Oak Tree House ★★★★
Contact: Harbour Holidays -
Rock, Estuary House, Rock Road,
Rock, Wadebridge, Cornwall
PL27 6NW
T: (01208) 862424
F: (01208) 862218
E: rockhols@aol.com
I: www.rockholidays.com

2 The Old Dairy ★★★★
Contact: Harbour Holidays -
Rock, Estuary House, Rock Road,
Rock, Wadebridge, Cornwall
PL27 6NW
T: (01208) 862424
F: (01208) 862218
E: rockhols@aol.com
I: www.rockholidays.com

Penkivel House ★★★★
Contact: Harbour Holidays -
Rock, Estuary House, Rock Road,
Rock, Wadebridge, Cornwall
PL27 6NW
T: (01208) 862424
F: (01208) 862218
E: rockhols@aol.com
I: www.rockholidays.com

Pond End ★★★★
Contact: Harbour Holidays -
Rock, Estuary House, Rock Road,
Rock, Wadebridge, Cornwall
PL27 6NW
T: (01208) 862424
F: (01208) 862218
E: rockhols@aol.com
I: www.rockholidays.com

Puffin House ★★★★
Contact: Harbour Holidays,
Estuary House, Rock Road, Rock,
Wadebridge, Cornwall
PL27 6NW
T: (01208) 862424
F: (01208) 862218
E: rockhols@aol.com
I: www.rockholidays.com

Rosewin Barn ★★★★
Contact: Harbour Holidays -
Rock, Estuary House, Rock Road,
Rock, Wadebridge, Cornwall
PL27 6NW
T: (01208) 862424
F: (01208) 862218
E: rockhols@aol.com
I: www.rockholidays.com

Rosewin Farmhouse ★★★★
Contact: Harbour Holidays -
Rock, Estuary House, Rock Road,
Rock, Wadebridge, Cornwall
PL27 6LD
T: (01208) 862424

The Roundhouse ★★★★
Contact: Harbour Holidays,
Estuary House, Rock Road, Rock,
Wadebridge, Cornwall
PL27 6NW
T: (01208) 862424
F: (01208) 862218
E: rockhols@aol.com
I: www.rockholidays.com

Tamarisk ★★★★
Contact: Harbour Holidays -
Rock, Estuary House, Rock Road,
Rock, Wadebridge, Cornwall
PL27 6NW
T: (01208) 862424
F: (01208) 862218
E: rockhols@aol.com
I: www.rockholidays.com

Tremaine ★★★★★
Contact: Harbour Holidays -
Rock, Estuary House, Rock Road,
Rock, Wadebridge, Cornwall
PL27 6NW
T: (01208) 862424
F: (01208) 862218
E: rockhols@aol.com
I: www.rockholidays.com

Trevells ★★★★
Contact: Harbour Holidays,
Estuary House, Rock Road, Rock,
Wadebridge, Cornwall
PL27 6NW
T: (01208) 862424
F: (01208) 862218
E: rockhols@aol.com
I: www.rockholidays.com

Valerian ★★★
Contact: Harbour Holidays -
Rock, Estuary House, Rock Road,
Rock, Wadebridge, Cornwall
PL27 6NW
T: (01208) 862424
F: (01208) 862218
E: rockhols@aol.com
I: www.rockholidays.com

Wedge Cottage ★★★★
Contact: Harbour Holidays -
Rock, Estuary House, Rock Road,
Rock, Wadebridge, Cornwall
PL27 6NW
T: (01208) 862424
F: (01208) 862218
E: rockhols@aol.com
I: www.rockholidays.com

ST NEWLYN EAST
Cornwall

Penty Gwyn ★★★
Contact: Powell's Cottage
Holidays, High Street,
Saundersfoot, Dyfed SA69 9EJ
T: (01834) 812791
F: (01834) 811731
E: info@powells.co.uk
I: www.powells.co.uk

ST STEPHEN
Cornwall

**Court Farm Cottages
★★★-★★★★**
Contact: Mr W Truscott, Court
Farm Cottages, St Stephen, St
Austell, Cornwall PL26 7LE
T: (01726) 822727 &
07971 971673
F: (01726) 822685
E: truscott@ctfarm.freeserve.
co.uk

ST TEATH
Cornwall

Barn Farm ★★★-★★★★
Contact: CH
ref:1042,10262,8775,14636,
Holiday Cottages Group, Spring
Mill, Earby, Barnoldswick,
Lancashire BB18 6RN
T: (01282) 445096
F: (01282) 844299
E: ch.sales@ttging.co.uk
I: www.country-holidays.co.uk

Cocks Cottage ★★★
Contact: Mr & Mrs Bowater,
Helpful Holidays, Mill Street,
Chagford, Newton Abbot, Devon
TQ13 8AW
T: (01647) 433593
F: (01647) 433694
E: help@helpfulholidays.com
I: www.helpfulholidays.com

**Tregreenwell Farm Cottage
★★★★**
Contact: Mr Peter Morris, Farm
& Cottage Holidays, Victoria
House, 12 Fore Street, Northam,
Bideford, Devon EX39 1AW
T: (01237) 479146
F: (01237) 421512
E: farmcott@cix.co.uk
I: www.farmcott.co.uk

ST TUDY
Cornwall

Colesent Cottages ★★★
Contact: Mrs S Zamaria,
Colesent Cottages, St Tudy,
Bodmin, Cornwall PL30 4QX
T: (01208) 850112
F: (01208) 850112
E: zamaria_colesent@msn.com
I: www.colesent.co.uk

5 Liam Bungalows ★★
Contact: 'Holidays', 101
Coventry Road, Coleshill,
Birmingham B46 3EX
T: 0870 4423684
F: 0870 4423685
E: heather@holidays-cornwall.
com
I: www.holidays-cornwall.com

SALCOMBE
Devon

Coxswain's Watch ★★★
Contact: Mr Andrew Oulsnam,
Robert Oulsnam & Co, 79 Hewell
Road, Barnt Green, Birmingham
B45 8NL
T: (0121) 445 3311
F: (0121) 445 6026
E: barntgreen@oulsnam-online.
com

Longridge ★★★★
Contact: Mr B Curry, Meriden
Cottage, Longburton, Sherborne,
Dorset DT9 5PH
T: (01963) 210622

SALISBURY
Wiltshire

**12 Charter Court
Rating Applied For**
Contact: Mrs P Moore, 28
RIverside Close, Salisbury,
SP1 1QW
T: (01722) 320188

Cherry Tree Cottage ★★★★
Contact: Mrs J Murphy, Cherry
Tree Cottage, 1a Grasmere Close,
Harnham, Salisbury, SP2 8DG
T: (01722) 326144
F: (01722) 326144
I: www.
cherrytreecottage@hotmail.
com

The Old Stables ★★★★
Contact: Mr G Gould, The Old
Stables, Bridge Farm, Lower
Road, Britford, Salisbury
SP5 4DY
T: (01722) 349002
F: (01722) 349003
E: mail@old-stables.co.uk
I: www.old-stables.co.uk

Weavers Cottage ★★★
Contact: CH ref: 8210, Holiday
Cottages Group Owner Services
Department, Spring Mill, Earby,
Barnoldswick, Lancashire
BB18 6RN
T: (01282) 445096
F: (01282) 844299
E: ch.sales@ttgihg.co.uk
I: www.country-holidays.co.uk

SALWAY ASH
Dorset

**Brinsham Farm
Rating Applied For**
Contact: Ms V Harding,
Caryswood Ltd, Bentley
Cottages, Bentleys Farm Lane,
Higher Whitley, Warrington
WA4 4PZ
T: (01925) 730634 & 730006

Chapel Cottage ★★★★
Contact: CH Ref: 14285, Holiday
Cottages Group Owner Services
Department, Spring Mill, Earby,
Barnoldswick, Lancashire
BB94 0AA
T: (01282) 445096
F: (01282) 844299
E: ch.sales@ttgihg.co.uk
I: www.country-holidays.co.uk

SAMPFORD ARUNDEL
Somerset

Gorlegg Cottage ★★★
Contact: Mr Peter Morris, Farm
& Cottage Holidays, Victoria
House, 12 Fore Street, Northam,
Bideford, Devon EX39 1AW
T: (01237) 479146
F: (01237) 421512
E: farmcott@cix.co.uk
I: www.farmcott.co.uk

SAMPFORD BRETT
Somerset

The Granary ★★★
Contact: CH ref: 68042, Holiday
Cottages Group Owner Services
Department, Spring Mill, Earby,
Barnoldswick, Lancashire
BB18 6RN
T: (01282) 445096
F: (01282) 844299
E: ch.sales@ttgihg.co.uk
I: www.country-holidays.co.uk

Establishments printed in blue have a detailed entry in this guide

SAMPFORD COURTENAY
Devon

Culverhayes Cottages ★★★★
Contact: Mr & Mrs Martin & Sue
Roberts, Culverhayes Cottages,
Culverhayes, Rectory Hill,
Sampford Courtenay,
Okehampton, Devon EX20 2TG
T: (01837) 89150
F: (01837) 82431
E: culverhayes@excite.co.uk

SAMPFORD SPINEY
Devon

Withill Cottage ★★★
Contact: Mr Peter Morris, Farm
& Cottage Holidays, Victoria
House, 12 Fore Street, Northam,
Bideford, Devon EX39 1AW
T: (01237) 479146
F: (01237) 421512
E: farmcott@cix.co.uk
I: www.farmcott.co.uk

SANDYWAY
Devon

Barkham Cottage ★★★★
Contact: Mr & Mrs J Adie,
Barkham, Sandyway, South
Molton, Devon EX36 3LU
T: (01643) 831370
F: (01643) 831370
E: adie.exmoor@btinternet.com
I: www.exmoor-visitus.com
I: www.exmoor-visitus.co.uk

SAUNTON
Devon

Lankham Cottage ★★★
Contact: Marsden's Cottage
Holidays, 2 The Square,
Braunton, Devon EX33 2JB
T: (01271) 813777
F: (01271) 813664
E: holidays@marsdens.co.uk
I: www.marsdens.co.uk

Rhu and Little Rhu
★★★–★★★★
Contact: Marsden's Cottage
Holidays, 2 The Square,
Braunton, Devon EX33 2JB
T: (01271) 813777
F: (01271) 813664
E: holidays@marsdens.co.uk
I: www.marsdens.co.uk

Saunton Heath ★★★
Contact: Marsden's Cottage
Holidays, 2 The Square,
Braunton, Devon EX33 2JB
T: (01271) 813777
F: (01271) 813664
E: holidays@marsdens.co.uk
I: www.marsdens.co.uk

SEATON
Devon

Bishopswood ★★★★
Contact: Jean Bartlett Cottage
Holidays, Fore Street, Beer,
Seaton, Devon EX12 3JB
T: (01297) 23221
F: (01297) 23303
E: jeanb@netbreaks.com
I: www.netbreaks.com/jeanb

Caruso ★★★
Contact: Milkbere Cottage
Holidays, Milkbere House, 14
Fore Street, Seaton, Devon
EX12 2LA
T: (01297) 20729
F: (01297) 24831
E: info@milkbere.com
I: www.milkbere.com

The Chalet ★★★
Contact: Jean Bartlett Cottage
Holidays, Fore Street, Beer,
Seaton, Devon EX12 3JB
T: (01297) 23221
F: (01297) 23303
E: jeanb@netbreaks.com
I: www.netbreaks.com/jeanb

Cliff Hollow ★★★★★
Contact: Mr & Mrs R Pocock,
Cliff Hollow, Beer Road, Seaton,
Devon EX12 2QB
T: (01297) 23707
E: cliffhollow@talk21.com

Coniston ★★
Contact: Milkbere Cottage
Holidays, Milkbere House, 14
Fore Street, Seaton, Devon
EX12 2LA
T: (01297) 20729
F: (01297) 24831
E: info@milkbere.com
I: www.milkbere.com

Flat 4 Homestead★★
Contact: Jean Bartlett Cottage
Holidays, Fore Street, Beer,
Seaton, Devon EX12 3JB
T: (01297) 23221
F: (01297) 23303
E: jeanb@netbreaks.com
I: www.netbreaks.com/jeanb

Fuchsias ★★★
Contact: Milkbere Cottage
Holidays, 14 Fore Street, Seaton,
Devon EX12 2LA
T: (01297) 20729
F: (01297) 24831
E: info@milkbere.com
I: www.milkbere.com

Hydrangea Cottage ★★★
Contact: Milkbere Cottage
Holidays, 14 Fore Street, Seaton,
Devon EX12 2LA
T: (01297) 20729
F: (01297) 24831
E: info@milkbere.com
I: www.milkbere.com

1 Inkerman Court ★★★★
Contact: Milkbere Cottage
Holidays, 14 Fore Street, Seaton,
Devon EX12 2LA
T: (01297) 20729
F: (01297) 24831
E: info@milkbere.com
I: www.milkbere.com

Laburnum ★★★
Contact: Milkbere Cottage
Holidays, 14 Fore Street, Seaton,
Devon EX12 2LA
T: (01297) 20729
F: (01297) 24831
E: info@milkbere.com
I: www.milkbere.com

Langdale ★★★
Contact: Milkbere Cottage
Holidays, 14 Fore Street, Seaton,
Devon EX12 2LA
T: (01297) 20729
F: (01297) 24831
E: info@milkbere.com
I: www.milkbere.com

Last Penny Cottage ★★★
Contact: Milkbere Cottage
Holidays, Milkbere House, 14
Fore Street, Seaton, Devon
EX12 2LA
T: (01297) 20729
F: (01297) 24831
E: info@milkbere.com
I: www.milkbere.com

Little Cot ★★★
Contact: Jean Bartlett Cottage
Holidays, Fore Street, Beer,
Seaton, Devon EX12 3JB
T: (01297) 23221
F: (01297) 23303
E: jeanb@netbreaks.com
I: www.netbreaks.com/jeanb

3 Lyme Mews ★★★★
Contact: Jean Bartlett Cottage
Holidays, Fore Street, Beer,
Seaton, Devon EX12 3JB
T: (01297) 23221
F: (01297) 23303
E: jeanb@netbreaks.com
I: www.netbreaks.com/jeanb

Manor Farm Cottages
★★★–★★★★
Contact: Mrs Parr, Manor Farm,
Harepath Hill, Seaton, Devon
EX12 2TF
T: (01297) 625349

Pippins ★★
Contact: Milkbere Cottage
Holidays, 14 Fore Street, Seaton,
Devon EX12 2LA
T: (01297) 20729
F: (01297) 24831
E: info@milkbere.com
I: www.milkbere.com

Primrose Cottage ★★★★
Contact: Jean Bartlett Cottage
Holidays, Fore Street, Beer,
Seaton, Devon EX12 3JB
T: (01297) 23221
F: (01297) 23303
E: jeanb@netbreaks.com
I: www.netbreaks.com/jeanb

Rosemead ★★★
Contact: Milkbere Cottage
Holidays, 14 Fore Street, Seaton,
Devon EX12 2LA
T: (01297) 20729
F: (01297) 24831
E: info@milkbere.com
I: www.milkbere.com

10 Seafield Road ★★★
Contact: Milkbere Cottage
Holidays, 14 Fore Street, Seaton,
Devon EX12 2LA
T: (01297) 20729
F: (01297) 24831
E: info@milkbere.com
I: www.milkbere.com

Seagulls ★★★
Contact: Milkbere Cottage
Holidays, Milkbere House, 14
Fore Street, Seaton, Devon
T: (01297) 20729
F: (01297) 24831
E: info@milkbere.com
I: www.milkbere.com

Seaside Flat 3★★★
Contact: Jean Bartlett Cottage
Holidays, Fore Street, Beer,
Seaton, Devon EX12 3JB
T: (01297) 23221
F: (01297) 23303
E: jeanb@netbreaks.com
I: www.netbreaks.com/jeanb

West Ridge Bungalow ★★★
Contact: Mrs H Fox, West Ridge
Bungalow, Harepath Hill,
Seaton, Devon EX12 2TA
T: (01297) 22398
F: (01297) 22398
E: foxfamily@westridge.
fsbusiness.co.uk
I: www.cottageguide.
co.uk/westridge

Westward Apartments ★★★
Contact: Milkbere Cottage
Holidays, Milkbere House, 14
Fore Street, Seaton, Devon
EX12 2LA
T: (01297) 20729
F: (01297) 24831
E: info@milkbere.com
I: www.milkbere.com

Windrush ★★★
Contact: Jean Bartlett Cottage
Holidays, Fore Street, Beer,
Seaton, Devon EX12 3JB
T: (01297) 23221
F: (01297) 23303
E: jeanb@netbreaks.com
I: www.netbreaks.com/jeanb

SEATOWN
Dorset

The Guard House ★★★★★
Contact: Mrs Joyce Whittaker,
Seatown House, Seatown,
Chideock, Bridport, Dorset
DT6 6JU
T: (01297) 489417
F: (01297) 489151
E: info@guardhouse.co.uk
I: www.guardhouse.co.uk

SECTOR
Devon

Primrose Cottage ★★★★
Contact: Jean Bartlett Cottage
Holidays, Fore Street, Beer,
Seaton, Devon EX12 3JB
T: (01297) 23221
F: (01297) 23303
E: jeanb@netbreaks.com
I: www.netbreaks.com/jeanb

SELWORTHY
Somerset

**Old Rectory Holiday Flats
★★★**
Contact: Mr & Mrs Clarke, Old
Rectory Holiday Flats, The Old
Rectory, Selworthy, Minehead,
Somerset TA24 8TW
T: (01643) 862233

SENNEN
Cornwall

3 & 4 Wesley Cottages ★★★
Contact: Mrs Jane Davey,
Rosteague, Raginnis Farm,
Mousehole, Penzance, Cornwall
TR19 6NJ
T: (01736) 731933
F: (01736) 732344
E: wesley@raginnis.demon.
co.uk
I: www.wesleyatnanquidno.
co.uk

The Old Dairy ★★★
Contact: Cornish Cottage
Holidays, The Old Turnpike Dairy,
Godolphin Road, Helston,
Cornwall TR13 8AA
T: (01326) 573808
F: (01326) 564992
E: enquiry@
cornishcottageholidays.co.uk
I: www.cornishcottageholidays.
co.uk

Tregiffian Studios ★★–★★★
Contact: Mrs R Vigano,
Tregiffian Farmhouse, Sennen,
Penzance, Cornwall TR19 7BE
T: (01736) 871658

Wellfield Farmhouse and Cottages ★★★
Contact: Cornish Cottage Holidays, The Old Turnpike Dairy, Godolphin Road, Helston, Cornwall TR13 8AA
T: (01326) 573808
F: (01326) 564992
E: enquiry@cornishcottageholidays.co.uk
I: www.cornishcottageholidays.co.uk

SENNEN COVE
Cornwall

Huer's Rock ★★★
Contact: Mr Richard Puddiphatt, 34 Westbridge Cottages, Tavistock, Devon PL19 8DQ
T: (01822) 615320
E: puddy90@hotmail.com

Jubilee Cottage ★★★
Contact: Mr J Nicholas, Harbour View, Sennen Cove, Penzance, Cornwall TR19 7DE
T: (01736) 871206
F: (01736) 871206
E: susannecook@supanet.com
I: www.pop3susannecook@supanet.com

Lynwood House ★★★
Contact: Mr J Nicholas, Harbour View, Sennen Cove, Penzance, Cornwall TR19 7DE
T: (01736) 871206
F: (01736) 871206
E: susannecook@supanet.com

The Old Success Inn ★★
Contact: Mr Martin Brookes, The Old Success Inn, Sennen Cove, Lands End, TR19 7DG
T: (01736) 871232
F: (01736) 871457
E: theoldsuccessinn.co.uk

o SEVERN BEACH
Gloucestershire

Gorse Cottage ★★★
Contact: Mr Clive Churchill, 87 Bradley Crescent, Shirehampton, Bristol BS11 9SB
T: (0117) 982 0022 & 982 2088
F: (0117) 982 1292
E: info@gorse-cottage.freeserve.co.uk

SHALDON
Devon

Badgers Brook Holiday Cottages★★
Contact: Mr & Mrs KT Price, Badgers Brook, Higher Gabwell, Stoke-in-Teignhead, Newton Abbot, Devon TQ12 4QW
T: (01803) 327398
F: (01803) 327398
E: badgers@aisthorpe.freeserve.co.uk

Barton Cottage ★★★
Contact: Miss Susan Elizabeth Witt, Barton Cottage Holiday Lettings, Court Barton, Stokeinteignhead, Newton Abbot, Devon TQ12 4QL
T: (01626) 872441 & 07703 240218
E: bartoncottage@stokeinteignhead.freeserve.co.uk

Coombe Close Holidays ★★★
Contact: Mr & Mrs M&P Huff, Coombe Close Holidays, Coombe Close, Brim Hill, Maidencombe, Torquay, Devon TQ1 4TR
T: (01803) 327215
F: (01803) 327215
E: peterhuff@onetel.net.uk
I: www.shines.net/maidencombe

Longmeadow Farm ★★
Contact: Mrs A Mann, Longmeadow Farm, Coombe Road, Ringmore, Shaldon, Teignmouth, Devon TQ14 0EX
T: (01626) 872732
F: (01626) 872323

Pear Tree Cottage ★★★
Contact: Mr& Mrs P H Colley, Pear Tree Cottage, Higher Ringmore Road, Shaldon, Teignmouth, Devon TQ14 0HG
T: (01626) 873300
E: nataliacolley@onetel.net.uk
I: www.colleycottage.co.uk

SHEBBEAR
Devon

Apple Loft ★★★★
Contact: Mr Peter Morris, Farm & Cottage Holidays, Victoria House, 12 Fore Street, Northam, Bideford, Devon EX39 1AW
T: (01237) 479146
F: (01237) 421512
E: farmcott@cix.co.uk
I: www.farmcott.co.uk

SHEEPWASH
Devon

Swardicott Farm ★★★
Contact: Mrs M Purser, Swardicott Farm, Sheepwash, Beaworthy, Devon EX21 5PB
T: (01409) 231633
F: (01409) 231361
E: mpurser@btinternet.com
I: www.holidaycottages-devon.co.uk

SHELDON
Devon

Droughtwell Farm ★★★
Contact: Mrs Susan Cochrane, Droughtwell Farm, Sheldon, Honiton, Devon EX14 4QW
T: (01404) 841349
F: (01404) 841349

SHEPTON BEAUCHAMP
Somerset

Cowleaze ★★★★
Contact: CH ref: 1101, Holiday Cottages Group, Spring Mill, Earby, Barnoldswick, Lancashire BB18 6RN
T: (01282) 445096
F: (01282) 844299
E: ch.sales@ttgihg.co.uk
I: www.country-holidays.co.uk

SHEPTON MALLET
Somerset

Bridge Cottage ★★★★
Contact: Ms Paula Blight, DCC Associates Ltd, PO Box 1641, Frome, Somerset BA11 1YY
T: (01373) 812080
F: (01373) 813636

Knowle Farm Cottages ★★★
Contact: Mrs J A Boyce, Knowle Farm Cottages, West Compton, Shepton Mallet, Somerset BA4 4PD
T: (01749) 890482
F: (01749) 890405

Leigh Holt ★★★★
Contact: Mrs Pamela Hoddinott, Burnt House Farm, Waterlip, Shepton Mallet, Somerset BA4 4RN
T: (01749) 880280
F: (01749) 880004
🅰

Middle Farm ★★★★
Contact: Mr Mark Evans, Middle Farm, Hornblotton, Shepton Mallet, Somerset BA4 6SF
T: (01963) 240446

SHERBORNE
Dorset

1 & 2 Trill Cottages ★★★
Contact: Mrs J Warr, 1 & 2 Trill Cottages, Trill House, Thornford, Sherborne, Dorset DT9 6HF
T: (01935) 872305
E: trill.cottages@ic24.net

Blackberry Cottage ★★★
Contact: Mr John Michael Farr, 17 Marsh Lane, Yeovil, Somerset BA21 3BX
T: (01935) 423148 & 433538

Carpenters ★★★
Contact: Mrs S J Dixon, Carpenters, Neals Lane, Chetnole, Sherborne, Dorset DT9 6PF
T: (01935) 872695
E: D.Dixon@farmline.com

Grange Farm ★★★★
Contact: Mrs K Flannery, Grange Farm, Oborne, Sherborne, Dorset DT9 4LA
T: (01935) 812793

Millers Loft ★★★
Contact: Mrs B Buckland, Millers Loft, The Mill, Goathill, Sherborne, Dorset DT9 5JD
T: (01963) 250380

Old Orchard Cottage ★★★★
Contact: Mrs Alexa Buckland, Old Orchard Cottage, Goathill Farm, Goathill, Sherborne, Dorset DT9 5JD
T: (01963) 251365
F: (01963) 251365

Stable Cottage Terrace★★★
Contact: Mrs R E Dimond, Stable Cottage Terrace, Bridleways, Oborne Road, Sherborne, Dorset DT9 3RX
T: (01935) 814716
F: (01935) 814716

SHERRINGTON
Wiltshire

Gingerbread Cottage ★★★★
Contact: Ms Gabrielle Lewis, Gingerbread Cottage, Sheepfold Cottage, Sherrington, Warminster, Wiltshire BA12 0SN
T: (01985) 850453
F: (01985) 850453
E: patlewis@lineone.net
I: www.gingerbreadcottage.co.uk

SHERSTON
Wiltshire

May Cottage ★★★★
Contact: Mrs S M Bristow, Mill Cottage, Thompsons Hill, Sherston, Malmesbury, Wiltshire SN16 0NE
T: (01666) 840655

SHILLINGFORD
Devon

South Hayne Farm ★★★
Contact: Mr Peter Morris, Farm & Cottage Holidays, Victoria House, 12 Fore Street, Northam, Bideford, Devon EX39 1AW
T: (01237) 479146
F: (01237) 421512
E: farmcott@cix.co.uk
I: www.farmcott.co.uk

SHIPTON GORGE
Dorset

Dolphins ★★★★
Contact: Mrs J D Sorrell, The Croft, Bonscombe Lane, Shipton Gorge, Bridport, Dorset DT6 4LJ
T: (01308) 897277 & 07790 580589

SHUTE
Devon

Higher Watchcombe Farmhouse and Country Cottages★★★★
Contact: Mr & Mrs Paul & Jane Galloway, Higher Watchcombe Farmhouse and Country Cottages, Shute, Axminster, Devon EX13 7QN
T: (01297) 552424
F: (01297) 552424
E: galloways@ukgateway.net
I: www.galloways@ukgateway.net

SIDBURY
Devon

Lower Knapp Farm Holidays ★★★★
Contact: Mr and Mrs J D Baxter, Lower Knapp Farm Holidays, Sidbury, Sidmouth, Devon EX10 0QN
T: (01404) 871438
F: (01404) 871597
E: lowknapp@aol.com

SIDMOUTH
Devon

Boswell Farm Cottages ★★★★
Contact: Mr & Mrs B P Dillon, Boswell Farm Holiday Cottages, Boswell Farm, Sidford, Sidmouth, Devon EX10 0PP
T: (01395) 514162
F: (01395) 514162
E: dillon@boswell-farm.co.uk
I: www.boswell-farm.co.uk

Bringewood ★★★
Contact: CH ref: 50269, Holiday Cottages Group Owner Services Dept, Spring Mill, Earby, Barnoldswick, Lancashire BB18 6RN
T: (01282) 445096
F: (01282) 844299
E: ch.sales@ttgihg.co.uk
I: www.country-holidays.co.uk

Cliffe Cottage ★★★★
Contact: Jean Bartlett Cottage Holidays, Fore Street, Beer, Seaton, Devon EX12 3JB
T: (01297) 23221
F: (01297) 23303
E: jbean@netbreaks.com
I: www.netbreaks.com/jeanb

Establishments printed in blue have a detailed entry in this guide

Drupe Farm ★★★★
Contact: Miss G Elliott, Drupe
Farm, Colaton Raleigh,
Sidmouth, Devon EX10 0LE
T: (01395) 568838
F: (01395) 567882
E: mail@drupefarm.co.uk
I: www.drupefarm.co.uk

Higher Thorn Barn ★★★★
Contact: Mrs Margaret Evans,
Higher Thorn Cottage, Trow,
Salcombe Regis, Sidmouth,
Devon EX10 0PA
T: (01395) 513813

Leigh Farm ★★★★
Contact: Mr & Mrs Geoff & Gill
Davis, Leigh Farm, Weston,
Sidmouth, Devon EX10 0PH
T: (01395) 516065
F: (01395) 579582
E: leigh.farm@virgin.net
I: www.streets-ahead.
com/leighfarm

Melody ★★★
Contact: Mrs S Broom, 187
Manstone Avenue, Sidmouth,
Devon EX10 9TJ
T: (01395) 512967

Paccombe Cottage ★★★
Contact: Jean Bartlett Cottage
Holidays, Fore Street, Beer,
Seaton, Devon EX12 3JB
T: (01297) 23221
F: (01297) 23303
E: jeanb@netbreaks.com
I: www.netbreaks.com/jeanb

Riverside Cottage ★★
Contact: Jean Bartlett Cottage
Holidays, Fore Street, Beer,
Seaton, Devon EX12 3JB
T: (01297) 23221
F: (01297) 23303
E: jeanb@netbreaks.com
I: www.netbreaks.com/jeanb

Springfield Lodge ★★★★
Contact: Jean Bartlett Cottage
Holidays, Fore Street, Beer,
Seaton, Devon EX12 3JB
T: (01297) 23221
F: (01297) 23303
E: jeanb@netbreaks.com
I: www.netbreaks.com/jeanb

Waterside ★★
Contact: Jean Bartlett Cottage
Holidays, Fore Street, Beer,
Seaton, Devon EX12 3JB
T: (01297) 23221
F: (01297) 23303
E: jeanb@netbreaks.com
I: www.netbreaks.com/jeanb

SIMONSBATH
Somerset

Pound Cottage ★★★
Contact: Mrs Margaret
Billington, Pottery Cottage,
Simonsbath, Minehead,
Somerset TA24 7SH
T: (01643) 831443

Wintershead Farm ★★★★
Contact: Mrs J Styles,
Wintershead Farm, Simonsbath,
Minehead, Somerset TA24 7LF
T: (01643) 831222
F: (01643) 831628
I: www.wintershead.co.uk

SITHNEY
Cornwall

**Tregathenan Barns Long Barn,
Hayloft & Granary
★★★-★★★★**
Contact: Mrs Furness, The Old
Farmhouse, Tregathenan,
Sithney, Helston, Cornwall
TR13 0RZ
T: (01326) 569840 & 572852
F: (01326) 572852

SLAPTON
Devon

Dittiscombe ★★★-★★★★
Contact: Mrs Ruth Saunders,
Dittiscombe, Slapton,
Kingsbridge, Devon TQ7 2QF
T: (01548) 521272
F: (01548) 521425
E: jonmsaunders@lineone.net

SLAUGHTERFORD
Wiltshire

Carters Cottage ★★★
Contact: Mrs J M Jones,
Fairhaven Holiday Cottages,
Derby House, 123 Watling
Street, Gillingham, Kent
ME7 2YY
T: (01249) 782243

SOMERTON
Somerset

**Sleepy Hollow Double Gates
Drove★★★★★**
Contact: Mr & Mrs P Raine,
Sleepy Hollow Double Gates
Drove, Mill Road, Barton St
David, Somerton, Somerset
TA11 6DF
T: (01458) 850584
F: (01458) 850584
E: paul&rhian@
sleepyhollowcottages.com
I: www.sleepyhollowcottages.
com

Tiddlywinks ★★★
Contact: Mr Graham Slocombe,
Home Farm, Upton, Long Sutton,
Langport, Somerset TA10 9NW
T: (01458) 241117
E: slocombe@globalnet.co.uk

SOUTH BRENT
Devon

**High Leigh
Rating Applied For**
Contact: Mrs Reynolds, High
Leigh, South Brent, Devon
TQ10 9DS
T: (01364) 73396

SOUTH BREWHAM
Somerset

**Magpie Cottage & Jackdaw
Cottage ★★★★**
Contact: Mr DRD Dabinett,
Haven Farm, South Brewham,
Bruton, Somerset BA10 0JZ
T: (01749) 850441
E: david@havenfarm.co.uk
I: www.havenfarm.co.uk

SOUTH MILTON
Devon

Nancy's Cottage ★★
Contact: Mrs R J Jones, 139
Franche Road, Kidderminster,
Worcestershire DY11 5AP
T: (01562) 66930

SOUTH MOLTON
Devon

**Drewstone Farm
★★★-★★★★**
Contact: Mrs Ruth Ley,
Drewstone Farm, South Molton,
Devon EX36 3EF
T: (01769) 572337
F: (01769) 572337
I: www.devonfarms.co.uk

Great Whitstone Farm ★★★
Contact: Mrs Sally Meikle, Great
Whitstone Farm, Meshaw, South
Molton, Devon EX36 4NH
T: (01884) 860914

**North Lee Farm Holiday
Cottages ★★★★**
Contact: Mr Roy Hancocks,
North Lee Farm Holiday
Cottages, Hacche Lane, South
Molton, Devon EX36 3EH
T: (01598) 740248 & 740675
F: (01598) 740248
E: sue@
northleeholidaycottages.co.uk
I: www.northleeholidaycottages.
co.uk

The Willows ★★★★
Contact: Marsden's Cottage
Holidays, 2 The Square,
Braunton, Devon EX33 2JB
T: (01271) 813777
F: (01271) 813664
E: holidays@marsdens.co.uk
I: www.marsdens.co.uk

SOUTH PETHERTON
Somerset

Tanwyn ★★★★
Contact: Mr & Mrs Rodney &
Ann Tanswell, Planhigyn,
Penylan Road, St Brides Major,
Bridgend, Mid Glamorgan
CF32 0SB
T: (01656) 880524 & (029) 2054
0000
F: (01656) 880524
E: rtanswel@globalnet.co.uk

SOUTH POOL
Devon

The Roundhouse ★★★★
Contact: Mr & Mrs Bowater,
Helpful Holidays, Mill Street,
Chagford, Newton Abbot, Devon
TQ13 8AW
T: (01647) 433593
F: (01647) 433694
E: help@helpfulholidays.com
I: www.helpfulholidays.com

SOUTHSTOKE
Bath and North East Somerset

Top Flat ★★★
Contact: Mr Philip Raby, Top
Flat, Southstoke House,
Packhorse Lane, Southstoke,
Bath BA2 7DJ
T: (01225) 837121 & 462033
F: (01225) 836090
E: jennymac@netgates.co.uk

STANTON DREW
Bath and North East Somerset

Druid Farm ★★★
Contact: Mr Peter Morris, Farm
& Cottage Holidays, Victoria
House, 12 Fore Street, Northam,
Bideford, Devon EX39 1AW
T: (01237) 479146
F: (01237) 421512
E: farmcott@cix.co.uk
I: www.farmcott.co.uk

STAPLE FITZPAINE
Somerset

**Mill Farm Holiday Cottages
★★★**
Contact: Mr & Mrs Stan & Alison
Moore, Mill Farm Holiday
Cottages, Staple Fitzpaine,
Taunton, Somerset TA3 5SP
T: (01823) 481214
F: (01823) 481214

STAPLETON
Bristol

**Carleton Estates Ltd
Rating Applied For**
Contact: Ms G Carleton,
Carleton Estates Ltd, Stoke Park,
Stapleton, Bristol SN4 7HN
T: (01793) 850421

STARCROSS
Devon

Regent House ★★★★
Contact: Mrs Jewel Goss, Regent
House, Starcross, Exeter EX6 8PA
T: (01626) 891947
F: (01626) 206077
E: regenthouse@eclipse.co.uk
I: www.smoothhound.
co.uk/hotels/regenth.html

STAVERTON
Devon

The Kingston Estate ★★★★
Contact: Mr Mark Stevens,
Kingston House, Staverton,
Totnes, Devon TQ9 6AR
T: (01803) 762235
F: (01803) 762444
E: info@kingston-estate.net
I: www.kingston-estate.net

STEEPLE ASHTON
Wiltshire

Elwyns Cottage ★★★★
Contact: CH Ref: B4773, Holiday
Cottages Group, Spring Mill,
Earby, Barnoldswick, Lancashire
BB18 6RN
T: (01282) 445096
F: (01282) 844299
E: ch.sales@ttgihg.co.uk
I: www.country-holidays.co.uk

Jasmine Cottage ★★★
Contact: Mr NA Sharples, 4 St
Margarets, Little Aston, Sutton
Coldfield, West Midlands
B74 4HU
T: (0121) 353 5258
E: jasminecottage@
netscapeonline.co.uk
I: www.jasminecottage.co.uk

STITHIANS
Cornwall

Chy Gwyn Cottage ★★★
Contact: Mrs B Rayner, Chy
Gwyn Cottage, Crellow Lane,
Stithians, Truro, Cornwall
TR3 7BB
T: (01209) 860702

Higher Trewithen ★★★
Contact: Mrs Avril Stokes,
Higher Trewithen, Stithians,
Truro, Cornwall TR3 7DR
T: (01209) 860863 &
07785 752373
F: (01209) 860785
E: trewithen@talk21.com
I: www.
trewithenholidaycottages.co.uk

STOCKLAND
Devon

Brindley Fold Annexe ★★★
Contact: Mr HB Ref: B5043,
Holiday Cottages Group, Spring
Mill, Earby, Barnoldswick,
Lancashire BB18 6RN
T: (01282) 445096
F: (01282) 844299
E: ch.sales@ttgihg.co.uk
I: www.country-holidays.co.uk

STOGUMBER
Somerset

Periwinkle Cottage ★★★★
Contact: Miss Sheila Hubbard,
Puzzle Tree, Wootton Courtenay,
Minehead, Somerset TA24 8RD
T: (01643) 841413

STOKE ABBOTT
Dorset

**Number 2 Manor Farm
Cottages ★★★**
Contact: Mrs Margaret Shreeve,
Vern Path, Melplash, Bridport,
Dorset DT6 3UD
T: (01308) 488470
F: (01308) 488470

STOKE GABRIEL
Devon

Adams Nest ★★★
Contact: Mr S Alty, Ardencote, 6
Bodyhayes Close, Stoke Gabriel,
Totnes, Devon
T: (01803) 782625 & 865860
F: (01803) 864404

The Boathouse ★★★★★
Contact: Mr Brian Train, 69
Seymour Road, Newton Abbot,
Devon TQ12 2PX
T: (01626) 366592
F: (01626) 334490
E: billc@ula.com
I: www.ula.co

STOKE ST GREGORY
Somerset

Holly Farm ★★★★
Contact: Mr & Mrs R&E
Hembrow & Smith, Holly
Cottage, Stoke St Gregory,
Taunton, Somerset TA3 6HS
T: (01823) 490828 &
0777 5993716
F: (01823) 490590
E: robhembrow@btinternet.com
I: www.somerset-farm-holiday.
co.uk

**Lovells Cottage
Rating Applied For**
Contact: Ms & Mr S&G
Oppenlander/Bolton, Lovells
Cottage, Dark Lane, Stoke St
Gregory, Taunton, Somerset
TA3 6EU
T: (01823) 491437

Sedgemoor Cottage ★★★★
Contact: Mr & Mrs R&I
Browning, Rose & Crown,
Woodhill, Stoke St Gregory,
Taunton, Somerset TA36 EW
T: (01823) 490296
F: (01823) 490996
E: ron.browning@virgin.net

STOKE ST MARY
Somerset

Owl Cottage ★★★
Contact: Mrs Mary Hamlyn, Owl
Cottage, The White House, Stoke
St Mary, Taunton, Somerset
TA3 5DD
T: (01823) 442234
F: (01823) 442234

Stoke Hill Studio ★★
Contact: Mr Alan Coles, Stoke
Hill Barn, Stoke St Mary,
Taunton, Somerset TA3 5BT
T: (01823) 443759
F: (01823) 443759
E: ajcoles@supanet.com

STOKE SUB HAMDON
Somerset

East Stoke House ★★
Contact: Mrs C M Shuldham,
East Stoke House, Stoke sub
Hamdon, Somerset TA14 6UF
T: (01935) 823558 & 823558
F: (01935) 824596

Fairhaven ★★★
Contact: Mrs M Wilson,
Fairhaven, Montacute Road,
Stoke sub Hamdon, Somerset
TA14 6UQ
T: (01935) 823534 &
0775 2596778
E: frank@fairhaven70.freeserve.
co.uk

One Fair Place ★★★★
Contact: Mrs A A Wright, Holly
Lodge, 39 The Avenue,
Crowthorne, Berkshire
RG45 6PB
T: (01344) 772461
F: (01344) 772461
E: petewright@compuserve.
com

Top o Hill ★★★
Contact: Mrs Mary Gane, Top o
Hill, Percombe, Stoke sub
Hamdon, Somerset TA14 6RD
T: (01935) 822089

STOKEINTEIGNHEAD
Devon

Dean Cottage ★★★★
Contact: Holiday Homes &
Cottages South West, 365a
Torquay Road, Paignton, Devon
TQ3 2BT
T: (01803) 663650
F: (01803) 664037
E: holcotts@aol.com
I: www.swcottages.co.uk

Rocombe Cottage ★★
Contact: Holiday Homes &
Cottages South West, 365A
Torquay Road, Paignton, Devon
TQ3 2BT
T: (01803) 663650
F: (01803) 664037
E: holcotts@aol.com
I: www.swcottages.co.uk

STONEY STRATTON
Somerset

Limekiln Farm ★★★★
Contact: Mrs Y Hemmens,
Limekiln Farm, Stoney Stratton,
Shepton Mallet, Somerset
BA4 6HJ
T: (01749) 830346

STOODLEIGH
Devon

2 Lower Ford Cottage ★★★★
Contact: Ms Holton, Ford
Barton, Stoodleigh, Tiverton,
Devon EX16 9PP
T: (01398) 351139 & 351206
F: (01398) 351157
E: cottage@fordbarton.co.uk
I: www.fordbarton.co.uk

STRATTON
Cornwall

Coachman's House ★★★★
Contact: Mr Peter Morris, Farm
& Cottage Holidays, Victoria
House, 12 Fore Street, Northam,
Bideford, Devon EX39 1AW
T: (01237) 479146
F: (01237) 421512
E: farmcott@cix.co.uk
I: www.farmcott.co.uk

Kitts Cottage ★★★
Contact: Mr Peter Morris, Farm
& Cottage Holidays, Victoria
House, 12 Fore Street, Northam,
Bideford, Devon EX39 1AW
T: (01237) 479146
F: (01237) 421512
E: farmcott@cix.co.uk
I: www.farmcott.co.uk

**Old Sanctuary Cottages
★★★★**
Contact: Mrs Jane Berry, Old
Sanctuary, Diddies Road,
Stratton, Bude, Cornwall
EX23 9DW
T: (01288) 353159
F: (01288) 353159

Ronjon ★★★
Contact: CH ref: 11610,15102,
Holiday Cottages Group Owner
Services Dept, Spring Mill, Earby,
Barnoldswick, Lancashire
BB18 6RN
T: (01282) 445096
F: (01282) 844299
E: ch.sales@ttgihg.co.uk
I: www.country-holidays.co.uk

Tree Cottage ★★★
Contact: Mrs Fran Hunt, Elm
House, Marhamchurch, Bude,
Cornwall EX23 0EN
T: (01288) 361899
F: (01288) 361899
E: hunt@emlhouse.freeserve.
co.uk
I: www.elmhouse.freeserve.co.uk

STREET
Somerset

**36 Blagrove Close
Rating Applied For**
Contact: Mrs S A Stratta, 183
Weald Drive, Furnace Green,
Crawley, West Sussex RH10 6NZ
T: (01293) 412587 &
(01458) 446371

Blue Lias ★★★
Contact: Mr Mark Foot, 8
Kingston Drive, Nailsea, Bristol,
BS48 4RB
T: (01275) 853612
F: (01275) 544936

SWANPOOL
Cornwall

**Mobri
Rating Applied For**
Contact: Mrs M Broughton,
Mobri, 1b Madeira Walk,
Swanpool, Falmouth, Cornwall
TR11 4EJ
T: (01326) 314348

SWIMBRIDGE
Devon

Lane End ★★★
Contact: Marsden's Cottage
Holidays, 2 The Square,
Braunton, Devon EX33 2JB
T: (01271) 813777
F: (01271) 813664
E: holidays@marsdens.co.uk
I: www.marsdens.co.uk

SWINDON
Wiltshire

The Cottage ★★★★
Contact: Mrs Judith Stares, The
Cottage, 101 Bath Road, Old
Town, Swindon, SN1 4AX
T: (01793) 485461
F: (01793) 485462
E: judith@stares.co.uk
I: www.stares.co.uk

SYDLING ST NICHOLAS
Dorset

Grace Cottage ★★★
Contact: Mrs Nicky Willis,
Lamperts Cottage, Sydling St
Nicholas, Dorchester, Dorset
DT2 9NU
T: (01300) 341659
F: (01300) 341699
E: mikywillis@aol.com

The Stock Barn ★★★
Contact: Mrs P A Gill, The Old
Manor, Stratton, Dorchester,
Dorset DT2 9RY
T: (01305) 263475
F: (01305) 263475

Swain Cottage ★★★
Contact: Mrs B Bryant, 9
Dorchester Road, Sydling St
Nicholas, Dorchester, Dorset
DT2 9NU
T: (01300) 341382

SYMONDSBURY
Dorset

Bathsheba ★★★★
Contact: Mrs Shelagh Mullins,
The Barn, Shutes Lane,
Symondsbury, Bridport, Dorset
DT6 6HF
T: (01308) 425261
F: (01308) 425261
E: shelaghmullins@aol.com
I: www.shelaghsbathsheba.co.uk

TALATON
Devon

Westcot House Farm ★★★
Contact: Miss Melanie Peters,
Westcot House Farm, Talaton,
Exeter, Devon EX5 2RN
T: (01404) 822320
F: (01404) 823847
E: m.peters@farming.co.uk

TAUNTON
Somerset

Masons Arms ★★
Contact: Mr Jeremy Leyton,
Masons Arms, Magdalene Street,
Taunton, Somerset TA1 1SG
T: (01823) 288916
E: jjmax@jleyton.freeserve.co.uk
I: www.masonsarms.freeuk

Meare Court Holiday Cottages
★★★
Contact: Mrs E J Bray, Meare
Court Holiday Cottages, Meare
Court, Wrantage, Taunton,
Somerset TA3 6DA
T: (01823) 480570 &
07980 601670
F: (01823) 481123
E: mearecourt@farming.co.uk
I: www.mearecourt.co.uk

TAVISTOCK
Devon

Acorn Cottage – Cedar Lodge
★★★
Contact: Mrs Vivien Powell-
Thomas, Acorn Cottage,
Heathfield, Tavistock, Devon
PL19 0LQ
T: (01822) 810038
E: viv@acorncot.fsnet.co.uk
I: www.fsmail.net

Ashwood ★★★
Contact: Dr & Mrs C Hunter,
Ashwood, 11 Plymouth Road,
Tavistock, Devon PL19 8AU
T: (01822) 615616

Edgemoor Cottage ★★★★
Contact: Mrs Mary Susan Fox,
Edgemoor, Middlemoor,
Tavistock, Devon PL19 9DY
T: (01822) 612259
F: (01822) 617625
E: foxesuk@compuserve.com

Higher Chaddlehanger Farm
★★★
Contact: Mrs R Cole, Higher
Chaddlehanger Farm, Tavistock,
Devon PL19 0LG
T: (01822) 810268
F: (01822) 810268

TAWSTOCK
Devon

Park Farm Cottages ★★★★
Contact: Marsden's Cottage
Holidays, 2 The Square,
Braunton, Devon EX33 2JB
T: (01271) 813777
F: (01271) 813664
E: holidays@marsdens.co.uk
I: www.marsdens.co.uk

TEIGNGRACE
Devon

Twelve Oaks Holiday Cottages
★★★
Contact: Mrs M A Gale, Twelve
Oaks Holiday Cottages, Twelve
Oaks Farm, Teigngrace, Newton
Abbot, Devon TQ12 6QT
T: (01626) 352769
F: (01626) 352769

TEIGNMOUTH
Devon

Grendons Holiday Apartments
★★★
Contact: Mrs Wendy Valentine,
Grendons Holiday Apartments,
58 Coombe Vale Road,
Teignmouth, Devon TQ14 9EW
T: (01626) 773667
F: (01626) 773667
E: grendonsholapt@cix.co.uk

High Tide ★★
Contact: Holiday Homes &
Cottages South West, 365A
Torquay Road, Paignton, Devon
TQ3 2BT
T: (01803) 663650
F: (01803) 664037
E: holcotts@aol.com
I: www.swcottages.co.uk

THORNBURY ◉
Devon

Dairy Cottage ★★★★
Contact: Mr Peter Morris, Farm
& Cottage Holidays, Victoria
House, 12 Fore Street, Bideford,
Devon EX39 1AW
T: (01237) 479146
F: (01237) 421512
E: farmcott@cix.co.uk
I: www.farmcott.co.uk

THORNCOMBE
Dorset

Thatch Cottage
Rating Applied For
Contact: Mr & Mrs John & Eileen
Mercer, 53 Heatherside Road,
West Ewell, Epsom, Surrey
KT19 9QS
T: (0208) 393 8165

THORNE ST MARGARET
Somerset

Church Cottage ★★★★
Contact: Mr & Mrs Bowater,
Helpful Holidays, Mill Street,
Chagford, Newton Abbot, Devon
TQ13 8AW
T: (01647) 433593
F: (01647) 433694
E: help@helpfulholidays.com
I: www.helpfulholidays.com

THROWLEIGH
Devon

Sue's House & The Cottage
★★-★★★
Contact: Mrs Joan White, Sue's
House & The Cottage, Aysh
Farm, Throwleigh, Okehampton,
Devon EX20 2HY
T: (01647) 231266

THURLESTONE
Devon

April Cottage ★★★★
Contact: Mrs Joy Jordan, F P
Holidays, 76 Main Road, Long
Bennington, Newark,
Nottinghamshire NG23 5DJ
T: (01400) 281937
F: (01400) 282051
E: joy.jordan@focalpointuk.com
I: www.fpholidays.com

9 Court Park ★★★★
Contact: CH ref: 11131, Holiday
Cottages Group, Spring Mill,
Earby, Barnoldswick, Lancashire
BB18 6RN
T: (01282) 445096
F: (01282) 844299
E: ch.sales@ttgihg.co.uk
I: www.country-holidays.co.uk

TIMBERSCOMBE
Somerset

Mill Leat ★★★★
Contact: Mrs Judith Ford, Rowan
Cottage, Great House Street,
Timberscombe, Minehead,
Somerset TA24 7TQ
T: (01643) 841336

TINCLETON
Dorset

Hastings Farm Cottages
★★★★
Contact: Mr David John Hills,
Hastings Farm Cottages,
Hastings Farm, Tincleton,
Dorchester, Dorset DT2 8QP
T: (01305) 848627
E: djh@hastingsfarm.freeserve.
co.uk
I: www.hastingsfarm.freeserve.
co.uk

The Old Dairy Cottage and
Clyffe Dairy Cottage★★★★
Contact: Mr R Coleman, The
Old Dairy Cottage and Clyffe
Dairy Cottage, Clyffe Farm,
Tincleton, Dorchester, Dorset
DT2 8QR
T: (01305) 848252
F: (01305) 848702
E: coleman.clyffe@virgin.net
I: www.heartofdorset.easynet.
co.uk

TIPTON ST JOHN
Devon

Summer Cottage ★★★★
Contact: Mrs R Ashford, Rose
Cottage, Frogmore Road, East
Budleigh, Budleigh Salterton,
Devon 01395
T: (01395) 442442 & 446080

TIVERTON
Devon

Cider Cottage ★★★★
Contact: Mrs Sylvia Hann, Cider
Cottage, Great Bradley Farm,
Withleigh, Tiverton, Devon
EX16 8JL
T: (01884) 256946
F: (01884) 256946
E: hann@agriplus.net
I: www.devonfarms.co.uk

Lilac Cottage ★★★★
Contact: Mrs R J Venner, Lilac
Cottage, Battens Farm,
Sampford Peverell, Tiverton,
Devon EX16 7EE
T: (01884) 820226

Lower Ingrams ★★★
Contact: Mr & Mrs Ron &
Margaret Tidball, Lower Ingrams
Farmhouse, Loxbeare, Tiverton,
Devon EX16 8BY
T: (01884) 881362
F: (01884) 881362

Lower Yeadbury ★★
Contact: Miss N Croft, Lower
Yeadbury, Tiverton, Devon
EX16 8LH
T: (01363) 866243

Tiverton Castle ★★★★
Contact: Mrs A Gordon, Tiverton
Castle, Tiverton, Devon
EX16 6RP
T: (01884) 253200 & 255200
F: (01884) 254200
E: tiverton.castle@ukf.net
I: www.tivertoncastle.com

TIVINGTON
Somerset

Tethinstone Cottage ★★★★
Contact: Mr N G Challis,
Tethinstone Cottage, Tivington,
Minehead, Somerset TA24 8SX
T: (01643) 706757
F: (01643) 706757

TOLLER PORCORUM
Dorset

11 High Street ★★★
Contact: Mrs Dot Thornton, 2
The George Yard, Broad Street,
Alresford, Hampshire SO24 9EF
T: (01962) 732700

TOLPUDDLE
Dorset

Cob Cottage ★★★★
Contact: Miss Hilary Cobban,
The Old Mill, Tolpuddle,
Dorchester, Dorset DT2 7EX
T: (01305) 848552
F: (01305) 848552
E: hlcobban@lineone.net

TORPOINT
Cornwall

Robins Post ★★
Contact: Mrs Ann May, Masra
Ltd, 19 Seafield Close, Seaford,
East Sussex BN25 3JP
T: (01323) 892550 &
07885 594149

TORQUAY
Devon

3 Abbey Mews ★★★★
Contact: Holiday Homes &
Cottages South West, 365a
Torquay Road, Paignton, Devon
TQ3 2BT
T: (01803) 663650
F: (01803) 664037
E: holcotts@aol.com
I: www.swcottages.co.uk

25 and 27 Lydwell Park Road
★★★
Contact: Holiday Homes &
Cottages South West, 365A
Torquay Road, Paignton, Devon
TQ3 2BT
T: (01803) 663650
F: (01803) 664037
E: holcotts@aol.com
I: www.swcottages.co.uk

Ashfield Rise Holiday Flats
★★-★★★
Contact: Mr & Mrs Skinner,
Ashfield Rise Holiday Flats,
Ruckamore Road, Chelston,
Torquay, Devon TQ2 6HF
T: (01803) 605156 & 605846
F: (01803) 607373
E: su8681@eclipse.co.uk
I: www.ashfieldrise.co.uk

Aster House Apartments
★★-★★★
Contact: Mr C Coleman, Aster
House Apartments, Warren
Road, Torquay, TQ2 5TR
T: (01803) 292747
E: info@asterhouse.freeserve.
co.uk
I: www.asterhouse.freeserve.
co.uk

Bay Fort Mansions ★★★★
Contact: Mr & Miss Paul & Maria
Freeman & Young, Bay Fort
Mansions, Warren Road,
Torquay, TQ2 5TN
T: (01803) 213810
F: (01803) 209057
E: freeman@bayfortapartments.
co.uk
I: www.bayfortapartments.co.uk

Bedford House ★★-★★★
Contact: Mrs E J MacDonald-Smith, Bedford House, 517 Babbacombe Road, Torquay, Devon TQ1 1HJ
T: (01803) 296995
F: (01803) 296995
E: macdonald-smith@torquay41.freeserve.co.uk
I: www.bedfordhouse.fsnet.co.uk

1 Brunel Avenue ★★★★
Contact: Holiday Homes & Cottages South West, 365A Torquay Road, Paignton, Devon TQ3 2BT
T: (01803) 663650
F: (01803) 664037
E: holcotts@aol.com
I: www.swcottages.co.uk

Burley Court Apartments ★★★
Contact: Mrs B Palmer, Burley Court Apartments, Wheatridge Lane, Livermead, Torquay, TQ2 6RA
T: (01803) 607879 & 606101
F: (01803) 605516

Cliff Court Holiday Apartments ★★★
Contact: Mr & Mrs Gary and Denise Tudor, Cliff Court Holiday Apartments, Cliff Road, Livermead, Torquay, TQ2 6RE
T: (01803) 294687
E: gary@cliffcourt.co.uk
I: www.cliffcourt.co.uk

The Coach House ★★★★
Contact: Mr Hedges, Barters Old Farmhouse, Whilborough, Newton Abbot, Devon TQ12 5LP
T: (01803) 873213
F: (01803) 875096
E: holcot@eclipse.co.uk

The Corbyn ★★★★★
Contact: Mrs S Stamp, Brights of Nettlebed, The Corbyn, Torbay Road, Torquay, Devon TQ2 6RH
T: (01803) 215595
F: (01803) 200568

Corbyn Lodge ★★
Contact: Holiday Homes & Cottages South West, 365A Torquay Road, Paignton, Devon TQ3 2BT
T: (01803) 663650
F: (01803) 664037
E: holcotts@aol.com
I: www.swcottages.co.uk

Delamere Court ★★★★
Contact: Mr & Mrs Trevor & Diane Hammond, Delamere Court, St Mark's Road, Meadfoot, Torquay, Devon TQ1 2EH
T: (01803) 293428 & 07989 456529
F: (01803) 215570
E: trevor@delamerecourt.co.uk
I: www.delamerecourt.co.uk

Evergreen Lodge ★★-★★★
Contact: Mr & Mrs James & Ann Boase, Evergreen Lodge, Ruckamore Road, Chelston, Torquay, TQ2 6HF
T: (01803) 605519
E: evergreenlodge@aol.com
I: www.members.aol.com/evergreenlodge

Flat 3 Woodlands ★★★★
Contact: CH ref: 11247, Holiday Cottages Group Owner Services Dept, Spring Mill, Earby, Barnoldswick, Lancashire BB18 6RN
T: (01282) 445096
F: (01282) 844299
E: ch.sales@ttgihg.co.uk
I: www.country-holidays.co.uk

17 Gainsborough Close ★★★
Contact: Holiday Homes & Cottages South West, 365A Torquay Road, Paignton, Devon TQ3 2BT
T: (01803) 663650
F: (01803) 664037
E: holcotts@aol.com
I: www.swcottages.co.uk

Harbour Cottage ★★★
Contact: Holiday Homes & Cottages South West, 365A Torquay Road, Paignton, Devon TQ3 2BT
T: (01803) 663650
F: (01803) 664037
E: holcotts@aol.com
I: www.swcottages.co.uk

Hollington House Apartments ★★★
Contact: Mr & Mrs RVA Vaughton, Hollington House Apartments, Acadia Road, Wellswood, Torquay, Devon TQ1 2PL
T: (01803) 293555
E: aldworth@caribbeancourt.co.uk
I: www.caribbeancourt.co.uk

36 Hollywater Close ★★★
Contact: Holiday Homes & Cottages South West, 365A Torquay Road, Paignton, Devon TQ3 2BT
T: (01803) 663650
F: (01803) 664037
E: holcotts@aol.com
I: www.swcottages.co.uk

Little Walderlea ★★
Contact: Holiday Homes & Cottages South West, 365A Torquay Road, Paignton, Devon TQ3 2BT
T: (01803) 663650
F: (01803) 664037
E: holcotts@aol.com
I: www.swcottages.co.uk

Lorna Doone Holiday Apartments ★★
Contact: Mr Lee & Max Chapman, Teddesley Leisure Limited, Longmynd Hotel, Cunnery Road, Church Stretton, Shropshire SY6 6AG
T: (01694) 722244
F: (01694) 722718
E: reservations@longmynd.co.uk
I: www.longmynd.co.uk

45 Lyme View Road ★★
Contact: Holiday Homes & Cottages South West, 365A Torquay Road, Paignton, Devon TQ3 2BT
T: (01803) 663650
F: (01803) 664037
E: holcotts@aol.com
I: www.swcottages.co.uk

Marina & Bay View ★★★
Contact: Holiday Homes & Cottages South West, 365A Torquay Road, Paignton, Devon TQ3 2BT
T: (01803) 663650
F: (01803) 664037
E: holcotts@aol.com
I: www.swcottages.co.uk

Maxton Lodge Holiday Apartments★★★
Contact: Mr Richard Hassell, Maxton Lodge Holiday Apartments, Rousdown Road, Chelston, Torquay, Devon TQ2 6PB
T: (01803) 607811
F: (01803) 605357
E: stay@redhouse-hotel.co.uk
I: www.redhouse-hotel.co.uk

Moongate Cottages ★★★
Contact: Holiday Homes & Cottages South West, 365A Torquay Road, Paignton, Devon TQ3 2BT
T: (01803) 663650
F: (01803) 664037
E: holcotts@aol.com
I: www.swcottages.co.uk

Moorcot Self Contained Holiday Apartments★★★
Contact: Mrs MC Neilson, Moorcot Self Contained Holiday Apartments, Kents Road, Wellswood, Torquay, TQ1 2NN
T: (01803) 293710
E: margaret-neilson@moorcot.fsnet.co.uk
I: www.moorcot.fsnet.co.uk

Moorhaven Holiday Flats ★★★
Contact: Mr & Mrs T&J Chandler, Moorhaven Holiday Flats, 43 Barton Road, Torquay, TQ1 4DT
T: (01803) 328567
E: info@moorhaven.co.uk
I: www.moorhaven.co.uk

Muntham Holiday Apartments ★★★★
Contact: Mr & Mrs Peter & Trudie Cross, Muntham Holiday Apartments, Barrington Road, Wellswood, Torquay, Devon TQ1 1SG
T: (01803) 292958
F: (01803) 291715
E: muntham@btinternet.com
I: www.torbay.gov.uk

33 Reddenhill Road ★★
Contact: Holiday Homes & Cottages South West, 365A Torquay Road, Paignton, Devon TQ3 2BT
T: (01803) 663650
F: (01803) 664037
E: holcotts@aol.com
I: www.swcottages.co.uk

South Sands Apartments ★★★
Contact: Mr P W Moorhouse, South Sands Apartments, Torbay Road, Torquay, TQ2 6RG
T: (01803) 293521
F: (01803) 293502
E: southsands.torquay@virgin.net
I: www.southsands.co.uk

Stillmeadow ★★★★
Contact: Holiday Homes & Cottages South West, 365A Torquay Road, Paignton, Devon TQ3 2BT
T: (01803) 663650
F: (01803) 664037
E: holcotts@aol.co.uk
I: www.swcottages.co.uk

Suncourt ★★★
Contact: Holiday Homes & Cottages South West, 365A Torquay Road, Paignton, Devon TQ3 2BT
T: (01803) 663650
F: (01803) 664037
E: holcotts@aol.com
I: www.swcottages.com

Suncrest Lodge ★★★★
Contact: Holiday Homes & Cottages South West, 365A Torquay Road, Paignton, Devon TQ3 2BT
T: (01803) 663650
F: (01803) 664037
E: holcotts@aol.com
I: www.swcottages.co.uk

Sunningdale Apartments ★★★
Contact: Mr Allan Carr, Sunningdale Apartments, 11 Babbacombe Downe Road, Torquay, TQ1 3LF
T: (01803) 325786
F: (01803) 329611
I: www.sunningdaleapartments.co.uk

Vane Tower ★★★★
Contact: Holiday Homes & Cottages South West, 365A Torquay Road, Paignton, Devon TQ3 2BT
T: (01803) 663650
F: (01803) 664037
E: holcotts@aol.com
I: www.swcottages.co.uk

Vanessa Apartment 4★★★
Contact: Holiday Homes & Cottages South West, 365A Torquay Road, Paignton, Devon TQ3 2BT
T: (01803) 663650
F: (01803) 664037
E: holcotts@aol.com
I: www.swcottages.co.uk

Villa Capri ★★★★
Contact: Mr E A Turner, Villa Capri, Daddyhole Road, Meadfoot, Torquay, Devon TQ1 2ED
T: (01803) 297959 & 294278
F: (01803) 297959
E: villcapr@btinternet.com
I: www.english-riviera.co.uk

Woodfield Holiday Apartments ★★★
Contact: Mr and Mrs T W Gaylard, Woodfield Holiday Apartments, Lower Woodfield Road, Torquay, TQ1 2JY
T: (01803) 295974

Wrenwood ★★★
Contact: Holiday Homes &
Cottages South West, 365A
Torquay Road, Paignton, Devon
TQ3 2BT
T: (01803) 663650
F: (01803) 664037
E: holcotts@aol.com
I: www.swcottages.co.uk

TORRINGTON
Devon

Hill Farm Cottages ★★★★
Contact: Mrs Mary Vickery, Hill
Farm Cottages, Hill Farm, Weare
Trees Hill, Torrington, Devon
EX38 7EZ
T: (01805) 622432
F: (01805) 622432

Orford Mill ★★★–★★★★
Contact: Mr R Cooper, Best
Leisure, North Hill, Shirwell,
Barnstaple, Devon EX31 4LG
T: (01271) 850611
F: (01271) 850693
I: www.bestleisure.co.uk

**Stowford Lodge & South Hill
Cottages★★★**
Contact: Mrs S Milsom,
Stowford Lodge, Langtree,
Torrington, Devon EX38 8NU
T: (01805) 601540
F: (01805) 601487
E: stowford@dial.pipex.com
I: www.stowford.dial.pipex.com

Week Farm Flat ★★★
Contact: Mrs D R Bealey, Week
Farm Flat, Week Farm,
Torrington, Devon EX38 7HU
T: (01805) 623029 &
07971 251361
F: (01805) 623029
E: glenn.bealey@btinternet.com

TOTNES
Devon

The Annexe, The Talus ★★★
Contact: Mr and Mrs A Pedley,
The Annexe, The Talus, 12 Quarry
Close, Follaton, Totnes, Devon
TQ9 5FA
T: (01803) 865647
E: theannexe@talk21.com

Hood Barton Barns ★★★★
Contact: Mrs P Baxendale, The
Hayloft, Hood Barton Barns,
Dartington, Totnes, Devon
TQ9 6AB
T: (01803) 762756
F: (01803) 762756
E: ap.bax@tesco.net
I: www.hoodbartonbarns.co.uk

The Little Elbow Room ★★★
Contact: Mrs A W Savin, The
Elbow Room, North Street,
Totnes, Devon TQ9 5NZ
T: (01803) 863480
F: (01803) 863480

Wedge Cottage ★★★★
Contact: Mrs S Seymour, 17
Bridgetown, Totnes, Devon
TQ9 5BA
T: (01803) 862893

TOWNSHEND
Cornwall

Godolphin Bridge Farm ★★★
Contact: Mr & Mrs Bowater,
Helpful Holidays, Mill Street,
Chagford, Newton Abbot, Devon
TQ13 8AW
T: (01647) 433593
F: (01647) 433694
E: help@helpfulholidays.com
I: www.helpfulholidays.com

TREBETHERICK
Cornwall

**Bar House
Rating Applied For**
Contact: Dr AT Hambly, Bodrean
Manor, St Clements, Truro,
Cornwall TR4 9AG
T: (01872) 264400
F: (01872) 264400
E: anthonyhambly@hotmail.
com
I: www.cornishholidays.uk.com

Boskenna ★★★★
Contact: Diana Bullivant
Holidays, South Winds, Trebell
Green, Lanivet, Bodmin,
Cornwall PL30 5HR
T: (01208) 831336
F: (01208) 831336
E: diana@dbullivant.fsnet.co.uk
I: www.cornwall-online.
co.uk/diana-bullivant

Highcliffe ★★★★
Contact: Mr Robert Mably,
Highcliffe Agency Ltd,
Bosneives, Withiel, Bodmin,
Cornwall PL30 5NQ
T: (01208) 831167 &
07768 586807
F: (01208) 831198
E: sales@highcliffeagency.com
I: www.highcliffeholidays.co.uk

Saint Moritz Villas ★★★★
Contact: Miss J Cutler, Saint
Moritz Villas, Trebetherick,
Wadebridge, Cornwall PL27 6SD
T: (01208) 862242
F: (01208) 862262
E: info@stmoritzhotel.co.uk

TREDETHY
Cornwall

**Brinkywell Holiday Cottages
★★★**
Contact: Mr Brian Tocknell,
Treetops, Ashmead Green,
Dursley, Gloucestershire
GL11 5EW
T: (01453) 545184
E: brian.tocknell@treetopscam.
freeserve.co.uk
I: www.brinkywell.co.uk

TREGONY
Cornwall

The Bolt Hole ★★★★
Contact: Ms B F Hunt, The Pines,
Lower Golf Links Road,
Broadstone, Dorset BH18 8BG
T: (01202) 693817 &
07885 951942
E: barbara@aaacott.freeserve.
co.uk

TREMAINE
Cornwall

Tremaine Barn ★★★★
Contact: Mr & Mrs Alan & Jillie
Lamb, Tremaine Barn, West
Tremaine, Tremaine, Launceston,
Cornwall PL15 8SA
T: (01566) 781636
F: (01566) 781309
E: welcome@stay-in-cornwall.
co.uk
I: www.stay-in-cornwall.co.uk

TRENARREN
Cornwall

East Wing Apartment ★★★
Contact: Mrs A J Treleaven,
Trevissick Farm, Trenarren, St
Austell, Cornwall PL26 6BQ
T: (01726) 72954
F: (01726) 72954
E: d.treleaven@farmline.com

TRENEGLOS
Cornwall

Tregerry Farm ★★★★
Contact: Mr Peter Morris, Farm
& Cottage Holidays, Victoria
House, 12 Fore Street, Northam,
Bideford, Devon EX39 1AW
T: (01237) 479146
F: (01237) 421512
E: farmcott@cix.co.uk
I: www.farmcott.co.uk

TRENTISHOE
Devon

The Old Farmhouse ★★★
Contact: Mr & Mrs Ian & Ann
Wright, The Old Farmhouse,
Trentishoe, Barnstaple, Devon
EX31 4QD
T: (01598) 763495
E: ian@oldfarmhouse.co.uk
I: www.oldfarmhouse.co.uk

TREQUITE
Cornwall

**Tregoid Manor Farm Cottage
★★★**
Contact: Diana Bullivant
Holidays, South Winds, Trebell
Green, Lanivet, Bodmin,
Cornwall PL30 5HR
T: (01208) 831336
F: (01208) 831336
E: diana@dbullivant.fsnet.co.uk
I: www.cornwall-online.
co.uk/diana-bullivant

TRESARRETT
Cornwall

**Merry Meeting Farmhouse
★★★**
Contact: Mr & Mrs Bowater,
Helpful Holidays, Mill Street,
Chagford, Newton Abbot, Devon
TQ13 8AW
T: (01647) 433593
F: (01647) 433694
E: help@helpfulholidays.com
I: www.helpfulholidays.com

TRESCO
Cornwall

Boro Chalets ★★★
Contact: Mrs M Christopher,
Boro Chalets, Boro Farm, Tresco,
Isles of Scilly TR24 0PX
T: (01720) 422843

Borough Farm Chalets ★★★
Contact: Mrs Ann Oyler, The
Bungalow, Borough, Tresco, Isles
of Scilly TR24 0PX
T: (01720) 422840

TRESPARRETT
Cornwall

Underlanes ★★
Contact: Mrs S Prout,
Penventon, St Juliot, Boscastle,
Cornwall PL35 0DA
T: (01840) 250289

TREVONE
Cornwall

Furlongs ★★★
Contact: Mrs Gill Vivian, Gambia,
4 St Saviours Lane, Padstow,
Cornwall PL28 8BD
T: (01841) 533791
E: gill.price2@virgin.net
I: www.holiday-padstow.co.uk

TREVOSE
Cornwall

**Coastguard Cottage West
★★★★**
Contact: Cornish Horizons
Holiday Cottages, Higher
Trehemborne, St Merryn,
Padstow, Cornwall PL28 8JU
T: (01841) 520889 & 521333
F: (01841) 521523
E: cottages@cornishhorizons.
co.uk
I: www.cornishhorizons.co.uk

TRUDOXHILL
Somerset

Courtyard Cottages ★★★★
Contact: Mrs Annie Hill,
Courtyard Cottages, Knoll Hill
Farm, Trudoxhill, Frome,
Somerset BA11 5DP
T: (01373) 836266
E: courtyardcottages@
btinternet.com
I: www.courtyardcottages.com

TRURO
Cornwall

Ancarva Cottage ★★★
Contact: Mrs Margie Lumby,
Special Places, Poachers Reach,
Feock, Truro, Cornwall TR3 6SQ
T: (01872) 864400
F: (01872) 864400
E: office@
specialplacescornwall.co.uk
I: www.specialplacescornwall.
co.uk

The Anchorage ★★★
Contact: Mrs Margie Lumby,
Special Places, Poachers Reach,
Feock, Truro, Cornwall TR3 6SQ
T: (01872) 864400
F: (01872) 864400
E: office@
specialplacescornwall.co.uk
I: www.specialplacescornwall.
co.uk

**The Coach House
Rating Applied For**
Contact: Dr AT Hambly, The
Coach House, Bodrean Manor,
St Clements, Truro, Cornwall
TR4 9AG
T: (01872) 264400
F: (01872) 264400
E: anthonyhambly@hotmail.
com
I: www.cornishholidays.uk.com

Establishments printed in blue have a detailed entry in this guide

Hill View
Rating Applied For
Contact: CH ref: 1122, Holiday
Cottages Group Owner Services
Dept, Spring Mill, Earby,
Barnoldswick, Lancashire
BB18 6RN
T: (01282) 445096
F: (01282) 844299
E: ch.sales@ttgihg.co.uk
I: www.country-holidays.co.uk

TRUSHAM
Devon

Tucketts Barn ★★★★
Contact: CH ref: 6412, Holiday
Cottages Group Owner Services
Dept, Spring Mill, Earby,
Barnoldswick, Lancashire
BB18 6RN
T: (01282) 445096
F: (01282) 844299
E: ch.sales@ttgihg.co.uk
I: www.country-holidays.co.uk

UGBOROUGH
Devon

Venn Farm ★★★★
Contact: Mr & Mrs Bowater,
Helpful Holidays, Mill Street,
Chagford, Newton Abbot, Devon
TQ13 8AW
T: (01647) 433593
F: (01647) 433694
E: help@helpfulholidays.com
I: www.helpfulholidays.com

UPHILL
North Somerset

Lindsey House
Rating Applied For
Contact: Mrs Jeanne Champion,
Knoll Farm, Jarvis Lane, East
Brent, Highbridge, Somerset
TA9 4HS
T: (01278) 760227

UPLODERS
Dorset

The Hayloft ★★★★
Contact: Mrs P Harding, The
Hayloft, Brook Barton, Uploders,
Bridport, Dorset DT6 4NT
T: (01308) 485266

Moens Dairyhouse ★★★
Contact: Mrs Eleanor Cobbold,
Marston Properties Ltd, 1
Stephendale Road, Fulham,
London SW6 2LU
T: (020) 7736 7133
F: (020) 7731 8412
E: ellie@marstonproperties.
co.uk
I: www.marstonproperties.co.uk

Tiddlers Cottage ★★★
Contact: Mrs J E Gawman,
Springside Cottage, Uploders,
Bridport, Dorset DT6 4NU
T: (01308) 485478

UPLYME
Devon

The Bower ★★★★
Contact: Mrs Paula Wyon-
Brown, The Bower, Hill Barn,
Gore Lane, Uplyme, Lyme Regis,
Dorset DT7 3RJ
T: (01297) 445185
E: jwb@
lymeregis-accommodation.com
I: www.
lymeregis-accommodation.com

Lym Croft D4227 ★★★★
Contact: Lyme Bay Holidays,
Boshouse, 44 Church Street,
Lyme Regis, Dorset DT7 3DA
T: (01297) 443363
F: (01297) 445576
E: email@lymebayholidays.
co.uk
I: www.lymebayholidays.co.uk

Mount View ★★★
Contact: Jean Bartlett Cottage
Holidays, Fore Street, Beer,
Seaton, Devon EX12 3JB
T: (01297) 23221
F: (01297) 23303
E: jeanb@netbreaks.com
I: www.netbreaks.com/jeanb

The Old Barn B4078 ★★
Contact: Lyme Bay Holidays,
Boshouse, 44 Church Street,
Lyme Regis, Dorset DT7 3DA
T: (01297) 443363
F: (01297) 445576
E: email@lymebayholidays.
co.uk
I: www.lymebayholidays.co.uk

Old Orchard ★★★
Contact: Mr G L Smith,
Cannington Farm, Cannington
Lane, Uplyme, Lyme Regis,
Dorset DT7 3SW
T: (01297) 443172
F: (01297) 445005
E: tvecs@aol.com

**Sherwood Apartments
★★-★★★**
Contact: Mrs W Blinman,
Sherwood Apartments,
Sherwood, Uplyme, Lyme Regis,
Dorset DT7 3LS
T: (01297) 445753
F: (01297) 443863
E: information@sherwoodapts.
freeserve.co.uk
I: www.lymeregis.
com/sherwood-apartments/htm

Yawl House ★★★
Contact: Lyme Bay Holidays,
Boshouse, 44 Church Street,
Lyme Regis, Dorset DT7 3DA
T: (01297) 443363
F: (01297) 445576
E: email@lymebayholidays.
co.uk
I: www.lymebayholidays.co.uk

UPOTTERY
Devon

The Haybarton ★★★★★
Contact: CH Ref: B5605, Holiday
Cottages Group Owner Services
Department, Spring Mill, Earby,
Barnoldswick, Lancashire
BB18 6RN
T: (01282) 445096
F: (01282) 844299
E: ch.sales@ttgihg.co.uk
I: www.country-holidays.co.uk

Hoemoor Bungalow ★★★
Contact: Mrs P Phillips,
Hoemoor Bungalow, Upottery,
Honiton, Devon EX14 9PB
T: (01823) 601265 &
07977 542620

UPPER CASTLE COMBE
Wiltshire

Garden Cottage ★★★★
Contact: Mr V G Fortune, The
Cottage, Upper Castle Combe,
Chippenham, Wiltshire
SN14 7HD
T: (01249) 782174
F: (01249) 782174

UPTON
Cornwall

Rockhaven ★★
Contact: Mrs Marjorie Anderson,
Rockhaven, Upton, Bude,
Cornwall EX23 0LY
T: (01288) 359175

**West Withy Farm Holiday
Cottages ★★★★**
Contact: Mr & Mrs Gareth &
Mary Hughes, West Withy Farm
Holiday Cottages, West Withy
Farm, Upton, Taunton, Somerset
TA4 2JH
T: (01398) 371258
F: (01398) 371123
E: g.hughes@irisi.u-net.com
I: www.greencountry.
co.uk/westwithyfarm

URCHFONT
Wiltshire

**Breach Cottage and The
Pottery ★★**
Contact: Mr and Mrs Philip and
Clare Milanes, Breach House,
Cuckoo Corner, Urchfont,
Devizes, Wiltshire SN10 4RA
T: (01380) 840050 & 840402
F: (01380) 840150
E: breachhouse@freenetname.
co.uk

VERYAN
Cornwall

Mill Cottage ★★★
Contact: Cornish Cottage
Holidays, Godolphin Road,
Helston, Cornwall TR13 8AA
T: (01326) 573808
F: (01326) 564992
E: enquiry@
cornishcottageholidays.co.uk
I: www.cornishcottageholidays.
co.uk

WADEBRIDGE
Cornwall

Coombe Mill ★★-★★★★
Contact: Mrs & Mr Pippa & Mark
Colton-Taylor, Coombe Mill, St
Breward, Bodmin, Cornwall
PL30 4LZ
T: (01208) 850344
F: (01208) 850452
E: mail@coombemill.com
I: www.chycor.
co.uk/coombe-mill

**Polgrain Holiday Cottages
★★★**
Contact: Mrs Sandra Perry,
Polgrain Holiday Cottages,
Higher Polgrain, St Wenn,
Cornwall PL30 5PR
T: (01637) 880637 & 881944
F: (01637) 881944
E: polgrainholidaycottages@
ukgateway.net
I: www.selfcateringcornwall.uk.
com

Rensburg ★★★★
Contact: Mr & Mrs Bowater,
Helpful Holidays, Mill Street,
Chagford, Newton Abbot, Devon
TQ13 8AW
T: (01647) 433593
F: (01647) 433694
E: help@helpfulholidays.com
I: www.helpfulholidays.com

Rock Barn ★★★★
Contact: Cornish Cottage
Holidays, The Old Turnpike Dairy,
Godolphin Road, Helston,
Cornwall TR13 8AA
T: (01326) 573808
F: (01326) 564992
E: enquiry@
cornishcottageholidays.co.uk
I: www.cornishcottageholidays.
co.uk

Treforest ★★★
Contact: CH Ref: 12507, Holiday
Cottages Group Owner Services
Department, Spring Mill, Earby,
Barnoldswick, Lancashire
BB18 6RN
T: (01282) 445096
F: (01282) 844299
E: ch.sales@ttgihg.co.uk
I: www.country-holidays.co.uk

**Tregolls Farm Cottages
★★★★**
Contact: Mrs Marilyn Hawkey,
Tregolls Farm, St Wenn, Bodmin,
Cornwall PL30 5PG
T: (01208) 812154
F: (01208) 812154
E: tregollsfarm@btclick.com
I: www.tregollsfarm.co.uk

WAMBROOK
Somerset

Little Pulleys ★★★★
Contact: Mrs Kay Clegg, Little
Pulleys, Wambrook, Chard,
Somerset TA20 3DF
T: (01460) 62583

WARBSTOW
Cornwall

**Fentrigan Manor Farm Cottage
★★★★**
Contact: Mr Peter Morris, Farm
& Cottage Holidays, Victoria
House, 12 Fore Street, Bideford,
Devon EX39 1AW
T: (01237) 479146
F: (01237) 421512
E: farmcott@cix.co.uk
I: www.farmcott.co.uk

WARKLEIGH
Devon

**The Lodge at Cleave Copse
★★★★**
Contact: Marsden's Cottage
Holidays, 2 The Square,
Braunton, Devon EX33 2JB
T: (01271) 813777
F: (01271) 813664
E: holidays@marsdens.co.uk
I: www.marsdens.co.uk

WARLEGGAN
Cornwall

Treveddoe ★★★
Contact: Lady A Hill-Norton, The
Barns, Newton Valence, Alton,
Hampshire GU34 3RB
T: (01420) 588302 &
07967 007604
E: jennic@hill-norton.freeserve.
co.uk
I: www.cornwall-online.
co.uk/treveddoe

WARMINSTER
Wiltshire

The Annex ★★
Contact: Mrs S Allery, The Annex, 'Wayside', 64 Weymouth Street, Warminster, Wiltshire BA12 9NT
T: (01985) 218158

The Coach House ★★★★
Contact: Mrs Lynn Corp, Sturford Mead Farm, Corsley, Warminster, Wiltshire BA12 7QU
T: (01373) 832213
F: (01373) 832213
E: lynn_sturford.cottage@virgin.net

WARMWELL
Dorset

Apple Orchard ★★
Contact: Mr Geoffrey Stuart Murgatroyd, Apple Orchard, Skippet Heath, Warmwell Road, Warmwell, Dorchester, Dorset DT2 8JD
T: (01305) 853702
F: (01305) 853702

Beech Farm ★★★
Contact: Mrs R Goldsack, Beech Farm, Warmwell, Dorchester, Dorset DT2 8LZ
T: (01305) 852414
F: (01305) 852414
E: rugold@lineone.net

WASHAWAY
Cornwall

Park Farmhouse ★★
Contact: Mr & Mrs Bowater, Helpful Holidays, Mill Street, Chagford, Newton Abbot, Devon TQ13 8AW
T: (01647) 433593
F: (01647) 433694
E: help@helpfulholidays.com
I: www.helpfulholidays.com

WASHFORD
Somerset

Meadstone ★★★★
Contact: Mr J K Westcott, Stonebank, 14 West Street, Chickerell, Weymouth, Dorset DT3 4DY
T: (01305) 760120
F: (01305) 760871
E: meadstone@stonebank-chickerell.co.uk
I: www.stonebank-chickerell.com

Monksway ★★★★★
Contact: Mr J K Westcott, Stonebank, 14 West Street, Chickerell, Weymouth, Dorset DT3 4DY
T: (01305) 760120 & (01643) 704209
F: (01305) 760871
E: monksway@stonebank-chickerell.co.uk

WATCHET
Somerset

The Croft Holiday Cottages ★★★★
Contact: Mr D Albutt, The Croft Holiday Cottages, The Croft, Anchor Street, Watchet, Somerset TA23 0BY
T: (01984) 631121
F: (01984) 631121
E: croftcottages@talk21.com
I: www.cottageguide.co.uk/croft-cottages

Roseville ★★★★
Contact: CH ref: 10619, Holiday Cottages Group Owner Services Dept, Spring Mill, Earby, Barnoldswick, Lancashire BB18 6RN
T: (01282) 445096
F: (01282) 844299
E: ch.sales@ttgihg.co.uk
I: www.country-holidays.co.uk

The Square ★★
Contact: Mrs C Court, 31 North Croft, Williton, Taunton, Somerset TA4 4RP
T: (01984) 639089
E: square@bestweb.net

5 Washford Hill ★★★
Contact: CH ref: 1673, Holiday Cottages Group Owner Services Dept, Spring Mill, Earby, Barnoldswick, Lancashire BB18 6RN
T: (01282) 445096
F: (01282) 844299
E: ch.sales@ttgihg.co.uk
I: www.country-holidays.co.uk

WATERROW
Somerset

Halsdown Farm Holiday Cottages★★★
Contact: Mrs A James, Halsdown Farm Holiday Cottages, Halsdown Farm, Waterrow, Taunton, Somerset TA4 2QU
T: (01984) 623493

Handley Farm ★★★★
Contact: Mr Peter Morris, Farm & Cottage Holidays, Victoria House, 12 Fore Street, Northam, Bideford, Devon EX39 1AW
T: (01237) 479146
F: (01237) 421512
E: farmcott@cix.co.uk
I: www.farmcott.co.uk

The Manor Mill ★★★
Contact: Ms Jane Arnell, The Manor Mill, Waterrow, Taunton, Somerset TA4 2AY
T: (01984) 623317
F: (01984) 623317
E: manormill@lineone.net
I: www.travel-uk.net/manormill

WEARE GIFFARD
Devon

2 Dock Cottages ★★
Contact: CH ref: 2465, Holiday Cottages Group, Spring Mill, Earby, Barnoldswick, Lancashire BB18 6RN
T: (01282) 445096
F: (01282) 844299
E: ch.sales@ttgihg.co.uk
I: www.country-holidays.co.uk

Honeycomb ★★★★
Contact: Mr Peter Morris, Farm & Cottage Holidays, Victoria House, 12 Fore Street, Northam, Bideford, Devon EX39 1AW
T: (01237) 479146
F: (01237) 421512
E: farmcott@cix.co.uk
I: www.farmcott.co.uk

Sealock ★★★
Contact: Mr Peter Morris, Farm & Cottage Holidays, Victoria House, 12 Fore Street, Northam, Bideford, Devon EX39 1AW
T: (01237) 479146
F: (01237) 421512
E: farmcott@cix.co.uk
I: www.farmcott.co.uk

WEDMORE
Somerset

Blandings ★★★
Contact: Mr & Mrs EFP Metters, Porch House, West End, Wedmore, Somerset BS28 4BA
T: (01934) 712515

The Coach House ★★★
Contact: CH ref: 9730, Holiday Cottages Group Owner Services Dept, Spring Mill, Earby, Barnoldswick, Lancashire BB18 6RN
T: (01282) 445096
F: (01282) 844299
E: ch.sales@ttgihg.co.uk
I: www.country-holidays.co.uk

WELCOMBE
Devon

Mead Barn Cottages ★★★
Contact: Mrs Valerie Price, Mead Barn Cottages, Mead Barns, Welcombe, Bideford, Devon EX39 6HQ
T: (01288) 331721
E: meadbarns@aol.com
I: www.meadbarns.com

Old Smithy Bungalows ★★★
Contact: CH Ref: 13727, Holiday Cottages Group, Spring Mill, Earby, Barnoldswick, Lancashire BB18 6RN
T: (01282) 445096
F: (01282) 844299
E: ch.sales@ttgihg.co.uk
I: www.country-holidays.co.uk

Underhill ★★★★
Contact: CH ref: 10957, Holiday Cottages Group Owner Services Dept, Spring Mill, Earby, Barnoldswick, Lancashire BB18 6RN
T: (01282) 445096
F: (01282) 844299
E: ch.sales@ttgihg.co.uk
I: www.country-holidays.co.uk

WELLINGTON
Somerset

Togwells ★★★★
Contact: Mr Eric Smith, Bishops Barton, Greenham, Wellington, Somerset TA21 0JJ
T: (01823) 672969
E: bishopsbarton@talk21.com

Tonedale House
Rating Applied For
Contact: Ms Dee Friend, Tonedale House, Wellington, Somerset TA21 0EZ
T: (01823) 662673
F: (01823) 663558
E: party@thebighouseco.com
I: www.thebighouseco.com

White Barn ★★★★
Contact: Mrs AM Reeve, White Barn, Ford St Hill, Wellington, Somerset TA21 9PD
T: (01823) 663874

WELLOW
Bath and North East Somerset

Holly Cottage ★★★★
Contact: Mr & Mrs Alick & Mari Bartholowmew, Holly Cottage, The Hollies, Mill Hill, Wellow, Bath, North Somerset BA2 8QJ
T: (01225) 840889
E: enquiries@bath-holidays.co.uk
I: www.bath-holidays.co.uk

WELLS
Somerset

Garslade Cottage ★★★
Contact: Mrs Bridget Gooden, Garslade Farm Wing, Garslade Farm, Godney, Wells, Somerset BA5 1RX
T: (01458) 833801
E: gooden@firenet.ws

5 High Street ★★★★
Contact: Mr & Mrs Alan & Margaret Southwood, 40a South Street, Wells, Somerset BA5 1SL
T: (01749) 675510

Model Farm Cottages ★★-★★★
Contact: Mrs Gill Creed, Model Farm Cottages, Model Farm, Milton, Wells, Somerset BA5 3AE
T: (01749) 673363
F: (01749) 671566
E: creedmodelfarm@faxvia.net

The Old Barn ★★★
Contact: Mrs Lameece Davies, The Old Inn, Green Ore, Wells, Somerset BA5 3ES
T: (01761) 241433 & 07831 272984
E: sagem03153@talk21.com

Shalom ★★
Contact: Mrs R L Rees, 60 Eastgrove Avenue, Sharples, Bolton, Lancashire BL1 7HA
T: (01204) 418576
F: (01204) 303810

Spiders End ★★★★
Contact: Mr & Mrs J Van Bergen-Henegouwen, Potting Shed Holidays, Harters Hill Cottage, Pillmoor Lane, Coxley, Wells, Somerset BA5 1RF
T: (01749) 672857
E: cjvbhhol.gaol.com
I: www.pottingshedholidays.co.uk

Spindlewood Lodges ★★★★
Contact: Mr & Mrs Dick and Jean Skidmore, Spindlewood Lodges, Wellhayes Farm, Lower Westholme, Pilton, Shepton Mallet, Somerset BA4 4HW
T: (01749) 890367
F: (01749) 890367
E: mail@hoseasons.co.uk
I: www.hoseasons.co.uk

WEMBDON
Somerset

Grange Farm Cottage ★★★★
Contact: English Country Cottages, Stoney Bank, Earby, Barnoldswick, Lancashire BB94 0AA
T: 0870 585 1155
F: 0870 585 1150
I: www.english-country-cottages.co.uk

WEMBURY
Devon

Traine Farm ★★★–★★★★
Contact: Mrs S Rowland, Traine Farm, Wembury, Plymouth, Devon PL9 0EW
T: (01752) 862264
F: (01752) 862264
E: rowland.trainefarm@eclipse.co.uk
I: www.traine-holiday-cottages.co.uk

WEMBWORTHY
Devon

Taw Mill ★★★★★
Contact: Mr Roger Bowley, Taw Mill, Wembworthy, Chulmleigh, Devon EX18 7SW
T: (01837) 83931
E: sheila@tawmill.com
I: www.tawmill.com

WEST ALVINGTON
Devon

Granary Cottage ★★★
Contact: Mrs J Y Philcox, Easton Farm, West Alvington, Kingsbridge, Devon TQ7 3BD
T: (01548) 852397
F: (01548) 892397
I: philcox@easton-farm.freeserve.co.uk

Sunshine Cottage ★★★★
Contact: Mr Nicholas Pash, Hideaways, Chapel House, Luke Street, Berwick St John, Shaftesbury, Dorset SP7 0HQ
T: (01747) 828170 & 828000
F: (01747) 829090
E: enq@hideaways.co.uk
I: www.hideaways.co.uk

WEST ANSTEY
Devon

Churchtown Farm ★★★
Contact: Mr R Tarr, Churchtown Farm, West Anstey, South Molton, Devon EX36 3PE
T: (01398) 341391
F: (01398) 341391
E: r.tarr@ukf.net
I: www.churchtownholidays.co.uk

Deer's Leap Country Cottages ★★★★
Contact: Mr & Mrs Michael & Frances Heggadon, Deer's Leap Country Cottages, West Anstey, South Molton, Devon EX36 3NZ
T: (01398) 341407 & 07702 637904
F: (01398) 341407
E: deersleapcottages@lineone.net
I: www.deersleap.com

Dunsley Farm ★★★
Contact: Mrs I M Robins, Dunsley Farm, West Anstey, South Molton, Devon EX36 3PF
T: (01398) 341246
F: (01398) 341246

Dunsley Mill ★★★★
Contact: Mr and Mrs John and Helen Sparrow, Dunsley Mill, West Anstey, South Molton, Devon EX36 3PF
T: (01398) 341374 & 341444
F: (01398) 341374
E: helen@dunsleymill.co.uk
I: www.dunsleymill.co.uk

WEST BAY
Dorset

15 Bramble Drive ★★★
Contact: Mr & Mrs G&J Paget, 3 Boundary Close, Tanners Brook, Southampton, SO15 4PE
T: (02380) 345836

28 Chesil House ★★★
Contact: Mrs Frances Hunt, Stoney Mead, Curry Rivel, Langport, Somerset TA10 0HW
T: (01458) 251203
F: (01458) 251203
E: frances.hunt@curryrivel.freeserve.co.uk
I: www.somersetcook.freeserve.co.uk

Flat F ★★★
Contact: Mr DA Kimber, 5 Flaxfield Court, Basingstoke, Hampshire RG21 8FX
T: (01256) 470927 & 07714 701208

Seafront Chalet ★★
Contact: Mrs T A Visram, 224 Perth Road, Gants Hill, Ilford, Essex IG2 6DZ
T: (020) 8554 1543
F: (020) 8491 8971
E: Teresa.Visram@virgin.net

Westpoint Apartments ★★★–★★★★★
Contact: Mr & Mrs D&B Slade, Westpoint Apartments, The Esplanade, West Bay, Bridport, Dorset DT6 4HG
T: (01308) 423636
F: (01308) 458871
E: bea@westpoint-apartments.co.uk
I: www.westpoint-apartments.co.uk

WEST BEXINGTON
Dorset

Gorselands ★★–★★★★
Contact: Mrs S J Northover, Gorselands, West Bexington, Dorchester, Dorset DT2 9DJ
T: (01308) 897232
F: (01308) 897239

Tamarisk Farm Cottages ★★★–★★★★★
Contact: Mrs Josephine Pearse, Tamarisk Farm Cottages, West Bexington, Dorchester, Dorset DT2 9DF
T: (01308) 897784
F: (01308) 897784
E: tamarisk@eurolink.ltd.net
I: www.tamariskfarm.co.uk

WEST BUCKLAND
Devon

Taddiport Cottage ★★★
Contact: Mrs M Hawkins, Taddiport, West Buckland, Barnstaple, Devon EX32 0SL
T: (01598) 760287
E: Maureen.V.Hawkins@ukgateway.net

WEST CHINNOCK
Somerset

Weavers Cottage ★★★★
Contact: Lt Col & Mrs Patricia & Gordon Piper, Weavers Cottage, 48 Higher Street, West Chinnock, Crewkerne, Somerset TA18 7QA
T: (01935) 881370
E: thepipers@btinternet.com

Yeoman Cottage ★★★★
Contact: Mrs M Wheatley, Yeoman Cottage, Yeoman Wake, Higher Street, West Chinnock, Crewkerne, Somerset TA18 7QA
T: (01935) 881421
F: (01935) 881421
E: jonwheat@cs.com

WEST DOWN
Devon

Kings Close ★★★★
Contact: Marsden's Cottage Holidays, 2 The Square, Braunton, Devon EX33 2JB
T: (01271) 813777
F: (01271) 813664
E: holidays@marsdens.co.uk
I: www.marsdens.co.uk

Myrtle Cottage ★★★
Contact: Marsden's Cottage Holidays, 2 The Square, Braunton, Devon EX33 2JB
T: (01271) 813777
F: (01271) 813664
E: robin@data-sphere.co.uk
I: www.myrtle-cottage-devon.co.uk

Rock Cottage ★★★
Contact: Mrs Virginia Sprason, 36 Ferndale Park, Stourbridge, West Midlands DY9 0RB
T: (01562) 883038
F: (01562) 886592
E: rock.cottage@virgin.net
I: www.freespace.virgin.net/keith.sprason/cottage/

Tawny Cottage ★★★★
Contact: Marsden's Cottage Holidays, 2 The Square, Braunton, Devon EX33 2JB
T: (01271) 813777
F: (01271) 813664
E: holidays@marsdens.co.uk
I: www.marsdens.co.uk

WEST MILTON
Dorset

Gore Cottage ★★★
Contact: Hon Mrs E G Maude, Sparrow Court, Chalk Hill Road, Kingsdown, Deal, Kent CT14 8DP
T: (01304) 389253
F: (01304) 389016

Leopard Cottage ★★★★
Contact: Milkbere Cottage Holidays, Milkbere House, 14 Fore Street, Seaton, Devon EX12 2LA
T: (01297) 20729
F: (01297) 24831
E: info@milkbere.com
I: www.milkbere.com

WEST STAFFORD
Dorset

Barton House Loft ★★★
Contact: Mrs J M Robertson, Barton House Loft, Barton Close, West Stafford, Dorchester, Dorset DT2 8AD
T: (01305) 250472
F: (01305) 250472

Lewell Mill Farm ★★★★
Contact: Mrs Kate Lousley, Lewell Mill Farm, The Barn, Lewell Mill Farm, West Stafford, Dorchester, Dorset DT2 8AN
T: (01305) 269681 & 768888
F: (01305) 768777
E: cfl@pengillymdge.loaw.co.uk

WESTBURY
Wiltshire

Iron Box Cottage ★★★★
Contact: Mrs SA Hansford, 1 Carpenters Lane, Bratton, Westbury, Wiltshire BA13 4SS
T: (01380) 830169 & 830670
E: sue.hansford@tesco.net

WESTBURY-SUB-MENDIP
Somerset

Old Apple Loft ★★★
Contact: Mrs Anne Flintham, Old Apple Loft, Westbury Cross House, Crow Lane, Westbury-sub-Mendip, Wells, Somerset BA5 1HB
T: (01749) 870557 & 07974 417623

WESTHAY
Somerset

The Courtyard New House Farm★★★★
Contact: Mr P W Bell, The Courtyard New House Farm, Burtle Road, Westhay, Glastonbury, Somerset BA6 9TT
T: (01458) 860238
F: (01458) 860568
E: newhousefarm@farmersweekly.net

WESTLEIGH
Devon

Farleigh Cottage ★★★★
Contact: Mr Peter Morris, Farm & Cottage Holidays, Victoria House, 12 Fore Street, Bideford, Devon EX39 1AW
T: (01237) 479146
F: (01237) 421512
E: farmcott@cix.co.uk
I: www.farmcott.co.uk

WESTON-SUPER-MARE
North Somerset

Batch Farm Cottage ★★
Contact: Mrs I D Wall, Batch Farm, Lympsham, Weston-super-Mare BS24 0EX
T: (01934) 750287

The Charlton Luxury Holiday Flats★★★
Contact: Mr and Mrs L T Pople, The Charlton Luxury Holiday Flats, 3 Charlton Road, Weston-super-Mare, BS23 4HB
T: (01934) 629896
E: charlton.wsm@btinternet.com
I: www.btinternet.com/charlton.wsm/firstpage/index.htm

Clarence View ★★★★
Contact: Ms A Cantle, Champagne Holiday Lets, Broomrigg House, Broomrigg Road, Fleet, Aldershot, Hampshire GU13 8LR
T: (01252) 622789 & 07831 845643
F: (01252) 812948
E: alison@broomrigg.madasafish.com
I: www.holiday-rentals.com

Doubleton Farm Cottages
★★★
Contact: Mr & Mrs John &
Victoria Southwood, Doubleton
Farm Cottages, Hewish, Weston-
super-Mare BS24 6RB
T: (01934) 520225
F: (01934) 520225
E: info@doubleton.com
I: www.doubleton.com

Hope Farm Cottages ★★★★
Contact: Mrs Liz Stirk, Hope
Farm Cottages, Brean Road,
Lympsham, Weston-super-Mare
BS24 0HA
T: (01934) 750506
F: (01934) 750506
E: stirk@hopefarm.totalserve.
co.uk
I: www.hopefarmcottages.co.uk

Manor House Cottages
★★★-★★★★
Contact: Mrs V Hart, Manor
House, Bleadon Road, Bleadon,
Weston-super-Mare BS24 0PY
T: (01934) 812689
F: (01934) 812689
E: valerie@
manor-house-cottages.com
I: www.manor-house-cottages.
com

Royal Sands ★★★★
Contact: Ms A Cantle,
Champagne Holiday Lets,
Broomrigg House, Broomrigg
Road, Fleet, Aldershot,
Hampshire GU13 8LR
T: (01252) 622789 &
07831 845643
F: (01252) 812948
E: alison@broomrigg.
madasafish.com
I: www.holiday-rentals.com

Sandhurst ★★★★
Contact: Ms Alision Cantle,
Champayne Holiday Lets,
Broomrigg House, Broomrigg
Road, Fleet, Aldershot,
Hampshire GU13 8LR
T: (01252) 622789 &
07831 845643
F: (01252) 812948
E: alison@broomrigg.
madusafish.com

Saxonhurst ★★-★★★
Contact: Mr P Norris,
Saxonhurst, 36 All Saints Road,
Weston-super-Mare, Somerset
BS23 2NN
T: (01934) 415997
E: saxonhurst@
patricknorrisassociates.co.uk

Westward Ho! Holiday Flats
★★-★★★
Contact: Mr and Mrs K Everard,
Westward Ho! Holiday Flats, 39
Severn Road, Weston-super-
Mare, Somerset BS23 1DP
T: (01934) 629294
E: kenandjanet@
westwardhohols.fsnet.co.uk

WESTPORT
Somerset

Riverside ★★★
Contact: Mrs Caroline King,
Dunns Green Farm, Hemyock,
Cullompton, Devon
T: (01823) 680447
F: (01823) 681008
E: cking@dunnsgreen.fsnet.
co.uk

Wind in the Willows Cottage
★★★
Contact: Mr C Baker, Hillside,
Cooks Lane, Axminster, Devon
EX13 5SQ
T: (01297) 32051 &
(01460) 281821
F: (01297) 32051
E: cjbaker@eggconnect.net

WESTWARD HO!
Devon

Fairway Cottage ★★
Contact: Appledore Holiday
Letting Agency, 20 Market
Street, Appledore, Bideford,
Devon EX39 1PW
T: (01237) 476191
F: (01237) 479621
E: enquiries@appledore-letting.
co.uk
I: www.appledore-letting.co.uk

**West Pusehill Farm Holiday
Cottages★★★-★★★★**
Contact: Mr/Ms John/Anna
Violet/Lacey, West Pusehill Farm
Holiday Cottages, West Pusehill
Farm, Westward Ho!, Bideford,
Devon EX39 5AH
T: (01237) 475638 & 470216
F: (01237) 425979
I: www.wpfcottages.co.uk

WEYMOUTH
Dorset

**Bay Lodge Self-Catering
Accommodation**
★★★-★★★★★
Contact: Mr and Mrs G Dubben,
Bay Lodge, 27 Greenhill,
Weymouth, Dorset DT4 7SW
T: (01305) 782419
F: (01305) 782828
E: barbara@baylodge
I: www.baylodge.co.uk

Beachside - Weymouth
Rating Applied For
Contact: Mr CF Tarrant,
Beachside - Weymouth, 45
Southwell, Portland, Dorset
DT5 2DP
T: (01305) 824108
F: (01305) 823182
E: eats@tesco.net

Belvidere House Holiday Flats
★★★
Contact: Mrs V J Brown, 16
Nottington Lane, Weymouth,
Dorset DT3 5DF
T: (01305) 814152
F: (01305) 5760301
E: enquiries@belviderehouse.
co.uk
I: www.belviderehouse.co.uk

3 Cove Street ★★★
Contact: Mrs J Creed, Propect
House, The Street, Yatton
Keynell, Chippenham, Wiltshire
SN14 7BQ
T: (01249) 782713

Glenthorne ★★★
Contact: Mrs Olivia Nurrish,
Glenthorne, Castle Cove, 15 Old
Castle Road, Weymouth, Dorset
DT4 8QB
T: (01305) 777281 &
07831 751526

**Howard Cottage 33 Walpole
Street★★★**
Contact: Mrs B A Willy, 5
Helston Close, Portesham,
Weymouth, Dorset DT3 4EY
T: (01305) 871799

8 North Square
Rating Applied For
Contact: CH ref: 8834, Holiday
Cottages Group Owner Services
Dept, Spring Mill, Earby,
Barnoldswick, Lancashire
BB18 6RN
T: (01282) 445096
F: (01282) 844299
E: ch.sales@ttgihg.co.uk
I: www.country-holidays.co.uk

Queensway Holiday Flats
Rating Applied For
Contact: Mr MR Kelly, 46 Park
Street, Weymouth, Dorset
DT4 7DF
T: (01305) 760747
I: www.precision.clara.
net/queensway

Stavordale House Holiday Flats
★★★
Contact: Mr AP Wallace, 49
Roman Road, Weymouth, Dorset
DT3 5JH
T: (01305) 789004

Stonebank Cottage ★★★★
Contact: Mrs P Westcott,
Stonebank, 14 West Street,
Chickerell, Weymouth, Dorset
DT3 4DY
T: (01305) 760120
F: (01305) 760871
E: annexe@
stonebank-chickerell.co.uk
I: www.stonebank-chickerell.
co.uk

Sunnywey Apartments
★★★★
Contact: Mrs L Bond, Sunnywey
Apartments, 27 Kirtleton
Avenue, Weymouth, Dorset
DT4 7PS
T: (01305) 781767
F: (01305) 785761
E: bond@sunnywey.co.uk
I: www.sunnywey.co.uk

**Weymouth Bay Holiday
Apartments**
Rating Applied For
Contact: Mrs A Blake,
Weymouth Bay Holiday
Apartments, 56 Greenhill,
Weymouth, Dorset DT4 7SL
T: (01305) 785003

WHEDDON CROSS
Somerset

Cutthorne Farm ★★★★
Contact: Mrs Ann Durbin,
Cutthorne Farm, Luckwell
Bridge, Wheddon Cross,
Minehead, Somerset TA24 7EW
T: (01643) 831255
F: (01643) 831255
E: durbin@cutthorne.co.uk
I: www.cutthorne.co.uk

Mill Cottage ★★★★
Contact: Mrs Ratcliff, Mill
Cottage, Ford Farm, Draypers
Way, Wheddon Cross, Minehead,
Somerset TA24 7EE
T: (01643) 841251
F: (01643) 841251
E: ratcliff@ford-farm.freeserve.
co.uk

Pembroke ★★★
Contact: Mrs J Escott, Brake
Cottage, Wheddon Cross,
Minehead, Somerset TA24 7EX
T: (01643) 841550

Triscombe Farm
★★★-★★★★
Contact: Mrs Ruth Brinkley,
Triscombe Farm, Wheddon
Cross, Minehead, Somerset
TA24 7HA
T: (01643) 851227
F: (01643) 851227

WHIMPLE
Devon

Higher Yellands Cottage
Rating Applied For
Contact: Mrs S Farmer, Higher
Yellands Cottage, Higher
Yellands, Whimple, Exeter
EX5 2QX
T: (01404) 822265
E: nfarmer@ic24.net

LSF Holiday Cottages ★★
Contact: Mrs S Lang, LSF Holiday
Cottages, Lower Southbrook
Farm, Southbrook Lane,
Whimple, Exeter, Devon EX5 2PG
T: (01404) 822989
F: (01404) 822989
E: angela.lang@btinternet.com

WHITCHURCH CANONICORUM
Dorset

Berehayes Farm Cottages
★★★★
Contact: Mr and Mrs
Winterbourne, Berehayes Farm
Cottages, Berehayes Farm,
Whitchurch Canonicorum,
Bridport, Dorset DT6 6RQ
T: (01297) 489093
F: (01297) 489093
E: berehayes@tesco.net
I: www.berehayes.co.uk

**Blackmore Farmhouse X3443
Dairy Cottage,Hayborn
W3434/5★★★★★**
Contact: Lyme Bay Holidays,
Boshouse, 44 Church Street,
Lyme Regis, Dorset DT7 3DA
T: (01297) 443363
F: (01297) 445576
E: email@lymebayholidays.
co.uk
I: www.lymebayholidays.co.uk

Bonhayes Farm ★★-★★★
Contact: Mr C Hendley,
Bonhayes Farm, Whitchurch
Canonicorum, Dorset DT6 6RF
T: (01297) 489615

Hinkhams Farm ★★
Contact: Mrs Ray, Hinkhams
Farm, Whitchurch Canonicorum,
Bridport, Dorset DT6 6RJ
T: (01297) 489311

Jenny Wrens V4262 ★★★★
Contact: Lyme Bay Holidays,
Boshouse, 44 Church Street,
Lyme Regis, Dorset DT7 3DA
T: (01297) 443363
F: (01297) 445576
E: email@lymebayholidays.
co.uk
I: www.lymebayholidays.co.uk

Old Dairy Cottage
Rating Applied For
Contact: Old Dairy Cottage,
Bonhayes Farm, Whitchurch
Canonicorum

**Taphouse Farmhouse &
Courthouse Farmhouse** ★★
Contact: Mrs S M Johnson,
Cardsmill Farm, Whitchurch
Canonicorum, Bridport DT6 6RP
T: (01297) 489375
F: (01297) 489375
E: cardsmill@aol.com
I: www.farmhousedorset.com

Vale View (X4024) ★★★
Contact: Lyme Bay Holidays,
Boshouse, 44 Church Street,
Lyme Regis, Dorset DT7 3DA
T: (01297) 443363
F: (01297) 445576
E: email@lymebayholidays.
co.uk
I: www.lymebayholidays.co.uk

WHITFORD
Devon

The Old Methodist Chapel
★★★★
Contact: Jean Bartlett Cottage
Holidays, Fore Street, Beer,
Seaton, Devon EX12 3JB
T: (01297) 23221
F: (01297) 23303
E: jeanb@netbreaks.com
I: www.netbreaks.com/jeanb

Parklands Cottage ★★★
Contact: Jean Bartlett Cottage
Holidays, Fore Street, Beer,
Seaton, Devon EX12 3JB
T: (01297) 23221
F: (01297) 23303
E: jeanb@netbreaks.com
I: www.netbreaks.com/jeanb

WICK
Gloucestershire

Greenway Farm ★★★
Contact: Mrs L Hooper,
Greenway Farm, Bath Road,
Wick, Bristol B30 5RL
T: (0117) 937 3201

WIDEMOUTH BAY
Cornwall

Quinceborough Farm Cottages
Rating Applied For
Contact: Mrs P M Rowland,
Quinceborough Farm Cottages,
Quinceborough Farm, Leverlake
Road, Widemouth Bay, Bude,
Cornwall EX23 ONA
T: (01288) 361236

WIDWORTHY
Devon

Sutton Barton ★★★★★
Contact: Jean Bartlett Cottage
Holidays, Fore Street, Beer,
Seaton, Devon EX12 3JB
T: (01297) 23221
F: (01297) 23303
E: jeanb@netbreaks.com
I: www.netbreaks.com/jeanb

WILLITON
Somerset

Daisy Cottage ★★★★
Contact: Mrs A Bishop, 6 North
Street, Williton, Taunton,
Somerset TA4 4SL
T: (01984) 632657
F: (01984) 632657

WINGFIELD
Wiltshire

Romsey Oak Cottages ★★
Contact: Mr Alan Briars, Romsey
Oak Cottages, Romsey Oak
Farmhouse, Bradford Road,
Wingfield, Trowbridge, Wiltshire
BA14 9LS
T: (01225) 753950
F: (01225) 753950
E: enquiries@
romseyoakcottages.co.uk
I: www.romsleyoakcottages.
co.uk

WINSCOMBE
North Somerset

**Mulberry South Wing of
Winscombe Court** ★★★★
Contact: Mrs J Symons,
Winscombe Court, Winscombe
Hill, Winscombe, BS25 1DE
T: (01934) 842171 & 844665
F: (01934) 842171
E: jsymons@winscombecourt.
fsnet.co.uk
I: www.winscombecourt.co.uk

Uplands Cottages ★★★
Contact: Mrs A Webb, Uplands
Cottages, Shipham Lane,
Winscombe, Somerset BS25 1PX
T: (01934) 842257

WINSFORD
Somerset

Ball Cottage ★★★
Contact: Mrs Wilkinson, 44
Guildford Road, London
SW8 2BU
T: (0207) 6226757
E: wilkinson.ballcottage@virgin.
net
I: www.ball-cottage.co.uk

East Galliford Cottage ★★★
Contact: Mr Alexander, 28 Friars
Stile Road, Richmond, Surrey
TW10 6NE
T: (020) 8940 8078
F: (020) 8940 6871
E: beverleymca@compuserve.
com

Hill House ★★
Contact: Mrs S Maxse,
Homestead Farm, Selborne,
Alton, Hampshire GU34 3LN
T: (01420) 511216
F: (01420) 511024

WINTERBOURNE ABBAS
Dorset

Garden Studio ★★★
Contact: Mrs Anne Slattery, 14
Diggory Crescent, Dorchester,
Dorset DT1 2SP
T: (01305) 259127
E: anne@slattery.fsnet.co.uk

WINTERBOURNE STOKE
Wiltshire

Scotland Lodge ★★
Contact: Mrs Jane Singleton,
Scotland Lodge, Winterbourne
Stoke, Salisbury, Wiltshire
SP3 4TF
T: (01980) 620943 &
07957 856302
F: (01980) 621403
E: scotland.lodge@virgin.net.
co.uk
I: www.scotland-lodge.co.uk

WITHERIDGE
Devon

The Furrows ★★★
Contact: The Proprietor, The
Furrows, Wheadon Farm,
Witheridge, Tiverton, Devon
EX16

WITHYPOOL
Somerset

Landacre Bungalow ★★★
Contact: Mrs P G Hudson,
Landacre Cottage, Landacre
Farm, Withypool, Minehead,
Somerset TA24 7SD
T: (01643) 831223 & 831487

WIVELISCOMBE
Somerset

Hurstone Farmhouse
Rating Applied For
Contact: Mr J Bone, Hurstone
Farmhouse, Waterrow,
Wiveliscombe, Taunton,
Somerset TA4 2AT
T: (01984) 623441

Upton Farmhouse Wing
★★★★
Contact: CH ref: 10140, Holiday
Cottages Group Owner Services
Dept, Spring Mill, Earby,
Barnoldswick, Lancashire
BB18 6RN
T: (01282) 445096
F: (01282) 844299
E: ch.sales@ttgihg.co.uk
I: www.country-holidays.co.uk

WOODBURY
Devon

**The Thatched Cottage
Company** ★★★★★
Contact: Mrs G M Barlow, The
Thatched Cottage Company, 56
Fore Street, Otterton, Budleigh
Salterton, Devon EX9 7HB
T: (01395) 567676
F: (01395) 567440

The Warren ★★★★
Contact: Jean Bartlett Cottage
Holidays, Fore Street, Beer,
Seaton, Devon EX12 3JB
T: (01297) 23221
F: (01297) 23303
E: jeanb@netbreaks.com
I: www.netbreaks.com/jeanb

WOOLACOMBE
Devon

The Apartment ★★★★
Contact: Marsden's Cottage
Holidays, 2 The Square,
Braunton, Devon EX33 2JB
T: (01271) 813777
F: (01271) 813664
E: holidays@marsdens.co.uk
I: www.marsdens.co.uk

Barton Court ★★★
Contact: Marsden's Cottage
Holidays, 2 The Square,
Braunton, Devon EX33 2JB
T: (01271) 813777
F: (01271) 813664
E: holidays@marsdens.co.uk
I: www.marsdens.co.uk

Bayview ★★★★
Contact: Marsden's Cottage
Holidays, 2 The Square,
Braunton, Devon EX33 2JB
T: (01271) 813777
F: (01271) 813664
E: holidays@marsdens.co.uk
I: www.marsdens.co.uk

**Beachcroft Holiday
Apartments** ★★★
Contact: Mrs G Barr, Beachcroft
Holiday Apartments, Beach
Road, Woolacombe, Devon
EX34 7BT
T: (01271) 870655
F: (01271) 870655

40 Chichester Park ★★★
Contact: Marsden's Cottage
Holidays, 2 The Square,
Braunton, Devon EX33 2JB
T: (01271) 813777
F: (01271) 813664
E: holidays@marsdens.co.uk
I: www.marsdens.co.uk

79 Chichester Park ★★★
Contact: Marsden's Cottage
Holidays, 2 The Square,
Braunton, Devon EX33 2JB
T: (01271) 813777
F: (01271) 813664
E: holidays@marsdens.co.uk
I: www.marsdens.co.uk

1 Europa Park ★★
Contact: Mrs Rosemary Ann
Facey, Sticklepath Lodge, Old
Sticklepath Hill, Barnstaple,
Devon EX31 2BG
T: (01271) 343426
E: rosemary.facey@talk21.com

Kirton ★★★
Contact: Marsdens Cottage
Holidays, 2 The Square,
Braunton, Devon EX33 2JB
T: (01271) 813777
E: holidays@marsdens.co.uk
I: www.marsdens.co.uk

Lundy Set ★★★★
Contact: Marsden's Cottage
Holidays, 2 The Square,
Braunton, Devon EX33 2JB
T: (01271) 813777
F: (01271) 813664
E: holidays@marsdens.co.uk
I: www.marsdens.co.uk

Ocean View ★★★
Contact: Marsden's Cottage
Holidays, 2 The Square,
Braunton, Devon EX33 2JB
T: (01271) 813777
F: (01271) 813664
E: holidays@marsdens.co.uk
I: www.marsdens.co.uk

4 Pandora Court ★★★★
Contact: Marsden's Cottage
Holidays, 2 The Square,
Braunton, Devon EX33 2JB
T: (01271) 813777
F: (01271) 813664
E: holidays@marsdens.co.uk
I: www.marsdens.co.uk

5 Pandora Court ★★★★
Contact: Marsden's Cottage
Holidays, 2 The Square,
Braunton, Devon EX33 2JB
T: (01271) 813777
F: (01271) 813664

Patscombe Cottage ★★★
Contact: Marsden's Cottage
Holidays, 2 The Square,
Braunton, Devon EX33 2JB
T: (01271) 813777
F: (01271) 813664
E: holidays@marsdens.co.uk
I: www.marsdens.co.uk

Establishments printed in blue have a detailed entry in this guide

Puffin ★★★★
Contact: Marsden's Cottage
Holidays, 2 The Square,
Braunton, Devon EX33 2JB
T: (01271) 813777
F: (01271) 813664
E: holidays@marsdens.co.uk
I: www.marsdens.co.uk

Seawatch ★★★
Contact: Marsden's Cottage
Holidays, 2 The Square,
Braunton, Devon EX33 2JB
T: (01271) 813777
F: (01271) 813664

Tysoe ★★★★
Contact: Marsden's Cottage
Holidays, 2 The Square,
Braunton, Devon EX33 2JB
T: (01271) 813777
F: (01271) 813664
E: holidays@marsdens.co.uk
I: www.marsdens.co.uk

West View ★★★
Contact: Marsdens Cottage
Holidays, 2, The Square,
Braunton, Devon EX33 2JB
T: (01271) 813777
F: (01271) 813664
E: holidays@marsdens.co.uk
I: www.marsdens.co.uk

WOOLAVINGTON
Somerset
Primrose Cottage ★★★★
Contact: Mr & Mrs Jon &
Christine Brinkman, Chestnut
House, Hectors Stone, Lower
Road, Woolavington,
Bridgwater, Somerset TA7 8EQ
T: (01278) 683658
F: (01278) 683658
I: www.chestnuthouse.freeserve.
co.uk

WOOLFARDISWORTHY
Devon
The Old Coach House ★★★
Contact: Mr Peter Morris, Farm
& Cottage Holidays, Victoria
House, 12 Fore Street, Northam,
Bideford, Devon EX39 1AW
T: (01237) 479146
F: (01237) 421512
E: farmcott@cix.co.uk
I: www.farmcot.co.uk

WOOTTON COURTENAY
Somerset
Old Parlour Cottage
Rating Applied For
Contact: Mr EG Bishop, Old
Parlour Cottage, Hanny Cottage,
Wootton Courtenay, Minehead,
Somerset TA24 8RE
T: (01643) 841440
E: bishop.dunn@virgin.net

Rose Cottage ★★★
Contact: Mr B Fawcett, The
Paddocks, Pilgrims Way, Chew
Stoke, Bristol BS40 8TZ
T: (01275) 332574
F: (01275) 331123
E: bryanfawcett@lineone.net

WOOTTON FITZPAINE
Dorset
Champernhayes Cottages
★★★★★
Contact: Mrs E R Thompson,
Champernhayes Cottages,
Champernhayes, Wootton
Fitzpaine, Bridport, Dorset
DT6 6DF
T: (01297) 560853
F: (01297) 561155
E: champhayes@aol.com
I: www.champernhayes.com

Cowslip,Foxglove & Bluebell
Cottages ★★★★
Contact: Lyme Bay Holidays,
Boshouse, 44 Church Street,
Lyme Regis, Dorset DT7 3DA
T: (01297) 443363
F: (01297) 445576
E: email@lymebayholidays.
co.uk
I: www.lymebayholidays.co.uk

Marsh Farm ★★★
Contact: Mr J Mansbridge,
Marsh Farm, Wootton Fitzpaine,
Bridport, Dorset DT6 6DF
T: (01297) 560600

WRANTAGE
Somerset
Ludwells Barn
Rating Applied For
Contact: Mr DJ Dodd, Ludwells
Barn, Ludwells Farm, Wrantage,
Taunton, Somerset TA3 6DQ
T: (01823) 480316

WYKE
Devon
Rose Cottage ★★★★
Contact: Jean Bartlett Cottage
Holidays, Fore Street, Beer,
Seaton, Devon EX12 3JB
T: (01297) 23221 & 20973
F: (01297) 23303
E: jeanb@netbreaks.com
I: www.netbreaks.com/jeanb

YARNSCOMBE
Devon
Moos ★★
Contact: Mr Peter Morris, Farm
& Cottage Holidays, Victoria
House, 12 Fore Street, Northam,
Bideford, Devon EX39 1AW
T: (01237) 479146
F: (01237) 421512
E: farmcott@cix.co.uk
I: www.farmcott.co.uk

YELLAND
Devon
Ballards Retreat ★★★
Contact: Mrs Butler, 1 Ballards
Crescent, Yelland, Barnstaple,
Devon EX31 3EU
T: (01271) 861126

YEOVIL
Somerset
Pound Cottage ★★★★
Contact: Mr and Mrs P
Clutterbuck, Cloverleaf Farm,
East Chinnock, Yeovil, Somerset
BA22 9DJ
T: (01935) 863149
F: (01935) 863149
E: pllva@clover-leaf.demon.
co.uk

YETMINSTER
Dorset
The White Hart Inn ★★★
Contact: Mr & Mrs J&C Bayfield,
The White Hart Inn, High Street,
Yetminster, Sherborne, Dorset
DT9 6LF
T: (01935) 872338
E: jimbayfield@bun.com

ZEAL MONACHORUM
Devon
Gillhouse Cottage ★★★
Contact: Ms Vicki Mills,
Gillhouse Farm, Zeal
Monachorum, Crediton, Devon
EX17 6LE
T: (01363) 82465
F: (01363) 82944
E: victoria.mchugh@virgin.net
I: www.cottagesdirect.com

ZELAH
Cornwall
Little Callestock Farm
★★★-★★★★
Contact: Country Hols
Ref:R792,11396, Holiday
Cottages Group Limited, Spring
Mill, Earby, Barnoldswick,
Lancashire BB94 0AA
T: (01282) 445096
F: (01282) 844288
I: www.country-holidays.co.uk

SOUTH OF ENGLAND

ABINGDON
Oxfordshire
Kingfisher Barn Holiday
Cottages ★★★
Contact: Ms Liz Beaumont,
Kingfisher Barn Holiday
Cottages, Kingfisher Barn Ltd,
Rye Farm, Abingdon, Oxfordshire
OX14 3NN
T: (01235) 537538
F: (01235) 537538
E: info@kingfisherbarn.com
I: www.kingfisherbarn.com

The Old School ★★★
Contact: Mrs C A Radburn, The
Old School, 16 High Street,
Drayton, Abingdon, Oxfordshire
OX14 4JL
T: (01235) 531557
E: gordon@theoldschool.
freeserve.co.uk

ALTON
Hampshire
Woodside Farm Annexe ★
Contact: Miss V A Crisp & Mrs K
Ormsby, Woodside Farm,
Gosport Road, Privett, Alton,
Hampshire GU34 3NJ
T: (01730) 828359
F: (01730) 828006

ALVERSTOKE
Hampshire
28 The Avenue ★★
Contact: Mr Martin Lawson, 18
Upper Paddock Road, Watford,
Hertfordshire WD1 4DZ
T: (01923) 244042
F: (01923) 244042

ALVERSTONE
Isle of Wight
Combe View ★★★
Contact: Mrs G D Oliver, Kern
Farm, Alverstone, Sandown, Isle
of Wight PO36 0EY
T: (01983) 403721

West Wing Kern Farmhouse
★★★★
Contact: Mrs G D Oliver, Kern
Farm, Alverstone, Sandown, Isle
of Wight PO36 0EY
T: (01983) 403721

The Willows ★★★
Contact: Mrs Honor Vass, Island
Cottage Holidays, The Old
Vicarage, Kingston, Corfe Castle,
Wareham, Dorset BH20 5LH
T: (01929) 480080
F: (01929) 481070
E: ich@cottageholidays.demon.
co.uk
I: www.cottageholidays.demon.
co.uk.

AMPORT
Hampshire
The Thatched Barn ★★
Contact: Mrs Carolyn Mallam,
Broadwater, Amport, Andover,
Hampshire SP11 8AY
T: (01264) 772240
F: (01264) 772240
E: carolyn@dmac.co.uk
I: www.dmac.co.uk/carolyn

ASCOTT-UNDER-WYCHWOOD
Oxfordshire
Crown Farm ★★★★
Contact: Mr & Mrs Chris and
Janet Badger, Crown Farm Bed &
Breakfast, Crown Farm, 13 The
Green, Ascott-under-
Wychwood, Oxford, Oxfordshire
OX7 6AB
T: (01993) 832083 & 830045
F: (01993) 832083
E: chrisandjanet@farming.co.uk
I: www.crown-farm.co.uk

Hedera Cottage ★★★★
Contact: Mrs Jennie Lougher, 25
High Street, Ascott-under-
Wychwood, Chipping Norton,
Oxfordshire OX7 6AW
T: (01993) 832119
E: j.lougher@talk21.com

AYLESBURY
Buckinghamshire

Appletrees ★★★★
Contact: Mrs V Rayner, 94
Vicarage Road, Marsworth,
Buckinghamshire HP23 4LU
T: (01296) 661967

BAMPTON
Oxfordshire

Green Acres
Rating Applied For
Contact: Mrs Isobel Evers, Green
Acres, Cote, Bampton,
Oxfordshire OX18 2EG
T: (01993) 850526 &
(01235) 530074

Haytor Cottage ★★★
Contact: Mrs S M Phillips,
Haytor, Lavender Square,
Bampton, Oxfordshire OX18 2LR
T: (01993) 850321

Tom's Barn ★★
Contact: Mr Thomas Freeman,
Radcot Bridge House, Radcot,
Bampton, Oxfordshire OX18 2SX
T: (01367) 810410
E: tmfreeman@btinternet.co.uk

BANBURY
Oxfordshire

Millstream Cottages ★★
Contact: Mrs Patricia Ritter &
Michael Canning, La Madonette
Country Guest House, North
Newington, Banbury,
Oxfordshire OX15 6AA
T: (01295) 730212
F: (01295) 730363
E: lamadonett@aol.com
I: www.lamadonette.co.uk

The Wickets ★★★
Contact: Mrs E Halcro-Johnston,
Orphir House, Orphir, Orkney,
Isle of Orkney
T: (01856) 811200

BARTON ON SEA
Hampshire

Cleeve House ★★★
Contact: Mrs Eileen Carter,
Cleeve House, 58 Barton Court
Avenue, Barton on Sea, New
Milton, Hampshire BH25 7HG
T: (01425) 615211
F: (01425) 615211
E: cleeve.house@btinternet.com

Waters Edge ★★★★
Contact: Mrs Y Murphy, Waters
Edge, 10 Marine Drive West,
Barton on Sea, New Milton,
Hampshire BH25 7QH
T: (01425) 615485
F: (01425) 615485

BEACONSFIELD
Buckinghamshire

Roselands ★★★
Contact: Mrs June Koderisch,
Roselands, 3 Beechwood Road,
Beaconsfield, Buckinghamshire
HP9 1HP
T: (01494) 676864
F: (01494) 676864
E: dkoderisch@iname.com

BEAULIEU
Hampshire

Eaglesham ★★★★
Contact: Mrs Ruth Phillips, 1
Newlands Manor, Everton,
Lymington, Hampshire SO41 0JH
T: (01590) 644140
F: (01590) 644141
E: derek.phillips@tesco. net

**Hill Top House Cottage
★★★★**
Contact: Mr & Mrs Brett
Johnson, Hill Top House, Palace
Lane, Beaulieu, Hampshire
SO42 7YG
T: (01590) 612731 &
07836 247896
F: (01590) 612743
E: bretros@cs.com

Ivy Cottage ★★★
Contact: Mr & Mrs B R Gibb, 28
Church Street, Littlehampton,
West Sussex BN17 5PX
T: (01903) 715595 &
07778 933172
E: gibb28@breathemail.net

Mares Tails Cottage ★★★★
Contact: Mrs Alice Barber, Mares
Tails, Furzey Lane, Beaulieu,
Brockenhurst, Hampshire
SO42 7WB
T: (01590) 612160
E: marestails612160@cs.com

Old Stables Cottage ★★★★
Contact: Mr & Mrs P Whapham,
Myrtle Farm, East boldre,
Beaulieu, Brockenhurst,
Hampshire SO42 7WU
T: (01590) 626707
E: oldstablescott@cs.com

BEMBRIDGE
Isle of Wight

Allandale ★★
Contact: Mr Peter de Ferrars,
Bembridge Holiday Homes, 9
Meadow Close, Bembridge, Isle
of Wight PO35 5YJ
T: (01983) 873163
F: (01983) 873163
E: bembridge@deferrars.
freeserve.co.uk

Cara Cottage ★★★
Contact: Mr Peter de Ferrars,
Bembridge Holiday Homes, 9
Meadow Close, Bembridge, Isle
of Wight PO35 5YJ
T: (01983) 873163
F: (01983) 873163
E: bembridge@deferrars.
freeserve.co.uk

Cliff Cottage ★★★
Contact: Ms Lisa Baskill, Home
from Home Holidays, 31 Pier
Street, Ventnor, Isle of Wight
PO38 1SX
T: (01983) 854340
F: (01983) 855524

Crossways ★★★
Contact: Mr Peter de Ferrars,
Bembridge Holiday Homes, 9
Meadow Close, Bembridge, Isle
of Wight PO35 5YJ
T: (01983) 873163
F: (01983) 873163
E: bembridge@deferrars.
freeserve.co.uk

8 Downsview Road ★★
Contact: Mr Peter de Ferrars,
Bembridge Holiday Homes, 9
Meadow Close, Bembridge, Isle
of Wight PO35 5YJ
T: (01983) 873163
F: (01983) 873163
E: bembridge@deferrars.
freeserve.co.uk

3 Fairhaven Close ★★
Contact: Mr Peter de Ferrars,
Bembridge Holiday Homes, 9
Meadow Close, Bembridge, Isle
of Wight PO35 5YJ
T: (01983) 873163
F: (01983) 873163
E: bembridge@deferrars.
freeserve.co.uk

The Finches ★★★
Contact: Mr Peter de Ferrars,
Bembridge Holiday Homes, 9
Meadow Close, Bembridge, Isle
of Wight PO35 5YJ
T: (01983) 873163
F: (01983) 873163
E: bembridge@deferrars.
freeserve.co.uk

Forelands Cottage ★
Contact: Mr Peter de Ferrars,
Bembridge Holiday Homes, 9
Meadow Close, Bembridge, Isle
of Wight PO35 5YJ
T: (01983) 873163
F: (01983) 873163
E: bembridge@deferrars.
freeserve.co.uk

Harbour Farm Cottage ★★★
Contact: Mrs D Hicks, Harbour
Farm, Embankment Road,
Bembridge, Isle of Wight
PO35 5NS
T: (01983) 872610 & 874080
F: (01983) 874080
I: www.isle_of_wight_holiday_
directory.co.uk.

3 Harbour Strand ★★
Contact: Ms Lisa Baskill, Home
from Home Holidays, 31 Pier
Street, Ventnor, Isle of Wight
PO38 1SX
T: (01983) 854340
F: (01983) 855524

Hilvana ★★
Contact: Mr Peter de Ferrars,
Bembridge Holiday Homes, 9
Meadow Close, Bembridge, Isle
of Wight PO35 5YJ
T: (01983) 873163
F: (01983) 873163
E: bembridge@deferrars.
freeserve.co.uk

Honeysuckle Haven ★★★
Contact: Mr Peter de Ferrars,
Bembridge Holiday Homes, 9
Meadow Close, Bembridge, Isle
of Wight PO35 5YJ
T: (01983) 873163
F: (01983) 873163
E: bembridge@deferrars.
freeserve.co.uk

Howe Lodge ★★
Contact: Mr Peter de Ferrars,
Bembridge Holiday Homes, 9
Meadow Close, Bembridge, Isle
of Wight PO35 5YJ
T: (01983) 873163
F: (01983) 873163
E: bembridge@deferrars.
freeserve.co.uk

Kingsmere ★★
Contact: Mrs M Kersley,
Kingsmere, Lane End,
Bembridge, Isle of Wight
PO35 5TB
T: (01983) 872778

Little Forelands ★★★★
Contact: Mr Peter de Ferrars,
Bembridge Holiday Homes, 9
Meadow Close, Bembridge, Isle
of Wight PO35 5YJ
T: (01983) 873163
F: (01983) 873163
E: bembridge@deferrars.
freeserve.co.uk

Mill Reach ★★
Contact: Mr Peter de Ferrars,
Bembridge Holiday Homes, 9
Meadow Close, Bembridge, Isle
of Wight PO35 5YJ
T: (01983) 873163
F: (01983) 873163
E: bembridge@deferrars.
freeserve.co.uk

Nine ★★
Contact: Mrs B C Cripps, High
Point, Brook Green, Cuckfield,
Haywards Heath, West Sussex
RH17 5JJ
T: (01444) 454474

**Port & Starboard Cottages
★★★★**
Contact: Mr & Mrs C B Trapp,
Hoe Cottage, 15 Westfield Park,
Ryde, Isle of Wight PO33 3AB
T: (01983) 563764

11 Port St Helens ★★
Contact: Mr Peter de Ferrars,
Bembridge Holiday Homes, 9
Meadow Close, Bembridge, Isle
of Wight PO35 5YJ
T: (01983) 873163
F: (01983) 873163
E: bembridge@deferrars.
freeserve.co.uk

Portland House ★★★★
Contact: Mr Peter de Ferrars,
Bembridge Holiday Homes, 9
Meadow Close, Bembridge, Isle
of Wight PO35 5YJ
T: (01983) 873163
F: (01983) 873163
E: bembridge@deferrars.
freeserve.co.uk

**Princessa Cottage &
Coastwatch Cottage★★★**
Contact: Mrs S Hargreaves, 1
Norcott Drive, Bembridge, Isle of
Wight PO35 5TX
T: (01983) 874403

The Retreat ★★
Contact: Mr Peter de Ferrars,
Bembridge Holiday Homes, 9
Meadow Close, Bembridge, Isle
of Wight PO35 5YJ
T: (01983) 873163
F: (01983) 873163
E: bembridge@deferrars.
freeserve.co.uk

Sandpipers ★
Contact: Mr Peter de Ferrars,
Bembridge Holiday Homes, 9
Meadow Close, Bembridge, Isle
of Wight PO35 5YJ
T: (01983) 873163
F: (01983) 873163
E: bembridge@deferrars.
freeserve.co.uk

Establishments printed in blue have a detailed entry in this guide

Seahorses ★★★
Contact: Mr Peter de Ferrars, Bembridge Holiday Homes, 9 Meadow Close, Bembridge, Isle of Wight PO35 5YJ
T: (01983) 873163
F: (01983) 873163
E: bembridge@deferrars.freeserve.co.uk

September Cottage ★
Contact: Mr Peter de Ferrars, Bembridge Holiday Homes, 9 Meadow Close, Bembridge, Isle of Wight PO35 5YJ
T: (01983) 873163
F: (01983) 873163
E: bembridge@deferrars.freeserve.co.uk

Ship-n-Shore ★★★★
Contact: Mrs C M Morris, Ash Hill Farm, Atherfield, Chale, Ventnor, Isle of Wight PO38 2LH
T: (01983) 551350

Sundowner ★★★
Contact: Mr & Mrs David & Deanne Selby, Old Garth Cottage, 98 High Street, Bembridge, Isle of Wight PO35 5SF
T: (01983) 874724
E: dmselby@dial.pipex.com

4 Swains Villas ★★★
Contact: Mr Peter de Ferrars, Bembridge Holiday Homes, 9 Meadow Close, Bembridge, Isle of Wight PO35 5YJ
T: (01983) 873163
F: (01983) 873163
E: bembridge@deferrars.freeserve.co.uk

Will-o-Cott ★
Contact: Mrs B C Cripps, High Point, Brook Green, Cuckfield, Haywards Heath, West Sussex RH17 5JJ
T: (01444) 454474

Windmill Cottage ★★★★
Contact: Mrs L Miles, Windmill Hotels Ltd, 1 Steyne Road, Bembridge, Isle of Wight PO35 5UH
T: (01983) 872875 & 566884
F: (01983) 874760

BERE REGIS
Dorset

Troy, Bathsheba & Oak Cottages ★★★★
Contact: Mr Ian Ventham, Shitterton Farmhouse, Bere Regis, Wareham, Dorset BH20 7HU
T: (01929) 471480
E: ventham@shitterton.com
I: www.shitterton.com

Victoria Cottage ★★★★
Contact: Mrs Patricia Sage, Regency Cottage, Church Lane, Wool, Wareham, Dorset BH20 6DD
T: (01929) 462229
F: (01929) 462229
I: agbrend@fricsfcciarb.demon.co.uk

BICESTER
Oxfordshire

Pimlico Farm Country Cottages ★★★★
Contact: Mr & Mrs John & Monica Harper, Pimlico Farm Country Cottages, Pimlico Farm, Tusmore, Bicester, Oxfordshire OX27 7SL
T: (01869) 810306 & 07774 940321
F: (01869) 810309
E: enquiries@pimlicofarm.co.uk
I: www.pimlicofarm.co.uk

BLANDFORD FORUM
Dorset

The Lodge, the Stable & Plumtree Cottage★★★
Contact: Mrs P A Cooper, Dairy House Farm, Woolland, Blandford Forum, Dorset DT11 0EY
T: (01258) 817501
F: (01258) 818060
E: penny.cooper@farming.co.uk
I: www.self-cateringholidays4u.co.uk

Shepherds Cottage ★★★
Contact: CH ref; 8002, 8003, 8322, Country Holidays, Spring Mill, Earby, Barnoldswick, Lancashire BB94 0AA
T: 08700 723723
F: (01282) 844288
E: sales@ttgihg.co.uk
I: www.country-holidays.co.uk

BOLDRE
Hampshire

Close Cottage ★★
Contact: Mr or Mrs C J White, Close Cottage, Brockenhurst Road, Battramsley, Boldre, Lymington, Hampshire SO41 8PT
T: (01590) 675343

Fernbrake House ★★★
Contact: Mrs P Hall, Fernbrake, Coxhill, Boldre, Lymington, Hampshire SO41 8PS
T: (01590) 622257
F: (01590) 624256

Orchard House ★★★
Contact: Mrs Valerie Barnes, Orchard House, Battramsley, Boldre, Lymington, Hampshire SO41 8ND
T: (01590) 676686

Springfield Wing, Boldre ★★★
Contact: Mr & Mrs David or Rosemary Scott, Springfield, Spring Hill, Boldre, Lymington, Hampshire SO41 8NG
T: (01590) 672491
E: david.scott@nfdc.gov.uk

BONCHURCH
Isle of Wight

Ashcliff Holiday Apartments ★★★★
Contact: Mr & Mrs T J Foley, Ashcliff Holiday Apartments, The Pitts, Bonchurch, Ventnor, Isle of Wight PO38 1NT
T: (01983) 853919
E: ashcliff.iow@virgin.net

Fernwood Cottage ★
Contact: Ms Lisa Baskill, Home from Home Holidays, 31 Pier Street, Ventnor, Isle of Wight PO38 1SX
T: (01983) 854340
F: (01983) 855524

Halcyon ★★★
Contact: Mrs Rowena Reedman, Stoneleigh, Beggars Lane, Longworth, Abingdon, Oxfordshire OX13 5BL
T: (01865) 820744

Jasmine Cottage ★★★
Contact: Mrs Honor Vass, Island Cottage Holidays, The Old Vicarage, Kingston, Corfe Castle, Wareham, Dorset BH20 5LH
T: (01929) 480080
F: (01929) 481070
E: ich@cottageholidays.demon.co.uk
I: www.cottageholidays.dmon.co.uk.

Regent Court Holiday Bungalows ★★★
Contact: Mrs G M Smith, Windycroft, Park Road, Wootton Bridge, Ryde, Isle of Wight PO33 4RL
T: (01983) 883782
E: smith.windycroft@tinyworld.co.uk
I: www.cottageguide.co.uk/regentcourt

Uppermount ★★★★
Contact: Mrs Honor Vass, Island Cottage Holidays, The Old Vicarage, Kingston, Corfe Castle, Wareham, Dorset BH20 5LH
T: (01929) 480080
F: (01929) 481070
E: ich@cottageholidays.demon.co.uk
I: www.cottageholidays.demon.co.uk.

Woodlynch Holiday Flats ★★
Contact: Mr & Mrs C Tasker, Woodlynch Holiday Flats, Shore Road, Bonchurch, Ventnor, Isle of Wight PO38 1RF
T: (01983) 852513

Wyndcliffe Holiday Apartments ★★★★
Contact: Mrs Rosalind Young, Wyndcliffe Holiday Apartments, 16 Spring Gardens, Bonchurch, Ventnor, Isle of Wight PO38 1QX
T: (01983) 853458
F: (01983) 853272

BORDON
Hampshire

Tunford Cottage Lodge ★★
Contact: Mrs Anne Symon, Tunford Cottage Lodge, Tunford Cottage, Oakhanger, Bordon, Hampshire GU35 9JE
T: (01420) 473159 & 544288
E: symon@tunford.freeserve.co.uk

BORTHWOOD
Isle of Wight

Willow Cottage
Rating Applied For
Contact: Mrs Honor Vass, Island Cottage Holidays, The Old Vicarage, Kingston, Corfe Castle, Wareham, Dorset BH20 5LH
T: (01929) 480080
F: (01929) 480080
E: ich@cottageholidays.demon.co.uk
I: www.cottageholidays.demon.co.uk

BOSCOMBE
Dorset

Flat 2 St George's Mansions
Rating Applied For
Contact: Mr A Palmer, 9 Quail Close, Stratford-upon-Avon, Warwickshire CV37 9FF
T: 07711 802788

Lynton Holiday Apartments ★-★★★★
Contact: Mr Patrick Macdona, 85 Harewood Avenue, Bournemouth, Dorset BH7 6NN
T: (01202) 424075
F: (01202) 246079
E: info@macdona.com
I: www.macdona.com

BOULDNOR
Isle of Wight

Amulet ★★★★
Contact: Mr Colin Nolson, Holiday Homes Owners Services (West Wight), 18 Solent Hill, Freshwater, Isle of Wight PO40 9TG
T: (01983) 753423
F: (01983) 753423
E: holidayhomesiow@ic24.net

BOURNEMOUTH
Dorset

Amberwood Grange
Rating Applied For
Contact: Mr & Mrs A M Bayliss, Amberwood Grange, 30 Dean Park Road, Bournemouth, Dorset BH1 1HY
T: (01202) 290920
F: (01202) 319122
E: reservations@amberwood.demon.co.uk
I: www.amberwood.demon.co.uk

The Black House
Rating Applied For
Contact: Mr Andrew Brown, 51 Carbery Avenue, Southbourne, Bournemouth, Dorset BH6 3LN
T: (01202) 779488 & 07855 280191
F: (01202) 483555

2 Cedar Avenue ★★★
Contact: Country Hols ref : 6954 Sales, Country Holidays, Spring Mill, Earby, Barnoldswick, Lancashire BB18 6RN
T: 08700 723723
F: (01282) 844288
E: sales@ttgihg.co.uk
I: www.country-holidays.co.uk

Flat 2, 44A Seymour Road
★★★
Contact: Mrs Zandra Knight, 15
Torbay Road, Lower Parkstone,
Poole, Dorset BH14 9JQ
T: (01202) 718671 &
07973 884760
F: (01202) 718671
E: zandraknight@talk21.com

39 R L Stevenson Avenue
★★★
Contact: Mr Paul Dredge,
Rumsey Holiday Homes, 2 Banks
Road, Sandbanks, Poole, Dorset
BH13 7QD
T: (01202) 707357
F: (01202) 701955
E: info@rhh.org
I: www.rhh.org

Loxley ★★★★
Contact: Mrs Honor Vass, Island
Cottage Holidays, The Old
Vicarage, Kingston, Corfe Castle,
Wareham, Dorset BH20 5LH
T: (01929) 480080
F: (01929) 481070
E: ich@cottageholidays.demon.
co.uk
I: www.cottageholidays.dmon.
co.uk.

Romana Holiday Apartments
★-★★★
Contact: Mr Patrick Macdona,
85 Harewood Avenue,
Bournemouth, Dorset BH7 6NN
T: (01202) 424075
F: (01202) 264079
E: info@macdonna.com
I: www.macdona.com

Saltaire ★★★★
Contact: Mr D H Counter,
Saltaire, Sea Road, Southbourne,
Bournemouth, Dorset BH6 4BT
T: (01202) 420296 & 422875
F: (01202) 417660

Sea Road Holiday Apartments
★★★
Contact: Mr D L Jenkin, Sea
Road Holiday Apartments,
Excelsior House, 22A Sea Road,
Bournemouth, Dorset BH5 1DD
T: (01202) 721666
F: (01202) 721666

Shalbourne House Holiday
Flats ★★★
Contact: Mrs Margaret Stubbs,
83 Southbourne East Road,
Bournemouth, BH6 4DX
T: (01202) 432735 &
0797 9492252

Willow Mead ★★★
Contact: Mrs June Woods, 225
Broadway Lane, Throop,
Bournemouth, Dorset BH8 0AE
T: (01202) 519737
F: (01202) 533325
E: woodsjune@aol.com

Woodview Holiday Apartments
★★★★
Contact: Mr Shane Busby,
Woodview Holiday Apartments,
6 St Anthony's Road, Meyrick
Park, Bournemouth, Dorset
BH2 6PD
T: (01202) 290027
F: (01202) 295959
E: woodview.holidays@virgin.
net
I: www.SmoothHound.
co.uk/hotels/woodview.html

BOURTON
Dorset

Badger Cottage ★★★
Contact: Mr J Freeman, Bullpits,
Bourton, Gillingham, Dorset
SP8 5AX
T: (01747) 840084
F: (01747) 840302

Deer Cottage ★★★★
Contact: Mr J Freeman, Bullpits,
Bourton, Gillingham, Dorset
SP8 5AX
T: (01747) 840084
F: (01747) 840302

Dovehayes Cottage ★★★
Contact: Mr J Freeman, Bullpits,
Bourton, Gillingham, Dorset
SP8 5AX
T: (01747) 840084
F: (01747) 840302

The Honey House ★★★
Contact: Mr J Freeman, Bullpits,
Bourton, Gillingham, Dorset
SP8 5AX
T: (01747) 840084
F: (01747) 840302

Iron Cottage ★★★
Contact: Mr J Freeman, Bullpits,
Bourton, Gillingham, Dorset
SP8 5AX
T: (01747) 840084
F: (01747) 840302

The Malthouse
Rating Applied For
Contact: Mr P J Whaley, The
Malthouse, Bourton, Gillingham,
Dorset SP8 5DB
T: (01747) 840475

BOXFORD
Berkshire

Willows End ★★★★
Contact: Mr & Mrs D Squire,
Willows End, Westbrook,
Boxford, Newbury, Berkshire
RG20 8DN
T: (01488) 608506

BRADING
Isle of Wight

Moles Leap ★
Contact: Ms Lisa Baskill, Home
from Home Holidays, 31 Pier
Street, Ventnor, Isle of Wight
PO38 1SX
T: (01983) 854340
F: (01983) 855524

Morton Mews Self-Catering
Apartments ★★★★
Contact: Mr G S Redfern,
Morton Mews Self-Catering
Apartments, Morton Old Road,
Brading, Isle of Wight PO36 0EN
T: (01983) 406132
F: (01983) 408923
E: morton@isle-of-wight.uk.
com
I: www.mortonmews.com

Plovers ★★
Contact: Ms Lisa Baskill, Home
from Home Holidays, 31 Pier
Street, Ventnor, Isle of Wight
PO38 1SX
T: (01983) 854340
F: (01983) 855524

The Stables ★★★
Contact: Mrs Diane Morris, New
Farm, Coach Lane, Brading,
Sandown, Isle of Wight
PO36 0JQ
T: (01983) 407371
F: (01983) 401531
E: morris.rwbo@farmersweekly.
net

Thistle Waite ★★★★
Contact: Mrs Jan Hegarty, Rock
Cottage, Melville Street,
Sandown, Isle of Wight
PO36 9JW
T: (01983) 409707
E: jananddon-rock2@yahoo.
com

BRAISHFIELD
Hampshire

Meadow Cottage & Rosie's
Cottage ★★★
Contact: Mrs J W Graham, Farley
Farm Cottage Holidays, Farley
Farm, Braishfield, Romsey,
Hampshire SO51 0QP
T: (01794) 368265
F: (01794) 367847

BRANKSOME
Dorset

Danehurst Holiday Flat ★★★
Contact: Mr John Richings,
Danehurst Holiday Flat, 15
Brunstead Road, Branksome,
Poole, Dorset BH12 1EJ
T: (01202) 768632

BRANKSOME PARK
Dorset

Silwood ★★
Contact: Mrs M Matthews,
Silwood, 5 Forest Road,
Branksome Park, Poole, Dorset
BH13 6DQ
T: (01202) 761424
E: bowlers2@btinternet.com

Woodlea Holiday Flats ★★
Contact: Mr Michael Clarke,
Woodlea Holiday Flats, 24 Tower
Road, Branksome Park, Poole,
Dorset BH13 6HZ
T: (01202) 763692 &
07703 513063

BRIANTSPUDDLE
Dorset

The Stable Door Flat ★★★
Contact: Mr & Mrs R T Smith,
The Old School, Briantspuddle,
Dorchester, Dorset DT2 7HR
T: (01929) 471919
F: (01929) 471919
E: rtsmith121@aol.com
I: www.netoffice.
co.uk/stable-door

BRIGHSTONE
Isle of Wight

The Brew House ★★★★
Contact: Mrs Honor Vass, Island
Cottage Holidays, The Old
Vicarage, Kingston, Corfe Castle,
Wareham, Dorset BH20 5LH
T: (01929) 480080
F: (01929) 481070
E: ich@cottageholidays.demon.
co.uk.
I: www.cottageholidays.dmon.
co.uk.

Casses ★★★★
Contact: Mr & Mrs J K Nesbitt,
Kerrich House, Peartree Court,
Old Orchards, Lymington,
Hampshire SO41 3TF
T: (01590) 679601
E: jkn@casses.fsbusiness.co.uk

Chilton Farm Cottages ★★★
Contact: Mrs Susan Fisk, Chilton
Farm Cottages, Chilton Farm,
Chilton Lane, Brighstone, Isle of
Wight PO30 4DS
T: (01983) 740338
F: (01983) 741370
E: info@chiltonfarm.co.uk
I: www.chiltonfarm.co.uk

2 The Granary ★★★★
Contact: Mr & Mrs David &
Vanessa Lovett, 29 Bulls Lane,
North Mymms, Hatfield,
Hertfordshire AL9 7NY
T: (01707) 267976

Grange Farm ★★★
Contact: Mr D J Dungey, Grange
Farm, Grange Chine, Military
Road, Brighstone, Newport, Isle
of Wight PO30 4DA
T: (01983) 740296
F: (01983) 741233
E: grangefarm@brighstonebay.
fsnet.co.uk
I: www.brighstonebay.fsnet.
co.uk/main.htm

Leiston ★★
Contact: Mr A Hands, Riverdene,
Salisbury Road, Hoddesdon,
Hertfordshire EN11 0HX
T: (01992) 441095

Memories
Rating Applied For
Contact: Ms Lisa Baskill, Home
from Home Holidays, 31 Pier
Street, Ventnor, Isle of Wight
PO38 1SX
T: (01983) 854340
F: (01983) 855524

Pool Cottage
Rating Applied For
Contact: Mr John Russell,
Thorncross Farm, Brighstone,
Newport, Isle of Wight
PO30 4PN
T: (01983) 740291
F: (01983) 741408

Rose Cottage ★★★★★
Contact: Mr John Russell,
Thorncross Farm, Brighstone,
Newport, Isle of Wight
PO30 4PN
T: (01983) 740291
F: (01983) 741408

St Crispin ★★
Contact: Mr C Leake, 42
Sandown Park, Royal Tunbridge
Wells, Kent TN2 4RN
T: (01892) 822492

Stable Cottage ★★★
Contact: Mrs Honor Vass, Island
Cottage Holidays, The Old
Vicarage, Kingston, Corfe Castle,
Wareham, Dorset BH20 5LH
T: (01929) 480080
F: (01929) 481070
E: ich@cottageholidays.demon.
co.uk.
I: www.cottageholidays.dmon.
co.uk.

Establishments printed in blue have a detailed entry in this guide

BROCKENHURST
Hampshire

Gorse Cottage ★★★★★
Contact: Mr & Mrs J Bareford,
Whins, Hook Heath Avenue,
Woking, Surrey GU22 0HN
T: (01483) 760803
F: (01483) 764227
E: jon@bareford.com
I: www.bareford.com

Heywood House ★★★★
Contact: Adam Ogilvie, 4 Quay
Hill, Lymington, Hampshire
SO41 3AR
T: (01590) 679655
F: (01590) 670989
I: www.newforestcottages.co.uk

Setley Brake East ★★★
Contact: Mr John Gorton, Setley
Brake East, Tile Barn Lane,
Brockenhurst, Hampshire
SO42 7UE
T: (01590) 622160

2 Waters Green Court ★★★★
Contact: Mrs Sharon Hough, 5
Barton Drive, Knowle, Solihull,
West Midlands B93 0PE
T: (01564) 771582
F: (01564) 774733
E: sharon.hough@talk21.com

BROOK
Isle of Wight

Brook Farm Cottages ★★★
Contact: Mrs Sonia Fry, Brook
Farmhouse, Brook, Newport, Isle
of Wight PO30 4ES
T: (01983) 740387

Brookdown Cottage ★★
Contact: Mr Colin Nolson,
Holiday Homes Owners Services
(West Wight), 18 Solent Hill,
Freshwater, Isle of Wight
PO40 9TG
T: (01983) 753423
F: (01983) 753423
E: holidayhomesiow@ic24.net

1A Coastguard Cottage ★★★
Contact: Mr Colin Nolson,
Holiday Homes Owners Services
(West Wight), 18 Solent Hill,
Freshwater, Isle of Wight
PO40 9TG
T: (01983) 753423
F: (01983) 753423
E: holidayhomesiow@ic24.net

Moreys Lodge ★★★★
Contact: Mr Colin Nolson,
Holiday Homes Owners Services
(West Wight), 18 Solent Hill,
Freshwater, Isle of Wight
PO40 9TG
T: (01983) 753423
F: (01983) 753423
E: holidayhomesiow@ic24.net

Summerlea ★★★★
Contact: Mr Colin Nolson,
Holiday Homes Owners Services
(West Wight), 18 Solent Hill,
Freshwater, Isle of Wight
PO40 9TG
T: (01983) 753423
F: (01983) 753423
E: holidayhomesiow@ic24.net

BUCKINGHAM
Buckinghamshire

**The Courtyard Centre at
Barton Manor ★★★★**
Contact: Mrs Susannah Petszaft,
The Courtyard Centre at Barton
Manor, Barton Hartshorn,
Buckingham, Buckinghamshire
MK18 4JU
T: (01280) 848943
F: (01280) 847517
E: enquiries@bartonmanor.
co.uk
I: www.bartonmanor.co.uk

Huntsmill Holidays ★★★★
Contact: Mrs Fiona Hilsdon,
Huntsmill Holidays, Huntsmill
Farm, Shalstone, Buckingham,
Buckinghamshire MK18 5ND
T: (01280) 704852
F: (01280) 704852

BURFORD
Oxfordshire

**Bruern Stable Cottages
★★★★★**
Contact: Ms Frances Curtin, Red
Brick House, Bruern, Chipping
Norton, Oxfordshire OX7 6PY
T: (01993) 830415
F: (01993) 831750
E: judy.astor@easynet.co.uk
I: www.bruern.co.uk

Candlemas ★★★★
Contact: Manor Cottages,
Manor Cottages & Cotswolds
Retreats, Priory Mews, 33A
Priory Lane, Burford, Oxford,
West Oxfordshire OX18 4SG
T: (01993) 824252
F: (01993) 824443

The Mill at Burford ★★-★★★
Contact: Mr & Mrs Tony
Waddell, The Mill at Burford, 83
Witney Street, Burford,
Oxfordshire OX18 4RX
T: (01993) 822379 & 878151
F: (01993) 822759
E: cottages@themillatburford.
co.uk
I: www.themillatburford.co.uk

Park House Lodge ★★★
Contact: Mrs Therese Kennard,
Park House Lodge, Park House,
Witney Street, Burford, Oxford,
Oxfordshire OX18 4SN
T: (01993) 823460
F: (01993) 823460
E: dken768542@aol.com

Riders ★★★
Contact: Mrs Rebecca Burnside,
The Fullers Cottage, 23 Witney
Street, Burford, Oxford,
Oxfordshire OX18 4RX
T: (01993) 822878
F: (01993) 700366

BURGATE
Hampshire

Burgate Farmhouse ★★★
Contact: Mrs Christine Bennett,
Burgate Farmhouse, Burgate,
Fordingbridge, Hampshire
SP6 1LX
T: (01425) 655909
E: christine@burgatefarm.
freeserve.co.uk

BURITON
Hampshire

18 High Street ★★
Contact: Mr Michael Ayling, 14
High Street, Buriton, Petersfield,
Hampshire GU31 5RX
T: (01730) 260366
E: rosecottage18@hotmail.com

Rose Cottage ★★★★
Contact: Mr Michael Ayling, 14
High Street, Buriton, Petersfield,
Hampshire GU31 5RX
T: (01730) 260366
E: rosecottage18@hotmail.com
I: www.rosecot18.fsnet.co.uk

BURLEY
Hampshire

Brackenwood ★★★★★
Contact: Mrs Carole Stewart,
Great Wells House, Beechwood
Lane, Burley, Ringwood,
Hampshire BH24 4AS
T: (01425) 402302
F: (01425) 402302
E: greatwells@cs.com
I: www.smoothhound.
co.uk/hotels/greatwel

**Burbush Farm Cottages
★★★★★**
Contact: Mrs Carole Hayles,
Burbush Farm, Pound Lane,
Burley, Ringwood, Hampshire
BH24 4EF
T: (01425) 403238 &
07711 381924
F: (01425) 403238
E: burbush-farm@excite.com
I: www.burbush-farm.co.uk

**Cherry Tree Cottage
Rating Applied For**
Contact: Mr & Mrs J Pannell,
West Cliff Sands Hotel, 9 Priory
Road, West Cliff, Bournemouth,
Dorset BH2 5DF
T: (01202) 557013

**Honeysuckle Cottage
Rating Applied For**
Contact: Mrs Wanda Williams,
Oakapple Cottage, 5 Garden
Road, Burley, Ringwood,
Hampshire BH24 4EA
T: (01425) 402489
F: (01425) 402489
E: wanda@oakapplecottage.
fsnet.co.uk
I: www.oakapplecottage.fsnet.
co.uk

BURSLEDON
Hampshire

62 Goodlands Vale ★★★
Contact: Mr & Mrs Mike & Sue
Batley, Town or Country
Serviced Apartments & Houses,
60 Oxford Street, Southampton,
Hampshire SO14 3BL
T: (023) 8088 1000
F: (023) 8088 1010
E: town@interalpha.co.uk
I: www.intent.
co.uk/southampton/hotels/
townorc/index.htm

CADNAM
Hampshire

2 The Terrace ★★★
Contact: Ms Diane Spearing or
Ms C Roberts, Greenlees, 16
Woodlinken Drive, Verwood,
Dorset BH31 6BN
T: (01202) 820589
F: (01202) 820589

CALBOURNE
Isle of Wight

**Little Chessell Cottage
Rating Applied For**
Contact: Mrs Hilary Jane Spence,
Little Chessell, Calbourne,
Newport, Isle of Wight PO30 4JP
T: (01983) 531326

CANFORD CLIFFS
Dorset

Flat 2 Cliffside ★★★★
Contact: Mr Paul Dredge,
Rumsey Holiday Homes, 2 Banks
Road, Sandbanks, Poole, Dorset
BH13 7QD
T: (01202) 707357
F: (01202) 701955
E: unfo@rhh.org
I: www.rhh.org

Flat 4 Harbour Court ★★★★
Contact: Mr Paul Dredge,
Rumsey Holiday Homes, 2 Banks
Road, Sandbanks, Poole, Dorset
BH13 7QD
T: (01202) 707357
F: (01202) 701955
E: info@rhh.org
I: www.rhh.org

CARISBROOKE
Isle of Wight

Alvington Manor Farm ★★
Contact: Mrs Margaret Marsh,
Alvington Manor Farm,
Carisbrooke, Newport, Isle of
Wight PO30 5SP
T: (01983) 523463
F: (01983) 523463

Clatterford Coach House ★★
Contact: Ms Sylvia Clare,
Clatterford Coach House,
Clatterford House, Clatterford
Shute, Carisbrooke, Newport,
Isle of Wight PO30 1PD
T: (01983) 537338
E: sylvia.clare@btinternet.com
I: www.claritybooks.co.uk

Dairy Cottage ★★★★
Contact: Mrs E R Yapp,
Luckington Farm, Bowcombe
Road, Carisbrooke, Newport, Isle
of Wight PO30 3HT
T: (01983) 822951

**Froglands Farm
★★★-★★★★**
Contact: Mrs L J Dungey,
Froglands Farm, Carisbrooke,
Newport, Isle of Wight
PO30 3DU
T: (01983) 821027

CASTLETHORPE
Buckinghamshire

**Balney Grounds
★★★-★★★★**
Contact: Mrs Mary Stacey,
Balney Grounds, Home Farm,
Hanslope Road, Castlethorpe,
Milton Keynes, Buckinghamshire
MK19 7HD
T: (01908) 510208
F: (01908) 516119
E: mary.stacey@tesco.net
I: www.lets-stay-mk.co.uk

CAVERSFIELD
Oxfordshire
Grooms Cottage ★★★
Contact: Mr Albert Phipps, Grooms Cottage, Home Farm, Caversfield, Bicester, Oxfordshire OX6 9TG
T: (01869) 249307
F: (01869) 246739

CHADLINGTON
Oxfordshire
Petrie Cottage ★★★★
Contact: Ms Catherine Hillbourne, Chadlington House, Chapel Road, Chadlington, Chipping Norton, Oxfordshire OX7 3LZ
T: (01608) 676437
F: (01608) 676437
E: info@chadlingtonhouse.com
I: www.holiday-rentals.com

CHALE
Isle of Wight
Atherfield Green Farm Holiday Cottages★★★★
Contact: A Jupe, The Laurels, High Street, Newchurch, Sandown, Isle of Wight PO36 0NJ
T: (01983) 867613
F: (01983) 868214
E: alistair.jupe@btinternet.com

The Cart House ★★★★★
Contact: Mrs Caroline Smith, Gotten Manor, Gotten Lane, Chale, Ventnor, Isle of Wight PO38 2HQ
T: (01983) 551368
F: 0870 136 9453
E: caroline@gottenmanor.co.uk
I: www.gottenmanor.co.uk

Chapel Cottage
Rating Applied For
Contact: Ms Lisa Baskill, Home from Home Holidays, 31 Pier Street, Ventnor, Isle of Wight PO38 1SX
T: (01983) 854340
F: (01983) 855524

The Old Rectory ★★★★
Contact: Mrs Mary Coward, The Old Rectory, Chale Street, Chale, Ventnor, Isle of Wight PO38 2HE
T: (01983) 551393
I: www.froglet.demon.co.uk/holiday/wight.htm

CHALE GREEN
Isle of Wight
Greenedge ★★★
Contact: Mrs Jacqueline Miles, Greenedge, Chale Green, Ventnor, Isle of Wight PO38 2JR
T: (01983) 551419

North Appleford Cottages ★★
Contact: Mrs Jan Clarke, Great Appleford Farm, Whitwell, Ventnor, Isle of Wight PO38 2PH
T: (01983) 551227

CHALFONT ST GILES
Buckinghamshire
Studio Flat at Applewood ★★★
Contact: Mr & Mrs J E Newcombe, Applewood, Mill Lane, Chalfont St Giles, Buckinghamshire HP8 4NX
T: (01494) 873343
E: JnA@stgiles98.fsnet.co.uk

CHANDLERS FORD
Hampshire
Rawa ★★★★
Contact: Mrs Mary Forshaw, Rawa, 24 Baddesley Road, Chandlers Ford, Eastleigh, Hampshire SO53 5NG
T: (023) 8026 3043 &
07703 137387
F: (023) 8027 0978
E: david.forshawl@ntlworld.com

CHARLBURY
Oxfordshire
Banbury Hill Farm Cottages ★★★
Contact: Mrs Angela Widdows, Banbury Hill Farm, Charlbury, Oxford, Oxfordshire OX7 3JH
T: (01608) 810314
F: (01608) 811891
E: angelawiddows@gfwiddowsf9.co.uk
I: www.charlburyoxfordaccom.co.uk

26 The Green ★★★
Contact: Mrs Katharine Brown, Hill Grove Farm, Crawley Road, Minster Lovell, Oxford, Oxfordshire OX8 5NA
T: (01993) 703120
F: (01993) 700528
E: kbrown@eggconnect.net

CHILD OKEFORD
Dorset
Gold Hill Organic Farm ★★
Contact: Mr D N Cross, Gold Hill Organic Farm, Child Okeford, Blandford Forum, Dorset DT11 8HP
T: (01258) 860293

CHILLERTON
Isle of Wight
Roslin Farm Annexe ★★
Contact: Mrs Evelyn Murdoch, Roslin Farm Annexe, Roslin, Chillerton, Newport, Isle of Wight PO30 3HG
T: (01983) 721662

The Willows
Rating Applied For
Contact: Mrs Muriel Burns, Dove Cottage, Brook Lane, Chillerton, Newport, Isle of Wight PO30 3EW
T: (01983) 721630

CHILWORTH
Hampshire
Rose Cottage ★★★
Contact: Mrs Gwendolyn Young, 61 Clifton Road, Regents Park, Southampton, Hampshire SO15 4GY
T: (023) 8077 1729

CHIPPING NORTON
Oxfordshire
Compton House ★★★★
Contact: Mrs J Roach, Compton House, 71 Burford Road, Chipping Norton, Oxfordshire OX7 5EE
T: (01608) 642964 & 644575
F: (01608) 642964
E: mark@questfs.co.uk

Heath Farm Holiday Cottages
★★★★
Contact: Mr & Mrs David Barbour, Heath Farm Holiday Cottages, Heath Farm, Swerford, Chipping Norton, Oxfordshire OX7 4BN
T: (01608) 683270 & 683204
F: (01608) 683222
E: barbours@heathfarm.com
I: www.healthfarm.com

Stone Farm Cottage ★★★
Contact: Mrs J S Parris, Stone Farm Cottage, Stone Farm, Lidstone, Chipping Norton, Oxfordshire OX7 4HL
T: (01608) 677088

CHRISTCHURCH
Dorset
Avon Reach ★★★★
Contact: Mrs M Wynne, 15 Halls Farm Close, Winchester, Hampshire SO22 6RE
T: (01962) 883454
F: (01962) 884486

Burridge Lettings ★★-★★★
Contact: Mr Mark Pope, Burridge Lettings, 3 Mudeford, Christchurch, Dorset BH23 3NQ
T: (01202) 481810
F: (01202) 476677
E: enquiries@burridge-property.co.uk
I: www.burridge-property.co.uk

The Causeway ★-★★
Contact: Mrs L Tomkinson, The Causeway, 32-34 Stanpit, Mudeford, Christchurch, Dorset BH23 3LZ
T: (01202) 470149 &
07979 607993
F: (01202) 477558
E: thecauseway@nascr.net

The Holiday Cottage ★★
Contact: Mr & Mrs John Brewer, 61 Southwick Road, Bournemouth, Dorset BH6 5PR
T: (01202) 420673

Mallard Cottage ★★★
Contact: Mr & Mrs David Pearce, Swan Lodge, 17 Willow Way, Christchurch, Dorset BH23 1JJ
T: (01202) 480805
F: (01202) 480805

Riverbank Holidays ★★★
Contact: Mr & Mrs E G Gibson, Riverbank Holidays, Toad Hall, 8 Willow Way, Christchurch, Dorset BH23 1JJ
T: (01202) 477813

CHURCHILL
Oxfordshire
The Little Cottage ★★★
Contact: Mr David Sheppard, Gables Cottage, Junction Road, Churchill, Chipping Norton, Oxfordshire OX7 6NW
T: (01608) 658674
E: enquiries@littlecottage.co.uk
I: www.littlecottage.co.uk

CLANFIELD
Oxfordshire
Grafton Manor Wing ★★★
Contact: Ms Sandra Eddolls, Manor Farm, Grafton, Clanfield, Bampton, Oxfordshire OX18 2RY
T: (01367) 810237

COLWELL BAY
Isle of Wight
Chalet 14 Island View Chalet Park ★
Contact: Ms Dorothea Lutticke, Unterer Hasselbach 14, 34359 Reinhardshagen, Germany
T: 0049 5544 7328 & 0049 177 2425679
F: 0049 5544 7328
E: dorothealutticke@hotmail.com

Honeysuckle Chalet ★
Contact: Mr Colin Nolson, Holiday Homes Owners Services (West Wight), 18 Solent Hill, Freshwater, Isle of Wight PO40 9TG
T: (01983) 753423
F: (01983) 753423
E: holidayhomesiow@ic24.net

Solent Heights ★★★
Contact: Mrs Honor Vass, Island Cottage Holidays, The Old Vicarage, Kingston, Corfe Castle, Wareham, Dorset BH20 5LH
T: (01929) 480080
F: (01929) 481070
E: ich@cottageholidays.demon.co.uk.
I: www.cottageholidays.demon.co.uk

COMPTON ABBAS
Dorset
The Smithy ★★★★
Contact: Mrs L Kerridge, The Old Forge, Fanners Yard, Compton Abbas, Shaftesbury, Dorset SP7 0NQ
T: (01747) 811881
F: (01747) 811881
E: theoldforge@hotmail.com
I: www.smoothhound.co.uk

CORFE CASTLE
Dorset
Heatherlands ★★
Contact: Mr & Mrs John Shelton, Brinkhill, Winton Close, Andover Road, Winchester, Hampshire SO22 6AB
T: (01962) 856617
F: (01962) 856617

Kingston Country Courtyard ★★★
Contact: Mrs Ann Fry, Kingston Country Courtyard, Greystone Court, Kingston, Corfe Castle, Wareham, Dorset BH20 5LR
T: (01929) 481066
F: (01929) 481256
E: annfry@kingstoncountrycourtyard.co.uk
I: www.kingstoncountrycourtyard.co.uk

Scoles Manor ★★★★
Contact: Mr & Mrs Peter Bell, Scoles Manor, Kingston, Corfe Castle, Dorset BH20 5LG
T: (01929) 480312
F: (01929) 481237
E: peter@scoles.co.uk
I: www.scoles.co.uk

COWES
Isle of Wight

10A & 11A High Street ★★★
Contact: Ms Sarah Marshall, 238
Park Road, Cowes, Isle of Wight
PO31 7NQ
T: (01983) 291369 &
07802 269221
F: (01983) 291369
E: sarahj.marshall@virgin.net

Apartment Marivent ★★★
Contact: Mr & Mrs J Segui,
Apartment Marivent, 75 High
Street, Cowes, Isle of Wight
PO31 7AJ
T: (01983) 292148
F: (01983) 280174
E: julia.segui@talk21.com
I: www.marivent.co.uk

Farthings ★★★
Contact: Mr Michael Rabjohns,
Firestone Cottage, Kite Hill,
Wootton Bridge, Ryde, Isle of
Wight PO33 4LE
T: (01983) 884122

Florist House ★★
Contact: Mrs Deborah Hall,
Beresford, 2 Shooters Hill,
Cowes, Isle of Wight PO31 7BE
T: (01983) 293863
F: (01983) 293863
E: floristhouse@sailing.co.uk
I: www.beresfordsbarbershop.
co.uk./accommodation.

Georgette Cottage ★★
Contact: Mrs M T Pallett, 22
Ambleside Crescent, Enfield,
Middlesex EN3 7LZ
T: (020) 8292 0418
F: (020) 8292 0418
E: georgettecottage@
mailexcite.com

Greenside ★★★★
Contact: Mrs Honor Vass, Island
Cottage Holidays, The Old
Vicarage, Isle of Wight,
Wareham, Dorset BH20 5LH
T: (01929) 480080
F: (01929) 481070
E: ich@cottageholidays.demon.
co.uk
I: www.cottageholidays.demon.
co.uk

110 Gurnard Pines ★★
Contact: Mr Graham Reed, 21
Roull Road, Corstorphine,
Edinburgh, EH12 7JW
T: (0131) 334 9184 &
07966 726389
E: reedg@callnetuk.com
I: www.callnetuk.
com/home/reedg

127 Gurnard Pines ★★
Contact: Mrs Karin Wales,
Hazelmount Lodge, Church
Road, Binstead, Ryde, Isle of
Wight PO33 3TB
T: (01983) 567484 &
07884 364717
E: karin-wales@hotmail.com

Halyards ★★★
Contact: Mrs Susan Gibbs,
Caulkhead Properties, 68
Worsley Road, Gurnard, Cowes,
Isle of Wight PO31 8JX
T: (01983) 298704 &
07970 415633
F: (01983) 290300
E: sgibbs4870@aol.com

12 Harbour View ★★★★
Contact: Mrs Suzanne Thomas,
69 Airedale Avenue, Chiswick,
London W4 2NN
T: (020) 8994 0856
F: (020) 8994 0856

The Hut ★
Contact: Ms Mary Mcbride,
Furzyhurst Farmhouse, 69
Oxford Street, Northwood,
Cowes, Isle of Wight PO31 8PT
T: (01983) 292513 &
07930 942692
F: (01983) 294802
E: marymcbrideuk@yahoo.co.uk
I: www.geocities.
com/furzyhurst/hut/

1 Middleton Terrace ★★★
Contact: Mrs Sarah Cotton, 49
Linden Road, Newport, Isle of
Wight PO30 1RJ
T: (01983) 523648

78 Park Road ★★★
Contact: Mrs Patricia Rooke, 202
Park Road, Cowes, Isle of Wight
PO31 7NE
T: (01983) 298976
E: trish.rooke@virgin.net
I: www.zenalt.
com/cowesholidayhomes

41 Pelham Road ★★★
Contact: Mrs Christine Hunter,
10 Lark Close, Kempshott,
Basingstoke, Hampshire
RG22 5PX
T: (01256) 327096 &
07971 818153

**Point House, Point Quay &
Midpoint ★★★**
Contact: County Hols Ref,
Country Holidays, Spring Hill,
Earby, Barnoldswick, Lancashire
BB94 0AA
T: 08700 723723
F: (01282) 844288
E: sales@ttging.co.uk
I: www.country-holidays.co.uk

**2 South Road
Rating Applied For**
Contact: Mr Andrew Davies, 25A
Church Street, Romsey,
Hampshire SO51 8BT
T: 07867 511265

Thorness Cross Farm ★★
Contact: Mr Albert Cosh,
Thorness Cross Farm, Thorness,
Cowes, Isle of Wight PO31 8NQ
T: (01983) 524365

64 York Street ★★
Contact: Mrs Patricia Rooke, 202
Park Road, Cowes, Isle of Wight
PO31 7NE
T: (01983) 298976
E: trish.rooke@virgin.net
I: www.seault.
com/cowesholidayhomes

DENMEAD
Hampshire

Flint Cottage ★★★
Contact: Mr & Mrs John & Sheila
Knight, High Trees, Ashling
Close, Denmead, Waterlooville,
Hampshire PO7 6NQ
T: (023) 9226 6345
E: sheila@flintcottagehants.
fsnet.co.uk

DINTON
Buckinghamshire

Wallace Farm Cottages ★★
Contact: Mrs J M Cook, Wallace
Farm, Dinton, Aylesbury,
Buckinghamshire HP17 8UF
T: (01296) 748660
F: (01296) 748851
E: jackiecook@wallacefarm.
freeserve.co.uk
I: www.country-accom.co.uk

DOWNEND
Isle of Wight

**Lilac Cottage & The Old Barn
★★–★★★**
Contact: Mrs Anne Kennerley,
Duxmore Farm, Downend,
Newport, Isle of Wight
PO30 2NZ
T: (01983) 883993

EARLEY
Berkshire

Bulmershe Court ★★★
Contact: Mrs Lesley Gosden, The
University of Reading
Residential & Catering Services,
Palmer Building, Whiteknights,
Reading, Berkshire RG6 6AH
T: (0118) 931 8427
F: (0118) 931 4714
I: www.reading.ac.uk/confoff

EAST BOLDRE
Hampshire

Greycott ★★
Contact: Ms Catherine Gray, The
Bungalow, Main Road, East
Boldre, Brockenhurst, Hampshire
SO42 7WL
T: (01590) 612162
F: (01590) 612162

EAST CHALDON
Dorset

Kay's Cottage ★★★
Contact: Mrs Noel Hosford,
Heart of Dorset, Mill Cottage,
Bramblecombe Farm, Melcombe
Bingham, Dorchester, Dorset
DT2 7QA
T: (01258) 880248
F: (01258) 880248
E: noelhosford@hotmail.com
I: www.heartofdorset.easynet.
co.uk/

EAST HAGBOURNE
Oxfordshire

The Oast House ★★★★
Contact: Mr R W Harries, Manor
Farm, East Hagbourne, Didcot,
Oxfordshire OX11 9ND
T: (01235) 815005

EAST ORCHARD
Dorset

Bowling Green Farm ★
Contact: Mrs Susan Benefer,
Bowling Green Farm, East
Orchard, Shaftesbury, Dorset
SP7 0LG
T: (01747) 811588
F: (01747) 811588

EMSWORTH
Hampshire

Hermitage Cottage ★★★
Contact: Mrs Sarah Evans,
Kimlas, School Lane, Nutbourne,
Chichester, West Sussex
PO18 8RZ
T: (01243) 372554
F: (01243) 370193
E: sally@seeksys.demon.co.uk
I: www.seeksys.demon.
co.uk/cottage.html

2 Heron Quay ★★★
Contact: Mrs L M Sprules, 16
Godstone Road, Old Oxted,
Oxted, Surrey RH8 9JS
T: (01883) 732144
F: (01883) 722510

Westview Holiday Flat ★★★
Contact: Mrs Julia Oakley, 61
Bath Road, Emsworth,
Hampshire PO10 7ES
T: (01243) 373002

EPWELL
Oxfordshire

**The Retreat of Church Farm
★★★★**
Contact: Mrs Dawn Castle,
Church Farm, Epwell, Banbury,
Oxfordshire OX15 6LD
T: (01295) 788473

EVERTON
Hampshire

Gothic Cottage ★★★
Contact: Mrs Mary Brockett, The
Old Boathouse, 13 Newlands
Manor, Everton, Lymington,
Hampshire SO41 0JH
T: (01590) 645941

10 Newlands Manor ★★★
Contact: Mr & Mrs G G Rhoden,
10 Newlands Manor, Everton,
Lymington, Hampshire SO41 0JH
T: (01590) 642830
F: (01590) 642830
E: newlandsmanor@eurolink.
ltd.net

Wheatley Cottage ★★★
Contact: Mrs J S Taylor, Three
Corners, Centre Lane, Everton,
Lymington, Hampshire SO41 0JP
T: (01590) 645217

EXTON
Hampshire

**Beacon Hill Farm Cottages
★★★★**
Contact: Mrs J Smith, The Farm
Office Manor Farm, Beacon Hill
Lane, Warnford Road, Exton,
Southampton, Hampshire
SO32 3NW
T: (01730) 829724
F: (01730) 829833
E: chris.martin@farmline.com
I: www.beaconhillcottages.co.uk

FAREHAM
Hampshire

Manor Croft ★★★★
Contact: Mr A Thomson, Manor
Croft Clinic Ltd, Manor Croft,
Church Path, Fareham,
Hampshire PO16 7DT
T: (01329) 280750
F: (01329) 280750
E: accom@btconnect.com
I: www.manor-croft-health.
co.uk

FARINGDON
Oxfordshire

Coxwell House ★★★★
Contact: Mrs EAG Crossley
Cooke, Little Coxwell House,
Little Coxwell, Faringdon,
Oxfordshire SN7 7LP
T: (01367) 241240
F: (01367) 240911
E: elspeth@coxwell.u-net.com
I: www.farm-holidays.co.uk

FIFEHEAD MAGDALEN
Dorset

**Stable Cottage, Shire Cottage
& Granary Cottage
★★★–★★★★**
Contact: Mrs R Trevor, Middle
Farm, Fifehead Magdalen,
Gillingham, Dorset SP8 5RR
T: (01258) 820220 & 821074
F: (01258) 820220

FIFEHEAD ST QUINTON
Dorset

**Lower Fifehead Farm Cottage
★★**
Contact: Mrs J M Miller, Lower
Fifehead Farm Cottage, Lower
Fifehead Farm, Fifehead St
Quinton, Sturminster Newton,
Dorset DT10 2AP
T: (01258) 817335
F: (01258) 817335

FIFIELD
Oxfordshire

Peacocks ★★★
Contact: Mrs Rosemary
Alexander, Peacocks, The Folly,
Fifield, Chipping Norton,
Oxfordshire OX7 6HW
T: (01993) 830484
F: (01993) 832022
E: rosemaryalex@onetel.co.uk

FILKINS
Oxfordshire

**Sunnyside Garden Cottage
★★★★**
Contact: Mrs Marjorie Burrell,
Sunnyside Garden Cottage,
Broughton Poggs, Filkins,
Lechlade, Gloucestershire
GL7 3JH
T: (01367) 860047
F: (01367) 860146
E: info@cotswold-cottage.com

FINSTOCK
Oxfordshire

Wychwood ★★
Contact: Mrs Bodil Grain, 40
School Road, Finstock, Oxford,
Oxfordshire OX7 3DJ
T: (01993) 868249
E: bgrain@wychwoodcottage.
co.uk
I: www.wychwoodcottage.co.uk

FORDINGBRIDGE
Hampshire

**Burgate Manor Farm Holidays
★★★★**
Contact: Mrs Bridget Stallard,
Burgate Manor Farm Holidays,
Burgate Manor Farm,
Fordingbridge, Hampshire
SP6 1LX
T: (01425) 653908
F: (01425) 653908
E: holidays@newforestcottages.
com
I: www.newforestcottages.com

Garden Cottage ★★★
Contact: Mr & Mrs A Holmes,
The Dial House, Rockbourne,
Fordingbridge, Hampshire
SP6 3NA
T: (01725) 518083
F: (01725) 518083
E: rockbourneprop@freeuk.com
I: www.rockbourne.4dw.com

Glencairn ★★★
Contact: Mrs C Tiller, 2 Fernlea,
Sandleheath, Fordingbridge,
Hampshire SP6 1PN
T: (01425) 652506

**Redbrook Farm Cottage
Rating Applied For**
Contact: Mrs Madge Bastable,
Redbrook Farm, Fordingbridge,
Hampshire SP6 2ET
T: (01425) 653208

**5 Riverside Place
Rating Applied For**
Contact: Ms Lindsay Burgess, 71
Christchurch Road, Ringwood,
Hampshire BH24 1DH
T: (01425) 476106
F: (01425) 479097

Twin Oaks ★
Contact: Mr John Leach,
Newton, Whiteparish, Salisbury,
Wilts SP5 2QQ
T: (01794) 884428
F: (01794) 884428
I: www.independent-traveler.
com/UK/THC

Warren Park Farm ★★–★★★
Contact: Mrs V A Huzzey,
Warren Park Farm, Alderholt,
Fordingbridge, Hampshire
SP6 3DE
T: (01425) 653340
F: (01425) 653340
E: jvhuzzey@farmersweekly.net

FORDWELLS
Oxfordshire

**Forge Cottage & Little Forge
Cottage★★–★★★**
Contact: Country Hols
REF;50244,50245, Country
Holidays, Spring Mill, Earby,
Barnoldswick, Lancashire
BB94 0AA
T: 08700 723723
F: (01282) 844288
E: sales@ttgihg.co.uk
I: www.country-holidays.co.uk

FRESHWATER
Isle of Wight

103 Brambles Chine ★★
Contact: The Lettings
Administrator, Linstone Chine
Holiday Services Ltd, Brambles
Office, Monks Lane, Freshwater,
Isle of Wight PO40 9NQ
T: (01983) 755933 & 752015
F: (01983) 752015

107 Brambles Chine ★★★
Contact: The Lettings
Administrator, Linstone Chine
Holiday Services Ltd, Brambles
Office, Monks Lane, Freshwater,
Isle of Wight PO40 9NQ
T: (01983) 755933 & 752015
F: (01983) 752015

110 Brambles Chine ★★
Contact: The Lettings
Administrator, Linstone Chine
Holiday Services Ltd, Brambles
Office, Monks Lane, Freshwater,
Isle of Wight PO40 9NQ
T: (01983) 755933 & 752015
F: (01983) 752015

160 Brambles Chine ★★
Contact: The Lettings
Administrator, Linstone Chine
Holiday Services Ltd, Brambles
Office, Monks Lane, Freshwater,
Isle of Wight PO40 9NQ
T: (01983) 755933 & 752015
F: (01983) 752015

168 Brambles Chine ★★
Contact: Mr Colin Nolson,
Holiday Homes Owners Services
(West Wight), 18 Solent Hill,
Freshwater, Isle of Wight
PO40 9TG
T: (01983) 753423
F: (01983) 753423
E: holidayhomesiow@ic24.net

176 Brambles Chine ★★
Contact: Mr Neil Andrew Cain,
18 Osborn Gardens, Mill Hill
East, London NW7 1DY
T: (020) 8346 6308 & 7551 5532

197 Brambles Chine ★★
Contact: The Lettings
Administrator, Linstone Chine
Holiday Services Ltd, Brambles
Office, Monks Lane, Freshwater,
Isle of Wight PO40 9NQ
T: (01983) 755933 & 752015
F: (01983) 752015

203 Brambles Chine ★★★
Contact: Mr Colin Nolson,
Holiday Homes Owners Services
(West Wight), 18 Solent Hill,
Freshwater, Isle of Wight
PO40 9TG
T: (01983) 753423
F: (01983) 753423
E: holidayhomesiow@ic24.net

222 Brambles Chine ★★
Contact: The Lettings
Administrator, Linstone Chine
Holiday Services Ltd, Brambles
Office, Monks Lane, Freshwater,
Isle of Wight PO40 9NQ
T: (01983) 755933 & 752015
F: (01983) 752015

233 Brambles Chine ★★
Contact: The Lettings
Administrator, Linstone Chine
Holiday Services Ltd, Brambles
Office, Monks Lane, Freshwater,
Isle of Wight PO40 9NQ
T: (01983) 755933 & 752015
F: (01983) 752015

238 Brambles Chine ★★
Contact: Mr Colin Nolson,
Holiday Homes Owners Services
(West Wight), 18 Solent Hill,
Freshwater, Isle of Wight
PO40 9TG
T: (01983) 753423
F: (01983) 753423
E: holidayhomesiow@ic24.net

42 Brambles Chine ★
Contact: Mr Colin Nolson,
Holiday Homes Owners Services
(West Wight), 18 Solent Hill,
Freshwater, Isle of Wight
PO40 9TG
T: (01983) 753423
F: (01983) 753423
E: holidayhomesiow@ic24.net

60 Brambles Chine ★★
Contact: The Lettings
Administrator, Linstone Chine
Holiday Services Ltd, Brambles
Office, Monks Lane, Freshwater,
Isle of Wight PO40 9NQ
T: (01983) 755933 & 752015
F: (01983) 752015

64 Brambles Chine ★★★
Contact: The Lettings
Administrator, Linstone Chine
Holiday Services Ltd, Brambles
Office, Monks Lane, Freshwater,
Isle of Wight PO40 9NQ
T: (01983) 755933 & 752015
F: (01983) 752015

65 Brambles Chine ★★★★
Contact: The Lettings
Administrator, Linstone Chine
Holiday Services Ltd, Brambles
Office, Monks Lane, Freshwater,
Isle of Wight PO40 9NQ
T: (01983) 755933 & 752015
F: (01983) 752015

67 Brambles Chine ★★
Contact: The Lettings
Administrator, Linstone Chine
Holiday Services Ltd, Brambles
Office, Monks Lane, Freshwater,
Isle of Wight PO40 9NQ
T: (01983) 755933 & 752015
F: (01983) 752015

73 Brambles Chine ★★
Contact: The Lettings
Administrator, Linstone Chine
Holiday Services Ltd, Brambles
Office, Monks Lane, Freshwater,
Isle of Wight PO40 9NQ
T: (01983) 755933 & 752015
F: (01983) 752015

87 Brambles Chine ★★
Contact: The Lettings
Administrator, Linstone Chine
Holiday Services Ltd, Brambles
Office, Monks Lane, Freshwater,
Isle of Wight PO40 9NQ
T: (01983) 755933 & 752015
F: (01983) 752015

91 Brambles Chine ★★
Contact: The Lettings
Administrator, Linstone Chine
Holiday Services Ltd, Brambles
Office, Monks Lane, Freshwater,
Isle of Wight PO40 9NQ
T: (01983) 755933 & 752015
F: (01983) 752015

92 Brambles Chine ★★
Contact: The Lettings
Administrator, Linstone Chine
Holiday Services Ltd, Brambles
Office, Monks Lane, Freshwater,
Isle of Wight PO40 9NQ
T: (01983) 755933 & 752015
F: (01983) 752015

Brambles Farm ★★★
Contact: Mrs P Osman, Brambles
Farm, Colwell Road, Freshwater,
Isle of Wight PO40 9SS
T: (01983) 753270
F: (01983) 753270

Establishments printed in blue have a detailed entry in this guide

1 Cliff End ★★
Contact: The Lettings
Administrator, Linstone Chine
Holiday Services Ltd, Brambles
Office, Monks Lane, Freshwater,
Isle of Wight PO40 9NQ
T: (01983) 755933 & 752015
F: (01983) 752015

12A Cliff End ★★
Contact: The Lettings
Administrator, Linstone Chine
Holiday Services Ltd, Brambles
Office, Monks Lane, Freshwater,
Isle of Wight PO40 9NQ
T: (01983) 755933 & 752015
F: (01983) 752015

16 Cliff End ★★
Contact: The Lettings
Administrator, Linstone Chine
Holiday Services Ltd, Brambles
Office, Monks Lane, Freshwater,
Isle of Wight PO40 9NQ
T: (01983) 755933 & 752015
F: (01983) 752015

20 Cliff End ★★
Contact: The Lettings
Administrator, Linstone Chine
Holiday Services Ltd, Brambles
Office, Monks Lane, Freshwater,
Isle of Wight PO40 9NQ
T: (01983) 755933 & 752015
F: (01983) 752015

26 Cliff End ★★
Contact: The Lettings
Administrator, Linstone Chine
Holiday Services Ltd, Brambles
Office, Monks Lane, Freshwater,
Isle of Wight PO40 9NQ
T: (01983) 755933 & 752015
F: (01983) 752015

30 Cliff End ★★
Contact: Mr Colin Nolson,
Holiday Homes Owners Services
(West Wight), 18 Solent Hill,
Freshwater, Isle of Wight
PO40 9TG
T: (01983) 753423
F: (01983) 753423
E: holidayhomesiow@ic24.net

32 Cliff End ★★
Contact: Mr Colin Nolson,
Holiday Homes Owners Services
(West Wight), 18 Solent Hill,
Freshwater, Isle of Wight
PO40 9TG
T: (01983) 753423
F: (01983) 753423
E: holidayhomesiow@ic24.net

48 Cliff End ★★
Contact: Mr Colin Nolson,
Holiday Homes Owners Services
(West Wight), 18 Solent Hill,
Freshwater, Isle of Wight
PO40 9TG
T: (01983) 753423
F: (01983) 753423
E: holidayhomesiow@ic24.net

65 Cliff End ★★
Contact: Mrs Helen Long,
Windrush, Wellow, Yarmouth,
Isle of Wight PO41 0TA
T: (01983) 761506
E: Hugh7@Bushinternet.com

70 Cliff End ★★
Contact: Mr R Armour,
Glebelands, Afton Road,
Freshwater, Isle of Wight
PO40 9TP
T: (01983) 754453

Finsbury Cottage ★★★
Contact: Mr Colin Nolson,
Holiday Homes Owners Services
(West Wight), 18 Solent Hill,
Freshwater, Isle of Wight
PO40 9TG
T: (01983) 753423
F: (01983) 753423
E: holidayhomesiow@ic24.net

The Flat, Rose Cottage ★★
Contact: Mr Colin Nolson,
Holiday Homes Owners Services
(West Wight), 18 Solent Hill,
Freshwater, Isle of Wight
PO40 9TG
T: (01983) 753423
F: (01983) 753423
E: holidayhomesiow@ic24.net

Freshfields ★★★
Contact: Mr & Mrs D Barry, 26
Calbourne Road, Carisbrooke,
Newport, Isle of Wight
PO30 5AP
T: (01983) 529901

1 London House Cottages ★★
Contact: Mrs Jill Wareham,
Wellgrounds, Moor Lane,
Brighstone, Newport, Isle of
Wight PO30 4DL
T: (01983) 741068
F: (01983) 741068
E: jill_wareham@hotmail.com

St Martins Holiday Flats ★★
Contact: Mr & Mrs John Finch,
St Martins Holiday Flats, Afton
Down, Freshwater Bay,
Freshwater, Isle of Wight
PO40 9TY
T: (01983) 752389

Sunnyside ★★
Contact: Mrs M Lavington, West
Horton Farm, Bishopstoke,
Eastleigh, Hampshire SO50 8LT
T: (023) 8069 2783

Sunsets ★★
Contact: The Lettings
Administrator, Linstone Chine
Holiday Services Ltd, Brambles
Office, Monks Lane, Freshwater,
Isle of Wight PO40 9NQ
T: (01983) 755933 & 752015
F: (01983) 752015

Tops ★★★
Contact: Mr Colin Nolson,
Holiday Homes Owners Services
(West Wight), 18 Solent Hill,
Freshwater, Isle of Wight
PO40 9TG
T: (01983) 753423
F: (01983) 753423
E: holidayhomesiow@ic24.net

FRESHWATER BAY
Isle of Wight

Links View ★★★
Contact: Mr Colin Nolson,
Holiday Homes Owners Services
(West Wight), 18 Solent Hill,
Freshwater, Isle of Wight
PO40 9TG
T: (01983) 753423
F: (01983) 753423
E: holidayhomesiow@ic24.net

FRITHAM
Hampshire

Valletta House ★★★★
Contact: Mrs Pauline McCulloch,
The Royal Oak, Fritham,
Lyndhurst, Hampshire SO43 7HJ
T: (023) 8081 2606
F: (023) 8081 4066

GATCOMBE
Isle of Wight

**The Dairy, the Parlour & the
Stable ★★★★**
Contact: Mrs Diane Harvey,
Newbarn Farm, Gatcombe,
Newport, Isle of Wight
PO30 3EQ
T: (01983) 721202

GILLINGHAM
Dorset

Meads Farm ★★★★
Contact: Mrs June Wallis, Meads
Farm, Stour Provost, Gillingham,
Dorset SP8 5RX
T: (01747) 838265
F: (01258) 821123

Top Stall ★★★
Contact: Mrs Kathleen Jeanes,
Top Stall, Factory Farm, Fifehead
Magdalen, Gillingham, Dorset
SP8 5RS
T: (01258) 820022
F: (01258) 820022
E: factoryfarm@agriplus.net

Woolfields Barn ★★★★
Contact: Mr & Mrs B Thomas,
Woolfields Barn, Woolfields
Farm, Milton on Stour,
Gillingham, Dorset SP8 5PX
T: (01747) 824729 &
07836 772264
F: (01747) 824986
E: OThomas453@aol.com

GODSHILL
Isle of Wight

**1, 2 & 3 Barwick Cottages
★★★–★★★★**
Contact: Mrs P J Wickham,
Barwick Cottage, Rookley Farm
Lane, Niton Road, Rookley,
Ventnor, Isle of Wight PO38 3PA
T: (01983) 840787 &
0797 7926841
E: pam@barwickcottages.co.uk
I: www.barwickcottages.co.uk

Bagwich Cottage ★★★
Contact: Mrs Honor Vass, Island
Cottage Holidays, The Old
Vicarage, Kingston, Corfe Castle,
Wareham, Dorset BH20 5LH
T: (01929) 480080
F: (01929) 481070
E: ich@cottageholidays.demon.
co.uk
I: www.cottageholidays.demon.
co.uk

The Coach House Studio ★★★
Contact: Mrs Honor Vass, Island
Cottage Holidays, The Old
Vicarage, Kingston, Corfe Castle,
Wareham, Dorset BH20 5LH
T: (01929) 480080
F: (01929) 481070
E: ich@cottageholidays.demon.
co.uk.
I: www.cottageholidays.demon.
co.uk.

Demelza ★★★★
Contact: Mrs Honor Vass, Island
Cottage Holidays, The Old
Vicarage, Kingston, Corfe Castle,
Wareham, Dorset BH20 5LH
T: (01929) 480080
F: (01929) 481070
E: ich@cottageholidays.demon.
co.uk.
I: www.cottageholidays.dmon.
co.uk.

**Glebelands Holiday
Apartments ★★★**
Contact: Mrs Iris Beardsall,
Glebelands Holiday Apartments,
Church Hollow, Godshill,
Ventnor, Isle of Wight PO38 3DR
T: (01983) 840371 & 862616
F: (01983) 867482
E: glebelands@beardsalls.com

Godshill Park House ★★★★
Contact: Mrs Nora Down,
Godshill Park House, Godshill,
Ventnor, Isle of Wight PO38 3JF
T: (01983) 840271

Graylands Cottage ★★
Contact: Professor Ian Bruce, 54
Mall Road, Hammersmith,
London W6 9DG
T: (020) 8748 0611
F: (020) 8741 5621
E: tinab@cocoon.co.uk

Keepers Cottage ★★★★
Contact: Mrs Honor Vass, Island
Cottage Holidays, The Old
Vicarage, Kingston, Corfe Castle,
Wareham, Dorset BH20 5LH
T: (01929) 480080
F: (01929) 480080
E: ich@cottageholidays.demon.
co.uk
I: www.cottageholidays.demon.
co.uk

**Lambourn View Holiday
Annexe ★★**
Contact: Mrs Maureen Plumbley,
Lambourn View Holiday Annexe,
Beacon Alley, Godshill, Ventnor,
Isle of Wight PO38 3JX
T: (01983) 840293

**Loves Cottage & Pilgrims
Lodge ★★★–★★★★**
Contact: Mrs Honor Vass, Island
Cottage Holidays, The Old
Vicarage, Kingston, Corfe Castle,
Wareham, Dorset BH20 5LH
T: (01929) 480080
F: (01929) 481070
E: ich@cottageholidays.demon.
co.uk
I: www.cottageholidays.dmon.
co.uk

Milk Pan Farm ★★★
Contact: Mr & Mrs J A Morrish,
Milk Pan Farm, Bagwich Lane,
Godshill, Ventnor, Isle of Wight
PO38 3JY
T: (01983) 840570

Pheasant Cottage ★★★
Contact: Mrs Honor Vass, Island
Cottage Holidays, The Old
Vicarage, Kingston, Corfe Castle,
Wareham, Dorset BH20 5LH
T: (01929) 480080
F: (01929) 480080
E: ich@cottageholidays.demon.
co.uk
I: www.cottageholidays.demon.
co.uk

Rosemary Cottage ★★★★
Contact: Mrs Honor Vass, Island
Cottage Holidays, The Old
Vicarage, Kingston, Corfe Castle,
Wareham, Dorset BH20 5LH
T: (01929) 480080
F: (01929) 481070
E: lch@cottageholidays.demon.
co.uk
I: http://www/cottageholidays/
demon.co.uk

Seymour Cottages ★★★
Contact: Mr & Mrs P Lazenby, Seymour Cottages, Lower Yard Farm, Godshill, Ventnor, Isle of Wight PO38 3LY
T: (01983) 840536

Stag Cottage ★★★★
Contact: Mrs Honor Vass, Island Cottage Holidays, The Old Vicarage, Kingston, Corfe Castle, Wareham, Dorset BH20 5LH
T: (01929) 480080
F: (01929) 481070
E: ich@cottageholidays.demon.co.uk.
I: www.cottageholidays.dmon.co.uk

GODSHILL WOOD
Hampshire

The Lodge (Ref: H212) ★★★★
Contact: Mr Nick Pash, Hideaways, Chapel House, Luke Street, Berwick St John, Shaftesbury, Dorset SP7 0HQ
T: (01747) 828170
F: (01747) 829090
I: www.hideaways.co.uk/property2.cfm?ref=H212GodshillWood

GOSPORT
Hampshire

Captains Folly ★★★
Contact: Mr J M White, 8 Cambridge Road, Lee on the Solent, Hampshire PO13 9DH
T: (023) 9255 0883

Dolphins ★★★
Contact: Mrs A Donnelly, 28 Crescent Road, Gosport, Hampshire PO12 2DJ
T: (023) 9258 8179

Flat 1 Tregantle Mews ★★★
Contact: Mrs Carole Rudin, 1 Madden Close, Alverstoke, Gosport, Hampshire PO12 2PT
T: (023) 9258 3637
E: carole.rudin@btinternet.com

Keefons ★★
Contact: Mr & Mrs Keith & Yvonne Hoskins, 6 Village Road, Alverstoke, Gosport, Hampshire PO12 2LF
T: (023) 9252 0982

GREAT MILTON
Oxfordshire

Views Farm Barns ★★★★
Contact: Mr & Mrs C O Peers, Views Farm Barns, Views Farm, Great Milton, Oxford, Oxfordshire OX44 7NW
T: (01844) 279352 & 07836 273541
F: (01844) 279362
E: viewsfarm@callnetuk.com

GREAT ROLLRIGHT
Oxfordshire

Blackbird Cottage ★★★★
Contact: Mrs Carol Dingle, Tyte End Cottage, Great Rollright, Chipping Norton, Oxfordshire OX7 5RU
T: (01608) 737676
F: (01608) 737330
E: paul@pcdingle.freeserve.co.uk

GURNARD
Isle of Wight

5 & 101 Gurnard Pines ★★★
Contact: Mrs Geraldine Jarvis, 158 Gurnard Pines, Cockleton Lane, Cowes, Isle of Wight PO31 8RW
T: (01983) 289863
E: gerry@holly2.demon.co.uk
I: www.holly2.demon.co.uk/g&tr.html

136 Gurnard Pines ★★
Contact: Mr Nigel Haward, 23 Highfield Road, Cowes, Isle of Wight PO31 7UF
T: (01983) 297294

97 Gurnard Pines Holiday Village
Rating Applied For
Contact: M A Bowerman, 97 Gurnard Pines, 65 The Avenue, Camberley, Surrey GU15 3NF
T: (01276) 21488

Solent Lodge ★★
Contact: Mr Steve Russell, Alford Cottage, Latimer Road, St Helens, Ryde, Isle of Wight PO33 1TP
T: (01983) 616449 & 822036
E: solentlodge@hotmail.com
I: www.netguides.co.uk/wight/solent.html

Wishing Well ★★
Contact: Mrs Cheryl Greene, Wishing Well, 7A Woodvale Road, Gurnard, Cowes, Isle of Wight PO31 8EH
T: (01983) 294479
F: (01983) 282383
E: cheryl/peter@virgin.net

HAILEY
Oxfordshire

The Hovel & Tallet
Rating Applied For
Contact: Mr & Mrs Benfield, Gigley Farm, Hailey, Witney, Oxfordshire OX8
T: (01993) 868715

HARTGROVE
Dorset

Hartgrove Farm ★★★–★★★★★
Contact: Mrs Susan Smart, Hartgrove Farm, Hartgrove, Shaftesbury, Dorset SP7 0JY
T: (01747) 811830
F: (01747) 811066
E: cottages@hartgrovefarm.com
I: www.hartgrovefarm.co.uk

HARTLEY WINTNEY
Hampshire

Wintney Stable ★★★
Contact: Mr & Mrs Bernard Kilroy, 10 Hunts Common, Hartley Wintney, Hook, Hampshire RG27 8NT
T: (01252) 843133
F: (01252) 843133
E: bk22@tutor.open.ac.uk

HAYLING ISLAND
Hampshire

44 Bembridge Drive ★★
Contact: Mr Roy Pine, Millers of Hayling, Regal House, 46 Mengham Road, Hayling Island, Hampshire PO11 9BL
T: (023) 9246 5951
F: (023) 9246 1321
E: millers@haylingproperty.co.uk
I: www.haylingproperty.co.uk

1 Bosmere Road ★
Contact: Mr Roy Pine, Millers of Hayling, Regal House, 46 Mengham Road, Hayling Island, Hampshire PO11 9BL
T: (023) 9246 5951
F: (023) 9246 1321
E: millers@haylingproperty.co.uk
I: www.haylingproperty.co.uk

17 Eastoke Avenue ★
Contact: Mr Roy Pine, Millers, 19 Mengham Road, Hayling Island, Hampshire PO11 9BG
T: (023) 9246 5951
F: (023) 9246 1321
E: millers@haylingproperty.co.uk
I: www.haylingproperty.co.uk

15 Fairlight Chalets ★
Contact: Mr Roy Pine, Millers, 19 Mengham Road, Hayling Island, Hampshire PO11 9BG
T: (023) 9246 5951
F: (023) 9246 1321
E: millers@haylingproperty.co.uk
I: www.haylingproperty.co.uk

16 Fairlight Chalets
Rating Applied For
Contact: Mr Roy Pine, Millers, 19 Mengham Road, Hayling Island, Hampshire PO11 9BG
T: (023) 9246 5951
F: (023) 9246 1321
E: millers@haylingproperty.co.uk
I: www.haylingproperty.co.uk

30 Fairlight Chalets ★
Contact: Mr Roy Pine, Millers, 19 Mengham Road, Hayling Island, Hampshire PO11 9BG
T: (023) 9246 5951
F: (023) 9246 1321
E: millers@haylingproperty.co.uk
I: www.haylingproperty.co.uk

63 North Shore Road ★★
Contact: Mr Roy Pine, Millers, 19 Mengham Road, Hayling Island, Hampshire PO11 9BG
T: (023) 9246 5951
F: (023) 9246 1321
E: millers@haylingproperty.co.uk
I: www.haylingproperty.co.uk

1 Ramsey Road ★
Contact: Mr Roy Pine, Millers, 19 Mengham Road, Hayling Island, Hampshire PO11 9BG
T: (023) 9246 5951
F: (023) 9246 1321
E: millers@haylingproperty.co.uk
I: www.haylingproperty.co.uk

20 Sandy Beach Estate ★
Contact: Mr Roy Pine, Millers, 19 Mengham Road, Hayling Island, Hampshire PO11 9BG
T: (023) 9246 5951
F: (023) 9246 1321
E: miller@haylingproperty.co.uk
I: www.haylingproperty.co.uk

78 Sandypoint Road ★★
Contact: Mr Roy Pine, Millers, 19 Mengham Road, Hayling Island, Hampshire PO11 9BG
T: (023) 9246 5951
F: (023) 9246 1321
E: millers@haylingproperty.co.uk
I: www.haylingproperty.co.uk

Seagazers
Rating Applied For
Contact: Mrs S A Weatherley, Rose Cottage, St Peters Road, Hayling Island, Hampshire PO11 0RX
T: (023) 9246 2975
F: (023) 9246 2975

128a Southwood Road ★★
Contact: Mr Roy Pine, Millers, 19 Mengham Road, Hayling Island, Hampshire PO11 9BG
T: (023) 9246 5951
F: (023) 9246 1321
E: millers@haylingproperty.co.uk
I: www.haylingproperty.co.uk

88 Southwood Road ★★
Contact: Mr Roy Pine, Millers, 19 Mengham Road, Hayling Island, Hampshire PO11 9BG
T: (023) 9246 5951
F: (023) 9246 1321
E: millers@haylingproperty.co.uk
I: www.haylingproperty.co.uk

88c Southwood Road ★★
Contact: Mr Roy Pine, Millers, 19 Mengham Road, Hayling Island, Hampshire PO11 9BG
T: (023) 9246 5951
F: (023) 9246 1321
E: millers@haylingproperty.co.uk
I: www.haylingproperty.co.uk

5 Webb Close ★★
Contact: Mr Roy Pine, Millers, 19 Mengham Road, Hayling Island, Hampshire PO11 9BG
T: (023) 9246 5951
F: (023) 9246 1321
E: millers@haylingproperty.co.uk
I: www.haylingproperty.co.uk

4 Wittering Road ★★
Contact: Mr Roy Pine, Millers of Hayling, Regal House, 46 Mengham Road, Hayling Island, Hampshire PO11 9BL
T: (023) 9246 5951
F: (023) 9246 1321
E: millers@haylingproperty.co.uk
I: www.haylingproperty.co.uk

HEDGE END
Hampshire

Twin Oaks
Rating Applied For
Contact: Mrs Yvonne Main, Twin Oaks, 14 Upper Northam Road, Hedge End, Southampton, Hampshire SO30 4EA
T: (01489) 690054

HENLEY-ON-THAMES
Oxfordshire

The Clock Tower & Beechwood Cottage ★★★★
Contact: Mrs E Martin, The Clock Tower & Beechwood Cottage, Lovegroves Barn, Gallowstree Common, Wyfold, Reading, Berkshire RG4 9HS
T: (0118) 972 2365

Flat at Cedar ★★★
Contact: Mrs R B Foster, Cedar, Upper Bolney Road, Harpsden, Henley-on-Thames, Oxfordshire RG9 4AH
T: (01491) 573855 &
07768 724341
F: (01491) 573855

141 Greys Road ★★★★
Contact: Mrs J King, Jersey Farmhouse, Colmore Lane, Kingwood Common, Henley-on-Thames, Oxfordshire RG9 5LX
T: (01491) 628486
F: (01491) 628015
E: mjking@btinternet.com
I: www.holiday.btinternet.co.uk

Jersey Farmhouse ★★★
Contact: Mrs J King, Jersey Farmhouse, Colmore Lane, Kingwood Common, Henley-on-Thames, Oxfordshire RG9 5LX
T: (01491) 628486
F: (01491) 628015
E: mjking@btinternet.com
I: www.holiday.btinternet.co.uk

HERMITAGE
Berkshire

The Garden Flat ★★★★
Contact: Country Hols ref; 9310, Country Holidays, Spring Mill, Earby, Barnoldswick, Lancashire BB94 0AA
T: 08700 723723
F: (01282) 844288
E: sales@ttgihg.co.uk
I: www.country-holidays.co.uk

HIGHCLERE
Hampshire

Glencross Annexe ★★★
Contact: Mr Martyn Alexander, Glencross, Mount Road, Highclere, Newbury, Berkshire RG20 9QZ
T: (01635) 253244
F: (01635) 253244
E: glenalex@hotmail.com

HIGHCLIFFE
Dorset

Cairnleigh ★★★★
Contact: Mr Paul Dredge, Rumsey Holiday Homes, 2 Banks Road, Sandbanks, Poole, Dorset BH13 7QD
T: (01202) 707357
F: (01202) 701955
E: info@rhh.org
I: www.rhh.org

The Flat Briarwood ★★★
Contact: Mrs Stella Ward, Briarwood, 1 Dunbar Crescent, Highcliffe, Christchurch, Dorset BH23 5RY
T: (01425) 275523

Pedralves ★★
Contact: Mr J A Kenney, Pedralves, 48 Nea Road, Highcliffe, Christchurch, Dorset BH23 4NB
T: (01425) 273858

Wingfield Holiday Bungalow ★★★
Contact: Mrs Josephine Stevens, 15 Wingfield Avenue, Highcliffe, Christchurch, Dorset BH23 4NR
T: (01425) 278583
F: (01425) 278583

HILTON
Dorset

Crown Farm ★★
Contact: Mrs Pamela Crocker, Crown Farm, Duck Street, Hilton, Blandford Forum, Dorset DT11 0DQ
T: (01258) 880259

HORDLE
Hampshire

Bell Cottage ★★
Contact: Mrs Marian Nickels, 168 Everton Road, Hordle, Lymington, Hampshire SO41 0HB
T: (01425) 618383
E: barrenick@email.msn.com

HORNDEAN
Hampshire

Dairy Cottage ★★★★★
Contact: Country Holidays ref: 1539, Holiday Cottages Group Owner Services Dept, Spring Mill, Earby, Barnoldswick, Lancashire BB18 6RN
T: 0870 444 6603
F: (01282) 841539
E: ownerservices@ttgihg.co.uk
I: www.country-holidays.co.uk

HULCOTT
Buckinghamshire

Lizzies Cottage ★★★
Contact: Mrs Elizabeth Arnold, 4 The Green, Hulcott, Aylesbury, Buckinghamshire HP22 5AX
T: (01296) 394916
F: (01296) 394916

HURN
Dorset

The Old Farmhouse ★★★
Contact: Mrs Jennifer Burford, The Old Farmhouse, Pitt House Farm, Hurn, Christchurch, Dorset BH23 6AU
T: (01202) 479483

HYTHE
Hampshire

Waterfront House ★★★★
Contact: Mr & Mrs A Cunningham, Shalimar, Lime Walk, Dibden Purlieu, Southampton, Hampshire SO45 5RA
T: (023) 8084 2460
E: alex_cunningham@msn.com
I: www.cunningham100.fsnet.co.uk

IBSLEY
Hampshire

Crofton ★★★★★
Contact: Mrs Julie Hordle, Air View, Mockbeggar Lane, Ibsley, Ringwood, Hampshire BH24 3PR
T: (01425) 471829
F: (01425) 461350

IPSDEN
Oxfordshire

The Old Stables at Wellplace Barns ★★★★
Contact: Mr Robert Booth, The Old Stables at Wellplace Barns, Wellplace, Ipsden, Wallingford, Oxfordshire OX10 6QY
T: (01491) 381158 & 682929
F: (01491) 681158
E: robertbooth@beeb.net

IVINGHOE
Buckinghamshire

Town Farm Holiday Cottages ★★★
Contact: Mrs Angie Leach, Town Farm Holiday Cottages, Town Farm, Ivinghoe, Leighton Buzzard, Bedfordshire LU7 9EL
T: (01296) 668455 &
07774 217722
F: (01296) 668455
E: w.h.leach.and.sons@farmline.com.uk
I: www.members.farmline.com/angie

KILMESTON
Hampshire

College Down Farm Self Catering Holidays ★★★★
Contact: Mr Eric Ruff, College Down Farm Self Catering Holidays, College Down Farm, Kilmeston, Alresford, Hampshire SO24 0NS
T: (01962) 771345

KINGHAM
Oxfordshire

Church Farm Cottage
Rating Applied For
Contact: Country Hols ref : 1330 Sales, Country Holidays, Spring Mill, Earby, Barnoldswick, Lancashire BB94 0AA
T: (01282) 445096
F: (01282) 844288
I: www.country-holidays.co.uk

Ducktails
Rating Applied For
Contact: Mrs J M Sleath, Ducktails, 48 West End, Kingham, Oxford, Oxfordshire OX7 6YL

LAKE
Isle of Wight

Greenfields ★★-★★★
Contact: Mrs June Boyce, Greenfields, Newport Road, Lake, Sandown, Isle of Wight PO36 9PE
T: (01983) 402004

LANGTON MATRAVERS
Dorset

Flat 5 Garfield House ★★★
Contact: Miss Susan Inge, Flat A, 147 Holland Road, London W14 8AS
T: (020) 7602 4945
E: sueinge@hotmail.com

LAVENDON
Buckinghamshire

The Annexe ★★★
Contact: Mrs Marion Rutherford, 37 Northampton Road, Lavendon, Olney, Buckinghamshire MK46 4EY
T: (01234) 712755 &
07765 951177
E: mruther21@aol.com

Bell Cottage ★★★
Contact: Mrs Sally Wetherall, Bell House, 35 High Street, Lavendon, Olney, Buckinghamshire MK46 4HA
T: (01234) 712614
F: (01234) 712614

LEDWELL
Oxfordshire

Chapel Cottage ★★★
Contact: Country Hols ref : 12510 Sales, Country Holidays, Spring Mill, Earby, Barnoldswick, Lancashire BB94 0AA
T: 08700 723723
F: (01282) 844288
E: Sales@ttgihg.co.uk
I: www.country-holidays.co.uk

LEE ON THE SOLENT
Hampshire

The Chart House ★★★
Contact: Ms Marion Kinnear-White, 6 Cambridge Road, Lee on the Solent, Hampshire PO13 9DH
T: (023) 9255 4145 & 9255 0883
E: marion_kinnear-white@talk21.com

Kinderton House ★★★
Contact: Mrs Jean Miller, Kinderton House, 31 Marine Parade West, Lee on the Solent, Hampshire PO13 9LW
T: (023) 9255 2056

Kings Retreat ★★★
Contact: Mrs Bernadette Griffiths, 6 Bell Davies Road, Hill Head, Fareham, Hampshire PO14 2DW
T: (01329) 665914 & 0780 800 8199

LYMINGTON
Hampshire

8 Admirals Court ★★★★
Contact: Mrs S E Mayes, Ridgeway Rents New Forest Cottages, 4 Quay Hill, Lymington, Hampshire SO41 3AR
T: (01590) 679655
F: (01590) 670989
E: holidays@newforestcottages.co.uk
I: www.newforestcottages.co.uk

Bourne House ★★★
Contact: Mr & Mrs P J Mare, Maybury Wood Cottage, The Ridge, Woking, Surrey GU22 7EG
T: (01483) 772086
F: (01483) 772086
E: jppmare@aol.com

The Chantry ★★★★
Contact: Country Holidays ref: 9805, Holiday Cottages Group Owner Services Dept, Spring Mill, Earby, Barnoldswick, Lancashire BB94 0AA
T: 0870 444 6603
F: (01282) 844288
E: ownerservices@ttgihg.co.uk
I: www.country-holidays.co.uk

Corner Cottages ★★★★
Contact: Mrs Ginny Neath, Courtyard Cottage, Main Road, East Boldre, Brockenhurst, Hampshire SO42 7WD
T: (01590) 612080
F: (01590) 612080
E: rg.neath@virgin.net

7a Fairlea Road
Rating Applied For
Contact: Mrs Megan Hall, 1
Medley Close, Eaton Bray,
Dunstable, Bedfordshire
LU6 2DX
T: (01525) 220652

Fir Tree Cottage ★★★
Contact: Mrs B Saword, 1
Merlewood Court, Lyon Avenue,
New Milton, Hampshire
BH25 6AP
T: (01425) 617219

The Nuthatch ★★★★
Contact: Mrs Sue Wise, 15 The
Orchard, Milford-on-Sea,
Lymington, Hampshire
SO41 0SR
T: (01590) 645036

Rainbow Cottage ★★★
Contact: Mr & Mrs P J Mare,
Maybury Wood Cottage, The
Ridge, Woking, Surrey GU22 7EG
T: (01483) 772086
F: (01483) 772086
E: jppmare@aol.com

LYNDHURST
Hampshire

Acorn Cottage ★★★★
Contact: Mrs April Robinson,
Lyndhurst Cottages, Boltons
House, Princes Crescent,
Lyndhurst, Hampshire SO43 7BS
T: (023) 8028 3000
F: (023) 8028 3000
E: lyndhurstcottages@supanet.
com
I: www.lyndhurstcottages.
supanet.com

**Alice Cottage, Dormouse
Corner & Duchess Place
★★★-★★★★**
Contact: Mr Mike Saqui, The
Penny Farthing Hotel, Romsey
Road, Lyndhurst, Hampshire
SO43 7AA
T: (023) 8028 4422
F: (023) 8028 4488
E: cottages@
pennyfarthinghotel.co.uk
I: www.pennyfarthinghotel.
co.uk

The Cottage ★★★
Contact: Mrs Sheila Robinson,
The Cottage, The Old Stables,
Pikes Hill, Lyndhurst, Hampshire
SO43 7AY
T: (023) 8028 3697

95B High Street ★★
Contact: Mr & Mrs John
Langston, Monkton Cottage, 93
High Street, Lyndhurst,
Hampshire SO43 7BH
T: (023) 8028 2206
F: (023) 8028 2206

Holly Cottage ★★★★
Contact: Mr & Mrs F S Turner,
Greensward, The Crescent,
Woodlands Road, Ashurst,
Southampton, Hampshire
SO40 7AQ
T: (023) 8029 2374
F: (023) 8029 2374

Link Place ★★★★
Contact: Mrs April Robinson,
Lyndhurst Cottages, Boltons
House, Princes Crescent,
Lyndhurst, Hampshire SO43 7BS
T: (023) 8028 3000
F: (023) 8028 3000
E: lyndhurstcottages@supanet.
com
I: www.lyndhurstcottages.
supanet.com

Yorke Cottage ★★★★
Contact: Mr John Drew,
Burwood Lodge, 27 Romsey
Road, Lyndhurst, Hampshire
SO43 7AA
T: (023) 8028 2445
F: (023) 8028 4104
E: burwoodl@ukonline.co.uk

MAIDENHEAD
Berkshire

11 Cadwell Drive ★★★
Contact: Mrs V Williams, 32 York
Road, Maidenhead, Berkshire
SL6 1SF
T: (01628) 627370
F: (01628) 627370

Courtyard Cottages
Rating Applied For
Contact: Mrs Carol Bardo, Moor
Farm, Ascot Road, Holyport,
Maidenhead, Berkshire SL6 2HY
T: (01628) 633761
F: (01628) 636167
E: moorfm@aol.com

MAPLEDURHAM
Oxfordshire

**Mapledurham Holiday
Cottages ★★-★★★★**
Contact: Mrs Lola Andrews, The
Estate Office, Mapledurham
House, Mapledurham, Reading,
Berkshire RG4 7TR
T: (0118) 972 4292
F: (0118) 972 4016
E: mtrust1997@aol.com
I: www.mapledurham.co.uk

MARNHULL
Dorset

Trooper Farm ★★
Contact: Mr Cyril Bastable,
Trooper Farm, Love Lane,
Marnhull, Sturminster Newton,
Dorset DT10 1PT
T: (01258) 820753

MILBORNE ST ANDREW
Dorset

Orchard Cottage ★★★
Contact: Mrs C Martin, 1 Deverel
Cottages, Deverel Farm,
Milborne St Andrew, Blandford
Forum, Dorset DT11 0HX
T: (01258) 837195 &
0797 0358774
F: (01258) 837227
E: deverel@dialstart78.fsnet.
co.uk

The Retreat ★★★
Contact: Mrs June Jenkins, 27
Fourgates Road, Dorchester,
Dorset DT1 2NL
T: (01305) 269194
E: junejenkins56@hotmail.com

MILFORD-ON-SEA
Hampshire

Forest Farm ★★
Contact: Ms Debbie Butler,
Forest Farm, Barnes Lane,
Milford-on-Sea, Lymington,
Hampshire SO41 0RR
T: (01590) 644365
F: (01590) 644365
E: driving@ffarm.fsnet.co.uk
I: www.forestfarmdriving.com

Harmony ★★★★
Contact: Mrs C R Ling, 9 The
White House, Westover Road,
Milford-on-Sea, Lymington,
Hampshire SO41 0PW
T: (01590) 641779 &
07808 215567

The Old Bakery ★★★
Contact: Mrs A Braithwaite, Bay
Tree Cottage, Bashley Common
Road, New Milton, Hampshire
BH25 5SQ
T: (01425) 620733

Penny Pot ★★★★
Contact: Mrs C M Plummer,
Penny Pot, Ha'penny House, 16
Whitby Road, Milford-on-Sea,
Lymington, Hampshire
SO41 0ND
T: (01590) 641210
F: (01590) 623872
E: admin@hapennyhouse.co.uk

Pine View Cottage ★★★★
Contact: Mrs Sheri Gadd, Cherry
Trees, Lymington Road, Milford-
on-Sea, Lymington, Hampshire
SO41 0QL
T: (01590) 643746 &
07976 382828
E: cherrytrees@beeb.net
I: www.theea.
co.uk/region12/98653.
htmlwww.newforest.demon.
co.uk/cherrytrees.htm

Windmill Cottage ★★★
Contact: Mrs S M Perham,
Danescourt, 14 Kivernell Road,
Milford-on-Sea, Lymington,
Hampshire SO41 0PQ
T: (01590) 643516
F: (01590) 641255

MILTON ABBAS
Dorset

Little Hewish Barn ★★★★★
Contact: Mr Terry Dunn, 2 Little
Hewish Cottages, Milton Abbas,
Blandford Forum, Dorset
DT11 0DP
T: (01258) 881235 &
07778 966843
F: (01258) 881393
E: terry@littlehewish.co.uk
I: www.littlehewish.co.uk

Luccombe Farm ★★★★
Contact: Mr & Mrs Murray &
Amanda Kayll, Luccombe Farm,
Milton Abbas, Blandford Forum,
Dorset DT11 0BE
T: (01258) 880558
F: (01258) 881384

Park Farm ★★-★★★★
Contact: Mrs Audrey Burch, Park
Farm, Milton Abbas, Blandford
Forum, Dorset DT11 0AX
T: (01258) 880828
F: (01258) 881788
E: burch@parkfarmcottages.
co.uk
I: www.parkfarmcottages.co.uk

Primrose Cottage ★★★
Contact: Mrs G D Garvey, Brook
Cottage, 1 Long Street, Cerne
Abbas, Dorchester, Dorset
DT2 7JF
T: (01300) 341352
F: (01300) 341352
E: tgarvey@ragtime99.
freeserve.co.uk

MILTON KEYNES
Buckinghamshire

Arena Apartments ★★★
Contact: Ms Jules Hardy, Valley
Lodge, Whaddon Road, Shenley
Brook End, Milton Keynes,
Buckinghamshire MK5 7AF
T: (01908) 502397
F: (01908) 502397
E: arenamk@talk21.com
I: www.arena-apartments.co.uk

35 Brookside Close ★★★
Contact: Mrs A Hepher, The Old
Bakery Hotel, Main Street,
Cosgrove, Milton Keynes
MK19 7JL
T: (01908) 262255
F: (01908) 263620
E: avh@hepher.demon.co.uk

MILTON-UNDER-WYCHWOOD
Oxfordshire

Lambley Cottage ★★★
Contact: Mrs Jill Fox, Quartern,
The Heath, Milton-under-
Wychwood, Chipping Norton,
Oxfordshire OX7 6LG
T: (01993) 830975
E: j.fox6@nHworld.com

London House Cottage ★★
Contact: Country Holidays ref:
50248, Holiday Cottages Group
Owner Services Dept, Spring
Mill, Earby, Barnoldswick,
Lancashire BB94 0AA
T: 0870 444 6603
F: (01282) 844288
E: ownerservices@ttgihg.co.uk
I: www.country-holidays.co.uk

Washpool Cottage ★★★★
Contact: Mrs Angela Richards,
Priory Mews, 33A Priory Lane,
Burford, Oxford, Oxon OX18 4SG
T: (01993) 824252 & 824443
F: (01993) 824443

MINSTER LOVELL
Oxfordshire

Hill Grove Cottage ★★
Contact: Mrs Katharine Brown,
Hill Grove Farm, Crawley Road,
Minster Lovell, Oxford,
Oxfordshire OX29 0NA
T: (01993) 703120
F: (01993) 700528

MOLLINGTON
Oxfordshire

The Yews ★★-★★★
Contact: Mr & Mrs Darrel & Gail
Jeffries, Anitas Holiday Cottages,
The Yews, Church Farm,
Mollington, Banbury,
Oxfordshire OX17 1AZ
T: (01295) 750731

MONXTON
Hampshire

The Den at Millcroft ★★★★
Contact: Mrs Pat Hayward, Millcroft, Chalkpit Lane, Monxton, Andover, Hampshire SP11 8AR
T: (01264) 710618 &
07787 552170
F: (01264) 710618

MORETON
Dorset

The Courtyard ★★★
Contact: Mrs J P Lofts, The Courtyard, Moreford Hall, Moreton, Dorchester, Dorset DT2 8BA
T: (01305) 853499
E: famlofts@aol.com

Glebe Cottage ★★
Contact: Mrs C L Gibbens, Glebe Cottage, Moreton, Dorchester, Dorset DT2 8RQ
T: (01929) 462468

MOTCOMBE
Dorset

The Dairy House
Rating Applied For
Contact: Mr Gilbert Archdale, Church Farm, Motcombe, Shaftesbury, Dorset SP7 9NT
T: (01747) 854844 & 850968
F: (01747) 853459
E: enquiries@thedairyhouse. com
I: www.thedairyhouse.com

MUDEFORD
Dorset

Flat 1 Digby Court ★★
Contact: Mrs K Spreadbury, Merbury House, Vaggs Lane, Hordle, Lymington, Hampshire SO41 0FP
T: (01425) 615605

NEW MILTON
Hampshire

53 & 63 Bayview ★★
Contact: Mrs D A Orchard, Daphne's Chalet, 54 Westwoods Park, Bashley Cross Road, New Milton, Hamphire BH25 5TB
T: (01425) 619630
E: priscilla.may@virgin.net

The Granary ★★
Contact: Mrs Jane Fish, Woodcutters, St Johns Road, Bashley, New Milton, Hampshire BH25 5SD
T: (01425) 610332
E: danfishsurface@onetel.net.uk

NEWBRIDGE
Isle of Wight

Laurel Cottage ★★
Contact: Mrs Jill Nicholson, 10 Valley Close, Goring, Reading, Berkshire RG8 0AN
T: (01491) 875998
F: (01491) 874198

NEWBURY
Berkshire

Barn House ★★★★
Contact: Mrs M Edwards, Enborne Street Farm, Enborne, Newbury, Berkshire RG20 0JP
T: (01635) 253443
F: (01635) 253443

Peregrine Cottage ★★★★★
Contact: Mrs Elizabeth Knight, Peregrine House, Enborne Street, Enborne, Newbury, Berkshire RG14 6RP
T: (01635) 42585
F: (01635) 528775
E: lizziek1eak@hotmail.com

Yaffles ★★★–★★★★
Contact: Mr & Mrs Tony & Jean Bradford, Yaffles, Red Shute Hill, Hermitage, Thatcham, Berkshire RG18 9QH
T: (01635) 201100 &
0777 5681821
F: (01635) 201100
E: yaffles@ukonline.co.uk
I: www.cottagesdirect. com/yaffles

NEWCHURCH
Isle of Wight

Barn Cottage ★★★
Contact: Mrs P A Corbin, Knighton Barn, Knighton Shute, Newchurch, Sandown, Isle of Wight PO36 0NT
T: (01983) 865349
F: (01983) 865349

Clematis ★★★
Contact: Mr & Mrs A G Jupe, The Laurels, High Street, Newchurch, Sandown, Isle of Wight PO36 0NJ
T: (01983) 867613
F: (01983) 868214
E: alistair.jupe@btinternet.com
I: www.btinternet.com/~alistair.jupe/

Hill Farm House ★★★★★
Contact: Mrs Honor Vass, Island Cottage Holidays, The Old Vicarage, Kingston, Corfe Castle, Wareham, Dorset BH20 5LH
T: (01929) 480080
F: (01929) 481070
E: ich@cottageholidays.demon. co.uk
I: www.cottageholidays.dmon. co.uk

Knighton Gorges ★★★
Contact: Mrs Honor Vass, Island Cottage Holidays, The Old Vicarage, Kingston, Corfe Castle, Wareham, Dorset BH20 5LH
T: (01929) 480080
F: (01929) 4810700
E: ich@cottageholidays.demon. co.uk
I: www.cottageholidays.demon. co.uk

Mersley Farm ★★★
Contact: Mrs Jennifer Boswell, Mersley Farm, Newchurch, Sandown, Isle of Wight PO36 0NR
T: (01983) 865213
F: (01983) 862294
E: jenny@mersleyfarm.co.uk
I: www.mersleyfarm.co.uk

Owl Cottage & Paperbarn Cottage ★★★★
Contact: Mrs Honor Vass, Island Cottage Holidays, The Old Vicarage, Kingston, Corfe Castle, Wareham, Dorset BH20 5LH
T: (01929) 480080
F: (01929) 481070
E: ich@cottageholidays.demon. co.uk
I: www.cottageholidays.demon. co.uk.

NEWPORT
Isle of Wight

Bethel Cottage ★★★
Contact: Mrs Bridget Lewis, Channers Ltd, Blackbridge Brook House, Main Road, Havenstreet, Ryde, Isle of Wight PO33 4DR
T: (01983) 884742
E: bridget_lewis@talk21.com

The Cottage ★★★★
Contact: Mrs Honor Vass, Island Cottage Holidays, The Old Vicarage, Kingston, Corfe Castle, Wareham, Dorset BH20 5LH
T: (01929) 480080
F: (01929) 481070
E: ich@cottageholidays.demon. co.uk
I: www.cottageholidays.demon. co.uk

Durrants Farm ★★★
Contact: Mr Arthur Attrill, Durrants Farm, Newtown, Newport, Isle of Wight PO30 4PE
T: (01983) 523981

Nobbys Cottage
Rating Applied For
Contact: Mrs Honor Vass, Island Cottage Holidays, The Old Vicarage, Kingston, Corfe Castle, Wareham, Dorset BH20 5LH
T: (01929) 480080
F: (01929) 481070
E: enq@islandcottageholidays. com
I: www.islandcottageholidays. com

NINGWOOD
Isle of Wight

The Granary ★★★★
Contact: Mrs Honor Vass, Island Cottage Holidays, The Old Vicarage, Kingston, Corfe Castle, Wareham, Dorset BH20 5LH
T: (01929) 480080
F: (01929) 481070
E: ich@cottageholidays.demon. co.uk
I: www.cottageholidays.demon. co.uk

NITON
Isle of Wight

Gate Lodge ★★
Contact: Ms Lisa Baskill, Home from Home Holidays, 31 Pier Street, Ventnor, Isle of Wight PO38 1SX
T: (01983) 854340
F: (01983) 855524

Hoyes Farmhouse ★★
Contact: Mr & Mrs S Willis, Ladyacre Farm, Pan Lane, Niton, Ventnor, Isle of Wight PO38 2BU
T: (01983) 730015 & 0797 785 6795

Pollard Willow ★★
Contact: The Proprietor, Pollard Willow, Pan Cottages, Pan Lane, Niton, Ventnor, Isle of Wight PO38 2BU

Southcliffe ★★
Contact: Ms Lisa Baskill, Home from Home Holidays, 31 Pier Street, Ventnor, Isle of Wight PO38 1SX
T: (01983) 854340
F: (01983) 855524

Sundial Cottage ★★
Contact: Ms Lisa Baskill, Home from Home Holidays, 31 Pier Street, Ventnor, Isle of Wight PO38 1SX
T: (01983) 854340
F: (01983) 855524

NITON UNDERCLIFF
Isle of Wight

Puckaster Main House, Puckaster Wing & Puckaster Cottage ★★★★–★★★★★
Contact: Mrs Honor Vass, Island Cottage Holidays, The Old Vicarage, Kingston, Corfe Castle, Wareham, Dorset BH20 5LH
T: (01929) 480080
F: (01929) 481070
E: ich@cottageholidays.demon. co.uk
I: www.cottageholidays.co.uk.

The Well House ★★★★
Contact: Mrs Honor Vass, Island Cottage Holidays, The Old Vicarage, Kingston, Corfe Castle, Wareham, Dorset BH20 5LH
T: (01929) 480080
F: (01929) 481070
E: ich@cottageholidays.demon. co.uk
I: www.cottageholidays.demon. co.uk

NORLEYWOOD
Hampshire

The Bee Garden ★★★★
Contact: Mr R J Mayes, Ridgeway Rents New Forest Cottages, 4 Quay Hill, Lymington, Hampshire SO41 3AR
T: (01590) 679655
F: (01590) 670989
E: members.aol.com/nfcottages

NORTH LEIGH
Oxfordshire

Churchmead Cottage
Rating Applied For
Contact: Mr & Mrs Hugh Wheeler, End House, Chilson, Chipping Norton, Oxfordshire OX7 3HU
T: (01608) 676452
F: (01608) 676452
E: hugh@johnfrancis.freeserve. co.uk

Wylcot Cottage ★★★
Contact: Mrs Joy Crew, Hollywell Cottage, New Yatt, Witney, Oxfordshire OX29 6TF
T: (01993) 868614

NORTHMOOR
Oxfordshire

Rectory Farm Cottages
★★★★
Contact: Mrs Mary Anne Florey,
Rectory Farm, Northmoor,
Oxford, Oxfordshire OX8 1SX
T: (01865) 300207
F: (01865) 300559
E: pj.florey@farmline.com

OKEFORD FITZPAINE
Dorset

Stonyford Cottage ★★★
Contact: Mrs Susan Godden,
Stresa House, Lower Street,
Okeford Fitzpaine, Blandford
Forum, Dorset DT11 0RN
T: (01258) 860763
F: (01258) 860763

OLD CHALFORD
Oxfordshire

Beech House ★★★★★
Contact: Mrs Dorothy Canty,
Oak House, Chalford Park, Old
Chalford, Chipping Norton,
Oxfordshire OX7 5QR
T: (01608) 641435
F: (01608) 641435

OLDBROOK
Buckinghamshire

Arena Apartments ★★★
Contact: Ms Jules Hardy, Valley
Lodge, Whaddon Road, Shenley
Brook End, Milton Keynes,
Buckinghamshire MK5 7AF
T: (01908) 502397
F: (01908) 502397
E: arenamk@talk21.com

Arena Apartments ★★★
Contact: Ms Jules Hardy, Valley
Lodge, Whaddon Road, Shenley
Brook End, Milton Keynes,
Buckinghamshire MK5 7AF
T: (01908) 502397
F: (01908) 502397
E: arenamk@talk21.com

OLNEY
Buckinghamshire

Hyde Farm Cottages ★★★★
Contact: Mrs Penny Reynolds,
Hyde Farm Cottages, Hyde Farm,
Warrington Road, Olney,
Buckinghamshire MK46 4DU
T: (01234) 711223 &
07778 412975

The Old Stone Barn
★★★–★★★★
Contact: Mr & Mrs G J Pibworth,
Home Farm, Warrington, Olney,
Buckinghamshire MK46 4HN
T: (01234) 711655
F: (01234) 711855
E: accommodation@
oldstonebarn.co.uk
I: www.oldstonebarn.co.uk

OXFORD
Oxfordshire

7 Bannister Close ★★★
Contact: Mr I M Priestly, 7
Bannister Close, Iffley Road,
Oxford, Oxfordshire OX4 1SH
T: (01865) 251095
F: (01865) 251095

Chilswell Farm ★★
Contact: Mrs H Farrant,
Chilswell Farm, Boars Hill,
Oxford, Oxfordshire OX1 5EP
T: (01865) 735223

17 Kingston Road ★★★
Contact: Mrs Pru Dickson, 17
Kingston Road, Oxford,
Oxfordshire OX2 6QR
T: (01865) 516913
F: (01865) 516913
E: pru.dickson@tesco.net
I: www.oxfordcity.
co.uk/accom/studioflat/

Otmoor Holidays ★★★★
Contact: Mrs Emma Righton,
Otmoor Holidays, Lower Farm,
Noke, Oxford, Oxfordshire
OX3 9TX
T: (01865) 373766
F: (01865) 371911
E: info@oxfordholidays.co.uk
I: www.oxfordholidays.co.uk

St Thomas' Mews ★★★★★
Contact: Reception, St Thomas'
Mews Apartments in Oxford
Limited, 58 St Thomas Street,
Oxford, Oxford, Oxfordshire
OX1 1JP
T: (01865) 254000
F: (01865) 254001
E: based@oxstay.co.uk
I: www.oxstay.co.uk

73 St Clements Street ★★★
Contact: Mrs A Winston-
Lawton, Little Barn House, Crow
Lane, Great Bourton, Banbury,
Oxfordshire OX17 1RL
T: (01295) 758814
F: (01295) 758978

PANGBOURNE
Berkshire

Brambly Thatch ★★★
Contact: Mr & Mrs J N Hatt,
Merricroft Farming, Goring
Heath, Reading, Berkshire
RG8 7TA
T: (0118) 984 3121
F: (0118) 984 4662
E: hatts@merricroft.demon.
co.uk

The Old Rectory Cottage ★★★
Contact: Mrs J H Short, The Old
Rectory Cottage, Lower
Basildon, Pangbourne, Reading,
Berkshire RG8 9NH
T: (01491) 671344

Pennycroft ★★★★
Contact: Mr C J Collingwood, 34
Ambleside Avenue, London
SW16 1QP
T: (020) 8769 2742
F: (020) 8677 3023
E: pennycroft@cwcom.net
I: www.pennycroft.cwc.net

Soldalen Annexe ★★
Contact: Mrs B Kirk, Soldalen,
Riverview Road, Pangbourne,
Reading, Berkshire RG8 7AU
T: (0118) 984 2924
F: (0118) 984 2924

PARKSTONE
Dorset

25 Anthony's Avenue ★★★
Contact: Mr Paul Dredge,
Rumsey Holiday Homes, 2 Banks
Road, Sandbanks, Poole, Dorset
BH13 7QD
T: (01202) 707357
F: (01202) 701955
E: info@rhh.org
I: www.rhh.org

10 Austin Avenue ★★★
Contact: Mr Paul Dredge,
Rumsey Holiday Homes, 2 Banks
Road, Sandbanks, Poole, Dorset
BH13 7QD
T: (01202) 707357
F: (01202) 701955
E: info@rhh.org
I: www.rhh.org

3 Brownsea Court ★★★
Contact: Mr Paul Dredge,
Rumsey Holiday Homes, 2 Banks
Road, Sandbanks, Poole, Dorset
BH13 7QD
T: (01202) 707357
F: (01202) 701955
E: info@rhh.org
I: www.rhh.org

10 Grandier Court ★★★★
Contact: Mr Paul Dredge,
Rumsey Holiday Homes, 2 Banks
Road, Sandbanks, Poole, Dorset
BH13 7QD
T: (01202) 707357
F: (01202) 701955
E: info@rhh.org
I: www.rhh.org

3 Wentworth ★★★
Contact: Mr Paul Dredge,
Rumsey Holiday Homes, 2 Banks
Road, Sandbanks, Poole, Dorset
BH13 7QD
T: (01202) 707357
F: (01202) 701955
E: info@rhh.org
I: www.rhh.org

POOLE
Dorset

5 Bay Harbour View ★★★★
Contact: Mr Paul Dredge,
Rumsey Holiday Homes, 2 Banks
Road, Sandbanks, Poole, Dorset
BH13 7QD
T: (01202) 707357
F: (01202) 701955
E: info@rhh.org
I: www.rhh.org

The Boat House ★★★
Contact: Mrs Suzanne Fuller,
Hollymoors, Holtwood,
Wimborne Minster, Dorset
BH21 7DR
T: (01258) 840377
F: 08701 672994
E: baiter.holidays@btinternet.
com
I: www.baiter.holidays.
btinternet.co.uk

The Breakers ★★
Contact: Mr Paul Dredge,
Rumsey Holiday Homes, 2 Banks
Road, Sandbanks, Poole, Dorset
BH13 7QD
T: (01202) 707357
F: (01202) 701955
E: info@rhh.org
I: www.rhh.org

37 Brownsea Road ★★★★
Contact: Mr Paul Dredge,
Rumsey Holiday Homes, 2 Banks
Road, Sandbanks, Poole, Dorset
BH13 7QD
T: (01202) 707357
F: (01202) 701955
E: info@rhh.org
I: www.rhh.org

106 Catalina Drive ★★★
Contact: Mr Paul Dredge,
Rumsey Holiday Homes, 2 Banks
Road, Sandbanks, Poole, Dorset
BH13 7QD
T: (01202) 707357
F: (01202) 701955
E: info@rhh.org
I: www.rhh.org

14A Chaddesley Wood Road
★★★★
Contact: Mr Paul Dredge,
Rumsey Holiday Homes, 2 Banks
Road, Sandbanks, Poole, Dorset
BH13 7QD
T: (01202) 707357
F: (01202) 701955
E: info@rhh.org
I: www.rhh.org

16 Chaddesley Wood Road
★★★★
Contact: Mr Paul Dredge,
Rumsey Holiday Homes, 2 Banks
Road, Sandbanks, Poole, Dorset
BH13 7QD
T: (01202) 707357
F: (01202) 701955
E: info@rhh.org
I: www.rhh.org

22 Chaddesley Wood Road
★★★
Contact: Mr Paul Dredge,
Rumsey Holiday Homes, 2 Banks
Road, Sandbanks, Poole, Dorset
BH13 7QD
T: (01202) 707357
F: (01202) 701955
E: info@rhh.org
I: www.rhh.org

7 Compass Point ★★★★
Contact: Mr Paul Dredge,
Rumsey Holiday Homes, 2 Banks
Road, Sandbanks, Poole, Dorset
BH13 7QD
T: (01202) 707357
F: (01202) 701955
E: info@rhh.org
I: www.rhh.org

7 Daylesford Close ★★★
Contact: Mr Paul Dredge,
Rumsey Holiday Homes, 2 Banks
Road, Sandbanks, Poole, Dorset
BH13 7QD
T: (01202) 707357
F: (01202) 701955
E: info@rhh.org
I: www.rhh.org

**Dolphin Cottage, Seahorse &
Starfish Apartments**★★★
Contact: Mrs Middler, The
Grovefield Manor Hotel, 18
Pinewood Road, Branksome
Park, Poole, Dorset BH13 6JS
T: (01202) 766798

Egret Cottage ★★★
Contact: Mr & Mrs P Cocklin, 46
Perry Gardens, Poole, Dorset
BH15 1RA
T: (01202) 670046

12 Fairwinds ★★
Contact: Mr Paul Dredge,
Rumsey Holiday Homes, 2 Banks
Road, Sandbanks, Poole, Dorset
BH13 7QD
T: (01202) 707357
F: (01202) 701955
E: info@rhh.org
I: www.rhh.org

Establishments printed in blue have a detailed entry in this guide

2 Fairwinds ★★★
Contact: Mr Paul Dredge,
Rumsey Holiday Homes, 2 Banks
Road, Sandbanks, Poole, Dorset
BH13 7QD
T: (01202) 707357
F: (01202) 701955
E: info@rhh.org
I: www.rhh.org

9 Fairwinds ★★★
Contact: Mr Paul Dredge,
Rumsey Holiday Homes, 2 Banks
Road, Sandbanks, Poole, Dorset
BH13 7QD
T: (01202) 707357
F: (01202) 701955
E: info@rhh.org
I: www.rhh.org

First Floor Flat 53 Panorama Road★★★
Contact: Mr Paul Dredge,
Rumsey Holiday Homes, 2 Banks
Road, Sandbanks, Poole, Dorset
BH13 7QD
T: (01202) 707357
F: (01202) 701955
E: info@rhh.org
I: www.rhh.org

Flat 1 Wykeham Lodge ★★★
Contact: Mr Paul Dredge,
Rumsey Holiday Homes, 2 Banks
Road, Sandbanks, Poole, Dorset
BH13 7QD
T: (01202) 707357
F: (01202) 701955
E: info@rhh.org
I: www.rhh.org

Flat 10 Fairwinds ★★★
Contact: Mr Paul Dredge,
Rumsey Holiday Homes, 2 Banks
Road, Sandbanks, Poole, Dorset
BH13 7QD
T: (01202) 707357
F: (01202) 701955
E: info@rhh.org
I: www.rhh.org

Flat 12 Golden Gates ★★★★
Contact: Mr Paul Dredge,
Rumsey Holiday Homes, 2 Banks
Road, Sandbanks, Poole, Dorset
BH13 7QD
T: (01202) 707357
F: (01202) 701955
E: info@rhh.org
I: www.rhh.org

Flat 16 Golden Gates ★★★
Contact: Mr Paul Dredge,
Rumsey Holiday Homes, 2 Banks
Road, Sandbanks, Poole, Dorset
BH13 7QD
T: (01202) 707357
F: (01202) 701955
E: info@rhh.org
I: www.rhh.org

Flat 2 Mansard Court ★★★★
Contact: Mr Paul Dredge,
Rumsey Holiday Homes, 2 Banks
Road, Sandbanks, Poole, Dorset
BH13 7QD
T: (01202) 707357
F: (01202) 701955
E: info@rhh.org
I: www.rhh.org

Flat 2 Port Iona ★★★
Contact: Mr Paul Dredge,
Rumsey Holiday Homes, 2 Banks
Road, Sandbanks, Poole, Dorset
BH13 7QD
T: (01202) 707357
F: (01202) 701955
E: info@rhh.org
I: www.rhh.org

Flat 2 Sandhaven Court ★★★★
Contact: Mr Paul Dredge,
Rumsey Holiday Homes, 2 Banks
Road, Sandbanks, Poole, Dorset
BH13 7QD
T: (01202) 707357
F: (01202) 701955
E: info@rhh.org
I: www.rhh.org

Flat 4 Sandhaven Court ★★★★
Contact: Mr Paul Dredge,
Rumsey Holiday Homes, 2 Banks
Road, Sandbanks, Poole, Dorset
BH13 7QD
T: (01202) 707357
F: (01202) 701955
E: info@rhh.org
I: www.rhh.org

Flat 5 Mansard Court ★★★
Contact: Mr Paul Dredge,
Rumsey Holiday Homes, 2 Banks
Road, Sandbanks, Poole, Dorset
BH13 7QD
T: (01202) 707357
F: (01202) 701955
E: info@rhh.org
I: www.rhh.org

Flat 6 Compass Point ★★★★
Contact: Mr Paul Dredge,
Rumsey Holiday Homes, 2 Banks
Road, Sandbanks, Poole, Dorset
BH13 7QD
T: (01202) 707357
F: (01202) 701955
E: info@rhh.org
I: www.rhh.org

Flat 6 Sandhaven Court ★★★★
Contact: Mr Paul Dredge,
Rumsey Holiday Homes, 2 Banks
Road, Sandbanks, Poole, Dorset
BH13 7QD
T: (01202) 707357
F: (01202) 701955
E: info@rhh.org
I: www.rhh.org

Flat 8 Sandacres ★★
Contact: Miss M Barker-Smith, 7
Keythorpe, 27 Manor Road,
Bournemouth, Dorset BH1 3ER
T: (01202) 316230 &
07771 985511

Flats 5 & 6 Sandacres ★★-★★★
Contact: Mrs Rosemary Bond,
Beacon Hill Touring Park,
Blandford Road North, Near
Lytchett Minster, Poole, Dorset
BH16 6AB
T: (01202) 631631
F: (01202) 625749

Flintshore ★★
Contact: Mr Paul Dredge,
Rumsey Holiday Homes, 2 Banks
Road, Sandbanks, Poole, Dorset
BH13 7QD
T: (01202) 707357
F: (01202) 701955
E: info@rhh.org
I: www.rhh.org

5 Fourwinds ★★★
Contact: Mr Paul Dredge,
Rumsey Holiday Homes, 2 Banks
Road, Sandbanks, Poole, Dorset
BH13 7QD
T: (01202) 707357
F: (01202) 701955
E: info@rhh.org
I: www.rhh.org

11 Golden Gates ★★★
Contact: Mr Paul Dredge,
Rumsey Holiday Homes, 2 Banks
Road, Sandbanks, Poole, Dorset
BH13 7QD
T: (01202) 707357
F: (01202) 701955
E: info@rhh.org
I: www.rhh.org

15 Golden Gates ★★★
Contact: Mr Paul Dredge,
Rumsey Holiday Homes, 2 Banks
Road, Sandbanks, Poole, Dorset
BH13 7QD
T: (01202) 707357
F: (01202) 701955
E: info@rhh.org
I: www.rhh.org

4 Golden Gates ★★★
Contact: Mr Paul Dredge,
Rumsey Holiday Homes, 2 Banks
Road, Sandbanks, Poole, Dorset
BH13 7QD
T: (01202) 707357
F: (01202) 701955
E: info@rhh.org
I: www.rhh.org

8 Golden Gates ★★★★
Contact: Mr Paul Dredge,
Rumsey Holiday Homes, 2 Banks
Road, Sandbanks, Poole, Dorset
BH13 7QD
T: (01202) 707357
F: (01202) 701955
E: info@rhh.org
I: www.rhh.org

17 Green Gardens ★★★
Contact: Ms Christina Harris,
Victoria, Beech Close, Spetisbury,
Blandford Forum, Dorset
DT11 9HG
T: (01258) 456609
E: christina.harris@breathemail.net

Ground Floor Flat 53 Panorama Road★★★
Contact: Mr Paul Dredge,
Rumsey Holiday Homes, 2 Banks
Road, Sandbanks, Poole, Dorset
BH13 7QD
T: (01202) 707357
F: (01202) 701955
E: info@rhh.org
I: www.rhh.org

12 Haven Court ★★★
Contact: Mr Paul Dredge,
Rumsey Holiday Homes, 2 Banks
Road, Sandbanks, Poole, Dorset
BH13 7QD
T: (01202) 707357
F: (01202) 701955
E: onfo@rhh.org
I: www.rhh.org

Hemingways ★★★★
Contact: Mr Paul Dredge,
Rumsey Holiday Homes, 2 Banks
Road, Sandbanks, Poole, Dorset
BH13 7QD
T: (01202) 707357
F: (01202) 701955
E: info@rhh.org
I: www.rhh.org

Holwell ★★
Contact: Mr Paul Dredge,
Rumsey Holiday Homes, 2 Banks
Road, Sandbanks, Poole, Dorset
BH13 7QD
T: (01202) 707357
F: (01202) 701955
E: info@rhh.org
I: www.rhh.org

75 Labrador Drive ★★★
Contact: Mr Paul Dredge,
Rumsey Holiday Homes, 2 Banks
Road, Sandbanks, Poole, Dorset
BH13 7QD
T: (01202) 707357
F: (01202) 701955
E: info@rhh.org
I: www.rhh.org

91 Labrador Drive ★★★
Contact: Mrs Diane Lee, Forest
Edge, Holtwood, Wimborne
Minster, Dorset BH21 7DX
T: (01258) 840952 &
(01202) 403780
E: diane@leedpm.fsnet.co.uk

19 Lander Close ★★
Contact: Mr Paul Dredge,
Rumsey Holiday Homes, 2 Banks
Road, Sandbanks, Poole, Dorset
BH13 7QD
T: (01202) 707357
F: (01202) 701955
E: info@rhh.org
I: www.rhh.org

42 Lander Close ★★★
Contact: Mrs J A Marchant,
Sylbury, 3 Newhaven,
Winterbourne Steepleton,
Dorchester, Dorset DT2 9LH
T: (01305) 889449
E: imarchant@aol.com

60 Lander Close ★★★
Contact: Mr Paul Dredge,
Rumsey Holiday Homes, 2 Banks
Road, Sandbanks, Poole, Dorset
BH13 7QD
T: (01202) 707357
F: (01202) 701955
E: info@rhh.org
I: www.rhh.org

Lymington Lodge ★★
Contact: Mr Paul Dredge,
Rumsey Holiday Homes, 2 Banks
Road, Sandbanks, Poole, Dorset
BH13 7QD
T: (01202) 707357
F: (01202) 701955
E: info@rhh.org
I: www.rhh.org

3 Mansard Court ★★★
Contact: Mr Paul Dredge,
Rumsey Holiday Homes, 2 Banks
Road, Sandbanks, Poole, Dorset
BH13 7QD
T: (01202) 707357
F: (01202) 701955
E: info@rhh.org
I: www.rhh.org

4 Mansard Court ★★★
Contact: Mr Paul Dredge,
Rumsey Holiday Homes, 2 Banks
Road, Sandbanks, Poole, Dorset
BH13 7QD
T: (01202) 707357
F: (01202) 701955
E: info@rhh.org
I: www.rhh.org

6 Mansard Court ★★★
Contact: Mr Paul Dredge,
Rumsey Holiday Homes, 2 Banks
Road, Sandbanks, Poole, Dorset
BH13 7QD
T: (01202) 707357
F: (01202) 701955
E: info@rhh.org
I: www.rhh.org

2 Marina Court ★★★
Contact: Mr Paul Dredge,
Rumsey Holiday Homes, 2 Banks
Road, Sandbanks, Poole, Dorset
BH13 7QD
T: (01202) 707357
F: (01202) 701955
E: info@rhh.org
I: www.rhh.org

40 Panorama Road ★★★
Contact: Mr Paul Dredge,
Rumsey Holiday Homes, 2 Banks
Road, Sandbanks, Poole, Dorset
BH13 7QD
T: (01202) 707357
F: (01202) 701955
E: info@rhh.org
I: www.rhh.org

9 Panorama Road ★★★
Contact: Mr Paul Dredge,
Rumsey Holiday Homes, 2 Banks
Road, Sandbanks, Poole, Dorset
BH13 7QD
T: (01202) 707357
F: (01202) 701955
E: info@rhh.org
I: www.rhh.org

1 Peninsula Court ★★★★
Contact: Mr Paul Dredge,
Rumsey Holiday Homes, 2 Banks
Road, Sandbanks, Poole, Dorset
BH13 7QD
T: (01202) 707357
F: (01202) 701955
E: info@rhh.org
I: www.rhh.org

3 Peninsula Court ★★★
Contact: Mr Paul Dredge,
Rumsey Holiday Homes, 2 Banks
Road, Sandbanks, Poole, Dorset
BH13 7QD
T: (01202) 707357
F: (01202) 701955
E: info@rhh.org
I: www.rhh.org

The Quarries ★★★
Contact: Mr Paul Dredge,
Rumsey Holiday Homes, 2 Banks
Road, Sandbanks, Poole, Dorset
BH13 7QD
T: (01202) 707357
F: (01202) 701955
E: rumseyholidayhome@
compuserve.com
I: www.rhh.org

Quay Side ★★★
Contact: Mrs Suzanne Fuller,
Hollymoors, Holtwood,
Wimborne Minster, Dorset
BH21 7DR
T: (01258) 840377
F: 08701 672994
E: baiter.holidays@btinternet.
com
I: www.baiter.holidays.
btinternet.co.uk

Quayside ★★★
Contact: Mr Richard Ball, 59
Oakwood Avenue, Beckenham,
Kent BR3 6PT
T: (0208) 663 6426
F: (0208) 663 0038
E: quayside@oakwood59.
freeserve.co.uk

**Quayside Close Holiday
Apartments ★★★**
Contact: Mr & Mrs David Ellison,
3 Flaghead Road, Canford Cliffs,
Poole, Dorset BH13 7JN
T: (01202) 708195 &
07860 708676
F: (01202) 708195
E: quaysideclose@aol.co.uk
I: www.quayside.co.uk
I: www.quayside.co.uk

3 Red Sails ★★★★
Contact: Mr Paul Dredge,
Rumsey Holiday Homes, 2 Banks
Road, Sandbanks, Poole, Dorset
BH13 7QD
T: (01202) 707357
F: (01202) 701955
E: info@rhh.org
I: www.rhh.org

10 Sandacres ★★
Contact: Mr Paul Dredge,
Rumsey Holiday Homes, 2 Banks
Road, Sandbanks, Poole, Dorset
BH13 7QD
T: (01202) 707357
F: (01202) 701955
E: info@rhh.org
I: www.rhh.org

18 Sandacres ★★
Contact: Mr Paul Dredge,
Rumsey Holiday Homes, 2 Banks
Road, Sandbanks, Poole, Dorset
BH13 7QD
T: (01202) 707357
F: (01202) 701955
E: info@rhh.org
I: www.rhh.org

5 Sandbanks Court ★★★
Contact: Mr Paul Dredge,
Rumsey Holiday Homes, 2 Banks
Road, Sandbanks, Poole, Dorset
BH13 7QD
T: (01202) 707357
F: (01202) 701955
E: info@rhh.org
I: www.rhh.org

1 Sandhaven Court ★★★★
Contact: Mr Paul Dredge,
Rumsey Holiday Homes, 2 Banks
Road, Sandbanks, Poole, Dorset
BH13 7QD
T: (01202) 707357
F: (01202) 701955
E: info@rhh.org
I: www.rhh.org

7 Sandhaven Court ★★★★
Contact: Mr Paul Dredge,
Rumsey Holiday Homes, 2 Banks
Road, Sandbanks, Poole, Dorset
BH13 7QD
T: (01202) 707357
F: (01202) 701955
E: info@rhh.org
I: www.rhh.org

1 Sandhills ★★★★
Contact: Mr Paul Dredge,
Rumsey Holiday Homes, 2 Banks
Road, Sandbanks, Poole, Dorset
BH13 7QD
T: (01202) 707357
F: (01202) 701955
E: info@rhh.org
I: www.rhh.org

2 Sandhills ★★★
Contact: Mr Paul Dredge,
Rumsey Holiday Homes, 2 Banks
Road, Sandbanks, Poole, Dorset
BH13 7QD
T: (01202) 707357
F: (01202) 701955
E: info@rhh.org
I: www.rhh.org

5 Sandhills ★★★
Contact: Mr Paul Dredge,
Rumsey Holiday Homes, 2 Banks
Road, Sandbanks, Poole, Dorset
BH13 7QD
T: (01202) 707357
F: (01202) 701955
E: info@rhh.org
I: www.rhh.org

6 Sandhills ★★★
Contact: Mr Paul Dredge,
Rumsey Holiday Homes, 2 Banks
Road, Sandbanks, Poole, Dorset
BH13 7QD
T: (01202) 707357
F: (01202) 701955
E: info@rhh.org
I: www.rhh.org

3 Seahaven ★★★★
Contact: Mr Paul Dredge,
Rumsey Holiday Homes, 2 Banks
Road, Sandbanks, Poole, Dorset
BH13 7QD
T: (01202) 707357
F: (01202) 701955
E: info@rhh.org
I: www.rhh.org

4 Seahaven ★★★
Contact: Mr Paul Dredge,
Rumsey Holiday Homes, 2 Banks
Road, Sandbanks, Poole, Dorset
BH13 7QD
T: (01202) 707357
F: (01202) 701955
E: info@rhh.org
I: www.rhh.org

28 Seaview Road ★
Contact: Mr Paul Dredge,
Rumsey Holiday Homes, 2 Banks
Road, Sandbanks, Poole, Dorset
BH13 7QD
T: (01202) 707357
F: (01202) 701955
E: info@rhh.org
I: www.rhh.org

Self catering in Poole ★★★
Contact: Mrs C Webster, 38
Springdale Road, Broadstone,
Dorset BH18 9BU
T: (01202) 604295
E: christine@websterp43.
freeserve.co.uk
I: websterp43.freeserve.co.uk

Seymour ★★★
Contact: Mr Paul Dredge,
Rumsey Holiday Homes, 2 Banks
Road, Sandbanks, Poole, Dorset
BH13 7QD
T: (01202) 707357
F: (01202) 701955
E: info@rhh.org
I: www.rhh.org

**Sunridge Shades
Rating Applied For**
Contact: Ms Jacqueline Moore,
83 Wedgwood Drive, Lilliput,
Poole, Dorset BH14 8EW
T: (01202) 737790 & 0774 089
7694

22 Vallis Close ★★
Contact: Mr Paul Dredge,
Rumsey Holiday Homes, 2 Banks
Road, Sandbanks, Poole, Dorset
BH13 7QD
T: (01202) 707357
F: (01202) 701955
E: info@rhh.org
I: www.rhh.org

43 Vallis Close ★★★
Contact: Miss P A Thomas, 65
Parr Street, Parkstone, Poole,
Dorset BH14 0JX
T: (01202) 743768

29 Waldren Close ★★★
Contact: Mr Paul Dredge,
Rumsey Holiday Homes, 2 Banks
Road, Sandbanks, Poole, Dorset
BH13 7QD
T: (01202) 707357
F: (01202) 701955
E: info@rhh.org
I: www.rhh.org

37 Waldren Close ★★★★
Contact: Mr Paul Dredge,
Rumsey Holiday Homes, 2 Banks
Road, Sandbanks, Poole, Dorset
BH13 7QD
T: (01202) 707357
F: (01202) 701955
E: info@rhh.org
I: www.rhh.org

Windward ★★
Contact: Mrs Karen Preece,
Ashbourne House, Sandhurst
Lane, Sandhurst, Gloucester,
Gloucestershire GL2 9NP
T: (01452) 308585
F: (01452) 308585
E: windward.sandbanks@
btinternet.com

Establishments printed in blue have a detailed entry in this guide

**Wychcott, Spinnaker Reach &
Quay Cottage★★**
Contact: Mrs B Saunders,
Wychcott, Spinnaker Reach &
Quay Cottage, 1 Harbour
Shallows, 15 Whitecliff Road,
Poole, Dorset BH14 8DU
T: (01202) 741637

2 Wykeham Lodge ★★★
Contact: Mr Paul Dredge,
Rumsey Holiday Homes, 2 Banks
Road, Sandbanks, Poole, Dorset
BH13 7QD
T: (01202) 707357
F: (01202) 701955
E: info@rhh.org
I: www.rhh.org

PORCHFIELD
Isle of Wight

Herons Ghyll ★★★
Contact: Mr Colin Nolson,
Holiday Homes Owners Services
(West Wight), 18 Solent Hill,
Freshwater, Isle of Wight
PO40 9TG
T: (01983) 753423
F: (01983) 753423
E: holidayhomesiow@ic24.net

Squirrels
Rating Applied For
Contact: Mrs Bridget Lewis,
Channers Ltd, Blackbridge Brook
House, Main Road, Havenstreet,
Ryde, Isle of Wight PO33 4DR
T: (01983) 884742
E: bridget_lewis@talk21.com

PORTSMOUTH & SOUTHSEA
Hampshire

Alamar ★
Contact: Mr Alan Hyde, 1
Eastlake Heights, Horse Sands
Close, Southsea, Hampshire
PO4 9UE
T: (023) 9229 6442 &
07973 549608

The Apartments ★★
Contact: Mrs D Sullivan, 42A St
Catherines Road, Hayling Island,
Hampshire PO11 0HF
T: (023) 9263 7068
E: robert.sullivan2@virgin.net

Atlantic Apartments ★★★
Contact: Mr F Hamdani, 61A
Festing Road, Southsea,
Hampshire PO4 0NQ
T: (023) 92735574 & 92734233
F: (023) 92820955
E: feris@oceanhotel.freeserve.
co.uk
I: www.oceanhotel.freeserve.
co.uk

45 Exmouth Road ★★
Contact: Mrs Sarah Moss,
Pillmead Cottage, North Lane,
Buriton, Petersfield, Hampshire
GU31 5RS
T: (01730) 825076 &
(01428) 717231
E: mosscottage@btinternet.com

**Geminair Holiday & Business
Flats ★★★**
Contact: Mrs Pamela Holman,
Geminair Holiday & Business
Flats, 1 Helena Road, Southsea,
Hampshire PO4 9RH
T: (023) 9282 1602
E: gemflat@aol.com
I: www.gemflat.co.uk

**Helena Court Apartments
★★★**
Contact: Mrs Wendy Haley-
Firman, Helena Court
Apartments, 3 Helena Road,
Southsea, Hampshire PO4 9RH
T: (023) 9273 2116
F: (023) 9282 2698
E: tikitouch@hotmail.com

**Kenilworth Court Holiday Flats
★★★★**
Contact: Mrs T Sparrowhawk, 1
Kenilworth Road, Southsea,
Hampshire PO5 2PG
T: (023) 9273 4205
F: (023) 9273 4205

**Lakeside Holiday & Business
Apartments★★★**
Contact: Mrs V Hamza, Lakeside
Holiday & Business Apartments,
5 Helena Road, Southsea,
Portsmouth, Hampshire
PO4 9RH
T: (023) 9282 0690
F: (023) 9282 0690

Ocean Apartments ★★★
Contact: Mrs Dawn Sait, Ocean
Apartments, 8-10 St Helens
Parade, Southsea, Portsmouth,
Hampshire PO4 0RW
T: (023) 92734233 & 92734342
F: (023) 92297046
E: feris@oceanhotel.freeserve.
co.uk
I: www.oceanhotel.freeserve.
co.uk

**South Parade Apartments
★★★**
Contact: Mr & Mrs Sait, South
Parade Apartments c/o, 61A
Festing Road, Southsea,
Hampshire PO4 0NQ
T: (023) 92817007 & 92734342
F: (023) 92297046
E: feris@oceanhotel.freeserve.
co.uk
I: www.oceanhotel.freeserve.
co.uk

Sovereign Holiday Flatlets ★★
Contact: Mr & Mrs Michael
Cummings, Sovereign Holiday
Flatlets, 18 Victoria Grove,
Southsea, Portsmouth,
Hampshire PO5 1NE
T: (023) 9281 1398

Tramways House ★★★
Contact: Mr B Brown,
Woodthorpe, 18 Wilson Grove,
Southsea, Portsmouth,
Hampshire PO5 1PD
T: (023) 9273 0433
F: (023) 9273 0433

University of Portsmouth ★★
Contact: Mrs Anne-Marie
Harrison, University of
Portsmouth, Langstone Centre,
Furze Lane, Southsea,
Hampshire PO4 8LW
T: (023) 9284 4884
F: (023) 9284 4848
E: reservation@port.ac.uk
I: www.port.ac.
uk/decr/HAAHSCaL.html

32 Victoria Road South ★
Contact: Mr K Patel, A C
Property Services Ltd, 4
Highland Road, Southsea,
Portsmouth, Hampshire
PO4 9AH
T: (023) 9273 2111 &
07850 547551
F: (023) 9273 2555
E: acpropertys@newnet.co.uk
I: www.portsnet.
com/acpropertys

Wallington Court ★-★★
Contact: Mr Paul Stretton,
Wallington Court, 64
Craneswater Avenue, Southsea,
Hampshire PO4 0PD
T: (023) 9283 3831 &
07721 399910

PRINCES RISBOROUGH
Buckinghamshire

**Old Callow Down Farm
★★-★★★**
Contact: Mrs N E Gee, Old
Callow Down Farm, Wigans
Lane, Bledlow Ridge, High
Wycombe, Buckinghamshire
HP14 4BH
T: (01844) 344416
F: (01844) 344703
E: oldcallow@aol.com

RINGWOOD
Hampshire

Beech Cottage ★★★
Contact: Peter Grisdale, Flat 2
Canford Heights, 7 Western
Road, Poole, Dorset BH13 7BE
T: (01202) 707885

Glenavon ★★★
Contact: Mrs C D Wareham,
Glenavon, 12 Boundary Lane, St
Leonards, Ringwood, Hampshire
BH24 2SE
T: (01202) 873868
E: enquiries@glenavonhol.co.uk
I: www.glenavonhol.co.uk

Heather Cottage ★★★
Contact: Mr & Mrs Peter Harper,
The Gables, 93 Southampton
Road, Ringwood, Hampshire
BH24 1HR
T: (01425) 474567
F: (01425) 474567
E: pjh.hols@btinternet.com

Karelia Holidays ★★★
Contact: Mr R Gleed, Karelia
Holidays, c/o The Studio, Ashley,
Ringwood, Hampshire BH24 2EE
T: (01425) 478920
F: (01425) 480479
E: kareliahol@aol.com
I: http://members.aol.
com/kareliahol

ROMSEY
Hampshire

**Dunwood Manor Golf Club
★★★★-★★★★★**
Contact: Mr Roger Basford,
Dunwood Manor Golf Club,
Danes Road, Awbridge, Romsey,
Hampshire SO51 0GF
T: (01794) 340549
F: (01794) 341215
E: admin@dunwood-golf.co.uk
I: www.dunwood-golf.co.uk

The Old Smithy ★★★
Contact: Mr Paul Reeves, The
Old Smithy, Awbridge Hill,
Romsey, Hampshire SO51 0HF
T: (01794) 511778 &
07831 452018
F: (01794) 521446
E: paul@
paulreevesphotography.co.uk

ROOKLEY
Isle of Wight

Coastal Cottages ★★★
Contact: Mrs Jean Linaker, Little
Pidford Farm, Blackwater
Hollow, Rookley, Ventnor, Isle of
Wight PO38 3NL
T: (01983) 721841

ROPLEY
Hampshire

Dairy Cottage ★★★
Contact: Country Holidays ref:
10912, Country Holidays ref :
10912 Sales, Country Holidays,
Spring Mill, Earby, Barnoldswick,
Lancashire BB94 0AA
T: 08700 444 6603
F: (01282) 844244
E: ownerservices@ttgihg.co.uk
I: www.country-holidays.co.uk

RYDE
Isle of Wight

Ascot House ★
Contact: Mrs Cynthia Grace,
Ascot House, 27 The Strand,
Ryde, Isle of Wight PO33 1JF
T: (01983) 811716
F: (01983) 811716

Beachcomber ★★
Contact: Ms Tina Clift,
Beachcomber, 18 The Esplanade,
Ryde, Isle of Wight PO33 2DZ
T: (01983) 566333

Claverton ★★★★
Contact: Dr H Metz, Claverton,
12 The Strand, Ryde, Isle of
Wight PO33 1JE
T: (01983) 613015
E: lwdims@aol.com

Coast View ★★★
Contact: Mr & Mrs Richard &
Lynn Pester, Cynara, Winford
Road, Newchurch, Sandown, Isle
of Wight PO36 0NE
T: (01983) 865373
F: (01983) 865373

Fucshia House ★★
Contact: Mrs Bernadette
Sessions, 42 Fishbourne Lane,
Ryde, Isle of Wight PO33 4EX
T: (01983) 564370 &
07974 125676

Garden Flat
Rating Applied For
Contact: Ms Rowena Nihell,
Garden Flat, 54 The Strand,
Ryde, Isle of Wight PO33 1JD
T: (01983) 563432
F: (01983) 563432

Holmwood ★★★★
Contact: Ms Nicola Pitt,
Holmwood, 7 Argyll Street, Ryde,
Isle of Wight PO33 3BZ
T: (01983) 614852

Kemphill Farm ★★★★★
Contact: Mr Ronald Holland, Kemphill Farm, Stroudwood Road, Upton, Ryde, Isle of Wight PO33 4BZ
T: (01983) 563880
F: (01983) 563880
E: ron.holland@farming.co.uk
I: www.kemphill.com

Lionstone House
Rating Applied For
Contact: Mrs J C Hermiston-Hooper, Lionstone House, 13 The Strand, Ryde, Isle of Wight PO33 1JE
T: (01983) 563496 & 882688
F: (01983) 563496

Oak Lawn Holiday Cottages ★★★★
Contact: Mrs Lynette Haywood, Corner House, Oak Lawn, Woodside, Wootton Bridge, Ryde, Isle of Wight PO33 4JR
T: (01983) 884080

The Oaks ★–★★★
Contact: Mrs Christine Rossall, The Oaks, 56 West Hill Road, Ryde, Isle of Wight PO33 1LW
T: (01983) 565769

33 St Thomas' Street
Rating Applied For
Contact: Mr Derek Dart, 1 Manor Farm Cottage, Stratford Tony, Salisbury, Wiltshire SP5 4AX
T: (01722) 718675 & 07747 000023

Strand House ★★★
Contact: Ms Jan Johnston, Strand House, 17 The Strand, Ryde, Isle of Wight PO33 1JE
T: 07973 683722

Tavern Cottage ★★★
Contact: Miss Christine James, 21 Marina Avenue, Appley, Ryde, Isle of Wight PO33 1NG
T: (01983) 563036 & 565356
F: (01983) 565356
E: chrisjames@care4free.net
I: www.chris-james.co.uk

Upwood Holiday Flats ★★–★★★
Contact: Mrs Angela Harris, Upwood Holiday Flats, East Hill Road, Ryde, Isle of Wight PO33 1LS
T: (01983) 568965
E: angie.harris@virgin.net

The Victorian Lodge ★
Contact: Mrs Herbert, The Victorian Lodge, 8 Easthill Road, Ryde, Isle of Wight PO33 1LS
T: (01983) 563366

ST CROSS
Hampshire

North Cottage
Rating Applied For
Contact: Mrs C Wilson, The Mill House, St Cross, Winchester, Hampshire SO23 9RU
T: (01962) 861750

ST HELENS
Isle of Wight

1 & 2 Glade House ★★★★
Contact: Mrs Peggy Stephens, Old Mill Holiday Park, Mill Road, St Helens, Ryde, Isle of Wight PO33 1UE
T: (01983) 872507
E: oldmill@fsb.dial.co.uk
I: www.oldmill.co.uk

Bay Cottage
Rating Applied For
Contact: Ms Lisa Baskill, Home from Home Holidays, 31 Pier Street, Ventnor, Isle of Wight PO38 1SX
T: (01983) 854340
F: (01983) 855524

6 Broomlands Close ★★★
Contact: Ms Lisa Baskill, Home from Home Holidays, 31 Pier Street, Ventnor, Isle of Wight PO38 1SX
T: (01983) 854340
F: (01983) 855524

Carpenters Farm ★★
Contact: Mrs M Lovegrove, Carpenters Farm, Carpenters Road, St Helens, Ryde, Isle of Wight PO33 1YL
T: (01983) 872450

The Haven ★★
Contact: Mr Peter de Ferrars, Bembridge Holiday Homes, 9 Meadow Close, Bembridge, Isle of Wight PO35 5YJ
T: (01983) 873163
F: (01983) 873163
E: bembridge@deferrars.freeserve.co.uk

Isola ★★★★
Contact: Mr & Mrs Tim & Anne Baker, 16 Dorset Road, Ealing, London W5 4HU
T: (020) 8840 6053

The Little Shell House ★★★
Contact: Mrs Christina Hind, 11 Byng Road, High Barnet, Barnet, Hertfordshire EN5 4NW
T: (0208) 449 8867
F: (0208) 449 8867
E: thehinds@ntlworld.com

The Poplars ★★★
Contact: Mrs Honor Vass, Island Cottage Holidays, The Old Vicarage, Kingston, Corfe Castle, Wareham, Dorset BH20 5LH
T: (01929) 480080
F: (01929) 481070
E: ich@cottageholidays.demon.co.uk.
I: www.cottageholidays.demon.co.uk.

9 Port St Helens ★★★
Contact: Mrs Peggy Stephens, Old Mill Caravan Park, Mill Road, St Helens, Ryde, Isle of Wight PO33 1UA
T: (01983) 872507
E: old_mill@netguides.co.uk
I: www.oldmill.co.uk

ST LAWRENCE
Isle of Wight

Heshcot ★★★
Contact: Ms Lisa Baskill, Home from Home Holidays, 31 Pier Street, Ventnor, Isle of Wight PO38 1SX
T: (01983) 854340
F: (01983) 855524

Manor Retreat ★★★
Contact: Mrs Jeanie Brown, Manor Retreat, Salem Manor, Salem Close, St Lawrence, Ventnor, Isle of Wight PO38 1XN
T: (01983) 854485

Orchard Edge ★★★
Contact: Mrs Heather Nolan, Little Orchard, Undercliff Drive, St Lawrence, Ventnor, Isle of Wight PO38 1YA
T: (01983) 731106

Seven Sisters House Annexe ★★★
Contact: Ms Lisa Baskill, Home from Home Holidays, 31 Pier Street, Ventnor, Isle of Wight PO38 1SX
T: (01983) 854340
F: (01983) 855524

The Spinaker ★★★
Contact: Mr Derek Morris, Undercliff Glen Caravan Park, The Undercliffe Drive, St Lawrence, Ventnor, Isle of Wight PO38 1XY
T: (01983) 730261
F: (01983) 730261

Timber Top ★★★
Contact: Ms Lisa Baskill, Home from Home Holidays, 31 Pier Street, Ventnor, Isle of Wight PO38 1SX
T: (01983) 854340
F: (01983) 855524

ST MARY BOURNE
Hampshire

Trestan Cottage ★★★
Contact: Mrs Carolann Sutton, Trestan Cottage, Church Street, St Mary Bourne, Andover, Hampshire SP11 6BL
T: (01264) 738380

SALFORD
Oxfordshire

Mill Cottage ★★★★
Contact: Mr Charles Teall, Salford Mill, Salford, Chipping Norton, Oxfordshire OX7 5YQ
T: (01608) 641304 & 642849
F: (01608) 644442
E: teall@compuserve.com

Stable Cottage & The Granary ★★★★
Contact: Mrs Barbara Lewis, Larches Farmhouse, Salford, Chipping Norton, Oxfordshire OX7 5YY
T: (01608) 643398
E: babbylew@supanet.com

SANDLEHEATH
Hampshire

Plum Tree Cottage ★★★
Contact: Mrs Susan Sollars, Plum Tree Cottage, Sandleheath, Fordingbridge, Hampshire SP6 1QF
T: (01425) 653032
E: roy.sollars@virgin.net

SANDOWN
Isle of Wight

173, 174 & 179 Sandown Bay Holiday Centre★–★★
Contact: Mr & Mrs Paul Horobin, 22 St Boniface Cliff Road, Shanklin, Isle of Wight PO37 6ET
T: (01983) 868184
F: (01983) 868184

Barcelona Holiday Flats ★★★
Contact: Mr Stuart Marlow, 42 Fitzroy Street, Sandown, Isle of Wight PO36 8HZ
T: (01983) 402481
E: barcelonaflats@aol.com
I: barcelonahouse.co.uk

Beaulieu Cottage ★★★
Contact: Mrs Honor Vass, Island Cottage Holidays, The Old Vicarage, Kingston, Corfe Castle, Wareham, Dorset BH20 5LH
T: (01929) 480080
F: (01929) 481070
E: ich@cottageholidays.demon.co.uk.
I: www.cottageholidays.dmon.co.uk.

2 Hill Street ★★★★
Contact: Mrs Julia Clift, 2 Nunwell Street, Sandown, Isle of Wight PO36 9DE
T: (01983) 400447

Hope Cottage ★★
Contact: Ms Gail Whiting, 5 Witbank Gardens, Shanklin, Isle of Wight PO37 7JE
T: (01983) 864103

Kintore Court Holiday Apartments ★★★
Contact: Mr and Mrs D Allman, Kintore Court Holiday Apartments, 15 Broadway, Sandown, Isle of Wight PO36 9BY
T: (01983) 402507

Little Parklands Holiday Apartments ★★★
Contact: Mrs Janet Little, Little Parklands Holiday Apartments, 7 Winchester Park Road, Sandown, Isle of Wight PO36 8HJ
T: (01983) 402883 & 07747 623970
F: (01983) 402883

Parklands Apartments ★★
Contact: Mr Hugh McGee, Parklands Apartments, 9 Winchester Park Road, Sandown, Isle of Wight PO36 8HJ
T: (01983) 409602

Parterre Holiday Flats ★★★
Contact: Mr Roger Hollis, Parterre Holiday Flats, 34 Broadway, Sandown, Isle of Wight PO36 9BY
T: (01983) 403555
E: roger@parterre.freeserve.co.uk

The Retreat ★★
Contact: Ms Lisa Baskill, Home from Home Holidays, 31 Pier Street, Ventnor, Isle of Wight PO38 1SX
T: (01983) 854340
F: (01983) 855524

Establishments printed in blue have a detailed entry in this guide

Rose Bay ★★★
Contact: Mr Roy Cole, 81 Spring Lane, Great Horwood, Milton Keynes, Buckinghamshire MK17 0QP
T: (01296) 712319 &
(01908) 684471
F: (01296) 714063
E: roycole@breathe.com

Royal Court & Garden Apartments ★★★★
Contact: Mr & Mrs Blake, The Town House, 12 Beachfield Road, Sandown, Isle of Wight PO36 8ND
T: (01983) 405032

Sandown Bay Holiday Centre Chalet 103★
Contact: Mr & Mrs M W Leonard, 19 Wetherby Close, Milborne St Andrew, Blandford Forum, Dorset DT11 0JN
T: (01258) 837582

35 Sandown Bay Holiday Centre ★★
Contact: Mr & Mrs G Sitton, 'Cascade', 34 Hartswood Avenue, Reigate, Surrey RH2 8ET
T: (01737) 221074 &
07974 971595
F: 001775 6402669
E: grahamsitton@hotmail.com

Sandy Cove Holiday Chalet Chalet 102★★
Contact: Mr D L Puttick, Woodlands, 21 The Hedges, St Georges, Weston-super-Mare, Avon BS22 7BU
T: (01934) 520549 & (0117) 934 9344

Sunnymede ★★★
Contact: Mrs Honor Vass, Island Cottage Holidays, The Old Vicarage, Kingston, Corfe Castle, Wareham, Dorset BH20 5LH
T: (01929) 480080
F: (01929) 481070
E: ich@cottageholidays.demon.co.uk.
I: www.cottageholidays.demon.co.uk.

Sunnyside Holiday Chalet ★★★
Contact: Mrs Ann Roberts, 26 Hampshire Close, Bury, Lancashire BL9 9EZ
T: (0161) 280 7352
F: (0161) 763 3303

Valros ★★
Contact: Ms Lisa Baskill, Home from Home Holidays, 31 Pier Street, Ventnor, Isle of Wight PO38 1SX
T: (01983) 854340
F: (01983) 855524

Victoria Lodge ★★★
Contact: Mr W G Gibbens & Mrs P Jackson, Victoria Lodge, 4-6 Victoria Road, Sandown, Isle of Wight PO36 8AP
T: (01983) 403209

Whyte Chalets ★★
Contact: Mr & Mrs M Whyte, 9 Greenlydd Close, Niton, Ventnor, Isle of Wight PO38 2BJ
T: (01983) 730269

SEAVIEW
Isle of Wight

Elgin House
Rating Applied For
Contact: Mrs Julia Barber, Holiday Home Services (Seaview), Madeira Road, Seaview, Isle of Wight PO34 5HD
T: (01983) 811418
F: (01983) 616900
E: holiday~homes@netguides.co.uk
I: www.netguides.co.uk./wight/services.html

Pepita ★★
Contact: Ms Lisa Baskill, Home from Home Holidays, 31 Pier Street, Ventnor, Isle of Wight PO38 1SX
T: (01983) 854340
F: (01983) 855524

1 Pond Lane ★★
Contact: Mrs P A Bruce, Wheel House, 16a Woodside Avenue, Alverstone Garden Village, Sandown, Isle of Wight PO36 0JD
T: (01983) 408722 & 406180
F: (01983) 406180
E: PAMawford@aol.com

5 Sandpipers
Rating Applied For
Contact: Mrs Julia Barber, Holiday Home Services (Seaview), Madeira Road, Seaview, Isle of Wight PO34 5HD
T: (01983) 811418
F: (01983) 616900
E: holiday~homes@netguides.co.uk
I: www.netguides.co.uk./wight/services.html

Tides Reach
Rating Applied For
Contact: Mrs Julia Barber, Holiday Home Services (Seaview), Madeira Road, Seaview, Isle of Wight PO34 5HD
T: (01983) 811418
F: (01983) 616900
E: holiday~homes@netguides.co.uk
I: www.netguides.co.uk./wight/services.html

SHAFTESBURY
Dorset

Dairy Cottage ★★
Contact: Mrs Mary Pryce, Broadlea Farm, Sutton Waldron, Blandford Forum, Dorset DT11 8NS
T: (01747) 811330
F: (01747) 811330
E: mary2@tinyworld.co.uk

Elmvale & South View ★★★
Contact: Mr J K Westcott, Stonebank, 14 West Street, Chickerell, Weymouth, Dorset DT3 4DY
T: (01305) 760120
F: (01305) 760871
E: keithstonebank@aol.com
I: www.stonebank-chickerell.com

The Old Rectory Annexe ★★★
Contact: Country Hols ref: 7936, Country Holidays Sales, Country Holidays, Spring Mill, Earby, Barnoldswick, Lancashire BB94 0AA
T: (01282) 445096
F: (01282) 844288

Vale Farm Holiday Cottages ★★★★
Contact: Mrs Sarah Drake, Vale Farm, Sutton Waldron, Blandford Forum, Dorset DT11 8PG
T: (01747) 811286
F: (01747) 811286

Well Cottage ★★★★
Contact: Mrs Susan Smart, Hartgrove Farm, Hartgrove, Shaftesbury, Dorset SP7 0JY
T: (01747) 811908
F: (01747) 811066
E: cottages@hartgrove.co.uk
I: www.hartgrovefarm.co.uk

SHALCOMBE
Isle of Wight

Chessell Farmhouse ★★
Contact: Mr John Francis, Chessell Farmhouse, Chessell Pottery, Shalcombe, Yarmouth, Isle of Wight PO41 0UE
T: (01983) 531248
F: (01983) 531210
E: chessell-pottery@iga.uk.com
I: www.isle-of-wight.uk.com/chessell
I: www.chessellpottery.co.uk

Quarry Farm Cottage ★★
Contact: Mr Colin Nolson, Holiday Homes Owners Services (West Wight), 18 Solent Hill, Freshwater, Isle of Wight PO40 9TG
T: (01983) 753423
F: (01983) 753423
E: holidayhomesiow@ic24.net

SHALFLEET
Isle of Wight

Hebberdens
Rating Applied For
Contact: Mrs A J Ridler-Lee, Hebberdens, Yarmouth Road, Shalfleet, Newport, Isle of Wight PO30 4NB
T: (01983) 531364
F: (01983) 531364

SHANKLIN
Isle of Wight

Braeholme ★★★
Contact: Mr Roger Charlo, Braeholme, 8 Arthurs Hill, Shanklin, Isle of Wight PO37 6EF
T: (01983) 862673

Broadslade Court ★★★-★★★★★
Contact: Mr & Mrs Mike & Marilyn Spanner, Broadslade Court, Westhill Road, Shanklin, Isle of Wight PO37 6PZ
T: (01983) 865861
F: (01983) 865861

Byre Cottage ★★★
Contact: Ms Lisa Baskill, Home from Home Holidays, 31 Pier Street, Ventnor, Isle of Wight PO38 1SX
T: (01983) 854340
F: (01983) 855524

Central Holiday Flat
Rating Applied For
Contact: Mr & Mrs W R Piche, Central Holiday Flat, 15 High Street, Shanklin, Isle of Wight PO37 6JZ
T: (01983) 866288
F: (01983) 864611

Chelsea ★★
Contact: Mrs B E Walker, 14 Hungerberry Close, Shanklin, Isle of Wight PO37 6LX
T: (01983) 863194

Dairymaid Cottage ★★★
Contact: Ms Lisa Baskill, Home from Home Holidays, 31 Pier Street, Ventnor, Isle of Wight PO38 1SX
T: (01983) 854340
F: (01983) 855524

Fernhurst Holiday Apartments ★★★
Contact: Mrs Sandra Petcher, Fernhurst Holiday Apartments, 42 Western Road, Shanklin, Isle of Wight PO37 7NF
T: (01983) 862126 &
0778 8757167
E: dpetcher@talk21.com
I: www.isleofwight.uk.com/fernhurst

28 Grange Road
Rating Applied For
Contact: Mr J Derbyshire, 94 High Street, Shanklin, Isle of Wight PO37 6NS
T: (01983) 862363

Green Gable
Rating Applied For
Contact: Ms Lisa Baskill, Home from Home Holidays, 31 Pier Street, Ventnor, Isle of Wight PO38 1SX
T: (01983) 854340
F: (01983) 855524

Heatherdene ★★★
Contact: Ms Lisa Baskill, Home from Home Holidays, 31 Pier Street, Ventnor, Isle of Wight PO38 1SX
T: (01983) 854340
F: (01983) 855524

Laramie ★★★
Contact: Mrs Honor Vass, Island Cottage Holidays, The Old Vicarage, Kingston, Corfe Castle, Wareham, Dorset BH20 5LH
T: (01929) 480080
F: (01929) 481070
E: sally@ranson2.screaming.net
I: www.cottageholidays.dmon.co.uk

Laurel Court Holiday Apartments ★★
Contact: Mrs E W Thompson, Laurel Court Holiday Apartments, 40 Atherley Road, Shanklin, Isle of Wight PO37 7AU
T: (01983) 862203
E: laurel.court@zoom.co.uk

Lavender Cottage & Magnolia Cottage ★★★★
Contact: Mrs Honor Vass, Island Cottage Holidays, The Old Vicarage, Kingston, Corfe Castle, Wareham, Dorset BH20 5LH
T: (01929) 480080
F: (01929) 481070
E: ich@cottageholidays.demon.co.uk.
I: www.cottageholidays.demon.co.uk

Lovecombe Cottage ★★★
Contact: Mrs Anne Kennerley, Duxmore Farm, Downend, Newport, Isle of Wight PO30 2NZ
T: (01983) 883993

Luccombe Villa ★★★
Contact: Mrs Christine Williams, Luccombe Villa, 9 Popham Road, Shanklin, Isle of Wight PO37 6RF
T: (01983) 862825
F: (01983) 862362

4 Napier Apartments ★
Contact: Ms Lisa Baskill, Home from Home Holidays, 31 Pier Street, Ventnor, Isle of Wight PO38 1SX
T: (01983) 854340
F: (01983) 855524

The Old Grange Apartments ★★★★
Contact: Mr W M Douglas, The Old Grange Apartments, 9 Eastcliff Road, Shanklin, Isle of Wight PO37 6AA
T: (01983) 862385
F: (01983) 868385

Percy Cottage ★★★
Contact: Mr David Hirst, 47 George Street, Hoyland, Barnsley, South Yorkshire S74 9AE
T: (01226) 744754 &
07889 335455

25 Savoy Court ★★★★
Contact: Mrs Nadine Randall, Spring Chase, Westhill Manor, Shanklin, Isle of Wight PO37 6QB
T: (01983) 863962

Shanklin Manor Mews ★★★★
Contact: Mr T McLinden, Shanklin Manor House Hotel, Manor Road, Old Village, Shanklin, Isle of Wight PO37 6QX
T: (01983) 862777
F: (01983) 863464
I: www.hotels.iow.co.uk

Summerhill Apartments ★★★
Contact: Pat, Summerhill Apartments, 4 Culver Road, Shanklin, Isle of Wight PO37 6ER
T: (01983) 865545
F: (01983) 865545
I: www.summerhill.f9.co.uk

Upper Chine Holiday Cottages & Apartments★★★★
Contact: Mr Henry Butcher, Upper Chine Holiday Cottages & Apartments, 22a Church Road, Old Village, Shanklin, Isle of Wight PO37 6QU
T: (01983) 867900
I: www.upperchinecottages.co.uk

SHIPTON-UNDER-WYCHWOOD
Oxfordshire

Turkey Cottage ★★★★
Contact: Cottage in the Country, Forest Gate, Frog Lane, Milton-under-Wychwood, Chipping Norton, Oxfordshire OXY 6JZ
T: (01993) 831495
F: (01993) 831095
E: cottage@cottageinthecountry.co.uk
I: www.cottageinthecountry.co.uk

6 Westgate ★★★
Contact: Mrs Helen Harrison, Northgate, Shipton Court, Shipton-under-Wychwood, Oxfordshire OX7 6DG
T: (01993) 830202
F: (01993) 830202

SHORWELL
Isle of Wight

Bucks Farm Holidays ★★★★
Contact: Mrs Carol Jones, Bucks Farm Holidays, Bucks Farm, Shorwell, Newport, Isle of Wight PO30 3LP
T: (01983) 551206 &
0797 4054975
F: (01983) 551206
E: carol@bucksfarm.co.uk
I: www.bucksfarm.co.uk

Marylands ★★★
Contact: Mrs Honor Vass, Island Cottage Holidays, The Old Vicarage, Kingston, Corfe Castle, Wareham, Dorset BH20 5LH
T: (01929) 480080
F: (01929) 481070
E: ich@cottageholidays.demon.co.uk.
I: www.cottageholidays.dmon.co.uk.

SOUTH GORLEY
Hampshire

Little Horseshoes ★★★
Contact: Mrs Jenny Monger, Horseshoes, Gorley Road, South Gorley, Ringwood, Hampshire BH24 3NL
T: (01425) 479340
E: jenny@littlehorseshoes.co.uk
I: www.littlehorseshoes.sco.uk

SOUTHAMPTON
Hampshire

Bridge Terrace Apartments ★★
Contact: Mr & Mrs Mike & Sue Batley, Town or Country Serviced Apartments & Houses, 60 Oxford Street, Southampton, Hampshire SO14 3BL
T: (023) 8088 1000
F: (023) 8088 1010
E: town@interalpha.co.uk
I: www.intent.co.uk/southampton/hotels/townorc/index.htm

Bridge Terrace Studio Apartments ★★
Contact: Mr & Mrs Mike & Sue Batley, Town or Country Serviced Apartments & Houses, 60 Oxford Street, Southampton, Hampshire SO14 3BL
T: (023) 8088 1000
F: (023) 8088 1010
E: town@interalpha.co.uk
I: www.intent.co.uk/southampton/hotels/townorc/index.htm

---

11 Calshot Court ★★★
Contact: Mr & Mrs Mike & Sue Batley, Town or Country Serviced Apartments & Houses, 60 Oxford Street, Southampton, Hampshire SO14 3BL
T: (023) 8088 1000
F: (023) 8088 1010
E: town@interalpha.co.uk
I: www.intent.co.uk/southampton/hotels/townorc/index.htm

14 Calshot Court ★★★★
Contact: Mr & Mrs Mike & Sue Batley, Town or Country Serviced Apartments & Houses, 60 Oxford Street, Southampton, Hampshire SO14 3BL
T: (023) 8088 1000
F: (023) 8088 1010
E: town@interalpha.co.uk
I: www.intent.co.uk/southampton/hotels/townorc/index.htm

4 Canada Place ★★★★
Contact: Mr & Mrs Mike & Sue Batley, Town or Country Serviced Apartments & Houses, 60 Oxford Street, Southampton, Hampshire SO14 3BL
T: (023) 8088 1000
F: (023) 8088 1010
E: town@interalpha.co.uk
I: www.intent.co.uk/southampton/hotels/townorc/index.htm

7 Canada Place ★★★★
Contact: Mr & Mrs Mike & Sue Batley, Town or Country Serviced Apartments & Houses, 60 Oxford Street, Southampton, Hampshire SO14 3BL
T: (023) 8088 1000
F: (023) 8088 1010
E: town@interalpha.co.uk
I: www.intent.co.uk/southampton/hotels/townorc/index.htm

Pimms Hotel Apartments ★★★
Contact: Ms Brenda Collins, PJC Property Manager, 44 Winn Road, Southampton, Hampshire SO17 1EQ
T: (023) 8055 5102
E: pimmg.ug@virgin.net
I: www.hotelapartments.co.uk

Pinewood Lodge Apartments ★★★
Contact: Dr or Mrs S W Bradberry, Pinewood Lodge Apartments, Pinewood Lodge, Kanes Hill, Southampton, Hampshire SO19 6AJ
T: (023) 8040 2925

1 Vectis Court ★★★
Contact: Mr & Mrs Mike & Sue Batley, Town or Country Serviced Apartments & Houses, 60 Oxford Street, Southampton, Hampshire SO14 3BL
T: (023) 8088 1000
F: (023) 8088 1010
E: town@interalpha.co.uk
I: www.intent.co.uk/southampton/hotels/townorc/index.htm

---

16 Vectis Court ★★★
Contact: Mr & Mrs Mike & Sue Batley, Town or Country Serviced Apartments & Houses, 60 Oxford Street, Southampton, Hampshire SO14 3BL
T: (023) 8088 1000
F: (023) 8088 1010
E: town@interalpha.co.uk
I: www.intent.co.uk/southampton/hotels/townorc/index.htm

STANDLAKE
Oxfordshire

Gaunt Mill Cottage & Fishermans Loft★★★
Contact: Mrs Moira Glynn, Gaunt Mill Cottage & Fishermans Loft, Standlake, Witney, Oxfordshire OX8 7QA
T: (01865) 300227
F: (01865) 300117
E: moiraglynn@aol.com

STANFORD IN THE VALE
Oxfordshire

The Paddock ★★★★
Contact: Cottag in the Country, Forest Gate, Frog Lane, Milton-under-Wychwood, Oxford OX7 6JZ
T: (01993) 831495 & 831743
E: cottage@cotswold0.demon.co.uk

STANTON HARCOURT
Oxfordshire

Akers ★★★★★
Contact: Ms Barbara Harding, Lower Farm, Duck End Lane, Sutton, Stanton Harcourt, Oxfordshire OX29 5RH
T: (01865) 881553
E: barbaraharding@yahoo.co.uk
I: www.oxfordshirecottages.com

STEEPLE ASTON
Oxfordshire

Westfield Farm Motel ★★★
Contact: Mrs Julie Hillier, Westfield Farm Motel, Fenway, Steeple Aston, Bicester, Oxfordshire OX25 4SS
T: (01869) 340591

STOCKBRIDGE
Hampshire

7 Prospect Place ★★★
Contact: Mrs Caroline Sellick, Parfitts Farm, Chequers Lane, Eversley Cross, Hook, Hampshire RG27 0NT
T: (01189) 732155

STOKENCHURCH
Buckinghamshire

5 Gardens Close ★★★
Contact: Mrs M J Langston, Box Tree Cottage, Postcombe, Thame, Oxfordshire OX9 7DY
T: (01844) 281501

STOUR ROW
Dorset

Stable Cottage ★★
Contact: Mrs N Speers, Hill Farm, Stour Row, Shaftesbury, Dorset SP7 0QF
T: (01747) 838730

Establishments printed in blue have a detailed entry in this guide

STUDLAND
Dorset

Corner Cottage ★★
Contact: Mrs Antonia Ives,
Faun's Cottage, Swanage Road,
Studland, Swanage, Dorset
BH19 3AE
T: (01929) 450309
E: antonia2@dcives.fsnet.co.uk

STURMINSTER NEWTON
Dorset

Barn Cottage ★★★★
Contact: Mr Paul Gardiner,
Rivers Corner House,
Sturminster Newton, Dorset
DT10 2AB
T: (01258) 472326
F: (01258) 471211
E: paulgardiner@iname.com
I: www.heartofdorset.easynet.
co.uk

The Homestead
Rating Applied For
Contact: Mrs Carol Townsend,
The Homestead, Hole House
Lane, Sturminster Newton,
Dorset DT10 2AA
T: (01258) 471390
F: (01258) 471090
E: townsend@dircon.co.uk
I: www.townsend.dircon.co.uk

Owl Barn ★★★★
Contact: Mrs R Baynes, Wool
House Farm, Hole House Lane,
Glue Hill, Sturminster Newton,
Dorset DT10 2AA
T: (01258) 472238
F: (01258) 472238
E: bob.baynes@ukgateway.net

SWANAGE
Dorset

Flat 7 Grand View★★★
Contact: Mrs Linda Benfield,
Wyke Holiday Properties, 137A
High Street, Swanage, Dorset
BH19 2NB
T: (01929) 422776
F: (01929) 422002
I: www.apexweb.co.uk/whp

13 The Haven ★★★★
Contact: Mrs Linda Benfield,
Wyke Holiday Properties, 137A
High Street, Swanage, Dorset
BH19 2NB
T: (01929) 422776
F: (01929) 422002

Island View ★★★
Contact: Mr & Mrs R Jones,
Island View, 19A Priests Road,
Swanage, Dorset BH19 2RG
T: (01929) 426614

The Isles Apartments
★★-★★★
Contact: Mr Andrew Robinson,
Errinco UK Ltd, 1 King's Road,
Crowthorne, Berkshire RG45 7BF
T: (01344) 750777
F: (01344) 750222

SWAY
Hampshire

Dormie ★★★★★
Contact: Mr Chris Cutting, 9
Munnery Way, Orpington, Kent
BR6 8QD
T: (01689) 862709
F: (01689) 862533

Hackney Park ★★★
Contact: Mrs Helen Beale,
Hackney Park, Mount Pleasant
Lane, Sway, Lymington,
Hampshire SO41 8LS
T: (01590) 682049

Highbank ★★
Contact: Mr Stuart Bailey,
Homefield, Silver Street, Sway,
Lymington, Hampshire
SO41 6DG
T: (01590) 682025 & 683410
F: (01590) 683782
E: baileyhome@aol.com
I: www.stuartbailey.net

Middle Cottage ★★★
Contact: Mrs Ann Gimeno, 5
Fernglade, Manor Road, New
Milton, Hampshire BH25 5NZ
T: (01425) 623172
E: fairways@swayroad.co.uk

TARRANT GUNVILLE
Dorset

Underwood ★★★
Contact: Mrs M E Belbin, Home
Farm, Tarrant Gunville,
Blandford Forum, Dorset
DT11 8JW
T: (01258) 830208

THAME
Oxfordshire

Goldsworthy Cottage ★★★
Contact: Mrs Janet Eaton, Cuttle
Cottage, 17 Southern Road,
Thame, Oxfordshire OX9 2EE
T: (01844) 213035
E: janet-.eaton@virgin.net
I: www.cotswoldo.demon.co.uk

The Hollies ★★★★
Contact: Ms Julia Tanner, Little
Acre, 4 High Street, Tetsworth,
Thame, Oxfordshire OX9 7AT
T: (01844) 281423 &
07798 625252
E: info@theholliesthame.co.uk
I: www.theholliesthame.co.uk

Honeysuckle Cottage ★★★
Contact: Mr & Mrs A Lester,
Honeysuckle Cottage, Frogmore
Lane, Long Crendon, Aylesbury,
Buckinghamshire HP18 9DZ
T: (01844) 208697

THORNESS BAY
Isle of Wight

New Stable & Old Stable
Cottages ★★★★
Contact: Country Hols ref:
13509 Sales, Country Holidays,
Spring Mill, Earby, Barnoldswick,
Lancashire BB94 0AA
T: 08700 723723
F: (01282) 844288
E: sales@ttgihg.co.uk
I: www.country-holidays.co.uk

THREE LEGGED CROSS
Dorset

The Gables
Rating Applied For
Contact: Mr & Mrs David Priest,
The Gables, Verwood Road,
Three Legged Cross, Wimborne
Minster, Dorset BH21 6RW
T: (01202) 821322
F: (01202) 821322

TINGEWICK
Buckinghamshire

Lily Cottage ★★★
Contact: Mrs Rosemary Shahani,
Carolyn Cottage, 22 Main Street,
Tingewick, Buckingham,
Buckinghamshire MK18 4NN
T: (01280) 848047
F: (01280) 848047
E: rshahani@compuserve.com

TOTLAND BAY
Isle of Wight

Alum Bay House ★★
Contact: Mr Geoffrey Hurrion,
Alum Bay House, Alum Bay Old
Road, Totland Bay, Isle of Wight
PO39 0JA
T: (01983) 754546
I: www.cottageguide.
co.ukheritageholidays

Cliffway ★★★
Contact: Ms Katharine Gillings,
63 High Street, Codicote,
Hitchin, Hertfordshire SG4 8XD
T: (01438) 820220
F: (01438) 821360
E: kg@choros.com

The Coach House ★★★
Contact: Mr C E Boatfield,
Frenchman's Cove Country
Hotel, Alum Bay Old Road, Alum
Bay, Totland Bay, Isle of Wight
PO39 0HZ
T: (01983) 752227
F: (01983) 755125
E: boatfield@which.net

27 Granville Road ★★
Contact: Mr Colin Nolson,
Holiday Homes Owners Services
(West Wight), 18 Solent Hill,
Freshwater, Isle of Wight
PO40 9TG
T: (01983) 753423
F: (01983) 753423
E: holidayhomesiow@ic24.net

Heatherwood Holidays
★★★-★★★★★
Contact: Mrs Pamela Lodge,
Heatherwood Holidays,
Heatherwood, Church Hill,
Totland Bay, Isle of Wight
PO39 0ET
T: (01983) 752216
F: (01983) 752216

32 Lanes End ★★★
Contact: Mrs E J Osman, Warren
Farm, Alum Bay, Totland Bay,
Isle of Wight PO39 0AL
T: (01983) 753200

56 Lanes End ★★
Contact: Mr Colin Nolson,
Holiday Homes Owners Services
(West Wight), 18 Solent Hill,
Freshwater, Isle of Wight
PO40 9TG
T: (01983) 753423
F: (01983) 753423
E: holidayhomesiow@ic24.net

Nodewell House ★★★
Contact: Mrs Angela Morgan,
Westways, The Mall, Totland
Bay, Isle of Wight PO39 0DS
T: (01983) 753157

Sea Haven ★★★★
Contact: Mrs Honor Vass, Island
Cottage Holidays, The Old
Vicarage, Kingston, Corfe Castle,
Wareham, Dorset BH20 5LH
T: (01929) 480080
F: (01929) 480080
E: ich@cottageholidays.demon.
co.uk
I: www.cottageholidays.demon.
co.uk

Seaward ★★
Contact: Ms Lisa Baskill, Home
from Home Holidays, 31 Pier
Street, Ventnor, Isle of Wight
PO38 1SX
T: (01983) 854340
F: (01983) 855524

Seawinds Self-Catering
Holidays ★★
Contact: Mrs Jacquie Simmonds,
Norton Lodge, Granville Road,
Totland Bay, Isle of Wight
PO39 0AZ
T: (01983) 752772

The Shieling ★
Contact: Ms Lisa Baskill, Home
from Home Holidays, 31 Pier
Street, Ventnor, Isle of Wight
PO38 1SX
T: (01983) 854340
F: (01983) 855524

Stabula ★★
Contact: Country Holidays Ref;
7311, Country Holidays, Spring
Mill, Earby, Barnoldswick,
Lancashire BB94 0AA
T: 08700 723723
F: (01282) 844288
E: sales@ttgihg.co.uk
I: www.country-holidays.co.uk

Stonewind Farm ★★★
Contact: Mrs Pat Hayles, Barn
Cottage, Middleton, Freshwater,
Isle of Wight PO40 9RW
T: (01983) 752912
F: (01983) 752912

TURNWORTH
Dorset

The Old Post Office ★★★
Contact: Ms Adele Martin,
Okeden House, Turnworth,
Blandford Forum, Dorset
DT11 0EE
T: (01258) 454331
F: (01258) 454331

TWYFORD
Dorset

Buddens Farm Holidays ★★★
Contact: Mrs Sarah Gulliford,
Buddens Farm Holidays,
Buddens Farm, Twyford,
Shaftesbury, Dorset SP7 0JE
T: (01747) 811433
F: (01747) 811433

UPTON
Dorset

Sandon House ★
Contact: Mrs J Whittingham,
Sandon House, 641-643
Blandford Road, Upton, Poole,
Dorset BH16 5ED
T: (01202) 622442

VENTNOR
Isle of Wight

Bay House ★★
Contact: Mrs Janet Scovell, Bay House, Shore Road, Ventnor, Isle of Wight PO38 1RN
T: (01983) 852464
E: jdscovell@21.com

Bayview Holiday Flat ★★★
Contact: Country Hols Ref;13009, Country Holidays, Spring Mill, Earby, Colne, Lancashire BB18 6RN
T: 08700 723723
F: (01282) 844288
E: sales@ttgihg.co.uk
I: www.country-holidays.co.uk

Casuara ★★
Contact: Ms Lisa Baskill, Home from Home Holidays, 31 Pier Street, Ventnor, Isle of Wight PO38 1SX
T: (01983) 854340
F: (01983) 855524

Clarence House ★★★★
Contact: Mr C A Cooper & Mrs S M Lawson, Clarence House, Park Avenue, Ventnor, Isle of Wight PO38 1LE
T: (01983) 852875
F: (01983) 855006
E: c.a.c@btinternet.com
I: www.iowholidayapartments.co.uk

Daisy Cottage ★★
Contact: Mr V Anderson, Mari Laetare, Esplanade, Ventnor, Isle of Wight PO38 1JX
T: (01983) 855189 & 07790 396383
F: (01983) 855189
E: samval@marilaetare.freeserve.co.uk

Engleberg ★★★
Contact: Ms Mary Bell, Engleberg, 31 Alpine Road, Ventnor, Isle of Wight PO38 1BU
T: (01983) 852631
E: mrjbell@hotmail.com

Flat 2 56 St Catherines Street
Rating Applied For
Contact: Ms Linda Bruce, Flat 3, 56 St Catherines Street, Ventnor, Isle of Wight PO38 1HN
T: (01983) 856283

Garfield Holiday Flats ★★★
Contact: Mrs Susan Stead, Garfield Holiday Flats, 13 Spring Gardens, Ventnor, Isle of Wight PO38 1QX
T: (01983) 854084

Glenlyn
Rating Applied For
Contact: Mr Louis Stritton, c/o Eversley Hotel, Park Avenue, Ventnor, Isle of Wight PO38 1LB
T: (01983) 852244
F: (01983) 856534
E: eversleyhotel@fsbdial.co.uk
I: www.eversleyhotel.com

Glenwood ★★★
Contact: Ms Lisa Baskill, Home from Home Holidays, 31 Pier Street, Ventnor, Isle of Wight PO38 1SX
T: (01983) 854340
F: (01983) 855524

Jules Cottage ★★★★
Contact: Ms Lisa Baskill, Home from Home Holidays, 31 Pier Street, Ventnor, Isle of Wight PO38 1SX
T: (01983) 854340
F: (01983) 855524

Marina Apartments ★★★★
Contact: Mr P L Redding, Marina Apartments, Marine Parade, Ventnor, Isle of Wight PO38 1JN
T: (01983) 852802
E: marina_apts@madasafish.com
I: www.marinaapartments.co.uk

Marula ★★
Contact: Ms Lisa Baskill, Home from Home Holidays, 31 Pier Street, Ventnor, Isle of Wight PO38 1SX
T: (01983) 854340
F: (01983) 855524

Micklepage Holiday Flats ★★
Contact: Mr & Mrs Roy Dicker, Micklepage Holiday Flats, 12 Spring Gardens, Ventnor, Isle of Wight PO38 1QX
T: (01983) 852120

No 1 St Catherines View ★★
Contact: Ms Lisa Baskill, Home from Home Holidays, 31 Pier Street, Ventnor, Isle of Wight PO38 1SX
T: (01983) 854340
F: (01983) 855524

2 Palmerston House ★★★
Contact: Ms Lisa Baskill, Home from Home Holidays, 31 Pier Street, Ventnor, Isle of Wight PO38 1SX
T: (01983) 854340
F: (01983) 855524

Seagate Lodge ★★★
Contact: Ms Julia Warr, 8 Dartmouth Park Road, London NW5 1SY
T: (0207) 4854809

Seahaze ★★★
Contact: Ms Lisa Baskill, Home from Home Holidays, 31 Pier Street, Ventnor, Isle of Wight PO38 1SX
T: (01983) 854340
F: (01983) 855524

Sunrise ★★
Contact: Mrs Cherry Owens, Appletrees, Post Office Road, Inkpen, Hungerford, Berkshire RG17 9PU
T: (01488) 668216

Valerian ★★★
Contact: Mrs Margaret Louise Brown, Home from Home Holidays, 31 Pier Street, Ventnor, Isle of Wight PO38 1SX
T: (01983) 854340
F: (01983) 855524

Ventnor Holiday Villas ★-★★
Contact: Mr Stephen King, Ventnor Holiday Villas, Old Fort Place (Reception), Wheelers Bay Road, Ventnor, Isle of Wight PO38 1HR
T: (01983) 852973
F: (01983) 855401
E: steve@ventnor-holidayvillas.co.uk
I: ventnor-holidayvillas.co.uk

Westfield Lodges ★★★
Contact: Mrs J MacLean, Westfield Lodges, Shore Road, Bonchurch, Ventnor, Isle of Wight PO38 1RH
T: (01983) 852268
F: (01983) 853992
E: info@westfieldlodges.fsnet.co.uk
I: www.westfieldlodges.co.uk

Winyards ★★★★
Contact: Mrs Honor Vass, Island Cottage Holidays, The Old Vicarage, Kingston, Corfe Castle, Wareham, Dorset BH20 5LH
T: (01929) 480080
F: (01929) 481070
E: ich@cottageholidays.demon.co.uk
I: www.cottageholidays.dmon.co.uk

Woodcliffe Holiday Apartments ★★★
Contact: Mr Bryce Wilson, Woodcliffe Holiday Apartments, Undercliff Drive, St Lawrence, Ventnor, Isle of Wight PO38 1XJ
T: (01983) 852397
F: (01983) 852397
E: bryce.wilson@virgin.net
I: www.business.virgin.net/bryce.wilson

Worsley Cottage & Haddon Suite ★★★★
Contact: Mr & Mrs J Sharp, Old Park Hotel, St Lawrence, Ventnor, Isle of Wight PO38 1XS
T: (01983) 852583
F: (01983) 854920
E: thornton@old-park.demon.co.uk
I: www.parkhotel.co.uk

VERWOOD
Dorset

Forest Edge ★★★
Contact: Mr Patrick Singleton, Forest Edge, 59 Coopers Lane, Verwood, Wimborne Minster, Dorset BH31 7PG
T: (01202) 822093
E: psingle@waitrose.com

West Farm Lodges & West Farm Cottage ★★★
Contact: Mr & Mrs R J Froud, West Farm, Romford, Verwood, Dorset BH31 7LE
T: (01202) 822263
F: (01202) 821040

WALLINGFORD
Oxfordshire

The Annexe ★★★
Contact: Mrs R A Ryder, The Annexe, Alders Croft, South Moreton, Didcot, Oxfordshire OX11 9AD
T: (01235) 813104
F: (01235) 813104

WAREHAM
Dorset

East Creech Farm House ★★★
Contact: Mrs V Best, East Creech Farm House, East Creech, Wareham, Dorset BH20 5AP
T: (01929) 480519 & 481312
F: (01929) 481312
E: debbie.best@euphony.net
I: www.pages.euphony.net/debbie.best/holiday

WARSASH
Hampshire

The White House Flat B ★★★
Contact: Mrs E Paxton, 39 Warsash Road, Warsash, Southampton, Hampshire SO31 9HW
T: (01489) 572907

WATCHFIELD
Oxfordshire

The Coach House ★★★★★
Contact: Cottage in the Country Cottage Holidays, Forest Gate, Frog Lane, Milton-under-Wychwood, Oxford, Oxfordshire OX7 6JZ
T: (01993) 831495
F: (01993) 831095
E: info@cottageinthecountry.co.uk

WELLOW
Isle of Wight

Blakes Barn & Dairy Cottages ★★★★
Contact: Mr & Mrs Alan Milbank, Mattingley Farm, Main Road, Wellow, Yarmouth, Isle of Wight PO41 0SZ
T: (01983) 760503
F: (01983) 760503
E: i.milbank@btinternet.com

Brook Cottage & Mrs Tiggywinkles Cottage
Rating Applied For
Contact: Mrs Anne Longford, Warren Holidays, The Warren, 1 Elenors Grove, Ryde, Isle of Wight PO33 4HE
T: (01983) 883364
F: (01983) 884980
E: anne.longford@btinternet.com
I: www.warrenholidays.com

Jubilee Villa ★★★★
Contact: Mr & Mrs Steve & Jill Cowley, Coast and Country, Lee Farm, Wellow, Yarmouth, Isle of Wight PO41 0SY
T: (01983) 760327
F: (01983) 760327

WEST MELBURY
Dorset

Allans Farm Cottage ★★★
Contact: Ms Sally Nutbeem, Allans Farm, West Melbury, Shaftesbury, Dorset SP7 0BX
T: (01747) 852153
F: (01747) 852153
E: sally@eurolink.ltd.net

WEST PARLEY
Dorset

Church Farm ★★
Contact: Mr Andrew Ross, Church Farm, Church Lane, West Parley, Wimborne Minster, Dorset BH22 8TR
T: (01202) 579515
F: (01202) 591763

WEST TYTHERLEY
Dorset

Brightside Cottage Annexe ★★★
Contact: Mrs Barbara Wilks, Brightside Cottage, 19 Church Lane, West Tytherley, Salisbury, Wiltshire SP5 1JY
T: (01794) 341391
F: (01794) 341775
E: bwilks@talk21.com

Establishments printed in blue have a detailed entry in this guide

WHITELEY BANK
Isle of Wight

The Annexe ★★★★
Contact: Miss S Wilson,
Fowlsdown Farm, Whiteley
Bank, Ventnor, Isle of Wight
PO38 3AF
T: (01983) 866260

WHITWELL
Isle of Wight

Ashdale ★★★
Contact: Mr A V Woodford, Lane
End Nursery Cottage, Macketts
Lane, Arreton, Newport, Isle of
Wight PO30 3AS
T: (01983) 865727

43 Bannock Road ★★★
Contact: Mrs Sally Morris, 1
Upper Ash Drive, Whitwell,
Ventnor, Isle of Wight PO38 2PD
T: (01983) 730153

Downcourt Manor Farm
Rating Applied For
Contact: Mrs S R Harvey,
Downcourt Manor Farm, St
Catherines Down, Whitwell,
Ventnor, Isle of Wight PO38 2PJ
T: (01983) 730329
E: boharvey@farming.co.uk

2 Farm Cottages ★★
Contact: Ms Lisa Baskill, Home
from Home Holidays, 31 Pier
Street, Ventnor, Isle of Wight
PO38 1SX
T: (01983) 854340
F: (01983) 855524

Fossil Cottage ★★★
Contact: Mrs Honor Vass, Island
Cottage Holidays, The Old
Vicarage, Kingston, Corfe Castle,
Wareham, Dorset BH20 5LH
T: (01929) 480080
F: (01929) 480080

Greystone Cottage ★★
Contact: Mrs L M Steele,
Mardon, 79 New Road, Brading,
Sandown, Isle of Wight
PO36 0AG
T: (01983) 407221

Nettlecombe Farm ★★★
Contact: Mrs Jose Morris,
Jolliffes Farm, Whitwell,
Ventnor, Isle of Wight PO38 2AF
T: (01983) 730783
F: (01983) 730783

The Old Barn Cottage ★★★★
Contact: Mrs Honor Vass, Island
Cottage Holidays, The Old
Vicarage, Kingston, Corfe Castle,
Wareham, Dorset BH20 5LH
T: (01929) 480080
F: (01929) 481070
E: ich@cottageholidays.demon.
co.uk.
I: www.cottageholidays.demon.
co.uk.

The Old Dairy ★★★
Contact: Mrs E M Denham,
Lower Dolcoppice Farm,
Dolcoppice Lane, Whitwell,
Ventnor, Isle of Wight PO38 2PB
T: (01983) 551445
F: (01983) 551445

Sundew ★★★
Contact: Ms Lisa Baskill, Home
from Home Holidays, 31 Pier
Street, Ventnor, Isle of Wight
PO38 1SX
T: (01983) 854340
F: (01983) 855524

Sunglaze ★★★★
Contact: Mrs A M Evans,
Kingsmede, Kemming Road,
Whitwell, Ventnor, Isle of Wight
PO38 2QX
T: (01983) 730867

Union Cottage ★★
Contact: Ms Lisa Baskill, Home
from Home Holidays, 31 Pier
Street, Ventnor, Isle of Wight
PO38 1SX
T: (01983) 854340
F: (01983) 855524

Whitwell Station ★★★
Contact: Mrs Julia Carter, Old
Station House, Nettlecombe
Lane, Whitwell, Ventnor, Isle of
Wight PO38 2QA
T: (01983) 730667
F: (01983) 730667
E: enqs@whitwellstation.co.uk
I: www.whitwellstation.co.uk

Willow Bank ★★★
Contact: Mrs G J Eldridge, 28
Mulgrave Road, Ealing, London
W5 1LE
T: (020) 8997 7903

The Wing ★★★
Contact: Mrs Honor Vass, Island
Cottage Holidays, The Old
Vicarage, Kingston, Corfe Castle,
Wareham, Dorset BH20 5LH
T: (01929) 480080
F: (01929) 481070
E: ich@cottageholidays.demon.
co.uk.
I: www.cottageholidays.demon.
co.uk.

WICKHAM
Hampshire

Meonwood Annexe ★★★
Contact: Mrs Susan Wells,
Meonwood, Heath Road,
Wickham, Fareham, Hampshire
PO17 6JZ
T: (01329) 834130
F: (01329) 834380
E: sue.wells@pop3.hiway.co.uk

WIMBORNE MINSTER
Dorset

Hillberry ★
Contact: Mr & Mrs P L Cheyne,
Hillberry, Blandford Road, Corfe
Mullen, Wimborne Minster,
Dorset BH21 3HF
T: (01202) 658906

Millstream ★★★★
Contact: Mrs Mary Ball, 59
Oakwood Avenue, Beckenham,
Kent BR3 6PT
T: (020) 8663 6426
F: (020) 8663 0038
E: millstream@oakwood59.
freeserve.co.uk

Owls Lodge ★★★
Contact: Miss Mary King, Hope
Farm, Holtwood, Wimborne
Minster, Dorset BH21 7DU
T: (01258) 840239
E: kinger@owls-lodge.
freeservenet.co.uk

Spinney Cottage ★★★★
Contact: Mrs P N Ruddick,
Spinney Cottage, Arrowsmith
Road, Wimborne Minster, Dorset
BH21 3BE
T: (01202) 884725
F: (01202) 884725
E: ruddick1@globalnet.co.uk

Warriors Keep ★★★
Contact: Mr & Mrs Philip Stoate,
Warriors Keep, Keepers Lane,
Stapehill, Wimborne Minster,
Dorset BH21 7NE
T: (01202) 871061
F: (01202) 855992
E: Holidays@warriors-keep.
freeserve.co.uk
I: www.warriors-keep.freeserve.
co.uk

WINCHESTER
Hampshire

Flat 7 Kingsway Court ★★
Contact: Mr Peter Bulmer, Flat
14 Kingsway Court, Kingsway
Gardens, Chandlers Ford,
Eastleigh, Hampshire SO53 1FG
T: (023) 8025 3159

Gyleen ★★★★
Contact: Mr & Mrs Paul Tipple, 9
Mount View Road, Olivers
Battery, Winchester, Hampshire
SO22 4JJ
T: (01962) 861918
F: 0870 0542801
E: pauliz@tipple.demon.co.uk
I: www.cottageguide.
co.uk/gyleen

WINDSOR
Berkshire

9 The Courtyard ★★★
Contact: Mrs N J Hitchcock, 1
Agar's Place, Datchet, Slough,
Berkshire SL3 9AH
T: (01753) 545005
F: (01753) 545005
E: jhhitchcock@btinternet.com

Manor View Apartment ★★★
Contact: Mrs M C Smith, 32
Matthews Chase, Binfield,
Bracknell, Berkshire RG42 4UR
T: (01344) 485658
E: manorview@care4free.net
I: www.manorview.care4free.net

WINTERBORNE WHITECHURCH
Dorset

3 Rose Cottages ★★★
Contact: Mrs Anne Macfarlane,
Barn Court, West Street,
Winterborne Kingston,
Blandford Forum, Dorset
DT11 9AX
T: (01929) 471612
F: (01929) 472293
E: rosecottages5137@aol.com
I: www.cottageguide.co.uk/rose.
cottage

WITNEY
Oxfordshire

Gleann Cottages ★★★
Contact: Mr S Murtagh, Gleann
Cottages, Northfield Farm,
Woodstock Road, Witney,
Oxfordshire OX8 6UH
T: (01993) 778007
F: (01993) 775957
I: www.cottageguide.
co.uk/gleanncottages

Melrose Villa & Mews ★★★
Contact: Mrs Susan Petty,
Applegarth, Holloway Road,
Witney, Oxfordshire OX28 6NF
T: (01993) 703035
F: (01993) 771014

WOODLANDS
Hampshire

Purlins
Rating Applied For
Contact: Mrs Kay Lindsell,
Purlins, 159 Woodlands Road,
Woodlands, Southampton,
Hampshire SO40 7GL
T: (023) 8029 3833
F: (023) 8029 3855
E: kay@PeterLindsell.co.uk
I: www.purlins.net

WOOTTON BRIDGE
Isle of Wight

Grange Farm ★★★
Contact: Mrs Rosemarie Horne,
Grange Farm, Staplers Road,
Wootton Bridge, Ryde, Isle of
Wight PO33 4RW
T: (01983) 882147

**Wootton Keepers Cottage
★★★**
Contact: Mrs Honor Vass, Island
Cottage Holidays, The Old
Vicarage, Kingston, Corfe Castle,
Wareham, Dorset BH20 5LH
T: (01929) 480080
F: (01929) 481070
E: ich@cottageholidays.demon.
co.uk.
I: www.cottageholidays.dmon.
co.uk.

WORTH MATRAVERS
Dorset

One London Row ★★★
Contact: Mr & Mrs Philip &
Monica Sanders, 54 Hillway,
Highgate, London N6 6EP
T: (020) 8348 9815
F: (020) 8347 7124
E: ps@philamonic.com
I: www.philamonic.com

WROXALL
Isle of Wight

**Appuldurcombe Holiday
Cottages ★★★-★★★★**
Contact: Mrs C J Owen,
Appuldurcombe Holiday
Cottages, Wroxall, Ventnor, Isle
of Wight PO38 3EW
T: (01983) 840188 & 852484
F: (01983) 840188
I: www.appuldurcombe.co.uk

**The Brewhouse & Stable
Cottage ★★★**
Contact: Mrs Felcity Corry, Little
Span Farm, Rew Lane, Wroxall,
Ventnor, Isle of Wight PO38 3AU
T: (01983) 852419
F: (01983) 852419
E: info@spanfarm.co.uk
I: www.spanfarm.co.uk

Malmesbury Cottage ★★★
Contact: Ms Lisa Baskill, Home
from Home Holidays, 31 Pier
Street, Ventnor, Isle of Wight
PO38 1SX
T: (01983) 854340
F: (01983) 855524

Sunflower Holiday Lodges ★
Contact: Ms Melinda Johnson,
Sundance Lodge Sunflower
Holiday Lodges, Clevelands
Road, Wroxall, Ventnor, Isle of
Wight PO38 3DZ
T: (01983) 853194

Wroxall Manor Farmhouse
★★★
Contact: Mrs Virginia Grace,
Wroxall Manor Farmhouse,
Manor Road, Wroxall, Ventnor,
Isle of Wight PO38 3DH
T: (01983) 854033

YARMOUTH
Isle of Wight

Alma Cottage ★★★★
Contact: Mr Colin Nolson,
Holiday Homes Owners Services
(West Wight), 18 Solent Hill,
Freshwater, Isle of Wight
PO40 9TG
T: (01983) 753423
F: (01983) 753423
E: holidayhomesiow@ic24.net

Bay Cottage ★★★
Contact: Mr Colin Nolson,
Holiday Homes Owners Services
(West Wight), 18 Solent Hill,
Freshwater, Isle of Wight
PO40 9TG
T: (01983) 753423
F: (01983) 753423
E: holidayhomesiow@ic24.net

Grove Cottage ★★★
Contact: Mr Colin Nolson,
Holiday Homes Owners Services
(West Wight), 18 Solent Hill,
Freshwater, Isle of Wight
PO40 9TG
T: (01983) 753423
F: (01983) 753423
E: holidayhomesiow@ic24.net

Ivy Cottage ★★★
Contact: Mr Colin Nolson,
Holiday Homes Owners Services
(West Wight), 18 Solent Hill,
Freshwater, Isle of Wight
PO40 9TG
T: (01983) 753423
F: (01983) 753423
E: holidayhomesiow@ic24.net

2 Locksley Mews ★★★
Contact: Mr Colin Nolson,
Holiday Homes Owners Services
(West Wight), 18 Solent Hill,
Freshwater, Isle of Wight
PO40 9TG
T: (01983) 753423
F: (01983) 753423
E: holidayhomesiow@ic24.net

5 Locksley Mews ★★★
Contact: Mr Colin Nolson,
Holiday Homes Owners Services
(West Wight), 18 Solent Hill,
Freshwater, Isle of Wight
PO40 9TG
T: (01983) 753423
F: (01983) 753423
E: holidayhomesiow@ic24.net

Mallard House ★★★
Contact: Mr Colin Nelson,
Holiday Home Owner Services,
Westwight, 18 Solent Hill,
Freshwater, Freshwater, Isle of
Wight PO40 9TG
T: (01983) 753423

Marston Mews ★★★
Contact: Mr Colin Nolson,
Holiday Homes Owners Services
(West Wight), 18 Solent Hill,
Freshwater, Isle of Wight
PO40 9TG
T: (01983) 753423
F: (01983) 753423
E: holidayhomesiow@ic24.net

Prosper Cottage ★★★
Contact: Mrs Susan Robinson,
The Loft, High Street, Yarmouth,
Isle of Wight PO41 0PL
T: (01983) 760987
F: (01983) 760245

2 Providence Villas ★★
Contact: Mr Colin Nolson,
Holiday Homes Owners Services
(West Wight), 18 Solent Hill,
Freshwater, Isle of Wight
PO40 9TG
T: (01983) 753423
F: (01983) 753423
E: holidayhomesiow@ic24.net

Tree Tops ★★★★
Contact: Mr Colin Nolson,
Holiday Homes Owners Services
(West Wight), 18 Solent Hill,
Freshwater, Isle of Wight
PO40 9TG
T: (01983) 753423
F: (01983) 753423
E: holidayhomesiow@ic24.net

The Wight House ★★★★
Contact: Ms Lisa Baskill, Home
from Home Holidays, 31 Pier
Street, Ventnor, Isle of Wight
PO38 1SX
T: (01983) 854340
F: (01983) 855524

SOUTH EAST ENGLAND

ACRISE
Kent

Ladwood Farm Cottages ★★★
Contact: Fairhaven Holiday
Cottages, Derby House, 123
Watling Street, Gillingham, Kent
ME7 2YY
T: (01303) 891328 & 891427
E: mail@ladwood.com
I: www.ladwood.com

ALCISTON
East Sussex

Rose Cottage Flat ★★★
Contact: Mrs Brenda Beck,
Freedom Holiday Homes, St
David's Bridge, Cranbrook, Kent
TN17 3HJ
T: (01580) 720770
F: (01580) 720771
E: freedomholsuk@clara.net
I: www.freedomholidayhomes.
co.uk

Southdown Barn ★★★
Contact: Mrs R T Salmon, Best of
Brighton & Sussex Cottages Ltd,
Windmill Lodge, Vicarage Lane,
Rottingdean, Brighton, East
Sussex BN2 7HD
T: (01273) 308779 &
07956 662457
F: (01273) 300266

ALDINGTON
Kent

The Cottage ★★★★
Contact: Mrs Brenda Beck,
Freedom Holiday Homes, St
David's Bridge, Cranbrook, Kent
TN17 3HJ
T: (01580) 720770
F: (01580) 720771
E: freedomholsuk@clara.net
I: www.freedomholsuk.clara.net

ALFRISTON
East Sussex

Danny Cottage ★★★★★
Contact: Mr Michael Ann, France
Hill, Alfriston, Polegate, East
Sussex BN26 5XN
T: (01323) 870406 & 871343
F: (01323) 870406
E: Michael@annassociates.
demon.co.uk
I: www.annassociates.demon.
co.uk

Flint Cottage ★★★★
Contact: Mrs Linda Garwood,
Downland Cottages, Allington
Lodge, Allington Lane, Offham,
Lewes, East Sussex BN7 3QJ
T: (01273) 477044
F: (01273) 479855
E: cgarwood@dircon.co.uk
I: www.flintcottagesussex.co.uk

The Pony House ★★★★
Contact: Mrs Sandy Hernu, The
Old Forge, Sloe Lane, Alfriston,
Polegate, East Sussex BN26 5UP
T: (01323) 870303
F: (01323) 871664
E: hernu@nupanet.com

APPLEDORE
Kent

Ashby Farms Ltd ★★-★★★
Contact: Mr K P Ashby, Ashby
Farms Ltd, Place Farm,
Kenardington, Ashford, Kent
TN26 2LZ
T: (01233) 733332
F: (01233) 733326
I: www.stay.at/ashby.farms/

ARDINGLY
West Sussex

Townhouse Bothy
Rating Applied For
Contact: Mr & Mrs John
Campbell, Fairhaven Holiday
Rentals, Derby House, 123
Watling Street, Gillingham, Kent
ME7 2YY
T: (01634) 300089
F: (01634) 570157
E: fairhaven@pavilion.co.uk
I: www.fairhaven-holidays.co.uk

ARUNDEL
West Sussex

The Coachman's Flat and the
Cottage ★★
Contact: Mrs Sarah Fuente, Mill
Lane House, Slindon, Arundel,
West Sussex BN18 0RP
T: (01243) 814440
F: (01243) 814436

5 Hazel Grove ★★★★
Contact: Mrs Pauline Bitten, 5
Hazel Grove, Arundel, West
Sussex BN18 9JD
T: (01903) 883260

Village Holidays – Walberton
★★★-★★★★
Contact: Mrs G Pilkington, Elm
Cottage, Dairy Lane, Walberton,
Arundel, West Sussex BN18 0PT
T: (01243) 551073 & 552696
F: (01243) 551073

ASH
Kent

Hawthorn Farm ★★★
Contact: Mr & Mrs John Baker,
Hawthorn Farm, Corner Drove,
Ware, Ash, Canterbury, Kent
CT3 2LU
T: (01304) 813560
F: (01304) 812482
E: info@hawthornfarm.co.uk
I: www.hawthornfarm.co.uk

ASHBURNHAM
East Sussex

Slivericks Farm Folly
Rating Applied For
Contact: Mrs Brenda Beck,
Freedom Holiday Homes, St
David's Bridge, Cranbrook, Kent
TN17 3HJ
T: (01580) 720770
F: (01580) 720771
E: freedomholsuk@clara.net
I: www.freedomholidayhomes.
co.uk

ASHFORD
Kent

Dean Farm ★★★★
Contact: Mrs Brenda Beck,
Freedom Holiday Homes, St
David's Bridge, Cranbrook, Kent
TN17 3HJ
T: (01580) 720770
F: (01580) 720771
E: freedomholsuk@clara.net
I: www.freedomholsuk.clara.net

Establishments printed in blue have a detailed entry in this guide

Eversleigh Woodland Lodges
★★★
Contact: Mrs C J Drury,
Eversleigh Woodland Lodges,
Eversleigh House, Hornash Lane,
Shadoxhurst, Ashford, Kent
TN26 1HX
T: (01233) 733248 &
07703 349744
F: (01233) 733248
E: cjdrury@freeuk.com

The Old Dairy ★★★
Contact: Mrs June Browning,
Whatsole Street Farm, Elmsted,
Ashford, Kent TN25 5JW
T: (01233) 750238

BARNHAM
West Sussex

Welldiggers ★★★★
Contact: Mrs Penelope
Crawford, Church Farm Barns,
Hill Lane, Barnham, Bognor
Regis, West Sussex PO22 0BN
T: (01243) 555119
F: (01243) 552779
E: welldiggers@hotmail.com
I: www.welldiggers.co.uk

BATTLE
East Sussex

Highfields ★★★
Contact: Mr & Mrs Martin
Holgate, Highfields, Telham
Lane, Battle, East Sussex
TN33 0SN
T: (01424) 774865

Lonicera Lodge ★★★
Contact: Mrs Annette Hedges,
Lonicera, 114 Hastings Road,
Battle, East Sussex TN33 0TQ
T: (01424) 772835

Netherfield Hall Cottages
★★★
Contact: Mrs Jean Hawes,
Netherfield Hall Cottages,
Netherfield Hall, Netherfield,
Battle, East Sussex TN33 9PQ
T: (01424) 774450
F: (01424) 774450

Prior's Well ★★★
Contact: Mrs Yvonne Apps, 50
Wellington Gardens, Battle, East
Sussex TN33 0HD
T: (01424) 772914 &
0796 7902183

BEARSTED
Kent

The Haven ★★★★
Contact: Mrs Valerie Jensen,
Parsonage Cottage, The Green,
Bearsted, Maidstone, Kent
ME14 4DL
T: (01622) 737479
E: johnvaljensen@aol.com

Laurel Cottage ★★★
Contact: Mrs Chris Street, 43
The Landway, Bearsted,
Maidstone, Kent ME14 4BG
T: (01622) 739713
F: (01622) 631249

The Water Tower ★★★★
Contact: Country Holidays Ref:
13684, Country Holidays, Spring
Mill, Earby, Barnoldswick,
Lancashire BB94 0AA
T: 08700 723723
F: (01282) 844288
E: sales@ttgihg.co.uk
I: www.country-holidays.co.uk

BECKLEY
East Sussex

Church Cottage
Rating Applied For
Contact: Mrs Brenda Beck,
Freedom Holiday Homes, St
David's Bridge, Cranbrook, Kent
TN17 3HJ
T: (01580) 720770
F: (01580) 720771
E: freedomholsuk@clara.net
I: www.freedomholidayhomes.
co.uk

Fantails Cottage ★★★
Contact: Mrs Brenda Beck,
Freedom Holiday Homes, St
David's Bridge, Cranbrook, Kent
TN17 3HJ
T: (01580) 720770
F: (01580) 720771
E: freedomholsuk@clara.net
I: www.freedomholidayhomes.
co.uk

BENENDEN
Kent

Coopers Cottage
Rating Applied For
Contact: Mrs Gill Winter &
Patrick Tierney, Garden of
England Cottages, The Mews
Office, 189a High Street,
Tonbridge, Kent TN9 1BX
T: (01732) 369168
F: (01732) 358817
E: goec@dial.pipex.com
I: www.
gardenofenglandcottages.co.uk

Standen Barn ★★★★
Contact: Mrs Gill Winter &
Patrick Tierney, Garden of
England Cottages, The Mews
Office, 189a High Street,
Tonbridge, Kent TN9 1BX
T: (01732) 369168
F: (01732) 358817
E: goec@dial.pipex.com
I: www.
gardenofenglandcottages.co.uk

BEPTON
West Sussex

The Coach House ★★★
Contact: Dr Jennifer Randall, The
Coach House, Bepton, Midhurst,
West Sussex GU29 0HZ
T: (01730) 812351

BETHERSDEN
Kent

Brissenden Court ★★★★
Contact: Mrs Gill Winter &
Patrick Tierney, Garden of
England Cottages, The Mews
Office, 189a High Street,
Tonbridge, Kent TN9 1BX
T: (01732) 369168
F: (01732) 358817
E: goec@dial.pipex.com
I: www.
gardenofenglandcottages.co.uk

Huntsman Cottage ★★★★
Contact: Mrs Gill Winter &
Patrick Tierney, Garden of
England Cottages, The Mews
Office, 189a High Street,
Tonbridge, Kent TN9 1BX
T: (01732) 369168
F: (01732) 358817
E: goec@dial.pipex.com
I: www.
gardenofenglandcottages.co.uk

Mill Barn
Rating Applied For
Contact: Mrs Brenda Beck,
Freedom Holiday Homes, St
David's Bridge, Cranbrook, Kent
TN17 3HJ
T: (01580) 720770
F: (01580) 720771
E: freedomholsuk@clara.net
I: www.freedomholidayhomes.
co.uk

BEXHILL
East Sussex

2 Cantelupe Court ★★★
Contact: Mrs V Mathews,
Miraleisure Ltd, 51 Marina,
Bexhill, East Sussex TN40 1BQ
T: (01424) 730298
F: (01424) 212500

4 Carlton Court ★★★
Contact: Mrs V Mathews,
Miraleisure Ltd, 51 Marina,
Bexhill, East Sussex TN40 1BQ
T: (01424) 730298
F: (01424) 212500

1 Crossway Mansions ★★★
Contact: Mrs V Mathews,
Miraleisure Ltd, 51 Marina,
Bexhill, East Sussex TN40 1BQ
T: (01424) 730298
F: (01424) 212500

2 Crowhurst Court ★★★
Contact: Mrs V Mathews,
Miraleisure Ltd, 51 Marina,
Bexhill, East Sussex TN40 1BQ
T: (01424) 730298
F: (01424) 212500

1 Dalmore Court ★★★
Contact: Mrs V Mathews,
Miraleisure Ltd, 51 Marina,
Bexhill, East Sussex TN40 1BQ
T: (01424) 730298
F: (01424) 212500

11 Dalmore Court ★★
Contact: Mrs V Mathews,
Miraleisure Ltd, 51 Marina,
Bexhill, East Sussex TN40 1BQ
T: (01424) 730298
F: (01424) 212500

5 De la Warr Court ★★
Contact: Mrs V Mathews,
Miraleisure Ltd, 51 Marina,
Bexhill, East Sussex TN40 1BQ
T: (01424) 730298
F: (01424) 212500

Flat 2, 6 Middlesex Road
★★★★
Contact: Mrs V Mathews,
Miraleisure Ltd, 51 Marina,
Bexhill, East Sussex TN40 1BQ
T: (01424) 730298
F: (01424) 212500

Flat 2, 9 Bolebroke Road ★★★
Contact: Mrs V Mathews,
Miraleisure Ltd, 51 Marina,
Bexhill, East Sussex TN40 1BQ
T: (01424) 730298
F: (01424) 212500

Flat 3, 43 Eversley Road ★★
Contact: Mrs V Mathews,
Miraleisure Ltd, 51 Marina,
Bexhill, East Sussex TN40 1BQ
T: (01424) 730298
F: (01424) 212500

Flat 3, 6 Middlesex Road
★★★
Contact: Mrs V Mathews,
Miraleisure Ltd, 51 Marina,
Bexhill, East Sussex TN40 1BQ
T: (01424) 730298
F: (01424) 212500

Flat 4, 6 Middlesex Road
★★★
Contact: Mrs V Mathews,
Miraleisure Ltd, 51 Marina,
Bexhill, East Sussex TN40 1BQ
T: (01424) 730298
F: (01424) 212500

Flat 4 Cantelupe Court ★★★
Contact: Mrs V Mathews,
Miraleisure Ltd, 51 Marina,
Bexhill, East Sussex TN40 1BQ
T: (01424) 730298
F: (01424) 212500

Flat 5, 6 Middlesex Road
★★★
Contact: Mrs V Mathews,
Miraleisure Ltd, 51 Marina,
Bexhill, East Sussex TN40 1BQ
T: (01424) 730298
F: (01424) 212500

Flat 5 Cantelupe Court ★★★
Contact: Mrs V Mathews,
Miraleisure Ltd, 51 Marina,
Bexhill, East Sussex TN40 1BQ
T: (01424) 730298
F: (01424) 212500

Flat 6, 6 Middlesex Road
★★★
Contact: Mrs V Mathews,
Miraleisure Ltd, 51 Marina,
Bexhill, East Sussex TN40 1BQ
T: (01424) 730298
F: (01424) 212500

Gulls Nest ★★
Contact: Mrs V Mathews,
Miraleisure Ltd, 51 Marina,
Bexhill, East Sussex TN40 1BQ
T: (01424) 730298
F: (01424) 212500

Henry House ★
Contact: Mr Adrian Hazell, 4
Burhill Way, St Leonards on Sea,
St Leonards, East Sussex
TN38 0XP
T: (01424) 438702
E: sylvia.laidlaw@henry.dialnet.
com

4 Knole Court ★★★★
Contact: Mrs V Mathews,
Miraleisure Ltd, 51 Marina,
Bexhill, East Sussex TN40 1BQ
T: (01424) 730298
F: (01424) 212500

Miramar Holiday Flats
★★–★★★
Contact: Mrs Carolyn
Simmonds, Miramar Holiday
Flats, De La Warr Parade, Bexhill,
East Sussex TN40 1NR
T: (01424) 220360

Mulberry ★★★
Contact: Mrs Valerie Passfield,
Mulberry, 31 Warwick Road,
Bexhill, East Sussex TN39 4HG
T: (01424) 219204

6 Pevensey Court ★★★
Contact: Mrs V Mathews,
Miraleisure Ltd, 51 Marina,
Bexhill, East Sussex TN40 1BQ
T: (01424) 730298
F: (01424) 212500

7 Pevensey Court ★★★
Contact: Mrs V Mathews,
Miraleisure Ltd, 51 Marina,
Bexhill, East Sussex TN40 1BQ
T: (01424) 730298
F: (01424) 212500

Sackville Hotel ★★★★
Contact: Ms Amanda Fiora,
Sackville Hotel, De La Warr
Parade, Bexhill-on-Sea, Bexhill,
East Sussex TN40 1LS
T: (01424) 224694
F: (01424) 734132

5 Shellbourne House ★★★
Contact: Mrs V Mathews,
Miraleisure Ltd, 51 Marina,
Bexhill, East Sussex TN40 1BQ
T: (01424) 730298
F: (01424) 212500

26 St Lucia ★★
Contact: Mrs V Mathews,
Miraleisure Ltd, 51 Marina,
Bexhill, East Sussex TN40 1BQ
T: (01424) 730298
F: (01424) 212500

8 Wilton Court ★★★
Contact: Mrs V Mathews,
Miraleisure Ltd, 51 Marina,
Bexhill, East Sussex TN40 1BQ
T: (01424) 730298
F: (01424) 212500

BIDDENDEN
Kent

Frogs Hole Barn ★★★★
Contact: Mrs Penelope Pellett,
Frogs Hole Barn, Sissinghurst
Road, Biddenden, Ashford, Kent
TN27 8EY
T: (01580) 291845
F: (01580) 291845

Tanyard Barn ★★★★
Contact: Mrs Gill Winter &
Patrick Tierney, Garden of
England Cottages, The Mews
Office, 189a High Street,
Tonbridge, Kent TN9 1BX
T: (01732) 369168
F: (01732) 358817
E: goec@dial.pipex.com
I: www.
gardenofenglandcottages.co.uk

BILSINGTON
Kent

Cydonia Cottage ★★★★
Contact: Mrs Brenda Beck,
Freedom Holiday Homes, St
David's Bridge, Cranbrook, Kent
TN17 3HJ
T: (01580) 720770
F: (01580) 720771
E: freedomholsuk@clara.net
I: www.freedomholsuk.clara.net

Stonecross Farm Barn ★★★★
Contact: Mrs Jane Hickman,
Stonecross Farm Barn,
Stonecross Farm, Stonecross,
Bilsington, Ashford, Kent
TN25 7JJ
T: (01233) 720397

BIRCHINGTON
Kent

Rossetti Cottage ★★★
Contact: Mrs Jill Edwards, Band
Box, 79 Station Road,
Birchington, Kent CT7 9RE
T: (01843) 841101 & 841146

BIRDHAM
West Sussex

Croftside Cottage ★★★★
Contact: Mrs Susan Muffett,
Croftside Cottage, Main Road,
Birdham, Chichester, West
Sussex PO20 7HS
T: (01243) 512864 &
07721 325755
F: (01243) 512864
E: connex@cwcom.net
I: www.travellingsouth.co.uk

The Old Dairy ★★★
Contact: Mrs Diana Strange,
Carthagena Farm, Bell Lane,
Birdham, Chichester, West
Sussex PO20 7HY
T: (01243) 513885
E: strange.carthagina@virgin

BLEAN
Kent

Bay Tree House ★★★
Contact: Mr King, 21 Blean
Common, Blean, Canterbury,
Kent CT2 9EX
T: (01227) 472337
E: godfrey.king2000@virgin.net

50 School Lane ★★★
Contact: Mrs Brenda Beck,
Freedom Holiday Homes, St
David's Bridge, Cranbrook, Kent
TN17 3HJ
T: (01580) 720770
F: (01580) 720771
E: freedomholsuk@clara.net
I: www.freedomholsuk.clara.net

BOGNOR REGIS
West Sussex

Victorian House ★★
Contact: Mrs Jacqueline Thomas,
8 Leinster Gardens, Bognor
Regis, West Sussex PO22 7RE
T: (01243) 584959
F: (01243) 584959

BONNINGTON
Kent

Bonnington Court ★★
Contact: Mrs Monika Mann,
Bonnington Court, Bonnington,
Ashford, Kent TN25 7BA
T: (01233) 720521
F: (01233) 720521

**The Old School House
Rating Applied For**
Contact: Mr Stephen Drew, The
Old School House, The Green,
Bonnington, Ashford, Kent
TN25 7BN
T: (01233) 720955
F: (01233) 720606

BOSHAM
West Sussex

The Warren ★★★
Contact: Mrs G M Odell, The
Warren, Main Road, Bosham,
Chichester, West Sussex
PO18 8PL
T: (01243) 573927
F: (01243) 573927

BOUGHTON MONCHELSEA
Kent

Dovecote ★★★★
Contact: Mrs Gill Beveridge,
Dovecote, Wierton Oast, Wierton
Hill, Boughton Monchelsea,
Maidstone, Kent ME17 4JT
T: (01622) 741935
F: (01622) 741935
E: gill.beveridge@lineone.net

BOWLHEAD GREEN
Surrey

**The Barn at Heath Hall Farm
★★**
Contact: Mrs Susanna Langdale,
Heath Hall Farm, Bowlhead
Green, Godalming, Surrey
GU8 6NW
T: (01428) 682808
F: (01428) 684025
E: heathhallfarm@btinternet.
com

BOXLEY
Kent

Styles Cottage ★★
Contact: Mrs Sue Mayo, Styles
Cottage, Styles Lane, Boxley,
Maidstone, Kent ME14 3DZ
T: (01622) 757567
E: sue.mayo@virgin.net
I: www.freespace.virginnet.
co.uk/styles.cottage/

BRACKLESHAM BAY
West Sussex

Broadwater ★★★★
Contact: Mr & Mrs Michael or
Susan Wright, Broadwater, West
Bracklesham Drive, Bracklesham
Bay, Chichester, West Sussex
PO20 8PH
T: (01243) 670059
F: (01243) 670059

39 Marineside ★★★
Contact: Mrs Kirsten Spanswick,
33 Cartier Close, Old Hall,
Warrington, Cheshire WA5 5TD
T: (01925) 652334
F: (01925) 499552
E: spanners@westbrook.u-net.
com
I: www.westbrook.u-net.com

41 Marineside ★★★
Contact: Mrs Joan Welch,
Sheepwash House, West
Wittering, Chichester, West
Sussex PO20 8QN
T: (01243) 512846

Sea Ride ★★★
Contact: Ms Karen Brooker,
Baileys Estate Agents, 17 Shore
Road, East Wittering, Chichester,
West Sussex PO20 8DY
T: (01243) 672217
F: (01243) 670100
E: info@baileys.uk.com
I: www.baileys.uk.com
I: www.baileys.uk.com

BRASTED
Kent

Courtside Cottage ★★★
Contact: Mrs J R Couch,
Courtside Lodge, Station Road,
Brasted, Westerham, Kent
TN16 1NT
T: (01959) 561494 & 0774 020
1313
E: info@13thfloorcompany.com
I: welcome.to/courtside-cottage

BRENCHLEY
Kent

1 & 2 May Cottages ★★★
Contact: Mrs M E Allen, 12
Amberleaze Drive, Pembury,
Royal Tunbridge Wells, Kent
TN2 4HF
T: (01892) 824373
E: margaret.allen@lineone.net

BOWLHEAD GREEN
Surrey

**Great Worge Farm Barn
★★★★**
Contact: Mrs Brenda Beck,
Freedom Holiday Homes, St
David's Bridge, Cranbrook, Kent
TN17 3HJ
T: (01580) 720770
F: (01580) 720771
E: freedomholsuk@clara.net
I: www.freedomholidayhomes.
co.uk

BRIGHTLING
East Sussex

BRIGHTON & HOVE
East Sussex

**The Abbey Self-Catering
Flatlets ★-★★**
Contact: Reservations, The
Abbey Self-Catering Flatlets,
14-19 Norfolk Terrace, Brighton,
East Sussex BN1 3AD
T: (01273) 778771
F: (01273) 729147
E: theabbey@brighton.co.uk
I: www.brighton.
co.uk/hotels/theabbey

22 Albany Towers ★★★
Contact: Mrs R T Salmon, Best of
Brighton & Sussex Cottages Ltd,
Windmill Lodge, Vicarage Lane,
Rottingdean, Brighton, East
Sussex BN2 7HD
T: (01273) 308779 &
07956 662457
F: (01273) 300266

31 Albany Towers ★★★
Contact: Mrs R T Salmon, Best of
Brighton & Sussex Cottages Ltd,
Windmill Lodge, Vicarage Lane,
Rottingdean, Brighton, East
Sussex BN2 7HD
T: (01273) 308779 &
07956 662457
F: (01273) 300266

37 The Albemarle ★★★
Contact: Mrs R T Salmon, Best of
Brighton & Sussex Cottages Ltd,
Windmill Lodge, Vicarage Lane,
Rottingdean, Brighton, East
Sussex BN2 7HD
T: (01273) 308779 &
07956 662457
F: (01273) 300266

Bella Vista Holiday Flats ★★★
Contact: J D Mason, Telephone
Enquiries only, Hove, Brighton
T: (01273) 421897

52 Blenheim Court ★★★
Contact: Mrs R T Salmon, Best of
Brighton & Sussex Cottages Ltd,
Windmill Lodge, Rottingdean, Brighton, East
Sussex BN2 7HD
T: (01273) 308779 &
07956 662457
F: (01273) 300266

40 Borough Street ★★★
Contact: Mr Trevor Jones, 40
Borough Street, 40 Borough
Street, Brighton, East Sussex
BN1 3BG
T: 07711 712117

Brighton Holiday Flats ★★★
Contact: Mrs L Bowler, Little
Shepham, Shepham Lane,
Polegate, East Sussex BN26 6NB
T: (01323) 483119
F: (01323) 488322
E: bookings@brightonflats.co.uk
I: www.brightonflats.co.uk

Brighton Lanes ★★-★★★
Contact: Miss Frances Hix or
Carol Coates, Brighton Lanes,
Gordon House, 14A Ship Street,
Brighton, East Sussex BN1 1AD
T: (01273) 325315
F: (01273) 323882
E: intermkt@pavilion.co.uk
I: www.brighton.
co.uk/hotels/brightonlanes

Brighton Marina Apartments
★★
Contact: Mr & Mrs Richard &
Lorna Gartside, 16 Orchard
Gardens, Hove, East Sussex
BN3 7BJ
T: (01273) 737006
E: bton-marina-apts@mistral.
co.uk

**Brighton Marina Holiday
Apartments**★★★★
Contact: Mrs S B Wills, Brighton
Marina Holiday Apartments, 5
Mariners Quay, Brighton Marina
Village, Brighton, East Sussex
BN2 5UZ
T: (01273) 693569
F: (01273) 693569

18 Bristol Road ★★
Contact: Mrs R T Salmon, Best of
Brighton & Sussex Cottages Ltd,
Windmill Lodge, Vicarage Lane,
Rottingdean, Brighton, East
Sussex BN2 7HD
T: (01273) 308779 &
07956 662457
F: (01273) 300266

67 Britannia Court ★★★
Contact: Mrs R T Salmon, Best of
Brighton & Sussex Cottages Ltd,
Windmill Lodge, Vicarage Lane,
Rottingdean, Brighton, East
Sussex BN2 7HD
T: (01273) 308779 &
07956 662457
F: (01273) 300266

9 Brunswick Mews ★★
Contact: Mrs R T Salmon, Best of
Brighton & Sussex Cottages Ltd,
Windmill Lodge, Vicarage Lane,
Rottingdean, Brighton, East
Sussex BN2 7HD
T: (01273) 308779 &
07956 662457
F: (01273) 300266

6 Burleigh Court ★★
Contact: Mrs R Hall, 25 Fairoak
Drive, Eltham, London SE9 2QG
T: (020) 8850 1892
F: (020) 8850 1892

The Cabin ★★
Contact: Mrs R T Salmon, Best of
Brighton & Sussex Cottages Ltd,
Windmill Lodge, Vicarage Lane,
Rottingdean, Brighton, East
Sussex BN2 7HD
T: (01273) 308779 &
07956 662457
F: (01273) 300266

43 Chain Pier House ★★★
Contact: Mrs R T Salmon, Best of
Brighton & Sussex Cottages Ltd,
Windmill Lodge, Vicarage Lane,
Rottingdean, Brighton, East
Sussex BN2 7HD
T: (01273) 308779 &
07956 662457
F: (01273) 300266

**34 Chartwell Court
Rating Applied For**
Contact: Mrs R T Salmon, Best of
Brighton & Sussex Cottages Ltd,
Windmill Lodge, Vicarage Lane,
Rottingdean, Brighton, East
Sussex BN2 7HD
T: (01273) 308779 &
07956 662457
F: (01273) 300266

Cobblers Cottage ★★★
Contact: Mrs R T Salmon, Best of
Brighton & Sussex Cottages Ltd,
Windmill Lodge, Vicarage Lane,
Rottingdean, Brighton, East
Sussex BN2 7HD
T: (01273) 308779 &
07956 662457
F: (01273) 300266

**Dale Court Family Holiday
Flats** ★★★
Contact: Ms Bettina Goodman,
Dale Court Family Holiday Flats,
9 Florence Road, Brighton, East
Sussex BN1 6DL
T: (01273) 326963

**6 East Drive
Rating Applied For**
Contact: Mrs R T Salmon, Best of
Brighton & Sussex Cottages Ltd,
Windmill Lodge, Vicarage Lane,
Rottingdean, Brighton, East
Sussex BN2 7HD
T: (01273) 308779 &
07956 662457
F: (01273) 300266

44 Eastern Concourse ★★★
Contact: Mrs Pat Lowe, Palms
Property Sales & Letting, Marine
Trade Centre, Brighton Marina,
Brighton, East Sussex BN2 5UG
T: (01273) 626000

Flat 1 12 Palmeira Avenue
★★★
Contact: Mrs R T Salmon, Best of
Brighton & Sussex Cottages Ltd,
Windmill Lodge, Vicarage Lane,
Rottingdean, Brighton, East
Sussex BN2 7HD
T: (01273) 308779 &
07956 662457
F: (01273) 300266

Flat 1 14 Old Shoreham Road
★★
Contact: Mrs R T Salmon, Best of
Brighton & Sussex Cottages Ltd,
Windmill Lodge, Vicarage Lane,
Rottingdean, Brighton, East
Sussex BN2 7HD
T: (01273) 308779 &
07956 662457
F: (01273) 300266

Flat 1 22 Brunswick Square
★★★
Contact: Mrs R T Salmon, Best of
Brighton & Sussex Cottages Ltd,
Windmill Lodge, Vicarage Lane,
Rottingdean, Brighton, East
Sussex BN2 7HD
T: (01273) 308779 &
07956 662457
F: (01273) 300266

Flat 1 68 Marine Parade★★★
Contact: Mrs R T Salmon, Best of
Brighton & Sussex Cottages Ltd,
Windmill Lodge, Vicarage Lane,
Rottingdean, Brighton, East
Sussex BN2 7HD
T: (01273) 308779 &
07956 662457
F: (01273) 300266

Flat 1 91 Lansdowne Place
★★★
Contact: Mrs R T Salmon, Best of
Brighton & Sussex Cottages Ltd,
Windmill Lodge, Vicarage Lane,
Rottingdean, Brighton, East
Sussex BN2 7HD
T: (01273) 308779 &
07956 662457
F: (01273) 300266

**Flat 1 Ground Floor 44
Brunswick Square**★★★★
Contact: Mrs R T Salmon, Best of
Brighton & Sussex Cottages Ltd,
Windmill Lodge, Vicarage Lane,
Rottingdean, Brighton, East
Sussex BN2 7HD
T: (01273) 308779 &
07956 662457
F: (01273) 300266

Flat 10 4 Adelaide Mansions
★★★
Contact: Mrs R T Salmon, Best of
Brighton & Sussex Cottages Ltd,
Windmill Lodge, Vicarage Lane,
Rottingdean, Brighton, East
Sussex BN2 7HD
T: (01273) 308779 &
07956 662457
F: (01273) 300266

Flat 11 4 Adelaide Mansions
★★★★
Contact: Mrs R T Salmon, Best of
Brighton & Sussex Cottages Ltd,
Windmill Lodge, Vicarage Lane,
Rottingdean, Brighton, East
Sussex BN2 7HD
T: (01273) 308779 &
07956 662457
F: (01273) 300266

**Flat 12 37 Brunswick Terrace
Rating Applied For**
Contact: Mrs R T Salmon, Best of
Brighton & Sussex Cottages Ltd,
Windmill Lodge, Vicarage Lane,
Rottingdean, Brighton, East
Sussex BN2 7HD
T: (01273) 308779 &
07956 662457
F: (01273) 300266

**Flat 14, 37-38 Adelaide
Crescent**★★★★
Contact: Mrs R T Salmon, Best of
Brighton & Sussex Cottages Ltd,
Windmill Lodge, Vicarage Lane,
Rottingdean, Brighton, East
Sussex BN2 7HD
T: (01273) 308779 &
07956 662457
F: (01273) 300266

Flat 2 34 Bedford Square★★★
Contact: Mrs R T Salmon, Best of
Brighton & Sussex Cottages Ltd,
Windmill Lodge, Vicarage Lane,
Rottingdean, Brighton, East
Sussex BN2 7HD
T: (01273) 308779 &
07956 662457
F: (01273) 300266

Flat 3 1 Third Avenue★★★
Contact: Mrs R T Salmon, Best of
Brighton & Sussex Cottages Ltd,
Windmill Lodge, Vicarage Lane,
Rottingdean, Brighton, East
Sussex BN2 7HD
T: (01273) 308779 &
07956 662457
F: (01273) 300266

**Flat 3 127 Kings Road
Rating Applied For**
Contact: Mrs R T Salmon, Best of
Brighton & Sussex Cottages Ltd,
Windmill Lodge, Vicarage Lane,
Rottingdean, Brighton, East
Sussex BN2 7HD
T: (01273) 308779 &
07956 662457
F: (01273) 300266

Flat 3 34 Brunswick Terrace
★★★★
Contact: Mrs R T Salmon, Best of
Brighton & Sussex Cottages Ltd,
Windmill Lodge, Vicarage Lane,
Rottingdean, Brighton, East
Sussex BN2 7HD
T: (01273) 308779 &
07956 662457
F: (01273) 300266

Flat 3 35 First Avenue★★
Contact: Mrs R T Salmon, Best of
Brighton & Sussex Cottages Ltd,
Windmill Lodge, Vicarage Lane,
Rottingdean, Brighton, East
Sussex BN2 7HD
T: (01273) 308779 &
07956 662457
F: (01273) 300266

Flat 3 6 Evelyn Terrace★★★
Contact: Mrs R T Salmon, Best of
Brighton & Sussex Cottages Ltd,
Windmill Lodge, Vicarage Lane,
Rottingdean, Brighton, East
Sussex BN2 7HD
T: (01273) 308779 &
07956 662457
F: (01273) 300266

Flat 3 68 Marine Parade★★★
Contact: Mrs R T Salmon, Best of
Brighton & Sussex Cottages Ltd,
Windmill Lodge, Vicarage Lane,
Rottingdean, Brighton, East
Sussex BN2 7HD
T: (01273) 308779 &
07956 662457
F: (01273) 300266

Flat 4 20 Fourth Avenue★★★
Contact: Mrs R T Salmon, Best of
Brighton & Sussex Cottages Ltd,
Windmill Lodge, Vicarage Lane,
Rottingdean, Brighton, East
Sussex BN2 7HD
T: (01273) 308779 &
07956 662457
F: (01273) 300266

Flat 5 35 First Avenue★★
Contact: Mrs R T Salmon, Best of
Brighton & Sussex Cottages Ltd,
Windmill Lodge, Vicarage Lane,
Rottingdean, Brighton, East
Sussex BN2 7HD
T: (01273) 308779 &
07956 662457
F: (01273) 300266

Establishments printed in blue have a detailed entry in this guide

Flat 5 37 Brunswick Terrace ★★★
Contact: Mrs R T Salmon, Best of Brighton & Sussex Cottages Ltd, Windmill Lodge, Vicarage Lane, Rottingdean, Brighton, East Sussex BN2 7HD
T: (01273) 308779 &
07956 662457
F: (01273) 300266

Flat 5 4 Medina Terrace★★★
Contact: Mrs R T Salmon, Best of Brighton & Sussex Cottages Ltd, Windmill Lodge, Vicarage Lane, Rottingdean, Brighton, East Sussex BN2 7HD
T: (01273) 308779 &
07956 662457
F: (01273) 300266

Flat 5 5–6 Sussex Square★★★
Contact: Mrs R T Salmon, Best of Brighton & Sussex Cottages Ltd, Windmill Lodge, Vicarage Lane, Rottingdean, Brighton, East Sussex BN2 7HD
T: (01273) 308779 &
07956 662457
F: (01273) 300266

Flat 56 Brittania Court
Rating Applied For
Contact: Mrs R T Salmon, Best of Brighton & Sussex Cottages Ltd, Windmill Lodge, Vicarage Lane, Rottingdean, Brighton, East Sussex BN2 7HD
T: (01273) 308779 &
07956 662457
F: (01273) 300266

Flat 6, 63 Regency Square ★★★
Contact: Mrs R T Salmon, Best of Brighton & Sussex Cottages Ltd, Windmill Lodge, Vicarage Lane, Rottingdean, Brighton, East Sussex BN2 7HD
T: (01273) 308779 &
07956 662457
F: (01273) 300266

Flat 6 Glenside Court ★★★
Contact: Mrs R T Salmon, Best of Brighton & Sussex Cottages Ltd, Windmill Lodge, Vicarage Lane, Rottingdean, Brighton, East Sussex BN2 7HD
T: (01273) 308779 &
07956 662457
F: (01273) 300266

Flat 6 Lansdowne Court
Rating Applied For
Contact: Mr R T Harris, Best of Brighton & Sussex Cottages, Windmill Lodge, Vicarage Lane, Rottingdean, Brighton, East Sussex BN2 7HD
T: (01273) 308779
F: (01273) 300266
E: brightoncottages@pavilion.co.uk
I: www.bestofbrighton.co.uk

Flat 8 2 Wellington Court
Rating Applied For
Contact: Mrs R T Salmon, Best of Brighton & Sussex Cottages Ltd, Windmill Lodge, Vicarage Lane, Rottingdean, Brighton, East Sussex BN2 7HD
T: (01273) 308779 &
07956 662457
F: (01273) 300266

Flat 8 The Georgian House ★★★
Contact: Mrs R T Salmon, Best of Brighton & Sussex Cottages Ltd, Windmill Lodge, Vicarage Lane, Rottingdean, Brighton, East Sussex BN2 7HD
T: (01273) 308779 &
07956 662457
F: (01273) 300266

Flat 9 28 Brunswick Terrace ★★★
Contact: Mrs R T Salmon, Best of Brighton & Sussex Cottages Ltd, Windmill Lodge, Vicarage Lane, Rottingdean, Brighton, East Sussex BN2 7HD
T: (01273) 308779 &
07956 662457
F: (01273) 300266

Florence House ★★
Contact: Mr Geoff Hart, 47 Wayland Avenue, Brighton, East Sussex BN1 5JL
T: (01273) 506624
F: (01273) 506624

The Garden Flat ★★★
Contact: Mrs R T Salmon, Best of Brighton & Sussex Cottages Ltd, Windmill Lodge, Vicarage Lane, Rottingdean, Brighton, East Sussex BN2 7HD
T: (01273) 308779 &
07956 662457
F: (01273) 300266

Gloucester House ★★★
Contact: Mr Brian Starey, 44 Palmersfield Road, Banstead, Surrey SM7 2LD
T: (01737) 354813
F: (01737) 354813
E: brian@starey.freeserve.co.uk
I: www.brighton.co.uk/hotels/gloucester/

Ground Floor Flat 12 Arundel Terrace★★★★
Contact: Mrs R T Salmon, Best of Brighton & Sussex Cottages Ltd, Windmill Lodge, Vicarage Lane, Rottingdean, Brighton, East Sussex BN2 7HD
T: (01273) 308779 &
07956 662457
F: (01273) 300266

Holiday Flat 16 Lancaster Court★★
Contact: Mr Peter Anthony, Merrydown, 1A Fairfields, St Ives, Huntingdon, Cambridgeshire PE27 5QQ
T: (01480) 495914
F: (01480) 495914

2 Ivy Mews ★★★
Contact: Mrs R T Salmon, Best of Brighton & Sussex Cottages Ltd, Windmill Lodge, Vicarage Lane, Rottingdean, Brighton, East Sussex BN2 7HD
T: (01273) 308779 &
07956 662457
F: (01273) 300266

3 Kemp Town Mews ★★★
Contact: Mrs R T Salmon, Best of Brighton & Sussex Cottages Ltd, Windmill Lodge, Vicarage Lane, Rottingdean, Brighton, East Sussex BN2 7HD
T: (01273) 308779 &
07956 662457
F: (01273) 300266

13c Kemp Town Place ★★★★
Contact: Mrs R T Salmon, Best of Brighton & Sussex Cottages Ltd, Windmill Lodge, Vicarage Lane, Rottingdean, Brighton, East Sussex BN2 7HD
T: (01273) 308779 &
07956 662457
F: (01273) 300266

93 Kingsway Court ★★★★
Contact: Mrs R T Salmon, Best of Brighton & Sussex Cottages Ltd, Windmill Lodge, Vicarage Lane, Rottingdean, Brighton, East Sussex BN2 7HD
T: (01273) 308779 &
07956 662457
F: (01273) 300266

Lower Ground Floor Flat
Rating Applied For
Contact: Mrs R T Salmon, Best of Brighton & Sussex Cottages Ltd, Windmill Lodge, Vicarage Lane, Rottingdean, Brighton, East Sussex BN2 7HD
T: (01273) 308779 &
07956 662457
F: (01273) 300266
E: brightoncottages@pavilion.co.uk
I: www.bestofbrighton.co.uk

Marine House ★★★
Contact: Mrs R T Salmon, Best of Brighton & Sussex Cottages Ltd, Windmill Lodge, Vicarage Lane, Rottingdean, Brighton, East Sussex BN2 7HD
T: (01273) 308779 &
07956 662457
F: (01273) 300266

3 Mariners Quay ★★★★
Contact: Mrs Pat Lowe, Palms Property Sales & Letting, Marine Trade Centre, Brighton Marina, Brighton, East Sussex BN2 5UG
T: (01273) 626000

3A Metropole Court ★★★
Contact: Mr & Mrs Nigel & Viv Earwicker, Nivian Apartments, Acorn Cottage, Tudor Close, Pulborough, West Sussex RH20 2EF
T: (01798) 875513 &
07798 744574
E: nivianinc@aol.com

Metropole Court Apartments ★★★–★★★★
Contact: Mr & Mrs Harold & Valerie Williams, Cliff Edge, 28 Marine Drive, Rottingdean, Brighton, East Sussex BN2 7HQ
T: (01273) 302431
F: (01273) 307744
E: harval@brighton-apartments.com
I: www.brighton-apartments.com

New Beams
Rating Applied For
Contact: Mrs R T Salmon, Best of Brighton & Sussex Cottages Ltd, Windmill Lodge, Vicarage Lane, Rottingdean, Brighton, East Sussex BN2 7HD
T: (01273) 308779 &
07956 662457
F: (01273) 300266

19 North Gardens ★★★★
Contact: Mrs R T Salmon, Best of Brighton & Sussex Cottages Ltd, Windmill Lodge, Vicarage Lane, Rottingdean, Brighton, East Sussex BN2 7HD
T: (01273) 308779 &
07956 662457
F: (01273) 300266

22 Palmeira House
Rating Applied For
Contact: Mrs R T Salmon, Best of Brighton & Sussex Cottages Ltd, Windmill Lodge, Vicarage Lane, Rottingdean, Brighton, East Sussex BN2 7HD
T: (01273) 308779 &
07956 662457
F: (01273) 300266

Regency Seafront Holiday Flats ★★
Contact: Mrs B M Edwards, 6 Highcroft Villas, Brighton, East Sussex BN1 5PS
T: (01273) 556227

3 Russell Mews ★★★
Contact: Mrs R T Salmon, Best of Brighton & Sussex Cottages Ltd, Windmill Lodge, Vicarage Lane, Rottingdean, Brighton, East Sussex BN2 7HD
T: (01273) 308779 &
07956 662457
F: (01273) 300266

Seapoint ★★★★
Contact: Mrs R T Salmon, Best of Brighton & Sussex Cottages Ltd, Windmill Lodge, Vicarage Lane, Rottingdean, Brighton, East Sussex BN2 7HD
T: (01273) 308779 &
07956 662457
F: (01273) 300266
E: brightoncottages@pavilion.co.uk
I: www.bestofbrighton.co.uk

2A St Catherines Terrace ★★
Contact: Mrs R T Salmon, Best of Brighton & Sussex Cottages Ltd, Windmill Lodge, Vicarage Lane, Rottingdean, Brighton, East Sussex BN2 7HD
T: (01273) 308779 &
07956 662457
F: (01273) 300266

5 St Johns Mews
Rating Applied For
Contact: Mrs R T Salmon, Best of Brighton & Sussex Cottages Ltd, Windmill Lodge, Vicarage Lane, Rottingdean, Brighton, East Sussex BN2 7HD
T: (01273) 308779 &
07956 662457
F: (01273) 300266

4 St Marks Street ★★★
Contact: Mrs R T Salmon, Best of Brighton & Sussex Cottages Ltd, Windmill Lodge, Vicarage Lane, Rottingdean, Brighton, East Sussex BN2 7HD
T: (01273) 308779 &
07956 662457
F: (01273) 300266

18 St Vincents Court ★★★★
Contact: Mrs Pat Lowe, Palms Property Sales & Letting, Marine Trade Centre, Brighton Marina, Brighton, East Sussex BN2 5UG
T: (01273) 626000

Establishments printed in blue have a detailed entry in this guide

Star Cottage
Rating Applied For
Contact: Mrs R T Salmon, Best of Brighton & Sussex Cottages Ltd, Windmill Lodge, Vicarage Lane, Rottingdean, Brighton, East Sussex BN2 7HD
T: (01273) 308779 &
07956 662457
F: (01273) 300266

9 Starboard ★★★
Contact: Mrs Pat Lowe, Palms Property Sales & Letting, Marine Trade Centre, Brighton Marina, Brighton, East Sussex BN2 5UG
T: (01273) 626000

6 Starboard Court ★★★
Contact: Mrs R T Salmon, Best of Brighton & Sussex Cottages Ltd, Windmill Lodge, Vicarage Lane, Rottingdean, Brighton, East Sussex BN2 7HD
T: (01273) 308779 &
07956 662457
F: (01273) 300266

31 Trafalgar Gate ★★★★
Contact: Mr & Mrs Jeremy & Debbie Quick, 20 Whitehorn Gardens, Shirley Park, Croydon, Surrey CR0 7LL
T: (020) 8654 4757 &
07973 907871

12 Western Concourse ★★★
Contact: Mrs M Bowen, 2 Lincoln Avenue, Peacehaven, East Sussex BN10 7HL
T: (01273) 584347

BROAD OAK
East Sussex

Austens Wood Farm ★★★★
Contact: Mrs Brenda Beck, Freedom Holiday Homes, St David's Bridge, Cranbrook, Kent TN17 3HJ
T: (01580) 720770
F: (01580) 720771
E: freedomholsuk@clara.net
I: www.freedomholidayhomes.co.uk

BROADSTAIRS
Kent

Beach Lodge Holiday Apartment ★
Contact: Mrs M Choudhury, 43 Bateman Road, London E4 8ND
T: (020) 8531 4198

Beacon Light Cottage ★★★
Contact: Mr Patrick Vandervorst, Duinhelmlaan 11, B-8420 Wenduine, Belgium
T: 0032 504 23207 & 504 12566
F: 0032 504 23207
E: beaconlight.cottage@worldonline.be
I: www.beaconlightcottage.com

Bray Holiday Homes ★★★
Contact: Mr D J Bray, 34 Smithamdowns Road, Purley, Surrey CR8 4ND
T: (020) 8660 1925

Broadstairs Holiday House ★★★
Contact: Mrs L E Bull, Millstone Cottage, 16 Beulah Road, Epping, Essex CM16 6RH
T: (01992) 576044
E: lynn.bull@btinternet.com

2 Church Square ★★
Contact: Mr Philip Dennis, 8 St Mildreds Avenue, Broadstairs, Kent CT10 2BX
T: (01843) 601996
E: phildennis@btclick.com

Clifftop Family House ★★★
Contact: Mrs D Coleman, Trosley Lodge, Firle, Lewes, East Sussex BN8 6LQ
T: (01273) 858420
F: (01273) 858010
E: deborah.coleman@virgin.net

Coachmans Flat ★★★
Contact: Mrs Ellen Barrett, Coachmans Flat, White Lodge, 4 Reading Street, Broadstairs, Kent CT10 3BD
T: (01843) 867925
F: (01843) 867925
E: ellen@stonar.com

1 Darren Gardens ★★★★
Contact: Mrs Jean Lawrence, J N Lawrence, 24 Winterstoke Crescent, Ramsgate, Kent CT11 8AH
T: (01843) 591422
F: (01843) 591422
E: ali-keir@dutton94freeserve.co.uk

Fisherman's Cottage ★★★★
Contact: Ms Linda Spillane, 33 St James' Drive, Wandsworth, London SW17 7RN
T: (0208) 672 4150

Flat 2 8 Chandos Road★★
Contact: Mrs Edwina Coyne, Fuchsia Cottage, The Street, Woodnesborough, Sandwich, Kent CT13 0ND
T: (01304) 612664

Harbour Holidays (Thanet) Ltd ★★★
Contact: Mr M W Ward-Athey, Harbour Holidays (Thanet) Ltd, The Lees House, St George's Lees, Sandwich, Kent CT13 9JS
T: (01304) 613027
F: (01304) 613445

Homehaven House ★★★
Contact: Mrs Barbara Vandervord, 13 Granville Avenue, Ramsgate, Kent CT12 6DX
T: (01843) 585798

2 Paragon Lodge
Rating Applied For
Contact: Mrs Ruth Kelsey, The Farmhouse, Stanhill Farm, Birchwood Road, Wilmington, Dartford, Kent DA2 7HD
T: (01322) 669711 &
07778 549442
F: (01322) 619037
E: rkelsey@farming.co.uk

Ramsgate Holiday Homes ★★★★
Contact: Mrs P J Martin, Ramsgate Holiday Homes, 21 Avebury Avenue, Ramsgate, Kent CT11 8BB
T: (01843) 592945
F: (01843) 599063
E: penny@martinramsgate.freeserve.co.uk

Ramsgate Holiday Homes ★★★★
Contact: Mrs P J Martin, Ramsgate Holiday Homes, 21 Avebury Avenue, Ramsgate, Kent CT11 8BB
T: (01843) 592945
F: (01843) 599063
E: penny@martinramsgate.freeserve.co.uk

Spero Court Apartments Flat 13★★★
Contact: Miss Carol Bowerman, 28 Heather Drive, Dartford, Kent DA1 3LE
T: (01322) 224869

BROOKLAND
Kent

Puddock Farm Pine Lodges ★★★★
Contact: Mrs Amanda Skinner, Puddock Farm Pine Lodges, Puddock Farm, Fairfield, Brookland, Romney Marsh, Kent TN29 9SA
T: (01797) 344440
F: (01797) 344440
E: amanda_skinner@talk21.com
I: www.cottageguide.co.uk/puddockfarmpinelodges

BURGESS HILL
West Sussex

Farnaby ★★★
Contact: Mrs R T Salmon, Best of Brighton & Sussex Cottages Ltd, Windmill Lodge, Vicarage Lane, Rottingdean, Brighton, East Sussex BN2 7HD
T: (01273) 308779 &
07956 662457
F: (01273) 300266

BURWASH
East Sussex

Battenhurst Barn ★★★
Contact: Mrs Gill Winter & Patrick Tierney, Garden of England Cottages, The Mews Office, 189a High Street, Tonbridge, Kent TN9 1BX
T: (01732) 369168
F: (01732) 358817
E: goec@dial.pipex.com
I: www.gardenofenglandcottages.co.uk

1 Rose Hill Cottages ★★★
Contact: Country Holidays Ref: 2805, Country Holidays Sales, Spring Mill, Earby, Barnoldswick, Lancashire BB94 0AA
T: 08700 723 723
F: (01282) 844288
E: sales@ttgihg.co.uk
I: www.country-holidays.co.uk

CAMBER
East Sussex

Bridle Cottage & Horseshoe Cottage & Poundfield Bungalow★★★★
Contact: Mrs Gill Winter & Patrick Tierney, Garden of England Cottages, The Mews Office, 189a High Street, Tonbridge, Kent TN9 1BX
T: (01732) 369168
F: (01732) 358817
E: goec@dial.pipex.com
I: www.gardenofenglandcottages.co.uk

CANTERBURY
Kent

The Canterbury Hotel & Apartments ★★★★
Contact: Mr D Standen, The Canterbury Hotel and Apartments, 71 New Dover Road, Canterbury, Kent CT1 3DZ
T: (01227) 450551
F: (01227) 780145
E: canterbury.hotel@btinternet.com
I: www.canterbury-hotel-apartments.co.uk

16 Church Street ★★★★
Contact: Mrs M Cain, 6 Dunstan Court, London Road, Canterbury, Kent CT2 8LF
T: (01227) 769955

Curiosity Cottage ★★★★
Contact: Mr R E Allcorn, Abberley House, 115 Whitstable Road, Canterbury, Kent CT2 8EF
T: (01227) 450265
F: (01227) 478626

11 Dunstan Court ★★★
Contact: Mrs M Cain, 6 Dunstan Court, London Road, Canterbury, Kent CT2 8LF
T: (01227) 769955

Ebury Hotel Cottages ★★★★
Contact: Mr Henry Mason, Ebury Hotel, New Dover Road, Canterbury, Kent CT1 3DX
T: (01227) 768433 & 811550
F: (01227) 459187
E: info@ebury-hotel.co.uk
I: www.ebury-hotel.co.uk

Haybarn ★★★★
Contact: Mrs Sheila Wilton, Walnut Tree Farm, Upper Hardres, Canterbury, Kent CT4 6EG
T: (01227) 709375
F: (01227) 709544

Henry's of Ash ★★★
Contact: Mr P H Robinson, Henry's of Ash, Darrington, Durlock Road, Ash, Canterbury, Kent CT3 2HU
T: (01304) 812563

Luxury Holiday Apartment ★★★★
Contact: Mrs H A Homerstone, Courtfields, Lees Road, Brabourne Lees, Ashford, Kent TN25 6RN
T: (01303) 814020
F: (01303) 812333

67 Martysfield Road ★★
Contact: Mrs Debbie Pearson, Bleanhyrst, Honey Hill, Blean, Canterbury, Kent CT2 9JP
T: (01227) 472431
I: k.w.pearsons@BTconnect.com

Millers Quern ★★★★
Contact: S Harman, 34 Nunnery Fields, Canterbury, Kent CT1 3JT
T: (01227) 762660
F: (01227) 766992
E: quern@care4free.net

Pilgrims End ★★★
Contact: Mrs J M Reed, 11
Woodlands Avenue, New
Malden, Surrey KT3 3UL
T: (020) 8942 0342 &
07710 591735
F: (020) 8942 0342
E: janette.reed@cwcom.net

Queensview Cottage ★★★★
Contact: Mrs M Woodifield,
Braymor House, Queens Avenue,
Canterbury, Kent CT2 8AY
T: (01227) 471914
F: (01227) 785348
E: Braymor@talk21.com
I: www.cottagesguide.
co.uk/queensview

**R N K Holiday Lets
Rating Applied For**
Contact: Mrs Kathryn Nevell, 14
Craythorne, Tenterden, Kent
TN30 6SD
T: (01580) 766628
F: (01580) 761830
E: rnevell@aol.com

**134 Station Road West
★★★★**
Contact: Mrs Julie Metcalf,
Albany House, 21 High Street,
Bridge, Canterbury, Kent CT4 5JZ
T: (01227) 831787 & 477038
F: (01795) 535128

Steam Packet Cottages ★★★
Contact: Mrs Alison Rogers, The
Winch, Steam Packet Yard,
North Lane, Canterbury, Kent
CT2 7EB
T: (01227) 763099

**Swarling Manor Oast
★★★-★★★★**
Contact: Mr & Mrs D&G
Braddon, Coach Cottage,
Swarling Manor, Petham,
Canterbury, Kent CT4 5QW
T: (01227) 700393 & 700377
F: (01227) 700393
E: swarlingmanor@gbraddon.
freeserve.co.uk
I: www.member.xoom.
com/gbraddon/index_2html

**Wagoners & Shepherds
Cottage ★★★**
Contact: Mrs M K Heathcote,
Wagoners & Shepherds Cottage,
Denstroude Farm, Blean,
Canterbury, Kent CT2 9JZ
T: (01227) 471513

Yew Tree Park ★★★
Contact: Mr Derek Zanders, Yew
Tree Park, Stone Street, Petham,
Canterbury, Kent CT4 5PL
T: (01227) 700306
F: (01227) 700306
E: enquiries@yewtreepark.com
I: www.yewtreepark.com

CATERHAM
Surrey

Underwood ★★★
Contact: Mrs Georgina Salmon,
Woodridge, The Ridge,
Woldingham, Caterham, Surrey
CR3 7AH
T: (01883) 653250
F: (01883) 653250
E: jdystersalmon@hotmail.com

The White Cottage ★★★
Contact: Mrs Josephine Crux,
Birchwood House, Woldingham
Road, Woldingham, Caterham,
Surrey CR3 7LR
T: (01883) 343287
F: (01883) 348066
E: jocrux@birchwoodhouse.
freeserve.co.uk
I: www.oas.co.uk/ukcottages

CATSFIELD
East Sussex

**Owl's Beam & Ox Shoe
★★★★**
Contact: Mr & Mrs John
Campbell, Fairhaven Holiday
Rentals, Derby House, 123
Watling Street, Gillingham, Kent
ME7 2YY
T: (01634) 300089
F: (01634) 570157
E: fairhaven@pavilion.co.uk
I: www.fairhaven-holidays.co.uk

CHARCOTT
Kent

**The Old Dairy & Stable Cottage
★★★★**
Contact: Mrs Sandra Bell, The
Old Barn, Charcott Farm,
Charcott, Tonbridge, Kent
TN11 8LG
T: (01892) 870138 &
07850 018811
F: (01892) 870138

CHARLTON
West Sussex

Orchard Cottage ★★★
Contact: Mrs E Jeffries, 34
Foxhall Lane, Charlton,
Chichester, West Sussex
PO18 0HU
T: (01243) 811338

CHART SUTTON
Kent

Park House Farm ★★★
Contact: Mrs Brenda Beck,
Freedom Holiday Homes, St
David's Bridge, Cranbrook, Kent
TN17 3HJ
T: (01580) 720770
F: (01580) 720771
E: freedomholsuk@clara.net
I: www.freedomholidayhomes.
co.uk

CHICHESTER
West Sussex

24 & 26 Oaklands Court ★★★
Contact: Mr G Ryan & Mr M
Stait, 7 Loretto Gardens, Harrow,
Middlesex HA3 9LY
T: (020) 8204 1188
F: (020) 8906 1940
E: southerncountieslets@
hmeth.fsnet.co.uk
I: www.
southerncountieslettings.com

The Annexe ★★★
Contact: Mrs Janet Lawrence,
The Annexe, 85 Adelaide Road,
Chichester, West Sussex
PO19 4NA
T: (01243) 783840
F: (01243) 783840
E: janet.lawrence2@ntlworld.
com

5 Caledonian Road ★★★★
Contact: Miss Victoria Chubb, 33
Hillier Road, London SW11 6AX
T: (020) 7924 5446
E: victoriachubb@hotmail.com
I: www.sussexlive.com

Cornerstones ★★★★
Contact: Mrs V J Higgins,
Greenacre, Goodwood Gardens,
Runcton, Chichester, West
Sussex PO20 6SP
T: (01243) 839096
F: (01243) 779658
E: vjrmhiggins@hotmail.com
I: www.visitbritain.com

Cygnet Cottage ★★★★
Contact: Mrs V J Higgins,
Greenacre, Goodwood Gardens,
Runcton, Chichester, West
Sussex PO20 6SP
T: (01243) 839096
F: (01243) 779658
E: vjrmhiggins@hotmail.com
I: www.visitbritain.com

**Flat 2, 4 Guildhall Street
★★★**
Contact: Mr G Ryan & Mr M
Stait, 7 Loretto Gardens, Harrow,
Middlesex HA3 9LY
T: (020) 8204 1188
F: (020) 8906 1940
E: southerncountieslets@
hmeth.fsnet.co.uk
I: www.
southerncountieslettings.com

**Flats 1 & 5 West Broyle House
Rating Applied For**
Contact: Mrs Penelope Gurland,
Flat 6, 21 De Vere Gardens,
London W8 5AN
T: (0207) 937 6337
F: (0207) 938 2199
E: penelope.gurland@lineone.
net

Footpath Nursery ★★★★
Contact: Mr & Mrs Noel
Bettridge, Footpath Nursery,
Post Office Lane, North
Mundham, Chichester, West
Sussex PO20 6JY
T: (01243) 779823
F: (01243) 779823
E: noeljenny@onetel.net.uk

Hunston Mill ★★★★
Contact: Mr & Mrs R Beeny,
Hunston Mill, Selsey Road,
Hunston, Chichester, West
Sussex PO20 6AU
T: (01243) 783375
F: (01243) 785179
E: hunston.mill@virgin.net
I: www.hunstonmill.co.uk

22 Kings Avenue ★★★
Contact: Country Hols Ref: 112,
Country Holidays, Spring Hill,
Earby, Barnoldswick, Lancashire
BB94 0AA
T: 0870 072 3723
F: (01282) 844288
E: dales@ttgihg.co.uk
I: www.country-holiays.co.uk

33 Melbourne Road ★★★
Contact: Mrs Jane Donnelly,
Clevelands, Fordwater Road,
Chichester, West Sussex
PO19 4PS
T: (01243) 537737

**Muttons Farm House
★★★★★**
Contact: Mr & Mrs P T Rist,
Muttons Farm House, Keynor
Lane, Sidlesham, Chichester,
West Sussex PO20 7NG
T: (01243) 641675
F: (01243) 641675
I: www.smoothhound.
co.uk/hotels/muttons.html

Oak Apple Barn ★★★
Contact: Ms Siobain Davies, Oak
Apple Barn, The Lane,
Summersdale, Chichester, West
Sussex PO19 4PY
T: (01243) 771669
I: www.siobaindavies@virgin.
net

2 Rumbolds Close ★★★
Contact: Dr & Mrs Ian White, 35
Baldwin Avenue, Eastbourne,
East Sussex BN21 1UL
T: (01323) 648291
E: irwhite@aol.com

CHIDDINGLY
East Sussex

Bull River Farm ★★★★
Contact: Mrs Gill Winter &
Patrick Tierney, Garden of
England Cottages, The Mews
Office, 189a High Street,
Tonbridge, Kent TN9 1BX
T: (01732) 369168
F: (01732) 358817
E: goec@dial.pipex.com
I: www.
gardenofenglandcottages.co.uk

Pekes ★★★-★★★★
Contact: Ms Eva Morris, 124 Elm
Park Mansions, Park Walk,
London SW10 0AR
T: (020) 7352 8088
F: (020) 7352 8125
E: pekes.afa@virgin.net

CHIDDINGSTONE
Kent

**Larkins Barn & Larkins Stable
★★★**
Contact: Mrs Gill Winter &
Patrick Tierney, Garden of
England Cottages, The Mews
Office, 189a High Street,
Tonbridge, Kent TN9 1BX
T: (01732) 369168
F: (01732) 358817
E: goec@dial.pipex.com
I: www.
gardenofenglandcottages.co.uk

CHIDDINGSTONE CAUSEWAY
Kent

Whitepost Oast ★★★★
Contact: Mr Nicholas De Maid,
Whitepost Oast, Chiddingstone
Causeway, Tonbridge, Kent
TN11 8JH
T: (01892) 870115 & 870116
E: elliotthale@onet.co.uk

CHIDHAM
West Sussex

Canute Cottages ★★★★
Contact: Ms Diana Beale, Cobnor
House, Chidham, Chichester,
West Sussex PO18 8TE
T: (01243) 572123
E: taylorbeales@yahoo.co.uk
I: www.canutecottages.co.uk

Establishments printed in blue have a detailed entry in this guide

CHILHAM
Kent

Monckton Cottages ★★★
Contact: Dr R W Kirwan,
Monckton Cottages, Heron
Manor, Mountain Street,
Chilham, Canterbury, Kent
CT4 8DG
T: (01227) 730256
F: (01227) 730256
E: monckton@rw-kirwan.
demon.co.uk

CHOBHAM
Surrey

Swallow Barn Cottage ★★★★
Contact: Mrs Joan Carey,
Swallow Barn, Milford Green,
Chobham, Woking, Surrey
GU24 8AU
T: (01276) 856030 &
07768 972904
F: (01276) 856030
E: swallowbarn@compuserve.
com

CLIMPING
West Sussex

The Dairy Cottage ★★★
Contact: Ms Sue Beckhurst, The
Dairy, Brookpit Lane, Climping,
Littlehampton, West Sussex
BN17 5QU
T: (01903) 724187
F: (01903) 724187
E: suebeckhurst@genie.co.uk

COBHAM
Surrey

Cherry Court ★★★
Contact: Mr & Mrs Gordon
Faulkner, Cherry Court, 140 Tilt
Road, Cobham, Surrey KT11 3HR
T: (01932) 860189 &
07767 432550
F: (01932) 860189

COMPTON
West Sussex

**3 The Old School House
★★★★**
Contact: Mr & Mrs Brian & Val
Parkinson, 47-48 Castle Garden,
Petersfield, Hampshire
GU32 3AG
T: (01730) 233747 &
0870 0549604
F: 0870 8317730
E: info@comptoncottage.co.uk
I: www.comptoncottage.co.uk

Yew Tree House Annexe ★★★
Contact: Mr & Mrs James
Buchanan, Yew Tree House
Annexe, Compton, Chichester,
West Sussex PO18 9HD
T: (023) 9263 1248 & 9232 4555
F: (023) 9264 6555
E: d.buchanan@btinternet.com

COUSLEY WOOD
East Sussex

**The Cowshed at the Carriage
House ★★★**
Contact: Mrs Maureen Parker,
The Carriage House, Monks Lane,
Cousley Wood, Wadhurst, East
Sussex TN5 6EN
T: (01892) 783188 & 723800
F: (01892) 784380

**The Mill House Cottage
Rating Applied For**
Contact: Mrs Brenda Beck,
Freedom Holiday Homes, St
David's Bridge, Cranbrook, Kent
TN17 3HJ
T: (01580) 720770
F: (01580) 720771
E: freedomholsuk@clara.net
I: www.freedomholidayhomes.
co.uk

CRANBROOK
Kent

The Annexe Hadleigh★★★
Contact: Mrs Brenda Beck,
Freedom Holiday Homes, St
David's Bridge, Cranbrook, Kent
TN17 3HJ
T: (01580) 720770
F: (01580) 720771
E: freedomholsuk@clara.net
I: www.freedomholidayhomes.
co.uk

**The Annexe to The Old Barn
★★★**
Contact: Mrs Patricia Redmayne,
The Annexe to The Old Barn,
Rocks Hill, Cranbrook, Kent
TN17 2BL
T: (01580) 715449
F: (01580) 715443

Bakersbarn ★★★
Contact: Dr & Mrs J Hooper,
Bakersbarn, Golford Road,
Cranbrook, Kent TN17 3NW
T: (01580) 713344

**The Little Barn (Ref: H762)
★★★★**
Contact: Mr Nick Pash,
Hideaways, Chapel House, Luke
Street, Berwick St John,
Shaftesbury, Dorset SP7 0HQ
T: (01747) 828170
F: (01747) 829090
I: www.hideaways.
co.uk/property2.cfm?ref=H762

Mill Cottage ★★★★
Contact: Mrs Gill Winter &
Patrick Tierney, Garden of
England Cottages, The Mews
Office, 189a High Street,
Tonbridge, Kent TN9 1BX
T: (01732) 369168
F: (01732) 358817
E: goec@dial.pipex.com
I: www.
gardenofenglandcottages.co.uk

Oak Cottage ★★
Contact: Mrs Brenda Beck,
Freedom Holiday Homes, St
David's Bridge, Cranbrook, Kent
TN17 2LG
T: (01580) 720770
F: (01580) 720771
E: freedomholsuk@clara.net
I: www.freedomholsuk.clara.net

Turnden Wing ★★★-★★★★★
Contact: Mr Peter Hopper,
Turnden, Hartley Road,
Cranbrook, Kent TN17 3QX
T: (01580) 713183
F: (01580) 713183
E: turnden@globalnet.co.uk

CROSS-IN-HAND
East Sussex

Oast House ★★★★
Contact: Country Hols Ref:
9989, Country Holidays, Spring
Mill, Earby, Barnoldswick,
Lancashire BB18 6RN
T: 08700 723723
F: (01282) 844288
I: www.country-holidays.co.uk

CROWBOROUGH
East Sussex

Cleeve Lodge ★★★★
Contact: Mr & Mrs Edward &
Nina Sibley, The Old House,
Harlequin Lane, Crowborough,
East Sussex TN6 1HS
T: (01892) 654331
E: nina@the-old-house.co.uk
I: www.the-old-house.co.uk

**Cruickshanks Oast Holiday
Apartments★★-★★★**
Contact: Mr & Mrs Michael &
Deborah Harris, Cruickshanks
Oast Holiday Apartments,
Cruickshanks Oast, Boars Head,
Crowborough, East Sussex
TN6 3HD
T: (01892) 655156
F: (01892) 611799
E: freedomholsuk@clara.net
I: www.freedomholsuk.clara.net

Hodges ★★★★
Contact: Mrs Hazel Colliver,
Hodges, Eridge Road,
Crowborough, East Sussex
TN6 2SS
T: (01892) 652386

CROWHURST
East Sussex

**Ye Olde Shoppe Cottage
★★★★**
Contact: Mr & Mrs John
Campbell, Fairhaven Holiday
Cottages, Derby House, 123
Watling Street, Gillingham, Kent
ME7 2YY
T: (01634) 300089
F: (01634) 570157
E: fairhaven@pavilion.co.uk
I: www.fairhaven-holidays.co.uk

CRUNDALE
Kent

Farnley Little Barn ★★★★
Contact: Mrs Sylvia Hope,
Farnley Little Barn, Denwood
Street, Crundale, Canterbury,
Kent CT4 7EF
T: (01227) 730510
F: (01227) 730510
E: farnleylittlebarn@supaworld.
com

Ripple Farm ★★
Contact: Ms Maggie Baur, Ripple
Farm, Crundale, Canterbury,
Kent CT4 7EB
T: (01227) 730748
F: (01227) 730748

CUDHAM
Kent

Fairmead Cottage ★★★★
Contact: Mr & Mrs John
Campbell, Fairhaven Holiday
Cottages, Derby House, 123
Watling Street, Gillingham, Kent
ME7 2YY
T: (01959) 532662
F: (01959) 534274
E: fairhaven@pavilion.co.uk
I: www.fairhaven-holidays.co.uk

DALLINGTON
East Sussex

**Little Pines
Rating Applied For**
Contact: Mrs Sarah Wall, Little
Pines, Bakers Lane, Dallington,
Heathfield, East Sussex TN21 9JS
T: (01435) 831048

DANEHILL
East Sussex

Sliders Farm Barn ★★★★
Contact: Mrs R T Salmon, Sliders
Farm Barn, Furners Green,
Danehill, Uckfield, East Sussex
TN22 3RT
T: (01825) 790258
F: (01825) 790258

Sliders Farm Cottage ★★★★
Contact: Mrs R T Salmon, Sliders
Farm Cottage, Furners Green,
Danehill, Uckfield, East Sussex
TN22 3RT
T: (01825) 790258
F: (01825) 790258

DEAL
Kent

30 Nelson Street ★★
Contact: Mr Nick Pash,
Hideaways, Chapel House, Luke
Street, Berwick St John,
Shaftesbury, Dorset SP7 0HQ
T: (01747) 828170
F: (01747) 829090
I: www.hideaways.
co.uk/property2.cfm?ref=H765

DENTON
Kent

Low Borrans ★★★★
Contact: Mr & Mrs P Lucock,
Low Borrans, The Street, Denton,
Canterbury, Kent CT4 6QZ
T: (01303) 844289
F: (01303) 844289
E: paul@downland-cycles.
freeserve.co.uk

DITCHLING
East Sussex

Tovey Cottage ★★★★
Contact: Mrs R T Salmon, Best of
Brighton & Sussex Cottages Ltd,
Windmill Lodge, Vicarage Lane,
Rottingdean, Brighton, East
Sussex BN2 7HD
T: (01273) 308779 &
07956 662457
F: (01273) 300266

Tovey Flat ★★★
Contact: Mrs R T Salmon, Best of
Brighton & Sussex Cottages Ltd,
Windmill Lodge, Vicarage Lane,
Rottingdean, Brighton, East
Sussex BN2 7HD
T: (01273) 308779 &
07956 662457
F: (01273) 300266

DODDINGTON
Kent

The Old School House ★★★★
Contact: Mrs Gill Winter &
Patrick Tierney, Garden of
England Cottages, The Mews
Office, 189a High Street,
Tonbridge, Kent TN9 1BX
T: (01732) 369168
F: (01732) 358817
E: goec@dial.pipex.com
I: www.
gardenofenglandcottages.co.uk

DORKING
Surrey

Bulmer Farm ★★★
Contact: Mrs Gill Hill, Bulmer
Farm, Holmbury St Mary,
Dorking, Surrey RH5 6LG
T: (01306) 730210

DOVER
Kent

Meggett Farm Cottage
★★★★
Contact: Mr & Mrs Simon Price,
Meggett Farm, Meggett Lane,
Alkham, Dover, Kent CT15 7BS
T: (01303) 252764 &
07831 834094
F: (01303) 252764
E: simon-price.dover@virgin.net

DYMCHURCH
Kent

Dank U Well ★★★
Contact: Mr & Mrs John
Campbell, Fairhaven Holiday
Rentals, Derby House, 123
Watling Street, Gillingham, Kent
ME7 2YY
T: (01634) 300089
F: (01634) 570157
E: fairhaven@pavilion.co.uk
I: www.fairhaven-holidays.co.uk

Seabreeze Holiday Homes
★★-★★★
Contact: Mr Peter Checksfield,
Seabreeze Holiday Homes, 1 Sea
Wall, Dymchurch, Romney
Marsh, Kent TN29 0TG
T: (01303) 874116 & 260027

EARNLEY
West Sussex

Mill House ★★★
Contact: Mrs E P Harrison, Mill
House, Earnley, Chichester, West
Sussex PO20 7JD
T: (01243) 512389

The Stable Flat ★★
Contact: Ms Karen Brooker,
Baileys Estate Agents, 17 Shore
Road, East Wittering, Chichester,
West Sussex PO20 8DY
T: (01243) 672217
F: (01243) 670100
E: info@bailey.uk.com
I: www.bailey.uk.com

EAST DEAN
West Sussex

The Hurdlemakers Cottage ★★
Contact: Mr Roger Waller, The
Hurdlemakers Cottage, Main
Road, East Dean, Chichester,
West Sussex PO18 0JG
T: (01243) 811318
F: (01243) 821294

EAST FARLEIGH
Kent

2 The Malthouse ★★★★
Contact: Mrs Gill Winter &
Patrick Tierney, Garden of
England Cottages, The Mews
Office, 189a High Street,
Tonbridge, Kent TN9 1BX
T: (01732) 369168
F: (01732) 358817
E: goec@dial.pipex.com
I: www.
gardenofenglandcottages.co.uk

EAST LAVANT
West Sussex

40 Pook Lane ★★
Contact: Mr & Mrs R V Warren,
30 Sherwood Close,
Leatherhead, Surrey KT22 9QT
T: (01372) 450191 & 0781 552
2595

EAST PECKHAM
Kent

Middle Cottage ★★★★
Contact: Mrs Gill Winter &
Patrick Tierney, Garden of
England Cottages, The Mews
Office, 189a High Street,
Tonbridge, Kent TN9 1BX
T: (01732) 369168
F: (01732) 358817
E: goec@dial.pipex.com
I: www.
gardenofenglandcottages.co.uk

EAST WITTERING
West Sussex

Brambles End ★★
Contact: Ms Karen Brooker,
Baileys Estate Agents, 17 Shore
Road, East Wittering, Chichester,
West Sussex PO20 8DY
T: (01243) 672217
F: (01243) 670100
E: info@baileys.uk.com
I: www.baileys.uk.com

Fairhaven ★★★
Contact: Ms Karen Brooker,
Baileys Estate Agents, 17 Shore
Road, East Wittering, Chichester,
West Sussex PO20 8DY
T: (01243) 672217
F: (01243) 670100
E: info@baileys.uk.com
I: www.baileys.uk.com

Little Thatch ★
Contact: Ms Karen Brooker,
Baileys Estate Agents, 17 Shore
Road, East Wittering, Chichester,
West Sussex PO20 8DY
T: (01243) 672217
F: (01243) 670100
E: info@baileys.uk.com
I: www.baileys.uk.com

Memphis ★
Contact: Ms Karen Brooker,
Baileys Estate Agents, 17 Shore
Road, East Wittering, Chichester,
West Sussex PO20 8DY
T: (01243) 672217
F: (01243) 670100
E: info@baileys.uk.com
I: www.baileys.uk.com

20 Seagate Court ★★★
Contact: Mr G Ryan & Mr M
Stait, 7 Loretto Gardens, Harrow,
Middlesex HA3 9LY
T: (020) 8204 1188
F: (020) 8906 1940
E: southerncountieslets@
hmeth.fsnet.co.uk
I: www.
southerncountieslettings.com

3 Seagate Court ★★
Contact: Ms Karen Brooker,
Baileys Estate Agents, 17 Shore
Road, East Wittering, Chichester,
West Sussex PO20 8DY
T: (01243) 672217
F: (01243) 670100

30 Seagate Court ★★
Contact: Ms Karen Brooker,
Baileys Estate Agents, 17 Shore
Road, East Wittering, Chichester,
West Sussex PO20 8DY
T: (01243) 672217
F: (01243) 670100

31 Seagate Court ★★★
Contact: Ms Karen Brooker,
Baileys Estate Agents, 17 Shore
Road, East Wittering, Chichester,
West Sussex PO20 8DY
T: (01243) 672217
F: (01243) 670100
E: info@baileys.uk.com
I: www.baileys.uk.com

37 Seagate Court ★★★
Contact: Ms Karen Brooker,
Baileys Estate Agents, 17 Shore
Road, East Wittering, Chichester,
West Sussex PO20 8DY
T: (01243) 672217
F: (01243) 670100
E: info@baileys.uk.com
I: www.baileys.uk.com

Sunnyside ★★
Contact: Ms Karen Brooker,
Baileys Estate Agents, 17 Shore
Road, East Wittering, Chichester,
West Sussex PO20 8DY
T: (01243) 672217
F: (01243) 670100
E: info@baileys.uk.com
I: www.baileys.uk.com
I: www.baileys.uk.com

Tofts Chalet ★
Contact: Ms Karen Brooker,
Baileys Estate Agents, 17 Shore
Road, East Wittering, Chichester,
West Sussex PO20 8DY
T: (01243) 672217
F: (01243) 670100
E: info@baileys.uk.com
I: www.baileys.uk.com

EASTBOURNE
East Sussex

Black Robin Farm ★★★★
Contact: Mrs Jane Higgs, Black
Robin Farm, Beachy Head,
Eastbourne, East Sussex
BN20 7XX
T: (01323) 643357 &
0797 0905809
F: (01323) 643357

4 Boship Cottages ★★★★
Contact: Country Hols Ref:
11983, Country Holidays, Spring
Mill, Earby, Barnoldswick,
Lancashire BB94 0AA
T: 08700 723 723
F: (01282) 844288
E: sales@ttgihg.co.uk
I: www.country-holidays.co.uk

Courtney House Holiday Flats
★★★★
Contact: Mr A Beney, Courtney
House Holiday Flats, 53 Royal
Parade, Eastbourne, East Sussex
BN22 7AQ
T: (01323) 410202 & 732697
E: holidays@courtneyhouse.org.
uk
I: www.eastbourne-web.
co.uk/sites/courteneyhouse/
index.html

Lake View ★★★
Contact: Country Hols Ref: 728,
Country Holidays Spring Mill,
Earby, Barnoldswick, Lancashire
BB94 0AA
T: 0870 072 3723
F: (01282) 844288
E: sales@ttgihg.co.uk
I: www.country-holidays.co.uk

Oysters ★★★★★
Contact: Mrs R T Salmon, Best of
Brighton & Sussex Cottages Ltd,
Windmill Lodge, Vicarage Lane,
Rottingdean, Brighton, East
Sussex BN2 7HD
T: (01273) 308779 &
07956 662457
F: (01273) 300266

Quayside ★★★★★
Contact: Mrs R T Salmon, Best of
Brighton & Sussex Cottages Ltd,
Windmill Lodge, Vicarage Lane,
Rottingdean, Brighton, East
Sussex BN2 7HD
T: (01273) 308779 &
07956 662457
F: (01273) 300266

**Sussex House Holiday
Apartments** ★★★
Contact: Mr C Parsons, 6
Sunstar Lane, Polegate, East
Sussex BN26 5HS
T: (01323) 487272 & 412415
F: (01323) 412415

**Tom Thumb Cottages &
Latimer Lodge Holiday Flats**
★★-★★★
Contact: Mr & Mrs Roger Clark,
52 Royal Parade, Eastbourne,
East Sussex BN22 7AQ
T: (01323) 723248
F: (01323) 723248
E: info@
eastbourne-holidayflats.co.uk
I: www.eastbourne-holidayflats.
co.uk

EASTCHURCH
Kent

**Connetts Farm Holiday
Cottages** ★★★
Contact: Fairhaven Holiday
Cottages, Derby House, 123
Watling Street, Gillingham, Kent
ME7 2YY
T: (01634) 300089
F: (01634) 570157
E: fairhaven@pavilion.co.uk
I: www.fairhaven-holidays.co.uk

EASTERGATE
West Sussex

Eastmere ★★★
Contact: Mr & Mrs B Lane,
Eastmere House, Eastergate
Lane, Eastergate, Chichester,
West Sussex PO20 6SJ
T: (01243) 544204
E: bernardlane@hotmail.com
I: www.eastmere.com

EGERTON
Kent

**Coldharbour Farm Oast & Pond
Cottage** ★★★-★★★★
Contact: Mrs Lisa Fraser,
Coldharbour Farm, Egerton,
Ashford, Kent TN27 9DD
T: (01233) 756548 & 756770
F: (01233) 756770

Establishments printed in blue have a detailed entry in this guide

The Dering Suite & The Old Bakery ★★★
Contact: Mrs Brenda Beck, Freedom Holiday Homes, St David's Bridge, Cranbrook, Kent TN17 3HJ
T: (01580) 720770
F: (01580) 720771
E: freedomholsuk@clara.net
I: www.freedomholsuk.clara.net

Ragged Barn Court ★★★
Contact: Mrs Sarah Browning, Ragged Barn Court, Munday Bois Road, Egerton, Ashford, Kent TN27 9ER
T: (01233) 756358
F: (01233) 756358
E: browning@raggedbarn.fsnet.co.uk

EGHAM
Surrey
Burford
Rating Applied For
Contact: Mr David Coltman, Burford, 59 Egham Hill, Egham, Surrey TW20 0ER
T: (01784) 432196 & (020) 8982 1820

ELMSTED
Kent
Great Holt Farm ★★★
Contact: Mrs Gill Winter & Patrick Tierney, Garden of England Cottages, The Mews Office, 189a High Street, Tonbridge, Kent TN9 1BX
T: (01732) 369168
F: (01732) 358817
E: goec@dial.pipex.com
I: www.gardenofenglandcottages.co.uk

EPSOM
Surrey
7 Great Tattenhams ★★★
Contact: Mrs Mary Willis, 7 Great Tattenhams, Epsom, Surrey KT18 5RF
T: (01737) 354112

ETCHINGHAM
East Sussex
Moon Cottage ★★★
Contact: Mrs Jan Chapman, The White Cottage, Union Street, Flimwell, Wadhurst, East Sussex TN5 7NT
T: (01580) 879328 & 07989 278160
F: (01580) 879729
E: jan.chapman@virgin.net

EWHURST GREEN
East Sussex
Waterman's Farm ★★★
Contact: Mrs Brenda Beck, Freedom Holiday Homes, St David's Bridge, Cranbrook, Kent TN17 3HJ
T: (01580) 720770
F: (01580) 720771
E: freedomholsuk@clara.net
I: www.freedomholsuk.clara.net

FARNHAM
Surrey
High Wray ★★
Contact: Mrs Alexine Crawford, High Wray, 73 Lodge Hill Road, Farnham, Surrey GU10 3RB
T: (01252) 715589
F: (01252) 715746
E: crawford@highwray73.co.uk

FAVERSHAM
Kent
Country Retreat ★★★
Contact: Mrs Carol Batchelor, Country Retreat, Yew Tree Cottage, Syndale Park, Faversham, Kent ME13 0RH
T: (01795) 531257

Monks Cottage ★★★
Contact: Mr & Mrs Graham Darby, Monks Cottage, Leaveland, Faversham, Kent ME13 0NP
T: (01233) 740419
F: (01233) 740419

Old Dairy ★★★
Contact: Mrs G Falcon, Shepherds Hill, Selling, Faversham, Kent ME13 9RS
T: (01227) 752212
F: (01227) 752212
E: ag@agfalcon.f9.co.uk

Uplees Farm ★★★
Contact: Mr & Mrs Chris & Heather Flood, Uplees Farm, Uplees Road, Luddenham, Faversham, Kent ME13 0QR
T: (01795) 532133

FAWKHAM
Kent
Three Gates Stables Holiday Cottages★★★
Contact: Mr Thomas Cramer, Three Gates Stables Holiday Cottages, Speedgate Hill, Fawkham, Longfield, Kent DA3 8NJ
T: (01474) 872739
F: (01474) 879455

FELPHAM
West Sussex
Felpham Bungalow ★★★
Contact: Mrs Janet Yabsley, 4 Nicholas Road, Beddington, Croydon, Surrey CR0 4QS
T: (0208) 680 4761

Lily Cottage ★★★
Contact: Mrs M Bird, 5 Firs Close, Dorking, Surrey RH4 3AW
T: (01306) 882489
F: (01306) 882489

FERRING
West Sussex
The Bungalow ★★★★
Contact: Mr D R Baggs, Teigncombe, Park View Road, Woldingham, Caterham, Surrey CR3 7DL
T: (01883) 653289

5 Lamorna Gardens
Rating Applied For
Contact: Mrs Elsden & Mary Fitzgerald, Torrington Holiday Flats, 60 Manor Road, Worthing, West Sussex BN11 4SL
T: (01903) 238582 & 07860 699268
F: (01903) 230266

FISHBOURNE
West Sussex
The Tidings ★★★
Contact: Mrs M Davies, The Tidings, Appledram Lane North, Fishbourne, Chichester, West Sussex PO19 2PW
T: (01243) 773958

The Willows ★★
Contact: Mrs Linda Proctor, The Willows, Main Road, Fishbourne, Chichester, West Sussex PO18 8AX
T: (01243) 576645
E: linda@proctor50.freeserve.co.uk

FIVE OAK GREEN
Kent
Stable Cottage
Rating Applied For
Contact: Mrs Brenda Beck, Freedom Holiday Homes, St David's Bridge, Cranbrook, Kent TN17 3HJ
T: (01580) 720770
F: (01580) 720771
E: freedomholsuk@clara.net
I: www.freedomholidayhomes.co.uk

FOLKESTONE
Kent
Bybrook Cottage ★★★
Contact: Mrs Gwendoline Baker, Bybrook House, The Undercliffe, Folkestone, Kent CT20 3AT
T: (01303) 248255

Merriwinds ★★★★
Contact: Country Hols Ref: 11232, Country Holidays Spring Mill, Earby, Barnoldswick, Lancashire BB94 0AA
T: 08700 723 723
F: (01282) 844288
E: sales@ttgihg.co.uk
I: www.country-holidays.co.uk

Parkview Apartments ★★★
Contact: Miss Paula McGlynn, Parkview Apartments, 1 Grimston Gardens, Folkestone, Kent CT20 2PT
T: (01303) 251482
E: paulamcglynn6@hotmail.com

FOLKINGTON
East Sussex
The Old Rectory
Rating Applied For
Contact: Mrs Janet Macdonald, The Old Rectory, Folkington, Polegate, East Sussex BN26 5SD
T: (01323) 483367
F: (01323) 488156
E: geradin@pobox.com

FRITTENDEN
Kent
2 The Old Farmhouse ★★★
Contact: Mrs Brenda Beck, Freedom Holiday Homes, St David's Bridge, Cranbrook, Kent TN17 3HJ
T: (01580) 720770
F: (01580) 720771
E: freedomholsuk@clara.net
I: www.freedomholidayhomes.co.uk

Street Farm Cottage
Rating Applied For
Contact: Mrs Brenda Beck, Freedom Holiday Homes, St David's Bridge, Cranbrook, Kent TN17 3HJ
T: (01580) 720770
F: (01580) 720771
E: freedomholsuk@clara.net
I: www.freedomholidayhomes.co.uk

Weavers Oast ★★★★
Contact: Mrs Gill Winter & Patrick Tierney, Garden of England Cottages, The Mews Office, 189a High Street, Tonbridge, Kent TN9 1BX
T: (01732) 369168
F: (01732) 358817
E: goec@dial.pipex.co.uk
I: www.gardenofenglandcottages.co.uk

FUNTINGTON
West Sussex
The Courtyard ★★★★
Contact: Ms Claire Hoare, 3 The Cottages, Adsdean Farm, Funtington, Chichester, West Sussex PO18 9DN
T: (01243) 575464
F: (01243) 575586
E: tim.hoare@farming.co.uk

Dellfield ★★★★
Contact: Mr M A Hall Hall, Dellfield, Downs Road, Funtington, Chichester, West Sussex PO18 9LS
T: (01243) 575244
F: (01243) 578916
E: holidays@dellfield.com
I: www.dellfield.com

GLYNDE
East Sussex
Caburn Cottages ★★★★
Contact: Mr & Mrs P Norris, Caburn Cottages, Ranscombe Farm, Glynde, Lewes, East Sussex BN8 6AB
T: (01273) 858062

GODALMING
Surrey
Magpie Cottage ★★★
Contact: Mrs Gabrielle Mabley, Tigbourne Wood, New Road, Wormley, Godalming, Surrey GU8 5SU
T: (01428) 682702
E: Gabrielle.Mabley1@btinternet.com

GORING-BY-SEA
West Sussex
Sea Place ★★
Contact: Mr Robert Brew, Promenade Holiday Homes, 165 Dominion Road, Worthing, West Sussex BN14 8LD
T: (01903) 201426 & 07711 102397
F: (01903) 201426

GOUDHURST
Kent
4 Clay Cottages ★★★★
Contact: Mrs Gill Winter & Patrick Tierney, Garden of England Cottages, The Mews Office, 189a High Street, Tonbridge, Kent TN9 1BX
T: (01732) 369168
F: (01732) 358817
E: goec@dial.pipex.com
I: www.gardenofenglandcottages.co.uk

The Coach House ★★★
Contact: Mrs Diana Lusty, The Coach House, c/o Thorford Hall Farm, Goudhurst Road, Goudhurst, Cranbrook, Kent TN12 0HQ
T: (01580) 891353
E: r.lusty@virgin.net
I: www.thorfordhall.co.uk

Etchinghill Cottage ★★★★
Contact: Mrs Gill Winter &
Patrick Tierney, Garden of
England Cottages, The Mews
Office, 189a High Street,
Tonbridge, Kent TN9 1BX
T: (01732) 369168
F: (01732) 358817
E: goec@dial.pipex.com
I: www.
gardenofenglandcottages.co.uk

Risebridge Farm ★★★
Contact: Ms Alex Hillier,
Risebridge Farm, Ranters Lane,
Goudhurst, Cranbrook, Kent
TN17 1HN
T: (01580) 212097
F: (01580) 211984
E: enquiries@risebridge.co.uk
I: www.risebridge.co.uk

Three Chimneys Farm ★★★★
Contact: Mrs Marion Fuller,
Three Chimneys Farm,
Bedgebury Road, Goudhurst,
Cranbrook, Kent TN17 2RA
T: (01580) 212175 &
07785 734639
F: (01580) 212175
E: marionfuller@
threechimneysfarm.co.uk
I: www.threechimneysfarm.
co.uk

GRAFTY GREEN
Kent

2 Fermor Cottages ★★★
Contact: Mrs Rosemary Smith,
Fermor Cottage, Headcorn Road,
Grafty Green, Maidstone, Kent
ME17 2AN
T: (01622) 850526
F: (01622) 850526

GROOMBRIDGE
East Sussex

Hollambys ★★★
Contact: Mr Andrew Joad & I
Smith, Hollambys, Eridge Road,
Groombridge, Royal Tunbridge
Wells, Kent TN3 9NJ
T: (01892) 864203
E: ajoad@hollambys.force9.
co.uk

Sherlocks Cottage ★★★★
Contact: Mrs Brenda Beck,
Freedom Holiday Homes, St
David's Bridge, Cranbrook, Kent
TN17 3HJ
T: (01580) 720770
F: (01580) 720771
E: freedomholsuk@clara.net
I: www.freedomholsuk.clara.net

GUESTLING
East Sussex

Lord's Wood Studio ★★★
Contact: Mrs Brenda Beck,
Freedom Holiday Homes, St
David's Bridge, Cranbrook, Kent
TN17 3HJ
T: (01580) 720770
F: (01580) 720771
E: freedomholsuk@clara.net
I: www.freedomholidyhomes.
co.uk

GUILDFORD
Surrey

University of Surrey ★★
Contact: Conference Office,
University of Surrey, Stag Hill,
Guildford, Surrey GU2 5XH
T: (01483) 259093 & 259157
F: (01483) 579266
E: k.stacey@surrey.ac.uk
I: www.surrey.ac.uk/conferences

GUSTON
Kent

Owl Cottage ★★★★
Contact: English Country
Cottages:PXK, English Country
Cottages, Stoney Bank, Earby,
Barnoldswick, Lancashire
BB94 0EE
T: 0870 5851155
F: 0870 5851150

HAILSHAM
East Sussex

**Little Marshfoot Farmhouse
★★★★**
Contact: Ms Kathryn Webster,
Little Marshfoot Farmhouse, Mill
Road, Hailsham, East Sussex
BN27 2SJ
T: (01323) 844690
E: kathryn.webster@which.net

**The Old Orchard Bungalow
★★★**
Contact: Mr Brian Bennett, The
Old Orchard House, The Platt,
Bottom of Caburn Way,
Hailsham, East Sussex BN27 3LX
T: (01323) 440977
F: (01323) 440977

HALLAND
East Sussex

Little Tamberry ★★★★
Contact: Mrs Brenda Beck,
Freedom Holiday Homes, St
David's Bridge, Cranbrook, Kent
TN17 3HJ
T: (01580) 720770
F: (01580) 720771
E: freedomholsuk@clara.net
I: www.freedomholidayhomes.
co.uk

HARTFIELD
East Sussex

Yew Tree Cottage ★★★
Contact: Mrs Gill Winter &
Patrick Tierney, Garden of
England Cottages, The Mews
Office, 189a High Street,
Tonbridge, Kent TN9 1BX
T: (01732) 369168
F: (01732) 358817
E: goec@dial.pipex.com
I: www.
gardenofenglandcottages.co.uk

HARTLEY
Kent

Highfields Cottage ★★
Contact: Country Holidays
ref:1861, Holiday Cottages
Group Owner Services
Department, Spring Mill, Earby,
Barnoldswick, Lancashire
BB18 6RN
T: 0870 444 6603
F: (01282) 841539
E: ownerservices@ttgihg.co.uk
I: www.country-holidays.co.uk

HASLEMERE
Surrey

Sheps Hollow ★★
Contact: Mrs Elizabeth Cattell,
Sheps Hollow, Henley Common,
Fernhurst, Haslemere, Surrey
GU27 3HB
T: (01428) 653120

HASTINGLEIGH
Kent

Staple Farm ★★★★
Contact: Mr & Mrs C H
Martindale, Staple Farm,
Hastingleigh, Ashford, Kent
TN25 5HF
T: (01233) 750248
F: (01233) 750249

HASTINGS
East Sussex

**Brooklands Coach House
★★★**
Contact: Mrs Caroline McNally,
Brooklands Coach House, 61 Old
London Road, Hastings, East
Sussex TN35 5NB
T: (01424) 421957
F: (01424) 437003
E: brooklandscoachhouse@
talk21.com

Bryn-Y-Mor ★★★-★★★★
Contact: Mrs D P Karen-Alun,
Bryn-Y-Mor, 12 Godwin Road,
Hastings, East Sussex TN35 5JR
T: (01424) 722744
F: (01424) 445933

The Chestnuts ★★★
Contact: Country Holidays Ref:
8021, Country Holidays, Spring
Mill, Earby, Barnoldswick,
Lancashire BB18 6RN
T: 08700 723723
F: (01282) 844288
E: sales@ttgihg.co.uk
I: www.country-holidays.co.uk

12 The Coastguards ★★★
Contact: Mrs J Doyle, Merton
House, 11 Barrack Street,
Bridport, Dorset DT6 3LX
T: (01308) 423180

Lionsdown House ★★★★
Contact: Mrs Sharon Bigg,
Lionsdown House, 116 High
Street, Old Town, Hastings, East
Sussex TN34 3ET
T: (01424) 420802
F: (01424) 420802
E: sharonlionsdown@aol.com
I: www.lionsdowhouse.co.uk

Number Six ★
Contact: Mr & Mrs C J Hart,
Number Six, 6 Stanley Road,
Hastings, East Sussex TN34 1UE
T: (01424) 431984 & 432690
E: famhart@supanet.com

**14 Old Humphrey Avenue
Rating Applied For**
Contact: Mrs Chris Nixey, 4
Southfield Cottages, Chalkshire
Road, Butlers Cross, Aylesbury,
Buckinghamshire HP17 0TS
T: (01296) 625780
F: (01296) 625780

Rocklands Holiday Park ★★★
Contact: Mr & Mrs J Guilliard,
Rocklands Holiday Park,
Rocklands Lane, East Hill,
Hastings, East Sussex TN35 5DY
T: (01424) 423097

**Rose House
Rating Applied For**
Contact: Mrs Susan Hill, 1
Beauport Gardens, St Leonards-
on-Sea, St Leonards, Hastings,
East Sussex TN37 7PQ
T: (01424) 754812 & 421973
F: (01424) 754812

St Marys Holiday Flats ★-★★
Contact: Mr Donald Edwards, 6
Highcroft Villas, Brighton, East
Sussex BN1 5PS
T: (01273) 556227

**Tillys Cottage
Rating Applied For**
Contact: Ms Celia Tully, 25
Alleyns Road, Old Town,
Stevenage, Hertfordshire
SG1 3PG
T: (01438) 216787

**Wellington Holiday
Apartments ★★**
Contact: Mrs Joan Stevens,
Wellington, Ashen Grove Road,
East Hill, Knatts Valley,
Sevenoaks, Kent TN15 6YE
T: (01959) 524260

**Westcliff Lodge
Rating Applied For**
Contact: Ms Celia Tully, 25
Alleyns Road, Old Town,
Stevenage, Hertfordshire
SG1 3PG
T: (01438) 216787

HAWKHURST
Kent

Baretilt Farm ★★★
Contact: Mrs Brenda Beck,
Freedom Holiday Homes, St
David's Bridge, Cranbrook, Kent
TN17 3HJ
T: (01580) 720770
F: (01580) 720771
E: freedomholsuk@clara.net
I: www.freedomholidayhomes.
co.uk

**Kent Bridge Croft Annexe
★★★**
Contact: Mrs Brenda Beck,
Freedom Holiday Homes, St
David's Bridge, Cranbrook, Kent
TN17 3HJ
T: (01580) 720770
F: (01580) 720771
E: freedomholsuk@clara.net
I: www.freedomholidayhomes.
co.uk

The Stables ★★★★
Contact: Mrs Gill Winter &
Patrick Tierney, Garden of
England Cottages, The Mews
Office, 189a High Street,
Tonbridge, Kent TN9 1BX
T: (01732) 369168
F: (01732) 358817
E: goec@dial.pipex.com
I: www.
gardenofenglandcottages.co.uk

**Woodham Hall Holiday
Studios ★★**
Contact: Mrs Sandra Liddiard,
Woodham Hall Hotel, Rye Road,
Hawkhurst, Kent TN18 5DA
T: (01580) 753428
F: (01580) 752304
E: ss@woodham hall.demon.
co.uk
I: www.woodhamhall.demon.
co.uk

HAWKINGE
Kent

1 North Downs Cottage ★★★★
Contact: Mrs Brenda Beck, Freedom Holiday Homes, St David's Bridge, Cranbrook, Kent TN17 3HJ
T: (01580) 720770
F: (01580) 720771
E: freedomholsuk@clara.net
I: www.freedomholsuk@clara.net

HAWLEY
Kent

Kingsley Holiday Flat
Rating Applied For
Contact: Mrs Una Warnes, Kingsley, Cross Road, Hawley, Dartford, Kent DA2 7RS
T: (01322) 225566

HEATHFIELD
East Sussex

Boring House Farm ★★★
Contact: Mrs A Reed, Boring House Farm, Vines Cross, Heathfield, East Sussex TN21 9AS
T: (01435) 812285
E: anne.read@ic24.net

HENFIELD
West Sussex

Dears Farm ★★
Contact: Mrs M G Paul, Dears Farm, West End Lane, Henfield, West Sussex BN5 9RD
T: (01273) 492334

New Hall Cottage & New Hall Holiday Flat★★★
Contact: Mrs M W Carreck, New Hall, Small Dole, Henfield, West Sussex BN5 9YJ
T: (01273) 492546

HERNE BAY
Kent

Arlington Lodge ★★★★
Contact: Mr A F Webb, 45A Warren Road, Reigate, Surrey RH2 0BN
T: (01737) 244385

Golf Lodge Cottage ★★★
Contact: Mrs Mariam Smallridge, 166 Mickleburgh Hill, Herne Bay, Kent CT6 6JZ
T: (01227) 740342
F: (01227) 740342

Iluka ★★★
Contact: Ms M S Hyde, Yamba, Spa Esplanade, Herne Bay, Kent CT6 8EP
T: (01227) 372282
I: iluka@coa.org.uk

83 Selsea Avenue ★★
Contact: Mr & Mrs John Campbell, Fairhaven Holiday Rentals, Derby House, 123 Watling Street, Gillingham, Kent ME7 2YY
T: (01634) 300089
F: (01634) 570157
E: fairhaven@pavilion.co.uk
I: www.fairhaven-holidays.co.uk

The South Wing Gothic House ★★★★
Contact: Mrs Maria McArdle, Fairhaven Holiday Cottages, Derby House, 123 Watling Street, Gillingham, Kent ME7 2YY
T: (01634) 300089
F: (01634) 570157
E: fairhaven@pavilion.co.uk
I: www.fairhaven-holidays.co.uk

Umballa ★★★
Contact: Mrs A Campbell, Fairhaven Holiday Cottages, Derby House, 123 Watling Street, Gillingham, Kent ME7 2YY
T: (01634) 300089
F: (01634) 570157
E: fairhaven@pavilion.co.uk
I: www.fairhaven-holidays.co.uk

Westcliff ★★★
Contact: Fairhaven Holiday Rentals, Derby House, 123 Watling Street, Gillingham, Kent ME7 2YY
T: (01634) 300089 & 570157
F: (01634) 570157
E: fairhaven@pavilion.co.uk
I: www.fairhaven-holidays.co.uk

49 Western Esplanade ★★
Contact: Mr Michael Hedger, 49 Western Esplanade, Herne Bay, Kent CT6 8JA
T: (01227) 375941

HERONS GHYLL
East Sussex

Home Farm ★★★★
Contact: Mrs Brenda Beck, Freedom Holiday Homes, St David's Bridge, Cranbrook, Kent TN17 3HJ
T: (01580) 720770
F: (01580) 720771
E: freedomholsuk@clara.net
I: www.freedomholidayhomes.co.uk

HIGH HALDEN
Kent

Crampton Lodge ★★★★
Contact: Mrs Brenda Beck, Freedom Holiday Homes, St David's Bridge, Cranbrook, Kent TN17 3HJ
T: (01580) 720770
F: (01580) 720771
E: freedomholsuk@clara.net
I: www.freedomholidayhomes.co.uk

The Granary at Hales Place ★★★★
Contact: Mrs Brenda Beck, Freedom Holiday Homes, St David's Bridge, Cranbrook, Kent TN17 3HJ
T: (01580) 720770
F: (01580) 720771
E: freedomholsuk@clara.net
I: www.freedomholidayhomes.co.uk

Heron Cottage ★★★
Contact: Mrs Gill Winter & Patrick Tierney, Garden of England Cottages, The Mews Office, 189a High Street, Tonbridge, Kent TN9 1BX
T: (01732) 369168
F: (01732) 358817
E: goec@dial.pipex.com
I: www.gardenofenglandcottages.co.uk

Mallard Cottage ★★★
Contact: Mrs Gill Winter & Patrick Tierney, Garden of England Cottages, The Mews Office, 189a High Street, Tonbridge, Kent TN9 1BX
T: (01732) 369168
F: (01732) 358817
E: goec@dial.pipex.com
I: www.gardenofenglandcottages.co.uk

Pine Tree Cottage Annexe ★★★
Contact: Mrs Brenda Beck, Freedom Holiday Homes, St David's Bridge, Cranbrook, Kent TN17 3HJ
T: (01580) 720770
F: (01580) 720771
E: freedomholsuk@clara.net
I: www.freedomholsuk.clara.net

Ransley Oast ★★★
Contact: Ms Emma MacLennan, Ransley Oast, Ashford Road, High Halden, Ashford, Kent TN26 3LL
T: (01233) 850057
F: (01233) 850136

HILDENBOROUGH
Kent

Coldharbour Farm Holiday Cottages ★★★★
Contact: Mr & Mrs M J Wilson, Coldharbour Farm, Coldharbour Lane, Hildenborough, Tonbridge, Kent TN11 9JX
T: (01732) 832085
F: (01732) 832228
E: hg.letting@virgin.net
I: www.holiday-rentals.co.uk

The Cottage ★★★★
Contact: Mr D W Hurrell, The Cottage, Court Lodge, Coldharbour Lane, Hildenborough, Tonbridge, Kent TN11 9LE
T: (01732) 832081
F: (01732) 832081

HINDHEAD
Surrey

Tyndalls Cottage ★★★★
Contact: Mrs Christine Foster, Tyndalls Cottage, 26 Tyndalls, Hindhead, Surrey GU26 6AP
T: (01428) 609028
F: (01428) 609028
E: tyndallscottage@tinyworld.co.uk

HOO
Kent

Whitehall Farmhouse ★★★★
Contact: Mr Dennis Reavell, Whitehall Farmhouse, Whitehall Farm, Stoke Road, Hoo, Rochester, Kent ME3 9BP
T: (01634) 250251
F: (01634) 251112
E: reavell@waystarltd.freeserve.co.uk

HORSHAM
West Sussex

Walnut Barn & Walnut Cottage ★★★★-★★★★★★
Contact: Mrs Sally Cole, Walnut Barn & Walnut Cottage, Hard's Farm Cottage, Kerves Lane, Horsham, West Sussex RH13 6RJ
T: (01403) 249159
E: jpcole@lineone.net
I: www.sussexholidaycottages.com

HORSMONDEN
Kent

Bainden Barn
Rating Applied For
Contact: Mrs Brenda Beck, Freedom Holiday Homes, St David's Bridge, Cranbrook, Kent TN17 3HJ
T: (01580) 720770
F: (01580) 720771
E: freedomholsuk@clara.net
I: www.freedomholidayhomes.co.uk

Field Cottage ★★★
Contact: Mrs Gill Winter & Patrick Tierney, Garden of England Cottages, The Mews Office, 189a High Street, Tonbridge, Kent TN9 1BX
T: (01732) 369168
F: (01732) 358817
E: goec@dial.pipex.com
I: www.gardenofenglandcottages.co.uk

Heathside ★★★★
Contact: Mrs Gill Winter & Patrick Tierney, Garden of England Cottages, The Mews Office, 189a High Street, Tonbridge, Kent TN9 1BX
T: (01732) 369168
F: (01732) 358817
E: goec@dial.pipex.com
I: www.gardenofenglandcottages.co.uk

HUNTON
Kent

Woolhouse Barn ★★★★
Contact: Mrs Gill Winter & Patrick Tierney, Garden of England Cottages, The Mews Office, 189a High Street, Tonbridge, Kent TN9 1BX
T: (01732) 369168
F: (01732) 358817
E: goec@dial.pipex.com
I: www.gardenofenglandcottages.co.uk

HYTHE
Kent

5B Hillside Street ★★★
Contact: Mrs Brenda Beck, Freedom Holiday Homes, St David's Bridge, Cranbrook, Kent TN17 3HJ
T: (01580) 720770
F: (01580) 720771
E: freedomholsuk@clara.net
I: www.freedomholsuk.clara.net

40 Stade Street ★★
Contact: Mrs Anne Ambrose, Driffield Manor, Driffield, Cirencester, Gloucestershire GL7 5PZ
T: (01285) 851205

Uppermill ★★★
Contact: Mrs Eleanor Cobbold, Marston Properties Ltd, 1 Stephendale Road, London SW6 2LU
T: (020) 7736 7133
F: (020) 7731 8412
E: ellie@marstonproperties.co.uk
I: www.marstonproperties.co.uk

Establishments printed in blue have a detailed entry in this guide

ICKLESHAM
East Sussex

Broadstreet House ★★★★
Contact: Mrs Gill Winter &
Patrick Tierney, Garden of
England Cottages, The Mews
Office, 189a High Street,
Tonbridge, Kent TN9 1BX
T: (01732) 369168
F: (01732) 358817
E: goec@dial.pipex.com
I: www.
gardenofenglandcottages.co.uk

Garden Cottage ★★★
Contact: Mrs Gill Winter &
Patrick Tierney, Garden of
England Cottages, The Mews
Office, 189a High Street,
Tonbridge, Kent TN9 1BX
T: (01732) 369168
F: (01732) 358817
E: goec@dial.pipex.com
I: www.
gardenofenglandcottages.co.uk

Oast House Cottage ★★★★
Contact: Mrs Brenda Beck,
Freedom Holiday Homes, St
David's Bridge, Cranbrook, Kent
TN17 3HJ
T: (01580) 720770
F: (01580) 720771
E: freedomholsuk@clara.net
I: www.freedomholidayhomes.
co.uk

The Stable ★★★
Contact: Mrs Gill Winter &
Patrick Tierney, Garden of
England Cottages, The Mews
Office, 189a High Street,
Tonbridge, Kent TN9 1BX
T: (01732) 369168
F: (01732) 358817
E: goec@dial.pipex.com
I: www.
gardenofenglandcottages.co.uk

IPING
West Sussex

The Studio ★★★
Contact: Mrs & Mr Claudia
Callingham, Kinrose House, Titty
Hill, Iping, Midhurst, West
Sussex GU29 0PL
T: (01428) 741561
F: (01428) 741561

KEMSING
Kent

6 Dippers Close ★★
Contact: Mr & Mrs Ronald Rose,
6 Dippers Close, Kemsing,
Sevenoaks, Kent TN15 6QD
T: (01732) 761937

KINGSDOWN
Kent

**Chalet 115 Kingsdown Park
★★★**
Contact: Mrs Anne Hayward,
Homestall, Fairmead, Elmswell,
Bury St Edmunds, Suffolk
IP30 9HT
T: (01359) 242342
F: (01359) 240837
E: hayward@homestall.com
I: www.homestall.com

**Chalets 11 & 12 Kingsdown
Park★★★**
Contact: Mrs C Cross & Mr D
Withers, 167 Percy Avenue,
Kingsgate, Broadstairs, Kent
CT10 3LE
T: (01843) 863612
E: decccec@aol.com

47 Kingsdown Park ★★★
Contact: Mrs Brenda Beck,
Freedom Holiday Homes, St
David's Bridge, Cranbrook, Kent
TN17 3HJ
T: (01580) 720770
F: (01580) 720771
E: freedomholsuk@clara.net
I: www.freedomholidayhomes.
co.uk

KINGSTON
East Sussex

Nightingales ★★★★
Contact: Mrs Jean Hudson,
Nightingales, The Avenue,
Kingston, Lewes, East Sussex
BN7 3LL
T: (01273) 475673
F: (01273) 475673
E: Nightingales@totalise.co.uk
I: www.user.totalise.
co.uk/nightingales/

KNOWLTON
Kent

**Knowlton Court
★★★-★★★★**
Contact: Mrs Mary Smith,
Knowlton Court, The Estate
Office, Knowlton Court,
Knowlton, Canterbury, Kent
CT3 1PT
T: (01304) 842402
F: (01304) 842403
E: knowlton.cottages@farmline.
com

LAMBERHURST
Kent

Goldings Barn ★★★
Contact: Mrs Brenda Beck,
Freedom Holiday Homes, St
David's Bridge, Cranbrook, Kent
TN17 3HJ
T: (01580) 720770
F: (01580) 720771
E: freedomholsuk@clara.net
I: www.freedomholidayhomes.
co.uk

**Oast Cottage, Orchard Cottage
& The Oast House★★★**
Contact: Mrs Brenda Beck,
Freedom Holiday Homes, St
David's Bridge, Cranbrook, Kent
TN17 3HJ
T: (01580) 720770
F: (01580) 720771
E: freedomholsuk@clara.net
I: www.freedomholidayhomes.
co.uk

Owls Castle Oast ★★★★
Contact: Mrs B Bingham, Owls
Castle Oast, Hoghole Lane,
Lamberhurst, Royal Tunbridge
Wells, Kent TN3 8BN
T: (01892) 890758
F: (01892) 890215

The White Magpie ★★★★
Contact: Mrs P I Spencer, The
White Magpie, Hog Hole Lane,
Lamberhurst, Royal Tunbridge
Wells, Kent TN3 8BN
T: (01892) 617136 & 890341

LAUGHTON
East Sussex

Holly Cottage ★★★
Contact: Mr & Mrs David & Pat
Fuller, Holly Cottage, Lewes
Road, Laughton, Lewes, East
Sussex BN8 6BL
T: (01323) 811309
F: (01323) 811106
E: hollycottage@tinyworld.
co.uk

LAVANT
West Sussex

South Cottage ★★★★
Contact: Mr Graham Davies,
Raughmere House, Raughmere
Drive, Lavant, Chichester, West
Sussex PO18 0AB
T: (01243) 527120
E: gmd@lix.co.uk

LEEDS
Kent

**1 & 2 Orchard View
Rating Applied For**
Contact: Mrs Gill Winter &
Patrick Tierney, Garden of
England Cottages, The Mews
Office, 189a High Street,
Tonbridge, Kent TN9 1BX
T: (01732) 369168
F: (01732) 358817
E: goec@dial.pipex.com
I: www.
gardenofenglandcottages.co.uk

LEIGH
Kent

The Old Stables ★★★★★
Contact: Mr & Mrs Nicholas
Morris, Charcott Farmhouse,
Charcott, Leigh, Tonbridge, Kent
TN11 8LG
T: (01892) 870024
F: (01892) 870158
E: nicholasmorris@charcott.
freeserve.co.uk
I: www.smoothhound.
co.uk/hotels/charcott

LENHAM
Kent

7 Church Square ★★
Contact: Mrs Brenda Beck,
Freedom Holiday Homes, St
David's Bridge, Cranbrook, Kent
TN17 3HJ
T: (01580) 720770
F: (01580) 720771
E: freedomholsuk@clara.net
I: www.freedomholsuk.clara.net

**Newage Farmhouse
Rating Applied For**
Contact: Mrs Brenda Beck,
Freedom Holiday Homes, St
David's Bridge, Cranbrook, Kent
TN17 3HJ
T: (01580) 720770
F: (01580) 720771
E: freedomholsuk@clara.net
I: www.freedomholidayhomes.
co.uk

LEWES
East Sussex

5 Buckhurst Close ★★★
Contact: Mrs S Foulds, 66
Houndean Rise, Lewes, East
Sussex BN7 1EJ
T: (01273) 474755
F: (01273) 474755

17 Cluny Street ★★★
Contact: Mrs R T Salmon, Best of
Brighton & Sussex Cottages Ltd,
Windmill Lodge, Vicarage Lane,
Rottingdean, Brighton, East
Sussex BN2 7HD
T: (01273) 308779 &
07956 662457
F: (01273) 300266

1 Roots Cottages ★★★★
Contact: Mr & Mrs Hedley
Cornwell, Camoys Farmhouse,
Barcombe, Lewes, East Sussex
BN8 5BH
T: (01273) 400662
E: hedley.reinie@tinyworld.
co.uk

24 St Johns Terrace ★★★
Contact: Mrs R T Salmon, Best of
Brighton & Sussex Cottages Ltd,
Windmill Lodge, Vicarage Lane,
Rottingdean, Brighton, East
Sussex BN2 7HD
T: (01273) 308779 &
07956 662457
F: (01273) 300266

**Sussex Countryside
Accommodation ★★★★**
Contact: Mrs Hazel Gaydon,
Sussex Countryside
Accommodation, Crink House,
Barcombe Mills, Lewes, East
Sussex BN8 5BJ
T: (01273) 400625
E: crinkhouse@hgaydon.fsnet.
co.uk

LINTON
Kent

Loddington Oast ★★★★
Contact: Mr & Mrs R Martin,
Loddington Oast, Loddington
Lane, Linton, Maidstone, Kent
ME17 4AG
T: (01622) 747777
E: rm_trsystems@btinternet.
com

LITTLEHAMPTON
West Sussex

10 Mariners Quay ★★★★★
Contact: Mrs R T Salmon, Best of
Brighton & Sussex Cottages Ltd,
Windmill Lodge, Vicarage Lane,
Rottingdean, Brighton, East
Sussex BN2 7HD
T: (01273) 308779 &
07956 662457
F: (01273) 300266

Racing Greens ★★★
Contact: Ms Edith Ballantine,
Racing Greens, 70 South
Terrace, Littlehampton, West
Sussex BN17 5LQ
T: (01903) 732972 &
07887 572098
F: (01903) 732932
E: urban.surfer@easynet.co.uk

Victoria Holidays ★★
Contact: Mrs S Ogrodnik,
Victoria Holidays, 86 South
Terrace, Littlehampton, West
Sussex BN17 5LJ
T: (01903) 722644

Establishments printed in blue have a detailed entry in this guide

LOOSE
Kent

Bockingford Steps Barn ★★★
Contact: Mrs Jennifer Buckley,
Bockingford Steps, Bockingford
Lane, Loose, Maidstone, Kent
ME15 6DP
T: (01622) 756030

LOWER BEEDING
West Sussex

**Black Cottage, the Little Barn
& the Old Dairy★★-★★★★**
Contact: Mrs V Storey, Newells
Farm, Newells Farmhouse,
Newells Lane, Lower Beeding,
Horsham, West Sussex
RH13 6LN
T: (01403) 891326
F: (01403) 891530

LYDD ON SEA
Kent

69 Coast Drive ★★★
Contact: Mrs Brenda Beck,
Freedom Holiday Homes, St
David's Bridge, Cranbrook, Kent
TN17 3HJ
T: (01580) 720770
F: (01580) 720771
E: freedomholsuk@clara.net
I: www.freedomholidayhomes.
co.uk

MAIDSTONE
Kent

Brook House Barn ★★★★★
Contact: Mrs Linda Doust, Brook
House, Old Loose Hill,
Maidstone, Kent ME15 0BL
T: (01622) 743703
F: (01622) 747828

Lavender Cottage ★★
Contact: Mr & Mrs John
Campbell, Fairhaven Holiday
Cottages, Derby House, 123
Watling Street, Gillingham, Kent
ME7 2YY
T: (01634) 300089
F: (01634) 570157
E: fairhaven@pavilion.co.uk
I: www.fairhaven-holidays.co.uk

Orchard Flat ★★
Contact: Mrs Pamela Clark,
Orchard Flat, Ferlaga, Vicarage
Lane, East Farleigh, Maidstone,
Kent ME15 0LX
T: (01622) 726919

MARDEN
Kent

Redstock ★★★★
Contact: Mrs Gill Winter &
Patrick Tierney, Garden of
England Cottages, The Mews
Office, 189a High Street,
Tonbridge, Kent TN9 1BX
T: (01732) 369168
F: (01732) 358817
E: goec@dial.pipex.com
I: www.
gardenofenglandcottages.co.uk

MARGATE
Kent

Smugglers Cottage ★★
Contact: Ms Susan Anderson, 10
Royal Crescent, Ramsgate, Kent
CT11 9PD
T: (01843) 594207

63 Staplehurst Gardens ★★★
Contact: Mrs P F Bowles, 57
Rectory Lane North, Leybourne,
West Malling, Kent ME19 5HD
T: (01732) 843396
F: (01732) 843396

MAYFIELD
East Sussex

Fair Oak Farm Oast ★★★★
Contact: Mr Martin Saker, Fair
Oak Farm, Witherenden Lane,
Mayfield, East Sussex TN20 6RS
T: (01435) 882344
F: (01435) 883376

MEOPHAM
Kent

54 Beechwood Drive ★★★★
Contact: Mrs Brenda Beck,
Freedom Holiday Homes, St
David's Bridge, Cranbrook, Kent
TN17 3HJ
T: (01580) 720770
F: (01580) 720771
E: freedomholsuk@clara.net
I: www.freedomholsuk.clara.net

MEREWORTH
Kent

The Dairy ★★★★
Contact: BI Hols
Ref:KC89,90,91,etc, Blakes
Holidays in Britain Sales, Stoney
Bank Road, Earby, Barnoldswick,
Lancashire BB94 0AA
T: 08700 723723
F: (01282) 844288
E: sales@ttgihg.co.uk
I: www.country-holidays.co.uk

MERSHAM
Kent

Gill Farm ★★★★
Contact: Mrs Jan Bowman, Gill
Farm, Gill Lane, Mersham,
Ashford, Kent TN25 7HZ
T: (01303) 261247 &
(01233) 720345
F: (01303) 261249
E: janbowman@studio2uk.
com/gillfarm
I: www.studio2uk.com/gillfarm

MINSTER-IN-THANET
Kent

April Cottage ★★★
Contact: Ms Sylvie Dalton, 34
Rogers Hill, Worcester,
Worcester WR3 8AQ
T: (01905) 613066

The Coach House ★★★
Contact: Mrs Brenda Beck,
Freedom Holiday Homes, St
David's Bridge, Cranbrook, Kent
TN17 3HJ
T: (01580) 720770
F: (01580) 720771
E: freedomholsuk@clara.net
I: www.freedomholsuk.clara.net

Durlock Lodge ★★★
Contact: Mr David Sworder,
Durlock Lodge, Durlock, Minster-
in-Thanet, Ramsgate, Kent
CT12 4HD
T: (01843) 821219
E: david@durlocklodge.co.uk
I: www.durlocklodge.co.uk

NEW ROMNEY
Kent

Boxted Lodge Farm ★★★★
Contact: Mrs Jane Apps, Boxted
Lodge Farm, Brookland, Romney
Marsh, Kent TN29 9QU
T: (01797) 344295
F: (01797) 344295

Romney Farm ★★★
Contact: Mrs Gill Winter &
Patrick Tierney, Garden of
England Cottages, The Mews
Office, 189a High Street,
Tonbridge, Kent TN9 1BX
T: (01732) 369168
F: (01732) 358817
E: goec@dial.pipex.com
I: www.
gardenofenglandcottages.co.uk

NEWENDEN
Kent

The Bothy ★★★
Contact: Mrs Brenda Beck,
Freedom Holiday Homes, St
David's Bridge, Cranbrook, Kent
TN17 3HJ
T: (01580) 720770
F: (01580) 720771
E: freedomholsuk@clara.net
I: www.freedomholidayhomes.
co.uk

NEWICK
East Sussex

Manor House Cottage ★★★★
Contact: Mrs Jane Roberts, The
Manor House, Church Road,
Newick, Lewes, East Sussex
BN8 4JZ
T: (01825) 722868
E: jane.roberts@tinyworld.co.uk

NORTHBOURNE
Kent

New Mill ★★★
Contact: Mrs Brenda Beck,
Freedom Holiday Homes, St
David's Bridge, Cranbrook, Kent
TN17 3HJ
T: (01580) 720770
F: (01580) 720771
E: freedomholsuk@clara.net
I: www.freedomholidayhomes.
co.uk

NUTBOURNE
West Sussex

**Loveders Farm Cottage
★★★★**
Contact: Mr & Mrs P R Mansell,
Loveders Farm Cottage, Loveders
Farm, Priors Leaze Lane,
Nutbourne, Chichester, West
Sussex PO18 8RH
T: (01243) 371943
E: mansell@tinyworld.co.uk

NUTLEY
East Sussex

**Whitehouse Farm Holiday
Cottages ★★-★★★★**
Contact: Mr Keith Wilson,
Whitehouse Farm Holiday
Cottages, Whitehouse Farm,
Horney Common, Nutley,
Uckfield, East Sussex TN22 3EE
T: (01825) 712377
F: (01825) 712377
E: keith.g.r.wilson@btinternet.
com
I: www.streets-ahead.
com/whitehousefarm
🏠

OTHAM
Kent

The Library ★★★★
Contact: Mr & Mrs J Barker, The
Library, Gore Court, Church
Road, Otham, Maidstone, Kent
ME15 8RF
T: (01622) 863029

**2 Primrose Cottage
Rating Applied For**
Contact: Mrs S Malone, 69 Lion
Road, Bexleyheath, Kent
DA6 8NW
T: (0208) 303 1369 &
07767 346974

OTTERDEN
Kent

Frith Farm House ★★★★
Contact: Mrs Susan Chesterfield,
Frith Farm House, Otterden,
Faversham, Kent ME13 0DD
T: (01795) 890701
F: (01795) 890009
E: markham@frith.force9.co.uk

PADDOCK WOOD
Kent

4 Maidstone Road ★★★★
Contact: Mrs Gill Winter &
Patrick Tierney, Garden of
England Cottages, The Mews
Office, 189a High Street,
Tonbridge, Kent TN9 1BX
T: (01732) 369168
F: (01732) 358817
E: goec@dial.pipex.com
I: www.
gardenofenglandcottages.co.uk

PEACEHAVEN
East Sussex

Highseas ★★★
Contact: Mrs R T Salmon, Best of
Brighton & Sussex Cottages Ltd,
Windmill Lodge, Vicarage Lane,
Rottingdean, Brighton, East
Sussex BN2 7HD
T: (01273) 308779 &
07956 662457
F: (01273) 300266

Pampass ★★★★★
Contact: Mrs R T Salmon, Best of
Brighton & Sussex Cottages Ltd,
Windmill Lodge, Vicarage Lane,
Rottingdean, Brighton, East
Sussex BN2 7HD
T: (01273) 308779 &
07956 662457
F: (01273) 300266

PEASMARSH
East Sussex

Pond Cottage ★★★★
Contact: Mr & Mrs A Reeve, A
Reeve & Son, Clayton Farm,
Church Lane, Peasmarsh, Rye,
East Sussex TN31 6XS
T: (01797) 230394 &
07761 742664
E: peasmarsh68.fsnet.co.uk
I: rye.tourism.co.uk/pondcottage

PEMBURY
Kent

2 Cornford Close ★★★
Contact: Mrs Gill Winter &
Patrick Tierney, Garden of
England Cottages, The Mews
Office, 189a High Street,
Tonbridge, Kent TN9 1BX
T: (01732) 369168
T: (01732) 358817
E: goec@dial.pipex.com
I: www.
gardenofenglandcottages.co.uk

Wysteria Cottage ★★★
Contact: Mrs T M Graham,
Wysteria Cottage, Hazelwood,
Romford Road, Pembury, Royal
Tunbridge Wells, Kent TN2 4BA
T: (01892) 822645
F: (01892) 823274

PETHAM
Kent

**Slippery Sam's Holiday
Cottages ★★★**
Contact: Mr Ian Wallace,
Slippery Sam's Holiday Cottages,
Slippery Sam's, Stone Street,
Petham, Canterbury, Kent
CT4 5PR
T: (01227) 700044
E: slipperysams@postmaster.
co.uk
I: www.slipperysams.fsnet.co.uk

PETT LEVEL
East Sussex

**Anchor Cottage
Rating Applied For**
Contact: Mrs Brenda Doherty,
Harlyn, Brampton Road, Alston,
Cumbria CA9 3AA
T: (01434) 381034

Laughing Water ★★★
Contact: Mrs L Robinson,
Laughing Water, 80 Hayes
Chase, West Wickham, Bromley,
Kent BR4 0JA
T: (020) 8777 7517 &
(01732) 863061

PETWORTH
West Sussex

Duncton Mill Ltd ★★★★
Contact: Mrs Sheila Bishop,
Duncton Mill House, Dye House
Lane, Dunctun, Petworth, West
Sussex GU28 0LF
T: (01798) 342294
F: (01798) 344122
E: sheila@dunctonmill.com
I: www.dunctonmill.com

The Old Dairy ★★★★
Contact: Mrs Rosaleen Waugh,
Coultershaw Farm House,
Petworth, West Sussex
GU28 0JE
T: (01798) 342900
E: peter_waugh@compuserve.
com

PEVENSEY BAY
East Sussex

Sunpatch ★★★★
Contact: Mr Lindsay Davis,
Willow Cottage, 8 Kingswood
Way, Selsdon, South Croydon,
Surrey CR2 8QP
T: (020) 8651 2444 &
07711 616550
E: lindsay.davis@btinternet.com
I: www.beachbungalow.
freeservers.com

The Yellow House ★★★★
Contact: Mrs R T Salmon, Best of
Brighton & Sussex Cottages Ltd,
Windmill Lodge, Vicarage Lane,
Rottingdean, Brighton, East
Sussex BN2 7HD
T: (01273) 308779 &
07956 662457
F: (01273) 300266

PLAXTOL
Kent

**Golding Hop Farm Cottage
★★★**
Contact: Mrs J Vincent, Golding
Hop Farm, Bewley Lane, Plaxtol,
Sevenoaks, Kent TN15 0PS
T: (01732) 885432
F: (01732) 885432
E: adrian@mvvincent.freeserve.
co.uk
I: www.mvvincent.freeserve.
co.uk

**3 Shields Cottages
Rating Applied For**
Contact: Mrs Gill Winter &
Patrick Tierney, Garden of
England Cottages, The Mews
Office, 189a High Street,
Tonbridge, Kent TN9 1BX
T: (01732) 369168
F: (01732) 358817
E: goec@dial.pipex.com
I: www.
gardenofenglandcottages.co.uk

PLUCKLEY
Kent

Little Caradon ★★★
Contact: Mrs Diana Birch,
Caradon, Mill Lane, Pluckley,
Ashford, Kent TN27 0SL
T: (01233) 840353
F: (01233) 840353
E: caradon@btinternet.com

POLEGATE
East Sussex

Barn Cottage ★★★★★
Contact: Mrs R T Salmon, Best of
Brighton & Sussex Cottages Ltd,
Windmill Lodge, Vicarage Lane,
Rottingdean, Brighton, East
Sussex BN2 7HD
T: (01273) 308779 &
07956 662457
F: (01273) 300266

PORTSLADE
East Sussex

**Ground Floor Apartment 1 St
Aubyns Road★★**
Contact: Mrs R T Salmon, Best of
Brighton & Sussex Cottages Ltd,
Windmill Lodge, Vicarage Lane,
Rottingdean, Brighton, East
Sussex BN2 7HD
T: (01273) 308779 &
07956 662457
F: (01273) 300266

PRINSTED
West Sussex

4 The Square ★★
Contact: Mr Martin Body, 7
Addington Square, London
SE5 7JZ
T: (020) 7703 4351
F: (020) 7703 1047

PULBOROUGH
West Sussex

Bignor Park Estate ★★★
Contact: Diana Robertson, 1
Bignor Park Cottages, Bignor
Park, Pulborough, West Sussex
RH20 1HG
T: (01798) 869227
F: (01798) 869227
E: info@bignorpark.co.uk
I: www.bignorpark.co.uk

RAMSGATE
Kent

Crescent Apartments ★★
Contact: Mrs Penelope Perrott,
Crescent Apartments, 4 Nelson
Crescent, Ramsgate, Kent
CT11 9JF
T: (01843) 593947
F: (01843) 851255

**Hamilton House Holiday Flats
★-★★**
Contact: Mrs Ann Burridge,
Hamilton House Holiday Flats, 5
Nelson Crescent, Ramsgate,
Kent CT11 9JF
T: (01843) 582592

23 The Lawns ★★★★
Contact: Mrs Jean Lawrence, J N
Lawrence, 24 Winterstoke
Crescent, Ramsgate, Kent
CT11 8AH
T: (01843) 591422
F: (01843) 591422
E: ali-keir@dutton94freeserve.
co.uk

**Ramsgate Holiday Homes
★★★**
Contact: Mrs P J Martin,
Ramsgate Holiday Homes, 21
Avebury Avenue, Ramsgate,
Kent CT11 8BB
T: (01843) 592945
F: (01843) 599063
E: penny@martinramsgate.
freeserve.co.uk

**Ramsgate Holiday House
★★★**
Contact: Mrs W E Martin, 20
Swinburne Avenue, Broadstairs,
Kent CT10 2DP
T: (01843) 863014
E: wend-liz@jules85.fsnet.co.uk

**White Lodge
Rating Applied For**
Contact: Mrs Frances Doyle, 26
London Road, Ramsgate, Kent
CT11 0DB
T: (01843) 592903

RIVER
West Sussex

Timekeepers ★
Contact: Mrs Joanna Clevely,
Tanners, River, Petworth, West
Sussex GU28 9AY
T: (01798) 861394
F: (01798) 861669

ROBERTSBRIDGE
East Sussex

**Frendes Cottage
Rating Applied For**
Contact: Mrs Brenda Beck,
Freedom Holiday Homes, St
David's Bridge, Cranbrook, Kent
TN17 3HJ
T: (01580) 720770
F: (01580) 720771
E: freedomholsuk@clara.net
I: www.freedomholsuk.clara.net.

Fuggles & Hop Cottage ★★★
Contact: Mrs Gill Winter &
Patrick Tierney, Garden of
England Cottages, The Mews
Office, 189a High Street,
Tonbridge, Kent TN9 1BX
T: (01732) 369168
F: (01732) 358817
E: goec@dial.pipex.com
I: www.
gardenofenglandcottages.co.uk

**Garden Cottage Annexe &
Studio ★★-★★★**
Contact: Mrs Brenda Beck,
Freedom Holiday Homes, St
David's Bridge, Cranbrook, Kent
TN17 3HJ
T: (01580) 720770
F: (01580) 720771
E: freedomholsuk@clara.net
I: www.freedomholidayhomes.
co.uk

Holly Cottage ★★★
Contact: Mrs Judy Phillips,
Fairhaven Holiday Cottages,
Derby House, 123 Watling
Street, Gillingham, Kent
ME7 2YY
T: (01634) 300089
F: (01634) 570157
E: fairhaven@pavilion.co.uk
I: www.fairhaven-holidays.co.uk

3 Saxon Terrace ★★★★
Contact: Mrs Brenda Beck,
Freedom Holiday Homes, St
David's Bridge, Cranbrook, Kent
TN17 3HJ
T: (01580) 720770
F: (01580) 720771
E: freedomholsuk@clara.net
I: www.freedomholsuk.clara.net

ROCHESTER
Kent

**The Bungalow
Rating Applied For**
Contact: Mr T G Terry, 5 Trevale
Road, Rochester, Kent ME1 3NZ
T: (01634) 848614
E: papa@tterry7.fsnet.co.uk

Merton Villa ★★
Contact: Mrs Nicola Radford,
Merton Villa, 38 Maidstone
Road, Rochester, Kent ME1 1RJ
T: (01634) 817190

Newlands Farm House ★★★★
Contact: Mrs Patricia Kelly,
Newlands Farm House, Fenn
Corner, St Mary Hoo, Rochester,
Kent ME3 8RE
T: (01634) 253083 & 272388
F: (01634) 255053
E: knweld@aol.com

**Stable Cottages
Rating Applied For**
Contact: Mr & Mrs Jason
Symonds, Stable Cottages, Fenn
Croft, Newlands Farm Road, St
Mary's Hoo, Rochester, Kent
ME3 8QS
T: (01634) 272439
F: (01634) 272205

RODMELL
East Sussex

**Deep Thatch Cottage Annexe
★★★**
Contact: Mrs Carol Ashplant,
Deep Thatch Cottage, The Street,
Rodmell, Lewes, East Sussex
BN7 3HF
T: (01273) 477086

Establishments printed in blue have a detailed entry in this guide

ROTTINGDEAN
East Sussex

11 Highcliffe Court ★★
Contact: Mrs R T Salmon, Best of Brighton & Sussex Cottages Ltd, Windmill Lodge, Vicarage Lane, Rottingdean, Brighton, East Sussex BN2 7HD
T: (01273) 308779 &
07956 662457
F: (01273) 300266

Horseshoe Cottage ★★★
Contact: Reservations, Best of Brighton & Sussex Cottages Ltd, Windmill Lodge, Vicarage Lane, Rottingdean, Brighton, East Sussex BN2 7HD
T: (01273) 308779 &
07956 662457
F: (01273) 300266
E: brightoncottages@pavilion.co.uk
I: www.bestofbrighton.co.uk

Kilcolgan Bungalow ★★★★
Contact: Mrs R T Salmon, Best of Brighton & Sussex Cottages Ltd, Windmill Lodge, Vicarage Lane, Rottingdean, Brighton, East Sussex BN2 7HD
T: (01273) 308779 &
07956 662457
F: (01273) 300266

7 Park Crescent ★★★
Contact: Mrs R T Salmon, Best of Brighton & Sussex Cottages Ltd, Windmill Lodge, Vicarage Lane, Rottingdean, Brighton, East Sussex BN2 7HD
T: (01273) 308779 &
07956 662457
F: (01273) 300266

ROYAL TUNBRIDGE WELLS
Kent

Broad Oak House ★★★
Contact: Ms Tina Seymour, Broad Oak House, 9 Linden Park Road, Royal Tunbridge Wells, Kent TN2 5QL
T: (01892) 619065 & 619064
F: (01892) 619064
E: tina@tlctraing.co.uk

Flat 4 76 London Road
Rating Applied For
Contact: Mrs Brenda Beck, Freedom Holiday Homes, St David's Bridge, Cranbrook, Kent TN17 3HJ
T: (01580) 720770
F: (01580) 720771
E: freedomholsuk@clara.net
I: www.freedomholidayhomes.co.uk

Ford Cottage ★★★
Contact: Mrs Wendy Cusdin, Ford Cottage, Linden Park Road, Royal Tunbridge Wells, Kent TN2 5QL
T: (01892) 531419
E: fordcottage@tinyworld.co.uk

Itaris Properties Limited
★★★★
Contact: Mr Edward Chattell, Itaris Properties Ltd, 12 Mount Ephraim, Royal Tunbridge Wells, Kent TN4 8AS
T: (01892) 511065
F: (01892) 540171
E: aechattell@msn.com
I: www.itaris.co.uk

1 Stable Mews ★★★
Contact: Mrs Brenda Beck, Freedom Holiday Homes, St David's Bridge, Cranbrook, Kent TN17 3HJ
T: (01580) 720770
F: (01580) 720771
E: freedomholsuk@clara.net
I: www.freedomholidayhomes.co.uk

RUCKINGE
Kent

The Old Granary ★★★★
Contact: Mrs Brenda Beck, Freedom Holiday Homes, St David's Bridge, Cranbrook, Kent TN17 3HJ
T: (01580) 720770
F: (01580) 720771
E: freedomholsuk@clara.net
I: www.freedomholidayhomes.co.uk

Willow Court ★★★
Contact: Mrs Brenda Beck, Freedom Holiday Homes, St David's Bridge, Cranbrook, Kent TN17 3HJ
T: (01580) 720770
F: (01580) 720771
E: freedomholsuk@clara.net
I: www.freedomholsuk.clara.net

RUSHLAKE GREEN
East Sussex

The Coach House ★★★★
Contact: Mrs J B Desch, Beech Hill Farm, Cowbeech Road, Rushlake Green, Heathfield, East Sussex TN21 9QB
T: (01435) 830203
F: (01435) 830203

3 Foords Cottages ★★★
Contact: Mrs Brenda Beck, Freedom Holiday Homes, St David's Bridge, Cranbrook, Kent TN17 3HJ
T: (01580) 720770
F: (01580) 720771
E: freedomholsuk@clara.net
I: www.freedomholsuk.clara.net

RUSTINGTON
West Sussex

The Bungalow ★★★★
Contact: Mr D R Baggs, Teigncombe, Park View Road, Woldingham, Caterham, Surrey CR3 7DL
T: (01883) 653289

The Bungalow ★★★★
Contact: Mr D R Baggs, Teigncombe, Park View Road, Woldingham, Caterham, Surrey CR3 7DL
T: (01883) 653289

8 Mariners Walk ★★
Contact: Mr Robert Brew, Promenade Holiday Homes, 165 Dominion Road, Worthing, West Sussex BN14 8LD
T: (01903) 201426 &
07711 102397
F: (01903) 201426

Seaway ★★★
Contact: Mrs M E Millidge, Four Seasons, 27 Mill Lane, Rustington, Littlehampton, West Sussex BN16 3JR
T: (01903) 772548

RYE
East Sussex

Apothecary House ★★★★
Contact: Mrs Gill Winter & Patrick Tierney, Garden of England Cottages, The Mews Office, 189a High Street, Tonbridge, Kent TN9 1BX
T: (01732) 369168
F: (01732) 358817
E: goec@dial.pipex.com
I: www.gardenofenglandcottages.co.uk

Brandy's Cottage
Rating Applied For
Contact: Mrs Jane Apperly, Brandy's Cottage, Cadborough Farm, Udimore Road, Rye, East Sussex TN31 6AA
T: (01797) 225426
F: (01797) 224097
I: www.marcomm.co.uk/cadborough/

Chapel Cottage
Rating Applied For
Contact: Mrs Gill Winter & Patrick Tierney, Garden of England Cottages, The Mews Office, 189a High Street, Tonbridge, Kent TN9 1BX
T: (01732) 369168
F: (01732) 358817
E: goec@dial.pipex.com
I: www.gardenofenglandcottages.co.uk

Cuckoo Cottage ★★★
Contact: Ms Jane Wood, 35 Denham Way, Camber, Rye, East Sussex TN31 7XR
T: (01797) 227391
E: simon.wood@zoom.co.uk

9 East Street ★★★
Contact: Mrs M H Bird, 10 East Street, Rye, East Sussex TN31 7JY
T: (01797) 225030

2 Hucksteps Row ★★
Contact: Mrs Brenda Beck, Freedom Holiday Homes, St David's Bridge, Cranbrook, Kent TN17 3HJ
T: (01580) 720770
F: (01580) 720771
E: freedomholsuk@clara.net
I: www.freedomholsuk.clara.net

Oak Cottages & Rose Cottage ★★★
Contact: Mr A Reeve, Clayton Farm, Church Lane, Peasmarsh, Rye, East Sussex TN31 6XS
T: (01797) 230394 &
07761 742664
E: jackiereeve@peasmarsh68.fsnet.co.uk

Ockman Cottage
Rating Applied For
Contact: Mrs Brenda Beck, Freedom Holiday Homes, St David's Bridge, Cranbrook, Kent TN17 3HJ
T: (01580) 720770
F: (01580) 720771
E: freedomholsuk@clara.net
I: www.freedomholidayhomes.co.uk

2 Ryford Court ★★★★
Contact: Mrs Brenda Beck, Freedom Holiday Homes, St David's Bridge, Cranbrook, Kent TN17 3HJ
T: (01580) 720770
F: (01580) 720771
E: freedomholsuk@clara.net
I: www.freedomholidayhomes.co.uk

Strand Gate ★★
Contact: Mr & Mrs John Campbell, Fairhaven Holiday Rentals, Derby House, 123 Watling Street, Gillingham, Kent ME7 2YY
T: (01634) 300089
F: (01634) 570157
E: fairhaven@pavilion.co.uk
I: www.fairhaven-holidays.co.uk

RYE HARBOUR
East Sussex

1a Coastguard Square ★★★
Contact: Mrs Brenda Beck, Freedom Holiday Homes, St David's Bridge, Cranbrook, Kent TN17 3HJ
T: (01580) 720770
F: (01580) 720771
E: freedomholsuk@clara.net
I: www.freedomholsuk.clara.net

Harbour Lights ★★★
Contact: Mrs Penelope Webster, 24 Moorcroft Close, Sheffield, S10 4GU
T: (0114) 230 6859

Harbour Point South
Rating Applied For
Contact: Mrs Brenda Beck, Freedom Holiday Homes, St David's Bridge, Cranbrook, Kent TN17 3HJ
T: (01580) 720770
F: (01580) 720771
E: freedomholsuk@clara.net
I: www.freedomholsuk.clara.net

Mermaid Cottage ★★
Contact: Mrs Brenda Beck, Freedom Holiday Homes, St David's Bridge, Cranbrook, Kent TN17 3HJ
T: (01580) 720770
F: (01580) 720771
E: freedomholsuk@clara.net
I: www.freedomholidayhomes.co.uk

ST LEONARDS
East Sussex

Flat 1 60 Warrior Square ★★★★
Contact: Mrs Brenda Beck, Freedom Holiday Homes, St David's Bridge, Cranbrook, Kent TN17 3HJ
T: (01580) 720770
F: (01580) 720771
E: freedomholsuk@clara.net
I: www.freedomholsuk.clara.net

Flat 4 42 Marina ★★★★
Contact: Mrs Brenda Beck, Freedom Holiday Homes, St David's Bridge, Cranbrook, Kent TN17 3HJ
T: (01580) 720770
F: (01580) 720771
E: freedomholsuk@clara.net
I: www.freedomholidayhomes.co.uk

Glastonbury Guest House and Holiday Flats★★
Contact: Mr B Toloui, Glastonbury Guest House, 45 Eversfield Place, St Leonards On Sea, Hastings, East Sussex TN37 6DB
T: (01424) 444711 & 422280
E: glastonburyselfcatering@btinternet.com
I: www.hastings.gov.uk

Greystones
Rating Applied For
Contact: Country Holidays Ref: 9308, Country Holidays, Spring Mill, Earby, Barnoldswick, Lancashire BB94 0AA
T: 0700 723 723
F: (01282) 844288
E: sales@ttgihg.co.uk
I: www.country-holidays.co.uk

Little Highlands Mews ★★★
Contact: Mrs Brenda Beck, Freedom Holiday Homes, St David's Bridge, Cranbrook, Kent TN17 3HJ
T: (01580) 720770
F: (01580) 720771
E: freedomholsuk@clara.net
I: www.freedomholsuk.clara.net

71a Marina ★★
Contact: Mrs V Mathews, Miraleisure Ltd, 51 Marina, Bexhill, East Sussex TN40 1BQ
T: (01424) 730298
F: (01424) 212500

ST MARGARET'S BAY
Kent

The Edge ★★★
Contact: Mrs Jennifer Chambers, Applegarth, Matfield, Tonbridge, Kent TN12 7LQ
T: (01892) 722919
F: (01892) 723078
E: chamapple@hotmail.com

Reach Court Farm Cottages ★★★★
Contact: Mrs J Mitchell, Reach Court Farm Cottages, Reach Court Farm, St Margaret's Bay, Dover, Kent CT15 6AQ
T: (01304) 852159
F: (01304) 853902

57 St Margarets Holiday Park ★★★
Contact: Mrs Christine Tuck, 57 St Margarets Holiday Park, Reach Road, St-Margarets-at-Cliffe, Dover, Kent CT15 6AE

ST MARY'S BAY
Kent

Edenhurst ★★★
Contact: Country Holidays Ref : 4691, Country Holidays Ref :4691 Sales, Country Holidays, Spring Mill, Earby, Barnoldswick, Lancashire BB94 0AA
T: 0870 072 3723
F: (01282) 844288
E: sales@ttgihg.co.uk
I: www.country-holidays.co.uk

ST MICHAELS
Kent

Boundary Cottage
Rating Applied For
Contact: Mrs Brenda Beck, Freedom Holiday Homes, St David's Bridge, Cranbrook, Kent TN17 3HJ
T: (01580) 720770
F: (01580) 720771
E: freedomholsuk@clara.net
I: www.freedomholsuk.clara.net

6 The Terrace ★★★
Contact: Mrs Brenda Beck, Freedom Holiday Homes, St David's Bridge, Cranbrook, Kent TN17 3HJ
T: (01580) 720770
F: (01580) 720771
E: freedomholsuk@clara.net
I: www.freedomholidayhomes.co.uk

SALTDEAN
East Sussex

Marsom ★★★
Contact: Mrs R T Salmon, Best of Brighton & Sussex Cottages Ltd, Windmill Lodge, Vicarage Lane, Rottingdean, Brighton, East Sussex BN2 7HD
T: (01273) 308779 & 07956 662457
F: (01273) 300266

11b Nutley Avenue ★★★★★
Contact: Mrs R T Salmon, Best of Brighton & Sussex Cottages Ltd, Windmill Lodge, Vicarage Lane, Rottingdean, Brighton, East Sussex BN2 7HD
T: (01273) 308779 & 07956 662457
F: (01273) 300266

Westpoint ★★★
Contact: Mrs R T Salmon, Best of Brighton & Sussex Cottages Ltd, Windmill Lodge, Vicarage Lane, Rottingdean, Brighton, East Sussex BN2 7HD
T: (01273) 308779 & 07956 662457
F: (01273) 300266

SANDWICH
Kent

The Old Dairy ★★★★
Contact: Mrs J R Montgomery, Little Brooksend Farm, Birchington, Kent CT7 0JW
T: (01843) 841656
F: (01843) 841656

2 Worth Farm Cottages ★★★
Contact: Mrs Patricia Mallett, Vine Farm, Marshborough, Sandwich, Kent CT13 0PG
T: (01304) 812276
F: (01304) 812694

SEAFORD
East Sussex

Ann Boleyn Cottage
Rating Applied For
Contact: Mrs R T Salmon, Best of Brighton & Sussex Cottages Ltd, Windmill Lodge, Vicarage Lane, Rottingdean, Brighton, East Sussex BN2 7HD
T: (01273) 308779 & 07956 662457
F: (01273) 300266

4 Beach Cottages ★★★
Contact: Ms Julia Lewis, 47 Wandle Bank, Wimbledon, London SW19 1DW
T: (020) 8542 5073
E: 101527.2647@compuserve.com
I: www.ourworld.compuserve.com/homepages/julialewis

24 Cliff Close ★★★
Contact: Mrs R T Salmon, Best of Brighton & Sussex Cottages Ltd, Windmill Lodge, Vicarage Lane, Rottingdean, Brighton, East Sussex BN2 7HD
T: (01273) 308779 & 07956 662457
F: (01273) 300266

Cuilfail ★★★
Contact: Mrs Lois Fuller, Cuilfail, Firle Road, Seaford, East Sussex BN25 2JD
T: (01323) 898622

Dymock Farm ★★★
Contact: Mrs M White, Dymock Farm, Chyngton Lane North, Seaford, East Sussex BN25 4AA
T: (01323) 892982

2 Kingsway Court ★★★
Contact: Mrs Pauline Gower, 6 Sunningdale Close, Southdown Road, Seaford, East Sussex BN25 4PF
T: (01323) 895233 & 07889 310414
E: sific@bgower.f9.co.uk

21 Marine Parade ★★★
Contact: Mrs R T Salmon, Best of Brighton & Sussex Cottages Ltd, Windmill Lodge, Vicarage Lane, Rottingdean, Brighton, East Sussex BN2 7HD
T: (01273) 308779 & 07956 662457
F: (01273) 300266

SEDLESCOMBE
East Sussex

Acorn Chalet ★★★★
Contact: Mrs Gill Winter & Patrick Tierney, Garden of England Cottages, The Mews Office, 189a High Street, Tonbridge, Kent TN9 1BX
T: (01732) 369168
F: (01732) 358817
E: goec@dial.pipex.com
I: www.gardenofenglandcottages.co.uk

Platnix Farm Oast
Rating Applied For
Contact: Mrs Brenda Beck, Freedom Holiday Homes, St David's Bridge, Cranbrook, Kent TN17 3HJ
T: (01580) 720770
F: (01580) 720771
E: freedomholsuk@clara.net
I: www.freedomholidayhomes.co.uk

SELLINDGE
Kent

Barnhaven
Rating Applied For
Contact: Mr M R Old, Gibbins Brook Farm, Sellindge, Ashford, Kent TN25 6HZ
T: (01303) 813521

SELLING
Kent

Hop-Pickers East ★★★
Contact: Country Holidays, Country Holidays, Spring Mill, Barnoldswick, Lancashire BB94 0AS
T: (01282) 445444
F: (01282) 841539
I: www.country-holidays.co.uk

SELSEY
West Sussex

1 Fraser Close ★★
Contact: Mr Andrew Bartlett, High House, 67 West Street, Selsey, Chichester, West Sussex PO20 9AG
T: (01243) 604318
E: jaab@tesco.net

12 Fraser Close ★★★
Contact: Mrs Heather Birchall, Sea Spangles, 75 West Street, Selsey, Chichester, West Sussex PO20 9AG
T: (01243) 606892

100 Kingsway ★★★
Contact: Mrs Karen Rayner, 39 Ullswater Avenue, West End, Southampton, Hampshire SO18 3QS
T: (023) 8048 8482 & 07730 263523

Stable Annexe ★★
Contact: Mr & Mrs Kenneth Child, Post Cottage, Rectory Lane, Selsey, Chichester, West Sussex PO20 9DU
T: (01243) 604264

SEVENOAKS
Kent

The Flat Eagles' Nest★★
Contact: Mrs Sinyee Adams, The Flat Eagles' Nest, Bayley's Hill, Sevenoaks, Kent TN14 6HS
T: (01732) 455310

Harveys ★★★
Contact: Mrs Pat Harvey, Harveys, 143 West End, Kemsing, Sevenoaks, Kent TN15 6QJ
T: (01732) 761862

Linden Beeches Cottages ★★★
Contact: Mr Peter Gilbert, Linden Beeches Cottages, 81 Bradbourne Park Road, Sevenoaks, Kent TN13 3LQ
T: (01732) 461008
E: lindenbeeches@rmplc.co.uk

SHIPBOURNE
Kent

The Old Stables ★★★★
Contact: Mrs E A Cohen, Great Oaks House, Puttenden Road, Shipbourne, Tonbridge, Kent TN11 9RX
T: (01732) 810739
F: (01732) 810738
E: kent.lets@virgin.net
I: www.heartofkent.org.uk

Violets ★★★
Contact: Owner Services Ref: 5883, Country Holidays Owner Services Dept, Spring Mill, Earby, Barnoldswick, Lancashire BB94 0AA
T: 0870 444 6604
F: (01282) 841539
I: www.country-holidays.co.uk

Establishments printed in blue have a detailed entry in this guide

SHORTGATE
East Sussex

White Lion Farm Cottages
★★★
Contact: Mrs Diana Green,
White Lion Farm, Shortgate,
Lewes, East Sussex BN8 6PJ
T: (01825) 840288

SHOTTENDEN
Kent

The Barn ★★★★
Contact: Country Hols Ref:
7304, Country Holidays Ref:
7304 Sales, Spring Mill, Earby,
Barnoldswick, Lancashire
BB94 0AA
T: 08700 723 723
F: (01282) 844288
E: sales@ttgihg.co.uk
I: www.country-holidays.co.uk

SIDLESHAM
West Sussex

Cloverlands Cottage ★★★
Contact: Mrs Diana Pound,
Cloverlands Cottage, Chalder
Lane, Sidlesham, Chichester,
West Sussex PO20 7RJ
T: (01243) 641243
F: (01243) 641243

Little Durley ★★★★
Contact: Ms Deborah Clark,
Durley, Selsey Road, Sidlesham,
Chichester, West Sussex
PO20 7LS
T: (01243) 641858
F: (01243) 641231

SISSINGHURST
Kent

Satins Hill Oast ★★★★
Contact: Mrs Gill Winter &
Patrick Tierney, Garden of
England Cottages, The Mews
Office, 189a High Street,
Tonbridge, Kent TN9 1BX
T: (01732) 369168
F: (01732) 358817
E: goec@dial.pipex.com
I: www.
gardenofenglandcottages.co.uk

SMARDEN
Kent

The Cobbles ★★★
Contact: Mrs Brenda Beck,
Freedom Holiday Homes, St
David's Bridge, Cranbrook, Kent
TN17 3HJ
T: (01580) 720770
F: (01580) 720771
E: freedomholsuk@clara.net
I: www.freedomholidayhomes.
co.uk

The Mill House Annexe
★★★★
Contact: Mrs Brenda Beck,
Freedom Holiday Homes, St
David's Bridge, Cranbrook, Kent
TN17 3HJ
T: (01580) 720770
F: (01580) 720771
E: freedomholsuk@clara.net
I: www.freedomholidayhomes.
co.uk

SOUTH CHAILEY
East Sussex

Fantasy Cottages ★★★
Contact: Mrs Alison Bullar,
Fantasy Cottages, Fantasy,
Kilnwood Lane, South Chailey,
Lewes, East Sussex BN8 4AU
T: (01273) 400445 & 401619
F: (01273) 400445
E: comesailing@btinternet.com

ST-MARGARETS-AT-CLIFFE
Kent

Bungalow 142 ★★
Contact: Mr Peter Kennett, 4
Churchill Close, St-Margarets-
at-Cliffe, Dover, Kent
T: (01304) 852968

Bungalows 105 & 107 ★★★
Contact: Mr Geoffrey Lear,
Martin Farmhouse, Martin,
Dover, Kent CT15 5JL
T: (01304) 852881 & 852587
F: (01304) 852587
E: geofflear@aol.com

116 St Margarets Holiday Park
★★★★
Contact: Mrs Christine
Ellerington, 1 Knights Templar,
Western Heights, Dover, Kent
CT17 9DX
T: (01304) 211289

STAPLE
Kent

Piglet Place ★★★★
Contact: Mr & Mrs Richard &
Bronwen Barber, Greengage
Cottage, Lower Road, Barnsole,
Staple, Canterbury, Kent
CT3 1LG
T: (01304) 813321 & 812312
F: (01304) 812312

STAPLEHURST
Kent

6 Headcorn Road ★★
Contact: Mrs I B Maxted, 6
Headcorn Road, Staplehurst,
Tonbridge, Kent TN12 0BT
T: (01580) 891219

Rose Cottage Oast ★★★
Contact: Mrs Brenda Beck,
Freedom Holiday Homes, St
David's Bridge, Cranbrook, Kent
TN17 3HJ
T: (01580) 720770
F: (01580) 720771
E: freedomholsuk@clara.net
I: www.freedomholidayhomes.
co.uk

STELLING MINNIS
Kent

Great Field Farm Annexe
★★★
Contact: Mrs L Castle, Great
Field Farm, Misling Lane, Stelling
Minnis, Canterbury, Kent
CT4 6DE
T: (01227) 709223
F: (01227) 709223
E: greatfieldfarm@aol.com

North End Barn ★★★
Contact: Mr & Mrs C K Robbins,
Church Lane Cottage, Harvest
Lane, Stelling Minnis,
Canterbury, Kent CT4 6AX
T: (01227) 709552

STEYNING
West Sussex

Wappingthorn Farm ★★
Contact: Mrs Arianne Shapland,
Wappingthorn Farmhouse,
Horsham Road, Steyning, West
Sussex BN44 3AA
T: (01903) 813236
F: (01903) 813236
E: arianne@wappingthorn.
demon.co.uk
I: www.wappingthorn.demon.
co.uk

STOCKBURY
Kent

The Old Dairy ★★
Contact: Mrs M Anthony,
Wheatsheaf Farm, Hazel Street,
Stockbury, Sittingbourne, Kent
ME9 7SA
T: (01622) 884222

STONE CROSS
East Sussex

**The Little House Stone Cross
Farm** ★★★
Contact: Mrs B M Dixon, Stone
Cross Farm, Burnt Oak Lane,
Stone Cross, Crowborough, East
Sussex TN6 3SJ
T: (01892) 652603

STONE-IN-OXNEY
Kent

Old Forge Cottage ★★★
Contact: Mrs Brenda Beck,
Freedom Holiday Homes, St
David's Bridge, Cranbrook, Kent
TN17 3HJ
T: (01580) 720770
F: (01580) 720771
E: freedomholsuk@clara.net
I: www.freedomholidayhomes.
co.uk

STORRINGTON
West Sussex

Byre Cottages ★★★
Contact: Mr & Mrs John
Campbell, Fair Haven Holiday
Cottages, Derby House, 123
Watling Street, Gillingham, Kent
ME7 2YY
T: (01634) 300089
F: (01634) 570157
E: fairhaven@pavilion.co.uk
I: www.fairhaven-holidays.co.uk

Greenacres Country Holidays
★★
Contact: Mrs E Redfern,
Greenacres Country Holidays,
Washington Road, Storrington,
Pulborough, West Sussex
RH20 4AF
T: (01903) 742538 & 264303
F: (01903) 740017
E: greenacres5@supanet.com

SUTTON VALENCE
Kent

Sparks Oast ★★
Contact: Mrs Brenda Beck,
Freedom Holiday Homes, St
David's Bridge, Cranbrook, Kent
TN17 3HJ
T: (01580) 720770
F: (01580) 720771
E: freedomholsuk@clara.net
I: www.freedomholsuk.clara.net

TELSCOMBE
East Sussex

The Coach House ★★★★
Contact: Mrs Elizabeth
Hollington, Duck Barn,
Telscombe Village, Telscombe,
Lewes, East Sussex BN7 3HY
T: (01273) 301844
F: (01273) 300935

TELSCOMBE CLIFFS
East Sussex

Old Coast Guard Cottage
Rating Applied For
Contact: Ms Gail Latimer, 61
Chestnut Drive, Pinner,
Middlesex HA5 1LX
T: (020) 8868 0761
F: (020) 8868 0700
E: gail@laltd.demon.co.uk

438a South Coast Road
Rating Applied For
Contact: Mrs R T Salmon, Best of
Brighton & Sussex Cottages Ltd,
Windmill Lodge, Vicarage Lane,
Rottingdean, Brighton, East
Sussex BN2 7HD
T: (01273) 308779 &
07956 662457
F: (01273) 300266

TENTERDEN
Kent

Cromwell Cottage ★★★
Contact: Mrs Valerie Ernst,
Aventine, Ingleden Park Road,
Tenterden, Kent TN30 6NS
T: (01580) 762958
F: (01580) 762958
E: val@cromwellcottage.fsnet.
co.uk

Plummer Farm ★★★
Contact: Mrs Brenda Beck,
Freedom Holiday Homes, St
David's Bridge, Cranbrook, Kent
TN17 3HJ
T: (01580) 720770
F: (01580) 720771
E: freedomholsuk@clara.net
I: www.freedomholsuk.clara.net

Quince Cottage ★★★★
Contact: Mrs H E Crease,
Laurelhurst, 38 Ashford Road,
Tenterden, Kent TN30 6LL
T: (01580) 765636
F: (01580) 765922
E: quincott@zetnet.co.uk
I: www.quincecottage.co.uk

44 Rogersmead ★★★★
Contact: Mrs Brenda Beck,
Freedom Holiday Homes, St
David's Bridge, Cranbrook, Kent
TN17 3HJ
T: (01580) 720770
F: (01580) 720771
E: freedomholsuk@clara.net
I: www.freedomholidayhomes.
co.uk

Summit Villa
Rating Applied For
Contact: Mrs Brenda Beck,
Freedom Holiday Homes, St
David's Bridge, Cranbrook, Kent
TN17 3HJ
T: (01580) 720770
F: (01580) 720771
E: freedomholsuk@clara.net

Tamworth Cottage & Meadow Cottage ★★★★
Contact: Mrs P Cooke, Great Prawls Farm, Stone-in-Oxney, Tenterden, Kent TN30 7HB
T: (01797) 270539 &
07770 788475
E: P.cooke.Prawls@Tinyworld.co.uk

TONBRIDGE
Kent

88 Avebury Avenue ★★★★★
Contact: Mrs Gill Winter & Patrick Tierney, Garden of England Cottages, The Mews Office, 189a High Street, Tonbridge, Kent TN9 1BX
T: (01732) 369168
F: (01732) 358817
E: goec@dial.pipex.com
I: www.gardenofenglandcottages.co.uk

3 Church Street ★★★
Contact: Mrs Brenda Beck, Freedom Holiday Homes, St David's Bridge, Cranbrook, Kent TN17 3HJ
T: (01580) 720770
F: (01580) 720771
E: freedomholsuk@clara.net
I: www.freedomholsuk.clara.net

Goldhill Mill Cottages ★★★★★
Contact: Mr & Mrs V Cole, Goldhill Mill Cottages, Goldhill Mill, Golden Green, Tonbridge, Kent TN11 0BA
T: (01732) 851626
F: (01732) 851881
E: vernon.cole@virgin.net
I: www.goldhillmillcottages.co.uk

High Barn Farm Cottage ★★★★
Contact: Mrs S P Brooks, High Barn, High Barn Farm, Hildenborough, Tonbridge, Kent TN11 9JR
T: (01732) 832490
F: (01732) 832490

7 Lodge Road ★★★★
Contact: Mrs Gill Winter & Patrick Tierney, Garden of England Cottages, The Mews Office, 189a High Street, Tonbridge, Kent TN9 1BX
T: (01732) 369168
F: (01732) 358817
E: goec@dial.pipex.com
I: www.gardenofenglandcottages.co.uk

Oast Barn ★★★★
Contact: Mrs Gill Winter & Patrick Tierney, Garden of England Cottages, The Mews Office, 189a High Street, Tonbridge, Kent TN9 1BX
T: (01732) 369168
F: (01732) 358817
E: goec@dial.pipex.com
I: www.gardenofenglandcottages.co.uk

Postern Heath Oast
Rating Applied For
Contact: Mrs Brenda Beck, Freedom Holiday Homes, St David's Bridge, Cranbrook, Kent TN17 3HJ
T: (01580) 720770
F: (01580) 720771
E: freedomholsuk@clara.net
I: www.freedomholidayhomes.co.uk

TUDELEY
Kent

Latters Oast ★★★★
Contact: Mrs Gill Winter & Patrick Tierney, Garden of England Cottages, The Mews Office, 189a High Street, Tonbridge, Kent TN9 1BX
T: (01732) 369168
F: (01732) 358817
E: goec@dial.pipex.com
I: www.gardenofenglandcottages.co.uk

UDIMORE
East Sussex

Finlay Cottage & Tibbs Bungalow ★★★★
Contact: Mrs Gill Winter & Patrick Tierney, Garden of England Cottages, The Mews Office, 189a High Street, Tonbridge, Kent TN9 1BX
T: (01732) 369168
F: (01732) 358817
E: goec@dial.pipex.com
I: www.gardenofenglandcottages.co.uk

ULCOMBE
Kent

Apple Pye Cottage
Rating Applied For
Contact: Mrs Patricia Diane Leat, Bramley Knowle Farm, Eastwood Road, Ulcombe, Maidstone, Kent ME17 1ET
T: (01622) 858878
F: (01622) 851121
I: www.bramleyknowlefarm.co.uk

Kingsnorth Manor Farm
Rating Applied For
Contact: Mrs Brenda Beck, Freedom Holiday Homes, St David's Bridge, Cranbrook, Kent TN17 3HJ
T: (01580) 720770
F: (01580) 720771
E: freedomholsuk@clara.net
I: www.freedomholidayhomes.co.uk

WADHURST
East Sussex

Bewl Water Cottages ★★★★
Contact: Mr & Mrs M Bentsen, Bewl Water Cottages, Newbarn, Wards Lane, Wadhurst, East Sussex TN5 6HP
T: (01892) 782042
E: bentsen@bewlwatercottages.com
I: www.bewlwatercottages.com

Laundry Cottage
Rating Applied For
Contact: Mrs Brenda Beck, Freedom Holiday Homes, St David's Bridge, Cranbrook, Kent TN17 3HJ
T: (01580) 720770
F: (01580) 720771
E: freedomholsuk@clara.net
I: www.freedomholsuk.clar.net

Old Stables ★★★
Contact: Mrs D S Le May, Old Stables, Ladymeads Farm, Lower Cousley Wood, Wadhurst, East Sussex TN5 6HH
T: (01892) 783240
F: (01892) 783240
E: camrosa.equestrian@virgin.net

WALMER
Kent

Brunswick Cottage ★★★
Contact: Mr Martin O'Neill, Rashleigh, 9a Liverpool Road, Walmer, Deal, Kent CT14 7HN
T: (01304) 239201

The Coach House ★★
Contact: Mr Martin O'Neill, Rashleigh, 9a Liverpool Road, Walmer, Deal, Kent CT14 7HW
T: (01304) 239201

Cottage In Deal ★★
Contact: Mr A S Hay, Leipziger Str 13D, 91058 Erlangen, Germany
T: 00499 131 65921 &
(01304) 381160
F: 00499 131 65733
E: alan.hay@t-online.de

Fisherman's Cottage ★★
Contact: Dr & Mrs A S Morris, 39 Dorset Road, Merton Park, London SW19 3EZ
T: (020) 8542 5086 & 8540 9443
F: (020) 8540 9443

Holm Oaks ★★★
Contact: Mrs Annie Spencer-Smith, Holm Oaks, 72 The Strand, Walmer, Deal, Kent CT14 7DL
T: (01304) 367365
E: holm_oaks@hotmail.com

WALTHAM
Kent

Springfield Cottage and Springfield Barn ★★★
Contact: Mrs Gill Winter & Patrick Tierney, Garden of England Cottages, The Mews Office, 189a High Street, Tonbridge, Kent TN9 1BX
T: (01732) 369168
F: (01732) 358817
E: goec@dial.pipex.com
I: www.gardenofenglandcottages.co.uk

WALTON-ON-THAMES
Surrey

Guest Wing ★★★★
Contact: Mr A R Dominy, 30 Mayfield Gardens, Walton-on-Thames, Surrey KT12 5PP
T: (01932) 241223

WARBLETON
East Sussex

Threeways Farm Cottage ★★★★
Contact: Mrs Maureen Wheeler, Threeways Farm, Warbleton, Heathfield, East Sussex TN21 9BA
T: (01435) 830189
F: (01435) 830189

Well Cottage ★★★★
Contact: Mrs Gill Winter & Patrick Tierney, Garden of England Cottages, The Mews Office, 189a High Street, Tonbridge, Kent TN9 1BX
T: (01732) 369168
F: (01732) 358817
E: goec@dial.pipex.com
I: www.gardenofenglandcottages.co.uk

WATERSFIELD
West Sussex

Greenacres ★
Contact: Fairhaven Holiday Cottages, Derby House, 123 Watling Street, Gillingham, Kent ME7 2YY
T: (01634) 300089
F: (01634) 570157
E: fairhaven@pavilion.co.uk
I: www.fairhaven-holidays.co.uk

WEST ASHLING
West Sussex

Hills Cottage ★★★★
Contact: Mrs Virginia Jack, The Thatched House, Down Street, West Ashling, Chichester, West Sussex PO18 8DP
T: (01243) 574382
E: hills.cottage@tesco.net
I: www.hillscottage.com

WEST FARLEIGH
Kent

Mill Cottage ★★★★
Contact: Mrs Gill Winter & Patrick Tierney, Garden of England Cottages, The Mews Office, 189a High Street, Tonbridge, Kent TN9 1BX
T: (01732) 369168
F: (01732) 358817
E: goec@dial.pipex.com
I: www.gardenofenglandcottages.co.uk

5 Mill Cottages ★★★
Contact: Mr & Mrs John Campbell, Fairhaven Holiday Rentals, Derby House, 123 Watling Street, Gillingham, Kent ME7 2YY
T: (01634) 302300
F: (01634) 302300
E: fairhaven@pavilion.co.uk
I: www.fairhaven-holidays.co.uk

WEST MALLING
Kent

Meadowbank Court Flat B ★★★★
Contact: Mrs Gill Winter & Patrick Tierney, Garden of England Cottages, The Mews Office, 189a High Street, Tonbridge, Kent TN9 1BX
T: (01732) 369168
F: (01732) 358817
E: goec@dial.pipex.com
I: www.gardenofenglandcottages.co.uk

Establishments printed in blue have a detailed entry in this guide

The Shire ★★★★
Contact: Mrs R Lambert, Manor Farm, St Leonard's Street, West Malling, Kent ME19 6PD
T: (01732) 842091
F: (01732) 873784
E: barbaralambert@lineone.net

WEST MARDEN
West Sussex

Barley Cottage ★★★★
Contact: Mr & Mrs Martin Edney, West Marden Farmhouse, West Marden, Chichester, West Sussex PO18 9ES
T: (023) 9263 1382
E: carole.edney@btinternet.com

Groom & Laundry Cottage ★★★★
Contact: Mrs J M Baker, Watergate House, West Marden, Chichester, West Sussex PO18 9EQ
T: (023) 9263 1470
F: (023) 9263 1767

WEST PECKHAM
Kent

Beech Farmhouse
Rating Applied For
Contact: Mr & Mrs H Wooldridge, Beech Farmhouse, Stan Lane, West Peckham, Maidstone, Kent ME18 5JT
T: (01622) 812360
F: (01622) 814659

WEST WITTERING
West Sussex

Brendon ★★
Contact: Ms Karen Brooker, Baileys Estate Agents, 17 Shore Road, East Wittering, Chichester, West Sussex PO20 8DY
T: (01243) 672217
F: (01243) 670100

59 Marine Drive ★★★★
Contact: Ms Karen Brooker, Baileys Estate Agents, 17 Shore Road, East Wittering, Chichester, West Sussex PO20 8DY
T: (01243) 672217
F: (01243) 670100
E: info@baileys.uk.com
I: www.baileys.uk.com

9 Marine Drive ★★
Contact: Ms Karen Brooker, Baileys Estate Agents, 17 Shore Road, East Wittering, Chichester, West Sussex PO20 8DY
T: (01243) 672217
F: (01243) 670100
E: info@baileys.uk.com
I: www.baileys.uk.com

21 Owers Way ★★
Contact: Ms Karen Brooker, Baileys Estate Agents, 17 Shore Road, East Wittering, Chichester, West Sussex PO20 8DY
T: (01243) 672217
F: (01243) 670100
E: info@baileys.uk.com
I: www.baileys.uk.com

WESTBOURNE
West Sussex

4 Manchester Terrace
Rating Applied For
Contact: Mrs Charlotte Edworthy, 11A Chancellors Street, London W6 9RN
T: (0208) 748 2380 &
07973 670965
F: (0208) 563 2199
E: charlyfane@aol.com

WESTCOTT
Surrey

The Garden Flat ★★★★
Contact: Ms Louise Scillitoe Brown, The Garden Flat, Chartfield, Guildford Road, Westcott, Dorking, Surrey RH4 3LG
T: (01306) 883838
F: (01306) 883838

WESTERHAM
Kent

The Barn at Bombers
Rating Applied For
Contact: Mrs Gill Winter & Patrick Tierney, Garden of England Cottages, The Mews Office, 189a High Street, Tonbridge, Kent TN9 1BX
T: (01732) 369168
F: (01732) 358817
E: goec@dial.pipex.com
I: www.gardenofenglandcottages.co.uk

Le Chalet ★★★
Contact: Mrs Nancy Aspinwall, Totem Ridge, 85 Paynesfield Road, Tatsfield, Westerham, Sevenoaks, Kent TN16 2BQ
T: (01959) 577778
F: (01959) 577778
E: mary.aspinwall@getreal.co.uk

WHITSTABLE
Kent

19 Acton Road ★★★
Contact: Ms Stephanie Brunton, Georgia, 17 Pierpoint Road, Whitstable, Kent CT5 4NW
T: (01227) 272206
E: stormbrunton@clara.co.uk
I: www.whitstableaccommodation.co.uk

Fairway View ★★★
Contact: Mrs Maria Hudson, 35 Cedar Road, Romford, Essex RM7 7JS
T: (01708) 766599 &
07885 346330
E: brian_hudson@novar.com

3 Harbour Mews
Rating Applied For
Contact: Mr & Mrs John Kaye, 46 Marine Parade, Whitstable, Kent CT5 2BE
T: (01227) 280391
E: jkaye46@hotmail.com

4 Saxon Shore ★★★★
Contact: Mr & Mrs John Campbell, Fairhaven Holiday Rentals, Derby House, 123 Watling Street, Gillingham, Kent ME7 2YY
T: (01634) 300089
F: (01634) 570157
E: fairhaven@pavilion.co.uk
I: www.fairhaven-holidays.co.uk

Stag Cottage
Rating Applied For
Contact: Mrs Brenda Beck, Freedom Holiday Homes, St David's Bridge, Cranbrook, Kent TN17 3HJ
T: (01580) 720770
F: (01580) 720771
E: freedomholsuk@clara.net
I: www.freedomholsuk.clara.net

Trappers End ★★★
Contact: Mrs J M Reed, 11 Woodlands Avenue, New Malden, Surrey KT3 3UL
T: (020) 8942 0342 &
07710 591735
F: (020) 8942 0342
E: janette.reed@cwcom.net

WILLESBOROUGH
Kent

Rosemary ★★★
Contact: Mr Philip McGoldrick, Rosemary, 68 Kennington Road, Willesbrough Lees, Willesborough, Ashford, Kent TN24 0NS
T: (01233) 613826
I: philipmcgoldrick@virgin.net

WINCHELSEA BEACH
East Sussex

Tamarix ★★★
Contact: Mr & Mrs M J Miller, Sanderlings, Plovers Barrows, Buxted, Uckfield, East Sussex TN22 4JP
T: (01825) 732034

WISBOROUGH GREEN
West Sussex

Fowlers Cottage ★★★★
Contact: Mrs Jennie Burr, Fowlers, Fittleworth Road, Wisborough Green, Billingshurst, West Sussex RH14 0HB
T: (01403) 700607

WOODCHURCH
Kent

The Little House ★★★★
Contact: Mrs Brenda Beck, Freedom Holiday Homes, St David's Bridge, Cranbrook, Kent TN17 3HJ
T: (01580) 720770
F: (01580) 720771
E: freedomholsuk@clara.net
I: www.freedomholholidayhomes.co.uk

The Stable ★★★
Contact: Mrs Carol Vant, The Stable, Coldblow Lodge, Woodchurch, Ashford, Kent TN26 3PH
T: (01233) 860388
F: (01233) 860388
E: Carol.Vant@btinternet.com
I: www.lineone.net/~carol.vant/index.htm

WOODNESBOROUGH
Kent

Sonnet Cottage ★★
Contact: Mrs Brenda Beck, Freedom Holiday Homes, St David's Bridge, Cranbrook, Kent TN17 3HJ
T: (01580) 720770
F: (01580) 720771
E: freedomholsuk@clara.net
I: www.freedomholidayhomes.co.uk

WOOTTON
Kent

Captains & Colonels ★★★
Contact: Mrs Brenda Beck, Freedom Holiday Homes, St David's Bridge, Cranbrook, Kent TN17 3HJ
T: (01580) 720770
F: (01580) 720771
E: freedomholsuk@clara.net
I: www.freedomholsuk.clara.net

WORTHING
West Sussex

Aldine House ★★★
Contact: Mr & Mrs G Hills, 311 South Farm Road, Worthing, West Sussex BN14 7TL
T: (01903) 266980
E: hills-aldine@supanet.com

12 Byron Road ★
Contact: Mr Robert Brew, Promenade Holiday Homes, 165 Dominion Road, Worthing, West Sussex BN14 8LD
T: (01903) 201426 &
07711 102397
F: (01903) 201426

Exmoor House ★
Contact: Mr & Mrs A R Harrison, Exmoor House, 32 Chesswood Road, Worthing, West Sussex BN11 2AD
T: (01903) 208856

7 Ferring Grange Gardens ★★★
Contact: Country Holidays Ref: 7277, Country Hols Ref: 7277 Sales, Country Holidays, Spring Mill, Earby, Barnoldswick, Lancashire BB94 0AA
T: (01282) 445096
F: (01282) 844288
E: sales@ttgihg.co.uk
I: www.country-holidays.co.uk

Flat 16 Heene Court Mansions ★★
Contact: Mr Robert Brew, Promenade Holiday Homes, 165 Dominion Road, Worthing, West Sussex BN14 8LD
T: (01903) 201426 &
07711 102397
F: (01903) 201426

Flat 3 15 West Buildings★
Contact: Mr Robert Brew, Promenade Holiday Homes, 165 Dominion Road, Worthing, West Sussex BN14 8LD
T: (01903) 201426 &
07711 102397
F: (01903) 201426

12 Hampton Court ★★★
Contact: Mr & Mrs M E Tyson, 32 Victoria Road, Worthing, West Sussex BN11 1XB
T: (01903) 533742 &
(019732) 477090

2 Harley Court
Rating Applied For
Contact: Mr Robert Brew, Promenade Holiday Homes, 165 Dominion Road, Worthing, West Sussex BN14 8LD
T: (01903) 201426 &
07711 102397
F: (01903) 201426
E: robert@promhols.fsbusiness.co.uk

6 Heene Terrace ★★
Contact: Mr Robert Brew,
Promenade Holiday Homes, 165
Dominion Road, Worthing, West
Sussex BN14 8LD
T: (01903) 201426 &
07711 102397
F: (01903) 201426

Holiday Bungalow ★★★
Contact: Mr & Mrs Graham
Haynes, Bahnstrasse 59, 3008
Bern, Switzerland
T: 004131 381 1876
F: 004131 381 1876

2 Knightsbridge House ★★★
Contact: Ms Greta Paull, 35
Cheyne Avenue, South
Woodford, London E18 2DP
T: (020) 8530 2336
F: (020) 8530 2336

Navarino Flat ★★★
Contact: Mrs Cynthia Hanton,
Navarino Flat, 46 Navarino
Road, Worthing, West Sussex
BN11 2NF
T: (01903) 205984
F: (01903) 520620
E: chantan@cwctv.net

17 Pendine Avenue ★★★
Contact: Mrs Sue Harding, 17
Pendine Avenue, Worthing, West
Sussex BN11 2NA
T: (01903) 202833
E: sue_harding23@hotmail.com

Seashells ★★
Contact: Mr Harry Fenn, 23
Arundel Road, Worthing, West
Sussex BN13 3EH
T: (01903) 525892

Smuggles ★★
Contact: Mr Mark Juby, c/o 18
Rogate Road, Worthing, West
Sussex BN13 2DS
T: (01903) 532437 &
07770 398077
F: (01903) 694692
E: markjuby@mcmail.com
I: www.smuggles.mcmail.com

Torrington Holiday Flats ★★
Contact: Mrs Elsden & Mary
Fitzgerald, Torrington Holiday
Flats, 60 Manor Road, Worthing,
West Sussex BN11 4SL
T: (01903) 238582 &
07860 699268
F: (01903) 230266

3 West Way ★★★
Contact: Mr Colin Eaton,
Millview, Ashurst, Steyning,
West Sussex BN44 3AP
T: (01403) 711504

WROTHAM
Kent

**Butts Hill Farm Country
Holidays** ★★★
Contact: Ms Kim Howard, Butts
Hill Farm Country Holidays,
Conningdale, Billets Hill, Ash,
Sevenoaks, Kent TN15 7HG
T: (01474) 871090
F: (01474) 871090

Establishments printed in blue have a detailed entry in this guide

Information

The English Tourism Council's quality assurance standards   670

General advice and information   671-672

About the guide entries   673

Travel information – by car and by train   674-675

Events for 2002   676-682

Calendars 2002/2003   683

Town index   684-688

The National
Quality Assurance
Standards

English Tourism Council

★ ★ ★
SELF CATERING

RATINGS YOU CAN TRUST

Wherever you see a national rating sign, you can be sure that one of our trained impartial assessors has been there before you, checking the place on your behalf - and will be there again, because every place with a national rating is assessed annually.

The Star ratings reflect the quality that you're looking for when booking accommodation. All properties have to meet an extensive list of minimum requirements to take part in the scheme. From there, increased levels of quality apply. For instance, you'll find acceptable quality at One Star, good to very good quality at Three Star and exceptional quality at Five Star establishments.

Quite simply, the more Stars, the higher the overall level of quality you can expect to find. Establishments at higher rating levels also have to meet some additional requirements for facilities.

Minimum entry requirements include the following:

- High standards of cleanliness throughout
- Pricing and conditions of booking made clear
- Local information to help you make the best of your stay
- Comfortable accommodation with a range of furniture to meet your needs
- Colour television (where signal available) at no extra charge
- Kitchen equipped to meet all essential requirements

The brief explanation of the Star ratings outlined below show what is included at each rating level.

● ONE STAR

An acceptable overall level of quality with adequate provision of furniture, furnishings and fittings.

● TWO STAR
(in addition to what is provided at ONE STAR):
A good overall level of quality. All units self-contained.

● THREE STAR
(in addition to what is provided at ONE and TWO STAR):
A good to very good overall level of quality with good standard of maintenance and decoration. Ample space, good quality furniture. All double beds have access from both sides. Microwave.

● FOUR STAR
(in addition to what is provided at ONE, TWO and THREE STAR):
An excellent overall level of quality with very good care and attention to detail throughout. Access to a washing machine and drier if not provided in the unit, or a 24-hour laundry service.

● FIVE STAR
(in addition to what is provided at ONE, TWO, THREE and FOUR STAR):
An exceptional overall level of quality with high levels of decor, fixtures and fittings with personal touches. Excellent standards of management, efficiency and guest services.

The rating is awarded to an establishment is a reflection of the overall standard, taking everything into account. It is a balanced view of what is provided and, as such, cannot acknowledge individual areas of excellence. Quality ratings are not intended to indicate value for money. A high quality product can be over-priced; a product of modest quality, if offered at a low price, can represent good value. The information provided by the quality rating will enable you to determine for yourself what represents good value for money.

ALL ASSESSED

All holiday homes listed in this guide have been assessed or are awaiting assessment under the English Tourism Council quality assurance standard. The ratings in the accommodation entries were correct at the time of going to press but are subject to change.

An information leaflet giving full details of the English Tourism Council quality assurance standard - which also covers hotels, motels, guesthouses, inns, B&Bs, farmhouses, motorway lodges and caravans, chalets and camping parks - is available from any Tourist Information Centre.

AWAITING CONFIRMATION OF RATING

If no rating appears in an entry it means that the establishment was awaiting assessment at the time of going to press.

For your information, the most up-to-date information regarding these establishments' ratings is in the listings pages at the back of this guide.

General Advice & Information

MAKING A BOOKING

When enquiring about accommodation, make sure you check prices and other important details. You will also need to state your requirements, clearly and precisely - for example:

- **Arrival and departure dates,** with acceptable alternatives if appropriate.
- **The accommodation you need.**
- **Number of people in your party,** and the ages of any children.
- **Special requirements,** such as ground-floor bathroom, garden, cot.

Booking by letter

Misunderstandings can easily happen over the telephone, so we strongly advise you to confirm your booking in writing if there is time.

Please note that the English Tourism Council does not make reservations - you should write direct to the accommodation.

PRICES

The prices shown in Where to Stay 2002 are only a general guide; they were supplied to us by proprietors in summer 2001. Remember, changes may occur after the guide goes to press, so we strongly advise you to check prices when you book your accommodation.

Prices are shown in pounds sterling and include VAT where applicable. The prices shown are per unit per week.

Also remember that prices may be higher in summer and during school holidays, and lower in the autumn, winter and spring.

DEPOSITS

When you book your self-catering holiday, the proprietor will normally ask you to pay a deposit immediately, and then to pay the full balance before your holiday date.

The reason for asking you to pay in advance is to safeguard the proprietor in case you decide to cancel at a late stage, or simply do not turn up. He or she may have turned down other bookings on the strength of yours, and may find it hard to re-let if you cancel.

CANCELLATIONS

Legal contract

When you accept accommodation that is offered to you, by telephone or in writing, you enter a legally binding contract with the proprietor.

This means that if you cancel your booking, fail to take up the accommodation or leave early, you will probably forfeit your deposit, and may expect to be charged the balance at the end of the period booked if the place cannot be re-let.

Where you have already paid the full amount before cancelling, the proprietor is likely to retain the money. If the accommodation is re-let, the proprietor will make a refund, normally less the amount of the deposit.

And remember, if you book by telephone and are asked for your credit card number, you should check whether the proprietor intends charging your credit card account should you later cancel your reservation. A proprietor should not be able to charge your credit card account with a cancellation unless he or she has made this clear at the time of your booking and you have agreed.

However, to avoid later disputes, we suggest you check with the proprietor whether he or she intends to charge your credit card account if you cancel.

Insurance

There are so many reasons why you might have to cancel your holiday, which is why we strongly advise people to take out a cancellation insurance policy. In fact, many self-catering agencies now insist their customers take out a policy when they book their holiday.

CODE OF CONDUCT

All the places featured in this guide have agreed to observe the following Codes of Conduct:

1   To ensure high standards of courtesy and cleanliness, catering and service appropriate to the type of establishment.

2   To describe fairly to all visitors and prospective visitors the amenities, facilities and services provided by the establishment, whether by advertisement, brochure, word of mouth or any other means. To allow visitors to see accommodation, if requested, before booking.

3   To make clear to visitors exactly what is included in all prices quoted, including service charges, taxes and other surcharges. Details of charges, if any, for heating or additional service or facilities should also be made clear.

4   To adhere to, and not to exceed, prices current at time of occupation for accommodation or other services.

5   To advise visitors at the time of booking, and subsequently of any change, if the accommodation offered is in an unconnected annexe, or similar, or by boarding out; and to indicate the location of such accommodation and any difference in comfort or amenities from accommodation in the main establishment.

6   To give each visitor, on request, details of payments due and a receipt if required.

7   To deal promptly and courteously with all enquiries, requests, reservations, correspondence and complaints from visitors.

8   To allow an English Tourism Council representative reasonable access to the establishment, on request, to confirm that the Code of Conduct is being observed.

COMMENTS AND COMPLAINTS
Information

The proprietors themselves supply the descriptions of their establishments and other information for the listings, and they pay to have their entries included in the guide. They have all signed a declaration that their information conforms to the Trade Description Acts 1968 and 1972. All the places featured in the guide have also been assessed or have applied for assessment under the English Touism Council quality assurance scheme.

The English Tourism Council cannot guarantee accuracy of information in this guide, and accepts no responsibility for any error or misrepresentation.

All liability for loss, disappointment, negligence or other damage caused by reliance on the information contained in this guide, or in the event of bankruptcy or liquidation or cessation of trade of any company, individual or firm mentioned, is hereby excluded.

We strongly recommend that you carefully check prices and other details when you book your accommodation.

Problems

Of course, we hope you will not have cause for complaint, but problems do occur from time to time.

If you are dissatisfied with anything, make your complaint to the management immediately. Then the management can take action at once to investigate the matter and put things right. The longer you leave a complaint, the harder it is to deal with it effectively.

In certain circumstances, the English Tourism Council may look into complaints. However, the Council has no statutory control over establishments or their methods of operating. The Council cannot become involved in legal or contractual matters.

If you do have problems that have not been resolved by the proprietor and which you would like to bring to our attention, please write to: Quality Standards Department, English Tourism Council, Thames Tower, Black's Road, Hammersmith, London W6 9EL.

About the
Guide Entries

LOCATIONS

Places to stay are listed under the town, city or village where they are located. If a place is out in the countryside, you may find it listed under a nearby village or town.

Town names are listed alphabetically within each regional section of the guide, along with the name of the county or unitary authority they are in (see note on page 15), and their map reference.

MAP REFERENCES

These refer to the colour location maps at the front of the guide. The first figure shown is the map number, the following letter and figure indicate the grid reference on the map. Some entries were included just before the guide went to press, so they do not appear on the maps.

ADDRESSES

County names, which appear in the town headings, are not normally repeated in the entries. When you are writing, you should of course make sure you use the full address and postcode.

PRICES

The prices shown are only a general guide; they were supplied to us by proprietors in summer 2001. A number of establishments have included in their enhanced entry information about any special offers, short breaks, etc. that are available. Please see page 671 for further details about prices.

OPENING PERIOD

All places are open for the months indicated in their entry.

SYMBOLS

The at-a-glance symbols included at the end of each entry show many of the facilities and equipment available at each place. You will find the key to these symbols on the back cover flap.

SMOKING

Some places prefer not to accommodate smokers and in such cases the accommodation entry makes this clear.

PETS

Many places accept guests with dogs, but we do advise that you check this when you book, and ask if there are any extra charges or rules about exactly where your pet is allowed. The acceptance of dogs is not always extended to cats and it is strongly advised that cat owners contact the establishment well in advance. Some establishments do not accept pets at all. Pets are welcome where you see this symbol 🐕 .

The quarantine laws have recently changed in England and a Pet Travel Scheme (PETS) is currently in operation. Under this scheme pet dogs are able to come into Britain from over 35 countries via certain sea, air and rail routes into England.

Dogs that have been resident in these countries for more than 6 months may enter the UK under the Scheme providing they are accompanied by the appropriate documentation.

For dogs to be able to enter the UK without quarantine under the PETS Scheme they will have to meet certain conditions and travel with the following documents: the Official PETS Certificate, a certificate of treatment against tapeworm and ticks and a declaration of residence.

For details of participating countries, routes, operators and further information about the PETS Scheme, please contact the PETS Helpline, DEFRA (Department for Environment, Food and Rural Affairs),1a Page Street, London SW1P 4PQ

Tel: +44 (0) 870 241 1710 Fax: +44 (0) 20 7904 6834 Email: pets.helpline@defra.gsi.gov.uk, or visit their web site at www.defra.gov.uk/animalh/quarantine

CREDIT AND CHARGE CARDS

The credit and charge cards accepted by a place are listed in the entry.

If you do plan to pay by card, check that the establishment will take your card before you book.

Some proprietors will charge you a higher rate if you pay by credit card rather than cash or cheque. The difference is to cover the percentage paid by the proprietor to the credit card company.

If you are planning to pay by credit card, you may want to ask whether it would, in fact, be cheaper to pay by cheque or cash. When you book by telephone, you may be asked for your credit card number as 'confirmation'. But remember, the proprietor may then charge your credit card account if you cancel your booking. See under Cancellations on page 671.

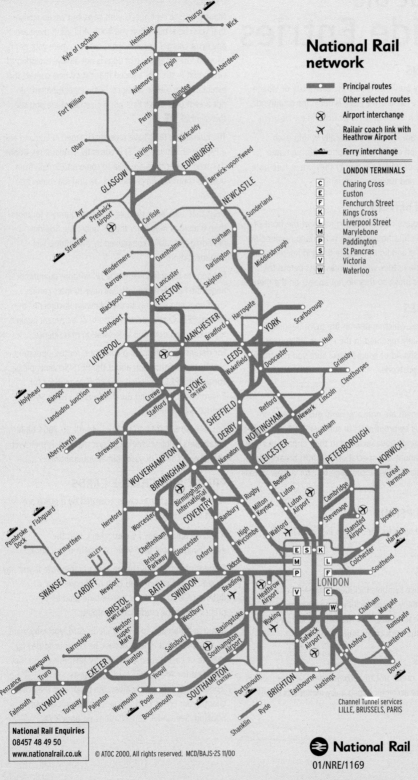

National Rail network

	Principal routes
	Other selected routes
✈	Airport interchange
✈	Railair coach link with Heathrow Airport
⛴	Ferry interchange

LONDON TERMINALS

C	Charing Cross
E	Euston
F	Fenchurch Street
K	Kings Cross
L	Liverpool Street
M	Marylebone
P	Paddington
S	St Pancras
V	Victoria
W	Waterloo

Channel Tunnel services
LILLE, BRUSSELS, PARIS

National Rail Enquiries
08457 48 49 50
www.nationalrail.co.uk

© ATOC 2000. All rights reserved. MCD/BAJS-2S 11/00

National Rail

01/NRE/1169

Distance Chart

The distances between towns on the chart below are given to the nearest mile, and are measured along routes based on the quickest travelling time, making maximum use of motorways or dual-carriageway roads. The chart is based upon information supplied by the Automobile Association.

To calculate the distance in kilometres multiply the mileage by 1.6

For example: Brighton to Dover
82 miles x 1.6
=131.2 kilometres

	Aberdeen	Aberystwyth	Barnstaple	Birmingham	Brighton	Bristol	Cambridge	Cardiff	Carlisle	Carmarthen	Colchester	Dorchester	Dover	Edinburgh	Exeter	Fort William	Glasgow	Gloucester	Guildford	Holyhead	Hull	Inverness	Kendal	Leeds	Lincoln	Liverpool	Maidstone	Manchester	Middlesbrough	Newcastle	Norwich	Nottingham	Oxford	Penzance	Perth	Plymouth	Sheffield	Southampton	Stranraer	Taunton	York
Aberystwyth	468																																								
Barnstaple	603	214																																							
Birmingham	431	124	180																																						
Brighton	605	288	208	171																																					
Bristol	513	128	99	90	169																																				
Cambridge	462	215	267	97	120	170																																			
Cardiff	531	110	127	109	201	44	203																																		
Carlisle	231	236	372	199	375	282	257	300																																	
Carmarthen	513	48	190	171	264	106	266	67	282																																
Colchester	516	289	292	171	112	195	48	227	310	290																															
Dorchester	595	206	94	172	119	62	179	119	363	182	206																														
Dover	587	325	273	207	82	206	124	238	400	301	116	200																													
Edinburgh	125	335	470	298	473	380	333	398	98	381	385	462	458																												
Exeter	585	196	53	162	175	82	249	109	353	172	274	55	245	453																											
Fort William	156	446	581	409	584	491	466	509	209	491	518	573	590	133	563																										
Glasgow	147	333	468	296	472	379	353	397	96	379	405	461	478	49	451	102																									
Gloucester	479	111	125	56	155	35	150	61	247	124	171	117	192	347	107	456	343																								
Guildford	563	224	175	128	44	106	91	138	332	201	103	97	97	432	147	541	428	99																							
Holyhead	459	101	339	167	343	250	259	201	227	149	333	332	369	327	322	436	323	215	300																						
Hull	375	228	321	140	258	231	138	249	170	312	191	313	262	247	303	379	266	196	239	219																					
Inverness	106	494	630	457	633	540	514	558	257	540	566	622	639	158	612	66	174	505	591	485	428																				
Kendal	279	190	325	153	329	236	245	254	47	236	319	318	355	147	308	256	143	201	286	181	164	305																			
Leeds	331	174	302	121	263	212	146	230	126	220	200	294	271	202	284	335	222	177	220	165	60	383	71																		
Lincoln	387	199	276	89	216	186	95	204	182	267	147	245	220	258	258	391	278	151	173	204	46	439	176	72																	
Liverpool	357	110	274	102	277	184	193	202	126	163	268	266	304	225	256	335	222	150	235	101	128	383	79	74	140																
Maidstone	548	286	234	168	50	167	85	199	361	262	77	161	41	419	206	570	458	153	58	329	223	619	315	233	181	263															
Manchester	356	134	261	89	264	171	160	189	123	180	212	253	291	223	243	332	219	137	222	125	97	381	77	44	85	35	251														
Middlesbrough	276	245	357	177	318	268	198	286	95	291	251	350	322	147	340	280	191	233	276	236	89	308	84	63	123	145	283	115													
Newcastle	234	276	388	208	349	299	229	317	60	322	282	381	353	106	371	239	154	264	307	267	142	266	102	94	154	176	314	146	38												
Norwich	488	277	329	159	171	233	63	264	282	327	61	241	175	359	311	491	379	212	162	320	150	540	276	173	104	241	135	186	223	254											
Nottingham	393	162	234	54	195	144	86	163	188	226	139	226	218	265	216	397	284	110	153	178	92	446	164	74	38	112	179	71	129	160	119										
Oxford	503	159	170	68	109	73	81	105	271	168	124	115	146	371	152	480	367	48	67	239	189	529	225	171	130	173	106	161	226	257	144	103									
Penzance	697	308	108	274	287	194	361	221	465	284	386	167	357	565	111	674	562	219	259	433	414	723	419	396	369	367	317	355	451	482	423	328	264								
Perth	87	382	518	345	521	428	402	446	145	428	454	510	527	42	500	102	62	393	478	373	315	114	193	268	327	271	487	266	192	151	428	334	418	611							
Plymouth	628	239	67	205	218	125	292	152	396	215	316	98	288	496	45	605	492	150	190	364	345	654	350	326	300	298	248	286	382	413	354	259	195	77	542						
Sheffield	365	167	272	76	233	182	122	201	159	264	176	264	247	236	254	368	255	148	191	158	66	417	125	36	47	79	207	39	100	131	147	44	141	366	281	297					
Southampton	570	225	142	135	66	106	131	138	339	201	159	53	152	439	109	548	435	100	49	307	257	596	292	238	197	241	112	228	293	324	193	171	67	221	484	152	208				
Stranraer	232	342	478	305	481	388	363	406	106	388	415	470	487	133	460	188	86	354	439	333	276	258	153	228	288	231	448	226	201	163	388	294	378	572	146	503	265	446			
Taunton	554	165	50	132	160	51	218	79	323	142	243	45	224	423	32	532	419	77	126	291	272	581	276	253	227	225	184	212	308	339	280	186	121	144	469	75	223	94	429		
York	322	202	315	134	276	225	155	243	117	248	209	307	280	193	297	326	213	191	233	193	38	374	91	24	80	103	240	72	50	89	180	86	184	409	238	340	58	251	223	266	
London	544	238	216	120	59	120	60	152	313	215	61	128	79	413	198	522	409	102	30	281	186	571	266	198	143	215	39	202	253	284	115	131	56	310	458	241	168	80	419	167	211

A selection of events for 2002

This is a selection of the many cultural, sporting and other events that will be taking place throughout England during 2001. Please note, as changes often occur after press date, it is advisable to confirm the date and location before travelling.

* Provisional at time of going to press.

January 2002

1 January
The New Year's Day Parade - London
Parliament Square,
SW1 to Berkeley Square, London W1
Tel: (020) 8566 8586
Email: markp@londonparade.co.uk
www.londonparade.co.uk

3-13 January
London International Boat Show
Earls Court Exhibition Centre, Warwick Road,
London SW5 9TA
Tel: (01784) 472222 (Boatline)
www.bigblue.org.uk

13 January
Antique and Collectors' Fair
Alexandra Palace,
Alexandra Palace Way, London N22 7AY
Tel: (020) 8883 7061
Email: info@pigandwhistlepromotions.com
www.allypally-uk.com

27 January
Charles I Commemoration
Banqueting House,
Whitehall, London SW1A 2ER
Tel: (01430) 430695

31 January-3 February
**Wakefield Rhubarb Trail and Festival
of Rhubarb**
Various venues, Wakefield
Tel: (01924) 305841
Email: pventom@wakefield.gov.uk
www.wakefield.gov.uk

February 2002

1 February*
Cheltenham Folk Festival
Town Hall, Imperial Square, Cheltenham
Tel: (01242) 226033
Email: Antoniac@cheltenham.gov.uk
www.visitcheltenham.gov.uk

9-16 February
Jorvik Viking Festival - Jolablot 2002
Various venues - Jorvik, Coppergate, York
Tel: (01904) 643211
Email: marketing.jorvik@lineone.net
www.jorvik-viking.centre.co.uk

17 February
Chinese New Year Celebrations
Centered on Gerrard Street and Leicester Square,
London WC2
Tel: (020) 7287 1118

17 February-24 March
Lambing Sunday and Spring Bulb Days
Kentwell Hall, Long Melford, Sudbury

26 February-3 March
Fine Art and Antiques Fair
Olympia, Hammersmith Road, London W14
Tel: (020) 7370 8212
Email: olympia.antiques@eco.co.uk
www.olympia-antiques.co.uk

March 2002

6 March-1 April
Ideal Home Show
Earls Court Exhibition Centre,
Warwick Road, London SW5 9TA
Tel: (0870) 606 6080

7 March-10 March*
Crufts 2002
National Exhibition Centre, Birmingham

12 March-14 March
**Cheltenham Gold Cup National Hunt
Racing Festival**
Cheltenham Racecourse, Prestbury Park, Cheltenham
Tel: (01242) 513014
www.cheltenham.co.uk

16 March-17 March
Ambleside Daffodil and Spring Flower Show
The Kelsick Centre, St Mary's Lane, Ambleside
Tel: (015394) 32252
www.ambleside-show.org.uk

17 March
Antique and Collectors' Fair
Alexandra Palace, Alexandra Palace Way,
London N22 7AY
Tel: (020) 8883 7061
Email: info@pigandwhistlepromotions.com
www.allypally-uk.com

23 March
Head of the River Race
River Thames, London
Tel: (01932) 220401
Email: secretary@horr.co.uk
www.horr.co.uk

23 March-24 March*
Thriplow Daffodil Weekend
Various Venues, Thriplow, Royston
Tel: (01763) 208132
Email: jmurray@thriplow.fsnet.co.uk
www.thriplow.org.uk

29 March
British and World Marbles Championship
Greyhound Public House,
Radford Road, Tinsley Green, Crawley
Tel: (01403) 730602

29 March-5 April*
Harrogate International Youth Music Festival
Various venues, Harrogate
Tel: (01306) 744360
Email: peurope@kuoni.co.uk
www.performeurope.co.uk

29 March-6 April
Ulverston Walking Festival
Various Venues, Ulverston
Tel: (01229) 585588

30 March
Oxford and Cambridge Boat Race
River Thames, London
Tel: (020) 7611 3500

April 2002

1 April
Old Custom: World Coal Carrying Championship
Start: Royal Oak Public House,
Owl Lane, Ossett
Tel: (01924) 218990
Email: bwilding@gawthorpe.ndo.co.uk
www.gawthorpe.ndo.co.uk

1 April
London Harness Horse Parade
Battersea Park, London SW11
Tel: (01733) 371156
Email: t-g@ic24.net
www.eastofengland.org.uk

1 April-30 April*
Old Custom: Pace Egg Plays
Upper Calder Valley, Various venues, Todmorden,
Heptonstall, Hebden Bridge
Tel: (01422) 843831
Email: calderdale_tourism@lineone.net

1 April-30 April*
Trigg Morris Men's Easter Monday Tour
Various Venues Starting in the
Market Square, Launceston
Tel: (01637) 880394
www.triggmorris.freeserve.co.uk

4 April-6 April*
Horse-racing: Martell Grand National Festival
Aintree Racecourse,
Ormskirk Road, Aintree, Liverpool
Tel: (0151) 523 2600
Email: aintree@rht.net
www.aintree.co.uk

14 April
London Marathon
Greenwich Park, London SE10
Tel: (020) 8948 7935

18 April-20 April
Maltings Beer Festival
Tuckers Maltings, Teign Road, Newton Abbot
Tel: (01626) 334734

20 April-6 May
World Snooker Championships
Crucible Theatre, Norfolk Street, Sheffield
Tel: (0114) 249 6006
www.embassysnooker.com

24 April-27 April
Bury St Edmunds Beer Festival
Corn Exchange, Cornhill, Bury St Edmunds
Tel: (01842) 860063

25 April-28 April
Harrogate Spring Flower Show
Great Yorkshire Showground, Harrogate
Tel: (01423) 561049
Email: info@flowershow.org.uk
www.flowershow.org.uk

May 2002

1 May-6 May*
Cheltenham International Jazz Festival
Various venues throughout Cheltenham

1 May-31 May*
Bexhill 100 Festival of Motoring
Seafront, De La Warr Parade, Bexhill
Tel: (01424) 730564
Email: brian@bexhill100.co.uk
www.bexhill100.co.uk

1 May-31 May*
Hay on Wye Literature Festival
Various Venues in Hay-on-Wye,
Hay-on-Wye, Hereford
Tel: (01497) 821299

1 May-31 May*
Jennings Keswick Jazz Festival
Keswick
Tel: (01900) 602122
Email: carnegie@allerdale.gov.uk

1 May-31 Aug
Glyndebourne Festival Opera
Glyndebourne Opera House,
Glyndebourne, Glynde, Lewes

3 May-6 May
**Hastings Traditional Jack in the
Green Morris Dance and Folk Festival**
Various venues, Hastings
Tel: (01424) 781122
Email: greenman@britishlibrary.net
www.jack-in-the-park.co.uk

4 May*
Downton Cuckoo Fair
Village Centre, Downton, Salisbury
Tel: (01725) 510646

4 May-27 May*
Rhododendron and Azalea Time
Leonardslee Gardens,
Lower Beeding, Horsham
Tel: (01403) 891212
Email: leonardslee.gardens@virgin.net
www.leonardslee.com

5 May-6 May*
2002 Dover Pageant
Dover College Grounds, Dover
Tel: (01304) 242990
Email: pageant@port-of-dover.com
www.port-of-dover.com/pageant

6-May
Dunstable Carnival
Bennett Memorial Recreation Ground,
Bull Pond Lane, Dunstable
Tel: (01582) 607895
Email: promotions.dunstable@towns.bedfordshie.gov.uk

11 May-19 May*
Tiverton Spring Festival
Various venues, Tiverton
Tel: (01884) 258952

12-May
Antique and Collectors' Fair
Alexandra Palace, Alexandra Palace Way,
London N22 7AY
Tel: (020) 8883 7061
Email: info@pigandwhistlepromotions.com
www.allypally-uk.com

12-May
South Suffolk Show
Point-to-Point Course, Ampton Park,
Ingham, Bury St Edmunds
Tel: (01638) 750879
Email: geoff@southsuffolkshow.co.uk
www.southsuffolkshow.co.uk

15 May-19 May
Royal Windsor Horse Show
Home Park, Windsor Castle, Windsor
Tel: (01753) 860633
Email: olympia-show-jumping@eco.uk
www.olympia-show-jumping.co.uk

18 May-19 May
London Tattoo
Wembley Arena, Empire Way, Wembley
Tel: (01189) 303239
Email: normanrogerson@telinco.co.uk
www.telinco.co.uk/maestromusic

21 May-24 May
Chelsea Flower Show
Royal Hospital Chelsea, Royal Hospital Road,
Chelsea, London SW3 4SR

24 May-27 May*
Old Custom: The Hunting of the Earl of Rone
Various venues, Combe Martin, Ilfracombe
Tel: (01271) 882 366
Email: tom.brown1@virgin.net

25 May-26 May*
Air Fete
RAF Mildenhall,
100ARW/CV USAF, Mildenhall, Bury St Edmunds
Tel: (01638) 543341
www.mildenhall.af.mil/airfete

25 May-26 May
Hertfordshire County Show
Hertfordshire Agricultural Society, Dunstable Road,
Redbourn, St Albans
Tel: (01582) 792626

26 May-27 May
Battle Medieval Fair
Abbey Green, High Street, Battle
Tel: (01424) 774447
Email: chpsmith@lineone.net

27 May-7 Jun
Isle of Man T.T. Motorcycle Festival
Various venues Isle of Man
Tel: (01624) 686801

29 May-30 May
Corpus Christi Carpet of Flowers and Floral Festival
Cathedral of Our Lady and St Philip Howard,
Cathedral House, Arundel
Tel: (01903) 882297
Email: aruncathl@aol.com

31 May-2 Jun
Holker Garden Festival
Holker Hall and Gardens, Cark in Cartmel,
Grange-over-Sands
Tel: (015395) 58328
Email: publicopening@holker.co.uk
www.holker-hall.co.uk

June 2002

1 June-3 June*
Orange WOW
North Shields Fishquay and Town Centre, North Shields
Tel: (0191) 200 5164
Email: carol.alevroyianni@northtyneside.gov.uk
www.orangewow.co.uk

1 June-4 June*
Chatham Navy Days
The Historic Dockyard, Chatham
Tel: (01634) 823800
www.worldnavalbase.org.uk

1 June-31 July*
Exeter Festival
Various Venues, Exeter
Tel: (01392) 265118
www.exeter.gov.uk

6 June-12 June
Appleby Horse Fair
Fair Hill, Roman Road,
Appleby-in-Westmorland
Tel: (017683) 51177
Email: tic@applebytowncouncil.fsnet.co.uk
www.applebytowncouncil.fsnet.co.uk

6 June-16 June
Fine Art and Antiques Fair
Olympia, Hammersmith Road, London W14
Tel: (020) 7370 8212
Email: olympia.antiques@eco.co.uk
www.olympia-antiques.com

7 June*
Robert Dover's Cotswold Olimpick Games
Dovers Hill, Weston Subedge, Chipping Campden
Tel: (01384) 274041
Email: a.greenwood@cix.co.uk

7 June-8 June*
Vodafone Derby Horse Race Meeting
Epsom Racecourse, Epsom
Tel: (01372) 470047
Email: epsom@rht.net
www.epsomderby.co.uk

11 June-13 June*
Three Counties Show
Three Counties Showground, Malvern
Tel: (01684) 584900
Email: info@threecounties.co.uk
www.threecounties.co.uk

12 June-18 June
Grosvenor House Art and Antiques Fair
Le Meridien Grosvenor House, Park Lane,
London W1A 3AA
Tel: (020) 7399 8100
Email: olivia@grosvenor-antiquesfair.co.uk
www.grosvenor-antiquesfair.co.uk

15 June
Trooping the Colour - The Queen's Birthday Parade
Horse Guards Parade, London SW1
Tel: (020) 7414 2479

15 June-23 June
Broadstairs Dickens Festival
Various Venues, Broadstairs
Tel: (01843) 865265
www.broadstairs.gov.uk/dickensfestival.html

18 June-19 June*
Cheshire County Show
The Showground, Tabley, Knutsford
Tel: (01829) 760020

18 June-21 June
Royal Ascot
Ascot Racecourse, Ascot
Tel: (01344) 876876
www.ascot.co.uk

19 June-23 June
Covent Garden Flower Festival
Covent Garden Piazza, London WC2
Tel: 09064 701 777 (60p per minute)
Email: info@cgff.co.uk
www.cgff.co.uk

21 June-30 June
Newcastle Hoppings
Town Moor, Grandstand Road, Newcastle upon Tyne
Tel: (07831) 458774

22 June
HOYA Round the Island Race
Isle of Wight Coast, c/o Island Sailing Club,
70 High Street, Cowes
Tel: (01983) 296621
Email: islandsc.org.uk
www.island.org.uk

24 June-7 July
Wimbledon Lawn Tennis Championships
All England Lawn Tennis and Croquet Club,
Church Road, London SW19 5AE
Tel: (020) 8946 2244

28 June-30 June*
The Ordnance Survey Balloon and Flower Festival
Southampton Common, The Avenue, Southampton
Tel: (023) 8083 2525
Email: southampton.gov.uk

29 June-17 July*
Chester Mystery Plays
Cathedral Green, Chester
Tel: (01244) 6826176 July-7 July

July 2002

5 July-14 July
Lichfield International Arts Festival
Throughout City of Lichfield
Tel: (01543) 306270
Email: Lichfield.fest@Lichfield-arts.org.uk
www.lichfieldfestival.org

5 July-14 July
York Early Music Festival
Various venues, York
Tel: (01904) 645738
Email: enquiry@yorkearlymusic.org
www.yorkearlymusic.org

6 July-7 July
Sunderland International Kite Festival
Northern Area Playing Fields, District 12, Washington
Tel: (0191) 514 1235
Email: jackie.smithr@edcom.sunderland.gov.uk
www.sunderland.gov.uk/kitefestival

6 July-18 August
Cookson Country Festival
Various Venues in South Shields
Tel: (0191) 424 7985
Email: andy.buyers@s-tyneside-mbc.gov.uk
www.s-tyneside-mbc.gov.uk

10 July-14 July*
Henley Festival
Royal Regatta, Henley-on-Thames
Tel: (01491) 843400
Email: info@henley-festival.co.uk
www.henley-festival.co.uk

13 July
Tendring Hundred Show
Lawford House Park, Lawford, Manningtree
Tel: (01206) 571517
Email: anne@tendringshow.demon.co.uk
www.tendringshow.demon.com

13 July-14 July
Tewkesbury Medieval Festival
The Gastons, Gloucester Road, Tewkesbury
Tel: (01386) 871908

19 July-21 July*
Netley Marsh Steam and Craft Show
Meadow Farm, Ringwood Road, Netley Marsh,
Southampton
Tel: (023) 8086 7882

19 July-14 September
BBC Henry Wood Promenade Concerts
Royal Albert Hall, Kensington Gore, London SW7 2AP
Tel: (020) 7765 5575
Email: proms@bbc.co.uk
www.bbc.co.uk/proms

23 July-28 July*
Chulmleigh Old Fair
Various Venues, Chulmleigh
Tel: (01769) 580276

25 July-4 August*
Manchester 2002
- The 17th Commonwealth Games
Various venues, Manchester
Tel: (0161) 228 2002

26 July-28 July
Gateshead Summer Flower Show
Gateshead Central Nurseries, Whickham Highway, Lobley
Hill, Gateshead
Tel: (0191) 433 3838
Email: g.scott@leisure.gatesheadmbc.gov

27 July-28 July*
Sunderland International Air Show
Promenade, Sea Front, Seaburn, Sunderland
Tel: (0191) 553 2000

31 July
Nantwich and South Cheshire Show
Dorfold Hall, Nantwich
Tel: (01270) 780306

August 2002

1 August-30 August
Last Night of the Proms Outdoor Concert
Castle Howard, York
Tel: (01653) 648444
Email: mec@castlehoward.co.uk
www.castlehoward.co.uk

1 August-31 August*
Lowther Horse Driving Trials and Country Fair
Lowther Castle , Lowther Estate, Lowther, Penrith
Tel: (01931) 712378

1 August-31 August*
Maryport Songs of the Sea Festival
The Harbour, Maryport
Tel: (01900) 813738

3 August*
Stoke Gabriel Grand Carnival Procession
Village Centre, Stoke Gabriel, Totnes
Tel: (01803) 782483

3 August-4 August
Woodvale International Rally
R A F Woodvale, 43 Kenilworth Road, Southport
Tel: (01704) 578816

4 August-11 August
Alnwick International Music Festival
Market-place, Alnwick
Tel: (01665) 510417
Email: jim@alnwick0.demon.co.uk

10 August-17 August
Billingham International Folklore Festival
Town Centre, Queensway, Billingham
Tel: (01642) 651060
www.billinghamfestival.co.uk

16 August-26 August*
Ross on Wye International Festival
Various venues around Ross on Wye, mainly by the
riverside, Rope Walk, Ross-on-Wye
Tel: (01594) 544446
Email: info@festival.org.uk
www.festival.org.uk

22 August-27 August
International Beatles Festival
Various venues, Liverpool
Tel: (0151) 236 9091
Email: cavern@fsb.dial.co.uk
www.cavern-liverpool.co.uk

25 August-26 August
Western Union Notting Hill Carnival
Streets around Ladbroke Grove , London W11
Tel: (020) 8964 0544

28 August-1 September
Great Dorset Steam Fair
South Down Farm, Tarrant Hinton, Blandford Forum
Tel: (01258) 860361
Email: enquiries@steam-fair.co.uk
www.steam-fair.co.uk

30 August-3 November
Blackpool Illuminations
Promenade, Blackpool
Tel: (01253) 478222
Email: tourism@blackpool.gov.uk
www.blackpooltourism.gov.uk

31 August-1 September*
Lancashire Vintage and Country Show
Hamilton House Farm, St Michael's on Wyre, Preston
Tel: (01772) 687259

September 2002

1 September*
Egremont Crab Fair and Sports
Baybarrow, Orgill, Egremont
Tel: (01946) 821554
Email: crabfair.homestead.com/mainpage.html

1 September*
Kendal Torchlight Procession
Kendal
Tel: (015395) 63018
Email: ronc@torchlight.net1.co.uk
www.lakesnet.co.uk/kendaltorchlight

1 September-30 September*
Southampton International Boat Show
Western Esplanade, Southampton
Tel: (01784) 223600
Email: boatshow@boatshows.co.uk
www.bigblue.org.uk

5 September-8 September
**The Blenheim Petplan International
Three Day Event**
Blenheim Palace, Woodstock
Tel: (01993) 813335
Email: blenheimht@btconnect.com

7 September-8 September
Berwick Military Tattoo
Berwick Barracks, Berwick-upon-Tweed
Tel: (01289) 307426

7 September-8 September*
Kirkby Lonsdale Victorian Fair
Kirkby Lonsdale
Tel: (015242) 71570

13 September-15 September
Thames Festival
River Thames, London
Tel: (020) 7928 0960
Email: festival@coin-street.org
www.ThamesFestival.org

18 September-21 September*
Barnstaple Ancient Chartered Fair
Seven Brethren Bank, Barnstaple
Tel: (01271) 373311
Email: barnstaple_com_council@northdevon.gov.uk

21 September-22 September*
Newbury and Royal County of Berkshire Show
Newbury Showground, Priors Court, Hermitage,
Thatcham

22 September
Antique and Collectors' Fair
Alexandra Palace, Alexandra Palace Way,
London N22 7AY
Tel: (020) 8883 7061
Email: info@pigandwhistlepromotions.com
www.allypally-uk.com

October 2002

1 October-6 October
Horse of the Year Show
Wembley Arena, Empire Way, Wembley
Tel: (020) 8900 9282
Email: info@hoys.co.uk
www.hoys.co.uk

11 October-19 October
Hull Fair
Walton Street Fairground, Walton Street, Hull
Tel: (01482) 615625
Email: city.entertainments@hull.gov.uk

20 October
Trafalgar Day Parade - The Sea Cadet Corps
Trafalgar Square, London WC2
Tel: (020) 7928 8978
Email: rbusby@sea-cadets.org

November 2002

1 November-30 November*
International Guitar Festival of Great Britain
Various venues, Wirral
Tel: (0151) 666 5060
Email: rob@bestguitarfest.com
www.bestguitarfest.com

1 November-31 December*
Marwell's Winter Wonderland
Marwell Zoological Park, Colden Common, Winchester
Tel: (01962) 777407
Email: events@marwell.org.uk

3 November
London to Brighton Veteran Car Run
Hyde Park, London W2
Tel: (01753) 765035

9 November
Lord Mayor's Show
City of London, London
Tel: (020) 7606 3030

10 November
Remembrance Day Service and Parade
Cenotaph, Whitehall, London SW1
Tel: (020) 7273 3498
Email: frances.bright@homeoffice.gsi.gov.uk

11 November*
**Highbridge and Burnham-on-Sea
Guy Fawkes Carnival**
Town Centre, Burnham-on-Sea
Tel: (01278) 794557

16 November-23 December
Thursford Christmas Spectacular
Thursford Collection, Thursford Green,
Thursford, Fakenham
Tel: (01328) 878477

17 November
Antique and Collectors' Fair
Alexandra Palace, Alexandra Palace Way,
London N22 7AY
Tel: (020) 8883 7061
Email: info@pigandwhistlepromotions.com
www.allypally-uk.com

December 2002

18 December-22 December
**Showjumping: Olympia International
Championships**
Olympia, Hammersmith Road, London W14
Tel: (020) 7370 8206
Email: olympia-show-jumping@eco.co.uk
www.olympia-show-jumping.co.uk

Calendar 2002

JANUARY						
M	T	W	T	F	S	S
1	2	3	4	5	6	
7	8	9	10	11	12	13
14	15	16	17	18	19	20
21	22	23	24	25	26	27
28	29	30	31			

FEBRUARY						
M	T	W	T	F	S	S
				1	2	3
4	5	6	7	8	9	10
11	12	13	14	15	16	17
18	19	20	21	22	23	24
25	26	27	28			

MARCH						
M	T	W	T	F	S	S
				1	2	3
4	5	6	7	8	9	10
11	12	13	14	15	16	17
18	19	20	21	22	23	24
25	26	27	28	**29**	30	31

APRIL						
M	T	W	T	F	S	S
1	2	3	4	5	6	7
8	9	10	11	12	13	14
15	16	17	18	19	20	21
22	23	24	25	26	27	28
29	30					

MAY						
M	T	W	T	F	S	S
		1	2	3	4	5
6	7	8	9	10	11	12
13	14	15	16	17	18	19
20	21	22	23	24	25	26
27	28	29	30	31		

JUNE						
M	T	W	T	F	S	S
					1	2
3	**4**	5	6	7	8	9
10	11	12	13	14	15	16
17	18	19	20	21	22	23
24	25	26	27	28	29	30

JULY						
M	T	W	T	F	S	S
1	2	3	4	5	6	7
8	9	10	11	12	13	14
15	16	17	18	19	20	21
22	23	24	25	26	27	28
29	30	31				

AUGUST						
M	T	W	T	F	S	S
			1	2	3	4
5	6	7	8	9	10	11
12	13	14	15	16	17	18
19	20	21	22	23	24	25
26	27	28	29	30	31	

SEPTEMBER						
M	T	W	T	F	S	S
30						1
2	3	4	5	6	7	8
9	10	11	12	13	14	15
16	17	18	19	20	21	22
23	24	25	26	27	28	29

OCTOBER						
M	T	W	T	F	S	S
	1	2	3	4	5	6
7	8	9	10	11	12	13
14	15	16	17	18	19	20
21	22	23	24	25	26	27
28	29	30	31			

NOVEMBER						
M	T	W	T	F	S	S
				1	2	3
4	5	6	7	8	9	10
11	12	13	14	15	16	17
18	19	20	21	22	23	24
25	26	27	28	29	30	

DECEMBER						
M	T	W	T	F	S	S
30	31					1
2	3	4	5	6	7	8
9	10	11	12	13	14	15
16	17	18	19	20	21	22
23	24	**25**	**26**	27	28	29

Calendar 2003

JANUARY						
M	T	W	T	F	S	S
		1	2	3	4	5
6	7	8	9	10	11	12
13	14	15	16	17	18	19
20	21	22	23	24	25	26
27	28	29	30	31		

FEBRUARY						
M	T	W	T	F	S	S
					1	2
3	4	5	6	7	8	9
10	11	12	13	14	15	16
17	18	19	20	21	22	23
24	25	26	27	28		

MARCH						
M	T	W	T	F	S	S
					1	2
3	4	5	6	7	8	9
10	11	12	13	14	15	16
17	18	19	20	21	22	23
24	25	26	27	28	29	30
31						

APRIL						
M	T	W	T	F	S	S
	1	2	3	4	5	6
7	8	9	10	11	12	13
14	15	16	17	**18**	19	20
21	22	23	24	25	26	27
28	29	30				

MAY						
M	T	W	T	F	S	S
			1	2	3	4
5	6	7	8	9	10	11
12	13	14	15	16	17	18
19	20	21	22	23	24	25
26	27	28	29	30	31	

JUNE						
M	T	W	T	F	S	S
						1
2	3	4	5	6	7	8
9	10	11	12	13	14	15
16	17	18	19	20	21	22
23	24	25	26	27	28	29
30						

JULY						
M	T	W	T	F	S	S
	1	2	3	4	5	6
7	8	9	10	11	12	13
14	15	16	17	18	19	20
21	22	23	24	25	26	27
28	29	30	31			

AUGUST						
M	T	W	T	F	S	S
				1	2	3
4	5	6	7	8	9	10
11	12	13	14	15	16	17
18	19	20	21	22	23	24
25	26	27	28	29	30	31

SEPTEMBER						
M	T	W	T	F	S	S
1	2	3	4	5	6	7
8	9	10	11	12	13	14
15	16	17	18	19	20	21
22	23	24	25	26	27	28
29	30					

OCTOBER						
M	T	W	T	F	S	S
		1	2	3	4	5
6	7	8	9	10	11	12
13	14	15	16	17	18	19
20	21	22	23	24	25	26
27	28	29	30	31		

NOVEMBER						
M	T	W	T	F	S	S
					1	2
3	4	5	6	7	8	9
10	11	12	13	14	15	16
17	18	19	20	21	22	23
24	25	26	27	28	29	30

DECEMBER						
M	T	W	T	F	S	S
1	2	3	4	5	6	7
8	9	10	11	12	13	14
15	16	17	18	19	20	21
22	23	24	**25**	**26**	27	28
29	30	31				

TOWN INDEX

The following cities, towns and villages all have accommodation listed in this guide. If the place where you wish to stay is not shown, the location maps (starting on page 18) will help you to find somewhere suitable in the same area.

A — PAGE

Abberley *Worcestershire*	173
Abbotsbury *Dorset*	285
Abingdon *Oxfordshire*	356
Accrington *Lancashire*	120
Alcester *Warwickshire*	174
Aldeburgh *Suffolk*	241
Alderton *Gloucestershire*	174
Alfreton *Derbyshire*	174
Alfriston *East Sussex*	386
Allendale *Northumberland*	90
Allerford *Somerset*	286
Allerston *North Yorkshire*	134
Allonby *Cumbria*	50
Alnmouth *Northumberland*	90
Alnwick *Northumberland*	91
Alresford *Essex*	243
Alstonefield *Staffordshire*	175
Alton *Staffordshire*	175
Alverstoke *Hampshire*	357
Ambleside *Cumbria*	50
Amesbury *Wiltshire*	286
Ampleforth *North Yorkshire*	134
Appleby-in-Westmorland *Cumbria*	52
Appley *Somerset*	286
Arkengarthdale *North Yorkshire*	135
Arundel *West Sussex*	387
Ashbourne *Derbyshire*	175
Ashbrittle *Somerset*	286
Ashburton *Devon*	287
Ashby-De-La-Zouch *Leicestershire*	176
Ashdown Forest (See under Nutley)	
Ashford *Kent*	387
Ashford in the Water *Derbyshire*	176
Ashwater *Devon*	287
Atherstone *Warwickshire*	177
Axminster *Devon*	288

B — PAGE

Bacton *Norfolk*	243
Bailey *Cumbria*	52
Bakewell *Derbyshire*	177
Bamburgh *Northumberland*	92
Bamford *Derbyshire*	179
Bampton *Devon*	288
Bardon Mill *Northumberland*	94
Barnard Castle *Durham*	94
Barnham *West Sussex*	388
Barnstaple *Devon*	289
Bashall Eaves *Lancashire*	120
Baslow *Derbyshire*	179
Bassenthwaite *Cumbria*	53
Batcombe *Somerset*	289
Bath *Bath and North East Somerset*	289
Battle *East Sussex*	388
Baumber *Lincolnshire*	179
Beachamwell *Norfolk*	243
Beadnell *Northumberland*	95
Beaminster *Dorset*	290
Beamish *Durham*	95

Bearsted *Kent*	388
Beaulieu *Hampshire*	357
Beccles *Suffolk*	243
Beckenham *Greater London*	42
Belchamp St Paul *Essex*	243
Bellingham *Northumberland*	96
Belstone *Devon*	290
Bembridge *Isle of Wight*	357
Berkhamsted *Hertfordshire*	244
Berrynarbor *Devon*	291
Berwick-upon-Tweed *Northumberland*	96
Beverley *East Riding of Yorkshire*	135
Bibury *Gloucestershire*	179
Bideford *Devon*	291
Bigbury-on-Sea *Devon*	291
Billericay *Essex*	244
Birch Vale *Derbyshire*	180
Bishop Monkton *North Yorkshire*	135
Bishop Thornton *North Yorkshire*	136
Bishop's Castle *Shropshire*	180
Black Torrington *Devon*	292
Blackpool *Lancashire*	121
Blakeney *Norfolk*	244
Blanchland *Northumberland*	96
Blankney *Lincolnshire*	181
Blockley *Gloucestershire*	181
Bodenham *Herefordshire*	182
Bodmin *Cornwall*	292
Boldre *Hampshire*	358
Borrowdale *Cumbria*	53
Boscastle *Cornwall*	292
Bosley *Cheshire*	122
Boston *Lincolnshire*	182
Bothel *Cumbria*	53
Bournemouth *Dorset*	358
Bourton-on-the-Water *Gloucestershire*	182
Bowden *Devon*	293
Bowes *Durham*	96
Bradford-on-Avon *Wiltshire*	293
Brancaster *Norfolk*	245
Brancaster Staithe *Norfolk*	245
Brandon *Suffolk*	246
Bratton *Somerset*	293
Brayford *Devon*	294
Brean *Somerset*	294
Bridgnorth *Shropshire*	183
Bridlington *East Riding of Yorkshire*	136
Bridport *Dorset*	294
Brighstone *Isle of Wight*	358
Brighton & Hove *East Sussex*	388
Brigsley *Lincolnshire*	137
Brinscall *Lancashire*	122
Bristol	294
Brixham *Devon*	295
Broad Campden *Gloucestershire*	184
Broadstairs *Kent*	389
Broadway *Worcestershire*	185
Brockenhurst *Hampshire*	359
Bromsgrove *Worcestershire*	185
Broughton-in-Furness *Cumbria*	54
Buckingham *Buckinghamshire*	359
Buckland Newton *Dorset*	295

Buckland St Mary *Somerset*	295
Bude *Cornwall*	296
Burford *Oxfordshire*	360
Burnham-on-Sea *Somerset*	298
Burnham Overy Town *Norfolk*	246
Burnsall *North Yorkshire*	137
Burrowbridge *Somerset*	298
Burton Bradstock *Dorset*	298
Burton-in-Lonsdale *North Yorkshire*	137
Burton Leonard *North Yorkshire*	137
Burwarton *Shropshire*	185
Bury St Edmunds *Suffolk*	247
Butcombe *North Somerset*	299
Buxton *Derbyshire*	185
Byrness *Northumberland*	97

C — PAGE

Caldbeck *Cumbria*	54
Cambridge *Cambridgeshire*	247
Canterbury *Kent*	390
Carisbrooke *Isle of Wight*	360
Carleton *Cumbria*	54
Carlisle *Cumbria*	55
Carlton *North Yorkshire*	138
Carsington *Derbyshire*	186
Cartmel *Cumbria*	55
Castle Acre *Norfolk*	248
Castle Carrock *Cumbria*	56
Castle Cary *Somerset*	299
Castle Hedingham *Essex*	248
Castleside *Durham*	97
Caterham *Surrey*	390
Cattistock *Dorset*	299
Cawton *North Yorkshire*	138
Chale *Isle of Wight*	360
Chalfont St Giles *Buckinghamshire*	361
Challacombe *Devon*	300
Chapel Amble *Cornwall*	300
Chapel Stile *Cumbria*	56
Charcott *Kent*	391
Charlbury *Oxfordshire*	361
Charsfield *Suffolk*	249
Chathill *Northumberland*	97
Cheddar *Somerset*	300
Chelmorton *Derbyshire*	186
Cheltenham *Gloucestershire*	186
Chester *Cheshire*	123
Chesterfield *Derbyshire*	187
Chichester *West Sussex*	391
Chideock *Dorset*	301
Chilham *Kent*	392
Chippenham *Wiltshire*	301
Chipping *Lancashire*	124
Chipping Campden *Gloucestershire*	188
Chipping Norton *Oxfordshire*	361
Chop Gate *North Yorkshire*	138
Chopwell *Tyne and Wear*	98
Christchurch *Dorset*	361
Chudleigh *Devon*	301
Chulmleigh *Devon*	302
Church Stretton *Shropshire*	188
Cirencester *Gloucestershire*	190
Cley Next the Sea *Norfolk*	249

Clifton upon Teme *Worcestershire* 191
Clitheroe *Lancashire* 124
Cloughton *North Yorkshire* 139
Cockermouth *Cumbria* 56
Cockfield *Durham* 98
Colchester *Essex* 250
Coleford *Gloucestershire* 192
Colyton *Devon* 303
Combe Martin *Devon* 303
Combs *Derbyshire* 192
Compton *West Sussex* 393
Compton Abdale *Gloucestershire* 192
Coniston *Cumbria* 56
Corbridge *Northumberland* 98
Corfe Castle *Dorset* 362
Costock *Nottinghamshire* 193
Cotherstone *Durham* 99
Cotswolds *Heart of England*
(See under Alderton, Bibury,
Blockley, Bourton-on-the-Water,
Broad Campden, Broadway,
Cheltenham, Chipping Campden,
Cirencester, Compton Abdale,
Daglingworth, Dursley, Gloucester,
Lower Slaughter, Miserden,
Moreton-in-Marsh, Naunton,
Owlpen, Stanton, Stow-on-the-
Wold, Tetbury, Tewkesbury, Upton St
Leonards, Winchcombe, Witcombe
See also Cotswolds in South of
England region)
Cotswolds *South of England*
(See under Burford, Chesterton,
Deddington, Steeple Aston, Witney
See also Cotswolds in Heart of
England region)
Cotton *Suffolk* 251
Cousley Wood *East Sussex* 393
Cowes *Isle of Wight* 362
Crackington Haven *Cornwall* 303
Cranbrook *Kent* 393
Cranmer *Norfolk* 251
Cratfield *Suffolk* 251
Craven Arms *Shropshire* 193
Cressbrook *Derbyshire* 193
Creswell *Derbyshire* 193
Cromer *Norfolk* 251
Cropton *North Yorkshire* 139
Croyde *Devon* 304
Croydon *Greater London* 43

D PAGE

Daglingworth *Gloucestershire* 194
Dallinghoo *Suffolk* 252
Danby *North Yorkshire* 139
Darlington *Durham* 99
Dartmoor
(See under Ashburton, Belstone,
Dunsford, Moretonhampstead,
Okehampton, Tavistock)
Dartmouth *Devon* 304
Dawlish *Devon* 305
Dawlish Warren *Devon* 305
Dent *Cumbria* 59
Denton *Kent* 393
Denver *Norfolk* 252
Derby *Derbyshire* 194
Devizes *Wiltshire* 305
Diddlebury *Shropshire* 194
Dilham *Norfolk* 252
Diss *Norfolk* 253
Docking *Norfolk* 253
Dorchester *Dorset* 306

Dore *South Yorkshire* 139
Dorking *Surrey* 394
Dorrington *Lincolnshire* 194
Drimpton *Dorset* 306
Dulverton *Somerset* 306
Dunsford *Devon* 307
Dunster *Somerset* 307
Duntisbourne Abbots
Gloucestershire 195
Durham *Durham* 99
Dursley *Gloucestershire* 195

E PAGE

Easby *North Yorkshire* 139
East Allington *Devon* 307
East Bergholt *Suffolk* 253
East Dereham *Norfolk* 254
East Haddon *Northamptonshire* 195
East Harling *Norfolk* 254
East Runton *Norfolk* 254
Eastbourne *East Sussex* 394
Ebberston *North Yorkshire* 140
Edale *Derbyshire* 195
Edlingham *Northumberland* 100
Elterwater *Cumbria* 59
Ely *Cambridgeshire* 255
Embleton *Northumberland* 100
Epperstone *Nottinghamshire* 196
Epsom *Surrey* 394
Erpingham *Norfolk* 255
Eskdale *Cumbria* 60
Evesham *Worcestershire* 196
Exbourne *Devon* 308
Exmoor
(See under Allerford, Bratton,
Brayford, Challacombe, Combe
Martin, Dulverton, Dunster, Lynton,
Minehead, North Molton,
Parracombe, Porlock, Timberscombe,
Winsford, Withypool, Parracombe)
Exton *Hampshire* 363
Eyam *Derbyshire* 196
Eye *Suffolk* 255

F PAGE

Falmouth *Cornwall* 308
Far Forest *Worcestershire* 197
Faulkland *Somerset* 309
Faversham *Kent* 394
Fawkham *Kent* 395
Felixstowe *Suffolk* 255
Fifehead Magdalen *Dorset* 363
Filey *North Yorkshire* 140
Finstock *Oxfordshire* 363
Folkestone *Kent* 395
Fordingbridge *Hampshire* 364
Forest of Dean *Oxfordshire*
(See under Coleford, Lydney,
Soudley, Whitecroft)
Fownhope *Herefordshire* 197
Foxley *Norfolk* 256
Frampton-on-Severn
Gloucestershire 197
Frinton-on-Sea *Essex* 256
Frome *Somerset* 309
Funtington *West Sussex* 395
Fylingthorpe *North Yorkshire* 140

G PAGE

Gatwick Airport
(See under Horsham)

Giggleswick *North Yorkshire* 141
Gilling West *North Yorkshire* 141
Gillingham *Dorset* 364
Glanton *Northumberland* 101
Glastonbury *Somerset* 309
Gloucester *Gloucestershire* 198
Godshill *Isle of Wight* 365
Goodrington *Devon* 309
Gorran Haven *Cornwall* 309
Gosport *Hampshire* 365
Goudhurst *Kent* 395
Grafty Green *Kent* 396
Grange-over-Sands *Cumbria* 60
Grantham *Lincolnshire* 198
Grasmere *Cumbria* 60
Grassington *North Yorkshire* 141
Great Broughton *Cumbria* 61
Great Carlton *Lincolnshire* 198
Great Cheverell *Wiltshire* 310
Great Dunmow *Essex* 256
Great Hucklow *Derbyshire* 198
Great Langdale *Cumbria* 62
Great Langton *North Yorkshire* 142
Great Milton *Oxfordshire* 365
Gresham *Norfolk* 256
Groombridge *East Sussex* 396
Guildford *Surrey* 396
Gunnerside *North Yorkshire* 142

H PAGE

Halifax *West Yorkshire* 143
Halstead *Essex* 257
Haltwhistle *Northumberland* 101
Hamsterley *Durham* 102
Hamsterley Forest
(See under Barnard Castle,
Stanhope, Wolsingham)
Harrogate *North Yorkshire* 143
Hartington *Derbyshire* 198
Hartland *Devon* 310
Haslemere *Surrey* 396
Hastingleigh *Kent* 397
Hathersage *Derbyshire* 199
Hatton *Lincolnshire* 200
Hatton *Warwickshire* 199
Haughley *Suffolk* 257
Haverhill *Suffolk* 257
Haverigg *Cumbria* 62
Hawkshead *Cumbria* 62
Hawling *Gloucestershire* 200
Haworth *West Yorkshire* 145
Haydon Bridge *Northumberland* 102
Hayfield *Derbyshire* 200
Heacham *Norfolk* 257
Hebburn *Tyne and Wear* 102
Hebden Bridge *West Yorkshire* 146
Heddon-on-the-Wall
Northumberland 103
Helmsley *North Yorkshire* 146
Henfield *West Sussex* 397
Heptonstall *West Yorkshire* 146
Hereford *Herefordshire* 200
Hexham *Northumberland* 103
Hickling *Norfolk* 258
High Bentham *North Yorkshire* 147
High Lorton *Cumbria* 64
Hinckley *Leicestershire* 201
Hindhead *Surrey* 397
Hingham *Norfolk* 258
Hinton St George *Somerset* 310
Hitcham *Suffolk* 259
Hockwold *Norfolk* 259

Holme Next the Sea *Norfolk* 259
Holmfirth *West Yorkshire* 147
Holsworthy *Devon* 310
Holymoorside *Derbyshire* 201
Hope *Derbyshire* 201
Hope Cove *Devon* 311
Horning *Norfolk* 260
Horsham *West Sussex* 398
Horsington *Lincolnshire* 201
Hove
(See under Brighton & Hove)
Huddersfield *West Yorkshire* 147
Hunstanton *Norfolk* 260
Huxham *Devon* 311

I	PAGE

Iken *Suffolk* 261
Ilfracombe *Devon* 311
Ilkley *West Yorkshire* 147
Ilminster *Somerset* 312
Ingram *Northumberland* 103
Ipswich *Suffolk* 261
Ironbridge *Shropshire* 201
Isle of Wight
(See under Bembridge, Brighstone,
Carisbrooke, Chale, Cowes, Godshill,
Sandown, Shanklin, Totland Bay,
Ventnor)
Isles of Scilly 312

K	PAGE

Kelsall *Cheshire* 124
Kendal *Cumbria* 64
Kenilworth *Warwickshire* 202
Kenley *Shropshire* 202
Kessingland *Suffolk* 261
Keswick *Cumbria* 65
Kettlewell *North Yorkshire* 148
Kielder Forest
(See under Bellingham, West
Woodburn)
Kielder Water *Northumberland* 104
King's Lynn *Norfolk* 262
King's Meaburn *Cumbria* 68
King's Nympton *Devon* 312
Kingsbridge *Devon* 312
Kingston upon Thames *Greater
London* 43
Kiplin *North Yorkshire* 148
Kirkby Fleetham *North Yorkshire* 148
Kirkby Stephen *Cumbria* 68
Kirkbymoorside *North Yorkshire* 148
Kirkoswald *Cumbria* 68
Knapton *Norfolk* 262
Knaresborough *North Yorkshire* 149
Kniveton *Derbyshire* 202
Knowlton *Kent* 398

L	PAGE

Lacock *Wiltshire* 313
Lambley *Nottinghamshire* 202
Lamplugh *Cumbria* 69
Langdale *Cumbria* 69
Langport *Somerset* 313
Langton Matravers *Dorset* 365
Lanner *Cornwall* 313
Lanreath-By-Looe *Cornwall* 314
Launceston *Cornwall* 314
Lavenham *Suffolk* 262
Laxfield *Suffolk* 263
Lealholm *North Yorkshire* 149

Leamington Spa *Warwickshire* 202
Leasgill *Cumbria* 69
Ledbury *Herefordshire* 203
Lee *Devon* 315
Lee on the Solent *Hampshire* 366
Leintwardine *Herefordshire* 203
Leominster *Herefordshire* 203
Lewes *East Sussex* 398
Leyburn *North Yorkshire* 150
Lincoln *Lincolnshire* 203
Liskeard *Cornwall* 315
Little Henham *Essex* 263
Little Hucklow *Derbyshire* 204
Little Langdale *Cumbria* 70
Little Walden *Essex* 264
Littlehampton *West Sussex* 398
Liverton *Devon* 315
Llanyblodwel *Shropshire* 205
Lofthouse *North Yorkshire* 150
London 37
Long Melford *Suffolk* 264
Longhoughton *Northumberland* 104
Longsleddale *Cumbria* 70
Looe *Cornwall* 316
Lostwithiel *Cornwall* 317
Louth *Lincolnshire* 205
Lower Beeding *West Sussex* 399
Lower Benefield *Northamptonshire* 206
Lower Slaughter *Gloucestershire* 206
Loweswater *Cumbria* 70
Ludlow *Shropshire* 206
Lullington *Derbyshire* 208
Lydney *Gloucestershire* 208
Lyme Regis *Dorset* 317
Lymington *Hampshire* 366
Lyndhurst *Hampshire* 366
Lynton *Devon* 318

M	PAGE

Macclesfield *Cheshire* 125
Madeley *Shropshire* 208
Malmesbury *Wiltshire* 318
Malton *North Yorkshire* 150
Malvern *Worcestershire* 208
Manchester *Greater Manchester* 125
Manchester Airport
(See under Manchester)
Marazion *Cornwall* 318
Mark *Somerset* 319
Market Rasen *Lincolnshire* 209
Marske-By-The-Sea *Tees Valley* 104
Martham *Norfolk* 264
Matlock *Derbyshire* 210
Mealsgate *Cumbria* 70
Melkridge *Northumberland* 104
Membury *Devon* 319
Menheniot *Cornwall* 319
Mevagissey *Cornwall* 320
Mickleton *Durham* 105
Middleham *North Yorkshire* 151
Middleton-By-Youlgreave
Derbyshire 211
Middleton-in-Teesdale *Durham* 105
Milburn *Cumbria* 70
Milford-on-Sea *Hampshire* 367
Millbeck *Cumbria* 71
Miller's Dale *Derbyshire* 211
Milton Abbas *Dorset* 367
Milton Keynes *Buckinghamshire* 369
Milwich *Staffordshire* 211
Mindrum *Northumberland* 106
Minehead *Somerset* 320

Minions *Cornwall* 320
Minster-in-Thanet *Kent* 399
Minsterley *Shropshire* 211
Miserden *Gloucestershire* 212
Modbury *Devon* 321
Mollington *Oxfordshire* 369
Morcombelake *Dorset* 321
Moreton-in-Marsh *Gloucestershire* 212
Moretonhampstead *Devon* 321
Mosterton *Dorset* 321
Mothecombe *Devon* 322
Mullion Cove *Cornwall* 322
Mylor *Cornwall* 322

N	PAGE

Nanstallon *Cornwall* 322
Nantwich *Cheshire* 125
Narborough *Norfolk* 264
Naunton *Gloucestershire* 212
Nawton *North Yorkshire* 151
New Forest
(See under Beaulieu, Boldre,
Brockenhurst, Fordingbridge,
Lymington, Lyndhurst, Milford-on-
Sea, Sway)
New Mills *Derbyshire* 212
Newbury *Berkshire* 369
Newby Bridge *Cumbria* 71
Newcastle-under-Lyme
Staffordshire 213
Newcastle upon Tyne *Tyne and
Wear* 106
Newmarket *Suffolk* 265
Newsham *North Yorkshire* 151
Newton-By-the-Sea
Northumberland 106
Newton Ferrers *Devon* 323
Newton-on-Rawcliffe *North
Yorkshire* 152
Norfolk Broads
(See under Beccles, Hickling,
Horning, Norwich, Salle, Sprowston,
Stalham, Wroxham)
North Leigh *Oxfordshire* 370
North Molton *Devon* 323
Northallerton *North Yorkshire* 152
Northampton *Northamptonshire* 213
Norwich *Norfolk* 265
Nutley *East Sussex* 399

O	PAGE

Oakford *Devon* 323
Okehampton *Devon* 324
Olney *Buckinghamshire* 370
Orcop *Herefordshire* 213
Orford *Suffolk* 265
Oundle *Northamptonshire* 214
Overstrand *Norfolk* 266
Ovington *Durham* 107
Ovington *Northumberland* 107
Owermoigne *Dorset* 325
Owlpen *Gloucestershire* 214
Oxford *Oxfordshire* 370

P	PAGE

Padstow *Cornwall* 325
Pangbourne *Berkshire* 371
Parracombe *Devon* 326
Pateley Bridge *North Yorkshire* 152
Patterdale *Cumbria* 71

Peak District
(See under Alstonefield, Ashbourne,
Ashford in the Water, Bakewell,
Bamford, Baslow, Buxton,
Chelmorton, Cressbrook, Edale,
Eyam, Calver, Great Hucklow,
Hartington, Hathersage, Hayfield,
Hope, Middleton-by-Youlgreave,
Miller's Dale, New Mills, Tideswell,
Youlgreave
See also Dore in Yorkshire region)
Peldon *Essex* 266
Pembridge *Herefordshire* 214
Penrith *Cumbria* 71
Penzance *Cornwall* 326
Perranporth *Cornwall* 327
Pevensey Bay *East Sussex* 399
Pickering *North Yorkshire* 153
Pinner *Greater London* 43
Plaxtol *Kent* 400
Plungar *Leicestershire* 215
Polperro *Cornwall* 327
Poole *Dorset* 371
Pooley Bridge *Cumbria* 72
Porlock *Somerset* 328
Port Isaac *Cornwall* 328
Portland *Dorset* 328
Portreath *Cornwall* 328
Portsmouth & Southsea *Hampshire* 372
Poulton-le-Fylde *Lancashire* 125
Praa Sands *Cornwall* 329
Preston *Gloucestershire* 215
Preston *Lancashire* 126

R	PAGE

Ravenstonedale *Cumbria* 72
Ribble Valley
(See under Chipping, Clitheroe)
Richmond *North Yorkshire* 154
Rillington *North Yorkshire* 155
Ringstead *Norfolk* 266
Ripon *North Yorkshire* 155
Robin Hood's Bay *North Yorkshire* 155
Rochester *Kent* 400
Romsey *Hampshire* 372
Rosedale Abbey *North Yorkshire* 156
Ross-on-Wye *Herefordshire* 215
Rothbury *Northumberland* 107
Rottingdean *East Sussex* 400
Royal Tunbridge Wells *Kent* 400
Rugby *Warwickshire* 217

S	PAGE

Saffron Walden *Essex* 266
St Albans *Hertfordshire* 267
St Austell *Cornwall* 329
St Ives *Cornwall* 329
St Johns-in-the-Vale *Cumbria* 73
St Just-in-Penwith *Cornwall* 330
St Keverne *Cornwall* 330
St Margaret's Bay *Kent* 401
St Mawgan *Cornwall* 331
Salcombe *Devon* 331
Salisbury *Wiltshire* 332
Salisbury Plain
(See under Amesbury, Hindon, Great
Cheverell, Salisbury, Winterbourne
Stoke)
Salle *Norfolk* 267
Sandown *Isle of Wight* 373
Sandringham *Norfolk* 267
Sawrey *Cumbria* 73

Saxmundham *Suffolk* 268
Scarborough *North Yorkshire* 156
Scotch Corner *North Yorkshire* 156
Seahouses *Northumberland* 108
Seaton *Devon* 332
Sedbergh *Cumbria* 73
Sedbusk *North Yorkshire* 157
Sedgeberrow *Worcestershire* 217
Selsey *West Sussex* 401
Selside *North Yorkshire* 157
Shaftesbury *Dorset* 373
Shaldon *Devon* 332
Shanklin *Isle of Wight* 373
Shardlow *Derbyshire* 217
Sheen *Staffordshire* 217
Sheffield *South Yorkshire* 157
Shepton Mallet *Somerset* 333
Sherborne *Dorset* 333
Sheringham *Norfolk* 268
Sherston *Wiltshire* 333
Sherwood Forest
(See under Epperstone)
Shipston-on-Stour *Warwickshire* 217
Shipton-under-Wychwood
Oxfordshire 374
Shrewsbury *Shropshire* 218
Sidmouth *Devon* 334
Silverdale *Lancashire* 126
Skipton *North Yorkshire* 157
Slaggyford *Northumberland* 108
Slaley *Northumberland* 108
Snailbeach *Shropshire* 218
Snape *Suffolk* 268
Snettisham *Norfolk* 269
Soudley *Gloucestershire* 218
South Chailey *East Sussex* 401
South Mimms *Hertfordshire* 269
South Shields *Tyne and Wear* 109
Southampton *Hampshire* 374
Southport *Merseyside* 126
Southsea
(See under Portsmouth & Southsea)
Southwold *Suffolk* 269
Spark Bridge *Cumbria* 74
Spilsby *Lincolnshire* 218
Sprowston *Norfolk* 270
Staintondale *North Yorkshire* 158
Staithes *North Yorkshire* 158
Stalham *Norfolk* 270
Stanhope *Durham* 109
Stanton *Gloucestershire* 219
Stanton Harcourt *Oxfordshire* 374
Stanton-on-the-Wolds
Nottinghamshire 219
Staveley *Cumbria* 74
Steeple Ashton *Wiltshire* 334
Stiffkey *Norfolk* 270
Stithians *Cornwall* 335
Stocksfield *Northumberland* 109
Stoke-on-Trent *Staffordshire* 219
Stoke Sub Hamdon *Somerset* 335
Stonyhurst *Lancashire* 127
Stow-on-the-Wold *Gloucestershire* 220
Stowmarket *Suffolk* 270
Stratford-upon-Avon *Warwickshire* 222
Sutton on the Hill *Derbyshire* 223
Swanton Morley *Norfolk* 271
Sway *Hampshire* 374
Swinhoe *Northumberland* 109

T	PAGE

Tattersett *Norfolk* 271

Taunton *Somerset* 335
Tavistock *Devon* 335
Tebay *Cumbria* 75
Tenterden *Kent* 402
Tetbury *Gloucestershire* 223
Tewkesbury *Gloucestershire* 224
Thame *Oxfordshire* 375
Thaxted *Essex* 271
Thirsk *North Yorkshire* 158
Thornham *Norfolk* 271
Thornley *Lancashire* 127
Thornthwaite *Cumbria* 75
Thorpeness *Suffolk* 272
Threlkeld *Cumbria* 75
Thurlestone *Devon* 336
Thurstonfield *Cumbria* 75
Thwaite *North Yorkshire* 158
Tideswell *Derbyshire* 224
Timberscombe *Somerset* 336
Tirril *Cumbria* 75
Tiverton *Devon* 336
Todmorden *West Yorkshire* 159
Torquay *Devon* 336
Torrington *Devon* 339
Tosside *Lancashire* 127
Totland Bay *Isle of Wight* 375
Trebetherick *Cornwall* 340
Trefonen *Shropshire* 224
Tregony *Cornwall* 340
Tremaine *Cornwall* 340
Troutbeck *Cumbria* 76
Tunbridge Wells
(See under Royal Tunbridge Wells)

U	PAGE

Ullswater *Cumbria* 76
Ulverston *Cumbria* 77
Upper Slaughter *Gloucestershire* 224
Uppingham *Rutland* 225
Upton St Leonards *Gloucestershire* 225

V	PAGE

Ventnor *Isle of Wight* 375
Verwood *Dorset* 376

W	PAGE

Waddingworth *Lincolnshire* 225
Wadebridge *Cornwall* 340
Wallingford *Oxfordshire* 376
Walsham-le-Willows *Suffolk* 272
Walton-on-Thames *Surrey* 402
Wareham *Dorset* 376
Waren Mill *Northumberland* 110
Warkworth *Northumberland* 110
Warwick *Warwickshire* 225
Wasdale *Cumbria* 77
Wellington *Shropshire* 225
Wellow *Bath and North East
Somerset* 341
Wells *Somerset* 341
Wells-Next-the-Sea *Norfolk* 273
Wembdon *Somerset* 341
Wennington *Lancashire* 127
West Bay *Dorset* 342
West Raynham *Norfolk* 273
West Woodburn *Northumberland* 110
Westbury *Wiltshire* 342
Westgate-in-Weardale *Durham* 110
Weston-Super-Mare *North
Somerset* 342
Wetton *Staffordshire* 225

Weybourne Norfolk	273	Winscombe North Somerset	344	Worsbrough South Yorkshire	161
Weymouth Dorset	343	Winsford Somerset	344	Worthing West Sussex	403
Whimple Devon	344	Winston Durham	111	Wroxham Norfolk	274
Whitbourne Herefordshire	226	Winterborne Whitechurch Dorset	377	Wye Valley	
Whitby North Yorkshire	159	Winterbourne Abbas Dorset	344	(See under Fownhope, Hereford,	
Whitecroft Gloucestershire	226	Winterbourne Stoke Wiltshire	344	Ross-on-Wye)	
Whitehaven Cumbria	78	Wirksworth Derbyshire	227	Wythall Worcestershire	228
Whitstable Kent	402	Wisbech Cambridgeshire	274		
Wickham Skeith Suffolk	273	Witcombe Gloucestershire	228		
Wigton Cumbria	78	Witherslack Cumbria	81		
Willoughby Warwickshire	226	Witton-le-Wear Durham	111	Yardley Gobion Northamptonshire	228
Wimborne Minster Dorset	376	Wolsingham Durham	111	Yeadon West Yorkshire	161
Winchcombe Gloucestershire	226	Woodbridge Suffolk	274	York North Yorkshire	161
Winchester Hampshire	376	Woodbury Devon	345	Youlgreave Derbyshire	229
Windermere Cumbria	78	Woodhall Spa Lincolnshire	228		
Windsor Berkshire	377	Wooler Northumberland	112		

Y   PAGE

USE YOUR *i*s

There are more than 550 Tourist Information Centres throughout England offering friendly help with accommodation and holiday ideas as well as suggestions of places to visit and things to do. There may well be a centre in your home town which can help you before you set out. You'll find addresses in the local Phone Book.